TEXT-BOOK OF ANATOMY

Oliver Sheppard, R.H.A., fecit.

DANIEL JOHANNES CUNNINGHAM ADHUC LOQUITUR

DEMONSTRATOR OF ANATOMY, UNIVERSITY OF EDINBURGH, 1874–1882

PROFESSOR OF ANATOMY, ROYAL COLLEGE OF SURGEONS, DUBLIN, 1882–1883

PROFESSOR OF ANATOMY, TRINITY COLLEGE, UNIVERSITY OF DUBLIN, 1883–1903

PROFESSOR OF ANATOMY, UNIVERSITY OF EDINBURGH, 1903–1909

OXFORD MEDICAL PUBLICATIONS

CUNNINGHAM'S
TEXT-BOOK

OF

ANATOMY

EDITED BY

J. C. BRASH, M.A., M.D., F.R.C.S. Ed.

PROFESSOR OF ANATOMY, UNIVERSITY OF EDINBURGH

AND

E. B. JAMIESON, M.D.

LECTURER ON ANATOMY, UNIVERSITY OF EDINBURGH

SEVENTH EDITION

ILLUSTRATED BY 1171 TEXT FIGURES, 653 OF WHICH ARE
PRINTED IN COLOURS, AND 76 PLATES INCLUDING 121 RADIOGRAPHS

NEW YORK

OXFORD UNIVERSITY PRESS

London   Edinburgh   Glasgow   Toronto
Melbourne   Cape Town   Bombay
Calcutta   Madras   Shanghai

MCMXXXVII

TO

Sir William Turner, K.C.B.

LL.D., D.C.L., M.B., D.Sc., F.R.S.

PROFESSOR OF ANATOMY, UNIVERSITY OF EDINBURGH, 1867-1903
VICE-CHANCELLOR AND PRINCIPAL, 1903-1916

IN RECOGNITION OF

HIS EMINENCE AS AN ANATOMIST

AND HIS INFLUENCE AS A TEACHER

THE FIRST EDITION

OF

THIS VOLUME

WAS DEDICATED

BY THOSE OF HIS FORMER PUPILS AND ASSISTANTS

WHO CONTRIBUTED

TO ITS PAGES

Printed in Great Britain by R. & R. CLARK, LIMITED, *Edinburgh.*

From a drawing by]   [*William Hole in 1884*

WILLIAM TURNER
ANATOMIST

FIRST EDITION . . . 1902 ⎫
SECOND EDITION . . 1905 ⎬ D. J. CUNNINGHAM
THIRD EDITION . . . 1909 ⎭

FOURTH EDITION . . 1913 ⎫
   REVISED . . . 1915 |
     SECOND IMPRESSION 1917 |
      THIRD IMPRESSION 1920 ⎬ ARTHUR ROBINSON
FIFTH EDITION . . . 1922 |
    SECOND IMPRESSION 1928 |
SIXTH EDITION . . . 1931 ⎭

SEVENTH EDITION . . 1937

PREFACE TO THE SEVENTH EDITION

THE retirement of Professor Arthur Robinson, under whose guidance Cunningham's *Text-Book of Anatomy* has prospered for nearly twenty-five years, has entailed a change not only in the editorship of the seventh edition but also in the charge of certain of its sections. The revision of the chapters on Human Embryology and the Blood Vascular and Lymphatic Systems, of which Professor Robinson was one of the original authors, has been undertaken by one of the editors, who has also revised and extended the Introduction. This arrangement and the retirement of Professor J. T. Wilson have called for the services of two new contributors. Professor R. D. Lockhart, University of Birmingham, taking over the chapter on Myology, has revised the accounts of muscle action and has introduced photographic and other new illustrations; Professor A. B. Appleton, St. Thomas's Hospital Medical School, University of London, succeeding Professor Wilson in charge of the chapter on the Ductless Glands, has partly rewritten that section from a more functional standpoint.

With deep regret we record the death of Professor A. Francis Dixon, which took place while the preparation of this edition was still in progress. He was the last of the original contributors to retain a share in the work, and his name still stands in the list of authors, for he had just completed the revision of the text of his section before he was overtaken by his last illness. After thirty-three years he showed, in conversation and correspondence, an undiminished interest both in his own section and in the book as a whole; and for this edition he made fruitful suggestions regarding the reproduction of his illustrations, in which he took a just pride.

We desire to thank all the contributors for their harmonious and considerate co-operation; and Sir Grafton Elliot Smith desires us to express also his personal indebtedness to two members of his staff in University College, London—Dr. Una Fielding and Dr. Archibald Durward (the latter now Professor of Anatomy in the University of Leeds)—for the valuable and willing assistance they have given him in the revision of the text of the section on the Central Nervous System and bringing it up to date; to which we would add that the editors also are indebted to them for the careful and efficient manner in which they have carried out their task. We owe thanks also to Professor J. Kay Jamieson, University of Leeds, and now of Trinity College, Dublin, for valuable suggestions regarding the Lymphatic System and for assistance in the preparation of new illustrations in that section; and to Professor J. Brontë Gatenby, Trinity College, Dublin, for kindly advising about the redrawing of Figs. 28 and 29 and for revising the relevant text.

Our thanks are due also to those readers of the last edition who have kindly drawn our attention to misprints and to errors and obscurities of statement. Among them we would specially mention Dr. Thomas H. Evans and Dr. Dwight M. Palmer, who have made many valuable suggestions upon which we have been glad to act.

No great time has passed since the issue of the last edition, and substantial changes were therefore called for in only a few sections; but the whole text has undergone careful revision, and, where required, has been brought into harmony with modern views and methods in the teaching of Anatomy.   This is reflected in the illustrations.   New illustrations partly replace old figures and partly supplement them ; but the chief change of this kind is the introduction of a series of Plates with photographs of the living body showing the effects of muscles in action, and a large number of radiographs (in negative reproduction) illustrating the structure and growth of the skeleton and the position and form of the various organs in the living body.

The new drawings are the careful and skilful work of Mr. R. W. Matthews and Mr. A. K. Maxwell ; the photographic illustrations of the chapter on Myology were made by Messrs. H. J. Whitlock & Sons, Birmingham, under the supervision of Professor Lockhart ; and the majority of the new radiographs have been prepared by Dr. E. Ll. Godfrey in this Department.

For other radiographs, which are duly acknowledged in their place, we have to thank Professor D. M. Blair, Professor John Fraser, Professor R. D. Lockhart, Mr. F. E. Jardine, Dr. J. F. Brailsford, Dr. R. McWhirter, Dr. J. Duncan White, and, through Professor T. Wingate Todd, Dr. B. Holly Broadbent and Dr. Eugene Freedman of Cleveland, Ohio.

Professor Lockhart desires us to say that, with the exception of those of the shoulder in Plate XXII, which are the work of the late Dr. A. Fowler, Aberdeen, all the radiographs supplied by him were made by Dr. J. F. Brailsford.

We should mention that the negative prints for the reproduction of almost all the radiographs were prepared by Mr. John Borthwick of this Department.

A number of the new illustrations have been borrowed from other publications. The source of each is duly acknowledged, and we desire to record our appreciation of the courtesy of the authors and publishers concerned in granting us the permission to use them.   Acknowledgment, not otherwise recorded, is due to the following publishers for the use of the figures mentioned : Messrs. Baillière, Tindall & Cox (Fig. 789) ; Messrs. Lea & Febiger (Fig. 675) ; Messrs. Longmans, Green & Co., Ltd. (Figs. 650, 990, 1082) ; Messrs. Macmillan & Co., Ltd. (Fig. 41) ; Messrs. W. B. Saunders Company (Figs. 664, 678, 981, 982).

The preparation of a new edition has enabled us to introduce the revision of the *Basle Nomina Anatomica* that was approved by the Anatomical Society of Great Britain and Ireland at Birmingham in 1933.   We should like to explain to those who might prefer to adhere to the *B.N.A.* that the revision is not a sweeping one and that much of the apparent change is merely the result of a freer translation of the *B.N.A.* into English than had been in use hitherto—a change which we are confident will in itself make the text of this edition easier to read and more easily understood by the student.   For the convenience of those accustomed to the *B.N.A.* we have inserted a glossary which shows what changes have been made in the nomenclature ; and throughout the text the Basle names have been inserted [in square brackets] after the *B.R.* names where there is a radical difference between them.   Here and there (in ordinary brackets) there are explanatory insertions of the Latin terms.

We cannot close this preface without a further reference to Professor Robinson, whose name has been so long associated with this book.   Even in his retirement, he retains so much interest in the work that he offered to read some of the proofs— an offer of which we gladly took advantage.

J. C. Brash.
E. B. Jamieson.

Department of Anatomy,
    University of Edinburgh,
        December 1936.

LIST OF CONTRIBUTORS

A. B. APPLETON, M.A., M.D.
 Professor of Anatomy, St. Thomas's Hospital Medical School, London
  (*Ductless Glands*)

D. M. BLAIR, M.B., Ch.B., D.Sc.(Lond.)
 Professor of Anatomy, University of Glasgow
  (*Arthrology*)

J. C. BRASH, M.C., M.A., M.D., F.R.C.S.Ed.
 Professor of Anatomy, University of Edinburgh
  (*Human Embryology, Blood Vascular and Lymphatic Systems*)

A. FRANCIS DIXON, M.B., D.Sc. (Dublin)
 Professor of Anatomy, Trinity College, University of Dublin
  (*Uro-Genital System*)

JOHN FRASER, M.C., M.D., Ch.M., F.R.C.S.Ed.
 Professor of Clinical Surgery, University of Edinburgh
  (*Surface and Surgical Anatomy*)

E. B. JAMIESON, M.D.
 Lecturer on Anatomy, University of Edinburgh
  (*Osteology*)

R. D. LOCKHART, M.D., Ch.M.
 Professor of Anatomy, University of Birmingham
  (*Myology*)

Sir GRAFTON ELLIOT SMITH, M.A., Litt.D., D.Sc., M.D., F.R.C.P., F.R.S.
 Professor of Anatomy, University College, London
  (*Central Nervous System*)

J. S. B. STOPFORD, M.D., F.R.S.
 Professor of Anatomy, University of Manchester
  (*Peripheral Nervous System*)

T. WINGATE TODD, M.B., Ch.B., F.R.C.S.
 Professor of Anatomy, Western Reserve University, Cleveland
  (*Respiratory System*)

DAVID WATERSTON, M.A., M.D., F.R.C.S.Ed.
 Professor of Anatomy, University of St. Andrews
  (*Digestive System*)

C. M. WEST, M.C., M.B., B.Ch., D.Sc.(Dublin)
 Professor of Anatomy, University College of South Wales and
  Monmouthshire, Cardiff
  (*Organs of the Senses and the Skin*)

ix

CONTENTS

CONTENTS

ARTHROLOGY

Professor D. M. BLAIR

MYOLOGY

Professor R. D. LOCKHART

DIGESTIVE SYSTEM

Professor DAVID WATERSTON

RESPIRATORY SYSTEM

Professor T. WINGATE TODD

URO-GENITAL SYSTEM

Professor A. FRANCIS DIXON

ORGANS OF THE SENSES AND THE SKIN   Professor C M. WEST

BLOOD VASCULAR AND LYMPHATIC SYSTEMS   Professor J. C. BRASH

SURFACE AND SURGICAL ANATOMY
Professor JOHN FRASER

GLOSSARY

MODIFICATIONS OF THE BASLE NOMINA ANATOMICA ADOPTED BY THE ANATOMICAL
SOCIETY OF GREAT BRITAIN AND IRELAND AT BIRMINGHAM IN 1933

The names in the first column are the anglicised version of the altered and added terms, and those in
the second column are their Latin form ; the third column contains the B.N.A. equivalents. The
Anatomische Gesellschaft, after discussion of a preliminary report by a Nomenklatur Kommission, adopted
a modification of the B.N.A. at Jena in 1935.[1] The fourth column in this Glossary contains the terms,
corresponding to these of the B.R. in the first column, which also differ from the B.N.A. Some of these are
identical with the B.R. terms : the complete list, however, includes others which differ from the B.N.A. but
have not been altered in the B.R.

GENERAL TERMS AND PARTS OF HUMAN BODY

B.R.	Latin Form of B.R.	B.N.A.	N.K.
Cephalic	*Cephalicus*	*Cranialis*	
Coronal	Coronalis	Frontalis	
Anterior and palmar	Anterior ; palmaris	Volaris	
Horizontal planes	Plana horizontalia		
Sagittal planes	Plana sagittalia		
Coronal planes	Plana coronalia		
Hilum	Hilum	Hilus	
Cortex	Cortex	Substantia corticalis	Cortex
Medulla	Medulla	Substantia medullaris	Medulla
Mucous membrane	Membrana mucosa	Tunica mucosa	
Neck	Cervix	Collum	
Nape of neck	Nucha		
Nuchal furrow	Sulcus nuchæ	Fovea nuchæ	
Root of neck	Radix cervicis		
Suprasternal fossa	Fossa suprasternalis	Fossa jugularis	
Infraclavicular fossa	Fossa infraclavicularis	Trigonum deltoideo-pectorale	
Epigastric fossa	Fossa epigastrica	Scrobiculus cordis	
Upper limb	Membrum superius	Extremitas superior	Extremitas thoracica
Palm of hand	Palma manus	Vola manus	
Lower limb	Membrum inferius	Extremitas inferior	Extremitas pelvina
Fold of buttock	Sulcus natis	Sulcus glutæus	
Natal cleft	Fissura natalis		
Popliteal fossa	Fossa poplitea		Fossa poplitea

OSTEOLOGY

Epiphyseal cartilage	Cartilago epiphysealis		
Epiphyseal line	Linea epiphysealis		
Endosteum	Endosteum		Endosteum

Vertebral Column

Superior costal facet (of vertebræ)	Facies costalis superior	Fovea costalis superior	Fovea costalis cranialis
Inferior costal facet	Facies costalis inferior	Fovea costalis inferior	Fovea costalis caudalis
Pedicle (of vertebral arch)	Pediculus (arcus vertebræ)	Radix arcus vertebræ	
Lamina (of vertebral arch)	Lamina (arcus vertebræ)		
Neural arch	*Arcus neuralis*		
Centrum	*Centrum*		
Neuro-central joint	Articulatio neuro-centralis		
Superior articular facet of atlas	Facies articularis superior	Foveæ articulares superiores	Foveæ articulares craniales

[1] *Nomina Anatomica.* G. Fischer, Jena, 1936.

B.R.	Latin Form of B.R.	B.N.A.	N.K.
Facet for odontoid process	Facies processus odontoidei	Fovea dentis	Facies articularis dentalis
Axis (vertebra)	Axis	Epistropheus	
Odontoid process	Processus odontoideus	Dens epistrophei	
Lateral mass of sacrum	Massa lateralis ossis sacri	Pars lateralis oss. sac.	
Spinous tubercles of sacrum	Tubercula spinosa ossis sacri	Crista sacralis media	
Transverse tubercles of sacrum	Tubercula transversa ossis sacri	Cristæ sacrales laterales	
Articular tubercles of sacrum	Tubercula articularia ossis sacri	Cristæ sacrales articulares	

Ribs and Sternum

Inlet of thorax	Aditus thoracis	Apertura thoracis superior	Apertura thoracis cranialis
Outlet of thorax	Exitus thoracis	Apertura thoracis inferior	Apertura thoracis caudalis
Head of rib	Caput costæ	Capitulum costæ	
Tubercle for serratus anterior	Tuberculum m. serrati anterioris	Tuberositas costæ II	
Suprasternal notch	Incisura suprasternalis	Incisura jugularis	

Skull

Foramen magnum	Foramen magnum	Foramen occipitale magnum	
Groove for inferior petrosal sinus	Sulcus sinus petrosi inferioris	Sulcus petrosus inferior	
Condylar part of occipital bone	Pars condylaris	Pars lateralis	
Posterior condylar canal	Canalis condylaris posterior	Canalis condyloideus	Canalis condylicus
Anterior condylar canal	Canalis condylaris anterior	Canalis hypoglossi	
Inion	Inion		
Groove for transverse sinus	Sulcus sinus transversi	Sulcus transversus	
Optic groove (of sphenoid)	Sulcus opticus	Sulcus chiasmatis	
Jugum sphenoidale	Jugum sphenoidale		
Lesser wing	Ala minor	Ala parva	
Greater wing	Ala major	Ala magna	
Emissary sphenoidal foramen	F. sphenoidale emissarium		
Infratemporal surface (of greater wing)	Facies infratemporalis		Facies infratemporalis
Spine of sphenoid	Spina oss. sphenoidei	Spina angularis	Spina ossis sphenoidis
Groove for pharyngo-tympanic tube	Sulcus tubæ pharyngo-tympanicæ	Sulcus tubæ auditivæ	Sulcus tubæ pharyngo-tympanicæ
Lateral pterygoid plate	Lamina pterygoidea lateralis	Lamina lateralis processus pterygoidei	Lamina lateralis processus pterygoidis
Medial pterygoid plate	Lamina pterygoidea medialis	Lamina medialis processus pterygoidei	Lamina medialis processus pterygoidis
Palatino-vaginal canal	Canalis palatino-vaginalis	Canalis pharyngeus	Canalis pharyngicus
Vomero-vaginal canal	Canalis vomero-vaginalis	Canalis basi-pharyngeus	C. basi-pharyngicus
Groove for sigmoid sinus	Sulcus sinus sigmoidei	Sulcus sigmoideus	Sulcus sinus sigmoidis
Hiatus for greater superficial petrosal nerve	Hiatus n. petrosi superficialis majoris	Hiatus canalis facialis	Hiatus canalis n. facialis
Borders of petrous temporal	Margines	Anguli pyramidis	Crista pyramidis (for superior border)
Groove for superior petrosal sinus	Sulcus sinus petrosi superioris	Sulcus petrosus superior	Sulcus cristæ pyramidis
Auditory meatus	Meatus auditorius	Meatus acusticus	
Canal for facial nerve	Canalis n. facialis	Canalis facialis	Canalis nervi facialis
Notch for glosso-pharyngeal nerve	Incisura n. glosso-pharyngei		
Canaliculus for tympanic nerve	C. n. tympanici	C. tympanicus	

B.R.	Latin Form of B.R.	B.N.A.	N.K.
Canal for tensor tympani	C. m. tensoris tympani	Semicanalis m. tens. tym.	
Canal of pharyngo-tympanic tube	C. tubæ pharyngo-tympanicæ	Semicanalis tubæ auditivæ	
Anterior canaliculus for chorda tympani	C. anterior chordæ tymp.	C. chordæ tympani	
Posterior canaliculus for chorda tympani	C. posterior chordæ tymp.		
Squamo-tympanic fissure	Fissura squamo-tympanica	⎱ Fissura petro-tympanica ⎰	
Petro-tympanic fissure	Fissura petro-tympanica		
Zygomatic process (zygoma)	Processus zygomaticus (zygoma)	Processus zygomaticus	
Roots of zygoma	Radices zygomatis		
Tubercle of root of zygoma	Tuberculum radicis z.		
Infratemporal surface (of squamous temporal)	Facies infratemporalis		
Articular fossa (of temporal bone)	Fossa articularis	Fossa mandibularis	
Articular eminence	Eminentia articularis	Tuberculum articulare	
External surface (of parietal bone)	Facies externa	Facies parietalis	
Internal surface	Facies interna	Facies cerebralis	
Parietal eminence	Eminentia parietalis	Tuber parietale	
Groove for sigmoid sinus	Sulcus sinus sigmoidei	Sulcus transversus	
Frontal eminence	Eminentia frontalis	Tuber frontale	
Orbital plate (of frontal)	Lamina orbitalis	Pars orbitalis	
Trochlear fossa	Fossa trochlearis	Fovea trochlearis	Foveola trochlearis
Nasal spine (of frontal)	Spina nasalis	Spina frontalis	Spina nasalis
Cribriform plate (of ethmoid)	Lamina cribriformis	Lamina cribrosa	Lamina cribriformis
Ala of crista galli (R. & L.)	Ala cristæ galli (dext. et sinist.)	Processus alaris	
Ethmoidal sinuses	Sinus ethmoidales	Cellulæ ethmoidales	Sinus ethmoideus
Orbital plate (of ethmoid)	Lamina orbitalis	Lamina papyracea	Lamina orbitalis (papyracea)
Crest of lacrimal bone	Crista ossis lacrimalis	Crista lacrimalis posterior	Crista lacrimalis orbitalis
Posterior surface (of maxilla)	Facies posterior	Facies infratemporalis	
Dental foramina	Foramina dentalia	Foramina alveolaria	
Dental canals	Canales dentales	Canales alveolares	
Naso-lacrimal groove	Sulcus naso-lacrimalis	Sulcus lacrimalis	
Lacrimal crest (of maxilla)	Crista lacrimalis	Crista lacrimalis anterior	
Alveolar arch	Arcus alveolaris	Limbus alveolaris	Margo alveolaris
Perpendicular plate (of palatine bone)	Lamina perpendicularis	Pars perpendicularis	Lamina maxillaris
Greater palatine groove	Sulcus palatinus major	Sulcus pterygo-palatinus	
Lesser palatine canals	Canales palatini minores	Canales palatini	
Horizontal plate	Lamina horizontalis	Pars horizontalis	Lamina palatina
Tubercle (of p. bone)	Tuberculum (oss. pal.)	Processus pyramidalis	
Palatine crest	Crista palatina		
Lateral surface (of zygomatic bone)	Lateral surface	Facies malaris	
Frontal process (of z. bone)	Processus frontalis	Processus fronto-sphenoidalis	Processus fronto-sphenoideus
Marginal tubercle	Tuberculum marginale	(Processus marginalis)	
Alveolar arch (of mandible)	Arcus alveolaris	Limbus alveolaris	Margo alveolaris
External surface (of m.)	Facies externa		
Internal surface	Facies interna		
Genial tubercles	Tubercula geniaca	Spina mentalis	Spinæ mandibulares
Sublingual fossa	Fossa sublingualis	Fovea sublingualis	
Submandibular fossa	Fossa submandibularis	Fossa submaxillaris	
Head of mandible	Caput mandibulæ	Capitulum processus condyloidei mand.	Capitulum mandibulæ

B.R.	Latin Form of B.R.	B.N.A.	N.K.
Base of skull	Basis cranii		Basis cranii
Lower surface	Facies inferior	Basis cranii externa	Facies externa
Upper surface	Facies superior	Basis cranii interna	Facies interna
Impressions for (cerebral) gyri	Impressiones gyrorum (cerebri)	Impressiones digitatæ	Impressiones gyrorum
Granular pits	Fossulæ granulares	Foveolæ granulares (Pacchioni)	Foveolæ granulares
Pterygo-maxillary fissure	Fissura pterygo-maxillaris		
Greater palatine canal	Canalis palatinus major	Canalis pterygo-palatinus	
Bony palate	Palatum osseum	Palatum durum	Palatum osseum
Incisive fossa	Fossa incisiva	Foramen incisivum	
Incisive foramina	Foramina incisiva		
Anterior bony aperture of nose	Apertura ossea nasi anterior	Apertura piriformis	
Posterior bony aperture of nose	Apertura ossea nasi posterior	Choana	
Bony part of septum of nose	Pars ossea septi nasi	Septum nasi osseum	
Anterior fontanelle	Fonticulus anterior	Fonticulus frontalis (major)	Fonticulus major
Posterior fontanelle	Fonticulus posterior	Fonticulus occipitalis (minor)	Fonticulus minor
Postero-lateral fontanelle	Fonticulus postero-lateralis	Fonticulus mastoideus	
Antero-lateral fontanelle	Fonticulus antero-lateralis	Fonticulus sphenoidalis	Fonticulus sphenoideus

Bones of Upper Limb

B.R.	Latin Form of B.R.	B.N.A.	N.K.
Shoulder girdle	Cingulum membri superioris	Cingulum extremitatis superioris	Ossa cinguli extremitatum thoracicarum
Crest (of spine of scapula)	Crista (spinæ scapulæ)		
Angle of acromion	Angulus acromialis		
Medial border of scapula	Margo medialis	Margo vertebralis	
Lateral border of scapula	Margo lateralis	Margo axillaris	
Superior angle	Angulus superior	Angulus medialis	Angulus cranialis
Suprascapular notch	Incisura suprascapularis	Incisura scapulæ	
Spino-glenoid notch	Incisura spino-glenoidalis		
Conoid tubercle (of clavicle)	Tuberculum conoideum	Tuberositas coracoidea	
Trapezoid ridge (of clavicle)	Linea trapezoidea		
Impression for costo-clavicular lig.	Impressio lig. costo-clavicularis	Tuberositas costalis	
Tuberosities (of humerus)	Tuberositates	Tubercula	
Bicipital groove	Sulcus m. bicipitis	Sulcus intertubercularis	
Lateral lip	Labium laterale	Crista tuberculi majoris	
Medial lip	Labium mediale	Crista tuberculi minoris	
Medial supracondylar ridge	Crista supracondylaris medialis		
Lateral supracondylar ridge	Crista supracondylaris lateralis		
Anterior border (of humerus)	Margo anterior		
Spiral groove	Sulcus spiralis	Sulcus n. radialis	
Head of radius	Caput radii	Capitulum radii	
Interosseous border	Margo interossea	Crista interossea	
Posterior border	Margo posterior	Margo dorsalis	
Anterior border	Margo anterior	Margo volaris	
Anterior surface	Facies anterior	Facies volaris	
Posterior surface	Facies posterior	Facies dorsalis	
Dorsal tubercle	Tuberculum dorsale		
Trochlear notch (of ulna)	Incisura trochlearis	Incisura semilunaris	
Interosseous border	Margo interossea	Crista interossea	
Posterior border	Margo posterior	Margo dorsalis	

B.R.	Latin Form of B.R.	B.N.A.	N.K.
Anterior border	Margo anterior	Margo volaris	
Anterior surface	Facies anterior	Facies volaris	
Posterior surface	Facies posterior	Facies dorsalis	
Head of ulna	Caput ulnæ	Capitulum ulnæ	
Scaphoid bone	Os scaphoideum	Os naviculare manus	
Trapezium	Os trapezium	Os multangulum majus	
Crest of trapezium	Crista ossis trapezii	Tuberculum ossis. m. majoris	
Trapezoid	Os trapezoideum	Os multangulum minus	
Head of metacarpal bone	Caput ossis metac.	Capitulum	
Proximal phalanx	Phalanx proximalis	Phalanx prima	Phalanx proximalis
Middle phalanx	Phalanx media	Phalanx secunda	Phalanx media
Distal phalanx	Phalanx distalis	Phalanx tertia	Phalanx distalis
Tuberosity of distal phalanx	Tuberositas phalangis distalis	Tuberositas unguicularis	
Head of phalanx	Caput phalangis	Trochlea phalangis	

Bones of Lower Limb

B.R.	Latin Form of B.R.	B.N.A.	N.K.
Pelvic Girdle	Cingulum membri inferioris	Cingulum extremitatis inferioris	Ossa cinguli extremitatum pelvinarum
Articular surface (of acetabulum)	Facies articularis	Facies lunata	
Tubercle of iliac crest	Tuberculum cristæ iliacæ		
Intermediate area (of crest)	Area intermedia	Linea intermedia	
Gluteal surface (of ilium)	Facies glutæa		
Middle gluteal line	Linea glutæa media	Linea glutæa anterior	Linia glutæa cranialis
Sacro-pelvic surface	Facies sacro-pelvina		
Pelvic surface of ischium	Facies pelvina		
Dorsal surface of ischium	Facies dorsalis		
Femoral surface of ischium	Facies femoralis		
Ramus of ischium	Ramus ossis ischii	Ramus inferior ossis ischii	Pars pubica rami ossis ischii
Pubic crest	Crista ossis pubis		
Pelvic surface of sup. ramus	Facies pelvina		
Pectineal surface of sup. ramus	Facies pectinea		
Obturator surface of sup. ramus	Facies obturatoria		
Pectineal line	Linea pectinea	Pecten ossis pubis	
Ilio-pubic eminence	Eminentia ilio-pubica	Eminentia ilio-pectinea	
False pelvis	Pelvis spuria	Pelvis major	
True pelvis	Pelvis vera	Pelvis minor	
Inlet of pelvis	Aditus pelvis (veræ)	Apertura pelvis (minoris) superior	Aditus pelvis
Outlet of pelvis	Exitus pelvis (veræ)	Aperture pelvis (minoris) inferior	Exitus pelvis
Arcuate line	Linea arcuata	Linea terminalis	
Pectineal line	Linea pectinea		
Pubic crest	Crista ossis pubis		
Sub-pubic angle	Angulus sub-pubicus	Angulus pubis	
Pit on head of femur	Fossula capitis femoris	Fovea capitis femoris	
Trochanteric line	Linea trochanterica	L. intertrochanterica	
Trochanteric crest	Crista trochanterica	C. intertrochanterica	
Spiral line	Linea spiralis		
Supracondylar lines	Lineæ supracondylares		
Intercondylar notch	Incisura intercondylaris	Fossa intercondyloidea	Fossa intercondylica
Popliteal surface	Facies poplitea	Planum popliteum	
Adductor tubercle	Tuberculum adductorium		
Tubercle of tibia	Tuberculum tibiæ	Tuberositas tibiæ	
Intercondylar area	Area intercondylaris	{ Fossa intercondyloidea anterior / Fossa intercondyloidea posterior	

B.R.	Latin Form of B.R.	B.N.A.	N.K.
Soleal line	Linea m. solei	Linea poplitea	
Vertical line	Linea perpendicularis		
Anterior border	Margo anterior	Crista anterior	
Interosseous border	Margo interossea	Crista interossea	
Groove for tibialis posterior	Sulcus tendinis m. tibialis posterioris	Sulcus malleolaris	Sulcus malleoli tibiæ
Head of fibula	Caput fibulæ	Capitulum fibulæ	
Styloid process	Processus styloideus	Apex capituli fibulæ	
Anterior border	Margo anterior	Crista anterior	
Interosseous border	Margo interossea	Crista interossea	
Posterior border	Margo posterior	Crista lateralis	Crista fibularis
Anterior surface	Facies anterior	Facies medialis (pars anterior)	}Facies tibialis
Posterior surface	Facies posterior	{ Facies medialis (pars posterior) Facies posterior	
Malleolar fossa	Fossa malleoli lateralis		Fossa malleoli fibulæ
Tarsal bones	Ossa tarsalia	Ossa tarsi	
Medial surface of talus	Facies medialis tali		
Malleolar facet	Facies articularis malleolaris medialis	Facies malleolaris medialis	Facies malleolaris tibialis
Lateral surface	Facies lateralis		
Malleolar facet	Facies articularis mall. lat.	Facies malleolaris lateralis	Facies malleolaris fibularis
Lateral tubercle (of talus)	Tuberculum laterale	Processus lateralis ,	
Medial tubercle	Tuberculum mediale	}	{Tuberculum tibiale
Posterior tubercle	Tuberculum posterius }	Processus posterior	{Tuberculum fibulare
Anterior surface (of talus)	Facies anterior		
Lower surface	Facies inferior		
Posterior surface	Facies posterior		
Calcaneum	Calcaneum	Calcaneus	
Posterior surface	Facies posterior	Tuber calcanei	
Lower surface	Facies inferior		
Medial tubercle	Tuberculum mediale	Processus medialis tuberis calcanei	Tuberculum tibiale tuberis calcanei
Lateral tubercle	Tuberculum laterale	Processus lateralis tuberis calcanei	Tuberculum fibulare tuberis calcanei
Anterior tubercle	Tuberculum anterius		
Medial surface	Facies medialis		
Upper surface	Facies superior		
Anterior facet for talus	Facies articularis talaris anterior	Facies articularis anterior	
Middle facet for talus	Facies articularis talaris media	Facies articularis media	
Posterior facet for talus	Facies articularis talaris posterior	Facies articularis posterior	
Lateral surface (Peroneal tubercle)	Facies lateralis (Tuberculum tendinum mm. peronæorum)	(Processus trochlearis)	
Anterior surface	Facies anterior		
Medial cuneiform bone	Os cuneiforme mediale	Os cuneiforme primum	
Intermediate cuneiform bone	Os cuneiforme intermedium	Os cuneiforme secundum	
Lateral cuneiform bone	Os cuneiforme laterale	Os cuneiforme tertium	
Head of metatarsal bone	Caput	Capitulum	
Proximal phalanx	Phalanx proximalis	Phalanx prima	Phalanx proximalis
Middle phalanx	Phalanx media	Phalanx secunda	Phalanx media
Distal phalanx	Phalanx distalis	Phalanx tertia	Phalanx distalis
Head of phalanx	Caput phalangis	Trochlea phalangis	
Tuberosity of distal phalanx	Tuberositas phalangis distalis	Tuberositas unguicularis	

ARTHROLOGY

ARTHROLOGY	ARTHROLOGIA	SYNDESMOLOGIA	JUNCTURAE OSSIUM
Joint	Articulatio	Junctura ossium	Articulus
Fibrous joint	Articulatio fibrosa	Synarthrosis	
Denticulate suture	Sutura denticulata		

B.R.	Latin Form of B.R.	B.N.A.	N.K.
Flat suture	S. plana	Harmonia	
Limbous suture	S. limbosa		
Wedge and groove suture	Schindylesis		
Primary cartilaginous joint	Artic. cartilaginea primaria	Synchondrosis	
Secondary cartilaginous joint	Artic. cartilaginea secundaria	Amphiarthrosis	
Synovial joint	Artic. synovialis	Diarthrosis	
Plane joint	Artic. plana	Arthrodia	
Ball and socket joint	Artic. cotylica	Enarthrosis	Enarthrosis sphæroidea
Condyloid joint	Artic. condyloidea		
Capsular ligament	Lig. capsulare	Stratum fibrosum capsulæ articularis	
Synovial membrane	Membrana synovialis	Stratum synoviale capsulæ articularis	

Joints of Axial Skeleton

Intervertebral discs	Disci intervertebrales	Fibro-cartilagines intervertebrales	Disci intervertebrales
Sacro-coccygeal joint	Articulatio sacro-coccygea	Symphysis sacro-coccygea	Symphysis sacro-coccygica
Superficial posterior sacro-coccygeal lig.	Lig. sacro-coccygeum posterius superficiale	Lig. sacro-coccygeum posterius superficiale	
Intercornual ligs.	Ligg. intercornualia		
Alar ligs. of odontoid process	Ligg. proc. odont. alaria	Ligg. alaria	
Apical lig. of odontoid process	Lig. apicis proc. od.	Lig. apicis dentis	
Longitudinal bands (of cruciate lig.)	Fasciculi longitudinales		
Intra-articular lig. (of joint of head of rib)	Lig. (capitis costæ) intra-articulare	Lig. capituli costæ interarticulare	
Lateral costo-transverse lig.	Lig. costo-transversarium laterale	Lig. tuberculi costæ	
Inferior costo-transverse lig.	Lig. costo-transversarium inferius	Lig. colli costæ	
Superior costo-transverse lig.	Lig. costo-transversarium superius	Lig. costo-transversarium anterius	Lig. costo-transversarium internum
Manubrio-sternal joint	Artic. manubrio-sternalis	Synchondrosis sternalis	Symphysis sterni
Xiphi-sternal joint	Artic. xiphi-sternalis		
Intra-articular (sterno-costal) ligs.	Ligg. (sterno-costalia) intra-articularia	Lig. sterno-costale interarticulare	Lig. sterno-costale intra-articulare

Joints of Upper Limb

Suprascapular lig.	Lig. suprascapulare	Lig. transversum scapulæ superius	
Spino-glenoid lig.	Lig. spino-glenoidale	Lig. transversum scapulæ inferius	
Posterior sterno-clavicular lig.	Lig. sterno-claviculare posterius		
Transverse lig. (of shoulder joint)	Lig. transversum		
Anterior lig. (of elbow joint)	Lig. anterius		
Posterior lig. (of elbow joint)	Lig. posterius		
Lateral lig. (of elbow joint)	Lig. laterale	Lig. collaterale radiale	
Medial lig. (of elbow joint)	Lig. mediale	Lig. collaterale ulnare	
Quadrate lig.	Lig. quadratum		
Anterior radio-carpal lig.	Lig. radio-carpeum anterius	Lig. radio-carpeum volare	
Posterior radio-carpal lig.	Lig. radio-carpeum posterius	Lig. radio-carpeum dorsale	

B.R.	Latin Form of B.R.	B.N.A.	N.K.
Lateral lig. (of wrist)	Lig. laterale (carpi)	Lig. collaterale carpi radiale	
Medial lig. (of wrist)	Lig. mediale (carpi)	Lig. collaterale carpi ulnare	
Palmar intercarpal ligs.	Ligg. intercarpea palmaria	Ligg. intercarpea volaria	
Palmar carpo-meta-carpal ligs.	Ligg. carpo-metacarpea palmaria	Ligg. carpo-metacarpea volaria	
Dorsal metacarpal ligs.	Ligg. metacarpea dorsalia	Ligg. basium (oss. metacarp.) dorsalia	
Palmar metacarpal ligs.	Ligg. metacarpea palmaria	Ligg. basium (oss. metacarp.) volaria	
Interosseous metacarpal ligs.	Ligg. metacarpea interossea	Ligg. basium (oss. metacarp.) interossea	
Palmar lig. (of digits)	Lig. palmaria	Ligg. accessoria volaria	
Deep transverse ligs. of palm	Ligg. palmæ transversa profunda	Ligg. capitulorum (oss. metacarp.) transversa	

Joints of Pelvis and Lower Limb

B.R.	Latin Form of B.R.	B.N.A.	N.K.
Inferior pubic lig.	Lig. pubicum inferius	Lig. arcuatum pubis	
Anterior pubic lig.	Lig. pubicum anterius		
Posterior pubic lig.	Lig. pubicum posterius		
Interpubic disc	Discus interpubicus	Lamina fibro-cartilaginea interpubica	
Ischio-femoral lig.	Lig. ischio-femorale	Lig. ischio-capsulare	
Pubo-femoral lig.	Lig. pubo-femorale	Lig. pubo-capsulare	
Labrum acetabulare	Labrum acetabulare	Labrum glenoidale	Labium articulare
Lig. of head of femur	Lig. capitis femoris	Lig. teres femoris	Lig. capitis femoris
Lateral lig. (of knee)	Lig. laterale (genu)	Lig. collaterale fibulare	
Medial lig. (of knee)	Lig. mediale (genu)	Lig. collaterale tibiale	
Oblique posterior lig. (of knee)	Lig. posterius obliquum	Lig. popliteum obliquum	
Arcuate lig.	Lig. arcuatum	Lig. popliteum arcuatum	
Semilunar cartilages	Cart. semilunares	Menisci	
Infrapatellar synovial fold	Plica infrapatellaris	Plica synovialis patellaris	
Superior tibio-fibular joint	Artic. tibio-fibularis superior	Artic. tibio-fibularis	
Inferior tibio-fibular joint	Artic. tibio-fibularis inferior	Syndesmosis tibio-fibularis	
Interosseous tibio-fibular lig.	Lig. tibio-fibulare interosseum		
Anterior inferior tibio-fibular lig.	Lig. tibio-fibulare inferius anterius	Lig. malleoli lateralis anterius	Lig. tibio-fibulare anterius
Posterior inferior tibio-fibular lig.	Lig. tibio-fibulare inferius posterius	Lig. malleoli lateralis posterius	Lig. tibio-fibulare posterius
Transverse tibio-fibular lig.	Lig. tibio-fibulare inferius transversum		
Anterior lig. (of ankle joint)	Lig. anterius		
Posterior lig. (of ankle joint)	Lig. posterius		
Lateral lig. (of ankle joint)	Lig. laterale		
Lateral calcaneo-navicular lig.	Lig. calcaneo-naviculare laterale	Pars calcaneo-navicularis lig. bifurcati	Pars calcaneo-navicularis lig. bipartiti
Medial calcaneo-cuboid lig.	Lig. calcaneo-cuboideum mediale	Pars calcaneo-cuboidea lig. bifurcati	Pars calcaneo-cuboidea lig. bipartiti
Short plantar lig.	Lig. plantare breve	Lig. calcaneo-cuboideum plantare	Lig. calcaneo-cuboideum plantare obliquum
Interosseous metatarsal ligs.	Ligg. metatarsea interossea	Ligg. basium (oss. metatars.) interossea	
Dorsal metatarsal ligs.	Ligg. metatarsea dorsalia	Ligg. basium (oss. metatars.) dorsalia	
Plantar metatarsal ligs.	Ligg. metatarsea plantaria	Ligg. basium (oss. metatars.) plantaria	
Plantar ligs. (of digits)	Ligg. plantaria	Ligg. accessoria plantaria	
Deep transverse ligs. of sole	Ligg. plantæ transversa profunda	Ligg. capitulorum (oss. metars.) transversa	

MYOLOGY

B.R.	Latin Form of B.R.	B.N.A.	N.K.
Tendinous intersection	Intersectio tendinea	Inscriptio tendinea	
Synovial sheath	Vagina synovialis	Vagina mucosa	Vagina synovialis
Synovial bursa	Bursa synovialis	Bursa mucosa	Bursa synovialis
Deep fascia	Fascia profunda		

Muscles of the Back

Ilio-costo-cervicalis	Idem	M. ilio-costalis	
Ilio-costalis	Idem	M. ilio-costalis lumborum	} M. ilio-costalis
Costalis	Idem	M. ilio-costalis dorsi	
Costo-cervicalis	Idem	M. ilio-costalis cervicis	
Longissimus thoracis	Idem	M. longissimus dorsi	
Spinalis thoracis	Idem	M. spinalis dorsi	
Semispinalis thoracis	Idem	M. semispinalis	
Lumbar fascia	Fascia lumbalis	F. lumbo-dorsalis	

Muscles of Head and Neck

Occipito-frontalis	Idem	M. epicranius	Mm. epicranii
Frontal belly	Venter frontalis	M. frontalis	
Occipital belly	Venter occipitalis	M. occipitalis	
Epicranial aponeurosis	Aponeurosis epicranialis	Galea aponeurotica	
Compressor naris	Idem	Pars transversa m. nasalis	} M. nasalis
Dilator naris	Idem	Pars alaris m. nasalis	
Levator labii superioris alæque nasi	Idem	Caput angulare m. quadrati labii superioris	M. levator nasi et labii maxillaris medialis
Levator labii superioris	Idem	Caput infra-orbitale m. quad. labii superioris	M. levator nasi et labii maxillaris lateralis
Zygomaticus minor	Idem	Caput zygomaticum m. quad. labii superioris	M. zygomaticus minor
Zygomaticus major	Idem	M. zygomaticus	M. zygomaticus major
Levator anguli oris	Idem	M. caninus	
Depressor anguli oris	Idem	M. triangularis	
Depressor labii inferioris	Idem	M. quadratus labii inferioris	M. quadratus labii mandibularis
Parotid fascia	F. parotidea	F. parotideo-masseterica	F. masseterica
Lateral pterygoid muscle	M. pterygoideus lateralis	M. pterygoideus externus	M. pterygoideus lateralis
Medial pterygoid muscle	M. pterygoideus medialis	M. pterygoideus internus	M. pterygoideus medialis
Longus cervicis	Idem	M. longus colli	
Cervical fascia	F. cervicis	F. colli.	Fasciæ colli
Pretracheal fascia	F. pretrachealis		

Muscles of Thorax

Anterior intercostal membranes	Membranæ intercostales anteriores	Ligg. intercostalia externa	
Posterior intercostal membranes	Membranæ intercostales posteriores	Ligg. intercostalia interna	
Transversus thoracis	Idem		
Sterno-costalis	Idem	M. transversus thoracis	
(Innermost intercostals)	(Mm. intercostales intimi)		
Subcostals	Mm. subcostales	Mm. subcostales	
Vertebral part of diaphragm	Pars vertebralis	Pars lumbalis	
Crus	Crus	{ Crus laterale Crus intermedium Crus mediale	} Crus laterale Crus mediale
Central tendon	Tendo centralis	Centrum tendineum	
Vena-caval opening	Hiatus venæ cavæ	Foramen venæ cavæ	
Lateral arcuate lig.	Lig. arcuatum laterale	Arcus lumbo-costalis lateralis (Halleri)	Arcus lumbo-costalis lateralis
Medial arcuate lig.	Lig. arcuatum mediale	Arcus lumbo-costalis medialis (Halleri)	Arcus lumbo-costalis medialis
Median arcuate lig.	Lig. arcuatum medianum		

Muscles of Abdomen and Pelvis

B.R.	Latin Form of B.R.	B.N.A.	N K.
Arcuate line (of sheath of rectus)	Linea arcuata	Linea semicircularis (Douglasi)	
Pectineal part of inguinal lig.	Pars pectinea lig. ing.	Lig. lacunare (Gimbernati)	
(Reflected part of inguinal lig.)	(Pars reflexa)	Lig. inguinale reflexum	
Pectineal lig.	Lig. pectineale		
Conjoint tendon	Tendo conjunctus	Falx aponeurotica inguinalis	Falx inguinalis
Superficial inguinal ring	Annulus inguinalis superficialis	Annulus inguinalis subcutaneus	
Deep inguinal ring	Annulus inguinalis profundus	Annulus inguinalis abdominalis	Anulus inguinalis præperitonealis
Levator ani	Idem	M. levator ani	
Pubo-coccygeus	Idem		
Levator prostatæ	Idem		
Pubo-rectalis	Idem		
Ilio-coccygeus			
		F. pelvis	Fasciæ pelvis
		F. endopelvina	F. intrapelvina
Fascia of pelvic muscles	F. musculorum pelvinorum	F. diaphragmatis pelvis	
Fascia of pelvic viscera	F. viscerum pelvinorum	F. diaphragmatis urogenitalis superior	F. diaph. urog. interna
(Fascial) sheath of prostate	Vagina (fascialis) prostatæ	F. prostatæ	
Retro-pubic space	Spatium retropubicum		Spatium prævesicale
Retro-pubic pad of fat	Corpus adiposum retropubicum		
Ano-coccygeal body	Corpus ano-coccygeum	Lig. ano-coccygeum	Septum ano-coccygicum
Bulbo-spongiosus	Idem	M. bulbo-cavernosus	
Sphincter urethræ	Idem	M. s. u. membranaceæ	M. s. u. diaphragmaticæ
Perineal membrane	Membrana perinealis	Fascia diaphragmatis urogenitalis inferior	F. diaph. urogen. externa
Transverse lig. of perineum	Lig. perinei transversum	Lig. transversum pelvis	Lig. præurethrale
Perineal body	Corpus perineale		
Membranous layer of superficial fascia	Lamina membranacea		
Fatty layer of superficial fascia	Lamina adiposa		
Ischio-rectal pad of fat	Corpus adiposum ischio-rectale		
Pudendal canal (in obturator fascia)	Canalis pudendalis		

Muscles of Upper Limb

(Dorso-epitrochlearis)	Idem		
Clavi-pectoral fascia	F. clavi-pectoralis	F. coraco-clavicularis	F. coraco-clavi-pectoralis
Bicipital aponeurosis	Aponeurosis m. bicipitis	Lacertus fibrosus	
Humero-ulnar head of flexor digitorum sublimis	Caput humero-ulnare	Caput humerale	Caput humerale m. flexoris digitorum superficialis
Extensor digitorum	Idem	M. ext. dig. communis	
Extensor digiti minimi	Idem	M. ext. digiti quinti	
Extensor indicis	Idem	M. ext. indicis proprius	
Oblique head of adductor pollicis	Caput obliquum		Caput obliquum
Transverse head of adductor pollicis	Caput transversum		Caput transversum
Abductor digiti minimi	Idem	M. abd. dig. quinti	
Flexor digiti minimi	Idem	M. fl. dig. quinti brevis	
Opponens digiti minimi	Idem	M. opponens dig. quinti	
Palmar interossei	Mm. interossei palmares	Mm. interossei volares	
Extensor retinaculum	Retinaculum tendinum mm. extensorum	Lig. carpi dorsale	

B.R.	Latin Form of B.R.	B.N.A.	N.K.
Superficial transverse lig. of palm	Lig. palmæ transversum superficiale	Fasciculi transversi	
Flexor retinaculum	Retinaculum tendinum mm. flexorum	Lig. carpi transversum	
Superficial part	Pars superficialis	Lig. carpi volare	
Synovial sheaths	Vaginæ synoviales	Vaginæ mucosæ	Vaginæ synoviales
Fibrous flexor sheaths	Vaginæ fibrosæ digitales tendinum mm. flexorum		

Muscles of Lower Limb

B.R.	Latin Form of B.R.	B.N.A.	N.K.
Saphenous opening	Hiatus saphenus	Fossa ovalis	
Cribriform fascia	F. cribriformis	F. cribrosa	Lamina cribriformis
Subsartorial canal	Canalis subsartorialis	C. adductorius (Hunteri)	
Opening in adductor magnus	Hiatus m. adductoris magni	Hiatus tendineus (adductorius)	Hiatus canalis adductorii
Abductor digiti minimi (Abductor ossis metatarsi quinti)	Idem Idem	M. abductor dig. quinti	
Flexor digiti minimi brevis	Idem	M. flexor digiti quinti brevis	
Flexor digitorum accessorius	Idem	M. quadratus plantæ	
Superior extensor retinaculum	Retinaculum tendinum mm. extensorum superius	Lig. transversum cruris	
Inferior extensor retinaculum	Retinaculum tendinum mm. extensorum inferius	Lig. cruciatum cruris	Lig. cruciforme
Flexor retinaculum	Retinaculum tendinum mm. flexorum	Lig. laciniatum	
Superficial transverse lig. of sole	Lig. plantæ transversum superficiale		
Synovial sheaths	Vaginæ synoviales	Vaginæ mucosæ	Vaginæ synoviales
Fibrous flexor sheaths	Vaginæ fibrosæ digitales tendinum mm. flexorum		

Bursæ

B.R.	Latin Form of B.R.	B.N.A.	N.K.
Bursa of superior oblique muscle of eye	Bursa m. obliqui superioris oculi	Bursa m. trochlearis	
Retrohyoid bursa	B. retrohyoidea		
Bursa of extensor carpi ulnaris	B. m. extensoris carpi ulnaris		
Bursa of tendon of triceps	B. tendinis m. tricipitis	B. subtendinea olecranoidea	
Dorsal digital bursæ	Bursæ digitorum dorsales	Bb. subcutaneæ digitorum dorsales	
Trochanteric bursa of gluteus medius	B. trochanterica m. glutei medii	B. troch. m. gl. med. anterior	
Bursa of obturator externus	B. m. obturatoris externi		
Bursa of psoas major	B. tendinis psoadis majoris	B. ilio-pectinea	
Tibial intertendinous bursa	B. intertendinea tibialis	{ B. m. sartorii propria { B. anserina	

DIGESTIVE SYSTEM

DIGESTIVE SYSTEM	SYSTEMA DIGESTORIUM	APPARATUS DIGESTORIUS	SYSTEMA DIGESTORIUM
Alimentary canal	Canalis alimentarius	Tubus digestorius	
The mouth	Os		
Palato-glossal arch	Arcus palato-glossus	Arcus glosso-palatinus	
Oro-pharyngeal isthmus	Isthmus oro-pharyngeus	Isthmus faucium	
Sublingual papilla	Papilla sublingualis	Caruncula sublingualis	Carunculæ sublinguales
Submandibular gland	Glandula sub-mandibularis	Gl. submaxillaris	Gl. submandibularis
Submandibular duct	Ductus sub-mandibularis	D. submaxillaris (Whartoni)	D. submandibularis

B.R.	Latin Form of B.R.	B.N.A.	N.K.
Foramen of root of tooth	Foramen radicis dentis	F. apicis dentis	
Dentine (Ivory)	Ebur	Substantia eburnea	
Enamel	Adamas dentis	Substantia adamantina	
Cement	Cæmentum	Substantia ossea	
Wisdom tooth	Dens sapientiæ	Dens serotinus	
Folia linguæ	Idem	Papillæ foliatæ	{ Regio foliata Folia
Palato-glossus	Idem	M. glosso-palatinus	
Palato-pharyngeus	Idem	M. pharyngo-palatinus	
Levator palati	Idem	M. levator veli palatini	
Tensor palati	Idem	M. tensor veli palatini	
Glosso-epiglottic fold	Plica glosso-epiglottica	P. glosso-epiglottica mediana	
Pharyngo-epiglottic fold	Plica pharyngo- epiglottica	P. glosso-epiglottica lateralis	
Tonsil	Tonsilla	Tonsilla palatina	
Intratonsillar cleft	Fissura intratonsillaris	Fossa supratonsillaris	
Palato-pharyngeal arch	Arcus palato- pharyngeus	Arcus pharyngo- palatinus	
Pharyngeal isthmus	Isthmus pharyngeus		
Naso-pharyngeal tonsil	Tonsilla naso-pharyngea	T. pharyngea	
Piriform fossa	Fossa piriformis	Recessus piriformis	
Pterygo-mandibular lig.	Lig. pterygo- mandibulare	Raphe pterygo- mandibularis	Rhaphe buci-pharyngea
Cardiac orifice (of stomach)	Orificium cardiacum		
Cardiac notch	Incisura cardiaca		
Angular notch	Incisura angularis		Incisura angularis
Pyloric canal	Canalis pyloricus		
Pyloric constriction	Strictura pylorica		
Pyloric orifice	Orificium pyloricum		
First part (of duodenum)	Pars prima	Pars superior	Pars cranialis
Second part	Pars secunda	Pars descendens	
Third part	Pars tertia	Pars horizontalis (inferior)	Pars caudalis
Fourth part	Pars quarta	Pars ascendens	
Ampulla of bile duct	Ampulla ductus choledochus		
Ileo-colic orifice	Orificium ileo-colicum		Ostium ileo-caeco- colicum
Ileo-colic valve	Valvula ileo-colica	Valvula coli	
Vermiform appendix	Appendix vermiformis	Processus vermiformis	
Descending colon	Colon descendens	Colon descendens	C. descendens
Pelvic colon	Colon pelvinum	Colon sigmoideum	C. sigmoides
Rectum	Intestinum rectum	Intestinum rectum	Intest. rectum
Sacculations of colon	Sacculi coli	Haustra coli	
Longitudinal layer (of rectum)	Stratum longtitudinale		
Circular layer (of rectum)	Stratum circulare		
Rectal glands	Gl. rectales	Gl. intestinales (Lieberkuhni)	
Horizontal folds	Plicæ horizontales	Plicæ transversales	
Anal canal	Canalis analis	Pars analis recti	
Anal columns	Columnæ anales	C. rectales (Morgagnii)	
Anal valves	Valvulæ anales		
Anal sinuses	Sinus anales	S. rectales	
Neck of pancreas	Collum pancreatis		
Right surface (of liver)	Facies dexter		
Anterior surface	Facies anterior		
Lower (or visceral) surface	Facies inferior (visceralis)	F. inferior	F. visceralis
Lower border (of liver)	Margo inferior	Margo anterior	M. ventralis
Notch for lig. teres	Incisura lig. teretis	Incisura umbilicalis	Incisura hepatis
Fissure for lig. teres	Fissura lig. teretis	Fossa venæ umbilicalis	Pars fissuræ sagittalis chordæ venæ um- bilicalis
Fissure for lig. venosum	Fissura lig. venosi	Fossa ductus venosi	Pars chordæ ductus venosi
Groove for vena cava	Sulcus venæ cavæ	Fossa venæ cavæ	
Hepato-biliary capsule	Capsula hepato-biliaris	Capsula fibrosa (Glissoni)	Capsula hepatis

B.R.	Latin Form of B.R.	B.N.A.	N.K.
Bile ductules	Ductuli biliferi	Ductus biliferi	
Right hepatic duct	Ductus hepaticus dexter		
Left hepatic duct	Ductus hepaticus sinister		
Common hepatic duct	Ductus hepaticus communis	D. hepaticus	

RESPIRATORY SYSTEM

RESPIRATORY SYSTEM	SYSTEMA RESPIRATORIUM	APPARATUS RESPIRATORIUS	SYSTEMA RESPIRATORIUM
Posterior apertures of nose	Aperturæ nasi posteriores	Choanæ	
Cartilaginous part (of septum)	Pars cartilaginea	Septum cartilagineum	Pars cartilaginea
Membranous part (of septum)	Pars membranacea	Septum membranaceum	Pars cutanea
Bony part (of septum)	Pars ossea		Pars ossea
Movable part (of septum)	Pars mobilis	Septum mobile	
Upper nasal cartilage	Cartilago nasi superior	C. nasi lateralis	Lamina dorsi nasi septo-dorsalis
Lower nasal cartilage	Cartilago nasi inferior	C. nasi alaris	C. apicis nasi
Septal process	Processus septalis	Crus mediale	
Small cartilages of ala	Cartilagines parvæ alæ	C. alares minores	C. nasales accessoriæ
Subvomerine cartilage	Cartilago subvomerina	C. vomero-nasalis (Jacobsoni)	C. vomero-nasalis
Ethmoidal sinuses	Sinus ethmoidales	Cellulæ ethmoidales	Sinus ethmoidei
Thyroid notch	Incisura thyreoidea	In. thyr. superior	In. thyr. cranialis
Thyro-hyoid membrane	Membrana thyreo-hyoidea	Memb. hyo-thyreoidea	
Median thyro-hyoid lig.	Lig. thyreo-hy. medianum	Lig. hyo-thyr. medium	
Lateral thyro-hyoid lig.	Lig. thyreo-hy. laterale	Lig. hyo-thyr. laterale	
Crico-vocal membrane	Membrana crico-vocalis	Conus elasticus	
Crico-thyroid lig.	Lig. crico-thyreoideum	Lig. crico-thyr. medium	Pars libera coni elastici
Vestibular lig.	Lig. vestibulare	Lig. ventriculare	
Thyro-arytenoid muscle	M. thyreo-arytænoideus	M. thyreo-ary. (externus)	Pars lateralis m. thyreo-arytænoidei
Vestibular fold	Plica vestibularis	Plica ventricularis	
Interarytenoid fold	Plica interarytænoidea		
Sinus of larynx	Sinus laryngis	Ventriculus laryngis (Morgagnii)	Ventriculus laryngis
Saccule of larynx	Sacculus laryngis	Appendix ventriculi	
Trachealis muscle	M. trachealis		
Eparterial bronchus	Br. eparterialis	Ramus bronchialis eparterialis	} Rami bronchales
Hyparterial bronchi	Br. hyparteriales	Rami bronchiales hyparteriales	
Bronchial cartilages	Cartilagines bronchiales		
Posterior border of lung	Margo posterior		
Medial surface	Facies medialis		
Vertebral part	Pars vertebralis		
Mediastinal part	Pars mediastinalis	Facies mediastinalis	
Oblique fissure	Fissura obliqua	Incisura interlobaris	Fissura interlobaris
Horizontal fissure	Fissura horizontalis		F. accessoria pulmonis dextri
Intra-pulmonary bronchi	Bronchi intra-pulmonales	Rami bronchiales	Rami bronchales
Terminal bronchioli	Bronchioli terminales	Br. respiratorii	Bronchuli respiratorii
Cervical pleura	Pleura cervicalis	Cupula pleuræ	
Suprapleural membrane	Membrana supra-pleuralis		
Recesses of pleura	Recessus pleuræ	Sinus pleuræ	
Costo-mediastinal recess	Recessus costo-mediastinalis	Sinus costo-mediastinalis	Sinus costo-mediastinales
Costo-diaphragmatic recess	Recessus costo-diaphragmaticus	Sinus phrenico-costalis	
Phrenico-pleural fascia	Fascia phrenico-pleuralis		

B.R.	Latin Form of B.R.	B.N.A.	N.K.
Mediastinum	Idem	Septum mediastinale	Mediastinum
Anterior mediastinum	Med. thoracis anterius	Cavum mediastinale anterius	Pars ventralis
Posterior mediastinum	Med. thoracis posterius	Cavum mediastinale posterius	Pars dorsalis
Middle mediastinum	Med. thoracis medium		
Superior mediastinum	Med. thoracis superius		Pars cranialis

URO-GENITAL SYSTEM

Uro-Genital System	Systema Uro-Genitale	Apparatus Uro-Genitalis	
Renal fat	Adeps renis	Capsula adiposa	
Renal fascia	Fascia renis		
Fibrous capsule	Capsula fibrosa	Tunica fibrosa	
Convoluted tubules	Tubuli convoluti	T. contorti	
Urine	Urina		
Pelvis of ureter	Pelvis ureteris	Pelvis renalis	
Apex of bladder	Apex vesicæ	Vertex vesicæ	
Median umbilical lig.	Lig. umbilicale medianum	Lig. umb. medium	Chorda urachi
Superior surface	Facies superior		
Infero-lateral surfaces	Facies infero-laterales		
Neck of bladder	Cervix vesicæ		
Sphincter of bladder	Sphincter vesicæ		Sphincter vesicæ
Rugæ (of mucous membrane)	Rugæ		
Interureteric ridge	Crista interureterica		
Stratum spongiosum (of female urethra)	Stratum spongiosum urethræ	Corpus spongiosum urethræ	
Prostatic sinus	Sinus prostaticus		
Spongy part of urethra	Pars spongiosa	Pars cavernosa	
Intrabulbar fossa	Fossa intrabulbaris		
Fossa terminalis	Idem	Fossa navicularis urethræ (Morgagnii)	Fossa navicularis urethræ
Neck of penis	Collum penis	Collum glandis	
Corpus cavernosum penis (R. and L.)	Corpus cavernosum penis (Dextrum et Sinistrum)	Corpus cavernosum penis	
Corpus spongiosum penis	Idem	Corpus cavernosum urethræ	
Bulb of penis	Bulbus penis	Bulbus urethræ	B. corporis cav. ur.
Superficial fascia (of penis)	Fascia superficialis		
Deep fascia	Fascia profunda	Fascia penis	
Smegma penis	Idem	Smegma præputii	
Dartos muscle	M. dartos	Tunica dartos	
Septa of testis	Septa testis	Septula testis	
Lobes of testis	Lobi testis	Lobuli testis	
Convoluted seminiferous tubules	Tubuli seminiferi convoluti	Tub. sem. contorti	Tubuli contorti
Canal of epididymis	Canalis epididymidis	Ductus epipidymidis	
(Vestige of processus vaginalis)	(Vestigium processus vaginalis)	Rudimentum proc. vag,	
Internal spermatic fascia	Fascia spermatica interna	Tunica vaginalis communis (testis et funiculi spermatici)	
External spermatic fascia	Fascia spermatica externa		
Vas deferens	Idem	Ductus deferens	
Sheath of prostate	Vagina (fascialis) prostatæ	Fascia prostatæ	Capsula prostatæ
Capsule of prostate	Capsula prostatæ		
Infero-lateral surfaces	Facies infero-laterales		
Median lobe	Lobus medianus	L. medius	
Lig. of ovary	Lig. ovarii	Lig. ovarii proprium	Chorda utero-ovarica
Ovarian follicles	Folliculi ovarici	F. oöphori	F. ovarii
Cumulus ovaricus	Idem	C. oöphorus	

B.R.	Latin Form of B.R.	B.N.A.	N.K.
Duct of ep-oöphoron	Ductus ep-oöphori	Ductus ep-oöphori longitudinalis (Gartneri	
Tubules of ep-oöphoron	Tubuli ep-oöphori	Ductuli transversi	
Pelvic opening (of uterine tube)	Ostium pelvinum	Ostium abdominale	
Subserous coat (of uterine tube)	Tunica subserosa	Tunica adventitia	
Border of uterus (R. and L,)	Margo (dext. et sinist.)	Margo lateralis	
Cavity of body (of uterus)	Cavum corporis		Cavum corporis
Internal os (of uterus)	Os uteri internum	Orificium internum	Or. internum canalis cervicis
Canal of cervix	Canalis cervicis	Canalis cervicalis	Canalis cervicis
Arbor vitæ uteri	Idem	Plicæ palmatæ	
External os	Os uteri externum	Orificium externum	Or. externum canalis cervicis
Hymen of vagina	Hymen vaginæ	Hymen femininus	Hymen vaginæ
Vestibular fossa	Fossa vestibuli vaginæ	Fossa navicularis	
Commissure of bulbs	Commissura bulborum		

Ontogenetic Terms

Decidua	*Membrana decidua*	Membranæ deciduæ	
Decidua parietalis	Idem	*Decidua vera*	
Uterine part of placenta	*Pars uterina placentæ*	*Placenta uterina*	
Fœtal part	*Pars fœtalis*	*Placenta fœtalis*	
Mesonephros	Idem	*Corpus Wolffii*	
Mesonephric duct	*Ductus mesonephricus*	*Ductus Wolffii*	
Paramesonephric duct	*Ductus para- mesonephricus*	Ductus Muelleri	

PERITONEUM

Extraperitoneal tissue	Tela extraperitonæalis	Tela subserosa	
Greater sac (of peritoneum)	Saccus peritonæi major		
Lesser sac	Saccus peritonæi minor	Bursa omentalis	
Opening into lesser sac	Aditus ad saccum minorem	Foramen epiploicum (Winslowi)	
Gastro-phrenic lig.	Lig. gastro-phrenicum		Pars phrenico-gastrica mesogastrii dorsalis
Lieno-renal lig.	Lig. lieno-renale		
Pelvic mesocolon	Mesocolon pelvinum {	Mesocolon sigmoideum Mesorectum	} Mesosigmoideum
Mesentery of vermiform appendix	Mesenterium appendicis vermiformis	Mesenteriolum pro- cessus vermiformis	
Superior duodenal recess	Recessus duodenalis superior	R. duodeno-jejunalis	
Inferior duodenal recess	Recessus duodenalis inferior		
Paraduodenal recess	Recessus paraduodenalis		
Retroduodenal recess	Recessus retroduodenalis		
Superior duodenal fold	Plica duodenalis superior	Pl. duodeno-jejunalis	Pl. duodeno-mesocolica cranialis
Inferior duodenal fold	Plica duodenalis inferior		
Paraduodenal fold	Plica paraduodenalis		
Vascular fold of cæcum	Plica cæcalis vascularis		Plica ileo-cæcalis cranialis
Recess of pelvic mesocolon	Recessus mesocoli pelvini	Recessus intersigmoideus	
Paracolic grooves	Sulci paracolici	Recessus paracolici	
Median umbilical fold	Plica umbilicalis mediana	Pl. umb. media	
Fold of epigastric artery	Plica art. epigastricæ	Pl. epigastrica	
Infundibulo-pelvic lig.	Lig. infundibulo- pelvinium	Lig. suspensorium ovarii	Plica suspensoria ovarii

B.R.	Latin Form of B.R.	B.N.A.	N.K.
Sacro-genital fold	Plica sacro-genitalis	Plica recto-vesicalis	
Recto-uterine (or recto-vaginal) pouch	Excavatio recto-uterina (recto-vaginalis)	Excav. recto-uterina (Cavum Douglasi)	Excavatio recto-uterina

DUCTLESS GLANDS

DUCTLESS GLANDS	GLANDULÆ SINE DUCTIBUS	GLANDULÆ CLAUSÆ	
Parathyroid glands	Glandulæ parathyreoideæ		Gll. parathyreoideæ
Medial end (of spleen)	Extremitas medialis	Extr. superior	Extr. vertebralis
Lateral end (of spleen)	Extremitas lateralis	Extr. inferior	Extr. ventralis
Upper border	Margo superior	Margo anterior	M. acutus
Lower border	Margo inferior	Margo posterior	M. obtusus
Visceral surface	Facies visceralis		F. visceralis
Renal impression	Impressio renalis	Facies renalis	Pars renalis
Gastric impression	Impressio gastrica	Facies gastrica	Pars gastrica
Pancreatic impression	Impressio pancreatica		
Colic impression	Impressio colica		

NEUROLOGY

Central Nervous System	Systema Nervosum Centrale	Systema Nervorum Centrale	
Spinal cord	**Chorda spinalis**	**Medulla spinalis**	
Regions (of spinal cord)	Regiones		
Segments (of spinal cord)	Segmenta		
White columns (of spinal cord)	Columnæ albæ	Funiculi medullæ spinalis	Fasciculi medullæ spinalis
Grey columns (Horns in section)	Columnæ griseæ (Cornua)	C. griseæ	
White commissure	Commissura alba	C. anterior alba	C. ventralis alba
Grey commissure	Commissura grisea {	C. anterior grisea C. posterior	C. grisea
Thoracic nucleus	N. thoracicus	N. dorsalis (Stillingi ; Clarki)	N. dorsalis
Intersegmental tracts	Fasciculi intersegmentales	F. proprii	
Anterior spino-thalamic tract	Fasciculus spino-thalamicus anterior		Tractus spino-thalamicus
Vestibulo-spinal tract	F. vestibulo-spinalis		Tractus vest.-spin.
Olivo-spinal tract	F. olivo-spinalis		Tractus olivo-spinalis
Anterior spino-cerebellar tract	F. spino-cerebellaris anterior	F. antero-lateralis superficialis (Gowersi)	T. cerebello-spinalis ventralis
Posterior spino-cerebellar tract	F. spino-cerebellaris posterior	F. cerebello-spinalis	T. cerebello-spinalis dorsalis
Postero-lateral tract	F. postero-lateralis		
Lateral spino-thalamic	F. spino-thalamicus lateralis		
Spino-tectal tract	F. spino-tectalis		Tractus spino-tectalis
Tecto-spinal tract	F. tecto-spinalis		Tractus tecto-spinalis
Rubro-spinal tract	F. rubro-spinalis		Tractus rubro-spinalis
Ponto-spinal fibres	Fibræ ponto-spinales		
Septo-marginal tract	Fasc. septo-marginalis		
Semilunar tract	F. semilunaris		

Brain

Base of brain	Basis encephali	Basis cerebri	Facies basialis cerebri
Vallecula of cerebrum	Vallecula cerebri		Vallecula cerebri lateralis
Inferior cerebellar peduncle	Pedunculus cerebelli inferior	Corpus restiforme	Crus medullo-cerebellare
Middle cerebellar peduncle	Pedunculus cerebelli medius	Brachium pontis	Crus ponto-cerebellare
Superior cerebellar peduncle	Pedunculus cerebelli superior	Brachium conjunctivum	Crus cerebello-cerebrale

B.R.	Latin Form of B.R.	B.N.A.	N.K.
Fasciculus cuneatus	Idem	Funiculus cuneatus ⎫	Partes lateralis et
Fasciculus gracilis	Idem	Funiculus gracilis ⎭	medialis fasc. dorsalis
Gracile tubercle	Tuberculum gracile	Clava	
Anterior and posterior external arcuate fibres	Fibræ arcuatæ externæ anteriores et posteriores	Fibræ arcuatæ externæ	Fibræ arcuatæ externæ ventrales et dorsales
Circumolivary bundle of pyramid	Fasc. circumolivaris pyramidis		
Nucleus of circum-olivary bundle	Nucleus fasc. circum-olivaris		
Median raphe (of medulla and pons)	Raphe medianum	Raphe	Rhaphe
Reticular formation	Formatio reticularis	Substantia reticularis	
Dorsal nucleus of vagus	N. dorsalis n. vagi	N. alæ cinereæ	
Gracile nucleus	N. gracilis	N. funiculi gracilis ⎫	Nn. partium medialis et
Cuneate nucleus	N. cuneatus	N. funiculi cuneati ⎭	lateralis fasc. dors.
Olivary nucleus	N. olivaris	N. olivaris inferior	N. olivæ
Sensory decussation	Decussatio sensoria	D. lemniscorum	
Olivo-cerebellar tract	Fasc. olivo-cerebellaris	Fibræ cerebello-olivares	Tractus olivo-cerebellares
Inferior salivary nucleus	N. salivarius inferior		N. (originis) salivatorius medullæ oblongatæ
Ventral and dorsal cochlear nuclei	Nuclei n. cochlearis, ventralis et dorsalis	Nuclei n. cochlearis	Nuclei terminales ventralis et dorsalis n. cochleæ
Lateral, medial, superior and inferior vestibular nuclei	Nuclei n. vestibularis lateralis et medialis et superior et inferior	Nuclei n. vestibularis	Nuclei terminales later-alis, medialis, dor-salis, spinalis, n. vestibuli
Motor nucleus of tri-geminal nerve	Nucleus motorius n. trigemini	Nuclei motorii n. tri-gemini	Nucleus originis n. trigemini
Superior sensory nucleus of trigeminal	Nucleus sensorius superior n. trigemini		Nucleus terminalis n. trigemini
Mesencephalic tract of trigeminal nerve	Tractus mesen-cephalicus n. trigemini	Radix descendeus (mesencephalica) n. trigemini	
Superior salivary nucleus	N. salivarius superior		N. (originis) salivatorius pontis
Dorsal nucleus of corpus trapezoideum	N. dorsalis corporis trapezoidei	N. olivaris superior	N. olivaris metencephali
Ventral n. of c. trap.	N. ventralis corp. trap.		
Transverse fibres of pons	Fibræ pontis transversæ	⎧ Fibræ pontis profundæ ⎨ Fibræ pontis super-⎩ ficialis	
Cerebellar folia	Folia cerebelli	Gyri cerebelli	
Fissures of cerebellum	Fissuræ cerebelli	Sulci cerebelli	
Anterior lobe	Lobus anterior		
Lobulus culminis	Idem	Culmen monticuli	
Anterior lunate lobule	Lobulus lunatus anterior	Pars anterior lobuli quadrangularis	
Fissura prima	Idem		
Middle lobe	Lobus medius		
Lobulus clivi	Idem	Declive monticuli	
Lobulus folii	Idem	Folium vermis	
Lobulus tuberis	Idem	Tuber vermis	
Post-pyramidal fissure	Fissura post-pyramidalis		
Posterior lunate lobule	Lobulus lunatus posterior	Pars posterior lobuli quadrangularis	
Ansiform lobule, superior surface	Lobulus ansiformis, facies superior	Lobulus semilunaris superior	
Horizontal fissure	Fissura horizontalis	Sulcus horizontalis	
Ansiform lobule, in-ferior surface	Lobulus ansiformis, facies inferior	⎧ Lobulus semilunaris ⎨ inferior ⎨ Lobulus gracilis ⎩ Lobulus biventer	
Retro-tonsillar fissure	Fissura retro-tonsillaris		
Parafloccular fissure	Fissura parafloccularis		
Posterior lobe	Lobus posterior		
Fissura secunda	Idem		

B.R.	Latin Form of B.R.	B.N.A.	N.K.
Postnodular fissure	Fissura postnodularis		
Paraflocculus	Idem		
Molecular layer	Stratum moleculare	Stratum cinereum	
White matter (of cerebellum)	Substantia alba	Corpus medullare	
White laminæ	Laminæ albæ	Laminæ medullares	
Floor of fourth ventricle	Solum ventriculi quarti	Fossa rhomboidea	Fossa rhomboides
Lateral recess of fourth ventricle	Recessus lateralis ventriculi quarti	Recessus lat. fossæ rhomboideæ	
Vagal triangle	Trigonum n. vagi	Ala cinerea	
Vestibular area	Area nucleorum n. vestibularis	Area acustica	
Auditory striæ	Striæ auditoriæ	Striæ medullares	
Superior medullary velum	Velum medullare superius	Velum medallare anterius	
Inferior medullary velum (R. & L.)	Velum medullare inferius (dext. et sinist.)	Velum medullare posterius	
Median aperture of fourth vent.	Apertura mediana vent. quarti	Ap. medialis v. q. (foramen Magendii)	Ap. mediana rhombinecphali
Medial sulcus (of midbrain)	Sulcus medialis	S. n. oculomotorii	
Tectum (of midbrain)	Tectum (mesencephali)	Lamina quadrigemina	
Superior quadrigeminal body	Corpus quadrigeminum superius	Colliculus superior	Colliculus rostralis
Inferior quadrigeminal body	Corpus quadrigeminum inferius	Colliculus inferior	Colliculus caudalis
Nucleus of sup. q. body	Nucleus corp. quad. sup.	Stratum griseum coll. sup.	Str. gris. coll. rostralis
Aqueduct of midbrain	Aquæductus mesencephali	Aquæductus cerebri (Sylvii)	Aquæductus mesencephali
Central gray matter	Substantia grisea centralis	Stratum griseum centrale	
Mesencephalic nucleus of trigeminal nerve	Nucleus mesencephalicus n. trigemini	Nucleus radicis descendentis n. trigemini	Nucleus originis accessorius n. trigemini
Decussation of superior cerebellar peduncles	Decussatio pedunculorum cerebellarium superiorum	Decussatio brachii conjunctivi	D. crurum cerebellocerebralium
Decussation of tecto-spinal tracts	Decussatio fasciculorum tecto-spinalium		
Decussation of rubro-spinal tracts	Decussatio fasciculorum rubro-spinalium		
Cerebro-spinal fibres	Fibræ cerebro-spinales		Tractus cortico-spinalis
Cerebro-pontine fibres	Fibræ cerebro-pontiles		Tractus cortico-pontini
Interpeduncular nucleus	N. interpeduncularis	Ganglion interpedunculare	
Subthalamic nucleus	N. subthalamicus	N. hypothalamicus (corpus Luysii)	
Mamillo-thalamic tract	Fasc. mamillo-thalamicus	Fasc. thalamo-mamillaris (Vicq d' Azyr)	Fasc. mamillo-thalamicus
Mamillo-peduncular tract	Fasc. mamillo-peduncularis	Fasciculi pedunculo-mamillares	Tractus mamillo-tegmentalis
Mamillo-tegmental tract	Fasc. mamillo-tegmentalis		
Connexus interthalamicus	Idem	Massa intermedia	
Stria habenularis	Idem	Stria medullaris	
Archipallium	Idem		
Neopallium	Idem		
Supero-lateral surface (of hemisphere)	Facies supero-lateralis	F. convexa	
Lateral sulcus	Sulcus lateralis	Fissura cerebri lateralis (Sylvii)	Fissura cerebri lateralis
Precentral gyrus	Gyrus præcentralis	G. centralis anterior	G. præcentralis
Middle frontal sulcus	Sulcus frontalis medius		
Posterior part (of inf. frontal gyrus)	Pars posterior	Pars opercularis	
Inferior temporal sulcus	S. temporalis inferior	S. temporalis medius	
Postcentral gyrus	G. postcentralis	G. centralis posterior	G. postcentralis

B.R.	Latin Form of B.R.	B.N.A.	N.K.
Postcentral sulcus	S. postcentralis	} S. interparietalis	{ S. postcentralis
Intraparietal sulcus	S. intraparietalis		{ S. interparietalis
Anterior part (of inferior parietal lobule)	Pars anterior	Gyrus supramarginalis	G. circumflexus
Middle part	Pars media	G. angularis	
Posterior part	Pars posterior		
Lunate sulcus	S. lunatus		
Long gyri of insula	G. longi insulæ	Gyrus longus insulæ	
Opercula	Idem	Operculum	
Orbital operculum	Op. orbitale	} Pars frontalis	Operculum frontale
Frontal operculum	Op. frontale	Pars parietalis	Operculum parietale
Fronto-parietal	Op. fronto-parietale		
Paraterminal gyrus	G. paraterminalis	G. subcallosus (pedunculus corporis callosi)	
Suprasplenial sulcus	S. suprasplenialis	S. subparietalis	
Parieto-occipital sulcus	S. parieto-occipitalis	Fissura parieto-occipitalis	S. parieto-occipitalis
Calcarine sulcus	S. calcarinus	} Fissura calcarina	S. calcarinus
Post-calcarine sulcus	S. post-calcarinus		
Medial frontal gyrus	G. frontalis medialis		
Inferior surface of cerebral hemisphere	Facies inferior hemisphærii cerebri		
Orbital surface	Facies orbitalis		
Tentorial surface	Facies tentorialis		
Collateral sulcus	S. collateralis	Fissura collateralis	S. collateralis
Rhinal sulcus	S. rhinalis		
(Hippocampal sulcus)	(S. hippocampalis)	Fissura hippocampi	S. hippocampi
Isthmus of gyrus cinguli	Isthmus gyri cinguli	Isthmus gyri fornicati	
Occipito-temporal sulcus	S. occipito-temporalis	S. temporalis inferior	S. temporalis basialis
Medial occipito-temporal gyrus	G. occipito-temporalis medialis	G. fusiformis	G. occipito-temporalis lateralis
Lateral occipito-temporal gyrus	G. occipito-temporalis lateralis		
Olfactory part (of anterior commissure)	Pars olfactoria	Pars anterior	Pars olfactoria (commissuræ rostalis)
Forceps minor (of corpus callosum)	Forceps minor		
Forceps major (of corpus callosum)	Forceps major		
Roots (of olfactory tract)	Radices	Striæ	
Olfactory pyramid	Pyramis olfactoria	Trigonum olfactorium	
Diagonal band (of ant. perf. substance)	Fasciculus diagonalis		
Piriform area	Area piriformis		
Hippocampal formation	Formatio hippocampalis		
Indusium griseum	Idem		Stratum griseum
Pes hippocampi	Idem	Digitationes hippocampi	
Dentate gyrus	G. dentatus	Fascia dentata hippocampi	G. dentatus
Tail of dentate gyrus	Cauda gyri dentatis		
Splenial gyrus	G. splenialis	Fasciola cinerea	G. fasciolaris
Anterior column (of fornix)	Columna anterior	Columna fornicis	
Posterior column (of fornix)	Columna posterior	Crus fornicis	
Septum lucidum	Idem	S. pellucidum	
Choroid fissure	Fissura chorioidea		
Basal nuclei	Nuclei basales		
Body of caudate nucleus	Corpus nuclei caudati		
Amygdaloid nucleus	N. amygdaloideus	N. amygdalæ	
Stria semicircularis	Idem	Stria terminalis	
Strata of cortex (cerebri)	Strata corticis		
Striate area	Area striata		
Visual stria	Stria visualis		
Association fibres	Fibræ annectantes	Fibræ arcuatæ cerebri	Tractus nervosi associationis

B.R.	Latin Form of B.R.	B.N.A.	N.K.
Fronto-occipital bundle	Fasc. fronto-occipitalis		
Itinerant fibres	Fibræ itinerantes		Tractus nervosi projectionis
Base of corona radiata	Basis coronæ radiatæ		
Anterior limb (of internal capsule)	Crus anterius	Pars frontalis	Crus frontale
Posterior limb	Crus posterius	Pars occipitalis	Crus occipitale
Lentiform part	Pars lentiformis		
Retro-lentiform part	Pars retro-lentiformis		
Optic radiation	Radiatio optica	R. occipito-thalamica (Gratioleti)	Radiatio optica (Gratioleti)
Auditory radiation	Radiatio auditoria		
Thalamo-cortical fibres	Fibræ thalamo-corticales		Tractus thalamo-corticales

Meninges

B.R.	Latin Form of B.R.	B.N.A.	N.K.
Extra-dural space	Cavum extradurale	Cavum epidurale	Cavum extradurale
Cavum trigeminale	Cavum trigeminale		
Arachnoid mater	Arachnoidea mater	Arachnoidea	Arachnoides
Subarachnoid space	Cavum subarachnoideum	C. subarachnoideale	C. lepto-meningicum
Subarachnoid cisterns	Cisternæ subarachnoideæ	C. subarachnoideales	C. lepto-meningicæ
Cistern of lateral sulcus	Cisterna sulci lateralis	C. fossæ lateralis cerebri	
Arachnoid villi	Villi arachnoidei		
Arachnoid granulations	Granulationes arachnoideæ	G. arachnoideales (Pacchioni)	Granula meningica
Posterior median cervical septum	Septum cervicale medianum posterius	Septum cervicale intermedium	

Peripheral Nervous System	Systema Nervosum Periphericum	Systema Nervorum Periphericum	N.K.
Communicating branch	Ramus communicans	Ramus anastomoticus	Ramus communicans
Cranial nerves	**Nervi craniales**	**Nervi cerebrales**	**Nervi capitales**
Motor root of ciliary ganglion	Radix motoria g. ciliaris	Radix brevis ganglii ciliaris	
Sensory root (of trigeminal nerve)	Radix sensoria	Portio major	
Motor root (of trigeminal nerve)	Radix motoria	Portio minor	
Trigeminal ganglion	Ganglion n. trigemini	G. semilunare	
Communicating branch with ciliary ganglion	Ramus communicans cum ganglio ciliari	Radix longa g. ciliaris	
Internal nasal branches (of anterior ethmoidal nerve)	Rami nasales interni {	Rami nasales anteriores R. nasales interni R. nasales mediales R. nasales laterales	
Ganglionic branches (of maxillary nerve)	Rami communicantes cum ganglio spheno-palatino	Nn. spheno-palatini	Nn. pterygo-palatini
Superior dental nerves	Nervi dentales superiores	Rami alveolares superiores	Rami alveolares maxillares
Inferior dental nerve	Nervus dentalis inferioris	Nervus alveolaris inferior	N. alveolaris mandibularis
Short spheno-palatine nerves	Nn. spheno-palatini breves	{ Rami nasales posteriores superiores laterales et mediales	
Long spheno-palatine nerve	N. spheno-palatinus longus	N. naso-palatinus (Scarpæ)	N. naso-palatinus
Greater palatine nerve	N. palatinus major	N. palatinus anterior	N. palatinus major
Lesser palatine nerves	Nn. palatini minores	N. palatinus medius et posterior	Nn. palatini medius et minor
Buccal nerve	N. buccalis	N. buccinatorius	N. buccalis
Submandibular ganglion	G. submandibulare	G. submaxillare	G. submandibulare
Glandular branches	Rami glandulares	R. submaxillares	R. glandulares

B.R.	Latin Form of B.R.	B.N.A.	N.K.
Sublingual ganglion	G. sublinguale		G. sublinguale (var.)
Motor root (of facial nerve)	Radix motoria		
Sensory root	Radix sensoria	N. intermedius	
Genu of facial nerve	Genu n. facialis	Geniculum n. facialis	
Ganglion of facial nerve	Ganglion n. facialis	G. geniculi	
Root of lesser superficial petrosal nerve (from VII)	Radix n. petrosi superficialis minoris		
Mandibular branch (of facial)	Ramus mandibularis	Ramus marginalis mandibulæ	
Auditory nerve	N. auditorius	N. acusticus	N. stato-acusticus
Inferior ganglion (of glosso-phar. n.)	G. inferius	G. petrosum	G. extracraniale
Root of lesser superficial petrosal n. (from tympanic plexus)	Radix n. petrosi superficialis minoris		
Superior ganglion (of vagus)	G. superius	G. jugulare	
Inferior ganglion.	G. inferius	G. nodosum	
External laryngeal nerve	N. laryngeus externus	Ramus externus nervi laryngei superioris	Ramus externus nervi laryngici cranialis
Internal laryngeal nerve	N. laryngeus internus	Ramus internus nervi laryngei superioris	
Cardiac branches (of vagus)	Rami cardiaci	Rami cardiaci superiores	Rami cardiaci craniales
Recurrent laryngeal nerve	N. laryngeus recurrens	N. recurrens	
Cardiac branches	Rami cardiaci	Rami cardiaci inferiores	Rami cardiaci caudales
Pharyngeal branches	Rami pharyngei	{ N. laryngeus inferior { Ramus anterior { Ramus posterior	N. laryngeus caudalis Ramus ventralis Ramus dorsalis
Laryngeal branches	Rami laryngei		
Pulmonary branches (of vagus)	Rami pulmonales	Rami bronchiales anteriores et posteriores	Rr. br. ventrales et dorsales
Œsophageal plexus	Plexus œsophageus	Plexus œsoph. ant. et post.	Pl. œs. ventralis et dorsalis
Cranial root (of accessory nerve)	Radix cranialis		Radix myelencephalica
Spinal root (of accessory nerve)	Radix spinalis		Radix spinalis
Accessory branch to vagus	Ramus accessorius ad n. vagum	Ramus internus	Ramus medialis
Terminal branches of XII	Rami terminales	Rami linguales	

Spinal Nerves

B.R.	Latin Form of B.R.	B.N.A.	N.K.
Posterior primary ramus (of spinal nerve)	Ramus primarius posterior	Ramus posterior	Ramus dorsalis
Anterior primary ramus (of spinal nerve)	Ramus primarius anterior	Ramus anterior	Ramus ventralis
Grey and white rami communicantes	Rami communicantes, grisei et albi	Ramus communicans	
Anterior cutaneous nerve of neck	N. cutaneus cervicis anterior	N. cutaneus colli	
Lateral supraclavicular nerves	Nn. supraclaviculares laterales	Nn. supraclaviculares posteriores	⎫
Intermediate supra-clavicular nerves	Nn. supraclaviculares intermedii	Nn. supraclaviculares medii	⎬ Nn. supraclaviculares
Medial supraclavicular nerves	Nn. supraclaviculares mediales	Nn. supraclaviculares anteriores	⎭
Nervus descendens cervicalis	Idem		N. cervicalis descendens
Roots of brachial plexus	Radices plexus		Radices plexus
Nerve to rhomboids	N. mm. rhomboideorum	N. dorsalis scapulæ	
Nerve to serratus anterior	N. m. serrati anterioris	N. thoracalis longus	N. thoracicus longus
Upper trunk (of brachial plexus)	Truncus superior		Truncus cranialis
Middle trunk (of brachial plexus)	Truncus medius		Truncus intermedius

B.R.	Latin Form of B.R.	B.N.A.	N.K.
Lower trunk (of brachial plexus)	Truncus inferior		Trucus candalis
Pectoral nerves	Nn. pectorales	Nn. thoracales anteriores	Nn. thoracici ventrales
Nerve to latissimus dorsi	N. m. latissimi dorsi	N. thoraco-dorsalis	
Circumflex nerve	N. circumflexus	N. axillaris	
Upper lateral cutaneous nerve of upper arm	N. cutaneus brachii lateralis superior	N. cutaneus brachii lateralis	N. cutaneus brachii radialis
Radial nerve	N. radialis	{ N. radialis / Ramus superficialis	
Posterior interosseous nerve	N. interosseus posterior	{ Ramus profundus / N. interosseus dorsalis	
Lower lateral cutaneous nerve of upper arm	N. cutaneus brachii lateralis inferior	} N. cutaneus anti- brachii dorsalis	
Posterior cutaneous nerve of forearm	N. cutaneus antebrachii posterior		
Roots of median nerve	Radices n. mediani		
Anterior interosseous nerve	N. interosseus anterior	N. interosseus volaris	
Palmar cutaneous branch	Ramus palmaris cutaneus	Ramus palmaris	
Palmar digital nerves	Nn. digitales palmares	{ Nn. digitales volares communes / Nn. dig. vol. proprii	
Superficial terminal branch (of ulnar)	Ramus terminalis superficialis	Ramus superficialis	
Deep terminal branch (of ulnar)	Ramus terminalis profundus	Ramus profundus	
Subcostal nerve	N. subcostalis		N. subcostalis
Gluteal branches (of lumbar ns.)	Rami glutæi	Nn. clunium superiores	Nn. clunium craniales
Gluteal branches (of sacral ns.)	Rami glutæi	Nn. clunium medii	
Gluteal branches (of post. cutan. n.)	Rami glutæi	Nn. clunium inferiores	Nn. clunium caudales
Genital branch (of genito-femoral)	Ramus genitalis	N. spermaticus externus	Ramus genitalis
Femoral branch (of genito-femoral)	Ramus femoralis	N. lumbo-inguinalis	Ramus femoralis
Medial and intermediate cutaneous nerves of thigh	Nn. cutanei femoris medialis et intermedius	Rami cutanei anteriores (n. femoralis)	Rami cutanei ventrales
N. to quadratus femoris	N. m. quadrati femoris		
N. to obturator internus	N. m. obturatoris interni		
Perforating cutaneous nerve	N. cutaneus perforans		
Perineal branch of fourth sacral	Ramus perinealis n. sacralis quarti		
Lateral popliteal nerve	N. popliteus lateralis	N. peronæus communis	N. fibularis communis
Sural communicating branch	Ramus communicans cum n. surali	Ramus anastomoticus peronæus	Ramus communicans fibularis
Musculo-cutaneous nerve	N. musculo-cutaneus	N. peronæus superficialis	N. fibularis superficialis
Medial branch	Ramus medialis	N. cutaneus dorsalis medialis	N. cutaneus dorsi pedis tibialis
Lateral branch	Ramus lateralis	N. cutaneus dorsalis intermedius	N. cutaneus dorsi pedis medius
Anterior tibial nerve	N. tibialis anterior	N. peronæus profundus	N. fibularis profundus
Digital branch	Ramus digitalis	Nn. digitales dorsales hallucis lateralis et digiti secundi medialis	
Medial popliteal nerve	N. popliteus medialis	} N. tibialis	
Posterior tibial nerve	N. tibialis posterior		
Nerve to popliteus	N. m. poplitei		
Sural nerve	N. suralis	N. cutaneus suræ medialis	N. suralis
Plantar digital nerves	Nn. digitales plantares	{ Nn. digitales plantares communes / Nn. dig. pl. proprii	

B.R. Autonomic Nervous System	Latin Form of B.R. Systema Nervosum Autonomicum	B.N.A.	N.K.
Sympathetic root of submandibular ganglion	Radix sympathica ganglii submandibularis	Radix sympathica ganglii submaxillaris	Radix sympathica g. submandibularis (et sublingualis)
Sympathetic root of sublingual ganglion	Radix sympathica ganglii sublingualis		
Sympathetic root of otic ganglion	Radix sympathica ganglii otici		Radix symp. g. otici
Thyroid branches (of middle ganglion)	Rami thyreoidei		
Cardiac branches (of thoracic sympathetic)	Rami cardiaci		
Œsophageal branches (of thoracic sympathetic)	Rami œsophagei		
Lumbar part of sympathetic system	Pars lumbalis	Pars abdominalis	
Ganglion impar	Idem		
Pelvic plexus	Plexus pelvinus		
Plexus of vas deferens	Plexus vasis deferentis	Plexus deferentialis	
Parasympathetic nervous system	Systema nervosum parasympathicum		Systema nervorum parasympathicum
Cranial part	Pars cranialis		Pars encephalica
Spinal part	Pars spinalis		Pars sacralis
Pelvic splanchnic nerves	Nn. splanchnici pelvini		
Parasympathetic ganglia	Ganglia parasympathica		

ORGANS OF THE SENSES

Eye

Optic vesicle	*Vesicula optica*	*Vesicula ophthalmica*	
Optic cup	*Caliculus opticus*	*Caliculus ophthalmicus*	
Mesothelium of anterior chamber	Mesothelium cameræ anterioris	Endothelium cameræ anterioris	
Irido-corneal angle	Angulus irido-cornealis	Angulus iridis	Angulus irido-cornealis
Lens	Lens	Lens crystallina	
Optic disc	Discus opticus	Papilla n. optici	P. fasciculi optici
Fascial sheath of eyeball	Vagina fascialis bulbi	Fascia bulbi (Tenoni)	Capsula bulbi
Muscles of orbit	Musculi orbitæ	Musculi oculi	Musculi bulbi
Tarsus of upper eyelid	Tarsus palpebræ superioris	Tarsus superior	Tarsi palpebrarum
Tarsus of lower eyelid	Tarsus palpebræ inferioris	Tarsus inferior	
Lateral palpebral lig.	Lig. palpebrale laterale		Lig. palpebrale laterale
Ocular part of conjunctiva	Pars ocularis conjunctivæ	Tunica conjunctiva bulbi	
Palpebral part of conjunctiva	Pars palpebralis conjunctivæ	Tunica conjunctiva palpebrarum	
Lacrimal gland	Glandula lacrimalis	Gl. lacrimalis superior	Pars orbitalis (gl. lac.)
Palpebral process	Processus palpebralis	Gl. lacrimalis inferior	Pars palpebralis
Ducts	Ductus	Ductuli excretorii	
Lacrimal canaliculi	Canaliculi lacrimales	Ductus lacrimales	Ductuli lacrimales

Ear

Maculæ of membranous labyrinth	Maculæ labyrinthi membranacei	Maculæ acusticæ	Maculæ staticæ
Macula of utricle	Macula utriculi	Macula acustica utriculi	Macula statica utriculi
Macula of saccule	Macula sacculi	Macula acustica sacculi	Macula statica sacculi
Aqueduct of cochlea	Aquæductus cochleæ	Ductus perilymphatici	Ductus perilymphacei
Duct of cochlea	Ductus cochleæ	D. cochlearis	
Foramina for nerves	Foramina nervorum	F. nervosa	
Semicircular canals	Canales semicirculares	C. S. ossei	
Auditory meatus	Meatus auditorius	Meatus acusticus	
Middle ear (tympanum)	Auris media (tympanum)		Tympanum

B.R.	Latin Form of B.R.	B.N.A.	N.K.
Roof of tympanum	Tegmen tympani	Paries tegmentalis	
Floor of tympanum	Solum tympani	Paries jugularis	
Anterior wall of tympanum	Paries anterior	Paries carotica	Paries caroticus
Posterior wall of tympanum	Paries posterior	Paries mastoidea	P. mastoideus
Medial wall of tympanum	Paries medialis	Paries labyrinthica	P. labyrinthicus
Lateral wall of tympanum	Paries lateralis	Paries membranacea	P. membranaceus
Pyramid of tympanum	Pyramis tympani	Eminentia pyramidalis	
Radial fibres of tymp. memb.	Fibræ radiatæ	Stratum radiatum	
Circular fibres of tymp. memb.	Fibræ circulares	Stratum circulare	
Head of stapes	Caput stapedis	Capitulum stapedis	
Short process of incus	Processus brevis	Crus breve	
Long process of incus	Processus longus	Crus longum	
Lentiform nodule	Nodulus lentiformis	Processus lenticularis	
Head of malleus	Caput mallei	Capitulum mallei	
Mastoid air cells	Cellulæ pneumaticæ mastoideæ	Cellulæ mastoideæ	
(Tympanic air cells)	(Cellulæ pneumaticæ tympanicæ)	Cellulæ tympanicæ	
Pharyngo-tympanic tube	Tuba pharyngo-tympanica	Tuba auditiva	Tuba pharyngo-tympanica
Antihelix (of auricle)	Antihelix	Anthelix	
Scaphoid fossa	Fossa scaphoidea	Scapha	

Skin

B.R.	Latin Form of B.R.	B.N.A.	N.K.
Zones of epidermis	Zonæ epidermidis	Strata epidermidis	
Subcutaneous fatty tissue	Tela adiposa subcutanea	Panniculus adiposus	
Oval corpuscles	Corpuscula ovalia	Corp. tactus (Meissneri)	Corpuscula tactus
Collateral borders (of nails)	Margines collaterales	Margines laterales	
Zones (of nails)	Zonæ unguis	Strata unguis	
Mammary gland	Glandula mammaria		
Lobes of mammary gland	Lobi gl. mammariæ	Lobi mammæ	
Male mammary gland	Gl. mammaria virilis	Mamma virilis	
Accessary mammary glands	Gl. mammariæ accessoriæ	Mammæ accessoriæ	

BLOOD VASCULAR SYSTEM

Blood Vascular System	Systema Vasorum Sanguineorum	Angiologia	Systema Vasorum

Heart

B.R.	Latin Form of B.R.	B.N.A.	N.K.
Left surface (of heart)	Facies sinistra		
Anterior interventricular groove	Sulcus interventricularis anterior	S. longitudinalis anterior	S. interventricularis ventralis
Inferior interventricular groove	Sulcus interventricularis inferior	S. longitudinalis posterior	S. interventricularis dorsalis
Auricles of atrium	Auriculæ atriorum	Auricula cordis	
Membranous part (of septum)	Pars membranacea	Septum membranaceum	Pars membranacea
Right atrio-ventricular (tricuspid) orifice	Orificium (tricuspidatum) atrio-ventriculare dextrum	} Ostium venosum	Ostia venosa { Ostium atrio-ventriculare dextrum, O. a.-v. sinistrum
Left atrio-ventricular (mitral) orifice	Orificium (mitrale) atrio-ventriculare sinistrum		
Pulmonary orifice	Orificium trunci pulmonalis	} Ostium arteriosum	Ostium arteriosum dextrum
Aortic orifice	Orificium aortæ		Ostium arteriosum sinistrum
Annulus ovalis	Idem	Limbus fossæ ovalis (Vieussenii)	

B.R.	Latin Form of B.R.	B.N.A.	N.K.
Right atrio-ventricular (tricuspid) valve	Valvula (tricuspidalis) atrio-ventricularis dextra	Valvula tricuspidalis	
Inferior cusp	Cuspis inferior	Cuspis posterior	Cuspis dorsalis
Infundibulo-ventricular crest	Crista infundibulo-ventricularis	C. supra-ventricularis	
Infundibulum	Idem	Conus arteriosus	
Pulmonary valve	Valvula trunci pulmonalis	Valvulæ semilunares a. pulm.	Valvula a. pulmonalis
Right cusp	Cuspis dextra	Valvula semilunaris anterior	Velum semilunare sinistrum
Posterior cusp	Cuspis posterior	Valvula semilunaris dextra	Velum semilunare dextrum
Left cusp	Cuspis sinistra	Valvula semilunaris sinistra	Velum semilunare dorsale
Anterior papillary muscle	M. papillaris anterior		M. papillaris ventralis
Inferior papillary muscle	M. papillaris inferior ⎫		Mm. papillares parvi
Septal papillary muscles	Mm. papillares septales ⎭		
Moderator band	Fasciculus moderator		Trabecula septo marginalis
Left atrio-ventricular (mitral) valve	Valvula (mitralis) atrio-ventricularis sinistra	Valvula bicuspidalis (mitralis)	
Aortic vestibule	Vestibulum aortæ		
Aortic valve	Valvula aortæ	Valvulæ semilunares aortæ	Valvula aortæ
Left cusp	Cuspis sinistra	Valvula semilunaris posterior	Velum semilunare dextrum
Right cusp	Cuspis dextra	Valvula semilunaris dextra	Velum semilunare ventrale
Anterior cusp	Cuspis anterior	Valvula semilunaris sinistra	Velum semilunare sinistra
Superior papillary muscle	M. papillaris superior		M. papillaris sinister
Inferior papillary muscle	M. papillaris inferior		M. papillaris dexter
Neuro-myocardium	Idem		
Sinu-atrial node	Nodulus sinu-atrialis		Nodus sinu-atrialis
Atrio-ventricular node	Nodulus atrio-ventricularis		Nodus fasciculi atrio-ventricularis
Atrio-ventricular bundle	Fasciculus atrio-ventricularis		Fasc. atrio-ventricularis

Pericardium

B.R.	Latin Form of B.R.	B.N.A.	N.K.
Fibrous pericardium	Pericardium fibrosum		
Serous pericardium	Pericardium serosum		
Parietal layer	Lamina parietalis		
Visceral layer (epicardium)	Lamina visceralis (epicardium)	Epicardium	
Oblique sinus	Sinus obliquus		
Fold of left vena cava	Plica v. cavæ sinistræ		Plica v. cavæ cranialis

Arteries

B.R.	Latin Form of B.R.	B.N.A.	N.K.
Pulmonary trunk (stem)	Truncus pulmonalis	A. pulmonalis	
Right pulmonary artery	A. pulmonalis dextra	Ramus dexter	
Left pulmonary artery	A. pulmonalis sinistra	Ramus sinister	
Interventricular branch (of coronary artery)	Ramus interventricularis	Ramus descendens	Ramus interventricularis
Innominate artery	A. innominata	A. anonyma	Truncus brachio-cephalicus
Carotid sinus	Sinus carotis		
Infrahyoid artery	A. infrahyoidea	Ramus hyoideus (a. thyr. sup.)	
Suprahyoid artery	A. suprahyoidea	R. hyoideus (a. lingualis)	
Facial artery	A. facialis	A. maxillaris externa	A. facialis
Sterno-mastoid branches (of occipital)	Rr. sterno-cleido-mastoidei	A. sterno-cleido-mastoidea (of external carotid)	
Zygomatic branch (of superficial temporal)	Ramus zygomaticus	A. zygomatico-orbitalis	

B.R.	Latin Form of B.R.	B.N.A.	N.K.
Anterior branch (of superficial temporal)	Ramus anterior	R. frontalis	
Posterior branch (of superficial temporal)	Ramus posterior	R. parietalis	
Maxillary artery	A. maxillaris	A. maxillaris interna	A. maxillaris
Inferior dental artery	A. dentalis inferior	A. alveolaris inferior	A. alveolaris mandibularis
Buccal artery	A. buccalis	A. buccinatoria	A. buccalis
Posterior superior dental arteries	Aa. dentales superiores posteriores	A. alveolaris superior posterior	A. alveolaris maxillaris posterior
Anterior superior dental arteries	Aa. dentales superiores anteriores	Aa. alveolares superiores anteriores	Aa. alveolares maxillares anteriores
Palpebral arches	Arcus palpebrales	Arcus tarsei	
Supra-trochlear artery	A. supra-trochlearis	A. frontalis	A. frontalis medialis
Anterior choroid artery	A. chorioidea anterior	A. chorioidea	
Arteries of brain	Aa. encephali	Aa. cerebri	Aa. encephali
Central branches	Rr. centrales		
Striate branches	Rr. striati		
Posterior choroid artery	A. chorioidea posterior		
Cortical branches	Rr. corticales		
Orbital branches	Rr. orbitales		
Frontal branches	Rr. frontales		
Temporal branches	Rr. temporales		
Parietal branches	Rr. parietales		
Occipital branches	Rr. occipitales		
Parieto-occipital branches	Rr. parieto-occipitales		
Anterior intercostal arteries	Aa. intercostales anteriores	Rami intercostales	
Transverse cervical artery	A. cervicalis transversa	A. transversa colli	
Superficial branch	Ramus superficialis	R. ascendens	
Deep branch	Ramus profundus	R. descendens	
Suprascapular artery	A. suprascapularis	A. transversa scapulæ	A. suprascapularis
Superior intercostal artery	A. intercostalis superior	A. intercostalis suprema	
Posterior intercostal arteries (I and II)	Aa. intercostales posteriores (I and II)		
Superior thoracic artery	A. thoracalis superior	A. thoracalis suprema	A. thoracica suprema
Acromio-thoracic artery	A. acromio-thoracalis	A. thoraco-acromialis	
Clavicular branch	R. clavicularis		
Nutrient branch to humerus (from brachial and profunda)	R. nutritius humeri		
Ascending branch (of profunda)	R. ascendens	R. deltoideus	
Anterior descending branch	R. descendens anterior	A. collateralis radialis	Ramus volaris
Posterior descending branch	R. descendens posterior		Ramus dorsalis
Ulnar collateral artery	A. collateralis ulnaris	A. col. uln. superior	A. coll. uln. proximalis
Supratrochlear artery	A. supratrochlearis	A. col. uln. inferior	A. coll. uln. distalis
Anterior interosseous artery	A. interossea anterior	A. interossea volaris	
Posterior interosseous artery	A. interossea posterior	A. interossea dorsalis	
Anterior carpal branch	R. carpeus anterior	R. carpeus volaris	R. carpicus volaris
Posterior carpal branch	R. carpeus posterior	R. carpeus dorsalis	R. carpicus dorsalis
Posterior carpal arch	Arcus carpeus posterior	Rete carpi dorsale	
Anterior carpal arch	Arcus carpeus anterior		
Deep branch (of ulnar)	Ramus profundus	R. volaris profundus	
Superficial palmar arch	Arcus palmaris superficialis	Arcus volaris superficialis	
Deep palmar arch	Arcus palmaris profundus	Arcus volaris profundus	

B.R.	Latin Form of B.R.	B.N.A.	N.K.
Palmar digital arteries	Aa. digitales palmares	Aa. digitales volares communes Aa. digitales volares propriæ	
Radialis indicis artery	A. radialis indicis	A. volaris indicis radialis	
Descending thoracic aorta	Aorta thoracalis descendens	Aorta thoracalis	Aorta thoracica
Phrenic branches	Rr. phrenici	Aa. phrenicæ superiores	Aa. phrenicæ craniales
Posterior intercostal arteries (III-XI)	Aa. intercostales posteriores (III-XI)	Aa. intercostales	
Cutaneous branches	Rr. cutanei	A. cutaneus lateralis A. cutaneus medialis	
Collateral branch	R. collateralis		
Mammary branch	R. mammarius	Rr. mammarii laterales	
Subcostal artery	A. subcostalis		
Phrenic artery	A. phrenica	A. phrenica inferior	A. phrenica abdominalis
Posterior branch (of lumbar artery)	R. posterior	R. dorsalis	
Median sacral artery	A. sacralis mediana	A. sacralis media	Aorta caudalis
Fifth lumbar artery	A. lumbalis quinta	A. lumbalis ima	
Omental branches (of gastro-epiploic)	Rami epiploici		
Superior left colic artery	A. colica sinistra superior	A. colica sinistra	
Inferior left colic arteries	Aa. colicæ sinistræ inferiores	Aa. sigmoideæ	
Rectal arteries	Aa. rectales	Aa. hæmorrhoidales	Aa. rectales
Ureteric branches	Rami ad ureterem		
Internal iliac artery	A. iliaca interna	A. hypogastrica	A. ilica interna
Lateral sacral arteries	Aa. sacrales laterales	A. sacralis lateralis	
Superficial branch (of superior gluteal)	R. superficialis	R. superior	R. superficialis (a. gluteæ cranialis)
Deep branch (of superior gluteal)	R. profundus	R. inferior	R. profundus (a. gluteæ cranialis)
Coccygeal branches (of inferior gluteal)	Rr. coccygei		
Transverse perineal artery	A. perinei transversa	A. perinei	
Artery to cremaster	A. m. cremasteris	A. spermatica externa	A. m. cremasteris
Ascending branch (of deep circumflex iliac)	Ramus ascendens		
Ascending and transverse branches of medial circumflex	Rr. ascendens et transversus	R. profundus	
Transverse branch (of lateral circumflex)	R. transversus		
Descending genicular artery	A. genu descendens	A. genu suprema	A. genus descendens
Circumflex fibular branch	Ramus circumflexus fibulæ	Ramus fibularis	
Superficial branch (of lateral plantar)	R. superficialis		

Veins

B.R.	Latin Form of B.R.	B.N.A.	N.K.
Cardiac veins	Venæ cardiacæ	Vv. cordis	
Right superior intercostal vein	V. intercostalis superior dextra		
Inferior hemiazygos vein	V. hemiazygos inferior	V. hemiazygos	V. thoracica longitudinalis sinistra
Superior hemiazygos vein	V. hemiazygos superior	V. hemiazygos accessoria	V. thoracica longitudinalis accessoria
Bronchial veins	Vv. bronchiales	Vv. bronchiales posteriores	Vv. bronchales dorsales
Pericardial veins	Vv. pericardiacæ		
Mediastinal veins	Vv. mediastinales		
Phrenic tributaries	Rr. phrenici		
Subcostal vein	V. subcostalis		
Posterior intercostal veins	Vv. intercostales posteriores	Vv. intercostales	

xliv GLOSSARY

B.R.	Latin Form of B.R.	B.N.A.	N.K.
Lateral cutaneous tributary	R. cutaneus lateralis		
Posterior tributary	R. posterior	R. dorsalis	
Spinal veins	Vv. spinales	Vv. spinales internæ / Vv. spinales externæ anteriores et posteriores	
Innominate veins	V in nominatæ	Vv. anonymæ	Vv. brachio-cephalicæ
Musculo-phrenic veins	Vv. musculo-phrenicæ		
Anterior intercostal veins	Vv. intercostales anteriores		
Perforating veins	Vv. perforantes		
First (posterior) intercostal vein	V. intercostalis (posterior) prima	V. intercostalis suprema	
Left superior intercostal vein	V. intercostalis superior sinistra		
Anterior vertebral vein	V. vertebralis anterior		
Sub-occipital plexus	Plexus venosus sub-occipitalis		Plexus venosus sub-occipitalis
Occipital veins	Vv. occipitales		V. occipitalis
Acromio-thoracic vein	V. acromio-thoracica	V. thoraco-acromialis	
Palmar venous arches	Arcus venosi palmares	Arcus venosi volares	
Palmar metacarpal veins	Vv. metacarpeæ palmares	Vv. metacarpeæ volares	
Palmar digital veins	Vv. digitales palmares	Vv. digitales volares communes / Vv. digitales volares propriæ	
(Posterior external jugular vein)	(V. jugularis externa posterior)		
Suprascapular vein	V. suprascapularis	V. transversa colli	V. suprascapularis
Transverse cervical veins	Vv. cervicales transversæ	Vv. transversæ colli	
Middle thyroid vein	V. thyreoidea media		
Superior thyroid vein	V. thyreoidea superior	(Vv. thyreoideæ superiores)	V. thyreoidea cranialis
Venæ comitantes of lingual	Vv. comitantes a. lingualis		
Profunda vein of tongue	V. profunda linguæ		
Supratrochlear veins	Vv. supratrochleares	Vv. frontales	V. naso-frontalis
Deep facial vein	V. facialis profunda		
External palatine vein	V. palatina externa	V. palatina	
Maxillary vein (or veins)	V. (vv.) maxillaris		
Pterygoid veins	Vv. pterygoideæ		
Masseteric veins	Vv. massetericæ		
Inferior dental vein	V. dentalis inferior		
Mylohyoid vein	V. mylohyoidea		
Infra-orbital vein	V. infra-orbitalis		
Superior dental veins	Vv. dentales superiores		
Buccal veins	Vv. buccales		
Spheno-palatine veins	Vv. spheno-palatinæ		
Internal nasal veins	Vv. nasales internæ		
Greater palatine veins	Vv. palatinæ majores		
Lesser palatine veins	Vv. palatinæ minores		
Venous sinuses (of dura mater)	Sinus venosi (duræ matris)	Sinus duræ matris	
Transverse sinus	Sinus transversus	Sinus transversus	
Sigmoid sinus	Sinus sigmoideus		
Network of basilar sinuses	Rete sinuum basilarium	Plexus basilaris	Plexus basialis
Emissary vein	V. emissaria	Emissarium	
Posterior condylar emissary vein	V. emissaria condylaris posterior	Emissarium condyloideum	Emissarium condylicum
Anterior condylar emissary vein	V. emissaria condylaris anterior	Rete canalis hypoglossi	
Emissary veins of carotid canal	Vv. emissariæ canalis carotici	Plexus venosus caroticus internus	
Veins of brain	Vv. encephali	Vv. cerebri	Vv. encephali
Superior anastomotic vein	V. anastomotica superior		
Inferior anastomotic vein	V. anastomotica inferior		

B.R.	Latin Form of B.R.	B.N.A.	N.K.
Superficial middle cerebral vein	V. cerebri media superficialis	V. cerebri media	
Deep middle cerebral vein	V. cerebri media profunda		
Anterior cerebral vein	V. cerebri anterior		
Striate veins	Vv. striatæ		
Thalamo-striate vein	V. thalamo-striata	V. terminalis	V. thalamo-striata
Phrenic vein	V. phrenica	V. phrenica inferior	V. phrenica abdominalis
Median sacral vein	V. sacralis mediana	V. sacralis media	
Internal iliac vein	V. iliaca interna	V. hypogastrica	V. ilica interna
Rectal veins	Vv. rectales	Vv. hæmorrhoidales	Vv. rectales
Vein of the bulb	V. bulbi penis (vestibuli)		
(Inferior) vesical veins	Vv. vesicales (inferiores)		
Deep dorsal vein of penis	V. dorsalis penis profunda	V. dorsalis penis	V. dorsalis penis subfascialis
Superficial dorsal veins of penis (or clitoris)	Vv. dorsales penis (clitoridis) superficiales	Vv. dorsales penis subcutaneæ	
Prostatic venous plexus	Plexus venosus prostaticus	Plexus pudendalis	
Vaginal vein	V. vaginalis		
Long saphenous vein	V. saphena longa	V. saphena magna	
Short saphenous vein	V. saphena brevis	V. saphena parva	
Genicular veins	Vv. genu		
Lateral and medial plantar veins	Vv. plantares laterales et mediales		
Plantar digital veins	Vv. digitales plantares	{ Vv. digitales communes pedis Vv. digitales plantares	
Ductus venosus, Lig. venosum	Idem	Ductus venosus (Arantii)	
Umbilical vein, Round lig. of liver	V. umbilicalis, Lig. teres hepatis	V. umbilicalis	
Left gastric vein	V. gastrica sinistra	V. coronaria ventriculi	
Right gastric vein	V. gastrica dextra		
Prepyloric vein	V. præpylorica		
Pancreatic veins	Vv. pancreaticæ		
Superior left colic vein	V. colica sinistra superior	V. colica sinistra	
Inferior left colic veins	Vv. colicæ sinistræ inferiores	Vv. sigmoideæ	
Jejunal and ileal veins	Vv. jejunales et ileæ	Vv. intestinales	
Appendicular vein	V. appendicularis		

LYMPHATIC SYSTEM

B.R.	Latin Form of B.R.	B.N.A.	N.K.
Mediastinal trunk	Truncus mediastinalis	Truncus broncho-mediastinalis	
Mastoid lymph glands	Lympho-glandulæ mastoideæ	Lg. auriculares posteriores	Lymphonodi retro-auriculares
Submandibular glands	Lg. submandibulares	Lg. submaxillares	Ln. submandibulares
Submental glands	Lg. submentales		Ln. submentales
Anterior cervical glands	Lg. cervicales anteriores		
Supratrochlear glands	Lg. supratrochleares	Lg. cubitales superficiales	
Paratracheal glands	Lg. paratracheales		
Tracheo-bronchial glands	Lg. tracheo-bronchiales	Lg. tracheales Lg. bronchiales	
Broncho-pulmonary glands	Lg. broncho-pulmonales		
Innominate glands	Lg. innominatæ	Lg. mediastinales anteriores	Ln. mediast. ventrales
Internal mammary glands	Lg. mammariæ internæ	Lg. sternales	
Diaphragmatic glands	Lg. phrenicæ		
Aortic glands	Lg. aorticæ	Lg. lumbales	
Left gastric glands	Lg. gastricæ sinistræ	Lg. gast. superiores	Ln. gast. craniales
Right gastro-epiploic glands	Lg. gastro-epiploicæ dextræ	Lg. gast. inferiores	Ln. gast. caudales
Pyloric glands	Lg. pyloricæ		
Ileo-colic glands	Lg. ileo-colicæ		

B.R.	Latin Form of B.R.	B.N.A.	N.K.
Middle colic glands	Lg. colicæ mediæ	Lg. mesocolicæ	
Inferior mesenteric glands	Lg. mesentericæ inferiores		
Left colic glands	Lg. colicæ sinistræ		
Common iliac glands	Lg. iliacæ communes	} Lg. iliacæ	Ln. ilici
External iliac glands	Lg. iliacæ externæ		
Internal iliac glands	Lg. iliacæ internæ	Lg. hypogastricæ	Ln. ilici interni
Inguinal glands	Lg. inguinales	{ Lg. inguinales Lg. subinguinales	Ln. subinguinales

TEXT-BOOK OF ANATOMY

◆

INTRODUCTION

ANATOMY is a comprehensive term, and includes several closely related branches of knowledge. Primarily it is equivalent to **dissection**, and therefore comes to mean knowledge of the form and relations of the parts into which the body may be resolved by that fundamental method of study. As the body is dissected region by region, or studied by means of sections taken in different planes, and as the knowledge so acquired is formulated in descriptions of all the features of each region taken together, such basic anatomical knowledge is known as *Regional* or *Topographical Anatomy*. But in the course of dissection it soon becomes evident that all regions of the body are built up of the same kinds of structures (bones, muscles, nerves, blood-vessels, etc.), and that the viscera are related to one another in special ways. The idea of **systems** of structures therefore arises, and the description of the same kinds of structures found throughout the body is known as *Systematic Anatomy*. The observation that there are different kinds of structures in the body inevitably leads to enquiry (speculative at first and then experimental) about what they do; and thus the idea of a community of **function** is inherent in the description of a "system" of parts or organs. *Functional Anatomy* may therefore be considered in a sense equivalent to Systematic Anatomy; but it has in fact a wider range and merges insensibly into Physiology.

Very closely related to the study of their function is the use of the microscope for resolving still further the structure of the parts of the body displayed by dissection and arranged in systems. The topography of the body as learned by the method of dissection is often referred to as *Gross* or *Macroscopic Anatomy*: the finer structure in contrast is known as *Microscopic Anatomy*. It will be easily understood by the student that there is no essential difference between the two— only one of method of study—and that even this difference may be bridged to some extent in the dissecting room by the habitual use of magnifiers of moderate power, by means of which many important details of the finer structure of organs may readily be observed. Microscopic Anatomy includes not only the minute structure of the organs and parts but also the still finer details of the **tissues** of which they are composed. The study of the minute structure of the tissues is called *Histology* [from ἱστός (histos), a web]; and it includes *Cytology* i.e. the study of the cells which, although far from simple, may be taken as the ultimate units of the body.

But the structure of the body is not the same at all stages of life. All the cells of the body are the descendants of the single cell—formed by the union of ovum and spermatozoon—which is the starting-point of each individual. This single-cell stage is obviously a very different thing from the finished organism represented by the adult; and the series of changes through which the organism passes until its structure is perfected constitute the phenomena of **development** and **growth**.

The general term "development" is not restricted to the various and striking structural changes which occur during the intra-uterine life of the individual, to the study of which the term *Embryology* is more specially applied; it includes also—in addition to alterations in proportions—many developmental and growth processes which occur after birth, such as the adjustment of the vascular system to its new requirements, the later stages in the ossification and growth of the bones, the eruption of the two sets of teeth, and the changes in the sex organs and the appearance of secondary sex characters at puberty. "Development" indeed in the wider sense continues throughout the natural span of life, and includes all changes in the body which are due to age.

In the mind of the thoughtful student, the study of Embryology in particular raises questions of the origin of Man, and indeed helps to answer them. Human Anatomy from this point of view is but part of a larger subject; Man as a mammalian vertebrate takes his place in the wider studies of *Comparative Anatomy* and *Comparative Embryology* with all the evidence that they have to offer in support of the theory of evolution. The broader conceptions of anatomy, which are obtained by taking a general survey of the structural aspects of the vertebrate animal kingdom, constitute *Vertebrate Morphology*. The morphologist investigates the laws of form and structure, and gives attention to detail only in so far as this is necessary for his argument.

The knowledge of anatomy which is required by the student of medicine is different. Though his education is incomplete without some appreciation of these wider issues, it is essential for him to be familiar with details of the structure of the human body; and many details that are important from the practical point of view have little or no morphological interest. Moreover, his knowledge is of little value if he is incapable of transferring it from the dissecting room to the bedside, and applying it in the examination and treatment of his living patients. Hence the importance of having his attention directed to the study of the anatomy of the living body. This may be done in several ways. One is the consideration of the relation of organs and other structures to the surface features of the body—*Surface Anatomy*; or the living body may be examined in the revealing light of the X-Rays—*Radiographic Anatomy*. By X-Ray examinations not only may the student's impressions of the form and position of organs obtained from the embalmed cadaver be suitably corrected, but his attention may also be drawn to many interesting observations which are important from the growth and functional points of view.

Finally, it should be understood that *Applied Anatomy* is not a separate division of the subject at all; it is the application of every kind of anatomical knowledge to practical problems in Medicine, Surgery, and other departments of clinical study. It should indeed be the aim of the student of medicine during his anatomical studies to obtain such a knowledge of the anatomy of the living human body that he will find no difficulty in applying it later in practice with understanding and confidence.

TOPOGRAPHICAL ANATOMY

As already explained, Anatomy is primarily a descriptive science founded on observation, and in order that precision and accuracy may be attained it is necessary to have a series of well-defined **descriptive terms**. It is in dissecting manuals that the regional or topographical method is followed; but such terms are just as necessary in a systematic text-book. It must therefore be clearly understood that all topographical descriptions are framed on the anatomical convention that the body is in the erect position, with the arms by the side, and held so that the palms of the hands look forwards. An imaginary plane of section, passing longitudinally through the body and dividing it accurately into a right and a left half, is called the **median plane**, Fig. 1 (M.P.). When the right and left halves of the body are studied it will be found that both are to a large extent formed of similar parts. The right and left limbs are alike; the right and left halves of the brain appear the same; there are a right and a left kidney and a right and a left lung, and so on. Many organs are therefore **symmetrically** arranged. But still a large amount of **asymmetry** may be observed. Thus, the chief bulk of the liver lies to the right side of the median plane, and the spleen is an organ which belongs wholly to the left half of the body. Indeed, it is well to state that

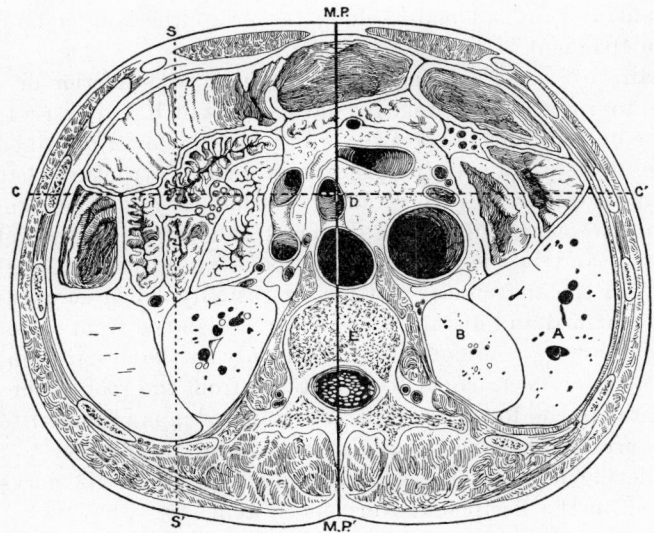

FIG. 1.—HORIZONTAL SECTION THROUGH THE TRUNK AT THE LEVEL OF THE FIRST LUMBAR VERTEBRA.

perfect symmetry never does exist. There always will be, and always must be, a certain want of balance between symmetrically placed parts of the body. Thus, the right upper limb is, as a rule, constructed upon a heavier and more massive plan than the left, and even in those organs where the symmetry appears most perfect, as for instance the brain and spinal cord, it requires only a closer study to reveal many points of difference between the right and left halves.

The line on the front of the body along which the median plane reaches the surface is termed the **anterior median line**; and the corresponding line behind is called the **posterior median line**.

It is convenient to employ other terms to indicate other imaginary planes of section through the body. The term **sagittal** is used to denote any plane which cuts through the body along a path parallel to the median plane (S S′); and the term **coronal** is given to any vertical plane which cuts the median plane at right angles (C C′). These two terms are derived from the names of two of the sutures of the skull. The term **horizontal**, as applied to a plane of section, requires no explanation.

Any structure which lies nearer to the median plane than another is said to be **medial** to that other; and any structure placed farther from the median plane than another is said to lie **lateral** to it. Thus in Fig. 1, A is lateral to B; and B is medial to A. The term **intermediate** may be employed to indicate the position of a third structure lying between two others that are medial and lateral.

The terms **internal** and **external** express relative distance from the centre of an organ or a cavity; thus, the ribs have external surfaces, that is, surfaces away from the cavity of the thorax, and internal surfaces adjacent to the cavity. The terms **superficial** and **deep** are also used to denote relative distance from the surface of the body, especially in the limbs.

The terms **anterior** and **ventral** are synonymous, and are used to indicate a structure (D) which lies nearer to the front or ventral surface of the body than another structure (E) which is placed nearer to the back or dorsal surface of the body, and is thus said to be **posterior** or **dorsal**. The terms "anterior" and "posterior" belong strictly to human descriptive anatomy, since they are applicable only to man in the erect attitude, and cannot be applied to a four-footed animal; the terms "ventral" and "dorsal" belong rather to the language of morphology, as they are independent of habitual position.

Similar pairs of terms are **superior** or **cephalic** and **inferior** or **caudal**, which are employed to indicate the relative levels at which two structures lie with reference to the upper or head end of the trunk, and the lower or tail end. The term **middle** may be used to indicate the position of a third structure that lies between two others that are either "superior" and "inferior" or "anterior" and "posterior."

In the hand we commonly speak of **dorsal** and **palmar** instead of "posterior" and "anterior"; and in the foot the corresponding surfaces though "superior" and "inferior" in the anatomical position, are usually called **dorsal** and **plantar**.

The terms **proximal** and **distal** denote relative distance from some central point agreed upon. They are commonly employed only in the description of the limbs, and then denote relative nearness to or distance from the root of the limb. Thus, the hand is distal to the forearm, whilst the upper arm is proximal to the forearm.

The terms **preaxial** and **postaxial** also are useful in relation to the axis of a limb in considering its development or the distribution of its nerves (see p. 310 and the chapter on the Peripheral Nervous System).

SYSTEMATIC ANATOMY

The description of the several systems of organs of which the human body is composed, separately and in logical order, constitutes "Systematic Anatomy," and is the plan upon which this treatise is based. The several parts of each system not only present a certain similarity of structure but are also associated in specialised functions. As already pointed out, "Functional Anatomy" merges insensibly into Physiology. It begins with simple ideas, such as that the skeleton has the primary function of a supporting framework of the body, and the muscles the primary function of moving the parts of the framework in relation to each other and the external world: it advances by deductions about the function of parts from their anatomical arrangement (such as Harvey's famous discovery of the Circulation of the Blood, from observations and simple experiments on the valves of the veins and of the heart): but it is also concerned with the wider field of the interrelations of parts belonging to different systems—for example, the anatomical localisation in the Central Nervous System of the origin of nerve fibres concerned with the regulation and control of the functions of different organs. Anatomy and Physiology are indeed but two different aspects of one subject, separated as a matter of convenience for investigation and study. Structure and function are in reality indissolubly associated ; and that is the basis of Systematic Anatomy. Thus there are—

1. The *Locomotor System*, which includes

A. The *Skeletal System*, composed of the bones and certain cartilaginous and membranous parts associated with them, the knowledge of which is known as **osteology**.

B. The *Articulatory System*, which includes the joints or articulations, the knowledge of which is termed **arthrology**.

C. The *Muscular System*, comprising the muscles, the knowledge of which constitutes **myology**. With the muscles are usually included fasciae, synovial sheaths of tendons, and synovial bursae.

2. The *Digestive System*, which consists of the alimentary canal and its associated glands, and parts such as the tongue, teeth, liver, pancreas, etc.

3. The *Respiratory System*, in which we place the nasal passages, larynx, windpipe, and lungs.

4. The *Urogenital System*, composed of the urinary organs and the genital organs—the latter differing in the two sexes.

5. The *Ductless Glands*, which though heterogeneous in their origin, structure, and particular functions, are conveniently grouped together as a " system," as they share the common functional feature of "**internal secretion**" and together have a profound influence on the functioning of the body as a whole : they include the thyroid and parathyroid glands, the thymus, the hypophysis cerebri and pineal body (these two are attached to the Brain), the suprarenal glands, and the spleen.

The term **splanchnology** denotes the knowledge of the organs included in the digestive, respiratory, and urogenital systems, and the ductless glands.

6. The *Nervous System*, which is subdivided into—

A. The *Central Nervous System*, including the brain and the spinal cord.

B. The *Peripheral Nervous System*, which consists of the cranial and the spinal nerves and their ganglia.

C. The *Autonomic Nervous System*, comprising the Sympathetic and Parasympathetic Systems of nerves and ganglia.

The knowledge of all these is included in the term **neurology**.

With the Nervous System may be included

D. The *Organs of the Special Senses* (Sight, Hearing, Smell, Taste) and also

E. The *Common Integument* (skin, nails, hair, etc.), which is also a great sense organ.

7. The *Blood Vascular System*, including the heart and blood vessels (arteries, veins, and capillaries).

8. The *Lymphatic System* of lymph vessels and lymph glands.

MICROSCOPIC ANATOMY AND HISTOLOGY

The organs which form the various systems of the body are themselves built up of **tissues**. Their intimate structure can be resolved only by the use of the microscope and is thus known as *Microscopic Anatomy*. The tissues themselves are built up of elements comprising **cells** and their products, and the study of these tissues constitutes *Histology*. These two together form an important branch of Anatomy requiring special technical methods for its study ; and since it involves finer description in great detail, special text-books are devoted to it. In a general text-book of Anatomy only outlines of this aspect of the subject can be presented; and in this text these outlines will be found in the several sections in relation to the systematic description of the organs. It is, however, necessary to give the student an introduction to the general structure of the ultimate units of the body—the cells—including their methods of reproduction; and to the kinds of tissues which they build up and which in turn form the basis of the micro-scopic anatomy of the organs. For further details the student is referred to one of the special text-books.[1]

THE STRUCTURE OF THE CELL

The human body is an aggregate of innumerable microscopic units called **cells**. The cells vary in size and shape, but all are very minute, the largest—apart from ova (p. 20) —rarely exceeding 80 μ in diameter (a μ = a micron, which is 1/1000 of a millimetre). In some tissues, as will be explained, the cells lie side by side, but in others they are separated from one another by a varying amount of intercellular substance. Each cell is a minute mass of the living substance called **protoplasm**, which is the "physical basis of life."

Protoplasm is a colourless, semi-transparent, mobile, irritable substance. It is a colloidal mixture of proteins and nucleo-proteins, with carbohydrates, fats, lipoids, in-organic salts, and water. Different kinds of protoplasm, containing different proportions of these constituents, are recognisable by their reactions to various staining agents.

Every typical animal cell has a **cell body**, which contains the following structures:—

> The **nucleus** with its **nucleolus** or nucleoli.
> The **centrosome** with its **centriole**.
> **Mitochondria**.
> The **Golgi apparatus**.

In addition, the cell body may contain a number of substances, more or less constant in different cells but not essential parts of their structure. They are classified collectively as **metaplasmic** contents; they are: (1) *Fats* and *Lipoids*, in the form of spherules of varying sizes; (2) *Carbo-hydrates*, including *Glycogen*; (3) *Vacuoles*, filled with fluid; (4) *Products of cell activity* (*e.g.* precursors of secretions) in the form of granules.

Much light has recently been thrown on the structure of the cell and the physical nature of its parts by the method of **micro-dissection** (Chambers).

The Cell Body.—The protoplasm of the cell body is called **cytoplasm**. It is probable that the living cyto-plasm has no special struc-tural arrangement, other than that due to its colloidal nature, and that the ap-parent structure, which has been variously described in the dead cell, is due to the action of fixing and staining chemicals.

The peripheral part of the cytoplasm forms a definite clear film called the **plasma**

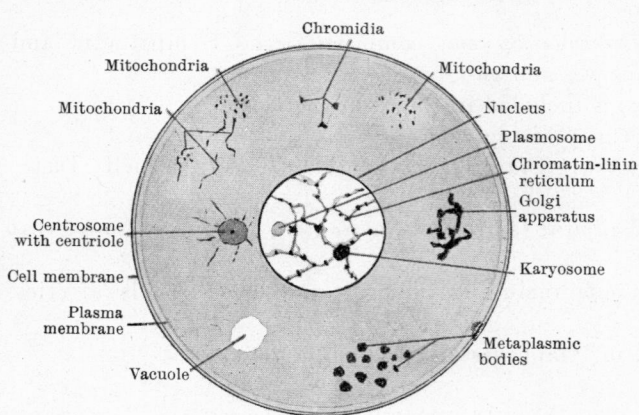

FIG. 2.—DIAGRAM OF AN ANIMAL CELL

Chromidia
Mitochondria
Mitochondria
Mitochondria
Nucleus
Plasmosome
Chromatin-linin reticulum
Golgi apparatus
Centrosome with centriole
Cell membrane
Plasma membrane
Karyosome
Vacuole
Metaplasmic bodies

---

[1] *Essentials of Histology*, Sharpey-Schafer and Carleton, 13th ed. 1934. *A Text-Book of Histology*, Maximow and Bloom, 1930.

membrane, outside which a definite **cell membrane** may or may not be present. These act as a semi-permeable membrane through which exchanges take place between the cell and its surroundings.

The Nucleus.—The protoplasm of the nucleus is called **karyoplasm,** and it is surrounded by a *nuclear membrane.* Contained within it are (1) the substance known as *chromatin*; (2) a *linin* network; and (3) one or more *nucleoli*, which are either (*a*) plasmosomes or (*b*) karyosomes, or both. The nucleus controls the metabolic changes in cells, and is also concerned with their reproduction by mitotic division.

The **chromatin** is present in the form of granules, and owes its name to the fact that it is very readily stained by basic dyes. In fixed cells it generally forms a beaded network, and during cell division it is aggregated into the specific bodies known as **chromosomes.**

The **linin** or "thread" material may be seen in fixed cells as a fine reticulum with which the independent chromatin network may be connected. It has an affinity for acid dyes, but is not easily stained. It may be an artifact due to fixation.

The **nucleoli** are small spheres of two kinds. (*a*) The *plasmosomes*, or true nucleoli, lie in the karyoplasm and stain, like cytoplasm, with acid dyes. (*b*) The *karyosomes* appear as knots in the chromatin network and stain, like chromatin, with basic dyes.

The **nuclear membrane** is the outer layer of the nucleus and stains like the chromatin with which it is connected. It disappears when cell division begins.

The Centrosome.—The essential part of this structure is a minute particle called the **centriole.** It is usually seen densely stained at the centre of a homogeneous sphere, different in appearance from the surrounding cytoplasm and placed near the nucleus. The centriole is the structure that appears to initiate cell division; it is present in all cells that have retained the power of division, and absent only in those so highly specialised (*e.g.* nerve cells) that they have lost that power.

Mitochondria.—These minute bodies are believed to play an important part in cell function, for example, in the production of *enzymes* (ferments). They occur as minute granules, rods, or filaments, and may be scattered throughout the cell or collected in groups. When a cell divides, the mitochondria are distributed between the two daughter cells.

The Golgi Apparatus.—This remarkable structure is not visible in living cells, but is displayed after the cell has been treated by special chemical reagents—silver and osmium. It varies greatly in shape and in size, according to the activity and function of the cell; it is often seen as a reticular formation, and it has no definitely fixed place in the cytoplasm. Like the mitochondria it appears to be very important in the functioning of the cell, and is believed to be concerned with metabolism and the formation of secretions. Like the mitochondria also, its material is shared between the two daughter cells when a cell divides.

The Life-History of Cells

The Necessities for Cell Life.—In order that an animal cell may live and perform its work, certain conditions are necessary : (1) a temperature which varies only within narrow limits ; (2) a certain amount of moisture in the form of water ; (3) oxygen ; and (4) a supply of food from which it can obtain the other chemical elements of its substance, more especially carbohydrates (in the form of sugar), fats, and proteins which contain the necessary nitrogen.

Reproduction of Cells.—Every animal cell is formed by the division of a pre-existing cell called the *mother cell.* The mother cell divides into two equal parts—*the daughter cells*—each of which, under ordinary conditions, possesses all the capabilities of its mother. Every new cell has a definite life-history. It grows and performs its proper functions ; it then ceases to exist, either by dividing into two daughter cells, or by dying and breaking up into fragments which disappear.

Any tissue or organ grows as long as the multiplication-rate of the cells exceeds the death-rate. When the multiplication-rate and the death-rate are equal, the tissue or organ is in a state of equilibrium. As soon as the death-rate exceeds the multiplication-rate, decay and atrophy set in ; and when the decay and atrophy have proceeded to such an extent that an important tissue or organ can no longer perform its proper functions, general death ensues.

General decay and death are the natural results of the loss of the power to divide by the cells of the body. Cell division is therefore a vital necessity, and it takes place in two ways—(1) by **amitotic division,** and (2) by **mitotic division.**

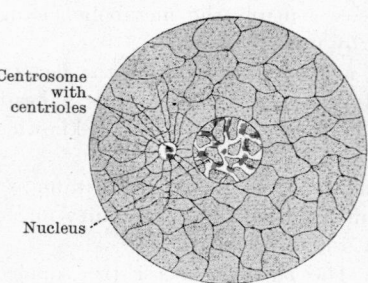

Centrosome
with
centrioles

Nucleus

FIG. 3.—SCHEMA OF ANIMAL CELL IN RESTING STAGE.

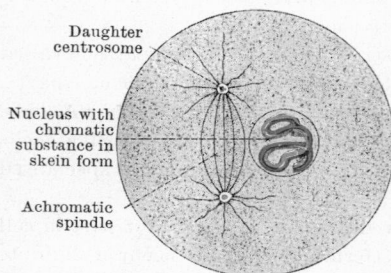

Daughter
centrosome

Nucleus with
chromatic
substance in
skein form

Achromatic
spindle

FIG. 4.—SCHEMA OF ANIMAL CELL IN EARLY PART OF PROPHASE OF MITOSIS.

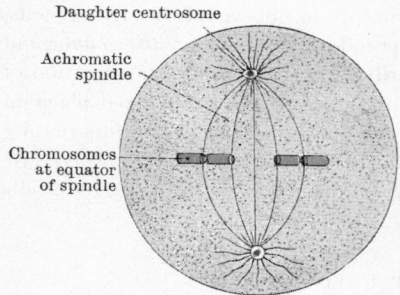

Daughter centrosome

Achromatic
spindle

Chromosomes
at equator
of spindle

FIG. 5.—SCHEMA OF ANIMAL CELL AT COMPLETION OF PROPHASE OF MITOSIS.

Amitotic Division.—The amitotic division of cells is an apparently simple process. First the nucleus is divided by an advancing constriction ; thereafter, the cell body is constricted and divided, and so two similar daughter cells are produced.

The nucleus of some cells (epithelium of urinary bladder, giant cells of bone marrow) may divide in this manner ; but complete amitotic division occurs rarely, if at all, in the cells of the human body, and it is not known whether the daughter cells produced can live and, in their turn, divide. Amitosis may be a degenerative process ; and in any case, in comparison with mitosis, it is certainly unimportant.

Mitotic Division.—Mitosis (so-called from the thread-like formation of the chromosomes) or *karyokinesis* (from the activity of the nucleus) is the more common, the more important, and by far the more complicated method of cell division.

The phenomena of mitosis occur in four phases termed (1) the prophase (or anaphase), (2) the metaphase, (3) the kataphase, and (4) the telophase.

The Prophase.—During the prophase the centrosome and the nucleus undergo very obvious changes.

The centrosome divides into two daughter centrosomes, of which one passes to one side and the other to the opposite side of the nucleus.

At the same time a spindle of achromatic fibrils appears, and extends from one daughter centrosome to the other (Fig. 4). In some cases the achromatic spindle is formed entirely outside the nucleus ; but more often it passes through the nucleus and may then appear to be derived from the linin reticulum.

The peripheral fibrils of the spindle are called the *mantle fibrils*; those which form the core of the spindle are called the *central fibrils.*

Other fibrils radiate peripherally from the daughter centrosomes into the surrounding cytoplasm. All these structures—daughter centrosomes, spindle, and radiating fibrils— collectively constitute the *achromatic figure.* It is thought that the fibres represent a physical change in the cytoplasm, and they appear to guide the movements of the chromosomes in the kataphase of division.

The nuclear transformation affects also the nuclear membrane, the nucleoli, and the chromatin. The nuclear membrane disappears as also do the nucleoli, sometimes after passing from the nucleus into the cytoplasm, but more commonly without such migration.

The chromatin, during the resting period, is dispersed in the nucleus in an apparently irregular and inconstant manner. As the prophase begins it is aggregated into small nodules, called *chromomeres*, which are strung together to form a series of nodulated filaments called **chromosomes**. In each species of animal the number of chromosomes found during cell division is constant and characteristic.

The filamentous chromosomes of the early prophase are bent, twisted, and intimately intermingled, so that, for a time, they simulate a convoluted *skein* (Fig. 4), and, indeed the individual filaments are sometimes united to one another end to end. Such a condition is, however, but a transitory connexion of the individual chromosomes, which soon reassert their independence. Gradually the thread-like chromosomes become shorter until the chromomeres are so compressed together that they are no longer distinguishable from one another.

When the shortening is completed the chromosomes appear in the form of rods, hooks, or V-shaped bars, of varying size, which are gathered together at the equator of the achromatic spindle, where they form collectively the *equatorial plate* of the prophase (Fig. 5). At this period, which is the end of the prophase, each chromosome is attached to one or more of the fibrils of the achromatic spindle.

V-shaped chromosomes at this stage, when seen from a pole of the spindle, form a star-like figure known as an *aster*.

The Metaphase.—During this phase each chromosome divides longitudinally into two equal daughter chromosomes (Fig. 6).

The division begins at the point where the chromosome is attached to the achromatic spindle ; and, as it proceeds, it becomes evident that one daughter chromosome is attached by one or more of the fibrils of the achromatic spindle to one centrosome and the other to the opposite centrosome.

When the division is completed the metaphase is ended, two daughter equatorial plates are present, and the number of chromosomes is doubled.

Although the division of the chromosomes occurs during the metaphase, it is often indicated in the prophase by the appearance of fine clear lines which run through the long axes of the chromosomes.

The Kataphase.—In the kataphase the chromosomes of each daughter equatorial plate move along the fibrils of the achromatic spindle towards the corresponding centrosome. As they approach the immediate neighbourhood of the centrosome, the body of the cell begins to be divided by a circular constriction which appears at the level of the equator of the achromatic spindle. The appearance of the constriction indicates the end of the kataphase and the commencement of the telophase (Fig. 7).

The Telophase.—In this terminal period of mitosis the constriction of the cell body deepens until the cell is divided into two daughter cells.

As the division of the cell body proceeds, the changes which occurred in the chromatin to form the chromosomes are reversed, so that first a skein and then a network are formed. A nuclear membrane is re-formed and nucleoli reappear. A new daughter nucleus is thus formed in each daughter cell ; and as the daughter nucleus is evolved the portions of the achromatic figure external to it disappear.

The result of mitotic division is therefore the formation of two daughter cells from a mother cell. Each daughter cell is necessarily smaller than the mother cell, but has the same constituent parts and the same number of chromosomes in its nucleus as the mother cell had (Fig. 8).

Heterotypical and Homotypical Mitosis.—The mechanism of mitosis just described applies to all somatic or body cells ; but in the maturation of the germ cells two special cell divisions occur which are known as "heterotypical" and "homotypical."

In **heterotypical mitosis** the number of chromosomes is reduced to half the characteristic number ; in **homotypical mitosis** the ordinary mechanism of cell division is applied to the daughter cells with the reduced number of chromosomes (see pp. 17 and 24).

Growth and Function Periods.—After cell division there is a variable period during which the daughter cells grow until they attain the adult size. Thereafter, until division again occurs, they perform the functions of the group of cells to which they belong.

The capability of cells to perform functions depends upon their chromatin contents as well as upon proper nutriment, warmth, and moisture, upon their relative positions in the body of which they form a part, and the provision of means whereby the products of the cell activity can be removed.

The Function of the Chromosomes.—As the chromosomes of the mother cells are split longitudinally, during mitosis, each daughter cell receives exactly the same number of chromosomes and presumably the same number of chromomeres as the mother cell from which it was derived, and in the case of cells in fully differentiated tissues it seems probable that the chromosomes carry with them the same possibilities for functional capacity that the mother cell possessed. This, however, cannot always be the case in the early stages of development, before the different tissues of the body are differentiated from one another, for in those stages some of the daughter cells of a group of mother cells take part in the formation of one tissue, and others in the formation of other tissues which ultimately perform quite different functions. It must be assumed, whilst the number of the chromosomes in all the cells of the body is the same, that the qualities of their chromomeres may be different.

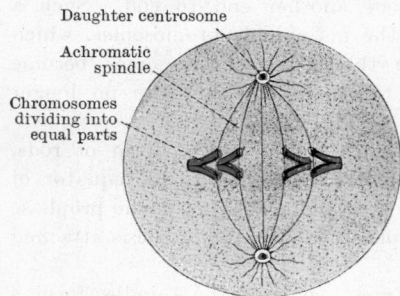

Daughter centrosome
Achromatic spindle
Chromosomes dividing into equal parts

FIG. 6.—SCHEMA OF ANIMAL CELL IN META-
PHASE OF MITOSIS.

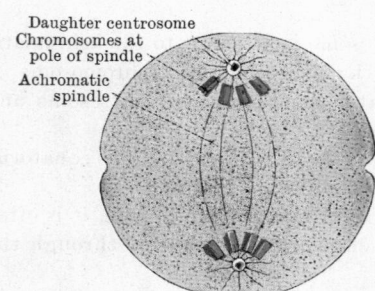

Daughter centrosome
Chromosomes at pole of spindle
Achromatic spindle

FIG. 7.—SCHEMA OF ANIMAL CELL AT END
OF KATAPHASE OF MITOSIS.

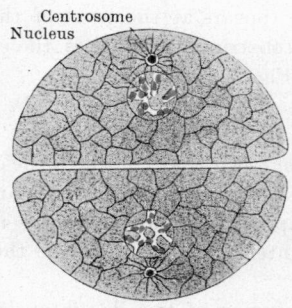

Centrosome
Nucleus

FIG. 8.—SCHEMA OF ANIMAL CELL AT END OF
TELOPHASE OF MITOSIS. The cell has
divided into two daughter cells. Red and
blue indicate the original paternal and
maternal derivatives.

The function of the chromosomes is therefore to transmit potentialities from one generation of cells to the next. This function has its supreme expression in the transmission through male and female germ cells of heritable characters from two parents to their offspring. The chromosomes are thus said to be "the material basis of inheritance."

It is believed that the chromomeres of the chromosomes consist of innumerable ultra-microscopic particles, called **genes**, in which, in some manner unknown, determinants of heritable characters are located, and that the capabilities and tendencies of each new individual depend upon the paternal and maternal genes which come together in a new combination in the fertilised ovum.

Further, the evidence available points to the conclusion that the chromomeres and their genes derived from the father never fuse with those derived from the mother, although they lie in close juxtaposition.

The Period of Cell Life.—As already pointed out, every new cell has a definite life-history. The period of cell life varies, but it always ends in death; for a time comes when cells no longer transmit to their descendants the power of division, or the capability of growth and function. If it were not so, growth and function, or at least maintenance and function, would continue uninterruptedly, and, in the absence of accident or disease, individual life would continue for ever, and "old age" would be unknown.

It appears therefore that the ancestors of certain tissue cells are capable of producing only a certain number of descendants that can grow to the normal size and perform their proper functions for a more or less fixed period, whilst in other cases the power of division appears to be transmitted continuously, but the more remote descendants become less and less capable of performing their proper functions. It is not known how the period of cell life is fixed; but it is believed that it is fixed by the character of the genes and their rearrangement in the fertilised ovum. When favourable combinations occur the individual may live for a hundred years or more. If the combinations of the genes are unfavourable the ova may die immediately after they are fertilised; or they may survive and develop for a time, only to die later at any stage of the intra-uterine period. Eventually all individuals must die—some killed by accident, others by microbic disease; but most because they have reached the limit originally determined by their inheritance (A. Robinson, Prenatal Death, *Edin. Med. Journ.* 1921. xxvi. 137).

The Tissues of the Body

There are only four main tissues in the body—**epithelial, connective, muscular, nervous**—and all parts of it are made up of combinations of varieties of these four in different proportions. All the tissues originally consist of cells; and the differences between the tissues are due to (1) changes in the cells in accordance with specialised functions; and (2) the formation of different kinds of extra-cellular materials—**intercellular substance**—which may surround the cells and separate them in varying degree.

The contents of the cells of some tissues are, however, not entirely separate, as in the stratum mucosum of the epidermis in which protoplasmic bridges pass between contiguous cells. Cell walls may even be absent so that the "cells" form a mass of multi-nucleated protoplasm known as a **syncytium** or a **plasmodium**, as in the outer layer of the "ovum" in early stages of development (p. 64).

In *epithelial tissue* extra-cellular material is at a minimum, and the varieties of the tissue depend upon the form of the comparatively simple cells according to their situation and function. In *connective tissue* intercellular substance is at a maximum, and its varieties depend mainly upon the nature of the intercellular substance and the appearance of different kinds of fibres in it. *Muscular tissue* and *nervous tissue* consist of very highly specialised cells which also show variations in form and complexity according to situation and function.

Embryology and Morphology

The study of the processes by which the parts of the body are gradually formed, and of the structural arrangements by means of which a temporary connexion, for the purpose of an interchange of nutritive and other materials, is established between the ovum and the mother, renders Embryology one of the most interesting of all the branches of Anatomy. Moreover, the early stages in the development of the embryo, and the mode of development of its organs, are of great morphological importance. The term **ontogeny** also is used to denote the development of the individual. There is, however, another form of development, slower but just as certain in its progress, which has affected all the members of the animal group to which the individual belongs. The theory of **evolution** leads us to believe that the wide structural gap between Man of the present day and his remote ancestors would, if the geological record were perfect, be completely occupied by long-lost intermediate forms. In the process of descent by evolution, structural changes have gradually taken place which have modified the entire race. The evolutionary phases through which it has passed constitute the ancestral history or **phylogeny** of the race. Ontogeny and phylogeny, moreover, are inter-twined in a remarkable manner. The ancestral evolutionary development appears to be so stamped upon an individual that it repeats certain of the phylogenetic stages with more or less clearness during the process of its own ontogenetic development. Thus, at an early period in the development of Man evanescent gill-pouches appear which are comparable with those of a fish, whilst a study of the development of his heart shows that it passes through transitory structural conditions similar, in many respects, to the permanent conditions of the heart in certain of the lower animals. Thus has arisen the picturesque phrase that every animal during its individual development climbs up its own genealogical tree—a saying which, taking it even in the broadest sense, is only partially true.

Speaking broadly, it may be said that during ontogeny only so much of the phylogenetic history is recapitulated as may be necessary to lay the foundation for further stages of development. Thus, although the embryos of the higher mammals have long since ceased to depend upon the storage of yolk in the egg for their nourishment, even in the human embryo a yolk-sac is well developed, since it is intimately related to the formation of the alimentary canal, and to the early appearance of blood-vessels and blood.

Certain terms employed in morphology require some explanation. The same organ repeated in two different animals is said to present a case of **homology**. But the morphological identity between the two organs must be proved beyond dispute before the homology between them can be allowed. The great and essential test is that the two organs in question should have a similar developmental origin. Thus, the fore-limb of a quadruped is homologous with the human upper limb; the puny collar-bone of a tiger, the fibrous thread which is the only representative of this bone in the horse, and the strongly marked clavicle of the ape or Man, are all, strictly speaking, homologous with one another. Homologous organs in different animals usually occupy a similar position and possess a similar structure, but not invariably so. It is not uncommon for a muscle to wander slightly from its original position, and many cases could be quoted in which parts have become completely transformed in structure, either from disuse or for the purpose of meeting some special demand in the animal economy. In the study of the muscles and ligaments instances of this will be brought under the notice of the reader.

The term **homoplasy** is sometimes used to express a form of correspondence between organs in different animals which cannot be included under the term homology. Two animal groups, which originally have sprung from the same stem-form, may exhibit convergence in evolution by developing independently a similar structural character which is altogether absent in the ancestor common to both. Thus the common ancestor of man and the carnivora in all probability possessed a smooth brain, and yet the human brain and the carnivore brain are both richly convoluted. Correspondence of this kind is included under the term " homoplasy." Another example is afforded by the heart of the mammal and that of the bird. In each of these groups the ventricular portion of the heart consists of a right and a left chamber, and yet the ventricular septum in the one is not strictly homologous with the corresponding septum in the other, because the common ancestor from which both have sprung possessed a heart with a single ventricular cavity, and the double-chambered condition has been a subsequent and independent development in the two groups.

Often organs which perform totally different functions are yet perfectly homologous. Thus, the wing of a bat or the wing of a bird, both of which are subservient to flight, are homologous with the human upper limb, the office of which is the different one of prehension. Identity or correspondence in the function performed by two organs in two different animals is not taken into consideration in deciding questions of homology. The gills of a fish and the lungs of a higher vertebrate perform very much the same physiological office, and yet they are not homologous. The term **analogy** is often used to express functional correspondence of this kind.

In the construction of vertebrates and certain other animal groups a series of similar parts are repeated along a longitudinal axis, one after the other. Thus the series of vertebræ which build up the backbone, the series of ribs which gird round each side of the chest, the series of intercostal muscles which fill up the intervals between the ribs, the series of nerves which arise from the brain and spinal cord, are all examples of this. Parts thus repeated are said to be **serially homologous**. An animal in which similar structures are thus repeated is said to present the **segmental type** of organisation. In the early stages of development this segmentation is much more strongly marked, and is to be seen in parts which subsequently lose all trace of such a subdivision. But there are other instances of serial homology besides those which are manifestly produced by segmentation. The upper limb is serially homologous with the lower limb : each is composed of parts which, to a large extent, are repeated in the other, and the correct adjustment of this comparison between the several parts of the upper and lower limbs constitutes one of the most difficult and yet interesting problems of morphology.

No student of Anatomy can proceed far without becoming aware that the human body, like all living things, is subject to **variation**. Many structural variations are recorded in the following pages. Apart altogether from **malformations**—due to aberrations in the course of the development of parts or organs of the body— most of them can be explained on morphological, genetic, or developmental grounds. But there are other kinds of variations in the human body that are not "structural" in the usual sense, and that are notably subject to the laws of **inheritance**. Even the chemistry of the body varies, and such variation may be inherited. The proportions of the body, the stature, the form of the skull and of the face, the texture and colour of the hair, the colour of the eyes and of the skin—all these and many other variable characters, in the skeleton and soft parts alike, make up in infinite variety the genetic constitution of individuals, and in characteristic combinations are the hall-marks of the varieties or races of mankind.

Such variations are the subject matter of *Physical Anthropology*, which not only deals with comparative racial anatomy, but is also concerned with the fascinating problems of the evolutionary origin and the early history of Man.

HUMAN EMBRYOLOGY

Originally written by the late A. H. Young, M.B., F.R.C.S.
Professor of Anatomy, University of Manchester

and Arthur Robinson, M.D., LL.D., F.R.C.S.
Emeritus Professor of Anatomy, University of Edinburgh

Revised by J. C. Brash

INTRODUCTION

Human Embryology—the study of the human embryo and its development—
treats of the phenomena of the intra-uterine period of life, from the fertilisation
of the ovum to the birth of the child. But there is a cycle in the developmental
relation of succeeding generations; and so it is necessary first to consider the life-
history of the germ cells which link one generation to the next.

It has been explained in the General Introduction that all the cells of the
body are the descendants of a single cell, which is the starting point of each
individual. The innumerable cells derived from the fertilised ovum are separable
into two main groups, a larger group—the **soma cells**—from which the body of the

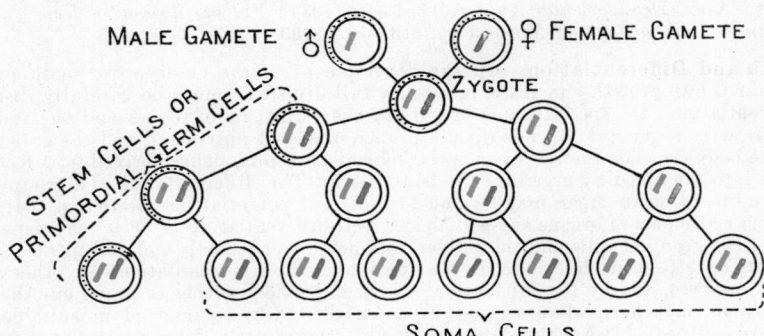

Fig. 9.—Diagram showing the Descent of Germ Cells and Soma Cells.

individual is developed, and a much smaller group—the **germ cells**—upon which
the life of the species depends (Fig. 9). The germ cells are lodged in the body of
the individual in relatively small organs called **sex glands** or **gonads**—ovaries in
the female, **testes** in the male.

A new individual is initiated by the union of a mature male germ cell, called a
spermatozoon or **male gamete**, with a mature female germ cell, called a **mature ovum**
or **female gamete**. The new cell thus formed is a **fertilised ovum** and is conveniently
called a **zygote**—a term indicating that it is formed by the yoking together of two
individuals and that therefore it contains the potentialities of both (Fig. 9).

The human zygote is about 200 μ in diameter and of scarcely measurable
weight. From it are produced not only a new individual and the germ cells of
the next generation, but also a series of membranes and appendages necessary for
growth and development during intra-uterine life.

The **ontogenetic** or **developmental history** of the individual is usually considered
to extend from the formation of the zygote to the attainment of full growth.

15

The **period of development** thus defined is divided into an **intra-uterine** or **pre-natal** period and an **extra-uterine** or **post-natal** period.

The intra-uterine life of human beings lasts for about nine months, and is itself divided into three secondary periods: (1) The **pre-embryonic period**, before the zygote is definitely separated into embryonic and non-embryonic portions; this period lasts about fourteen days. (2) The **embryonic period**, in which the rudiments of all the main organs of the adult are evolved, although the embryonic part has not yet assumed a definitely human form; this period runs to the end of the second month. (3) The **fœtal period**, from the end of the second month, when the embryo begins to assume a definitely human appearance and is called, thenceforth, a **fœtus**. The fœtal period ends at birth, when the fœtus becomes a child and passes into the stage of *post-natal development*.

During the fœtal period growth proceeds rapidly. It is especially rapid during the ninth month; and at birth the child usually weighs about seven pounds.

During the first-stages of the post-natal period—**infancy, childhood, adolescence**—growth and development still proceed until the adult condition is attained; then follows a period of **maturity**, which passes insensibly into the last stage of all—**senescence**—which ends in natural death. In the following pages it is the intra-uterine period of life which will be considered and more especially the phenomena of the first two months, the so-called pre-embryonic and embryonic periods.

The aim is to provide the student with a general account of the formation of the embryo, so that he may be in a position to understand the more detailed paragraphs on the development of organs which he will find throughout the text-book. Some account will also be given of those important extra-embryonic organs peculiar to intra-uterine life—the so-called **fœtal membranes**—which are responsible for the protection of the embryo and fœtus and, by the connexion established between one of them and the uterus of the mother, provide for its physiological needs.

For further information on human development the student should consult special works on the subject: Arey, *Developmental Anatomy*, 3rd edit., 1934; Frazer, *Manual of Embryology*, 1931; Keith, *Human Embryology and Morphology*, 5th edit., 1933.

Growth and Differentiation.—In the development of the embryo two main processes go hand in hand, but **growth**—increase in size by cell-division—must be carefully distinguished from **differentiation**—the specialisation of cells in the formation of tissues and the rudiments of organs. Growth in general depends upon a proper supply of nutriment, and the growth of some parts of the body depends further upon special chemical factors, either derived from food material or secreted into the blood by organs of the body itself. The differentiation of a group of cells to form the rudiment of an organ may be due to inherited potentialities located in that particular group—such rudiments of organs are said to be "self-differentiating"; or it may depend on the situation of the group of cells and the influence of neighbouring cells and rudiments upon them. Experiments have been made by the simple excision, or the transplantation into other regions, of portions of embryos, and by the cultivation of excised portions, either as grafts on other growing tissues (such as the chorio-allantoic membrane of the chick) or inserted in suitable nutritive media (tissue-culture). It has thus been shown that the power to form parts and organs may be more widespread in the cells of an embryonic layer than is apparent, and that their development in a particular place depends on the influence of other parts already differentiated. Such "dependent differentiation" of parts may be illustrated by two classical examples of the results obtained by the methods of *Experimental Embryology*.

The formation, and therefore the situation, of the axial structures in the embryonic area depends upon an influence exerted by the tissues in the primitive streak: these are believed to correspond with the dorsal lip of the blastopore in lower forms which, because it has this power, has been called the "Organiser" (Mangold and Spemann). The formation of the lens vesicle of the eye from the ectoderm depends, in some species, on the presence of the underlying optic cup—a self-differentiating structure which grows out from the fore-brain; if the optic cup is removed the lens does not appear, but a lens vesicle may be induced to form from another part of the ectoderm by transplanting the cup (Lewis, Spemann).

Progressive differentiation of the cells of a region is illustrated by experiments on limb buds. Part of a limb bud which if left *in situ* would form a particular part of the limb may, if transplanted soon enough, "regulate" so as to form a complete limb. After a time, however, the cells of the limb bud are differentiated, chemically if not morphologically, to form a "mosaic," any part of which has its particular destiny fixed and is incapable of "regulating" to form a whole limb; yet for a time it may still be capable of producing the whole of one segment of the limb. Thus, a portion of the thigh region of a chick embryo, transplanted (Murray & Huxley) or grown by tissue-culture methods (Fell & Robison), will produce not a complete limb but a femur only.

For further information on the control of development see *The Elements of Experimental*

Embryology, Huxley and de Beer, 1934, or the less detailed work, *How Animals Develop*, Waddington, 1935.

There are also many chemical problems in the development of the embryo, and for information on this aspect of the subject the student should consult *Chemical Embryology*, Needham, 1931, in which much interesting historical matter also will be found.

GERM CELLS

The majority of the multitudinous descendants derived from a zygote are soma cells, which form the tissues of the body; but a minority, which inherit all the potentialities of their parents, remain as **stem cells** or **primordial germ cells** (Fig. 9). Though the functions and the life histories of germ cells are quite different from those of soma cells, nevertheless the structural characters of the two groups of cells are very similar; in particular they both multiply by the same process of mitotic division (p. 8). Each primordial germ cell thus produces many descendants which are lodged in the sex glands—female sex cells or **oogonia** in the ovaries, male sex cells or **spermatogonia** in the testes—where they undergo further multiplication. Eventually they cease to multiply and enter upon a period of growth; the female cells are then known as **oocytes** and the male cells as

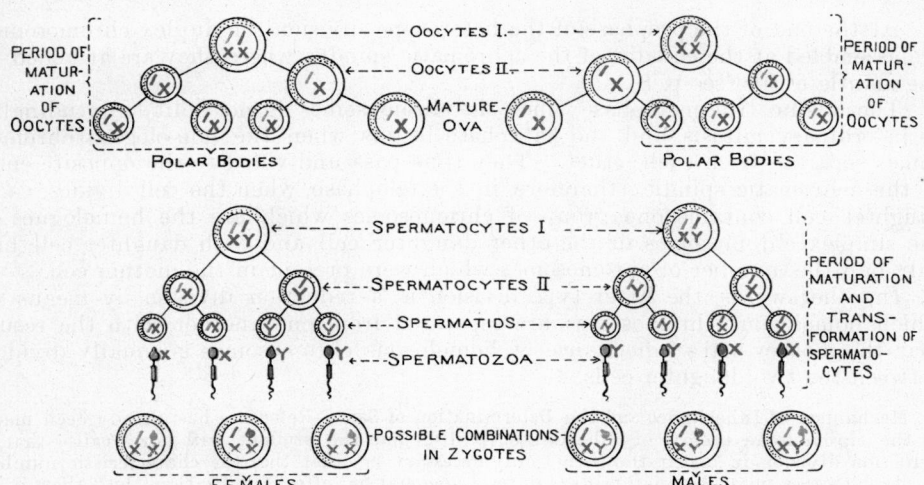

Fig. 10.—Diagram of the Behaviour of the Chromosomes during Maturation of the Germ Cells, including the XY Mechanism of Sex Determination.

spermatocytes. When the growth period is attained the power of division is not altogether lost; but each oocyte or spermatocyte is then capable of producing only four descendants by two final divisions, which are called the ripening or **maturation divisions.** The four descendants of an oocyte are a mature **ovum** and three small cells called *polar bodies*: the four descendants of a spermatocyte are four **spermatozoa** (Fig. 10). The mature germ cells (the ovum and the spermatozoon) are called **gametes.**

The first maturation division is "*heterotypical*" because the chromosomes do not split in the process, or "*meiotic*" [μειοῦν (meioun)—to lessen] because the result is a reduction of their number.

Heterotype Mitosis and **Meiosis.**—It has already been pointed out (p. 9) that the number of chromosomes in the dividing cells of any species of animal is always the same; the number varies greatly in different species, but is characteristically constant in each. The same number of chromosomes is found in the soma cells and primordial germ cells; and it is believed that they are arranged in pairs, called *homologous chromosomes*, one member of each pair being derived from the male parent and the other from the female parent.

In one of the maturation divisions of the germ cells the homologous chromosomes are separated, one of them going to one and the other to the other daughter cell : this is the essence of **heterotype mitosis** ; and **meiosis**, or the reduction of the number of chromosomes to half, is the result.

In Man and other mammals meiosis occurs in the first of the two maturation divisions.

During the early prophase of the reduction division the chromatin of the nucleus passes through a special series of changes in form to which various terms have been applied. These changes, which are related to the intricate mechanism of inheritance, occur in the spermatocyte immediately before the reduction division ; but in the oocyte they may occur long before, and are then followed by a long period of rest. In other words, the prophase of the reduction division in the spermatocyte is short, but in the oocyte it may be very prolonged. Finally, the homologous chromosomes appear and lie side by side (Fig. 17), each pair forming a *duplex* or twin chromosome—a stage also known as *conjugation of the chromosomes*. Thus, the apparent number of chromosomes is reduced to half the original number of the ordinary *simplex* chromosomes present in soma cells and in non-maturing germ cells.

The terms " diploid " and " haploid " are better avoided, as they have been used to mean not only the duplex and simplex *state*, but also the complete and reduced *number* of the chromosomes.

At the end of the prophase of the heterotype division the duplex chromosomes are assembled at the equator of the achromatic spindle, where they are attached to the mantle fibrils (see p. 8).

There is no true metaphase, since the chromosomes do not split longitudinally as in ordinary mitosis, and the kataphase begins when the homologous chromosomes separate from each other. They thus pass undivided to the opposite ends of the achromatic spindle ; therefore, in the telophase, when the cell divides, each daughter cell contains one group of chromosomes which are the homologues of the simplex chromosomes in the other daughter cell, and each daughter cell has only half the number of chromosomes which were present in the mother cell.

In other words, the heterotype division is a reduction division by means of which homologous chromosomes are separated from one another, with the result that the mother cell's inheritance of homologous chromosomes is equally divided between the two daughter cells.

Mechanism of Inheritance and the Determination of Sex.—Reference has already been made to the chromosome theory of inheritance (p. 10), and the student will now realise that a reduction division in maturation is not only necessary in order that the characteristic number of chromosomes may be maintained in each generation after fertilisation, but that it is part of the mechanism for that " shuffle and deal " of the parental chromosomes upon which, according to the theory of chance, the inheritance of the offspring depends.

In Fig. 10 the behaviour of *one pair* of homologous chromosomes (paternal, red ; maternal blue) in the maturation of germ cells is represented. But in studying this diagram the student should remember that in human oocytes and spermatocytes there are 23 such pairs, in addition to a special pair in each (oocyte, XX : spermatocyte, XY) which has special relation to the inheritance of sex. The statistical study of the mode of inheritance of pairs of characters, of which one may be *dominant* and the other *recessive*—**Mendelism**—is in accord with the behaviour of the chromosomes. As it appears to be a matter of chance into which daughter cells the members of one pair of homologous chromosomes may separately pass, it may be calculated that in the maturation and union in fertilisation of any two human germ cells there are over 281 *billions* of different possible combinations *of the chromosomes* alone.

Add to this that interchange of genes or groups of genes—*crossing-over*—is known to occur during the conjugation of the chromosomes in the prophase of the reduction division, and it is abundantly clear that the chromosome theory of inheritance is consistent with the infinite variety of individual characterisation.

Every normal individual must be either male or female ; and there is now conclusive evidence that sex is a heritable character, that it is determined at the time of the union of the gametes and that it is dependent upon special chromosomes, which, although they bear other genes than those that determine sex, are known for that reason as *sex chromosomes*. The relation of the behaviour of these special chromosomes to the sex of the offspring has been traced in many species of invertebrates and vertebrates. Although there are many variations of the mechanism in detail, the general principle disclosed is that one sex is characterised by the presence of a pair of similar sex chromosomes distinguished as X-chromosomes, and the other by the presence of only one X-chromosome, which may or may not be paired with another of dissimilar form known as the Y-chromosome. The determining factor is the formation by one sex of two kinds of gametes of different chromosome constitution. That sex (usually the male, but the female in many invertebrates and in birds) is therefore said to be *digametic* or *heterozygous* for sex ; while the other is said to be *monogametic* or *homozygous*.

In the determination of human sex, it is the male that is digametic. The human oocyte has 23 pairs of ordinary chromosomes and one pair of X-chromosomes—48 in all. Its chromosome constitution may thus be written 46XX : and every mature ovum therefore possesses an X-chromosome. Its formula is 23X. The formula of the spermatocyte, on the other hand, is 46XY ; when the reduction division occurs the X-chromosome passes into one spermatocyte II, the Y-chromosome to the other spermatocyte II. Therefore of the four spermatids two will have an X-chromosome and two will have a Y-chromosome. There are thus two kinds of spermatozoa, of 23X and 23Y constitution respectively. If an X-bearing spermatozoon unites with an ovum a female results, and if a Y-bearing spermatozoon unites with an ovum a male results (Fig. 10).

The chromosome constitution of human sex cells stated above is now generally accepted on the evidence of Painter (1923) and of Evans and Swezy (1929) ; but the view maintained by Winiwarter and Oguma (1912, 1926), that the female cell has 48 chromosomes and the male 47, there being no Y-chromosome present in the male, does not affect the principle of sex determination. Male sex depends on the absence of a second X rather than on the presence of a Y-chromosome, the physiological activity of which is in some doubt.

Moreover, the student should understand, although sex is said to be "determined" at fertilisation by the chromosome constitution of the nucleus of the zygote, that sex has to be "developed" in the individual. The rudiments of the organs of both sexes are formed in every embryo, and the actual sex depends upon physiological factors believed to be controlled by the chromosomes. But there is evidence, experimental and otherwise, to show that the normal mechanism may be deranged, with the production of the phenomena of inter-sex and sex-reversal, by changes in the environment either external or internal.

The cytological and other evidence upon which the chromosome theory of sex is based is confirmed by the observation that uni-ovular twins, *i.e.* twins developed from a single ovum, are always of the same sex, whilst bi-ovular twins may be of the same or of opposite sex. It is also strikingly confirmed by the phenomena of "sex linkage" in inheritance. The sex chromosomes are not solely concerned with sex ; they bear genes which control other heritable characters ; and these characters are linked to sex in their transmission from generation to generation. Sex-linked characters are of some importance in human inheritance, the best known example being the condition called *hœmophilia*, in which there is an abnormal tendency to spontaneous or excessive bleeding. It is believed that the determining factor of this condition is carried on the X-chromosome, which explains its characteristic mode of inheritance ; it is not transmitted from an affected father to his son, but only to a grandson through a "carrier" daughter who remains herself unaffected (see Fig. 10).

For further information on these interesting questions, the student is advised to consult Wilson, *The Cell in Development and Inheritance* ; Crew, *The Genetics of Sexuality in Animals*.

The Gametes.—Gametes are the final descendants of a line of germ cells which have changed from primordial germ cells to oocytes in the female and spermatocytes in the male ; the whole process is known as **gametogenesis** (Figs. 9 and 10).

By means of the two maturation divisions, the oocyte is transformed into the mature ovum or female gamete and three polar bodies which disappear, whilst the spermatocyte is transformed into four spermatids, which undergo metamorphosis into spermatozoa or mature male gametes.

Both female and male gametes are specialised cells, inasmuch as each possesses only half the number of chromosomes present in its grand-parent ; moreover, each is incapable, under ordinary circumstances, of undergoing cell division, and must either die or unite with a gamete of the opposite sex to produce a new rejuvenated cell called a zygote.

The ovum and the spermatozoon have their own special characteristics. The phenomena of **oogenesis** and **spermatogenesis** must, therefore, be considered separately.

OOGENESIS AND THE OVUM

The structure of the ovary and the development of oocytes from the germinal epithelium are described with the urogenital system.

Each **oocyte** lies at first in the cortical part of the ovary, surrounded by a single layer of cells known as the stratum granulosum, and the oocyte and the stratum granulosum constitute, together, a **primary ovarian follicle** (Fig. 11).

Gradually the oocyte increases in size until it attains a diameter of from

100 μ to 200 μ, and so becomes a relatively large cell. During the growth period changes occur both in the surroundings and in the contents of the oocyte.

The changes in the surroundings include increase in number of the cells of the stratum granulosum, changes in their form, subdivision of them into two groups by the appearance of a cavity amidst them, and the formation of a new envelope, called the *oolemma*, around the oocyte.

At first the cells of the stratum granulosum are flat plates. Then they become cubical and increase in number by mitosis, until they form several layers. Thereafter a cavity filled with a fluid called the *primary liquor folliculi* appears amidst the cells. It increases rapidly in size and separates the cells into two multicellular parts. One part forms the boundary of the cavity and is still called the *stratum granulosum*. The other projects into the cavity; it is called the *cumulus ovaricus*, and in it the oocyte is embedded. The primary ovarian follicle is thus converted into a *vesicular ovarian follicle* (Figs. 13, 14).

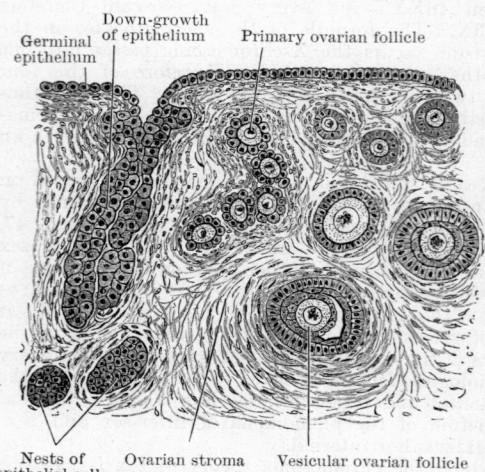

FIG. 11.—DIAGRAMMATIC REPRESENTATION OF THE MANNER IN WHICH VESICULAR FOLLICLES DEVELOP IN THE OVARY.

When the cells of the stratum granulosum have formed two layers, a glassy envelope begins to appear around the oocyte, separating it from the cells of the cumulus. The envelope is called the **oolemma.** It increases in thickness until the maturation of the oocyte begins, when it is an elastic pellucid membrane

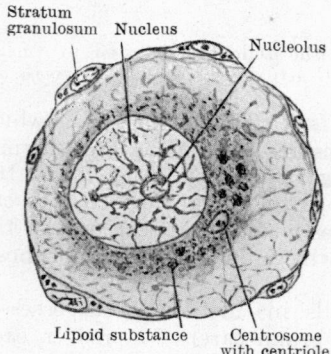

FIG. 12.—A HUMAN OOCYTE AT THE BEGINNING OF THE GROWTH PERIOD. Diameters 38 μ × 33 μ. The small black granules in the granulosa cells are lipoid granules.

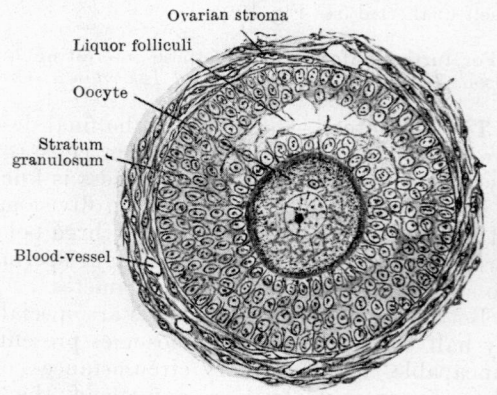

FIG. 13.—A HUMAN OVARIAN FOLLICLE AT THE BEGINNING OF THE VESICULAR STAGE. Diameters of follicle 155 μ × 155 μ × 120 μ.

(zona pellucida), sometimes faintly striated (zona striata), varying from 7 μ to 10 μ in thickness.

The oolemma is formed by the oocyte, and it appears to be traversed by processes of the surrounding cumulus cells, which gradually assume an elongated columnar form and constitute the *corona radiata* (Figs. 15 and 24).

It is the fine prolongations of the corona radiata cells, passing through the oolemma to the surface of the oocyte, which give rise to the striated appearance which has already been noted.

The changes which take place in the oocyte itself during the growth period concern the contents of the cytoplasm, and the position and relative size of the nucleus.

At the beginning of the growth period the oocyte (called *oocyte I* to differentiate it from one of its two immediate descendants) is an almost spherical cell; but it soon becomes ovoid and it retains its ovoid form in all subsequent periods. It consists of a cell body, containing a relatively large eccentrically placed nucleus and a centrosome. The centrosome lies near the central pole of the nucleus and contains one or two centrioles (Fig. 12).

The nucleus possesses one or two nucleoli, and its chromatic substance is dispersed through the linin reticulum.

Metaplasmic substance is already present in the oocyte; it lies in the cytoplasm, around the nucleus, and it is most abundant at the central pole of the nucleus around the centrosome (Fig. 12). As growth proceeds the metaplasmic substance becomes more diffused, but it is always most abundant in the central part of the cytoplasm, around the nucleus.

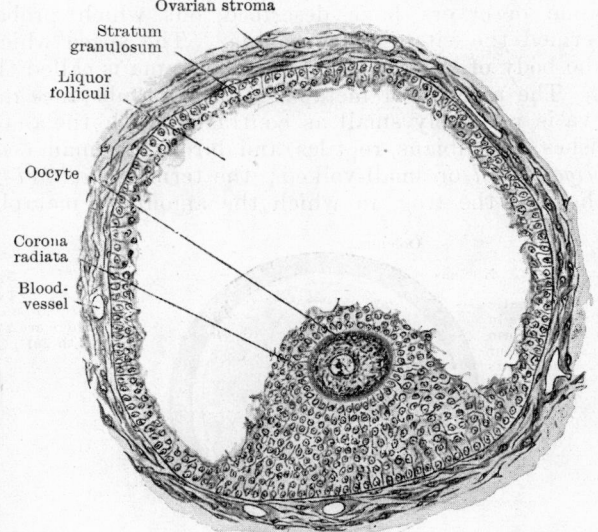

FIG. 14.—A HUMAN VESICULAR OVARIAN FOLLICLE.
Diameters of follicle 620 μ × 465 μ × 465 μ.

The nucleus gradually attains a central position in the oocyte (Fig. 13), but afterwards it migrates to the periphery of the oocyte, the centrosome disappears, and the process of maturation begins.

During the growth period the body of the oocyte grows more rapidly than the nucleus; and therefore at the end of the growth period the nucleus, though actually larger than it was at the beginning, is relatively smaller.

When growth is completed the full-grown oocyte I lies in the cumulus of a vesicular follicle in the cortical part of the ovary. It consists of a cell body which contains a nucleus, mitochondria and numerous highly refractive granules, called yolk granules. It possesses no proper cell membrane continuous with the cytoplasm, but it is enclosed in a definite sheath, called the oolemma, or zona pellucida, or zona striata.

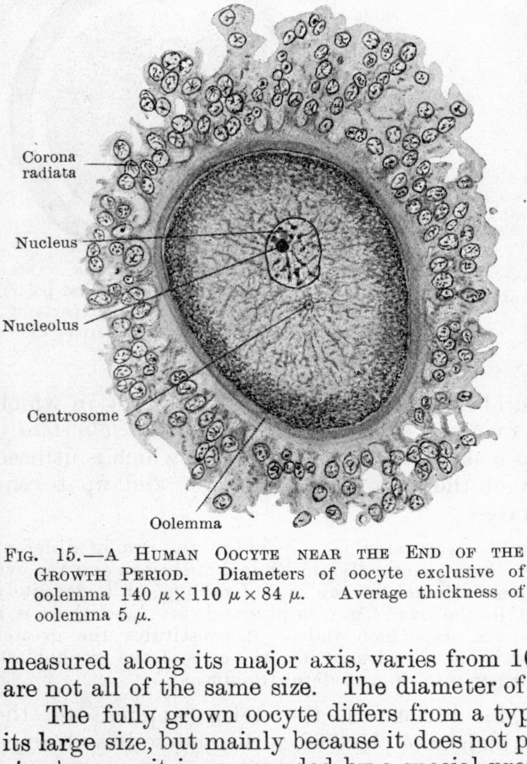

FIG. 15.—A HUMAN OOCYTE NEAR THE END OF THE GROWTH PERIOD. Diameters of oocyte exclusive of oolemma 140 μ × 110 μ × 84 μ. Average thickness of oolemma 5 μ.

The diameter of the cell body, measured along its major axis, varies from 100 μ to 200 μ, for full-grown oocytes are not all of the same size. The diameter of the nucleus varies from 25 μ to 50 μ.

The fully grown oocyte differs from a typical animal cell partly on account of its large size, but mainly because it does not possess a demonstrable centrosome, and also because it is surrounded by a special protective envelope—the oolemma.

2 a

The nucleus of the fully grown oocyte is frequently called the *germinal vesicle,* and the nucleolus the *germinal spot,* whilst the protoplasm of the cell body is spoken of as the *vitellus* or *yolk.* Consequently the cell membrane, which some observers have described, but which probably does not exist, has been termed the vitelline membrane. The space which sometimes appears between the body of the oocyte and the oolemma is called the *perivitelline space.*

The amount of metaplasm or yolk substance in human and most mammalian ova is relatively small as contrasted with the amount present in the oocytes of fishes, amphibians, reptiles, and birds. Human oocytes are said, therefore, to be *oligolecithal* or small-yolked; the term *telolecithal* is applied to oocytes, such as those of the frog, in which the amount of metaplasm is considerable, whilst the

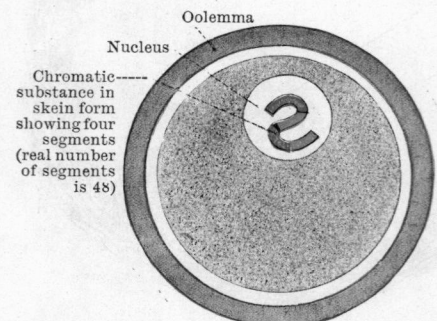

FIG. 16.—SCHEMA OF MATURATION OF OVUM, EARLY PART OF PROPHASE OF FIRST DIVISION.

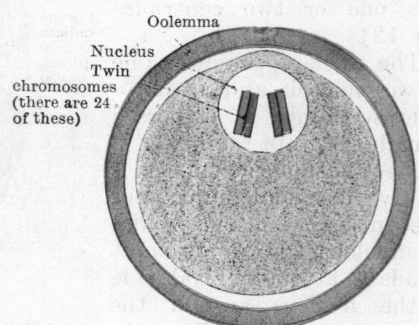

FIG. 17.—LATER PROPHASE OF FIRST DIVISION. The chromatic thread has divided into twin chromosomes. Each twin may be assumed to consist of a maternal and a paternal part.

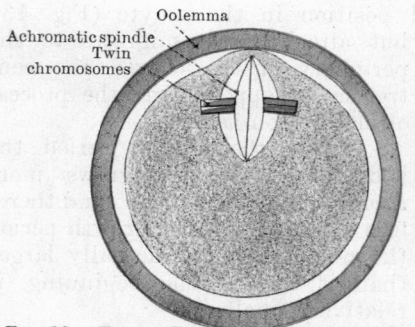

FIG. 18.—END OF PROPHASE OF FIRST DIVISION. The twin chromosomes lie at the equator of the achromatic spindle.

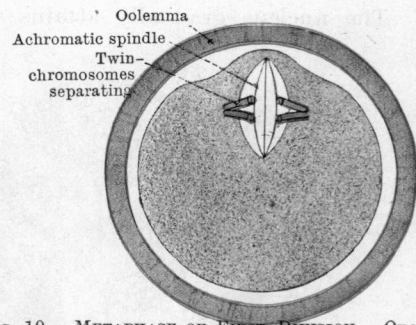

FIG. 19.—METAPHASE OF FIRST DIVISION. One pole of the spindle projects into the first polar bud, and the maternal and paternal parts of the chromosomes are separating from each other.

oocytes of birds, of many reptiles, and of monotremes amongst mammals, in which the metaplasm greatly preponderates over the cytoplasm, are called *eutelolecithal.*

The metaplasmic granules serve as a store of nutritive material which is utilised during the early stages of the growth of the zygote in mammals, and up to the period of birth in many other vertebrates.

There is great variation in the amount of unsaturated fat (lipoid) in the ova of different mammals, as shown by osmic acid staining. It is practically absent in human ova and the ova of rats and mice; a slight but variable amount is found in the ova of rabbits; it is definitely present, as spherules of relatively large size, in the ova of guinea pigs and cats; and there is a large amount in the ova of dogs and ferrets, in which indeed it constitutes the greater part of the volume of the ova. In the ferret it has been traced into the cells of the trophoblast, of the inner cell mass and the ectoderm, but not into the entoderm (Robinson).

Maturation of the Ovum.—Maturation is the term applied to the phenomena of the two cell divisions which take place after the oocyte has attained its full growth.

We have no thoroughly satisfactory knowledge of the phenomena of maturation in human oocytes and must therefore, at present, presume that they are the same as those which have been clearly demonstrated in many other mammals.

The first of the two divisions is meiotic or heterotypical. During its progress the nuclear membrane and the nucleolus or nucleoli disappear, and an achromatic spindle appears at one pole of the oocyte, in the situation previously occupied by the nucleus.

The spindle has no centrosomes at its extremities, and its long axis is at first parallel with the surface of the oocyte.

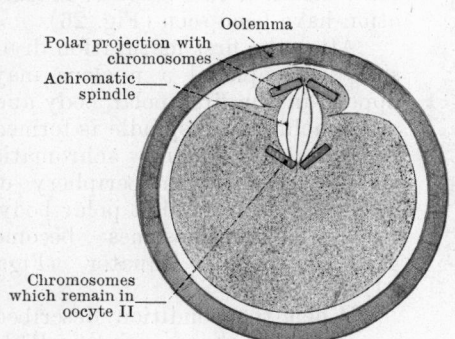

Fig. 20.—End of the Kataphase of the First Division. Two chromosomes (paternal or maternal) lie in the first polar bud and two in the larger part of the ovum which becomes oocyte II.

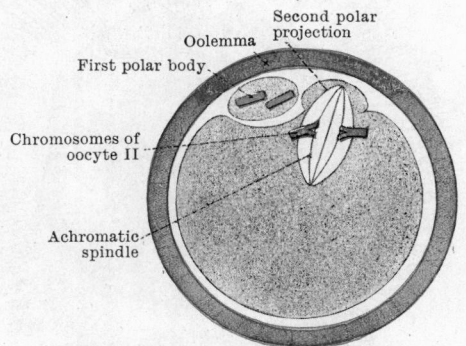

Fig. 21.—Beginning of the Metaphase of the Second Division.

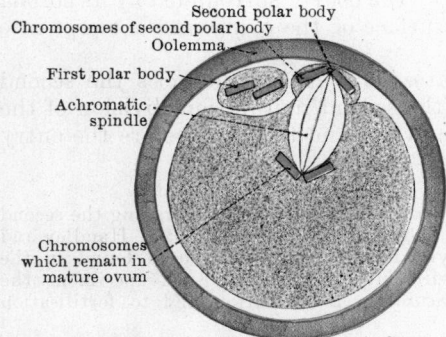

Fig. 22.—End of Kataphase of Second Division. The chromosomes of oocyte II have separated into equal parts which have passed to the opposite poles of the spindle.

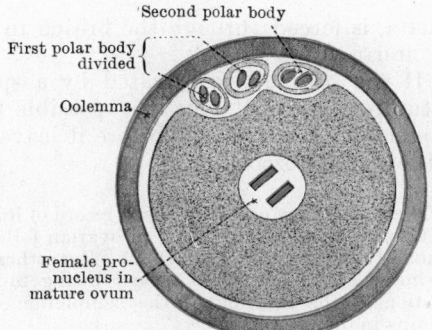

Fig. 23.—Schema of Maturation of Ovum, End of Telophase of Second Division. The four descendants of oocyte I are the mature ovum, with half the original number of chromosomes, and three polar bodies.

The chromosomes are aggregated together in pairs as twin or duplex chromosomes. They appear therefore to be only half the number of the chromosomes originally present in the oocyte; at the end of the prophase they lie at the periphery of the equator of the spindle. When this condition is attained the spindle rotates on its transverse axis, and one pole, carrying a little cytoplasm around it, projects beyond the general surface of the oocyte, forming the *first polar projection* (Fig. 19).

During the metaphase the two halves of each twin chromosome separate from each other, the two simplex chromosomes thus formed being each equivalent to a whole chromosome of an ordinary cell.

In the kataphase the halves of each twin chromosome travel to the opposite poles of the achromatic spindle, and those which travel to the peripheral pole enter the first polar projection (Figs. 19, 20).

During the telophase the first polar projection, with its included chromosomes and the part of the achromatic spindle next the periphery, is cut off from the main part of the oocyte. The first maturation division is then completed; *oocyte I* being divided into a large segment (*oocyte II*) and a small segment called the first

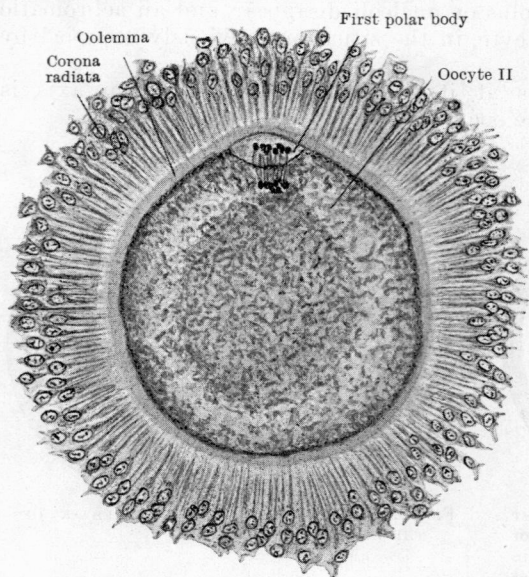

Oolemma

Corona radiata

First polar body

Oocyte II

polar body, both of which lie inside the oolemma and each of which contains half the number of chromosomes originally present in oocyte I (Figs. 20-26). Human ova which have attained this stage of maturation have been seen (Fig. 26).

After the first maturation division is completed a nucleus may appear in the first polar body and a new achromatic spindle is formed in oocyte II. The new achromatic spindle lies at the periphery of oocyte II near the first polar body, and the chromosomes become grouped at its equator (Figs. 21, 25).

When the condition described is attained the ovarian follicle ruptures, and the liquor folliculi (which has meanwhile increased in amount by the formation of *secondary liquor folliculi* in spaces in the cumulus), carrying with it the oocyte surrounded by its corona radiata, is forced through the breach in the surface of the ovary and is swept into the uterine tube.

FIG. 24.—OOCYTE OF A FERRET IN THE TELOPHASE OF THE FIRST MATURATION DIVISION. Diameters of oocyte exclusive of oolemma, 150 $\mu \times$ 125 $\mu \times$ 110 μ.

If the oocyte is penetrated by a spermatozoon it then undergoes the second maturation division; but it is possible that the second maturation division of the human oocyte may occur before it leaves the ovary, and therefore before the entry of the spermatozoon.

There are a few observations on record of human oocytes thought to be undergoing the second maturation division while still in ovarian follicles (Thomson, 1919; Dixon, 1927; Handley and Simon, 1928; Allen *et. al.* 1930). But other oocytes in that stage have been found in the uterine tubes (Allen *et. al.*); and owing to the difficulty of obtaining such specimens the question of the relation of the completion of maturation to ovulation and to fertilisation remains in doubt.

The phenomena of the second maturation division are those of **homotype mitosis**. One pole of the achromatic spindle, already present in oocyte II, projects beyond the surface of the oocyte, carrying with it a small amount of cytoplasm, and so forming the *second polar projection* (Fig. 21.) Thereafter each of the chromosomes at the equator of the achromatic spindle (which it must be remembered are only half as numerous as those originally present in oocyte I) splits longitudinally into equal parts. The opposite halves of the divided chromosomes then travel to the ends of the achromatic spindle; consequently one group enters the second polar projection and the other remains in the body of the oocyte (Fig. 22).

When the chromosomes reach the ends of the achromatic spindle the second polar projection is cut off from the body of the oocyte to form the *second polar body*. Thus, in the second maturation division, oocyte II is segmented into a smaller part (the second polar body) and a larger part, each of which contains half the number of chromosomes present in oocyte I.

As soon as the second polar body is separated off, a nuclear membrane appears around the chromosomes in the body of the oocyte; a linin reticulum is formed within the membrane, and the particles of the chromosomes are distributed along the reticulum; a nucleolus also is developed. The new nucleus, thus formed, is called the **female pronucleus,** and the maturation is completed.

As the second polar body is separated off, the first polar body not uncommonly divides into two parts. When that occurs the result of the two maturation divisions of the oocyte is the formation of one large cell (the mature ovum) and three polar bodies, all of which are enclosed within the oolemma (Fig. 23).

The exact position at which the polar bodies are extruded does not appear to be of any significance in the maturation of the mammalian ovum.

If the oocyte II does not meet with a spermatozoon it passes through the genital passages and is cast off and lost; or it breaks down, whilst still in the genital passages, into a detritus which disappears; but if it meets and unites with a spermatozoon a **zygote** is formed, from which a new individual may arise, and in that case the polar bodies persist until the zygote has undergone one or two divisions; but sooner or later they disappear, probably breaking down into fragments which are absorbed by the cells of the zygote.

Spermatogenesis and the Spermatozoon

When the male germ cells reach the period of growth they are called **spermatocytes of the first order** or spermatocytes I, which correspond morphologically with oocytes I (Fig. 10).

The spermatogonia and the spermatocytes lie in the walls of the seminiferous tubules of the testes or male sex glands. There their descendants become converted into spermatozoa.

Spermatocytes differ from oocytes in three important respects: (1) they have no protective membrane corresponding with the oolemma of the oocyte; (2) they are not enclosed in follicles; (3) they are not surrounded by definite encircling layers of cells similar to the cells of the stratum granulosum.

In the tubules of the testes the spermatocytes are intermingled with other cells called *supporting* or *nurse cells — cells of Sertoli*—amidst which they undergo their maturation divisions; their descendants become embedded in the nurse cells, where they are converted into spermatozoa. To a certain extent, therefore, the nurse cells may be looked upon as corresponding with the cells of the cumulus ovaricus, which surround the growing oocyte.

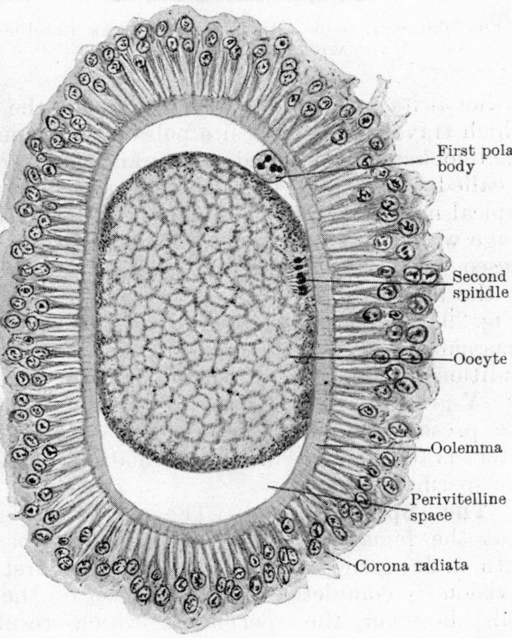

After it has reached its full growth each spermatocyte I, like each oocyte I, can produce only four descendants; the descendants, as in the case of the oocyte I, are formed by two successive mitotic divisions, of which the first is heterotypical and produces reduction of the chromosomes, and the second is homotypical.

FIG. 25.—Oocyte of a Ferret after Separation of the First Polar Body. Diameters of oocyte exclusive of oolemma, 110 μ × 110 μ × 41 μ.

The two divisions differ from the corresponding divisions of the oocytes in three important respects: (1) centrosomes are present; (2) the four granddaughter cells produced are of equal size and of equal value, as they are all capable of uniting with an ovum to form a zygote; (3) each of the four grand-daughter cells possesses two centrioles.

In the prophase of the first or *heterotype* division the nucleus and nucleolus disappear in the ordinary way. The centrosome divides, and an achromatic spindle appears, which has the daughter centrosomes at its poles and half the typical number of chromosomes at its equator. The chromosomes are twin chromosomes. During the metaphase the two segments of each twin chromosome separate from each other. In the kataphase they travel to the opposite poles of the achromatic spindle, and consequently, when the cell divides in the telophase, each daughter cell or **spermatocyte** II contains a centrosome and half the typical number of chromosomes (Fig. 10).

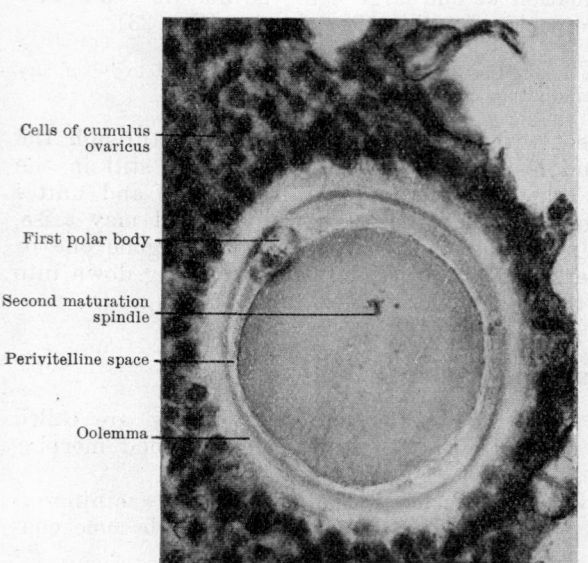

Cells of cumulus ovaricus

First polar body

Second maturation spindle

Perivitelline space

Oolemma

FIG. 26.—SECTION OF A HUMAN OVUM AFTER THE FIRST MATURATION DIVISION (A. F. Dixon).

The second maturation division, which takes place without the intervention of a resting stage, is of the *homotype* form. The centrosome divides, a new achromatic spindle appears, and the daughter chromosomes gather at its equator. In the metaphase the chromosomes divide into equal parts, which travel to the opposite poles of the spindle during the kataphase, and when the telophase is completed each grand-daughter cell, which is called a **spermatid**, possesses a centrosome and half the typical number of chromosomes (Fig. 10). In the resting stage which follows, the chromatic particles become enclosed in a new-formed nucleus, and the centriole passes to the surface of the cell and divides into two equal parts (Fig. 29(1)). The Golgi apparatus, which has been scattered, reassembles close to the opposite side of the nucleus. In addition to numerous mitochondria other particles, known as Y-granules, which may represent abortive yolk, are present, and there is also an *accessory body* which later is concerned in the formation of the neck of the spermatozoon.

The Spermatozoon.—The reader will have noted that the female gametes become ready for conjugation with male gametes directly after the first maturation division is completed. In the case of the male germ cells, however, the spermatids which result from the second maturation division have still to undergo a complicated process of transformation before they become converted to spermatozoa or mature male gametes. The process of transformation takes place in association with the cells of Sertoli in which the developing spermatozoa become embedded.

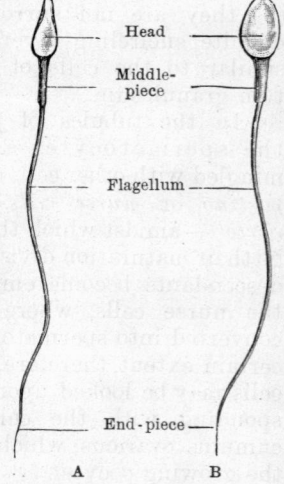

Head

Middle-piece

Flagellum

End-piece

A   B

FIG. 27.—HUMAN SPERMATOZOA (after Retzius).

A, Side view; B, Front view.

The details of the process of transformation are difficult to follow, and knowledge regarding them has been until quite recently rather indefinite. Gatenby and Beams (*Quart. Journ. Micr. Sci.*, Oct. 1935), however, have now provided us with an authentic account of human spermatogenesis, including very clear details of the metamorphosis of the spermatid (Fig. 29); but before these details are considered it is necessary that the reader should be acquainted with the anatomy of an adult spermatozoon.

A spermatozoon is a minute organism consisting of a head, a neck, a middle-piece or body, and a flagellum or tail. Its total length is about 50 μ, that is, its length is about the same as the diameter of the nucleus of the ovum.

The **head** has the form of a compressed ovoid. It contains the nucleus of the spermatid and is completely covered by a **head cap** which consists of two parts—an anterior part, the head-cap proper, and a posterior part, the post-nuclear cap. The length of the head is about 4·5 μ.

The **neck** is an extremely short constricted region between the head and the middle-piece. It contains a deeply staining "*neck body*" the exact significance of which is unknown. The **middle-piece** is about the same length as the head, and its constituent parts are: (1) the proximal centriole; (2) a portion of the axial filament with its sheath; (3) the mitochondrial sheath; and (4) the distal centriole.

The **axial sheath** is a thin layer of protoplasm immediately surrounding the **axial filament**, which extends from the **proximal centriole** through the middle-piece into the flagellum. The **mitochondrial sheath** surrounds the axial sheath, and is formed by numerous fused mitochondria. The **distal centriole** is ring-shaped, and through it the axial filament and its sheath pass from the middle-piece into the flagellum.

The **flagellum** or tail is long. It consists of prolongations of the axial filament and its sheath, and it terminates in a short thin *end-piece*, in which the axial filament appears free from the sheath.

Metamorphosis of Spermatid into Spermatozoon.—The **head** of the spermatozoon is formed from the nucleus of the spermatid, which becomes encased in a special sheath formed in two parts. The Golgi elements, which have been scattered during the maturation divisions, assemble on the surface of the nucleus as a single apparatus which contains a bead surrounded by a small vacuole. The bead is deposited on the nucleus to form the *acrosome* from which the **head-cap** proper is derived; the vacuole enlarges to form a semilunar space over the acrosome; and the Golgi apparatus then detaches itself from the nucleus and flows down into the cytoplasm of the spermatid to be discarded later.

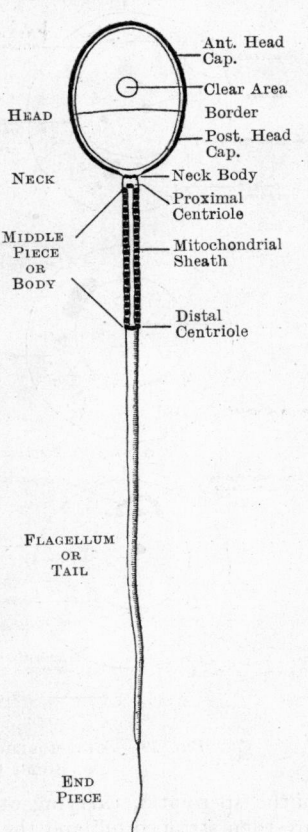

Fig. 28—Structure of a Human Spermatozoon (J. Brontë Gatenby and H. W. Beams).

After the second maturation division the centriole of the spermatid passes towards the cell-wall and divides into two; from the double centriole the **axial filament** then grows out through the surface of the cell. The double centriole moves inwards again, and can then be seen to consist of two separate parts—a **proximal centriole** (nearer the nucleus) which is granular and gives rise to the axial filament of the flagellum, and a **distal centriole** which appears as a *ring* threaded on the filament. The two centrioles continue to move in together and become applied to the nucleus on the side opposite to the attachment of the acrosome bead. The distal centriole grows very considerably and becomes a conspicuous object.

A new membranous structure has meanwhile appeared between the centrioles and the nucleus. This is the rudiment of the **post-nuclear cap**, which begins to grow upwards to meet the down-growing head-cap proper derived from the rapidly spreading acrosome. A clear area or vacuole (probably of nucleolar origin) has meanwhile appeared in the nucleus, and when the two parts of the head-cap meet, the sperm head is complete.

While the acrosome and the post-nuclear cap are spreading to form the complete head-cap, and before the separation of the two centrioles, the *accessory body* has been taken into the neck region, between the proximal centriole and the head, and becomes the *neck body*; and a collar-like structure (*manchette*) grows down from the nucleus and encloses the two centrioles. The manchette soon disappears, and its significance, like that of the neck body, is not known.

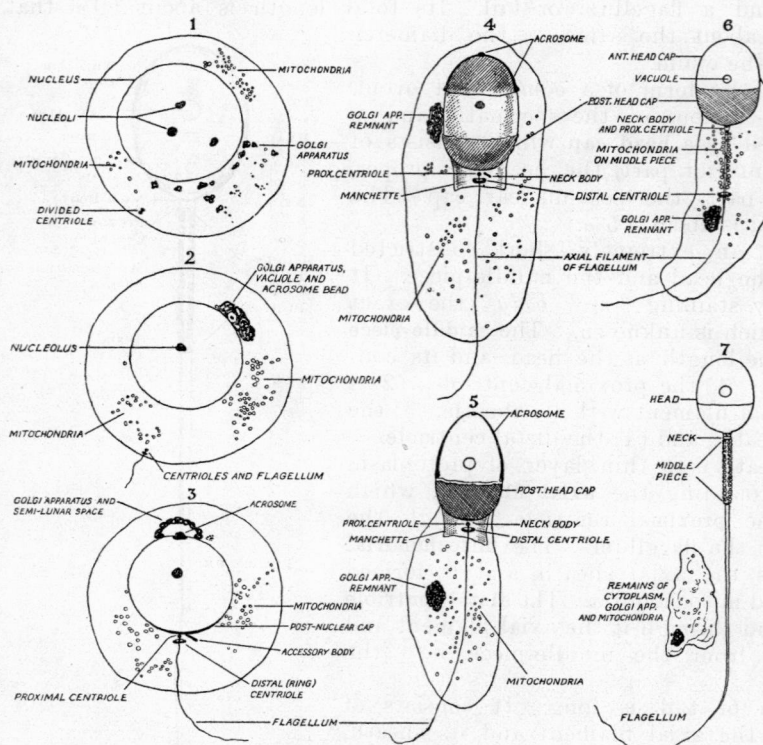

FIG. 29.—METAMORPHOSIS OF SPERMATID INTO SPERMATOZOON
(J. Brontë Gatenby and H. W. Beams).

The **middle piece** has still to be formed and the **flagellum** completed. The distal ring centriole slips down the axial filament for a distance about the length of the head, and leaves a space on to which most of the mitochondria crowd to form the **mitochondrial sheath**. The remains of the cytoplasm of the spermatid, carrying other mitochondria and the remnant of the Golgi apparatus, are then stripped off, and the spermatozoon is complete (Fig. 29 (7)).

FERTILISATION

The process of union of the male and female gametes to form a zygote is known as *fertilisation of the ovum*. It begins when a spermatozoon enters an ovum (either mature or in the last stage of maturation), and is completed when the nuclear elements of the two have combined.

Fertilisation of the human ovum has not been observed, but it may be assumed that all its essential features are the same as those which have been found to occur in other mammals. This assumption is the more justifiable because the phenomena of the maturation of the oocyte and fertilisation have been found to take place in the same manner, and to be essentially similar in detail, in several very different groups of mammals. It is believed that fertilisation takes place in the ampullary part of the uterine tube; and that the entry of one spermatozoon causes some change in the surface of the ovum that prevents the entry of others.

It has already been pointed out that maturation of the oocyte is usually not completed until after the spermatozoon has entered; thereafter the oocyte II divides and becomes the second polar body and the mature ovum in which a female pronucleus is formed. It has also been noted that the female pronucleus contains half the number of chromosomes present in the nucleus of the oocyte before the maturation began. As the female pronucleus forms, the flagellum or tail of the spermatozoon disappears, the head is transformed into the male pronucleus, and two centrosomes arise from the middle-piece. The male pronucleus is smaller than the female pronucleus, and it also contains only half the number of chromosomes present in the spermatocyte I from which it descended.

As soon as the female and male pronuclei are established they approach each other (Fig. 30), meet, and fuse together to form a single nucleus (Figs. 30, 31) called the *segmentation nucleus*, which contains the full number of chromosomes.

When fertilisation is completed, therefore, a new structure called a **zygote** is

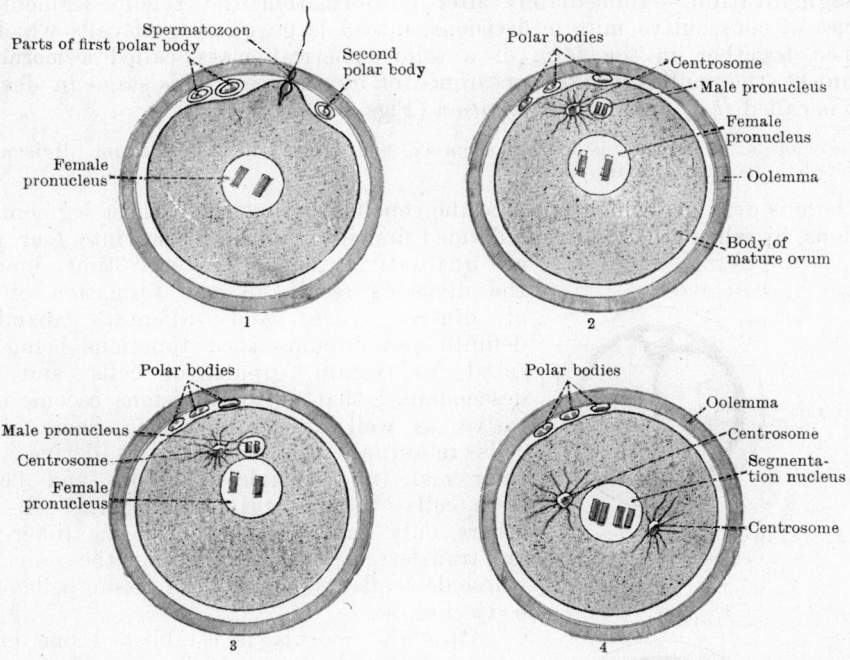

FIG. 30.—SCHEMA OF THE FERTILISATION OF THE MATURE OVUM AND THE FORMATION OF THE ZYGOTE.

formed. It lies, together with the polar bodies, inside the oolemma, and it consists of a cell body containing the segmentation nucleus, and two centrosomes, which lie at opposite poles of the nucleus. The only essential difference in appearance between an oocyte I and a zygote is the presence of two centrosomes in the zygote. But oocyte I is a cell almost at the end of its life period. It can have only one capable descendant and its chances of life are small, whilst the zygote is a rejuvenated cell with great possibilities, for it is endowed with the potentialities of its parents and is capable of producing a new member of the species.

There are therefore two factors in fertilisation. The first is the reconstitution in the segmentation nucleus of the number of chromosomes that is typical for the cells of the species to which the zygote belongs, half of them being derived from the female and half from the male ancestor of the zygote. The second factor

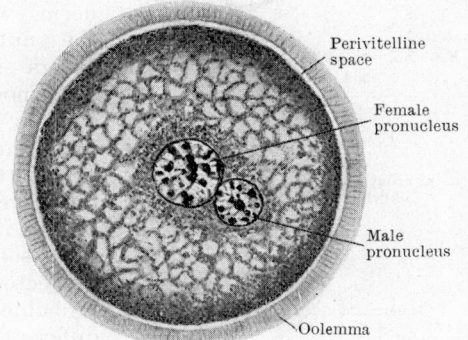

FIG. 31.—ZYGOTE OF A FERRET JUST BEFORE THE FUSION OF THE PRONUCLEI. Diameters of zygote exclusive of oolemma, 100 μ × 93 μ × 90 μ.

is the stimulus to division which the spermatozoon provides, a stimulus that is due to the physico-chemical influence exerted by the centrioles.

In the phenomena of *natural parthenogenesis* among invertebrates there are many interesting variations in the chromosome mechanism. Loeb and others have also shown experimentally—

artificial parthenogenesis—that it is possible, in the case of invertebrates like the sea-urchin, and even in the frog, to replace the stimulus normally supplied by the spermatozoon by chemical or mechanical means. For further information on the interesting cytological problems of partheno-genesis, consult the works already cited (p. 19), and also Loeb, *The Organism as a Whole.*

PRE-EMBRYONIC PERIOD

Segmentation.—Immediately after its formation the zygote segments, by a series of consecutive mitotic divisions, into a large number of cells which are grouped together in the form of a solid spherical mass, called a **morula** on account of the mulberry-like appearance of its surface. This stage in development is called *the period of segmentation* (Figs. 31-34).

The morula is formed inside the oolemma, and before the segmentation divisions are completed the polar bodies disappear.

There is evidence which tends to the conclusion that the earliest segmentation divisions, by which the zygote is divided first into two and then into four parts, are qualitatively equal. After a time, however, the divisions result in the formation of cells of different sizes and different capabilities, definite and circumscribed functions being allocated to certain groups of cells and their descendants; that is, the divisions become qualitative as well as quantitative. Some of the cells retain all the potentialities derived from their male and female ancestors and become stem cells—that is, primordial germ cells. To others only parts of the chromatic inheritance are transferred, and they become the soma cells whose descendants become the tissue cells of the body (Fig. 9).

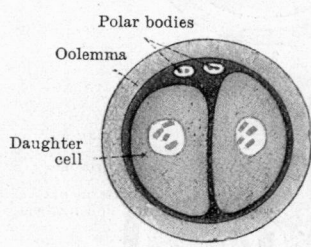

FIG. 32.—SEGMENTATION OF ZYGOTE. 2-Cell Stage.

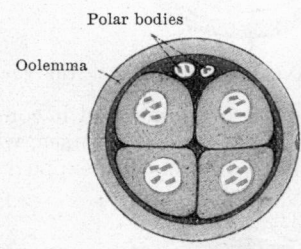

FIG. 33.—SEGMENTATION OF ZYGOTE. 4-Cell Stage.

After the morula is established one of the first definite changes which occur in its constitution is the differentiation of its cells into an outer layer and an inner mass (Fig. 34).

In the human zygote, as in that of many other mammals, the cells of the outer layer constitute the **trophoblast** or trophoblastic ectoderm, which plays a most important part in the nutrition of the embryo and fœtus. It enters into the formation of the **chorion**, or outermost envelope of the growing zygote. The chorion, which is subsequently differentiated into a placental and a non-placental portion, serves, in the first instance, as both a protective and a nutritive covering.

In many mammals the cells of the inner mass soon separate into two main groups, called the ectoderm and the entoderm; but it appears probable that in the human zygote they differentiate into four groups, named **amniotic ectoderm**, **ecto-mesoderm** (a term which will be presently explained, p. 33), **primary** or **extra-embryonic mesoderm**, and **entoderm**.

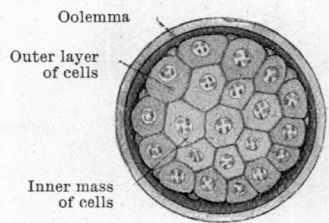

FIG. 34.—SEGMENTATION OF ZYGOTE. Morula Stage.

In the majority of mammals, during or immediately before the differentiation of the inner mass, a cavity appears in the zygote. The cavity is called the **segmentation cavity**, and as soon as it appears the zygote is called a **blastula**. The segmentation cavity enlarges until it separates the inner mass from the outer layer, except at one pole of the zygote, where the inner mass and the

outer layer remain in contact (Fig. 35). It appears, however, from the
evidence available, that a segmentation cavity is not formed in the human
zygote, and it therefore does not pass through
a true blastula stage. Instead, the primary
mesoderm proliferates and extends until it
separates the inner mass proper (that is the
ectoderm and the entoderm) from the outer layer
or trophoblast (Figs. 37, 38), and, immediately
thereafter, two cavities appear, one in the ectoderm and the other in the entodermal mass of
cells.

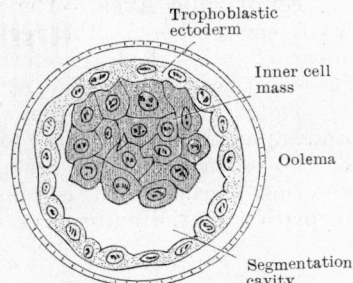

FIG. 35.—DIAGRAM OF MAMMALIAN
BLASTULA.

The zygote then consists of three vesicles,
one large and two small. The large vesicle is
bounded by the trophoblast; it contains the
two small vesicles embedded in the jelly-like
mass of primary mesoderm (Figs. 36, 39).

The two small vesicles lie eccentrically and close together in the interior of the
larger vesicle. The larger and more external of the two is the **ectodermal** or

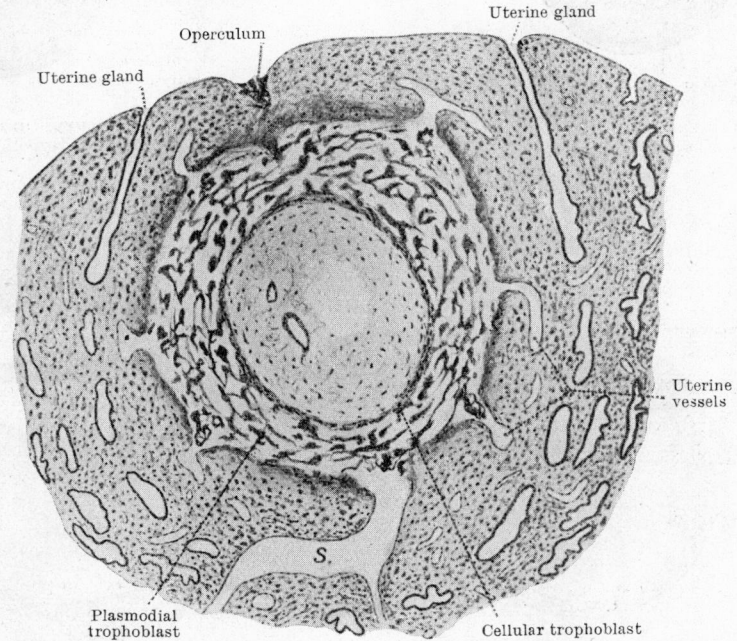

FIG. 36.—SECTION OF THE TEACHER BRYCE I EMBRYO SHOWING THE TWO INNER VESICLES EMBEDDED IN
PRIMARY MESODERM, AND THE RELATION OF THE TROPHOBLAST TO THE IMPLANTATION CAVITY IN THE
UTERINE DECIDUA. (T. H. Bryce, *Trans. Roy. Soc. Edin.*). *S*, venous sinus.

amnio-embryonic vesicle. It is separated from the trophoblast peripherally, and
the **entodermal** or **yolk-sac vesicle** centrally, by the surrounding primary mesoderm. That part of its wall which is in relation with the entodermal vesicle
consists of *ecto-mesoderm*—it will take part in the formation of the embryo; the
remainder is *amniotic ectoderm*.

This stage of human development is represented by the well-known Teacher
Bryce I embryo,[1] the age of which is estimated to have been 13-14 days
(Fig. 36).

The early appearance of the mesoderm in the zygote and its insinuation
at so early a period between the ectoderm and the entoderm are peculiarities

[1] T. H. Bryce. Observations on the Early Development of the Human Embryo. *Trans. Roy. Soc. Edin.*,
1924.

of human development.　In most mammals the mesoderm does not appear until the embryonic area and its primitive streak are defined.

Embryonic Area.—The area where the two inner vesicles lie in apposition with each other is the region of the zygote from which the embryo will be formed; it is called, therefore, the **embryonic area**, and at the time of its definition it consists of three layers—ecto-mesoderm, primary mesoderm, and entoderm.

The remainder of the zygote is utilised for the formation of membranes and appendages necessary for the protection, nutrition, respiration, and excretion of the offspring during the period of intra-uterine life.　It is uncertain whether the mesoderm which is present in the area at this period takes part in the formation of the embryo or is replaced at a later period by mesoderm derived

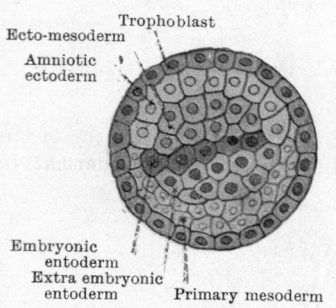

FIG. 37.—DIFFERENTIATION OF ZYGOTE AND CELLS (Hypothetical).

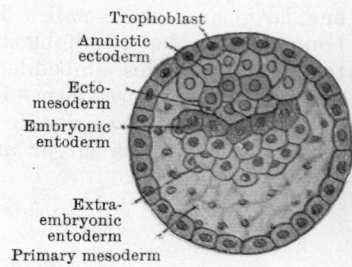

FIG. 38.—FURTHER DIFFERENTIATION OF ZYGOTE (Hypothetical).

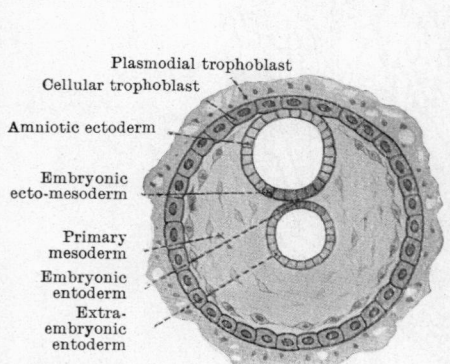

FIG. 39.—SCHEMA OF DIFFERENTIATION OF ZYGOTE (Teacher-Bryce I Ovum).

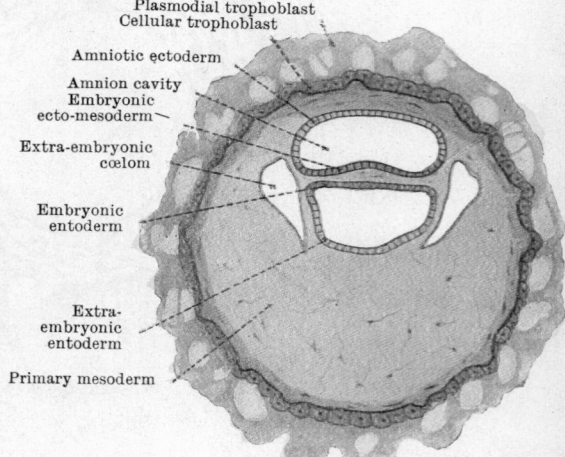

FIG. 40.—SCHEMA OF DIFFERENTIATION OF ZYGOTE (Peters Ovum).

from the cells of the ectodermal vesicle which is called the **secondary** or **embryonic mesoderm**; the latter certainly forms the greater part of the mesoderm of the embryo.

Extra-embryonic Cœlom.—The extra-embryonic cœlom is a space which appears as two clefts, one on each side of the embryonic area, in the primary mesoderm (Fig. 40).　The clefts fuse together round the periphery of the embryonic area, and the single space so formed expands rapidly until the mesoderm which originally filled the greater part of the larger vesicle becomes converted into two thin layers, one of which lines the inner surface of the trophoblast while the other covers the outer surfaces of the epithelial walls of the extra-embryonic parts of the two inner vesicles (Fig. 45).

The extra-embryonic cœlom does not extend into the embryonic area, and it never completely separates the amnio-embryonic vesicle from the inner surface of the trophoblast; on the contrary, the primary mesoderm on the outer surface of the vesicle retains its continuity with the mesoderm on the inner surface of the trophoblast until the end of intra-uterine life, and it takes part, as will be seen later, in the formation of the umbilical cord, which connects the fœtus with the placenta (p. 66).

Differentiation of Embryonic Area and Formation of Primary Axial Structures.—As the embryonic area is the area of contact between the ectodermal and the entodermal vesicles it is, at first, circular in outline. As growth continues the area becomes oval, and a linear streak, called the **primitive streak**, appears in that part of the oval which becomes the caudal part of the area (Fig. 44). Thus bilateral symmetry is impressed upon the embryonic area and the line of the axial structures of the developing embryo is laid down. From this point in development we can speak of **cephalic** and **caudal** ends of the embryonic area.

The cephalic and caudal ends of the embryonic area are often spoken of as "anterior" and "posterior"; but the student should note that in this connexion these terms are not used in the human anatomical sense as defined in the General Introduction.

At the same time the position of the mesodermal elements in the wall of the ectodermal vesicle is revealed, for the primitive streak is a thickened ridge of cells which grows from the part that has been termed "ecto-mesoderm" and projects against the entoderm in the caudal part of the embryonic area, pushing aside the primitive mesoderm which intervened between the adjacent parts of the walls of the two vesicles. The deeper cells of the ridge—those next the entoderm—are the mesodermal elements of the primitive ecto-mesoderm, and, by proliferation, they form the larger part, if not the whole, of the embryonic mesoderm and also give rise, after a series of remarkable developmental events, to an axial structure characteristic of all vertebrates, called the **notochord.** The mesoderm produced from the primitive streak may be termed the **secondary** or **embryonic mesoderm.**

Immediately after the formation of the primitive streak a groove, called the **neural groove**, appears in the cephalic part of the embryonic area. It is formed by the longitudinal folding of a thickened plate of ectoderm, called the **neural plate**, which is the rudiment of almost the whole nervous system, the only exceptions being the olfactory nerves, some parts of the ganglia of the cranial nerves, and the end organs of the sensory nerves. From it also are derived the cells of the primitive sheaths of the nerve-fibres and the chromaffin cells of the suprarenal glands and other chromaffin structures. The side walls of the neural groove are called the **neural folds.** Almost from the first the anterior ends of the neural folds are united together a short distance behind the head end of the embryonic area. Their posterior ends, which remain separate for a time, embrace the anterior part of the primitive streak.

In the meantime, however, a groove, called the **primitive groove**, has appeared on the surface of the primitive streak. The anterior end of the primitive groove deepens, until it forms a perforation which passes, through the anterior end of the streak and the subjacent entoderm, into the cavity of the entodermal vesicle. As this perforation passes from the floor of the posterior part of the neural groove into that part of the entodermal vesicle which afterwards becomes the primitive alimentary canal or enteron, it is called the **neurenteric canal** (Figs. 44, 101). The explanation of this curious phenomenon must be deferred until the formation of the notochord is considered; the neurenteric canal as such is but a transitory passage, and it disappears in Man and other mammals before the neural groove is converted into a closed neural tube.

After the appearance of the primitive groove and the neurenteric canal, the posterior ends of the neural folds converge, across the anterior part of the primitive streak and groove, and fuse together posterior to the neurenteric canal. The primitive streak is thus divided into two portions: (1) An anterior portion, which lies at first in the floor of the neural groove, and later in the floor or ventral wall of the posterior end of the spinal cord; and (2) a posterior portion, which remains on the surface and takes part in the formation of the median

3

portion of the posterior end of the body, forming the perineum, and the median part of the ventral wall of the body, from the perineum to the umbilicus.　It is through the perineal section of the posterior part of the primitive streak that the

anal and urogenital orifices of the body are formed at a later period of embryonic life (when it is known as the *cloacal membrane*).

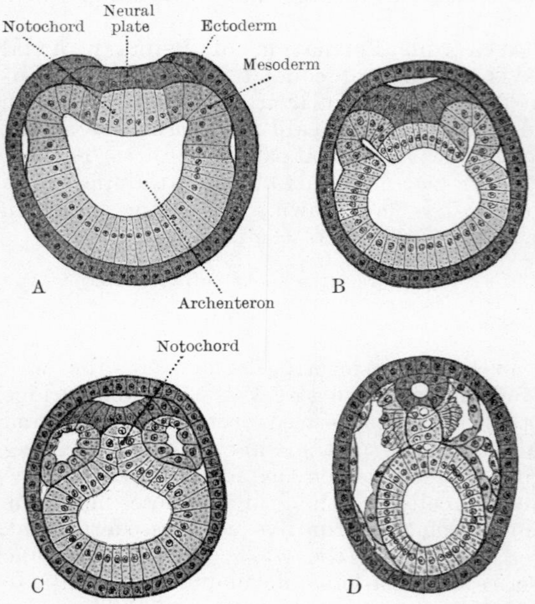

Formation of the Notochord and the Secondary Mesoderm.—The notochord and the secondary mesoderm are formed from the primitive streak—the notochord from its anterior end, and the secondary mesoderm from its lateral margins and posterior end.

In the primitive vertebrate *Amphioxus* in which a complete *gastrula* is formed, both the notochord and the mesoderm are derived from the inner layer of the wall of the gastrula, *i.e.* from the entoderm (Fig. 41).　Their connexion with the primitive streak in higher vertebrates is explained by the morphological interpretation that the primitive streak represents the fused and elongated lips of the *blastopore*, or opening into the entodermal cavity of the gastrula.　As an essential preliminary to the formation of the notochord, there appears a structure which corresponds, though remotely, to the part of the wall of a simple blastula that is invaginated to form the entodermal lining of the gastrula ; this is the *head process* to which further reference is made

Fig. 41.—Transverse Sections of Young *Amphioxus* illustrating the origin of the Notochord and the Mesoderm from the Entodermic Layer of the Gastrula (after Hatschek).　(J. Graham Kerr, *Text Book of Embryology*).

below.　Although the nature of this event in human development is greatly obscured by the precocious formation of other parts, and especially of a complete entodermal sac from the inner cell mass, and can be clarified only by extensive comparative studies, nevertheless it is an excellent example of that recapitulation with a purpose to which reference has been made in the General Introduction (p. 12).

As soon as the primitive streak is established its anterior end becomes a node or centre of growth—the *primitive node*—by means of which the length and, to a certain extent, the breadth of the body are increased.　The portion of the body formed by the activity of the primitive node is the dorsal portion, from the back part of the roof of the nose to the caudal end of the trunk.　The perineum and the ventral wall of the body, from the perineum to the umbilicus, are formed from the posterior part of the primitive streak.　Nevertheless, the primitive streak undergoes little or no increase in length ; indeed, as growth continues, it becomes relatively shorter as contrasted with the total length of the embryonic region ; for the new material, formed by its borders and its anterior extremity, is transformed into the tissues of the embryo as rapidly as it is created.

Notochord.—The notochord, or primitive skeletal axis, is formed indirectly by the proliferation of cells from the anterior end of the primitive streak.　On its first appearance it is a narrow rod of cells, called the **head process**, which projects forwards from the primitive node between the ectoderm and the entoderm. Shortly after its appearance the head process wedges its way between the entoderm cells, and so comes to form part of the wall of the primary entodermal cavity. From that period onwards, as its more posterior parts are formed by continued proliferation from the primitive node, they also are at once intercalated in the dorsal wall of the entodermal sac (Fig. 46).

The head process is at first solid, but presently a cavity appears in the rod of cells and tunnels it from the ectodermal surface of the primitive node forwards, though not quite to its cephalic end (Fig. 42). The floor of the tunnel, *i.e.* the cells next the cavity of the entodermic vesicle, then breaks down, the roof flattens out, and the head process is then represented by a plate of cells intercalated into the dorsal wall of the vesicle—the *notochordal plate*. As the tunnel in the head process breaks down, its caudal end is necessarily left as a passage from the cavity of the amnio-embryonic vesicle through the primitive node to the cavity of the entodermic vesicle—the *neurenteric canal*.

The tunnel which is formed in the head process is known as the *archenteric canal*, because it is thought to be homologous with the archenteron (entodermic cavity) of *Amphioxus*; from its relation to the formation of the notochord, it is also called the *notochordal canal*. The story of the head process seems to indicate that the entodermic vesicle is a precocious and specialised formation which does not contain the inherited potentiality of notochord formation. This resides in the primitive node, and before a notochord can be formed it is necessary that it should express itself in the formation of a more " primitive entoderm " which is carried forward into the roof of the " entodermic vesicle " by a modified process of gastrulation. When that has been accomplished, then the notochord is formed exactly as in *Amphioxus*.

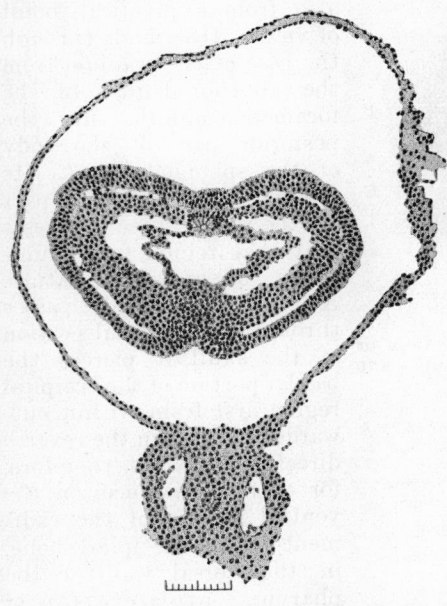

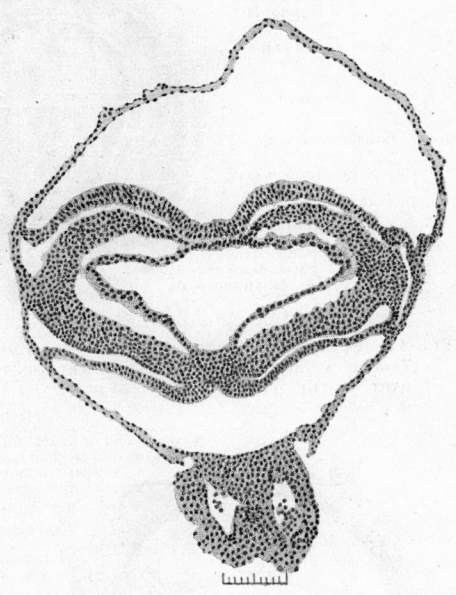

FIG. 42.—TRANSVERSE SECTION THROUGH 'TAIL-FOLD' OF YOUNG EMBRYO ENCLOSED IN AMNION. The archenteric canal in the head process is seen beneath the neural plate on the upper surface, the primitive streak and groove on the lower (reversed) surface. Between them is the posterior cul-de-sac of the yolk-sac, separated from the ectoderm by the secondary mesoderm spreading from the primitive streak ; below is the body stalk with the allantois and umbilical vessels.

FIG. 43.—TRANSVERSE SECTION OF SAME EMBRYO SIX SECTIONS NEARER THE HEAD END. The notochordal plate lies beneath the neural plate on the upper surface ; the primitive groove is on the lower surface ; the amnion cavity is divided into two parts as the primitive streak mesoderm is continuous with the mesoderm of the amnion. (Embryo M'Intyre. T. H. Bryce, *Trans. Roy. Soc. Edin.*, 1924).

At a later period the notochordal cells are excalated from the entoderm, and again form a cylindrical rod of cells in the median plane between the floor of the ectodermal neural groove and the reformed entodermal roof of the primitive alimentary canal, which, in the meantime, has been more or less moulded off from the dorsal part of the entodermal sac (Fig. 50, B). The neurenteric canal disappears, but for a time the caudal end of the notochord remains connected with the anterior end of the primitive streak. Its cephalic end is continuous with the entoderm of a small portion of the embryonic area which lies immediately in front of the anterior end of the neural groove and becomes bilaminar by the disappearance of the primary mesoderm. This region, because it afterwards forms the boundary membrane between the anterior end of the primitive entodermal canal and the primitive buccal cavity or oral pit, is called the **bucco-pharyngeal membrane** (Fig. 61, p. 50). It disappears about the third week of embryonic life, and immediately afterwards the anterior part of the notochord separates from the entoderm, but the posterior end remains continuous with the primitive streak until the formation of the neural tube is completed.

After a time the cylindrical notochordal rod is surrounded by secondary mesoderm which becomes converted into the vertebral column. As the vertebral column is formed the notochord is enlarged in the regions of the intervertebral discs and for a time assumes a nodulated appearance.

Ultimately the notochord disappears as a distinct structure, but remnants of it are believed to persist as the pulpy centres of the intervertebral discs. The extension of the notochord into the region of the head is of interest from a morphological, and possibly also from a practical, point of view. It extends through the base of the cranium from the anterior border of the foramen magnum into the posterior part of the body of the sphenoid bone. Its presence in the posterior part of the skull base suggests that that region was, primitively, of vertebral nature. As the notochord passes through the occipital portion of the skull it pierces the basilar portion of the occipital region first from within outwards and then in the reverse direction. It lies, therefore, for a short distance, on the ventral surface of the rudiment of the occipital bone, in the dorsal wall of the pharynx; proliferation of remnants of its pharyngeal portion may give rise to tumours known as *chordomata*.

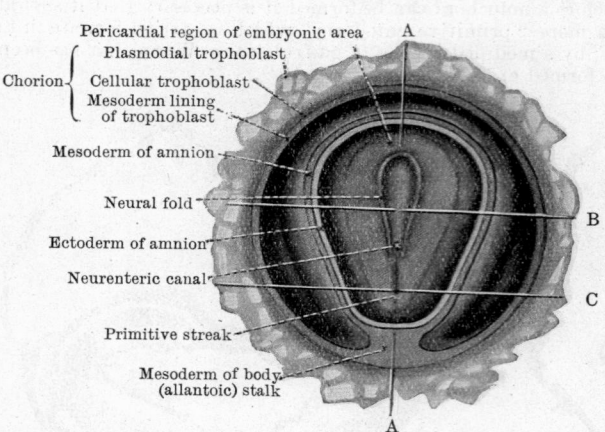

FIG. 44.—SCHEMA OF DORSAL SURFACE OF EMBRYONIC AREA OF ZYGOTE AFTER THE REMOVAL OF PART OF THE CHORION AND PART OF THE AMNION.

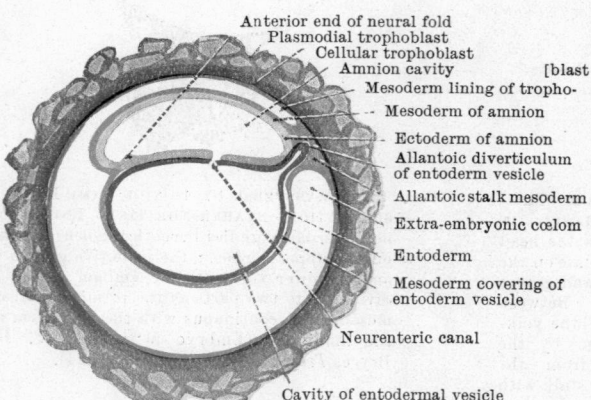

FIG. 45.—SCHEMA OF SAGITTAL SECTION OF ZYGOTE ALONG LINE A IN FIG. 44.

Differentiation of the Secondary Mesoderm.—It has already been noted that a portion of the inner mass of the human zygote becomes converted directly into mesoderm which may be called, for convenience, *primary mesoderm* or *extra-embryonic mesoderm*. It was stated also that the wall of the larger of the inner vesicles of the zygote consists of amniotic ectoderm and ecto-mesoderm, that being intended to convey the idea that the cells of the wall of the larger inner vesicle were the progenitors of the ectoderm of the amnion and the ectoderm and mesoderm of the embryo.

As soon as the larger of the two inner vesicles is formed two areas of its wall are defined : (1) the part in contact with the smaller inner or entodermal vesicle and (2) the remainder. As future events prove, the cells of the larger area, which is not in contact with the entodermal vesicle, simply produce ectodermal descendants which line the inner surface of a sac-like covering of the embryo termed the amnion ; they are, therefore, the predecessors of the *amniotic ectoderm*. The cells which lie adjacent to the smaller entoderm vesicle are separated from the entoderm merely by a thin layer of primary mesoderm. They take part in the formation of the embryo, forming, with the entoderm, the embryonic area from which the embryo is evolved. These cells are the forerunners of both ectoderm and mesoderm, and as the mesoderm developed from them is differentiated after the formation of the primary mesoderm it may be termed **secondary mesoderm** or **embryonic mesoderm** or, because it is differentiated in the region of the primitive streak, **primitive streak mesoderm**. It is the formation and fate of this primitive streak mesoderm which is now to be considered.

The primitive streak (Figs. 44, 47) is formed by the proliferation of the ecto-mesodermal cells of the caudal part of the embryonic area. The deeper cells of the streak, which displace the primary mesoderm from the median plane, and thus come into contact with the entoderm, are the rudiments of the secondary or primitive streak mesoderm (Figs. 42, 43, 47). The superficial cells form part of the surface ectoderm of the embryo.

At the anterior end of the primitive streak the meso-dermal elements of the streak fuse with the subjacent ento-derm in the formation of the **primitive node**.

It is uncertain whether or not the mesodermal cells budded off from the nodal point blend with the cells of the primary mesoderm, but there can be little doubt that they form by far the greater part, if not the whole, of the permanent mesoderm of the embryo.

Either by displacement of the primary mesoderm, or by union with it, the secondary mesoderm forms a continuous sheet of cells, in the embryo-nic area, on each side of the median plane.

Each of the lateral sheets

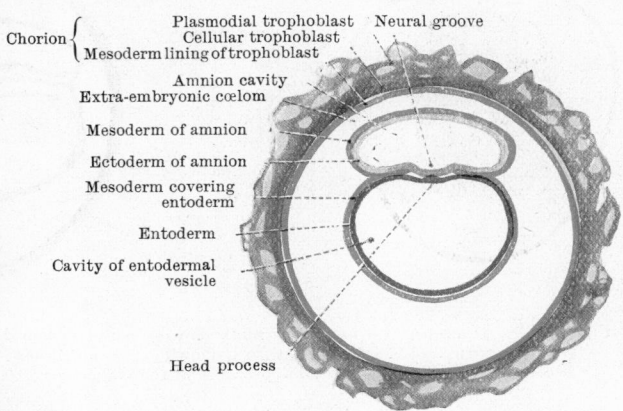

FIG. 46.—Schema of Transverse Section of Zygote along Line B in Fig. 44.

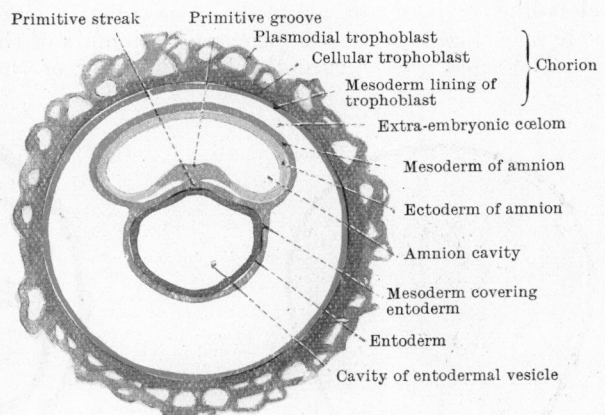

FIG. 47.—Schema of Transverse Section of Zygote along Line C in Fig. 44.

is thickest where it abuts against the notochord and the wall of the neural groove, and thinnest at its peripheral margin, where it is continuous with the primary mesoderm of the extra-embryonic area (Fig. 48, B).

At the cephalic end of the embryonic area the medial margins of the mesodermal sheets fuse together across the median plane, forming a transverse bar of mesodermal cells called the **pericardial mesoderm** (Fig. 59), because the pericardium is afterwards developed from it. The area in which this mesoderm lies is named the *pericardial region* of the embryonic area (Fig. 44).

Between the bar of pericardial mesoderm, the cephalic end of the neural groove, and the medial margins of the mesodermal plates lies a small segment of the embryonic area from which the primary mesoderm entirely disappears, leaving the ectoderm and entoderm in contact. This is the **bucco-pharyngeal area**. It afterwards becomes the **bucco-pharyngeal membrane** (Figs. 61, 70), which separates

the primitive mouth or oral pit from the cephalic end of the primitive entodermal alimentary canal. As already stated, the bucco-pharyngeal membrane
disappears during the third week, when the oral pit and the primitive alimentary
canal become continuous with each other.

Between the bucco-pharyngeal area and the cephalic end of the primitive
streak the medial margins of the mesodermal plates are separated from each

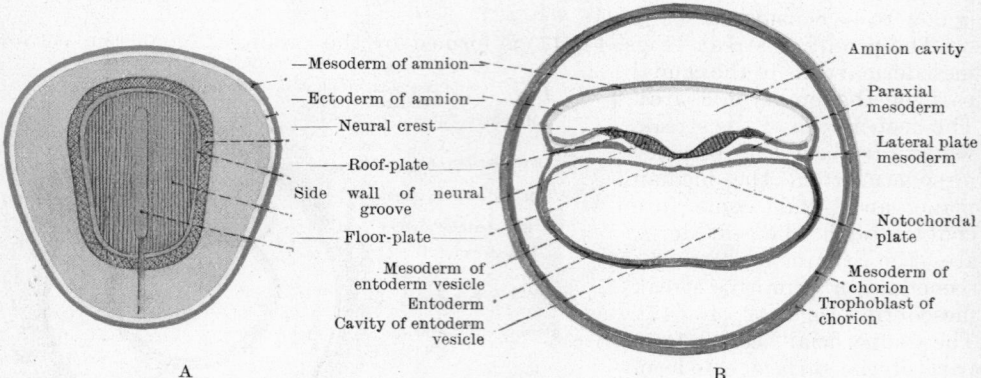

FIG. 48.—A. DIAGRAM OF EMBRYONIC AREA showing parts of neural plate and primitive streak.   B. TRANS-
VERSE SECTION OF THE SAME ZYGOTE, showing the constituent parts and an early stage of embryonic
secondary mesoderm before the appearance of the embryonic parts of the cœlom.

other by the notochord and the neural groove (Fig. 49, B), and still more caudally
they are united with the sides of the streak (Fig. 47).

After the permanent mesodermal plates are definitely established a series of
cleft-like cavities appear in their peripheral margins. These cavities, on each
side, soon fuse together to form the rudiments of the **embryonic cœlom** (Fig. 49, B).

The septum of cells at the lateral border of the embryonic area on each side,

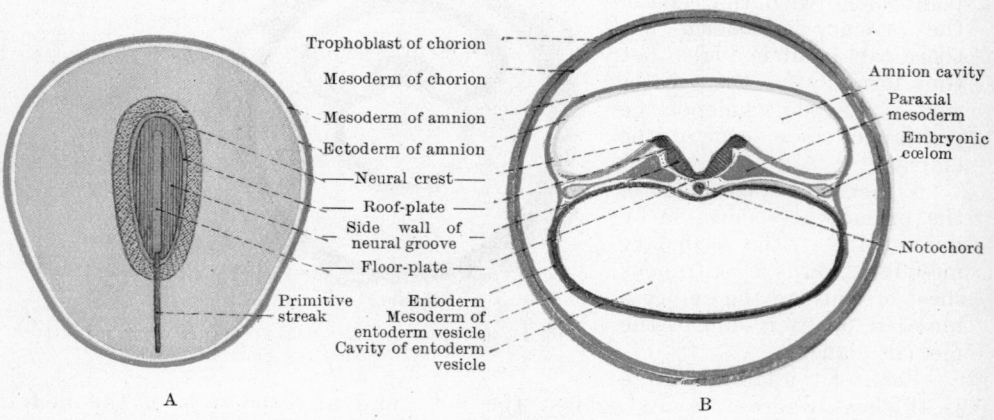

FIG. 49.—A. DIAGRAM OF EMBRYONIC AREA at later stage of development.   B. TRANSVERSE SECTION OF
THE SAME ZYGOTE, showing the formation of the neural groove and an early stage of development of
embryonic cœlom and differentiation of mesoderm.

which, for a time, separates the embryonic from the extra-embryonic cœlom,
soon disappears, and the cœlom becomes then one continuous cavity (Fig. 50, B).

The embryonic cœlom extends medially also, but the medial extension ceases
at some distance from the median plane, except at the cephalic end of the
embryonic area, where the two halves of the embryonic cœlom become continuous
with each other through the interior of the pericardial mesodermal bar (Figs. 60, 61).

As the embryonic cœlom is forming and extending, a longitudinal constriction
appears in each half of the mesoderm, a short distance from its medial border.

This constriction separates each plate into three parts: (1) a medial bar called the **paraxial mesoderm**, which lies at the side of the neural groove and the noto-chord; (2) the constricted portion, called the **intermediate cell mass**; and (3) the part lateral to the constriction, called the **lateral plate** (Fig. 50, B).

The embryonic cœlom is confined, in the human embryo, to the lateral plate, which it divides into a superficial layer next the ectoderm, called the **somatic mesoderm**, and a deeper layer next the entoderm, called the **splanchnic mesoderm**.

Ectoderm and somatic mesoderm together constitute the *somatopleure*: entoderm and splanchnic mesoderm are together known as the *splanchnopleure*.

The medial borders of the somatic and splanchnic mesoderm are continuous with each other round the medial border of the cœlom. The lateral border of the somatic mesoderm is continuous, at the margin of the embryonic area, with the mesoderm which covers the outer surface of the amnion; the lateral border of the splanchnic layer is continuous with the mesoderm on the wall of the extra-embryonic or yolk-sac portion of the entodermal sac.

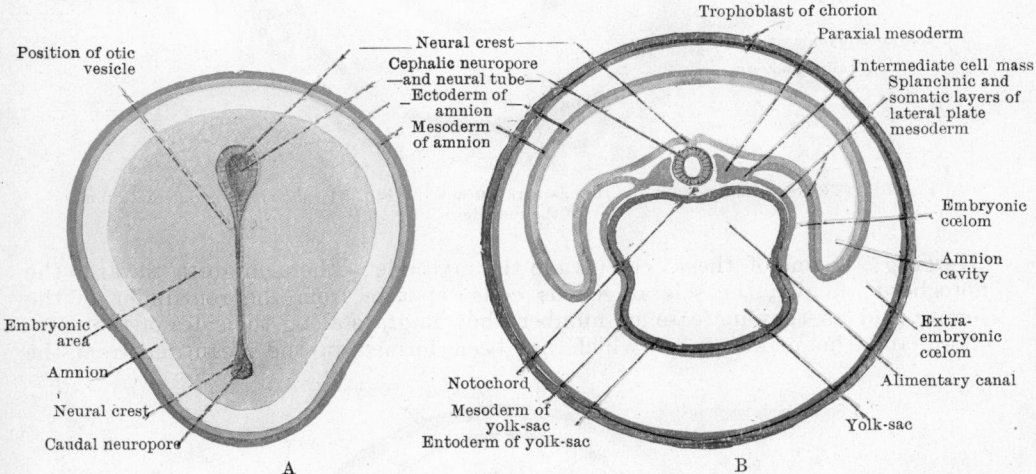

FIG. 50.—A. DIAGRAM OF EMBRYONIC AREA showing closure of neural groove with cephalic and caudal neuropores. Compare with surface view of embryo in Fig. 54. B. TRANSVERSE SECTION OF THE SAME ZYGOTE; the neural tube has formed but has not separated from the surface ectoderm. The section also shows union of intra- and extra-embryonic parts of cœlom, paraxial bars, intermediate masses and lateral plates of mesoderm, with separation of lateral plates into somatic and splanchnic layers by the intra-embryonic part of the cœlom.

Paraxial Mesoderm.—Each paraxial mesodermal bar soon assumes the form of a triangular prism. The cephalic portion of each paraxial bar, as far caudal-wards as the middle of the hind-brain (see p. 44), remains unsegmented, but the remainder is cut into a number of segments, called the **mesodermal somites**, by a series of transverse clefts (Fig. 54). The first cleft appears in the region of the hind-brain, and the others are formed successively, each caudal to its predecessor. Only three or four somites lie in the region of the head; the re-mainder are in the neck and trunk area of the embryonic region. The segmenta-tion of the paraxial bars begins before their elongation is completed, and the posterior somites are separated off as the paraxial bars are extended by the continued pro-liferation from the nodal point at the anterior end of the primitive streak.

When they are first defined the somites are solid masses of cells, but in a short time a cavity—the cœlom of the somite or **myocœle**—appears in each mass.

In many animals the myocœle is continuous through a cavity in the corresponding portion of the intermediate cell tract, the nephrocœle, with the more lateral parts of the cœlom, but that is not usually the case in human embryos.

The ventro-medial portion of the hollow mesodermal somite is known as the **sclerotome** (Goodsir), since it produces *scleratogenous cells* which are responsible for the formation of " hard " skeletal structures. The cells of the scleratogenous section of the somite undergo rapid proliferation, and assume the character of the variety of mesoderm to which the special name of **mesenchyme** has been given

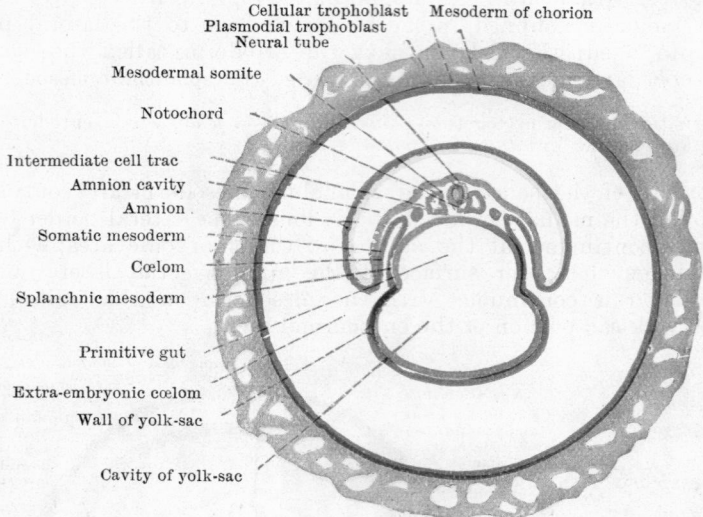

FIG. 51.—TRANSVERSE SECTION OF THE ZYGOTE SHOWN IN FIG. 54, showing the differentiation of the mesoderm.

(Hertwig). Some of these cells invade the myocœle ; others migrate towards the notochord ; finally, the scleratogenous cells separate from the remainder of the somite, and as they increase in number they migrate along the sides of the notochord and the neural tube (which has been formed in the meantime from the

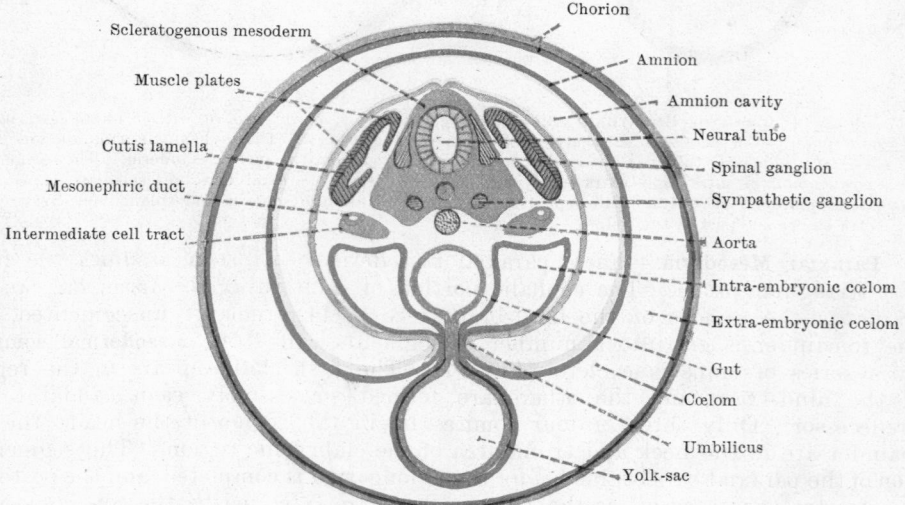

FIG. 52.—SCHEMA OF A TRANSVERSE SECTION OF A ZYGOTE, showing differentiation of mesoderm and extension of amnion.

neural groove) and mingle with those of the opposite side, and with those derived from adjoining cephalic and caudal somites. In this way a continuous sheath of mesoderm is formed around the neural tube and the notochord ; it is called the **membranous vertebral column**, and, in later stages, the following structures are differentiated from it—the vertebral column and its ligaments, and the dura mater of the brain and spinal cord (see p. 48).

The part of a mesodermal somite left after the separation of the sclerotome is called a **myotome**; each myotome gives rise to a flat plate with incurved dorsal and ventral margins, known as a **muscle plate**, because from these plates voluntary muscle fibres are derived.

In the opinion of some observers the outermost portion of each of the muscle plates is developed into subcutaneous connective tissue cells; consequently it is spoken of as the *cutis lamella*. According to this view the muscle cells are formed from the innermost cells and the incurved margins of the plates.

Intermediate Cell Mass.—The continuous tract of cells, lateral to the paraxial mesoderm on each side, to which this name is given, remains unsegmented; but as it gives rise to a series of excretory structures it corresponds to the segmented portions of mesoderm known in lower forms as **nephrotomes**. The intermediate cell mass gives rise to the greater part of the urogenital system, with the exceptions of the genital glands, most of the urinary bladder, the urethra, and the prostate.

Lateral Plates.—From the cells of the lateral plates are formed (1) the lining mesothelial cells of the great serous cavities of the body—the pleuræ, the pericardium, and the peritoneum; (2) the majority of the connective tissues (with the exception of those of the vertebral column and the head); (3) the greater part or all the mesoderm of the limbs; and, probably, (4) the unstriped muscle fibres of the walls of the alimentary canal and the blood-vessels. Most of these tissues are derived from mesenchymatous cells budded off from the lateral plates.

Cephalic Mesoderm.—It has already been noted that the mesoderm of the head becomes segmented only in the region of the caudal part of the hind-brain, where four cephalic mesodermal somites are formed on each side. From the scleratogenous portions of these somites the occipital part of the skull and the corresponding part of the dura mater of the brain are developed; and their muscle plates give rise to the intrinsic muscles of the tongue.

The unsegmented part of the cephalic mesoderm gives rise to the remaining muscles and connective tissues of the head region.

Mesenchyme.—Before the formation of the embryo many cells, of irregular form and wandering habits, appear between the more definite layers of mesoderm and the adjacent ectoderm and entoderm. They are called **mesenchyme cells**. The scleratogenous cells that wander out from the somites are of this nature; the remainder of the mesenchyme is derived largely from the lateral plates of mesoderm, though it may have other sources, possibly even from ectoderm and entoderm.

The complete rôle of the mesenchyme in development has not yet been elucidated, but in addition to connective tissues in general, the tissues of the vascular system, and plain muscle fibres in the walls of the alimentary canal and elsewhere, there is evidence to show that it is also concerned, *e.g.* in the limbs, with the development of striped muscles which are not directly derived from myotomes.

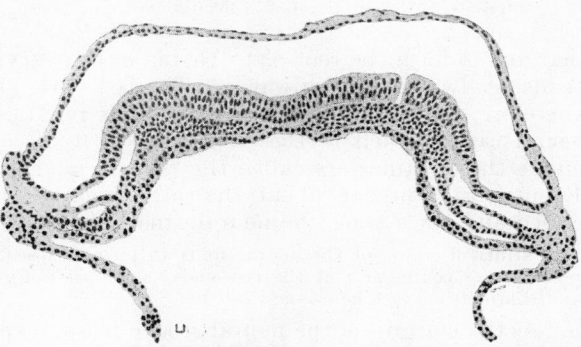

Fig. 53.—Transverse Section of the Same Young Human Embryo as in Figs. 42 and 43. The neural plate in a shallow neural groove is seen on the surface of the embryonic area; beneath it is the notochordal plate in the roof of the yolk-sac. Note the commencing cœlomic spaces in the sheets of lateral mesoderm which are continuous with the thickened paraxial mesoderm and the mesoderm of the amnion and yolk-sac. (Embryo M'Intyre. T. H. Bryce, *Trans. Roy. Soc. Edin.*, 1924).

Early Stages of the Development of the Nervous System.—No definite trace of the nervous system is present until the primitive streak has appeared and the embryonic area has passed from a circular to a pear-shaped form. Then an area of thickened ectoderm, called the **neural plate**, appears in the anterior part of the embryonic area. It begins to differentiate a little behind the cephalic end of the area, and its caudal extremity embraces the nodal end of the primitive streak. Its margins fade into the surrounding ectoderm; but, as the plate lengthens with the elongation of the embryonic area, its margins are elevated by the thickening mesoderm beneath them, and so they become distinct.

As the margins of the neural plate are raised the plate is necessarily folded longitudinally, and the sulcus so formed is called the **neural groove**. Each side wall of the neural groove, formed by the corresponding half of the neural plate, is a **neural fold**. At a very early period the neural folds unite to form a cephalic boundary of the neural groove, and, a little later, they also unite caudal to the neurenteric canal and across the primitive streak. After the neural groove is thus defined, in front, behind, and at the sides, the neural folds approach each other until they meet and fuse in the median plane, and the neural groove is converted into the **neural tube**. The tube possesses a floor or ventral wall, formed by the central part of the original neural plate and called the **basal plate** or floor-plate; a dorsal wall or **roof-plate** and two side walls are formed by the right and left halves of the neural plate.

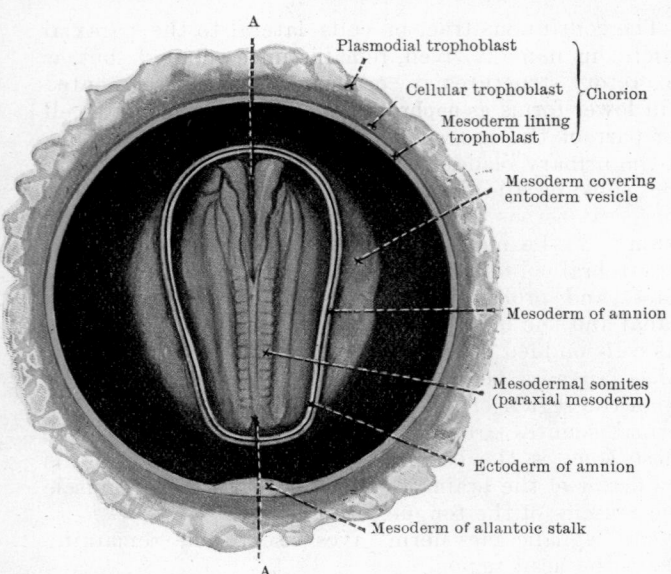

FIG. 54.—SCHEMA OF DORSAL ASPECT OF EMBRYO, showing partial closure of neural groove. For section along line A-A see Fig. 67.

Portions of the chorion and amnion have been removed. The neural folds have fused, except in the cephalic and caudal regions; both the cephalic and the caudal ends of the embryo have been bent ventrally and thirteen mesodermal somites have been formed.

The fusion of the margins to form the roof-plate begins in the cervical region, and from there it extends headwards and tailwards. The last parts of the roof-plate to be formed are, therefore, its cephalic and its caudal extremities; consequently, for a time, the **neural canal**, which is the cavity of the tube, opens on the surface at the two ends; the openings are called the **cephalic** and the **caudal neuropores** (Fig. 50, A). Eventually, however, about the third week of embryonic life, both apertures are closed and, for a time, the neural canal becomes a completely closed cavity.

Failure of union of the neural folds to form a closed neural canal, which may occur at any point but is commonest at the two ends, is the basis of gross malformations such as *anencephaly* and complete *spina bifida*.

As the margins of the neural groove rise and approach each other they carry with them the adjacent ectoderm to which they are attached, and which forms part of the surface covering of the embryo; consequently, when the lateral margins of the folds meet and unite, the tube, which is completed by their fusion, is embedded in the body of the embryo; but, for a time, its dorsal wall is attached to the surface ectoderm by a ridge of cells, formed by the fused margins of the neural plate. This ridge is called the **neural crest** (Figs. 48-50, 55).

The neural crest is the rudiment of the cranial and spinal nerve-ganglia, the sympathetic ganglia, the chromaffin cells of the chromaffin organs, and the cellular primitive sheaths of the peripheral nerves; the walls of the neural tube become transformed into the brain and spinal cord, the retinæ, and the optic nerves.[1]

---

[1] Some of the sympathetic nerve cells are said to be derived from the ventral parts of the lateral walls of the neural tube, from which they migrate, but there is some doubt whether this is so.

Formation of the Nerve Ganglia, the Chromaffin Tissues, and the Primitive Nerve-Sheaths.—The primitive ganglia grow as cell buds from the neural crest. In the neck and trunk regions they correspond in number with the spinal nerves and with the primitive segments into which the mesoderm becomes divided; but in the head region their arrangement is more irregular (Fig. 74), and some of the ganglia of the cranial nerves receive additional cell elements from the surface ectoderm or the entoderm.

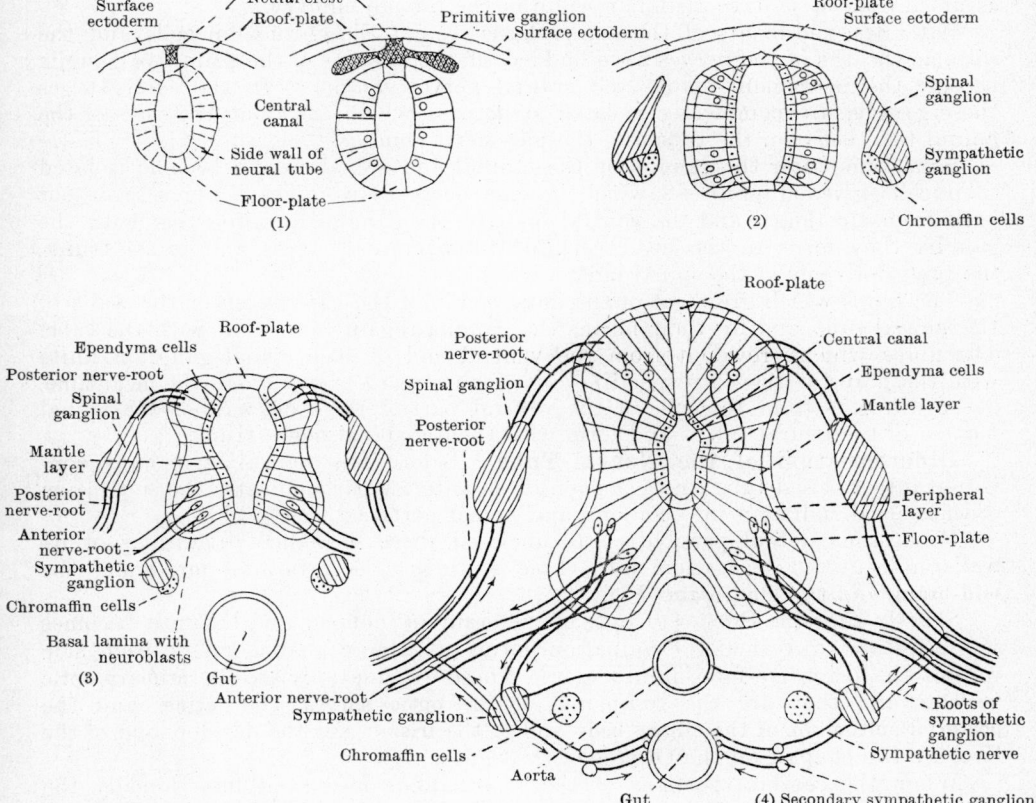

FIG. 55.—DIAGRAMS illustrating the formation of (1) the rudiments of the primitive ganglia from the neural crest. (2) The differentiation of different parts of the primitive ganglion into permanent root ganglion, sympathetic ganglion, and masses of chromaffin cells. (3) The formation of the anterior and posterior nerve-roots. (4) The differentiation of the walls of the neural tube into ependymal and peripheral layers.
The cells of the primitive ganglion which form the primitive sheaths of the nerves are not shown.

As soon as the ganglia have budded off, the neural crest disappears and the ganglia are left as isolated cell clumps. At this period, therefore, the nervous system consists of the neural tube and the primitive ganglia.

The primitive ganglia increase in size by the proliferation of their constituent cells, and they migrate ventrally by the sides of the neural tube; but the migration ceases before they reach the level of the ventral wall of the tube. As the migration proceeds clumps of cells are budded off from the ventral ends of the ganglia. These secondary cell buds are the rudiments of the sympathetic ganglia and of the chromaffin tissue which is found in the sympathetic nerve plexuses, in the medulla of the suprarenal glands, and in the carotid bodies. In the first instance the secondary cell buds which form the sympathetic ganglia wander ventrally and medially, until they attain the positions afterwards occupied by the ganglia of the sympathetic trunks. Buds of cells are given off from the primary sympathetic ganglia; these buds wander still farther ventrally to become the cells of the ganglia of the cardiac, cœliac, and other great ganglionic nerve plexuses, as well as to form the chromaffin cells of the chromaffin organs.

The exact manner in which the cells of the primitive sheaths of the nerves originate from the primitive ganglia in the human embryo is not known, but it has been shown by Harrison that if the primitive ganglia of the frog are destroyed, the sheaths of the nerves are not formed. In the frog, therefore, these sheaths are derived from cells produced by the primitive ganglia, and it is assumed that they have a similar origin in the human embryo.

After the rudiments of the sympathetic system, the chromaffin cells, and the cellular sheaths of the nerves have budded off, the remains of the primitive ganglia become the permanent spinal and cranial nerve - ganglia. In the early stages these ganglia are completely isolated structures which lie along the sides of the neural tube between the tube and the mesoderm somites.

Some time after the ganglia of the cranial and spinal nerves become isolated their cells give off processes which become nerve-fibres. These fibres grow out both from the dorsal and the ventral ends of the ganglia, and, together with the ganglia, they form, in the head, certain of the cranial nerves, and, in the trunk, the posterior roots of the spinal nerves.

The fibres which grow out of the dorsal ends of the ganglia enter the walls of the neural tube, and by their means the ganglia regain connexion with the tube. The fibres which grow out from the ventral end of each spinal ganglion unite with the fibres of the corresponding anterior nerve-root—which, in the meantime, has grown out from the cells of the ventral part of the side wall of the spinal portion of the neural tube—and form with them a spinal nerve-trunk.

Differentiation of the Neural Tube.—Before the neural groove is converted into a closed tube, an expansion of its anterior part indicates the separation of the neural rudiment into cerebral and spinal portions.

While the cerebral portion is still unclosed, three secondary dilatations of its walls indicate its separation into three sections—the primitive **fore-brain**, the **mid-brain**, and the **hind-brain** (Fig. 54).

Shortly after the three segments of the brain are defined, and before it becomes a closed tube, a vesicular evagination forms at the cephalic end of each side wall of the primitive fore-brain region. These evaginations are the **primary optic vesicles**, and they are the rudiments of the **optic nerves**, the **retinæ**, and the **posterior epithelium of the ciliary body** and of the **iris**. (For the development of the Eye, see the chapter on the Organs of the Senses).

When the cerebral portions of the neural folds meet and fuse dorsally the cerebral dilatations become the primitive brain vesicles, each vesicle possessing its own cavity and walls; but the cavities of the three vesicles are continuous with one another, and the cavity of the hind-brain vesicle is continuous, caudally, with the central canal of the spinal part of the neural tube.

After the three brain vesicles are formed, a diverticulum grows out from the cephalic end of the primitive fore-brain. This is the rudiment of the **secondary fore-brain**. Its cephalic end soon divides into right and left halves, which are the rudiments of the **cerebral hemispheres** of the adult brain.

After their formation the cerebral hemispheres expand rapidly in all directions. They soon overlap the primitive fore-brain and the mid-brain, and eventually the hind-brain also, and each gives off from the cephalic end of its ventral wall a tertiary vesicle—the **olfactory diverticulum**—which becomes converted, later, into the olfactory bulb and olfactory tract.

When the rudiments of the cerebral hemispheres first appear, they are connected together, across the median plane, by a part of the cephalic end of the wall of the secondary fore-brain dilatation which is called the **lamina terminalis**. This primitive connexion between the two cerebral hemispheres is supplemented, at a later period, by the formation of three secondary commissures : the *corpus callosum* and the *fornix*, which grow through the upper part of the lamina terminalis, and the *anterior commissure*, which grows through its lower part.

Structures derived from the Primitive Brain Vesicles.—The primitive hind-brain, which is also called the *rhombencephalon,* is separated in the later stages of development into two parts: (1) A caudal portion or *myelencephalon,* which is connected with the spinal cord and becomes the **medulla oblongata**; (2) a cephalic portion, which is continuous at one end with the medulla oblongata and at the other with the mid-brain. The ventral wall of the cephalic portion is ultimately converted into the **pons**. Its dorsal wall differentiates into two parts—a caudal part which becomes the **cerebellum**; and a cephalic part which is converted into the **superior medullary velum** and the **superior cerebellar peduncles** [brachia conjunctiva]. The superior peduncles connect the cerebellum with the ventral part of the mid-brain. The pons and cerebellum, together, constitute the *metencephalon,* whilst the superior cerebellar peduncles and the superior medullary velum belong to the *isthmus rhombencephali* (Fig. 56).

The ventral portion of the primitive mid-brain is converted into the two **cerebral peduncles**, and the dorsal portion is transformed into the **tectum**, in which four rounded elevations called the **corpora quadrigemina** are developed.

The transformations which take place in the region of the primitive fore-brain or *prosencephalon* are numerous and complicated; its ventral, lateral, and dorsal walls require, therefore, separate consideration.

By the expansion of its anterior end is formed the *telencephalon* (secondary fore-brain), which becomes partially divided, as already explained, into the two vesicles which are the rudiments of the **cerebral hemispheres**. The undivided part of the telencephalon between the cerebral hemispheres is continuous with the remainder of the fore-brain which constitutes the *diencephalon.*

The anterior end of the original cavity of the fore-brain (which becomes the third ventricle) is closed by the lamina terminalis, in association with which are subsequently developed the **anterior columns of the fornix**, which run dorso-ventrally, and three transverse commissures, two of which (the **corpus callosum** and the **anterior commissure**) connect the cerebral hemispheres, whilst the third is the **optic chiasma**, in which the medial fibres of the optic nerves decussate.

From the anterior end of the ventral wall of the diencephalon a diverticulum is projected ventrally towards the dorsal wall of the primitive mouth. The ventral end of this diverticulum becomes the posterior lobe of the **hypophysis cerebri**; the dorsal end becomes the **tuber cinereum**; and the middle part is the **infundibulum** which connects the tuber cinereum of the adult brain with the posterior lobe of the hypophysis.

Caudal to the hypophyseal diverticulum a single elevation appears in the ventral wall of the diencephalon. It is the **corpus mamillare**, which afterwards separates into the paired **mamillary bodies**.

Still more caudally the ventral wall of the diencephalon takes part in the formation of the **posterior perforated substance**, which lies between the two cerebral peduncles, and is partly developed from the ventral wall of the primitive mid-brain.

The greater part of the dorsal wall of the diencephalon is ultimately reduced to a single layer of epithelial cells, but near its caudal end a diverticulum is projected dorsally. This is the **pineal body**, which remains rudimentary in Man. At a later period two transverse bands of fibres appear in the dorsal wall of the diencephalon, one in front of the root of the pineal recess and the other immediately behind it. The anterior band is the **habenular commissure**, and the posterior is the **posterior commissure**.

These structures, collectively, together with a small diverticulum of the epithelial roof, which appears anterior to the habenular commissure and is called the supra-pineal recess, constitute the so-called **epithalamus**.

Each side wall of the diencephalon is differentiated into a dorsal and a ventral part. The dorsal part forms a large grey mass called the **thalamus**, and on the posterior end of the thalamus are developed two rounded elevations, called the **medial** and the **lateral geniculate bodies**, which constitute the **metathalamus**.

The ventral or basal portion of the lateral wall of the diencephalon, together with the adjacent part of the ventral wall, forms the **hypothalamus**.

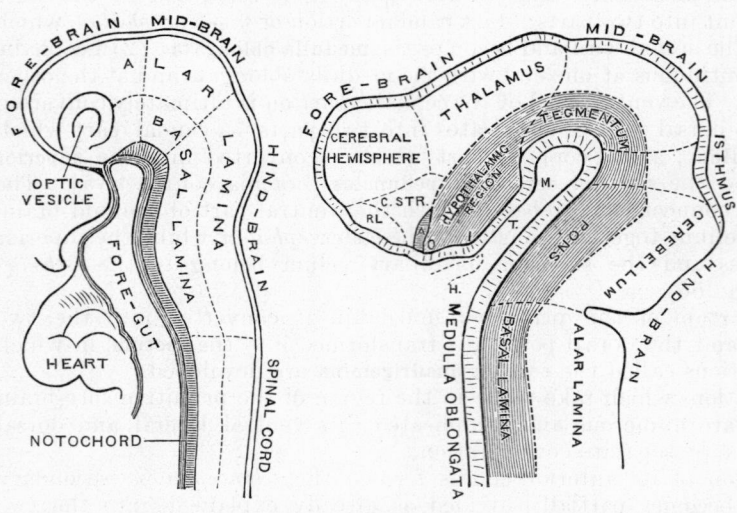

FIG. 56.—DIAGRAMS TO ILLUSTRATE THE ALAR AND BASAL LAMINÆ. In both cases the embryonic brain is represented in median section (His).

A. The different subdivisions of the brain are marked off from each other by dotted lines, and the dotted line running in the long axis of the neural tube indicates the separation of the alar from the basal lamina of the side wall.

B. Median section through the brain of a human embryo at the end of the first month. Dotted lines mark off the different regions and also the alar and basal laminæ from each other. H, Buccal part of hypophysis cerebri ; RL, Olfactory lobe ; C.STR, Corpus striatum ; A, Entrance to optic stalk ; O, Optic recess ; I, Infundibular recess ; T, Tuber cinereum ; M, Mamillary eminence.

Spinal Portion of the Primitive Neural Tube.—The spinal portion of the neural tube, during the first three months of intra-uterine life develops equally in its whole extent, but after that period a longer, cephalic (superior, in the erect posture) and a shorter, caudal portion are recognisable. The cephalic portion undergoes still further development and is converted into the spinal cord of the adult, but in the smaller caudal portion retrogressive changes occur, and it is transformed into the non-functional **filum terminale**.

(For further details of the development of Brain and Spinal Cord, see the chapter on the Central Nervous System.)

Histological Differentiation of the Walls of the Neural Tube.—In the earliest stages of its development the walls of the neural tube consist of a mass of nucleated protoplasm, more or less distinctly differentiated into cell areas of columnar form; these areas extend between and are connected with an **internal limiting membrane**, which bounds the neural canal, and an **external limiting membrane**, which surrounds the whole tube. At this time the outline of a transverse section of the primitive neural tube is more or less ovoid (Fig. 57). The cavity of the tube is compressed from side to side into a

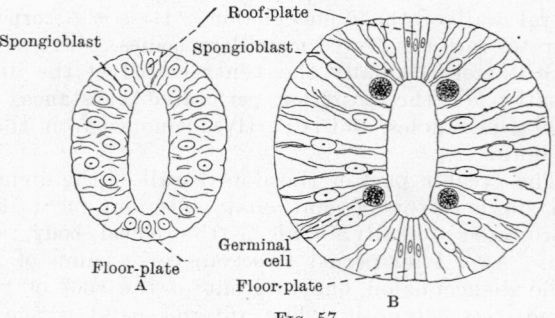

FIG. 57.

A. Diagram of a transverse section of a spinal cord which has not differentiated into groups of cells.

B. Diagram showing positions of germinal cells.

dorso-ventral cleft which is bounded by dorsal, ventral, and side walls. In the dorsal and ventral walls, called respectively the roof- and floor-plates, the columnar character of the primitive epithelial elements of the spinal cord is retained, but the peripheral parts of some of the cells are converted into fibrils.

In the side walls of the embryonic spinal cord some of the cells soon assume a spherical form. These spherical cells have large deeply staining nuclei, and they are termed **germinal cells.**

Some of the germinal cells are the predecessors of the primitive nerve elements or **neuroblasts** ; others, called **spongioblasts**, help to form the reticular sustentacular tissue of the central nervous system. There appear to be two groups of germinal cells; the descendants of one group are directly transformed into the ependymal or lining cells of the central canal, whilst those of the other group form in the first instance **indifferent cells**, some of whose descendants become neuroblasts and others spongioblasts.

All the nerve-cells are therefore the descendants of the germinal cells, but the spongioblasts which become developed into the cells of the **neuroglia** or susten-tacular reticulum are derived partly from the non-germinal cells of the primitive neural tube and, partly, they are descendants of the germinal cells.

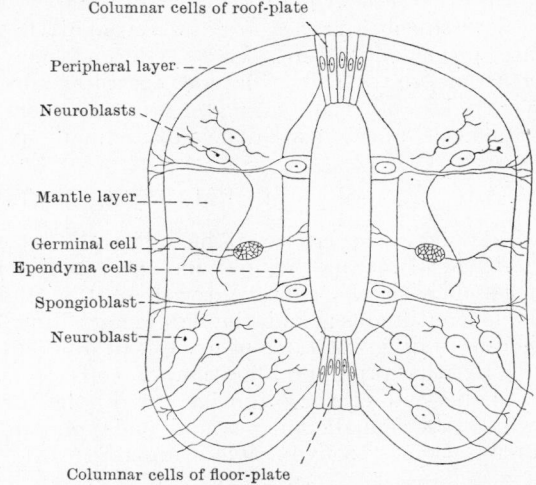

Columnar cells of roof-plate
Peripheral layer
Neuroblasts
Mantle layer
Germinal cell
Ependyma cells
Spongioblast
Neuroblast
Columnar cells of floor-plate

FIG. 58.—SHOWING ELEMENTS OF CENTRAL NERVOUS SYSTEM.

As differentiation proceeds three layers and two membranes are gradually defined in the walls of the neural tube : (1) a central layer of columnar **ependyma cells** immediately surrounding the central canal; (2) an intermediate or **mantle layer** consisting of neuroblasts, and their processes which are the nerve-fibres, intermingled with spongioblasts; (3) a **marginal reticular layer** consisting, at first, of processes of the spongioblasts. The membranes are an external limiting membrane, surrounding the exterior of the tube, formed by the fused outer ends of the spongioblastic cells, and an internal limiting membrane bounding the central canal and continuous with the inner ends of the ependyma cells.

Throughout the whole of the central nervous system, the ependyma cells become transformed into the columnar ciliated cells which line the cavities of the brain and spinal cord. The mantle layer becomes converted into the central grey matter of the central nervous system. The marginal reticular layer, in the spinal region, becomes permeated by nerve-fibres, which are merely processes of the nerve-cells, and it is thus converted into the white matter of the spinal cord. In the brain region it is either transformed in the same way into white matter, or it remains in a more rudimentary condition as a thin peripheral layer of neuroglia on the surface of the grey matter. In addition, in the brain region white matter is formed internal to the grey matter by the growth of nerve-fibres which insinuate themselves between the mantle layer externally and the bodies of the ependyma cells internally.

As the histological differentiation of the walls of the neural tube is proceeding a groove called the *sulcus limitans* divides each side wall into a dorsal part, called the **alar lamina**, and a ventral part called the **basal lamina**. After these sulci are formed the parts of the walls of the neural tube are a roof-plate, a floor-plate, and two side walls, each of which consists of an alar lamina, essentially sensory in function, and a basal lamina, essentially motor in function.

Cavities of the Neural Tube.—The cavity of the spinal portion of the primitive neural tube becomes the central canal of the spinal cord. The cavities of the primitive brain vesicles are transformed into the ventricles, foramina, and aqueduct of the brain. The cavities of the developing cerebral hemispheres become the **right** and **left lateral ventricles** of the brain. The cavity of the undivided portion of the telencephalon, together with the cavity of the diencephalon, becomes the **third ventricle**, and the apertures of communication between the third ventricle and the cerebral hemispheres are the **interventricular foramina**.

The cavity of the hind-brain vesicle becomes the **fourth ventricle**, and the cavity of the primitive mid-brain is converted into the **aqueduct of the mid-brain**, which connects the third ventricle with the fourth.

After the cephalic and caudal neuropores (p. 42) are closed, the cavity of the neural tube is, for a time, a completely enclosed space. Subsequently three membranous sheaths are developed around the tube; they are the **pia mater**, the **arachnoid mater**, and the **dura mater**. The dura mater, which is the outermost, is derived from the scleratogenous parts of the mesodermal somites; but the pia mater, which is the innermost, and the intervening arachnoid mater are possibly formed by ectodermal cells derived from the neural crest.

As the membranes are differentiated the **subdural** and the **subarachnoid spaces** are formed between them. After a time, the **median aperture of the fourth ventricle** and a pair of **lateral apertures** appear in the dorsal wall of the fourth ventricle and the pia mater which covers it, and thus the fourth ventricle becomes connected with the subarachnoid space.

FORMATION OF THE EMBRYO

The transformation of the relatively flat embryonic area into the form of the embryo is due, in the first instance, to the rapid extension of the area, as contrasted with the slower growth of the immediately adjacent parts with which it is continuous; and the later modelling of the various parts of the embryo is due to different rates of growth in different regions.

By the rapid proliferation of cells from the nodal growing point, at the cephalic end of the primitive streak, the surface length of the area is increased, whilst its cephalic and caudal ends remain relatively fixed; consequently the area becomes convex longitudinally. At the same time, the cephalic end of the neural groove is pushed away from the nodal point, until it lies at first dorsal to and then in front of the cephalic border of the area. As a result of this movement the bucco-pharyngeal and the pericardial areas become reversed in position, and a **head fold** is formed. This fold is bounded dorsally by what is now the head portion of the embryo, and ventrally by the reversed pericardial region.

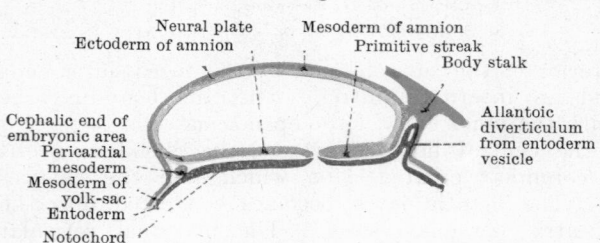

Neural plate   Mesoderm of amnion
Ectoderm of amnion   Primitive streak
    Body stalk
Cephalic end of
embryonic area   Allantoic
Pericardial   diverticulum
mesoderm   from entoderm
Mesoderm of   vesicle
yolk-sac
Entoderm
Notochord

FIG. 59.—SCHEMA OF SAGITTAL SECTION OF EMBRYONIC AREA AND AMNION BEFORE THE FOLDING OF THE AREA.

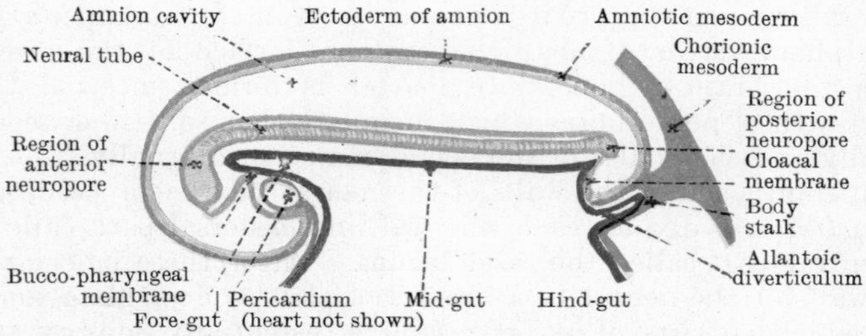

Amnion cavity   Ectoderm of amnion   Amniotic mesoderm
Neural tube   Chorionic
    mesoderm
    Region of
    posterior
Region of   neuropore
anterior   Cloacal
neuropore   membrane
    Body
    stalk
    Allantoic
    diverticulum
Bucco-pharyngeal
membrane   Pericardium   Mid-gut   Hind-gut
Fore-gut (heart not shown)

FIG. 60.—SCHEMA OF SAGITTAL SECTION OF EMBRYONIC AREA SHORTLY AFTER THE FOLDING HAS BEGUN. The pericardial mesoderm is carried into the ventral wall of the fore-gut, and the cœlom has extended through it. The cephalic end of the neural tube and the caudal part of the primitive streak are bent ventrally, and the latter now forms the cloacal membrane.

The growth at the nodal point not only produces a head fold, but at the same time it forces the rest of the primitive streak over the caudal end of the embryonic area, thus forming a **tail fold**.

As the head and tail folds of the embryo are produced by the longitudinal increase of the embryonic area, transverse growth of the area results in the formation of right and left **lateral folds** (Figs. 50, 51), and as the various folds are formed the embryo rises, like a mushroom, into the cavity of the amnion.

The portion of the entodermal sac which is enclosed within the hollow embryo, formed by the folding of the embryonic area, is the **primitive entodermal alimentary canal.** The part which remains outside the embryo is the **yolk-sac**; and the passage of communication between the two is the **vitello-intestinal duct** (Fig. 63.)

That portion of the primitive entodermal alimentary canal which lies in the head fold is termed the **fore-gut**, the part in the tail fold is the **hind-gut**, and the middle portion, which is in free communication with the yolk-sac, is the **mid-gut**.

As the extension of the embryonic area and its folding proceed, the margin of the area, which remains relatively stationary, becomes the margin of an orifice through which the primitive alimentary canal of the embryo communicates with the yolk-sac, and the intra-embryonic part of the cœlom with the extra-embryonic part. That orifice is the **primitive umbilical orifice.**

Not only does the primitive alimentary canal communicate with the yolk-sac, and the intra-embryonic with the extra-embryonic cœlom, at the margin of the umbilical orifice, but also the body walls of the embryo, formed by the somatopleure, become continuous at the same margin with the wall of the amnion.

The young embryo is connected also with the inner surface of the chorion by a band of tissue which is continuous with the caudal part of the wall of the amnion. The mesoderm in this region is thickened, and contains in its interior the **allantoic diverticulum**, which is primarily derived from the entodermal sac, but is afterwards connected with the hind-gut; it contains also the blood-vessels passing between the embryo and the chorion. This connecting band between embryo and chorion was called by His the **body stalk**, and is generally known by that name; but since it contains the entodermal diverticulum covered with mesoderm which represents the mammalian **allantois**, it has also been termed the **allantoic stalk**.

At first the umbilical orifice is relatively large as contrasted with the total size of the embryo, but as the embryo rapidly extends, in all directions, from its margins the orifice soon becomes relatively small. Ultimately the margins of the orifice are approximated until they fuse together, closing the opening and forming a cicatrix on the ventral wall of the abdomen known as the **umbilicus** or **navel**.

THE EMBRYO

Whilst the embryonic area is being folded into the form of the embryo, the neural groove on the surface of the area is being converted into the neural tube. After the neural tube is completely closed and separated from the surface, during the third week, the embryo is an elongated organism possessing a larger cephalic end, a smaller caudal end, and attached by the allantoic stalk to the chorion. Its dorsal surface is continuous and unbroken, but its ventral surface is separated into cephalic and caudal portions by the umbilical orifice, through which passes the vitello-intestinal duct. It has also a right and a left surface, and it contains three cavities: (1) The cavity of the neural tube; (2) the primitive alimentary canal, which is a portion of the entodermal vesicle constricted off during the folding of the embryonic area (Figs. 51, 52); (3) the embryonic cœlom.

The embryonic cœlom consists of a pericardial portion, which lies in a projection ventral to the fore-gut between the growing head and the umbilicus, and right and left lateral portions, which lie at the sides of the fore-gut, the mid-gut, and the hind-gut.

The right and left portions communicate with each other, ventral to the fore-gut, through the pericardial portion; ventral to the hind-gut, they communicate also with the extra-embryonic cœlom at the lateral and caudal margins of the umbilical orifice.

By this time the embryo has become easily distinguishable from the remainder of the zygote, and it is so far developed that indications of its general plan of organisation are discernible.

It has, as yet, no limbs, but the general contour of the head and body are defined. It possesses a primitive skeletal axis—the notochord—afterwards replaced by the permanent vertebral column. On the dorsal aspect of the notochord lies the neural tube, which is the rudiment of the brain and the spinal cord.

At the sides of the neural tube and the notochord are the mesodermal somites and the nerve ganglia (Figs. 51, 52).

Ventral to the notochord is the primitive alimentary canal closed at its cephalic end by the **bucco-pharyngeal membrane**, and at its caudal end by the **cloacal membrane**; this was originally the caudal portion of the primitive streak, and it now separates the amniotic cavity from the caudal end of the hind-gut, which becomes the **entodermal cloaca** (Fig. 61).

At the sides of the primitive alimentary canal are the right and left parts of the cœlom, and between the dorsal angle of each half of the cœlom and the mesodermal somites of the same side lies the intermediate cell mass, which is the rudiment of the greater part of the urogenital system (Figs. 51, 52).

Ventral to the fore-gut is the pericardial mesoderm, traversed by the pericardial portion of the cœlom, which is connected dorsally, on each side, with the

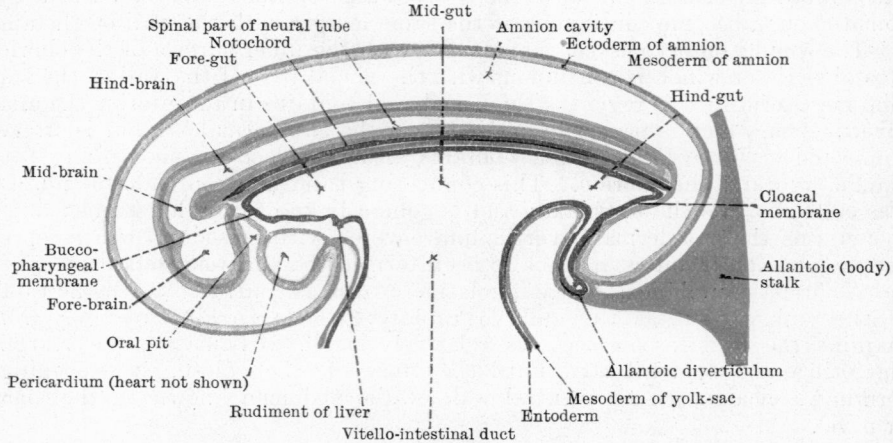

FIG. 61.—SCHEMA OF SAGITTAL SECTION OF EMBRYO AFTER THE FOLDING HAS DEFINED BOTH THE FORE-GUT AND HIND-GUT AREAS.

corresponding lateral portions of the cœlom; and ventral to the hind-gut is the cloacal membrane. Between the pericardial region at the one end and the cloacal membrane at the other lies the umbilical orifice, through which the mid-gut communicates with the yolk-sac, the intra-embryonic part of the cœlom with the extra-embryonic cœlom, and the allantoic diverticulum with the cloaca (Figs. 51, 61).

THE LIMBS

When it is first defined the embryo is entirely devoid of limbs (Fig. 102). During the fourth week a slight ridge appears on each side, opposite the intermediate cell mass in the interior. On this ridge the **limb buds**, which are the rudiments of the fore and hind limbs, are formed as secondary elevations; the fore-limb buds precede the hind-limb buds in time of appearance (Figs. 62, 105).

Shortly after each limb bud has appeared, it assumes a semilunar outline; it projects at right angles from the surface of the body, and it possesses dorsal and ventral surfaces, and cephalic or preaxial, and caudal or postaxial borders. The bud is the rudiment of the distal segment—hand or foot—of the future limb.

As the limb rudiment increases in length the more proximal segments of the limb are differentiated. At the same time the limbs are folded ventrally, so that their original ventral surfaces become medial and their original dorsal surfaces lateral, and the convexities of the elbows and knees are directed laterally. At a later period, on account of a rotation which takes place in opposite directions in the fore- and the hind-limbs, the convexity of the elbow is turned towards the caudal end of the body and that of the knee towards the head.

The terminal or distal segment of each limb is, at first, a flat plate with a rounded margin, but it soon differentiates into a proximal or basal part and a more flattened marginal portion. It is along the line where these two parts are continuous that the rudiments of the **digits** appear. They become evident as small elevations on the dorsal surface of the limb bud about the sixth week; they extend peripherally, and by the seventh week the fingers project beyond the margins of the hand segment, but the toes do not attain to a corresponding stage of development until the early part of the eighth week.

The **nails** are later developments. They appear at the third month and reach the ends of the digits at the sixth month.

Each limb bud is essentially an extension from a definite number of segments of the body. It consists, at first, of a core of mesenchyme covered by ectoderm. As it grows the anterior primary rami of the spinal nerves of the corresponding segments are prolonged into it, together with a number of blood-vessels. The nerves remain as the nerves of the fully developed limb, but the blood-vessels are reduced in number and are modified to form the permanent main trunks.

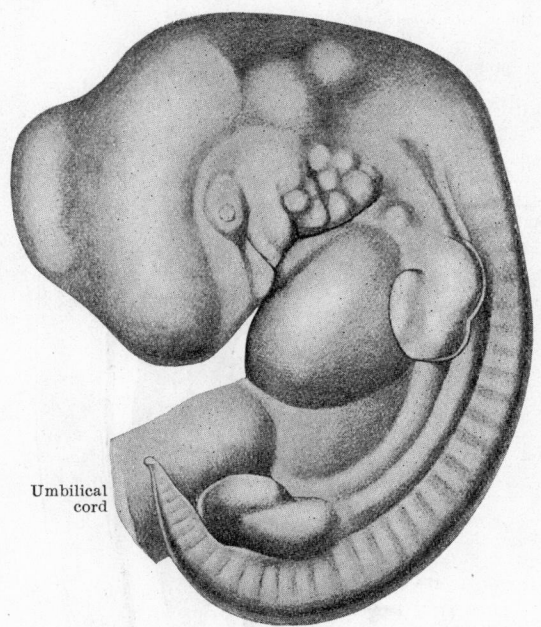

Umbilical cord

FIG. 62.—SIDE VIEW OF A HUMAN EMBRYO—11·5 mm. long. (Keibel and Elze, *Normentafeln*.)

The limb rudiments are bent ventrally and show differentiation into segments.

The greater part, if not the whole, of the mesenchymatous core of the primitive limb-rudiment is derived from somatic mesoderm of the lateral plate. As the development proceeds it is differentiated into the cartilaginous and other connective tissue elements which are the rudiments of the skeletal framework and the fasciæ of the fully formed limb.

The rudiments of the muscles of the limbs appear in the mesenchyme as **pre-muscle masses** which have no direct connexion with the myotomes of the segments to which the limb buds are related. There is evidence, however, that cells do migrate from the myotomes to mingle with the mesenchyme of the limbs; and in this way the myotomes may take part in the development of the limb muscles which are innervated by the nerves of the segments to which they belong.

EARLY DEVELOPMENT OF THE ALIMENTARY CANAL AND FORMATION OF ORAL AND ANAL PITS

The greater part of the permanent alimentary canal is derived from the entodermal vesicle and is therefore lined with entodermal cells. This part is enclosed in the embryo as it is folded off from the remainder of the zygote (Figs. 61, 67), but the two ends of the alimentary canal are formed by depressions of the surface of the embryo and are therefore lined with ectoderm.

The cephalic end of the alimentary canal is formed from a portion of a space called the **stomodæum** or **oral pit** which lies, at first, between the ventrally bent extremity of the head and the bulging pericardial region (Figs. 61, 63). At a later period it is enclosed at the sides by the rudiments of the maxillæ and of the mandible and caudally by the bucco-pharyngeal membrane.

When the oral pit first appears it is separated from the entodermal alimentary canal by the **bucco-pharyngeal membrane**, but when that septum disappears, during the third week, the oral pit communicates with the fore-gut. Later, it is separated into nasal and oral portions by the formation of the palate, and the oral portion forms that part of the mouth in which the gums and the teeth are developed.

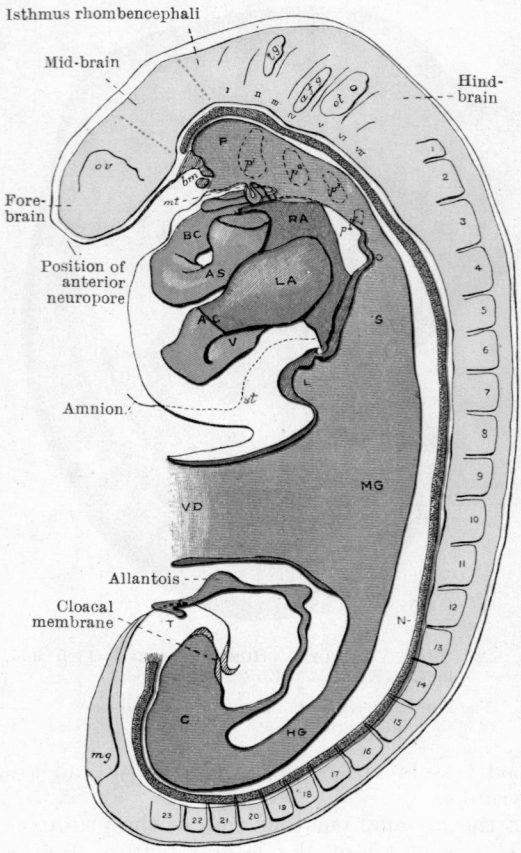

FIG. 63.—RECONSTRUCTION OF HUMAN EMBRYO, 2.5 MM. LONG, WITH TWENTY-THREE PAIRS OF SOMITES. (Peter Thompson, *Journ. Anat.*, 1907.)

o.v., optic vesicle; i.-vii., neuromeres of hind-brain; t.g., trigeminal ganglion; a.f.g., auditory-facial ganglion; o.t., otocyst; 1-23, somites; b.m., remains of bucco-pharyngeal membrane; m.t., median thyroid rudiment; P., pharynx; p.1-p.4, pharyngeal pouches; o., oesophagus; S., Stomach; L., liver; s.t., septum transversum; V.D., vitello-intestinal duct; M.G., mid-gut; N., notochord; H.G., hind-gut; C., cloaca; T., tail; m.g., neural groove (post. neuropore); R.A., L.A., right and left atria; A.C., atrio-ventricular canal; V., ventricle; B.C., bulbus cordis; A.S., truncus arteriosus.

The terminal portion of the permanent canal is formed by the elevation of a surface fold round a pit-like hollow called the **proctodæum** or **anal pit** (Fig. 77), which is separated from the blind end of the entodermal alimentary canal, until about the eighth week, by the **anal membrane** which is a portion of the more extensive cloacal membrane mentioned on p. 50.

Derivatives of the Oral Pit.—When the stomodæum or oral pit is definitely established, it is bounded cranially by the bent terminal part of the head, caudally by the conjoined ends of the mandibular arches, and laterally by the **maxillary processes**, which grow ventrally from the dorsal parts of the mandibular arches. The space is open ventrally, and it is closed dorsally by the bucco-pharyngeal membrane, which disappears during the third week so that the oral pit and the fore-gut become continuous (Fig. 63).

In the roof of the oral pit in front of the attachment of the bucco-pharyngeal membrane there is a depression which is deepened by the growth of mesoderm around it so that it appears as a diverticulum of the roof. It is lined with ectoderm and is known as **Rathke's pouch.** The blind end of the pouch comes into relation with the hypophyseal diverticulum from the floor of the third ventricle and dilates. The dilated part becomes the anterior lobe of the hypophysis; the rest disappears (Figs. 75, 76, 77). (For the development of the hypophysis, see the chapter on the Ductless Glands.)

Separation of the Oral Pit into Nose and Mouth.—The frontal end of the head lies in the cephalic boundary of the oral pit and is called the **fronto-nasal process.** A pair of shallow depressions, called the **olfactory pits**, divide it into a *median nasal process* and a pair of *lateral nasal processes*; and a median groove divides the median process into right and left *globular processes*. As the margins of these processes increase in height the olfactory pits deepen.

The lateral boundary of the oral pit is at first formed by the maxillary process springing from the dorsal part of the mandibular arch. But in the angle above the maxillary process is the projecting eye; and leading from it, between the maxillary process and the lateral nasal process, is the **naso-lacrimal sulcus.**

As growth proceeds and each maxillary process grows ventrally, it fuses with the lateral nasal process, and then, carrying the lateral nasal process with it, it fuses also with the globular process of the same side. The olfactory pits are thus completely separated, for a time, from the oral pit and they lie in the newly constituted ledge which now forms its boundary. This ledge consists of the two globular processes, fused into a single mass, and the two

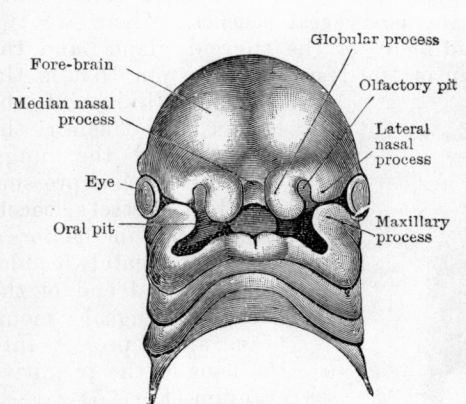

FIG. 64.—ANTERIOR VIEW OF BOUNDARIES OF STOMODÆUM BEFORE COMPLETION OF PRIMITIVE UPPER LIP.

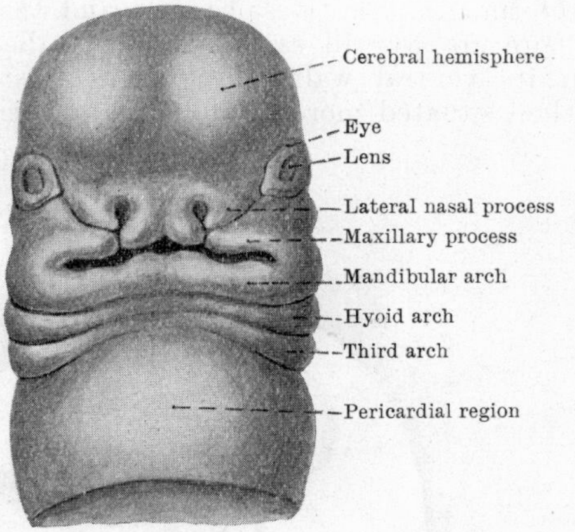

FIG. 65.—ANTERIOR VIEW OF THE HEAD OF A HUMAN EMBRYO SHOWING THE COMPLETION OF THE PRIMITIVE UPPER LIP.

maxillary processes—the lateral nasal processes being shut off from the margin of the ledge by the maxillary processes (Fig. 65).

Along the line of fusion of the maxillary and lateral nasal processes there remains a buried tract of ectodermal cells; it leads from the developing eye to the olfactory pit, and is the rudiment of the **naso-lacrimal duct.**

At this stage the blind ends of the olfactory pits are separated from the cavity of the oral pit by thin **bucco-nasal membranes,** but these soon disappear, and the olfactory pits then communicate directly with the cavity of the oral pit, through openings which are called the **primitive choanæ** or **posterior apertures of the nose.** The olfactory pits may now be called the **primitive nasal cavities;** they extend upwards and backwards excavating the roof of the main cavity of the oral pit on each side so that a median **nasal septum** appears between them.

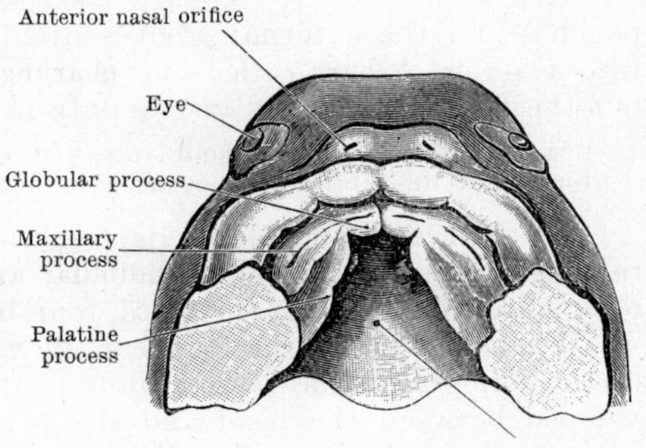

After the formation of the primitive choanæ a ledge grows from the medial surface of each maxillary process towards the median plane. These ledges—the **palatine processes**—are separated for a while by the developing tongue, but they meet and fuse during the third month of intra-uterine life, the fusion beginning

FIG. 66.—PORTION OF THE HEAD OF A HUMAN EMBRYO ABOUT 2½ MONTHS OLD (His). The lips are separated from the gums, and the line of the dental lamina is visible in the latter. The palatine processes are growing inwards from the maxillary processes.

ventrally and being completed dorsally in the region of the uvula. The cavity of the oral pit is thus separated into an upper and a lower portion. The upper portion is the **nasal cavity;** it is divided into lateral halves as the palatine processes fuse also with the free edge of the nasal septum. The lower portion of the cavity of the oral pit blends with the ventral part of the primitive pharynx. It forms the cavity of the vestibule of the mouth and from its walls the gums and teeth are developed.

The separation of the lips from the gums is described in the chapter on the Digestive System.

DIFFERENTIATION OF FORE-GUT

Derivatives of the Side Wall.—While still separated from the oral pit by the bucco-pharyngeal membrane the cephalic part of the fore-gut dilates to form the primitive pharynx, and thirteen depressions are formed in its walls. There are five in each side wall called the **pharyngeal pouches.** There are two in its ventral wall; the first is the rudiment of the thyroid gland; and the other, situated more caudally, is the origin of the respiratory system, that is, the epithelial lining of the larynx, the trachea, the bronchi, and the lungs. The thirteenth depression is called **Seessel's pouch.** It is formed in the dorsal wall, immediately caudal to the dorsal end of the bucco-pharyngeal membrane, and it projects into the floor of the primitive cranium (Fig. 75).

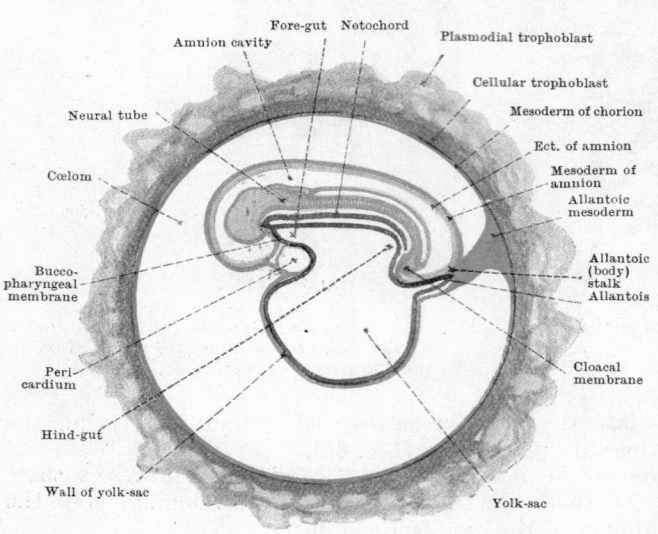

FIG. 67.—MEDIAN SECTION OF ZYGOTE SHOWN IN FIG. 54.

Simultaneously with the formation of the pharyngeal pouches internally a series of grooves appear externally. They correspond in position with the first four pharyngeal pouches, and they are called the **external pharyngeal grooves.**

The pharyngeal pouches and the external grooves divide each side wall of the primitive pharynx into a series of bars called the **pharyngeal arches.** The bars are five in number, but the fifth is distinctly visible only in the inner aspect of the pharynx.

Because of the obvious resemblance to the homologous parts in gill-breathing vertebrates, the formations described are often called **branchial** pouches, clefts, and arches.

The first pharyngeal bar is the rudiment of the maxillary and mandibular regions. It is called the **mandibular arch.** The second is the **hyoid arch.** The others are numbered as the third, fourth, and fifth arches.

When the arches first appear, they extend from the level of the dorsal wall of the fore-gut to the pericardium; but as growth proceeds, and the neck is developed between the head and the pericardium, the ventral ends of the arches come to lie in the ventral wall of the primitive pharynx, though the mandibular arch is the only one that meets its fellow of the opposite side externally (Frazer). The growth of the mandibular and the hyoid arches soon greatly exceeds that of the other arches, and the latter gradually recede from the surface until, on each side, they lie at the bottom of a depression—called the **precervical sinus**—overlapped by the caudal border of the hyoid arch. The increasing growth of the hyoid arch reduces the opening of the precervical sinus to a narrow channel called the *precervical duct*, but this is soon obliterated, and then the sinus becomes the *precervical vesicle*. The precervical vesicle lies at the side of the third pharyngeal groove, and it is associated with the second and fourth grooves by narrow canals called the "branchial" ducts, which are the remains of the external pharyngeal grooves or "branchial" clefts. Ultimately these submerged spaces (lined by ectoderm) are obliterated; but they may on occasion give rise to a *branchial cyst* or a *branchial fistula*.

Frazer (*Manual of Embryology*, 1931) gives a different interpretation of the changes in this region. His observations show that the area of the precervical sinus is reduced to a triangular field by a ridge which limits it behind, and a ventral (epipericardial) ridge which separates the ventral ends of the arches from the pericardial swelling. These ridges contain pre-muscle cells passing forwards from the occipital myotomes to the developing tongue. The fourth arch is covered in by the growth of the posterior ridge, and the flattened third arch remains on the surface, so that the closure of the precervical sinus is only partial.

The portion of the wall of the primitive pharynx which lies between any two adjacent arches and separates the external groove from the internal pouch is called the **separating membrane**. In the earliest stages it consists of ectoderm, mesoderm, and entoderm; then, for a time, the mesoderm disappears, but it reappears at a still later period.

Except as a malformation, the separating membranes are never perforated in mammalian development, so that no complete "cleft" ever exists.

The dorsal end of the first external groove becomes the **external auditory**

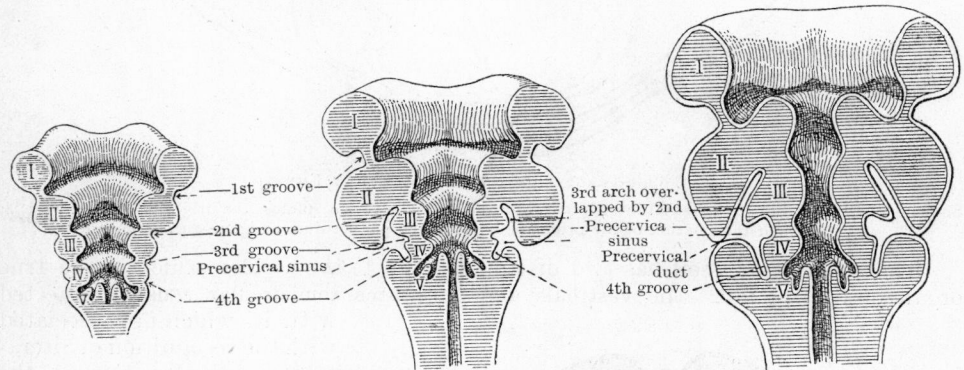

FIG. 68.—SCHEMA showing the formation and closure of the precervical sinus.

meatus, and a series of tubercles which appear at its margins develop into the **auricle** of the external ear (see p. 58). The **tympanic cavity** and the **pharyngo-tympanic tube** are developed from a lateral extension of the upper part of the cavity of the primitive pharynx between the first and third arches which contains in its floor the second arch, and parts of the first and second pouches, (see p. 57). A part of the cavity of the second pharyngeal pouch may be represented in the adult by the *intratonsillar cleft*, which passes into the upper part of the tonsil in the side wall of the pharynx (Fig. 72).

The third pharyngeal pouch opens, like the first and second, directly into the cavity of the fore-gut, but the communication is soon drawn out into a duct-like passage; the fourth and fifth pouches lie in the side wall of a common recess which opens by a single aperture or "duct" into the cavity of the primitive pharynx (Fig. 72).

The cavities of the third, fourth, and fifth pouches ultimately disappear. Before they disappear a diverticulum, at first hollow but afterwards solid, grows from the ventro-lateral wall of each, and a solid outgrowth, called an **epithelial body**, buds from the dorso-lateral wall of each of the third and fourth pouches (Fig. 72).

Tympanum and Pharyngo-Tympanic Tube.—The development of the organ of hearing is so intimately associated with the development of the pharyngeal portion of the primitive gut that a short consideration of the chief phenomena may with advantage be introduced here; but for the details of the development of the internal ear the student must refer to the chapter on the Organs of the Senses.

In Man as in other mammals, the organ of hearing consists of:—the **internal ear** or labyrinth; the middle ear or **tympanum**, with which is associated the **pharyngo-tympanic tube**; and the **external ear**, which includes the **external auditory meatus** and the **auricle**.

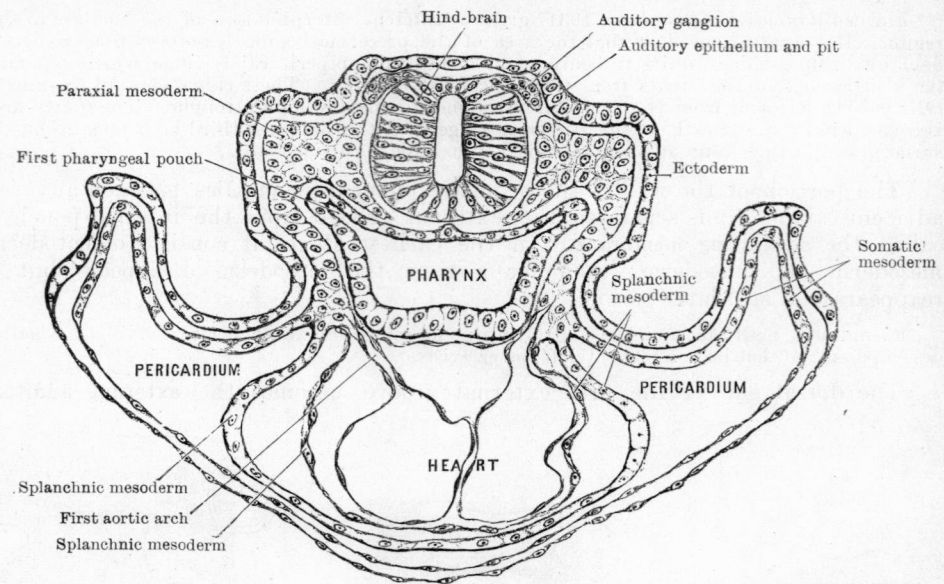

FIG. 69.—TRANSVERSE SECTION OF A RAT EMBRYO.

Showing the relation of the paraxial mesoderm of the head to the lateral plates, the origin of the otic vesicles and the relation of the primitive heart to the pericardium and fore-gut.

The **internal ear** itself has two distinct parts: (1) the **cochlea**, which is the true organ of hearing; (2) the **vestibule** and the **three semicircular canals** connected with it, which are associated with the recognition of alterations in the position of the head, and therefore with the maintenance of equilibrium.

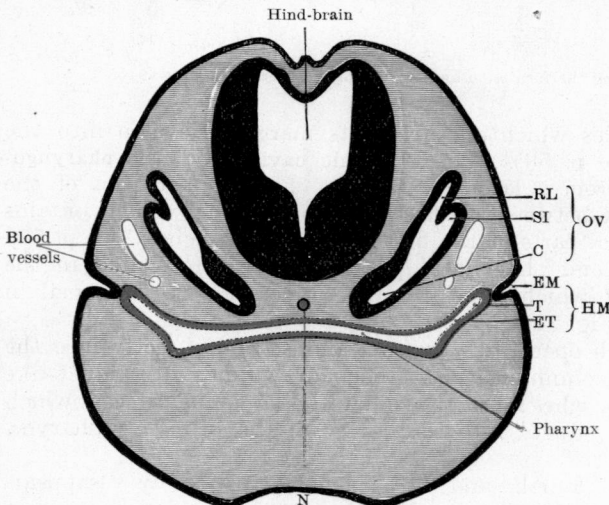

FIG. 70.—DIAGRAM OF TRANSVERSE SECTION THROUGH THE HEAD OF AN EMBRYO.

Showing the rudiments of the three parts of the ear and their relation to the tubo-tympanic recess and the first pharyngeal groove.

C.   Cochlea.
EM. Ext. auditory meatus.
ET. Pharyngo-tympanic tube.
HM. Tubo-tympanic recess and 1st pharyngeal groove.
N.   Notochord.
OV. Otic vesicle.
RL. Recessus labyrinthi.
SI. Stalk of invagination.
T.   Tympanum.

The whole of the internal ear is lined with ectoderm, called the **auditory epithelium**, which is derived from the surface of the head of the embryo in the region of the hind-brain, dorsal to the first pharyngeal groove (Fig. 69). It is recognisable in human embryos of the third week with five or six somites as a thickened and slightly depressed plate of ectodermal cells. The plate is gradually invaginated into the substance of the head, forming the **auditory pit**, which is transformed into a pear-shaped vesicle called the **otic vesicle** or **otocyst** (Figs. 63, 104). For a time the otic vesicle remains in communication with the exterior by a short tubular canal. As the canal disappears a diverticulum is formed from the vesicle at the medial side of the deep end of the canal. The diverticulum grows dorsally as a narrow tube called the *recessus labyrinthi*. It is ultimately transformed into the **endolymphatic duct** and sac.

After the otic vesicle is separated from the surface, it alters its position until its ventral end lies in close relation to the dorsal wall of the pharynx; at the same time, it undergoes alteration of shape. The ventral part of the vesicle grows towards the median plane, along the ventral wall of the hind-brain. It forms the cavity and the lining epithelium of the **cochlea**; but it remains in connexion with the dorsal part by means of a narrow tube called the **ductus reuniens**, and as it grows in length it is converted into a spiral tube.

The dorsal section of the primitive vesicle becomes converted into the three **semicircular ducts**, the **utricle**, and the **saccule**. All these parts with supporting mesoderm constitute the **membranous labyrinth** of the internal ear.

The cavity of the bony labyrinth is formed, outside the membranous labyrinth, by the appearance of lymph spaces between the walls of the various parts of the membranous labyrinth and the more external mesoderm.

The mesoderm outside the lymph spaces is converted first into the cartilage and then into the bone of the petrous part of the temporal bone. The dense bone immediately around the lymph spaces repeats their contours and is called the **bony labyrinth**.

The **tympanum** and the **pharyngo-tympanic tube** [tuba auditiva] are developed from a lateral extension of the upper part of the cavity of the primitive pharynx called the **tubo-tympanic recess** (Frazer). This recess is formed, not only from the first pharyngeal pouch, but also from a part of the second, since it is limited behind by the *third* arch.

The outer part of the recess expands and is converted into the cavity of the tympanum, whilst the inner part is gradually constricted from its lateral towards its medial end by the growth of tissue from the third arch in its posterior wall, and is converted into the

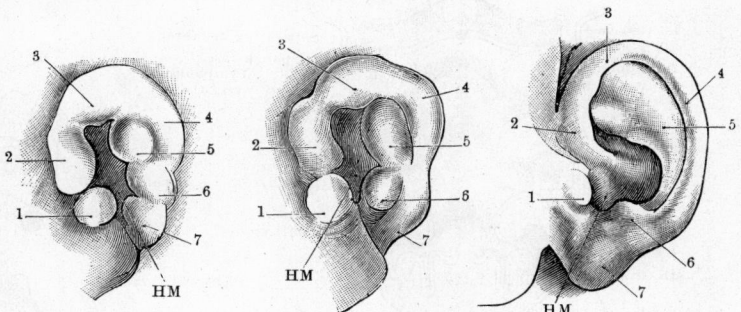

FIG. 71.—FIGURES, MODIFIED FROM HIS, ILLUSTRATING THE FORMATION OF THE AURICLE.

1. Tragus.   4. Tail of the helix.   7. Lobule.
2. Crus of helix. }   5. Antihelix.   HM. Hyomandibular (1st pharyn-
3. Helix.   6. Antitragus.   geal) groove.

pharyngo-tympanic tube. The constriction begins when the embryo has attained a length of about 20 mm. (that is, about the beginning of the eighth week), and is completed about the end of that week when the embryo is about 25 mm. long.

After the pharyngo-tympanic tube is defined it grows rapidly in length, and cartilage appears in its walls during the fourth month.

As the tympanic cavity increases in size the auditory ossicles—*malleus, incus,* and *stapes*—which are differentiated from the dorsal ends of the cartilages of the first and second arches, are invaginated into it.

The **tympanic membrane**, which separates the tympanum from the external auditory meatus, is formed in the position of a "separating membrane" between the first pharyngeal pouch and the first external groove. But it is formed indirectly. From the dorsal part of the groove ectodermal cells grow inwards to form a solid **meatal plug** which applies itself obliquely to the lateral end and floor of the tubo-tympanic recess. The plug breaks down in the centre to form the external auditory meatus, at the bottom of which the tympanic membrane is left. It consists, therefore, of an external covering of ectoderm, an internal lining of entoderm, and an intervening layer of fibrous tissue derived from the mesoderm.

The **external ear** is developed from the upper part and the boundaries of the first external pharyngeal (hyo-mandibular) groove. The deeper part of the *external auditory meatus* is formed by the breaking down of the meatal plug. On the mandibular and hyoid margins of the groove three eminences appear; from the eminences on the two arches, and from the skin immediately posterior to the eminences on the hyoid arch, are formed the various parts of the *auricle*; but the exact part played by the individual eminences is a matter of some doubt (Fig. 71).

Thymus, Parathyroid and Thyroid Glands.—The ventral diverticulum from the third pouch forms the main part of the corresponding lobe of the **thymus**; and the ventral diverticulum of the fourth pouch either takes part in the formation of the thymus or entirely disappears. The rudiment of the thymus is formed in the neck, but as the gland differentiates it extends and migrates caudally, until its cephalic end lies near the caudal end of the thyroid gland, at the level of the sixth ring of the trachea, and its caudal end is in the thorax at the level of the fourth costal cartilage.

The epithelial bodies derived from the walls of the third and fourth pouches

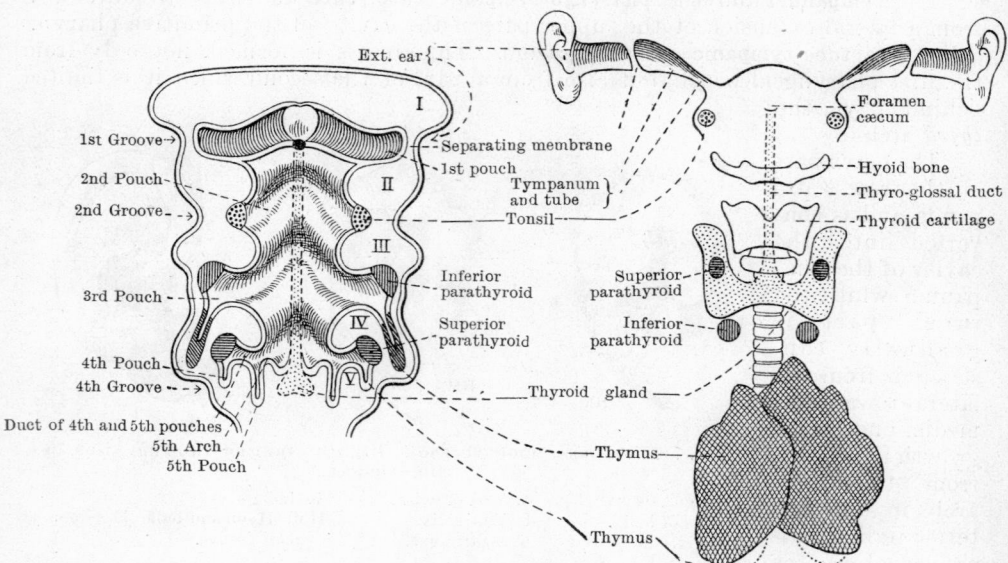

Fig. 72.—Schema showing the pharyngeal pouches, the external pharyngeal grooves, the pharyngeal arches, and the thyro-glossal duct and some of their derivatives. I, II, III, IV, and V, the five arches.

form the **parathyroid glands**. The one derived from the third pouch (parathyroid III) migrates caudally more rapidly than the one derived from the fourth pouch (parathyroid IV); consequently parathyroid III reaches the caudal end of the corresponding lobe of the thyroid gland whilst parathyroid IV is arrested at the middle of the dorsal border of the lobe (Fig. 72).

The diverticulum formed from the ventral part of the fifth pharyngeal pouch is the **ultimo-branchial body.** After it separates from the pouch it becomes solid and is associated with the corresponding lobe of the thyroid gland; and there is some evidence that the older view that it produces thyroid tissue and takes part in the formation of the lobe of the gland is correct (Weller). (See the chapter on Duct-less Glands).

Derivatives of the Ventral Wall.—The main rudiment of the **thyroid gland** appears first as a diverticulum from the ventral wall of the primitive fore-gut. It begins in the median plane, between the ventral ends of the mandibular and hyoid arches. It first grows ventrally, into the substance of the neck, and then caudally, passing ventral to the cartilage bars which appear in the second, third, and fourth arches and are developed into the hyoid bone and the cartilages of the larynx. When the caudal end of the diverticulum reaches the level of the origin of the trachea it becomes bilobed, and is thus differentiated into the isthmus and the adjacent parts of the two lobes of the permanent gland. The stalk of the diverticulum is the **thyro-glossal duct**. It extends from what becomes the oral part of the primitive pharynx to the isthmus of the gland. The position of its upper end is indicated by the **foramen cæcum**, which is situated in the dorsum of the tongue, at the junction of the anterior two-thirds with the posterior third. The caudal end sometimes persists and is transformed into the *pyramidal lobe of the thyroid* gland, which is attached to the isthmus (Figs. 72, 73).

A more caudally situated diverticulum from the ventral wall of the fore-gut is the **rudiment of the respiratory system** (Figs. 73, 75). It first appears as a longitudinal groove bounded at its cranial end and on each side by an elevated ridge, named by His the **furcula** (Fig. 73). The caudal end of the groove soon dilates into a pouch. Then the pouch and groove are separated from the more dorsal part of the fore-gut, which becomes the **œsophagus**, by a constriction which passes from the caudal towards the cranial end. The constricting process ceases before the separation reaches the cranial end of the respiratory rudiment, which therefore remains in communication with the pharynx and forms the permanent *inlet of the larynx*. As the groove is separated from the primitive

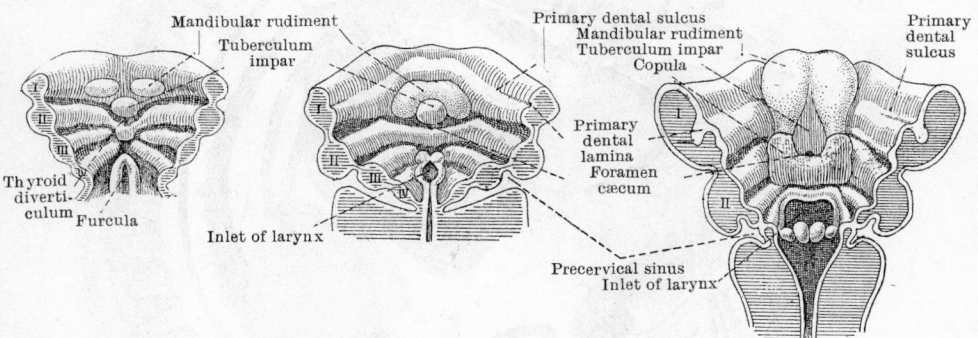

FIG. 73.—SCHEMA showing stages in the development of the tongue.

fore-gut it is converted into a tube which is gradually differentiated into the *larynx* and the *trachea*. The pouch at the caudal end of the tube soon divides into right and left lobes, each of which is the rudiment of the epithelium lining the bronchi and lung of the corresponding side.

The Tongue.—The mucous membrane of the tongue is formed by *four separate rudiments* which appear in the ventral wall of the primitive pharynx. Two of these are elevations formed on the ventral ends of the mandibular arches. The third is a median elevation, called the **tuberculum impar**, which is situated immediately caudal to the conjoined ventral ends of the mandibular arches. The fourth, called by His the **copula**, formed by the conjoined ventral ends of the second and third pairs of arches, is separated from the tuberculum impar by the orifice of the thyroid rudiment (Fig. 73).

The elevations on the mandibular arches unite to form the greater part of the anterior two-thirds of the tongue — the part on which all the papillæ are developed. The tuberculum impar helps to form the median part of the anterior two-thirds of the organ. The posterior third of the tongue, which lies in the ventral or anterior wall of the permanent pharynx, is formed by a ∧-shaped swelling which rises from the copula and blends with the anterior two-thirds along the line of the *sulcus terminalis*. The foramen cæcum is a depression left in the median plane at the junction of the two parts of the tongue, and it therefore indicates the site of origin of the thyroid gland.

According to Frazer's observations the lateral parts of the *furcula* represent obliquely situated *sixth* arches, and the median part is the rudiment of the epiglottis separated off from a median *hypobranchial eminence* which has previously appeared between the ventral ends of the third and fourth arches. The anterior part of this eminence corresponds to the *copula*, and from it the pharyngeal third of the tongue is derived, mainly from the third arches.

Derivative of the Dorsal Wall.—The only dorsal diverticulum from the cranial part of the fore-gut is **Seessel's pouch**, which enters the base of the occipital region of the primitive head. The ultimate fate of the pouch is unknown in the human subject, but it has been suggested that it is represented by a depression known as the *pharyngeal bursa* in the mucous membrane of the nasal part of the pharynx, close to the naso-pharyngeal tonsil.

The reader will have noted that the cranial portion of the fore-gut gives rise to the lower part of the mouth (with the exception of the lips, teeth, and gums) the pharynx, the thyroid gland, the thymus, the parathyroid glands, the respiratory organs, and the œsophagus.

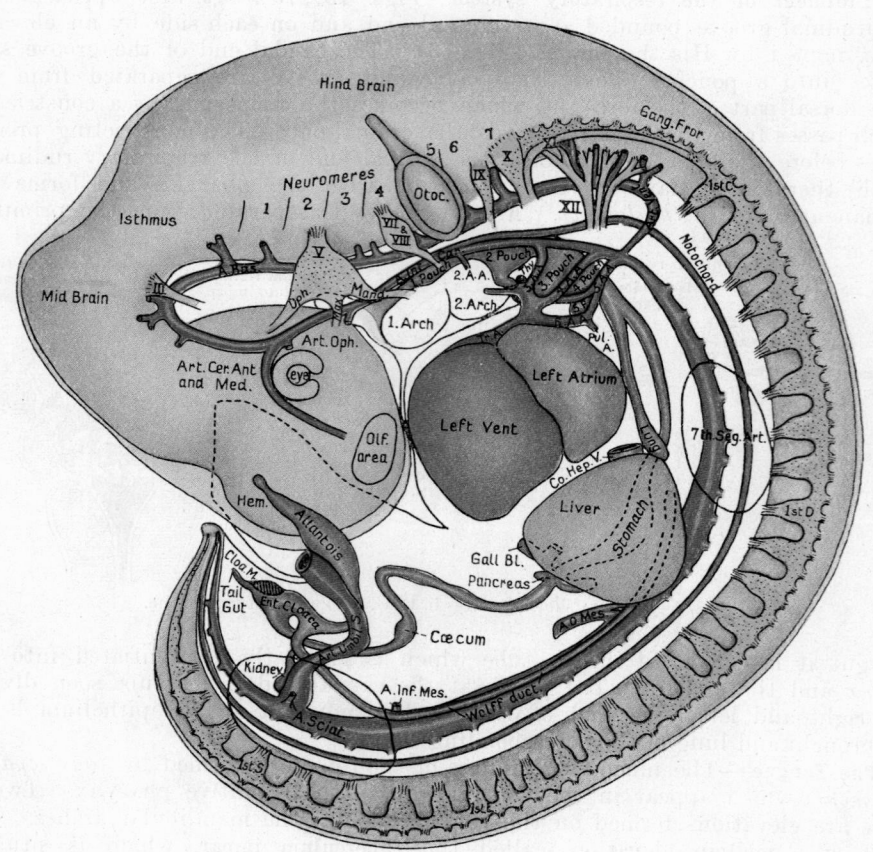

Fig. 74.—Reconstruction of Human Embryo, 7 mm. long. (Peter Thompson, *Studies in Anatomy*, University of Birmingham, 1915). Cf. Fig. 63 and subsequent figs. showing differentiation of the alimentary canal. *1st D*, 1st thoracic ganglion; *Co. Hep. V.*, Common hepatic vein; *Gang. Fror.*, Froriep's ganglion (XII); *Hem.*, cerebral hemisphere; *Wolff. duct*, mesonephric duct.

The remainder of the fore-gut is differentiated into the **stomach** and the first and second parts of the **duodenum**, and from it the liver and pancreas take origin, as outgrowths.

Liver and Pancreas.—When the embryo is about four weeks old and has attained a length of 2·5 mm. a diverticulum appears in the angle between the widely open vitello-intestinal duct and the ventral wall of the fore-gut (Fig. 63); and when the length of the embryo has increased to about 4 mm. another diverticulum is formed in the dorsal wall of the duodenal part of the fore-gut a little nearer the stomach. The ventral pouch is the rudiment of the *liver*, the *gall bladder*, the *bile-ducts*, and a portion of the *pancreas*. The remainder of the pancreas is formed from the dorsal diverticulum (Figs. 75, 76).

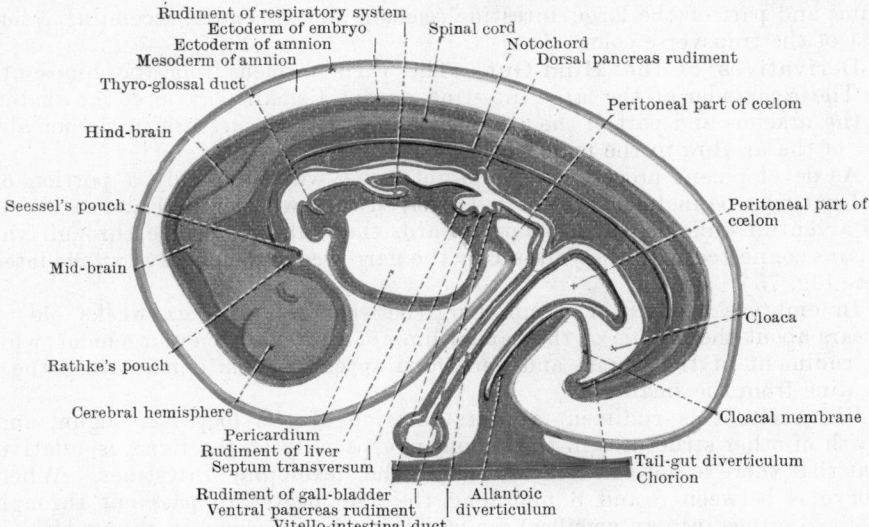

FIG. 75.—SCHEMA OF A LONGITUDINAL SECTION OF AN EMBRYO. (After Mall, modified.) Showing
dorsal and ventral diverticula of alimentary canal. The heart is not shown.

DIFFERENTIATION OF MID-GUT AND HIND-GUT

Derivatives of the Mid-Gut.—The mid-gut is that part of the primitive
alimentary tract which lies between the fore-gut and hind-gut ; it is less definitely

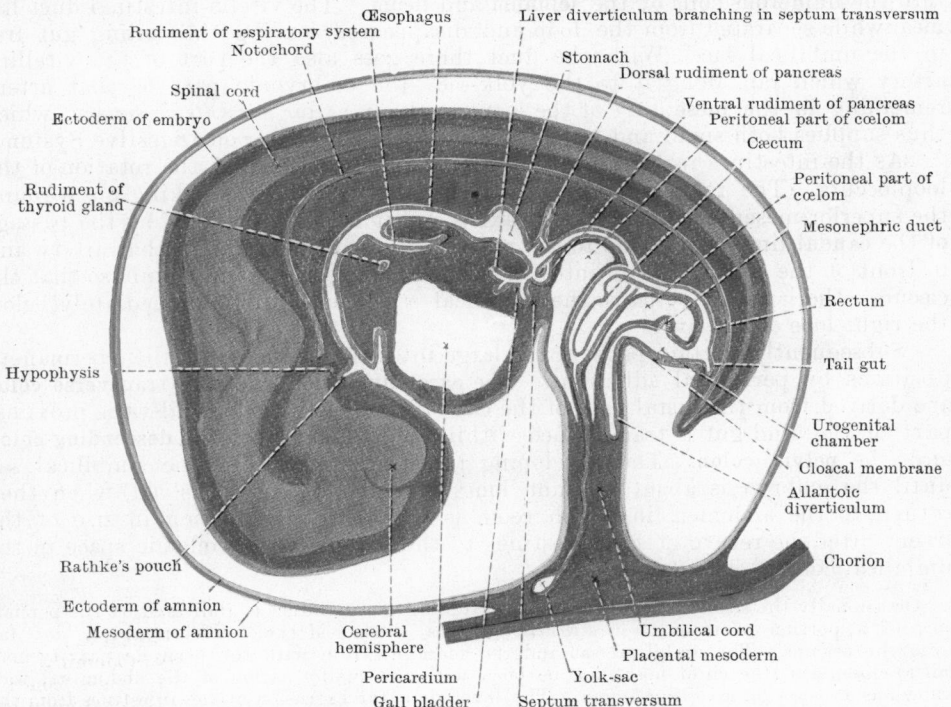

FIG. 76.—SCHEMA showing further stages in the development of the diverticula from the primitive gut and
rotation of the mid-gut loop in which the rudiment of the cæcum has appeared. The heart is not shown.
(After Mall, modified.)

enclosed than they are, as it is in free communication with the yolk-sac by the
vitello-intestinal duct. It is transformed into the greater part of the **small
ntestine** (from the entrance of the bile-duct into the duodenum to the end of the

ileum) and part of the large intestine (cæcum and appendix, ascending colon and most of the transverse colon).

Derivatives of the Hind-Gut.—The parts formed from the hind-gut are: (1) The remainder of the large intestine, except a small portion of the anal canal; (2) the urachus and part of the urinary bladder; (3) the urethra in the female, and part of the urethra in the male.

As development proceeds the mid-gut (with which possibly a portion of the hind-gut may be included) forms a U-shaped tube with cranial and caudal limbs, and a ventral knuckle which points towards the umbilical orifice, through which it remains connected with the yolk-sac by the narrowed and elongated **vitello-intestinal duct** (Fig. 75).

In embryos about 8 or 9 mm. long (between five and six weeks old) there appears about the middle of the caudal limb of the loop an enlargement which is the rudiment of the **cæcum** and **vermiform appendix**, thus demarcating the large intestine from the small.

But before this rudiment appears rotation of the loop has begun, and the growth of other structures in the abdomen, especially of the liver, is relatively so great that there is not sufficient room for the developing intestines. When the embryo is between 5 and 8 mm. long, the loop begins to pass out through the umbilical orifice into an **umbilical sac** which has been formed in the umbilical cord by the enclosure of part of the extra-embryonic coelom (Cf. Figs. 75, 76, 77,).

As it enters this sac the limbs of the loop lie already side by side—the cranial limb on the right, the caudal on the left—and there it remains for a considerable time while a further stage of its rotation and further development take place.

The chief change that now occurs is the rapid elongation of the part of the loop (mainly the cranial limb) that becomes small intestine, which is thrown into the numerous coils of the **jejunum** and **ileum**. The vitello-intestinal duct has meanwhile separated from the loop and disappeared, leaving the coiling gut free in the umbilical sac. With the duct there goes also the part of the vitelline artery which ran along it to the yolk-sac—the embryonic part of that artery remaining in the mesentery of the loop as the *superior mesenteric artery*, which thus supplies both small and large intestine (see the chapter on Digestive System).

As the intestines return into the abdomen the last stage of the rotation of the loop occurs. The rotation as a whole is usually described as taking place round the superior mesenteric artery as an axis; and it is now completed by the passage of the caudal limb of the loop to the right in front of the trunk of that artery and in front of the coils of small intestine derived from the cranial limb, so that the cæcum—the last part to leave the umbilical sac—comes to lie immediately below the right lobe of the liver.

Subsequently, certain parts of the large intestine are fixed in their permanent positions by peritoneal adhesions. The **ascending colon** and the **transverse colon** are derived from the distal part of the caudal limb of the loop, whilst the proximal part of the hind-gut is transformed within the abdomen into the **descending colon** and the **pelvic colon**. The developing intestines remain in the umbilical sac until the embryo is about 40 mm. long, and about ten weeks old, when they return to the abdomen, in which room is obtained by reduction in size of the liver; after the return of the intestines to the abdomen the cœlomic space in the umbilical cord is obliterated.

Occasionally the site of attachment of the vitello-intestinal duct is indicated by the persistence of a portion of it as a *diverticulum of the ileum* (Meckel's diverticulum) not far from the cæcum. The umbilical sac and its communication with the peritoneal cavity may fail to close; and the child may then be born with the malformation of the abdominal wall known as a *congenital umbilical hernia*. The developmental extrusion of the intestines from the abdomen of the embryo is so striking a phenomenon that it is often called the "normal umbilical hernia."

Development of the Posterior Part of the Hind-Gut.—When the hind-gut is first enclosed its blind end and its ventral wall are bounded by the caudal portion of the primitive streak, which is bent ventrally during the folding-off of the embryo.

The terminal part of this portion of the gut becomes expanded to form a chamber called the **entodermal cloaca**, into the ventral part of which the **mesonephric ducts** [ductus Wolffii] from the primitive kidneys open, one on each side.

The ventral part of the cephalic end of the cloaca is continuous with the allantoic diverticulum, and the dorsal part with that portion of the hind-gut which forms the descending colon and the pelvic colon.

As the temporary tail is formed and turned ventrally, by the growth energy of the nodal point situated at the caudal end of the neural tube, a diverticulum of the caudal end of the dorsal part of the cloaca is prolonged into it, forming the **tail gut**. This soon becomes shut off from the cloaca. It entirely disappears before the temporary tail is absorbed into the caudal end of the body (Figs. 75, 76, 77).

At a later period the cloaca itself is divided by a septum into a dorsal part,

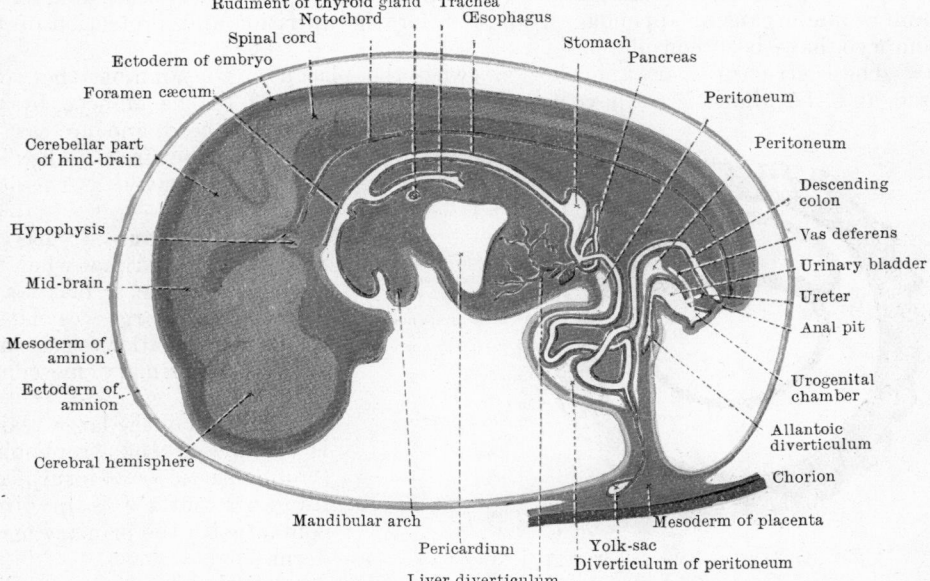

FIG. 77.—SCHEMA showing complete separation of cloaca into dorsal and ventral parts and the temporary ventral hernia of a portion of the gut through the umbilical orifice. The heart is not shown. (After Mall, modified.)

which becomes the **rectum**, and a ventral part called the **urogenital chamber**. The septum begins in the angle between the allantoic diverticulum and the ventral wall of the hind-gut, and grows downwards till it reaches and fuses with the cloacal membrane; the membrane is thus separated into urogenital and anal portions, both of which disappear about the eighth week.

In both sexes the urogenital chamber is separable into three portions: (1) a cephalic portion called the **urachus**, which becomes *the median umbilical ligament*; (2) a middle portion, which becomes the **urinary bladder**; and (3) a caudal portion, which becomes the **urethra** and the **vestibule of the vagina** in the female and part of the **urethra** in the male.

Urogenital System. — The development of the urogenital chamber and of the external genital organs is described in the account of the Urogenital System.

Derivative of the Anal Pit.—The anal pit is a surface depression which owes its origin to the elevation of the surface round the margin of the anal portion of the cloacal membrane. It forms the lowest portion of the **anal canal** of the adult.

FŒTAL MEMBRANES AND PLACENTA

Protection and Nutrition of the Embryo.—While the fertilised ovum is passing down the uterine tube, and for a brief period after it enters the uterus, it depends for its nutrition upon the yolk granules (metaplasm) embedded in its cytoplasm.

As the human ovum is small, and as it contains but little metaplasm, there is urgent necessity for an external source of nutritive supply ; that necessity leads to the early establishment of an intimate connexion between the zygote and the uterus which is one of the characteristic features of human development.

At an early stage, as the embryo is beginning to be moulded from the embryonic region, and before the paraxial mesoderm is segmented, a primitive heart and the rudiments of some well-defined blood-vessels are distinguishable in the embryo ; but the details of the establishment of the embryonic circulation cannot be well understood until the formation and structure of a group of closely associated extra-embryonic organs or appendages, adapted for the nutrition and protection of the embryo, have been considered.

These structures are the chorion (with the placenta), the amnion, the yolk-sac, and the allantois. They are all ultimately attached to the embryo by the umbilical cord, and are cast off when it is severed. They are known collectively as the *fœtal membranes.*

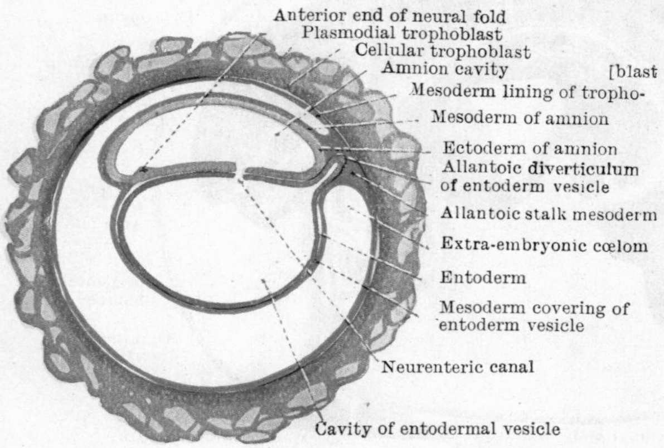

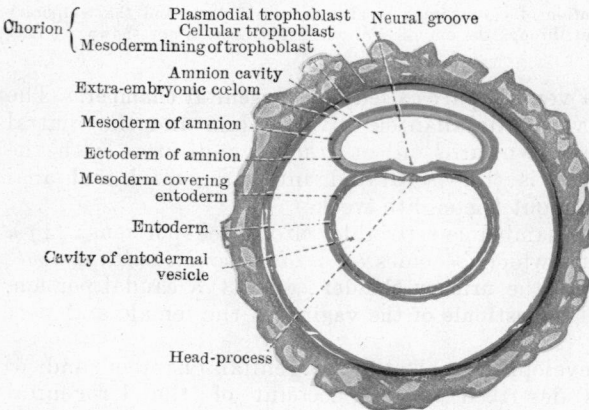

Anterior end of neural fold
Plasmodial trophoblast
Cellular trophoblast
Amnion cavity   [blast
Mesoderm lining of tropho-
Mesoderm of amnion

Ectoderm of amnion
Allantoic diverticulum of entoderm vesicle
Allantoic stalk mesoderm
Extra-embryonic cœlom
Entoderm
Mesoderm covering of entoderm vesicle

Neurenteric canal

Cavity of entodermal vesicle

Fig. 78.—Schema of Sagittal Section of Zygote along Line A in Fig. 44.

Chorion { Plasmodial trophoblast   Neural groove
Cellular trophoblast
Mesoderm lining of trophoblast

Amnion cavity
Extra-embryonic cœlom

Mesoderm of amnion

Ectoderm of amnion

Mesoderm covering entoderm

Entoderm

Cavity of entodermal vesicle

Head-process

Fig. 79.—Schema of Transverse Section of Zygote along Line B in Fig. 44.

The Chorion.—It has already been noted that when the zygote becomes a blastula it consists of a large vesicle enclosing two smaller vesicles and a mass of primary mesoderm (Fig. 39).

The wall of the large vesicle is composed of trophoblast (trophoblastic ectoderm), and its inner surface is in direct contact with the primary mesoderm.

A little later a cavity, called the **extra-embryonic cœlom**, appears in the primary mesoderm and separates it into two layers—one lining the inner surface of the trophoblast and the other covering the outer surfaces of the two inner vesicles (Figs. 78, 79).

As soon as the extra-embryonic cœlom is established the **chorion** is formed ; it consists of the trophoblast and its lining of mesoderm.

In the meantime the trophoblast has differentiated into two layers—an inner cellular layer, and an outer syncytial or plasmodial layer. In the plasmodial layer cell territories are not defined, and it consists therefore of multi-nucleated protoplasm. The differentiation of the trophoblast into two layers occurs after the ovum is embedded in the mucous coat of the uterus, which after modification for its reception is called the **decidua.**

As development proceeds, the trophoblast increases in thickness and invades the decidua. As this invasion occurs the plasmodial layer of the trophoblast becomes permeated with spaces which are continuous with the lumina of the maternal blood-vessels in the decidua, and are therefore filled with maternal blood. These blood-filled spaces divide the plasmodial trophoblast into branching, processes which separate the spaces from one another. The processes are the **primary chorionic villi**, and their central parts soon become cellular (Fig. 80).

After a time the primary villi are invaded by the chorionic mesoderm, and are thus converted into the **secondary chorionic villi**, which become vascularised by the growth of fœtal vessels into their mesodermal cores. The secondary villi consist, therefore, of a mesodermal core, continuous with the mesoderm of the chorion and covered by a layer of cellular trophoblast (*Langhan's layer*) and a layer of plasmodium. Still later the secondary villi send out numerous branches into the blood spaces, and thus increase greatly in complexity (Figs. 84, 85, 86).

As development progresses still further a part of the chorion is converted into the fœtal portion of an organ called the **placenta** (from its flat, cake-like form

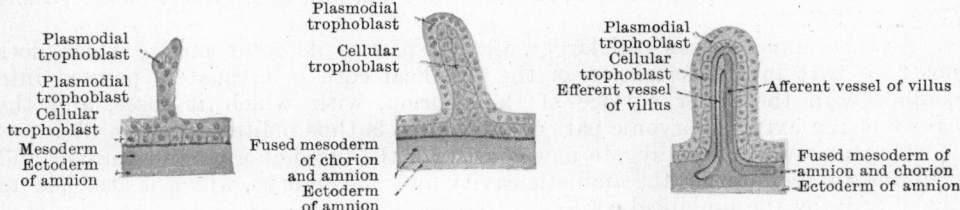

FIG. 80.—SCHEMA OF THREE STAGES IN THE FORMATION OF A CHORIONIC VILLUS.

when fully developed), and thus the chorion is divided into placental and non-placental regions. On the placental part the villi continue to increase, but they disappear entirely from the non-placental part, which remains smooth and is therefore called the **chorion læve** (Fig. 86).

The Amnion, the Body-Stalk, and the Umbilical Cord.—The **amnion** is formed from that portion of the wall of the ectodermal or amnio-embryonic vesicle (p. 31) which does not take part in the formation of the embryo. It consists of ectoderm cells covered externally by a layer of extra-embryonic mesoderm, and it is continuous with the margin of the embryonic area (Figs. 78, 79).

The cavity of the ectodermal vesicle, enclosed between the amnion and the embryonic area, is the **amnion cavity**; it is filled with fluid which raises the amnion in the form of a cupola over the embryonic region (Fig. 78).

Body-Stalk.—It has been noted already that the mesoderm of the median part of the caudal portion of the amnion becomes thickened. In the thickened strand lies the allantoic diverticulum of the entodermal vesicle (Fig. 78), whilst through it, on each side of the allantoic diverticulum, pass the umbilical arteries and veins, by means of which blood is conveyed between the embryo and the chorion. It is important to note that the blood-vessels which thus pass through the body-stalk enter or leave the body of the embryo through the umbilical orifice, which is, at first, a relatively large aperture (Fig. 60).

As the embryonic area is folded into the form of the embryo the amnion increases in extent, filling more and

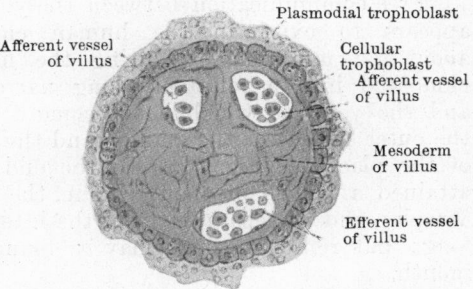

FIG. 81.—SCHEMA OF A TRANSVERSE SECTION OF A SECONDARY CHORIONIC VILLUS. A loop of the afferent vessel has been cut at two points.

more of the extra-embryonic cœlom, and the embryo rises into its cavity. In other words, the walls of the amnion bulge ventrally round the ends and the lateral borders of the embryo (Figs. 60, 61, 85). As the distension of the amnion still continues, the ventral bulging round the margin of the umbilical orifice becomes more pronounced, the yolk-sac is forced farther and farther away from the embryo, the vitello-intestinal duct is elongated and it is surrounded by a tube of mesoderm. The cavity of the tube is an elongated part of the extra-embryonic cœlom, and its walls are covered by the amnion (Figs. 75, 76, 77). The caudal wall of the tube necessarily consists of the elongated allantoic stalk.

Umbilical Cord.—As the distension of the amnion still continues, the walls of the tube are forced against the vitello-intestinal duct, and the amniotic mesoderm fuses with the mesoderm surrounding the duct. When the fusion is completed, a solid cord—the **umbilical cord**—is formed (Figs. 86, 87, 89). It consists of an external covering of amniotic ectoderm, and a core of mesoderm in which lie the two umbilical arteries, a single umbilical vein formed by the fusion of the two primitive umbilical veins, and the remains of the vitello-intestinal duct and the vitelline vessels. One end of the umbilical cord is connected with the embryo; the other end is attached to the chorion. Near this attachment, in the mesoderm of the chorion, lies the yolk-sac, now a relatively small vesicle (Figs. 76, 86).

As the amnion grows still larger, all that part of its outer surface which does not take part in the formation of the umbilical cord is ultimately pressed into contact with the inner surface of the chorion, with which it fuses, and the cavity of the extra-embryonic part of the cœlom is thus obliterated (Fig. 87).

The outer wall of the zygote now consists of the fused chorion and amnion, and contains in its interior the amniotic cavity and the embryo, which is attached to the chorion by the umbilical cord.

When the umbilical cord is first formed it is comparatively short, but as the amniotic cavity increases the cord elongates, until it attains a length of from 18 to 20 inches (45 to 50 cm.); it then allows the embryo to float freely in the fluid in the amniotic cavity, whilst its nutrition is provided for by the flow and return of blood, through the umbilical cord, to and from the placenta, where interchanges take place between the maternal and the fœtal blood.

The Yolk-Sac or Umbilical Vesicle.—When the embryonic area is folded into the form of the embryo, the entodermal vesicle is differentiated into three parts: (1) a part enclosed in the embryo, where it forms the **primitive entodermal alimentary canal**; (2) a part which lies external to the embryo in the extra-embryonic cœlom—this is the **yolk-sac** or **umbilical vesicle**; (3) the third portion is the **vitello-intestinal duct**, which connects the primitive alimentary canal and the yolk-sac together (Figs. 63, 75, 76).

The cavity of the yolk-sac is therefore in free communication with that of the alimentary canal, and their walls are continuous with each other and identical in structure, each consisting of an internal layer of entodermal cells and an external layer of mesoderm.

Free communication between the yolk-sac and the primitive alimentary canal appears to exist in the human embryo until it is four weeks old and about 2·5 mm. long. During the fifth week the vitello-intestinal duct is elongated into a relatively long narrow tube, lodged in the umbilical cord, and the yolk-sac, which has become a relatively small vesicle, is placed between the outer surface of the amnion and the inner surface of the chorion, in the region of the placenta (Fig. 76). By the end of the fifth week, when the embryo has attained a length of about 5 mm., the vitello-intestinal duct begins to undergo atrophy, and it separates from the intestine when the embryo is about 11 mm. long; but remnants of it may be found in the umbilical cord up to the third month.

The yolk-sac itself persists until birth, when it may be found as a minute object lying between the amnion and the placenta near the end of the umbilical cord.

At a very early period, before the paraxial mesoderm has commenced to divide into mesodermal somites, a number of **primitive vitelline arteries** are distributed to the yolk-sac from the primitive aortæ of the embryo, and the blood is returned from the yolk-sac to the embryo by a pair of **vitelline veins** (Fig. 91).

After a time the arteries are reduced to a single pair, and after the two primitive dorsal aortæ have fused into a single trunk, the pair of vitelline arteries also become converted into a single trunk, which passes through the umbilical orifice along the vitello-intestinal duct to the yolk-sac (Fig. 93).

The vitelline veins also pass through the umbilical orifice on their way to the heart of the embryo, and they become connected together, in the interior of the body of the embryo, by transverse anastomoses which are described in the account of the development of the Vascular System.

After the umbilical cord is formed, the extra-embryonic parts of the vitelline veins disappear, and can no longer be traced in the cord. The same fate overtakes the vitelline artery—all except the portion of its intra-embryonic part which persists as the *superior mesenteric artery*.

The Placenta.—The placenta is an organ developed for the purpose of providing the fœtus with food and oxygen, and removing the effete products produced by the metabolic processes which take place in the growing organism. It is formed partly from the chorion and partly from the decidua, which is the altered mucous coat of the uterus of the mother.

In the placenta the blood-vessels of the fœtus and the blood of the mother are brought into close relation, so that free interchanges may readily take place between the two blood streams; but the blood of the fœtus and the blood of the mother are always separated from each other by two or more layers of fœtal cells. The changes in the decidua and in the chorion, by which this intimate relation is attained, constitute the phenomena of the development of the placenta.

The details of the development of the human ovum for the first ten or twelve days after its fertilisation are not known. But the knowledge of what happens in other mammals justifies the belief that fertilisation takes place in the lateral part of the uterine tube, and that during the next ten to fourteen days the zygote passes along the tube towards the uterus, while undergoing the divisions which convert it into a morula.[1]

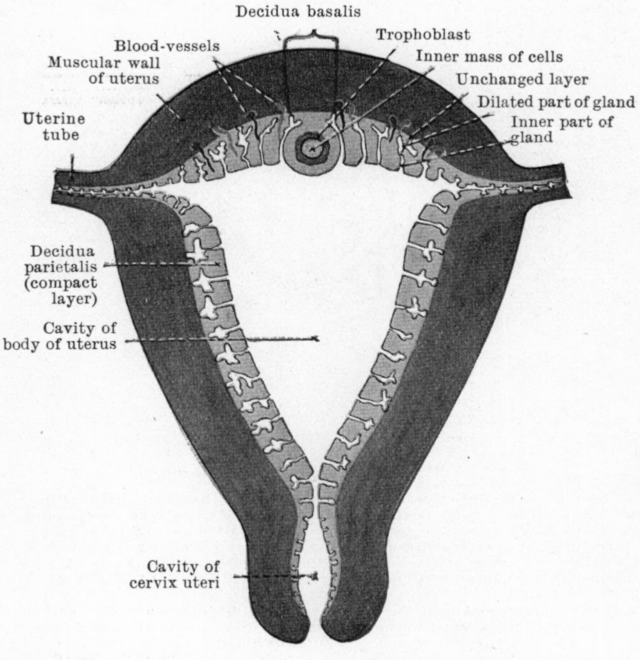

Formation of the Placenta. — The uterine mucous coat undergoes changes in preparation

FIG. 82.—SCHEMA OF A CORONAL SECTION OF THE UTERUS, showing the various parts of the decidua and a zygote embedded in it.

for the reception and retention of the zygote, and when the changes are completed the modified coat is known as the **uterine decidua.**

The changes which take place are, for the most part, hypertrophic in character. The vascularity of the mucous coat is increased, mainly by the dilatation of its capillaries. The tubular glands are elongated; they become tortuous, and dilatations form in their walls a short distance from their outer, closed extremities. At the same time the interglandular tissue increases in amount. As a result of

[1] This is an estimate, for there is no certain knowledge, and it is possible that the passage through the uterine tube is completed in seven or eight days or less.

5 a

the various changes the decidua is thicker, softer, more spongy, and more vascular than the mucous coat from which it was evolved.

Partly on account of the dilatation of the deep part of the glands and partly on account of differences in texture of the internal and the external part of the decidua, the membrane may be looked upon as consisting of three layers: (1) An internal layer, next the cavity, called the **stratum compactum.** (2) An intermediate layer—the **stratum spongiosum**—formed largely by the dilated parts of the glands. (3) An external **unchanged layer,** in which the comparatively unaltered outer ends of the glands lie.

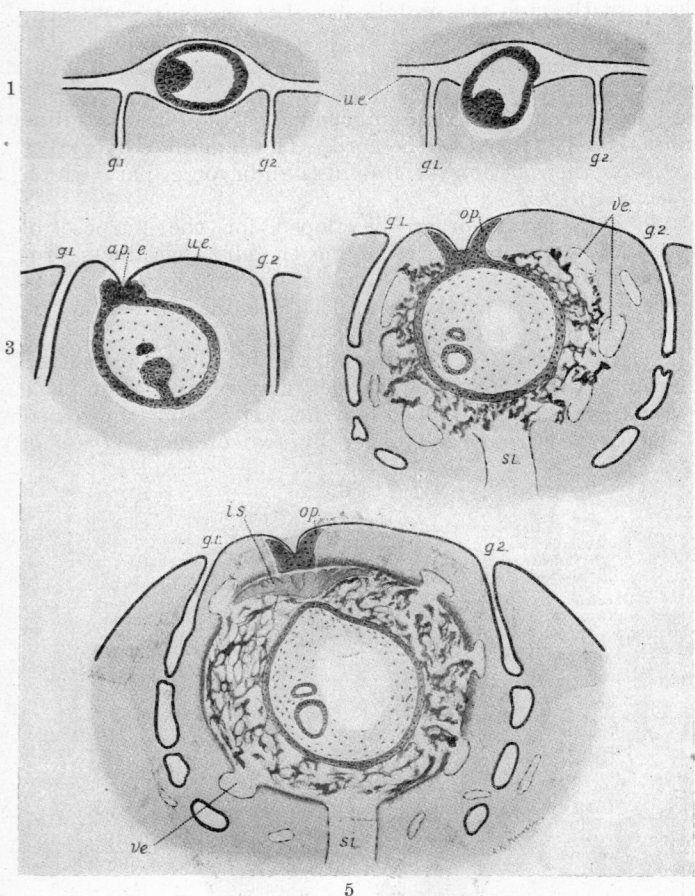

FIG. 83.—DIAGRAMS ILLUSTRATING THE IMPLANTATION OF THE HUMAN OVUM. (J. H. Teacher. *Journ. Obst. and Gyn.*, 1924).

1. Ovum free in uterine cavity. 2. Ovum passing through uterine epithelium into decidua. 3. About 24 hours after implantation; the trophoblast is spreading under the epithelium to form the operculum. 4. About 48 hours after implantation; the operculum has grown, is still continuous with the trophoblast and is attached to the epithelium. 5. Stage of Teacher-Bryce I embryo, about 72 hours after implantation; the operculum is detached from the trophoblast and separated from it by a mass of fibrin (cf. Fig. 36).

These diagrams also illustrate the progressive differentiation of the ovum, and the relation of the trophoblast to the implantation cavity and the uterine vessels.

ap.e., aperture of entrance; *g.l., g.2.,* uterine glands; *i.s.,* internal shield of fibrin; *op.,* operculum; *si.,* venous sinus; *u.e.,* uterine epithelium; *v.e.,* small vessels at periphery of implantation cavity.

When the zygote, in the morula stage, reaches the uterus, it acts as a parasite: it eats its way through the epithelium on the surface of the decidua, and implants itself in the stratum compactum. It may penetrate the decidua at any point of the wall of the uterine cavity; but it usually enters at some point of the dorsal or the ventral wall, and, pushing the glands aside, it becomes at once surrounded by the interglandular tissue of the stratum compactum of the decidua. The aperture through which it passes is closed by proliferation of a portion of the trophoblast which acts as a sealing plug—the *operculum* (J. H. Teacher [1]) (Fig. 83).

The portion of the decidua in which the zygote is embedded is thicker than the other parts of the membrane, and it is separated by the zygote into an internal part, called the **decidua capsularis,** and an external part—the **decidua basalis.** The remainder of the decidua, by far the larger portion, is the **decidua parietalis.**

As soon as the zygote becomes embedded in the decidua its trophoblast undergoes rapid proliferation. The superficial part of the growing trophoblast becomes

[1] "On the Implantation of the Human Ovum and the Early Development of the Trophoblast," *Journ. Obst. and Gyn. Brit. Emp.*, 1924.

converted into a mass of nucleated protoplasm—the plasmodial or syncytial layer—but the inner part remains more or less distinctly cellular.

The plasmodial portion of the trophoblast invades and destroys the surrounding decidual tissue, and at the same time spaces appear in its substance. As the plasmodium destroys the walls of the dilated maternal blood-vessels, channels are made through which the maternal blood flows into the spaces in the plasmodium and thus maternal blood begins to circulate in the trophoblast of the zygote.

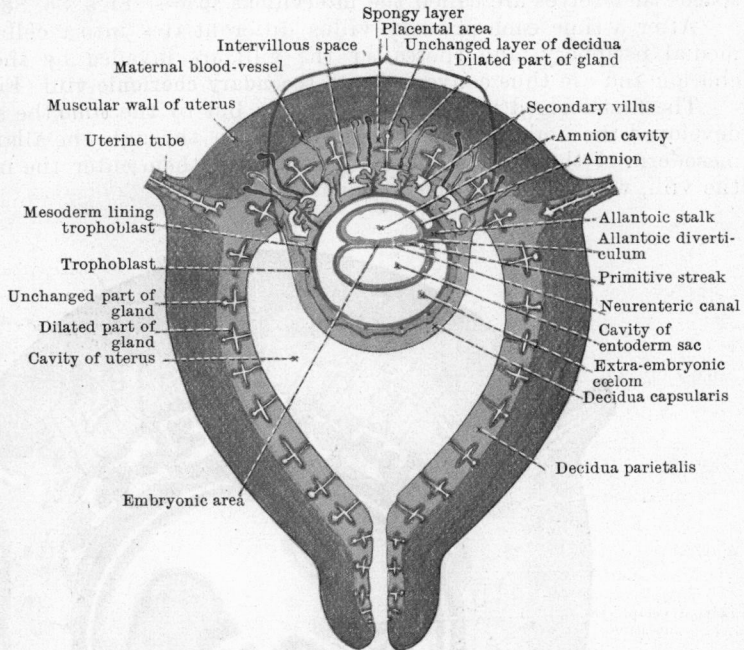

Fig. 84.—Schema of a Coronal Section of a Pregnant Uterus after the formation of the Intervillous Spaces.

In the meantime the extra-embryonic cœlom has appeared in the primary mesoderm of the zygote, and the outer layer of the mesoderm has associated itself with the trophoblast to form the chorion (see p. 64).

The spaces in the plasmodium enlarge rapidly after the maternal blood begins to circulate within them, and the plasmodium becomes divided into three series of parts: (1) The **primary chorionic villi**, which lie between adjacent blood spaces; (2) The parts which lie in contact with the mesoderm of the chorion, and form, with the mesoderm, the **chorion plate**; (3) The **basal layer**, composed of parts which cover the

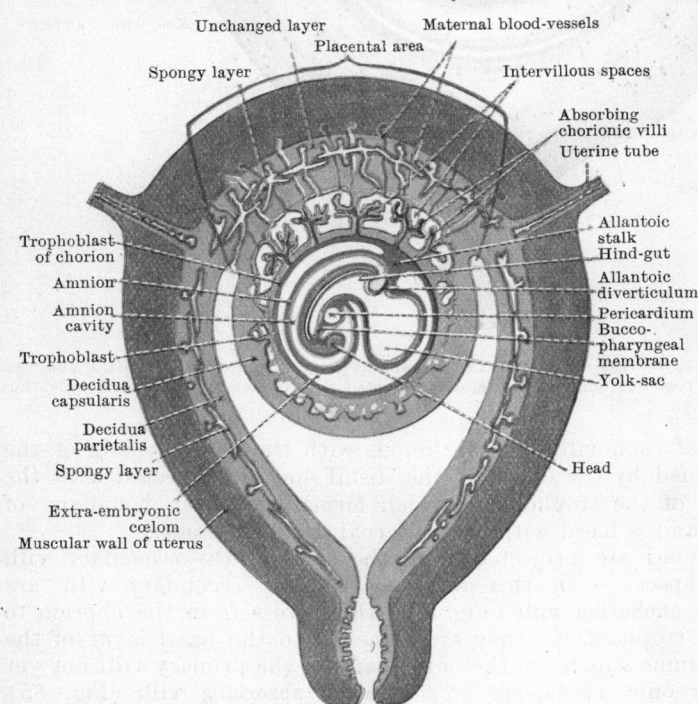

Fig. 85.—Schema of a Coronal Section of a Pregnant Uterus at the period of the Formation of the Embryo. Note extension of amnion as contrasted with stage shown in Fig. 84.

maternal tissues and form the outer boundaries of the blood spaces. The blood spaces themselves are called the **intervillous spaces** (Figs. 86, 88).

After a time each primary villus differentiates into a cellular core and plasmodial periphery, and thereafter the villi are invaded by the mesoderm of the chorion and are thus converted into **secondary chorionic villi** (Fig. 86).

The first-formed villi are non-vascular, but by the time the secondary villi have developed the umbilical arteries have grown through the allantoic stalk into the mesoderm of the chorion, and branches from them enter the mesodermal cores of the villi, which thus become vascular.

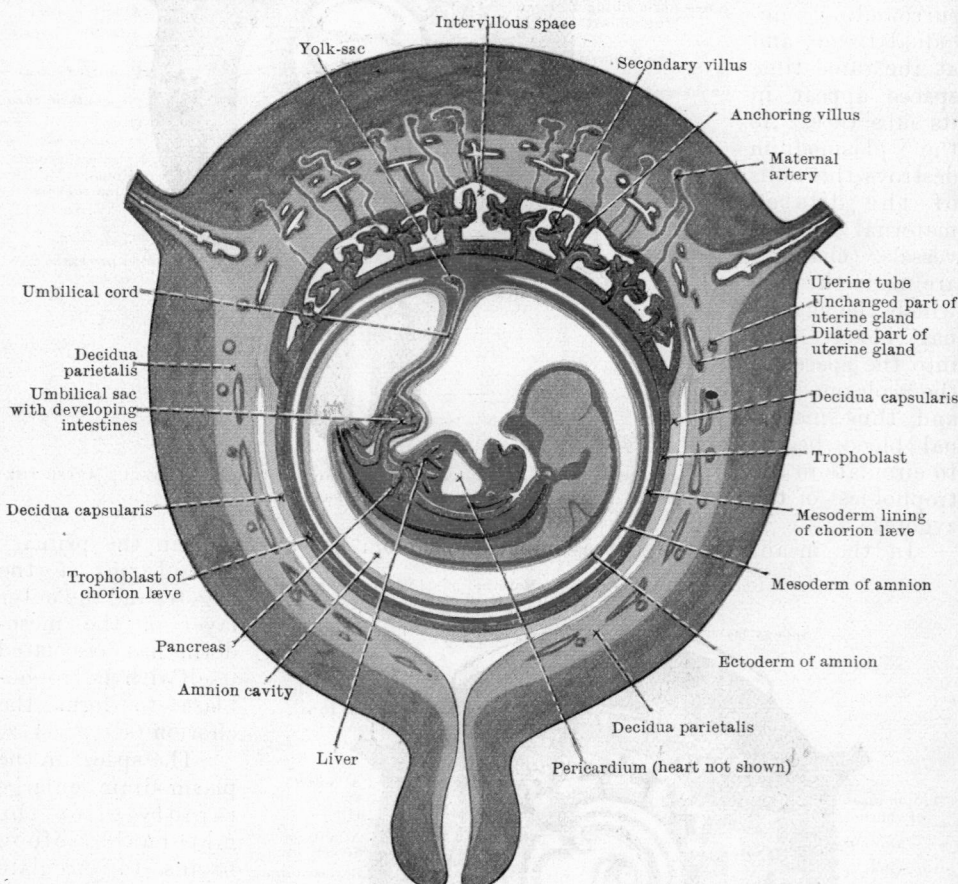

Fig. 86.—Schema of a Coronal Section of a Pregnant Uterus after the Formation of the Umbilical Cord. Note that the expanding amnion has almost obliterated the extra-embryonic cœlom which lies between it and the chorion.

The proximal end of each villus is continuous with the chorion plate of the intervillous spaces, formed by the chorion; the distal end is connected with the plasmodial basal layer of the trophoblast, which forms the outer boundary of the intervillous spaces and is fused with the maternal decidual tissue.

After a time branches are projected from the sides of the secondary villi into the intervillous spaces. In this way two sets of secondary villi are differentiated: (1) The **anchoring villi** (Fig. 88), which cross from the chorion to the basal layer of the trophoblast—they are attached to the basal layer of the trophoblast by cell columns which are the outer parts of the primary villi not yet invaded by the embryonic mesoderm; (2) **Free** or **absorbing villi** (Fig. 85), which extend from the sides of the original secondary villi into the blood in the intervillous spaces.

While the trophoblastic invasion of the compact layer of the decidua is proceeding, not only are the interglandular elements of the decidua destroyed, but the walls of the glands also; as a consequence, some of the glands in the decidua basalis open for a time into the intervillous spaces, and become filled with blood which passes from the spaces into the gland cavities. Frequently, however, before the glands are destroyed, their walls are converted into solid strands of cells, and thus the cavities of their more external undestroyed portions may become closed spaces.

In the early stages the whole trophoblast is differentiated in a similar manner, and thus, for a time, the whole of the surface of the chorion is covered with villi. As the embryo grows, and the amnion and the extra-embryonic cœlom are distended, the zygote increases in size, and the capsular portion of the decidua is stretched till its vascular supply is interfered with and the villi associated

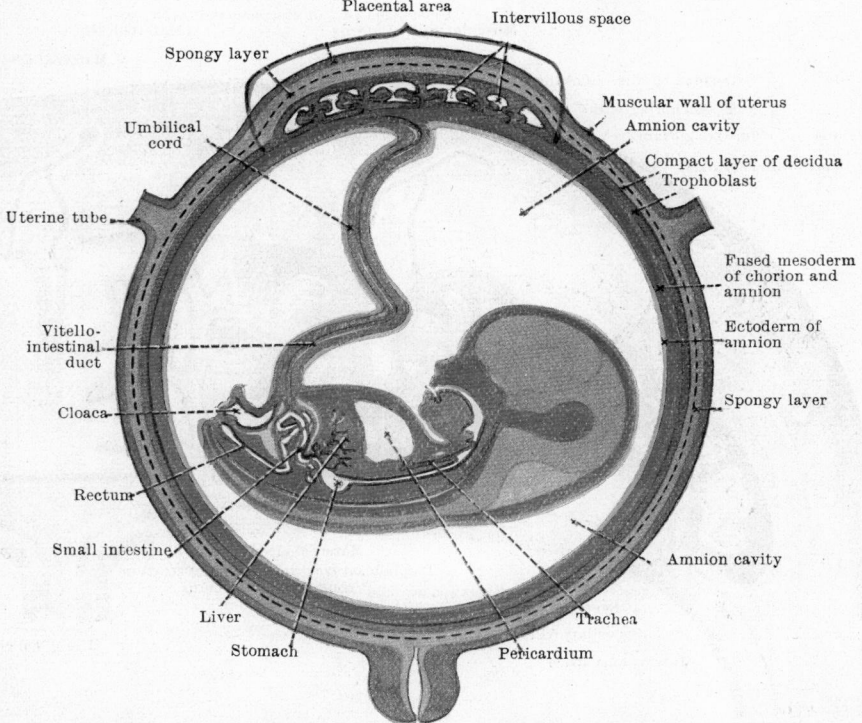

FIG. 87.—SCHEMA OF A SECTION OF A PREGNANT UTERUS AFTER FUSION OF AMNION AND CHORION.

with it undergo atrophy and disappear. When these degenerative changes have occurred, the portion of the chorion in association with the thinned decidua capsularis presents a relatively smooth surface, and is known as the **chorion læve**. In the meantime the decidua basalis increases in thickness, and the villi associated with it increase in size and in the complexity of their branches. The portion of the chorion from which these large villi spring is termed the **chorion frondosum**. It is this portion of the chorion which takes part in the formation of the **fœtal portion** of the placenta, the **maternal (uterine) part** of that organ being formed by the decidua basalis.

The placenta, therefore, is formed partly by the zygote and partly by maternal tissues, but the interchanges between the fœtal and the maternal blood take place in the substance of the zygote through the trophoblast which covers the surfaces of the villi.

As the growth of the embryo and the distension of the amnion continue, the amnion is gradually forced against the chorion and fuses with it. When fusion is complete the extra-embryonic cœlom is obliterated and the zygote contains only one extra-embryonic cavity—the amniotic cavity—which contains the fœtus surrounded and supported by the amnion fluid (Fig. 87).

At this period the amnion cavity is bounded by a wall composed of the fused amnion, chorion, and decidua.   In the meantime the chorion has differentiated into the chorion læve, fused with the decidua capsularis, and the chorion frondosum, fused with the decidua basalis.   As the distension of the amnion proceeds to a still greater extent, the part of the wall of the cavity formed by the fused amnion, chorion, læve, and the decidua capsularis bulges more and more into the cavity of the uterus, until it is forced against the surrounding wall of the uterine cavity, where it fuses with the decidua parietalis, and thus the cavity of the uterus is obliterated.   This fusion takes place towards the end of the second month, and as soon as it has occurred the discoid mass of placental tissue is continuous at its margin with the fused amnion, chorion, and decidua parietalis (Fig. 87).

After the second month the fœtus lies in the *amnion cavity*, which is bounded by

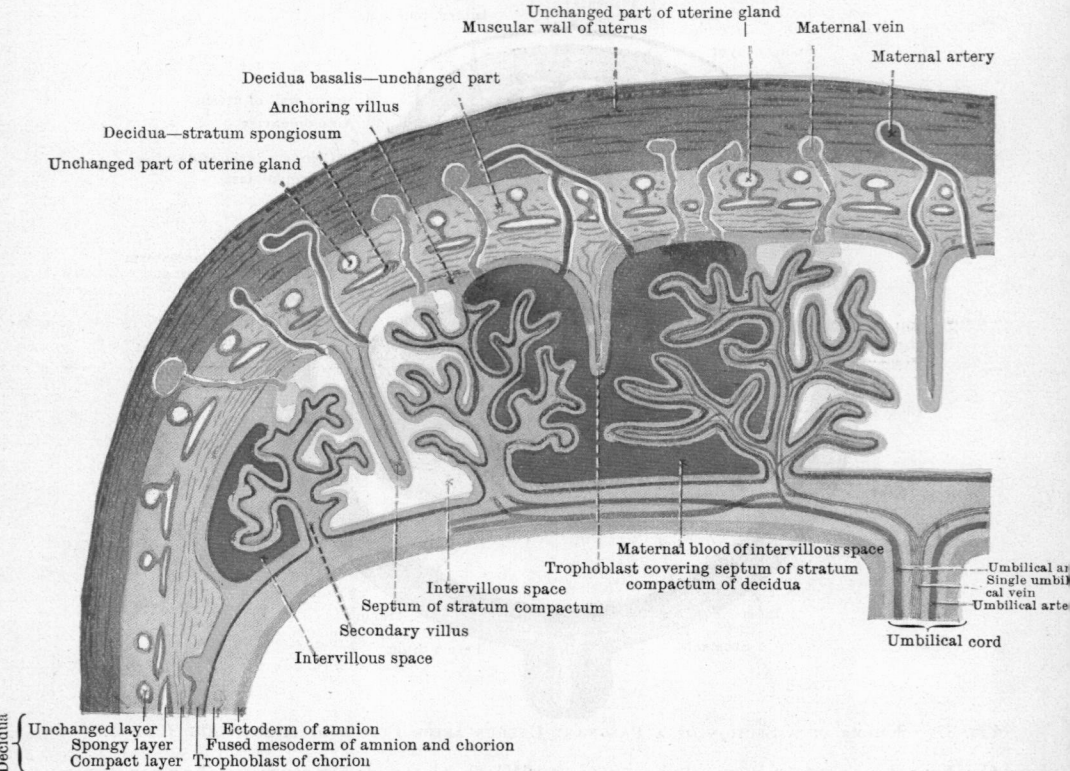

FIG. 88.—SCHEMA OF STRUCTURE OF COMPLETED PLACENTA.

the fused chorion and uterine wall, except at the lower end of the uterus, over the internal os uteri, where the cavity of the body of the uterus communicates with the canal of the cervix ; there the amniotic cavity is bounded by a membrane formed by the fused amnion, chorion læve, and the decidua capsularis only.

Completion of the Placenta.—It has already been stated that each absorbing villus consists of a vascular mesodermal core covered by a cellular and a plasmodial layer of trophoblast, the latter lying next the maternal blood in the intervillous spaces.   As development proceeds and the intervillous spaces become larger, the villi become longer and more complicated, and at the same time the cellular layer of the trophoblast largely disappears, until in the majority of the villi the plasmodial layer alone covers the vascular mesodermal core.

In still later stages, degeneration occurs not only in the villi, but also in the chorionic plate of the intervillous spaces and in the basal trophoblast which closes the spaces externally.   One of the results of the degenerative processes is the deposit of fibrinoid material in the place originally occupied by the trophoblast ; the fibrinous layers on the surfaces of adjacent villi adhere together, and the villi thus connected fuse into masses of intermingled fibrinous and vascular tissue.

When the fœtal (chorionic) part of the placenta is completed it consists of : (1) the chorion plate closing the intervillous spaces internally ; (2) the villi ; (3) the intervillous spaces ; and (4) the basal layer of the trophoblast, which closes the intervillous spaces externally, and is perforated by the maternal vessels passing to and from the spaces.

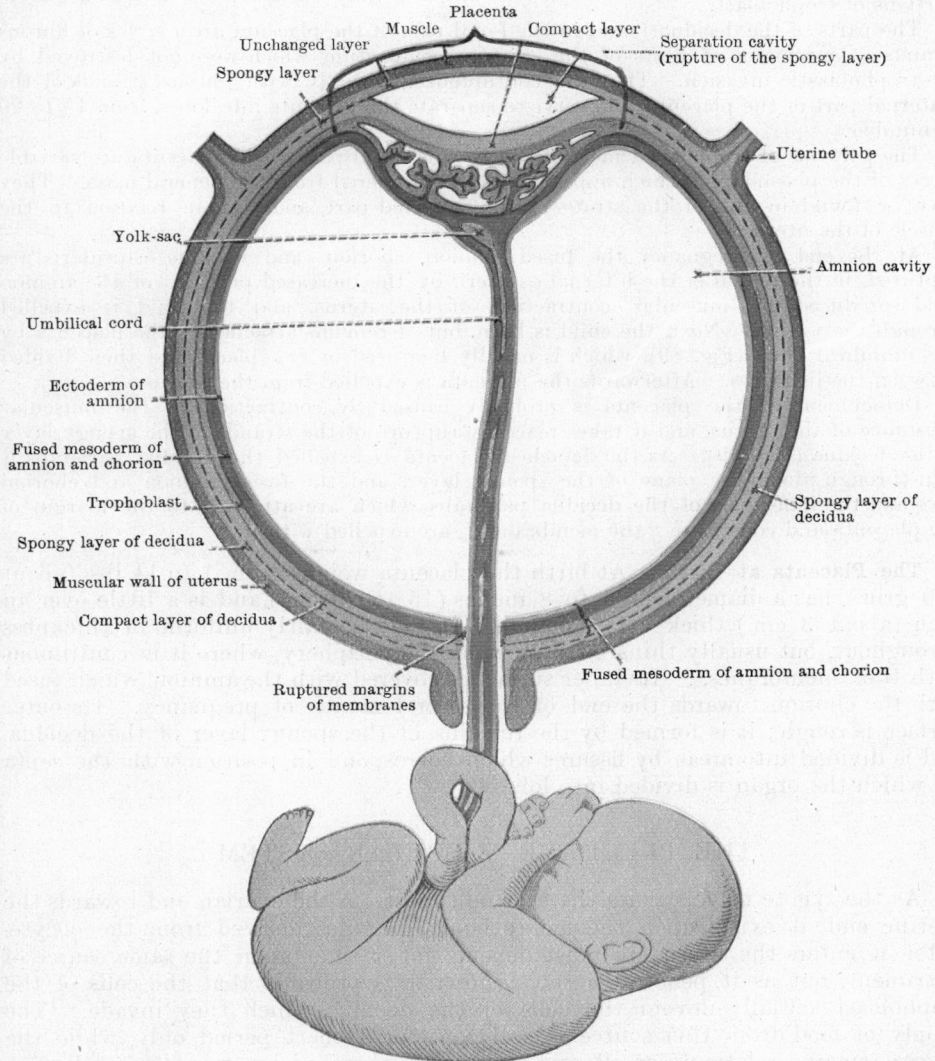

FIG. 89.—SCHEMA OF PREGNANT UTERUS IMMEDIATELY AFTER BIRTH OF THE CHILD, showing commencing separation of the placenta. Part of the umbilical cord is shown in section and part in surface view. The blue streaks in the former part indicate the position occupied by the vitello-intestinal duct in earlier stages.

The maternal (uterine) portion of the completed placenta consists from within out-wards of : (1) the basal layer of the decidua ; (2) the remains of the spongy layer of the decidua ; and (3) the unchanged layer.

The basal layer of the decidua is the remains of the compact part of the decidua basalis of earlier stages. It is fused internally with the basal plate of the trophoblast, and is continuous externally with the spongy layer. The spongy layer contains a series of cleft-like spaces. These spaces are cavities of the compressed remains of the earlier dilated portions of the glands of the stratum spongiosum, from which the epithelial lining has, to a great extent, disappeared. The spongy layer is continuous externally with the unchanged layer, in which the unaltered outer parts of the glands and the intervening interglandular tissue lie.

The maternal blood-vessels pass from the muscular wall of the uterus directly into the placenta, where they traverse the maternal portion and the basal plate of the trophoblast and open into the intervillous spaces. The arteries usually open on or near the septa and the veins begin in the intermediate areas.

In addition, however, to the constituent parts already described, the fœtal part of the placenta contains some strands of maternal tissue, and in the maternal part there are portions of trophoblast.

The parts of the decidua found in the fœtal part of the placenta are a series of fibrous strands—the remains of parts of the stratum compactum which were not destroyed by the trophoblastic invasion. They are continuous externally with fibrous strands of the maternal part of the placenta, and serve to separate the placenta into lobes, from 15 to 20 in number.

The portions of trophoblast met with in the maternal part of the placenta are variable pieces of the plasmodium which appear to have wandered from the general mass. They may be found in any of the strata of the maternal part, and even in relation to the muscle of the uterus.

At the end of pregnancy the fused amnion, chorion, and decidua capsularis are ruptured, in the region of the internal os uteri, by the increased pressure of the amnion fluid produced by muscular contraction of the uterus, and the fluid is expelled through the vagina. Next, the child is born, but it remains attached to the placenta by the umbilical cord (Fig. 89), which is usually ligatured in two places and then divided between the ligatures. Afterwards the placenta is expelled from the uterus.

Detachment of the placenta is probably caused by contraction of the muscular substance of the uterus, and it takes place by rupture of the strands of the spongy layer of the decidua (Fig. 89). As the detached placenta is expelled the decidua parietalis is torn through along the plane of the spongy layer, and the fused amnion and chorion læve and the inner part of the decidua parietalis, which are attached to the margin of the placenta and constitute "the membranes", are expelled with it.

The Placenta at Birth.—At birth the placenta weighs from 1 to $1\frac{1}{2}$ lbs. (about 500 grm.), has a diameter of 6 to 8 inches (15 to 20 cm.) and is a little over an inch (about 3 cm.) thick at its centre. It may be fairly uniform in thickness throughout, but usually thins off rapidly at the periphery, where it is continuous with the "membranes." Its inner surface is covered with the amnion, which fused with the chorion towards the end of the second month of pregnancy. Its outer surface is rough; it is formed by the remains of the spongy layer of the decidua, and is divided into areas by fissures which correspond in position with the septa by which the organ is divided into lobes.

THE PRIMITIVE VASCULAR SYSTEM

As the zygote travels along the uterine tube, from the ovarian end towards the uterine end, it exists upon the metaplasmic granules derived from the oocyte. After it enters the uterus it must depend, for a time, upon the same source of nutriment, but as it penetrates the decidua it is probable that the cells of the trophoblast actually devour the cells of the decidua which they invade. The supply of food from this source is sufficient for a short period only, while the zygote remains relatively small, and substances absorbed by its surface cells can be transmitted easily to all parts.

During this period, moreover, not only are the decidual tissues utilised as a food-supply, but fluids are absorbed from them and transmitted into the interior of the zygote to fill the expanding cavities of the amnion and the cœlom.

In all probability the fluids passed into the zygote contain nutritive materials which suffice for the requirements of the embryonic and non-embryonic parts of the zygote so long as both consist of comparatively thin layers of cells. But when the embryonic area increases in thickness, and begins to be moulded into the embryo, its association with adjacent fluids becomes less intimate, and as the development of its various parts progresses, the supply of food and oxygen required is greater than can be provided by osmosis from the adjacent fluid media. An imperative necessity thus arises for a method of food-supply adequate to the increasing requirements of continued development and growth.

To meet this necessity the **blood vascular system** is formed. The system is essentially an irrigation system. In its earliest stages it consists of a series of vessels in which the blood is kept circulating by the rhythmical contraction of the walls of the vessels; but, after a short time, parts of the vessels undergo changes which result in the formation of the **heart**. After the heart is established the continuance of the circulation of the blood depends upon the regular contractions of the muscular substance of its walls.

The corpuscular portions of the blood and the walls of the blood-vessels are formed from the cells of the zygote, but it is obvious that in the early stages at all events, the fluid portion of the blood must be obtained from the mother. It is necessary, therefore, both for this purpose and for the facilitation of interchanges between the fœtal and maternal blood streams, that the fœtal blood-vessels should be brought into close association with the maternal blood at an early period. This is accomplished by the appearance in the trophoblast of large spaces which become filled with blood from maternal vessels opened up by the destructive action of the trophoblast cells (p. 69); and by the subsequent invasion of these spaces by the chorionic villi, which contain branches of the blood-vessels of the embryo (Fig. 86). As soon as the intimate relationship between the chorionic villi and the maternal blood is established, fluids can readily pass from the maternal to the fœtal vessels; there can be no doubt that both food and oxygen pass from the maternal to the fœtal blood through and by the agency of the trophoblastic epithelium, whilst at the same time waste products of fœtal metabolism are passed from the fœtal to the maternal blood.

Germs of the Vascular System. — It has already been noted that the **mesenchyme cells** (which are probably derived from the paraxial mesoderm and the lateral plates) give rise to blood vessels and the cells of the blood. The development of the blood vessels takes place first in the wall of the yolk-sac and in the body stalk, but it occurs later in the mesenchyme of the embryo also.

On the wall of the yolk-sac the mesenchyme cells which are the rudiments of the blood vascular system become definitely spherical and their nuclei become relatively large; at the same time they are aggregated together into rounded patches called **blood islands** (Figs. 90, 101). As soon as the cells have attained their distinctive appearance they are

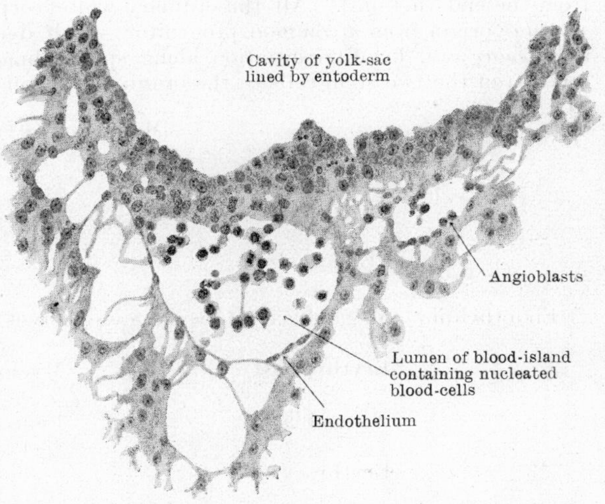

FIG. 90.—SECTION OF WALL OF YOLK-SAC OF YOUNG HUMAN EMBRYO (THIRD WEEK) SHOWING BLOOD-ISLANDS DEVELOPING IN THE MESENCHYME. (P. Thompson and J. C. Brash, *Journ. Anat.*, 1923).

known as *angioblasts*, and from them are derived both the endothelial walls of the blood-vessels and blood corpuscles.

According to one view the peripheral angioblasts become endothelial cells and those more centrally situated are the ancestors of all the blood corpuscles.

When the blood islands first become distinct in the walls of the yolk-sac they are isolated from one another, but the vessels of different islands soon join together to form a network of endothelial tubes in which fluid appears; there is thus established a plexus of anastomosing tubes filled with blood plasma in which the primitive nucleated blood corpuscles are suspended.

Most of the corpuscles of the blood, however, become non-nucleated and form the red corpuscles or *erythrocytes*. A small proportion (about $\frac{1}{6}$ per cent.) remain nucleated and form the white corpuscles or *leucocytes*, which are separable into several groups having distinctive characteristics. The blood-vessels also change as development proceeds, for the original plexuses are transformed into distinct stems and branches of varying size and importance. Therefore two groups of events in the development of the vascular system have to be considered—the evolution of the different kinds of blood corpuscles and the development of the main embryonic blood-vessels.

Development of the Blood Corpuscles.

— Numerous researches have been made with the object of discovering the mode of origin of the different kinds of blood corpuscles, but there is as yet no general agreement either with regard to their exact genesis or to the terminology to be used in describing the stages through which they pass.

It has been mentioned that the angioblast (derived from primitive mesenchyme cells) is considered by some to be the parent cell not only of the endothelium of blood vessels but also of all the blood corpuscles both red and white. This view has been elaborated by Maximow, and it implies either that blood formation in the growing embryo and fœtus takes place by the development of angioblastic cells from the mesenchyme in the same way as on the yolk-sac, or that the stem cells that give rise to all the varieties of blood corpuscles (hæmocytoblasts) are carried from the yolk-sac into the embryo to multiply there.

A single origin of all varieties of the cells of the blood is quite opposed to the older view of Ehrlich that the red blood corpuscles, the leucocytes, and the lymphocytes each have their own peculiar ancestral cells. An intermediate view, put forward by Sabin and others, is now gaining ground. According to Sabin, the angioblast produces the endothelium from which by *intra-vascular* budding the red blood corpuscles are derived. (A special kind of white corpuscle, few of which, however, are found in the blood stream and most in the connective tissues, called a *clasmatocyte* or *histiocyte*, is also said to arise from the endothelium). All the ordinary white corpuscles of the blood have an *extra-vascular* origin from a common progenitor—itself derived from the mesenchyme—called a *reticular cell*, by differentiation along special lines. The following scheme shows the relation of the two stem cells to the origin of the different kinds of blood corpuscles.

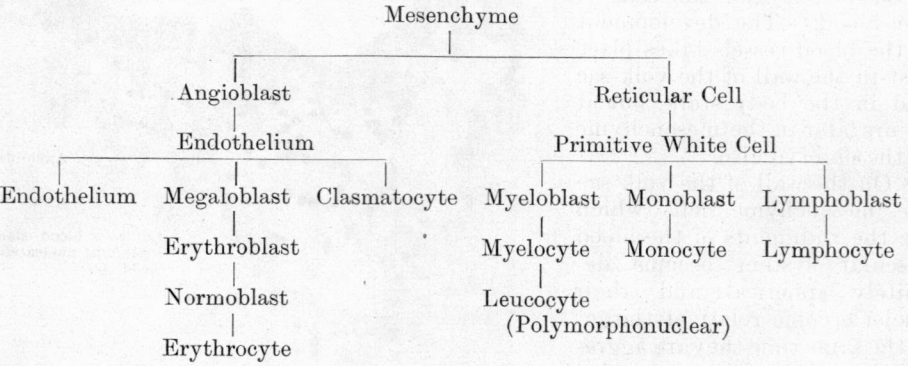

The original *erythroblasts* (nucleated red blood corpuscles) appear to be derived directly from the angioblasts in the blood-islands, but later are formed only from the endothelium. They pass through several stages to maturity; the erythroblasts become laden with hæmoglobin, and after the extrusion of their nuclei (contracted in the *normoblast* stage) become *erythrocytes* or mature red blood corpuscles.

This process goes on throughout life; it begins in the wall of the yolk-sac, is very active in the liver from the third month onwards, and occurs in the spleen in the later stages of intra-uterine life. When ossification begins, blood formation is actively carried on in the developing bone-marrow; and after birth the continuous formation of red blood corpuscles is entirely confined to that special hæmopoietic (blood-forming) tissue.

The three main kinds of white blood corpuscles are all, according to Sabin, developed from *reticular cells* in the fine reticular tissue outside the endothelial walls of the blood capillaries. These first give rise to primitive white cells which in turn become specialised to form *polymorphonuclear leucocytes, monocytes,* and *lymphocytes.* The bone-marrow is the great factory of the first two kinds (and their varieties) but the lymphocytes, which are relatively late in appearing, are formed in lymphoid (adenoid) tissue wherever it may be situated—in the spleen, in the mucous coat of the alimentary canal, and in the lymph glands. All these cells reach the blood stream by passing through the endothelial walls of blood capillaries, but lymphocytes also reach it in great numbers *via* the lymph vessels after the formation of lymph glands.

In very young embryos both immature and mature blood cells are present in the blood stream, the mature cells being developed from the immature in the stream; but after bone marrow and lymphoid tissue have been formed the proportion of immature cells decreases. After birth only mature erythrocytes pass into the blood stream; but under pathological conditions, in which there may be excessive formation of red corpuscles in the bone-marrow, immature reds (normoblasts) may again appear in the blood.

For a discussion of the origin of the blood corpuscles see *Recent Advances in Anatomy*, Woollard, 1927.

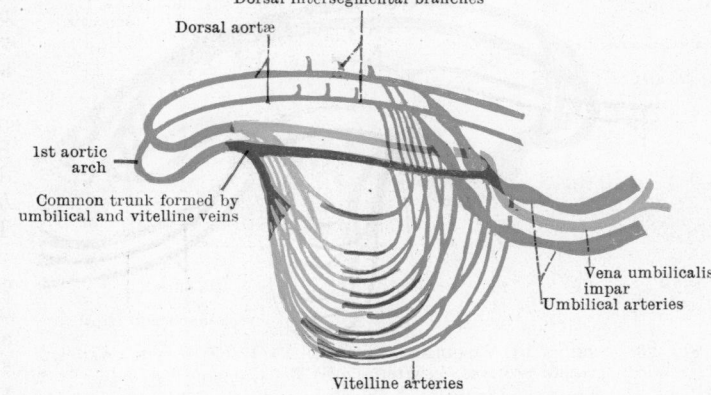

FIG. 91.—SCHEMA OF CIRCULATION OF AN EMBRYO, 1·35 MM. LONG, WITH SIX SOMITES. (After Felix, modified.)

Formation of the Primitive Blood-Vessels.—It has

been pointed out that in the yolk-sac area of the entodermal vesicle a plexiform system of tubes, filled with fluid and corpuscular elements, is formed from angioblastic cells.

Similar but less easily demonstrated plexuses are formed in the mesenchyme of the body stalk, and of the chorion, and also later in the embryonic area.

It is probable that the various plexuses become connected with one another very soon after they appear, so that a continuous capillary network is formed.

By enlargement in some places and diminution in others the general vascular network becomes more open, and from this *retiform* arrangement by further enlargement of definite channels there are evolved what may be called the primitive stem vessels of the embryo, through which the blood circulates from one area to another.

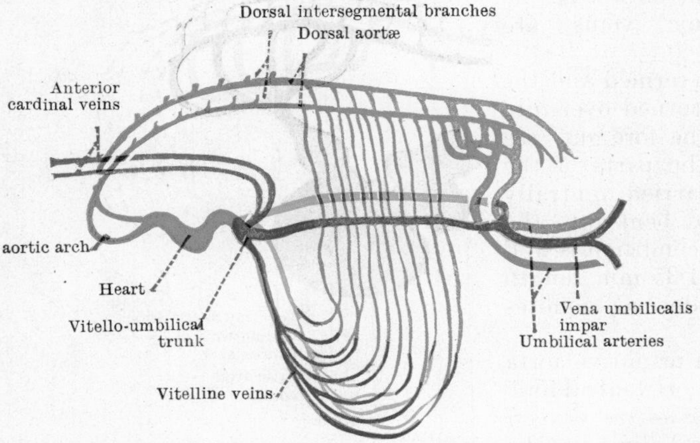

In the embryonic area a pair of main

FIG. 92.—SCHEMA OF VASCULAR SYSTEM OF AN EMBRYO, 2·6 MM. LONG, WITH FOURTEEN SOMITES. (Arteries after Felix, modified.)

stem vessels are first differentiated; they are the **primitive aortæ**.

The primitive aortæ appear in the splanchnic mesoderm of the pericardial region of the embryonic area, whence they extend to the caudal end of the area.

At their cephalic ends they are continuous with another pair of stem vessels, called the **vitelline veins**, which emerge from the vascular plexus in the wall of the yolk-sac.

As the primitive aortæ pass tailwards in the embryonic area, ventral to the paraxial bars of mesoderm (see p. 39), they give off a ventral series of paired branches, called **vitelline arteries**, which terminate in the vascular plexus in the yolk-sac wall; and from the caudal and dorsal part of that plexus, represented in Fig. 91 by a series of dilatations, a pair of vessels—the **umbilical arteries**—pass along the allantoic stalk to the vascular plexus in the chorion. Another stem vessel, called the **vena umbilicalis impar**, begins in the vascular plexus in the chorion and passes along the allantoic stalk to the caudal margin of the embryonic area, where it divides into *right* and *left umbilical veins.*

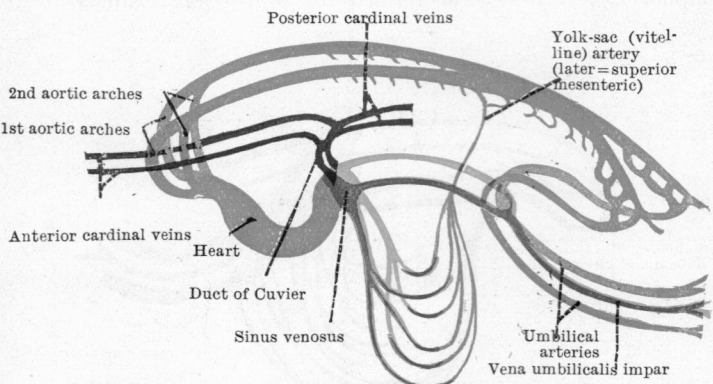

FIG. 93.—Schema of Vascular System of an Embryo with twenty-three Somites. (Arteries after Felix, modified.)

These two umbilical veins run along the corresponding margins of the embryonic area and fuse with the corresponding vitelline veins at the points where the latter join the primitive aortæ, forming with them **vitello-umbilical trunks**. Therefore, when rhythmic contraction begins in the pericardial portions of the primitive aortæ, the blood is driven through the primitive aortæ, and passes through their vitelline and umbilical branches to the yolk-sac and the chorion, whence it is returned to the aortæ by the vitelline and umbilical veins.

In the meantime lateral branches have been given off from the primitive aortæ, and in later stages, as the mesodermal somites are defined, they become the pre-segmental and inter-segmental arteries; but for a time no purely intra-embryonic veins are distinguishable.

As the head fold is formed and the pericardial region is turned over into the ventral wall of the fore-gut (see pp. 48, 49), the cephalic parts of the primitive aortæ are carried ventrally in the fold, and so are bent into the shape of hooks. That condition is well seen in an embryo of 1·35 mm. length which had six mesodermal somites (Fig. 91).

Three parts of each primitive aorta are now defined : the short ventral limb of the hook is the *primitive ventral aorta* ; the long dorsal limb is the *primitive dorsal aorta* ; and the bend, which connects the two limbs, is the *first aortic arch.* It runs along the

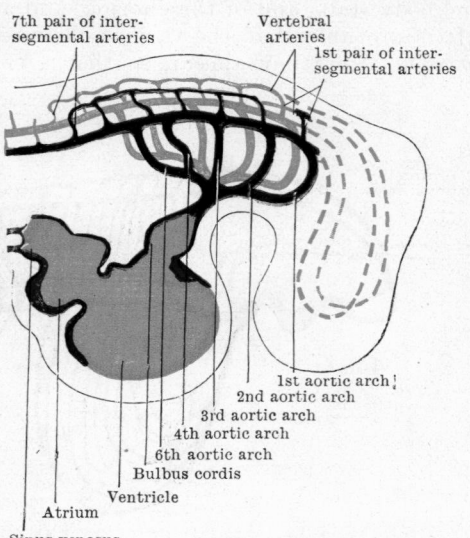

FIG. 94.—Diagram showing 5 mm. stage with five aortic arches.

side of the bucco-pharyngeal membrane, in the substance of the· mandibular arch. What were previously the cephalic ends of the primitive aortæ have now become the caudal ends of the primitive ventral aortæ ; they lie in the substance of the septum transversum—the bar of mesoderm which separates the pericardial cavity from the extra-embryonic cœlom at the cephalic margin of the umbilical orifice—and in that situation the common vitello-intestinal venous trunks are continuous with the primitive aortæ.

Three further important changes take place in the vascular system during the time in which the embryo grows a little more than another millimetre in length, and the tail fold and lateral folds are formed and the number of its mesodermal somites increases to fourteen pairs.

(1) The caudal parts of the primitive ventral aortæ fuse together to form a single, median, tubular heart, which is divided by dilatations and constrictions into six parts, named, from the caudal towards the cephalic end, the **sinus venosus**, the **atrium**, the **atrio-ventricular canal**, the **ventricle**, the **bulbus cordis**, and the **truncus arteriosus**. At the same time the heart increases in length more rapidly than the region in which it lies; it therefore becomes bent both in the longitudinal and the

transverse direction, and its caudal and cephalic ends begin to come close together (Fig. 92).

(2) The origins of the umbilical arteries are transferred from the vitelline plexus to the primitive dorsal aortæ, from which they arise by three roots for each (Fig. 92).

(3) The **anterior cardinal veins** are defined. They are the first pair of purely intra-embryonic veins. They begin in

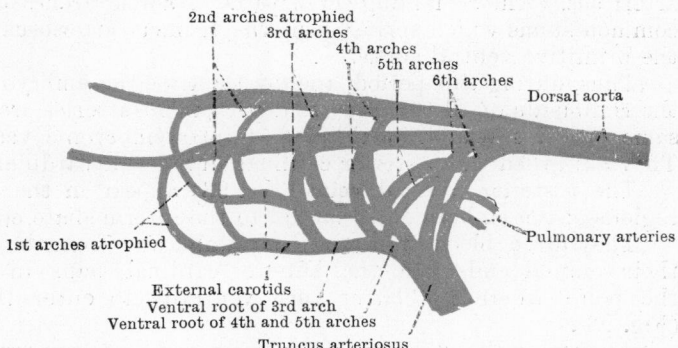

FIG. 95.—SCHEMA OF AORTIC ARCHES OF AN EMBRYO, 9 MM. LONG. (After Tandler, modified.) The first and second arches have atrophied and the transitory fifth has appeared.

the head and end in the sinus venosus, which they enter, in the septum transversum, close to the common vitello-umbilical veins. They bring back to the heart the blood which has been distributed by the pre-segmental and intersegmental arteries to the head, neck, and headward part of the trunk of the embryo.

As the embryo increases to about 5 mm. in length, by which time it is about five weeks old, its mesodermal somites increase to 38 pairs, and numerous changes take place in the cardiac, the arterial, and the venous parts of the vascular system, and the rudiments of all the main blood-vessels of the adult are defined.

In the heart its various chambers become more definitely demarcated, and the rudiments of the septa are formed. (For the further development of the heart see the chapter on the Vascular System.)

The changes in the arteries are brought about by fusions, reductions, transpositions, and additions.

Fusions.—The primitive dorsal aortæ fuse, from the region of the tenth (seventh cervical) somite tailwards, to form the permanent descending aorta (Fig. 93) and the median sacral artery.

At the same time each pair of ventral branches of the fused portions of the primitive dorsal aortæ fuse to form a single trunk; each trunk divides, on the dorsal aspect of the alimentary tube, into a right and a left branch which may reunite on the ventral wall of the tube and anastomose with neighbouring vessels.

Reductions.—Not only do the paired ventral or vitelline branches of the primitive dorsal aortæ fuse to form single trunks, but they also become reduced in number. A few remain in the thoracic region and become the bronchial and œsophageal branches of the descending aorta. In the abdominal region they are reduced to three main vessels—the cœliac artery, the superior mesenteric artery (which for a time passes to the yolk-sac as the vitelline artery) (Fig. 93), and the inferior mesenteric artery.

Additions.—Four additional aortic arches, connecting the unfused portions of the primitive ventral and dorsal aortæ, appear in the following sequence, the second, the third, the fourth, and the sixth—the temporary fifth arches appearing later. The second pair of arches is found in embryos possessing 23 mesodermal somites (Fig. 93): they spring from the truncus arteriosus close to the beginning of the primitive ventral aortæ.

Branches are given off from the ventro-lateral aspects of the descending aorta to the rudiments of the nephric or urinary system, which are developed from the intermediate cell mass, and to the rudiments of the genital glands.

By the time the embryo has fully attained a length of 5 mm. (Fig. 94) all five pairs of aortic arches are present, but in the meantime, coincidently with the elongation of the neck, the primitive ventral aortæ also have been elongated and the second pair of aortic arches has been transferred to them from the truncus arteriosus. The remaining three pairs of aortic arches originate from a pair of common stems which spring from the truncus arteriosus close to the origins of the primitive ventral aortæ.

Thus, during this period, and by the time the embryo is about five weeks old, the rudiments of all the important permanent arteries are evolved, and during the same period two additional pairs of intra-embryonic venous trunks are formed. They are called the posterior cardinal and the subcardinal veins.

The **posterior cardinal veins** (Fig. 93) appear in the thoracic and abdominal regions of the embryo dorso-lateral to the intermediate cell mass.

They drain blood from the body walls and from the nephric rudiments, and their cranial ends join the anterior cardinal veins in the thoracic region, at the point where the latter turn ventrally to enter the septum transversum (Fig. 93).

As soon as the union of the anterior and posterior cardinal veins is completed the parts of the anterior cardinals ventral to the points of union are called the **ducts of Cuvier.**

In the meantime the common vitello-umbilical venous trunks have been absorbed into the sinus venosus and the vitelline and umbilical veins now open independently into it; therefore, at the 5 mm. stage, three pairs of veins open into the sinus venosus of the heart. They are the ducts of Cuvier, the vitelline veins, and the umbilical veins.

The **subcardinal veins** appear in the abdominal region ventro-medial to the mesonephros—a large structure which contains nephric rudiments. They communicate both at their cranial and caudal ends with the posterior cardinal veins.

In addition, the anterior and posterior cardinal veins and the subcardinal vein become connected by anastomoses with their fellows of the opposite side, and the posterior cardinal vein anastomoses also with the subcardinal vein of the same side.

At a later period still another pair of intra-embryonic veins is established in the abdominal and thoracic regions. They are called the **supracardinal veins** and they appear dorso-lateral to the descending aorta. They communicate with each other across the median plane, and with the posterior cardinal and subcardinal veins. When their formation and anastomoses are completed the rudiments of the main stems of the venous system of the adult are established.

As these changes occur in the venous system the origins of the third and fourth pairs of aortic arches are transposed from their original positions to the primitive ventral aortæ, and a pair of fifth arches appear as a temporary connexion between the ventral aortæ and the dorsal ends of the sixth arches; pulmonary branches arise from the sixth arches and pass to the rudiments of the lungs; and the first two pairs of aortic arches have atrophied or have begun to undergo atrophy (Fig. 95).

In order to facilitate the description of the further changes which take place in association with the aortic arches it is customary to speak of the parts of the ventral aortæ which lie caudal to the respective arches as the *ventral roots* of those arches and the corresponding parts of the dorsal aortæ as the *dorsal roots*. (For the further history of the blood vessels and the fœtal circulation see the chapter on the Vascular System.)

THE CŒLOM

It has already been pointed out that there are two parts of the cœlom—the extra-embryonic and the intra-embryonic. They are derived independently as clefts in the mesoderm and are at first separate from each other (Figs. 49, B; 53); they become continuous, for a time, in the region of the then umbilical orifice (Fig. 50, B), but are separated from each other again when the umbilical orifice closes. Later the extra-embryonic cœlom disappears, but the intra-embryonic remains as the cavities of the pericardium, pleura, and peritoneum.

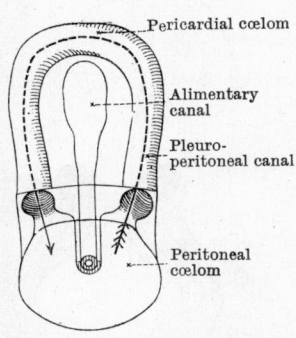

Extra-embryonic Cœlom.—The extra-embryonic cœlom appears in the primary mesoderm and divides it into a parietal and a visceral layer. The parietal layer covers the inner surface of the trophoblast and forms with it the chorion. It covers also the outer surface of the amnion. The visceral layer covers the outer surface of the yolk-sac.

The extra-embryonic portion is entirely obliterated when the outer surface of the expanding amnion fuses with the inner surface of the chorion (compare Figs. 85 and 86).

FIG. 96. — SCHEMA OF INTRA-EMBRYONIC CŒLOM SEEN FROM ABOVE BEFORE THE FOLDING OF THE EMBRYONIC AREA.

Intra-embryonic Cœlom.—The intra-embryonic cœlom appears as a series of cleft-like spaces in the margin of the embryonic mesoderm (Fig. 53). The

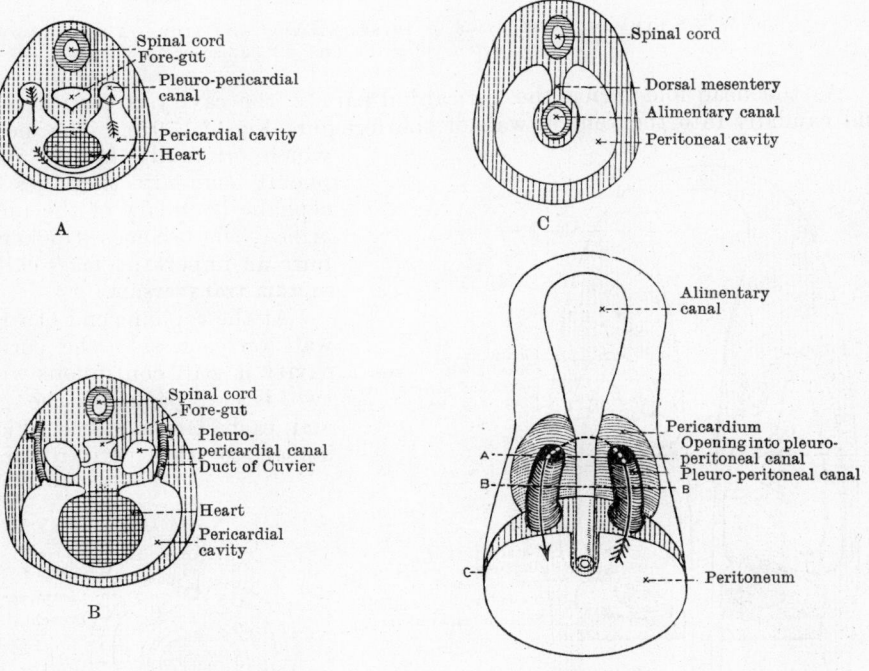

FIG. 97.—SCHEMATA OF EMBRYONIC CŒLOM AFTER FOLDING OF EMBRYONIC AREA BUT BEFORE THE SEPARATION OF THE VARIOUS PARTS. D from above; A, B, and C at levels of lines A, B, and C in Fig. D.

spaces fuse together to form a ∩-shaped cavity which divides the peripheral part of the embryonic mesoderm into a parietal or somatic layer, and a visceral or splanchnic layer. The bend of the ∩-shaped cavity lies in the margin of the cephalic part of the embryonic region, and it has no direct communication with the extra-embryonic cœlom, but the greater part of each limb of the cavity, on account of the disappearance of its lateral wall, soon opens, laterally, into the extra-embryonic cœlom.

The transverse portion of the ∩ is the **pericardial cavity**. The adjacent part of each limb of the cavity is the **pleuro-pericardial canal**, and it becomes a *pleural cavity*. The remaining portions of the two limbs unite ventrally, as the umbilical orifice closes, to form the single **peritoneal cavity**.

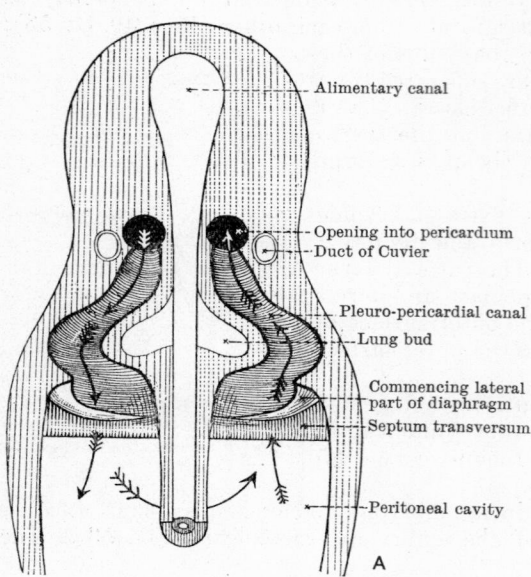

Alimentary canal

Opening into pericardium
Duct of Cuvier

Pleuro-pericardial canal
Lung bud

Commencing lateral part of diaphragm
Septum transversum

Peritoneal cavity

A

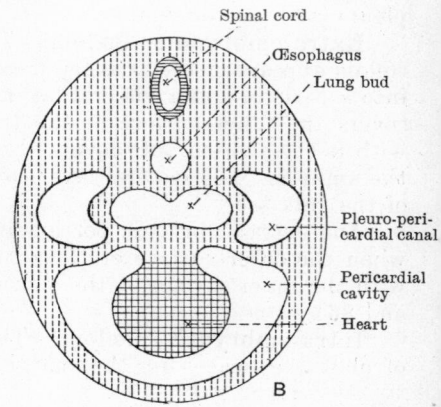

Spinal cord
Œsophagus
Lung bud

Pleuro-pericardial canal

Pericardial cavity

Heart

B

FIG. 98.—SCHEMA OF LATER STAGE OF DIFFERENTIATION OF CŒLOM.   A, from above. B, transverse section cut at the level of lung bud in A.

As the head fold forms, the pericardial part of the cavity is carried ventrally and caudally into the ventral wall of the fore-gut (Figs. 61, 97). The mesoderm which originally formed its peripheral boundary then lies in the cephalic boundary of the umbilical orifice; it becomes thickened to form an important mass called the **septum transversum**.

At the cephalic end of its dorsal wall, on each side, the pericardial cavity is still continuous with the two lateral parts of the cœlom; and each lateral part, which lies dorsal to the pericardium, and

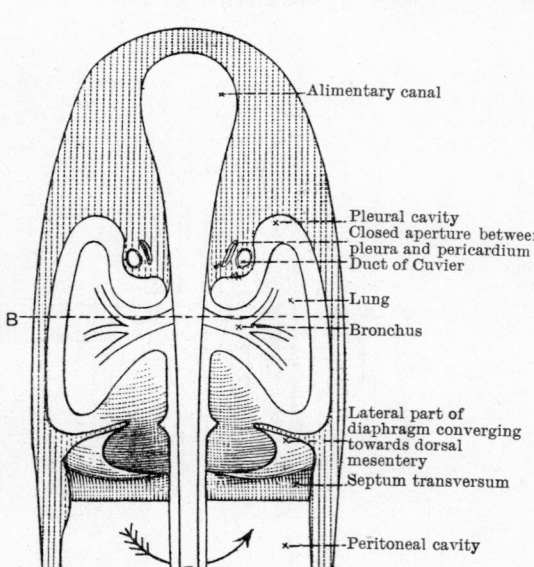

Alimentary canal

Pleural cavity
Closed aperture between pleura and pericardium
Duct of Cuvier

Lung

Bronchus

Lateral part of diaphragm converging towards dorsal mesentery
Septum transversum

Peritoneal cavity

A

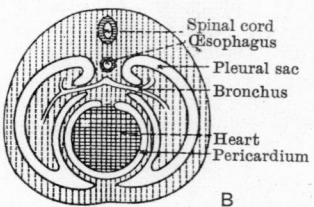

Spinal cord
Œsophagus

Pleural sac
Bronchus

Heart
Pericardium

B

FIG. 99.—SCHEMA OF STILL LATER STAGE OF CŒLOM DIFFERENTIATION. The pleuræ are separated from the pericardium, but still communicate with the peritoneum. A, from above. B, transverse section at level of line B, in Fig. A, showing ventral extension of the pleuræ.

between the fore-gut medially and the body wall laterally, is still a pleuro-pericardial canal.

Separation of Pericardial, Pleural, and Peritoneal Parts of Cœlom.—In the lateral wall of each pleuro-pericardial canal, near its cephalic end, lies the duct of Cuvier, passing towards the heart; and a lung bud containing a primitive bronchial tube forms in the medial wall and bulges into the cavity of each pleuro-pericardial canal (Fig. 97). As the lung buds grow the cavities of the pleuro-pericardial canals increase in size, and each passes ventrally round the side of the pericardium towards the ventral wall of the body, until it is separated from its fellow of the opposite side by a median interval only (filled with mesoderm), which becomes the anterior mediastinum and the anterior part of the superior mediastinum (Fig. 99, B). At the same time the cavity of each pleuro-pericardial canal and the growing lung bud grow towards the head of the embryo (Fig. 99, A). As the growing lung passes upwards it lies to the lateral side of the duct of Cuvier, which is thus forced against the cephalic end of the pleuro-pericardial canal, compressing it towards the median plane, against the sides of the trachea and the œsophagus, until its cavity is obliterated. When this occurs the pericardial cavity is entirely shut off from the remainder of the cœlom and it becomes a completely closed space (Fig. 99, B). Very rarely, as an abnormal condition, the pericardial cavity remains in communication on one or other side with a pleural cavity.

As the closure of the pericardial cavity is taking place a pair of wing-like folds of the mesoderm of the body walls appear caudal to the lungs. These *pleuro-peritoneal folds* are the rudiments of the lateral parts of the diaphragm; they are connected ventrally with the septum transversum and grow medially until they fuse with the mesoderm of the side wall of the fore-gut and with the dorsal mesentery (Figs. 97, 99, A). When this fusion is completed and the *pleuro-peritoneal opening* closed, the cavity of the portion of the cœlom surrounding the lung—the original pleuro-pericardial canal—is separated from the more caudal part of the cœlom, which now becomes the peritoneal cavity.

Only the broad outlines of the processes by which the pleuro-pericardial canals are separated from the pericardium and the peritoneum and so become the pleural sacs are mentioned in the preceding paragraphs. The details of the processes are too complicated for description in an ordinary text-book of anatomy.

Formation of the Diaphragm.—There are four main parts of the diaphragm —a ventral, a dorsal, and a right and a left lateral.

The ventral part is formed from the *septum transversum*, which is gradually differentiated into a caudal, a middle, and a cephalic part. The caudal part is transformed into (1) the mesodermal tissue of the liver, which grows towards the abdomen, (2) the falciform and coronary ligaments, and (3) the lesser omentum. The cephalic part becomes the caudal or diaphragmatic wall of the pericardium. The middle part is transformed into the ventral portion of the diaphragm.

The dorsal part of the diaphragm is developed from the mesoderm of the dorsal mesentery of the fore-gut. Each lateral part is derived from the pleuro-peritoneal folds mentioned above. The two lateral portions grow towards the median plane till they fuse with the dorsal portion; but sometimes, especially on the left side, the fusion is not completed. The pleuro-peritoneal opening then remains unclosed, and a portion of the abdominal contents may pass through it into the pleural sac, constituting a congenital *diaphragmatic hernia*.

SUMMARY OF THE EXTERNAL FEATURES OF THE HUMAN EMBRYO AND FŒTUS AT DIFFERENT PERIODS OF DEVELOPMENT

First Month.—During the first **fourteen days** after fertilisation the human ovum descends through the uterine tube, assumes the morula condition, enters the uterus (see p. 68), penetrates into the decidua compacta, and differentiates into three vesicles and a mass of primitive mesoderm (Fig. 36); but, probably, it is not until the beginning of the third week, if Bryce's calculations are correct, that a definite embryonic area is present. By that time the zygote is an ovoid vesicle measuring 2·4 by 1·8 mm. Its wall is formed by the trophoblast, and it contains two inner vesicles—the ectodermal amnio-embryonic vesicle and the entodermal yolk-sac vesicle. The inner vesicles are surrounded by a mass of primary mesoderm in which the extra-embryonic portion of the cœlom is beginning to appear. At that period the embryonic area is the region where the walls of the two inner vesicles lie in relation with each other, and in the Peters Ovum it is 0·19 mm. long (Fig. 40).

By the **eighteenth** or **nineteenth day** the area may be a little over 1 mm. long and about half as broad. It is pierced, about the middle of its length, by the neurenteric canal; the primitive streak has appeared on the dorsal surface of the area; the primitive groove is distinct, and the neural groove is indicated. The allantoic stalk is bent dorsally, at right angles with the area, and it contains the allantoic diverticulum, which has already been projected from the wall of the entodermal vesicle (Fig. 100).

By the **nineteenth** or **twentieth day** the length of the embryonic area may increase to about 1·5 mm.; the neurenteric canal is moved caudally to a point well behind the middle of the length of the area; the posterior part of the area is bent ventrally, forming the posterior boundary of the hind-gut region and indicating the position of the future cloacal membrane. The head fold has begun to form, and the pericardial region lies in the ventral wall of the rudimentary fore-gut (Figs. 60, 102).

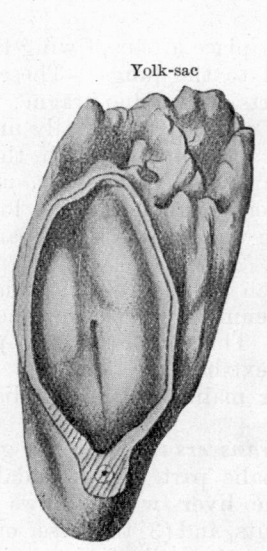

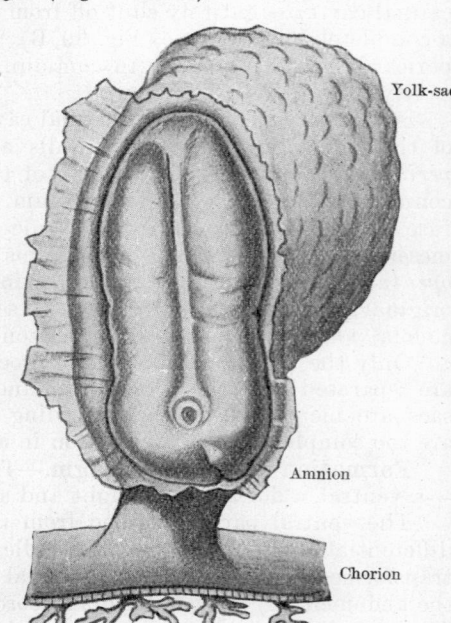

FIG. 100.—DORSAL VIEW OF HUMAN EMBRYO, estimated to be 18-19 days old (Bryce). The chorion is not shown. The upper part of the amnion is cut away, and the dorsal aspect of the embryonic area, 1·17 mm. long and ·6 mm. broad, is seen from above. In the centre of the area is the neurenteric canal and caudal to it is the primitive groove. Headwards of the neurenteric canal is the neural groove. At the lower (caudal) end of the fig. is seen a section of the allantoic stalk containing the allantoic diverticulum, and the nodulated area seen at the upper right part of the fig. is a portion of the yolk-sac. (Frassi's Embryo, from Keibel and Elze's *Normentafeln.*)

FIG. 101.—DORSAL VIEW OF HUMAN EMBRYO, of estimated age 19-20 days (Bryce). Length of embryonic area 1·54 mm. At the lower end of the fig. (caudal end of the embryo) is seen a portion of the chorion attached to the embryo by the allantoic stalk. A portion of the amnion is still attached to the margin of the embryonic area, the dorsal surface of which is exposed. In the median plane of the area is the neural groove, and at the caudal end of the groove is the neurenteric canal. The caudal part of the area is bent ventrally, and upon it is the remains of the primitive groove. The yolk-sac with blood-islands is seen at the upper and right part of the fig. (Von Spee's Gle. Embryo, from Keibel and Elze's *Normentafeln.*)

By the end of the **third week** the head and tail folds are distinctly formed, the neural folds are well developed, the neural groove is still completely open, and six pairs of mesodermal somites are visible (Fig. 102). The length of the embryo may now be nearly 2 mm.

In the next few days the neural groove closes except in the cranial and caudal regions, the mesodermal somites increase to fourteen pairs, and the cranial region begins to bend ventrally as the cervical flexure forms (Fig. 103).

By the end of the **fourth week** the length of the embryo is about 2·5 mm., the head is bent at right angles to the body, and indications of the limb rudiments are present. The rudiments of the otic vesicles have appeared as slight depressions in the region of the hind-brain. The anterior and posterior neuropores are still open (Figs. 63, 104).

Second Month.—During the **fifth week** the embryo attains a length of about 5·5 mm. The mesodermal somites increase to thirty-eight; the rudiments of the fore- and hind-limbs become quite distinct; the otic vesicles sink into the interior of the head but remain connected with the surface by a narrow canal; the tail becomes a very definite appendage; and the bulgings caused by the optic vesicles are quite obvious on the surface of the head. The cervical flexure remains acute, and the head bends at right angles upon

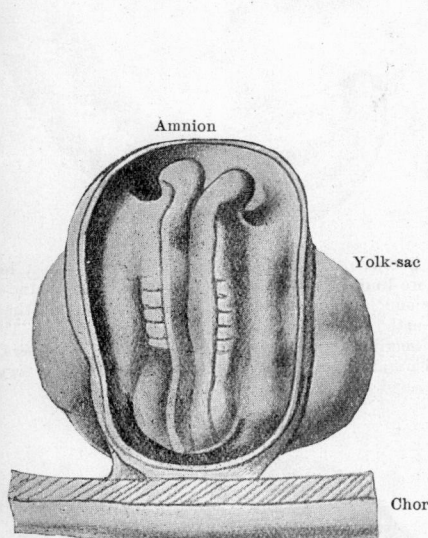

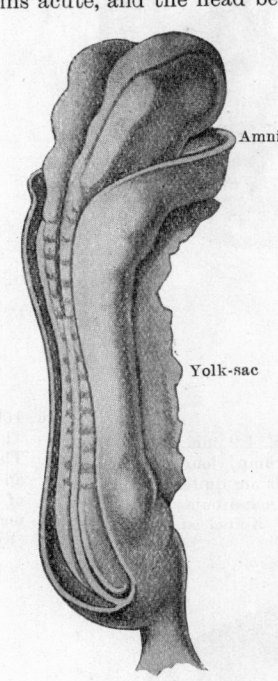

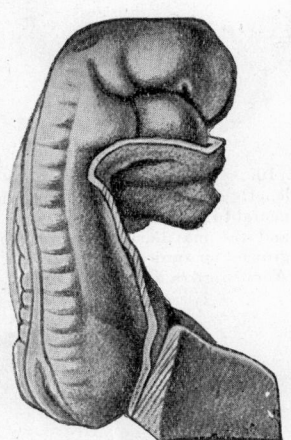

FIG. 102.—DORSAL VIEW OF EMBRYO (after formation of head and tail folds), 1·8 mm. long, and about three weeks old. At the lower end of the fig. (the caudal end of the embryo) are seen portions of the chorion and allantoic stalk. The cerebral portion of the neural rudiment is defined. Six pairs of mesodermal somites are present, but there are no signs of limbs. (Krœmer-Pfannenstiel Embryo, from Keibel and Elze's *Normentafeln.*)

FIG. 103.—EMBRYO, 2·5 mm. long (after hardening in alcohol). The neural groove is closed from the sixth somite to within a short distance of the caudal end. The hind-, mid-, and fore-brain regions and the optic vesicle can be distinguished. At the lower end of the fig. is the allantoic stalk, and at the right side a part of the yolk-sac. (Kollman's von Bulle Embryo, from Keibel and Elze's *Normentafeln.*)

FIG. 104.—EMBRYO, about 2·6 mm. long. The rudiment of the otic vesicle is seen above the second pharyngeal groove. The heart and pericardium form the bulging eminence below the head, and at the lateral border of the mesodermal somites is seen the ridge on which the limb buds develop. (Pfannenstiel's Embryo III, from Keibel and Elze's *Normentafeln.*)

itself in the region of the mid-brain, forming the cephalic flexure, with the result that the frontal region is turned towards the tail (Fig. 105).

By the end of the **sixth week** the length of the embryo has increased to 11 mm. (CR) [1] (Mall). Forty-three mesodermal somites are present, but only about twenty-one are visible on the surface. During the sixth week the lens of the eye appears as a thickening of the surface ectoderm, sinks into the interior of the eyeball, becomes a vesicle and separates from the surface. The three segments of the fore-limb become visible, and the rudiments of the fingers appear. The hind-limb is less advanced; the thigh segment is not distinct, and the rudiments of the toes are not yet visible. The third and fourth pharyngeal arches disappear from the surface and lie in the depths of the precervical sinus, overlapped by the caudal margin of the second arch (see p. 56) (Figs. 106, 107). During the sixth week the head grows rapidly, and becomes relatively very large in comparison with the trunk.

[1] CR indicates the crown-rump measurement which corresponds with the sitting height (Mall).

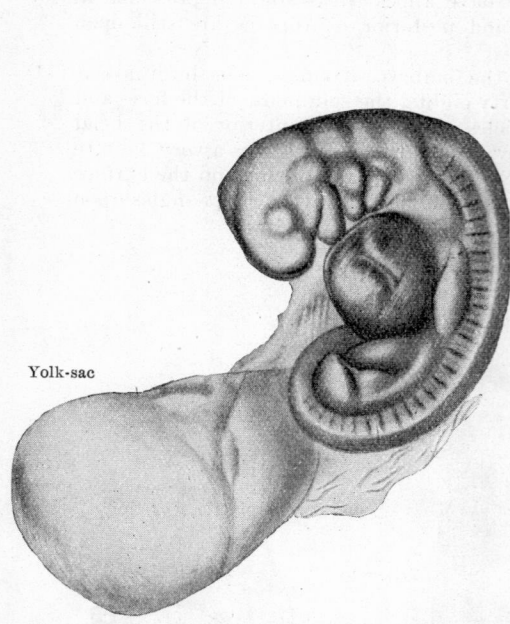

Yolk-sac

FIG. 105.—SIDE VIEW OF AN EMBRYO, 4·9 mm. greatest length and 4·7 mm. CR (crown-rump) length. The neural tube is closed. The limb buds are quite distinct, and the maxillary process of the mandibular bar has grown forward below the eye. (Keibel and Elze's *Normentafeln*.)

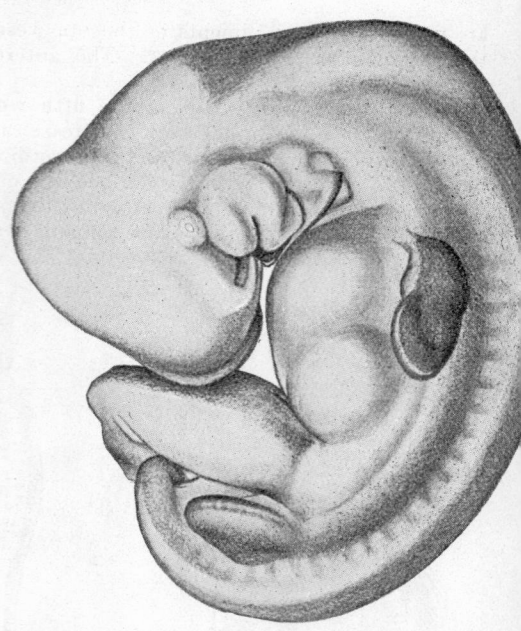

FIG. 106.—EMBRYO, 7·2 MM. CR, and 8·5 mm. greatest le The fore-limb is distinctly in advance of the hind- The second pharyngeal arch has begun to overlap the and fourth and to enclose the precervical sinus. Th of the maxillary process is in contact with the latera medial nasal processes at the margins of the olfactory (Keibel and Elze's *Normentafeln*.)

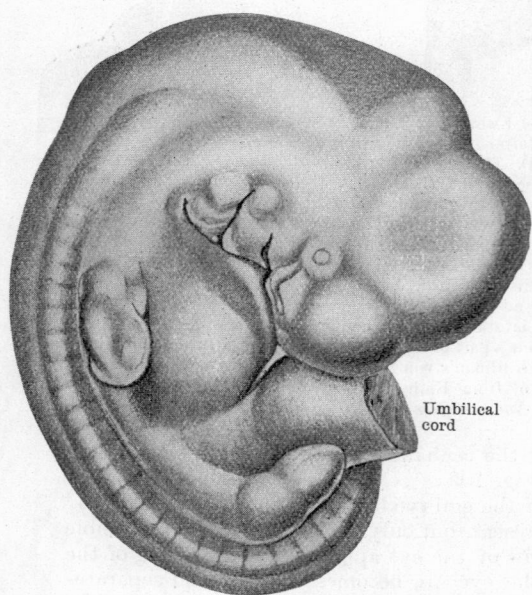

Umbilical cord

FIG. 107.—EMBRYO, 7·2 mm. CR, and 8 mm. greatest length. The limbs have begun to fold ventrally. The second arch has overlapped the third and fourth, which now lie in the precervical sinus, and the sinus still opens on the surface at the posterior border of the second arch. The lens of the eyeball is very evident, and rudiments of the auricle of the external ear have appeared on the first (mandibular) arch, and the second (hyoid) arch. (Keibel and Elze's *Normentafeln*.)

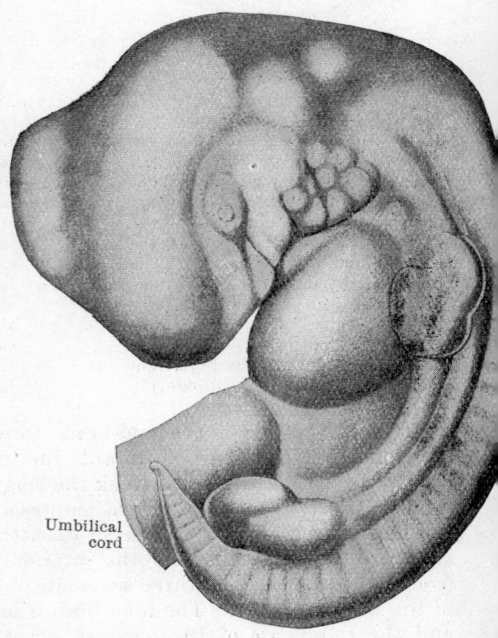

Umbilical cord

FIG. 108.—EMBRYO, 10·9 mm. CR, and 11·5 mm. grea length. The limbs are bent ventrally and show differe tion into segments. The precervical sinus is closed additional rudiments of the auricle of the external are present on the first and second arches. The no is no longer visible from the side. (Keibel and E *Normentafeln*.)

During this week also the olfactory pits appear between the median and the lateral nasal processes, and grow dorsally into the roof of the oral pit; the median process is divided into the two globular processes; and the maxillary processes of the mandibular arches, growing towards the median plane, fuse with the lateral nasal and the globular processes, so completing the lateral parts of the primitive upper lip (Figs. 64, 65, 66).

The nodular outgrowths which form the rudiments of the auricles appear on the margins of the first pharyngeal (hyo-mandibular) groove and fuse together, and by the end of the week traces of the tragus, the helix, and the antitragus are visible (Fig. 108).

By the **seventh week** the embryo has attained a length of 17 mm. (CR). The cervical flexure has begun to straighten. The rudiments of the eyelids have appeared. The globular

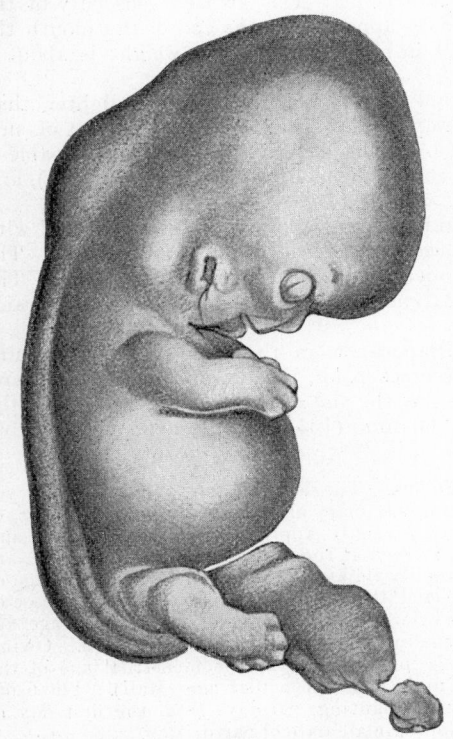

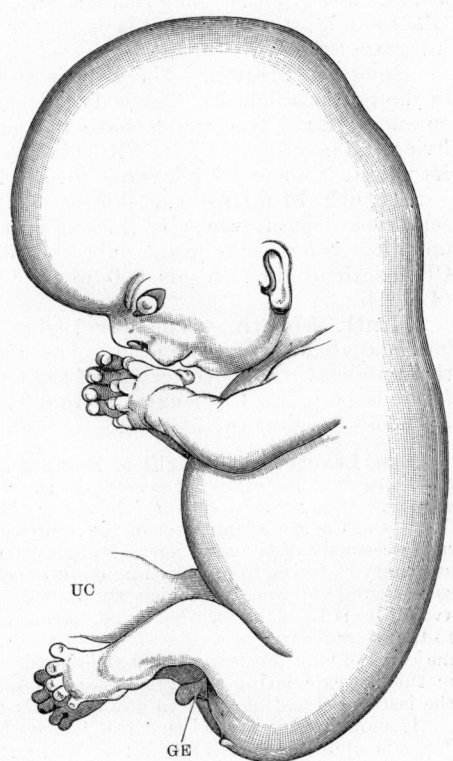

FIG. 109.—EMBRYO, 18·5 mm. greatest length, probably about seven weeks old. The abdomen is very prominent on account of the rapid increase of the liver. The digits of the hand and foot are distinct but not separated from one another. The margin of the auricle is completed. The eyelids have begun to form. (Keibel and Elze's *Normentafeln.*)

FIG. 110.—HUMAN FŒTUS ABOUT EIGHT AND A HALF WEEKS OLD. (After His.)

GE, Genital eminence; UC, Umbilical cord.

processes have fused together, but there is still a distinct notch in the middle of the upper lip. The margins of the auricles are now well defined; the hands are folded medially; the tips of the fingers are free, and the palms rest on the upper part of the distended abdomen. The thighs and the toes have appeared, and the tail has begun to fuse with the caudal end of the body (Fig. 109).

At the end of the **eighth week**, when the embryo becomes a fœtus, it has attained a length of about 25 mm. (CR). The auricles project from the sides of the head, the tail has almost disappeared from the surface, and the toes are free from one another. The cervical flexure is now very slight, and although the head is still relatively large, the disproportion between it and the trunk has begun to decrease (Fig. 110).

Third Month.—The head grows less rapidly, and, though it is still large, it is relatively smaller in proportion to the whole body. The eyelids close, and their margins fuse together. The neck increases in length. The various parts of the limbs assume their definite proportions, and nails appear on the fingers and toes. The anal pit is formed and the external genital organs are sufficiently differentiated for the sex to be distinguished. The skin is a rosy colour, thin and delicate, and of firmer consistence than in the preceding stages.   By the end of the third month the CR length of the fœtus is about 100 mm. (nearly 4 in.), and it weighs about 50 grams (2 oz.).

Fourth Month.—The skin is firmer, and fine hairs are developed.   The disproportion between the fore- and hind-limbs disappears.   A fœtus born at this period may live for a few hours.   Its CR length is 145 mm. ($5\frac{2}{3}$ in.), and it weighs 200 grams (7 oz.).

Fifth Month.—The skin becomes firmer, the hairs are more developed, and sebaceous matter appears on the surface of the body.   The lower limbs are longer than the upper, and the umbilicus is farther from the pubis.   At the end of the month the CR length of the fœtus is 190 mm. ($7\frac{1}{2}$ in.), and its average weight is 460 grams (about 1 lb.).

Sixth Month.—The skin is wrinkled and of a muddy reddish colour.   The hairs are stronger and darker.   The deposit of sebaceous matter is greater, especially in the armpits and groins.   The eyelashes and eyebrows appear.   At the end of the month the CR total length of the fœtus is 230 mm. (9 in.), and its average weight is about 1 kilogram ($2\frac{1}{5}$ lbs.).

Seventh Month.—The skin is still a muddy red colour, but it is lighter than in the previous month.   The body is more plump on account of a greater deposit of subcutaneous fat.   The eyelids have re-opened.   A fœtus born at this period is capable of living and may survive.   Its CR length at the end of the month is 265 mm. ($10\frac{1}{2}$ in.), and its weight is about 1·5 kilograms (over 3 lbs.).

Eighth Month.—The skin is of a bright red tint and is completely covered with sebaceous deposit, which is thickest on the head and in the armpits and groins.   The umbilicus is farther from the pubis, but it is not yet at the centre of the trunk.   The CR length of the fœtus is 300 mm. (12 in.), and its weight about 2 to 2·5 kilograms ($4\frac{1}{2}$-$5\frac{1}{2}$ lbs.).

Ninth Month. — The hair begins to disappear from the trunk, but it remains long and abundant on the head.   The skin becomes paler, the plumpness increases, and the umbilicus reaches the centre of the trunk.   At the end of the ninth month, when the fœtus is born, its CR length is from 340 to 360 mm. ($13\frac{1}{2}$-14 in.), and it weighs from 3 to 3·5 kilograms ($6\frac{1}{2}$-$7\frac{1}{2}$ lbs.).

Age, Length, and Weight of Embryo and Fœtus.—The lengths and weights of embryos and fœtuses at increasing ages given in the foregoing summary are compiled from a number of sources.   It must be understood however that they are only approximate, since embryos and fœtuses of the same length, or of the same weight, or even at the same stage of development, are not necessarily of the same age.   Moreover, it is usually impossible to calculate the *actual* age of an embryo (dating from the time of fertilisation) and the age assigned (except in the case of some young embryos for which the data necessary for the calculation of fertilisation age are available) is then the *menstrual* age, dating from the first day of the last menstruation.   Owing to the average time of ovulation in relation to the menstrual cycle, the menstrual age of the majority of embryos is probably at least ten days more than the actual age (Mall).   The usual method of calculating the duration of pregnancy by counting 280 days from the first day of the last menstruation gives in any case only the approximate date of parturition.

It should also be noted that the "greatest length" of an embryo (excluding the lower limbs) depends upon the cervical flexure.   While the head of the embryo is fully flexed the crown-rump measurement (CR) is less than the greatest length, but later the two measurements are the same.

Formulæ for the calculation of age from length have been devised, but it is more satisfactory to use tables and graphs (constructed from extensive data) from which the probable range of age can be read at a glance.   (See G. L. Streeter, *Contr. to Embryol.*, No. 55, Carnegie Institution of Washington, Pub. 274, 1920, p. 143.)

PLATE I

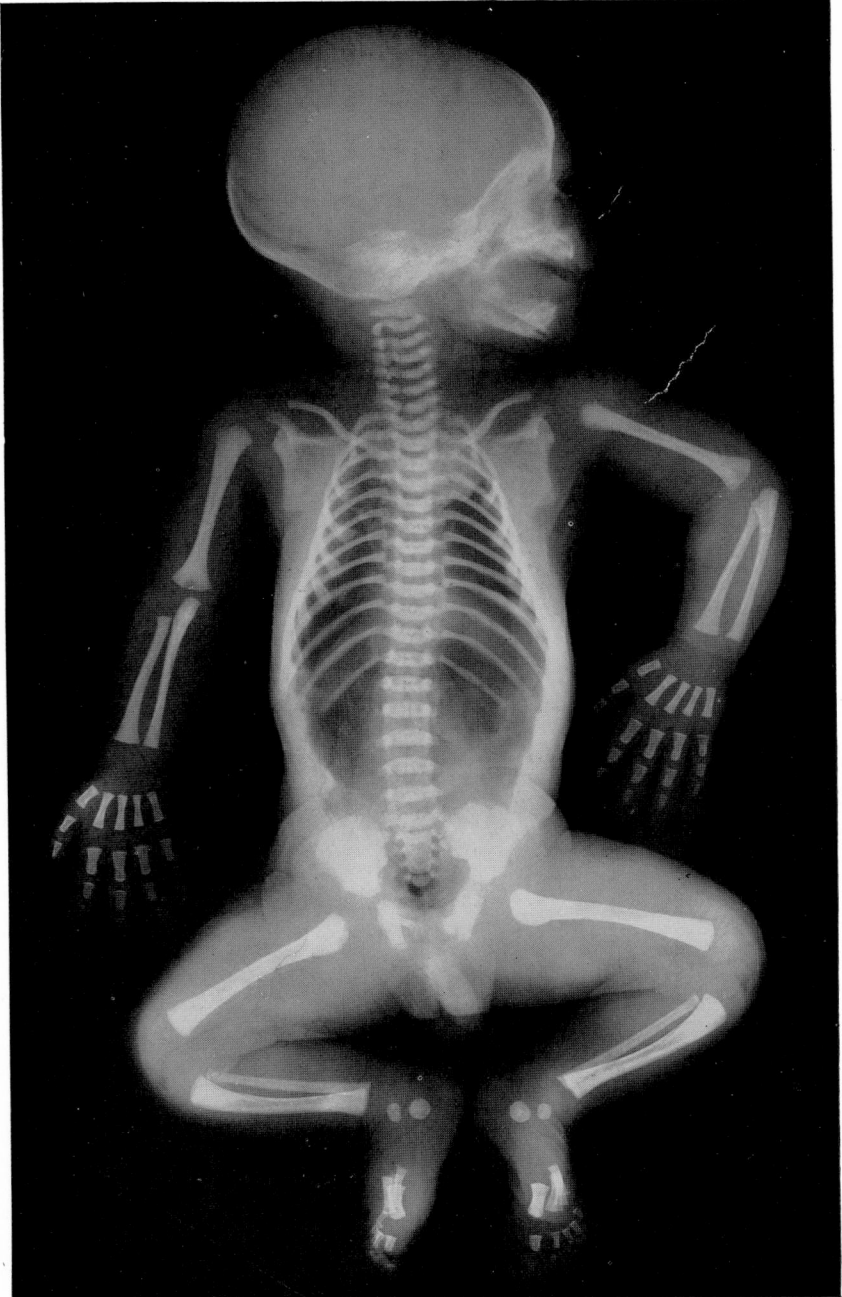

PLATE I.—RADIOGRAPH OF EIGHT MONTHS FŒTUS TO SHOW THE STATE OF OSSIFICATION OF THE SKELETON. THE RIGHT FOREARM IS SUPINATED, THE LEFT PRONATED.

Note the absence of ossific centres for the Carpus and the presence of centres for the Talus and Calcaneum (cf. Plate X, Fig. 1, and Plate XVI, Fig. 1). Minute centres of ossification for the lower epiphysis of the right Femur and the upper epiphysis of the left Tibia are also faintly visible.

PLATE II

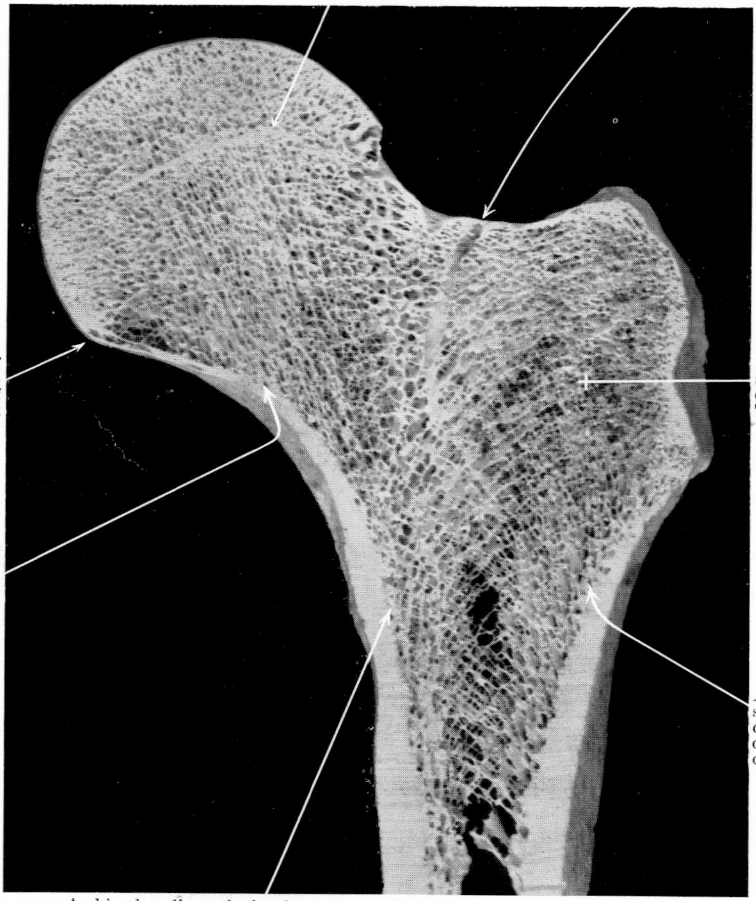

Epiphyseal scar

Vascular channel

Thin shell of
compact bone
at junction of
Head and Neck

Lamellæ
crossing in
spongy bone
of Greater
Trochanter

Straight lamellæ
running into
Head from com-
pact bone of Neck

Arching lamellæ
springing from
compact bone
of lateral side
of Shaft

Arching lamellæ springing from compact bone of
medial side of Shaft

FIG. 1.—PHOTOGRAPH OF CORONAL SECTION OF UPPER END OF LEFT FEMUR TO SHOW ITS ARCHITECTURE.

Note how the compact bone of the Shaft thins out over the Greater Trochanter and the
Head, and the manner of crossing of the different systems of lamellæ in the spongy bone.

Coarse lamellæ radiating from articular
facets and groove on upper surface

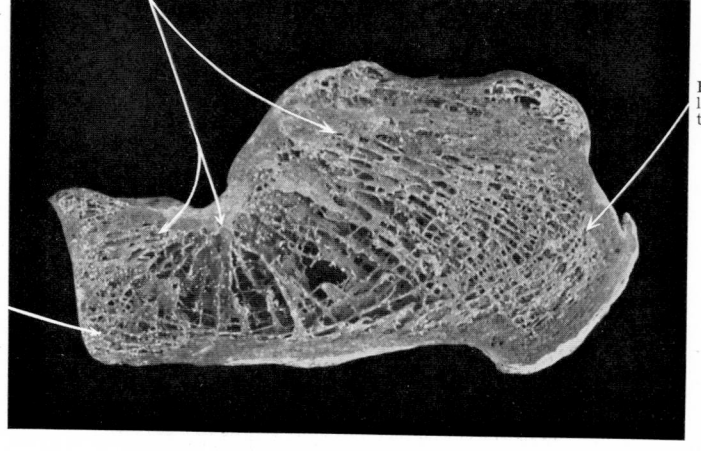

Finer curved
lamellæ crossing
the other system

Fine curved
lamellæ running
from anterior to
posterior surface

FIG. 2.—PHOTOGRAPH OF SAGITTAL SECTION OF CALCANEUM TO SHOW ITS ARCHITECTURE.

Note the thin shell of compact bone and the arrangement of the lamellæ of the
spongy bone in two main systems.

PLATE III

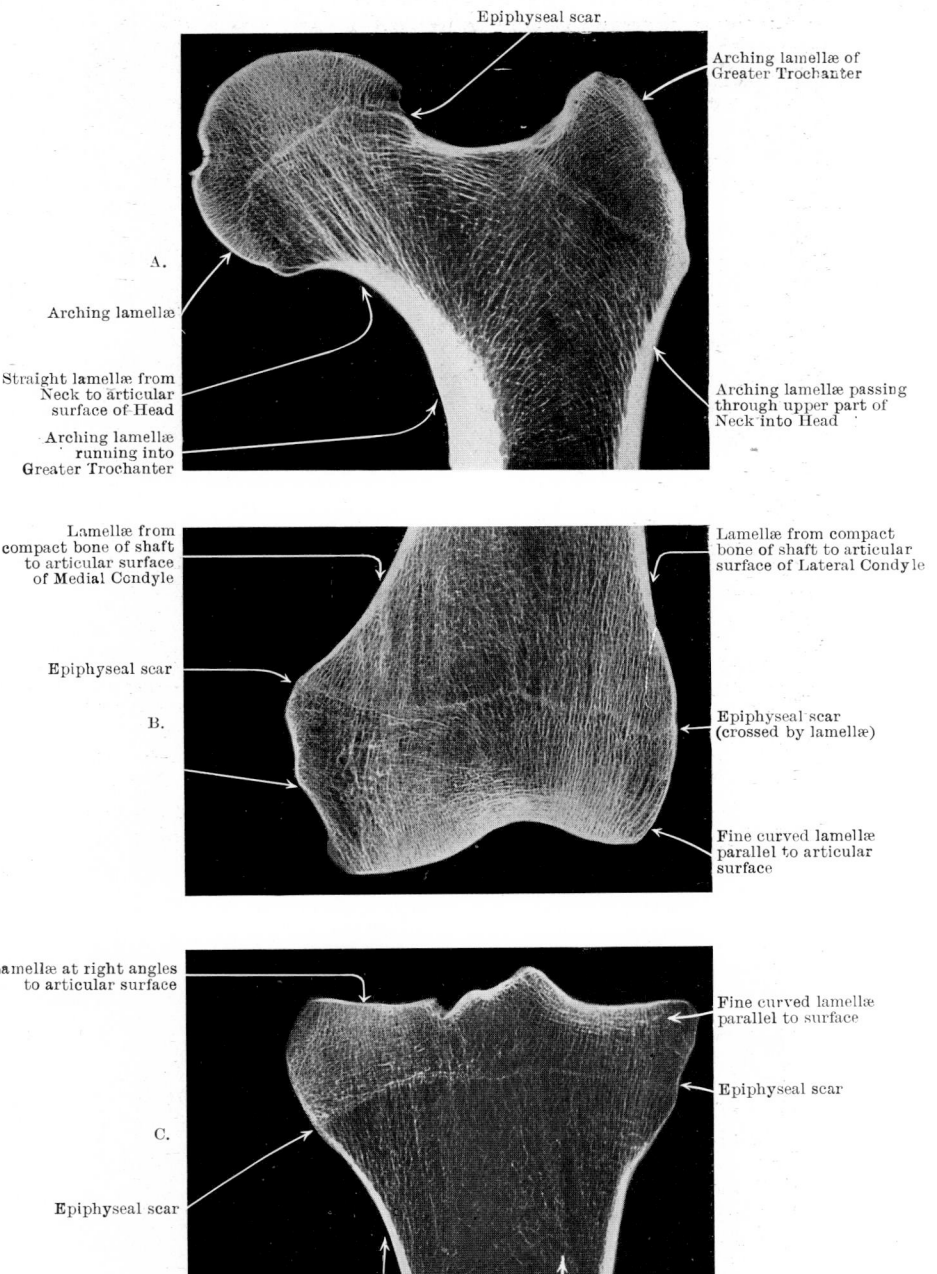

Epiphyseal scar

Arching lamellæ of
Greater Trochanter

A.

Arching lamellæ

Straight lamellæ from
Neck to articular
surface of Head

Arching lamellæ
running into
Greater Trochanter

Arching lamellæ passing
through upper part of
Neck into Head

Lamellæ from
compact bone of shaft
to articular surface
of Medial Condyle

Lamellæ from compact
bone of shaft to articular
surface of Lateral Condyle

Epiphyseal scar

B.

Epiphyseal scar
(crossed by lamellæ)

Fine curved lamellæ
parallel to articular
surface

Lamellæ at right angles
to articular surface

Fine curved lamellæ
parallel to surface

Epiphyseal scar

C.

Epiphyseal scar

Vertical lamellæ springing from compact bone of shaft   Vertical lamellæ of spongy bone

PLATE III.—RADIOGRAPHS OF CORONAL SECTIONS OF A. UPPER END OF FEMUR ;
B. LOWER END OF FEMUR ; C. UPPER END OF TIBIA, OF A WOMAN AGED 34.

Note the persisting epiphyseal scars and the arrangement of the systems of lamellæ in the spongy bone.

PLATE IV

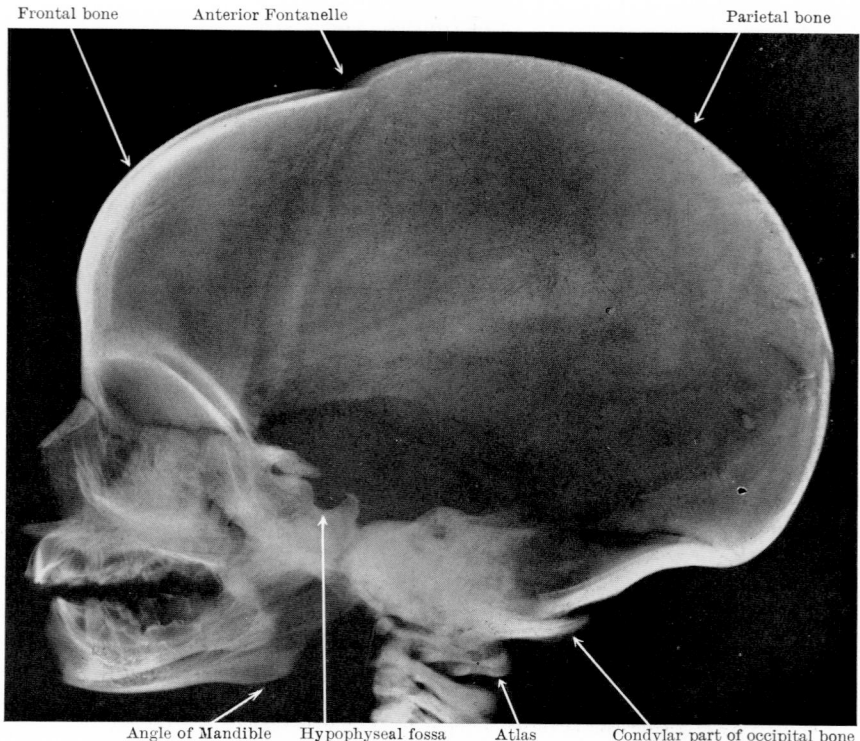

Frontal bone   Anterior Fontanelle   Parietal bone

Angle of Mandible   Hypophyseal fossa   Atlas   Condylar part of occipital bone
(overlapping supra-occipital part)

FIG. 1.—LATERAL RADIOGRAPH OF SKULL OF FULL-TIME FŒTUS.

Compare with Fig. 156, p. 194.

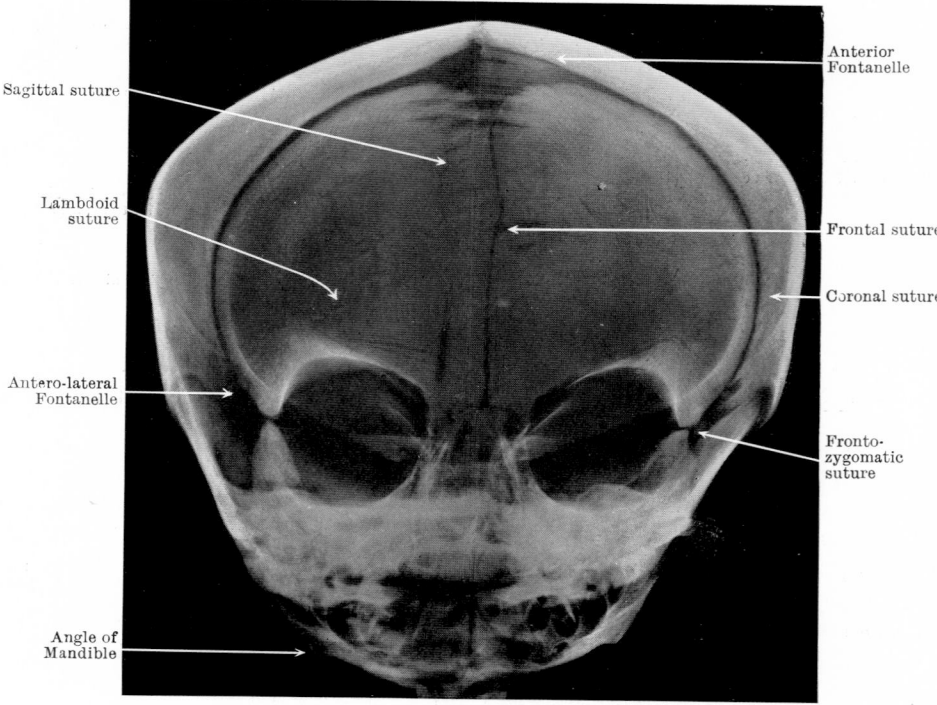

Anterior
Fontanelle

Sagittal suture

Lambdoid
suture

Frontal suture

Coronal suture

Antero-lateral
Fontanelle

Fronto-
zygomatic
suture

Angle of
Mandible

FIG. 2.—ANTERO-POSTERIOR RADIOGRAPH OF THE SAME SKULL OF A FULL-TIME FŒTUS.

Compare with Fig. 155, p. 193.

OSTEOLOGY

Originally written by the late ARTHUR THOMSON, M.A., M.B., LL.D., F.R.C.S.

Professor of Anatomy, University of Oxford

Revised and rewritten by E. B. JAMIESON

INTRODUCTION

BONES AND CARTILAGES

THE body is built around and supported by a framework of **bones** called the *skeleton* [σκελετός (skeletos) = dried], which accounts for about one-seventh of the body weight in a man and rather less in a woman; and the bones are supplemented in many places by gristle or **cartilage**—more so in a growing person than in an adult.

Uses of Bones.—Bones make up the framework on which the form of the body is moulded. They give support to the softer tissues which are situated around them. They provide surfaces and projections for the attachments of certain of the softer structures, such as the muscles, tendons, and ligaments. Some of the bones are connected together in such a way that they form the walls of cages and boxes for the lodgment of internal organs, for example, the heart and the lungs in the chest, the brain in the skull, and the spinal marrow in the backbone.

In addition, the bones throughout the adult body are the chief factory for the production of the cells of the blood, for they contain a special tissue, called *bone marrow*, in which the blood corpuscles are made; and, further, many of the bones are used as passive levers in the movements of the body.

Articulation of Bones (see Figs. in chapter on Joints).—Bones are held together indirectly by all the tissues which surround them and are attached to them, but bones which lie close to each other are connected together directly in a special way. The connexion or union between two or more adjacent bones is called a **joint** or articulation. The union is effected at most joints by special sheets and bands of fibrous tissue, called *ligaments*, which are fixed to adjoining parts of the two bones. The movements of the body take place at joints, and at those joints at which free movements are possible the bones are the levers by which they are brought about. [*Articulus*, diminutive of *artus* = a joint; cf. "articulation" in speech, meaning the junction of words or syllables. *Ligamentum* = a band or bandage, from *ligare* = to bind.]

Bones which are united together at a joint are said to *articulate* with each other at that joint, and the part of the one bone that comes into relation with the other bone is called its **articular** surface (or margin or end, as the case may be). At most of the joints of the *skull* there is a ribbon of fibrous tissue interposed between the two articular parts and firmly attached to both of them; and the articular parts are rough. At the joints between the *bodies* of the *vertebræ* (*i.e.* the segments of the backbone), and at the joint between the *two hip bones*, the articular parts are coated over with an adherent layer of **articular cartilage**, and interposed between them and firmly attached to them there is a plate or disc of a kind of cartilage called *fibro-cartilage*; at those joints also the articular parts of the bones are rough. But in the majority of joints the bones can either glide or rotate on each other; the articular parts are covered with an adherent layer of articular cartilage which is smooth and polished, and the underlying bone also is smooth, so that the articular part of a dried bone is easily identified, even though the articular cartilage has come off during the preparation of the bone.

Constituents of Bone.—Bone, or bony tissue, consists of equal parts of solids and water, and it is the hardest and most enduring tissue in the body, excepting only the enamel of the teeth. The solids are partly organic matter and partly inorganic. The *inorganic matter* consists of various *mineral salts*. About 70 per cent. of the solids are salts; the chief of them is phosphate of lime, which makes up about six-sevenths of the mineral or inorganic matter; and, because of its abundance, bones are one of the sources of phosphorus. The *organic matter* is *white fibrous tissue*. It consists of—(a) fine fibres imbedded in a little amorphous material, called "ground substance," which unites the fibres into interlacing bundles; (b) connective-tissue cells placed in rows among the bundles of fibres. The ground substance is completely impregnated with the mineral salts; and the cells are called *bone corpuscles*. The actual percentages of the components are :—organic matter, 31·03; calcium phosphate, 58·23; calcium carbonate, 7·32; calcium fluoride, 1·41; magnesium phosphate, 1·32; sodium chloride, 0.69. The mineral salts are so perfectly distributed through the fibrous tissue that a bone retains its shape both when the salts are dissolved out of it by immersion in acid, and when the fibrous tissue is burnt out of it. Bones are not only hard but are also exceedingly tough and elastic; they owe their toughness and elasticity to the fibrous tissue, and their hardness to the salts. In old age bones become more brittle owing to diminution of the elasticity of the fibrous tissue and not to any increase in the salts.

Structure of Bone.—There are two kinds of bone—compact bone and spongy bone. (See Fig. 239, p. 273.) **Compact bone** is hard and dense; this is seen and appreciated best in a bone such as the thigh bone when it is sawn across the middle. **Spongy bone** also is hard, but it is full of little cavities like a sponge; this is well seen in the end of a bone like the thigh bone, for the end consists of a mass of spongy bone covered with a thin surface shell of compact bone. When a bone is fresh the cavities of spongy bone are filled with a soft, reddish material known as *red marrow*. The cavities and their walls appear very irregular to a casual glance, but with careful examination it becomes apparent that the bony substance around the cavities in any bone is arranged so as best to withstand the strain and stress that will normally be put upon that bone. The bends, curves, and twists of the bones, the proportion of compact and spongy substance in them, and their internal architecture, all aim at a maximum strength with the utmost economy of material in order to secure a strong skeleton of minimum weight. Considering the amount of material used, the strength of bone is remarkable; bone is nearly as strong as cast-iron and nearly twice as strong as oak, and is able to resist a crushing strain of two tons weight to the cubic inch.

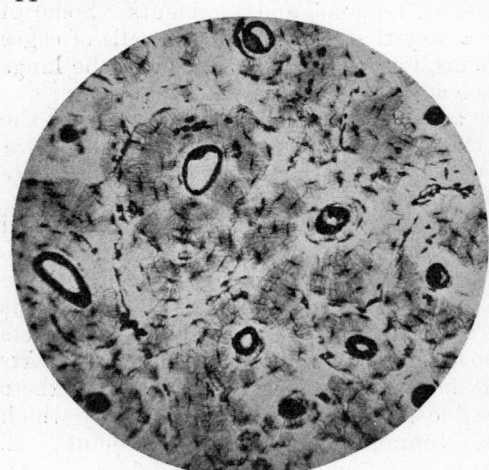

FIG. 111.—PHOTOGRAPH OF GROUND TRANSVERSE SECTION OF COMPACT BONE, showing Haversian systems (Haversian canal, concentric lamellæ, lacunæ, and canaliculi).

The **microscopical structure** of bony tissue is essentially the same in spongy and compact bone. The bony tissue is arranged in thin, closely applied sheets or layers called **bone lamellæ** [*lamella* or *lamina* = a leaf, blade, layer]. Here and there, between the lamellæ, there are minute cavities called **lacunæ** [*lacuna* = a pit, hole, or cavity], and in each lacuna, when the bone is fresh, there is a **bone corpuscle**. Several slender tubes or canals, called **canaliculi**, pass from a lacuna through the lamellæ and connect it with neighbouring lacunæ. A large number of the lamellæ are tubular, and are arranged in groups called **Haversian systems** (after Clopton Havers, who was the first to describe them in detail). In each group there are from three to ten tubes, called **Haversian lamellæ,** arranged concentrically one outside the other. The cavity of the central tube is called a **Haversian canal,** and contains blood-vessels, a lymph channel, a nerve, and some loose areolar tissue. The lacunæ of one system communicate by means of canaliculi with the other lacunæ in that system, but seldom with those of adjoining systems. Haversian systems are present in spongy bone and in thin compact bone, but they are most numerous in thick compact bone. Indeed, the compact substance of the shaft of a long bone is composed chiefly of Haversian systems, but at the surface of the bone there are circumferential lamellæ, and between the Haversian systems, there are interstitial lamellæ which are also parallel to the surface. These circumferential and interstitial lamellæ are called **periosteal lamellæ.** The circumferential lamellæ are pierced by calcified bundles of fibres, called the **perforating fibres** of Sharpey, which nail them together. These lamellæ are traversed also by tunnels through which the blood-vessels enter and leave the bone. The tunnels subdivide to become continuous with the Haversian canals, and their fibrous lining is continuous with the areolar tissue in those canals.

Classification of Bones.—The bones are divided into four classes according to their shape : long, short, flat, irregular.

Long bones are found in the limbs, *e.g.* the *humerus* or bone of the upper arm, and the *femur* or thigh bone. Small elongated bones, such as those of the fingers and toes, are called **miniature long bones.** Each long bone has a *shaft* and *two ends.* The **shaft** is a hollow, thick-walled rod of compact bone. The space inside is called the **medullary cavity,** and, when the bone is fresh, it is filled with soft, yellowish material known as *yellow marrow* [*medulla* = marrow] ; the yellow colour is due to abundance of fat. Around the medullary cavity, inside the compact bone, there is a layer of coarse spongy bone. The medullary cavity serves not only for the lodgment of the marrow. Its presence makes the bone lighter—with little diminution in strength, for up to a certain point a hollow cylinder is almost as resistant as a solid one of the same thickness and material. The shaft of a long bone is never quite straight ; it is curved usually in more than one plane ; its curvatures increase

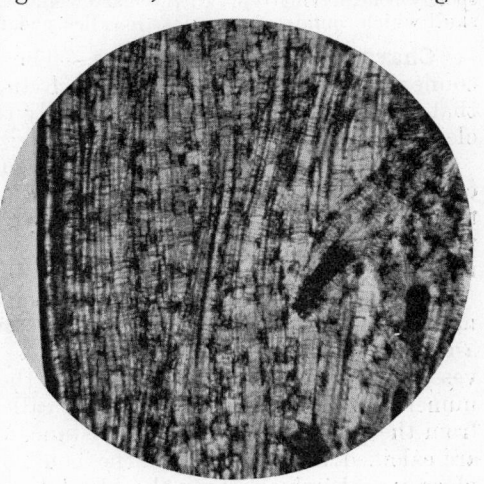

Fig. 112.—Photograph of Ground Longitudinal Section of Compact Bone, showing periosteal lamellæ parallel to surface on the left and Haversian systems cut obliquely on the right.

its strength and resistance, the more so as there is a greater thickness of compact bony tissue in the concavities of the curves than elsewhere. The **ends** of a long bone are broader and thicker than the shaft. They consist of spongy bone covered with a thin layer of compact bone ; the cavities in the sponge-work make the bone lighter. The objects gained by the greater bulk of the end of the bone are : (1) The surface for articulation is wider, and therefore movements at the joint can be regulated more precisely ; (2) the chances of dislocation are diminished ; (3) shocks received by the bone are diffused.

Short bones are more or less cubical in shape. They consist of spongy bone enclosed in a thin shell of compact bone. Examples of short bones are the eight *bones of the wrist* and the seven *bones of the hinder half of the foot.* **Sesamoid bones** are included among short bones. A sesamoid bone is one which is developed in the substance of a tendon or sinew ; the patella or knee cap is by far the largest of the sesamoid bones. They get their name from the resemblance that some of them have to sesame seeds.

Flat bones are such as the *ribs,* the *shoulder blade,* and the bones of the *skull cap.* They are **thin** rather than flat, for nearly all " flat " bones are curved or bent. Each is made up of two plates of compact bone which enclose between them a layer of spongy bone.   In the flat bones of the skull the layer of spongy substance is called the **diploë** [διπλόη (diploë) = a fold or doubling, a junction of two plates]; and in the diploë the marrow is largely replaced by venous blood.

Irregular bones are of various shapes, and include all those that cannot be classed as long, or short, or flat.   Many of the *skull bones* are irregular, and so are the *vertebræ*.   The thinner parts of irregular bones are like flat bones—two plates of compact substance with spongy substance between them.   The bulky parts, especially in vertebræ, are like short bones, and consist of spongy substance surrounded with a layer of compact substance.

In the skull, most of the flat bones and many of the irregular bones have spongy substance between their two layers of compact substance, but in some of them the spongy tissue is more or less completely removed, and is replaced by cavities containing air—the walls of the cavities being composed of compact bone.   Those cavities are called **air sinuses**; they give lightness to the bones and act as resonating chambers for the voice; they are extensions from the cavity of the nose, with which they are permanently in communication (Figs. 147, 148); their walls are lined on the inside with a membrane, called *muco-endosteum*, which is continuous with the muco-periosteum that lines the interior of the nose; inflammation of the mucous lining of the nose in a "cold in the head" extends to the lining of the sinuses and gives rise to dull headaches.   The air spaces in the part of the skull called the mastoid temporal are, however, rather different; they are extensions from the cavity of the tympanum or drum of the ear, and lie in the midst of spongy bone, having replaced the marrow and some of the spongy substance.   The bones of the skull which contain air cavities are called **pneumatic bones** [πνεῦμα (pneuma) = wind or air].

Characters of Living Bone.—The following five points are to be noted in connexion with a bone when it is living, or when it is in the "recent state"— that is, when it has been only recently removed from the body and has not been cleaned and dried.

(1) The articular parts of most bones are covered with a layer of cartilage called **articular cartilage**; and, at those joints at which the bones are free to move, the articular cartilage is smooth and polished to facilitate movement.   But the majority of the bones of the skull have no articular cartilage; their articulating margins are rough and are united by fibrous tissue.

(2) The whole of the bone, except the articular part, is covered with a laminated membrane of fibrous tissue called **periosteum** [περί (peri) = around; ὀστέον (osteon) = a bone].   The periosteum is adherent to the bone owing to the number of blood-vessels and nerves which pass from the periosteum into the bone, and because numerous minute bundles of fibres, called the *perforating fibres* of Sharpey, pass from the periosteum into the substance of the bone; within the bone the bundles are calcified like the rest of the bone, and nail the bone lamellæ together.   The blood-vessels which carry the blood to and from the bone and marrow lie in the periosteum before they enter the bone (arteries), and after they leave it (veins); if the periosteum is stripped off a living bone by accident or disease the under-lying part of the bone may die owing to the loss of its blood supply.

(3) The muscles, tendons, intermuscular fibrous septa [*septum* = a hedge, barrier, partition], and the ligaments are attached partly to the periosteum and partly to the bone directly.   In muscles with fleshy attachments the muscle fibres have microscopic tendinous ends which blend with the periosteum; some of the fibres of the tendons, the septa, and the ligaments blend with the periosteum, but a great many are prolonged into the bone as perforating fibres, and the tendons, etc., are therefore very firmly attached to bone.

(4) The medullary cavity is filled with yellow marrow, and the cavities in spongy bone with red marrow.

(5) The cavities in spongy bone are lined with a delicate membrane of fibrous tissue called **endosteum** [ἔνδον (endon) = within]; and, in a long bone, the medullary cavity is lined with endosteum continuous with that in the ends of the bone.   The endosteum within a bone is connected with the periosteum on the outside by means of the fibrous lining of the tunnels through which the blood-vessels pass.

Bone Marrow.—Both red and white blood corpuscles are formed in the bone marrow.   After birth the marrow is the only source of the red corpuscles; and, in adults, the marrow is the chief source of those varieties of white corpuscles that have distinctly stainable granules.   Blood platelets also are possibly formed in the marrow.   In infants the red marrow pervades all bones.

In the long bones, it is found not only in the spongy parts but also in the medullary cavity and even in the larger Haversian canals. It is gradually replaced by yellow marrow. At puberty the red marrow is found only in the spongy bone ; and, as age advances, it is replaced by yellow marrow in the spongy bone of peripheral parts—distal ends of long bones and the lower part of the backbone. But, in certain diseases of the blood, the red marrow may increase, invade its former territories and oust the yellow marrow from them.

The **yellow marrow** is simple in structure. It is adipose tissue, and is the most purely fatty tissue in the body ; but it contains also a few cells that give rise to blood corpuscles.

The **red marrow** is the important blood-forming organ. It consists of a large number of cells contained in the meshes of a delicate sponge-work of areolar tissue in which numerous blood-vessels—chiefly veins—ramify and anastomose. The red marrow owes its colour to the red cells inside and outside the vessels. The cells are of different kinds :—(1) A large number of amœboid marrow cells ; (2) white blood corpuscles ; (3) erythroblasts ; (4) red blood corpuscles ; (5) a few giant cells ; (6) a few large fat-cells. The **marrow cells** give rise to *white blood corpuscles* by mitotic division. The **erythroblasts** are nucleated cells of two varieties— a larger and a smaller—and are reddish [ἐρυθρός (erythros) = red]. The larger give rise to the smaller by mitotic division. The smaller ones give rise to the *red blood corpuscles* by losing their nuclei (probably by extrusion) and by becoming flattened discs. The **giant cells** resemble osteoclasts, and, indeed, are most numerous where bone is undergoing absorption, though they are not limited to such places. It has been said that amœboid processes project from them into blood-vessels, and are broken off to form the *blood platelets*.

The degenerated marrow found in the skull bones of aged people is called *gelatinous marrow*.

The **blood-vessels** reach the yellow marrow through the canals in the thick, compact bone of the shaft, and they supply the bony substance on their way through it. To reach the red marrow they have to pierce only the shell of compact bone ; they ramify in the red marrow, and send small twigs into the surrounding bone. Bone and fat are inactive tissues, requiring little blood ; the blood-vessels in the part of the shaft that encloses the medullary cavity are therefore small and relatively few. Red marrow is a very active tissue requiring a generous blood supply ; numerous blood-vessels of fairly large size therefore perforate the short and flat bones and the non-articular parts of long bones at and near their ends. The veins are larger and more numerous than the arteries ; for the veins are the channels by which newly-made blood corpuscles are taken away from the marrow. Inside the spongy bone the veins are large blood-spaces enclosed by thin walls without muscular tissue.

The **nerves** that accompany arteries into the bone are probably *nervi vasorum*.

The **lymph channels** are cleft-like spaces in the areolar sheaths of the blood-vessels ; and they end in the lymph vessels of the periosteum.

Appearances of a Dried Bone.—The bones used for study have been macerated and dried. Maceration is a process by which all the structures attached to a bone, including the periosteum and articular cartilage, are removed. In the subsequent drying the marrow and endosteum shrivel.

Though the articular cartilage is removed the **articular part** of a bone can still be identified. In the vertebræ the articular cartilage that covers the upper and lower surfaces of the bodies does not have a free surface itself but is adherent to fibro-cartilage (see p. 95), and the part covered by the articular cartilage can be recognised by its peculiar appearance, which resembles unglazed porcelain. But in most bones the articular cartilage has a free surface which is smooth and polished, and the bone covered by it also is smooth and polished ; some other parts of the bone may be quite smooth but do not have the polished or glazed appearance. Over all the surfaces of a bone, except the smooth articular surfaces, there are numerous small apertures ; the apertures are the outer ends of the canals or tunnels through which the blood-vessels pass on their way to and from the bone marrow and the substance of the bone. At the ends of a long bone, and on its shaft near the ends, those small foramina [*foramen* = a hole] are scattered, and are largest and most numerous near the margins of the articular surface. In the greater part of the shaft of a long bone the foramina are very minute, and are barely visible to the naked eye, but there is always one relatively large foramen, called the **nutrient foramen,** the position of which is fairly constant for the same bone in different subjects ; the tunnel into which it leads is the *nutrient canal*; the vessels which pass through it are called the *nutrient artery* and *vein,* and they convey the blood to and from the yellow marrow and the substance of the shaft. The ends of a long bone have a double blood supply—(1) from vessels that enter through their own non-articular surfaces ; (2) from vessels that run into them from the adjoining parts of the shaft. In a dried bone, some of the foramina on the shaft near the end can be seen to be directed towards the end.

On the exterior of bones there are many grooves and hollows, ridges, eminences, and projections. The depressions and elevations are chiefly for the attachment of muscles, tendons, and ligaments. For any one bone they vary in different subjects, but are sufficiently alike for a general description to be applicable to all. The **surfaces** of a bone are named usually from the direction in which they face; *e.g.* a surface directed *forwards* is called the *anterior* surface. Sometimes surfaces are named according to their relative propinquity to a cavity; *e.g.* the *outer* surface of a rib is the one farther away from the cavity of the chest. Some surfaces are named after neighbouring structures; *e.g.* the *costal* surface of the shoulder blade is the surface directed towards the ribs [*costa* = a rib]. The edge or ridge between two surfaces is called a **border** or margin, and is named from the direction in which it looks.

The depressions and elevations receive general names (most of which are included in the alphabetical list below) and special names according to their position or characters.

A student is often asked to say whether a given bone or other bilateral organ belongs to the right or the left half of the body. It is a ready means of testing whether he knows the broad, main features of the organ; for if a structure is held in the position it occupies in the erect body (*i.e.* with its upper end upwards and its anterior surface facing forwards), then its lateral surface or end or border will look towards the side to which it belongs. If a student does not know enough about a structure to enable him to distinguish which is the upper part, which is the front, and which is the lateral part, there is little merit and no advantage in his knowing whether it is left or right.

DEFINITION OF TERMS.

The terms *median, medial, lateral,* etc., are explained on pp. 3 and 4.

Aditus. The entrance into a cavity. [*Aditus* = an entrance.]

Ala. A projection or a surface shaped like a wing. [*Ala* = a wing.]

Alveolus. A deep narrow pit. [*Alveolus* = a small cavity.]

Antrum. A cavity or hollow filled with air and lined with mucous membrane in the interior of a bone. [Ἄντρον (antron) = a cave.]

Canal. A passage or tunnel; unlike the artificial watercourses of the same name, a canal has complete walls round about it.

Condyle. A smooth rounded eminence covered with articular cartilage. [Κόνδυλος (condylos) = a knuckle.]

Crest or *Crista.* A sharp upstanding ridge of bone.

Epicondyle. A prominence or projection situated above a smooth articular eminence, though that eminence may not be called a condyle. ['Επί (epi) = above or upon.]

Facet. A small smooth area usually covered with articular cartilage. Nearly all smooth articular surfaces on bones are referred to at times as facets.

Foramen. A hole; it may be an aperture through which one can see, or it may be the end of a canal.

Fossa. A depression, usually broad and shallow. [*Fossa* = a ditch.]

Hiatus. A slit or gap.

Labium or *Lip.* The margin of a groove or a hollow; when a ridge or a border is thick its margins are called its lips.

Lamina or *Lamella.* A thin plate or sheet.

Ligula or *Lingula.* A projection shaped like a tongue.

Line or *Linea.* A low ridge, usually narrow.

Meatus. A short canal. [*Meatus* = a way, passage.]

Process. Any kind of projection or prolongation.

Sinus. A cavity in a bone lined with mucous membrane and filled with air; used with very different meanings in other systems. [*Sinus* = a curve, fold, interior, hiding place, bay, or gulf.]

Spina or *Spine.* A sharp-pointed projection.

Squama. A portion of bone shaped like a scale. [*Squama* = a scale.]

Sulcus. A groove or furrow.

Trochlea. A pulley or pulley-shaped surface. [Τροχιλία (trochilia) = the sheave of a pulley.]

Tuber, Tubercle, and *Tuberosity* [*tuber* = a bump or swelling] are terms applied, without much distinction, to any kind of rounded swelling or eminence, large or small, smooth or rough. The term *tubercle,* with quite another meaning, is well known, owing to the endemic prevalence of disease caused by tubercle bacilli, but the origin of the term is the same. Tubercular diseases were so named because hard nodules or *tubercles* were found on the surface of affected organs.

Uncus. A part shaped like a hook. [*Uncus* = a hook or barb.]

Cartilage

Cartilage or gristle is present in many parts of the body. It is supplementary to bones, and in many situations it takes the place of bone. It is much more abundant in a young animal than in an adult, for much of the cartilage present in the young animal is replaced by bone during the period of growth;

but in many places cartilage persists throughout life. Cartilage is nourished by lymph. Neither blood-vessels nor nerves have been found in the actual substance of cartilage, though blood-vessels are present in the clefts in the larger pieces. It is elastic, but is not hard like bone; for it consists of collaginous material impregnated with chondro-sulphuric acid, with only a trace of lime salts. It is less yielding and pliable than tendons and ligaments, though it is cut more easily with a knife. Cartilage is covered with a fibrous membrane called **perichondrium**; the only exception is articular cartilage, which has a covering only on its margins. [Περί (peri) = around; χόνδρος (chondros) = cartilage.]

Classification of Cartilage.—There are three main varieties — hyaline cartilage; white fibro-cartilage; yellow fibro-cartilage.

Hyaline cartilage is bluish-white in colour, rather brittle, and easily cut into slices; the cut surface, to the naked eye, is homogeneous in texture, and a thin slice is translucent—hence the name "hyaline," from ὕαλος (hyalos) = glass. The following cartilages are of the hyaline variety : (1) The *costal cartilages*, which are connected with the anterior ends of the ribs. (2) The strips of cartilage between the segments of the body of the *sternum*, and a great part of the *xiphoid process*, which is the lowest part of the sternum. (3) The cartilages of the *nose*; most of the cartilages of the *larynx* or voice box; the cartilaginous rings of the *trachea* or windpipe and of the *bronchi*, which are the branches of the trachea. (4) The *cartilage which precedes bone*. At birth a great deal of that cartilage has been changed into bone already; but much of it still persists, especially at the ends of bones, and is gradually replaced by osseous tissue as growth goes on. In some bones the change is not complete until the body is fully grown; a growing person has therefore more hyaline cartilage in the body than an adult has; a ready example is furnished by edible animals : there is far more gristle about the bones in veal and lamb than in beef and mutton. (5) *Articular cartilage* is part of the hyaline cartilage in which a bone is formed; and it remains cartilaginous throughout life.

White fibro-cartilage consists of cartilage mixed with strong bundles of white fibrous tissue; it is therefore less homogeneous than hyaline cartilage and is tougher and more flexible; the fibrous tissue in it is most abundant at its attachments to bone. It is found in the following situations : (1) As *sesamoid cartilages* in a few tendons. (2) As *articular discs* in the joint between the lower jaw and the skull, the joint at each end of the collar bone, and at the wrist joint. (3) In the shoulder joint and the hip joint, as a ring-like *labrum* attached to the rim of the articular socket of the shoulder blade and the hip bone. [*Labrum* = labium = a lip.] (4) In the knee joint, as two crescentic bodies called *semilunar cartilages*. (5) In the backbone as thick *intervertebral discs*, one between the bodies of each two vertebræ and attached firmly to both of them, uniting them together; those discs account for most of the white fibro-cartilage in the body; they are easily recognised between the bodies of the vertebræ on the sawn surface of a sirloin of beef. (6) A similar plate unites the two hip bones at the *pubic symphysis* —that is, the joint in the middle line at the lower part of the front of the abdomen.

Yellow fibro-cartilage consists of cartilage mixed with bundles of yellow elastic fibres, and it contains little or no white fibrous tissue. It is found in the *ear*, in the *pharyngo-tympanic tube* (that is, the passage between the drum of the ear and the throat), and in some of the cartilages of the *larynx*.

Development of Bone

Bones are formed in mesodermal tissue (p. 36). In some parts, as in the vault of the skull, the mesoderm becomes fibrous tissue, and the bones are formed in it. In most parts, however, a small model of the bone is made of cartilage formed in the mesodermal tissue; the first step is a closer aggregation of the mesodermal cells in the situation where the model is to be made; the aggregation of cells is the **rudiment** of a bone, and the cells assume an appearance intermediate between fibrous tissue and cartilage, forming a substance called **pro-cartilage**, which is gradually transformed into true *hyaline cartilage*. The process of transformation of the fibrous tissue or of the cartilage into bone is called **ossification**. The bones ossified in fibrous tissue are called *membrane bones*, because the fibrous tissue is arranged in the form of a membrane. The bones which are preceded by cartilage are called *cartilage bones*.

Formation of Cartilage.—Each of the cells in the interior of the bone rudiment enlarges, and as it does so it makes a thick *capsule* or envelope round about itself, and then divides into two; each of the two enlarges, makes a capsule and divides; and so on—two new capsules being formed inside each older one. In that way the rudiment increases in size until a mass of tissue is formed consisting of cells—now called *cartilage cells*—which are imbedded in a dense substance of fused capsules made by the cells themselves and called the **cartilaginous periblast** (or *matrix*— an unsuitable name). The outermost part of the bone rudiment is retained as the **perichondrium**, which consists of an outer layer mainly fibrous, and an inner layer mainly cells and blood-vessels. [Περί (peri) = around; βλαστάνω (blastanō) = grow; χόνδρος (chondros) = cartilage.]

Appearance of Ossific Centres.—The process of ossification begins at different dates in different bones, but nearly all the bones begin to be ossified during the second month of intra-uterine life, and the date is fairly constant for any one bone in different subjects. The point in a bone where ossification begins is called a **centre of ossification**, and the centre is said to *appear* at such and such a date. Many of the bones are ossified from more than one centre. When a bone has several centres of ossification and the centres appear at widely separated dates, the first to appear is called the **primary centre** and the others are called **secondary centres**. By far the largest part of a bone is ossified from the primary centre. When ossification starts at more than one point in a bone about the same time, each of those centres is called a primary centre.

Ossification in Cartilage.—Ossification begins usually about the *middle* of a cartilage bone. At that point there is a great *increase* both in the size of the cartilage cells and in the amount of the substance around the cells; and the next step is the *deposition of lime salts* in that substance. As the process spreads from the centre the *cartilage cells* immediately ahead of the calcifying region *multiply* rapidly; in that way the size of the "bone" as a whole is increased—the multiplication and increase in a long bone taking place chiefly lengthwise. The deposit of lime salts goes on till, in a little while, the cartilage cells become imprisoned inside the calcareous walls built around them, and, having their supply of nutriment cut off at the same time, they die and shrivel, leaving the *spaces* they occupied *nearly empty*.

This calcified cartilage is not bone, though the process is called ossification; but while those changes have been taking place in the centre a similar change leading to the *production of real bone* has been taking place on the outside of the cartilage. The cells of the deeper layer of the perichondrium have formed a clear *ground-substance* round about themselves; fibres have been laid down in that, and **bone** is produced by the deposit of lime salts in the ground-substance between and among the cells and fibres, and, possibly, within the fibres themselves. The calcified cartilage in the interior is thus encased in bone formed by the perichondrium; the perichondrium, since it now surrounds bone, is called periosteum, and that bone is called **subperiosteal bone.**

The calcified cartilage is short-lived. Blood-vessels grow in from the deeper layers of the periosteum, and they are accompanied by more than one kind of cell. Some of those cells are called **osteoclasts** [κλάω (claō) = break, destroy]. They eat their way through the subperiosteal bone, making passages through it for the blood-vessels they accompany to run along; and when they come to the calcified cartilage they consume a great part of it and so enlarge the spaces in the interior. Other cells accompanying the blood-vessels are called *osteoblasts* or **bone-forming cells** [βλαστάνω (blastanō) = grow, produce]. They are the same kind of cells around which, and under the influence of which, the bone is formed underneath the periosteum; they form layers of bone on the calcified cartilage that the osteoclasts have so far left untouched, and thus enclose the enlarged spaces with bony walls; the spaces become filled with marrow by the multiplication of fat-cells and other cells that accompany the blood-vessels. The remains of the calcified cartilage on which those layers of bone are laid down become in time destroyed by the osteoclasts, until no vestige of cartilage or cartilage cells is left in the interior.

Both under the periosteum and in the interior some of the bone-forming cells are left in little cavities between succeeding layers of bone; but they are not cut off from nutritive supply, and survive, under the name of *bone corpuscles*, as long as the bone lives.

It is not only the calcified cartilage that is destroyed by osteoclasts. The cavities in spongy adult bone are much larger than the cavities in newly-formed bone. The cavities are larger because osteoclasts have removed a great quantity of the first-formed bone, so that several of the original cavities or spaces run into one. The strength of the bone, however, is maintained and increased because bone-forming cells lay down additional layers of bone on what remains of the original bone, and in that way the walls of the enlarged cavities are thickened. And it is not only in the bone which is formed in cartilage that those changes occur; the original subperiosteal bone also is largely destroyed and is replaced by a second osseous deposit. If the horizontal diameters of the body of a vertebra of a new-born child are compared with the diameters of the body of an adult vertebra, it will be clear that only a small part in the centre of the adult bone is pre-formed in cartilage. The greater part in those diameters is formed by layer after layer deposited under the periosteum. In that subperiosteal bone the same process has gone on as in the centre— ingrowth of blood-vessels, excavation by osteoclasts, and a rebuilding and a strengthening of the remains by bone-forming cells; and that strengthening is especially marked in the last-formed layers in the adult bone so as to produce the compact bone at the surface.

Some of the tissue which grows in with the blood-vessels from the periosteum becomes converted into the perforating fibres of Sharpey.

In bones that have a medullary cavity the osseous tissue which succeeds the calcified cartilage is entirely removed in order that the cavity may be created; and, further, while new bone is being formed on the outside under the periosteum, osteoclasts are continually eating away the bony tissue next the medullary cavity in order to enlarge the cavity both in length and width, until it attains adult size. In a bone like the femur none of the bony tissue present at birth and none that was created during early life is left at all, for the medullary cavity of the adult femur is larger than the whole femur of a child. Absorption of bone takes place also at the surface, especially at the ends of long bones—modelling them in order that their proper shape may be maintained as they grow.

The **Haversian systems** are produced in the following way: Blood-vessels from the periosteum grow into the original subperiosteal bone, and the osteoclasts create long and relatively wide spaces around those vessels. The bone-forming cells then multiply and arrange themselves round the inside of the wall of the space, and produce layer after layer around the space, forming a series of concentric tubes, the innermost one enclosing the original space, now called the Haversian canal. As successive layers are produced, bone-forming cells are left between them as bone-corpuscles in lacunæ. Among the Haversian systems a few of the original layers of the subperiosteal bone survive, and they are called *interstitial lamellæ*; while, at the surface of the bone, the last-formed layers of subperiosteal bone are left unaltered and are called *circumferential lamellæ*.

Ossification in membrane occurs in certain skull-bones, in the lower jaw bone and in part of the collar bone. The cartilaginous stage is missed out; in other respects the process of ossification is the same as in a cartilage bone. Osseous tissue is deposited in or underneath the outer layers of the sheet or membrane of mesoderm, which thereupon becomes periosteum; that is followed by excavation by osteoclasts and rebuilding by bone-forming cells—in the same sequence as in ossification under the periosteum of a bone pre-formed in cartilage.

Formation of Joints.—The mesodermal tissue between two developing bones becomes converted into the structures that bind the two bones together, and those structures vary according to the class of joint. In a **synovial joint**—that is one in which there is a cavity in the joint and the bones are free to move—the outer layers of the condensed mesoderm become converted into the *articular capsule* of the joint; the cells in the interior disappear and the *joint cavity* is formed. In certain joints the cells inside do not all disappear; those that remain give rise to the fibro-cartilaginous plates and the ligaments found in the interior of certain synovial joints. (See Figs. in chapter on Joints.)

Growth of Bones.—Most bones grow in two dimensions by deposition of osseous tissue under the periosteum, and in the third dimension by multiplication of cartilage cells prior to ossification. For example, the body of a vertebra grows in breadth and in thickness by subperiosteal deposit of bone, and in height by increase of cartilage at its upper and lower surfaces; a long bone grows in girth (*i.e.*, breadth and thickness) under the periosteum, and in length by increase of the cartilage at its ends. Some bones, on the contrary, grow in one dimension by subperiosteal deposit, and in the other two dimensions by increase of cartilage—for example, those cubical bones of the wrist and of the foot that have two sides covered with periosteum and four sides covered with articular cartilage. In bones such as those of the skull which are developed in membrane the growth takes place under the periosteum and in the membranous tissue that separates their margins from contiguous bones.

Some short bones and some flat bones are ossified wholly from the **primary centre** of ossification. They continue to grow: (1) in the case of flat bones developed in membrane, until the bone-forming cells in the periosteum and in the tissue separating the margins of bones cease to function as bone-forming cells; and (2) in the case of bones developed in cartilage, until the subperiosteal bone-forming cells cease to function and the cartilage cells in the cartilaginous covering of an articular surface cease to multiply. At the articular part of a bone the multiplication of cartilage cells and the process of ossification cease before the cartilage is all used up; a layer of articular cartilage is thus left, and it survives till death or until destroyed by disease.

All the long bones and many of the others acquire **secondary centres** that appear in outlying cartilaginous parts into which ossification from the primary centre has not had time to extend. Nearly all the secondary centres appear after birth, and the method of ossification from them is the same as from primary centres—multiplication of cartilage cells, calcification, subperiosteal deposit of bone, etc.

The part of a bone ossified from the primary centre is called (without good reason) the **diaphysis**. A part ossified from a secondary centre is called an **epiphysis**, and a secondary centre is therefore often called an *epiphyseal centre*. ['Επίφυσις from ἐπί (epi) = upon, φύω (phyō) = make to grow.]

Ossification in the cartilage (accompanied by ossification under the perichondrium) proceeds from the primary and secondary centres till only one part or two parts of the cartilage are left: (1) A thin plate, called the **epiphyseal cartilage**, persists for a time between the diaphysis and the epiphysis; its edge at the surface of the bone is called the **epiphyseal line**. (2) In a bone where the epiphysis is the articulating part the articular layer of cartilage survives.

As long as the epiphyseal cartilage lasts the bone continues to grow on each side of it—that is, both diaphysis and epiphysis continue to grow—the rate of growth being much more rapid in the diaphysis than in the epiphysis. The diaphysis continues to grow at the expense of the epiphyseal plate, and this enlarging part of a diaphysis is sometimes called the *metaphysis*. To maintain the existence of the plate, the cells farther away from the diaphysis go on multiplying; but a time comes when they cease to do so, and the ossifying process in the diaphysis—invading the cartilage—uses it up. The diaphysis and epiphysis are then osseously continuous; the epiphysis is said to have joined or *fused* with the diaphysis, and the bone ceases to grow in that situation. The epiphysis grows at the expense of the peripheral cartilage, whose cells multiply to maintain it; so growth goes on in the epiphysis until they cease to multiply—and that is about the same date as cessation in the epiphyseal plate. If the epiphysis is on a non-articulating part of the bone—*e.g.*, iliac crest—the cartilage is all replaced by bone; but in bones where the epiphysis is articular, its outermost layers of cartilage are not replaced by bone.

The growth of bone ceases when a person becomes an adult, but it can be resumed. Healthy periosteum retains the faculty of producing new bone when it is required; otherwise broken bones would not heal, nor would bony ridges become more pronounced to provide firmer attachments for muscles when they become stronger and larger as a result of unaccustomed exercise.

Epiphyses (Figs. 209, 243).—The shaft of a long bone is developed from a primary centre, and the shaft is therefore the diaphysis. Every long bone has an epiphysis at one end; most

7

of them have epiphyses at both ends; in some bones there are more than one epiphysis at the end, *e.g.*, the distal end of the humerus, the proximal end of the femur. When a long bone has an epiphysis at only one end, it is at the end at which there is the more movement. Most epiphyses are ossified from one centre, but some are ossified from more than one, and the different parts ossified from those separate centres coalesce before the union with the diaphysis, *e.g.*, the proximal end of the humerus. When there are more than one epiphyseal centre at the end of a bone, and the parts ossified from those centres do not coalesce but join the shaft separately, each part is called an epiphysis, *e.g.*, the parts at the proximal end of the femur.

Dates of Appearance of Epiphyses.—Though most epiphyseal centres appear after birth, there is one notable exception and sometimes three. The centre for the *distal end of the femur* appears during the ninth month of intra-uterine life; the centre for the proximal end of the tibia often appears towards the end of that month; and the centre for the head of the humerus sometimes does so also. A still-born child is assumed to be at full time if one of those epiphyses is present.

The other epiphyseal centres of *long bones* appear during **Infancy** and **Childhood**. A notable **exception** is the collar bone, which has an epiphysis only at its medial end, and the centre for that does not appear till the eighteenth or twentieth year. That epiphysis is one of the last to unite. Its presence is useful for determining approximately the age at death of a body found in a state of decomposition. If it is present, the age was between 18 and 30.

In any one long bone the epiphyseal centres do not appear at the same time : weeks, months, or even years may elapse between the appearance of its centres. Nor do the epiphyses fuse with the shaft at the same time; there may be an interval of months or years. The epiphysis whose centre appears first is the last to fuse; an exception is the *fibula*, whose distal epiphysis begins to ossify before the proximal but is no later in fusing; and the proximal and distal epiphyses of the femur (and also those of the tibia) may unite almost simultaneously, though they appear at different dates. The end of a bone at which the epiphyseal cartilage lasts longer is sometimes called the "growing end" of the bone; in those bones which, like the collar bone, have an epiphysis at only one end, that term applies to the end that has the epiphysis; at the "growing end" the increase not only goes on longer than at the other end but also is more rapid—for example, growth is both longer and faster at the distal end of the femur and the proximal end of the humerus than at their other ends. The nutrient canal of a long bone is directed away from the epiphysis which fuses last; when a bone has only one epiphysis the canal is directed away from the end that has the epiphysis. That is, the nutrient canal is directed away from the end that grows more rapidly. This has come to pass because the internal end of the canal remains near its original position, and is therefore relatively farther away from the more rapidly growing extremity of the bone than from the other extremity, while the external end maintains its original relative distance from both extremities. If, for example, the canal was originally near the middle of the bone, its external opening will remain near the middle, though the internal opening will be farther away from the growing end; for the parent vessel that gives rise to the nutrient artery keeps pace with the growth of the bone as a whole, and the part of it that was opposite the middle of the bone remains opposite the middle.

Many epiphyseal centres do not appear till **puberty**, *e.g.*, most of those of the *hip bone* and of the *shoulder blade*, those of the *ribs* and of the *vertebræ*. The most important of the epiphyses of a vertebra are those formed in the hyaline cartilage that covers the upper and lower surfaces of its body. In lower animals those epiphyses are thin plates; in Man they are flattened rings. Those ring-like epiphyses do not fuse with the body of the vertebra till the full adult stage is reached, and that stage may not be reached till the 25th year or later; the back, therefore, goes on growing for a longer time than the limbs do, for the limb bones have usually all ceased to grow before the 21st year.

For any one epiphysis, the date of appearance of its centre varies in different children by weeks or months, and sometimes by one or two years. The date of union varies even more, especially in the backbone; it is common knowledge that some people reach their full height in their 'teens, while others do not do so till after the age of 25. The sequence of the dates of union and the intervals between them remain proportionately the same in different people, and, therefore, if the first to join do so at an earlier age than usual, ossification throughout the body will be completed at an early age. Centres appear and union takes place earlier in girls than in boys. The dates given under the individual bones are approximate averages; those for most of the limb bones are taken from the table compiled by R. S. Paterson, and published in the *Journal of Anatomy*, October 1929; but see also the tables compiled by H. Flecker and published in the same journal in October 1932.

Separation of Epiphyses.—The epiphyseal plates of cartilage in long bones are not flat discs. If that was the case the epiphyses would be knocked off too easily, especially as the growing years of life are the most active and careless. The cartilages and the opposed surfaces of diaphyses and epiphyses have pronounced elevations and depressions which fit into one another, so that the bones can withstand knocks and jars and twists. None the less, an epiphysis sometimes is broken off. When a limb of an adult is subjected to great violence, a bone may be broken or put out of joint. Either accident may befall a boy or girl too, but while the bones are growing there is an added danger : an epiphysis may break away. When that happens, the epiphyseal cartilage is often so much injured that the bone ceases to grow at that end after diaphysis and epiphysis have re-united. When a bone is broken near one end in a young person, it may be either an ordinary fracture or a separation of the epiphysis. It is important to recognise at the outset which it is; and it is important, therefore, to remember the dates at

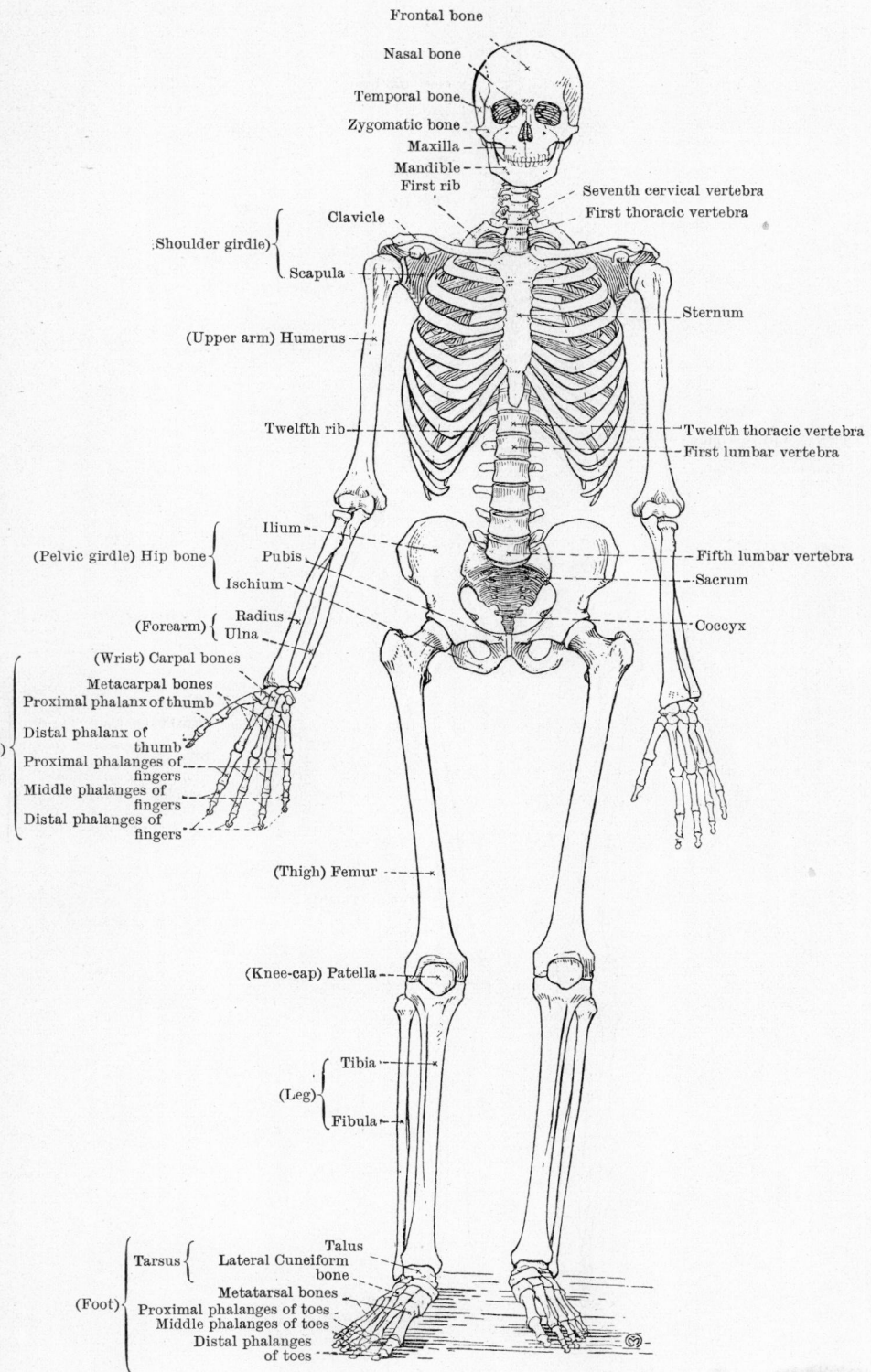

Frontal bone

Nasal bone

Temporal bone

Zygomatic bone

Maxilla

Mandible

First rib

Seventh cervical vertebra

First thoracic vertebra

Clavicle

(Shoulder girdle)

Scapula

Sternum

(Upper arm) Humerus

Twelfth rib

Twelfth thoracic vertebra

First lumbar vertebra

Ilium

(Pelvic girdle) Hip bone {

Pubis

Ischium

Fifth lumbar vertebra

Sacrum

Coccyx

(Forearm) {

Radius

Ulna

(Wrist) Carpal bones

Metacarpal bones

Proximal phalanx of thumb

Distal phalanx of thumb

(Hand) {

Proximal phalanges of fingers

Middle phalanges of fingers

Distal phalanges of fingers

(Thigh) Femur

(Knee-cap) Patella

Tibia

(Leg) {

Fibula

Talus

Tarsus {

Lateral Cuneiform bone

(Foot) {

Metatarsal bones

Proximal phalanges of toes

Middle phalanges of toes

Distal phalanges of toes

FIG. 113.—ANTERIOR VIEW OF THE SKELETON OF A MAN.
The bones of the left forearm and hand are in the position of pronation.

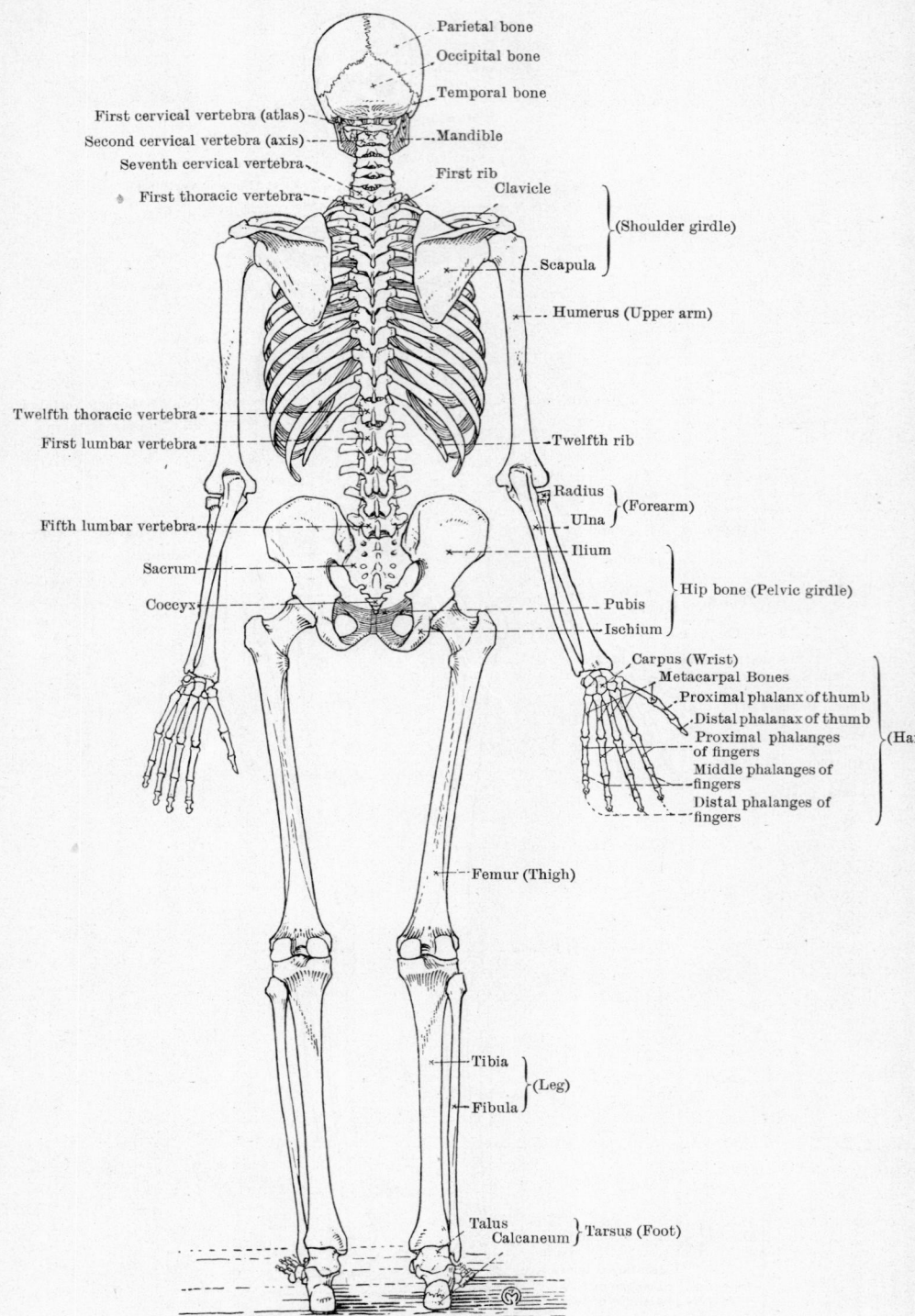

FIG. 114.—POSTERIOR VIEW OF THE SKELETON OF A MAN.
The bones of the left forearm and hand are in the position of pronation.

which epiphyses usually join. Moreover, in an X-ray photograph of a young person an epiphyseal cartilage appears as a clear line, and that line may be mistaken for a line of fracture, if it is forgotten that there is an unjoined epiphysis in the region.

Epiphyses can be seen in radiographs and in the skeletons of relatively young people and young animals in museums. They can be seen at home also : epiphyseal plates of vertebræ can be seen in a sirloin of young beef; epiphyses of limb bones can be found in a leg of lamb.

THE SKELETON

The human body is divided into the following parts : the **head** and **face** ; the **neck** ; the **trunk**, subdivided into the chest or *thorax* and the belly or *abdomen* ; a pair of **upper limbs** ; and a pair of **lower limbs**. The abdomen is further divided into a larger upper part called the *abdomen proper*, and a smaller part called the *pelvis*, situated below and behind the abdomen proper, between the two hips. The bones in the head, face, neck, and trunk are 80 in number in the adult and constitute what is called the *axial skeleton*. Excluding the small sesamoid bones, which are inconstant in number, there are 32 bones in each adult upper limb and 31 in each adult lower limb, and they constitute the *appendicular skeleton*.

The bones in the adult **axial skeleton** are—(*a*) the backbone or vertebral column, made up of 26 separate bones ; (*b*) the breastbone or sternum ; (*c*) 12 pairs of ribs ; (*d*) the skull, built up of 8 pairs of bones and 5 unpaired bones ; (*e*) the lower jawbone or mandible ; (*f*) the hyoid bone ; and (*g*) 3 pairs of tympanic ossicles.

The **vertebral column** is the fundamental part of the skeleton ; it is common to all the great class of animals called *vertebrates*, namely, fishes, amphibians, reptiles, birds, and mammals. It is situated in the median part of the back of the body and extends through the whole length of the neck and the trunk. The **sternum** lies in the median part of the front of the thorax. The twelve **ribs** make up the framework of the side and front and back of each half of the thorax. The **skull** is the skeleton of the head and the upper part of the face, and the **mandible** supports the lower part of the face. The **hyoid bone** lies in the front of the neck, below the mandible and the tongue. The **tympanic ossicles** are little bones situated in the drum of the ear or tympanic cavity.

The bones of the **appendicular skeleton** are summarised in the sections on limbs.

VERTEBRAL COLUMN

The vertebral column or backbone is a long, curved pillar (Fig. 124) composed of a number of segments, called **vertebræ**, which are placed in a series one above the other, and are connected together by discs of fibro-cartilage and by ligaments. The bulky part of each vertebra is its anterior part and is called its *body* (Fig. 115). The most posterior part of a vertebra is a projection called its *spine*, whence arose the names "spine" and "spinal column" used as synonyms for backbone. The spines can be felt in the floor of the median furrow that begins at the nape of the neck and ends between the buttocks.

In the **child** there are 33 separate vertebræ, but in the **adult** vertebral column there are only 26 separate bones, for the lowest nine vertebræ are fused together to form two single bones ; the upper of those two bones is called the *sacrum* and consists of 5 fused vertebræ ; the lower is called the *coccyx* and consists of 4 fused vertebræ (Fig. 125). The vertebræ are classified in five groups from above downwards :—

Child.					*Adult.*			
Cervical vertebræ	.	.	.	7	Cervical vertebræ	.	7	True or
Thoracic	,,	.	.	12	Thoracic ,,	.	12	movable
Lumbar	,,	.	.	5	Lumbar ,,	.	5	vertebræ
Sacral	,,	.	.	5	Sacrum	.	1 = 5	False or fixed
Coccygeal	,,	.	.	4	Coccyx	.	1 = 4	vertebræ
				33			26	

The **cervical vertebræ** constitute the bony axis of the *neck,* and form a very flexible part of the vertebral column [*cervix* = neck]. The **thoracic vertebræ** lie in the posterior wall of the *chest* and the 12 pairs of ribs are attached to them [θώραξ (thōrax) = a cuirass]. The **lumbar vertebræ** lie in the *loins* or "small of the back" [*lumbus* = the loin]; they are the only bones that belong exclusively to the *abdomen proper,* which is less supported by the skeleton than any other part of the body. The **sacrum** lies in the dorsal wall of the *pelvis* in the hollow between the upper part of the hips, and between the two hip bones, to which it is firmly attached by strong fibrous bands or ligaments [*os sacrum,* the "sacred" bone—called *luz* in ancient times—supposed to be able to resist decay and to be the seed from which the body

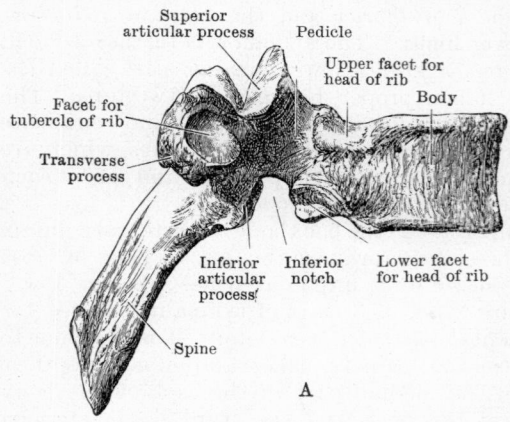

was resurrected]. The **coccyx** has a fancied resemblance to the bill of a bird [κόκκυξ (coccyx) = a cuckoo]. It is the lowest part of the vertebral column and lies below the sacrum in the dorsal wall of the *pelvis,* in the floor of the groove between the buttocks immediately above the *anus* or opening of the bowel.

Vertebræ belong to the class of *irregular* bones. Most of them have characters in common, but the vertebræ of each group have also special characters that distinguish them from those of the other groups; and, while each vertebra has the distinctive characters of its own group, many of them have their own special features by which they can individually be recognised at a glance.

A Typical Vertebra (Fig. 115). —It is usual to select a vertebra from the *middle* of the *thoracic* region as a type. The beginner can pick out a thoracic vertebra from among the others because it has articular *facets* on the sides of the body; none but a thoracic vertebra has those facets; and those in the middle of the thoracic region have long spines. The main parts of a vertebra are a *body* and an *arch*; they enclose a large hole called the *vertebral foramen*; and various processes jut out from the arch, namely, the *spine,* a pair of *trans-*

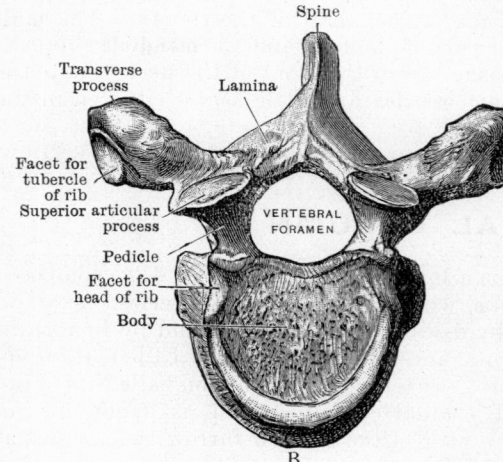

FIG. 115.—FIFTH THORACIC VERTEBRA, (A) as viewed from the right side, (B) as viewed from above.

verse processes, and two pairs of *articular processes*—a superior pair and an inferior.

The **body** is the bulky, anterior part. The **vertebral foramen,** behind the body, is large enough to admit a finger; when the vertebræ are in column the series of vertebral foramina makes a long tunnel, called the *vertebral canal,* for the lodgment of the spinal cord. The **vertebral arch** consists of four essential parts which bear the seven processes named above. The essential parts are a pair of *pedicles* at the sides of the foramen, and a pair of *laminæ* at the back; the two laminæ fuse together in the median plane. When the vertebræ are in column there is, on each side, a row of holes, called the *intervertebral foramina,* between the pedicles; a spinal nerve passes through each intervertebral foramen. The **spine** projects backwards and downwards from the junction of the two laminæ; its downward slant enables the beginner to distinguish the upper part of the vertebra from the lower; the tip of the spine is the only part of a vertebra that is *easily* felt in the living person, and, owing to the slope, it is at the level of the body next below. The other processes are at or near the junction of the pedicles with the laminæ; the **transverse processes** are the large projections that jut out from the sides of the arch; **superior articular processes** project upwards from the side of the arch; the **inferior** pair project downwards and articulate with the superior pair of the vertebra next below; in the thoracic vertebræ they are less distinct than the superior pair, and are on the laminæ near the pedicles.

The **body** has an *upper* and a *lower* surface; a *posterior* surface, forming the anterior boundary of the vertebral foramen; an *anterior* surface, merging into the *right* and *left* sides, so that the three form a continuous surface which is highly convex from side to side, and slightly concave from above downwards. The upper and lower surfaces are separated from the bodies of the vertebræ immediately above and below by thick *discs* of fibro-cartilage (which, at the same time, bind the bodies together); and two long fibrous ribbons, called the *anterior* and *posterior longitudinal ligaments,* lie on the front and the back of the bodies, and are attached to them and to the discs throughout the series of movable vertebræ.

The **pedicles** of the arch [radix arcus vertebræ] project backwards from the back of the body and are continuous with the laminæ posteriorly. The upper and lower borders of each pedicle are slightly concave, forming the floors of notches called the **superior** and **inferior vertebral notches**; in the thoracic and lumbar regions the superior notch is very shallow, for the pedicle springs from the upper part of the body. The pedicles are the only parts of two contiguous vertebræ that are not united by ligaments; they are separated by the **intervertebral foramen**, which is bounded *above* and *below* by the pedicles, *posteriorly* by the articular processes of the two vertebræ, *anteriorly* by the upper of the two bodies in the thoracic and lumbar regions and by both bodies in the cervical region. When the vertebræ are in column there is a linear series of intervertebral foramina on each side, through which the spinal nerves and vessels pass on their way from and to the spinal cord.

The **laminæ** are plates of bone that slope towards each other from the posterior ends of the pedicles and fuse together in the median plane behind the vertebral foramen. [*Lamina* = a plate, a leaf.] Their posterior surfaces are covered by muscles. Laminæ of contiguous vertebræ are united by flat, fibro-elastic bands, called *ligamenta flava* [*flavus* = yellow], which are attached to their borders and to the rough lower parts of their anterior or inner surfaces and the upper parts of their outer surfaces.

The **vertebral canal,** formed by the series of **vertebral foramina**, is bounded *anteriorly* by the bodies of the vertebræ, the discs, and the posterior longitudinal ligament, *posteriorly* by the laminæ and the ligamenta flava, *at each side* by the pedicles—between which there are the intervertebral foramina. The canal *contains* the spinal cord and its membranes, the roots of the spinal nerves, vessels supplying the spinal cord and the vertebræ, and a quantity of loose, semi-liquid fat. The canal is widest in the regions where the vertebral column is most movable —the neck and the loins.

Each **spine** has a median ridge superiorly, but widens out inferiorly into a surface bounded by a pair of ridges; and each ridge may end in a little tubercle at the tip. The spines are united by fibrous bands, called *interspinous ligaments,* which lie in the interval between each two, and *supraspinous ligaments,* which pass from tip to tip forming a continuous band from the sacrum to the neck; in the neck they form a wide sheet called the *ligamentum nuchæ* [*nucha* (derivation uncertain) = the nape of the neck]. The ligamentum nuchæ is set as a median partition between the muscles of the two sides of the back of the neck, and is attached superiorly to a median ridge, called the external occipital crest, on the posterior part of the base of the skull. Numerous muscles are attached to the spines (see p. 119).

The **transverse processes** give attachment to numerous muscles (see p. 118), and are connected with those of the vertebræ above and below by weak fibrous bands called *intertransverse ligaments.* In a typical thoracic vertebra each transverse process articulates with a rib, and has a facet on the front of its free end for that articulation, and is connected to ribs by ligaments.

The **articular processes** project upwards and downwards from a pair of *articular masses,* which are thickened parts of the pedicles and laminæ at and near their junction. The **superior processes** have smooth articular surfaces on their posterior aspects. The **inferior processes** are not so prominent; they are surfaces rather than processes in cervical and thoracic vertebræ, and look forwards to articulate with the superior pair of the vertebra below. The margins of the articulating surfaces give attachment to the *joint capsules,* and the non-articulating parts give attachment to muscles (see p. 118).

Structure.—All parts of a vertebra consist of spongy bone enclosed in compact bone. The compact bone is thinner in the body than in the other parts; it is thickest at the notches, the inner tables of the laminæ and the upper edge of the spine. The cervical vertebræ are denser in structure than those of the other regions. *Vascular foramina* are very small in the arch and processes; they are numerous and large on the front, sides, and back of the body; the largest is on the back, and transmits a vein.

Cervical Vertebræ

Cervical vertebræ are small. By their small size and uneven surface contours they can be identified as cervical at a glance; but their special distinctive character is that each of them has three holes in it—the large **vertebral foramen** in the middle, and a smaller hole at each side, called the **foramen transversarium** because it is partly bounded by the transverse process. The foramina transversaria form a vertical series on each side, and through

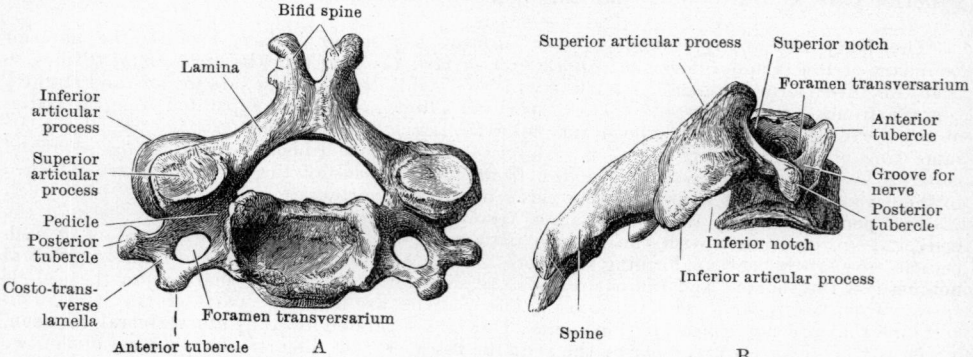

FIG. 116.—FOURTH CERVICAL VERTEBRA, (A) from above, and (B) from the right side.

the upper six of them there runs a large artery called the *vertebral artery*. In most cervical vertebræ the **transverse process** has two tubercles at its free end called the *anterior* and *posterior tubercles* of the transverse process. The free ends are little more than an inch from the median plane, and can be felt as an uneven bony resistance when pressure is made on the side of the neck. The lower border of the *third* vertebra is at the level of the upper border of the thyroid cartilage—that is, the prominence in the front of the neck known as the laryngeal prominence or "Adam's apple." The *sixth* vertebra is at the level of the cricoid cartilage—that is, the rounded bar felt in the front of the neck below the thyroid cartilage; the anterior tubercle of its transverse process is called the *carotid tubercle* because the carotid artery can be compressed against it.

The first and the second vertebræ are greatly modified to allow free movement of the head, and the seventh also has special characters, but the other four are very much alike and are regarded as typical cervical vertebræ.

A Typical Cervical Vertebra.—The **body** is small and is wider from side to side than from before backwards in the proportion of **3** to **2**. It is lipped up at the sides on the upper surface and correspondingly bevelled off on the lower surface; between the lip and the bevel of contiguous vertebræ there is a small synovial joint at the side of the intervertebral disc. The posterior surface is flat, and is pitted near its centre by holes for veins. The anterior surface is flat in the middle for the attachment of ligaments, and depressed at its side for muscular attachments; its lower part juts downwards and overlaps the disc below; the upper margin of the surface may be slightly bevelled.

The **vertebral foramen** is triangular, with rounded angles; and it is large in order that the spinal cord shall not be compressed in the movements of the neck, and also because the cord is thicker in the neck than it is lower down. The **pedicles** are short and rounded; they project laterally as well as backwards, and that contributes to the width of the vertebral foramen and its triangular outline. The superior and inferior **vertebral notches** are nearly equal in depth. The **laminæ** are thinner than in other regions, longer in their horizontal measurement, and narrower from above downwards.

The **spine** is short, and it overlaps the spine below; it is compressed from above downwards, and the median ridge is blunt and ill defined; the free end is bifid, because the pair of lateral ridges end in prominent spurs for the attachment of muscles—the spurs of the sixth being, however, short or absent.

The **articular masses** are large, and the series of them are built up to make a pair of rounded pillars behind the transverse processes; shallow, horizontal grooves on the sides of the third and fourth are for the accommodation of the posterior primary rami of the corresponding cervical nerves. The **articular processes** are merely the upper and lower parts of each articular mass; their articular surfaces are sloping and are nearly flat; the upper pair look backwards and upwards; the lower pair look in the opposite direction.

The **transverse processes** are short and inclined slightly downwards and forwards. Each has two distinct parts or roots—an anterior and a posterior. The *anterior root* corresponds to a rib and is sometimes called the *costal process*; it springs from the side of the body and ends laterally as the *anterior tubercle*. The *posterior root* is the true transverse process; it springs from the arch at the back of the articular pillar, and ends laterally as the *posterior tubercle*. Near their free ends the lower margins of the two roots are united by a curved bar of bone called the *costo-transverse lamella*. The posterior tubercle is farther from the median plane than the anterior tubercle is—jutting beyond the plane of the lateral surface of the articular pillar. The upper border of the anterior root is about the level of the upper surface of the body, and may be even higher. In the third it is at a higher level than the posterior root, and the costo-transverse lamella therefore slants downwards and backwards. In the fourth the anterior root is higher at its upper border and its costo-transverse lamella also is oblique, but the lower border is almost at the same level as the lower border of the posterior root. In the fifth and sixth the roots are nearly at the same level, and the lamella is therefore horizontal, but in the sixth the roots are farther apart and the lamella therefore longer.

The **foramen transversarium** is bounded by the side of the body, the pedicle, the two roots of the transverse process and the costo-transverse lamella; in some vertebræ it is divided into two by a spicule of bone. Except in the seventh, it transmits the vertebral artery surrounded by a network of veins and a network or plexus of delicate sympathetic nerves derived from the inferior cervical ganglion. The cervical nerves, on emerging from the intervertebral foramina, lie behind the vertebral artery, where each one divides into an anterior and a posterior primary ramus; the posterior ramus turns backwards above the posterior root of the transverse process across the side of the articular pillar; the anterior ramus proceeds in a lateral direction and lies on the costo-transverse lamella.

The **atlas** or **first cervical vertebra** is a ring of bone. It has no body and no spine; for the median part of the body has been detached from it and is fused with the upper surface of the body of the second vertebra, and a spine has not been developed on it because it would hamper the backward movement of the head. The two bulkier parts of it are called the **lateral masses**; they are united by two curved bars of bone called the **anterior arch** and the **posterior arch**, of which the posterior is much the longer. A **transverse process**, enclosing a **foramen transversarium**,

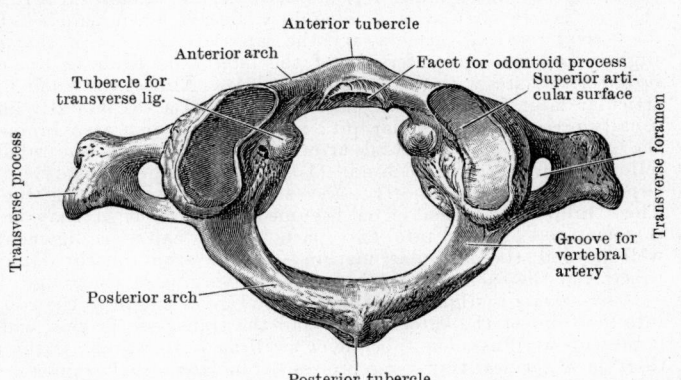

FIG. 117.—THE ATLAS FROM ABOVE.

projects laterally from each lateral mass. The transverse processes are farther apart than the transverse processes of other cervical vertebræ; the tip of each is an inch and a half from the median plane, and is the bone felt by the finger pressed into the hollow below the ear. The lateral masses rest upon the second cervical vertebra, and they support the skull—hence the name "atlas." Their upper and lower surfaces are readily distinguished, for the facets on their *lower* surfaces are fairly flat, while the facets on their *upper* surfaces are kidney-shaped and concave. The upper facets articulate with the occipital condyles at the sides of the foramen magnum—that is, with the smooth articular bosses at the sides of the large hole on the base of the skull (Fig. 139).

The **anterior arch** is short and is compressed from before backwards. The facet seen on the middle of its posterior surface is for articulation with a part of the second vertebra called the odontoid process. On the middle of its anterior surface there is a smooth eminence, called the **anterior tubercle** of the atlas, which gives insertion to the upper ends of the longus cervicis muscles. A continuation of the anterior longitudinal ligament is attached to the *lower margin* of the arch. A fibrous sheet, called the anterior atlanto-occipital membrane, stretches upwards from the *upper margin* to the anterior margin of the foramen magnum. .

The **posterior arch** is twice as long as the anterior arch, and is tilted slightly upwards. It springs on each side from the back of the lateral mass and the posterior root of the transverse process, and represents the pedicles and laminæ of a typical vertebra. On the middle of its posterior surface there is a small projection, called the **posterior tubercle** of the atlas, which corresponds to a spine, and gives origin to a pair of small muscles named the recti capitis posteriores minores. On the *upper surface* of the arch, close to each lateral mass, there is a broad, oblique groove in which the vertebral artery lies, as it runs from the first foramen transversarium to the foramen magnum, and the first cervical nerve lies in the groove below the artery. The remainder of the upper surface or border gives attachment to a thin fibrous sheet, called the posterior atlanto-occipital membrane, which stretches upwards to the posterior margin of the foramen magnum and also upwards and laterally to fuse with the capsule of the joint between the lateral mass and the skull; the infero-lateral margin of the membrane therefore bridges across the groove for the vertebral artery, and is sometimes ossified, converting the groove into a foramen. The *lower margin* of the arch is connected with the laminæ of the second vertebra by the first pair of ligamenta flava.

The **transverse processes** are longer and stronger than those of other cervical vertebræ, for they give attachment to the muscles that rotate the head, and are the levers on which these muscles act. The free end—though often tuberculated and sometimes bifid—corresponds only to the posterior tubercle of a typical cervical transverse process. The anterior root and tubercle have been absorbed into the front of the lateral mass (where they may be identified as a slight swelling), and the bar of bone that bounds the foramen anteriorly corresponds to a costo-transverse lamella. The free end is a little below the tip of the mastoid process of the temporal bone, but is slightly medial to that process and slightly in front of it, and the prominent, anterior part of the tip is the bone felt in the hollow below the ear. Each process gives origin to the following muscles—the rectus capitis lateralis, the obliquus capitis superior and slips of the levator scapulæ and scalenus medius—and insertion to the obliquus capitis inferior and a slip of the splenius cervicis.

The **lateral masses** do not correspond to the articular masses of the typical vertebræ but to the pedicles and to the lateral parts of the body—the parts that bear the lip and bevel united by synovial joints. Owing to the shortness of the anterior arch, the lateral masses are closer together in front than behind; and their upper and lower surfaces slope so markedly that the medial surface is of much less depth than the lateral surface. The *lower surface* of each is oblique, nearly circular, and is slightly concave when denuded of cartilage; it articulates with the second cervical vertebra, and the capsular ligament of that joint is attached to the rough, slightly grooved circumference of the lateral mass above the articular margin. The *upper surface* articulates with the occipital condyle. Almost the whole upper surface is occupied by the articular facet, but there are narrow, depressed areas laterally and medially—the medial part usually presenting a vascular pit; posteriorly, it juts as a prominent tubercle that overhangs the groove for the vertebral artery. The facet, like the whole lateral mass, is nearer its fellow in front than behind. To fit the occipital condyle, it is kidney-shaped, concave (especially antero-posteriorly), and slopes downwards from the lateral to the medial edge. The "hilum" or notch is on the medial side; but it may be notched on both sides, and is sometimes divided into two parts. The capsular ligament of the joint is attached well beyond the articular margins—to the front of the lateral mass, to the overhanging tubercle at the back, and to the outlying margins of the rough depressions at the sides. The *anterior surface* is slightly undulating, and gives origin to the rectus capitis anterior; it merges into the front of the anterior arch and the transverse process, and, near the transverse process, it presents a diffuse, low tubercle or swelling that represents the anterior root and tubercle of the typical cervical transverse process. The *lateral surface* gives origin to the transverse process, and is slightly excavated by the vertebral artery. The *posterior surface* is connected with the posterior arch; it is convex from side to side and grooved horizontally by the vertebral artery above the arch and by the anterior primary ramus of the second cervical nerve below the arch. The *medial surface* is small and uneven, and is seldom sharply marked off from the upper surface; its most conspicuous feature is a smooth, round *tubercle* for the attachment of the *transverse ligament* of the atlas, which stretches from one lateral mass to the other, across the back of the odontoid process, and keeps it in place against the anterior arch. The large hole surrounded by the lateral masses and the arches is divided by the transverse ligament into two parts—an anterior, which holds the odontoid process, and a posterior, which is the vertebral foramen and contains the spinal cord and its membranes.

The **second cervical vertebra** is called the **axis vertebra** [epistropheus]. It is the thickest and strongest of cervical vertebræ, and is easily distinguished. A thick process called the **odontoid process** [dens] stands up from the upper surface of the body. The **spine** is very thick compared with other cervical spines; it can be felt two or three inches below the *external occipital protuberance, i.e.,* the knob in the middle line where the back of the head joins the neck; the spine is the first bony resistance encountered by the finger drawn downwards from the protuberance.

The **axis vertebra**, when looked at from the front, is relatively very long in its vertical measurement, because of the upstanding odontoid process and because the lower part of the front of the body juts downwards very considerably. The **odontoid process** [ὀδούς (odous, *genitive* odontos) = dens = a tooth] is really the median part of the body of the atlas fused with the body of the axis. When the first two vertebræ are fitted together properly the odontoid process lies in the anterior compartment of the ring of the atlas, and, if the atlas is looked at from above, the whole of what is really its body is then seen—its own pair of lateral masses and the odontoid process of the axis. The upper part of the anterior surface of the odontoid process is smooth for articulation with the back of the anterior arch of the atlas; its posterior surface near its root also is smooth and even grooved for contact with the transverse ligament. Its top is pointed. A weak band of fibres, called the apical ligament of the odontoid process, stretches from the apex to the anterior margin of the foramen magnum; and a pair of strong bands of fibres, called the alar ligaments, stretch from the sides of the apex to tubercles on the sides of the foramen magnum. When the head and face are turned from side to side, the atlas, carrying the skull, pivots round the odontoid process (hence the name *axis*), and the movement is prevented from going too far by the alar ligaments.

The **inferior vertebral notches** are deep; the **superior** are absent; the **laminæ** are thick. The **spine** is deeply grooved on its lower surface and keeled on its upper surface. It is thick and

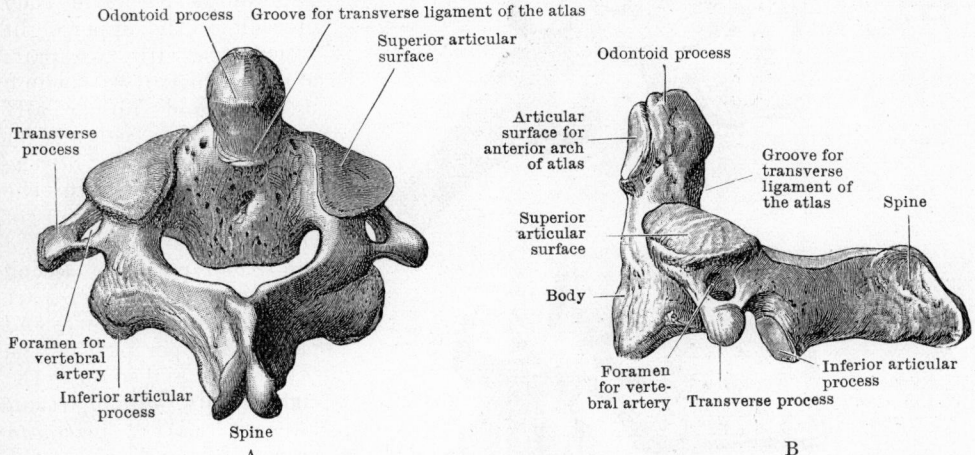

FIG. 118.—AXIS VERTEBRA, (A) from behind and above, (B) from the left side.

broad because of the number of muscles attached to it (p. 119). The most important of these are the rectus capitis posterior major and obliquus capitis inferior (which arise from it and move the head) and a great part of the semispinalis cervicis, which is inserted into it and bends the neck backwards. The **transverse processes** are the smallest of the series because the free end of each is not bifid and represents only the posterior tubercle. The anterior root is absorbed into the anterior surface of the upper articular part of the bone, and the anterior tubercle is either absent or is only a slight roughness near that surface. If the second and third vertebræ are placed together and looked at from the side, the change in the transverse process is obvious. The anterior boundary of the **foramen transversarium** is then seen to be chiefly the bar of bone that corresponds to the costo-transverse lamella of the third vertebra. The foramen is a short canal directed laterally as well as upwards, because the transverse process of the atlas is more laterally placed. The **inferior articular surfaces** are situated on typical *articular processes*. The **superior articular surfaces** are not situated on processes at the junction of the pedicles and the laminæ, but are placed on the body and the pedicles; they articulate with the lower surfaces of the lateral masses of the atlas, and through them the weight of the head is transmitted from the lateral masses to the bodies of the vertebræ below. The joints between them and the lateral masses of the atlas, and also those between the lateral masses and the occipital condyles correspond not to the joints between typical articular processes but to the small joints between the bodies of the cervical vertebræ at the sides of the intervertebral discs; the first and second cervical nerves issue therefore behind the joints that connect the atlas with the skull and with the axis, while other spinal nerves issue through the intervertebral foramina in front of the joints formed by the articular processes.

The **seventh cervical vertebra** is distinguished from the others because its **spine** is long, and is not bifid, but is thickened at its free end; the end of the spine is the upper of the two prominences at the root of the back of the neck, and on that account the seventh vertebra is called the *vertebra prominens*. The *posterior root* of the **transverse process** is a relatively wide triangular plate whose base or medial attached edge may reach almost as high a level as the top of the superior articular process, and its free end (*i.e.* the posterior tubercle) is in line with the tip of the first thoracic transverse process. The *anterior root* is slender and the *anterior tubercle* is often absent; but in some rare cases the anterior root is large and separate, forming a **cervical rib**. The **foramen transversarium** is usually small, for it does not transmit the vertebral artery; it transmits the posterior of the two vertebral veins when there are two of these veins instead of one; on one or both sides it may be double.

Thoracic Vertebræ

Thoracic vertebræ are of medium size, and increase in size from above downwards; their distinctive character is that they all have facets on their sides for articulation with the heads of ribs (see Figs. 115 and 119). The **body** of each of the upper eight articulates with two pairs of ribs—the pair with which it corresponds numerically and the pair below; for example, the body of the **first** articulates with the heads of the *first* pair of ribs and the upper part of the *second* pair; the **second** body with the lower part of the heads of the *second* pair and upper part of the *third* pair; and so on to the **eighth** body, which articulates with part of the *eighth* pair of ribs and part of the *ninth* pair. The bodies of the lower four articulate only with the ribs with which they correspond numerically.

The upper ten have a facet on each **transverse process** for articulation with the tubercle of the rib with which each corresponds numerically (see Fig. 131). The lower two do not have facets on the transverse processes. The thoracic transverse processes, are thick, their posterior surfaces lie under cover of the muscles of the back, and their tips are a little more than one inch from the median plane. The **spines** are long and sloping, especially in the middle of the series, where the slope is so steep that the spine is almost vertical, and one can

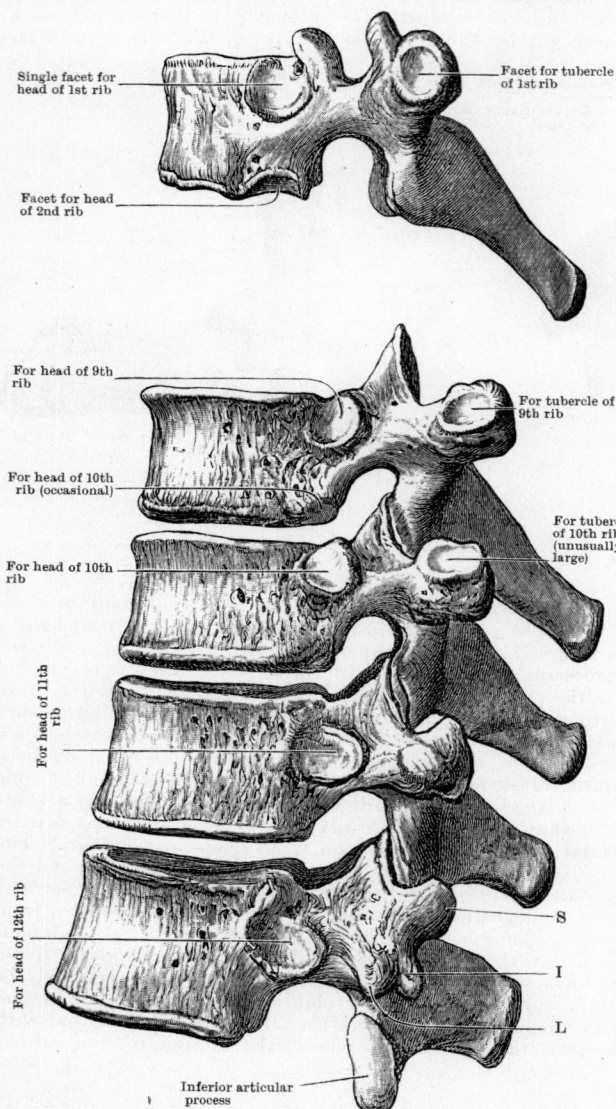

FIG. 119.—LEFT SIDE OF THE FIRST, NINTH, TENTH, ELEVENTH, AND TWELFTH THORACIC VERTEBRÆ.

S. Superior			Mamillary	
I. Inferior	} Tubercles corresponding to	{	Accessory	} of Lumbar.
L. Lateral			Transverse	

therefore say at once whether a given vertebra is from the middle of the series or not. In the upper and lower vertebræ the spines are shorter and slant very little in comparison; and the lower can be distinguished from the upper by the large size of the bodies. The tip of the spine of the *first* thoracic vertebra is the lower of the two knobs felt at the root of the back of the neck. The spine of the *third* is at the level of the point where the spine of the scapula joins the medial border, and that point is easily found in the living body. The spine of the *seventh* is at the level of the inferior angle of the scapula (Figs. 114, 135).

The first two thoracic vertebræ and the lower four have special characters by which they can be distinguished individually; the other six belong to a common type; but when the whole series in hand are from the same skeleton they are easily placed in their proper order, if the gradual changes in appearance are noted and experiments are made in fitting them together.

A Typical Thoracic Vertebra (Fig. 115).—The *upper* and *lower surfaces* of the **body** are almost flat, and are heart-shaped in outline. The *posterior surface* is slightly concave from side to side; it is slightly deeper than the *anterior surface*, and therefore from fœtal life onwards the thoracic part of the backbone is curved with the concavity forwards. There are two unequal *facets* on each side of the body, set far back at the widest part of the body, the larger one at the upper border and the smaller at the lower border. The lower facet of one vertebra is directly above the upper facet of the vertebra next below; the two facets, together with the side of the intervertebral disc, make a socket for the head of the rib that corresponds numerically with the lower of the two vertebræ.

The **pedicles** increase in thickness from above downwards. Each is compressed from side to side; it passes more directly backwards than in the cervical and lumbar regions, and is inclined upwards. It springs from the body nearer the upper border than the lower; the **superior vertebral notch** is therefore very shallow, and the **inferior** is deep. Owing to the direction of the pedicles, the **laminæ** are narrow, but they are deep and overlap the laminæ below; over-lapping of laminæ is called *imbrication* [*imbrex*=a tile]. The **vertebral foramen** is smaller than in the cervical and lumbar regions, as there is less movement in the thoracic region and less danger of compressing the spinal cord. The small size of the foramen and its circular outline are due to the direction of the pedicles and the narrowness of the laminæ.

The **spine** is long, slender, and three-sided, and its ridges converge on its free end, which is slightly thickened; it slopes so as to overlap the spine below. The **transverse processes** are long, thick, and rounded, and are inclined backwards and upwards. The free end of each is clubbed, is roughened for muscular and ligamentous attachments, and bears on its anterior surface a *facet* for articulation with the tubercle of the rib of corresponding number; owing to the back-ward inclination of the process, the facet looks laterally rather than forwards, and in the lower members it looks upwards as well; the process is connected with the corresponding rib by a joint capsule and by two bands called the lateral and inferior costo-transverse ligaments, and it is connected with the neck of the rib below by a flat band called the superior costo-transverse ligament. The *superior articular surfaces* are flat, and look backwards and slightly upwards and laterally; they are situated on distinct **articular processes**. The *inferior articular surfaces* are situated partly on the lower parts of the laminæ near the pedicles, and partly on short **articular processes** that jut downwards from the laminæ; their direction is the opposite of that of the superior surfaces.

The *body* of the **first thoracic vertebra** resembles that of a lower cervical vertebra in general outline, and also in that the postero-lateral part of the upper surface is raised up as a prominent lip which makes the superior vertebral notch deeper than that of any other thoracic vertebra. The body departs from type in its costal facets also; it has a complete, full-sized facet on each side, near the upper border, for the whole of the head of the first rib, and a small facet at the lower border for the upper part of the head of the second rib. The superior articular processes are wider than those of a typical vertebra and are less upright, and they encroach on the upper surfaces of the transverse processes.

The **second** often resembles the first, but the large facet at the upper border is not quite complete, and its superior vertebral notch and articular process conform to type.

The **ninth** has only one facet on the body; it is at the upper border—encroaching on the pedicle—and is incomplete; it is for articulation with the lower part of the head of the ninth rib. There may be a small facet at the lower border also, in which case the ninth would be a typical vertebra, and the tenth would resemble a ninth. Occasionally, the facet on the ninth is complete; in that case the eighth would resemble a ninth, and the ninth would not be readily distinguished from a tenth unless it was known that they both belonged to the same skeleton. The facet on the transverse process is on its upper surface rather than on the front.

The **tenth, eleventh,** and **twelfth** have *large bodies* resembling those of lumbar vertebræ, and each of them has only one pair of facets for the heads of ribs. The facet is large and com-plete, and is more on the pedicle than on the body; it is for articulation with the head of the rib of corresponding number. The facet on the *tenth* is near the upper border, while that on the *eleventh* is lower down; the tenth has a small facet on the upper surface of the transverse process, and the eleventh has none; these two, therefore, can usually be distinguished, though it is not always easy when they are from different skeletons. The **twelfth** is easily identified. Its *transverse processes* are each replaced by three small tubercles. Its costal facet is on the middle of the pedicle—or lower. The articular surfaces of the *inferior articular processes* look in a lateral direction, while in other thoracic vertebræ they look forwards. In some skeletons the inferior articular processes of the eleventh resemble those of the twelfth, but the transverse processes of the eleventh are not replaced by tubercles.

Lumbar Vertebræ

Lumbar vertebræ are large. Their *large size* distinguishes them at a glance from cervical vertebræ and most thoracic vertebræ; the *thin transverse processes* and *hatchet-shaped spine* distinguish them (all except the fifth) from the bulky lower thoracic vertebræ. The negative distinctive characters common to all lumbar vertebræ are the *absence* of a foramen in the transverse process and the *absence* of facets for ribs.

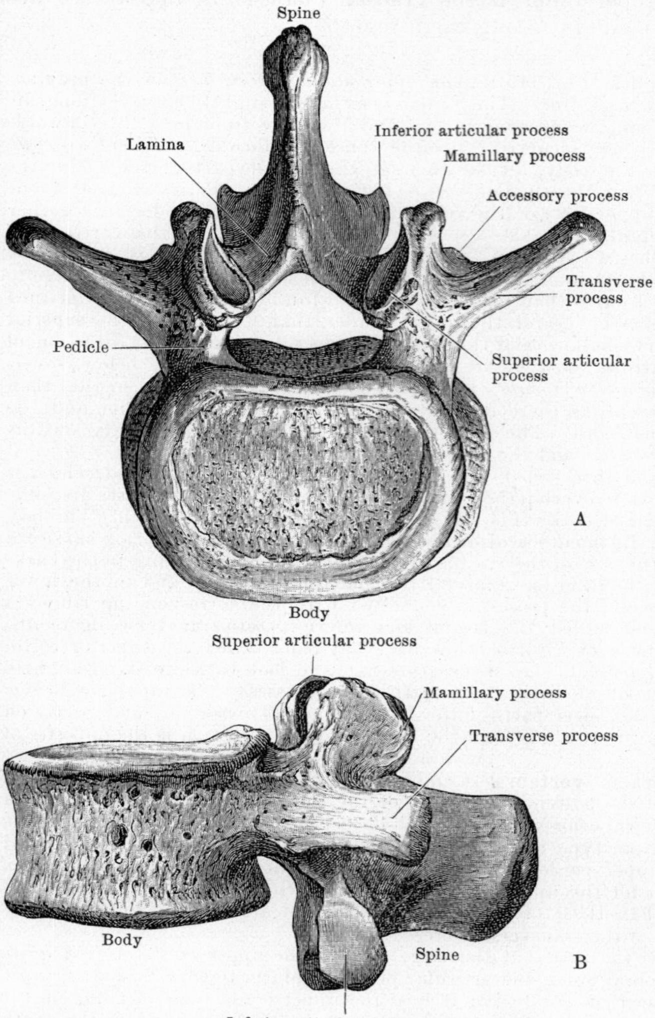

The **bodies** are about an inch in depth; they are almost two inches wide at their widest part, and therefore structures that lie alongside the bodies are about an inch from the median plane; and the tips of the **transverse processes** are rather more than an inch and a half from the median plane. The **umbilicus** is opposite the disc between the bodies of the *third* and *fourth*. The *fourth* is at the level of the *highest* part of the **iliac crest** (Fig. 134), and the *fifth* is at the level of the *tubercle* of the **iliac crest**. The **laminæ** droop considerably below the level of the pedicles, so that though the spine is nearly horizontal its posterior edge is at the level of the lower part of the body of its own vertebra and the upper part of the body next below. The laminæ do not overlap (Fig. 135); there is an interval between the spines and laminæ of two contiguous lumbar vertebræ through which an instrument can be passed into the vertebral canal in a living person—the operation being called *lumbar puncture*. Lumbar vertebræ measure about three inches from the posterior border of the spine to the front of the body, and therefore account for a large part of the antero-posterior diameter of the trunk about the level of the umbilicus.

FIG. 120.—THIRD LUMBAR VERTEBRA, (A) from above, and (B) from the left side.

The fifth lumbar vertebra has distinguishing features of its own; the others belong to a common type, though there are minor differences among them.

A Typical Lumbar Vertebræ.—The **body** is large; its *upper* and *lower surfaces* are nearly flat and have a slight resemblance to a kidney in outline; the *posterior surface* is slightly concave, and, in the lower three, is less in depth than the *anterior*, in conformity with the curve of the lumbar part of the backbone, which is convex forwards; the greater part of that convexity is, however, accounted for by the fact that the intervertebral discs are thicker in front than behind.

The **pedicles** are short, thick and horizontal, with a slight lateral inclination, and are compressed sideways. They spring from the upper part of the body ; therefore the **superior vertebral notches** are shallow and the **inferior** are deep. The **laminæ** are thick and uneven ; they droop considerably below the level of the pedicles, but do not imbricate. The **vertebral foramen** is triangular in outline with rounded corners ; it is larger than in the thoracic region owing to the larger size of the body, but smaller than in the cervical region as the pedicles are less oblique.

The **spine** is large and hatchet-shaped, and, owing to a great exaggeration of the median ridge, is almost horizontal. The **superior articular processes** are broad and uneven ; the articular surface is on the medial side, is concave from before backwards and faces medially and slightly backwards. The posterior border of each process is smooth, rounded, and slightly enlarged, and is called the *mamillary process* [*mamilla* = a nipple, a teat]. The **inferior articular processes** project downwards from the lower part of the laminæ, and are pointed at their lower ends. They fit in between the superior processes of the vertebra below ; they are therefore closer together than the superior pair, and the articular surfaces look in a lateral direction and are convex. The line of the joint is therefore almost in a sagittal plane ; but sometimes, in the lower members, the articular surfaces have a lessened convexity and look forwards as well as laterally ; the superior processes of the next vertebra are correspondingly altered, and the result is that the line of the joint is oblique or nearly transverse, and the inferior processes are nearly as far apart as the superior.

The **transverse processes** are long and thin, being compressed from before backwards, and they incline slightly backwards and upwards. In the lower vertebræ they spring from the pedicle as well as from the junction of pedicle and lamina, and the superior vertebral notch extends as a shallow groove on to the root of the process. On the back of the root of each process there is a little tubercle called the *accessory process*. The accessory process and the mamillary process correspond to the transverse process of a thoracic vertebra ; the transverse process of a lumbar vertebra is the homologue of a rib. If the last two thoracic vertebræ and the first lumbar vertebra are placed together in proper order, the transition from the thoracic transverse process to the lumbar mamillary and accessory processes can be seen. In some rare cases the transverse process of the first lumbar vertebra exists separately as a **lumbar rib**.

Certain minor differences among lumbar vertebræ may be noted. The body of the first may be deeper behind than in front, and those measurements may be equal in the second, while the others are deeper in front than behind. The third transverse process is usually the longest, and the others are shorter in this order—4th, 2nd, 1st, 5th. But these differences are inconstant, and it may be impossible to attach a number to one of the upper four unless the others are present. Progressive differences are then obvious. From above downwards, the bodies widen, the pedicles thicken, the articular processes are farther apart, the mamillary processes become less prominent, and the length of the whole articular column is reduced. The spines increase in depth to the third and then diminish.

The **fifth lumbar vertebra** is usually the largest of the lumbar vertebræ, though its body is usually of less depth than the fourth. The front of the **body** is usually much deeper than the back. The **spine** is small and its corners are rounded off. The **transverse process** is short, thick, and conical ; its root is attached not only to the junction of lamina and pedicle but also to the side of the pedicle and even to the side of the body ; a strong band called the ilio-lumbar ligament stretches from its tip to the adjoining part of the iliac crest ; the transverse process varies, however, both in length and in thickness. The **inferior articular processes** are as wide apart as the superior, or even wider, for they have to articulate with the widely separated superior articular processes of the sacrum. Their articular surfaces are less convex than in a typical vertebra and look forwards as well as laterally—sometimes more forward than laterally.

Sacrum and Coccyx

The **sacrum** is a large bone made up of the five sacral vertebræ, which are fused together in order to increase the stability of the pelvis. It lies below the small of the back between the upper parts of the two hips, and can be felt there as an uneven bony surface ; it is wedged in between the two hip bones and forms by far the greater part of the dorsal wall of the cavity of the pelvis ; it is held in place by exceedingly strong ligaments. It has the form of an inverted triangle, and possesses a wide upper end or **base**, a small lower end or **apex**, right and left **borders**, a rough, uneven **dorsal surface**, and a relatively smooth **pelvic surface**.

The **pelvic surface** is concave and looks downwards and forwards ; it presents a large median column of bone separated from a smaller mass on each side by a vertical series of four holes. The median column consists of the **bodies** of the five sacral vertebræ and the ossified intervertebral cartilages all fused together. The block of bone on each side is called the **lateral mass** of the sacrum. The four pairs of holes are called the **anterior sacral foramina** ; the anterior primary rami of the upper four pairs of sacral nerves issue through them. In specimens in which the coccyx has fused with the sacrum there are five pairs of foramina.

The **base** is directed forwards and upwards. In the middle there is the upper surface of the **body** of the first sacral vertebra; its anterior border is a prominent lip called the *promontory* of the sacrum. On each side of the body there is a wide, spreading surface called the **ala** of the sacrum; it is the upper end of the lateral mass. The promontory and the smooth anterior borders of the two alæ form the posterior part of the brim of the true pelvis. The **vertebral foramen** is the large opening behind the body and it leads into a tunnel called the *sacral canal*. The **superior articular processes** are the pair of upstanding projections at the sides of the vertebral foramen.

The **apex** is the lower surface of the body of the fifth sacral vertebra.

Each side or **border** of the sacrum is very thick above and much thinner below.

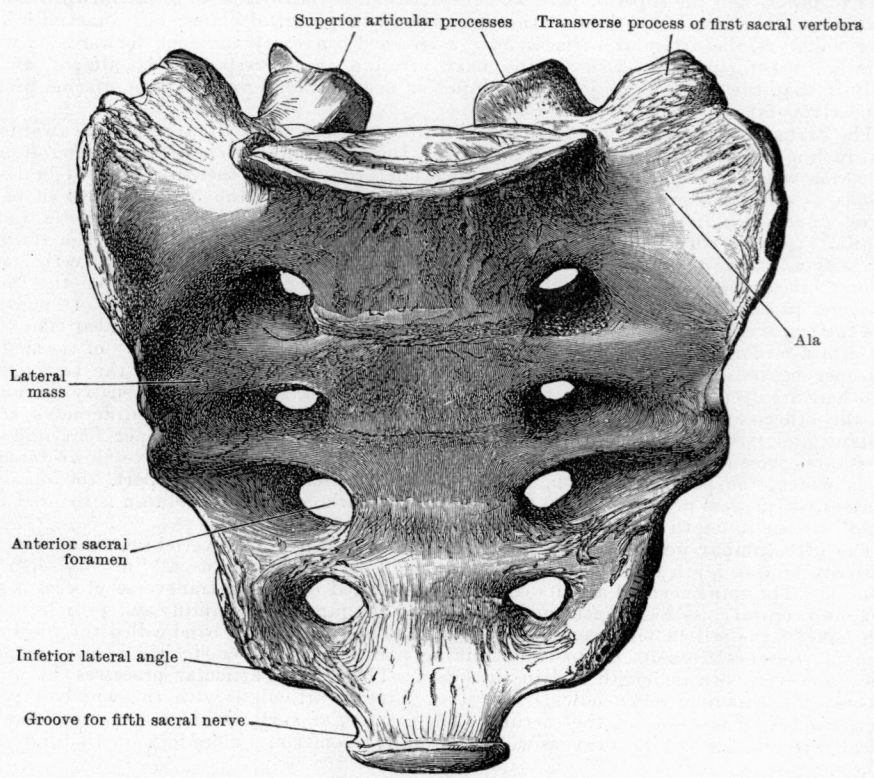

FIG. 121.—THE SACRUM (anterior view).

The upper part is a sharply defined area that has some resemblance to an ear (though turned the wrong way), and is therefore called the **auricular surface**; it articulates with a corresponding auricular surface on the hip bone to form the *sacro-iliac joint*. The thinner, lower part of the border, as it is traced downwards, turns abruptly towards the body of the fifth vertebra, where it ends; the point where the change of direction takes place is called the **inferior lateral angle** of the sacrum.

The **dorsal surface** is very rough and uneven, and is convex. In the median plane there is a row of **spinous tubercles**; they are the spines of the sacral vertebræ, and may be united by ossified ligaments into a median crest. The second spine or spinous tubercle is opposite the middle of the sacro-iliac joint, and, when the body is erect, it is at the same level as the promontory of the sacrum and the posterior superior iliac spine of the hip bone. About an inch lateral to the median plane there is a vertical row of four holes called the **posterior sacral foramina**; they are exactly opposite the anterior foramina, and the posterior primary rami of the upper four sacral nerves issue through them. The posterior parts of the vertebral arches of the lower two sacral vertebræ are absent; the row of spines therefore does not reach the lower end. The lowest complete vertebral foramen is the lower end of the sacral canal; it is an oblique opening; its margins are prolonged downwards to the fifth vertebra and end as two blunt projections called the **sacral cornua.**

The chief contents of the **sacral canal** are the roots of the sacral and coccygeal nerves, the filum terminale and the lowest parts of the dura mater and arachnoid mater. The lower end of the sacral canal gives exit to the fifth pair of sacral nerves, the pair of coccygeal nerves and the filum terminale. (Dura mater and arachnoid mater are the names given to the outer two of the three membranes that surround the spinal cord; they are continued downwards around the roots of the nerves as far as the second piece of the sacrum. The innermost membrane is called

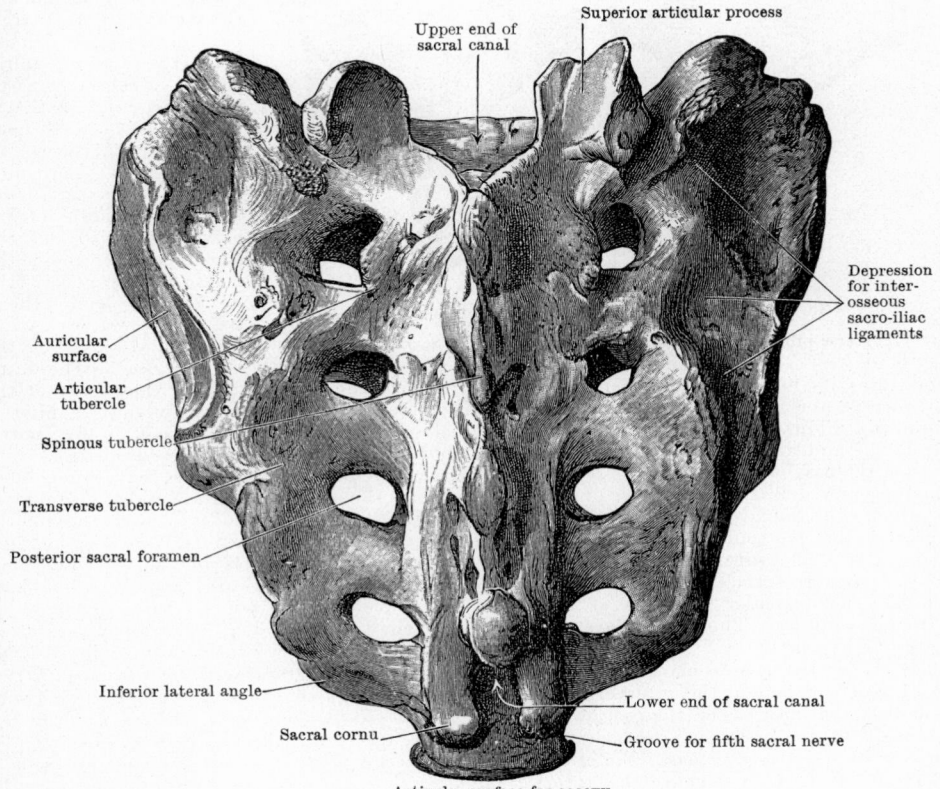

FIG. 122.—THE SACRUM (posterior view).

the pia mater; the filum terminale is a long, slender glistening thread continued downwards from the lower end of the pia mater and it ends by blending with the periosteum on the back of the coccyx.)

The **coccyx** is the lowest part of the backbone; it lies in the floor of the groove between the buttocks a little above the anus, and, at the same time, in the dorsal wall of the pelvis below the sacrum. It is made up of four small incomplete vertebræ fused together, and, like the sacrum, it is triangular in outline with the apex below. It has a base, an apex, a pelvic surface, a dorsal surface, and a pair of borders. The **first vertebra** is much the largest; its *upper surface* is the base of the coccyx and articulates with the apex of the sacrum; from its **dorsal surface** a pair of processes called the **coccygeal cornua** project upwards; and from each border a **transverse process** juts out. The lower three vertebræ are mere nodules of bone, usually diminishing in size from above downwards. Occasionally the coccyx consists of three or of five pieces instead of four.

8

The **pelvic surface** of the **sacrum** is concave from above downwards, and slightly concave from side to side also, the degree of concavity varying greatly in different specimens. The fact that there are five bodies in the median column is indicated by four *transverse ridges*, which are the edges of ossified intervertebral discs. The bodies diminish in width and thickness from above downwards and to a varying extent in depth ; and if a sagittal section is made, the remains of the discs are found between them. The four pairs of **anterior sacral foramina** are at the ends of the transverse ridges ; they also diminish in size from above downwards. Each foramen transmits the anterior primary ramus of a sacral nerve, a branch of a lateral sacral artery, and an accompanying vein ; a short, shallow groove, in which the ramus lies, extends from the foramen on to the lateral mass. The **lateral mass** is made up of the *transverse processes* of one side all fused together. In the sacral region, as in the cervical region, a transverse process is

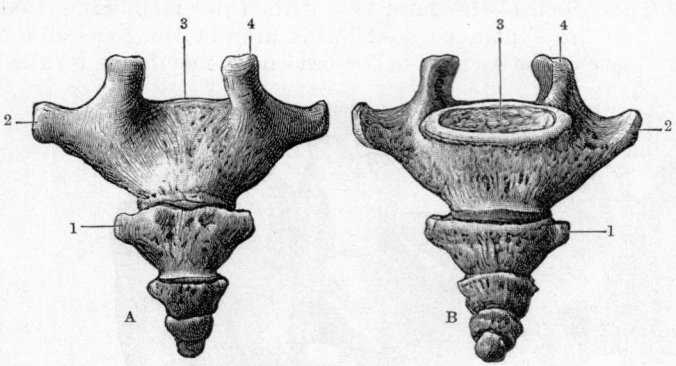

made up of a *rib element* in front and a *true transverse process* behind ; the costal elements are seen between the foramina, and they make up the larger part of the lateral mass (Fig. 128), especially in the upper three segments, which articulate with the ilium.

The median sacral artery, with a companion vein on each side, runs down the middle of the pelvic surface of the sacrum and ends on the pelvic surface of the coccyx. The sympathetic trunk runs down across the medial parts of the

FIG. 123.—THE COCCYX.

A. Dorsal Surface.   B. Pelvic Surface.

1. Transverse process.   2. Transverse process.   3. For Sacrum.   4. Cornu.

anterior sacral foramina and joins its fellow of the other side on the front of the coccyx. The greater part of the piriformis muscle arises from the middle three pieces of the sacrum between the anterior foramina. The rectum is closely related to the pelvic surface of the coccyx and of the sacrum up to the middle of the third piece ; the bodies above that are clothed with peritoneum.

On the **base** of the sacrum the constituent parts of the first sacral vertebra may be made out fairly clearly. The upper surface of the **body** resembles the body of the fifth lumbar vertebra in outline ; it is bound to that body by the lowest intervertebral disc and the lower ends of the anterior and posterior longitudinal ligaments. The **vertebral foramen** is large, sloping, and triangular. The **superior articular processes** stand up from the sides of the vertebral arch. Their articular surfaces are concave ; they look medially and backwards and articulate with the inferior articular processes of the fifth lumbar vertebra, to which they are bound by articular capsules. The **laminæ** are connected with the laminæ of that vertebra by the lowest pair of ligamenta flava. The **pedicle** is the part between the superior articular process and the body, and it may be marked off from the ala by a pit, or, in rare cases, by a foramen. It is the lower boundary of the intervertebral foramen through which the fifth lumbar nerve issues. The **vertebral notch** is on the root of the pedicle, and is continuous with two grooves : the one groove is for the posterior primary ramus of the nerve, and runs backwards between the articular process and the lateral mass ; the other is for the anterior primary ramus and runs forwards to the side of the body, whence the anterior ramus, running downwards, forwards, and laterally, sometimes makes a shallow groove on the ala. The **ala** is the transverse process ; its posterior part is the *true transverse process* and may be marked off from the rest by a slight depression ; the postero-lateral angle of the ala is the tip of the true transverse process and may be marked off from the margin in front of it by a notch. The ala is continuous with the floor of the iliac fossa of the hip bone when the bones are articulated ; the lumbo-sacral ligament and some fibres of the iliacus are attached to it. Its lateral margin is the anterior or upper boundary of the auricular surface.

The **apex** is attached to the body of the first coccygeal vertebra by an intervertebral disc and by the anterior and the deep posterior sacro-coccygeal ligaments.

The **lateral border** is curved sinuously as it is traced from base to apex, for the third piece of the sacrum is rather wider than the second, and the border turns abruptly towards the body of the fifth piece. The **auricular surface** belongs to the upper two or three pieces ; it is uneven and usually rough, though it is the articulating surface at a synovial joint ; its inequalities fit into reverse inequalities of the auricular surface of the hip bone, so that very little movement is possible at the joint. The anterior and lower parts of the joint capsule are together called the anterior sacro-iliac ligament, which is attached to the convex margin of the auricular surface ; the posterior or upper part is the interosseous sacro-iliac ligament, which is very thick and strong, and is attached to the concave margin of the surface and to the wide uneven depression above and behind it. The pelvic surface of the upper part of the sacrum is wider than the dorsal surface, and the auricular surface slopes accordingly ; in the articulated pelvis the sacrum is therefore the reverse of the keystone of an arch; the interosseous ligaments of the two sides are the principal factors in holding it in place.

The thinner, lower part of the lateral border gives attachment to part of the sacro-tuberous ligament; the upper parts of the sacro-spinous ligament and coccygeus muscle are attached to the side of the fifth piece in front of the sacro-tuberous ligament; and the **inferior lateral angle** is connected with the transverse process of the coccyx by the lateral sacro-coccygeal ligament.

The **dorsal surface** is directed upwards and backwards. The ridge of **spinous tubercles** varies greatly in its degree of prominence; its upper end gives attachment to a supraspinous and an interspinous ligament connecting it with the lowest lumbar spine, and the lower part of the lumbar fascia is attached to each lip of the ridge. At each side of the root of the ridge there is a rough plate of bone made up of the laminæ united by ossified ligaments. Lateral to that plate there are the four **posterior sacral foramina**; they diminish in size from above downwards, and each one transmits the posterior primary ramus of a sacral nerve, accompanied by small terminal branches of the lateral sacral vessels. At the medial margin of each foramen there is a small projection, called an **articular tubercle**, because it represents the inferior and superior articular processes of two contiguous sacral vertebræ fused together. The lowest of the series is the **sacral cornu**, which represents an inferior articular process of the fifth sacral vertebra; the two sacral cornua are connected by ligaments with the coccygeal cornua. Lateral to the posterior sacral foramina, on the back of the lateral mass, there is a row of **transverse tubercles**, representing the tips of the fused true transverse processes. The sacrospinalis muscle arises from the spinous and transverse tubercles, and the multifidus from the uneven surface that separates these two rows of tubercles. The short posterior sacro-iliac ligament is attached to the first and second transverse tubercles (the first being the postero-lateral angle of the ala); the long posterior sacro-iliac ligament to the third tubercle; part of the sacro-tuberous ligament to the fourth and fifth; fibres of the gluteus maximus arise from the back of the sacrum, but they spring from those ligaments and the lumbar fascia rather than from bone.

The **sacral canal** is the lowest part of the vertebral canal. It lies between the united bodies and the united laminæ. Its upper part is triangular; its lower part is flattened from before backwards. On each of its two margins there is a series of four large apertures that correspond to **intervertebral foramina**; they transmit the upper four sacral nerves, and each one divides into two parts which end as an anterior and a posterior sacral foramen. The canal *contains* (1) a quantity of soft fat in which there lie small arteries and fairly large, thin-walled veins, (2) the roots of the sacral and coccygeal nerves, (3) the filum terminale, (4) the lower part of the spinal dura mater and arachnoid mater down to the level of the second spine. The lower part of the posterior wall of the canal is deficient owing to the absence of the laminæ and spine of the fifth vertebra and, very often, of the fourth also. The lower opening of the canal is therefore very oblique, and is called the *hiatus sacralis*. It is closed by a thick membrane, called the superficial posterior sacro-coccygeal ligament, which extends from its upper and lateral margins to the back of the coccyx. The hiatus transmits the filum terminale and the primary rami of the coccygeal and fifth sacral nerves.

The coccygeal cornua correspond to pedicles and superior articular processes. In specimens in which the sacrum and coccyx are fused together the ligaments that connect the sacral and coccygeal cornua may be ossified, and so also may be the ligaments that connect the inferior lateral angles of the sacrum with the transverse processes of the coccyx; in such a specimen there are a *fifth pair* of intervertebral foramina and corresponding sacral foramina.

The back of the first piece of the **coccyx** gives attachment to the filum terminale, and a few fibres of the gluteus maximus. Its margin gives attachment to the lower parts of the sacro-tuberous ligament, the sacrospinous ligament, and the coccygeus muscle, in that order from behind forwards. The posterior fibres of the levator ani muscle are inserted into the side of the lower pieces; the sphincter ani externus and the ano-coccygeal body are attached to its apex.

Sexual Differences.—In the male the curve of the sacrum is fairly uniform and is deepest opposite the third piece. In the female the sacrum is flatter above and more sharply bent forwards below. In the female the auricular surface may be limited to the first two pieces; in the male it includes the third partly or wholly. The female sacrum is shorter and wider (in accordance with a shorter and wider pelvic cavity), and is set more obliquely—its pelvic surface looking more downwards than in the male. The coccyx is more movable in the female and less liable to be fused with the sacrum, and the first piece of the coccyx more often fails to fuse with the second piece than in the male.

VERTEBRAL COLUMN AS A WHOLE

The **vertebral column** is about 28 inches (70 cm.) long in a man and 24 inches (60 cm.) in a woman; and it is said to diminish nearly half an inch during the day. The discs account for nearly one-fourth of its length. In a man, approximate measurements for the different regions are: cervical, 5 in.; thoracic, 11 in.; lumbar, 7 in.; sacrum and coccyx, 5 in. The length increases up to the age of twenty-five or more; it diminishes in old age owing to reduction of the thickness of the discs and to exaggeration of the curve in the thoracic region. The proportion of its length to the whole length of the body is—3 : 4 at the third week of intra-uterine life; about 3 : 7 at birth; and 3 : 7·5 in a young man.

The column can bear a weight of nearly 7 cwt. without crushing, and a tearing strain of nearly 3 cwt. Its weakest part is between the second and third cervical vertebra ; the part most liable to injury is, however, at the twelfth thoracic, for at that level the column has the smallest transverse width (Fig. 125), is most movable, and is acted upon by the longest leverage.

The vertebræ are joined together by the discs between the bodies, and by the various ligaments that connect the body, laminæ, and processes of one vertebra with corresponding parts of its two immediate neighbours ; therefore the vertebræ make a strong column for the support of the trunk and neck and a pedestal for the head. It is not, however, a rigid column, but is flexible and resilient ; although the vertebræ are firmly bound together, a little movement is possible between each two (with the exception of the segments of sacrum and coccyx), and the sum of the movements between each two over the whole movable part of the column is very considerable. They derive their name from the rotatory movements between them.   [*Vertere* = to turn.]

The column of **bodies** is the chief axis of support ; the **vertebral arches** close in the vertebral canal, in which the spinal cord lies in safety ; the **articular processes** permit movement but also control its direction and help to limit its range ; the **spines** and **transverse processes** are levers to which muscles are attached.

Curvatures.—The column is not straight. **At birth** it has two curves, both concave forwards. They are called **primary curvatures**. The lower one, made by the sacral and coccygeal vertebræ, is for the accommodation of pelvic viscera, and begins to appear at the fifth month of intra-uterine life ; the upper one includes all the rest of the column, and is present from the earliest period ; the point where the two curves meet, at the junction of the last lumbar vertebra and the first sacral, is called the **sacro-vertebral angle**, which is more acute in the female than in the male.

In the adult there are four curves—cervical, thoracic, lumbar, and sacro-coccygeal. These curves help to break shocks, and they enable the column to bear vertical pressure better. They are maintained by the shape of the bodies and the discs and by the tension of the ligaments. Owing to them, the line of the centre of gravity passes not through the whole series of bodies but from the odontoid process through the front of the body of the second thoracic, the middle of the twelfth thoracic, and the back of the fifth lumbar body.

The **cervical curvature** is convex forwards. It begins at the atlas, culminates at the fifth cervical, and, at its lower part, merges into the thoracic curve ; the lower border of the second thoracic vertebra is taken as the level where the two curves meet, for that is the level of the upper border of the breast-bone, and the upper two thoracic vertebræ lie, therefore, in a sense, in the neck. The cervical curvature is the least marked of the four curves and is undone when the

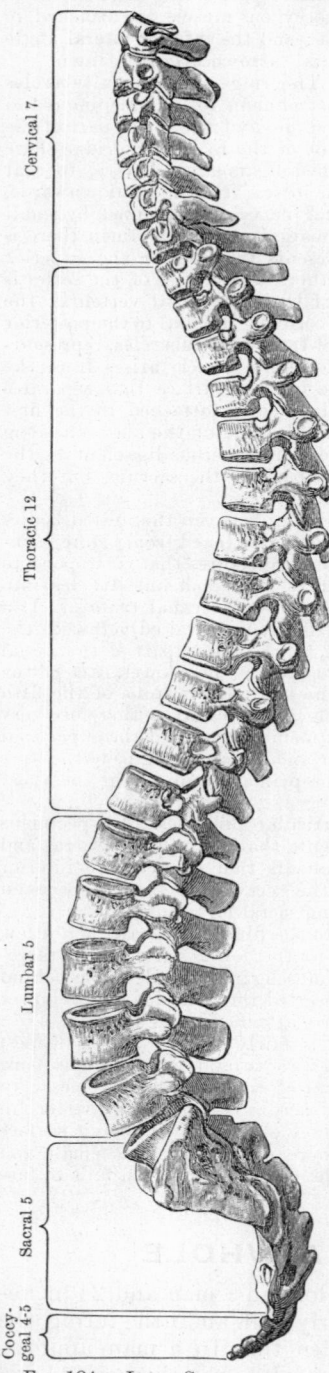

Fig. 124.—Left Side of the Vertebral Column.

neck is bent forwards. It is a *secondary* or *compensatory* curve and is due chiefly to the shape of the discs. It begins to be formed two or three months after birth, when the child begins to lift its head up from the chest; and it becomes further developed at the eighth or ninth month, when the child begins to sit upright. The **thoracic curvature** is concave forwards. It is deepest at the sixth thoracic vertebra, and extends to the twelfth, where it merges into the lumbar curve. It is a primary curve and is due to the shape of the bodies of the vertebræ. The **lumbar curvature** is convex forwards. It is more pronounced in a woman than in a man, and in a youth than in an elderly person. It culminates opposite the umbilicus, between the third and fourth lumbar vertebræ or at the fourth, and extends to the sacro-vertebral angle. It is a *secondary* or *compensatory* curve and is due chiefly to the shape of the discs. It begins a year after birth, when the child, adopting the erect attitude, lifts up its trunk, straightens out its lower limbs and begins to walk; it makes its first appearance immediately above the sacro-vertebral angle, and gradually extends upwards as the lower limbs come more into use. The **sacro-coccygeal curvature** is the original lower *primary curve* and is concave downwards and forwards.

Besides having those four curvatures the column of bodies is often slightly convex towards the right side in the thoracic region. That **lateral curvature** may be due to the greater muscularity and use of the right upper limb, for it is said to be convex towards the left in left-handed people; but much more probably it is due to the pressure that the upper part of the descending aorta exerts by its pulsations on the left side of the bodies of the middle four thoracic vertebræ, and in the rare cases in which the aorta is on the other side of those vertebræ the curve is convex towards the left. (The aorta is the great artery that springs from the heart and conveys blood to be distributed by its branches to all parts of the body.) When the lateral curvature is well marked there are compensatory curves, in the opposite direction, above and below it.

The curvatures of a line drawn along the tips of the spines are not repetitions of the curvatures of the bodies, owing to the varying length and obliquity of the spines; and lateral curvature of the spines may be greater or lesser in degree than that of the bodies. Occasionally one or more spines may be deflected very considerably to one side without corresponding rotation of the body towards the opposite side and without any sign of past disease or of recent accident.

Curvatures of the backbone may become accentuated and distortions may occur as a result of weakness, disease, or accident. With advancing years the column loses its flexibility and resilience and becomes more or less set and rigid, especially in rheumatic people. In many skeletons evidence of rheumatism is seen in the "lipping" of the margins of the vertebræ and rough ridges and protuberances here and there.

The following points may be noted in the vertebral column :—

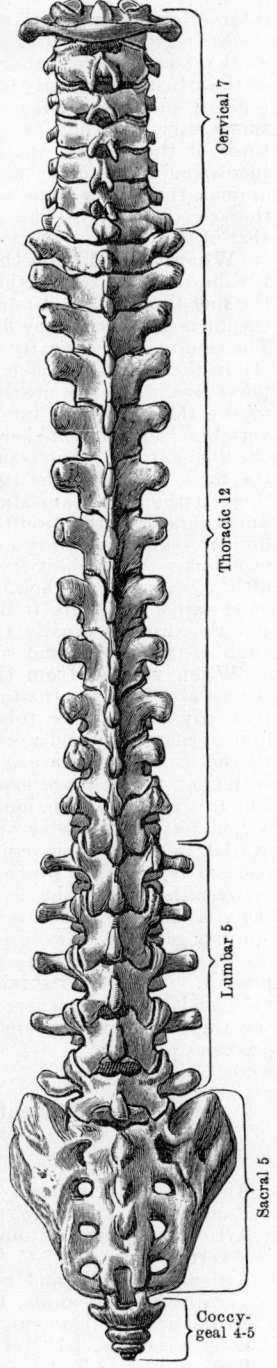

FIG. 125.—VERTEBRAL COLUMN SEEN FROM BEHIND.

When viewed from the Side.—(1) The four curvatures. (2) The antero-posterior diameters of the **bodies** increase gradually down to the *second lumbar*, and then gradually diminish. (3) The **costal facets** on the sides of the bodies, from the first thoracic downwards, gradually take up a position farther back till that on the twelfth is more on the pedicle than on the body. (4) The **intervertebral foramina** increase in size from above downwards. (5) The **transverse processes** of *cervical* and *lumbar* vertebræ are in front of the articular processes, while those of *thoracic* vertebræ are behind and have more of a backward inclination; they are between the intervertebral foramina in the *cervical* region, and behind the foramina in the *thoracic* and *lumbar* regions; the change of characters is abrupt between cervical and thoracic regions, and more gradual between thoracic and true lumbar transverse processes. (6) Owing to the direction of the **articular surfaces** the clefts of the joints between the articular processes are visible in the cervical and thoracic regions, but not in the lumbar region. (7) The length and slope of the **spines** vary, and there is consequent lack of conformity between the curves of the spines and those of the bodies; the slope of the spines, though varying greatly, is always downwards, increasing in obliquity down to the seventh thoracic and then diminishing; in most lower animals the spines slope towards an "anticlinal" vertebra situated in the hinder part of the thoracic region. (8) The antero-posterior diameter of the *lumbar vertebræ* is much greater than that of the others.

When viewed from the Front.—(1) The lateral curvatures, when present. (2) The column is widest at the base of the sacrum; the **bodies** increase in width from the second cervical to the first thoracic and diminish slightly from the first to the fourth; they increase gradually from the fifth thoracic to the first sacral, below which there is progressive diminution in width. (3) The side-to-side convexity of the bodies is sharper in the middle thoracic region than elsewhere. (4) In the vertical diameter the body of the second cervical vertebra is deeper than those of the lower five, which are nearly equal in depth; below that there is gradual increase in depth down to the third or fourth lumbar; the fifth lumbar is usually of less depth than the other lumbar vertebræ; in different skeletons any one of the thoracic vertebræ may be of less depth than the one above it. (5) The **transverse processes** of the *atlas* are outstanding and are wider apart than the next five pairs, the tips of which are at nearly equal distances from the median plane; those of the *seventh* are almost as long as the first thoracic; they gradually diminish from the first thoracic to the twelfth, where they are mere tubercles; they are outstanding again in the lumbar region and vary in length, and though the third is usually the longest, its tip is not necessarily the farthest from the median plane, owing to the greater width of the fourth and fifth vertebræ as a whole. (6) The *sacrum* and *coccyx* rapidly diminish in width from above downwards, but there is little difference between the second and third pieces of the sacrum, and the third is usually the wider; the diminution is very sudden below the inferior lateral angle of the sacrum, and, again, below the transverse process of the coccyx.

When viewed from the Back.—(1) Differences in the lengths of the **transverse processes** as seen also from the front; in the cervical region they are hidden by the articular processes, so that only the posterior tubercles are visible; the transition from thoracic transverse process to lumbar mamillary and accessory processes is well seen. (2) The **articular processes** of the lower six cervical vertebræ are at equal distances apart, and are wider apart than those of the thoracic vertebræ; the distance gradually diminishes from the first thoracic to the first lumbar, below which it increases; the joint clefts between articular processes are clearly visible in the lumbar region, less so in the cervical region, and not at all in the thoracic region. (3) The **laminæ** overlap in the thoracic region; in the lumbar region there are intervals between them; in the cervical region they overlap very slightly when the neck is straight, but there are intervals between them when the neck is bent forwards, and there is always a fairly wide interval between the atlas and the second vertebra, and also between the atlas and the skull. The widest inter-laminar gaps are between atlas and axis, fourth and fifth lumbar, and fifth lumbar and sacrum. (4) The different characters of the **spines** are seen, and their lateral curvatures or deflections, if present. (5) The **vertebral groove** is the wide furrow alongside the spines; it is shallow in the neck and the loins, where its floor is the laminæ and inferior articular processes, and deep in the thoracic region, where its floor is the laminæ, inferior articular processes and transverse processes.

Ligaments and Muscles attached to movable Vertebræ

Bodies.

Anterior and posterior longitudinal ligaments, 2 C to sacrum.
Articular capsules of joints at sides of intervertebral discs, 2-7 C.
Articular capsules and radiate ligaments of costo-vertebral joints, 1-12 T.
Medial arcuate ligament, 2 L.
Longus cervicis, 2-7 C, 1-3 T.
Psoas minor, 12 T, 1 L.
Psoas major, 12 T, 1-5 L.

Laminæ.

Ligamenta flava, ALL.
Rotatores, 1-11 T.

Articular processes.

Articular capsules, ALL.
Longissimus capitis ⎫
Semispinalis capitis ⎬ 4-7 C.
Semispinalis cervicis ⎭
Multifidus, 4-7 C, 1-5 L.

Transverse processes.

Intertransverse ligaments, ALL.
Suprapleural membrane, 7 C.
Articular capsules ⎫
Lateral costo-transverse ligament ⎬ 1-10 T.
Inferior and superior costo-transverse ligaments, 1-11 T.
Lumbo-costal ligament, 12 T, 1 L.

Transverse processes—(contd.)

Arcuate ligaments of diaphragm, 1 L.
Lumbar fascia, 1-5 L.
Ilio-lumbar ligament } 5 L.
Lumbo-sacral ligament }
Rectus capitis lateralis   }
Obliquus capitis superior } 1 C.
Obliquus capitis inferior   }
Levator scapulæ   } 1-4 C.
Splenius cervicis   }
Intertransversales, 1 C-5 L.
Scalenus medius, 1-6 C.
Longissimus cervicis, 2-6 C, 1-6 T.
Longus capitis   }
Longus cervicis   } 3-6 C.
Scalenus anterior   }
Scalenus posterior   } 4-6 C.
Costo-cervicalis   }
Levatores costarum, 7 C, 1-11 T.
Longissimus capitis   }
Semispinalis capitis   } 1-6 T.
Semispinalis cervicis   }
Multifidus, 1-12 T.
Longissimus thoracis, 1-12 T, 1-5 L.
Rotatores, 2-12 T.

Transverse processes—(contd.)

Semispinalis thoracis, 7-12 T.
Psoas major   } 1-5 L.
Quadratus lumborum }

Spines.

Ligamentum nuchæ, 2-7 C.
Interspinous and supraspinous }
    ligaments   } All T and L.
Lumbar fascia   }
Obliquus capitis inferior   } 2 C.
Rectus capitis posterior major }
Semispinalis cervicis, 2-5 C.
Spinalis cervicis, 2-4 C, 7 C-2 T.
Interspinales } 2 C-5 L.
Multifidus   }
Semispinalis thoracis, 6 C-4 T.
Rhomboideus minor, 7 C, 1 T.
Serratus posterior superior, 7 C-3 T.
Splenius, 7 C-5 T.
Trapezius, 7 C-12 T.
Rhomboideus major, 2-5 T.
Latissimus dorsi, 6-12 T.
Spinalis thoracis, 4-8 T, 11 T-2 L.
Sacro-spinalis, 1-5 L.

OSSIFICATION OF VERTEBRÆ

A **typical vertebra** is ossified from three primary centres and five secondary centres. The three **primary** centres are one in the *body* and one in each half of the *vertebral arch* (called also the *neural arch*); the five **secondary** centres appear at the tip of the *spine*, the tips of the *transverse processes*, the upper and lower surfaces of the *body*.

The *primary centres* for the **arch** appear gradually from above downwards, appearing first in the upper cervical region about the seventh week of intra-uterine life and reaching the sacrum about the twentieth week. They appear at the roots of the articular processes; the arch and its processes are ossified from them, and also the postero-lateral parts of the body—the parts of the body which, in thoracic vertebræ, articulate with the ribs.

The *centre* for the *centrum*, *i.e.* the median, larger part of the **body**, appears dorsal to the notochord, first in the lower thoracic region about the tenth week; the process spreads up and down till by the twentieth week centres have appeared in all the bodies except in the last two pieces of the sacrum, where they may not appear till the thirtieth week, and in the coccyx, where they do not appear till after birth. Occasionally a body has a pair of centres which coalesce, but may fail to do so, and the body may ossify therefore as two separate halves—or one half only may ossify.

At birth the vertebra is in three pieces—the median, larger part (the *centrum*) of the body and the two parts ossified from the centres for the arch. The laminæ are not osseously united; the spine is cartilaginous. The median part (centrum) of the body is joined to each postero-lateral part by a plate of cartilage; the joint is called the *neuro-central joint*; the line of the joint is anteroposterior in the cervical region, oblique in the thoracic, and nearly transverse in the lumbar region (Fig. 128).

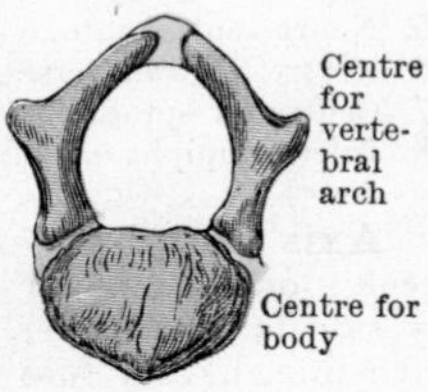

The union of laminæ begins in the lumbar region soon after birth, and, spreading upwards, is completed in the cervical region early in the second year, but is deferred in the sacrum till between the seventh and tenth years. After fusion of the laminæ the ossifying process extends into the spine. The union of the body and arch, *i.e.* the disappearance of the neuro-central joint, begins in the neck in the third year, and, spreading downwards, is completed in all regions in the sixth or seventh year.

Centre
for
verte-
bral
arch

Centre for
body

FIG. 126.—OSSIFICATION
OF VERTEBRÆ.

The *secondary centres* appear at puberty, and the epiphyses formed from them fuse with the rest of the bone at 25. The epiphyses on the body are in the form of flat rings on the circumferential part of the upper and lower surfaces. In the thoracic region the epiphysis on the tip of a transverse process includes part of the articular facet.

	Centres for arch.	Centre for body.	Laminæ unite.	Arch joins body.	Epiphyses appear.	Epiphyses join.
Cervical . .	7th week	15th week	Early 2nd yr.	3rd year	Puberty	25th year
Thoracic . .	10th ,,	10th ,,	1st year	4-5 years	,,	25th ,,
Lumbar . .	15th ,,	15th ,,	Early 1st yr.	6th year	,,	25th ,,
Sacral . .	20th ,,	20th ,,	7-10 years	7th year	18th year	25th ,,
Coccygeal . .	*none*	1st year to puberty	*none*	*none*	*none*	*none*

In many of the vertebræ the ossification departs from type.

In the **cervical region** the bifid tip of the **spine** has a *pair* of epiphyses.

Atlas Vertebra.—A primary centre for each half of the vertebral arch, including the lateral mass, appears at the seventh week. The two halves unite posteriorly in the third year, and their union may be preceded by a secondary centre in the cartilage between them. The anterior arch is cartilaginous at birth. One centre (or a pair) appears in it during the first year, and it fuses with the lateral masses about the seventh year. It includes the anterior part of the upper articular surface of the lateral mass. The epiphyses on the transverse processes unite about 18.

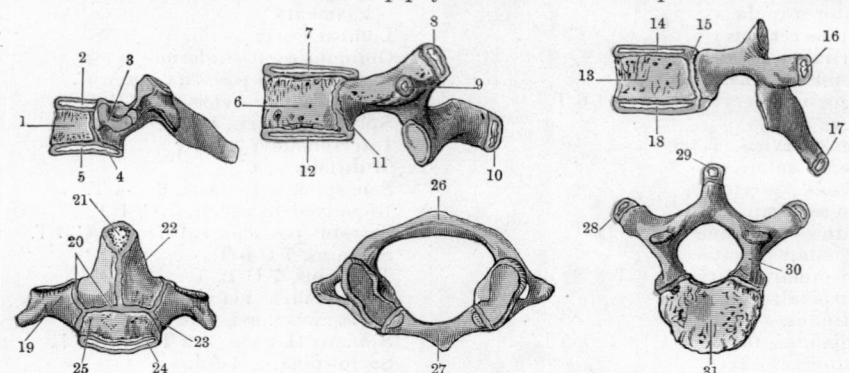

FIG. 127.—OSSIFICATION OF VERTEBRÆ.

Cervical vertebra.

1. Centre for body.
2. Superior epiphyseal ring.
3. Anterior bar of transverse process ossified by lateral extension from pedicle.
4. Neuro-central joint.
5. Inferior epiphyseal ring.

Lumbar vertebra.

6. Centre for body.
7. Superior epiphyseal ring.
8. Centre for mamillary process.
9. Centre for transverse process.
10. Centre for spine.
11. Neuro-central joint.
12. Inferior epiphyseal ring.

Thoracic vertebra.

13. Centre for body.
14. Superior epiphyseal ring.
15. Neuro-central joint.
16. Centre for transverse process.
17. Centre for spine.
18. Inferior epiphyseal ring.

Axis.

19. Centre for transverse process and vertebral arch.
20. Joints close about 3rd year.
21. Centre for summit of odontoid process.
22. Centre for lower part of odontoid process.
23. Neuro-central joint.
24. Inferior epiphyseal ring.
25. Single or double centre for body.

Atlas.

26. Posterior arch and lateral masses ossified from a single centre on each side. In this figure the posterior arch is represented complete by the union posteriorly of its posterior elements.
27. Anterior arch and portion of superior articular surface ossified from single or double centre.

Thoracic vertebra.

28. Centre for transverse process.
29. Centre for spine.
30. Centre for vertebral arch on each side. The arch is here shown complete posteriorly.
31. Centre for body.

Axis Vertebra.—A primary centre for each half of the vertebral arch appears in the seventh week ; one or two for the lower part of the body early in the fifth month ; a pair appear side by side for the upper part of the body and the lower part of the odontoid process later in the fifth month, and fuse during the seventh month. *At birth* the vertebra is in four bony pieces which unite between the third and sixth years. An epiphysis for the top of the odontoid process appears between the third and sixth years and fuses before 12 ; another appears on the lower surface of the body at puberty and fuses about 25.

The **sixth** and **seventh cervical vertebræ** may have separate primary centres in the costal processes ; these join the rest of the bone about the fifth year. Sometimes in the seventh it does not join but forms a cervical rib.

Lumbar vertebræ have additional epiphyses on the *mamillary processes*. The **first lumbar vertebra** may have a separate primary centre for its *transverse process*, and it may remain separate as a **lumbar rib**. The **fifth** may have two primary centres in each half of the arch ; the two parts of each half are then united by a plate of cartilage set obliquely between the superior and inferior articular processes. Its transverse process may have two epiphyses.

Sacrum.—**Primary centres** appear between the third and eighth months. One centre for each centrum and one for each half of the vertebral arch, and one for the costal element on each side in the upper three or four vertebræ. The costal parts fuse with the arches at the fifth year. The arches fuse with the centra a little later. The halves of the arches unite posteriorly between the seventh and tenth years. The segments of the lateral mass fuse together at puberty. **Epiphyseal centres** appear on the upper and lower surfaces of the bodies at puberty ; the epiphyses fuse with the bodies and the bodies fuse together from below upwards between 18 and 25. Numerous epiphyseal centres appear on the ends of the costal and true transverse processes at 18. From them are formed an epiphysis which covers the auricular surface, and another which completes the margin below the auricular surface.

The **coccyx** is cartilaginous at birth. Each segment has one **primary** centre. They appear, from above downwards, between the first year and puberty. Fusion between segments takes place from below upwards, but is very variable. Epiphyses on the surface of the bodies and in the cornua have been described.

VARIATIONS IN VERTEBRÆ

Variation in number is due usually to the coccygeal vertebræ being reduced to three or increased to five or even six. Variations in other regions may occur through increase or reduction or re-arrangement among the regions; the formula may be altered therefore in several ways, as follows :—

Cervical		7	7	7	6	7	7	7
Thoracic		13	12	12	13	13	12	12
Lumbar		5	6	4	5	4	6	4
Sacral		5	5	5	5	5	4	6
Coccygeal		4	4	4	4	4	4	4
		34	34	32	33	33	33	33

Atlas.—One or other of the arches may be incompletely ossified, or may have a facet for articulation with the margin of the foramen magnum. The foramen transversarium may be incomplete owing to absence of the anterior part of the transverse process. A bar of bone may bridge across the groove for the vertebral artery. The upper articular facet may be divided. The transverse process may be bifid ; and it may articulate with an occasional projection, called the *par-occipital process*, that juts from the jugular process of the occipital bone. The atlas may be partially fused with the occipital bone, or with the second cervical vertebra.

Axis.—It may be fused with the atlas or with the third vertebra. The odontoid process may articulate with the basi-occiput. It may be bifid or double, or may be a separate bone called the **os odontoideum**. Fusion of a detached odontoid process with the anterior arch of the atlas has been recorded. Its apical part may be partially or completely detached. The foramen transversarium may be incomplete, owing to imperfect development of the posterior part of the transverse process.

Nodules representing ribs have been seen once or twice in the **fourth** and **sixth** cervical vertebræ. The **seventh** has a cervical rib fairly often. One of its foramina transversaria may be absent.

The **first thoracic vertebra** may have its transverse process connected with the neck of the first rib by a bar of bone ; the posterior part of its arch may be separate. The facets on the body of the **ninth** are variable. The **tenth** may have no facets on its transverse processes ; and its spine may be shorter than that of the eleventh. The inferior articular processes of the **eleventh** may resemble those of the twelfth, and the superior processes of the **twelfth** correspondingly resemble those of a lumbar vertebra. Suppression of the right or left half of a lower thoracic vertebra (the remaining half being wedge-shaped) has been known to cause congenital scoliosis ; and so has the interpolation of a wedge-shaped half of a lumbar vertebra.

The mamillary and accessory processes of the **lumbar vertebræ** may be large, and occasionally are connected by a bridge of bone, enclosing a small foramen. The first transverse process may be separate, as a lumbar rib ; the fourth may spring from the side of the body, without connexion with the arch ; and the fifth may have a foramen in it. The posterior part of the arch of the fifth, comprising the spine, the laminæ, and inferior articular processes, is occasionally separate from the rest of the bone (union during life being effected by hyaline cartilage) ; the same condition has been seen in the fourth. The fifth may be fused with the sacrum partly or wholly, and may have pronounced sacral characters on one or both sides.

The **sacrum** may have six vertebræ, owing to inclusion usually of the first coccygeal, but sometimes of the fifth lumbar. More seldom there are only four vertebræ. Sometimes the first sacral is not united to the second, or only partially, and may resemble a lumbar vertebra on the un-united side. The posterior wall of the **sacral canal** may be defective in its whole length. A foramen may be present in the lateral part of the first sacral vertebra, between the pedicle and the costal element. The degree of curvature varies greatly in different specimens.

The **coccyx** varies in its number of segments and the extent to which they are fused together. A curved process jutting from the front of the first piece has been recorded. The second piece may have rudimentary transverse processes and pedicles.

SERIAL HOMOLOGIES OF VERTEBRÆ

The **body** is the only part present in every vertebra from the first cervical to the last coccygeal. The homology of the bodies is manifest throughout the series, except that the *median part* (centrum) of the body of the atlas is detached from its own vertebra and fused with the second, forming the odontoid process ; the *lateral parts, i.e.* the parts which in other vertebræ are ossified from the vertebral arch, form the anterior, larger parts of the lateral masses. The anterior arch of the atlas does not correspond to the front of the body of a vertebra, but is ossified from a persistent "hypochordal bow," which disappears in other vertebræ (p. 133).

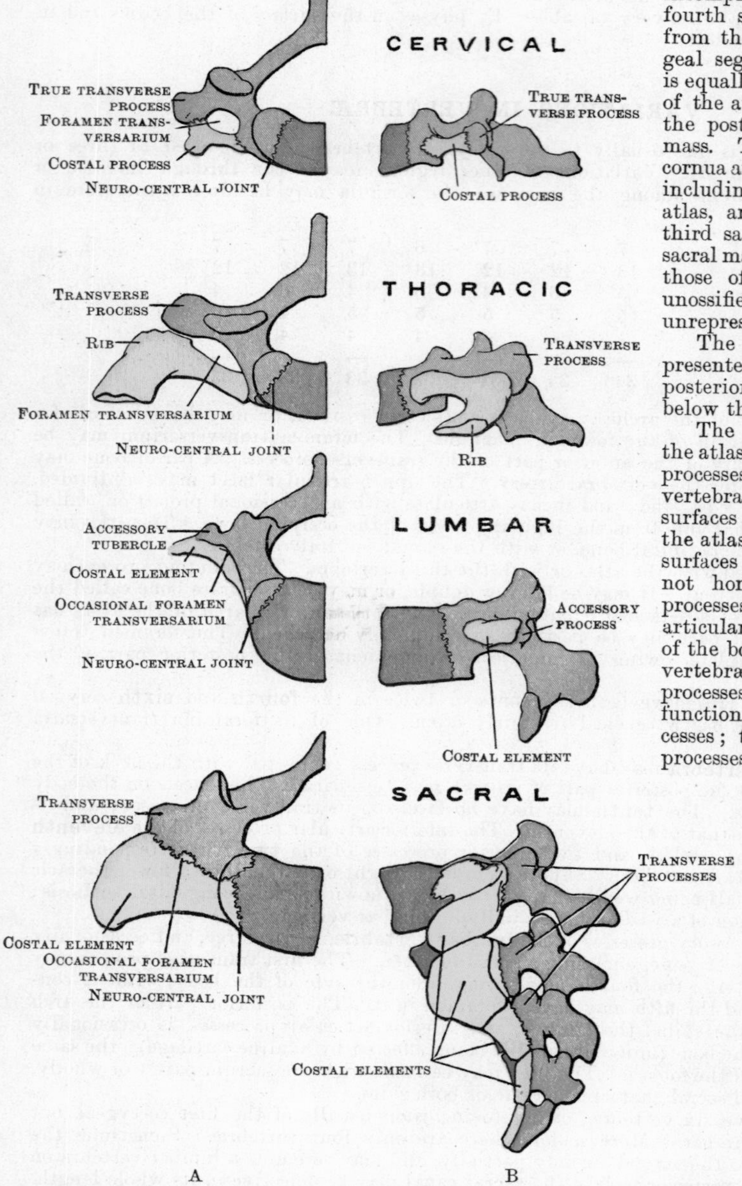

CERVICAL

TRUE TRANSVERSE PROCESS
FORAMEN TRANSVERSARIUM
COSTAL PROCESS
NEURO-CENTRAL JOINT

TRUE TRANSVERSE PROCESS
COSTAL PROCESS

THORACIC

TRANSVERSE PROCESS
RIB
FORAMEN TRANSVERSARIUM
NEURO-CENTRAL JOINT
RIB
TRANSVERSE PROCESS

LUMBAR

ACCESSORY TUBERCLE
COSTAL ELEMENT
OCCASIONAL FORAMEN TRANSVERSARIUM
NEURO-CENTRAL JOINT
ACCESSORY PROCESS
COSTAL ELEMENT

SACRAL

TRANSVERSE PROCESS
COSTAL ELEMENT
OCCASIONAL FORAMEN TRANSVERSARIUM
NEURO-CENTRAL JOINT
TRANSVERSE PROCESSES
COSTAL ELEMENTS

A   B

FIG. 128.—DIAGRAM TO ILLUSTRATE THE HOMOLOGOUS PARTS OF THE VERTEBRÆ.
Body, *purple*; arch and processes, *red*; costal element, *blue*.
A, from above.   B, from the side.

The **vertebral arches** are incomplete below the third and fourth sacral, and wholly absent from the third and fourth coccygeal segments. Their homology is equally obvious, but the **pedicle** of the atlas is partly obscured in the posterior part of the lateral mass. The roots of the coccygeal cornua are pedicles. The **laminæ**, including the posterior arch of the atlas, are complete down to the third sacral; those of the fourth sacral may or may not be complete; those of the fifth are usually unossified; and they are quite unrepresented in the coccyx.

The **spine** of the atlas is represented by the tubercle on the posterior arch. Spines are absent below the third sacral vertebra.

The **articular processes** of the atlas and the superior articular processes of the second cervical vertebra are absent; the articular surfaces of the lateral masses of the atlas and the upper articular surfaces of the second vertebra are not homologous with articular processes, but with the very small articular areas on the lateral parts of the bodies of the other cervical vertebræ. The superior articular processes of the first sacral vertebra function as ordinary articular processes; the other sacral articular processes are fused together to form the row of articular tubercles on the back of the sacrum, except the inferior articular processes of the fifth piece, which jut downwards as the sacral cornua. The upper parts of the coccygeal cornua are homologous with superior articular processes; they are absent from the other coccygeal segments.

The **transverse processes** are present in the whole series down to and including the first coccygeal vertebra; but their homologies are less obvious. The transverse processes of the **thoracic** vertebræ are taken as the type and standard.

In a **cervical** vertebra the true transverse process is represented by the posterior root; the remainder of the process is the homologue of a rib; the foramen transversarium is homologous with the interval between a transverse process and the neck of a rib. In a **lumbar** vertebra the process called the transverse process is the homologue of a rib; the true transverse process is represented by the mamillary process and the posterior part of the root of the transverse process, including the accessory process. No interval is left between the costal and true transverse elements as in the cervical and thoracic regions, except in the rare instance where there is a foramen in the fifth lumbar transverse process. In the **sacrum** the lateral mass is made of the true transverse processes posteriorly and the costal elements anteriorly, the ends of the true transverse processes being the row of transverse tubercles on the back; each transverse tubercle represents part of the ends of two true transverse processes, for the end of each process expands, growing upwards and downwards, and unites with similar expansions of the process above and below to form the tubercles lateral to the posterior sacral foramina.

STERNUM

The **sternum** or breast-bone [στέρνον (sternon) = the breast] is an elongated flat bone, six to eight inches long, shaped like a dagger. It lies in the anterior wall of the thorax in the median plane, extending from the root of the neck to the pit of the stomach, and it can be felt through the skin from end to end. It has an upper and a lower end, an anterior and a posterior surface, a right and a left border; the two clavicles articulate with its upper end, and the cartilages of the upper seven pairs of ribs articulate with it at intervals along its borders. It has three main parts, named, from above downwards, the *manubrium*, the *body*, and the *xiphoid process*; the body, in youth, is in four pieces—united by cartilage.

The **manubrium** [= a handle] is the widest piece of the sternum, and, unless the skeleton is that of an old person, it is a separate bone; for the manubrium and the body are united by cartilage and do not fuse together till an advanced age. It is triangular in outline, each side measuring about two inches; but the lower angle is cut off— giving it a short lower border. The *posterior surface* is slightly concave from side to side and is not so rough as the *anterior surface*. The *upper border* is the upper end of the sternum and is more than twice the width of the lower border. The middle part of the upper border is concave from side to side and can be felt in the root of the neck as the floor of the **suprasternal notch**; on each side of the suprasternal notch there is a larger notch for articulation with the medial end of the clavicle or collar bone. On the *right* and *left margins*, immediately below the **clavicular notch**, there is a rough mark or a pit on which the cartilage of the first rib is implanted.

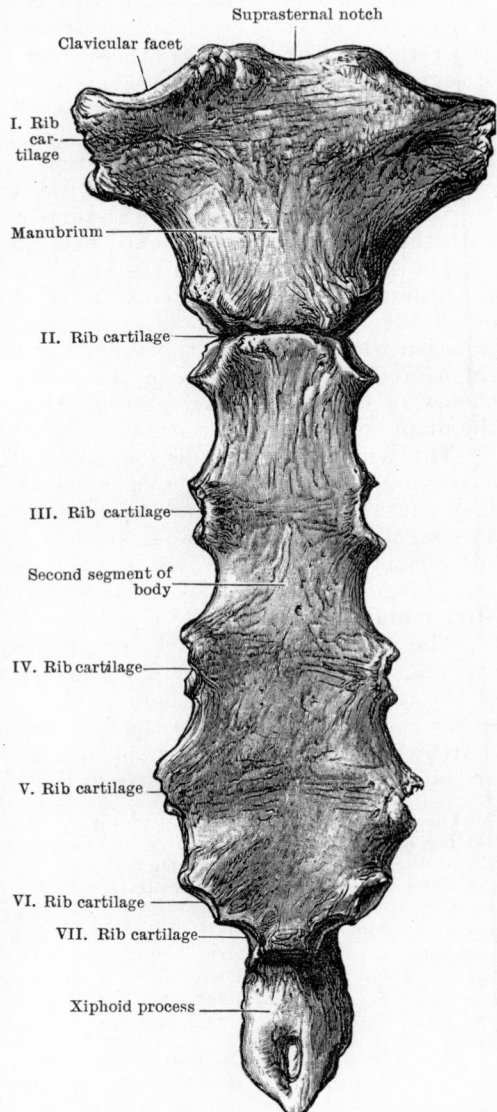

FIG. 129.—THE STERNUM (anterior view).

The lower border of the manubrium and the upper end of the body of the sternum, together, can be felt and often seen as a transverse ridge on the front of the chest, for the two bones are slightly thickened at their junction, and the manubrium is not quite in line with the body, but joins it at a very obtuse angle called the **sternal angle**. The ridge is about two inches below the upper end of the sternum; it can be felt in stout people as well as in thin, and is the most serviceable of the landmarks on the front of the chest. The cartilage of the second rib joins the side of the sternum at the junction of manubrium and body, *i.e.* at the sternal angle, and the second rib is therefore easily identified.

The **body** is the longest of the three parts of the sternum ; it is more than twice as long as the manubrium in men and rather less in women ; it is about an inch wide at its *upper end,* increases slightly down to the fourth segment and then dwindles in breadth, and the *lower end,* at its junction with the xiphoid process, is therefore the narrowest part. The *posterior surface* is slightly concave from above downwards and usually is smoother than the *anterior surface.* Each *margin* bears four pits for articulation with costal cartilages. The upper three pairs of pits are at the ends of indistinct **transverse lines** that indicate the subdivision of the body into four segments ; those three pairs of pits are therefore at the junction of segments ; the fourth pair is on the sides of the fourth segment. In addition there are, on each side, an articular pit or notch between the body and the manubrium, and one between the body and the xiphoid process—the latter notch being on the front of their junction rather than at its side. The second rib cartilage articulates with the notch between manubrium and body ; the third, fourth, fifth, and sixth with the pits or notches on the body ; and the seventh with that between the body and the xiphoid process.

The **xiphoid process** is the smallest piece of the sternum ; it juts down into the anterior wall of the abdomen in front of the liver. It can be felt in the floor of the depression known as the *epigastric fossa* or "pit of the stomach." Its junction with the body—the *xiphi-sternal joint*—can be felt as a short transverse ridge in the upper margin of that fossa ; the ridge marks the lower limit of the thorax in the middle line in front, and is the landmark, in the middle line, for the diaphragm, the upper surface of the liver, and the lower border of the heart.

The xiphoid process is usually flat and pointed [ξίφος (xiphos) = *ensis* = a sword ; εἶδος (eidos) = *forma* = shape], but it may be almost any shape ; it may have a hole in its middle or it may be bifid. It is made of cartilage with a core of bone ; the core enlarges with age at the expense of the cartilage, till the process is quite ossified ; it is more yielding therefore in youth than in old age. At first it is united to the body by cartilage, but fuses with it after middle age.

The sternum slopes from above downwards and forwards—the manubrium slanting more than the body. The **upper end** is on a level with the *lower* border of the body of the **second** thoracic vertebra (Fig. 134) ; the **sternal angle** with the *upper* border of the body of the **fifth** and with the interval between the third and fourth thoracic spines ; the **xiphi-sternal joint** with the **ninth** thoracic vertebra (at or below its middle), and the tip of the eighth thoracic spine.

The **manubrium** is thicker at its upper and lower parts than in the middle. The clavicular notches look upwards and laterally, and its thickest and strongest part is below and medial to them where it receives shocks transmitted through the clavicle. The slightly raised area on the *anterior surface,* below the medial part of the clavicular notch, gives origin to the sternal head of the sterno-mastoid ; part of the pectoralis major arises from the large concave area that accounts for most of each half of the front of the manubrium. On the *posterior surface* of the manubrium, part of the sterno-hyoid arises medial to the clavicular notch, and part of the sterno-thyroid about half-way down. The capsule of the sterno-clavicular joint is attached to the margins of the **clavicular notch** ; the articular disc of that joint to the junction of the manubrium and first costal cartilage ; the interclavicular ligament, slightly, to the floor of the **suprasternal notch.**

The chief structures *behind the manubrium* are : (1) the edges of the pleuræ and lungs, (2) the remains of the thymus, (3) the left innominate vein, (4) the arch of the aorta and its three branches, and (5) the trachea, which ends opposite the sternal angle.

The **body** is thinner along its middle than at the margins. Its *anterior surface* gives origin to part of the pectoralis major ; the lower part of its *posterior surface* to part of the sterno-costalis [transversus thoracis] ; the sterno-pericardial ligaments are attached to its upper and lower ends.

The chief structures *behind the body* are—the edges of the pleuræ and lungs, the pericardium and heart ; and the ascending aorta and right pulmonary artery, behind the first segment.

The **xiphoid process** is thicker in the middle than at the sides. It is thinner than the body, but their posterior surfaces are flush—hence the depression called the epigastric fossa. It varies in length, so that its lower end, though palpable, is of no use as a landmark.

The linea alba is attached to its *lower end.* Fibres of the rectus abdominis and of the external and internal oblique aponeuroses are inserted into its *anterior surface* ; of the internal oblique and transversus aponeuroses into its *margin* ; part of the sterno-costalis and a slip of the diaphragm arise from its *posterior surface*, to which the fascia transversalis and the falciform ligament of the liver also are attached.

The sterno-chondral ligaments are attached to the front and back of the sternum at the notches for the rib cartilages, and the intra-articular ligaments, when present, to their floors.

Ossification. — The following table gives the approximate dates of the appearance of centres and of fusion of segments, but there is a certain amount of variation, and centres for adjoining segments may appear almost simultaneously :—

	Manubrium.	Body, 1st Seg.	2nd Seg.	3rd Seg.	4th Seg.	Xiph. proc.
Centres (one or two) appear	5th month of intra-uterine life	6th m.	7th m.	8th m.	9th m.	3rd year
Parts unite	Old age	21st yr.	Puberty	Child	Middle age	

The fourth segment does not always have a separate centre. Epiphyses have been found at the clavicular notches in an adult.

Structure and Variations.—The sternum is composed of highly vascular spongy bone enclosed in thin compact bone. The *vascular foramina* are best marked on the back of the manubrium. Occasionally there is a hole in the lower part of the body, and more rarely the sternum is fissured longitudinally to a greater or lesser degree, the gap being wider above ; the cleft is sometimes associated with *ectopia cordis*—a condition incompatible with life. Deformities, such as a bending back of the lower part of the sternum, arise from disease and in certain occupations. The two halves of the sternum are often asymmetrical, the clavicular notch being higher and the costal notches more crowded together on one side, with the junction of manubrium and body oblique ; occupational use of the right upper limb may account for the asymmetry in some cases. Occasionally the manubrium includes the first segment of the body and carries three pairs of ribs, as in the gibbon ; the *sternal angle* is then between the third pair of costal cartilages, and is felt about 3 inches below the suprasternal notch. The eighth costal cartilage in about ten per cent. of bodies reaches the sternum, more often on the right side than on the left ; and in rare cases the seventh cartilage

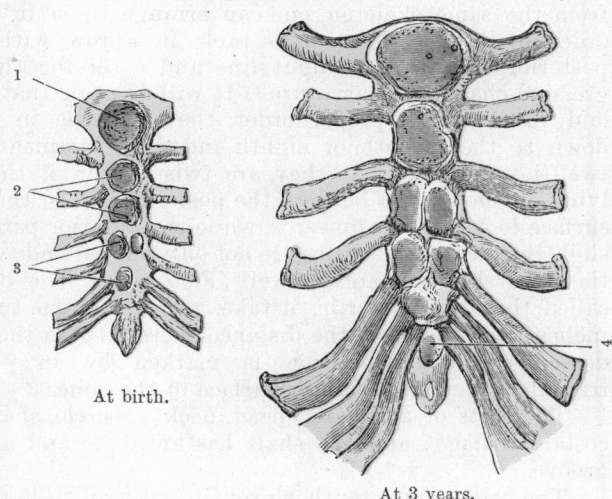

At birth.

At 3 years.

FIG. 130.—OSSIFICATION OF THE STERNUM.

1. Appears at 5th intra-uterine Month. 2. At 6th and 7th M.
3. At 8th and 9th M.   4. At 3rd Year.

fails to reach the sternum. Small ossicles called *suprasternal bones* are sometimes found in the ligaments of the sterno-clavicular joint.

In women the manubrium is at a rather lower level and is narrower and longer than in men, but the body of the sternum is wider and shorter.

RIBS (COSTÆ)

There are twelve **ribs** on each side in both sexes. They are thin, narrow, curved strips of bone, and, though elongated, they are classed among the " flat " bones. They are attached posteriorly to the thoracic vertebræ and curve round the sides of the chest, slanting downwards and forwards ; anteriorly each of them ends by joining a bar of cartilage called a **costal cartilage**. The ribs lie at the back, at the sides, and at the front of the thorax, and they provide protection for the sides and back of the upper part of the abdomen also. The upper seven ribs increase in length from above downwards and are called *true* ribs because their cartilages are attached to the side of the sternum. The lower five are called *false* ribs; they diminish in length from above downwards and their cartilages fail, by increasing distances, to reach the sternum; but the eighth, ninth, and tenth are each joined to the one above it, edge to edge. The cartilages of the eleventh and twelfth, however, are free, and they are called *floating* ribs.

A rib has an anterior and a posterior end, an external and an internal surface, and a superior and an inferior border. The *posterior end* is called the **head**, and is articular; the *anterior end* is hollowed out to form a pit into which the costal cartilage fits. The *upper*

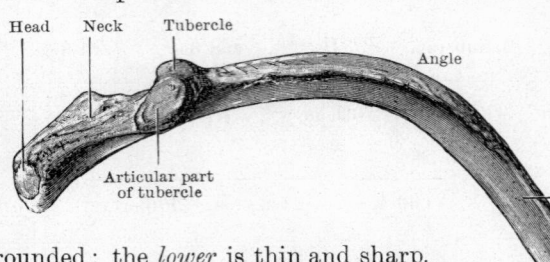

border is smooth and rounded; the *lower* is thin and sharp. The *outer surface* is convex; the *inner* is concave lengthwise.

The ribs are not all curved equally. The first rib has the sharpest curve, and the curve of each succeeding one is wider or more open; therefore, if the specimens are all from the same skeleton, one can arrange them in proper order by laying them on a table in a row with their posterior ends in a straight line and observing the progressive change of curvature. It will be seen that, when laid in a row in proper order, they increase in length down to the seventh or eighth and then diminish to the twelfth; and also that they are twisted, for, if they are lying on their lower borders, the posterior part of the inner surface looks largely upwards, while the anterior part looks slightly downwards. Ribs are not only curved and twisted, they are slightly bent as well (Fig. 132). The bend is called the *angle* of a rib; it takes place from one to three inches from the head, the distance increasing as the series descends, and its position is marked by an oblique, irregular ridge on the outer surface of the bone.

The **parts** of a rib are: head, neck, tubercle, shaft, and costal cartilage; and the shaft has an angle and a costal groove.

The first, second, tenth, eleventh, and twelfth have each some special characters of its own, but the third to the ninth belong to a common type.

A Typical Rib.—The **head** articulates with two thoracic vertebræ and therefore has two articular facets on it—an upper and a lower—which meet at a ridge. The two vertebræ with which a rib articulates are the one with which it is in numerical correspondence and the one above that, *e.g.* the fifth rib articulates with the fifth thoracic vertebra and with the fourth. The **neck** immediately succeeds the head and is about one inch long. Its surfaces are usually called *anterior* and *posterior*, though they are continuous respectively with the inner and outer surfaces of the shaft. The **tubercle** is situated on the outer

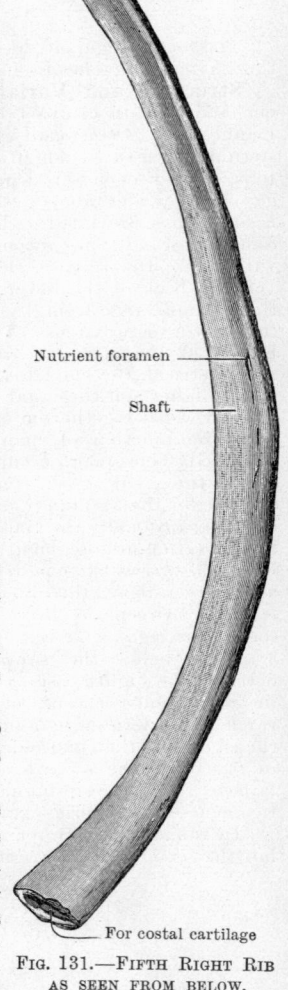

Fig. 131.—Fifth Right Rib as seen from below.

surface where the neck and shaft join; it articulates with the front of the tip of the transverse process of the vertebra with which the rib corresponds numerically. The **shaft** is all the rest of the bone. The ridge on the outer surface that marks the position of the **angle** is placed near the posterior end. In the first rib the angle is at the junction of neck and shaft and the ridge coincides with the tubercle; in the second rib the ridge is close to the tubercle; as the ribs are followed down the ridge gradually recedes from the tubercle, down to the eighth or ninth;

and below that the ridge becomes indistinct. The curve of a rib is not uniform, and it is sharpest at the angle; a curved bone is most likely to be broken where the curve is sharpest; therefore the rib is thickest there. The **costal groove** is the long, shallow groove on the inner surface of the shaft immediately above the lower border.

The articular surface of the **head** of a rib is surrounded by a joint capsule; the thick, anterior part of the capsular ligament is called the radiate ligament and is attached to the front of the head. Of the two facets the lower is the larger; the blunt ridge between them gives attachment to the intra-articular ligament which lies within the joint and binds the rib to the intervertebral disc.

The **neck** lies in front of the transverse process. The posterior surface is rough, and is bound to the transverse process by the inferior costo-transverse ligament; the upper border is rough and raised and is called the **crest**, from which the superior costo-transverse ligament stretches up to the transverse process next above. The lower part of the anterior surface is smooth and is covered with pleura, and is separated from the upper part by a faint ridge that gives attachment to the posterior intercostal membrane. The **tubercle** bulges backwards and downwards; it has a *facet* on its lower and medial part for articulation with the transverse process; an articular capsule surrounds the facet, and the lateral costo-transverse ligament connects the rough part of the tubercle with the tip of the transverse process.

The *upper border* of the **shaft** gives insertion in all its length to an external intercostal muscle, and, internal to that, a posterior intercostal membrane is attached between the neck and the angle, while an internal intercostal muscle is inserted into the rest of the length of the border. The **costal groove** is broad and well marked posteriorly, but indistinct in the anterior part of the rib; the intercostal vessels and nerve run along the groove. The groove has an upper and a lower lip, the lower lip being the sharp *lower border* of the bone; the external intercostal muscle arises from the whole length of its lower lip; the posterior intercostal membrane is attached to the floor of the groove between the tubercle and the angle; an internal intercostal muscle arises from the upper lip from the angle forwards. The rest of the *inner surface* of the rib is smooth and is covered with pleura.

Many muscles are attached to the *outer surface* of the ribs (p. 132). The *angle* is very obtuse, and is open upwards; the ridge that marks it is for the attachment of the ilio-costo-cervicalis—*i.e.* the lateral subdivision of the large

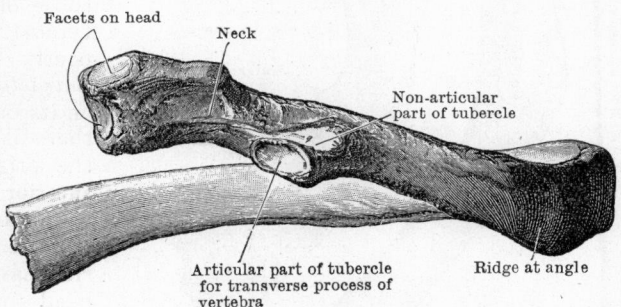

Facets on head

Neck

Non-articular part of tubercle

Articular part of tubercle for transverse process of vertebra

Ridge at angle

FIG. 132.—FIFTH RIGHT RIB AS SEEN FROM BEHIND.

composite mass of muscle, called sacro-spinalis, that lies alongside the spines of the vertebræ. On the longer ribs there is often a slight bend called the *anterior angle*, marked by an indistinct ridge on the outer surface two inches or more from the anterior end; the ridge is for the origin of slips of the serratus anterior and obliquus externus abdominis.

In each of the upper ten ribs the anterior end is the widest part of the rib.

The **first rib** is the shortest rib, except the twelfth; it is the most sharply curved, and it is broad in comparison with its length. It lies at the boundary between neck and thorax, largely under cover of the clavicle; its posterior end is above the level of the clavicle, and its anterior end is immediately below the clavicle (Fig. 134). Unlike the other ribs, it lies nearly all in one oblique plane, and its **surfaces** are *upper* and *lower*, its **borders** *inner* and *outer*. The inner border is concave; the outer border is convex. The surfaces are not always easily distinguished at first glance, but if the rib is laid on the table and its head touches the table, then its lower surface is looking downwards; if it is turned upside down the head stands away from the table.

The **head** is small; it articulates with only one vertebra, namely, the first thoracic, and it has therefore only one facet. The **neck** is relatively long, and is compressed from above downwards; the top of the pleura and lung lie immediately in front of it. The **tubercle** is situated on the outer border and is relatively large.

The outer part of the *lower surface* of the **shaft** is roughened by the attachment of the internal intercostal muscle; the inner part is covered with pleura, and is crossed obliquely by the first intercostal nerve, which may groove it. The subclavian artery and vein lie across the *upper surface*, producing broad, shallow grooves. The groove for the artery is about the middle of the body; the groove for the vein is nearer the anterior end. The scalenus anterior muscle is inserted into the **scalene tubercle** and a small rough triangular area that separates the two grooves; the scalene tubercle is a small projection on the *inner border* of the rib. The surface behind the groove for the artery—between that groove and the tubercle of the rib—gives insertion to the scalenus medius muscle, while the first digitation of the serratus anterior arises from it near the outer border immediately behind the groove for the artery. The greater part of the anterior primary ramus of the first thoracic nerve, on its way to join the brachial plexus, runs upwards and laterally in front of the neck and then lies in the posterior part of the groove for the artery, between the artery and the scalenus medius. On many specimens of the first rib the grooves and tubercle are faintly marked; while in others there is a special groove for the lodgment of the first thoracic nerve, or the lowest trunk of the brachial plexus, immediately behind the groove for the artery. The subclavius muscle and the costo-clavicular ligament are attached to the upper surface of the rib at its junction with the cartilage.

The external and internal intercostal muscles of the first space arise from the *outer border*. A fibrous sheet, called the suprapleural membrane, stretches fanwise from the transverse process of the seventh cervical vertebra to be attached to the *inner border*. (See also the list on p. 132.)

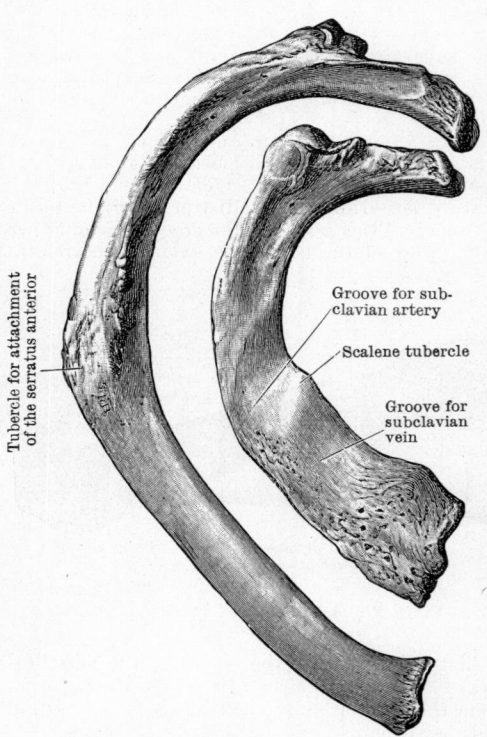

Tubercle for attachment of the serratus anterior

Groove for subclavian artery

Scalene tubercle

Groove for subclavian vein

FIG. 133.—FIRST AND SECOND RIGHT RIBS AS SEEN FROM ABOVE.

The **second rib** is about twice as long as the first, and the sharpness of its curve distinguishes it from one of the lower ribs of similar length; it is not twisted; its surfaces are, in direction, intermediate between those of a first rib and those of a typical rib, and its costal groove is poorly marked. But the *special character* of the second rib is that on its outer surface, about its middle, there is a broad rough **tubercle** for the origin of part of the **serratus anterior** muscle. No other rib has a similar tubercle.

The **tenth, eleventh,** and **twelfth** ribs have each only one facet on the head, for each articulates with only one vertebra and that is the thoracic vertebra of corresponding number. The tenth, however, may be a typical rib. The eleventh differs from the tenth mainly in that its tubercle is small and has no articular facet, and the angle is ill defined; but the tubercle and angle of the tenth also may be ill defined, so that it is sometimes difficult to say whether a given rib is tenth or eleventh if the other ribs of the same skeleton are not at hand.

The **twelfth rib** is small and slender. It may be as short as the first, or even shorter. *Tubercle, angle,* and *costal groove* are absent or are poorly marked. The **body** tapers off at the free end, while other ribs are nearly always slightly swollen at their anterior ends.

Costal Cartilages

The **costal cartilages** are bars of hyaline cartilage which are fitted into the pits at the anterior ends of the ribs; the cartilage is held in place because its perichondrium is continuous with the periosteum of the rib. They greatly increase the resilience of the framework of the thorax; they are seldom exactly alike on the two sides. Their perichondrium is so thick and strong that there is little or no displacement of the fragments when a costal cartilage is fractured. The **upper seven** pairs join the sternum and can be felt at its sides; they increase in length from above downwards, from one inch to four or five inches. The *first* cartilage is fitted on to a rough mark on the margin of the manubrium and is held in place by the continuity of its perichondrium with the periosteum of the sternum; the *other six* are joined to the sternum by synovial joints. The first and second slope downwards slightly from the bony rib to the sternum; the third is horizontal; the fourth inclines upwards; the fifth, sixth, and seventh continue the direction of the rib for about an inch, and then turn upwards, with increasing degrees of obliquity, to reach the sternum. The cartilages of the **lower five** ribs diminish in length from above downwards; they can be felt in the costal margin between the thorax and abdomen. The eighth, ninth, and tenth continue in the direction of their ribs for about an inch and then turn upwards; they fail, by increasing distances, to reach the sternum, and each tapers off to a point; they are each united edge to edge with the one above, forming synovial joints at the points of contact, except the tenth, which is separated from the ninth by the fibrous tissue that unites them. The eleventh and twelfth are mere pointed cartilaginous tips on the ends of the ribs.

THORAX

The **thorax** lodges the lungs and the heart and many other structures, and gives them protection; its skeleton provides attachment for many muscles besides those that belong to the thorax itself; but the chief use of the thorax in mammals is to act as a bellows by which air, for oxygenating the blood, can be drawn into the lungs. Its framework is a bony and cartilaginous cage the bars of which are arranged so that they not only resist atmospheric pressure as the bellows is opened, but also, by their mobility, take share in the expanding movement.

The skeleton or cage is made of the thoracic vertebræ and intervertebral discs, the sternum, the ribs, and their cartilages. It is barrel-shaped, but is narrower above than below. It is also longer behind than in front, and is compressed from before backwards, so that it is wider from side to side, the greatest width being at the level of the eighth or ninth rib. The antero-posterior diameter of its interior is greatly diminished by the bodies of the vertebræ. It communicates with the front of the neck by an inlet, and with the abdomen by an outlet.

The **inlet** [apertura thoracis superior] is small, and is kidney-shaped in outline; it slopes from above downwards and forwards; it measures about 2 inches or 50 mm. from before backwards, and 100 mm. across. It is bounded by the first thoracic vertebra behind, the manubrium in front, and the first pair of ribs and their cartilages at the sides. It is occupied by the apices of the lungs and pleuræ, the windpipe, the gullet, and numerous vessels and nerves that pass between neck and thorax.

The **outlet** [apertura thoracis inferior] is large and is uneven in outline. It is bounded by the xiphi-sternal joint, the lower six pairs of costal cartilages, the shafts of the twelfth pair of ribs, and the last thoracic vertebra. It is closed by the diaphragm, which separates the interior of the thorax from the interior of the abdomen, and forms a highly vaulted and very movable floor for the thorax and roof for the abdomen. The *infrasternal angle* is situated at the anterior part of the inferior aperture; its sides are the seventh pair of costal cartilages; its apex is the xiphi-sternal joint; and the xiphoid process juts down into the angle.

The **posterior wall** of the thorax is made up of the thoracic vertebræ and intervertebral discs and the posterior part of the ribs. The ribs have a backward sweep as far as their angles which makes their angles nearly flush with the tips of the spines of the vertebræ, so that Man, unlike most animals, can lie on his back with stability and ease. The forward projection of the vertebral bodies and the backward curve of the ribs create a large hollow, on each side, in the posterior part of the interior of the thorax for the lodgment of the thickest part of the lung.

In the **sides** of the thorax there are the shafts of the ribs. The ribs are not all the same distance apart, nor are they parallel. The upper intercostal spaces are wider than the lower; and the ribs slope downwards and forwards with an obliquity which increases from the first down to the ninth or tenth, and the intercostal spaces are wider therefore in front than behind; the obliquity is more marked in women than in men, and in the old than in the young. The sides slope outwards, down to the level of the eighth or ninth rib, and usually slope inwards slightly below that.

The **anterior wall** is made of the manubrium and body of the sternum, the anterior ends of the upper ten pairs of ribs and their cartilages. It is shorter than

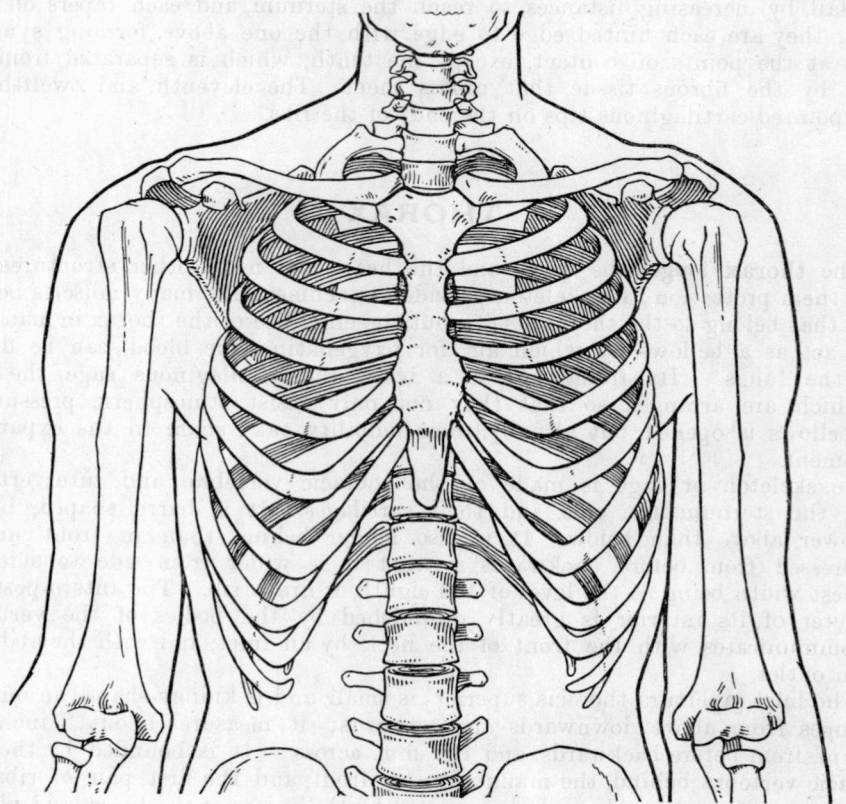

FIG. 134.—FRONT OF PORTION OF SKELETON SHOWING THORAX.

the posterior wall or the sides, especially in the median plane, for the upper border of the manubrium is opposite the lower border of the second thoracic vertebra and the xiphi-sternal joint is opposite the ninth.

In the fœtus the thorax is compressed from side to side. At birth its form alters with the expansion of the lungs, but full transverse expansion takes place only after the child begins to walk and to use its upper limbs more exclusively for prehensile purposes. *In a woman* the thorax is shorter and rounder than in a man, and the upper ribs are more movable.

Surface Relations.—The thorax is well covered externally with muscles belonging to the upper limb, the abdomen, the back, and the neck. There are only three parts that have no muscular covering. These are (1) a finger's-breadth down the middle of the sternum, (2) the median line of the back, (3) a portion of the seventh rib, just medial to the lower part of shoulder blade, especially when the shoulder is drawn forwards.

The **first rib** provides the bony resistance felt in the neck above the middle of the clavicle; its cartilage is immediately below the sternal end of the clavicle.

The **second rib** is the most easily identified of all on the front of the chest, because its cartilage joins the sternum at the **sternal angle**, which is always easily felt; both angle and second cartilage are often easily seen as well as felt. When ribs have to be counted, or when a particular rib has to be located in the living person, the best method is to find the second and count downwards from it. There are rough and ready, though uncertain, guides to some of the other ribs and cartilages. The *nipple* is usually opposite the **fourth intercostal space** between the anterior ends of the bony parts of the fourth and fifth ribs. The cartilage felt on

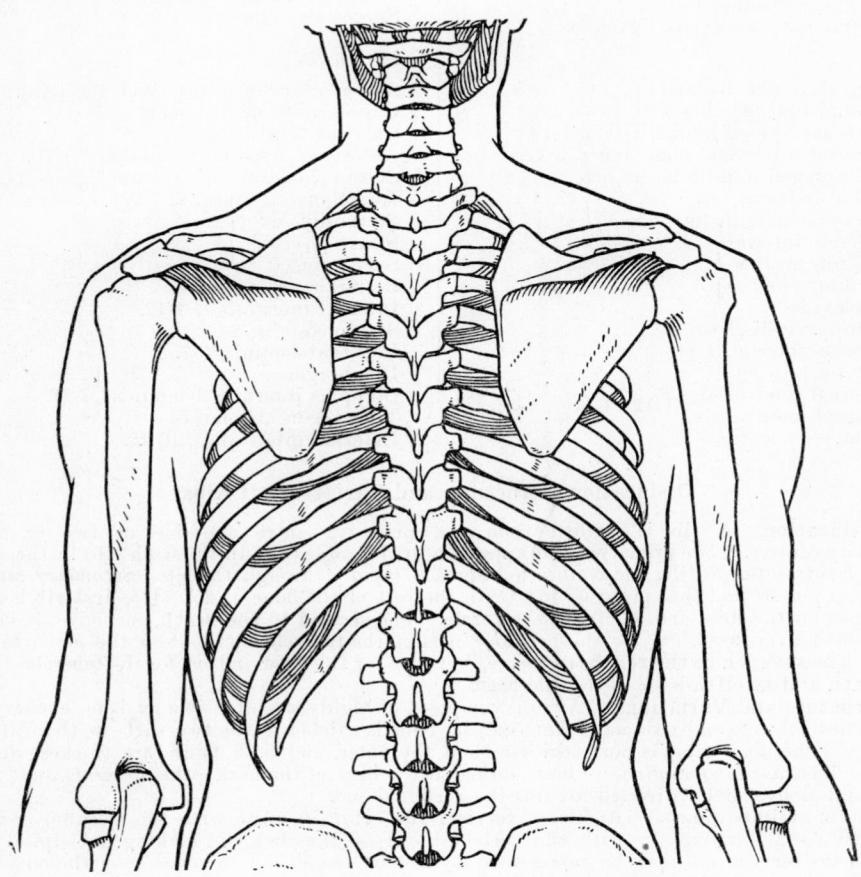

FIG. 135.—BACK OF PORTION OF SKELETON SHOWING THORAX.

the costal margin next the sternum is nearly always the **seventh**. The cartilage felt where the groove that marks the lateral margin of the rectus abdominis reaches the costal margin is usually the **ninth**. The **tenth** cartilage is the lowest one felt when the costal margin is examined from the front, and is at the level of the body of the *third lumbar vertebra*. A line drawn from the medial end of the clavicle to the point a thumb's-breadth behind the lowest point of the tenth cartilage will pass through or near the junction of ribs and cartilages from the second to the tenth. If the *posterior axillary line* is followed downwards, the lowest rib it crosses is the **eleventh**. The **twelfth** rib may be felt, but sometimes it is so short that it is hidden by the sacro-spinalis. **On the back** the point where the *spine of the scapula* meets the medial border overlies the **fourth** rib; and the *inferior angle* of the scapula overlies either the **seventh** intercostal space or the **eighth** rib.

9 *a*

Ligaments and Muscles attached to Ribs and their Cartilages

Heads.
- Articular capsules } 1-12.
- Radiate ligaments } 1-12.
- Intra-articular ligaments, 2-9.

Necks.
- Inferior costo-transverse ligaments, 1-12.
- Superior costo-transverse ligaments, 2-12.
- Lumbo-costal ligament, 12.

Tubercles.
- Articular capsules, 1-10.
- Lateral costo-transverse ligaments, 1-11.

Shafts.
- Costo-clavicular ligament, Suprapleural membrane } 1.
- Posterior layer of lumbar fascia, 1-12.
- Posterior intercostal membranes, 2-12.
- Anterior and middle layers of lumbar fascia, Lateral arcuate ligament } 12.
- Scalenus anterior, Scalenus medius, Sterno-thyroid, Subclavius } 1.
- Costo-cervicalis, 1-6.
- Serratus anterior, 1-8.
- Costalis, External intercostals, Internal intercostals, Levatores costarum } 1-12.

Shafts (contd.).
- Scalenus posterior, 2.
- Pectoralis minor, Serratus posterior superior } 2-5.
- Longissimus thoracis, 3-12.
- Obliquus externus abdominis, 5-12.
- Ilio-costalis [lumborum], 7-12.
- Latissimus dorsi, Serratus posterior inferior } 9-12.
- Obliquus internus abdominis, 10-12.
- Quadratus lumborum, 12.
- Subcostales, inconstant.

Costal Cartilages.
- Articular disc of sterno-clavicular joint, Costo-clavicular ligament, Clavi-pectoral fascia } 1.
- Anterior intercostal membranes, 1-10.
- Sterno-chondral capsules and ligaments, 2-7
- Interchondral capsules, 7-9.
- Sterno-hyoid, Sterno-thyroid, Subclavius } 1.
- Pectoralis major, 1-6.
- Internal intercostals, 1-12.
- Sterno-costalis, 2-6.
- Rectus abdominis, 5-7.
- Diaphragm, Obliquus internus abdominis, Transversus abdominis } 7-12.
- External intercostals, 10-12.

Ossification, Structure, and Variations of Ribs

Ossification.—A rib is ossified from one primary centre and one or two or three secondary centres. The **primary centre** appears near the angle (first in the sixth rib) in the sixth week of intra-uterine life, and ossification spreads rapidly through the rib. **Secondary centres** appear at *puberty* and the epiphyses fuse with the rest of the bone at 25. The **first rib** has *one* epiphysis for the **head** and *one* for the **tubercle.** The **second to the sixth**, inclusive, have *one* epiphysis for the **head**, *one* for the *articular* part of the **tubercle,** and *one* for the *non-articular* part. The **seventh to the tenth**, inclusive, have *one* for the **head** and *one* for the **tubercle.** The **eleventh and twelfth** have *one* for the **head.**

Structure and Variations.—A rib is composed of highly vascular spongy bone enclosed in a flattened tube of compact bone. The compact bone is thicker in the two surfaces than at the borders. The inner table is much thicker than the outer, and both tables are thickest at the angle. The *vascular foramina* are best marked at the back of the neck; the *nutrient canal* is in the costal groove, and is directed towards the vertebral end.

The most important variation is a **cervical rib.** It may unite with the sternum or with the first costal cartilage, or with the vertebral end of the first rib, making a bicipital rib. Part of the cervical rib may be represented by fibrous tissue, and in some cases the only part present is the sternal end. Occasionally increase of number is due to a lumbar rib. Diminution in number is rare, but sometimes the twelfth rib is absent, or the first rib is rudimentary and may fuse with the second, making a bicipital rib. Sometimes two ribs are partly fused together. Occasionally the posterior parts of two ribs are united by a projection jutting out from each and articulating with an intervening nodule of bone. The anterior end of a rib is sometimes very wide and may have a hole or a cleft in it. *Costal cartilages* also may be broad and perforated. The seventh cartilage sometimes throws out a projection which articulates with a similar projection from the sixth; the sixth may unite similarly with the fifth. The seventh sometimes fails to reach the sternum, but a commoner anomaly is that the eighth articulates with the sternum. In old age the cartilages may undergo partial ossification; this condition may be regarded as normal in the first costal cartilage in elderly people.

Development of Vertebræ, Ribs, and Sternum

Vertebræ.—In the Chapter on EMBRYOLOGY it is explained that the *paraxial mesoderm* is divided by transverse clefts into a number of segments called *mesodermal somites*, and that the cells of the ventro-medial or *scleratogenous* parts of the somites proliferate and form a continuous mesodermal sheath around the notochord and neural tube [σκληρός (sclēros) = hard; γεννάω (gennaō) = produce]. The sheath is called the **membranous vertebral column**: in it the vertebræ are formed, and pass through a pro-cartilage stage and a cartilage stage before ossification. A *pro-cartilage vertebra* has only a body enclosed in a horseshoe-shaped vertebral bow. The **body** surrounds the notochord, and its position is such that it corresponds to the contiguous halves of two adjacent somites, its middle being opposite an *intersegmental septum, i.e.* the interval between two somites. The middle part of the **vertebral bow** is sometimes called the *hypochordal bow* [ὑπό (hypo) = below]; it is ventral to the headward part of the body to which it belongs; the two limbs of the bow slant backwards to enclose the neural tube dorsal to the tailward part of the vertebral body; in time they meet each other dorsal to the neural tube, and thus form a *vertebral ring.*

About the fourth *week* of intra-uterine life, the scleratogenous tissue between two bodies, opposite the middle of a somite, begins to undergo fibrous and chondrifying changes, and becomes an *intervertebral disc*. About that time *chondrification* begins also in the **vertebral body** and

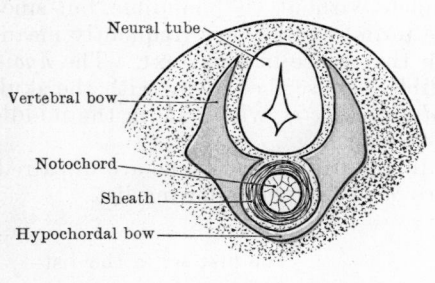
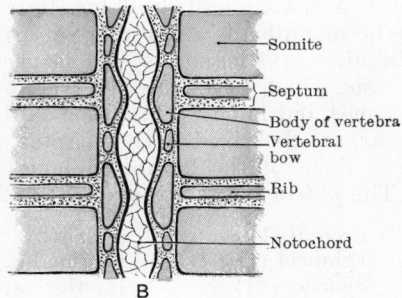

FIG. 136.—THE DEVELOPMENT OF THE MEMBRANOUS BASIS OF A VERTEBRA (after Keith).

A, in transverse section. B, in longitudinal section, showing the relation of the vertebræ to the primitive segments.

in the **limbs of the bow**; the body and the bow rapidly unite, and chondrification of the bow is completed dorsally during the fourth *month* of intra-uterine life. The body forms the median part (*centrum*) of a body of a vertebra. The limbs of the bow form the postero-lateral parts of a body and the vertebral arch and its processes; the transverse processes and the spine grow out from it into the intersegmental septum that lies between the two somites to which the vertebra corresponds. The scleratogenous tissue between the arches of two vertebræ becomes the ligamenta flava and the capsules that unite articular processes. *Ossification* begins at the seventh week of intra-uterine life in the arches and at the tenth week in the bodies.

The ventral or hypochordal part of the vertebral bow disappears, except in the **atlas** vertebra, where it chondrifies and ossifies to form the anterior arch. The atlas is therefore a complete vertebral **ring**; its centrum becomes the odontoid process, and its lateral masses correspond to the parts of the body of a typical vertebra that are formed from the vertebral bow. The ligaments that connect the odontoid process with the margins of the foramen magnum represent the disc between the atlas and the last occipital segment.

The rudimentary condition of a **coccygeal** vertebra is due to the failure of the limbs of the vertebral bow to develop. The incomplete condition of the laminæ of the last two **sacral** vertebræ is due to imperfect chondrification and ossification of vertebral bows. Imperfections in the formation of vertebral bows in regions farther up in the vertebral column give rise to the condition known as *spina bifida*.

The part of the *notochord* enclosed in the bodies of the vertebræ is first constricted, and finally disappears after ossification begins. The part enclosed in the discs persists in them as their pulpy centres.

Ribs.—The ribs are developed in the intersegmental septa, and pass through pro-cartilage and cartilage stages before ossification. Each articulates at first with only one vertebra—*i.e.*, the vertebra opposite the septum in which the rib is developed. Later, the vertebral ends of the ribs, except the first, tenth, eleventh, and twelfth, are shifted headwards, so that each articulates not only with its own vertebra but also with the disc and the vertebra above.

Sternum.—The sternum is formed from mesodermal tissue in front of the pericardium. The **manubrium** probably arises in association with the ventral part of the shoulder girdle, and the **body** and **xiphoid process** from a pair of *sternal bars* that grow from the mesodermal rudiment of the manubrium and fuse together in the median plane. After chondrification the sternum becomes connected with the costal cartilages by synovial joints.

THE SKULL

The **skull** is the skeleton of the head and face. It is made of 22 bones, including the mandible, which is the skeleton of the lower part of the face, and is a movable bone. The other 21 bones are so firmly knit together that they are taken apart with difficulty; they are built together in such a way that they enclose one large cavity and three smaller ones. The large cavity is called the *cranial cavity*, and contains the brain and its membranes; the smaller cavities are the *cavity of the nose*, and the two *orbits*, which hold the eyeballs. There are lesser cavities contained within certain of the skull bones; those cavities are the *middle ear*, the *internal ear*, and the *air sinuses*. The skull bones consist of two plates or **tables** of compact substance that enclose a layer of spongy substance between them; in skull bones this substance is called **diploë**. In some of them the diploë is absorbed, leaving cavities or air sinuses between the tables of compact bone; the sinuses communicate with the cavity of the nose, and have a mucous lining continuous with that of the nose.

A specimen of skull for study is not complete without the mandible, but since the mandible is a movable, separate bone, the term "skull" very frequently means skull *minus* mandible, and is used largely in that sense in this text. The *hyoid bone*, which lies in the neck below the mandible, is described along with the skull bones, but is not part of the skull. The *auditory ossicles*, which lie in the middle ear, are described in the chapter on Organs of Sense.

Some of the 21 united bones of the skull are paired and some are unpaired. The *paired* bones are bracketed (2), the *unpaired* (1), in the following list.

Frontal (1)	Nasal (2)	
Ethmoid (1)	Lacrimal (2)	The first six in the list—
Sphenoid (1)	Inferior nasal conchæ (2)	eight bones in all—are those
Occipital (1)	Vomer (1)	that share in the forma-
Parietal (2)	Maxillæ (2)	tion of the walls of the
Temporal (2)	Zygomatic (2)	cranial cavity.
	Palatine (2)	

In a young person, those 21 bones, though firmly bound together, are separable; the joints by which they are held together are either *sutures*, in which the articulating parts are connected by a ribbon of fibrous tissue, or *primary cartilaginous joints*, in which they are connected by hyaline cartilage. With advancing years the joints disappear and neighbouring bones fuse together gradually.

There is some confusion in regard to the meaning of *skull*, *cranium*, and *calvaria*, and the classification of the bones of the skull.

In ordinary English the word "Skull" denotes the skeleton of the head without the lower jaw bone, and in medical text-books the word "Cranium" is employed usually as a synonym for "skull" in that sense, though κρανίον (kranion) originally meant only the part of the head covered with hair; further, in medical text-books, "*calvaria*" (from *calvus* = bald) usually means the top part of the skull or skull-cap, though it is defined in Andrew's Latin dictionary as the *brain-pan*, *skull*, of man and beasts. But in catalogues of craniological collections the following meanings are attached to the terms: *Skull* = entire skeleton of head and face, including mandible; *Cranium* = skull without mandible; *Calvaria* = skull after bones of face have been removed or destroyed.

An old classification of the bones is: (1) Cranial bones = those that form the adult brain case; (2) Facial bones = all the others. In the Basle nomenclature the *ossa faciei* comprise maxilla, palatine, zygomatic, mandible, and the hyoid bone; *ossa cranii* comprise all the others; and there is a subdivision also into *cranium cerebrale* and *cranium viscerale*. Quain's *Anatomy*, 11th edition, suggests more than one classification. No classification has satisfied every one, and it is questionable if any classification of skull bones is either necessary or desirable.

It is much more important that the student should acquire a knowledge of the skull as a whole than of the separate bones. The detailed description of the separate bones is put at the end of the section for reference, and the skull as a whole is dealt with earlier. But so many of the parts of the skull are named from the particular bones to which they belong that it is necessary to give a few brief, preliminary notes on the individual bones; and the student, with a skull before him, and with the aid of the figures of the skull in the text, should identify each of the bones and note the aspects of the skull in which they are visible, before beginning to read the description of the skull as a whole. It is convenient, however, to locate at the outset the following parts, for they will be referred to as landmarks.

(1) The **orbits** are the pair of large pyramidal cavities in the front of the skull (Fig. 137). They are so named because the eyes rotate in them. [*Orbita* = a wheel rut, a circuit.]

(2) The **anterior bony aperture of the nose** is the large, egg-shaped hole between and below the two orbits; through it one can see into the cavities of the nose.

(3) The **external auditory meatus** or ear-hole (Fig. 138) is the small, round or oval hole or passage seen in the lower part of the side of the skull about midway between the front and the back. [*Meatus*=a passage.]

The proper position of the skull is not that which it occupies when it is set on a table. When the skull is held in its **proper position**, the lower margin of the orbit and the upper margin of the orifice of the meatus are at the same horizontal level.

(4) The **zygomatic arch** is the bridge of bone on the side of the skull that spans the interval between the lower part of the orbit and the front of the meatus [ζύγωμα (zygōma)=a bar, from ζυγόν=anything that connects two bodies].

(5) The **foramen magnum** is the large, round hole on the lower surface of the skull a little behind its centre (Fig. 139).

(6) The **posterior bony apertures of the nose** are a pair of large openings about two inches in front of the foramen magnum; they are oval and oblique, and are close together; through them one can see into the cavities of the nose from behind.

(7) The **bony palate** is the platform of bone that forms the median part of the front of the lower surface of the skull; its posterior edge is the *lower* margin of the posterior apertures of the nose (when the skull is held right way up).

(8) Examine the interior of the skull (Fig. 140). The cranial cavity has a very uneven floor, and is divisible into three main regions which are at different levels. Those regions are called the **anterior**, **middle**, and **posterior cranial fossæ**; each of them has a median part and a right and a left lateral part.

Bones of the Skull

The **frontal bone** (Figs. 137, 138) is the large shell of bone in the anterior part of the skull. [*Frons*=the brow.] It is the bone of the forehead and the anterior part of the top of the skull; and a pair of wide, thin shelves, called *orbital plates*, project backwards from its lower part and form the greater part of the roofs of the two orbits, and also of the floors of the two lateral parts of the anterior cranial fossa. In each half of the frontal bone there is a cavity, called the *frontal sinus*, situated immediately above the rim of the orbit and the root of the nose.

The **parietal bone** (Figs. 138, 160) is the large, convex, four-square bone that lies behind the frontal bone; it forms a large part of the side of the skull, and a large part of the top, meeting its fellow of the opposite side at the median line. [*Paries*=a wall.]

The **occipital bone** (Figs. 139, 140, 162) is the large bone at the back of the skull behind the two parietal bones. [*Occiput* (*ob, caput*) = the back of the head up to the crown, while *sinciput* (*semi, caput*)=the front part of the head from the crown to the forehead.] It is shaped like a leaf, and it is bent so that it lies in the base of the skull as well as at the back. The foramen magnum is in the occipital bone. The thick bar of bone in front of the foramen magnum is called the **basilar part** of the occipital bone or **basi-occiput**. The region at each side of the foramen magnum is called the **condylar part** of the occipital bone, because the pair of eminences with smooth articular surfaces at the sides of the foramen are called the occipital **condyles**.

The **temporal bone** (Figs. 138, 139, 140, 165) is partly in the side of the skull below the parietal bone, and partly in the base of the skull in front of the condylar part of the occipital bone. The external auditory meatus is in the temporal bone on the side of the head. The large piece of bone, shaped like a scale, that lies above the meatus is the *squamous part* of the temporal bone or **squamous temporal** [*squama* = a scale]; the *zygomatic process* of the temporal bone or **zygoma** is a projection from the squamous temporal, and it forms the posterior half or so of the zygomatic arch.   The bone behind the meatus is the *mastoid part* of the temporal bone or **mastoid temporal**, and its lower part is a large, rounded projection, called the **mastoid process**, which is easily felt behind the ear in the living head.   The mastoid process is named from its resemblance to a teat [μαστός (mastos) = the breast] and gives its name to the mastoid temporal.

The uneven plate of bone that forms the front and lower wall of the meatus, and part of the back wall, is the *tympanic part* of the temporal bone or **tympanic plate**.   The long, slender process (often broken off in specimens of skull) that projects downwards and forwards from behind the lower edge of the tympanic plate is called the **styloid process** [στῦλος (stylos) = a pillar, a stake, a pen].

The remaining part of the temporal bone is called the *petrous part* or **petrous temporal**, and gets its name from its hardness [πέτρος (petros) = a stone].   It is an uneven wedge of bone situated in the base of the skull on the medial side of the tympanic plate and in front of the condylar part of the occipital bone.   It is seen much better in the inside of the skull; it is the conspicuous elevation in each half of the floor, about midway between the front and the back of the cavity of the skull, between the middle and posterior cranial fossæ.

The temporal bone contains a number of important spaces, viz.—the *internal ear*, the *middle ear*, the *bony part of the external ear*, a small cavity called the *tympanic antrum*, and numerous small cavities called *mastoid air cells*.

The **sphenoid bone** (Figs. 138, 139, 140, 147, 169) is more difficult to identify, for it is wedged in among other bones of the skull [σφήν (sphēn) = a wedge].   Parts of it can be seen from various points of view—in the floor of the cranial cavity, on the lower surface of the base of the skull, in the side of the skull, and in the upper and lateral walls of both orbits.   The sphenoid bone has a body and three pairs of processes—lesser wings, greater wings, and pterygoid processes.

The **body** is the middle part of the bone; it lies in front of the basi-occiput, and fuses with it after the 25th year.   On the lower surface of the skull it is to a large extent hidden; in the floor of the cranial cavity it forms an uneven, median elevation that extends from a point about an inch in front of the foramen magnum to a point about an inch behind the anterior boundary of the floor.   The body is hollow; it is composed of a thin shell of bone enclosing a large air space, called the **sphenoidal sinus**, divided by a thin, bony septum into a right and a left half.

Each **lesser wing** is the posterior part of the roof of the orbit, but is seen best in the floor of the cranial cavity; it resembles the wing of a bird very closely, and extends laterally from the anterior part of the upper surface of the body.

The **greater wings** are behind the lesser wings and are at a lower level.   They are large plates that spread out from the sides of the body in the base of the skull, and their antero-lateral parts turn up into the sides of the skull.   One surface of a greater wing is seen in the floor and the side wall of the middle cranial fossa; another surface is seen in the orbit forming the greater part of its lateral wall; a third surface is seen on the side of the skull in front of the squamous temporal; and, continuous with that surface, a fourth surface is seen on the lower surface of the skull, lateral to the root of the pterygoid process.

The **pterygoid processes** resemble wings only remotely [πτέρυξ (pteryx) = a wing].   Each of them is a large process that projects downwards from the junction of body and greater wing and is seen on the lower surface of the skull forming the lateral boundary of a posterior aperture of the nose.   Each pterygoid process is divided by a deep, wide recess into two plates—a lateral and a medial.   It is the *medial plate* that forms the side of the posterior aperture of the nose like the jamb of a door; the recess between it and the *lateral plate* is called the *pterygoid fossa*.

The **ethmoid bone** (Figs. 140, 146, 147, 149, 172) lies in front of the body of the sphenoid and below the frontal bone, and is to a large extent hidden.   It is set between the two orbits, and the distance between the eyes depends therefore upon the breadth of the ethmoid.   Its parts are a perpendicular plate, a pair of cribriform plates, and a pair of labyrinths.

The **perpendicular plate** is a thin, median sheet of bone that forms part of the median partition or septum of the interior of the nose.   If it has not been broken

PLATE VII

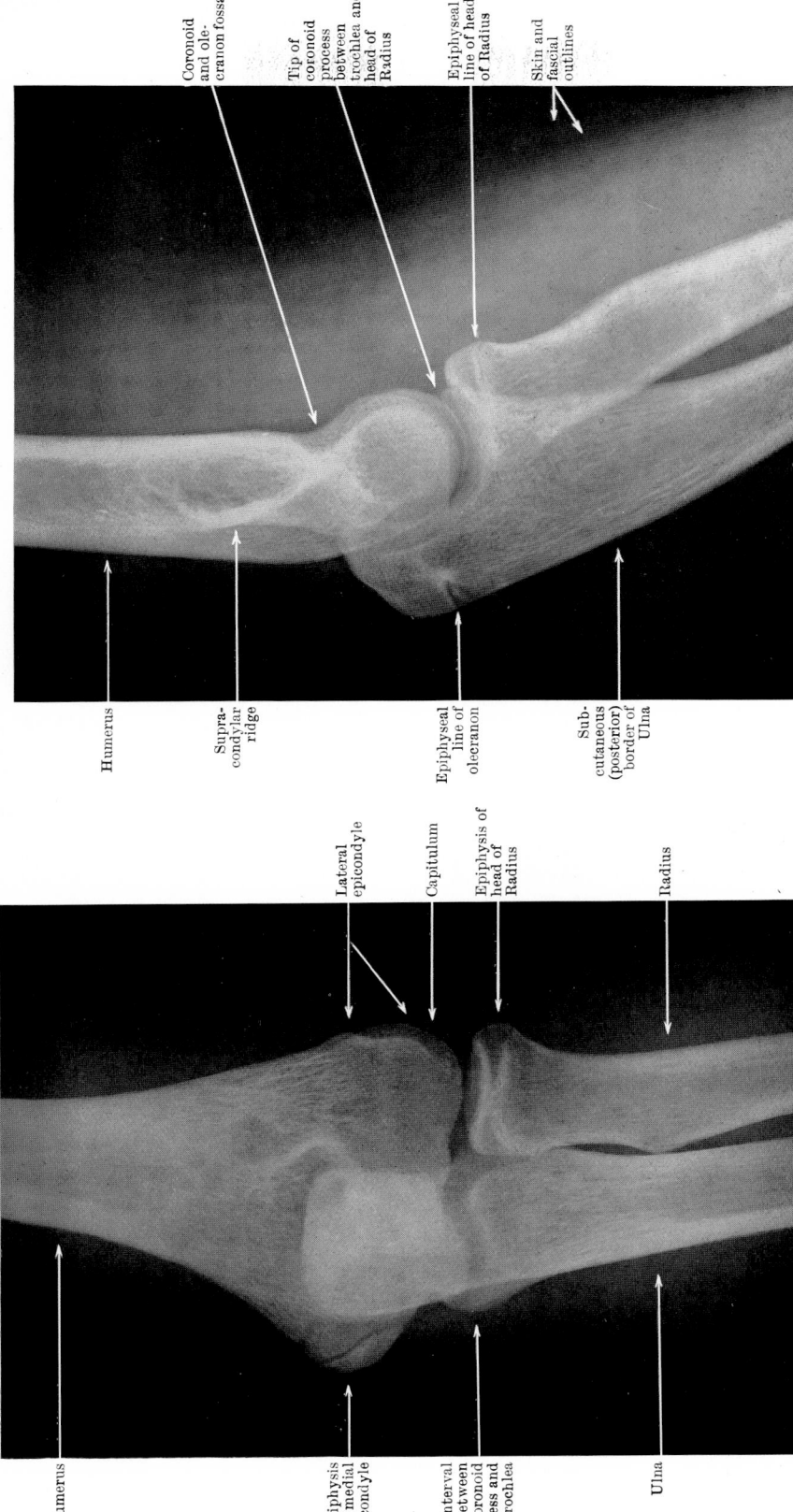

Coronoid and olecranon fossæ

Tip of coronoid process between trochlea and head of Radius

Epiphyseal line of head of Radius

Skin and fascial outlines

Humerus

Supra-condylar ridge

Epiphyseal line of olecranon

Sub-cutaneous (posterior) border of Ulna

FIG. 2.—LATERAL RADIOGRAPH OF THE SAME ELBOW (GIRL AGED 12), SLIGHTLY FLEXED.
Note the uniting Epiphyses of Head of Radius and Olecranon of Ulna.

Lateral epicondyle

Capitulum

Epiphysis of head of Radius

Radius

Humerus

Epiphysis of medial epicondyle

Interval between coronoid process and trochlea

Ulna

FIG. 1.—ANTERO-POSTERIOR RADIOGRAPH OF ELBOW OF GIRL AGED 12,
SHOWING EPIPHYSES OF MEDIAL EPICONDYLE OF HUMERUS AND
HEAD OF RADIUS NOT YET UNITED.

PLATE VIII

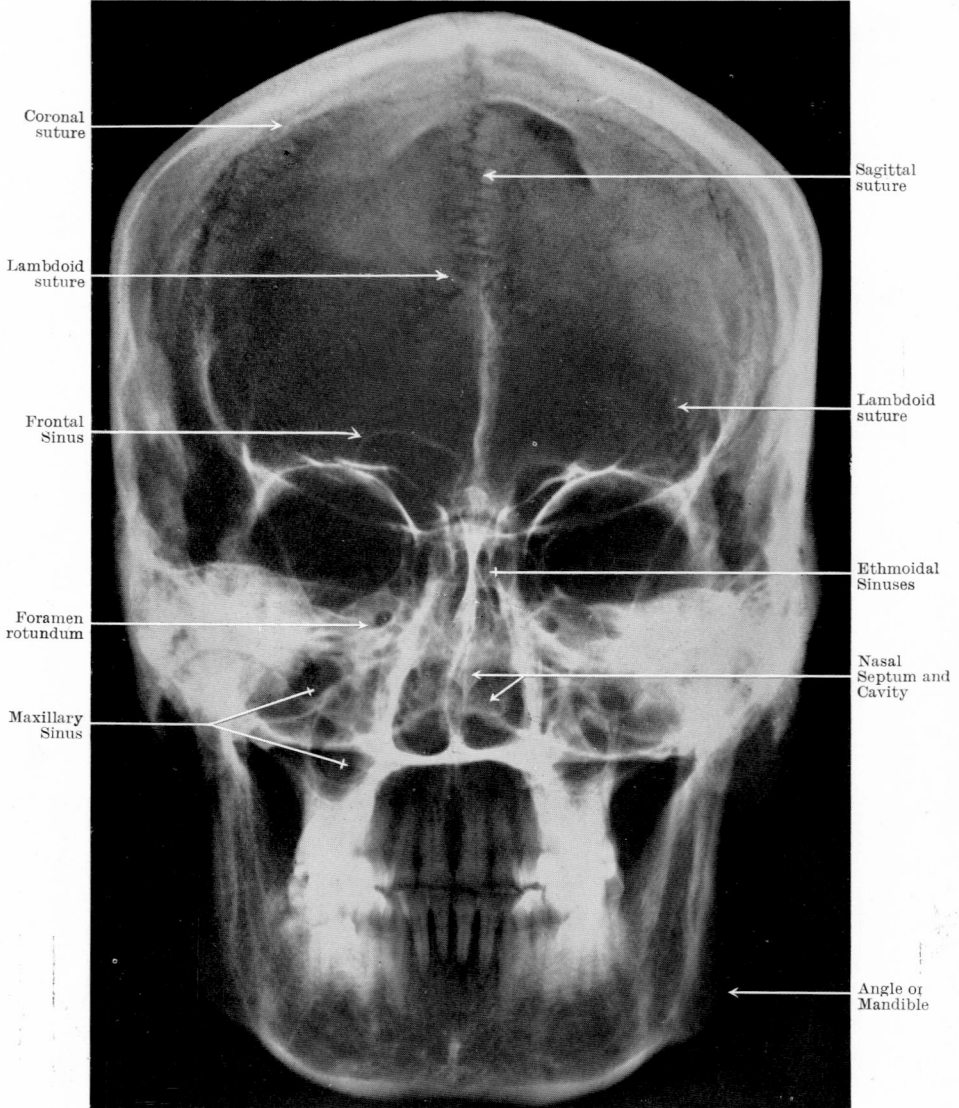

Coronal
suture

Lambdoid
suture

Frontal
Sinus

Foramen
rotundum

Maxillary
Sinus

Sagittal
suture

Lambdoid
suture

Ethmoidal
Sinuses

Nasal
Septum and
Cavity

Angle of
Mandible

PLATE VIII.—ANTERO-POSTERIOR RADIOGRAPH OF THE SAME MALE
SKULL AS IN PLATE V.

Compare with Fig. 137, p. 141; Fig. 148, p. 181; and, for variations in the extent of the
frontal sinuses, with Plate LVIII, Fig. 1. Note that in this skull the septum between the
two frontal sinuses is broad, which accounts for the fact that their cavities are not well
seen in Plate V.

away, one can see it by looking into the nasal cavity through the anterior aperture. The upper edge of the plate projects into the cranial cavity as a conspicuous crest, called the **crista galli** (comb of a cock), in the median part of the anterior cranial fossa.

The **cribriform plates** are narrow horizontal plates placed one on each side of the crista galli. They lie in the floor of the anterior cranial fossa and, at the same time, in the roof of the cavity of the nose. They are full of little holes through which the olfactory nerves pass up from the nose to reach the brain. ['Ηθμός (ēthmos) = a colander; *cribrum* = a sieve.]

The two **labyrinths** constitute the main part of the ethmoid bone. Each labyrinth is placed high up in the side wall of the cavity of the nose; the upper, narrow part of the nasal cavity separates it from the perpendicular plate in the septum. The labyrinth is composed of very thin, papery bone enclosing a number of irregular, small cavities which communicate with each other—hence the name "labyrinth." The cavities are called the **ethmoidal sinuses**. From the medial or nasal side of the labyrinth, two thin plates of bone project into the nasal cavity and then curl downwards; they are called the **superior** and **middle nasal conchæ** [κόγχη (conchē) = a mussel-shell]. The lateral surface of the labyrinth is a thin, smooth, four-sided sheet of bone called the *orbital plate*; it forms a great part of the medial wall of the orbit, where it is easily seen; its anterior end is about half an inch behind the rim of the orbit, and it measures over an inch from before backwards and over half an inch in height.

The two **nasal bones** lie side by side in the bridge of the nose.

The **lacrimal bone** (Figs. 137, 138, 177) is a thin, uneven scale of bone about the size of a finger-nail. It lies in the medial wall of the orbit near the orbital rim, immediately in front of the orbital plate of the ethmoid labyrinth. It is named "lacrimal" because its anterior part helps to form the groove in which the lacrimal sac lies. It is so thin that it is often broken away in a skull that has had much handling.

The **inferior nasal concha** (Figs. 146, 149, 176) is a thin, rough plate of bone attached by one of its edges to the lower part of the side wall of the nasal cavity; it projects into the cavity and its free edge curls downwards.

The **vomer** [= a ploughshare] is a thin bone that forms the posterior and postero-inferior part of the nasal septum (Figs. 139, 146, 178). It lies behind and below the perpendicular plate of the ethmoid. It is easily recognised in a skull turned upside down, for it is the partition between the two posterior apertures of the nose. At its upper end or border it splits into a right and a left half, called the **alæ** of the vomer, which spread out for a little distance on the lower surface of the body of the sphenoid bone [*ala* = a wing].

The two **maxillæ** form the upper jaw. Each maxilla has a main part or body and four processes—alveolar process, frontal process, palatine process, and zygomatic process (Figs. 137, 138, 139, 147, 181).

The **body** of the maxilla lies below the orbit, and lateral to the lower part of the nasal cavity. Its upper or *orbital surface* forms a large part of the floor of the orbit; its medial or *nasal surface* forms the lower part of the side wall of the cavity of the nose; its *anterior surface* is the bone alongside the lower part of the anterior aperture of the nose; its *posterior surface* is the rounded surface of bone that looks backwards into the space below the greater wing of the sphenoid. Those surfaces are like the outside of a box, for the body of the maxilla encloses a large cavity, called the **maxillary sinus**, which occupies its whole interior.

The **frontal process** of the maxilla is the projection that extends upwards to reach the frontal bone. It lies behind the nasal bone, taking share in the formation of the bony part of the external nose; it has a large share also in forming the medial part of the rim of the orbit.

The **zygomatic process** is the thick spur of bone that stands out from the junction of the anterior and posterior surfaces of the body, and is united to the zygomatic arch.

The **palatine process** is the horizontal shelf of bone that forms the anterior, larger part of its own half of the bony palate.

The **alveolar process** is the thick curved ridge that projects downwards from the body and carries the teeth. If the teeth have fallen out after the skull was dried, its lower border presents a row of *sockets* for the roots of the teeth. [*Alveolus* = a small cavity; *Maxilla*, a diminutive of *mala*, which = the bone of the cheek that carries the teeth.] When teeth are removed during life the walls of the corresponding sockets are soon absorbed and the alveolar process is greatly reduced in size at those points; in the skull of a person who had long lost all the teeth the alveolar process is a mere inconspicuous rim. The alveolar processes of the two maxillæ make a horseshoe-shaped ridge which bounds the bony palate in front and at the sides. The posterior part of the alveolar process is called the *tuberosity of the maxilla.*

The **zygomatic bone** (Figs. 137, 138, 186,) makes the hard, prominent part of the cheek; it forms the anterior part of the zygomatic arch and has a considerable share in forming the lower and lateral parts of the rim of the orbit. The part of the zygomatic bone that projects backwards to articulate with the zygoma of the temporal bone is called its **temporal process.** The part that projects upwards along the side of the orbit to articulate with the frontal bone is called its **frontal process**; posteriorly, it articulates with the greater wing of the sphenoid.

The **palatine bone** lies in the posterior part of the bony palate and in the side wall of the nasal cavity. It is a small bone, but has three parts, viz.: a horizontal plate, a perpendicular plate, and a tubercle. The horizontal plate is easily located; the other two parts are not (Figs. 139, 147, 184).

The **horizontal plate** is the thin, square plate of bone that forms the posterior quarter or third of the corresponding half of the bony palate.

The **perpendicular plate** is a still thinner sheet of bone; it lies on the side wall of the cavity of the nose, directly in front of the medial pterygoid plate, and in many skulls one can see the suture between its posterior edge and the pterygoid plate by looking into the nose through the posterior aperture. The anterior and larger part of its lateral surface is closely applied to the medial surface of the maxilla, but the posterior part is farther back than the maxilla and forms the medial wall of a space called the pterygo-palatine fossa that will be examined later. Its upper end is surmounted by two processes—an *orbital·process* in front and a *sphenoidal process* behind; the gap between the two processes is called the **spheno-palatine notch**.

The **tubercle** is irregular and is often so closely united to the bones among which it lies that it is difficult to see its outlines. It projects from the posterior border of the palatine bone where the horizontal and perpendicular plates join each other, and it fits in (1) between the tuberosity of the maxilla and the lower part of the pterygoid process of the sphenoid, and (2) between the lower parts of the two pterygoid plates.

The **mandible** (Figs. 137, 138, 150, 151), or lower jawbone, has a horseshoe-shaped **body** and two flat, broad **rami** that project upwards from the posterior parts of the two halves of the body. The body bears the teeth [*mandĕre* = to chew]. Two processes project upwards from the upper border of each ramus; the anterior one is named the **coronoid process**; the posterior is named the **condyloid process**, and is divided into a *head* and a *neck*. The head articulates with the temporal bone to form a synovial joint called the *mandibular joint*. In the living person, the projection that overlaps the ear-hole from in front is called the *tragus*. The head of the mandible can be felt immediately in front of the tragus when the mouth is shut; as the mouth is opened the head can be felt gliding downwards and forwards. The **angle** of the mandible is the point where the posterior border of the ramus joins the lower border; it is easily felt two or three finger-breadths below the lobule of the ear. The oblique opening on the medial side of the ramus is called the **mandibular foramen**; the narrow groove that extends downwards and forwards from the lower margin of the foramen is called the **mylo-hyoid groove**; the oblique ridge on the medial side of the body is called the **mylo-hyoid line**.

The mandible is a separate bone, and is not dealt with under the skull as a whole. It is an important bone, and is described on p. 185.

THE SKULL AS A WHOLE

The skull as a whole is slightly flattened from side to side. Looked at from above, it is smooth, but from below it is very uneven. It is never quite bilaterally symmetrical, but usually is nearly so.

The **exterior of the skull** is examined from five points of view: from the front, the back, above, below, and from the side. Each of those aspects is called a "norma" [=a square]; and they are named norma frontalis, occipitalis, verticalis, basalis, and lateralis. There are no boundary lines between the aspects, for they overlap one another to a large extent.

Norma Verticalis

The **top of the skull** has convex contours, so that any impact received at a particular point is distributed over a considerable area, and the danger of fracture is thereby lessened. The horizontal outline varies considerably in different specimens, but in most European skulls the outline is ovoid, the wider part being nearer the back than the front.

The top of the skull shows portions of four bones—the **frontal** bone in front, the **occipital** bone behind, and the right and left **parietal** bones in the middle between them—the occipital bone having only a very small share. The bones are united by serrated *sutures*—the jagged, saw-like edges of the bones interlocking with one another [*sutura* = a seam]. If the skull is that of a young adult the sutures are seen distinctly as irregular lines between the bones. If the skull is that of an old person the sutures are more or less obliterated and the bones are fused, but the positions of the sutures are usually indicated by narrow, irregular linear depressions. In many skulls small circumscribed pieces of bone, like islands, are seen in the sutures in certain places, and are called **sutural bones.**

The suture that unites the frontal bone to the two parietal bones arches across the skull from side to side, and is called the **coronal suture** [*corona* = a curved line, circle, crown]. The suture that unites the occipital bone to the two parietal bones is called the **lambdoid suture**, because it is shaped like the Greek capital letter *Lambda* [Λ = L]. The suture between the two parietal bones is called the **sagittal suture**; that name is given because in an infant's skull the sagittal suture, the lambdoid suture, and an unossified region, called the anterior fontanelle, together, resemble a heraldic arrow [*sagitta* = an arrow].

The point where the sagittal suture meets the coronal suture is called the **bregma** [βρέγμα = the front part of the head]. At birth the parts of the frontal and parietal bones around the bregma are not fully ossified, and leave a large, lozenge-shaped membranous area which is yielding to the touch and is called the *anterior fontanelle* [fonticulus frontalis], because it rises and falls with every beat of the heart; in a healthy child the bones approach each other and close the fontanelle by the end of the second year. The coronal suture slopes downwards and forwards from the top of the skull; the bregma is therefore the farthest back point on the suture; it is immediately in front of the mid point of a line drawn from one external auditory meatus to the other in the vertical transverse plane, and is occasionally felt as a depression in the living head. The *post-coronal depression* is the name given to a slight flattening or even hollowing seen in some skulls on the surface of each parietal bone behind and parallel to the coronal suture. Occasionally there is a broad, low ridge along the line of the sagittal suture.

The **lambda** is the point at which the sagittal and lambdoid sutures meet.

The **vertex**, or highest point of a skull held in proper position, is on the sagittal suture near its middle, but varies slightly in different skulls. The **parietal foramen** is a small hole present in many skulls in the parietal bone near the sagittal suture about 35 mm. from the lambda. It is usually only big enough to admit a pin; a small artery and vein pass through it; the vein connects the veins of the scalp with the superior sagittal venous sinus which lies along the middle line on the inside of the skull cap, and infection can travel along the vein from a wound in the scalp and attack the sinus. The sagittal suture is less serrated between the two parietal foramina than it is elsewhere.

The *sagittal fontanelle* is an unossified space in the region of the parietal foramina; it is usually closed at birth. If it is not closed at birth, the parietal foramen in the adult skull will probably be large enough to admit a match. The point on the sagittal suture between the two parietal foramina is called the **obelion** [ὀβελός (obelos) = ÷ (which is a mark used by literary commentators)].

The **parietal eminence** is the most convex part of the parietal bone, and is the region where the top of the skull and the side and the back merge into one another; its position varies with the shape of the skull, but none the less it is used as a landmark, for it is fairly easily identified in the living head. It overlies the most convex part of the surface of the brain.

The frontal eminences anteriorly and the temporal lines at the sides are visible, but will be dealt with later. In some specimens the zygomatic arches can be seen when the skull is looked at from above.

Norma Frontalis

The **front of the skull** (Fig. 137) is uneven in contour and outline. Almost more than any other aspect of the skull it varies with age, race, and sex, besides displaying individual variations in the details of its configuration.

The front of the skull is made up of: (1) the frontal region or forehead; (2) the two orbits; (3) the bony external nose, between and in front of the orbits; (4) the anterior bony aperture of the nose; (5) the two maxillæ, forming the upper jaw; (6) the zygomatic bone or cheek bone, below the lateral part of the orbit; and (7) the mandible, when it is in place.

Frontal Region.—The forehead is formed by the frontal bone, and is convex. Superiorly it merges into the top of the skull; inferiorly it is limited by the orbits and the root of the nose. The **nasion** is the point in the median plane at the root of the nose where the two nasal bones articulate with the frontal bone; it is opposite the anterior extremity of the brain. The **glabella** is the small region immediately above the nasion, between the two eyebrows [*glabellus* = without hair]. The **superciliary arch** is the smooth elevation that arches upwards and in a lateral direction from the glabella, a little above the margin of the orbit. Behind it, in the interior of the frontal bone, there is usually a large air-space, called the **frontal sinus** (Figs. 146, 149), from which a short channel leads down into the cavity of the nose. The **frontal eminence** is the most convex part of each half of the frontal bone; it is situated about two finger-breadths above the lateral end of the superciliary arch.

The **supra-orbital margin** or upper margin of the orbital opening is a curved border. At the highest point of the curve, about two finger-breadths from the median plane, there is usually a small notch called the **supra-orbital notch**; the notch can be felt in the living head by the thumb-nail pressed on the margin *from below*. Laterally, the supra-orbital margin ends in a prominent projection which is named the **zygomatic process** of the frontal bone because it curves downwards and articulates with the upstanding frontal process of the zygomatic bone. The zygomatic process is easily felt at the lateral end of the eyebrow hairs and is one of the most serviceable landmarks in the head. The ridge that curves upwards and backwards from it is the anterior part of the **temporal line**, and can be both felt and seen in thin people between the brow and the temple.

The two halves of the **frontal bone** are separable at birth and are not fused together completely till some period between the sixth and the tenth year. The suture between the halves is called the *frontal suture*. Remains of the suture can often be seen in the adult skull at and above the glabella, and in some skulls, especially in the more civilised races, the whole suture persists till late in life; it is sometimes called the *metopic suture* [μετόπη (metopē) = the interstice between two beam ends (in Doric architecture)]. The point in the middle of the forehead, on the shortest diameter between the two temporal lines, is usually a little above the glabella and is called the **ophryon** [ὀφρύς (ophrys) = the brow].

The **superciliary arch** is more prominent in men than in boys and women; the lower part of the forehead therefore protrudes more in a man, and the forehead is less vertical. Though the arch overlies the frontal sinus it is not produced by the sinus, for in a skull in which the sinus is small or absent the arch may be prominent. The upper part (corrugator supercilii) of the orbi-

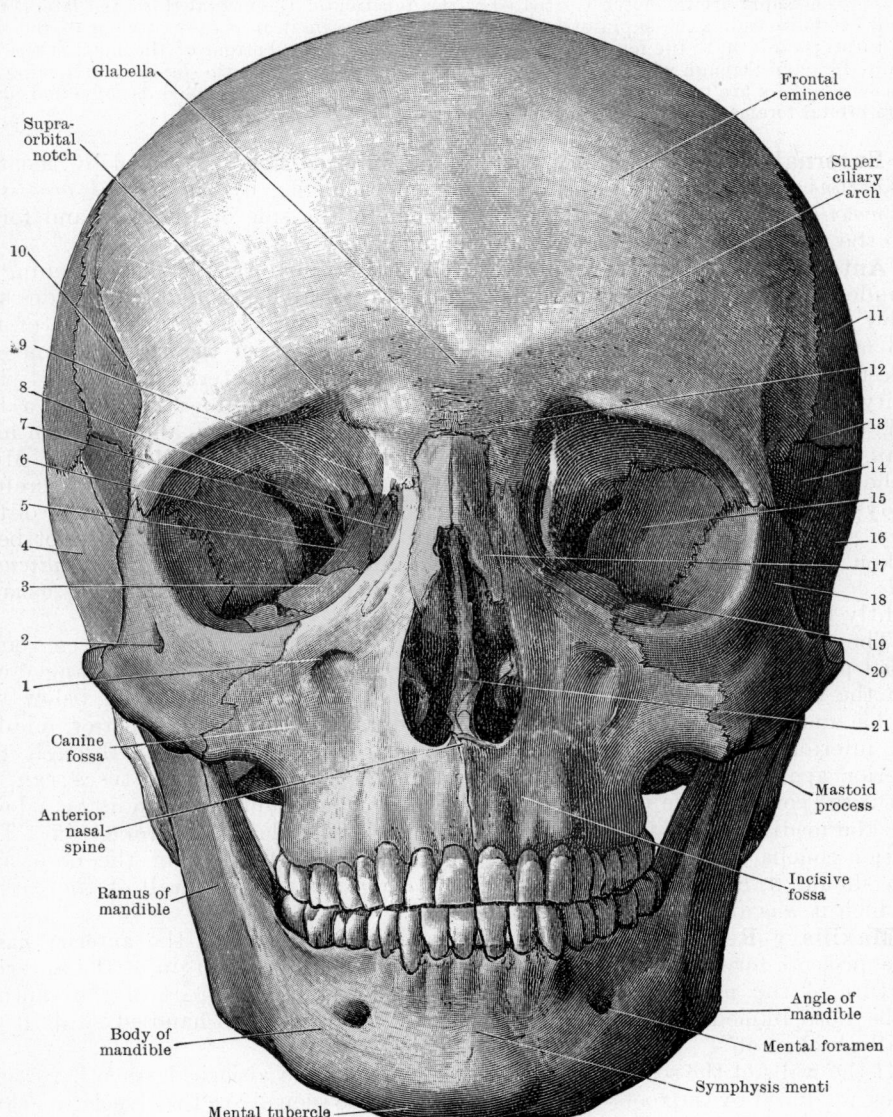

FIG. 137.—THE FRONT OF THE SKULL.

Red : parietal ; zygomatic ; orbital plate of ethmoid ; nasal ; vomer ; inferior concha.
Blue : sphenoid ; lacrimal ; perpendicular plate of the ethmoid and middle concha ; mandible.
Yellow : maxilla.   Uncoloured : frontal ; temporal.

1. Infra-orbital foramen.
2. Zygomatico-facial foramen.
3. Orbital surface of maxilla.
4. Squamous temporal.
5. Orbital plate of ethmoid.
6. Superior orbital fissure.
7. Lacrimal bone and groove.
8. Optic foramen.
9. Ethmoidal foramina.
10. Temporal line.
11. Parietal bone.
12. Naso-frontal suture.
13. Pterion.
14. Greater wing of sphenoid.
15. Orbital surface of greater wing.
16. Squamous part of temporal.
17. Left nasal bone.
18. Zygomatic bone.
19. Inferior orbital fissure.
20. Zygomatic arch.
21. Anterior aperture of nose.

cularis oculi arises from the medial end of the arch. The **frontal eminence** is the region where the views of the skull from the front, from above, and from the side overlap ; it is more conspicuous in boys and women than in men as their foreheads are more vertical ; it overlies the part of the brain called the middle frontal gyrus.

The **supra-orbital margin** is the lower limit of the forehead. Its lateral two-thirds is thin and sharp and bends down to the zygomatic process. The medial third is rounded ; it bends down into the medial margin of the orbit, and its end is sometimes called the *medial angular process*. The **supra-orbital notch** is situated at the junction of the medial third and lateral two-thirds of the margin ; the supra-orbital vessels and nerves lie in it as they pass out of the orbit and turn upwards on to the forehead to reach the scalp. In the bottom of the notch there is a minute foramen through which the frontal diploic vein passes to join the supra-orbital vein. In some skulls there are two shallow notches instead of one ; in others the notch is converted into a **supra-orbital foramen** by a bridge of bone.

External Nose.—The bony part of the external nose is formed by the two *nasal bones* in the bridge of the nose, and, on each side, by the *frontal process of the maxilla*, which lies behind the nasal bone in the side of the nose, and forms also the medial margin of the orbital opening.

Anterior Bony Aperture of Nose [Apertura piriformis].—This opening is bounded above by the lower margins of the two nasal bones, and at the sides and below by the sharp, anterior margins of the frontal processes and bodies of the two maxillæ. It is the anterior opening into the **cavity of the nose**, and one can look through it into the cavity and out through the posterior apertures. The cavity is divided by a thin, median partition or **septum** into a right and a left half. Each half is called a cavity of the nose or nasal cavity, and the term may mean, according to the context, either the whole cavity or one of the halves. Most of the anterior part of the septum is a plate of cartilage ; the septum is therefore always incomplete in a macerated and dried skull, and considerable parts of the bony septum may have been broken away. If the bony septum has not been broken the principal part seen through the anterior aperture is the *perpendicular plate of the ethmoid* bone, which forms the upper part of the septum ; it is usually slightly bent to one or other side.

The side wall of the nasal cavity is very uneven, because the three rough curled plates of bone called the *conchæ* project from the side wall and hang down into the cavity like curtains. The portions of the cavity which lie below the conchæ and lateral to them are called the *meatuses* of the nose—superior, middle, and inferior. The superior concha is too far back to be seen through the anterior aperture, but the inferior and middle conchæ and meatuses can be seen if the conchæ have not been broken away. The middle concha is on a level with the medial wall of the orbit, and is rather less liable to be broken off. The inferior concha is situated about half an inch above the floor of the nose, and even should it have been broken away the ridge on the side wall of the cavity to which it was attached can be seen.

Maxillary Region.—A sharp, median spur of bone, called the **anterior nasal spine**, projects forwards from the two maxillæ at the lower margin of the anterior aperture of the nose ; it is imbedded in the lower, mobile part of the septum of the nose immediately above the upper lip. In a much-handled skull it is usually broken off.

If the walls of the sockets for the teeth have not been absorbed, smooth vertical ridges, produced by the roots or fangs of the teeth, are seen above the alveolar margin. The largest of those ridges corresponds to the root of the canine tooth and is called the **canine eminence**. (The *canine* tooth is the third tooth, counting from the middle in front ; and the first two teeth are called *incisors*.) The **canine fossa** is the wide, shallow depression above and lateral to the canine eminence, reaching up almost to the lower margin of the orbit. The *infra-orbital foramen* is the opening immediately above the canine fossa, about 5 mm. below the lower margin of the orbit ; in the living person it is about a finger's-breadth lateral to the side of the nose, and may be felt indistinctly if pressure is made there with the finger-tip. It transmits the infra-orbital vessels and nerve.

Between the medial ends of the two supra-orbital margins there is a horseshoe-shaped suture uniting the frontal bone to the upper ends of the two nasal bones and frontal processes of the maxillæ. The middle of the suture is the **nasion**, from which a suture runs down the middle of the bridge of the nose between the two nasal bones ; the lower end of the suture is called the **rhinion** [ῥίς (rhis) = the nose]. On each side of the bony external nose there is a linear suture between the nasal bone and the frontal process of the maxilla. On the nasal bone, at a varying point, there is often a minute foramen through which a vein passes from the skin to the interior of the nose. Occasionally that vein continues upwards to join the commencement of the superior sagittal sinus in the cranial cavity, and then infection can pass along the vein and attack the sinus. At the lower end of the nasal bone there is very often a narrow notch that marks the point where the external nasal nerve escapes from the interior of the nose. Some fibres of the procerus are attached to the nasal bone. The levator labii superioris alæque nasi arises from the upper part of the frontal process of the maxilla; the compressor naris arises from the bone near the lower boundary of the anterior aperture of the nose.

The pliable, lower part of the external nose has a framework of cartilage united to the sharp margins of the anterior bony aperture by fibrous tissue. The **anterior bony aperture** is oblique, and is ovoid in outline with the narrow end above and in front. It measures about 30-35 mm. in height, and about 25 mm. across its widest part; it is shorter, wider, and more vertical in flat-nosed races. Parts of the septum and side walls of the **nasal cavity** can be seen through it, and also the floor and part of the roof when the skull is tilted.

If the bony **septum** is complete, its anterior edge forms an angle into which the septal cartilage fits. The upper limb of the angle is the perpendicular plate of the ethmoid. The lower limb is formed *posteriorly* by the lower and anterior part of the vomer and *anteriorly* by the prominent, anterior part of the *nasal crest* of the maxillæ (*i.e.*, a rough ridge that stands up from the junction of the palatine processes of the two maxillæ and is continuous with the anterior nasal spine). On the **side wall** note again the inferior and middle conchæ. The inferior concha reaches the anterior aperture. The middle concha is shorter than the inferior and does not reach so far forwards; the interval between it and the septum is very narrow, and also the part of the middle meatus that lies lateral to it is very narrow, because a part of the labyrinth of the ethmoid, called the *bulla ethmoidalis*, bulges into the meatus; the lower part of the middle meatus is roomier, and in its side wall the opening of the maxillary sinus can be found. Identify the floor of the fossa for the lacrimal sac in the orbit and locate it in the side wall of the nasal cavity, immediately in front of the middle meatus. The part of the **roof** visible is only the anterior, sloping part, which is formed by the nasal bone and the nasal part of the frontal bone and its nasal spine—a projection that juts down into the roof of the nose and is hidden from the exterior by the nasal bone. The whole **floor** can be seen. Though the upper part of the nasal cavity is very narrow, the floor is half an inch in width; it is made of the palatine process of the maxilla and the horizontal part of the palatine bone, which, at the same time, constitute the bony palate and are seen better on the lower surface of the skull.

The **anterior nasal spine** consists of a spicule from each maxilla; its apex is called the **akanthion** [ἄκανθα (akantha) = a thorn]. Running downwards from it there is the *intermaxillary suture*, the lower end of which, in the front of the alveolar margin, is called the **prosthion** [πρόσθιος = foremost]. On each side of the suture, immediately below the anterior aperture of the nose there is a shallow depression called the **incisive fossa**. The **canine fossa** lies below the infra-orbital foramen on the anterior wall of the maxillary sinus; the levator anguli oris arises from its floor. The levator labii superioris arises from the infra-orbital margin above the infra-orbital foramen; the incisive slips of the orbicularis oris arise from the incisive fossa and the canine eminence.

Lateral to the canine fossa, the suture between the maxilla and the zygomatic bone can be seen. It begins at the middle of the lower margin of the orbit and ends at the lower border of the zygomatic arch in line with the lateral margin of the orbit. The **zygomatico-facial foramen** is a small hole on the zygomatic bone about 5 mm. below the lateral part of the lower margin of the orbit; it is only big enough to admit a pin; it transmits the zygomatico-facial branch of the zygomatic nerve and a small branch of the lacrimal artery; sometimes it is represented by two openings instead of one. Below the foramen, a smooth low eminence gives origin to the zygomaticus major; the eminence is conspicuous in some thin people.

Orbit (Figs. 137, 148).—The orbit is a cavity of a shape not unlike a four-sided pyramid laid on one side. The sides are called the *roof*, the *floor*, the *medial wall* and the *lateral wall*. The *base* of the pyramid is the opening on to the face, and the boundaries of the base are the **margins of the orbit**. At the *apex* there is a large aperture; it is the medial and lower part of a cleft called the **superior orbital fissure** (Fig. 149); the rest of the fissure extends forwards, upwards, and in a lateral direction *between the roof and the lateral wall* of the orbit, becoming narrower as it does so. The fissure leads back into the middle cranial fossa, and its size varies in different skulls.

Between the roof and the medial wall there are three foramina—the optic and two ethmoidal. The **optic foramen** is the round aperture immediately above and medial to the apex of the orbit; it leads back into the middle cranial fossa. The **anterior** and **posterior ethmoidal foramina** are farther forward; they are about half an inch apart and the anterior is the larger. They lead into canals that open into the median part of the anterior cranial fossa, but their openings there are rather hidden under lips of bone.

The **fossa for the lacrimal gland** [*lacrima* = a tear] is a broad, smooth depression, of varying depth, in the anterior and lateral part of the roof of the orbit, under shelter of the zygomatic process of the frontal bone. The **fossa for the lacrimal sac** (Fig. 138) is on the medial wall close to the orbital margin. If the lacrimal bone is broken away, only part of the fossa will be seen, for it is a fairly broad, vertical groove, partly on the lacrimal bone and partly on the frontal process of the maxilla. The fossa becomes continuous with the **naso-lacrimal canal**, the upper opening of which is seen at the *junction of the medial wall and floor* of the orbit; the canal is a short tunnel that leads down into the inferior meatus of the nose under cover of the anterior part of the inferior concha—a fact which one can demonstrate by pushing a match down through the canal from the orbit. The lacrimal sac is a wide tube, blind at its upper end, and its lower end is continuous with the naso-lacrimal duct, which goes down through the canal into the nose. The lacrimal gland produces the lacrimal fluid; most of the fluid evaporates, and the remainder passes into the sac and thence into the nose—any excess of fluid overflowing the eyelids as tears. The gland is at the upper, lateral part of the orbit, and the sac is at the lower, medial part; that arrangement ensures that the front of the eye shall be well washed.

Between the floor and the lateral wall of the orbit there is a long cleft, called the **inferior orbital fissure**, which opens into a space behind the maxilla called the infra-temporal fossa. The **infra-orbital groove** is in the floor of the orbit. It begins about the middle of the inferior orbital fissure and runs nearly straight forwards. The anterior part of it has a thin roof of bone and is called the **infra-orbital canal**; and the canal opens on the face as the infra-orbital foramen. In one or both orbits the groove may be roofed over in all its length; one can then locate it by passing a pointer back through the infra-orbital foramen.

The chief **relations** (Figs. 148, 149) of the orbit are:—*Superiorly*—The frontal sinus to a varying extent; the anterior cranial fossa, containing the frontal lobe of the brain. *Inferiorly*—The maxillary sinus in the body of the maxilla. *Medially*—Near the apex, the sphenoidal sinus in the body of the sphenoid; farther forward, the ethmoidal sinuses, which separate the orbit from the cavity of the nose; within the orbital margin, the floor of the fossa for the lacrimal sac intervenes between the orbit and the nasal cavity, and is so thin that an operator can reach the lacrimal sac by passing from the nose through the floor of the fossa, if he wants to avoid a scar at the medial corner of the eye. *Laterally*—The posterior part of the orbit is related to the middle cranial fossa, which lodges the temporal lobe of the brain; the anterior part is related to the anterior part of the temporal fossa (p. 147).

The two **orbits** are placed so that their medial walls are almost parallel, while their lateral walls are nearly at right angles to each other; the axis of each orbit is directed therefore in a forward and lateral direction; none the less, the axes of the two eyeballs are antero-posterior and parallel. Each orbit is about 50 mm. long.

The **orbital opening** or base of the orbit is more or less four-square, measuring about 40 mm. each way; it is directed forwards and slightly in a lateral direction, and it is tilted so that the upper and lower margins slope slightly downwards from medial to lateral side. The *lower margin* of the opening is formed by the maxilla and the zygomatic bone. *The lateral margin* is formed by the frontal process of the zygomatic bone and the zygomatic process of the frontal bone; the suture between the processes, near the upper angle of the opening, can usually be felt in the living person; within the middle of the margin, about 10 mm. below the suture, there is a slight eminence (felt by the finger tip rather than seen), for the attachment of the lateral palpebral ligament and the check and suspensory ligaments of the eye. The *upper margin* is the supra-orbital margin of the frontal bone; its lateral two-thirds is sharp, and the medial third is smooth and rounded; the supra-orbital notch or foramen is at their junction; the supra-trochlear nerve and vessels, passing out of the orbit on to the forehead, cross the margin about 5 mm. medial to the supra-orbital notch and may produce a shallow groove. The *medial* margin is formed by the medial angular process of the frontal bone and the frontal process of the maxilla; the medial palpebral ligament and the orbicularis oculi are attached to the margin immediately in front of the groove for the lacrimal sac.

The orbit being pyramidal, its walls are more or less triangular in outline. The lateral wall is strong and fairly thick. The other walls are made of thin bone—especially the medial wall, where the bone is almost like paper.

The *roof* is concave; it is formed by the orbital plate of the frontal bone, comple-mented posteriorly by the lesser wing of the sphenoid. The frontal sinus extends for a variable distance backwards *in* the roof of the orbit between the two tables of the orbital plate. At the lateral angle of the roof there is the wide **fossa for the lacrimal gland** (*i.e.* the greater part of the gland ; the smaller part protrudes beyond the fossa into the upper eyelid). At the medial angle the trochlea is attached ; the attachment may be marked by a very small pit or by a spicule of bone, or by both (the **trochlear fossa** and **spine**) ; the trochlea is a small fibro-cartilaginous ring through which the tendon of the superior oblique muscle of the eyeball passes.

The greater part of the *lateral wall* is formed by the greater wing of the sphenoid, but the anterior part is formed by the frontal process of the zygomatic bone. On the anterior part there is a small aperture, called the **zygomatic foramen,** through which the zygomatic nerve leaves the orbit, accompanied by a small branch of the lacrimal artery ; sometimes there are two apertures instead of one. A great part of the lateral wall is separated posteriorly from the roof by the **superior orbital fissure,** which is bounded medially by the body of the sphenoid, above by the lesser wing, below and laterally by the greater wing. The two heads of the lateral rectus muscle of the eyeball lie across the wide, lower and medial part of the fissure. Some of the structures transmitted by the fissure pass between the two heads ; the others pass above both heads. They are :—

(*a*) *Between the Heads.*—The ophthalmic vein or veins, passing backwards to join the cavernous sinus [ὀφθαλμός (ophthalmos) = *oculus* = the eye] ; the abducent nerve, the naso-ciliary nerve, and the two divisions of the oculomotor nerve—all passing forwards.

(*b*) *Above the Heads.*—The trochlear nerve, the frontal nerve, and the lacrimal nerve, all passing forwards, in that order from medial to lateral side ; a small branch of the lacrimal artery passing backwards to the dura mater ; occasionally a small branch of the middle meningeal artery passing into the orbit ; and sympathetic twigs from the carotid plexus. [Μῆνιγξ (mēninx) = any membrane, but especially a membrane around the brain.]

The *floor* is formed chiefly by the orbital surface of the body of the maxilla, which is, at the same time, the roof of the maxillary sinus. But the antero-lateral corner of the floor is formed by the zygomatic bone ; and the posterior corner is formed by the orbital process of the palatine bone—that is, the anterior of the two projections on the upper end of its perpendicular plate.

A great part of the floor is separated from the lateral wall posteriorly by the **inferior orbital fissure.** The fissure is bounded *above* by the greater wing of the sphenoid, *below* by the orbital surface of the maxilla and the orbital process of the palatine bone ; its *anterior* end is closed either by the zygomatic bone or by an articulation between the greater wing and the maxilla. The posterior end of the inferior orbital fissure meets the medial end of the superior orbital fissure at the apex of the orbit. The greater part of the inferior fissure leads into the infra-temporal fossa behind the maxilla ; but its posterior part leads down into the pterygo-palatine fossa, which also is behind the maxilla and is below the most posterior part of the orbit. The inferior orbital fissure *transmits* : the maxillary nerve, as it changes its name to infra-orbital nerve ; the infra-orbital vessels ; the zygomatic nerve ; small twigs from the spheno-palatine ganglion to the lacrimal gland and the periosteum of the orbit ; a vein connecting the ophthalmic veins with the pterygoid venous plexus in the infra-temporal fossa.

The **infra-orbital groove** and **canal** run forwards in the floor of the orbit and the roof of the maxillary sinus. The infra-orbital nerve, accompanied by the infra-orbital vessels, traverses the groove and canal, sends down branches through the facial wall of the sinus to the incisor, canine, and premolar teeth, and enters the face through the infra-orbital foramen.

The upper end of the **naso-lacrimal canal** separates the anterior part of the floor from the medial wall ; and at the medial corner of the floor, immediately lateral to the canal, there is a shallow depression for the origin of the inferior oblique muscle of the eyeball.

The *medial wall* of the orbit is formed, from behind forwards, by : the anterior part of the side of the body of the sphenoid ; the orbital plate of the ethmoid ; the lacrimal bone ; and the posterior part of the frontal process of the maxilla. The optic foramen and the ethmoidal foramina lie between the medial wall and the roof. The **optic foramen** is bounded by the body of the sphenoid and the roots of the lesser wing ; it transmits the optic nerve and the ophthalmic artery ; note that the ophthalmic vein and artery pass through different apertures. The **anterior** and **posterior ethmoidal foramina** are the orbital ends of the anterior and posterior ethmoidal canals, which transmit vessels and nerves of the same name.

The **fossa for the lacrimal sac** grooves the anterior part of the lacrimal bone and the posterior part of the frontal process of the maxilla ; its margins are called the **lacrimal crests** ; the anterior crest is part of the medial margin of the orbit ; the posterior crest gives attachment to the pars lacrimalis of the orbicularis oculi muscle. The upper end of the suture between the two bones is called the **dacryon** [δάκρυον (dakryon) = *lacrima* = a tear].

Norma Occipitalis

The **back of the skull** is markedly convex and has the outline of a wide arch ; the arch is widest usually at the level of the parietal eminences. The bones seen are portions of the two parietal bones, a portion of the occipital, and the mastoid portion of the temporal bone and its mastoid process, which are visible at the lower corner on each side. The parts already seen on the top of the skull but seen again in the back are the parietal eminences, the posterior part of the sagittal suture, the parietal foramina, the lambda, and the lambdoid suture, which is now seen in the whole of its extent.

From the lower end of the lambdoid suture, on each side, the *occipito-mastoid suture* descends between the occipital bone and the mastoid temporal. The **mastoid foramen** is the aperture seen in the suture or on the mastoid temporal near the suture, and it varies in size from a pin point to a match ; it passes through the skull wall and opens internally in the posterior cranial fossa into the groove for the sigmoid venous sinus ; it transmits an emissary vein that connects the sinus with the veins on the outside of the head, and a small branch of the occipital artery ; it is at the level of the external auditory meatus and about three finger-breadths behind it.

The **external occipital protuberance** is the projection—usually well marked— in the median plane, at the lower part of the back of the skull, about midway between the lambda and the foramen magnum. It is easily felt in the living person immediately above the nape of the neck, and is a useful landmark. If two protuberances are felt there, one below the other, the lower one is the normal protuberance. The central point of the protuberance is called the **inion**. The **superior nuchal line** is the blunt, curved ridge that arches laterally from the protuberance. The protuberance and the right and left superior nuchal lines mark the boundary between the back of the head and the back of the neck [ἰνίον (inion)=back of head or nape of neck ; *nucha* =nape of neck]. The part of the skull seen in perspective below the protuberance and the superior nuchal lines belongs to the lower surface of the skull.

In some skulls a curved ridge is seen immediately above the superior nuchal line ; it is called the *highest nuchal line*, and gives attachment to the tendinous sheet in the scalp named the epicranial aponeurosis [galea aponeurotica, from *galea* = a helmet].

In most skulls the boss or most bulging part of the back of the head is not at the protuberance, but is a little above it. The degree of bulging of the occipital bone above the nuchal lines varies with the size and shape of the occipital lobes of the brain, and may be unequal on the two sides.

The **lambda** is situated between two and three inches above the protuberance. In many heads it can be felt by the finger tip as an apparent depression, owing to the prominence of the apical part of the occipital bone ; it overlies the interval between the two halves of the brain a little behind the cleft in the brain called the parieto-occipital sulcus.

Norma Lateralis

The **side of the skull** is divisible into two parts : a larger part above and behind ; a smaller part below and in front. The smaller part belongs to the face, and is very uneven. The larger part is the brain-case ; it is convex and ovoid.

Many of the parts seen already when the posterior and the upper and the anterior aspects of the skull were examined, are seen again in the lateral aspect. Identify again the superior nuchal line, the lambdoid suture, the occipito-mastoid suture, the mastoid foramen, the parietal eminence, the coronal suture, the frontal eminence, the superciliary arch, the bony external nose, the maxilla, the zygomatic bone, the margins of the orbit, and the zygomatic process of the frontal bone. The following parts are now to be looked for.

The **temporal line** is a long, curved ridge that begins at the zygomatic process of the frontal bone. From there it curves upwards and slightly medially and then arches backwards across the frontal bone along the lateral margin of the forehead ; then backwards over the parietal bone, passing immediately below the parietal eminence ; having passed the parietal eminence it bends downwards and slightly forwards, and it ends by joining a blunt, prominent ridge called the **supra-mastoid crest** ; that crest is situated on the squamous temporal near its junction with the mastoid temporal. The anterior part of the temporal line is easily felt in the living head above the zygomatic process of the frontal

bone, between the forehead and the temple. Its middle part is usually represented by two lines—an upper and a lower—about half an inch apart; the bone
between those lines is often more polished than that above and below, and if
the lines are indistinct they can often be identified as the margins of a smooth
strip along the upper part of the side of the skull. The posterior part of the
line is frequently very indistinct. [*Tempora* = the temples, from *tempus* = time:
grey hairs appear first in the temples.]

The **temporal fossa** is the wide space outlined by the temporal line and

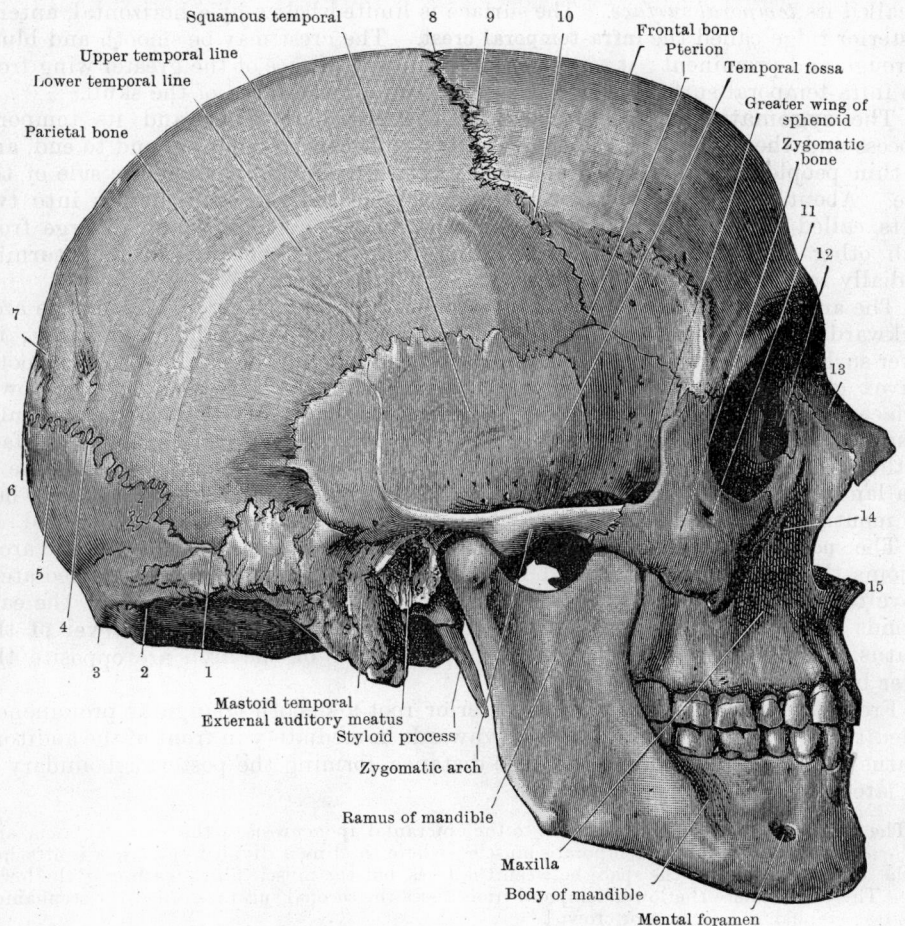

FIG. 138.—THE SIDE OF THE SKULL.

Red : parietal ; zygomatic ; nasal.   **Blue** : occipital ; sphenoid ; lacrimal ; mandible.
Uncoloured : temporal ; frontal ; ethmoid ; maxilla.

1. Asterion.	6. Lambda.	11. Zygomatico-facial foramen.
2. Superior nuchal line.	7. Obelion.	12. Fossa for lacrimal sac.
3. External occipital protuberance.	8. Bregma.	13. Nasal bone.
4. Lambdoid suture.	9. Coronal suture.	14. Infra-orbital foramen.
5. Occipital bone.	10. Stephanion.	15. Anterior nasal spine.

the zygomatic arch. Parts of four bones are seen in the **floor** of the fossa :
(1) the lower part of the *parietal* bone ; (2) the *squamous* part of the *temporal*
bone, below the parietal bone and united to it by a curved suture called the
squamous suture ; (3) a small part of the *frontal* bone, in the upper and anterior
part of the fossa ; (4) a part of the *greater wing of the sphenoid*, below the frontal
and in front of the squamous temporal. In the anterior part of the fossa the
four bones are so close together that a small circle, the size of a sixpence or a
shilling, would include portions of them all ; the region enclosed by such a circle

is called the **pterion**, because one of the pairs of Hermes' wings was attached to the corresponding part of his head-piece.   [πτέρυξ (pteryx)= a wing].

In an adult male skull, the centre of the pterion is 30 mm. behind the zygomatic process of the frontal bone and at a rather higher level (10 mm.).   It is a region made much use of as a guiding point when the position of deeper structures and their relations to the surface of the head are being explained.   In many skulls sutural bones are present in the region of the pterion.

The part of the greater wing of the sphenoid which is seen in the temporal fossa is called its *temporal surface*.   The surface is limited below by a horizontal, antero-posterior ridge called the **infra-temporal crest**.   The crest may be smooth and blunt or rough and prominent ; it separates the temporal surface of the greater wing from the infra-temporal surface, which is seen on the lower surface of the skull.

The **zygomatic arch** is formed by the zygomatic bone and its temporal process and the zygoma of the temporal bone ; it can be felt from end to end, and in thin people it stands out prominently between the temple and the side of the face.   About an inch in front of the auditory meatus the arch divides into two parts, called the **anterior** and **posterior roots** of the zygoma, which diverge from each other—the posterior root extending backwards, the anterior root turning medially towards the side of the skull.

The **anterior root** is easily found if one traces the lower border of the arch backwards ; it is broad and its two surfaces look upwards and downwards ; its lower surface is convex and is continuous, at the side of the skull, with a smooth, convex eminence, called the **eminentia articularis**, which is seen on the lower surface of the skull in the front of a smooth concavity called the **articular fossa** [fossa mandibularis] (Fig. 139).   The lateral end of the lower surface of the root is called the **tubercle of the root of the zygoma**, and is made use of as a landmark ; it is felt immediately in front of the head of the mandible when the mouth is shut, and immediately above the head when the mouth is opened.

The **posterior root** is continuous with the upper border of the zygomatic arch. It joins the side of the skull and is continued backwards as a ridge immediately above the external auditory meatus, and can be felt through the skin of the ear ; it ends by joining the supra-mastoid crest immediately behind the level of the meatus.   The posterior root and the upper border of the arch are opposite the lower border of the brain.

From the lower surface of the posterior root a smooth triangular prominence, called the **post-glenoid tubercle**, juts downwards immediately in front of the auditory meatus, and extends medially for some distance, forming the posterior boundary of the lateral part of the articular fossa.

The **temporal line** gives attachment to the epicranial aponeurosis, to the temporal fascia, and to the uppermost fibres of the temporalis muscle ; where the line is divided, the fascia is attached to the upper line and to the space between the lines, but the muscle fibres reach only the lower line.   The point where the lower temporal line crosses the coronal suture is called the **stephanion** [στέφανος (stephanos) = a circle or crown].

The **temporal fossa** contains the temporalis muscle, the middle and deep temporal vessels, the deep temporal nerves, the zygomatico-temporal branch of the zygomatic nerve, and a quantity of fat—all under cover of the temporal fascia ; and the chief structures on the surface of the fascia are the superficial temporal vessels, the auriculo-temporal nerve, and the temporal branches of the facial nerve.

The depth and width of the fossa depend, in a measure, on the size of the temporal muscle, which is proportional to the size and weight of the mandible.   The anterior and lower part of the fossa is much the deepest part and has an *anterior wall*, which separates it from the orbit ; the anterior wall is formed by the zygomatic process of the frontal, the frontal process of the zygomatic, and sometimes by the greater wing of the sphenoid where it articulates with that process of the zygomatic bone.   On the part of the wall formed by the zygomatic bone there is a small aperture, called the **zygomatico-temporal foramen**, which transmits the zygomatico-temporal nerve, accompanied by a small branch of the lacrimal artery.   The posterior border of the frontal process of the zygomatic bone gives attachment to the temporal fascia, and it shows a slight fulness or tubercle called the *marginal tubercle* ; the point where the posterior border of the frontal process joins the upper border of the zygomatic arch is called the **jugal point**.

The *floor* of the fossa gives origin to the temporalis muscle, and is limited below by the infra-temporal crest of the sphenoid, by the roots of the zygoma, and by a short, horizontal ridge on the squamous temporal between the anterior root and the infra-temporal crest ; that ridge separates the temporal surface of the squamous temporal from a small triangular area—its infra-temporal surface—which forms part of the roof of the infra-temporal fossa. The part of the floor formed by the greater wing sometimes shows grooves for the deep temporal arteries; and the part of the floor above the auditory meatus shows a long and narrow vertical groove for the middle temporal artery.

To find the centre of the **pterion** in the living head held in the proper position (p. 135), draw (1) a line horizontally backwards from the zygomatic process of the frontal bone for 30 mm., and (2) a line straight upwards from the posterior end of the first line for 10 mm. The pterion is opposite the point where the anterior branch of the middle meningeal artery is deeply imbedded in a groove on the inner side of the skull wall and is most liable to injury, and it is opposite the point on the brain where the stem of the lateral sulcus breaks up into its three rami.

The suture between the two constituent bones of the **zygomatic arch** runs obliquely from above downwards and backwards.

The *upper* border of the zygomatic arch—thin, sharp, and nearly horizontal—is formed chiefly by the zygoma, and gives attachment to the temporal fascia. The *lower* border, formed chiefly by the zygomatic bone, is thicker and rougher and extends much farther forwards, but not so far back; it slopes downwards as it is traced forwards, for the arch is much deeper in front than behind; the lower border gives origin to the masseter muscle, which arises also from the *deep* surface of the arch, while the *superficial* surface is subcutaneous. The **tubercle of the root of the zygoma** gives attachment to the temporo-mandibular ligament. The **anterior root** is not only continuous with the eminentia articularis but also forms part of it. The **posterior root** and the **supra-mastoid crest** give attachment to the temporal fascia.

A small portion of the squamous temporal lies below and behind the supra-mastoid crest. The anterior part of that portion sends downwards a pointed extension, called the **post-auditory process** (Fig. 165), which forms the upper part of the posterior wall of the external auditory meatus.

The *post-glenoid tubercle* corresponds to a prominent process developed in some mammals to prevent backward displacement of the mandible.

The **supra-meatal triangle** is a small (and often inconspicuous) depression below the posterior root of the zygoma, immediately behind the upper margin of the external auditory meatus. Although small, it is very important, for the tympanic antrum lies about half an inch directly medial to it. The tympanic antrum is a cavity in the temporal bone, and often has to be opened into when diseased; the road to it is through the supra-meatal triangle, the position of which, therefore, has to be accurately known. If the depression of the triangle is fairly well marked, one may be able to feel it in the living head by pulling the ear vigorously forwards and downwards, and pressing with the finger-tip immediately above and behind the meatus.

The entire **external auditory meatus** is about 25 mm. long, but only the medial, bony part of it is left in a dried skull; the lateral part is made of cartilage, and has been removed during maceration. The bony part is a tunnel about 15 mm. long. Its *inferior wall* and the greater part of the *anterior* and *posterior walls* are formed by the curled lateral half of the *tympanic plate*; the *upper wall* and small adjoining parts of the anterior and posterior walls are formed by the squamous temporal. The *medial end* of the meatus is closed up during life with a tense, vibratile membrane, called the **tympanic membrane,** which separates the meatus from the tympanic cavity or **middle ear** and forms the greater part of the lateral wall of the middle ear. The tympanic cavity or middle ear or drum of the ear [τύμπανον (tympanon) = a kettledrum] is a cavity in the temporal bone, and is narrow from side to side. The membrane is the drum head, and it, along with the contents of the middle ear, has been removed during maceration, and therefore, when one looks into the meatus, the bony surface seen at the far end is the medial wall of the middle ear (Figs. 141, 143).

The **styloid process**—a slender process about an inch long—projects downwards, forwards, and slightly medially from behind the lower edge of the tympanic plate; it is situated deeply in the interval between the mastoid process and the mandible. It is dealt with more fully when the lower surface of the skull is examined.

The **mastoid part** of the temporal bone lies behind the external meatus, wedged in between the parietal bone, the occipital bone, and the squamous temporal; it is united with the parietal and occipital by sutures, but is continuous with the squamous temporal; the line of fusion is a little below and behind the supra-mastoid crest (Fig. 165), but the crest approximately indicates the position of the junction of the two parts. The lower part of the mastoid temporal juts downwards as the thick, prominent *mastoid process.*

There may be no triangular depression to mark the **supra-meatal triangle** in the skull the student is using, and even a well-marked triangle measures only a few millimetres. The triangle is above and behind the opening of the meatus, close to the meatus, at the meeting of tangents drawn to the upper and posterior margins of the meatus. The *supra-meatal spine*, described as a spicule of bone on the antero-inferior side of the triangle, is seldom present.

The **external auditory meatus** is barely wide enough to admit an ordinary pencil. It passes in a medial direction and slightly forwards; its opening into the middle ear is very oblique, so that the tympanic membrane, which closes the opening, looks downwards and forwards as well as in a lateral direction. The outer orifice also is oblique—the upper margin overhanging the lower—and it is at a slightly higher level than the outer orifice of the cartilaginous part. The parts of the outer orifice formed by the lateral margin of the tympanic plate are rough for the attachment of the cartilage of the auricle; the auricularis posterior muscle arises from the bone behind the meatus.

In the child the meatus is very short, for the tympanic plate, which forms so much of the meatus, is at birth not a curved *plate* but an incomplete, slender *ring*; in a child, therefore, the tympanic membrane is quite near the surface of the head. In an infant's skull there is a foramen in the floor of the meatus; for, as the ring becomes a plate, ossification is incomplete in its lower part till the fifth year. Occasionally the foramen persists in the adult.

The meatus as a whole is described in the chapter on Organs of Sense; the student is liable to get misleading ideas about the meatus if he studies the osseous portion apart from the cartilaginous portion.

The **medial wall of the tympanic cavity**, seen when one looks into the meatus, is uneven, and has about its middle a white bulging called the **promontory**. If the meatus is fairly wide, and the skull is tilted this way and that, a little hole may be seen above the posterior part of the promontory; it is called the **fenestra vestibuli**, because it leads into a part of the internal ear named the *vestibule*. During life the footpiece of the auditory ossicle called the *stapes* or stirrup fits into it. [*Fenestra* = a window.]

The **tympano-mastoid fissure**, which transmits the auricular branch of the vagus nerve, is a narrow slit between the posterior part of the lateral margin of the tympanic plate and the front of the mastoid temporal. In many skulls the tympanic plate is so closely applied to the mastoid that the fissure is represented by a minute foramen just large enough to emit the nerve.

The mastoid portion of the temporal bone or **mastoid temporal** is more or less triangular in outline, the apical part being the mastoid process. Anteriorly it fuses with the squamous temporal a little behind and below the *supra-mastoid crest*, and, below that, it is closely related to the tympanic plate. Posteriorly it articulates with the occipital bone. Its upper border or base articulates with the truncated, postero-inferior angle of the parietal bone. The point, at the lateral angle of the occipital bone, where the lambdoid, parieto-mastoid, and occipito-mastoid sutures meet together, is called the **asterion** [ἀστήρ (astēr) = a star]; the superior nuchal line of the occipital bone, when well marked, reaches the asterion. In skulls in which the supra-mastoid crest is not a mere curved ridge but is a broad, blunt, prominent elevation, there is a depression behind the crest in the angle between the squamous temporal and the base of the mastoid temporal. Note that, in the living head, the depression is immediately behind the top of the root of the auricle—a full inch away from the meatus—and is not to be mistaken for the supra-meatal triangle; it is directly opposite the sigmoid venous sinus, immediately below its commencement.

The **mastoid process** juts down from the mastoid temporal, and is felt as a prominence behind the lower part of the auricle. It is opposite the foramen magnum, and a line drawn from one mastoid process to the other passes immediately below the foramen. It is absent at birth; it is small in a child, for it does not begin to appear till the second year and is not fully developed till after puberty; it is variable in size in the adult, and is usually larger in men than in women.

In the adult, the mastoid temporal (including the mastoid process) is permeated with small air spaces called the **mastoid air-cells**. The cells are diverticula from the tympanic antrum that replace the marrow and diploë in the mastoid temporal, and they may extend into adjoining parts of the petrous and squamous. They begin to develop at or shortly before birth. They increase in number and size slowly, and do not extend into the mastoid process till shortly before puberty; but at puberty they begin to enlarge rapidly and reach their full size in a year or two. They remain in communication with the tympanic antrum, and, like it, they are lined with a thin muco-endosteum which is continuous with the mucous lining of the tympanum and is covered with simple, flat epithelium. Occasionally in the adult the cells are few in number or are absent, the bone being diploëtic or even quite dense; on the other hand, the cells may extend to the mastoid process during childhood.

The sterno-mastoid muscle is inserted into a strip that extends from the tip of the mastoid process to the asterion and then includes the lateral third of the superior nuchal line; the splenius capitis into a strip immediately below that for the sterno-mastoid; the longissimus capitis into the back of the root of the mastoid process; and the posterior belly of the digastric arises from the well-marked groove, called the **mastoid notch**, at the medial side of the root of the mastoid process.

The **infra-temporal fossa** (Fig. 139) is the open space behind the maxilla; it communicates with the temporal fossa through a wide opening under cover of the zygomatic arch. Its *anterior wall*—full and rounded—is the posterior surface of the maxilla. The lowest part of that surface, behind the last molar tooth, is the **tuberosity of the maxilla.** (The *molar* teeth or grinders are the hindermost three teeth in a full set of eight a side.) Above the posterior surface of the maxilla, between it and the greater wing of the sphenoid, there is the horizontal cleft, called the **inferior orbital fissure,** by which the infra-temporal fossa communicates with the orbit, where the fissure has been seen already (pp. 144 and 145).

The greater part of the *roof* of the fossa is a large, fairly flat surface of bone already pointed out as the *infra-temporal surface* of the greater wing of the sphenoid; the lateral margin of the surface is the **infra-temporal crest,** which also has been referred to already (p. 148).

The *medial wall* of the fossa is the *lateral pterygoid plate.* This plate is thin and wide, and is set nearly perpendicularly behind the maxilla. Between its upper part and the upper part of the maxilla there is a narrow V-shaped cleft, called the **pterygo-maxillary fissure,** whose upper end joins the inferior orbital fissure at almost a right angle. A large artery, called the maxillary artery, passes out of the infra-temporal fossa through the pterygo-maxillary fissure into the *pterygo-palatine fossa.*

The **pterygo-palatine fossa** is the small, confined space one sees immediately beyond the pterygo-maxillary fissure. If a pin or a match is passed through the upper part of the fissure into the fossa, and onwards through the fossa, it appears in the nasal cavity. The hole in the medial wall of the fossa through which the pin enters the nose is called the **spheno-palatine foramen.**

The **infra-temporal fossa** is a roomy space containing the two pterygoid muscles, the spheno-mandibular ligament, the pterygoid venous plexus, the maxillary artery (first and second parts) and its branches, the mandibular nerve and its branches, and the chorda tympani nerve —all imbedded in a quantity of fat and lying under cover of the tendon of the temporalis, the coronoid process, and the ramus of the mandible and the masseter muscle. The coronoid process and the ramus constitute a *lateral wall* of the fossa; the temporalis tendon is inserted into the process; the masseter lies on the lateral surface of the process and the ramus, being inserted into the lateral surface of the ramus. [μασητήρ (masētēr)=a chewer.]

The *anterior wall* of the fossa (*i.e.* the posterior surface of the maxilla, ending inferiorly in the maxillary tuberosity) presents, about its middle, two or three small holes which are the upper ends of the **dental canals** [canales alveolares] through which vessels and nerves descend to the molar teeth of the upper jaw.

The *roof* of the fossa is chiefly the infra-temporal surface of the greater wing of the sphenoid, and partly also the infra-temporal surface of the squamous temporal, *i.e.* a small triangular area that lies in front of the medial part of the eminentia articularis. In the infra-temporal surface of the sphenoid, close to its posterior border, there are two holes, called the **foramen ovale** and **foramen spinosum,** which will be considered with the lower surface of the skull (p. 156).

The *medial wall* is the lateral pterygoid plate and a narrow strip of bone, belonging to the tubercle of the palatine bone, which is wedged in between the lower part of the plate and the maxilla; very often, however, the strip is so closely united to the bones between which it lies that it cannot be distinguished, and the lower part of the plate appears to be fused with the maxilla.

The **pterygo-palatine fossa** is a small space situated *below* the apex of the orbit, bounded *anteriorly* by the maxilla, *posteriorly* by the common root of the pterygoid process and greater wing of the sphenoid bone, and *medially* by the perpendicular plate of the palatine bone, which separates it from the cavity of the nose. The fossa is filled with fat in which there lie the third part of the maxillary artery and its branches, corresponding veins, the maxillary nerve, and the spheno-palatine ganglion and its branches.

The fossa communicates with the infra-temporal fossa by the **pterygo-maxillary fissure,** through which the maxillary artery enters it and the maxillary nerve leaves it. It is on a level with the zygomatic arch immediately below the jugal point, about two inches distant from the side of the head. In intractable neuralgia of the branches of the maxillary nerve a needle conveying analgesic fluid may be passed through the contents of the infra-temporal fossa into the pterygo-palatine fossa to reach the maxillary nerve.

The following apertures (several of which will be referred to more fully later), open into or out of the pterygo-palatine fossa: (1) the pterygo-maxillary fissure; (2) the inferior orbital fissure, through the posterior end of which the fossa communicates with the apical part of the orbit; (3) the greater palatine canal [canalis pterygo-palatinus], descending to the posterior corner of the bony palate; (4) the foramen rotundum, passing backwards into the middle cranial fossa; (5) the pterygoid canal, passing backwards through the root of the pterygoid process; (6) the palatino-vaginal canal [canalis pharyngeus], passing backwards and medially in the roof of the nose; (7) the spheno-palatine foramen.

The **spheno-palatine foramen** is in the medial wall of the fossa and is bounded by the spheno-palatine notch and the lower surface of the body of the sphenoid. It opens into the superior meatus of the cavity of the nose immediately above the posterior end of the middle concha, but during life is closed up by the mucous membrane. It transmits the spheno-palatine vessels and the long and short spheno-palatine nerves from the spheno-palatine ganglion. The foramen can be identified in the dried skull if a match is pushed onwards through the pterygo-palatine fossa into the nose, where one can see it by looking through the posterior aperture of that side; the foramen is large and round, but by frequent examination the thin bone around it may have been broken down, so that it may be a large opening with jagged margins.

Norma Basalis

When the skull is turned upside down for the examination of the **lower surface** of its base [basis cranii externa], many of the parts seen already from the other aspects or noted in connection with the individual bones of the skull are seen again, and those parts should be identified at once:—

The *foramen magnum*; the *basilar part* of the occipital bone in front, and the *occipital condyles* at the sides of the foramen. The *mastoid process*; the *styloid process*, in front of and medial to the mastoid process, may be broken off and only its root remain; the *tympanic plate*, in front of and above the styloid process, and forming a great part of the walls of the external auditory meatus. (The skull under examination is upside down, but in whatever position the skull is held all the terms, *above, upper*, etc., are used as if it was in its proper upright position.) The *zygomatic arch*; the *posterior root* of the zygoma extending backwards; the *anterior root* bent in a medial direction and continuous with the *eminentia articularis*, which is the anterior boundary of the *articular fossa*. The *infra-temporal surface* of the greater wing of the sphenoid, forming the greater part of the area in front of and medial to the eminentia articularis; the *infra-temporal crest* at the lateral margin of the infra-temporal surface; the *inferior orbital fissure* at the anterior margin of that surface; the *pterygoid process* and its *lateral* and *medial plates*, projecting downwards from the medial margin of that surface. The *posterior bony aperture of the nose*—the large oval opening at the medial side of the pterygoid process, separated from the aperture of the other side by the *vomer*. The *bony palate*, i.e. the large area of bone below and in front of the two apertures, bounded in front and at the sides by the *alveolar processes* of the two maxillæ.

The parts named in the foregoing paragraph are fairly large and easily identified, but, besides them, the lower surface of the skull abounds with smaller foramina, processes, etc., so that it is more difficult to learn than any other surface of the skull. The surface is so uneven and its component bones so interlock with one another that it does not lend itself readily to a natural subdivision into well-defined areas which would simplify description, and an attempt to subdivide it may only add new elements to the puzzle. The surface is naturally subdivided into a right and a left half; and a line drawn from one eminentia articularis to the other divides it into an anterior and a posterior part—though it is convenient to describe one or two points that lie behind that line along with points that lie in front of it, and *vice versa*.

Anterior Region of Lower Surface of Skull

In the middle in front there is the *bony palate*, bounded anteriorly and at the sides by the *alveolar processes*.

The **alveolar processes** of the two maxillæ are united to make a thick horseshoe-shaped ridge which carries the upper teeth. If the teeth have fallen out after death, the lower margin of each alveolar process exhibits a row of **sockets** for the roots of the teeth. The part of the margin behind the last molar tooth is called the **maxillary tuberosity**; it is not well developed till the third molar (the wisdom tooth) has erupted. If the teeth are all in place there are sixteen of them. On each side, beginning in front, there are two incisors, one canine, two premolars and three molars. If the teeth have fallen out after death there is a row of sockets, all single except those for the molar teeth (see p. 191). The walls of the sockets for teeth that have been removed some time before death are absorbed, and the corresponding part of the alveolar process is then nearly flush with the bony palate.

The **bony palate** [palatum durum] is the skeleton of the hard palate ; in lies in the roof of the mouth and, at the same time, in the floor of the nose. It is formed of the palatine processes of the two maxillæ anteriorly, and the horizontal plates of the two palatine bones posteriorly. Those four subdivisions are united by a transverse suture and a median longitudinal suture. At the anterior end of the longitudinal suture, behind the incisor teeth, there is a small pit called the **incisive fossa.**

The posterior margin of the bony palate is free and sharp, and the soft palate is attached to it ; from its middle a pointed process, called the **posterior nasal spine,** juts backwards. At each of the posterior corners of the bony palate, opposite the root of the last molar tooth, there is a hole almost wide enough to admit a match ; it is called the **greater palatine foramen** and is the lower end of the greater palatine canal [canalis pterygo-palatinus], the upper end of which opens into the pterygo-palatine fossa (p. 151).

The sides of the **alveolar processes** are covered with mucous membrane, and their free margins give attachment to the gums.

The **bony palate** is covered with the muco-periosteum of the roof of the mouth ; it is rough and pitted—especially anteriorly—by the numerous palatine glands that lie under cover of the mucous lining ; and the small vascular foramina, scattered here and there, are more numerous at the anterior part. The **incisive fossa,** situated behind the incisor sockets, is a pit into which four small foramina open. These four *incisive foramina* are not always easily seen, especially if the fossa is narrow and deep. They are the lower ends of a pair of divided incisive canals that lead up into the cavity of the nose (p. 178). Two of them are in the median plane, one in front of the other, and other two more laterally ; they are designated therefore *median* and *lateral.* The right and left long spheno-palatine nerves [nn. naso-palatini] descend from the nose through the median foramina—the left nerve in front of the right. The terminal branch of the greater palatine artery ascends to the nose through a lateral foramen.

If the skull is that of a young person, a faint irregular suture may be seen extending from the back of the incisive fossa towards the interval between the canine tooth and the lateral incisor tooth. That suture cuts off a part of the maxilla called the **pre-maxilla** ; the pre-maxilla carries the incisor teeth ; originally it is separate from the maxilla, and in some animals it remains a separate bone.

The palatine aponeurosis and part of the palato-pharyngeus muscle are attached to the *posterior border* of the bony palate, and the musculus uvulæ arises from the **posterior nasal spine.** A millimetre or two in front of the posterior border there is a ridge, called the **palatine crest,** into which part of the outspread tendon of the tensor palati is inserted ; the crest may be blunt or sharp, and its lateral part is immediately behind the greater palatine foramen.

The **greater palatine foramen** is the lower end of the **greater palatine canal.** If a pin is pushed up through the foramen and canal, its point appears in the pterygo-palatine fossa, where the canal begins. The canal lies in the posterior part of the side wall of the nasal cavity, between the maxilla and the perpendicular plate of the palatine bone. The greater palatine vessels from the third part of the maxillary vessels and the greater palatine nerve from the spheno-palatine ganglion descend through the canal and foramen and then run forwards in the poorly marked groove close to the alveolar process ; they are the chief supply of the palate.

The **lesser palatine foramina** are the small holes behind the palatine crest and greater palatine foramen ; there are usually two, but one of them may be so small that it almost escapes notice. The bone on which they are situated is the *tubercle* of the palatine bone [processus pyramidalis]. They lead up into the **lesser palatine canals,** which are branches of the greater palatine canal and convey the lesser palatine branches of the greater palatine vessels and nerve to the tissues of the soft palate.

Posterior bony apertures of the nose [Choanæ].—These are the two oval openings above the posterior edge of the bony palate—each of them large enough to admit the tips of two fingers. They are separated from each other by the posterior edge of the *vomer* ; through them the cavities of the nose open into the uppermost part of the cavity of the pharynx.

By looking into a posterior aperture one can get a partial view of the walls of a **nasal cavity,** and the following parts should be identified : The posterior part of the *floor,* formed by the horizontal plate of the palatine bone. The posterior part of the *septum,* formed by the vomer. The posterior part of the *roof,* formed chiefly by the body of the sphenoid. The posterior part of the *side wall,* formed by the medial pterygoid plate and, in front of that, the perpendicular plate of the palatine bone; the three nasal conchæ are seen projecting into the cavity from

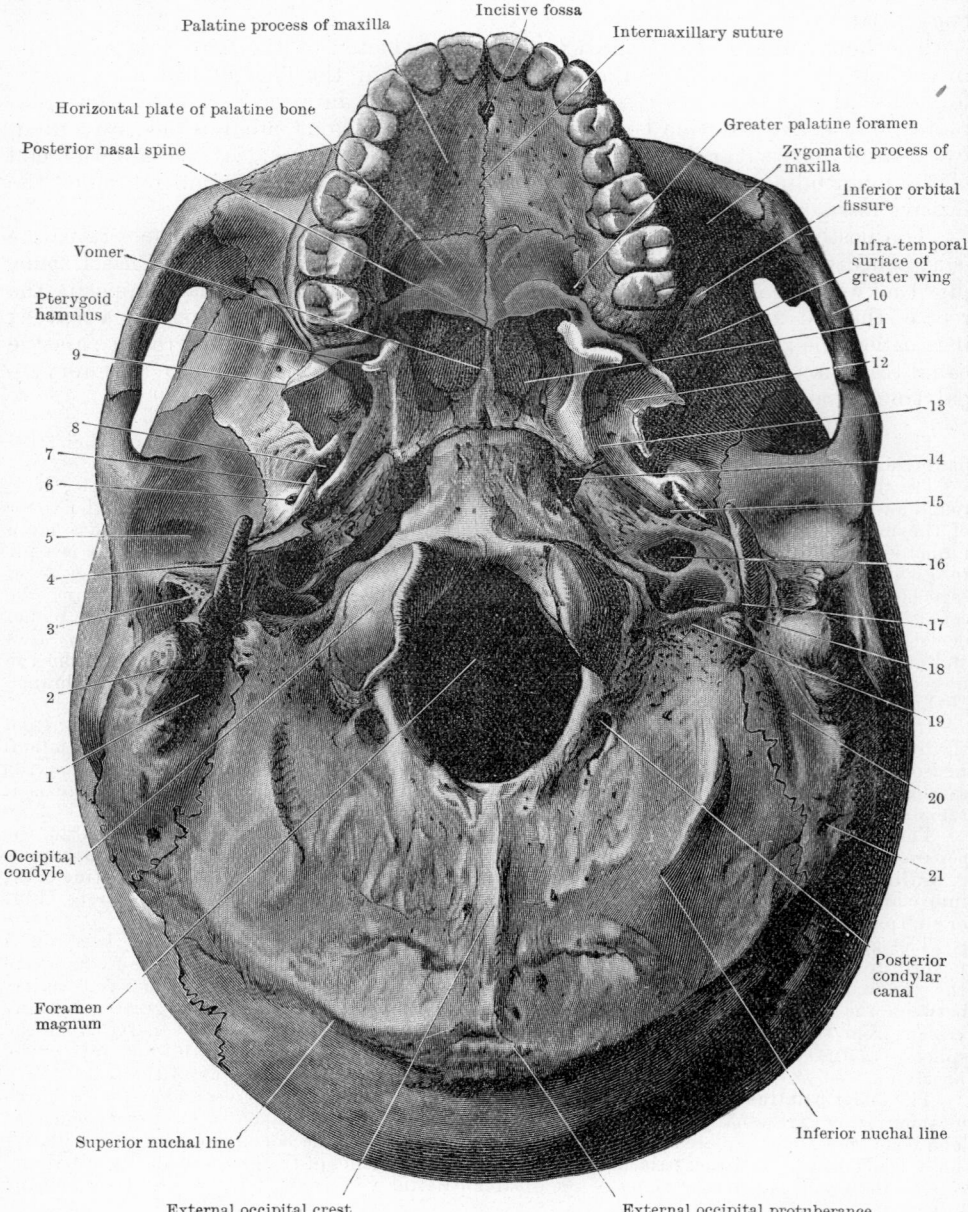

Palatine process of maxilla
Incisive fossa
Intermaxillary suture
Horizontal plate of palatine bone
Greater palatine foramen
Posterior nasal spine
Zygomatic process of maxilla
Inferior orbital fissure
Vomer
Infra-temporal surface of greater wing
Pterygoid hamulus
10
11
9
12
8
13
7
14
6
15
5
16
4
17
3
18
2
19
1
20
Occipital condyle
21
Foramen magnum
Posterior condylar canal
Superior nuchal line
Inferior nuchal line
External occipital crest
External occipital protuberance

FIG. 139.—LOWER SURFACE OF BASE OF SKULL.

Red: occipital; vomer; maxilla; zygomatic. Blue: palatine; temporal. Uncoloured: sphenoid; parietal

1. Mastoid notch.
2. Mastoid process.
3. External auditory meatus.
4. Styloid process.
5. Articular fossa.
6. Foramen spinosum.
7. Spine of the sphenoid.
8. Foramen ovale.
9. Lateral pterygoid plate.
10. Zygomatic arch.
11. Left posterior aperture of nose.
12. Pterygoid fossa.
13. Scaphoid fossa.
14. Foramen lacerum.
15. Opening of pharyngo-tympanic tube.
16. Carotid canal.
17. Jugular fossa.
18. Stylo-mastoid foramen.
19. Jugular process of occipital.
20. Groove for occipital artery.
21. Mastoid foramen.

the side wall, in front of the pterygoid plate; the inferior and middle conchæ have been identified already through the anterior aperture; their posterior parts are seen here, and the **spheno-palatine foramen** opens into the cavity immediately above the posterior end of the middle concha; the superior concha lies only a little distance above the posterior part of the middle concha, and is very much smaller—may, indeed, be no more than a sharp ridge of bone.

Each **posterior aperture of the nose** is bounded inferiorly by the bony palate, medially by the vomer, laterally by the medial pterygoid plate, and superiorly by the lower surface of the body of the sphenoid, which is, however, concealed by two thin pieces of bones, called the ala of the vomer and the vaginal process of the medial pterygoid plate, and they form the actual boundary. The upper boundary of the aperture is the junction of the roof of the nasal cavity with the roof of the nasal part of the pharynx.

The *ala of the vomer* spreads in a lateral direction from the upper end of the vomer and covers the part of the lower surface of the body of the sphenoid near the median plane. The *vaginal process* is a thin sheet of bone that extends in a medial direction from the upper end of the medial pterygoid plate; near the plate it is fused with the lower surface of the body of the sphenoid, but its medial part is free and its medial edge articulates with the edge of the ala of the vomer. In some skulls the upper lips of the articulating margins are separated by a linear interval, called the *vomero-vaginal canal* [canalis basipharyngeus], through which a small branch of the spheno-palatine artery runs backwards to the roof of the pharynx; the canal is unimportant, and is the occasionally persisting one of several vascular canals that are present in this neighbourhood in intra-uterine life. Anteriorly the vaginal process is overlapped by the *sphenoidal process of the palatine bone*, which bends in a medial direction, covering part of the lower surface of the body of the sphenoid in the roof of the nasal cavity, and reaching the edge of the ala of the vomer. On the lower surface of the vaginal process, near the pterygoid plate, there is a narrow, but fairly well marked, antero-posterior groove; the groove, when traced forwards, leads to a small foramen, which is the posterior end of the palatino-vaginal canal.

The **palatino-vaginal canal** [canalis pharyngeus] is a narrow, unimportant canal situated in the roof of the nasal cavity between the body of the sphenoid and the sphenoidal process of the palatine bone. Its anterior end opens into the pterygo-palatine fossa; its posterior end opens on the vaginal process in the roof of the posterior aperture of the nose. The pharyngeal branches of the spheno-palatine ganglion and of the third part of the maxillary vessels pass backwards through the canal and along the groove on the vaginal process to supply the muco-periosteum of the roof of the pharynx. In a much-handled skull the sphenoidal process is often broken away and the canal is destroyed.

The **pterygoid processes** are a pair of large processes that project downwards from the roots of the greater wings of the sphenoid bone. Each of them stands at the side of a posterior aperture of the nose, behind the maxilla, and separates the aperture from the infra-temporal fossa. It consists of two plates—a lateral and a medial—between which there is an interval, open posteriorly and nearly half an inch wide, called the **pterygoid fossa**.

The **lateral pterygoid plate** is the medial wall of the infra-temporal fossa. The **medial pterygoid plate** is the lateral boundary of the posterior aperture of the nose and also the most posterior part of the side wall of the nasal cavity. The lower end of its posterior border is continued into a slender process, called the **pterygoid hamulus**, which extends downwards, backwards, and in a lateral direction. The hamulus [= a hook] may be a mere stump, but it is usually 5 or 6 mm. long and is curved with its concavity upwards; it is very liable to be broken off in the dried skull. It can be felt, in the living head, by the thumb pressed against the lateral part of the roof of the mouth at the junction of hard palate and soft palate, rather behind the gum. The upper part of the posterior border of the medial pterygoid plate splits into two ridges which enclose a shallow oblong depression, about 3 mm. wide, called the **scaphoid fossa** [σκάφη (scaphē) = anything dug out, a trough, a boat].

The **infra-temporal surface** of the greater wing of the sphenoid is the wide, spreading horizontal surface of bone lateral to the upper end or root of the lateral pterygoid plate. Posteriorly, it extends backwards beyond the level of the lateral plate, and close to its posterior edge there are two holes—a larger and a smaller—set close together and called the foramen ovale and the foramen spinosum; both foramina lead directly up into the middle cranial fossa. The **foramen ovale** is the larger opening and is named from its shape; it lies behind and lateral to the upper end of the lateral pterygoid plate, and it is opposite the tubercle of the root of the zygoma and an inch and a half medial to it. The **foramen spinosum** is behind and lateral to the foramen ovale.

Behind and lateral to the foramen spinosum there is a sharp spur of bone which projects downwards from the posterior angle of the greater wing of the sphenoid. It is called the **spine of the sphenoid**, and gives its name to the foramen spinosum; it is close to the medial end of the eminentia articularis and articular fossa, and varies much in prominence in different skulls; in a few skulls a thin bar of bone stretches from the spine to the lateral pterygoid plate, converting the interval between them into a foramen.

The two **pterygoid plates** extend downwards to a level rather lower than that of the bony palate. Their posterior margins are free and sharp. The upper halves of their anterior borders are united together; the anterior surface of their junction is the posterior wall of the pterygo-palatine fossa, and the posterior surface is the upper part of the floor or anterior wall of the **pterygoid fossa**. The lower halves of the laminæ are quite separate from each other; that is, however, not apparent in the skull, for the tubercle of the palatine bone is wedged in between the maxilla and the lower part of the pterygoid process, filling in the interval between the lower halves of the anterior borders of the pterygoid plates; if the skull is that of a young adult, the Λ-shaped suture between the tubercle and the two plates can be seen in the lower part of the floor of the pterygoid fossa.

The **tubercle of the palatine bone**, though so frequently mentioned, is not of outstanding importance, but the origin of the medial pterygoid muscle cannot be fully understood unless the relations of the tubercle to the pterygoid plates are understood. Three surfaces of the process have now been seen : (1) the uneven surface, showing the lesser palatine foramina, behind the greater palatine foramen and between the lower ends of the two pterygoid plates; (2) an uneven Δ-shaped surface in the floor of the pterygoid fossa, between the lower halves of the two plates; (3) a narrow strip in the infra-temporal fossa, between the lower part of the maxilla and the lower part of the lateral pterygoid plate (p. 151).

The **medial pterygoid plate** is the most posterior bone in the side wall of the nasal cavity; inferiorly a portion of it stands also in the side wall of the nasal part of the pharynx (naso-pharynx), i.e. the uppermost subdivision of the interior of the pharynx; its medial surface is therefore clothed with mucous membrane. The posterior border is thin and sharp, and rather more than half-way up a sharp spur of bone sometimes juts backwards from it; above that spur, the border divides into two ridges which bound the **scaphoid fossa**, the medial margin of which is looked on as the real upper part of the border. The end of the pharyngo-tympanic [auditory] tube, as it opens on the side wall of the naso-pharynx, is closely related to the medial margin of the scaphoid fossa and is supported inferiorly by the spur of bone. The lower or palatine end of the posterior border is continued into the hooklet or **hamulus**, the concavity of which is directed backwards and upwards towards the base of the skull; the *lower* surface of the root of the hamulus is crossed by a groove. The anterior part of the tensor palati muscle arises from the scaphoid fossa, descends along the lateral surface of the medial pterygoid plate, and the slender tendon of the muscle turns at a right angle in a medial direction and forwards, in the groove on the lower surface of the hamulus, and spreads out as it enters the soft palate. The posterior border of the medial plate, in its whole length, gives attachment to the pharyngo-basilar fascia; its lower half or third, together with the hamulus, gives origin to the upper part of the superior constrictor of the pharynx; the tip of the hamulus gives attachment to a fibrous band, called the pterygo-mandibular ligament, which extends to the posterior end of the mylo-hyoid ridge of the mandible and gives origin to most of the remaining fibres of the superior constrictor.

The **lateral pterygoid plate** is wider than the medial plate, and its lower part is slightly bent in a lateral direction. Its posterior border is sharp and very uneven; its surfaces give origin to the pterygoid muscles. The lateral pterygoid muscle has two heads—an upper and a lower. The lower head arises from the lateral surface of the lateral pterygoid plate; the upper head arises from the infra-temporal surface and infra-temporal crest of the sphenoid. The two heads pass backwards, join together, and are inserted chiefly into the front of the neck of the mandible (the mandible should now be placed in position). The medial pterygoid muscle also has two heads—a superficial and a deep. The small, superficial head arises from the tuberosity of the maxilla and the strip of the tubercle of the palatine bone that appears between the maxilla and the lateral pterygoid plate; the large, deep head arises from the medial surface of the lateral pterygoid plate and the surface of the tubercle that appears in the pterygoid fossa; the two heads join and pass downwards and backwards to be inserted into the medial surface of the mandible above and in front of the angle.

The **infra-temporal surface** of the greater wing of the sphenoid is limited in front by the inferior orbital fissure, laterally by the infra-temporal crest, while posteriorly it extends back-wards and ends as the spine of the sphenoid, at the medial side of the articular fossa of the temporal bone. The **spine of the sphenoid** is grooved on its medial side by the chorda tympani nerve, and it gives attachment to (1) the posterior part of the tensor palati muscle, (2) the spheno-mandibular ligament, which stretches to the margin of the mandibular foramen, and (3) the pterygo-spinous ligament—a weak fibrous band that stretches to the posterior border of the lateral pterygoid plate, but may, however, be transformed into a bar of bone.

The **foramen spinosum** is antero-medial to the spine of the sphenoid. It transmits the middle meningeal vessels and sympathetic plexus, an unimportant nerve filament called the nervus spinosus, and lymph vessels from the meninges.

The **foramen ovale** is antero-medial to the foramen spinosum. The only large structure that it transmits is the mandibular nerve, including the motor root of the trigeminal nerve ; but there pass through it also the accessory meningeal artery, small veins connecting the cavernous venous sinus with the pterygoid venous plexus, lymph vessels from the meninges, and, sometimes, the lesser superficial petrosal nerve. The foramen ovale and spinosum began as notches on the posterior edge of the greater wing, and were gradually enclosed in bone.

Very frequently there is a small aperture, called the **emissary sphenoidal foramen,** situated antero-medial to the foramen ovale and close to the scaphoid fossa. It opens directly into the middle cranial fossa and transmits a small emissary vein that connects the cavernous sinus with the pterygoid plexus. In the same neighbourhood there are one or more minute foramina that transmit either emissary or diploic veins. And occasionally there is a very small unnamed hole behind the foramen ovale for the transmission of the lesser superficial petrosal nerve.

Posterior Region of Lower Surface of Skull

There are only three bones in the posterior part of the base of the skull—the occipital bone, and the right and left temporal bones. The **occipital** bone occupies a large part of the region in the middle and posteriorly ; the **temporal** bone is wedged in at the side, between the occipital bone and the greater wing of the sphenoid, and the details of its surface present more difficulties than those of the occipital bone.

The **occipital bone** is divided into four parts which surround the foramen magnum—the *basilar part (basi-occiput)* in front, a *condylar part* at each side, and a large, expanded *squamous part* behind. The four parts are separable at birth, but usually are fused together by the sixth year.

The **foramen magnum** is the large opening in which the medulla oblongata, or lowest subdivision of the brain, becomes continuous with the spinal cord. It is on a level with the mastoid process at the side of the head, and is opposite a point on the back of the neck midway between the external occipital protuberance and the spine of the second cervical vertebra.

The **foramen magnum** is usually ovoid in outline with the narrower part in front, and its antero-posterior diameter varies from 30 to 40 mm. It *contains* the upper end of the spinal cord with its membranes and blood-vessels, the spinal roots of the accessory nerves, the vertebral arteries surrounded by plexuses of sympathetic nerves derived from the inferior cervical ganglia, lymph vessels from the meninges of the brain ; the lowest part of the cerebellum lies in it ; and the membrana tectoria and upper band of the cruciate ligament pass upwards through it to be attached to the upper surface of the basi-occiput in front of the foramen magnum. The posterior atlanto-occipital membrane is attached to the posterior margin of the foramen magnum ; the anterior atlanto-occipital membrane and the apical ligament of the odontoid process to the anterior margin ; the alar ligament to the low tubercle on the medial surface of the occipital condyle on the side of the foramen magnum. The vertebral artery enters the foramen immediately behind the condyle, and sometimes grooves the margin of the foramen. The posterior margin of the foramen is in the same horizontal plane as the bony palate ; and its middle point is called the **opisthion** [ὀπίσθιος (opisthios) = posterior]. The anterior margin is usually a little higher, for the foramen is slightly oblique in white races ; the middle point of the margin is called the **basion**.

The **basilar part** of the occipital bone, or **basi-occiput**, is a wide bar of bone, thin at the margin of the foramen magnum, but thick at its anterior end, where it joins the body of the sphenoid. In youth it is united to the sphenoid by a plate of cartilage, and is fused with the sphenoid after the twenty-fifth year, but the position of their fusion may be indicated by an interrupted transverse depression. At the centre of the lower surface of the basi-occiput, about half an inch in front of the foramen magnum, there is a small elevation called the **pharyngeal tubercle** ; the surface of bone in front of the tubercle is clothed with the muco-periosteum of the roof of the pharynx, and is opposite and at the level of the upper part of the neck of the mandible.

The hole, with jagged edges, seen alongside the anterior part of the basi-occiput, is called the **foramen lacerum** ; it leads directly up into the middle cranial fossa. Look for the pterygoid tubercle and the pterygoid canal on its anterior margin, as seen from below. The *pterygoid tubercle* is a small rounded elevation at the extreme upper end of the medial pterygoid plate. The posterior end of the **pterygoid canal** is on the anterior margin of the foramen—immediately above the tubercle and rather hidden by it—and is only large enough to admit a thick pin ;

in some skulls it is so hidden that it cannot be seen, but a hook or a bent pin enables one to find it. The canal runs forwards through the root of the pterygoid process, and its anterior end opens into the pterygo-palatine fossa. (See also pp. 170 and 171.)

The **pharyngeal tubercle,** in an articulated skeleton, lies directly above the tubercle on the anterior arch of the atlas; the front of the cervical part of the vertebral column is therefore opposite a line drawn downwards and slightly backwards from the side of the neck of the mandible. The tubercle gives insertion to the uppermost bundle of fibres of the superior constrictor of the pharynx, and attachment to a median, fibrous longitudinal band, called the *pharyngeal raphe,* that lies in the posterior wall of the pharynx. The rectus capitis anterior is inserted into an impression on the basi-occiput in front of the occipital condyle, and the longus capitis into an impression lateral to the pharyngeal tubercle and in front of it; the back of the uppermost part of the pharynx is therefore recessed in between the right and left longus capitis muscles, and the prevertebral fascia is attached to a line which curves forwards from behind the pharyngeal tubercle to the front and lateral margins of the impression for the longus capitis.

The basi-occiput, the body of the sphenoid and the ethmoid form what is called the **basi-cranial axis;** a line drawn between the tips of the pterygoid tubercles marks the spheno-occipital junction. Posteriorly, the basicranial axis is wedge-shaped and solid; anteriorly it is thick but is hollow—owing to the sphenoidal and ethmoidal sinuses.

The **condylar parts** of the occipital bone lie at the sides of the anterior half of the foramen magnum, and are so named because they bear the occipital condyles.

The **occipital condyles** are the large, smooth, oblong protuberances that lie at the margins of the foramen magnum. They articulate with the lateral masses of the atlas vertebra, and through them the weight of the head is transmitted to the vertebral column. The nodding movements of the head take place at the joints between the condyles and the atlas. The condyle and the joint are at the level of the mastoid process, and are almost directly opposite it. The articular surface of each condyle is often notched at the sides, and in some skulls the notches meet and divide the articular surface into two parts.

The **condylar fossa** is the depression behind the condyle. In many skulls there is a canal that begins in the fossa, and passes obliquely forwards and upwards into the cranial cavity; it is named the *posterior condylar canal.* The bony wall of the fossa is thin and may have an artificial perforation in it that may be mistaken for the canal, but the artificial opening leads directly up into the cranial cavity, and not obliquely.

The **occipital condyles** lie alongside the anterior part of the foramen magnum. They are placed obliquely, their anterior ends being nearer each other than the posterior ends. The articular surface of each is convex from before backwards and slopes downwards from lateral to medial side. The articular capsule is attached to the margins of the articular surface, and the alar ligament is attached to the medial surface of the condyle.

The **condylar fossa** accommodates the upper part of the back of the lateral mass of the atlas when the head is bent backwards.

The **posterior condylar canal,** when present, passes above the posterior part of the condyle and opens, in the posterior cranial fossa, into (or near) the groove on the upper surface of the jugular process that lodges the lower end of the sigmoid venous sinus. The canal transmits a vein that connects the sinus with the sub-occipital venous plexus.

The external opening of the **anterior condylar canal** [canalis nervi hypoglossi] is above the lateral margin of the anterior part of the condyle; it is usually largely hidden by the condyle, and the skull has therefore to be tilted before the opening is seen. The beginner should not mistake the jugular foramen for it because the foramen chances to catch his eye first. The jugular foramen is a large irregular opening nearly half an inch away from the condyle, and through it one can see into the cranial cavity. The anterior condylar canal is only wide enough to admit a match; it is medial to the jugular foramen and quite close to the condyle; internally, it opens into the cranial cavity a little above the margin of the foramen magnum (p. 173).

The **jugular process** is the part of the occipital bone—about half an inch square—that lies lateral to the posterior half of the condyle. Its anterior border is the posterior margin of the jugular foramen; this border is concave from side to side and the concavity is called the **jugular notch.**

The **anterior condylar canal** passes in a medial direction and backwards above the anterior part of the condyle. The important structure that passes through it is the hypoglossal nerve; but it transmits also a meningeal branch of the ascending pharyngeal artery, veins connecting the meningeal veins and the veins of the medulla oblongata with the pharyngeal venous plexus, and lymph vessels from the meninges.

The **jugular process** is the homologue of the transverse process of a vertebra. It blends medially and posteriorly with the rest of the occipital bone; its anterior margin is free and bounds the **jugular notch**; its lateral margin is united to the petrous temporal by a plate of cartilage which may ossify after the twenty-fifth year; its lower surface is rough, and gives insertion to the rectus capitis lateralis; and the prevertebral fascia is attached to the anterior margin in front of the rectus; its upper surface, in the floor of the posterior cranial fossa, has a broad shallow groove which lodges the lower part of the sigmoid venous sinus.

In some skulls a curved process, called the *intra-jugular process*, projects from the floor of the jugular notch and partially or completely subdivides the jugular foramen. Occasionally a projection, called the *para-mastoid process*, juts downwards from the lateral part of the jugular process, and may be long enough to articulate with the transverse process of the atlas.

The **squamous part** is by far the largest subdivision of the occipital bone. It lies partly in the base and partly in the back of the skull. The *external occipital protuberance* and the *superior nuchal lines*, already examined (p. 146), are the boundary between the base and the back. The part in the base may be comparatively flat, or may be full and rounded, the contour varying with the size and shape of the part of the brain called the cerebellum, which lies on the upper surface of this part of the bone.

The **external occipital crest** is a median ridge that extends from the protuberance to the posterior margin of the foramen magnum; in some skulls it is very poorly marked.

The **inferior nuchal lines** are a pair of faint curved ridges, situated about midway between the foramen magnum and the superior nuchal lines. Each begins about the middle of the external occipital crest and arches in a lateral direction and forwards and downwards towards the side of the occipital bone.

The upper end or border of the ligamentum nuchæ is attached to the **external occipital crest** and **external occipital protuberance**; the protuberance and the medial part of the **superior nuchal line** give attachment to the epicranial aponeurosis [galea aponeurotica] and origin to the uppermost fibres of the trapezius; the lateral part of the line gives origin to the occipital belly of the occipito-frontalis and insertion to part of the sterno-mastoid and of the splenius capitis. The semispinalis capitis is inserted into the medial half of the area between the **superior** and **inferior nuchal lines**; the obliquus capitis superior into the lateral half; the rectus capitis posterior minor into the medial part of the area below or in front of the inferior nuchal line; the rectus posterior major into the lateral part. Though the oblique muscle and the two recti are small, their insertions are wide and in many skulls are mapped out by ridges. Place the atlas and the skull together properly and note the position and the direction taken by the obliquus superior as it passes from the transverse process of the atlas to its insertion into the occipital bone.

All the subdivisions of the **temporal bone** appear in the lower surface of the skull:—the lower end of the *mastoid temporal*; the *tympanic plate*; the lower surface of the *petrous temporal*, medial to the tympanic plate; the *styloid process*, emerging from behind the lower part of the tympanic plate; and the portion of the *squamous temporal* that bears the eminentia articularis and articular fossa, in front of the tympanic plate.

Certain parts that belong to the temporal bone (or placed close alongside it) have been noted already, and are easily identified again. (1) The **eminentia articularis** [tuberculum articulare] medial to the posterior part of the zygomatic arch and continuous with its anterior root; (2) the **articular fossa** [fossa mandibularis] behind the articular eminence; the head of the mandible is in relation with the fossa when the mouth is shut, and is pulled forwards and downwards into relation with the eminentia as the mouth is opened; (3) the **spine of the sphenoid**, medial to the eminence or medial to the fossa; (4) the **post-glenoid tubercle**, in the posterior boundary of the fossa immediately in front of the opening of the external auditory meatus; (5) the **tympanic plate**, behind and below the fossa; (6) the **mastoid process**, behind and below the external auditory meatus; (7) the **mastoid notch**, at the medial side of the root of the mastoid process; (8) the **foramen lacerum**, alongside the anterior part of the basi-occiput, between it and the petrous temporal.

The **mastoid notch** gives origin to the posterior belly of the digastric muscle. Close to the medial side of the notch and parallel with it, the occipital artery runs backwards and in a lateral direction, in contact with the mastoid temporal or with the suture between it and the occipital bone, and usually produces a groove on the bone. The entire absence of a groove indicates that the artery was lower than usual.

The following structures are opposite the mastoid process, *i.e.*, a line connecting the two mastoid processes would pass through or near them : The posterior belly of the digastric, the occipital artery, the posterior part of the rectus lateralis, the vertebral artery, the posterior part of the atlanto-occipital joint, and the upper end of the spinal cord—in that order latero-medially.

The **styloid process** lies deeply in the interval between the mastoid process and the mandible, and intervenes between the parotid gland and the internal jugular vein. It projects downwards, forwards, and medially from the petrous temporal, behind the lower part of the tympanic plate, which partly ensheaths its basal portion. Two ligaments and three muscles are attached to it. The stylo-hyoid ligament stretches from its tip to the hyoid bone ; the stylo-mandibular ligament (which is a thickened part of the fascia that covers the antero-medial surface of the parotid gland) extends from the front of it to the posterior border of the mandible. The stylo-glossus arises from the front of it near the tip ; the stylo-hyoideus, from the postero-lateral surface of the middle third ; the stylo-pharyngeus, from the medial side near the root. The styloid process is ossified in cartilage from two centres—an upper and a lower. The lower part of the process does not fuse with the upper till after puberty, and may remain a separate bone throughout life.

The following parts are now to be looked for :—

The **stylo-mastoid foramen** is the aperture immediately behind the root of the styloid process, between it and the mastoid process, in front of the mastoid notch. It is the lower end of a canal, in the substance of the temporal bone, through which the facial nerve travels on its way from the brain to the exterior of the skull; besides the facial nerve, it transmits the stylo-mastoid branches of the posterior auricular vessels, which pass upwards through it into the temporal bone.

The **jugular foramen** is a large opening with uneven margins situated a little to the medial side of the root of the styloid process, and it leads into the posterior cranial fossa. It is bounded anteriorly by the petrous temporal and posteriorly by the jugular process of the occipital bone.

The largest structure in the jugular foramen is the internal jugular vein, which begins in it as a continuation of the sigmoid venous sinus. The vein is dilated at its commencement and the dilatation is called the *superior bulb* of the internal jugular vein. To accommodate the bulb there is a concavity, called the **jugular fossa**, on the petrous temporal where it forms the antero-lateral wall of the jugular foramen.

The jugular foramen is opposite the external auditory meatus, and is almost at the level of its lower margin. A part of the bone that bounds the jugular fossa forms also the floor of the tympanic cavity or middle ear. That relationship can be verified if one looks at the medial wall of the tympanic cavity through the external meatus, and gauges the position of the floor of the cavity. In middle-ear disease, infection may pass through the bone, and attack the internal jugular vein.

The following parts lie opposite the *external auditory meatus, i.e.* a line drawn from one meatus to the other would pass through them or near them :—the root of the styloid process, the jugular foramen, the anterior condylar canal, the anterior end of the occipital condyle, and the anterior margin of the foramen magnum— in that order latero-medially.

The **jugular foramen** leads upwards and backwards into the cranial cavity, and the structures it transmits will be enumerated more intelligibly when it is examined from inside the skull (p. 175). Sometimes spicules of bone project across the foramen from its margins, and they may divide it into compartments.

The right internal jugular vein is usually larger than the left, and the right jugular foramen and fossa are therefore larger than the left. When the fossa is large there may be very little bony substance between it and the tympanic cavity and antrum, which lie above it.

On the lateral wall of the foramen, in the floor of the jugular fossa, there is a small "pin-point" aperture : it is the medial end of a narrow, horizontal canal, called the **mastoid canaliculus**, which passes through the temporal bone and opens laterally in the tympano-mastoid fissure. The canal is traversed by a slender but important nerve filament called the auricular branch of the vagus. It is not present at birth, but is formed as the growing tympanic plate and mastoid temporal enclose the nerve—which is outside the skull in an infant.

The **carotid canal** is a tunnel in the petrous temporal through which the internal carotid artery travels to reach the cranial cavity. The lower end of the canal is immediately in front of the jugular foramen and fossa, in the lower surface of the petrous temporal; it is a circular or oval opening, wide enough to admit a thin pencil. From this opening the canal leads upwards for a short distance and then, bending to become horizontal, it runs in a medial direction and forwards to open into the foramen lacerum. Since the lower end of the canal is anterior to the jugular foramen, the internal carotid artery, as it enters the bone, is in front of the internal jugular vein.

The lower end of the canal is opposite the anterior margin of the orifice of the external auditory meatus, and the ascending part of the canal lies below and in front of the middle ear and the internal ear; the thudding sound that one hears in the head during moments of excitement or after a spurt of violent exertion is due to the beating of the carotid artery against the bone which separates it from the internal ear.

The anterior margin of the jugular foramen and fossa is separated from the lower opening of the carotid canal by a ridge of bone on which there may be more than one small hole for small vessels that enter the bone. But one of those foramina is the lower end of the **tympanic canaliculus**, through which a small nerve, called the tympanic branch of the glosso-pharyngeal nerve, passes up to enter the tympanic cavity and form the tympanic plexus on its medial wall.

The **carotid canal** transmits the internal carotid artery, the internal carotid plexus of sympathetic nerves derived from the superior cervical ganglion, small veins that connect the cavernous venous sinus with the pharyngeal venous plexus, and lymph vessels from the meninges. On the postero-lateral wall of the canal, immediately above its lower aperture, there are the openings of two very narrow tunnels; they are the **carotico-tympanic canaliculi**, which transmit the tympanic branches of the carotid artery and of the carotid sympathetic plexus.

The **quadrate area** of the petrous temporal is the rough, nearly four-square area medial to and in front of the lower opening of the carotid canal, between that opening and the foramen lacerum. The *antero-lateral border* of the area lies against the posterior border of the greater wing of the sphenoid, *i.e.*, the border immediately behind the foramen ovale and foramen spinosum; the two borders may touch each other or there may be a narrow fissure between them. The *cartilaginous part* of the *pharyngo-tympanic tube* [tuba auditiva] lies along the fissure, or the line of contact, in a shallow groove shared by both the bones. The postero-lateral end of the groove is at the medial side of the spine of the sphenoid, and it is continuous there with two canals in the interior of the temporal bone. These canals are one above the other, and are separated by a thin, bony septum. The lower and wider is the **canal of the pharyngo-tympanic tube**—*i.e.*, the osseous part of the tube—and it passes obliquely into the middle ear or tympanic cavity. If a pin or a hook is run along the groove to its postero-lateral end and pushed onwards, it will pass, usually without difficulty, into the canal; and, if one looks through the external auditory meatus, the point of the hook will be seen in the tympanic cavity. The upper canal is the **canal for the tensor tympani**. That tiny muscle springs chiefly from the cartilage of the tube, runs in the canal above the bony part of the tube, enters the tympanic cavity and is inserted into one of the auditory ossicles, namely, the *malleus*.

Squamo-tympanic fissure is the name given to the narrow slit between the articular fossa of the squamous temporal and the upper edge of the tympanic plate. The lateral end of the slit is directly in front of the opening of the external auditory meatus; the medial end is directly behind the spine of the sphenoid.

The **foramen lacerum** can be seen between the petrous temporal and the basi-occiput, and the posterior end of the **pterygoid canal** is situated on the anterior margin of the foramen, above and lateral to the **pterygoid tubercle**; they will be dealt with more fully when the floor of the cranial cavity is examined (p. 171).

The **quadrate area** gives origin to the levator palati muscle. Cartilage, or dense fibrous tissue, unites the *postero-medial border* of the area to the basi-occiput, and its *antero-medial border* to the posterior border of the greater wing of the sphenoid; the cartilaginous part of the pharyngo-tympanic [auditory] tube lies along its line of union with the greater wing. The levator palati at its origin is therefore postero-medial to the tube. The tensor palati is a thin muscle with a triangular outline; the apex of the triangle is the tendon as it turns round the lower surface of the pterygoid hamulus, and the base is the origin of the muscle from the skull. It arises from the spine of the sphenoid and from the scaphoid fossa, and, between those points, from the cartilage of the tube; the upper part of the muscle therefore lies on the antero-lateral side of the tube and separates it from the mandibular nerve descending from the foramen ovale and the middle meningeal artery ascending to the foramen spinosum.

The **bony part of the pharyngo-tympanic tube** is about 10 mm. long. It is in the temporal bone, between the tympanic plate and the petrous temporal; and a thin bony septum separates it from the canal for the tensor tympani, which lies above it. One end opens into the anterior part of the tympanic cavity; from there the tube passes medially, forwards and slightly downwards, and opens on the lateral end of the groove for the cartilaginous part, at the medial side of the spine of the sphenoid, where the opening is easily found. Push a pin through the opening and along the tube to the tympanic cavity, and note that the tube has the ascending part of the carotid canal on its postero-medial side, and the mandibular joint on the antero-lateral side.

The **tympanic plate** has three surfaces. The medial part of the **posterior surface** is fused with the petrous temporal, and helps to form the anterior wall of the first part of the carotid canal; the lateral part is fused with the mastoid temporal and the post-auditory process of the squamous temporal, but is partly separated from the mastoid by the tympano-mastoid fissure. The **upper surface** is curved, for it belongs to the curled, lateral part of the plate; it forms the lower wall of the **external auditory meatus**, nearly the whole of its anterior wall and the greater part of its posterior wall; the rough, curved *lateral margin* of the plate gives attachment to the cartilage of the auricle. The **anterior surface** is free and concave, and is related to the upper part of the parotid gland, which separates it from the back of the head and neck of the mandible. Its *lower border* is uneven and sharp, and gives attachment to the fascia that covers the postero-medial surface of the parotid gland; its *upper border* forms the floor of the pharyngo-tympanic [auditory] tube and the posterior boundary of the squamo-tympanic fissure, and gives attachment to the fascia that covers the antero-medial surface of the parotid gland.

The *lateral part* of the **squamo-tympanic fissure** may be obliterated by fusion of the tympanic plate with the back of the post-glenoid tubercle. The *middle part* leads up into the tympanic cavity; the anterior process of the malleus is stuck into it; and the tympanic branch of the middle meningeal artery passes upwards through it. In many skulls a thin strip of bone is seen between the lips of the medial part of the fissure; that strip is the lower edge of the tegmen tympani (a part of the surface of the petrous temporal seen in the middle cranial fossa); to reach the fissure the tegmen is continued downwards as the antero-lateral wall of the bony part of the pharyngo-tympanic tube, and it divides the fissure into two slits—a **petro-squamous fissure**, in front of the edge of the tegmen, and a **petro-tympanic fissure**, which is more important; it is between the edge of the tegmen and the tympanic plate, and is below the tube. The chorda tympani nerve, having traversed the tympanic cavity from behind forwards, enters a small hole in the anterior wall of the cavity, runs obliquely downwards and forwards in the antero-lateral wall of the pharyngo-tympanic tube, and issues from the skull through the petro-tympanic fissure; it then runs in a medial direction and forwards and downwards, grooving the medial side of the spine of the sphenoid; and it ends by joining the lingual nerve below the foramen ovale.

The **articular fossa** and the **eminentia articularis** are for articulation with the head of the mandible, and their margins give attachment to the articular capsule, the thickened lateral part of which, called the temporo-mandibular ligament, is attached to the **tubercle of the root of the zygoma**; but the fossa and the eminence are separated from actual contact with the head of the mandible by an articular disc of fibro-cartilage which is attached by its circumference to the capsule, and divides the cavity of the joint into an upper and a lower part. The bone of the deepest part of the fossa is so thin that it is translucent.

CRANIAL CAVITY

The **cranial cavity** is the large cavity that lodges the brain. The bones which share in its formation are the frontal, the ethmoid, the sphenoid, the occipital, the two parietal, and the two temporal bones. The cavity is lined with the outermost of the three membranes or meninges of the brain, namely, the **dura mater**; the dura mater consists of two closely adherent fibrous layers, the *outer* of which clothes the bone, serving the purpose of periosteum, and is called the *endocranium*. The periosteum on the outside of the skull is called the *pericranium*. The pericranium and the endocranium are both continuous with the fibrous ribbons, called *sutural ligaments*, that lie between the articulating edges of the bones; and they are continuous also with each other round the lips of the various foramina and fissures that lead from the cranial cavity to the exterior.

Section of Skull.—The cranial cavity can be exposed for examination either by a median section which splits the skull into a right and a left half, or by a horizontal section which removes the skull-cap. The second method is the more common; the saw-cut is usually made to pass through the *frontal* bone immediately above the superciliary arches, through the two inferior angles of the *parietal* bone and the upper part of the *squamous temporal* on each side, and through the *occipital* bone immediately above the external occipital protuberance. The two parts are then examined separately: the skull-cap shows the roof of the cranial cavity; the lower part of the skull shows its floor; the front, the sides, and the back are included partly with the roof and partly with the floor.

The advantage of the median section is that it not only exposes the cranial cavity but also lays open the nasal cavity and the sphenoidal sinus. If the skull which the student has procured for himself has had the skull-cap removed, the lower part of the skull should be divided into a right and a left half. If he has an uncut specimen of skull he should remove the skull-cap by the saw-cuts indicated above, and then split the lower part of the skull into halves.

In making the sagittal section he should use a very fine saw, and should make the cut a little to one or other side of the median plane in order to avoid injury to the septum of the nose, but, at the same time, he must be careful not to injure the conchæ, which project from the side wall of the nasal cavity. The first cut should be made through the bony palate and the alveolar process of the maxilla; if they are not cut first they will break when the thicker parts of the skull are divided. The two halves can be tied together or hinged together with improvised pins and hooks when the student wants to examine both halves at once.

Thickness of Skull.—In cutting the skull the student will note that the inner table is thinner, harder and more brittle than the outer table, and that the whole thickness of the walls of the cranial cavity varies in different areas. The thicker and thinner areas are not all constant in position in different skulls, but the areas well covered with muscles are always thinner than those that are more exposed, *e.g.*, the floor of the temporal fossa and the floor of the posterior cranial fossa on each side of the median plane.

The bone of the skull as a whole is thicker in some races than in others (the more primitive races usually having the advantage of thicker skull bones); but in all races the skull bones are thinner in women and children than in men. The skull of a child is very thin, but it is more yielding and elastic than that of an adult and is less liable to fracture. There are, however, great differences in thickness in the skulls of adults of the same race and sex. About a quarter of an inch is an average thickness, but variations occur ranging from less than one-eighth of an inch to almost half an inch. There is no known relation between the thickness of the skull bones and the quality of the intelligence, but a thick skull obviously protects the brain more efficiently from injury by violence. It is not possible to gauge the thickness of the skull with any certainty during life, except during the course of an operation; and in the early steps of an operation on the skull it is safer to assume that the skull is thin.

Roof of Cranial Cavity

The **skull-cap** is the **roof** of the cranial cavity or **vault** of the skull. If the horizontal saw-cut has been made as indicated, the skull-cap includes part of the *frontal* bone in front, part of the *occipital* bone behind, nearly the whole of both *parietal* bones in the middle, and a very small part of the *squamous* portion of the *temporal* bone on each side, at the lower border of the parietal bone.

The internal or **cerebral surface** of the vault is highly concave in every direction. The dura mater is only loosely attached to the skull vault, except at the sutures, where, in a young adult skull, it is continuous with the sutural ligaments.

The **sutures** between the bones may be indistinct, for if their obliteration had begun it will be more advanced on the inner surface than on the outer; and if the skull is that of an old person the sutures may have disappeared. The sutures are:—The **sagittal suture**, uniting the two parietal bones; the **coronal suture**, uniting them to the frontal bone; the **lambdoid suture**, uniting them to the occipital bone; and the **squamous suture**, on each side, uniting the parietal bone to the squamous temporal. The squamous suture is at a lower level on the inside of the skull than on the outside, because the squamous temporal overlaps the parietal bone on the outside, and the saw-cut may have been at such a level that the suture is seen only on the outside.

The following additional parts are to be noted in the vault :—

The **frontal crest** (Fig. 140) is a median ridge on the anterior wall of the cranial cavity, on the lower part of the cerebral surface of the frontal bone, and it may extend far enough up to be seen on the skull-cap.

The **sagittal groove** is a shallow, median furrow on the cerebral surface of the vault, extending from above the root of the nose to the occipital protuberance. It begins on the frontal crest, passes upwards and backwards on the frontal bone, backwards along the sagittal suture, and downwards on to the occipital bone, widening progressively during its course. The superior sagittal venous sinus lies along it, in the upper border of the falx cerebri, which is attached to its lips. (The falx cerebri is a fold of the inner layer of the dura mater, projected downwards from the cranial vault as a tense, median partition, to keep the two halves of the cerebrum apart and prevent friction between them in sudden movements of the head.)

The **granular pits** are small irregular depressions that are placed here and there alongside the sagittal groove. They are more numerous and larger in the skull of an old person than in a young skull, and the bone in their floors may be thin enough to be translucent. They lodge arachnoid granulations, which are small bud-like growths that protrude from the arachnoid mater. (The arachnoid mater is the middle and the thinnest of the three membranes that enclose the brain) [ἀράχνιον (arachnion) = a spider's web].

The **parietal foramen** (p. 139), when present, is in the parietal bone, close to the sagittal groove, about an inch or an inch and a half above the lambdoid suture.

The **vascular grooves** (Fig. 147) are narrow branching grooves for meningeal vessels. They extend from the cut edges of the vault towards the top; the largest of them are on the parietal bone, and are for the branches and tributaries of the middle meningeal vessels; their direction is upwards and backwards. Small vascular foramina are numerous, especially in and near the grooves. The **impressions for cerebral gyri** [impressiones digitatæ] are the broad, shallow, ill-defined depressions, found all over the vault. They correspond to the gyri or convolutions on the surface of the brain.

Floor of Cranial Cavity

The **upper surface of the base of the skull** [basis cranii interna] is the floor of the cranial cavity. Grooves for meningeal vessels are seen on it; and the impressions for gyri are better marked than on the vault. The dura mater is more firmly attached to the bone of the floor than to that of the vault.

The floor is divided into three main districts, one behind the other and at different levels, corresponding to the anterior, middle, and posterior **cranial fossæ**, of which the anterior is at the highest level and the posterior at the lowest.

Anterior Cranial Fossa

The **anterior cranial fossa** contains the lower part of the frontal lobes of the brain. It is bounded in front and at the sides by the frontal bone; its floor is divided into :—(1) a median part, which is above the nasal cavity and is formed by the ethmoid bone and the body of the sphenoid; and (2) a right and a left lateral part, each of which is above the orbit and is made up of the orbital plate of the frontal bone and the lesser wing of the sphenoid.

In the **median subdivision** the chief parts to be looked for are :—

The **crista galli** is the upstanding, median process seen in front.

The **foramen cæcum** is the small pit in front of the crista galli [cæcum = blind]. The foramen, however, is not always blind: at its bottom there may be a small aperture which transmits a vein.

The **frontal crest** is the median ridge seen above the foramen cæcum, in the anterior boundary of the fossa; it extends upwards on to the vault and fades away there.

The **cribriform plates** of the ethmoid are a pair of narrow, horizontal plates of bone placed along the sides of the root of the crista galli; they are named " cribriform " because they are full of little holes [*cribrum* = a sieve]; they separate the cranial cavity from the nasal cavities (Figs. 147, 148).

Behind the cribriform plates there is a broad, fairly flat area of bone; it is the anterior part of the upper surface of the body of the sphenoid, and is called the **jugum sphenoidale** [from a resemblance to *jugum* = yoke]; it is limited behind by the **limbus sphenoidalis**—that is the anterior lip [*limbus* = edge] of a shallow transverse furrow, called the *optic groove*, that leads laterally on each side into an aperture called the *optic foramen*. The optic groove and foramen are, however, included in the middle cranial fossa.

By far the greater part of the **lateral subdivision** is formed by the orbital plate; only a small part posteriorly is formed by the lesser wing. The **orbital plate** separates the cranial cavity not only from the orbit but also from the ethmoidal air-sinuses; for the medial part of the plate overlies the labyrinth of the ethmoid—roofing in the sinuses. The *frontal sinus* extends backwards for a variable distance between the two tables of bone of which the plate is composed; and the upper table therefore separates the cranial cavity from part of the frontal sinus.

In the skull of an old person the suture between the orbital plate and the **lesser wing** may be obliterated, but if it is visible the outline of the wing can be made out—fairly broad at its medial end and tapering to a point at the lateral end. The posterior border of the lesser wing is the free, sharp margin of the floor of the lateral part of the fossa, and it ends *medially* in a prominent process, called the **anterior clinoid process,** that juts backwards behind the optic foramen.

Each lateral part of the floor of the anterior cranial fossa is convex, rather uneven, and slopes downwards towards the median portion, more so anteriorly than posteriorly, where both parts are smoother and more nearly horizontal. Together with the corresponding half of the median portion it supports the frontal lobe of the brain; the ridges and **impressions for gyri** on the lateral part correspond to the sulci and gyri on the orbital surface of the brain, and therefore vary in the pattern they make; they are much better marked in some skulls than others.

The antero-lateral margin of the orbital surface of the frontal lobe, *i.e.*, the superciliary margin of the brain, fits into the angle between the floor and the antero-lateral wall of the fossa, which corresponds, on the exterior, to a line drawn from the root of the nose upwards and then laterally along the superciliary arch and onwards to the root of the zygomatic process of the frontal bone, and then backwards to the pterion. The gyrus rectus, which is the most medial gyrus of the orbital surface, lies on the cribriform plate and on the jugum sphenoidale behind that; the olfactory tract and bulb are immediately lateral to the gyrus rectus, and lie on the jugum and on the orbital plate at the edge of the cribriform plate. The **cribriform plate** is at a lower level than the rest of the floor, and the holes in it are arranged in two irregular rows; the nerve filaments—twenty or so—which constitute the olfactory nerve come up from the nose through these foramina and end in the olfactory bulb.

In the lateral part of the fossa, especially in front and at the side, there are narrow branching *grooves for the anterior meningeal vessels* derived from the middle meningeal and ethmoidal vessels.

The **crista galli** is the upper anterior part of the perpendicular plate of the ethmoid projected upwards into the cranial cavity. It is highest and thickest in front, where it may contain either spongy bone or an air cavity which opens directly into the nose or into the frontal sinus; and from its anterior part two processes or *alæ* project forwards to articulate with the frontal bone and form the side boundaries of the **foramen cæcum,** which lies between the frontal bone and the crista galli.

The anterior end and anterior part of the convex border of the falx cerebri are attached to the sharp, sloping border of the crista galli and to the frontal crest. The anterior part of the superior sagittal sinus lies on the frontal crest in the convex border of the falx, and its commencement may be connected with the veins of the nose by a vein transmitted by the foramen cæcum.

The **nasal slit** is a short and narrow cleft—often difficult to find—situated between the anterior parts of the crista galli and cribriform plate; it leads down into the nasal cavity.

The **anterior** and **posterior ethmoidal canals** are narrow tunnels that begin at foramina of the same name between the roof and medial wall of the orbit (where they have been seen already). From these foramina they run in a medial direction, between the labyrinth of the ethmoid and the medial part of the orbital plate of the frontal bone, to open into the cranial cavity; their openings are often hidden by overhanging lips of bone. The *posterior* canal transmits the posterior ethmoidal vessels and opens at the junction of the cribriform plate with the front of the sphenoid. The posterior ethmoidal nerve, also contained in the canal, does not reach its

11 *a*

cranial end, being distributed to the mucous lining of the ethmoidal and sphenoidal sinuses. The *anterior* canal is larger; it opens at the side of the cribriform plate about the middle; it transmits the anterior ethmoidal vessels and the anterior ethmoidal nerve, which is a continuation of the

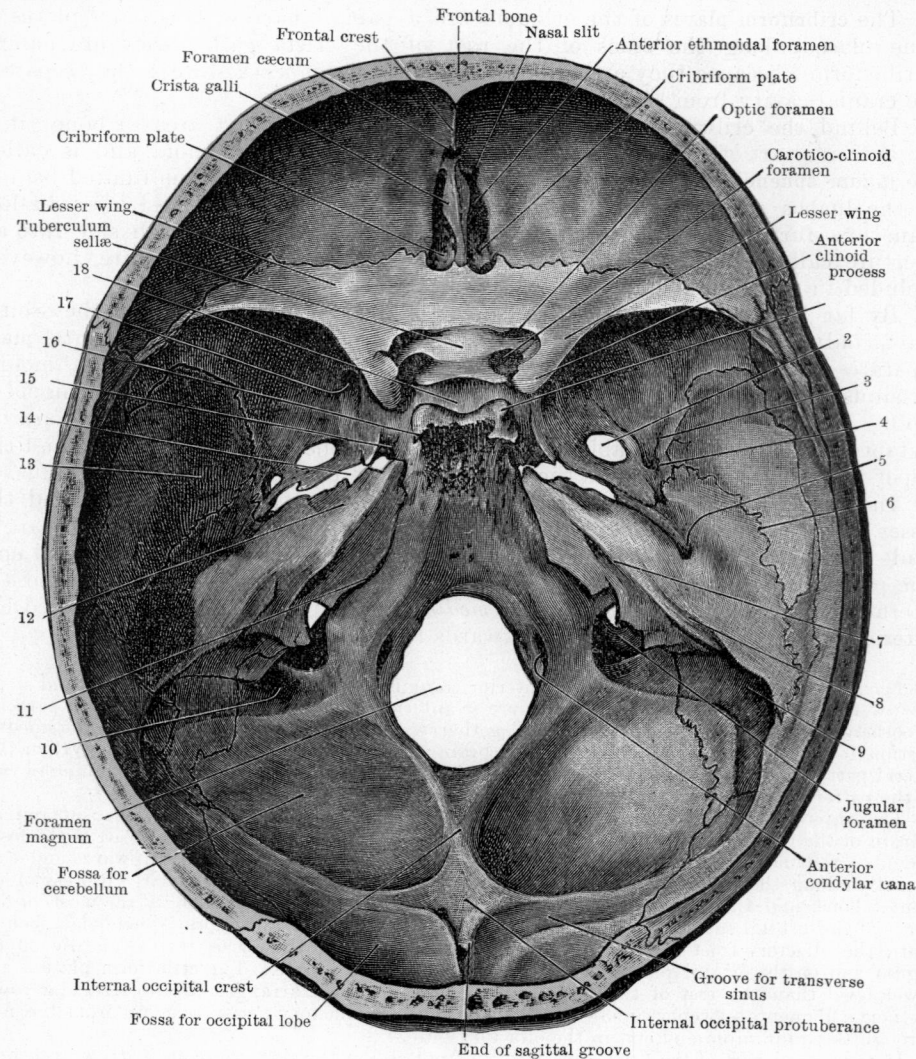

FIG. 140.—FLOOR OF CRANIAL CAVITY.

Red: frontal; occipital. **Blue**: ethmoid; temporal. **Orange**: parietal. **Uncoloured**: sphenoid.

1. Posterior clinoid process.
2. Foramen ovale.
3. Groove for middle meningeal vessels.
4. Foramen spinosum.
5. Hiatus for greater superficial petrosal nerve.
6. Occasional suture between petrous and squamous temporal.
7. Internal auditory meatus.
8. Groove for superior petrosal sinus.
9. Groove for sigmoid sinus.
10. Groove for sigmoid sinus.
11. Groove for the inferior petrosal sinus.
12. Impression for trigeminal ganglion.
13. Squamous temporal.
14. Spheno-petrous fissure.
15. Carotid groove, in front of foramen lacerum.
16. Dorsum sellæ of sphenoid.
17. Leads into foramen rotundum.
18. Hypophyseal fossa.

naso-ciliary nerve; the nerve runs forwards on the cribriform plate and descends to the nose through the **nasal slit** or through a foramen a little lateral to the slit, and is accompanied by small branches of the vessels.

The **lesser wing of the sphenoid** is triangular in outline and compressed from above downwards. It lies in the roof of the orbit and superior orbital fissure, and in the floor of the anterior cranial fossa; posteriorly, it overhangs the middle cranial fossa. It arises by two roots separated by the optic foramen : the *anterior root*—broad and flat—is continuous with the jugum sphenoidale ; the *posterior root*—much smaller—springs from the side of the body of the sphenoid and stands between the optic foramen and superior orbital fissure.   The spheno-parietal venous sinus lies in the dura mater on the lower surface of the posterior margin of the wing.   The **anterior clinoid process** is a flattened projection with a rounded free end ; it juts backwards from the postero-medial angle of the wing and gives attachment to the anterior end of the free margin of the tentorium cerebelli.

Middle Cranial Fossa

The **middle cranial fossa** is divided into a median part and a right and a left lateral part, and its floor resembles a bird with outspread wings.

MEDIAN PART OF MIDDLE CRANIAL FOSSA

The median part is elevated above the level of the lateral parts.   It is bounded *anteriorly* by the sphenoidal limbus, and *posteriorly* by an upstanding plate of bone called the dorsum sellæ.   Its floor is the body of the sphenoid, and is separated therefore from the cavity of the nose by the sphenoidal sinus enclosed within the bony shell of the body of the sphenoid (Fig. 147).   The parts to be looked for are the optic groove and foramina, the sella turcica, and the carotid grooves.

The **optic groove** [sulcus chiasmatis] is in the most anterior part of the floor, immediately behind the anterior cranial fossa ; it may be well defined or very shallow.   On each side the optic groove ends at the **optic foramen**, which opens into the medial side of the back of the orbit, where it has been seen already (pp. 143 and 145).

Sella turcica is the name given to the middle part of the upper surface of the body of the sphenoid, from a resemblance to a Turkish saddle.   The pommel is the transverse, oval elevation, called the **tuberculum sellæ**, situated directly behind the optic groove.   The seat is the wide, smooth depression behind the tuberculum ; it is called the **hypophyseal fossa** because a process of the brain called the hypophysis lies in it.   Behind the hypophyseal fossa there is an upstanding square plate of bone (broken off in many skulls) called the **dorsum sellæ** or back of the saddle.   The upper corners of the dorsum sellæ are called the **posterior clinoid processes**.   The anterior and posterior clinoid processes get their name from a fancied resemblance to the four posts of a bed [κλίνη (clinē)=a bed].

The **carotid groove** is a broad, shallow, ʃ-shaped groove on the upper part of the side of the body of the sphenoid.   It begins at the medial side of the foramen lacerum, ascends for a short distance, then runs forwards on the side of the sphenoid body, and finally turns upwards to end medial to the anterior clinoid process.   The internal carotid artery lies in it, and its sinuous bends indicate the course of the artery in the cranial cavity.

In many skulls there is a pair of **middle clinoid processes**.   Each middle clinoid process, when present, is usually a small tubercle situated a little behind the lateral end of the tuberculum sellæ.   In some skulls it is a large process and joins the anterior clinoid process, converting the termination of the carotid groove into a foramen called the **carotico-clinoid foramen**.   Occasionally it joins the posterior clinoid process instead, or it may branch and join both the anterior and the posterior clinoid process.

The **optic foramen** is a short, wide, nearly circular canal that passes in a lateral direction, forwards and slightly downwards from the cranial cavity into the orbit, and transmits the optic nerve and the ophthalmic artery.   It is bounded by the body of the sphenoid and the two roots of the lesser wing—the thin bone of the body separating it from the sphenoidal sinus. The **optic groove** connects the two optic foramina.   The optic chiasma, which connects the two optic nerves, does not, however, lie in the groove, but is situated a little distance above it.

The **hypophyseal fossa** lodges the hypophysis and is roofed over by a fold of dura mater, called the diaphragma sellæ, which has a hole in the middle of it for the stalk that connects the hypophysis with the brain.   The **posterior clinoid processes** give attachment to the anterior ends of the circumferential margin of the tentorium cerebelli.   Low down on the side of the dorsum sellæ, where its root joins the body of the sphenoid, there is a narrow groove that accommodates the medial margin of the beginning of the inferior petrosal sinus; the groove is only the width of a thick pin, but can usually be seen even when the dorsum sellæ is broken off.

The cavernous venous sinus lies at the side of the body of the sphenoid on the horizontal part of the **carotid groove**; its centre is opposite a point on the upper border of the zygomatic arch directly above the tubercle of the root of the zygoma. The carotid artery, lying in the carotid groove, is imbedded in the sinus, together with the carotid plexus, the oculo-motor, trochlear, ophthalmic, and abducent nerves; and the maxillary nerve runs forwards towards the foramen rotundum immediately below the carotid groove and cavernous sinus. Those structures are therefore all related to the body of the sphenoid—the cavernous sinus, the carotid artery, and the maxillary nerve being closely related to it and to the sphenoidal sinus within it. The two cavernous sinuses are connected by inter-cavernous sinuses that cross the back of the **tuberculum sellæ**, the front of the **dorsum sellæ**, and the floor of the **hypophyseal fossa**. The notch between the tuberculum sellæ and the anterior clinoid process is occupied by the carotid artery as it leaves the carotid groove.

Lateral Part of Middle Cranial Fossa

Each lateral subdivision of the middle cranial fossa is a wide, deep hollow limited *anteriorly* by the lesser wing of the sphenoid, and *posteriorly* by the upper border of the petrous temporal; it sinks to the level of the zygomatic arch and lower surface of the body of the sphenoid; it contains the temporal lobe of the brain. The principal parts on the exterior of the skull to which it is related are the orbit *in front*, the temporal fossa *laterally*, and the infra-temporal fossa and the mandibular joint *below*.

The bones in its walls are: (1) The petrous part of the temporal bone, *i.e.*, the pyramidal mass of bone that forms its posterior wall; (2) the squamous temporal, in front of the petrous, in the side wall of the fossa and slightly in the floor; (3) the greater wing of the sphenoid, partly in the side wall in front of the squamous temporal and partly in the anterior wall and in the floor in front of the petrous temporal. Beyond the limits of the fossa the lower part of the parietal bone lies in the side wall of the cranial cavity above the squamous temporal, and its antero-inferior angle articulates with the top of the greater wing.

The *anterior lip* of the hollow is the posterior margin of the anterior fossa; it overhangs the hollow, and ends laterally, on the side wall, **opposite the pterion**. The *posterior lip* is the upper margin of the petrous temporal; it is channelled lengthwise by a groove—sometimes well defined, but sometimes poorly marked and interrupted—which lodges the superior petrosal venous sinus; close to its medial end there is a wide, very shallow notch, called the *trigeminal notch*, on which the trigeminal or fifth cranial nerve lies.

The noteworthy feature in the *anterior boundary* of the fossa is the large, oblique gap between the wings of the sphenoid, called the **superior orbital fissure**, which opens into the orbit, where it has been examined already (pp. 143, 145).

The points to be noted in the *floor* are the foramen rotundum, foramen ovale, foramen lacerum, foramen spinosum, and the grooves for the meningeal vessels.

The **foramen rotundum** is the round hole situated almost directly below the medial end of the superior orbital fissure; it leads horizontally forwards into the upper part of the pterygo-palatine fossa, and transmits the maxillary nerve; if a pin is pushed forwards through the foramen, and the skull is looked at from the side, the point of the pin will be seen entering the pterygo-palatine fossa. The foramen is situated in the root of the greater wing, close to the body of the sphenoid, and is separated only by thin bone from the sphenoidal sinus.

The **foramen ovale** is almost half an inch behind the foramen rotundum, near the posterior border of the greater wing; it transmits the mandibular nerve, and has been seen already in the roof of the infra-temporal fossa (pp. 155, 156).

The **foramen spinosum**—behind and lateral to the foramen ovale and quite close to it—also has been seen from the infra-temporal fossa; it transmits the middle meningeal vessels.

The **grooves for the middle meningeal vessels** are usually sufficiently distinct to enable one to trace the course of the main trunk of the artery and its branches on the walls of the cranial cavity; their whole course is seen in a skull split into halves without previous removal of the skull cap (Fig. 147). The **main groove** begins at the foramen spinosum, runs forwards and in a lateral direction on the part of the squamous temporal that bears the eminentia articularis of the lower surface of the skull; and it divides into an anterior and a posterior branch at a point that varies but is usually near the side of the skull opposite a point on the upper margin of the zygomatic arch about midway between the auditory meatus and the margin of the orbit. The **anterior groove** extends from that point to the anterior inferior angle of the parietal bone *opposite the pterion*; in that region the groove is usually very deep and often roofed over and converted into a tunnel for a short distance; becoming a groove again, it extends upwards and backwards, branching over the parietal bone, the chief branch of the groove taking a line towards the point on the top of the skull midway between nasion and inion. The **posterior groove** extends backwards and upwards across the squamous temporal on to the parietal bone, branching as it goes—the chief branch taking a line towards the lambda. The meningeal vessels, since they are so closely related to the bone, are liable to be torn when the skull is injured during life—especially the veins, for they lie between the arteries and the bone. The chief point of danger is at the pterion, where the anterior branch is lodged in a deep groove and may lie in a

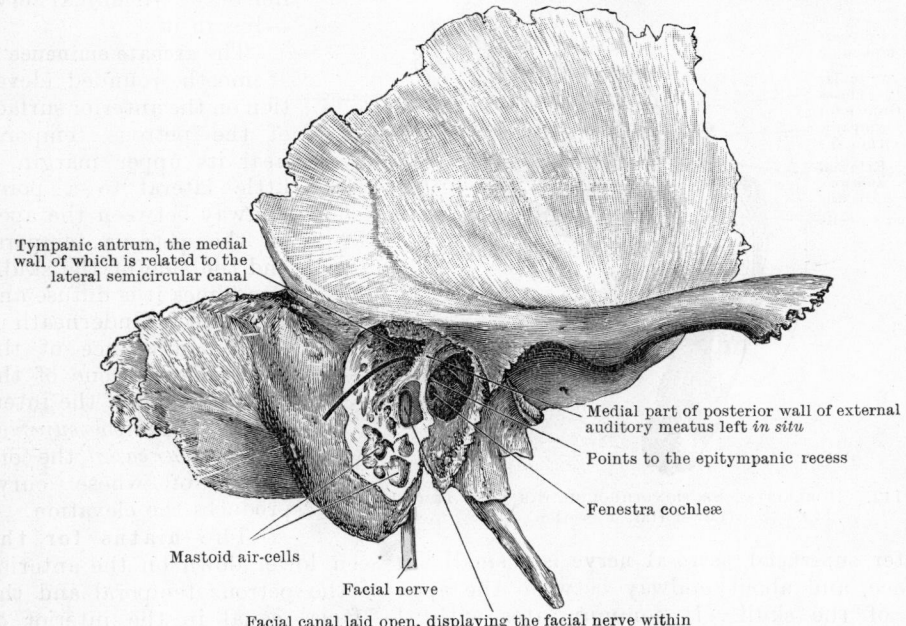

Tympanic antrum, the medial
wall of which is related to the
lateral semicircular canal

Medial part of posterior wall of external
auditory meatus left *in situ*

Points to the epitympanic recess

Fenestra cochleæ

Mastoid air-cells

Facial nerve

Facial canal laid open, displaying the facial nerve within

FIG. 141.

Preparation to show the tympanic antrum. The greater part of the posterior wall of the external auditory meatus has been removed, but a bridge of bone has been left at its medial end; under cover of this a bristle (thick black) passes from the tympanic antrum to the tympanic cavity through the posterior canaliculus of the chorda tympani.

tunnel. The grooves are in the inner table of the skull bones, which is more brittle than the outer table, and is sometimes called the *vitreous* table on that account [*vitreus* = like glass]; in an injury to the head the brittle, inner table may be cracked and the vessels torn, though the outer table is not broken.

The **foramen lacerum** is a large hole, with ragged margins, already seen on the lower surface of the skull. Seen in the floor of the cranial cavity, it is situated between the petrous temporal and the sphenoid. The carotid canal opens into it laterally, and the carotid artery crosses it to reach the carotid groove on the sphenoid. A spur of bone, called the **lingula**, projects obliquely backwards from the lateral margin of the carotid groove. In some skulls the lingula is a mere spicule of bone; in others it is long enough to reach the petrous temporal and form a complete lateral boundary for the foramen lacerum. In many skulls the roof of the carotid canal is deficient in bone, or has been partly broken away; in that case the jagged margins of the incomplete roof of the canal are continuous with the margins of the foramen lacerum. The posterior end of the **pterygoid canal** is on the anterior margin of the foramen lacerum almost directly below the lingula, but it is found more easily from the lower surface of the skull.

The *posterior wall* of the lateral part of the middle cranial fossa is the anterior face of the petrous temporal, and is nearly triangular in outline. The parts to be specially looked for in it are the trigeminal impression, the arcuate eminence, the tegmen tympani, and the hiatus for the greater superficial petrosal nerve.

The **trigeminal impression** is a shallow depression — barely wide enough to accommodate a finger tip —on the anterior surface of the petrous temporal near its apex or medial extremity, below the trigeminal notch. The trigeminal ganglion—the chief ganglion of the trigeminal nerve —lies in it.

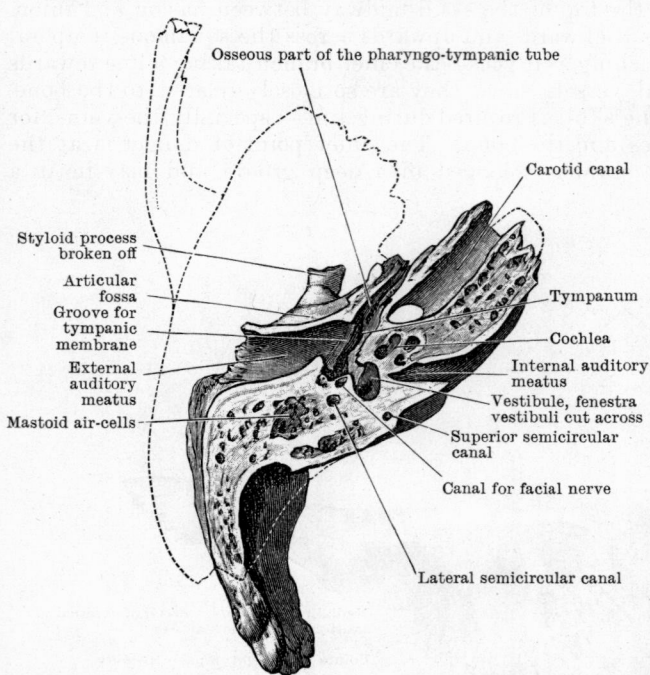

Fig. 142.—Horizontal Section through the Left Temporal Bone (Lower Half of Section).

The **arcuate eminence** is a smooth, rounded elevation on the anterior surface of the petrous temporal near its upper margin, a little lateral to a point midway between the apex of the petrous temporal and the side of the skull; sometimes it is diffuse and ill defined. Underneath it, in the substance of the bone, there is one of the curved canals of the internal ear, called the *superior semicircular canal*, the convexity of whose curve produces the elevation.

The **hiatus for the greater superficial petrosal nerve** is a small slit seen lower down on the anterior surface, and about midway between the apex of the petrous temporal and the side of the skull. It communicates with the facial canal in the interior of the bone, and transmits a slender nerve from which it takes its name. This nerve arises in the substance of the temporal bone from the facial nerve; it emerges from the hiatus and lies in a groove that runs in a medial direction and downwards and forwards to the foramen lacerum.

The **tegmen tympani** is the fairly smooth area of bone that forms the lateral part of the anterior surface of the petrous temporal, and is so named because part of it forms the roof of the middle ear or tympanum. It is made of thin bone; disease in the middle ear has therefore only a short way to travel to attack the membranes of the brain and the brain itself. The tegmen tympani is the roof not only of the tympanum but also of the canal for the tensor tympani and the tympanic antrum. The **tympanum** has been seen already at the far end of the external auditory meatus, and its position relative to the cranial cavity can be gauged from its position as seen through the meatus. The **canal for the tensor tympani** was located when the lower surface of the skull was examined. The **tympanic antrum** is a small but very important cavity. It lies in the substance of the temporal bone behind the tympanum and communicates with it by a wide opening; it is about half an inch medial to the suprameatal triangle; it communicates posteriorly with the air cells which pervade the mastoid portion of the temporal bone to a greater or lesser extent. The antrum is relatively large at birth; the mastoid cells grow as diverticula from the antrum—beginning at or shortly before birth, but not reaching full development till after puberty. If the student has a specimen of skull of his own, he would not be ill-advised to break through the tegmen tympani carefully and snip it away, in order to see the tympanic antrum and note its relation to the middle ear and to the exterior of the skull.

The *anterior lip* of the **lateral part of the middle cranial fossa** has a concave edge which begins medially at the anterior clinoid process and sweeps in a lateral direction and forwards and upwards to end at the side of the skull in the region of the pterion—the groove or tunnel for the anterior branch of the middle meningeal vessels being immediately behind its lateral extremity or even in it. The lip is formed chiefly by the lesser wing of the sphenoid, and is completed laterally by the frontal bone. It fits into the stem of the lateral sulcus of the cerebrum, *i.e.*, the cleft between the frontal and temporal lobes; the lateral end of the stem, where it breaks up into the rami of the sulcus, is therefore opposite the pterion.

The lower margin of the temporal lobe, *i.e.*, the anterior part of the infero-lateral margin of the cerebrum, fits into the ill-defined groove that marks the junction of the side wall of the fossa with the floor and posterior boundary; and it corresponds, on the exterior, to a line which begins near the anterior end of the upper border of the zygomatic arch, runs backwards along the upper border of the arch and the posterior root, and is continued backwards a short distance beyond the root to a point that corresponds, in the living head, to the place where the skin of the back of the root of the auricle joins the skin of the head.

The **foramen rotundum** was originally part of the superior orbital fissure, from which it was gradually cut off by the growth of bone. The **sphenoidal emissary foramen**—when present—is a little medial to the foramen ovale.

The **foramen lacerum** is a short, wide canal rather than a foramen; its lower end is on the lower surface of the skull and its upper end is in the floor of the middle cranial fossa. The carotid canal opens into its postero-lateral side near its upper end; and the carotid groove begins on the antero-medial boundary of the upper end. The **lower end** is bounded *postero-laterally* by the petrous temporal, *medially* by the basi-occipital and the body of the sphenoid, and *anteriorly* by the root of the greater wing and pterygoid process of the sphenoid. The **upper end** is bounded *postero-laterally* by the petrous temporal, *medially* and *anteriorly* by the carotid groove on the body and root of greater wing of the sphenoid; and the lingula—if long—completes the *lateral* boundary, which is defective if the lingula is short. The foramen *transmits* a meningeal branch of the ascending pharyngeal artery, some meningeal lymph vessels, and small veins that connect the cavernous sinus with the pharyngeal venous plexus. It *contains* (1) some cartilage, (2) the internal carotid artery, surrounded by the internal carotid plexus of sympathetic nerves and a plexus of tiny veins that connect the cavernous sinus and pharyngeal plexus, (3) the deep petrosal nerve, the termination of the greater superficial petrosal nerve, and the beginning of the nerve of the pterygoid canal. The cartilage fills the lower part of the foramen, and is pierced by the structures transmitted. The internal carotid artery, after it emerges from the carotid canal and as it bends up into the cranial cavity to enter the cavernous sinus, lies on the upper surface of the cartilage. While in the foramen the carotid nerve plexus gives off the deep petrosal nerve. The greater superficial petrosal nerve (a branch of the facial) runs in a groove on the anterior surface of the petrous temporal from its hiatus to the foramen lacerum, and joins the deep nerve to form the nerve of the pterygoid canal, which traverses that canal and joins the spheno-palatine ganglion.

The **pterygoid canal** is a narrow, horizontal tunnel, about half an inch long, which traverses the common root of the pterygoid process and greater wing of the sphenoid, and transmits the nerve of the pterygoid canal and an artery of the same name derived from the third part of the maxillary artery. The posterior end of the canal opens on the anterior margin of the foramen lacerum below the lingula and above the pterygoid tubercle. The anterior end opens on the posterior wall of the pterygo-palatine fossa below and medial to the foramen rotundum. The canal is in the floor of the sphenoidal sinus, and may raise a ridge in the floor.

The motor and sensory roots of the trigeminal nerve cross the **trigeminal notch** and enter the **trigeminal impression** on the roof of the medial end of the carotid canal, where the sensory root joins the trigeminal ganglion [g. semilunare]; the ganglion also lies partly in the impression and partly overlaps the carotid artery in the foramen lacerum. Three large nerves spring from the ganglion—(1) the ophthalmic, which runs forwards towards the superior orbital fissure but divides into branches before it gets there; (2) the maxillary, which runs forwards to the foramen rotundum; and (3) the mandibular, which descends to the foramen ovale. The motor root runs under cover of the ganglion and is incorporated in the mandibular nerve at the foramen ovale.

The **hiatus for the greater superficial petrosal nerve** transmits that nerve and the petrosal branch of the middle meningeal artery. The nerve runs in a groove medially and forwards, and has to pass under cover of the trigeminal ganglion or the mandibular nerve as it approaches the foramen lacerum.

Below the hiatus there is a small aperture through which the lesser superficial petrosal nerve issues from the substance of the temporal bone; continuous with the aperture there is a narrow groove which runs medially, forwards and downwards (on the roof of the canal for the tensor tympani) to the suture between the petrous temporal and the greater wing of the sphenoid. The aperture and the groove are often very difficult to identify. The nerve lies in the groove and leaves the skull either through that suture or through the foramen ovale or through a minute, unnamed hole, which, when present, is behind the foramen ovale.

Occasionally the remains of the original suture between petrous and squamous temporal can be seen in the adult near the side wall of the skull.

The following parts—which have been briefly defined in this section—are described fully in the chapter on The ORGANS OF THE SENSES : The **tympanum** ; the **internal ear**, which lies in the substance of the petrous temporal medial to the tympanum ; the **canals for the tensor tympani and bony part of pharyngo-tympanic tube**, which open out of the anterior part of the tympanum ; the **tympanic antrum**, behind the tympanum ; and the **mastoid air cells**, which communicate with the antrum.

Posterior Cranial Fossa

The **posterior cranial fossa** is in the part of the skull that is placed above the vertebral column and the muscles of the back of the neck. It is the largest and deepest of the cranial fossæ, and it lodges the hind-brain, *i.e.* cerebellum, pons and medulla oblongata.

The **bones** in its walls are : (1) the posterior part of the body of the **sphenoid**, including the *dorsum sellæ* ; (2) the posterior surface of the **petrous temporal** ; (3) the inner surface of the **mastoid temporal**, in the side wall behind the petrous temporal ; (4) the posterior inferior angle of the **parietal bone**, above the mastoid temporal ; (5) the whole of the **occipital bone**, except the part above the external occipital protuberance and the superior nuchal lines. The **basilar part** of the occipital bone is in the anterior wall of the fossa, above and in front of the foramen magnum, which occupies the lowest part of the floor. The **condylar part**, (including the jugular process), is in the floor, at the side of the foramen magnum. The lower, larger part of the **squamous part** is in the floor, in the side wall, and in the posterior wall, being behind the foramen magnum, behind the condylar part and behind the mastoid temporal and inferior angle of the parietal bone. In an adult over 25 years the basilar part is fused with the body of the sphenoid, the line of fusion being barely half an inch below the root of the dorsum sellæ.

The bones in the **rim** of the fossa are : (1) the **dorsum sellæ**, in the middle in front ; (2) in the middle posteriorly, a prominent elevation, called the **internal occipital protuberance**, which is nearly opposite the external protuberance ; (3) the **upper margin of the petrous temporal**, on each side in front ; (4) on each side, posteriorly a broad, shallow, horizontal groove, called the **transverse sulcus**, which begins at the side of the internal occipital protuberance, and passes laterally and forwards to the base or lateral end of the petrous temporal ; at that point the groove leaves the rim to become continuous with a deeper groove, called the sigmoid sulcus, which extends sinuously to the jugular foramen ; a large venous sinus, called the transverse sinus, lies in the transverse groove, and the sigmoid prolongation of that sinus lies in the sigmoid groove.

A wide fold of the inner layer of the dura mater, shaped like a tent and called the **tentorium cerebelli**, roofs over the posterior cranial fossa and keeps the weight of the hinder part of the cerebrum off the cerebellum. The circumferential or basal margin of the tentorium is attached to the lips of the transverse groove and the lips of the groove for the superior petrosal sinus on the upper margin of the petrous temporal.

The fossa is divisible into a median part and a right and a left lateral part.

MEDIAN PART OF POSTERIOR CRANIAL FOSSA

The parts to be noted in the median subdivision are the foramen magnum, the anterior condylar canals, the jugular tubercles, the clivus, the grooves for the inferior petrosal sinuses, and the internal occipital crest.

The **foramen magnum** is in the lowest part of the fossa. The medial surface of the occipital condyle can be seen at the anterior part of the margin on each side, and in many skulls the condyles encroach upon the foramen and reduce the width of its anterior part. (See also p. 157.)

The internal opening of the **anterior condylar canal** [canalis n. hypoglossi] is a little above the part of the margin of the foramen magnum that is formed by the condyle. The opening is rather hidden unless the skull is tilted; and it is often double on one or both sides. The external opening has been seen already on the lower surface of the skull (p. 158).

The **jugular tubercle** is the smooth, rounded elevation situated above and in front of the internal opening of the anterior condylar canal.

The **clivus** is the broad, sloping surface between the anterior margin of the foramen magnum and the root of the dorsum sellæ; it is formed by the upper surfaces of the basilar part of the occipital bone and of the posterior part of the body of the sphenoid; it is related to the pons and medulla oblongata of the brain. [*Clivus* = a slope.]

The **groove for the inferior petrosal sinus** lies along the suture between the basilar part of the occipital bone and the petrous temporal, and is shared by both bones.

The **internal occipital crest** is the strong, median ridge between the foramen magnum and the internal occipital protuberance.

The hypoglossal nerve pierces the dura mater as two bundles which unite in the **anterior condylar canal**. When the opening of the canal is double, the two bundles may enter the canal separate or they may both enter through one of the openings, while the other transmits a meningeal artery.

The **jugular tubercle** is at the medial side of the anterior part of the jugular foramen and overlies the anterior condylar canal; immediately behind and lateral to the tubercle there is a short, shallow groove in which the ninth, tenth, and eleventh cranial nerves lie, as they pass towards the jugular foramen.

The **clivus** is concave from side to side. Its upper part is related to the pons and the basilar artery, its lower part to the medulla oblongata and the vertebral arteries, and, near the foramen magnum, it is roughened by the attachments of the membrana tectoria and the upper band of the cruciate ligament. Between the two layers of the dura mater that cover the clivus there is a network of venous channels, called the plexus of basilar sinuses, which connect the right inferior petrosal sinus with the left. The abducent nerve, on each side, pierces the inner layer of the dura mater near the lateral margin of the clivus, about half an inch below the dorsum sellæ, and runs upwards on the clivus, between the two layers of the dura mater, across the inferior petrosal sinus to reach the apex of the petrous temporal; at that point, it crosses the petro-sphenoid joint below a slender fibrous band that is sometimes ossified; it then curves round the internal carotid artery to enter the cavernous sinus.

The **groove for the inferior petrosal sinus** begins at the apex of the petrous temporal, *i.e.*, at the medial end of its upper border, where the sinus is connected with the posterior end of the cavernous sinus; it runs obliquely downwards, backwards, and in a lateral direction, along the petro-occipital suture, to the jugular foramen, where the sinus, descending through the antero-medial part of the foramen, joins the commencement of the internal jugular vein.

The **internal occipital crest** gives attachment to a small fold of the inner layer of dura mater, called the falx cerebelli, which intervenes between the two hemispheres of the cerebellum. A small venous sinus, called the occipital sinus, lies along the edge of the crest between the two layers of the falx; sometimes the sinus is paired. The lower part of the crest sometimes divides to enclose a small depression related to a part of the cerebellum called the vermis.

The tentorium cerebelli, the falx cerebri, and the falx cerebelli are attached to the **internal occipital protuberance**; in its immediate neighbourhood the superior sagittal sinus and the straight sinus end, and the transverse sinuses and the occipital sinus begin; the posterior end of the cerebrum is immediately above and lateral to it. The internal occipital protuberance is seldom directly opposite the external protuberance (it is usually a little higher), but there is so little difference in their levels that the external protuberance is usually taken as the surface guide to the position of structures near the internal protuberance. Owing to the two protuberances, that region of the occipital bone is one of the thickest parts of the skull.

LATERAL PART OF POSTERIOR CRANIAL FOSSA

The chief parts to be noted in this subdivision are the cerebellar fossa, the transverse and sigmoid grooves, the jugular foramen, the posterior condylar canal, the mastoid foramen, and the internal auditory meatus. Points of less importance are the grooves for the meningeal arteries, the opening of the aqueduct of the vestibule, the subarcuate fossa, the notch for the glosso-pharyngeal nerve, and the external opening of the cochlear canaliculus.

The **cerebellar fossa** is the wide concavity between the transverse groove and the foramen magnum. Faint grooves made by meningeal vessels are seen in its floor.

The **transverse groove** begins at the side of the internal occipital protuberance and sweeps round the cranial wall to the lateral end of the upper margin of the petrous temporal, where it joins the sigmoid groove.

The **sigmoid groove** curves downwards and descends along the side wall of the skull to the floor, extends in a medial direction on the floor for an inch, and, finally, curves forwards to end at the jugular foramen. Its curves resemble those of the letter S; hence the name "sigmoid" [*sigma* is the Greek name for the letter S].

The position of the two grooves corresponds, on the exterior of the skull, to a line (1) which begins at the side of the external occipital protuberance, and is drawn almost horizontally, but with a slight upward convexity, to a point a little behind the place where the posterior root of the zygoma joins the supramastoid crest, and that point, on the living head, is where the skin of the upper part of the back of the root of the auricle joins the skin of the head; (2) from that point the line is drawn almost vertically downwards to a point about a finger's-breadth behind the lower margin of the external auditory meatus; (3) from there, forwards to the lower border of the meatus. The first or horizontal part of the line is opposite the transverse sinus and the attachment of the tentorium; the posterior part of the infero-lateral border of the cerebrum is above it; the margin of the cerebellum is below it. The second and third parts of the line correspond to the sigmoid sinus—which is the continuation of the transverse sinus.

The sigmoid groove is deeper than the transverse groove; in some skulls its upper part is so deep (at the expense of the petrous temporal) that it is quite close to the tympanic antrum, and the sigmoid sinus would be in considerable danger in an operation on the antrum.

The **mastoid foramen** is an aperture of variable size that leads from the exterior of the skull (p. 146) into the sigmoid groove on the side wall of the posterior fossa. The **posterior condylar canal**, when present, passes from the condylar fossa (p. 158) into the posterior cranial fossa and opens into the sigmoid groove on the floor of the fossa.

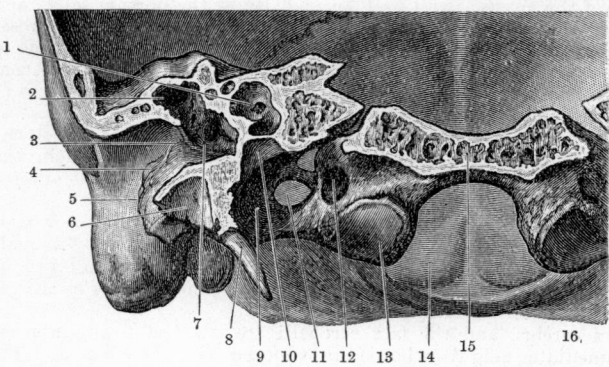

The posterior part of each transverse groove is situated on a thick, blunt ridge that extends in a lateral direction from the internal occipital protuberance for some distance. Above that ridge, on the posterior wall of the cranial cavity, there is a wide, well-marked depression, called the *posterior cerebral fossa*, which lodges the posterior end of the occipital lobe of the cerebrum. The right cerebral fossa is separated from the left by a thick vertical ridge which descends to the internal occipital

FIG. 143.—VERTICAL SECTION THROUGH BASE OF SKULL IMMEDIATELY IN FRONT OF ROOT OF STYLOID PROCESS.

1. Cochlea.	9. Jugular fossa.
2. Entrance to the antrum.	10. Lower end of carotid canal.
3. Tympanic sulcus.	11. Jugular foramen.
4. Tympanic plate	12. Anterior condylar canal.
5. Tympano-mastoid fissure.	13. Occipital condyle.
6. Tympanic plate.	14. Foramen magnum.
7. Tympanic cavity (floor).	15. Basi-occipital.
8. Styloid process.	16. Squama of occipital bone.

protuberance. Along that ridge the sagittal groove, seen already on the vault of the skull, runs down to the protuberance and becomes continuous with one or other of the transverse grooves, usually the right; occasionally it splits and becomes continuous with both transverse grooves.

The **transverse groove** begins at the internal occipital protuberance, passes across the occipital squama to its lateral angle, and then crosses the posterior inferior angle of the parietal bone to reach the mastoid temporal, where it becomes the sigmoid groove. The **sigmoid groove** turns downwards grooving the mastoid temporal and the petrous temporal, where it is separated by very thin bone from the mastoid air cells and may be very close to the tympanic antrum; reaching the floor, it passes off the mastoid temporal on to the upper surface of the jugular process of the occipital bone, on which it passes first in a medial direction and then forwards to the jugular foramen.

The right and left transverse grooves are seldom of equal size; the wider of the two is that which is joined by the sagittal groove, and it is usually the right; and the jugular foramen also is wider on that side than on the other.

The circumferential margin of the **tentorium cerebelli** is attached to the internal occipital protuberance, to the lips of the transverse groove, to the lips of the narrow, ill marked groove along the upper margin of the petrous temporal, and then is prolonged medially to be attached to the posterior clinoid process. Along the transverse groove it encloses the transverse sinus; along the margin of the petrous temporal it encloses the superior petrosal sinus, which runs from the cavernous sinus to the transverse sinus; and at the trigeminal notch the trigeminal nerve crosses beneath the sinus and the margin of the tentorium. The internal margin of the tentorium, *i.e.*, the margins of the door of the tentorium, is continued forwards, on each side, across the attached, circumferential margin at the apex of the petrous temporal, to be fastened to the anterior clinoid process.

The **cerebellar fossa** is of variable depth, and is often unequal on the two sides. Its floor is thin and translucent, and may be the thinnest part of the cranial wall. The cerebral fossæ also are seldom symmetrical.

Faint, narrow grooves are seen here and there in the walls of the posterior cranial fossa for the posterior meningeal vessels, which are derived from the vertebral, the occipital, and the ascending pharyngeal arteries; and some twigs of the posterior branch of the middle meningeal artery may descend into the fossa.

The **jugular foramen** is a large aperture, with irregular margins. It is in the anterior and medial part of the floor of the lateral subdivision of the fossa, between the petrous temporal and the jugular process of the occipital bone. It leads downwards and slightly forwards to the lower surface of the skull, where it is opposite the lower margin of the external auditory meatus.

The **jugular foramen** transmits three sets of structures, and small spicules of bone projecting from its margins may partly or completely divide it into corresponding compartments. By far the most important structures that pass through the foramen are the sigmoid sinus and the ninth, tenth and eleventh cranial nerves. The *antero-medial compartment* transmits the inferior petrosal sinus and a meningeal branch of the ascending pharyngeal artery. The *middle compartment* transmits the glosso-pharyngeal, vagus and accessory nerves—in that order from before backwards. The *postero-lateral compartment* is larger than the other two, and transmits the sigmoid sinus (as it becomes the internal jugular vein), a meningeal branch of the occipital artery, a meningeal branch of the vagus, and lymph vessels from the meninges. (See also p. 160.)

The posterior surface of the petrous temporal is the anterior wall of the lateral part of the fossa; the only conspicuous aperture in it is the oblique open-

ing of the **internal auditory meatus** [m. acusticus internus] (Fig. 147, 22, p. 179). The meatus is a short canal in the petrous temporal, nearly horizontal and nearly transverse; its lateral end is separated by thin bone from the internal ear. It is almost opposite the external meatus, and is about an inch and a half from the surface of the head.

The **internal auditory meatus** is about 8 mm. long and 3 to 5 mm. wide. It transmits the motor and sensory roots of the facial nerve, the auditory nerve, the internal auditory branch of the basilar artery and the internal auditory vein, which joins the inferior petrosal sinus. The lateral end of the meatus is called the **fundus** or bottom. The part of the petrous temporal bone that forms the

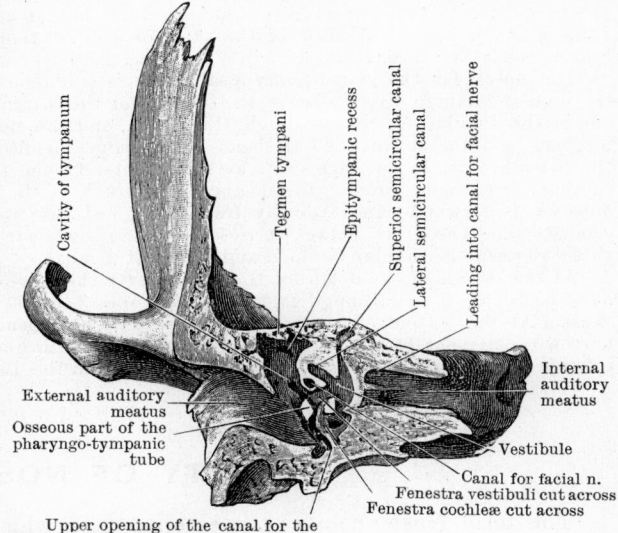

FIG. 144.—VERTICAL TRANSVERSE SECTION THROUGH THE LEFT TEMPORAL BONE (Anterior Half of Section).

fundus separates the meatus from the vestibule and cochlea of the internal ear. In the fundus there are several apertures that transmit the auditory vessels and the facial and auditory nerves. If the skull has been split into halves so that one can see into the meatus, the fundus and the holes in it are visible at the far end. The position of the internal ear can be gauged by an examination of the meatuses. The fundus of the internal meatus is the medial wall of the internal ear. The lateral wall of the internal ear is the medial wall of the tympanum or middle ear ; that wall can be seen through the external auditory meatus, and the bulge called the promontory seen there is produced by the basal curve of the cochlea, which is coiled like a snail shell [κοχλίας (cochlias) = a snail, a spiral]. The arcuate eminence of the anterior surface of the petrous temporal also is a guide, for it overlies the superior semicircular canal, which stands up from the posterior part of the vestibule of the inner ear like the handle of a pail. The facial nerve passes through one of the holes in the fundus of the internal meatus and enters the facial canal ; the canal conducts it through the temporal bone, passing first in a lateral direction, above the vestibule, to the anterior part of the upper border of the medial wall of the tympanum, then backwards in the medial wall near its upper border, and finally downwards behind the tympanum, and the canal ends as the stylo-mastoid foramen on the lower surface of the skull.

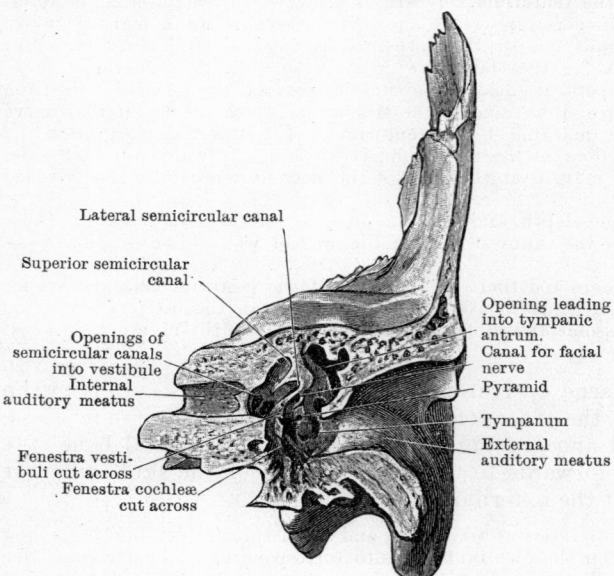

Lateral semicircular canal

Superior semicircular canal

Openings of semicircular canals into vestibule
Internal auditory meatus

Fenestra vestibuli cut across
Fenestra cochleæ cut across

Opening leading into tympanic antrum.
Canal for facial nerve
Pyramid

Tympanum
External auditory meatus

Fig. 145.—Vertical Transverse Section through the Left Temporal Bone (Posterior Half of Section).

A narrow canal about 8 mm. long, called the **aqueduct of the vestibule**, passes backwards from the vestibule and opens on the posterior surface of the petrous temporal ; this *external opening* is at the bottom of a small slit seen about half an inch lateral to the opening of the internal meatus ; the slit is overhung by a thin lip of bone. The canal transmits a tiny artery and vein and a delicate membranous tube called the *endolymphatic duct* ; this duct emerges from the external aperture and its blind terminal portion dilates to form a bag, called the *endolymphatic sac*, which lies under cover of the dura mater.

The **subarcuate fossa** is a small, ill-defined depression about midway between the opening of the meatus and the aperture of the aqueduct, but at a higher level than either of them. It is larger and better defined in the skull of a child than of an adult (Fig. 168, C, p. 208). Small vessels pass through its floor into the bone.

The **notch for the glosso-pharyngeal nerve** is a rounded notch on the anterior margin of the jugular foramen directly below the opening of the internal meatus ; the ninth cranial nerve enters the jugular foramen through this notch, and the notch is cut off from the rest of the foramen by a fibrous band. This band is sometimes ossified, but more usually the margins of the notch are prolonged backwards as little spurs of bone that partially or completely divide the jugular foramen into compartments. The notch is the upper end of a groove that runs downwards, forwards, and laterally from it, immediately in front of the jugular fossa. The groove lodges the ninth nerve ; it is seen on the lower surface of the skull, for it ends at the ridge between the jugular foramen and the carotid canal.

At the bottom of the notch for the ninth nerve there is a small pit hidden under an overhanging lip of bone, although it may in some specimens be seen from the lower surface of the skull. At the bottom of the pit there is the **external opening of the cochlear canaliculus**—a narrow canal about 15 mm. long, which leads from the cochlea and conducts a small vein to the inferior petrosal sinus and a tubular prolongation from the dura mater to the cochlea.

CAVITY OF NOSE

The term **Nose** includes the **external nose**, which juts from the face, and also the **cavity of the nose**, of which merely a small part lies in the external nose.

The **cavity of the nose** extends from the posterior bony apertures on the base of the skull to the anterior bony aperture on the front—or to the nostrils, when the soft parts are in place. It is above the cavity of the mouth, being separated therefrom by the hard palate ; and it lies below the anterior and middle cranial fossæ and the frontal and sphenoidal air sinuses.   In round numbers of millimetres, its length increases from 50 mm. at the floor to 75 mm. at the roof; its greatest height, about its middle, is 50 mm., and it diminishes to 30 mm. at the anterior aperture and 25 mm. at the posterior apertures.

It is divided into **right** and **left halves** by a median partition or **septum**, and the term "cavity of nose" or "nasal cavity" is applied sometimes to the whole cavity and sometimes to one or other of the halves—the context interpreting which is meant.   Each of the two cavities is narrow from side to side; the widest part, near the floor, measures only about 10 mm., while near the roof, except in its posterior section, it is only 1 or 2 mm.

Boundaries.— Each of the two nasal cavities has a *roof*, a *floor*, a *lateral* wall, and a *medial* wall — the medial wall being the septum between the cavities.

The **roof** is very narrow from side to side except at its posterior end.   It is horizontal in the middle, but slopes downwards in front and behind, and the anterior and posterior parts of the cavity are therefore of lesser vertical depth than the middle part.   The **middle** horizontal part is the cribriform plate of the ethmoid.   The **anterior** sloping part is formed by a small part of the frontal bone and by the nasal bone below that; and, still lower down, when the soft parts are in place, by the cartilages of the nose.   The **posterior** sloping part—a very steep slope—is formed by the anterior and inferior surfaces of the body of the sphenoid.

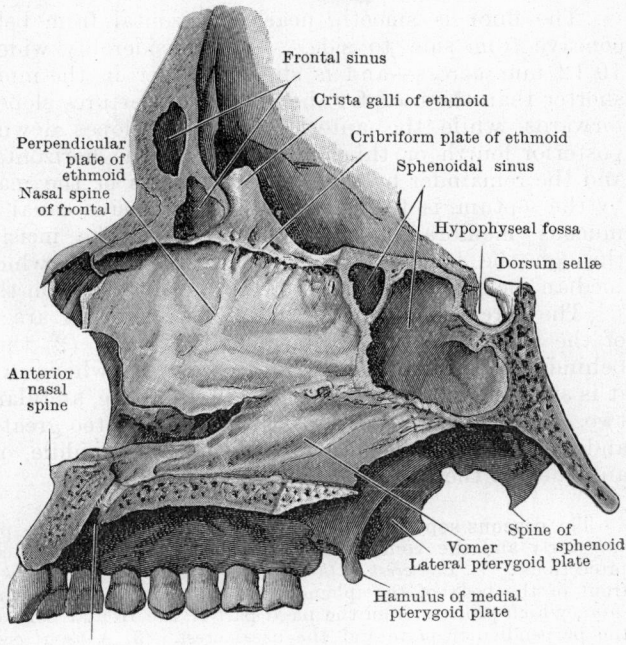

Fig. 146.—Roof, Floor, and Septum of Nose.

Red : Parts of frontal, sphenoid and maxilla.
Blue : Vomer ; basi-occiput ; part of nasal.|
White : Perpendicular plate of ethmoid ; horizontal plate of palatine.

The **roof of each nasal cavity**, in nearly the whole of its length, is only 1 or 2 mm. in width, but its most posterior part, which is formed by the lower surface of the body of the sphenoid, measures about 10 mm. across ; in a dried skull, that is also the lowest part of the roof— being on a level with the zygomatic arch at the side of the skull.   Though the anterior part of the lower surface of the body of the sphenoid is reckoned as part of the roof, yet the ala of the vomer and the sphenoidal process of the palatine bone, which are closely applied to it, shut it off from the nasal cavity, and are the actual bones clothed with the muco-periosteum of the posterior part of the roof.   The **palatino-vaginal canal** (p. 155) is situated in that part of the roof, between the sphenoidal process and the body of the sphenoid.

The part of the roof formed by the anterior surface of the body of the sphenoid looks forwards rather than downwards, and diminishes to 2 mm. in width as it is traced upwards and forwards, for the greater part of each half of the front of the body of the sphenoid articulates with the labyrinth of the ethmoid, leaving the smaller part alongside the median plane free to form a boundary for the nasal cavity.   In that area there is a round opening of considerable size which leads back into the *sphenoidal sinus*.

The anterior surface and anterior part of the lower surface of each half of the body of the sphenoid is made of bone which in early life is separate and is called the *sphenoidal concha*.

The part of the nasal cavity which is highest, and also nearest the cranial cavity, is the middle part ; it is roofed by the cribriform plate, which is at the level of the nasion, and is perforated by the olfactory nerves ; infection from a diseased nose has, at that part, only a very short distance to travel to reach the brain and its membranes.

The nasal surface of the frontal bone is only a very narrow strip that appears in the roof of

12

the nose in front of the cribriform plate ; it separates the nasal cavity from the frontal sinus, and it slopes downwards and forwards to the nasal bone. Those two bones form the anterior sloping part of the roof; along that part of the roof the anterior ethmoidal nerve (with companion vessels) runs downwards and forwards to emerge between the nasal bone and cartilage, under the name of the external nasal nerve, for the supply of the skin of the lower half of the external nose ; the nerve leaves a narrow groove on the surface of bone on which it runs.

The **floor** is smooth, nearly horizontal from before backwards, and slightly concave from side to side. It is considerably wider than the roof—measuring 10-12 mm. across—and is slightly wider in the middle than at its ends. It is shorter than the roof, for the posterior apertures slope from above downwards and forwards, while the anterior aperture slopes downwards and backwards. Its posterior fourth or third is formed by the horizontal plate of the palatine bone, and the remainder by the palatine process of the maxilla. Near the front, close by the septum, is the opening of the incisive canal, which is covered over with mucous membrane before maceration. The **incisive canal** passes downwards through the bone and divides into two parts which open, as the lateral and median incisive foramina, into the incisive fossa on the bony palate.

The three chief constituents of the **septum** are : (1) the perpendicular plate of the ethmoid, situated above and behind ; (2) the vomer, situated below and behind ; (3) the septal cartilage of the nose, which, in a dried skull, is destroyed ; it is situated anteriorly, and fills in the wide, angular interval between the other two. The superficial area of the septum is too great for the height of the cavity, and it is therefore bent to one side near its middle, or it is bent first to one side and then to the other.

The **osseous septum** is composed almost entirely of the perpendicular plate of the ethmoid superiorly and the vomer below and posteriorly, but it is completed by the following small projections : (1) The *crest of the sphenoid*, which projects forwards from the median line of the front of the body of the sphenoid to articulate with the perpendicular plate. (2) The *nasal spine*, which projects from the nasal part of the frontal bone downwards and forwards between the perpendicular plate and the nasal crest. (3) A *nasal crest* is formed by the lips of the margins of the nasal bones that articulate with each other ; that crest articulates, from above downwards, with the nasal spine of the frontal bone, the perpendicular plate, and the septal cartilage. (4) A *nasal crest*, to articulate with the lower edge of the vomer, is formed by sharp ridges that stand up from the horizontal part of the palatine bone and the palatine process of the maxilla where they articulate with their fellows of the other side. The anterior part of this crest stands up from the junction of the alveolar processes of the maxillæ ; it is thicker and higher than the rest ; and it articulates posteriorly with the vomer and superiorly with the sub-vomerine cartilage.

The upper part of the perpendicular plate of the ethmoid shows numerous small branching grooves that lodge olfactory nerves. Indistinct grooves for vessels may be seen on the vomer, and one long groove for the long spheno-palatine nerve and the spheno-palatine vessels, which enter the nose through the spheno-palatine foramen in the lateral wall, cross the roof and run downwards and forwards, grooving the vomer, to reach the incisive canal.

The *cartilaginous septum* is formed almost wholly by the septal cartilage, which, however, is aided by (1) the sub-vomerine cartilage (*i.e.* a small strip along its lower margin) ; and (2) the medial part of the right and left lower nasal cartilage, at the tip of the nose.

The **lateral wall** is very uneven and is composed of several bones, namely, the *nasal*, the *maxilla* and its *frontal process*, the *lacrimal*, the *labyrinth* of the ethmoid and its *conchæ*, the *inferior concha*, the perpendicular plate of the *palatine*, and the *medial pterygoid plate*.

Identify the conchæ at once. The **inferior nasal concha** is the rough plate of bone that projects from the side wall into the lower part of the nasal cavity for a little distance and then curves downwards ; it is a separate bone, and if it has been broken away, the line along which it was attached is seen as an irregular, broken ridge about half an inch above the floor of the nose. The **middle nasal concha** is situated about an inch above the inferior concha, which it resembles ; it is not a separate bone, but projects from the ethmoid labyrinth a little way into the nasal cavity and then turns downwards. The **superior nasal concha** also is a projection from the labyrinth. It is much smaller than the other conchæ ; it is the small ridge of bone situated a little above the posterior half of the middle concha. If a pair of forceps is passed into the living nose and opened vertically, it must be kept close to the septum, else the upper leg will be intercepted by the conchæ.

The **nasal bone** lies in the anterior and upper part of the lateral wall, as well as in the roof. The **frontal process of the maxilla** lies immediately behind and below the nasal bone. Those two bones form also the bony skeleton of the external

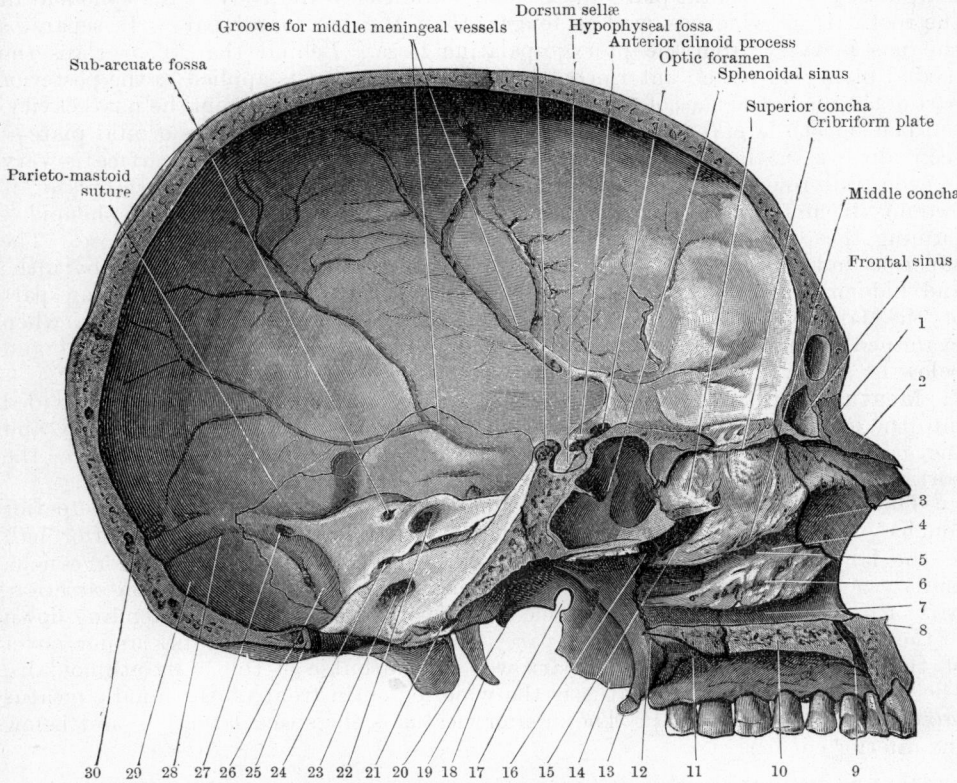

Fig. 147.—Medial Aspect of the Left Half of the Skull sagittally divided.

Red : parts of frontal, maxilla, and sphenoid. Blue : palatine ; nasal ; part of parietal. Purple : part of occipital squama. Yellow : part of basi-occiput. Uncoloured : left ala of vomer ; inferior concha ; ethmoid ; and other bones.

1. Near nasal spine of frontal.
2. Nasal bone.
3. Frontal process of maxilla (and atrium).
4. Lower part of middle meatus.
5. Near opening of maxillary sinus.
6. Inferior concha.
7. Inferior meatus.
8. Anterior nasal spine.
9. Incisive fossa and canal.
10. Palatine process of maxilla.
11. Horizontal plate of palatine.
12. Posterior nasal spine.
13. Hamulus of medial pterygoid plate.
14. Lateral pterygoid plate.
15. Superior meatus.
16. Spheno-palatine foramen.
17. Foramen formed by ossified pterygo-spinous lig.
18. Styloid process.
19. Spine of sphenoid.
20. Mastoid process.
21. Basion.
22. Internal auditory meatus.
23. Anterior condylar canal.
24. Groove for inferior petrosal sinus.
25. Opisthion.
26. Sigmoid groove.
27. Opening of mastoid foramen.
28. Transverse groove.
29. Cerebellar fossa.
30. Internal occipital protuberance.

nose. The **lacrimal bone**, seen already in the orbit, lies behind the frontal process ; only its lower and anterior part appears in the nose.

The **medial pterygoid plate** is the most posterior bone in the lateral wall of the nose. It forms the lateral boundary of the posterior aperture, and has been often referred to already.

The medial surface of the **body of the maxilla** lies in the lower part of the side wall of the nasal cavity, extending from the lower part of the anterior aperture backwards almost to the medial pterygoid plate. It is to a large extent concealed by other bones, among which there are two openings out of the maxillary sinus.

The **perpendicular plate of the palatine bone** lies in the posterior part of the lateral wall in front of the medial pterygoid plate. The horizontal plate is easily identified in the floor. The perpendicular plate lies directly above the lateral margin of the horizontal plate and extends upwards to the body of the sphenoid in the roof. It is wider, as well as longer, than the horizontal part. It separates the nasal cavity from the pterygo-palatine fossa. Behind that, it overlaps the medial pterygoid plate; anteriorly, the greater part of it is applied to the posterior part of the medial surface of the maxilla, shutting off that part from the nasal cavity.

The smooth lateral surface of the **labyrinth of the ethmoid** is its orbital plate— seen already in the orbit, behind the lacrimal bone. Its **medial surface** is very uneven and rough, and is now seen in the nose below the cribriform plate; it extends from the frontal process of the maxilla to the body of the sphenoid— forming the greater part of the upper half of the lateral wall of the nose. The superior and middle conchæ project from the medial surface of the labyrinth; and hidden under cover of the middle concha there is a rounded, bulging part of the labyrinth, called the **bulla ethmoidalis**, which can partly be seen when examined from the front [*bulla* = a bubble]. The bulla is bounded in front and below by a curved groove or slit called the **hiatus semilunaris**.

Meatuses of the Nose.—The lateral part of the cavity of the nose is divided into the *superior*, *middle*, and *inferior* meatuses, the *spheno-ethmoidal recess*, and the *atrium* of the middle meatus; and, when the soft parts are in place, the portion above the nostril is called the *vestibule* of the nose.

The **spheno-ethmoidal recess** is the small space above and behind the superior concha. The **superior meatus** is an oblique, cleft-like space in the posterior half of the labyrinth of the ethmoid; its slit-like orifice is below the superior concha and above the middle concha. The **middle meatus** is much larger than the superior; part of it is lateral to the middle concha and part of it is below—extending down to the inferior concha. The lower part is roomy; the part that lies under cover of the middle concha is greatly narrowed by the bulge of the bulla ethmoidalis. The **atrium** of the middle meatus is the wide region in front of the middle meatus [*atrium* = an entrance hall]. The **inferior meatus** is the space lateral to and below the inferior concha.

The **lateral wall** of the nasal cavity is more uneven and complicated than the other boundaries. It is also the most variable and most liable to injury in the dried skull, and the student may therefore have difficulty in applying any given description to the specimen he is using for study.

The groove made by the anterior ethmoidal nerve may be on the part of the **nasal bone** that lies in the lateral wall, rather than on the part in the roof.

The **frontal process of the maxilla** presents a wide area which forms the side wall of the *atrium* of the middle meatus. At the lower boundary of that area, where the frontal process joins the body of the maxilla, there is a horizontal ridge, called the *conchal crest*, which articulates with the anterior part of the inferior concha. At the upper boundary of the area there is a ridge called the *ethmoidal crest*. The anterior part of that ridge produces the elevation, called the *agger nasi*, in the un-macerated head. The posterior part articulates with the anterior end of the middle concha; the portion of the frontal process above that articulation is applied to the front of the labyrinth of the ethmoid and helps to close in the anterior ethmoidal sinuses.

The **lacrimal bone** also is applied to the labyrinth, forming a boundary to the anterior ethmoidal sinuses; but its antero-inferior portion appears in the side wall of the nose, and its lowest part projects downwards and helps to close the opening of the maxillary sinus.

The **labyrinth of the ethmoid**, situated between the orbit and the nasal cavity, bulges into the nasal cavity and greatly reduces the width of its upper part. It is composed of exceedingly thin, fragile bone. The upper half of its medial side is a wide area which, though far from smooth, is relatively even, and shows narrow grooves for the lateral group of olfactory nerves leading up to the holes in the cribriform plate. Inferiorly the posterior half of the area ends in the projecting ridge called the **superior concha**; the anterior half is continuous with the medial surface of the anterior part of the middle concha.

The **spheno-ethmoidal recess** is situated above and behind the posterior part of the superior concha, in front of the body of the sphenoid, and the sphenoidal sinus opens into it through a round hole.

The **middle concha** forms the roof and medial wall of the upper, narrow part of the middle meatus, and its rough medial surface is the lower and lesser half of the medial side of the labyrinth. It extends forwards to the frontal process of the maxilla, and backwards to the perpendicular part of the palatine bone—its anterior end being at a considerably higher level than the posterior end. The lower border is convex from before backwards, its lowest point being about the level of the floor of the orbit; this border is thickened and curled in a lateral direction, so that the lateral surface of the concha is concave and the medial surface is convex.

The **superior meatus** is bounded inferiorly by the posterior half of the middle concha, and superiorly by the superior concha and the walls of posterior ethmoidal sinuses; these sinuses open into it by two or three orifices in the dried skull, but mucous membrane covers one or two of the openings during life. The **spheno-palatine foramen** also opens into it at its posterior part, but is covered over with mucous membrane before maceration.

The **bulla ethmoidalis** bulges from the lateral wall into the upper part of the middle meatus, and is therefore hidden under cover of the middle concha; it varies considerably in size, and it encloses some of the middle ethmoidal sinuses.

From the labyrinth, in front of the bulla, there springs a long, thin process called the **uncinate process**: this process curves downwards and backwards, first in front of the bulla and then below it, and has a considerable share in covering the opening of the maxillary sinus.

The curved interval between the bulla and the uncinate process is the **hiatus semilunaris**; as the mucous lining passes from the bulla to the process, it dips into the hiatus to form a floor for it and convert it into a gutter-like groove. In some skulls, however, the uncinate process is closely applied to the bulla, and the hiatus is then a gutter-like groove on the process, the margins of which are curled to form the margins of the groove. The **infundibulum** [= a funnel], which leads downwards through the anterior part of the ethmoid labyrinth from the frontal sinus, opens into the hiatus.

The **middle meatus** extends from the attached margin of the middle concha down to the inferior concha, and is therefore of considerable height. The middle concha constitutes a medial wall for the upper, narrow part of the meatus; this part is at the level of the orbit, and is separated from the orbit by the lower part of the labyrinth, including the bulla. The lower, wide part of the meatus is open medially, and is situated below the labyrinth,

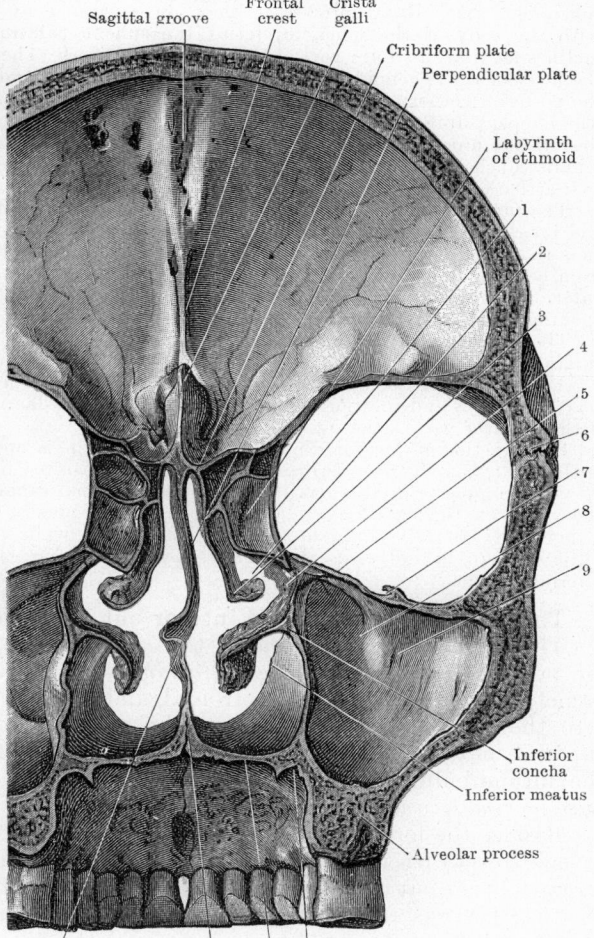

FIG. 148.—CORONAL SECTION PASSING INFERIORLY BETWEEN THE FIRST AND SECOND MOLAR TEETH.

Red: ethmoid; inferior concha; zygomatic.
Blue: frontal; maxilla. **Yellow**: vomer.

1. Orbital plate of ethmoid.
2. Middle meatus of nose.
3. Middle concha.
4. Opening of maxillary sinus.
5. Orbital surface of maxilla.
6. Zygomatico-frontal suture.
7. Infra-orbital groove.
8. Maxillary sinus.
9. Canal for the anterior dental nerve and vessels exposed.
10. Palatine process of maxilla.
11. Nasal crest of maxillæ.

opposite the upper part of the maxillary sinus, from which it is separated by the bones that close the opening of the sinus.

The *sinuses* leading into the meatus open into its upper part. The *middle ethmoidal* sinuses open into it on the surface of the bulla; the *maxillary* sinus opens into the lower part of the hiatus semilunaris; the infundibulum, leading from the *frontal* sinus, opens into the upper part of the hiatus; the *anterior ethmoidal* sinuses also open into the upper part of the hiatus and into the infundibulum. In the dried skull there are one or more additional openings out of the maxillary sinus into the lower part of the meatus, but they are closed with mucous membrane when the soft parts are in place.

The **perpendicular plate of the palatine bone** is a very thin plate of bone situated in the posterior part of the side wall of the nose. Its posterior edge articulates with the medial pterygoid plate and often overlaps it. Anteriorly, it is applied to the medial surface of the maxilla and takes a considerable share in closing the opening of the maxillary sinus. Between the upper parts of the maxilla and pterygoid process, it forms the medial wall of the pterygo-palatine fossa, from which the **greater palatine canal** descends to the hard palate; the canal is situated in the side wall of the nose between the palatine bone and the maxilla. Two processes project upwards from the upper end or margin of the palatine bone, namely, the sphenoidal and orbital processes; they are separated by the spheno-palatine notch, which, with the body of the sphenoid, forms the **spheno-palatine foramen**. The *sphenoidal process* inclines medially to form part of the roof of the nose. The *orbital process* is wedged in between the body of the sphenoid, the labyrinth of the ethmoid, and the body of the maxilla, and forms the posterior corner of the floor of the orbit; it often contains a cavity, called the *palatine sinus*, which opens into the sphenoidal sinus or into a posterior ethmoidal sinus. At the root of the orbital process, a ridge called the *ethmoidal crest* articulates with the posterior end of the middle concha; about 10 mm. from the lower end of the palatine bone, a ridge called the *conchal crest* articulates with the posterior end of the inferior concha.

The **inferior concha** extends between the conchal crests of the palatine bone and the maxilla, and its anterior attachment is the higher. It reaches a little farther forward and a little farther back than the middle concha does. Its lower border is slightly thickened, curled laterally, convex from before backwards, and is only a little distance above the level of the lower margin of the anterior bony aperture of the nose. The inferior concha passes across the lower part of the opening of the maxillary sinus and sends off processes which assist in closing the opening.

The **inferior meatus** extends from the attached margin of the inferior concha to the bony palate; the medial surface of the lower part of the maxilla is its lateral wall; and the concha provides it with a roof and a partial medial boundary. It is related laterally to the maxillary sinus and inferiorly to the mouth. The **naso-lacrimal canal** opens into it under cover of the anterior part of the inferior concha.

The junction of the middle meatus and its atrium is opposite the fossa for the lacrimal sac in the orbit, and the mucous lining of the nose is separated from the sac by the lacrimal bone and the frontal process of the maxilla. The **naso-lacrimal canal** is situated in the side wall of the nose between the nasal cavity and the maxillary sinus. It is 10 or 12 mm. in length, and is bounded laterally and antero-medially by the walls of a deep groove in the maxilla, while postero-medially it is bounded by the lower part of the lacrimal bone and the inferior concha.

The apertures which lead into or out of the nose are the following:—

The *posterior bony aperture*; the *anterior bony aperture*, or, when soft parts are present, the *nostril*; the *naso-lacrimal canal*; and the *openings of the sinuses*, namely, sphenoidal, ethmoidal, frontal, and maxillary. The **sphenoidal sinus** opens into the spheno-ethmoidal recess; the **posterior ethmoidal sinuses** open into the superior meatus; the **middle** and **anterior ethmoidal sinuses**, the **frontal sinus** *via* the infundibulum, and the **maxillary sinus** open into the middle meatus. The *naso-lacrimal canal* opens into the inferior meatus.

Besides the foregoing there are certain apertures in the dried skull which are covered over with mucous membrane before maceration, viz.: The *spheno-palatine foramen* opens out of the pterygo-palatine fossa into the posterior part of the superior meatus; there is an additional opening out of the maxillary sinus into the middle meatus; the *incisive canal* leads down from the anterior part of the floor of the nose into the incisive fossa; and the *foramina in the cribriform plate* in the roof transmit the olfactory nerves from the nose to the median part of the anterior cranial fossa.

General Relations of the Nose (Fig. 148).—**Superior,** from before backwards: the frontal sinus; the anterior or ethmoidal part of the median subdivision of the anterior cranial fossa; the sphenoidal sinus, separating the nose from the posterior part of that fossa and from the median subdivision of the middle cranial fossa. **Inferior:** the mouth. **Posterior:** the nasal part of the pharynx. **Lateral:** the pterygoid fossa, the pterygo-palatine fossa, and the greater palatine canal opposite the posterior section of the cavity; farther forward, the ethmoidal sinuses, the infundibulum, and the orbit, opposite the upper half of the middle section of the cavity, while opposite the lower half there are the maxillary sinus and the naso-lacrimal canal; the anterior section is situated in the external nose and is related laterally to the exterior.

PARANASAL SINUSES

The **paranasal air sinuses** (Figs. 148, 149) are cavities in the interior of certain of the skull bones, namely, the *frontal*, the *ethmoid*, the *sphenoid*, the *maxilla,* and the *palatine.* They all communicate either directly or indirectly with the cavity of the nose. The sphenoidal, ethmoidal, and maxillary communicate directly; the frontal and the palatine, indirectly. They are all lined with mucous membrane which is continuous, round the lips of the apertures of communication, with the mucous lining of the nose, and disease can readily spread from the nose to the sinuses. During a severe cold in the head, the inflammation often extends from the nasal mucous lining to the mucous lining of sinuses, giving rise to frontal headaches (frontal sinus), pain in the cheek (maxillary sinus), pain between the eyes (ethmoidal sinuses), deep-seated pain at the back of the eyes (sphenoidal sinus).

The walls of the sinuses are composed of compact bone; for, in the ethmoid, spongy bone is not formed, and in the other pneumatic bones the sinuses take the place of the spongy substance and its marrow, which have been absorbed to make room for them. They are lined with endosteum, which is blended with the mucous lining; and the mucous lining, like that of the nose, is covered with ciliated epithelium.

At birth the ethmoidal and sphenoidal sinuses are present but are very small; the maxillary sinus is a mere groove; the frontal appears during childhood. They all enlarge gradually till puberty, and rapidly after puberty till they attain their full adult size; in old age they enlarge further, owing to the absorption of the diploë adjoining them.

The sinuses act as resonating chambers for the voice; and by means of them the bones containing them, without increase of weight, gain increase of bulk and superficies necessary for the formation of the walls of the cavities of the nose, mouth, and orbits. They are relatively larger in men than in women.

The **maxillary sinus** (Figs. 148, 149) is a large cavity that occupies the body of the maxilla. It is *lateral* to the lower half of the nasal cavity, *below* the orbit, *in front of* infra-temporal fossa, and *above* the molar and premolar teeth—its deepest part being above the first molar and second premolar tooth. The opening out of it is on the medial side; in a separated maxilla the opening is very wide, but, when in position in the skull, that large opening is overlapped by adjoining bones and reduced to two small apertures, or perhaps three; when the mucous membrane is in place, only the uppermost of those apertures is left uncovered, and it opens out of the **uppermost** part of the sinus into the lower or posterior part of the hiatus semilunaris of the middle meatus.

The **maxillary sinus** is the largest of the sinuses; it is variable in size and may differ in the two sides of the same skull. Average measurements, in round numbers, are 35 mm. in height, 30 mm. in antero-posterior depth, and 25 mm. in width. In shape it resembles a pyramid laid on one side. The **apex** is situated in the zygomatic process of the maxilla. The **base** or **medial wall** separates it from the inferior meatus and the lower, wide part of the middle meatus, and is formed by the medial or nasal surface of the maxilla and the bones that almost completely close the large opening in the upper part of that surface, namely, portions of the uncinate process of the ethmoid, the palatine, the lacrimal, and the inferior concha.

The secretions of the mucous lining of the sinus are swept towards the orifice in the medial wall by the cilia of the epithelial covering of the mucous membrane; in inflammatory conditions, when the quality of the secretion clogs the action of the cilia or the quantity is too great for them to cope with, the sinus fills up, since the orifice is at its uppermost part.

The **floor** of the sinus is the alveolar process of the maxilla, and is the thickest wall of the sinus, though the process is excavated by the sockets for the teeth. The teeth whose roots are in relation to the floor vary from the three molars as a minimum to the molars, premolars, and the canine as a maximum. The roots of the first two molars produce eminences in the floor, and, though usually covered with thin bone, they may perforate the floor. Incomplete septa springing from the intervals between teeth may partially divide the sinus into compartments. The floor is below the level of the floor of the nose; the lowest part is about 10 mm. below the level of the nose, and overlies the roots of the first molar and second premolar teeth. The **posterior wall** is the bone of the posterior surface of the maxilla, which separates the sinus from the infra-temporal and pterygo-palatine fossæ. The **posterior dental canals,** conveying the vessels and nerves to the molar teeth, are in the lower part of the posterior wall. The **roof** is the bone of the orbital surface of the maxilla, which separates the sinus from the orbit. The **infra-orbital groove and canal** are in the roof and may produce a ridge, especially at the angle between roof and anterior wall. The anterior or **antero-lateral wall** is the bone of the anterior surface of the maxilla. The branches of the infra-orbital vessel and nerve to the premolar, canine, and incisor teeth descend through canals in the antero-lateral wall, but occasionally one or more of the canals may be defective; the corresponding vessels and nerve then lie between the bone and the mucous lining. The upper and anterior part of the sinus extends far enough forwards to be in front of the naso-lacrimal canal as well as lateral to it.

The maxillary sinus is the first sinus to appear; though, at birth, it is merely a groove on the medial side of the bone in the region of the middle meatus, yet that groove began to appear in the fourth month of intra-uterine life.

The **frontal sinus** is a cavity in the frontal bone; it is separated from its fellow by a complete bony septum which is usually bent to one or other

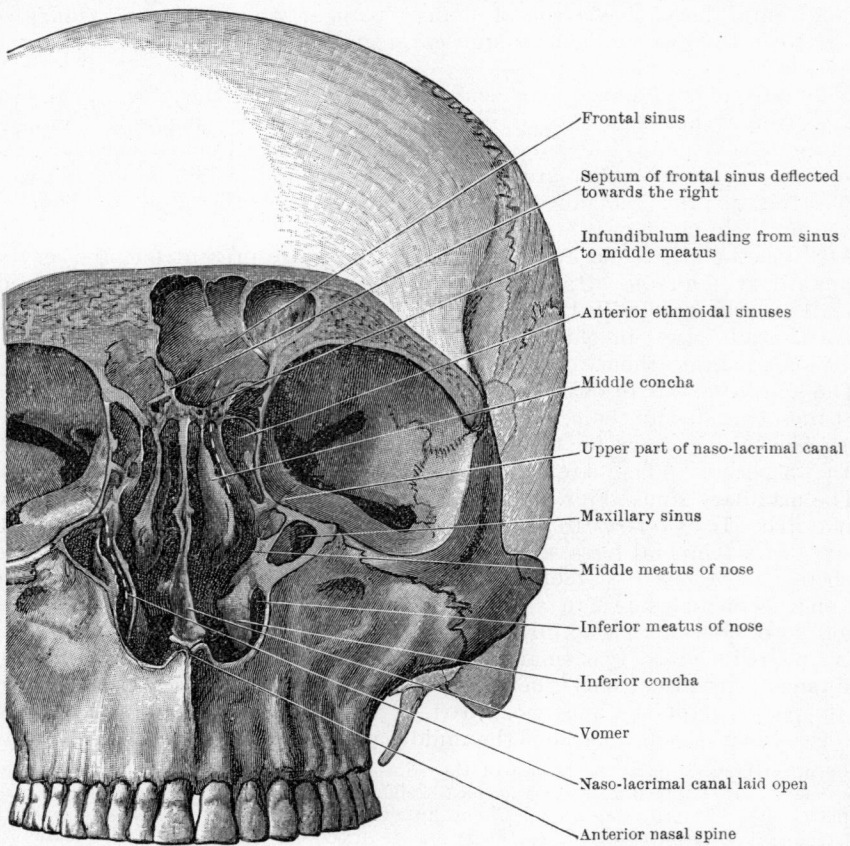

Frontal sinus

Septum of frontal sinus deflected towards the right

Infundibulum leading from sinus to middle meatus

Anterior ethmoidal sinuses

Middle concha

Upper part of naso-lacrimal canal

Maxillary sinus

Middle meatus of nose

Inferior meatus of nose

Inferior concha

Vomer

Naso-lacrimal canal laid open

Anterior nasal spine

FIG. 149.—PART OF THE FRONTAL, NASAL, AND MAXILLARY BONES REMOVED IN ORDER TO DISPLAY THE RELATION OF THE VARIOUS CAVITIES EXPOSED.

Red: ethmoid; inferior concha.   **Blue**: frontal and maxillary (where cut).   **Yellow**: lacrimal; vomer.

side. It is immediately above the supra-orbital margin and above the root of the nose. If large, it extends backwards in the roof of the orbit between the two tables of the orbital plate. The frontal sinus may open directly into the nasal cavity through an opening in the nasal part of the frontal bone, but more commonly one of the anterior ethmoidal sinuses is converted into a passage, called the **infundibulum**, by means of which the sinus drains into the middle meatus, for the upper end of the infundibulum opens into the sinus and its lower end opens into the upper or anterior end of the hiatus semilunaris.

The **ethmoidal sinuses** are numerous small thin-walled, intercommunicating cavities that occupy the labyrinth of the ethmoid. They are therefore between the orbit and the nasal cavity, and below the cranial cavity, from which they are separated by the medial part of the orbital plate of the frontal bone. They are divided into three groups—anterior, middle, and posterior. The **posterior sinuses** open into the superior meatus of the nose by one or more apertures. The **middle sinuses** open into the middle meatus on the surface of the bulla ethmoidalis by one or two apertures. The **anterior sinuses** open into the hiatus semilunaris of the middle meatus and into the infundibulum.

The **frontal sinus** varies greatly in size in different skulls, and may vary on the two sides of the same skull—the left usually being the larger. Average measurements are 30 mm. in height, 25 mm. in transverse width, and 20 mm. in antero-posterior depth. The configuration of the brow in the living person gives no indication of its size ; in a well-formed skull one or both may be absent, or it may extend laterally as far as the temporal fossa and backwards in the roof of the orbit as far as the optic foramen. The septum between the right and left sinuses is usually median inferiorly and bent to one side above. The sinus is related *inferiorly* to the orbit, the nose, and the anterior ethmoidal cells ; *postero-superiorly* to the cranial cavity and the brain.

An indication of the frontal sinus may be met with at the second year, but it cannot be definitely recognised till the seventh.

The walls of the **ethmoidal sinuses** are completed by the bones with which the ethmoid labyrinth articulates—the body of the sphenoid, the orbital process of the palatine bone, the orbital plate of the frontal bone, the lacrimal bone, the frontal process and the medial margin of the orbital surface of the maxilla. They are related *laterally* to the orbit ; *medially* to the upper half of the cavity of the nose ; *posteriorly* to the sphenoidal and palatine sinuses ; *superiorly* to the sphenoidal sinus, the frontal sinus, the anterior cranial fossa, and to the ethmoidal canals between the orbital plate and the ethmoidal labyrinth ; *inferiorly* the posterior sinuses are related to the superior meatus, into which they open, and the middle and anterior sinuses are related to the lower part of the middle meatus.

The ethmoidal sinuses begin to develop during the latter half of intra-uterine life, and the papery bone of the ethmoid is deposited around them in the cartilaginous nasal capsule.

The **sphenoidal sinus** is a large cavity in the body of the sphenoid bone. It is situated above the cavities of the naso-pharynx and nose, and below the median part of the cranial cavity. It is divided into right and left halves by a complete bony septum, which is usually bent to one or other side : each half may be referred to as a sphenoidal sinus, and it opens into the spheno-ethmoidal recess of the nose by a round aperture 4 or 5 mm. in diameter.

The **sphenoidal sinus** may be small and limited to the anterior part of the body of the sphenoid ; or it may occupy the whole of the body and extend into the roots of the wings and pterygoid processes, and backwards into the basilar part of the occipital bone. Its average dimensions are about 20 mm. each way.

Inferiorly it is related to the cavity of the naso-pharynx and posterior part of the nose and to the pterygoid canal with its contained nerve and vessels. *Anteriorly* it is related to the upper part of the middle section of the cavity of the nose and to the posterior ethmoidal sinuses. *Laterally* it is related : (1) to the optic nerve in the optic foramen, and to the apical part of the orbit ; (2) behind that, to the cavernous venous sinus, in the walls of which the internal carotid artery, the third, fourth, sixth, and ophthalmic nerves are imbedded ; (3) to the maxillary nerve, as it runs forwards along the lower border of the cavernous sinus and as it passes through the foramen rotundum. *Superiorly* it is related : (1) to the frontal lobes of the brain and the olfactory tracts, lying on the anterior part of the body of the sphenoid ; (2) more remotely, to the optic chiasma, which lies above the optic groove ; (3) to the hypophysis cerebri, lying in the hypophyseal fossa ; (4) to the pons and the basilar artery, lying on the clivus. The relation of the sinus and the nose to the hypophysis is of special interest because the hypophysis is subject to tumour growth and the operator may approach it through the nose and the sphenoidal sinus. The hypophysis is 60 mm. behind the nasion and at almost the same horizontal level. A line connecting the hypophysis with the lower margin of the anterior bony aperture of the nose is 75 mm. long and forms an angle of 45° with the floor of the nose.

The rudiments of the sphenoidal sinuses appear in the fifth month of intra-uterine life or a little later. They are recesses of the nasal cavity that are partly cut off from it and are enclosed within the sphenoidal conchæ (p. 209) when they begin to ossify. But those rudiments do not begin to extend into the body of the sphenoid till the seventh or eighth year.

The **palatine sinus**, when present, occupies the orbital process of the palatine bone, and opens either into the sphenoidal sinus or into a posterior ethmoidal sinus.

Mandible

The **mandible** or lower jaw bone lies below the anterior part of the cranium, and is the skeleton of the lower part of the face. It has a horseshoe-shaped **body** and a pair of flat, broad **rami**, which stand up from the posterior part of the body. Each ramus is surmounted by two processes, the anterior of which is named the **coronoid process**, and the posterior is the **condyloid process** ; the condyloid process has an articular part, called the **head**, supported on a more constricted part called the **neck**.

The right and left halves of the **body** of the mandible are fused together in the median plane in front, but widely separated behind. Their junction is called the

symphysis menti [σύν (syn)=together; φύω (phyō)=grow; *mentum*=the chin]. The halves are joined together by fibrous tissue at birth, but are fused together into one bone during the second year.

On the front of the mandible, along the line of the symphysis, there is a faint, vertical ridge. This ridge swells out inferiorly into a triangular elevation, of varying prominence, called the **mental protuberance**; the lower angles of the triangle are called the *mental tubercles*; in the region of the protuberance, the bone is bent forwards to produce the prominence of the **chin**. The forward projection of the lower part of the middle of the mandible to make the chin is a Human characteristic: among lower animals, not even the higher apes (Gibbon, Gorilla, Orang-utan, and Chimpanzee) have chins as an outstanding feature; and the prominence of the chin is not so marked in the primitive races of Men as in the higher, though the mandible as a whole may be a heavier bone.

Each half of the body of the mandible has an outer and an inner surface and an upper and a lower border. The surfaces slope so that the lower border of the whole bone makes a wider arch than the upper border.

The upper part is called the **alveolar** part, because it is occupied by a row of pits or **alveoli**; these are the sockets for the teeth, and they are visible on the *upper border* if the teeth have fallen out after death. On each side the sockets for the two incisors, the canine, and the two premolars are single, but those for the three molars are double, for each mandibular molar has two roots—an anterior and a posterior. When teeth are removed during life the walls of the sockets are gradually absorbed until no evidence of them is left; the upper border of the mandible in the region of

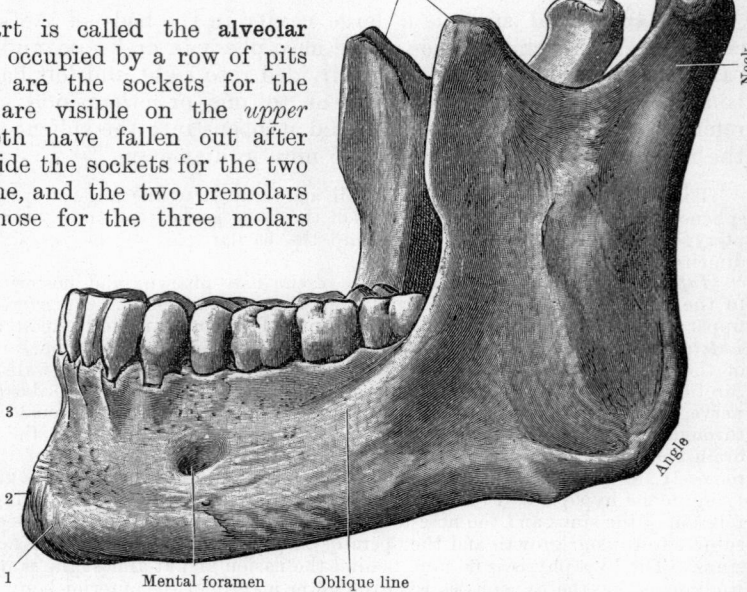

FIG. 150.—THE MANDIBLE AS SEEN FROM THE LEFT SIDE.
1. Mental tubercle.   2. Mental protuberance.   3. Symphysis.

the lost teeth is smooth, and the vertical diameter of the bone is reduced.

The *lower border* is the **base** of the mandible. On or behind this border, at the side of the symphysis, there is a broad, rough mark or depression called the **digastric fossa**. The rest of the border is smooth and rounded and has a slight fullness or downward convexity about its middle.

The **outer surface** is slightly convex, but has a broad, shallow depression alongside the symphysis, below the incisor teeth. An oblique opening is seen about an inch from the symphysis, below the second premolar or the interval between the premolars; it is called the **mental foramen**, and is about midway between the upper and lower borders if the sockets are present, but is near the upper border if the walls of the sockets have been absorbed. Below the mental foramen there is an ill defined ridge called the *oblique line*; it extends from the mental tubercle to the anterior border of the ramus, but is not well marked till it approaches the ramus.

The **inner surface** is undulating—being convex and concave at different parts. Low down on the back of the symphysis there is a rough mark which, when well developed, is divided into two pairs of little eminences called the **genial tubercles** [γένειον (geneion)=the chin].

At the side of the symphysis, a little above the digastric fossa, there is a smooth, shallow depression, about the width of a thumb-print, called the **sublingual fossa**. Farther back there is an elongated, shallow depression called the **submandibular fossa**, which extends on to the ramus; inferiorly it reaches the lower border of the mandible; superiorly it is bounded by an oblique ridge, called the **mylo-hyoid line**, which begins at the level of the socket of the last molar tooth and passes downwards and forwards to the posterior margin of the digastric fossa; the lower or anterior part of the line is faint, and separates the submandibular and sublingual fossæ from each other.

The **ramus** of the mandible is, properly, the broad, flattened plate that rises up above the level of the posterior part of the body; but for the sake of simplifying the description of the attachment of muscles it is convenient to include the bone down to the lower border under the term *ramus*; at the same time it is not necessary to subdivide the lower border: it is the lower border of the mandible, irrespective of subdivision into body and ramus. Each ramus has a lateral and a medial surface, an anterior and a posterior border, and an upper end or border surmounted by the coronoid and condyloid processes, which are separated by a wide gap called the **mandibular notch**.

The **lateral surface** is fairly flat, and rather rough. Where the ramus and body join, at the lower border of the bone, a faint groove may be detected; if the finger-tip is placed on the corresponding point in a living person the pulsing of an artery can be felt; that is the facial artery [a. maxillaris externa]—the chief artery of the face—as it crosses the lower border of the mandible and enters the face. The **medial surface** is more uneven. About its centre there is an oblique opening called the **mandibular foramen**; it leads into a **canal** which runs downwards and forwards in the substance of the bone and carries the vessels and nerves for the teeth; the spur of bone that overlaps the

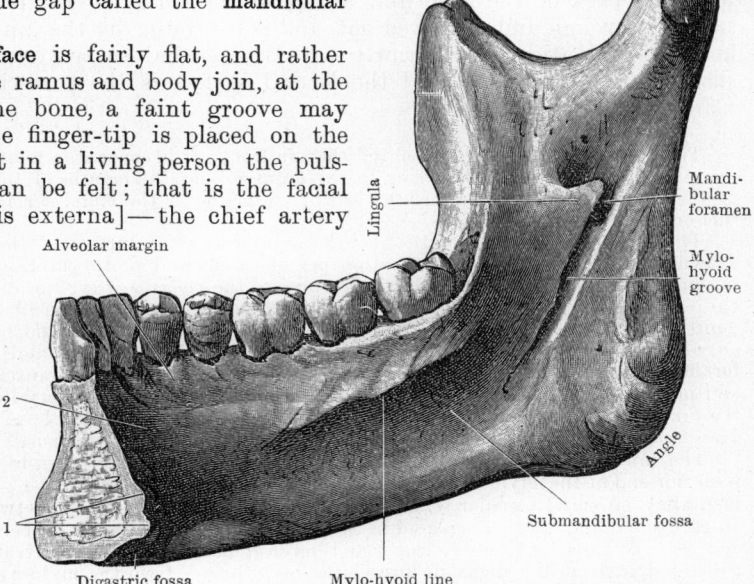

FIG. 151.—MEDIAL SURFACE OF RIGHT HALF OF MANDIBLE.

1. Upper and lower genial tubercles. 2. Above sublingual fossa.

foramen anteriorly is called the **lingula**. A narrow groove, called the **mylo-hyoid groove**, begins at the lower margin of the foramen, runs downwards and forwards and fades away in the mandibular fossa. The **anterior border** of the ramus is sharp, and is continuous with the oblique line of the body. The **posterior border** is smooth and rounded; the point where it meets the lower border is called the **angle of the mandible**—a point easily felt in the living and much used as a landmark.

The **coronoid process** is flattened and pointed; it is triangular in outline, and is named from its resemblance, when looked at sideways, to the beak of a bird [κορώνη (corōnē) = a sea crow]. Its anterior border is continuous with the anterior border of the ramus, and both can be felt inside the mouth, above and behind the last molar tooth. Its posterior border bounds the mandibular notch anteriorly. Its surfaces are continuous with those of the ramus; on its medial side a low blunt ridge begins near its top and extends down to the medial margin of the socket of the last molar tooth.

The **condyloid process** has two parts—an articular head or condyle supported on a constricted neck.

The **head** of the mandible is elongated transversely. It includes only the part that is smooth and coated with cartilage ; it has therefore an upper and a posterior surface and a small, negligible anterior surface. The head articulates with the articular fossa and eminence of the temporal bone—but not directly : an articular disc of fibro-cartilage separates the head from the temporal bone, and, since its circumference is attached to the capsular ligament of the joint, it divides the joint cavity into an upper and a lower compartment. When the mandible is at rest, with the mouth shut, the upper surface of the head is in contact with the disc, below the articular fossa ; as the mouth is opened the mandible rotates, and at the same time the head and the articular disc travel downwards and forwards till they come to lie beneath the articular eminence. The head can be felt in front of the auricle, and the finger can follow its movements as the mouth is opened and shut.

The **neck** of the mandible is obliquely compressed from before backwards. The *medial* and *lateral surfaces* are narrow, but widen out inferiorly as they merge into the surfaces of the ramus. The *posterior surface* is smooth, and is continuous with the back of the head and the posterior border of the ramus. The *anterior surface* is rough and hollowed out, and is overhung by the anterior margin of the head ; it is continuous inferiorly with the medial surface of the ramus, and the sharp margin between it and the lateral surface is the posterior boundary of the mandibular notch.

The **alveolar part** is thicker behind than in front ; it is covered on both surfaces with mucous membrane, and it gives attachment to the gums around the mouths of the sockets. The socket of the canine tooth may produce a vertical eminence on the labial surface of the bone, and the incisor sockets also may do so.

The mucous membrane of the mouth covers the **outer surface** of the body down to a line drawn from the last molar socket to the apex of the mental protuberance. The lower part of the buccinator arises from the lateral surface opposite the *molar sockets* ; the incisive muscle, opposite the *incisor sockets* ; the mentalis, from a point opposite the bottom of the *canine socket* ; the depressor labii inferioris, from a line joining the mental tubercle and foramen ; the depressor anguli oris, from the anterior part of the **oblique line**, below the mental foramen. The **mental foramen** opens obliquely in a lateral direction and upwards, and transmits the mental vessels and nerve ; it may be double on one or both sides. The facial artery lies on the mandible at the junction of body and ramus. The **lower border** of the mandible gives attachment to the deep fascia of the neck ; and the platysma is inserted into the anterior half.

The mucous membrane covers the **inner surface** of the body down to a line drawn from the posterior end of the mylo-hyoid line to a point immediately above the genial tubercles [spina mentalis]. A small vascular foramen is situated opposite the interval between the incisor sockets on each side ; and another is placed in the symphysis above the genial tubercles ; the genio-glossus and genio-hyoid arise from the upper and lower **genial tubercles** respectively ; the anterior belly, the digastric, from the **digastric fossa** ; the mylo-hyoid, from the **mylo-hyoid line**, the posterior end of which gives attachment also to fibres of the superior constrictor and the buccinator and to the lower end of the pterygo-mandibular ligament. The two mylo-hyoid lines are the sides of an arch which is smaller than the arches made by the upper border and the lower border ; for the surface above the lines slopes upwards and outwards, and the surface below slopes, to a still greater degree, downwards and outwards. The sublingual gland lies in the **sublingual fossa** ; and the submandibular gland lies in the **submandibular fossa.**

The **mandibular foramen** transmits the inferior dental vessels and nerve ; their mylo-hyoid branches run along the **mylo-hyoid groove**, which may be partly converted into a tunnel. The medial pterygoid muscle is inserted into the rough patch that separates the foramen and groove from the angle of the mandible. The spheno-mandibular ligament is attached to the **lingula** ; the stylo-mandibular ligament is attached to the **posterior border** *of the ramus* and also to the angle. The **angle** is usually everted, and is slightly obtuse in a well-formed adult jaw, more obtuse in childhood, and still more in old age after the teeth have been lost. In a young adult the slope of the jaw from angle to chin expresses almost the whole degree of obtuseness of the angle, for the posterior border of the ramus is nearly vertical ; but not so in old edentulous persons, for in them the posterior border of the ramus slants downwards and forwards, chiefly owing to the backward tilt of the condyloid process. In mandibles of old people the increase of obtuseness is not so much in the angle proper as in the angle between the anterior margin of the ramus and the upper margin of the body.

The masseter is inserted into the **lateral surface** of the ramus and covers the ramus and the coronoid process, leaving the head and neck without a covering of muscle ; the temporalis is inserted into the medial surface and the margins of the **coronoid process**, and also into the anterior margin of the ramus and the blunt ridge on the medial side. In some specimens an oblique canal traverses that ridge ; the canal transmits the buccal nerve. The coronoid process varies considerably in length, but its tip usually lies under cover of the anterior part of the zygomatic arch.

The long axis of the **head** is nearly horizontal and is directed latero-medially and backwards. The posterior surface is slightly convex ; so also is the upper surface, which overhangs the front of the neck, and ends in little tubercles that overhang the sides of the neck. The capsular ligament of the mandibular joint is attached to the margins of the articular surfaces of the head ; a thickened part of the capsule, called the temporo-mandibular ligament, is attached to the lateral side of the **neck**. The lateral pterygoid muscle is inserted into the front of the neck and the capsule. If the finger is placed in the auditory meatus, the meatus can be felt widening as the mouth is opened, for when the mouth is shut the back of the head exerts pressure on the meatus, though it is separated by a portion of the parotid gland ; the lateral side of the head and neck also is overlapped by the parotid gland and is crossed by the temporal and zygomatic branches of the facial nerve, which may be rolled between the finger and the bone. The external carotid artery ends behind the neck ; the superficial temporal artery, accompanied at that level by the posterior facial vein, runs upwards behind the lateral end of the head ; the maxillary artery passes forwards medial to the root of the neck ; the auriculo-temporal nerve winds round the medial side and the back of the neck and joins the superficial temporal artery. The vessels and nerves to the masseter pass in a lateral direction, through the **mandibular notch**, in front of the neck. When the mandible is in position in the head, a stilette inserted in front of the neck of the mandible can be thrust from one mandibular notch to the other ; it passes below the foramen ovale, and therefore would transfix the mandibular nerve.

Differences due to Age.—At birth the two halves are united by fibrous tissue ; the body is a mere shell that encloses the rudimentary *teeth*, which are imperfectly separated from one another ; the *mandibular canal* is relatively wide, and is near the lower border ; so also is the *mental foramen*, which is opposite the cavity for the first milk molar tooth. The *ramus* is relatively short ; the *condyloid process* is almost in line with the body, and the angle is therefore very obtuse ; the *head* is relatively large, and the *coronoid process* rises to a higher level than the head.

During the first year the halves unite from below upwards, and union is completed during the **second** year. As the teeth erupt and the child begins to chew, the depth of the body increases by the growth of the walls of the sockets, the lower part thickens, the rami enlarge and the angle becomes less obtuse, being about 140° in the fourth year. As growth advances the depth increases, and the body elongates, especially behind the mental foramen to provide room for the permanent molars ; the mental foramen assumes its adult position and the angle is reduced to 110°.

In **old age** after teeth are lost the walls

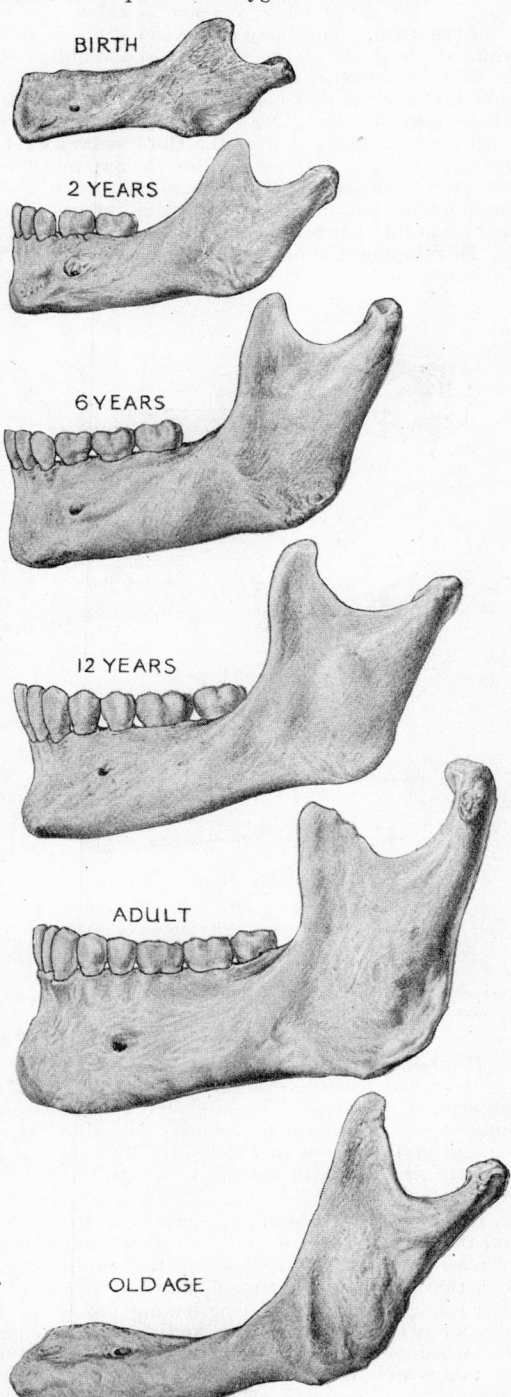

BIRTH

2 YEARS

6 YEARS

12 YEARS

ADULT

OLD AGE

FIG. 152. —FORM OF MANDIBLE AT DIFFERENT AGES. By the sixth year the first permanent molar has erupted behind the milk teeth ; by the twelfth year the milk teeth have been replaced by the corresponding permanent teeth, and the second permanent molar has erupted behind them.

of the sockets are absorbed; the chin appears therefore more prominent, and the mental foramen is near the upper border. The angle opens out to 140° and the condyloid process is bent back so that the mandibular notch is wider.

Structure.—The body of the mandible is thicker than the rami, and is thickest near the rami at the level of the mylo-hyoid and oblique lines, for there the mandible is subject to the greatest strain when the elevating muscles bring it into contact with the resisting upper jaw. The tables of compact bone are exceptionally dense and are very thick where they join together at the lower border. The lingual walls of the sockets are considerably thicker than the labial walls, except in the case of the **third molar** socket, where the labial wall is the thicker. The spongy substance is open-meshed below, but finer and more condensed in the walls of the sockets. The *canal* of the mandible is in the spongy substance, about the level of the mylo-hyoid line, and does not have a definite wall; the mental foramen branches off the canal, and so do the channels that carry blood-vessels and nerves to the teeth.

Development and Ossification.—The **mandible** begins to ossify during the sixth week of intra-uterine life—before any other bone in the body, except the clavicle. Each half is developed from (1) the membrane that overlies Meckel's cartilage, (2) the anterior portion of Meckel's cartilage, (3) certain accessory cartilages that appear between the eleventh and fourteenth weeks. The greater part of the mandible is developed from the membrane. The extreme anterior end of Meckel's cartilage disappears, but a part of it is incorporated in the mandible from a point near the symphysis backwards to the level of the mental foramen. One of the accessory cartilages forms the head and a narrow wedge-like part in the ramus; another forms a narrow strip along the front of the coronoid process; and some accessory nodules take a share in forming the symphyseal part of the bone. Those different structures are not ossified from separate centres. Each **half** of the mandible is ossified from **one** centre, and it appears in the membrane overlying the anterior part of Meckel's cartilage. The ossifying process spreads through the membrane

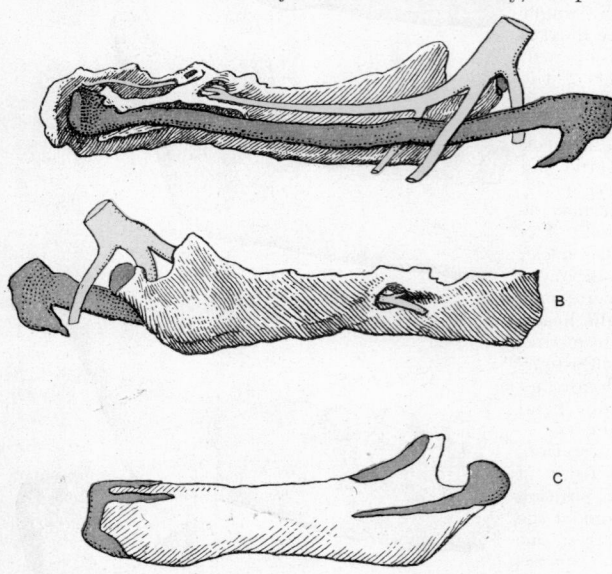

FIG. 153.—DEVELOPMENT OF THE MANDIBLE.

A, As seen from the medial side; B, from the lateral side; C, showing accessory (metaplastic) cartilages (blue).

(In A and B Meckel's cartilage is coloured blue.)

and envelops and invades the cartilages. Some small nodules, called *ossicula mentalia*, which appear at the symphysis shortly before birth and fuse with the mandible shortly after birth, may be derived from independent ossific centres in the accessory cartilages.

Meckel's cartilage is the cartilage of the first or **mandibular** arch of the embryo. Its posterior end is in the region of the ear; its anterior end almost meets its fellow of the other side. The posterior end ossifies to form two of the auditory ossicles, namely, *incus* and *malleus*; part of its anterior end is included in the mandible. The rest disappears; but the mylo-hyoid groove is the remains of the furrow in which part of it lay; and the *spheno-mandibular ligament* is derived from the fibrous sheath around it, though it has been argued that that ligament is the remnant of a muscular slip.

Growth.—The mandible grows in width between its angles as well as in length, height, and thickness. Increase of thickness is brought about chiefly by addition to the outer surfaces. Increase in height of the body is due mainly to growth at the alveolar border, and, associated with that, there is a continuous upward movement of the teeth in the bone before, during, and after their eruption. The lengthening process is chiefly backwards. It takes place partly by addition to the posterior border, and, owing to the lateral slope of the body from before backwards, that accounts for increase of width also. But the main increase depends upon the obliquity of the ramus and its processes in a young jaw. The growth of the condyloid process is not only upwards but also backwards and laterally, and it thus contributes to the total length as well as to height and width—a contribution that diminishes as the ramus becomes more vertical. The coronoid process grows upwards and backwards by addition to its tip. As the process grows, its sloping, anterior margin is encroached upon by the rising alveolar border, which thus becomes longer. This is the chief means of providing more room for the teeth as they rise with the alveolar border. As growth proceeds, modelling absorption maintains the shape of the condyle and the undulating curves of the anterior margin of the ramus and coronoid process. During the upward and backward growth of the ramus and coronoid process, the mandibular foramen maintains its relative position by a corresponding extension of its anterior lip, and the mandibular canal is thus lengthened. For further details see J. C. Brash, *Brit. Dent. Jour.* 1929, vol. l., pp. 611 and 776; *Edin. Med. Jour.* 1934, vol. xli., p. 378.

Dentes

There are two sets of **teeth**: the *deciduous* or milk teeth, which are shed during childhood; and those that are potentially *permanent*.

The **deciduous teeth** are 20 in number, 5 on each side of the upper and the lower jaws, namely, 2 incisors, 1 canine, and 2 molars, in that order from before backwards. There are 32 adult or **permanent teeth**, 8 on each side above and below, namely, 2 incisors, 1 canine, 2 premolars, and 3 molars. The permanent incisor and canine teeth replace those of the same name in the milk dentition; the premolar teeth replace the milk molars. The adult molars have no forerunners.

Each tooth is divided into—(1) a **crown**, above the level of the gum; (2) a **neck**, surrounded by the gum; and (3) a **root** or **roots**, imbedded in the jaw. The **crowns** are chisel-shaped in *incisor* teeth; peg-shaped in *canine* teeth; have two tubercles in *premolar* teeth, one tubercle medial and the other lateral; have several tubercles in *molar* teeth. The crown of the first upper incisor is considerably wider than that of any other incisor, and the crown of the first lower incisor is usually the narrowest; the crown of the third lower molar is larger than that of the third upper molar; therefore, with the exception of the first lower incisor and the last upper molar, each tooth meets two teeth of the opposing jaw. The upper teeth usually form a wider arch than the lower teeth, and therefore overlap them.

Each **root** or fang tapers to a point. The roots of the incisors, the canine, and the premolar teeth are single—except that the first upper premolar may be bifid at its tip. Each upper molar has three roots—two lateral and one medial—but those of the third molar may be clumped together; each lower molar has two roots—an anterior and a posterior—and both of those may be bifid at the point. If the teeth have all fallen out after death, those characters can be ascertained from their sockets.

The milk teeth are distinguished from adult teeth by their small size, their constricted necks, and, in the case of the molars, from the fact that the roots of the milk molars are more spread apart.

The bulk of each tooth is composed of an exceedingly hard substance called **ivory** or dentine. The crown is covered with a thin layer of still harder substance called **enamel**. The root is covered with a crust of modified bone called **cement**. A layer of fibrous tissue, called **alveolar periosteum**, lines the wall of the socket and surrounds the root, and is attached by Sharpey's fibres to both of them, binding them together. In the interior of each tooth there is a cavity, called the **pulp cavity**, containing areolar tissue, vessels, and nerves. The vessels and nerves enter the tooth through a foramen at the tip of each root, and traverse a canal in the root to reach the pulp cavity.

The first **deciduous** tooth to **erupt** is one of the **incisors**, and it should appear about *six* **months** after birth; all the milk teeth should have appeared by the end of the *second* year. The first **permanent** tooth to **erupt** is one of the **first molars** and it should appear during the *sixth* **year**. By the *twelfth* year all the permanent teeth should have erupted, except the third molar (dens serotinus or wisdom tooth), which appears at any time between 17 and 30, and may not erupt at all.

See Figures of teeth in the chapter on the Digestive System.

Hyoid Bone

The **hyoid bone** lies in the front of the neck, at the root of the tongue, between the mandible and the larynx. It is named from its resemblance to the letter U [the Greek letter *υ* aspirated thus *ὑ* = hy; εἶδος (eidos) = shape]. It does not articulate with any other bone. It has a *body*, a pair of *greater horns*, and a pair of *lesser horns*.

The **body** is the middle part or bottom of the U. It can be felt in the median line of the neck about a finger's-breadth above the laryngeal prominence when the chin is held up. When the chin is depressed the hyoid bone is at or

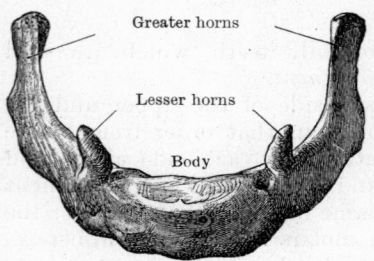

above the level of the point of the chin and is closer to the larynx. If one swallows or gulps while the finger is placed on the hyoid bone, the bone is felt rapidly ascending, for the tongue, the hyoid bone, and the larynx are all suddenly jerked upwards in the movement of swallowing.

The **greater horns** are the limbs of the U. They spring from the body about a finger's breadth from the median plane and extend backwards in the sides of the throat; they can be gripped between finger and thumb, but the tip of the greater horn, though often referred to as a land-

FIG. 154.—THE HYOID BONE.

mark, is overlapped by the anterior edge of the sterno-mastoid muscle, and cannot always be felt easily.

The **lesser horns** are small pointed nodules of bone that project upwards from the junction of the body with the greater horns.

The **body** is compressed from before backwards and is curved from side to side with the convexity forwards. It has an upper and a lower border, and an anterior and a posterior surface. The **anterior surface** is divided into an upper and a lower part by a transverse ridge on which there is sometimes a small median tubercle; the upper part looks upwards rather than forwards and is divided by a median ridge into right and left halves. The genio-hyoid is inserted into the upper part and a small adjoining area of the lower part. The anterior fibres of the hyo-glossus arise at the side of the genio-hyoid; part of the mylo-hyoid is inserted below the genio-hyoid. The deep fascia of the neck is attached below the mylo-hyoid. The levator glandulæ thyroideæ, when present, arises below the attachment of the fascia, near the median line.

The **lower border** gives insertion to the sterno-hyoid. The median thyro-hyoid ligament passes upwards behind the body to be attached to the **upper border**, which gives attachment also to the hyo-epiglottic ligament, and, occasionally, to some fibres of the genio-glossus. The **posterior surface** is smooth and concave; it is separated by some fat and a *bursa* from the median thyro-hyoid ligament, which, in turn, is separated by a pad of fat from the stem of the epiglottis. When the larynx is pulled up during swallowing, the posterior surface of the hyoid bone over-laps the thyroid cartilage of the larynx, and the bursa lessens the friction between them.

The **greater horns** not only pass backwards, but have an upward and lateral inclination as well; they taper as they pass backwards, but each ends in a slightly swollen **tip**, to which the lateral thyro-hyoid ligament is attached. They are compressed, so that each has a lateral and a medial surface and an upper and a lower border, but the compression is oblique, and the surfaces are sometimes named upper and lower respectively, and the borders medial and lateral.

The **medial surface** is related to the thyro-hyoid membrane, which passes upwards between it and the mucous membrane of the pharynx to be attached to the **upper border.** The **lateral surface** is continuous with the front of the body. It gives origin to the middle constrictor near the upper border, and to the hyo-glossus below that; the attachment of the fascial sling of the digastric tendon and the insertion of the stylo-hyoid are close to the junction with the body. The deep fascia of the neck is attached near the lower border. The **lower border**, in its anterior two-thirds, gives insertion to the thyro-hyoid; the superior belly of the omo-hyoid is inserted into the anterior third, superficial to the thyro-hyoid, and overlaps the insertion of the sterno-hyoid on the body.

The **lesser horn** is situated on the upper aspect of the junction of the body and the greater horn, and is often in line with the transverse ridge on the front of the body. It projects back-wards and slightly in a lateral direction as well as upwards; usually it is only a few millimetres in length, but may be 10 or 12 mm. A few fibres of the middle constrictor arise from its lateral surface, and the stylo-hyoid ligament is attached to its tip.

Development and Ossification.—The hyoid bone is developed from the cartilages of the second and third pharyngeal arches, the anterior ends of which are fused together. On each side, the greater horn and the greater part or whole of the body are derived from the cartilage of the third arch. The lesser horn and possibly the upper median part of the body are derived from the cartilage of the second or hyoid arch, which gives rise also to the stylo-hyoid ligament, the styloid process, and one of the auditory ossicles, namely, the *stapes.* Occasionally the stylo-hyoid ligament is ossified, and may be mistaken for a foreign body in the wall of the pharynx.

The hyoid bone is **ossified** from three pairs of centres. A pair (which soon unite into one) for the body, and one for each greater horn appear shortly before birth, and one for each lesser horn appears during the first year. The greater horn is united to the body of the bone by a plate of cartilage which ossifies at middle age. The lesser horn is united by a synovial joint, which may disappear in old age.

The Skull at Birth

At birth the skull, compared with other parts of the skeleton, is large—especially the vault. The facial region, however, compared with the rest of the skull, is small; in the adult the facial region, including the mandible, accounts for about one-half of the whole skull, but in the new-born child it is only one-eighth, for the teeth and the air sinuses are only rudimentary, and the mandible, the maxillæ, and the nasal cavities are therefore relatively small. A boy's head at birth is larger than a girl's, but so also is his body.

In the **vault**, the edges of the bones are not yet serrated, and are separated by linear intervals filled with strips of fibrous tissue continuous with the pericranium

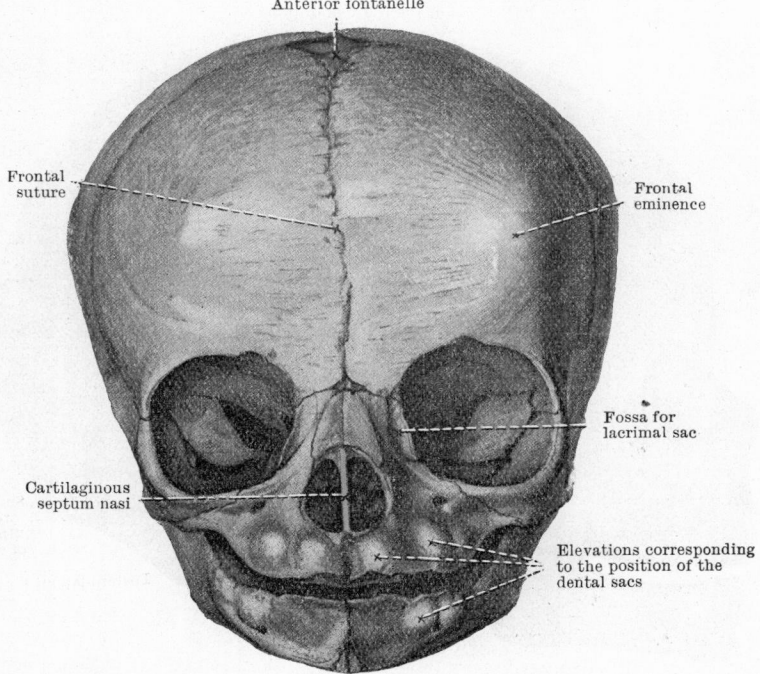

Anterior fontanelle

Frontal suture

Frontal eminence

Fossa for lacrimal sac

Cartilaginous septum nasi

Elevations corresponding to the position of the dental sacs

FIG. 155.—FRONTAL ASPECT OF THE SKULL AT BIRTH.

on the outer surface of the bones, and with the dura mater on the inner surface. Owing to the presence of those intervals, the bones of the vault have a degree of mobility that enables the head to be moulded into the required shape during the birth of the child. The bones are very thin, but they are little liable to fracture, for, in addition to their mobility, they are less brittle than in an adult, and the pericranium is very tough.

In certain situations there are areas, rather than linear intervals, between the bones of the vault. Those areas are called fontanelles. They are seven in number —anterior, sagittal, posterior, right and left antero-lateral and postero-lateral.

The **anterior fontanelle** [fonticulus frontalis] is much the largest, and is easily felt in the fore part of the top of the head in the new-born child. It is lozenge-shaped, and measures about an inch and a half antero-posteriorly and an inch across. It is situated between the two halves of the frontal bone and the two parietal bones. The ossifying process going on in those bones spreads into the fibrous membrane of the fontanelle; the bones meet and the fontanelle is closed during the second year.

13

The **sagittal fontanelle** is a small unossified space at the *obelion*; it extends like a cleft from the sagittal suture into the upper part of each parietal bone; it is often quite closed at birth. The parietal foramina in the adult are derived from it and indicate its position.

The **posterior fontanelle** [fonticulus occipitalis] is situated at the apex of the occipital bone between the two parietal bones. It is closed two months after birth.

The **antero-lateral fontanelle** [fonticulus sphenoidalis] is situated at the anterior inferior angle of the parietal bone. It is closed three months after birth.

The **postero-lateral fontanelle** [f. mastoideus] is situated at the postero-inferior angle of the parietal bone. It is closed at the end of the first year.

From irregularities in ossification **sutural bones** may be developed in various sutures, and at the fontanelles. Those formed at the antero-lateral fontanelle, being in the region of the pterion, are called **epipteric bones.**

At birth the *occipital* bone is in four separate pieces, and on each side of the squama there is a cleft partially separating the upper (interparietal) part of the bone from the rest; occasionally the two clefts meet. The *sphenoid* bone is in three parts—a median and a pair of lateral parts—in addition to the two sphenoidal conchæ (p. 209). The median part comprises the body with the lesser wings; each lateral part comprises the greater wing and the pterygoid process. The dorsum sellæ is still cartilaginous, and ossifies slowly. The lower surface of the body, between

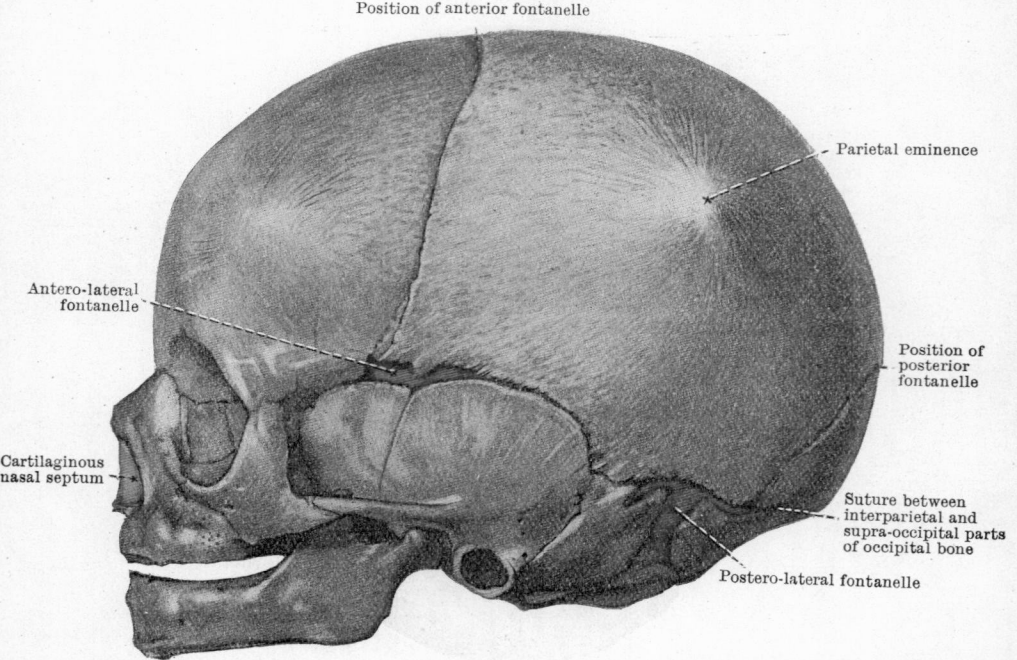

Position of anterior fontanelle

Parietal eminence

Antero-lateral fontanelle

Position of posterior fontanelle

Cartilaginous nasal septum

Suture between interparietal and supra-occipital parts of occipital bone

Postero-lateral fontanelle

FIG. 156.—LATERAL ASPECT OF THE SKULL AT BIRTH.

the conchæ, has a bullate appearance which it maintains for some years. The rudiments of the sphenoidal sinuses are present in the conchæ. The *temporal* bone is in four parts—petro-mastoid, squamous, tympanic, and the styloid process. The mastoid process has not begun to develop. The jugular fossa is poorly marked. The subarcuate fossa is large. The hiatus for the greater superficial petrosal nerve is an open groove. There is no *osseous* part of the external auditory meatus, for the tympanic part of the temporal bone is not a plate as yet, but is a mere ring—incomplete superiorly. The tympanic membrane is therefore near the surface of the head; the obliquity of the membrane is greater than in the adult; it looks downwards and forwards more than in a lateral direction. The styloid process and stylo-mastoid foramen also are near the side of the head, but gradually recede from it, after the second year, when the mastoid process begins to grow and the tympanic ring begins to become a plate. The articular fossa is shallow and relatively large, and looks in a lateral direction as well as downwards.

The halves of the *mandible* are separate. The ramus is relatively short but wide, the angle is very obtuse, and the coronoid process is at a higher level than the head. The body has little substance beyond the walls of a wide groove incompletely divided into compartments for the dental sacs; the mental foramen is near the lower border. (See also p. 189.)

The *maxilla* is vertical and of small height, for the maxillary sinus is a mere groove in the lateral wall of the middle meatus; the distance between palate and orbit is therefore short. The alveolar process is small, reaching only a little below the level of the zygomatic arch; and it is hollowed out for the dental sacs.

The perpendicular plates of the *palatine bones* are short; the *posterior apertures* and *cavity of the nose* are low. But the *bony anterior aperture* is relatively large and is a broad ovoid in outline; its lower margin is not far below the inferior orbital margin; for the nasal cavity is situated almost entirely between the orbits. The *nasal bones* are nearly flat.

The *ethmoid* is small. Its *perpendicular plate* is still cartilaginous, and is united to the labyrinth by a fibrous lamina. The *labyrinth* is already bony and contains the *sinuses* in the form of narrow pouches.

The *vomer* consists of two small plates of bone—a right and a left—separated by cartilage, but united along their lower edges; and they are not completely fused till puberty.

The *orbital opening* is large and nearly circular, and has sharp margins; the orbital fissures are wide; the fossa for the lacrimal gland is deep, and the fossa for the sac looks forwards rather than laterally. The supra-orbital notch is near the middle of the supra-orbital margin.

The *frontal* bone is divided into halves by the frontal suture. The frontal eminences are very prominent; their prominence, combined with the absence of superciliary arches, gives the bulging appearance to the child's forehead. The *parietal eminences* are even more prominent and convex, and are situated at the widest part of the head, and that is not always the case in the adult. The frontal and parietal eminences are more convex in the child than in the adult because the child's head is a smaller sphere.

Growth and Age Changes of Skull

The skull grows rapidly from birth till the seventh year, but in the brain box the greatest increase takes place during the first year. At the seventh year the orbits are almost as large as in the adult; the cribriform plates of the ethmoid, the body of the sphenoid, the petrous parts of the temporal bones and the foramen magnum have reached their full size; the jaws have enlarged in preparation for the eruption of the teeth and enlarge during their eruption—the chief enlargement being in the alveolar processes. For some years after the seventh growth is slower, but at puberty a rapid increase in the rate of growth takes place in all directions, especially in the frontal and facial regions, owing to the great increase of size of the air sinuses.

Growth in the thickness of the cranial bones takes place under the periosteum. Growth in the area of the flat bones, and consequently growth in the capacity of the cranial cavity, takes place at first at the articulating margins of the bones; but after the margins begin to interlock it is unlikely that any separating growth occurs between them. Increase in their area then depends on growth under the periosteum on the outside and absorption on the inside. The accretion and absorption are not equal and opposite, but take place in such a way that the bones become gradually less convex. It is only at the sagittal suture that the edges of the bones remain perpendicular to the surface; for, at the other sutures, as the skull grows, the edge of one bone creeps over the surface of the other and, to a varying extent, alters the position of the suture on the exterior.

Up to maturity the age of the person can be ascertained approximately from the skull and the teeth.

A deciduous incisor erupts at the *sixth month* after birth, and all the incisors, except the lower lateral, appear during the *first year*. During that year the portions of the temporal bone and of the sphenoid unite; the jugum sphenoidale is ossified by extension medially from each lesser wing; and the perpendicular plate of the ethmoid begins to ossify. During the *second year*, the rest of the deciduous teeth erupt; the halves of the mandible unite; the anterior fontanelle closes up; the cribriform plate ossifies and unites with the other parts of the ethmoid; and the mastoid process appears. The lateral parts of the occipital bone unite with the occipital squama during the *third year*, and with the basi-occiput during the *fourth or fifth year*. The halves of the frontal bone have almost completely united at the *sixth year*, and during that year the first of the permanent teeth—a first molar—erupts. The permanent incisors erupt during the *seventh and eighth years*, the premolars during the *ninth and tenth*, the canines during the *eleventh*, and the second molars during the *twelfth year*.

When the third molar is present the *seventeenth year* has been passed. If that tooth is present, and also the plate of cartilage between the body of the sphenoid and the occipital bone, the age is between 17 and 25. If the sphenoid and occipital are completely fused the age is over 25, for before that time (earlier in the female) the cartilage that unites the body of the sphenoid to the ethmoid and to the occipital bone disappears.

After maturity, the wear of the teeth and the degree of obliteration of the sutures may give a rough indication of the age. Obliteration of sutures in the cranial vault—first in the coronal, next in the sagittal, and third in the lambdoid—begins on the inner surface about ten years sooner than on the outer surface, and may begin between the *thirtieth and fortieth years*; but the order, the time, and the rate are all very variable, and complete obliteration does not take place till an advanced age.

In old age the skull vault may be thicker owing to deposit of bone on the inner surface; but in nearly all cases the skull bones are thinner, and the skull is lighter owing to absorption of diploë and the associated extension and enlargement of the sinuses. Consequent on loss of teeth there is diminution of the size of the jaws owing to absorption of the walls of the sockets; the chin protrudes and the angle of the mandible becomes more obtuse.

Sex Differences in the Skull

There is little difference between the skulls of boys and girls till the age of puberty; but the skull of a woman is, as a whole, smaller than that of a man, and the air sinuses are small relatively to the size of the skull. The capacity of the cranial cavity is one-tenth less than in a man of the same race, and that is more or less in conformity with the relative size of the whole body of women and men of respective average build. Very often it is not possible to say with certainty whether a given adult skull is that of a man or of a woman, but the sex may be determined if the following differences are well marked.

The skull of a *woman* is lighter than that of a man and retains more of the character of a young skull; the muscular ridges are less pronounced; the mastoid processes are relatively small. The glabella and superciliary arches are less prominent; the forehead is therefore more vertical, and the frontal eminences appear to bulge more; the upper margin of the orbital opening is sharper (a fact appreciated better by touch than by sight); the parietal eminences are more convex. The facial region is rounder, and the jaws and teeth are smaller. The vertex is said to be more flattened and the relative height of the skull to be less.

Development and Morphology of the Skull

At an early stage of development, the cerebral vesicles are enclosed in a membranous envelope derived from the mesoderm and called the **primordial membranous cranium.** In certain lower vertebrates (*e.g.*, elasmobranch fishes) a complete, thick-walled cartilaginous capsule is developed in the membranous envelope and is called the **primordial cartilaginous cranium ;** but in mammals, cartilage is developed only in the basal part; the roof, the greater part of the sides, and even part of the base of the skull remain membranous till bone is formed in them.

The **notochord** or chorda dorsalis [νῶτον (nōton) = the back] is imbedded in the basal part of the membranous envelope, but does not extend through the whole length of the base; its cephalic extremity reaches only to a point beneath the anterior end of the middle cerebral vesicle; and in the mammalian cartilaginous base it is related to that part which extends from the foramen magnum to the root of the dorsum sellæ. The cartilaginous base can therefore be divided into a **chordal** part and a **prechordal** part.

In the **human embryo** chondrification of the base of the cranium begins early in the second month and has almost attained its maximum about the end of the third month. Cartilage appears in the following situations.

(1) A pair of **parachordal cartilages** appear and fuse together around the notochord, to form a cartilaginous bar in which the *basi-occiput* ossifies. Extensions grow from its sides to form the cartilaginous precursors of the *condylar parts of the occipital bone* ; and they grow backwards to form the thin plate of cartilage in which the part of the *occipital squama* below the superior nuchal lines ossifies; the halves of the plate are tardy in uniting, so that the part immediately behind the foramen magnum remains membranous till shortly before birth, and is the commonest site for a cerebral meningocele.

(2) Chondrification takes place in the mesoderm around the internal ear, giving rise to what is called the **auditory capsule,** in which the *petrous* and *mastoid* parts of the *temporal* bone ossify.

(3) A small transverse strip of cartilage appears in front of the parachordal cartilages; it gives rise to the *dorsum sellæ.*

(4) Farther forward, a nodule of cartilage appears above and in front of the end of the notochord, and gives rise to the cartilaginous *body of the sphenoid* bone. It enlarges and sends forwards two extensions which pass one on each side of the cranio-pharyngeal canal—*i.e.*, the passage through which the pharyngeal part of the hypophysis enters the cranial cavity. Those extensions join together in front of the canal to form the anterior part of the cartilaginous body of the sphenoid, and so provide the canal with cartilaginous boundaries. The boundaries grow medially and usually occlude the canal during the third month, though occasionally it may remain open.

(The parachordal cartilages do not fuse together in such a way that the notochord traverses the basi-occipital bar lengthwise. The notochord lies in a groove on the posterior part of the cerebral surface of the bar, then pierces it to reach its pharyngeal surface, whence it runs upwards, between the basi-occipital and sphenoidal cartilages, to the root of the dorsum sellæ.)

(5) Chondrification occurs in the region that corresponds to the root of the *pterygoid process* and the root of the *greater wing* of the sphenoid, including the *lingula* and the part around the *foramen rotundum.*

(6) Chondrification occurs in the whole of the region of the lesser wing; in the cartilaginous state it is therefore bigger than the greater wing.

(7) Chondrification occurs in the region of the nose to form a cartilaginous **nasal capsule** during the third month. A cartilaginous plate, called the **paranasal cartilage,** appears in the lateral wall of the nasal cavity. It gives rise to the *labyrinth* of the ethmoid (including *its conchæ*) to the *inferior concha*, and to the *sphenoidal concha* ; part of it is included in the maxilla; and part persists through life as the *cartilages of the side* of the nose. Chondrification in the primitive septum takes place partly by extension from the cartilaginous sphenoid, and partly by the development of independent **paraseptal cartilages** in each side of the anterior part of the septum. The perpendicular plate of the ethmoid ossifies in the cartilaginous septum, but a great part of the cartilaginous septum persists throughout life; and the pair of sub-vomerine cartilages are

persistent parts of the paraseptal cartilages. The cartilaginous roof is formed partly by fusion of the cartilage in the side wall with that in the septum, and partly by independent chondrification of the mesoderm around the filaments of the olfactory nerve. Chondrification in the floor is very incomplete.

All the various chondrified areas of the mesoderm fuse together and form a cartilaginous platform in the base of the skull from which the cartilages of the pharyngeal arches are suspended. Most of the cartilage is ossified; part is replaced by bone ossified in the surrounding membrane; parts persist as the cartilages in the *sides* and *septum* of the nose and in the *foramina lacera*; and parts survive till maturity in the cartilaginous joints that unite the sphenoid to the ethmoid and to the occipital and between the occipital and the petrous temporal.

Some of the bones of the skull are ossified in the cartilage of the base, namely: the occipital bone, except the part of its squama above the nuchal lines; the petrous and mastoid parts of the

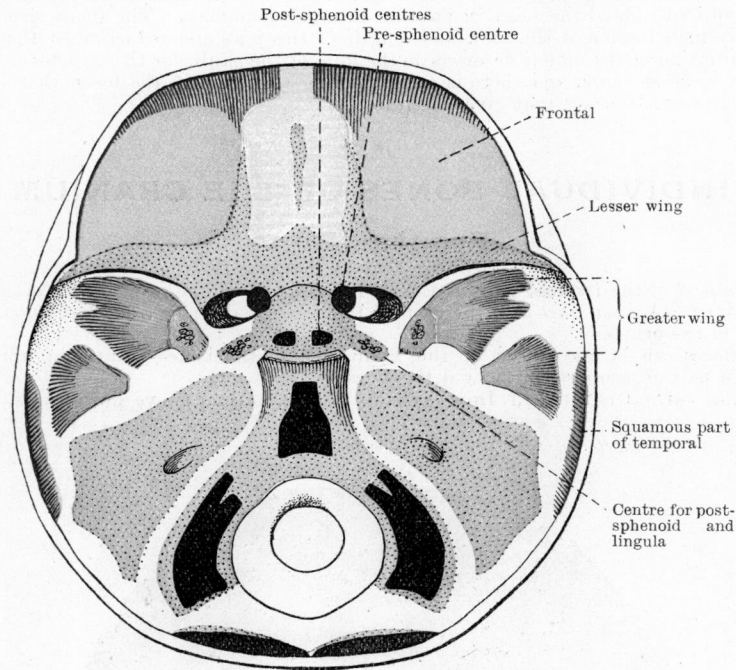

FIG. 157.—OSSIFICATION ON BASE AND SIDE WALLS OF SKULL OF A FOUR AND A HALF MONTHS' FŒTUS (Schultze's method).
Cartilage, blue; cartilage-bone, black; membrane-bone, red.

temporal bone; the body of the sphenoid, the lesser wings, the roots of the greater wings and of the pterygoid processes; the ethmoid; the inferior concha.

Some of them are ossified in the membrane overlying the cartilages of the nose, namely, the vomer, the lacrimal, the nasal, and the upper part of the maxilla.

Some are ossified from the membrane underlying the mucous lining of the bucco-pharyngeal cavity, namely, the lower part of the maxilla, the palatine, and the greater part of the pterygoid process.

The frontal, the parietal, the squamous temporal, the upper part of the occipital squama, and the greater wing of the sphenoid (all but its root) are ossified in the membranous brain envelope. The zygomatic bone ossifies in membrane which is continuous with the brain-case round the lateral margin of the orbit. The tympanic plate ossifies in membrane overlying the cartilaginous auditory capsule.

Although the skull never shows evidence of segmentation, probably owing to the need of stability even in the early evolutionary forms, it is assumed that the chordal part of the base has arisen by the fusion of segments equivalent to vertebræ, because—(1) of the presence of myotomes in the head region, (2) of the connexion with the series of pharyngeal arches, and (3) of the segmental arrangement of nerves. The guide to the disposition of the nerves is their points of exit through the dura mater, for that is derived from the inner part of the primitive brain envelope; owing to the evolutionary changes that have taken place in the outer parts of the mammalian brain envelope, the apertures through which the nerves leave the skull—though very constant in position—do not in every case correspond to the points where they pierce the dura, *e.g.*, the oculo-motor and the abducent nerves in the human head.

The mammalian occipital bone is regarded (Froriep) as the equivalent of four fused vertebræ, and there is reason to believe that in some vertebrates the occipital region of the

13 *a*

primordial cranium is increased by inclusion of vertebræ from the cephalic end of the vertebral column. The primitive cranial nerves are related to the chordal part of the primordial cranium (except the olfactory and the optic, which are metamorphosed parts of the brain); Gegenbauer concluded, from a study of the metameric arrangement of cranial nerves, that the chordal part was the equivalent of nine fused vertebræ, and he called the chordal part the **vertebral** part of the cranium. The prechordal part he called **evertebral** or non-vertebral, and regarded it as a new formation developed to contain and protect the enlarging brain and the organs of smell and sight.

The outstanding features that distinguish the human skull are the large size of the brain-case, the small size of the face, and the fact that the skull is poised on the end of the backbone. Its position on the vertebral column reacts on its outward configuration; the occipito-vertebral joints are placed so that the fore and hind parts of the head nearly balance each other; there is therefore an absence of the prominent ridges and crests for the attachment of the muscles and ligaments required to hold the head in position in lower mammals. The small size of the face is due chiefly to reduction of the bulk and length of the jaws and reduction of the size of the teeth. Diminution of the mandible reacts on the form of the skull, for the muscles of mastication do not need to be so large, and there is corresponding reduction in the fossæ that lodge them, and in the surfaces and crests that give origin to them.

INDIVIDUAL BONES OF THE CRANIUM
Frontal Bone

The *main part* of the **frontal bone** is the shell-like bone in the front of the skull above the orbital openings. A *nasal part* is in the roof of the nose; and a pair of *orbital plates* roof in the greater part of the orbits.

Four surfaces can be recognised in the main part of the bone—frontal in front, cerebral behind, and a pair of temporal surfaces at the sides.

The *frontal surface* is rounded from side to side and from above downwards. The most

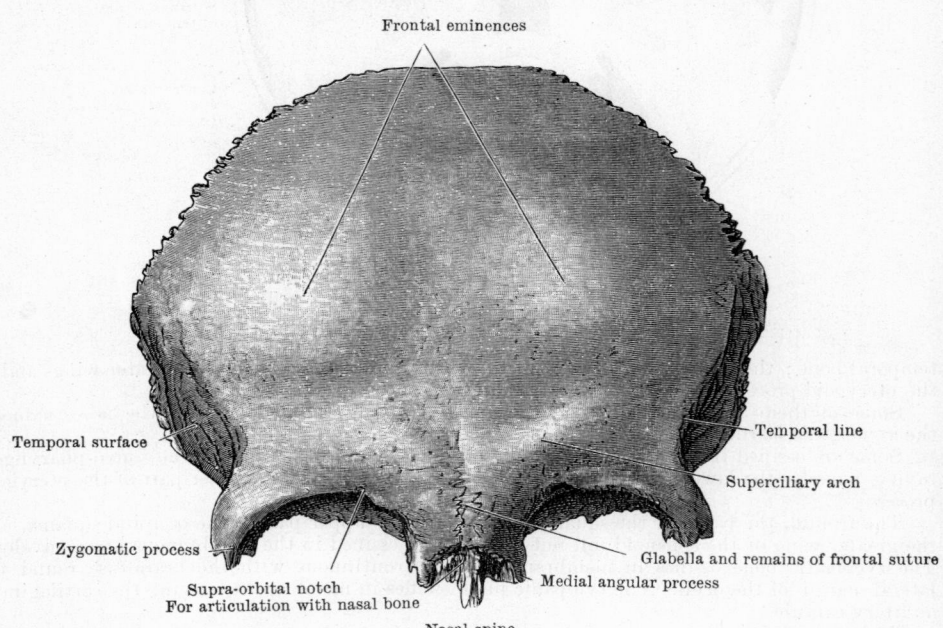

FIG. 158.—THE FRONTAL BONE (Anterior View).

pronounced parts of the convexity are a pair of **frontal eminences** seen about 35 mm. above the orbit. The surface ends inferiorly in a pair of concave edges separated by an articular area called the **nasal notch**. The concave edges are **supra-orbital margins**. Each margin ends later-ally in a prominent projection called the **zygomatic process**. The medial end descends to a slightly lower level and is called the **medial angular process**. Between its medial and inter-mediate thirds the margin is crossed by a groove, often converted into a foramen—the **supra-orbital notch** or **foramen**. Above the nasal notch there is a low elevation called the **glabella**, in which the remains of the frontal suture may be seen. On each side, the glabella is continuous with a curved elevation, of varying length and prominence, called the **superciliary arch**, which is a little above the supra-orbital margin.

From the zygomatic process a ridge, called the **temporal line**, curves upwards and backwards, separating the frontal from the *temporal surface*.

The *cerebral surface* is concave; it is marked by **impressions for the gyri** of the brain, and by narrow grooves for meningeal vessels; on each side of the median plane there are **granular pits**, varying in number and size, for the lodgment of arachnoid granulations. On the lower part of the surface there is a median ridge, called the **frontal crest**, which fades away as it is traced upwards. A groove called the **sagittal sulcus** begins on the crest and extends upwards to the margin of the bone, widening as it proceeds. A small hole, called the **foramen cæcum**, which is situated usually between the ethmoid and the lower end of the frontal crest, may sometimes be seen in its entirety on the separate frontal bone.

Each **orbital plate** is a thin, brittle, curved plate which is convex upwards and has the outline of a sextant. Its upper or *cerebral surface* is convex and uneven, showing ridges and depressions corresponding to the sulci and gyri of the frontal lobe, which lies on it; it shows also narrow grooves for meningeal vessels.

The larger, lateral part of the *inferior surface* is smooth and concave, and forms the greater part of the roof of the orbit, extending forward to the supra-orbital margin. In its antero-medial part there is either a very small depression **(trochlear fossa)**, or a spicule of bone

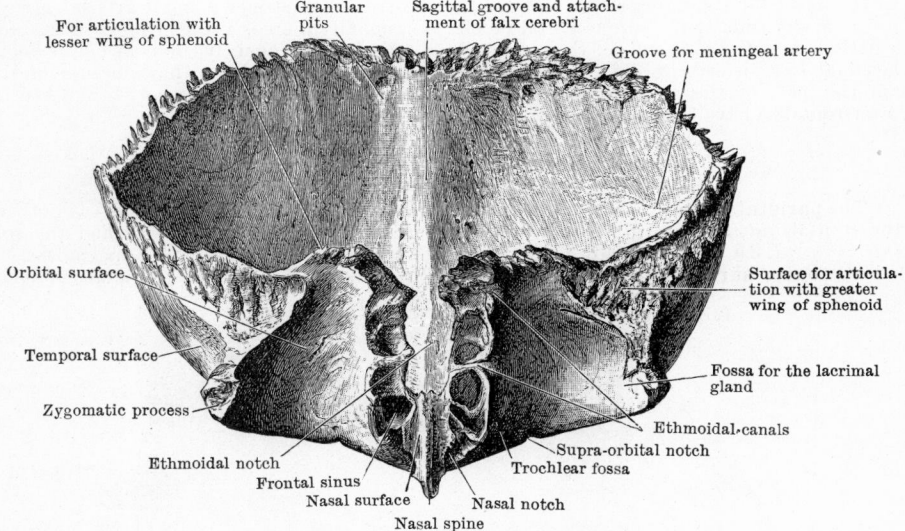

FIG. 159.—THE FRONTAL BONE AS SEEN FROM BELOW.

(trochlear spine), or both, for the attachment of the trochlea or pulley of the superior oblique muscle of the eyeball. Laterally the surface is overhung by the supra-orbital margin and the zygomatic process, so that a wide depression or **fossa for the lacrimal gland** is formed. The medial part of the inferior surface is a wide strip that overlies the labyrinth of the ethmoid, roofing in ethmoidal sinuses; it presents therefore a number of irregular depressions that correspond to the sinuses. Anteriorly the opening from the frontal sinus is seen. Farther back there are two narrow, nearly transverse grooves which, with corresponding grooves on the ethmoid labyrinth, form the **anterior** and **posterior ethmoidal canals**. The medial margins of the two orbital plates are parallel with each other. Their posterior halves, or more, are separated by an interval, called the **ethmoidal notch** because it is occupied by the cribriform plates of the ethmoid when the bones are articulated. The anterior halves of the margins are united to the nasal part of the bone.

The **nasal part** is the small portion of bone in front of the ethmoidal notch. From its centre the **nasal spine** projects downwards and forwards into the nasal septum between the nasal crest of the nasal bones and the perpendicular plate of the ethmoid, articulating with both. On each side of the root of the spine the nasal part presents a smooth, grooved surface that slopes from above downwards and forwards, and forms part of the roof of the nasal cavity.

Articulations.—The zygomatic process articulates with the frontal process of the zygomatic bone. Behind that, a rough, triangular area articulates with the greater wing of the sphenoid. Above that, the whole serrated *parietal margin* articulates with the two parietal bones. The posterior margin of the orbital plate articulates with the lesser wing of the sphenoid. The medial part of the inferior surface articulates with the labyrinth of the ethmoid. The medial angular process articulates with the lacrimal bone. Each half of the floor of the nasal notch articulates with the upper ends of the nasal bone and frontal process of the maxilla. The nasal spine articulates with the nasal bones and the perpendicular plate of the ethmoid.

13 *b*

Ossification.—Ossification begins in membrane from one centre for each half. Each centre appears about the sixth or seventh week in the region above the zygomatic process. Three pairs of centres are said to appear a little later—in the zygomatic processes, in the nasal spine, and at the trochlear fossæ. Fusion between these and the rest of the bone is complete about the sixth or seventh month of intra-uterine life. At birth the halves of the bone are separated by the *frontal suture*. Obliteration of the suture begins usually at the level of the frontal eminences, and gradually proceeds till, at the fifth or sixth year, the suture is almost closed, traces being left only above and below. In about 8 per cent. of Europeans the suture persists in the adult.

Structure and Variations.—Like other bones of the skull vault the frontal bone has two tables of compact substance with a layer of **diploë** between them. The diploë disappears from the part that encloses the frontal air sinuses. The zygomatic process is dense throughout and is shaped so as to meet the pressure transmitted through the zygomatic bone from the closed jaws.

The commonest variation is a persistence of the frontal suture. A persisting frontal suture is called a **metopic suture**; it is more common in the higher races than in the lower races, and has been said to be more frequent in the brachycephalic than in the dolichocephalic type. Sutural bones may occur at the anterior fontanelle; their fusion with one or other half of the frontal explains how the metopic suture is not always in line with the sagittal suture; occasionally they coalesce to form a *bregmatic bone*. In rare cases the frontal bone articulates directly with the orbital surface of the maxilla behind the lacrimal—a condition which exists normally in the skulls of the chimpanzee and gorilla. There is sometimes a small arterial groove close to the medial side of the supra-orbital notch; occasionally there is a second supra-orbital foramen a little lateral to the middle of the supra-orbital margin. Frequently the bone of the floor of the lacrimal fossa is cribriform. Independent ossicles (*supra-nasal bones*) have been found in the anterior part of the metopic suture; and a *metopic fontanelle, metopic canals* and *ossicles* (ossa interfrontalia) have been described.

Parietal Bones

The **parietal bones** form a great part of the vault. They articulate with each other, with the frontal *anteriorly*, with the occipital *posteriorly*, and with the temporal and the sphenoid *inferiorly*. Each bone has an outer and an inner surface, four borders, and four angles.

The **outer surface** is convex. The most convex region is called the **parietal eminence**, and

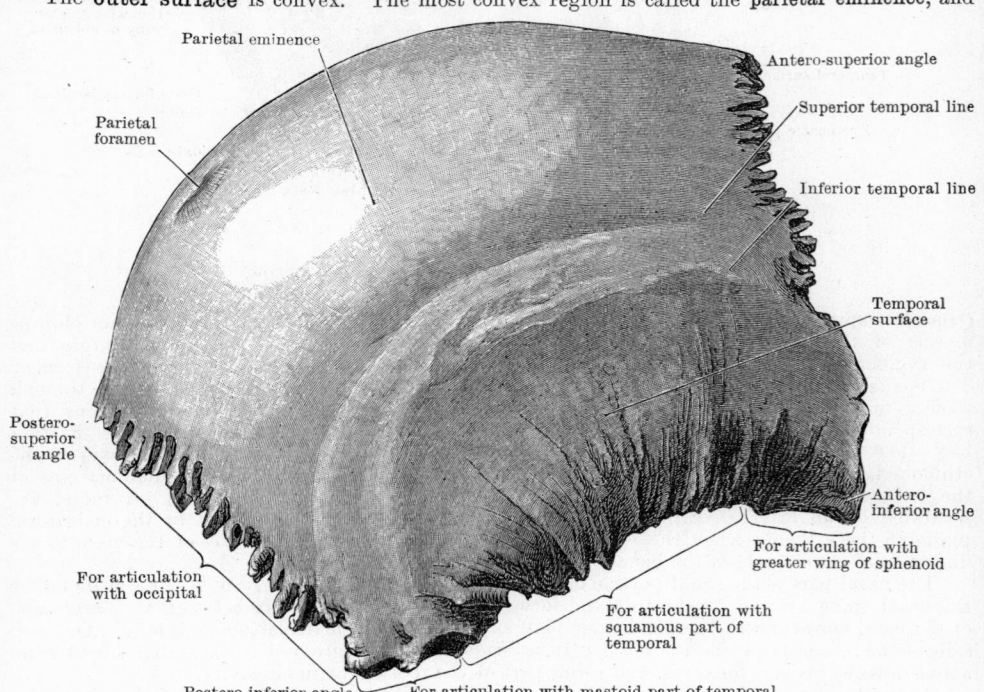

FIG. 160.—THE RIGHT PARIETAL BONE (Outer Surface).

marks the position of the ossific centre. At a variable distance from the inferior border of the bone, and more or less parallel to it, there are two parallel curved lines about half an inch apart. They are named the **superior** and **inferior temporal lines**, and are continuous with the two branches of the temporal line of the frontal bone. The **parietal foramen** is a small aperture near the upper border of the bone, and about an inch from its postero-superior angle.

The **inner surface** is concave, and displays impressions for the gyri of the brain. It presents also well-marked grooves for the branches of the middle meningeal vessels; the grooves radiate from the antero-inferior angle and the lower margin of the bone. Close to the upper margin there is a series of pits for arachnoid granulations, and along the margin the bone is grooved to form one half of the **sagittal groove**. At the postero-inferior angle the bone is slightly grooved by the transverse sinus.

The *anterior*, *superior*, and *posterior borders* are deeply serrated. The **anterior border** articulates with the frontal bone, forming with it the *coronal suture*. In the upper part of the suture the frontal bone overlaps the parietal, while the parietal overlies the frontal below. The **posterior border** is united with the occipital bone to form the *lambdoid suture*. The **superior border** articulates with its fellow to form the *sagittal suture*. The **antero-superior angle** is almost rectangular; the **postero-superior angle** is obtuse. The **inferior border** is sharp and curved, and is shorter than the others. It articulates with the squamous part of the temporal bone, which overlaps the parietal bone; the parietal bone, at its lower edge, is therefore bevelled at the expense of the outer table, and is grooved or fluted. The **antero-inferior angle** is acute; it articulates with the greater wing of the sphenoid. It is wedged into the angle between the greater wing and the frontal bone, and is bevelled at the expense of its inner table anteriorly,

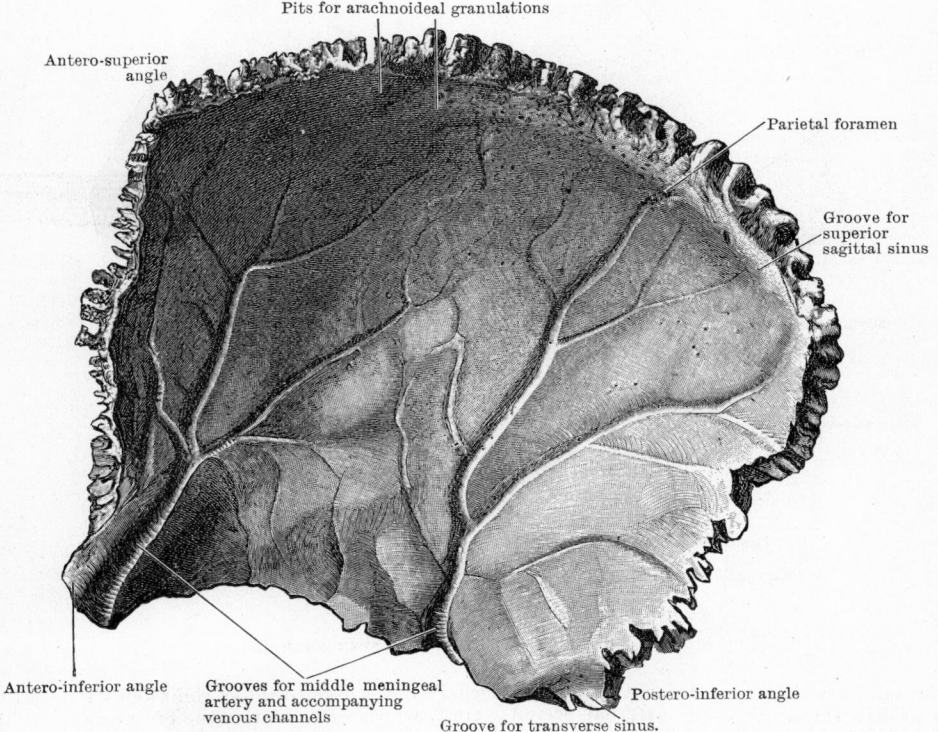

Pits for arachnoideal granulations

Antero-superior angle

Parietal foramen

Groove for superior sagittal sinus

Antero-inferior angle

Grooves for middle meningeal artery and accompanying venous channels

Groove for transverse sinus.

Postero-inferior angle

FIG. 161.—THE RIGHT PARIETAL BONE (Inner Surface).

and inferiorly it is thinned at the expense of its outer table. The **postero-inferior angle** is truncated and deeply serrated, and articulates with the mastoid part of the temporal bone.

Ossification.—In membrane by two centres that appear, one above the other at the parietal eminence, in the eighth week of intra-uterine life, and gradually unite during the fourth month. Ossification spreads radially towards the edges and angles; but at the angles the membranous condition persists for some time—hence the fontanelles. Ossification is a little delayed also in the region of the parietal foramina, so that a sagittal fontanelle is sometimes present at birth.

Structure and Variations.—The parietal bone is made of two tables of compact bone with a layer of diploë between them. It is thin towards its lower part, and is thickest along the upper border. Occasionally the outer table is very thin above the temporal lines.

The parietal bone is sometimes divided into an upper and lower part by an antero-posterior suture; in one case it was incompletely divided into an anterior and a posterior part by a vertical suture; and a tripartite condition also has been recorded. The parietal foramina vary greatly in size, and to some extent in position. They are sometimes absent on one or both sides. They correspond in position to the sagittal fontanelle. Sometimes the ossification of the sagittal fontanelle is incomplete and a small transverse fissure remains. Occasionally in the region of the anterior fontanelle an ossicle of variable size may be met with. According to its fusion with adjacent bones it may disturb the direction of the sagittal suture.

Occipital Bone

The four parts of the **occipital bone** are arranged around the foramen magnum. The expanded plate behind the foramen is the **squamous part**. The thick rod-like portion in front of the foramen is the **basilar part**. The pair of **condylar parts** are at the sides of the foramen.

The **squamous part** resembles a Gothic arch in outline, and is curved in every direction. Inferiorly it forms a small portion of the middle of the posterior boundary of the foramen magnum, and unites, on each side of that, with the condylar part of the bone.

About the centre of its *external surface* there is a prominence called the **external occipital protuberance**, and a pair of **superior nuchal lines** curve from it towards the lateral angles of the bone; above them there is occasionally another pair of curved ridges called the **highest**

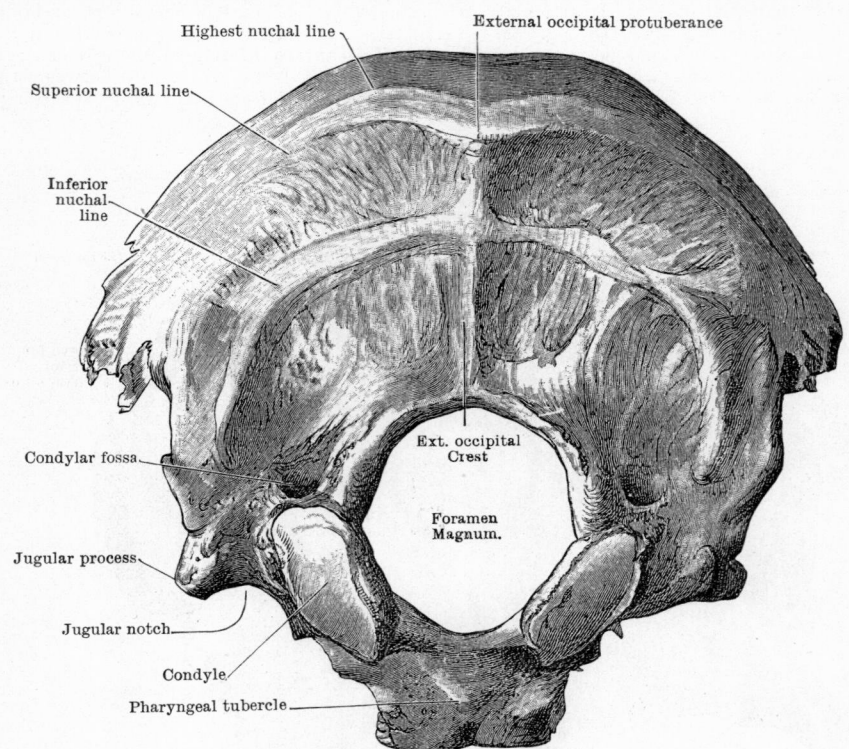

FIG. 162.—THE OCCIPITAL BONE AS SEEN FROM BELOW.

nuchal lines. The part below the superior nuchal lines is divided into a right and a left half by a median ridge, called the **external occipital crest**, which extends from the protuberance to the foramen magnum. From the middle of the crest a pair of **inferior nuchal lines** extends towards the lateral margins of the bone.

The *internal surface* is concave, and is subdivided into four fossæ by a cruciate arrangement of grooved ridges that meet at a prominence called the **internal occipital protuberance**, at one side of which there may be a fossa for the confluence of sinuses. The upper pair of fossæ lodge the occipital lobes of the cerebrum, and the hemispheres of the cerebellum occupy the lower pair. The ridge that extends from the protuberance to the foramen magnum is the **internal occipital crest**; the *grooves for the transverse sinuses* pass sideways from the protuberance; the *sagittal groove* descends to it, and usually runs into the right transverse groove.

The **superior angle**, more or less sharp and pointed, is wedged in between the two parietal bones, and the **superior borders**, much serrated, articulate with them—forming the **lambdoid suture**. Each **lateral angle** and **border** articulate with the mastoid portion of the temporal bone.

Each **condylar part** is placed at the side of the foramen magnum; on their lower surfaces they bear the **occipital condyles**, by which the skull articulates with the atlas. The condyles are elongated and oval; they are situated at the side of the anterior half of the foramen magnum; their anterior ends are closer together than their posterior ends; their articular surfaces are convex from before backwards and look in a lateral direction as well as downwards. Each articular surface is supported on a boss of bone through which the **anterior condylar canal** passes. The canal opens externally into a depression immediately lateral to the anterior part of the condyle; its internal opening is a little above the margin of the foramen magnum. The wide depression behind the condyle is the **condylar fossa**; the *posterior condylar canal* (when present) opens into it. The bone that lies lateral to the posterior half of the condyle is the **jugular process**; its *anterior* border, free and rounded, is the posterior margin of the jugular foramen and bounds the **jugular notch**. *Laterally*, the jugular process is united by cartilage to the petrous part of the temporal bone. *Posteriorly*, it is confluent with the occipital squama. Its *lower* surface is rough. The *upper* surface is grooved by the sigmoid sinus; the internal opening of the posterior condylar canal is in or near the groove. The **jugular tubercle** is a smooth eminence on the upper surface of the condylar part between the foramen magnum and the anterior part of the jugular foramen; its posterior part is often slightly grooved by the ninth, tenth and eleventh cranial nerves.

The **basilar part** extends forwards and upwards from the foramen magnum. Its anterior extremity is usually sawn across, as, after the twenty-fifth year, it is fused with the body of the sphenoid bone; the sawn surface is quadrilateral in outline. Posteriorly, where the basilar part bounds the foramen magnum, it is broad and thin. At the centre of its *lower surface* there

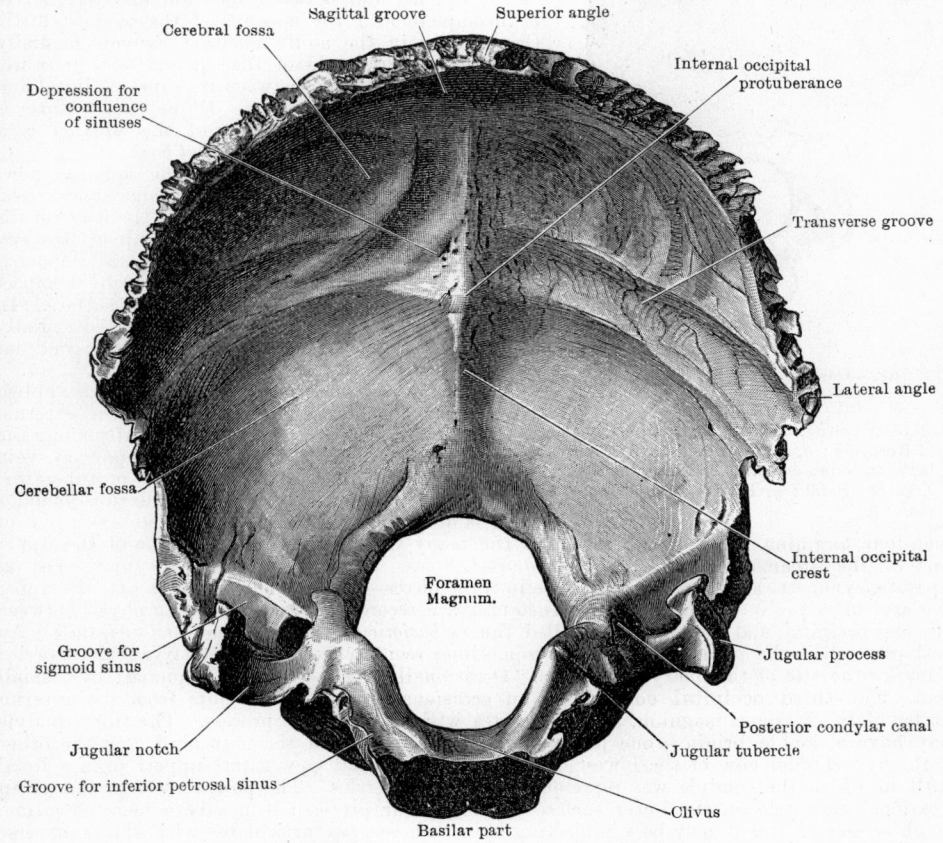

FIG. 163.—OCCIPITAL BONE (Internal Surface).

is a small elevation called the **pharyngeal tubercle**. The *upper surface* is the posterior part of the clivus of the skull, and is transversely concave. Each *lateral margin* is faintly grooved for the inferior petrosal venous sinus, and, below that, it is rough for the cartilage that unites it to the petrous part of the temporal bone.

The **foramen magnum** is variable in size and outline, but is usually ovoid, with the long axis antero-posterior. Anteriorly the condyles encroach upon it, and reduce its transverse diameter.

Ossification.—The part above the nuchal lines (*interparietal part*) is ossified in membrane, and the rest in cartilage.

The **basilar part** is ossified from one centre which appears in the sixth week of intra-uterine life; the anterior fourth of each condyle also is ossified from it. Each **condylar part** (including only the posterior three-fourths of the condyle) is ossified from one centre which appears at the eighth week. The *supra-occipital part* of the **squama** (*i.e.* the part below the highest nuchal line) is ossified from a pair of centres that appear at the position of the protuberance in the seventh week, and rapidly unite; the *interparietal part* also is ossified from a pair of centres that appear in the eighth week and soon fuse; osseous union of the two parts of the squama begins in the median plane during the third month, but is not quite completed at birth.

At birth the four component parts are separable bones united by cartilage. The two condylar parts fuse with the squama during the third year, and with the basilar part during the fourth or fifth year. The basilar part is united to the sphenoid by cartilage which begins to disappear between the eighteenth and twentieth years (earlier in the female), and is completely replaced by bone by the twenty-fifth year.

The single basilar centre may be the result of the speedy fusion of two centres—an anterior and a posterior—each of which may be a fused pair; and each of the two interparietal centres may be a fused pair. Small centres are sometimes seen in the cartilage between the squama and the condylar part; and occasionally an independent centre appears in the posterior margin of the foramen magnum at the end of the fourth month, and produces a nodule, called the *ossicle of Kerkring*, which fuses with the squama before birth.

Osseous union between the upper and lower parts of the squama and between its right and left halves is incomplete near the margins of the bone at birth. Occasionally in the adult a suture extends medially from the lateral angle of the squama, and indicates partial failure of union between its supra-occipital and interparietal parts. In some skulls the suture is complete, and the upper part of the squama is a separate bone called the *interparietal bone*.

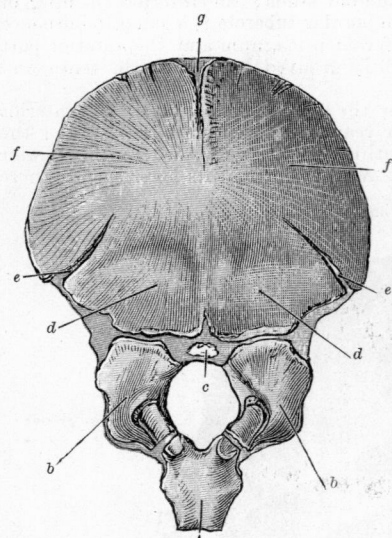

FIG. 164.—Ossification of the Occipital Bone.

a, Basilar centre; *b*, Condylar part; *c*, Ossicle of Kerkring; *d*, Supra-occipital; *e*, Fissure between supra-occipital and interparietal; *f*, Interparietal; *g*, Fissure between interparietals.

Structure and Variations.—The squama shows thickenings of compact bone at the ridges and crests, and it is thickest at the protuberances; the floors of the lower pair of fossæ are thinner than the upper pair and their lower parts have no diploë. The basilar part is made of spongy substance surrounded by compact substance which is thickest on the lower surface. In the condyles the spongy substance is arranged radially to the convex articular surfaces. The anterior condylar canal is surrounded by very dense bone.

The *torus occipitalis transversus* is the term applied to an occasional elevation which includes the external occipital protuberance and extends laterally along the superior nuchal line. Occasionally an emissary vein pierces the bone opposite the occipital protuberance. In about 15 per cent. of skulls the anterior condylar canal is double; much more rarely there are three or even four foramina. The most striking of the many variations is the separation of the upper part of the squama to form the *interparietal bone*. The interparietal bone may exist as separate, symmetrical halves; or it may be in three pieces—or even four, in which case the upper two are called *pre-interparietal* bones. Instances are recorded of a separate epiphysis between the basi-occipital and the sphenoid called the *os basioticum* or the *os pre-basi-occipitale*. An oval pit, called the *pharyngeal fossa*, is sometimes seen in front of the pharyngeal tubercle; it marks the site of the pharyngeal bursa. Occasionally the basilar part is pierced by a small vein. The **third occipital condyle** is an occasional process which juts from the anterior border of the foramen magnum, and articulates with the odontoid process. The third condyle may have a double origin—one part ossified in the sheath of the notochord, and the other in the hypochordal bow of the lowest occipital vertebra; that view gains support from a fœtal skull in which the condyle was represented by two tubercles. The *paramastoid process* is an occasional eminence on the lower surface of the jugular process; it may be a mere elevation, rough or smooth; or it may be a projecting spine whose apex articulates with the transverse process of the atlas. The size and shape of the foramen magnum vary much in different people and races, as also the disposition of its plane. The atlas is often fused with the occipital bone. Sometimes there is evidence of the intercalation of a new vertebral element (*pro-atlas*) between the atlas and the occipital bone.

Temporal Bones

Each **temporal bone** lies about the middle of the lower half of the side of the skull, and enters largely into the formation of the cranial base. It is placed between the occipital behind, the parietal above, the sphenoid in front, and the occipital and sphenoid medially and below. It has four main parts—squamous, petrous, mastoid, and tympanic.

The **squamous part** is a thin, scale-like plate of bone placed vertically in the side of the skull. It has a semicircular upper border, and cerebral, temporal and infra-temporal surfaces; the zygomatic process projects forwards from the lower part of its temporal surface; most of its infra-temporal surface is occupied by the articular eminence and fossa.

The anterior part of the **upper border** is nearly vertical and articulates with the greater wing of the sphenoid. The remainder of the border is bevelled at the expense of the inner table, overlaps and articulates with the parietal bone, and ends posteriorly by joining the mastoid part at an angle that accommodates the posterior inferior angle of the parietal bone.

The **cerebral surface** joins the petrous part inferiorly, and the remains of the suture between them can often be seen in the adult skull. The surface is marked by *impressions for gyri*, and is crossed by a groove or grooves for branches of the middle meningeal vessels. The **temporal surface**, smooth and slightly convex, is larger than the cerebral surface.

The **zygomatic process** or **zygoma** springs from the lower and anterior part of the temporal surface by two roots, and curves forwards to end in an oblique, serrated edge which articulates with the temporal process of the zygomatic bone. The *upper border* of the process is continuous with the posterior root. The *posterior root* is a salient ridge that extends backwards above the external auditory meatus and becomes continuous with a blunt low ridge, called the **supra-mastoid crest**, which curves upwards, and becomes continuous with the temporal lines of the parietal bone. The *lower border* of the zygomatic process is continuous with the *anterior*

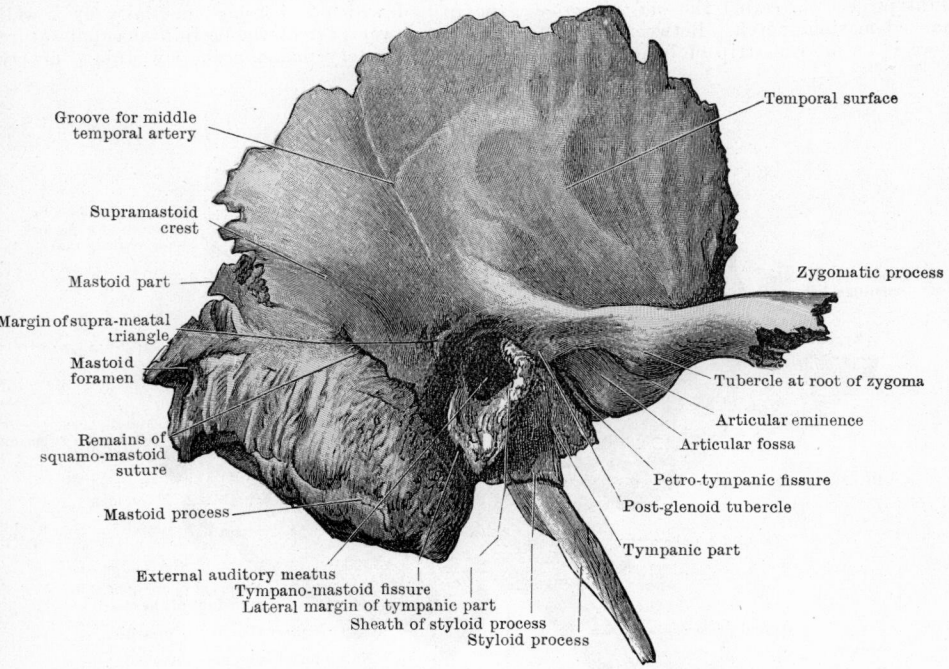

FIG. 165.—THE RIGHT TEMPORAL BONE (Lateral aspect).

Red : Mastoid part ; lower edge of tegmen tympani. **Blue :** Squamous part.
Uncoloured : Tympanic part ; styloid process.

root, which is a broad, thick bar of bone that turns abruptly in a medial direction to join the side of the skull. The lateral end of the root is prominent and is called the **tubercle** of the root of the zygoma ; the medial end is continuous with the **articular eminence**—the lower surface of the root forming part of the eminence. The anterior part of the eminence is in front of the eminence and articulates medially with the greater wing of the sphenoid.

The **articular fossa** [f. **mandibularis**] is the smooth hollow behind the eminence ; the *post-glenoid tubercle* is the lip on its posterior margin immediately in front of the opening of the external auditory meatus. The sloping plate behind the fossa is the tympanic part of the bone. The narrow cleft between them is the **squamo-tympanic fissure**. A thin edge of bone (the lower edge of the tegmen tympani) is usually seen in the medial part of the fissure, dividing it into two clefts—the *petro-tympanic fissure* behind the edge, and the *petro-squamous fissure* in front.

Behind the external auditory meatus, and below the supramastoid crest, the squamous element extends downwards as a pointed process, called the *post-auditory process* ; this process forms the lateral wall of the tympanic antrum, and helps to form the posterior wall of the meatus ; and its lower end unites with the tympanic part. In the adult the process is occasionally sharply defined posteriorly by an oblique irregular fissure—the remains of the squamo-mastoid suture—which is often not closed till puberty. The **supra-meatal triangle** is a small depression immediately above and behind the meatus.

The **tympanic part** of the temporal bone is a curved plate the concave **upper surface** of which forms the anterior, lower, and part of the posterior wall of the external auditory meatus. *Medially* it is fused with the petrous temporal. Its **anterior surface** is free and concave and has three borders. The *upper border* forms the posterior boundary of the squamo-tympanic and petro-tympanic fissures. The *lower border* is sharp and uneven, and partly ensheathes the root of the styloid process. The *lateral border*, curved, thick, and rough, gives attachment to the cartilage of the auricle. The part of the plate that curves upwards in the posterior wall of the meatus is united with the mastoid temporal and with the post-auditory process of the squamous temporal; but between it and the mastoid there is a narrow cleft—often very indistinct—called the **tympano-mastoid fissure.**

The **external auditory meatus** is a canal about 15 mm. long; it is directed obliquely medially and a little forwards, with a slight upward convexity. It is oval in outline, the long axis of the oval being nearly vertical near the lateral end, but oblique from above downwards and backwards near the medial end. The upper margin of the lateral orifice overhangs the lower margin, but the medial orifice, which is closed by the tympanic membrane, is so oblique that the lower wall of the meatus is almost, or quite, as long as the upper wall.

The **mastoid part** lies behind the squamous and tympanic parts. *Anteriorly* it is fused with those parts, and, more deeply, with the petrous part. Its *upper border* articulates with the parietal bone, and its *posterior border* with the occipital squama. *Inferiorly* it sends down a blunt projection, called the *mastoid process,* the root of which is bounded medially by a well marked **mastoid notch.** Between the notch and the lower part of the occipito-mastoid suture there is an uneven strip of bone on which the occipital artery makes a shallow groove nearly

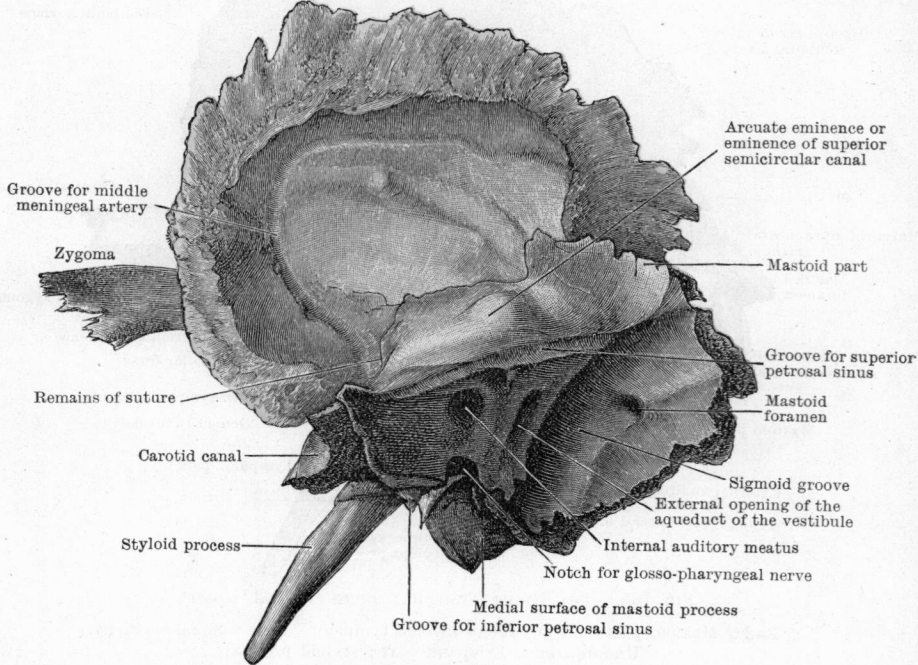

FIG. 166.—THE RIGHT TEMPORAL BONE (Cerebral aspect).
Red: Petro-mastoid.   **Blue:** Squamous.   **Uncoloured:** Zygoma; styloid process.

parallel to the notch. The *lateral surface* is convex and slightly roughened; the **mastoid foramen** opens on it near its posterior border or into the occipito-mastoid suture. The *medial surface* is in the side wall of the posterior cranial fossa. The *sigmoid groove* courses over the anterior part of this surface, and is partly on the petrous temporal.

The **petrous part** is shaped like a three-sided pyramid. By its base it is partly united obliquely to the other parts of the temporal bone, and is partly free, forming the medial wall of the tympanic cavity. Its apex is directed medially, forwards, and a little upwards. Its three surfaces are arranged as follows: The **anterior** looks upwards, slightly forwards, and a little laterally, and forms part of the posterior wall of the middle cranial fossa. The **posterior** is directed backwards and medially, and forms part of the anterior wall of the posterior cranial fossa. The **inferior** is seen on the lower surface of the skull, and is directed downwards. The margins are named anterior, superior, and posterior.

The **anterior margin** is partly united to the squamous temporal, but its medial part is a free edge that articulates with the posterior border of the greater wing of the sphenoid and forms an acute angle with the anterior border of the squamous part; within the angle is wedged the posterior corner of the greater wing. At the apex of the angle the openings of two canals are seen. These canals are separated by a thin, bony septum, and they lead backwards and laterally to the tympanic cavity. The upper is the *canal for the tensor tympani.* The lower is wider, and is the *bony part of the pharyngo-tympanic tube* [tuba auditiva].

The **posterior margin** is in part articular and in part non-articular. Posteriorly and laterally it corresponds to the upper margin of an area on the inferior surface which articulates with the jugular process of the occipital. Medial to that it is irregularly notched, and bounds the jugular foramen anteriorly. The remaining, antero-medial part articulates with the basilar part of the occipital bone; the inferior petrosal sinus runs along the articulation, grooving both bones.

The **superior margin** is a sinuous edge grooved lengthways for the superior petrosal sinus, and slightly depressed near the apex where it is crossed by the trigeminal nerve.

The inferior surface of the petrous part is rough and uneven. On it the following parts are to be noted: The **styloid process** projects downwards, forwards, and medially from behind the lower edge of the tympanic plate. The **stylo-mastoid foramen** is between the root of the styloid process and the mastoid notch. The **jugular fossa** is the concavity medial to the root of the styloid process. A small area behind and lateral to the fossa is united by cartilage to the jugular process of the occipital bone. A tiny aperture on the lateral part of the wall of the fossa is the medial end of the **mastoid canaliculus,** which opens laterally in the tympano-mastoid fissure. The oval or circular opening in front of the jugular fossa is the lower end of the **carotid canal**; the canal passes upwards for a short distance, and then, becoming horizontal, it passes medially and forwards, and ends at the apex as an oblique opening with jagged margins. On the lateral wall of the ascending part of the canal there are two or more small openings of **carotico-tympanic canaliculi,** which communicate with the tympanum. On the ridge between the carotid canal and the jugular fossa, there is the lower opening of the **tympanic canaliculus,** which leads up to the tympanum. The groove on the small area between the medial parts of the canal and fossa leads up to the **notch for the ninth nerve** on the margin of the jugular foramen. The *external opening of the cochlear canaliculus* is at the bottom of a pit in the notch. The **quadrate area** is the rough part medial to the opening of the carotid canal; a strip along its antero-lateral border articulates with the greater wing of

Temporal surface
Infra-temporal surface
Canal for chorda tympani
Zygomatic process
Pharyngo-tympanic tube
Carotid canal
Tubercle of root
Articular eminence
Articular fossa
Squamo-tympanic fissure
Tympanic plate
External meatus
Styloid process
Sheath of styloid process
Tympano-mastoid fiss.
stylo-mastoid foramen
Mastoid process
Mastoid notch for digastric muscle
Groove for occipital artery
Groove for inferior petrosal sinus
Groove for ninth nerve
Tympanic canaliculus
Jugular fossa
Mastoid canaliculus
Surface for articulation with jugular process of occipital

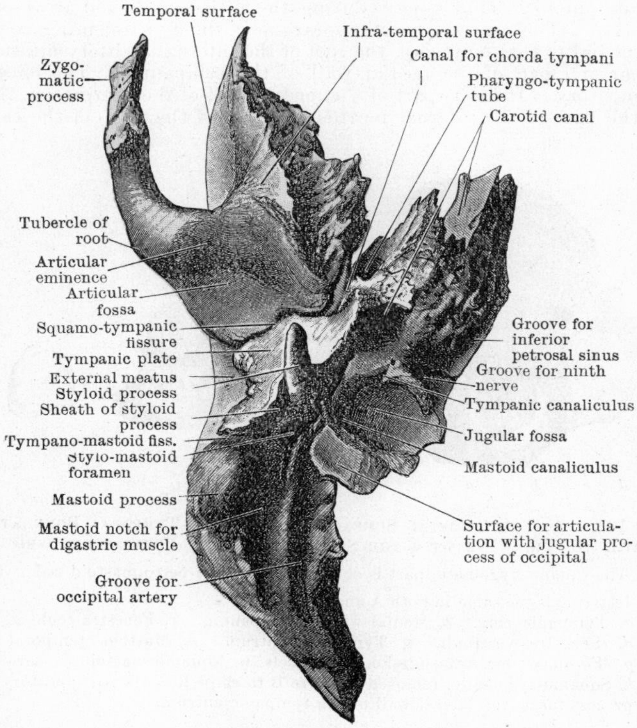

FIG. 167.—THE RIGHT TEMPORAL BONE (Inferior aspect).

Red: Petro-mastoid, including lower edge of tegmen tympani.
Blue: Squamous. **Uncoloured:** Tympanic part; styloid process.

the sphenoid and helps to form the groove for the cartilage of the pharyngo-tympanic tube; its postero-medial border is united to the occipital bone by dense fibrous tissue or cartilage—the gutter between the two bones being called the *petro-basilar fissure.*

The **anterior surface** of the petrous part bears the impress of gyri of the cerebrum; in addition, there is a distinct but shallow depression near the apex for the trigeminal ganglion [g. semilunare]. Lateral to the middle of the anterior surface, there is an elevation, called the **arcuate eminence,** which marks the position of the superior semicircular canal of the ear. A little below and medial to this, there is the small slit or *hiatus for the greater superficial petrosal nerve,* which is continued downwards and medially as a narrow groove; lateral to them there are a smaller opening and groove for the lesser superficial petrosal nerve. The bone forming the lateral part of the anterior surface, lateral to and in front of the arcuate eminence, is the **tegmen tympani**; it roofs over the tympanic cavity and antrum and the canal for the tensor tympani. The line of fusion between the petrous and squamous parts of the bone is often indicated by a faint, irregular **petro-squamous suture** along the lateral margin of the anterior surface of the petrous temporal.

The most conspicuous feature on the **posterior surface** of the petrous part of the bone is an oblique, oval aperture which leads into the internal auditory meatus. The **internal auditory meatus** is a canal about 10 mm. long that passes laterally and slightly downwards into the bone, and ends blindly, except that the bony substance at the **fundus** or far end has a number of small holes in it for the facial nerve and the nerves and vessels of the internal ear. Lateral to the meatus and above it, close to the upper border, there is an irregular depression called the **subarcuate fossa,** with one or two small foramina opening into it. It is often faintly marked; it is seen best in young bones (see Fig. 168, C), where it forms a distinct recess. About half an inch lateral to the meatus there is the *external aperture of the aqueduct of the vestibule,* often concealed in a narrow curved fissure overhung by a sharp scale of bone. The ridge above it corresponds to the upper half of the posterior semicircular canal.

Ossification.—The temporal bone of man represents the fused periotic, squamosal, and tympanic elements; the squamosal and tympanic are membrane bones, whilst the periotic is ossified in the cartilaginous auditory capsule. The cartilages of the first and second pharyngeal arches are also intimately associated with its development. The human temporal bone is characterised by the large proportionate size of the squamosal, the comparatively small size of the tympanic, the absence of an auditory bulla, and the large size of the mastoid process.

The **squamous part** is ossified from one centre that appears at the root of the zygoma about the end of the second month.

The **petro-mastoid part** is ossified from four centres, named pro-otic, opisthotic, pterotic, and epiotic. They appear during the fifth month and are more or less fused at the end of the sixth. The *pro-otic* centre appears near the arcuate eminence. It forms the part of the bone medial to that eminence, the roof of the internal auditory meatus, the upper part of the internal ear and part of the medial wall of the tympanum. The *opisthotic* centre appears at the promontory. It forms part of the medial wall of the tympanum, the lower part of the internal ear, the floor of the internal meatus and part of the walls of the carotid canal. The *pterotic* centre

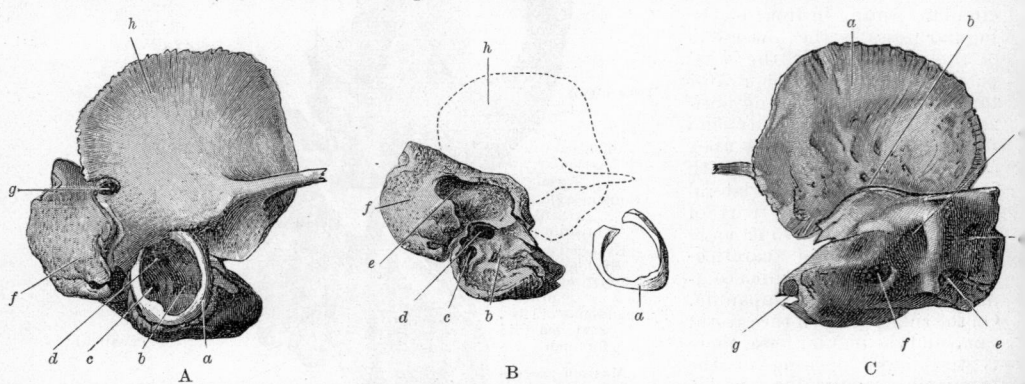

FIG. 168.—A. THE PARIETAL SURFACE OF THE RIGHT TEMPORAL BONE AT BIRTH. B. THE SAME WITH THE SQUAMO-ZYGOMATIC PORTION REMOVED.

C. CEREBRAL SURFACE OF THE RIGHT TEMPORAL BONE AT BIRTH.

The squamo-zygomatic part is coloured blue; the petro-mastoid red. The tympanic ring is left uncoloured.

The lettering is the same in both A and B.)
a, Tympanic ring. *b*, Medial wall of tympanum. *c*, Fenestra cochleæ. *d*, Fenestra vestibuli. *e*, Tympanic antrum. *f*, Mastoid temporal. *g*, Foramen for transmission of vessels in squamo-mastoid suture. *h*, Squamo-zygomatic, removed in figure B to show how its post-auditory process forms the lateral wall of the tympanic antrum.

a, Squamo - zygomatic. *b*, Petro-squamosal suture and foramen (just above the end of the lead line). *c*, Subarcuate fossa. *d*, Aquæductus vestibuli. *e*, Aquæductus cochleæ. *f*, Internal auditory meatus. *g*, Upper end of carotid canal.

appears in the roof of the tympanum. It forms the tegmen tympani; the part of it in the roof of the canal for the tensor tympani sends down a thin process that forms the lateral wall of the pharyngo-tympanic tube and appears in the squamo-tympanic fissure. The *epiotic* centre (or centres) appears in the base of the petrous part. It gives rise to the bone that encloses the posterior and lateral semicircular canals and forms the mastoid portion.

The **styloid process** is developed from the cranial part of the cartilage of the second pharyngeal arch. It is ossified from two centres. The upper centre (*tympano-hyal*) appears shortly before birth, and fuses with the petro-mastoid during the first year. The lower centre (*stylo-hyal*) appears in the cartilage shortly after birth; but the lower part ossifies slowly; it does not fuse with the upper part till after puberty, and may never do so.

The **tympanic part** is ossified from one centre which appears in the third month at the lower margin of the membranous lateral wall of the tympanum. Ossification proceeds in curved linear directions to form the *tympanic ring*, which is incomplete superiorly, and fuses with the petrous part medially. After birth it extends medially, laterally and downwards to form the tympanic plate.

Structure and Variations.—The temporal bone is remarkable for the hardness and density of its petrous part, which contains the osseous labyrinth, wherein are lodged the delicate organs of hearing and equilibration. The weakest part of the bone corresponds to a line that connects the two meatuses; for they are separated only by the cochlea and tympanum. It is usually in this position that fracture of the bone occurs.

The line of the petro-squamous suture is occasionally grooved for the lodgment of a sinus (petro-squamous); sometimes the posterior end of the groove is continuous with a canal that traverses the upper border of the bone and opens into the transverse groove. Anteriorly the groove may pass into a canal that traverses the root of the zygoma and appears externally above the lateral end of the squamo-tympanic fissure. They are the remains of channels through which the blood passed in the fœtal condition. Single cases have been recorded in which:—(1) the squamous part was pneumatic, the sinus reaching as high as the parietal bone; (2) the squamous part was separate from the rest of the bone in an adult; (3) the squamous part was divided into two by a transverse suture; (4) the zygoma was separated from the rest of the bone by a suture close to its root; (5) the zygoma was almost completely absent; (6) the carotid canal was rudimentary; (7) there was absence of the internal auditory meatus and the stylo-mastoid foramen and also of the jugular fossa, associated with a large mastoid foramen and partial absence of the transverse groove. In idiots and imbeciles a more pronounced form of post-glenoid tubercle has been noted and associated with regressive changes in the development of the temporal bone. Occasionally the temporal articulates with the frontal, as happens normally in the anthropoid apes.

Sphenoid Bone

The **sphenoid bone** lies in front of the basilar part of the occipital bone and the two temporal bones. It enters into the formation of the cranial, orbital, and nasal cavities, and also the temporal, infra-temporal, and pterygo-palatine fossæ. It has a body and three pairs of processes—the greater and lesser wings and the pterygoid processes.

The **body** is more or less cubical, and is hollow, for it contains the **sphenoidal air sinuses**. The sinuses are a right and left, separated by a partition. Each sinus communicates by a round aperture with the spheno-ethmoidal recess of the nose. In the adult the **posterior surface** of the body is a sawn surface because it is fused with the basi-occipital. The **superior surface** resembles an oriental saddle (**sella turcica**). The seat is a depression, called the **hypophyseal fossa**, that lodges the hypophysis of the brain. The fossa is overhung posteriorly by a sloping plate called the **dorsum sellæ**, the posterior surface of which is continuous with the clivus of the skull. The upper angles of the dorsum sellæ are prominent tubercles called the **posterior clinoid processes**. In front of the hypophyseal fossa there is a transverse elevation called the **tuberculum sellæ**, behind the lateral ends of which there are sometimes little spurs of bone called the **middle clinoid processes**. In front of the tuberculum sellæ there is the **optic groove**, which passes laterally into the optic foramina. The flat area in front of the optic groove is called the *jugum sphenoidale*; it is on the same plane as the upper surfaces of the lesser wings, and terminates anteriorly in a ragged edge that articulates with the cribriform plates of the ethmoid.

The lower part of each **side** of the body is fused with the greater wing, and in part also with the root of the pterygoid process. Curving along the side of the body, above its attachment to the greater wing, there is an *f*-shaped groove, called the **carotid groove**, in which the internal carotid artery lies. Posteriorly, the hinder margin of that groove, formed by the salient lateral edge of the posterior surface of the body, articulates with the apex of the petrous portion of the temporal bone.

The **anterior surface** of the body displays a median ridge, called the **crest of the sphenoid**, whose lower part is more prominent and is called the **rostrum**. The crest articulates with the perpendicular plate of the ethmoid. On each side of the median plane there is a triangular area which forms part of the roof of the nose; in that area there is an opening leading out of the sphenoidal sinus. The lateral part of the anterior surface, on each side, articulates with the labyrinth of the ethmoid and the orbital process of the palatine bone. The **sphenoidal rostrum** is continued backwards for some distance along the **inferior surface** of the body, where it forms a prominent keel that fits into the recess between the alæ of the vomer. Posteriorly, the inferior surface of the body of the sphenoid is rougher, and is covered with the muco-periosteum of the roof of the pharynx.

The **sphenoidal conchæ** are a pair of thin bones that are fused with the sphenoid, ethmoid, and palatine bones, and usually are partially destroyed when the skull is disarticulated. They form the anterior surface of the body of the sphenoid and the anterior part of its lower surface, except its crest and rostrum. Each resembles an inverted triangle, and is curved. Its smaller, apical part lies in the floor of the sphenoidal sinus and separates the sinus from the most posterior part of the roof of the nose, and its infero-lateral edge forms the upper margin of the spheno-palatine foramen. The remainder of the triangular plate lies in the anterior wall of the sinus, and is divisible into two parts. The lateral part forms the posterior wall of the posterior ethmoidal sinuses, and it articulates inferiorly with the orbital process of the palatine bone. The medial part is free in the roof of the nose, and in it there is the opening of the sphenoidal sinus.

The sphenoidal conchæ are formed, before birth, around the most posterior part of the cavity of the cartilaginous nasal capsule. That part of each half of the nasal cavity is a recess shut off from the rest of the cavity by membrane inferiorly, but anteriorly it communicates with the cavity by an aperture. In the fifth month, or later, ossification begins in the cartilaginous and membranous boundaries of the recess and converts them into the bony walls of a sphenoidal concha. In the infant, each concha is a hollow, three-sided pyramid. Its cavity is the rudiment of the sphenoidal sinus, but it was originally part of the cavity of the nose. It remains in communication with the nose; for the original aperture of communication is in the *base* of the pyramid, which partly is free in the roof of the nose, and partly fits on to the posterior surface of the ethmoid labyrinth and also articulates with the orbital process of the palatine bone. The *apex* articulates with the vaginal process of the medial pterygoid plate. The *infero-lateral wall* forms part of the roof of the nose and the upper boundary of the spheno-palatine foramen. The *superior wall* and the *medial wall* are applied to the antero-inferior aspect of the body of the sphenoid. In the fourth year, the concha fuses with the ethmoid and palatine bones, and its

14

superior and medial walls are absorbed. But the extension of the rudimentary sinus into the body of the sphenoid, by absorption of its spongy bone, does not begin till the seventh or eighth

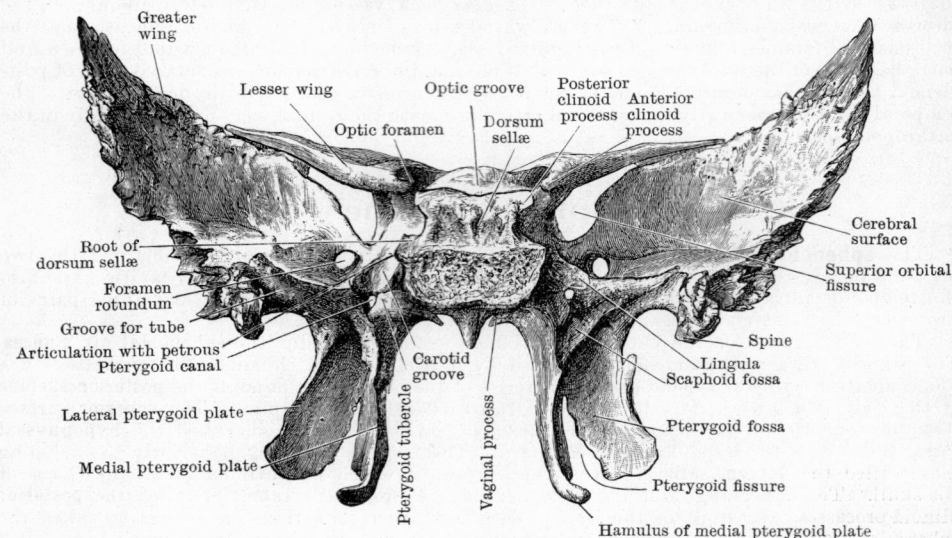

FIG. 169.—THE SPHENOID SEEN FROM BEHIND.

year; and fusion of the concha with the sphenoid does not take place till between the ninth and twelfth years.

The **lesser wings** are a pair of flattened, triangular plates that project laterally from the anterior and upper part of the body of the bone; each wing is united to the body by two roots—an anterior and a posterior—separated by the **optic foramen**. The posterior root springs from the body just wide of the tuberculum sellæ, separating the carotid groove behind from the optic foramen in front; laterally this root is confluent with the recurved posterior angle of the lesser wing, which projects backwards and is known as the **anterior clinoid process**. The anterior root, broad and compressed, joins the anterior part of the upper surface of the body.

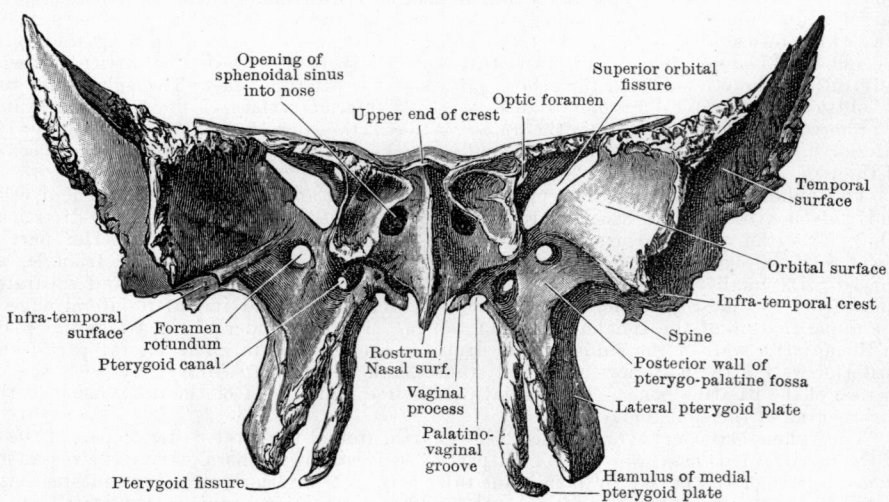

FIG. 170.—THE SPHENOID SEEN FROM THE FRONT.

Laterally, the pointed end of the wing reaches the region of the pterion and articulates there with the frontal, and may come in contact with the greater wing. The upper surface is smooth, and forms part of the floor of the anterior cranial fossa. The lower surface is the most posterior portion of the roof of the orbit, and is also the upper boundary of the **superior orbital fissure**, which separates the lesser wing from the greater wing. The anterior edge is ragged, and articulates with the orbital plate of the frontal bone. The posterior margin, sharp and sickle-shaped, separates the anterior from the middle cranial fossa, and ends medially in the anterior clinoid process.

Each **greater wing** spreads out from the side of the body of the sphenoid in the floor of the middle cranial fossa, and turns upward into the side wall of the skull. It has three surfaces —an internal or *cerebral*, an *orbital*, and an external, which is divided into a *temporal surface* and an *infra-temporal surface*.

The **cerebral surface** is concave and is marked by impressions for cerebral gyri and by grooves for meningeal vessels. Three foramina are seen in it and sometimes four. The **foramen rotundum** is a short horizontal canal that passes forwards below the medial part of the superior orbital fissure. The **foramen ovale** is situated about 10 or 12 mm. behind and lateral to the foramen rotundum. The **foramen spinosum** is the smaller aperture immediately behind and lateral to the foramen ovale. The fourth foramen, which is not always present, is a small hole, called the **sphenoidal emissary foramen**, situated medial to the foramen ovale. The *borders* of the cerebral surface are upper or anterior, medial, and posterior. The *medial border* is fused with the side of the body of the sphenoid. The *posterior border* is divided into two distinct parts that meet together posteriorly in a sharp projecting angle. The medial part is a short distance behind the foramen ovale and spinosum and is oblique in direction; laterally it articulates with the petrous temporal; medially it forms the anterior boundary of the foramen lacerum. There projects backwards from it a spur of bone of variable size, called the **lingula**, which forms the anterior or lateral margin of the commencement of the carotid groove; when the lingula is long enough it forms also the lateral margin of the foramen lacerum. The lateral part of the posterior border is a long, concave, serrated edge that articulates with the squamous temporal. The *upper border* also is divided into parts. The medial part, thin and sharp, forms the lower boundary of the superior orbital fissure; the next part articulates with the frontal bone; and the third part is the extreme upper part of the wing and articulates with the antero-inferior angle of the parietal bone.

The **orbital surface** is smooth, nearly flat, more or less quadrilateral, and forms a great part of the lateral wall of the orbit. Its *posterior border* is the medial part of the upper border of the cerebral surface and forms the lower margin of the superior orbital fissure. The *lower border* is smooth and forms the upper or lateral boundary of a cleft called the inferior orbital fissure; immediately below that border there is an oblique, horizontal groove that forms part of the posterior wall of the pterygo-palatine fossa. The *anterior border* articulates with the zygomatic bone; and the *upper border* articulates with the frontal bone.

The **temporal surface** is separated *posteriorly* from the cerebral surface by the border that articulates with the squamous temporal. *Anteriorly* it is separated from the orbital surface by the sharp crest that articulates with the zygomatic bone and sometimes also with the zygomatic process of the maxilla. *Superiorly* the uppermost part of the surface is separated from the cerebral surface by the short border that articulates with the parietal bone; in front of that it articulates with the frontal bone. The articulation of the greater wing with the frontal bone is by a rough triangular area bounded by the upper margins of the three surfaces of the wing. *Inferiorly* the temporal surface is limited by a rough, horizontal ridge called the **infra-temporal crest**.

The **infra-temporal surface** is almost at right angles to the temporal surface. The **foramen ovale** and **foramen spinosum** are seen in it near its posterior border, and the occasional *spenoidal emissary foramen* medial to the foramen ovale. The *posterior border* articulates with the petrous temporal and is grooved lengthwise for the cartilage of the pharyngo-tympanic tube, which lies along the junction of the two bones. *Medially* the surface is fused with the pterygoid process. *Anteriorly* it is bounded by a sharp margin behind the inferior orbital fissure. *Laterally* it is bounded by the infra-temporal crest, and behind that it is separated from the cerebral surface by the part of the posterior border that articulates with the lower part of the squamous temporal. That boundary and the posterior border which articulates with the petrous temporal meet at the angle which fits into the angular interval between the squamous and petrous temporal. From the angle a projection called the **spine** of the sphenoid juts downwards.

Each **pterygoid process** springs from the lower part of the side of the body and from the root of the greater wing, and passes vertically downwards. Its *lateral* and *medial* plates enclose the **pterygoid fossa** between them; the upper parts of their anterior borders are fused together.

The **lateral pterygoid plate**, thin and expanded, is directed obliquely backwards and laterally—its lower part being often slightly everted. Its posterior edge is sharp, and often has projecting from it one or two spines, one of which (*pterygo-spinous process*) gives attachment to the pterygo-spinous ligament, which stretches to the spine of the sphenoid.

The **medial pterygoid plate** is narrower and rather thicker. It is placed between the pterygoid fossa and the posterior part of the nasal cavity. Its posterior margin is sharp, and ends below as a slender, curved process, called the **pterygoid hamulus**, which, reaching a lower level than the lateral plate, curves backwards and laterally, and has a groove on its lower surface in which the tendon of the tensor palati muscle glides; superiorly, the posterior margin bifurcates to enclose a small, shallow, oval concavity called the **scaphoid fossa**; below the scaphoid fossa a small projection juts backwards from the posterior margin to support the cartilage of the pharyngo-tympanic tube. At the extreme upper end of the posterior margin plate, there is a small, blunt projection called the **pterygoid tubercle**. A thin lamina, called the **vaginal process**, passes medially from the upper end of the plate. Near the plate this process is fused with the lower surface of the body of the sphenoid. More medially it is free and is separated from the rostrum by a groove in which the edge of the ala of the vomer fits in the articulated skull, and it articulates with the ala. On the lower surface of the vaginal process, near the medial pterygoid plate, there is a groove which, in an articulated skull, leads forwards into the palatino-vaginal canal [canalis pharyngeus].

14 *a*

Above the pterygoid tubercle, and below the lingula, there is a small aperture that leads into the **pterygoid canal**, which passes forwards through the root of the pterygoid process. In front, at its root, the pterygoid process displays a broad, smooth surface which is confluent above with the root of the greater wing around the foramen rotundum, and forms the posterior wall of the **pterygo-palatine fossa.** Medial to the foramen rotundum, and below it, the anterior opening of the **pterygoid canal** is seen. The lower parts of the pterygoid plates are separated by an angular cleft called the **pterygoid fissure**; this fissure lodges the tubercle of the palatine bone, the margins of which articulate with the serrated edges of the fissure.

Ossification.—The sphenoid is ossified partly in cartilage and partly in membrane (p. 197). The body is at first in two parts—pre-sphenoid and post-sphenoid. The **pre-sphenoid** is the part in front of the tuberculum sellæ, and is connected with the lesser wings. The **post-sphenoid** is the rest of the body, and is connected with the pterygoid processes and the greater wings.

The ossific centres are in pairs, and appear as follows :—

One, at the eighth week, between the foramen ovale and foramen rotundum, for the **greater wing** and the **lateral pterygoid plate**.

One, at the eighth week, in the hypophyseal fossa at the side of the cranio-pharyngeal canal, for the main part of the **post-sphenoid**.

One, at the ninth week or later, near the carotid groove, for the side of the post-sphenoid and the **lingula**.

One, at the ninth week, in the **medial pterygoid plate**, for that plate and its hamulus.

One, at the ninth week, immediately lateral to the optic foramen, for the **lesser wing** and its roots and the jugum sphenoidale.

One, at the tenth week, medial to the optic foramen, for the main part of the **pre-sphenoid** (*i.e.* pre-sphenoid **minus** the jugum and the conchæ).

One (which may be quadruple), in the fifth month or later, for the **sphenoidal concha**.

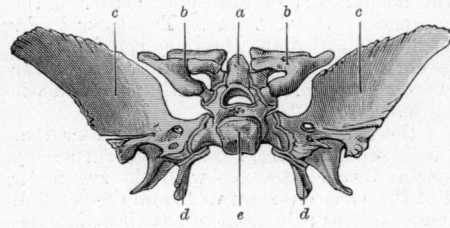

FIG. 171.—OSSIFICATION OF THE SPHENOID.

a, Pre-sphenoid; *b*, Lesser wings; *c*, Greater wings; *d*, Medial pterygoid plates; *e*, Post-sphenoid.

The medial pterygoid plate is the first part to be completely ossified; its hamulus is chondrified during the third month immediately before ossification spreads into it. The two pairs of centres for the post-sphenoid are fused by the sixth month; and the post-sphenoid unites with the pre-sphenoid in the seventh month. **At birth** the bone is in three pieces—the greater wing with the pterygoid process on each side, and the body with the lesser wings. They have fused by the end of the first year. During that year ossification spreads medially from the lesser wings to form the jugum sphenoidale. Occasionally two median foramina are seen in young skulls—one on the tuberculum sellæ and one farther forward—due to delayed fusion between the post-sphenoid and the jugum and between the halves of the jugum.

Variations.—The foramen spinosum and the foramen ovale are sometimes incomplete posteriorly. The superior orbital fissure, in rare cases, communicates with the foramen rotundum or with the optic foramen. The optic foramen has been found double—the optic nerve passing through one canal and the ophthalmic artery through the other. Ossification of fibrous bands leads to the formation of anomalous foramina, *e.g.* the *carotico-clinoid foramen*, between the anterior and middle clinoid processes; the *pterygo-spinous foramen*, enclosed by ossification of the band between the spine and the lateral pterygoid plate; the *porus crotaphitico-buccinatorius*, enclosed by ossification of a ligament below and lateral to the foramen ovale. The lesser superficial petrosal nerve sometimes passes through a minute, unnamed hole near the posterior border of the greater wing. The sphenoidal sinus varies in size; may be absent; and is occasionally multilocular.

Ethmoid Bone

The **ethmoid bone** lies in front of the sphenoid, between the orbits and the orbital plates of the frontal bone; it enters into the formation of the anterior cranial fossa, the orbits, and the nasal cavities. It is extremely light, and consists of a pair of cellular parts called the **ethmoidal labyrinths**, united superiorly to a median **perpendicular plate** by a pair of thin horizontal laminæ which, from their perforated condition, are called the **cribriform plates**.

The study of the ethmoid bone will be easier if one cribriform plate is cut through.

The **perpendicular plate** forms the upper part of the nasal septum and has an irregular pentagonal outline. Its **superior border** projects above the level of the cribriform plates into the cranial cavity to form a crest called the **crista galli**. The crest is thicker than the rest of the plate, and contains either spongy bone or an air cell. It is highest in front, and its lower part divides anteriorly into a pair of **alæ** which project forwards to articulate with the frontal bone, and enclose the **foramen cæcum**. The **posterior border** of the perpendicular plate articulates with the crest of the sphenoid. The **posterior inferior border** in the adult articulates with the vomer, and fuses with it after the fortieth year. The **anterior inferior border** is usually thicker than the others, and unites with the cartilaginous nasal septum. The **anterior superior border** articulates with the nasal spine of the frontal bone and with the median crest of the two nasal bones. The *surfaces* are fairly smooth, except superiorly, where there are short and shallow grooves that lead to the foramina in the cribriform plate.

Each **cribriform plate** occupies the interval between the orbital plate of the frontal bone

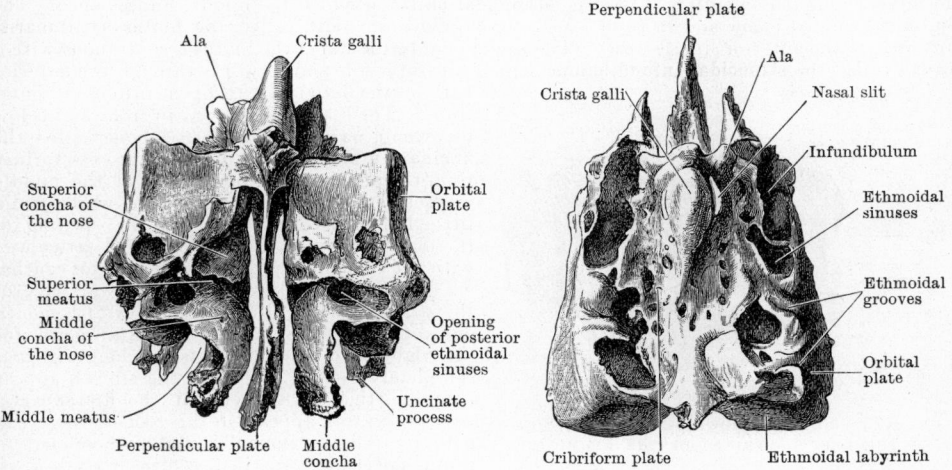

FIG. 172.—THE ETHMOID SEEN FROM BEHIND.   FIG. 173.—THE ETHMOID SEEN FROM ABOVE.

and the crista galli; it lies in the roof of the nose and in the floor of the anterior cranial fossa, and articulates posteriorly with the sphenoid.

The **ethmoidal labyrinth** is composed of exceedingly thin bone enclosing a large number of air sinuses; the sinuses are arranged in three groups—an anterior, a middle, and a posterior, the walls of which have been broken in the process of disarticulation.

The *posterior surface* of the labyrinth articulates with the front of the body of the sphenoid and the orbital process of the palatine bone, which close in the posterior sinuses. The *anterior surface* is oblique and is covered by the lacrimal bone and the upper part of the frontal process of the maxilla, which close the anterior sinuses. The *upper surface* is covered by the orbital plate of the frontal bone, which completes the sinuses superiorly; and it is crossed by two grooves which are converted into the **anterior** and **posterior ethmoidal canals** when the orbital plate is in position. *Laterally* the cells are closed in by a thin oblong lamina, called the **orbital plate** of the ethmoid [lamina papyracea], which forms a part of the medial wall of the orbit. The plate articulates *above* with the orbital plate of the frontal bone; *in front* with the lacrimal bone; *below* with the orbital surface of the maxilla; *behind* with the sphenoid; and, at its posterior inferior angle for a variable distance, with the orbital process of the palatine bone.

On the *medial surface* of the

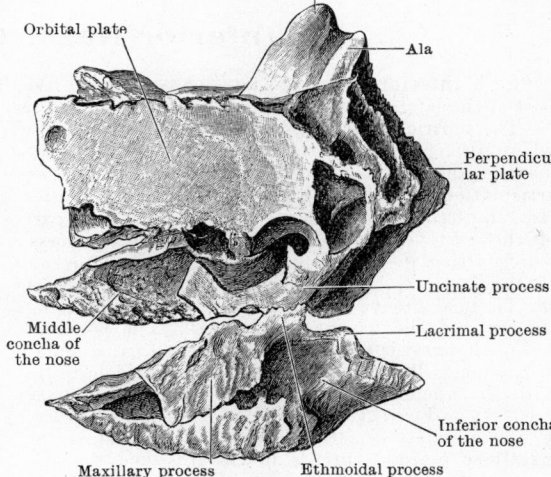

FIG. 174.—LATERAL SURFACE OF ETHMOID AND INFERIOR CONCHA.

labyrinth the sinuses are closed in by thin, rough bone, but they open into the nose by small apertures on this surface, which is free in the lateral wall of the nasal cavity. The surface is very uneven, and from it two thin, rough, curled plates of bone, called the superior and middle nasal conchæ, project medially into the cavity of the nose and then curve downwards.

The **superior concha** is small and may be a mere ridge. It projects from the posterior half of the surface, less than half an inch below the cribriform plate. The bone above the concha closes in the posterior ethmoidal sinuses, and is finely grooved for olfactory nerves; the grooves begin on the concha and run upwards and forwards to the lateral foramina of the cribriform plate. The space lateral to the concha, and between it and the middle concha, is called the **superior meatus** of the nose, and the posterior ethmoidal sinuses open into it. The bone in front of the superior meatus and superior concha closes in middle and anterior ethmoidal sinuses.

The **middle concha** is much deeper than the superior, and is as long as the labyrinth. Its anterior end articulates with the ethmoidal crest of the maxilla, and its posterior end with the ethmoidal crest of the palatine bone. The space lateral to it is the upper part of the **middle meatus** of the nose. The lower members of the middle ethmoidal sinuses bulge into the meatus, forming a rounded elevation, called the **ethmoidal bulla**, on which the middle sinuses open. The bulla is bounded below and in front by a curved groove or a slit, called the **hiatus semilunaris**, into which the anterior sinuses open. The upper or anterior end of the hiatus is continuous with a canal, called the **ethmoidal infundibulum**, which runs upwards and forwards through the anterior

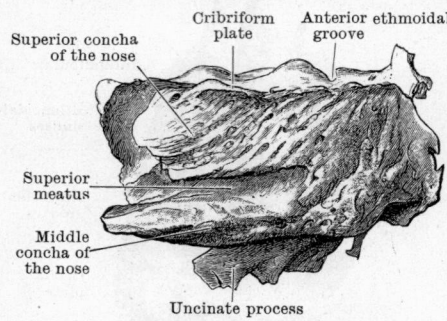

FIG. 175.—SECTION SHOWING THE NASAL SIDE OF THE LEFT LABYRINTH OF THE ETHMOID.

part of the labyrinth to open into the frontal sinus. The hiatus is bounded in front and below by a long, narrow, thin bar of bone called the **uncinate process**. The uncinate process springs from the anterior part of the roof of the middle meatus; it curves downwards, backwards and a little laterally, bridging across the opening of the maxillary sinus, and its lower end articulates with the ethmoidal process of the inferior concha.

Ossification takes place in the cartilage of the nasal capsule. In the fourth or fifth month one centre appears, near the orbital plate, for each **labyrinth** (including its conchæ), which is completely ossified at birth; the sinuses appear before birth. At the end of the first year, a pair of centres appear at the root of the crista galli for the **perpendicular plate**, whose ossification is not completed till the fifth or sixth year.

The **cribriform plate** is ossified during the second year by extension from the labyrinth and the perpendicular plate; and it fuses with the sphenoid after twenty-five.

Variations.—The orbital plate varies in size and shape. It is narrower from above downwards in the lower races than in the higher—in this respect resembling the condition in the anthropoids. And, as in the gorilla and chimpanzee, it may fail to articulate with the lacrimal, owing to a downgrowth of the frontal which articulates with the orbital surface of the maxilla (orbito-maxillary-frontal suture). It is sometimes divided by a vertical suture into an anterior and a posterior part. The number of the conchæ may be increased from two to four, or may be reduced to one.

Inferior Nasal Conchæ

Each **inferior concha** is an elongated, shell-like lamina of bone that lies along the lower part of the lateral wall of the nasal cavity. It has two surfaces and two borders.

The **superior** or **attached border** is thin and unevenly convex. It is sharp in front and behind, where it articulates with the conchal crests of the maxilla and the palatine bone. Between those two articulations the central part of the upper border rises in the form of a sharp crest; the anterior part of the crest forms the upstanding **lacrimal process**, which articulates above with the descending process of the lacrimal bone, and also with the edges of the lacrimal groove of the maxilla, thus completing the wall of the naso-lacrimal canal. The posterior end of the crest is elevated in the form of an irregular projection, called the **ethmoidal process**, which unites with the uncinate process of the ethmoid bone (see Fig. 174). From the middle of the upper border, on its lateral side, a thin irregular plate, called the **maxillary process**, spreads downwards and conceals

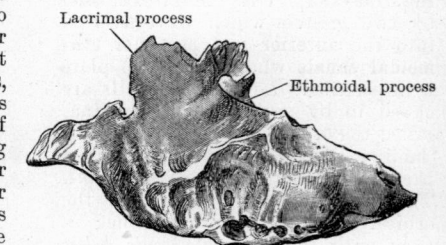

FIG. 176.—MEDIAL SURFACE OF RIGHT INFERIOR CONCHA.

part of the lateral surface of the bone; this process unites with the medial surface of the maxilla, partly helping to close the gap that leads into the maxillary sinus and partly hanging down in the sinus between its mucous lining and medial wall. The **inferior** or **free border** is gently curved from before backwards and turned slightly laterally, is rounded and full, is deeply pitted, and is of a slightly cellular character. The anterior and posterior ends of the bone are thin and sharp.

The **medial surface** is uneven and convex and bulges into the nasal cavity; it is rough and pitted, and is marked by some fine, scattered, and longitudinally directed vascular grooves. The **lateral surface** is concave and forms the medial boundary of the inferior meatus of the nose. It is smooth in front, where it corresponds to the opening of the naso-lacrimal canal; posteriorly and towards its inferior border it is irregular and pitted.

A case in which the inferior conchæ were absent has been recorded.

Ossification.—The inferior concha is ossified, in the cartilage of the lateral wall of the nasal capsule, from one centre which appears about the fifth month of intra-uterine life.

Lacrimal Bones

The **lacrimal bone**—a thin scale of bone about the size of a finger-nail—forms part of the medial orbital wall behind the frontal process of the maxilla. It is irregularly quadrangular, and has two surfaces—a medial and a lateral—and four borders.

The posterior part of the **medial surface** is uneven and cellular; it closes in some anterior ethmoidal sinuses and the ethmoidal infundibulum. The anterior part is smaller and smoother, and is separated from the posterior part by a shallow groove; it forms a small part of the lateral wall of the nose behind the frontal process of the maxilla and above the inferior concha. The **lateral surface** looks into the orbit, and is divided by a vertical ridge opposite the groove on the medial surface. This **crest** ends inferiorly as a hook-like process called the **lacrimal hamulus**. The hamulus curves forwards round the postero-lateral edge of the naso-lacrimal notch of the maxilla, and thus forms the postero-lateral boundary of the opening into the naso-lacrimal canal. The area behind the crest is nearly flat, and forms the part of the medial wall of the orbit in front of the orbital plate. The area in front of the crest is narrower and is concave, forming the floor of the **lacrimal groove**, which combines with the lacrimal groove on the frontal process of the maxilla to form the fossa for the lacrimal sac. The floor of the lacrimal groove is prolonged downwards beyond the main part of the bone as the **descending process**, which forms the medial boundary of the opening of the naso-lacrimal canal.

The **inferior border** articulates with the orbital surface of the maxilla, and, anteriorly, by the descending process, with the lacrimal process of the inferior concha. The **anterior border** articulates with the frontal process of the maxilla; the **superior border** with the frontal bone; the **posterior border** with the orbital plate of the ethmoid.

Ossification.—The lacrimal is ossified from one centre which appears in the third month of intra-uterine life in the membrane that covers the cartilaginous nasal capsule.

Variations.—The lacrimal bone is occasionally absent. In some skulls it is divided into two or more parts. The hamulus may be small; but in rare cases it extends forwards to the orbital margin, and shares in the formation of the face, as in lemurs.

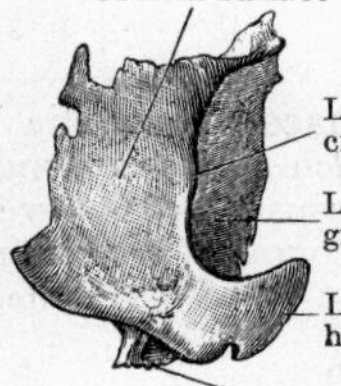

FIG. 177.—RIGHT LACRIMAL BONE (Orbital Surface).

Vomer

The **vomer** is placed in the posterior part of the nasal septum. It has four borders and two surfaces. The **superior border** is easily recognised, because it is split into a pair of everted lips or **alæ**. It articulates with the inferior surface of the body of the sphenoid, whose rostrum fits in between the alæ. Each **ala** is wedged in between the sphenoidal process of the palatine

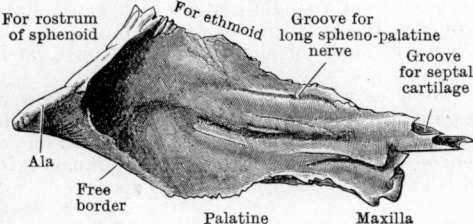

FIG. 178.—VOMER, FROM THE RIGHT SIDE.

FIG. 179.

VOMER AT BIRTH, consisting of two Osseous Laminæ united inferiorly. The figure to the right represents a vertical section at the point marked ✲ in the left figure.

bone and the vaginal process of the medial pterygoid plate. The **posterior border** is a free, sharp, slightly curved edge, and forms the posterior margin of the nasal septum. The **inferior border** articulates with the nasal crest formed by the maxillæ and the palatine bones. The **anterior edge** is the longest; it slopes obliquely from above downwards and forwards. Its upper half articulates with the perpendicular plate of the ethmoid, and is fused with it after middle age; its lower half is grooved to receive the septal cartilage of the nose. The **anterior end** of the bone is a truncated angle which articulates with the posterior border of the prominent, anterior part of the nasal crest of the maxillæ, and sends downwards a pointed process which passes between the incisive canals. The **surfaces** of the bone are smooth, except for a few vascular grooves; one groove, usually more distinct than the others, runs obliquely downwards and forwards, and lodges the long spheno-palatine nerve.

Ossification.—The vomer begins to ossify at the eighth week of intra-uterine life from a pair of centres that appear in the membrane on the postero-inferior part of the cartilaginous septum of the nose. They form a pair of plates of bone separated by cartilage. During the third month the plates unite along their lower edges, and their fusion is not much further advanced at birth. As growth goes on, the cartilage is absorbed, and fusion of the laminæ takes place from below upwards, and is almost complete at puberty; but, even in the adult, the bilaminar origin is indicated by the alæ and by the groove on the anterior border. The anterior end is partly ossified in cartilage by extension of the ossifying process into the paraseptal cartilages (p. 197).

Structure and Variations.—The bone is composed of two compact layers fused together, except at the grooves for the rostrum of the sphenoid and the septal cartilage, and also along a line where a canal runs horizontally from behind forwards in the substance of the bone. The canal is named the **spheno-vomerine canal**; it transmits the nutrient vessels, which enter the bone through a minute aperture at the posterior end of the groove between the alæ.

Owing to imperfect ossification there may be a deficiency in the bone—filled up during life with cartilage. The depth of the groove along the anterior border varies considerably; sometimes the two lamellæ are separated by a considerable cavity; and occasionally the sphenoidal sinus sends a small extension forwards between the lamellæ.

Nasal Bones

The **nasal bones** lie between the frontal processes of the maxillæ in the bridge of the nose. Each bone is elongated and quadrangular, having two surfaces and four borders, and is slightly constricted above its middle. The **outer surface** is convex from side to side, and slightly concavo-convex from above downwards. Near its centre there is usually the opening of a vascular canal. The **inner surface** or mucous surface forms part of the roof and side wall

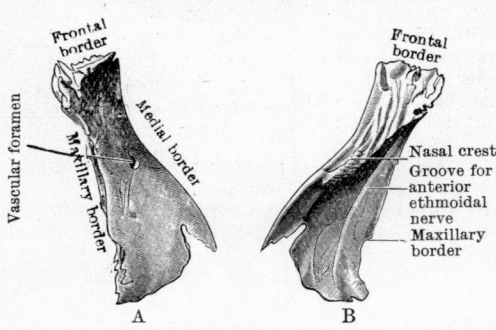

FIG. 180.—THE RIGHT NASAL BONE.
A, Outer aspect; B, Inner aspect.

of the cavity of the external nose. It is smooth and concave, and is triangular in outline. On its posterior part the anterior ethmoidal nerve makes a narrow, nearly vertical groove. The **medial border** articulates with its fellow of the other side. Inferiorly it is thin. Superiorly it widens out into a triangular area. The posterior edges of these triangular areas of the right and left bones are raised to form a narrow median ridge, called the **nasal crest**, which forms a small part of the nasal septum, and articulates, from above downwards, with the nasal spine of the frontal bone, the perpendicular ethmoidal plate, and the septal cartilage. The **lateral border**, usually the longest, is serrated and bevelled, and articulates with the anterior edge of the frontal process of the maxilla.

The **superior border** is a toothed surface which articulates with the frontal bone at the medial part of the nasal notch, and rests, posteriorly, on the root of the nasal spine. The **inferior border** is thin and sharp; it is connected with the lateral cartilage of the nose, and is often deeply notched near its medial extremity.

Ossification.—The nasal bones are each developed from a single centre which appears about the end of the second month in the membrane covering the cartilaginous nasal capsule.

Structure and Variations.—The nasal bone is made of dense compact tissue, and is strengthened by the formation of the nasal crest.

The nasal bones vary greatly in different people as well as in different races. As a rule they are large and prominent in the White races, and are small, flat, and depressed in Mongolians and Negroes. Absence has been recorded; and division into two or more parts; and one case of unusual extension downwards. Obliteration of the internasal suture is uncommon; it is stated to occur more frequently in negroes, and is the usual condition in adult apes.

Maxillæ

The two **maxillæ** form the upper jaw. Each has a **body** and four **processes**—**zygomatic, frontal, alveolar**, and **palatine**.

The **body** is pyramidal, and contains a cavity called the **maxillary sinus**. It has four surfaces—anterior, posterior, orbital, and nasal.

The **anterior surface** is concavo-convex. *Superiorly* it is limited, from behind forwards (or latero-medially), by the root of the zygomatic process, the smooth **infra-orbital margin**, and the root of the frontal process. *Anteriorly* it is limited by a sharp, curved edge that bounds a wide concavity called the **nasal notch**, and ends below in a pointed process. This process unites with the similar projection of the other maxilla to form a sharp spur, called the **anterior nasal spine**, which is situated at the upper end of the inter-maxillary suture. *Inferiorly* the surface is confluent with the alveolar process, which is ridged by the sockets of the teeth. The largest ridge is produced by the socket of the canine tooth, and is called the **canine eminence**. The shallow depression medial to the eminence overlies the upper parts of the incisor sockets. The wide depression that extends from the eminence to the zygomatic process is called the **canine fossa**; immediately above it, near the infra-orbital margin, is the **infra-orbital foramen**

Posteriorly the surface is limited by the zygomatic process and a blunt ridge that descends from it and fades away at the first or second molar socket.

The **posterior surface** is rounded and full. It forms the anterior walls of the infra-temporal and pterygo-palatine fossæ. *Laterally* it is separated from the anterior surface by the zygomatic process and the ridge. *Medially* it is separated from the nasal surface by an uneven, vertical margin. *Inferiorly* it ends as a rough, low prominence, called the **maxillary tuberosity,** which lies behind the last molar socket; above the tuberosity there are the openings of two or more **posterior dental canals** which convey the vessels and nerves down to the molar teeth. *Superiorly* the surface is limited by a rounded border that forms the anterior boundary of the inferior orbital fissure in the articulated skull.

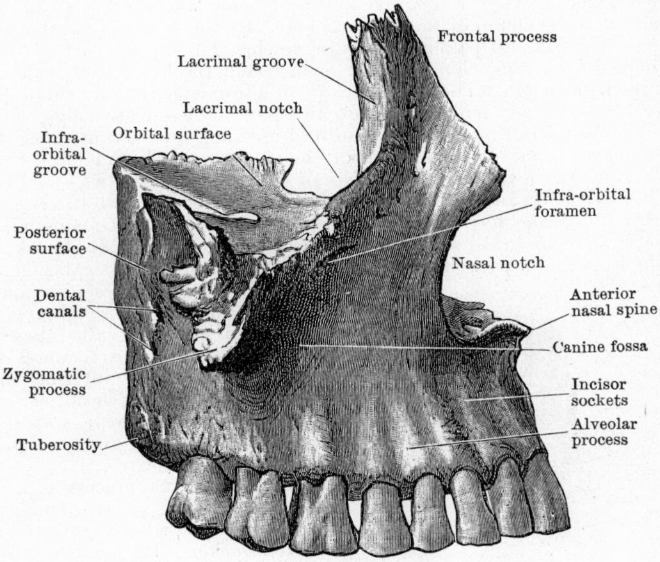

The **orbital surface** is smooth and flat, and is triangular in outline. It forms the greater part of the floor of the orbit. From behind forwards, the surface is traversed by the **infra-orbital groove** and **canal.** The canal ends as the infra-orbital foramen; and if it is laid open, small apertures are seen leading into the **middle** and **anterior dental canals,** which convey the vessels and nerves to the premolar, canine, and incisor teeth. The surface is limited *posteriorly* by the margin of the inferior orbital fissure, and *anteriorly* by the root of the zygomatic process and the infra-orbital margin. *Medially* it

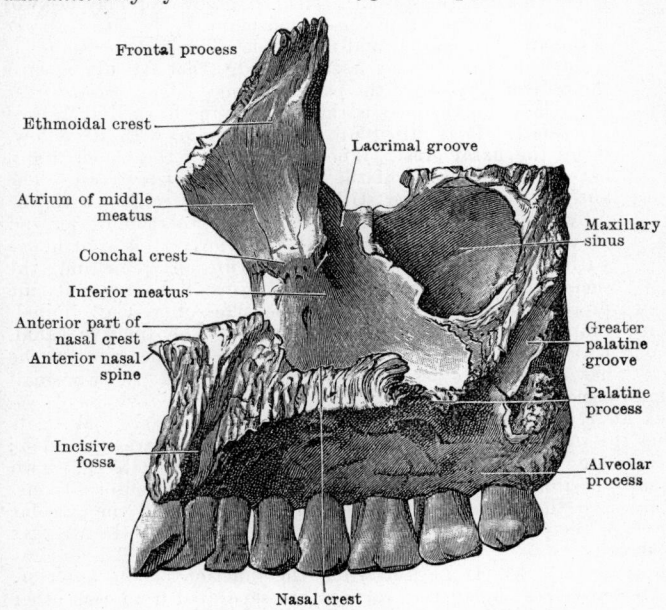

FIG. 181.—THE RIGHT MAXILLA (Lateral View).

is limited by a sharp margin whose anterior part bounds the **naso-lacrimal notch,** while the rest articulates, from before backwards, with the lacrimal bone, the orbital plate of the ethmoid, and the orbital process of the palatine bone.

The **nasal surface** forms part of the lateral wall of the cavity of the nose. It is limited *superiorly* by the medial margin of the orbital surface and the root of the frontal process, *posteriorly* by the medial margin of the posterior surface, *anteriorly* by the margin of the nasal notch, and *inferiorly* by the attachment of the palatine process. Above that attachment, there is a wide smooth area that forms the anterior and larger part of the lateral wall of the inferior meatus of the nose. Above and behind that area there is the large opening into the maxillary sinus; in the

FIG. 182.—THE RIGHT MAXILLA (Medial Aspect).

articulated skull the opening is to a large extent closed by the lacrimal, the ethmoid, the inferior concha, and the palatine bone. Behind the opening and also below it, there is a rough area for articulation with the perpendicular plate of the palatine bone; that area is traversed from above downwards and forwards by an oblique groove which, when the palatine bone is in place, is converted into the **greater palatine canal** (canalis pterygo-palatinus). In front of the opening there is a wide, vertical groove, called the **lacrimal groove,** which is converted into the

naso-lacrimal canal when the lacrimal and inferior concha are in place. In front of the groove, at the junction of the body and the frontal process, there is a low, horizontal ridge, called the **conchal crest**, which articulates with the inferior concha.

The **frontal process** is a long, wide, thin plate that stands up from the junction of the nasal, facial, and orbital surfaces. It lies in the side wall of the cavity of the nose, and forms a great part of the skeleton of the external nose. Its *upper end* is serrated and articulates with the frontal bone at the lateral part of the nasal notch. The upper part of the *anterior border* is rough or grooved for articulation with the nasal bone; the lower part is sharp, and bounds the upper part of the nasal notch. The *posterior border* is a thin edge that articulates with the lacrimal. The *lateral surface* is divided lengthwise into two parts by a smooth ridge, called the **lacrimal crest**, which forms the medial margin of the orbital opening, and is continuous with the infra-orbital margin. The part of the surface in front of the crest lies in the side of the external nose, and is confluent inferiorly with the anterior surface of the body; one or two vascular foramina may be seen on it. The part behind the crest is narrower, and forms the most anterior part of the medial wall of the orbit; it is the floor of a vertical groove which is continuous with the lacrimal groove of the body, and, combined with the groove of the lacrimal bone, forms the **fossa for the lacrimal sac**. The uppermost part of the *medial surface* is rough for articulation with the front of the ethmoid labyrinth, and it closes in some of the anterior ethmoidal sinuses. Below the rough area there is an ill-defined, nearly horizontal elevation called the **ethmoidal crest**. The posterior part of that crest articulates with the anterior end of the middle concha; its anterior part produces a slight elevation in the unmacerated head, called the **agger nasi**. The rest of the surface is the wide, smooth area between the ethmoidal and conchal crests, and it forms the side wall of the atrium of the middle meatus.

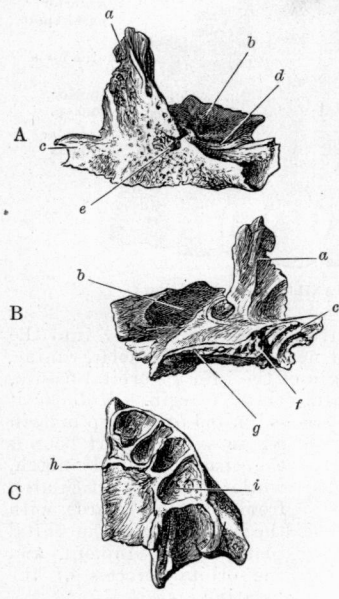

FIG. 183.—MAXILLA AT BIRTH.

A, Lateral side; B, Medial side; C, Under side. *a*, Frontal process; *b*, Orbital plate; *c*, Anterior nasal spine; *d*, Infra-orbital groove; *e*, Infra-orbital foramen; *f*, Incisive groove; *g*, Palatine process; *h*, Premaxillary suture; *i*, Alveolar process.

The **palatine process** is a horizontal plate attached to the medial side of the bone, at the junction of the body and alveolar process, from the incisor sockets to the second molar socket. It is much thinner behind than in front. It has two surfaces and three borders. The *upper surface* is smooth, and is slightly concave from side to side; it forms the anterior two-thirds of the floor of the nasal cavity. The *lower surface* lies in the roof of the mouth, forming the anterior two-thirds of its own half of the bony palate; it is rough, and is pitted for the palatine mucous glands; near its lateral margin there is an ill-defined groove (or may be two) for the greater palatine vessels and nerve. The *lateral border* is the attached border, and is curved. The *posterior border* is a notched, sharp, nearly horizontal edge that articulates with the horizontal plate of the palatine bone. The *medial border* is rough and articulates with its fellow in the median line of the palate. It is raised up as a lip which, with its fellow, forms the **nasal crest**. The lower edge of the vomer fits in between the two lips of the posterior part of the crest. The anterior part is raised still higher; it articulates with the subvomerine cartilages superiorly, and with the anterior end of the vomer posteriorly, while anteriorly it is continuous with the anterior nasal spine. Inferiorly, behind the incisor sockets, the articulating margins of the two palatine processes are grooved to form the sides of a small funnel-shaped pit called the **incisive fossa**. The **incisive canal**, which begins in the floor of the nose at the side of the nasal crest, divides to open into the fossa by two small apertures—a lateral and a **median incisive foramen**.

The **alveolar process** is thick and curved. It projects downwards from the body. With its fellow of the opposite side it forms the *alveolar arch*, in which the roots of the teeth are imbedded; when the adult dentition is complete, each alveolar process has sockets for eight teeth. Two small vascular foramina are usually visible on the lingual surface behind the incisor sockets. When any or all of the teeth are shed the walls of the sockets are absorbed, and the alveolar process may be reduced to the level of the plane of the palatine process. Posteriorly the alveolar process ends in the **maxillary tuberosity**.

The **zygomatic process** is short and thick. It projects from the junction of the anterior, posterior and orbital surfaces. Its *anterior* and *posterior surfaces* are separated from each other by a rounded, concave ridge that fades away at the socket of either the first or the second molar tooth. The *upper surface* is oblique and rough, and articulates with the zygomatic bone.

The **premaxillæ**, in most vertebrates, are a pair of independent bones that lie in front of the maxillæ. In Man and Apes they are the parts of the maxillæ that lie in front of the incisive fossa and carry the incisor teeth. But the premaxillary part is ossified separately, and, though the greater part of it fuses in intra-uterine life with the rest of the maxilla, yet, up to middle age, their independent origin is indicated by a faint suture that extends sinuously from the hinder part of the incisive fossa to the interval between the canine and lateral incisor sockets.

Ossification.—The **maxilla proper** is ossified in membrane in the wall of the buccal cavity from one centre which appears in the sixth week above the germ of the canine tooth. Ossification spreads rapidly in different directions to form the body of the bone and its processes. The infra-orbital nerve is at first placed considerably above the orbital surface of the maxilla, and comes in contact with it only in the second month, when a groove is formed on the bone; the groove is converted into the infra-orbital canal and foramen by the uprising and folding medialwards of its lateral boundary. In the early stages the alveolar part lies close below the infra-orbital groove; later, they are separated by the maxillary sinus, which first makes its appearance as a shallow fossa on the medial side of the bone about the fourth month of intra-uterine life.

The **premaxilla** is ossified from at least two centres. The first appears above the incisor tooth germs in the sixth week; from it, most of the premaxilla is ossified and also the anterior part of the frontal process; the bone formed from it fuses with the maxilla proper, beginning at the alveolar part almost at once. The second centre appears at the twelfth week and soon fuses with the rest; it forms the medial wall of the incisive canal. It may be that there are two main centres and that they fuse almost at once, but sometimes never fuse. For in some cases of lateral cleft palate the line of cleavage does not pass between the germs of the canine tooth and lateral incisor tooth (*i.e.* the cleft is not between the maxilla proper and the premaxilla), but passes between the germs of the two incisors, or even through the germ of the lateral incisor—accounting for the extra incisor sometimes found on the lateral side of the cleft.

Variations.—There may be a vertical suture in the infra-orbital margin above the infra-orbital foramen. The infra-orbital canal may be an open groove. Duckworth records four cases of a spine projecting upwards from the lower part of the nasal notch. A case has been described in which the premaxillæ and the incisor teeth were absent. A *torus palatinus* is not uncommon—*i.e.* a ridge along the median suture of the hard palate. The lacrimal groove may be constricted towards its centre. A part of the maxillary sinus may be constricted off anteriorly and, owing to its relation to the naso-lacrimal canal, is called the *lacrimal recess*. Almost complete septa in the maxillary sinus have been recorded.

Palatine Bones

Each **palatine bone** has two main parts—a **horizontal** and a **perpendicular plate**—united to each other like the limbs of the letter L. At their junction posteriorly there is an irregular projection called the **tubercle**. Two irregular projections stand up from the upper edge of the perpendicular plate; they are named the **sphenoidal** and **orbital processes**, and are separated by an interval called the **spheno-palatine notch**.

The **horizontal plate** is thin and square, having two surfaces and four borders. Its *upper surface* is smooth, is slightly concave from side to side, and forms the floor of the posterior part of the nasal cavity. Its *lower surface* is rougher, and forms the posterior third of the bony

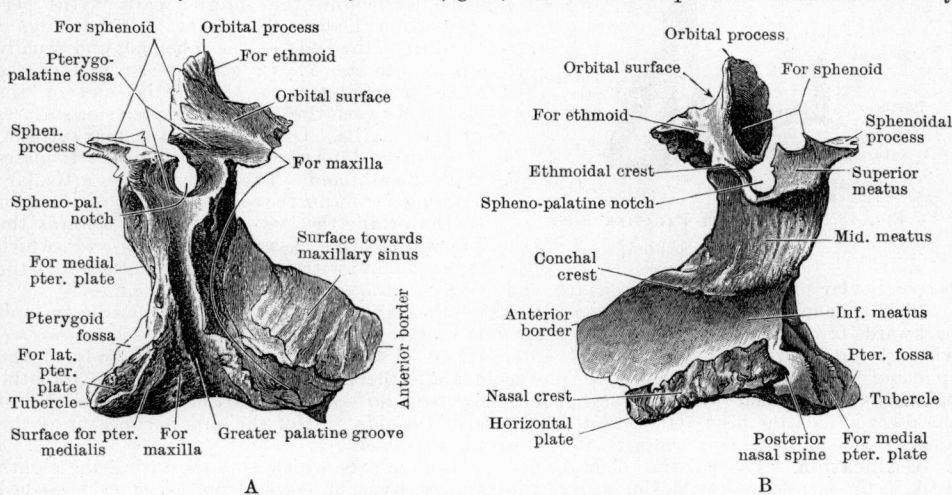

FIG. 184.—RIGHT PALATINE BONE.

A, As seen from the Lateral Side. B, As seen from the Medial Side.

palate; near its posterior edge there is a sharp, transverse ridge called the **palatine crest**. The *anterior border* is rough, and articulates with the palatine process of the maxilla. The *posterior margin* is free and concave; at the median plane it meets its fellow, and the two together send backwards a pointed process called the **posterior nasal spine**. The *medial border* is thick and rough, and articulates with its fellow; the two margins send up a median ridge called the **nasal** crest; it is continuous in front with the nasal crest of the maxilla, and the posterior part of the inferior border of the vomer fits in between its two lips. The *lateral border* joins the perpendicular plate at a right angle, and is grooved to form the medial margin of the **greater palatine foramen.**

The **perpendicular plate** also is thin, and has two surfaces and four borders. It is longer than the horizontal part, and much wider inferiorly. Its *medial surface* is crossed horizontally, about its middle, by the **conchal crest,** which articulates with the posterior part of the inferior concha; above and below the crest, the surface forms part of the lateral wall of the middle and inferior meatuses of the nose. Near the upper end of the surface there is another horizontal ridge, called the **ethmoidal crest,** which articulates with the posterior part of the middle concha. The *lateral surface,* for the most part, is applied to the medial side of the maxilla and helps to close the opening into the maxillary sinus; but the upper, posterior part—below the sphenoidal process and the spheno-palatine notch—is free, and forms the medial wall of the pterygo-palatine fossa. From that free area, the **greater palatine groove** runs downwards and forwards to the lower end of the plate. When the bone is in place, the groove, with the corresponding groove on the maxilla, forms the greater palatine canal, which leads from the pterygo-palatine fossa to the greater palatine foramen. The *anterior border* is a thin edge, of irregular outline, which articulates above with the ethmoid, with the posterior edge of the maxillary process of the inferior conchal bone about its middle, and below with the maxilla. The *posterior border* is thin above, where it articulates with the anterior part of the medial pterygoid plate, but expands below into the tubercle. The *lower border* is fused with the lateral edge of the horizontal plate. The *upper border* supports the **orbital** and **sphenoidal processes**; the notch between them is converted into the **spheno-palatine foramen** by the articulation of the palatine bone with the body of the sphenoid.

The **tubercle** [processus pyramidalis] is directed backwards and laterally from the junction between the perpendicular and horizontal plates. Its *posterior surface* presents a smooth, vertical groove bounded by two rough furrows that unite above in a ∧-shaped manner. The furrows articulate with the anterior parts of the lower portions of the two pterygoid plates, and the groove fits into the pterygoid fissure to form the floor of the lower part of the pterygoid fossa.

For sphenoid
Orbital process
Orbital surface
Sphenoidal process
Palatino-vaginal groove
Pterygo-palatine fossa
Spheno-palatine notch
Middle meatus
Greater palatine canal
Conchal crest
Inferior meatus
Nasal crest
For lateral pterygoid plate
Posterior nasal spine
Horizontal plate
Tubercle
Pterygoid fossa
For medial pterygoid plate

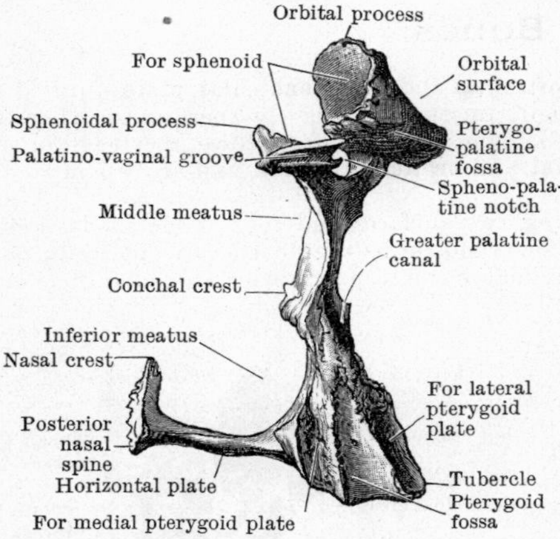

FIG. 185.—THE RIGHT PALATINE BONE.
As seen from behind.

The *lateral surface* of the tubercle is confluent with the lateral surface of the perpendicular plate; its anterior part is rough for articulation with the maxilla; its posterior part is a smooth, narrow triangle that fits into the interval between the tuberosity of the maxilla and the lateral pterygoid plate in the medial wall of the infra-temporal fossa. The **lesser palatine canals** descend through the tubercle and open on its lower surface as the **lesser palatine foramina.**

The **orbital process,** shaped like a hollow cube, surmounts the anterior part of the perpendicular plate. The mouth of the cube is applied to the body of the sphenoid, and usually opens into its cavity; the anterior part of the cube articulates with the medial end of the border between the orbital and posterior surfaces of the maxilla. Of the remaining four surfaces, one, directed forwards and medially, articulates with the ethmoid. The others are non-articular: the *superior* forms the posterior part of the floor of the orbit; the *lateral* is directed towards the pterygo-palatine fossa; whilst the *inferior,* which is confluent with the medial surface of the perpendicular plate, is of variable width, and overhangs the superior meatus of the nose.

The **sphenoidal process,** much smaller than the orbital, curves upwards, medially, and backwards from the posterior part of the summit of the perpendicular plate. Its *upper surface,* which is grooved, articulates with the anterior part of the lower surface of the body of the sphenoid and the root of the medial pterygoid plate, thereby converting the groove into the **palatino-vaginal canal** [canalis pharyngeus]. Its *lateral surface* forms part of the medial wall of the pterygo-palatine fossa. Its *medial surface* is in the side wall of the superior meatus of the nose; its medial edge is in contact with the ala of the vomer.

Ossification.—The palatine bone ossifies from one centre which appears during the eighth week in the membrane in the side wall of the nasal cavity. The orbital process may be ossified from an independent centre. Until the third year the antero-posterior width is greater than the vertical height, which increases as the maxillary sinus enlarges.

Structure and Variations.—The greater part of the palatine bone is composed of two thin plates of compact substance, which may be separated, in the horizontal plate, by an extension of the maxillary sinus. The lower part of the greater palatine canal may be completely bounded by the palatine bone. The orbital process varies greatly in size, and is not always pneumatic; occasionally it unites with the sphenoidal process and converts the spheno-palatine notch into a foramen, which may be divided into two by a bridge of bone

Zygomatic Bones

Each **zygomatic bone** lies below and lateral to the orbit, in the most prominent part of the cheek, and is hence often called the *cheek-bone*. It forms the lateral border of the orbit, and helps to separate it from the temporal fossa and the upper part of the infra-temporal fossa; below, it rests upon and is united to the maxilla; behind, it enters into the formation of the zygomatic arch. The zygomatic bone is described as having three *surfaces*, named the *lateral*, the *orbital*, and the *temporal*, two processes, named the *frontal* and the *temporal*, and a *marginal tubercle*.

The **lateral surface** is the largest surface; it is slightly convex and rather uneven; above its most elevated part there is a small aperture called the **zygomatico-facial foramen**, which is often double. The lower margin of the surface is free and rough, and is continuous with the lower edge of the zygomatic process of the maxilla. The upper margin is smooth and

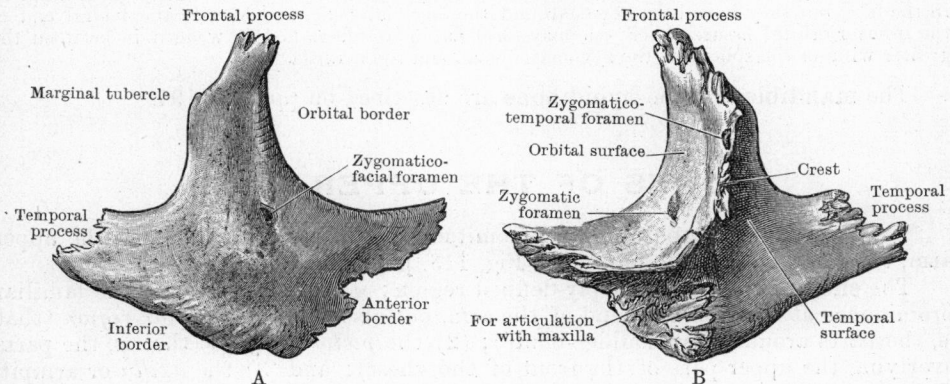

FIG. 186.—THE RIGHT ZYGOMATIC BONE. A, Lateral Side; B, Medial Side.

forms a great part of the infra-orbital margin. The anterior margin is oblique and is united to the zygomatic process of the maxilla. The posterior margin is continuous with the two processes. The **temporal process** projects backwards and articulates by an oblique, serrated extremity with the zygomatic process of the temporal bone. The **frontal process** is a large process that projects upwards; its medial margin is smooth and forms the greater part of the lateral margin of the orbit; its lateral or posterior margin meets the upper border of the temporal process almost at a right angle. About half-way up that margin there is usually a prominence called the **marginal tubercle**. The upper end of the frontal process articulates with the zygomatic process of the frontal bone; and from its deep surface a wide, thin, crest projects backwards in the lateral wall of the orbit, between the orbit and the temporal fossa, and articulates by its sharp, posterior edge with the greater wing of the sphenoid. That crest is continuous inferiorly with a small shelf of bone which projects backwards from the infra-orbital margin into the floor of the orbit and articulates with the maxilla. The crest and the shelf form the **orbital surface** of the bone; their free margins may be separated by a small, smooth notch that forms the anterior end of the inferior orbital fissure; at a varying point on the orbital surface there is an aperture, called the **zygomatic foramen**, which may be double.

The **temporal surface** is a large, concave surface which looks towards the temporal and infra-temporal fossæ, and includes the deep aspects of the temporal and frontal processes. On that part formed by the frontal process there is a small hole called the **zygomatico-temporal foramen**.

Besides the named surfaces there is a wide, rough, triangular area which articulates with the zygomatic process of the maxilla.

Ossification.—The zygomatic bone ossifies in membrane from one centre which appears between the eighth and the tenth week. There may be more than one centre, for the bone is sometimes divided in the adult. At birth there are narrow grooves or fissures on the temporal surface, produced by the overlapping edges of a cup-shaped and a club-shaped thickening of the bone; in some cases those grooves persist in the adult.

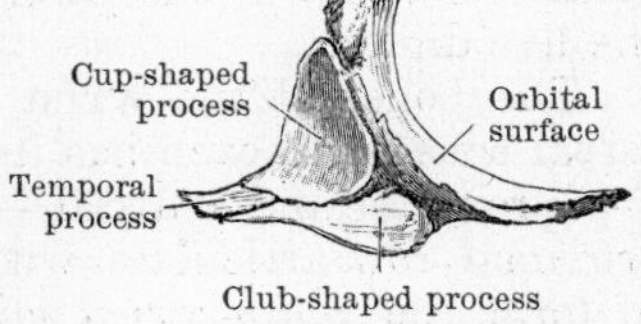

FIG. 187.—MEDIAL SURFACE OF THE ZYGOMATIC BONE AT BIRTH.

Structure and Variations.—In structure the zygomatic bone is compact, with little spongy tissue. Together with the zygomatic process of the temporal bone it forms the buttress which supports the maxilla and the lateral wall of the orbit. Additional strength is imparted to the bone by the angular mode of union of its orbital and facial parts.

The zygomatic bone is sometimes divided by a horizontal or a vertical suture. Partial separation of the upper and lower parts by a process from the maxilla has been recorded; and in one case an extension of the maxilla completely separated the two parts and articulated with the zygoma.   Cases have been noted where, owing to deficiency in the zygomatic bone, the zygomatic arch has been incomplete ; and a case of absence of the zygomatic arch has been recorded.

Sutural Bones

Sutural bones are isolated bones of variable size and shape occasionally met with in the sutures and at the fontanelles. They were once called Wormian bones after the Danish anatomist *Ole Worm*. They are ossified from independent centres, and usually include the whole thickness of the cranial wall, but they may involve only the outer or the inner table. They are most frequent at the lambda and in the lambdoid suture. They are common at the pterion ; in this situation they are called *epipteric bones*, and by their fusion with one or other of the adjacent bones they may lead to the occurrence of a fronto-squamosal suture. They have been seen in the sagittal suture, and sometimes in the inter-frontal suture of metopic skulls. They are occasionally met with at the asterion and more rarely at the obelion. They are infrequent in the face, but they have been noted around the lacrimal bone, and also at the lateral end of the inferior orbital fissure, where one may form an independent nodule wedged in between the greater wing of the sphenoid, the zygomatic bone, and the maxilla.

The **mandible** and the **hyoid bone** are described on pp. 185, 191.

BONES OF THE UPPER LIMB

The parts of the **upper limb** [extremitas superior] are the shoulder, the upper arm, the forearm, and the hand (see Fig. 113, p. 99).

The **shoulder** is not a sharply defined region ; it includes not only the familiar prominence at the proximal end of the arm, but also (1) the *scapular region* (that is, the parts around the shoulder-blade) ; (2) the *pectoral region* (that is, the parts overlying the upper part of the front of the chest) ; and (3) the *axilla* or armpit. The bones of the shoulder are the **scapula** or shoulder-blade and the **clavicle** or collar-bone. Those two bones constitute what is called the *shoulder girdle* ; they articulate with each other at the joint called the *acromio-clavicular joint*. The clavicle articulates with the upper end of the sternum or breastbone, forming with it the *sterno-clavicular joint* ; the scapula does not articulate with any part of the axial skeleton, being connected with it only by muscles.

The **upper arm** (brachium) extends from the shoulder to the elbow.   The bone of the upper arm is called the **humerus**.   The humerus articulates with the scapula to form the *shoulder joint*.

The **forearm** (ante-brachium) is continuous with the upper arm at the *elbow* (cubitus); there the humerus articulates with the two bones of the forearm to form the *elbow joint*.   The bones of the forearm are called the **radius** and the **ulna** ; they articulate with each other at their proximal and distal ends, forming *radio-ulnar joints*.

The **hand** (manus) has three parts : (1) the wrist ; (2) the hand proper, one surface of which is the palm and the other surface is the "back of the hand" ; (3) the five digits.

The bones of the **wrist** (carpus) are eight small bones, named collectively the **carpal bones**, and each has its own name besides. They are arranged in two rows —a proximal and a distal—four bones in each row. Three of the bones of the proximal row articulate with the radius and a fibro-cartilaginous *articular disc* to form the *radio-carpal joint* or *wrist joint*, where the hand joins the forearm. Each carpal bone articulates with the adjoining carpal bones, forming *inter-carpal joints*. Note that the " wrist " of every-day speech is the distal part of the fore-arm ; the anatomical *wrist* is lower, and is not marked off from the rest of the hand on the surface.

The bones of the **hand proper** (metacarpus) are called **metacarpal bones**. They are five in number—one corresponding to each digit. They are named **first** metacarpal, **second** metacarpal, etc., beginning with the one that corresponds to the thumb.   The metacarpal bones articulate with the distal row of carpal bones, forming *carpo-metacarpal joints* ; and they articulate with one another at their proximal ends, forming *inter-metacarpal joints* ; their distal ends are the rounded prominences known as the first row of *knuckles*.

Each of the **digits** is named: the thumb or *pollex*; the forefinger or *index*; the middle finger or *digitus medius*; the ring finger or *digitus annularis*; the little finger or *digitus minimus*. The bones of the digits are called **phalanges**. The thumb has two phalanges, named the **proximal** phalanx and the **distal** phalanx. Each finger has three phalanges: **proximal, middle**, and **distal**. The distal phalanx is sometimes called the *ungual phalanx*, because the *nail* (unguis) is associated with it. The proximal phalanx of each digit articulates with the distal end of the corresponding metacarpal bone to form a *metacarpo-phalangeal joint*. The ends of the middle phalanx articulate with the other two, forming *inter-phalangeal joints*.

Scapula

The **scapula** is a thin, wide, triangular bone [σκαπάνη (scapanē)=a digging tool] that lies obliquely in the upper part of the back and in the posterior wall of the axilla, opposite the second to the seventh ribs. It is classed as a "flat" bone and has a main part or **body** and three processes,[1] named the **spine**, the **acromion**, and the **coracoid process**. At one of its angles the body is greatly thickened and is coated with articular cartilage. The thickened angle is called the **head**, and the part contiguous to the head is called the **neck**. The spine is the large triangular plate attached to the posterior surface of the body; the acromion is the flattened piece of bone which is continuous with the spine at the angle between its two unattached borders; and the coracoid process is the thick, bent piece of bone that projects from the upper part of the head and neck.

The **body** is the blade proper; it is thin and even translucent in places, and is triangular in outline—having two surfaces, three borders, and three angles.

The **borders** of the scapula are named *superior, medial*, and *lateral*.

The **superior border** is the shortest of the three. At its lateral end, close to the root of the coracoid process, there is a notch called the *supra-scapular notch*; it may be wide and shallow, or narrow and deep; it is bridged across by a fibrous band called the *supra-scapular ligament* [lig. transversum scapulæ superius]; in some scapulæ the ligament is ossified, and the notch is thus converted into a foramen.

The **medial border** [margo vertebralis] is the longest of the three, and looks medially and backwards towards the spines of the vertebræ. When the shoulder is at rest the border lies two or three finger-breadths from those spines and can be both felt and seen in a thin person. It is divided into three parts:—a small part opposite the spine of the scapula, a part above that and a part below, the lowest part being by far the longest.

The **lateral border** [margo axillaris] looks in a lateral direction and forwards, and lies in the posterior wall of the axilla, where it may be indistinctly felt. The part of it immediately below the head is thick and rough, and is called the *infra-glenoid tubercle*; the rest of it is thin, though rough.

The **angles** of the scapula are named *superior, inferior*, and *lateral*.

The **superior angle** [angulus medialis] is the one between the superior and medial borders; it is so thickly covered with muscles that it can scarcely be felt.

The medial and lateral borders meet at the **inferior angle**, and it is the lowest part of the scapula. It is covered thinly with muscle and is easily felt; it is used as a landmark to locate spines of vertebræ, for, when the arm is hanging at rest, it is at the level of the spine of the *seventh* thoracic vertebra.

The **lateral angle** is between the lateral and superior borders. It is only nominally an angle, for it is truncated and thickened to form the **head**. The lateral surface of the head is slightly hollowed to form what is called the **glenoid cavity**; it is smooth, articular, and pear-shaped in outline; it is directed forwards and slightly upwards as well as laterally, and it articulates with the head of the humerus to form the shoulder joint [γλήνη (glēnē)=a socket]. The small rough area at the upper margin of the glenoid cavity is called the *supra-glenoid tubercle*.

The **surfaces** of the scapula are named *costal* and *dorsal*.

---

[1] Definitions of terms are given on pp. 3 and 94.

The **costal surface** looks towards the ribs and the greater part of it is concave; the concavity is referred to as the **subscapular fossa**, and is deepest opposite the spine. At the medial and lower angles there are usually flat, triangular areas marked off by ridges from the rest of the surface, and those two areas are connected by a very narrow raised strip alongside the medial border; the areas and the strip are for the insertion of a large muscle called the *serratus anterior*. All the rest of the costal surface (except a small part near the neck, Fig. 191) gives origin to a muscle called the *subscapularis*; and low ridges that run from the medial margin towards the neck give attachment to tendinous fibres in the substance of the subscapularis. A wide, blunt, smooth ridge begins at the neck, runs downwards near the lateral margin and fades away near the inferior angle. If the scapula is held up against the light, this will be seen to be the thickest part of the blade; and it is the barlike lever on which the serratus anterior acts when it moves the scapula.

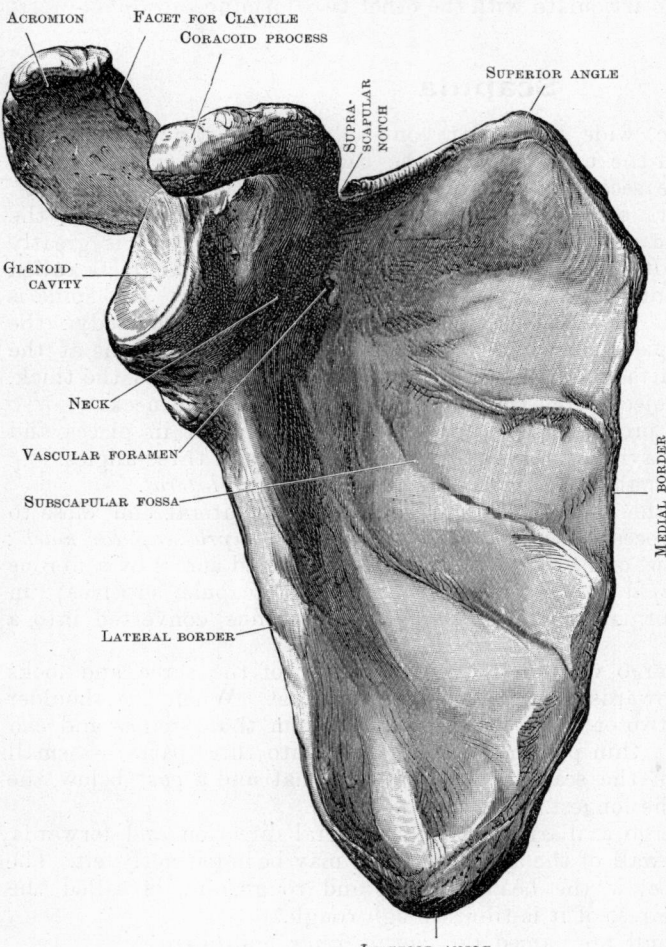

ACROMION   FACET FOR CLAVICLE
            CORACOID PROCESS

SUPRASCAPULAR NOTCH

SUPERIOR ANGLE

GLENOID CAVITY

NECK

VASCULAR FORAMEN

SUBSCAPULAR FOSSA

LATERAL BORDER

MEDIAL BORDER

INFERIOR ANGLE

FIG. 188.—RIGHT SCAPULA FROM THE FRONT.

The **dorsal surface** is divided into two unequal parts by the spine; the two parts are not in the same plane, for the scapula is bent at the attachment of the spine. The smaller, supraspinous part and the upper surface of the spine form the boundaries of a space called the **supraspinous fossa**. On the larger, infraspinous part there is a raised oval area, alongside the lower part of the lateral margin; this area gives origin to a muscle called the *teres major*. Above that area there is a raised narrow strip that reaches up to the head of the bone; the *teres minor* muscle arises from the strip, and crossing it there is a narrow, shallow groove produced by an artery called the circumflex scapular artery; occasionally there are two grooves, and they correspond to branches of the artery. The remainder of the lower part of the dorsal surface forms one wall of a space called the **infraspinous fossa**, while the lower surface of the spine is the other wall.

The **spine of the scapula** is a triangular plate of bone attached by one of its borders to the dorsum of the scapula. Another border of the spine looks in a lateral direction towards the shoulder joint; it is smooth and rounded, and the wide notch that separates it from the neck and head of the scapula is called the **spino-glenoid notch**. The notch is bridged by a weak fibrous band called the *spino-glenoid ligament* [lig. transversum scapulæ inferius]. The third border is called the **crest of the spine.** It is subcutaneous, and can be felt easily in all its length in the living person. It has fairly sharp *upper* and *lower lips* or edges; and the lower lip shows a low, wide *tubercle* or enlargement towards its medial end. At the medial margin of the blade the lips of the crest spread apart to enclose a small, smooth, triangular area which one can easily feel in the living person by pressing the finger along the crest; it is at the level of the spine of the *third* thoracic vertebra, and is used as a land-mark for locating the spines of the vertebræ.

The **acromion** is broad and flattened; it is continuous with the spine at the angle where the crest and the lateral border of the spine meet; it extends in a lateral direction and forwards, and over-hangs the shoulder joint above and behind. It lies at the top of the shoulder and is easily felt there, its upper surface being subcu-taneous and continuous with the crest of the spine [ἄκρον (acron) = highest point; ὦμος (ōmos) = shoulder (with upper arm)]. Its lateral border is long and is sharply bent to become continuous with the lower lip of the crest. The bend is called the **acromial angle**; it is easily located in the living person, and is used as a point from which measurements may be taken and as a guide to the back of the shoulder joint, which lies directly be-low and in front of it. The medial border of the acromion is short. It is continuous with

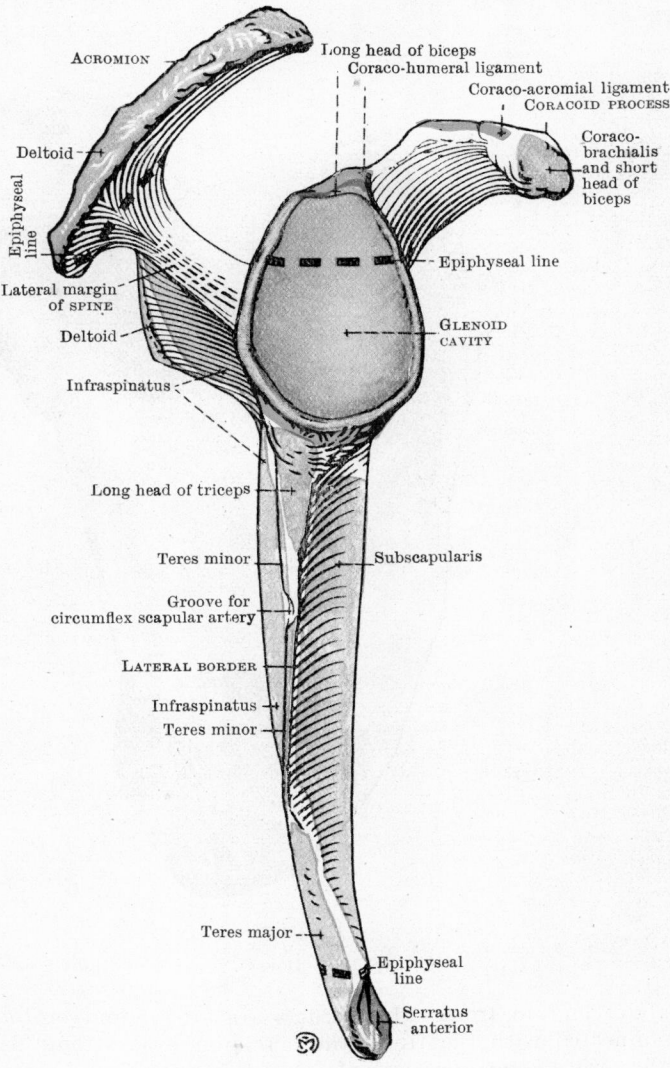

FIG. 189.—LATERAL VIEW OF RIGHT SCAPULA.

the upper lip of the crest, and its anterior and larger part is occupied by an oval facet for articulation with the lateral end of the clavicle at the *acromio-clavicular joint.*

The **coracoid process** is the stout, blunt process that projects from the upper margin of the neck and head of the scapula. In shape it has some resemblance to the bill of a bird [κόραξ (corax) = a raven or crow], and it is divisible into a root and a coracoid process proper.

The **root** projects upwards and forwards from the neck and head and is flattened from before backwards—its anterior and posterior surfaces being con-tinuous with the front and the back of the neck. Its medial border is the lateral

15

margin of the supra-scapular notch, and its lateral border is immediately above the glenoid cavity.

The **coracoid process proper** is fused with the top of the root and is almost horizontal. When the scapula is in its right position in the skeleton, with its glenoid cavity looking forwards as well as sideways, the coracoid process extends forwards and only slightly in a lateral direction, and overhangs the shoulder joint

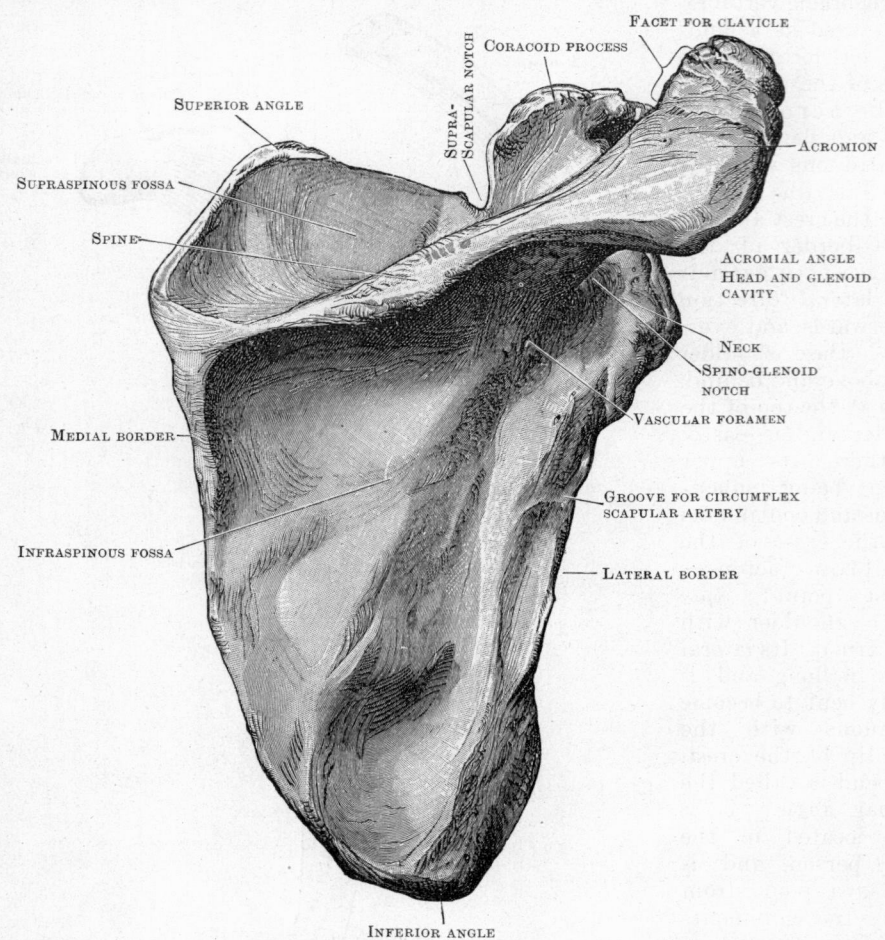

FIG. 190.—DORSAL SURFACE OF RIGHT SCAPULA.

above and in front. Its **borders** are *lateral* and *medial*. The lateral border is connected with the tip of the acromion by a strong, flat, triangular band called the *coraco-acromial ligament*; the two processes and the intervening ligament form a wide arch, called the **coraco-acromial arch**, which overhangs the shoulder joint and protects it. The **surfaces** of the coracoid process proper are *upper* and *lower*. The posterior part of the upper surface is roughened for the attachment of a thick, strong band, called the *coraco-clavicular ligament*, which binds it to the clavicle. The **tip of the coracoid process** is a landmark in the root of the upper limb. It is felt, rather indistinctly, as a hard, resisting object in the hollow on the front of the shoulder about an inch below the clavicle.

Nutrient foramina, by which arteries enter the bone and veins leave it, are scattered here and there, and are largest near the attached margin of the spine.

Attachments.—The **upper margin** of the scapula gives attachment to only one small muscle, namely, the inferior belly of the omo-hyoid, which arises from the supra-scapular ligament and the adjoining part of the upper margin. The **medial border** gives insertion to three muscles:

(1) the levator scapulæ, opposite the supraspinous fossa ; (2) the rhomboideus minor, opposite the spine ; and (3) the rhomboideus major, opposite the infraspinous fossa.

The **costal surface** gives attachment to (1) the serratus anterior, which is inserted into the small areas at the upper and lower angles and into the narrow strip along the medial border, and (2) the subscapularis, which arises from the whole costal surface except the parts for the insertion of the serratus anterior and a part near the neck ; a *bursa* protrudes from the capsule

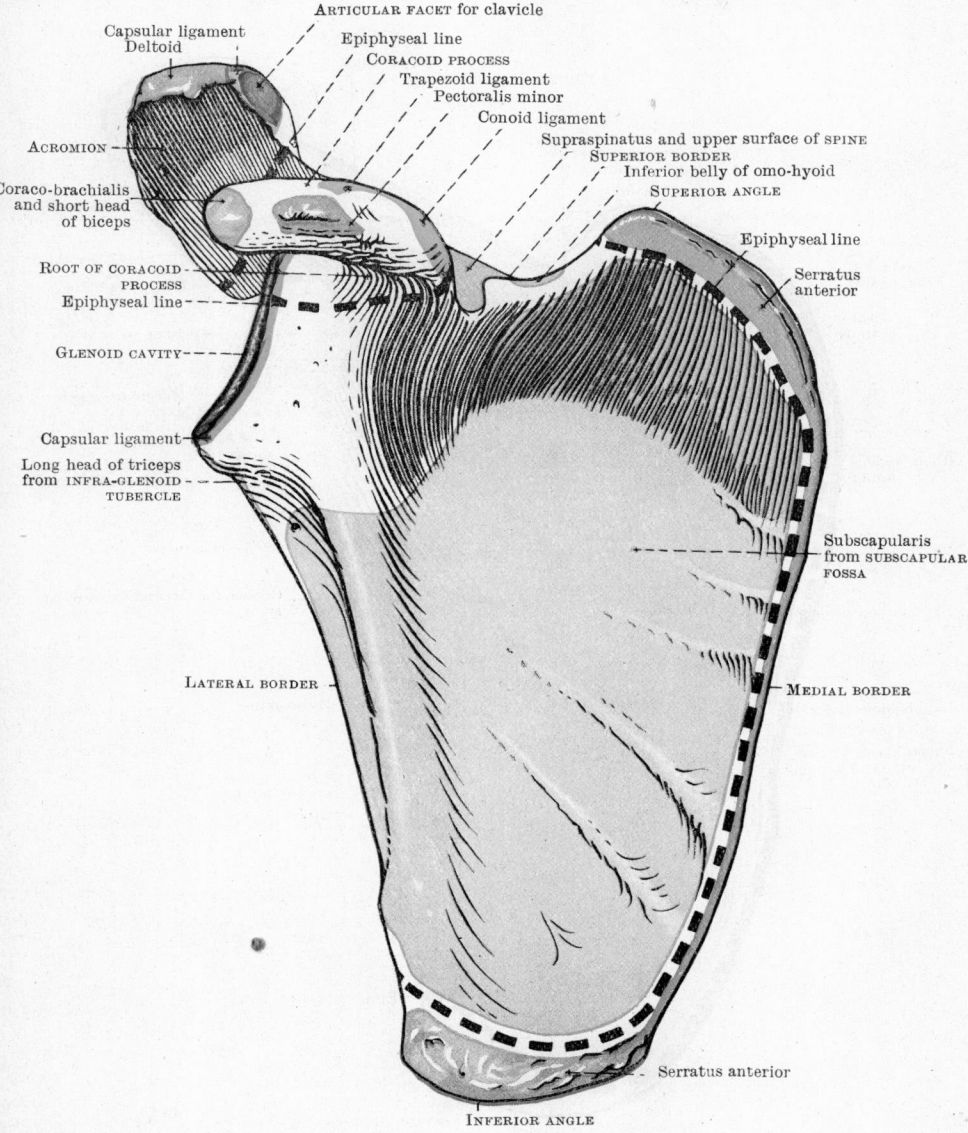

FIG. 191.—COSTAL SURFACE OF RIGHT SCAPULA.

of the shoulder joint and separates the subscapularis from the neck and from the root of the coracoid process, and those parts of the bone are smooth.

The **glenoid cavity** gives attachment by its circumference to a fibrous ring called the labrum glenoidale. The capsular ligament of the shoulder is attached to the rim of the cavity outside the labrum and to the labrum itself. The cavity looks almost directly upwards when the arm is raised above the head. The tendon of the long head of the biceps arises from the *supra-glenoid tubercle*, and some of the fibres of the tendon are incorporated in the labrum. The tendon of the long head of the triceps arises from the *infra-glenoid tubercle*, and that is the only muscle attached to the **lateral border.**

On the **dorsal surface** the teres major muscle arises from the oval or *triangular elevated area* near the inferior angle, and the latissimus dorsi muscle receives a small slip of origin from the lowest part of that area; the teres minor arises from the *elongated elevated area* that extends upwards to the head; the infraspinatus muscle arises from the walls of the **infraspinous fossa**, except a portion near the neck. The supraspinatus arises from the walls of the **supraspinous fossa**, except a part near the neck; as it passes over the shoulder joint towards its insertion into the humerus it is separated from the smooth, lower surface of the acromion by a *bursa* called the subacromial bursa.

The *upper* and *lower surfaces* of the **spine** help to bound the supra- and infraspinous fossæ and

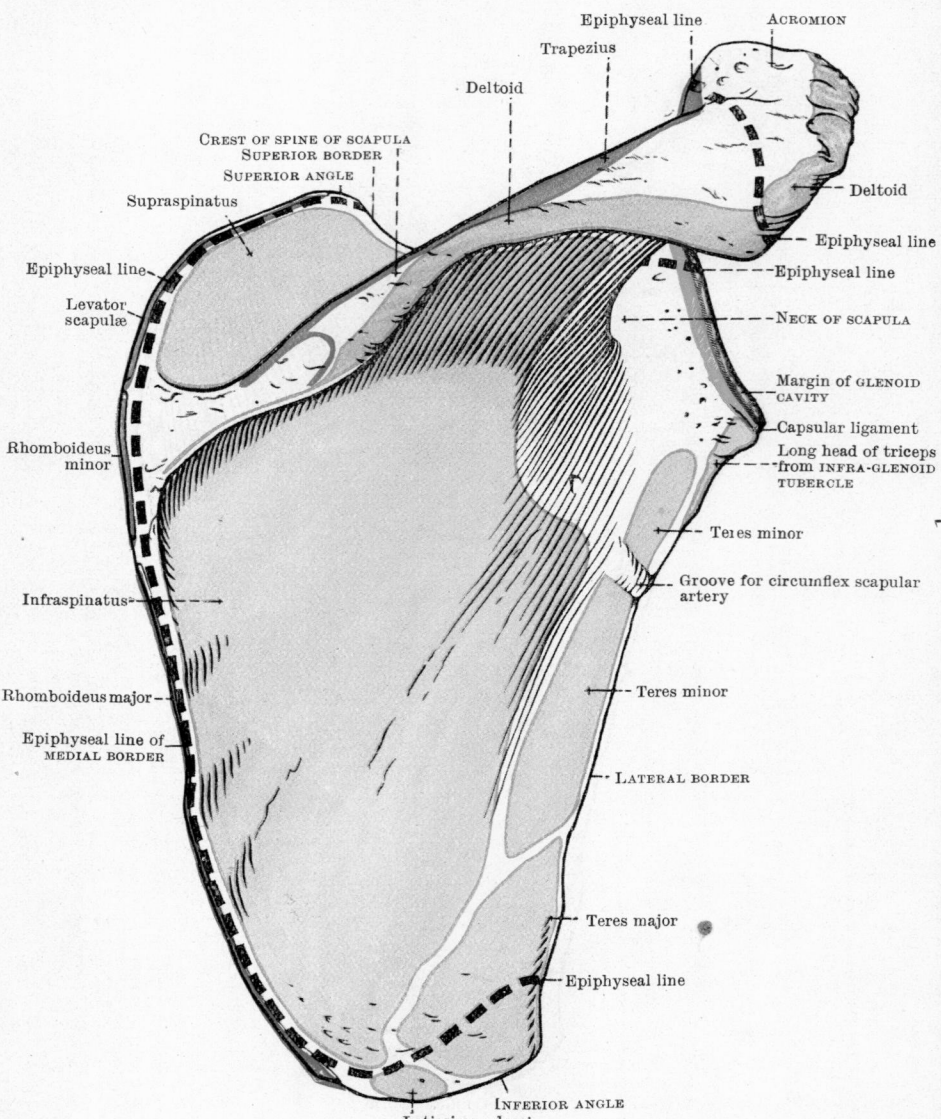

FIG. 192.—DORSAL SURFACE OF RIGHT SCAPULA.

give origin to some fibres of the supraspinatus and infraspinatus. The spino-glenoid ligament stretches from the *lateral margin* of the spine to the back of the **neck** of the scapula. The whole of the *lower lip* of the **crest** and the *lateral margin* of the **acromion** give origin to fibres of the deltoid muscle. The circumference of the *facet* on the medial margin of the acromion gives attachment to the capsule of the acromio-clavicular joint. The coraco-acromial ligament is attached to the *tip* of the acromion in front of the facet. Fibres of the trapezius muscle are inserted into the small part of the *medial margin* behind the facet, and into nearly the whole length of the *upper lip* of the **crest** and the **tubercle** on the *lower lip* of the crest; and a tendinous part of the trapezius, before reaching its insertion, plays over the smooth area where the spine joins the medial border, and is separated from that area by a small *bursa*.

The **coracoid process** gives attachment to numerous structures. The coraco-humeral ligament is attached to the *lateral margin* of its **root**, and the supra-scapular ligament to the *medial margin*. The coraco-brachialis muscle and the tendon of the short head of the biceps muscle arise conjointly from the *tip* of the **process proper**; the coraco-acromial ligament is attached to its *lateral margin*; the clavi-pectoral fascia to the posterior part of the *medial margin*; the pectoralis minor muscle is inserted into the anterior part of the *medial margin* and the adjoining part of the *upper surface*, and its attachment is sometimes marked by a ridge or a tubercle. The coraco-clavicular ligament is attached to the posterior part of the *upper surface*. The *lower surface* does not give attachment to any structure; it is smooth and is in relation with the subscapular *bursa* and muscle.

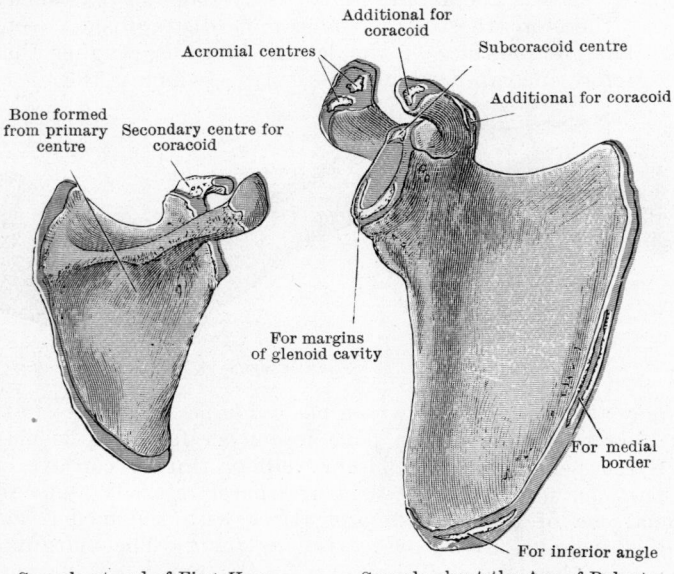

Scapula at end of First Year.   Scapula about the Age of Puberty.

FIG. 193.—OSSIFICATION OF THE SCAPULA.

Ossification.—The **primary** centre appears at the eighth week of intra-uterine life. At birth the acromion, the coracoid process, the glenoid cavity, the inferior angle, and the medial border are still cartilaginous.

Secondary Centre.	Appears at	Epiphysis fuses at	Relation of Epiphyseal line to Capsule of Neighbouring Joint.
For coracoid process (proper)	1st year	Puberty	None.
Subcoracoid, for lateral part of root of coracoid and upper third of glenoid cavity . .	10th year	Puberty	Partly outside, partly inside.
For margins of glenoid cavity	Puberty	20-25	Inside.
For inferior angle . .	Puberty	20-25	None.
For medial border .	Puberty	20-25	None.
Two for acromion . .	Puberty	20-25	Outside.

Occasionally the epiphysis formed from the two acromial centres fails to fuse with the rest of the bone, and the greater part of *the acromion is* **throughout life a separable bone** united to the rest of the bone by a cartilaginous or a synovial joint; the joint appears like a line of fracture in an X-ray photograph; the condition is usually alike on the two sides. The centre for the coracoid process may be regarded morphologically as a primary centre, and is sometimes present at birth; sometimes one or two additional centres appear on its surface after puberty and form small scaly epiphyses which join about the twentieth year.

Structure and Variations.—Two plates of compact bone separated by spongy tissue in the thicker parts and fused together in the thinner parts. In old people the bone may be absorbed in parts, but the periosteum remains. The coracoid process may be separate, but much more seldom than the acromion. In an infant the scapula is relatively wide.

Clavicle

The **clavicle** is an elongated, slender, curved bone [*clavicula*, diminutive of *clavis* = a key, or of *clavus* = nail or bolt]. It lies nearly horizontally in front of the upper part of the thorax at the root of the neck, stretching from the upper end of the sternum or breastbone to the acromion of the scapula and bracing the upper limb back so that the arm can swing to and fro clear of the trunk; it can be felt through the skin from end to end. It is a long bone and has a **shaft** and two slightly expanded **ends**. The *lateral third* of the bone is flattened from above downwards, and therefore the *lateral end* can be distinguished from the *medial end* at once; the lower surface of the lateral third is rougher than the upper surface, and therefore one can determine at a glance which is the *upper surface* and

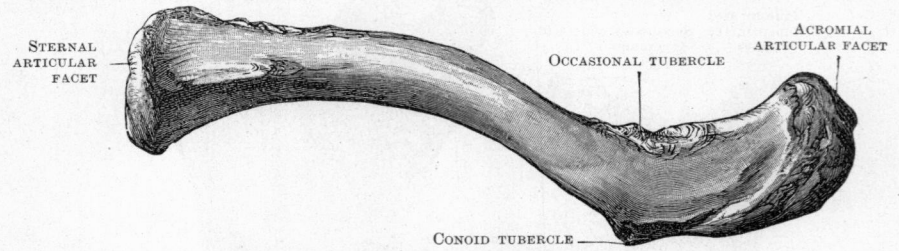

FIG. 194.—THE RIGHT CLAVICLE SEEN FROM ABOVE.

which is the *lower*. The bone as a whole has a double curve like the *italic* letter *f*: the **medial half or two-thirds** of the bone is convex forwards, as may be felt and seen in the living person, and the lateral half or third is concave forwards; the *anterior* and *posterior surfaces* of the bone are therefore easily identified.

The **acromial end** of the clavicle articulates with the medial margin of the acromion and is occupied by an oval *articular facet*. The margins of the facet are often raised or "lipped," and the ridge at the upper margin may assist one in locating the acromio-clavicular joint in the living person. Its articulation with the acromion is not direct, for an *articular disc* of fibro-cartilage intervenes between the two bones. The articular surface is oblique, looking downwards as well as laterally; when the bones are dislocated the clavicle therefore overrides the acromion, and is difficult to keep in place once dislocated.

The **sternal end** is thick. It articulates with the clavicular notch on the upper

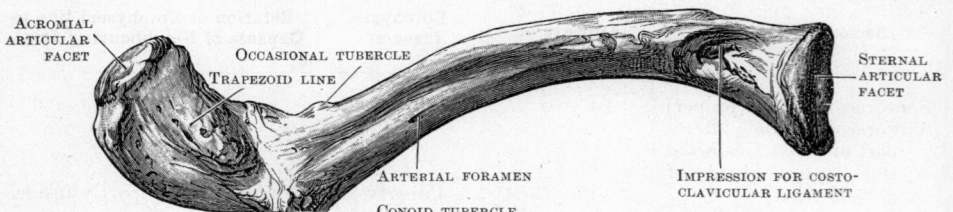

FIG. 195.—THE RIGHT CLAVICLE SEEN FROM BELOW.

end of the sternum and with the cartilage of the first rib at the side of the sternum, and the joint is called the *sterno-clavicular joint*. The end of the clavicle is larger than the clavicular notch on the sternum and its upper part can be felt above the level of the sternum; the *articular facet* occupies the lower three-fourths of the end of the clavicle, but it curves also on to the inferior surface for articulation with the first costal cartilage. In some clavicles the facet has been destroyed during maceration. The articulation with the sternum is not direct, for an *articular disc* separates the clavicle from actual contact with the sternum, though not from the first costal cartilage.

The **shaft** of the clavicle is divided, for descriptive purposes, into a lateral third and a medial two-thirds.

The **lateral third** has two surfaces, *upper* and *lower*, and two borders, *anterior* and *posterior*. The **anterior border** is rough and concave; the **posterior border** is smooth and convex. The **superior surface** is subcutaneous and is usually smooth, but may be rough near the borders, because the muscles attached to the borders sometimes extend their attachments on to the surface. The **inferior surface** is rough. At the posterior border there is a blunt, rounded prominence called the **conoid tubercle**; a broad, rough ridge, called the **trapezoid ridge**, extends from the tubercle towards the lateral end of the clavicle. The lateral third of the clavicle lies above the coracoid process of the scapula, and is attached to it by a strong, important band called the coraco-clavicular ligament; the ligament is in two parts named from their shape *conoid* and *trapezoid*, and they give the names to the tubercle and the ridge to which they are attached.

The **medial two-thirds** of the clavicle has four surfaces—anterior, posterior, superior, and inferior—separated by borders for which names are not necessary.

The **anterior surface** is the convex surface; laterally it narrows down to become continuous with the anterior border of the lateral third. Nearly all of it is occupied by an impression for the origin of part of a large muscle called the *pectoralis major*. The **posterior surface** is the concave surface; it is smooth and is continuous with the posterior border of the lateral third. The **upper surface** is

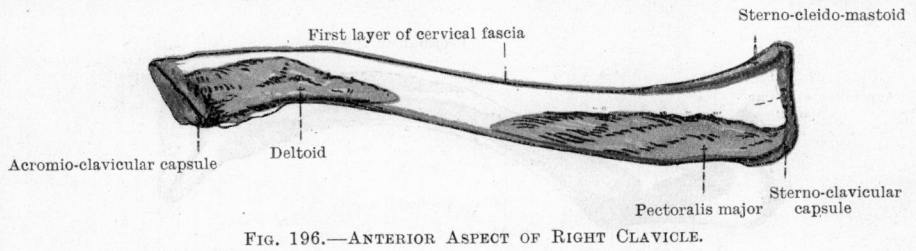

Fig. 196.—Anterior Aspect of Right Clavicle.

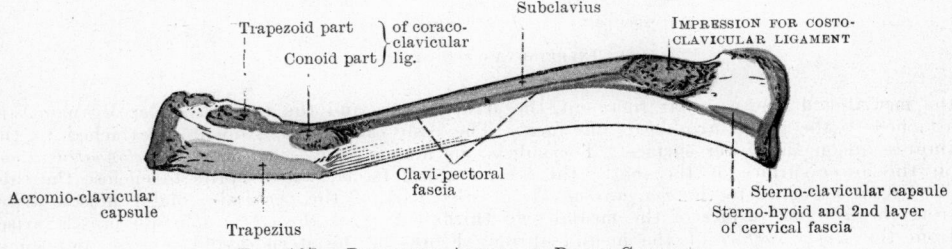

Fig. 197.—Posterior Aspect of Right Clavicle.

continuous with the upper surface of the lateral third, and is usually smooth and flat; it may be so narrow that it is a mere ridge, or it may be blended with the anterior surface.

Close to the medial end of the **lower surface** there is a rough impression of variable size and character; it may be an elevation or it may be a depression; it gives attachment to a strong fibrous band, called the *costo-clavicular ligament*, which binds the clavicle to the first rib. The lateral part of the lower surface of the medial two-thirds is occupied by a shallow groove which extends as far as the conoid tubercle and gives insertion to a small muscle called the *subclavius*. The rest of the surface may be of appreciable width, but in many clavicles it is narrowed down to a mere border.

The **nutrient foramen** is on the posterior surface near the junction of the lateral third with the medial two-thirds, and it is directed towards the lateral end.

The clavicle varies a great deal in different people, and the beginner may have difficulty in identifying the surfaces of the medial two-thirds if he is using a poorly developed bone as a specimen for study.

The clavicle is horizontal or nearly so when the body is in the upright position. But it slants upwards from medial to lateral end when the body is recumbent; for, in that position, the shoulder blades are moved upwards, and the lateral ends of the clavicles move with them. In a skiagram of a recumbent person the shadow of the clavicle is therefore very oblique. It is oblique also in skiagrams taken when the arm is held away from the side; for, in the movement of raising the arm, the scapula rotates, and the acromion, with the lateral end of the clavicle, is raised.

Attachments.—The capsule of the acromio-clavicular joint is attached to the margins of the *facet* on the **lateral extremity**. Part of the trapezius is inserted into the *posterior border* of the **lateral third**; part of the deltoid arises from the *anterior border*, on which there is occasionally a small, rough tubercle; the conoid and trapezoid ligaments are attached to the **conoid tubercle** and the **trapezoid ridge**.

The capsular ligament of the sterno-clavicular joint is attached to the margins of the *facet* at

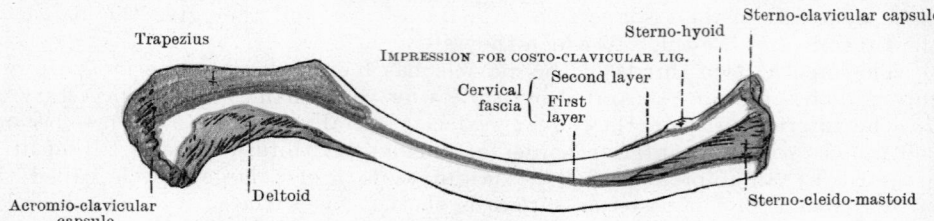

FIG. 198.—SUPERIOR ASPECT OF RIGHT CLAVICLE.

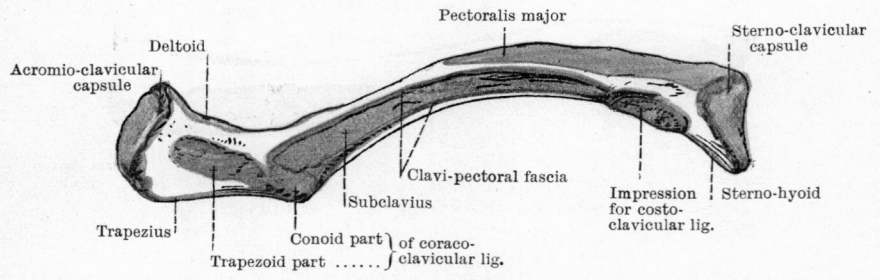

FIG. 199.—INFERIOR ASPECT OF RIGHT CLAVICLE.

the **medial end**; the capsular ligament, the articular disc and the interclavicular ligament are attached to the rough *area above the facet*. The costo-clavicular ligament is attached to the impression on the lower surface. The subclavius muscle is inserted into the *elongated groove* on the lower surface of the shaft; the clavi-pectoral fascia, which splits to enclose the sub-clavius, is attached to the *margins of the groove*. Part of the pectoralis major muscle arises from the *anterior surface* of the **medial two-thirds**. Part of the sterno-mastoid muscle arises from the *upper surface* of the medial third. Fibres of the sterno-hyoid muscle (and some-times sterno-thyroid) arise from the *posterior surface* near the medial end.

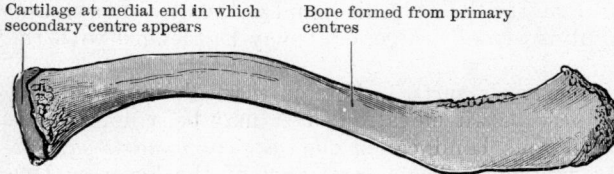

FIG. 200.—OSSIFICATION OF THE CLAVICLE.

Ossification.—The clavicle is the first bone in the body to begin to ossify, and is peculiar in its mode of ossification. Two **primary** centres appear in the fifth week of intra-uterine life in two separate portions of meso-dermal tissue which are at the pro-cartilage stage. When the tissue between those two portions also becomes pro-cartilage, the two centres coalesce to form one; ossification spreads from this centre into the cartilage that appears at the ends of the bone rudiment, and almost the whole bone is ossified from it.

Secondary Centre.	Appears at	Epiphysis fuses at	Epiphyseal Line is inside
For medial end	20th year	25	Capsule of sterno-clavicular joint.

Structure and Variations.—The clavicle, though a long bone, has no medullary cavity. It consists of spongy tissue surrounded by a shell of compact bone which is thickest in the middle. The nutrient artery is a branch of the supra-scapular. There may be two nutrient foramina, and one of them may be on the lower surface. The right clavicle is often longer, stronger, and more curved than the left.

The clavicle in women is shorter, smoother, and more slender than in men, and the curvatures are less marked; its acromial end is at a lower level than the sternal end, while in men the ends are at the same level or the acromial end is the higher. Occasionally the clavicle is perforated by one of the supra-clavicular nerves. In rare cases the clavicle is incompletely developed or is absent. A freely movable medial end and a bifurcated lateral part have been recorded. A small epiphysis may appear at the acromial end about 20, and unite rapidly.

Humerus

The **humerus** is the bone of the upper arm; its length is about one-fifth of the height of the person; though nearly all thickly covered with muscles it can be felt by deep palpation in all its length. It is a long bone with a **shaft** and **two ends**.

It is necessary first to distinguish the ends and ascertain the general direction of its surfaces. The **upper** end is the thick, rounded end, while the lower end is compressed from before backwards; there is a wide, deep hollow on the **back** of the lower end; the smooth, hemispherical part of the upper end looks in a **medial** direction.

The **upper end** includes the head, the anatomical neck, the greater and lesser tuberosities, and part of the bicipital groove.

The **head** is the large, convex, smooth articular part. It looks in a medial direction and also upwards, and, when the arm is hanging naturally by the side, it looks backwards as well. It articulates with the glenoid cavity of the scapula; and it may be indistinctly felt by the fingers pushed well up into the axilla.

The **lesser tuberosity** is the well-marked prominence on the front of the upper end; the part of it nearest the head has an impression, usually smooth, for the insertion of the tendon of the subscapularis. The lesser tuberosity can be felt in the

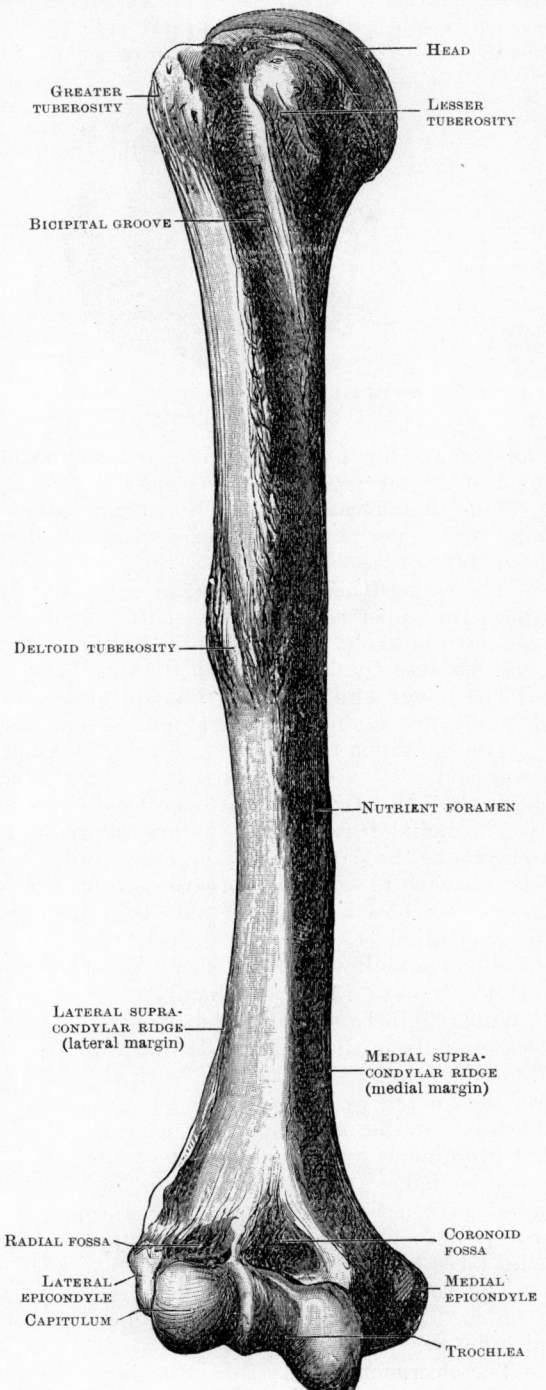

FIG. 201.—FRONT OF RIGHT HUMERUS.

front of the shoulder immediately lateral to the coracoid process (and may be mistaken for it) when the arm is hanging comfortably by the side, but at a little distance from that process when the limb is rotated so that the palm of the hand looks forwards.

The **greater tuberosity** is the prominence on the lateral side of the upper end. Though larger than the lesser tuberosity it is not so clearly defined, for its lateral surface shades off into the lateral side of the shaft. Its upper surface and its posterior surface have smooth impressions for the insertion of certain muscles.

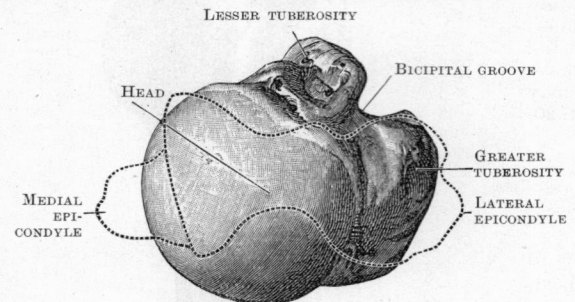

FIG. 202.—PROXIMAL ASPECT OF RIGHT HUMERUS (with the outline of lower end in relation to it in dotted line).

The greater tuberosity forms the "point of the shoulder," i.e., its most projecting lateral part, and may be felt there a little below the lateral margin of the acromion.

The **bicipital groove** [sulcus intertubercularis] is the clean-cut groove between the two tuberosities, and it is prolonged for two inches or more on to the shaft, where it is not so sharply defined. The tendon of the long head of the biceps, after it emerges from the shoulder joint, lies in the groove.

The **anatomical neck** is the narrow strip that encircles the margins of the head; its upper part is the narrow and shallow depression that separates the head from the tuberosities.

The **surgical neck** is the region immediately below the head and tuberosities—where the upper end joins the shaft. It does not have sharp limits, and may be reckoned as about a finger's breadth in extent all round the bone. The name is given because the bone is often fractured there.

The **lower end** includes the capitulum, the trochlea, the radial, coronoid and olecranon fossæ, and the lateral and medial epicondyles.

The **capitulum** is the smooth, rounded knob placed near the lateral part of the lower end. It is situated partly on the front and partly below, but not at all on the back. It articulates with the head of the radius.

The **radial fossa** is the shallow depression on the front of the bone, immediately above the capitulum; the margin of the head of the radius comes into close relation with it when the forearm is fully bent.

The **trochlea** is the wide, smooth, pulley-shaped surface at the medial side of the capitulum [τροχιλία (trochilia) = the sheave of a pulley]. It is situated on both the front and back and distal aspect. It winds slightly spirally from front to back, and its medial lip stands out as a prominent rim. It articulates with the trochlear notch, i.e. the wide concavity on the front of the upper end of the ulna. The prominence of the medial lip of the trochlea makes the distal surface ob-

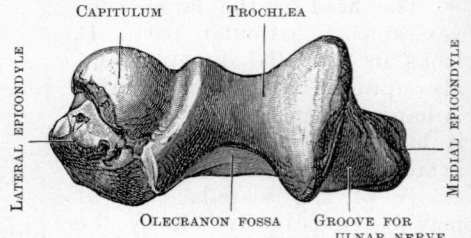

FIG. 203.—DISTAL ASPECT OF RIGHT HUMERUS.

lique; in consequence of that, the forearm is not quite in line with the upper arm when the limb is held so that the palm faces forwards.

The **coronoid fossa** is the depression on the front, immediately above the trochlea. It is related to the coronoid process of the ulna when the forearm is fully flexed.

The **olecranon fossa** is the large depression in a corresponding position on the back; the olecranon of the ulna fits into it when the forearm is straightened out. The bony substance between the coronoid and olecranon fossæ is very thin.

The **medial epicondyle** is the prominent projection on the medial side of the lower end. It is easily felt at the medial side of the elbow and can be gripped between finger and thumb. Its anterior surface has impressions on it for the origin of muscles; its posterior surface is smooth and has a shallow groove which

lodges the *ulnar nerve* as it passes from the upper arm into the fore-arm; the nerve can be felt and rolled between the finger and the bone.

The line or ridge (often poorly marked) that extends from the epicondyle on to the shaft for two or three inches is called the **medial supracondylar ridge.**

The **lateral epicondyle** is the projection on the lateral side of the lower end; it is not nearly so prominent as the medial epicondyle. Its anterior surface is small and is occupied by an impression for the origin of muscles. Its posterior surface is broad and smooth and sub-cutaneous; it can be felt on the back of the arm immediately above the lateral part of the elbow joint—that part of the joint being recognisable as a transverse depression.

The strong ridge which extends on to the shaft from the lateral epicondyle is called the **lateral supra-condylar ridge;** it is easily felt when the elbow joint is in the bent position and the muscles are relaxed.

When the upper limb is placed so that the palm looks forwards, the various parts of the humerus are in the position indicated in the description given; but when the limb hangs comfortably by the side with the palm looking towards the thigh, the directions in which the parts look are all altered—for example, the lateral epicondyle is felt on the antero-lateral aspect of the limb, and the medial epicondyle on the postero-medial aspect.

The **shaft** is more or less cylindrical in its upper half, but is rather compressed from before backwards in its lower part; it is described as having three borders and three surfaces. The **borders** are anterior, medial, and lateral; the **surfaces** are posterior, antero-lateral, and antero-medial.

The **anterior border** begins at the anterior margin of the greater tuberosity, runs along the front of the bone, and ends near the radial and coronoid fossæ; its upper third is the lateral lip of the bicipital groove.

The **medial border** begins at the lesser tuberosity and ends at the medial

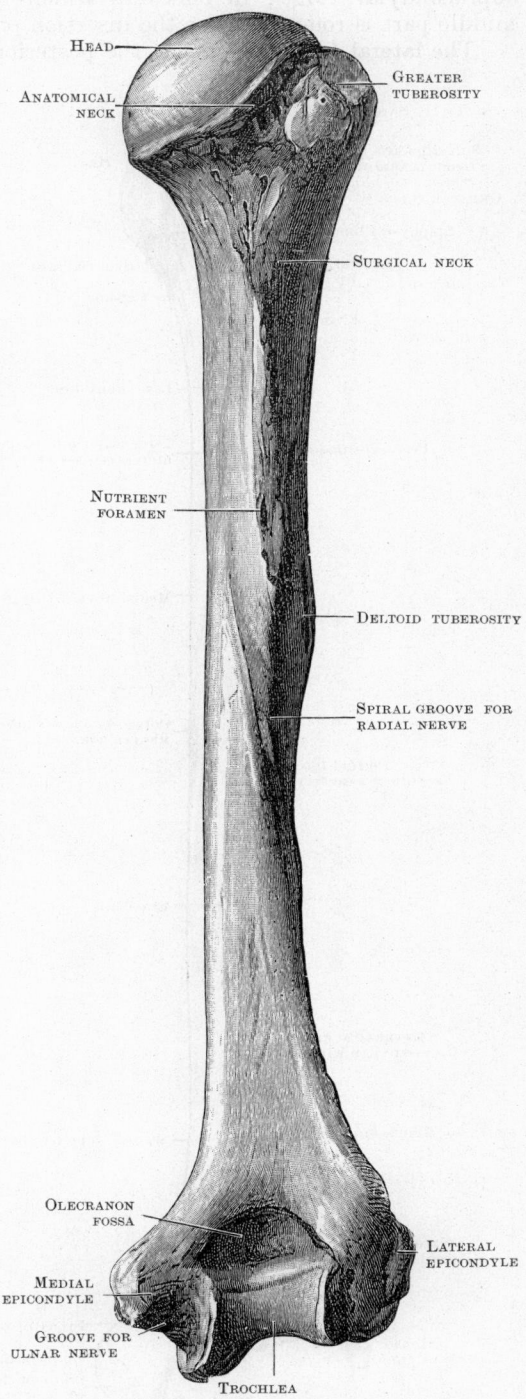

FIG. 204.—BACK OF RIGHT HUMERUS.

epicondyle. It is not nearly so well marked as the anterior border. Its upper third is the medial lip of the bicipital groove; its lower third is the medial supracondylar ridge; in bones in which muscular markings are well seen its middle part is roughened for the insertion of a muscle called coraco-brachialis.

The **lateral border** begins at the posterior surface of the greater tuberosity and

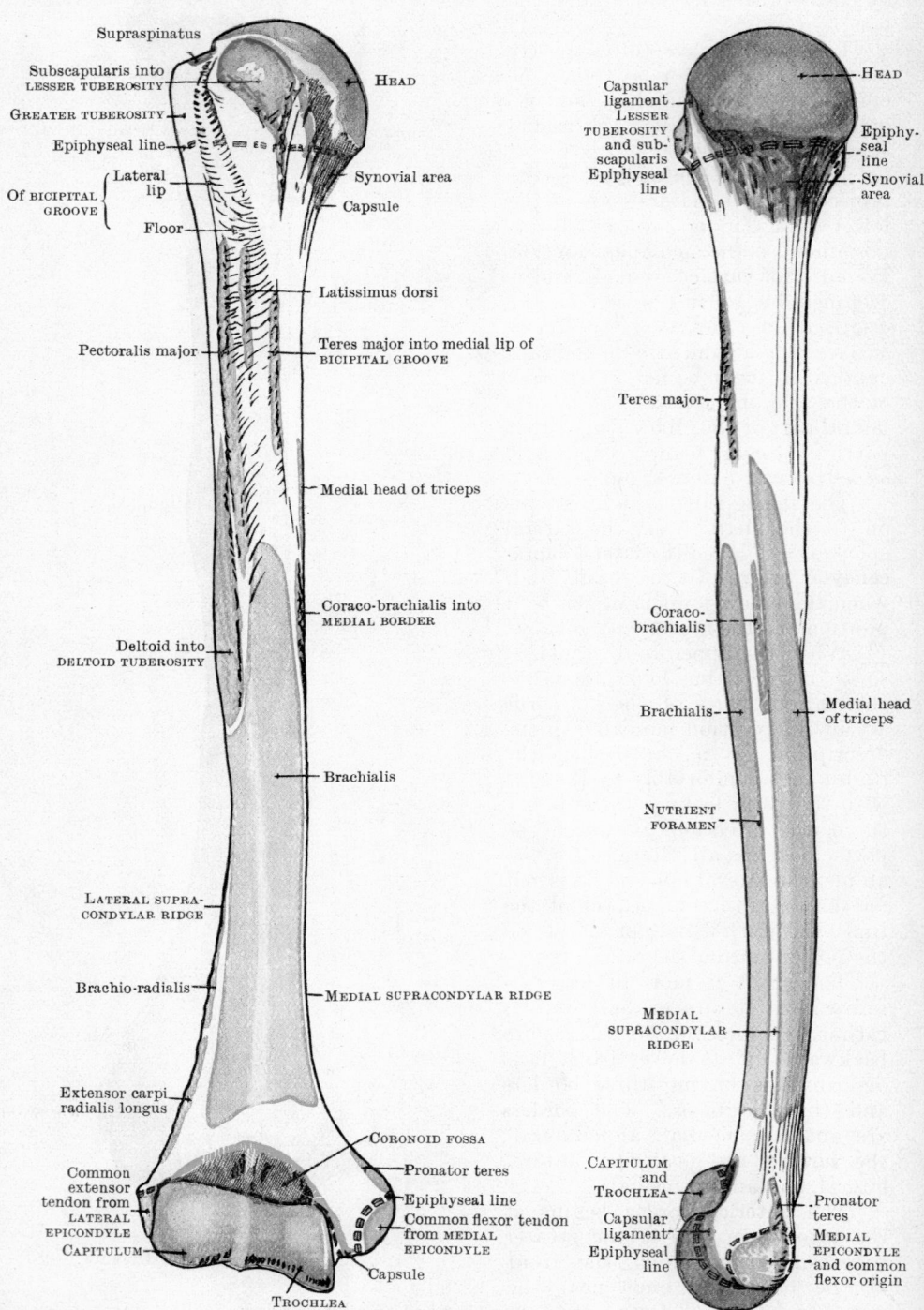

FIG. 205.—FRONT OF RIGHT HUMERUS.   FIG. 206.—MEDIAL ASPECT OF RIGHT HUMERUS.

ends at the lateral epicondyle. Its lower third is the lateral supracondylar ridge; its upper third is an indistinct ridge that descends from the back of the greater tuberosity; it is interrupted in its middle third by a broad, shallow groove which extends obliquely across it. The groove is named the **spiral groove**; it begins on

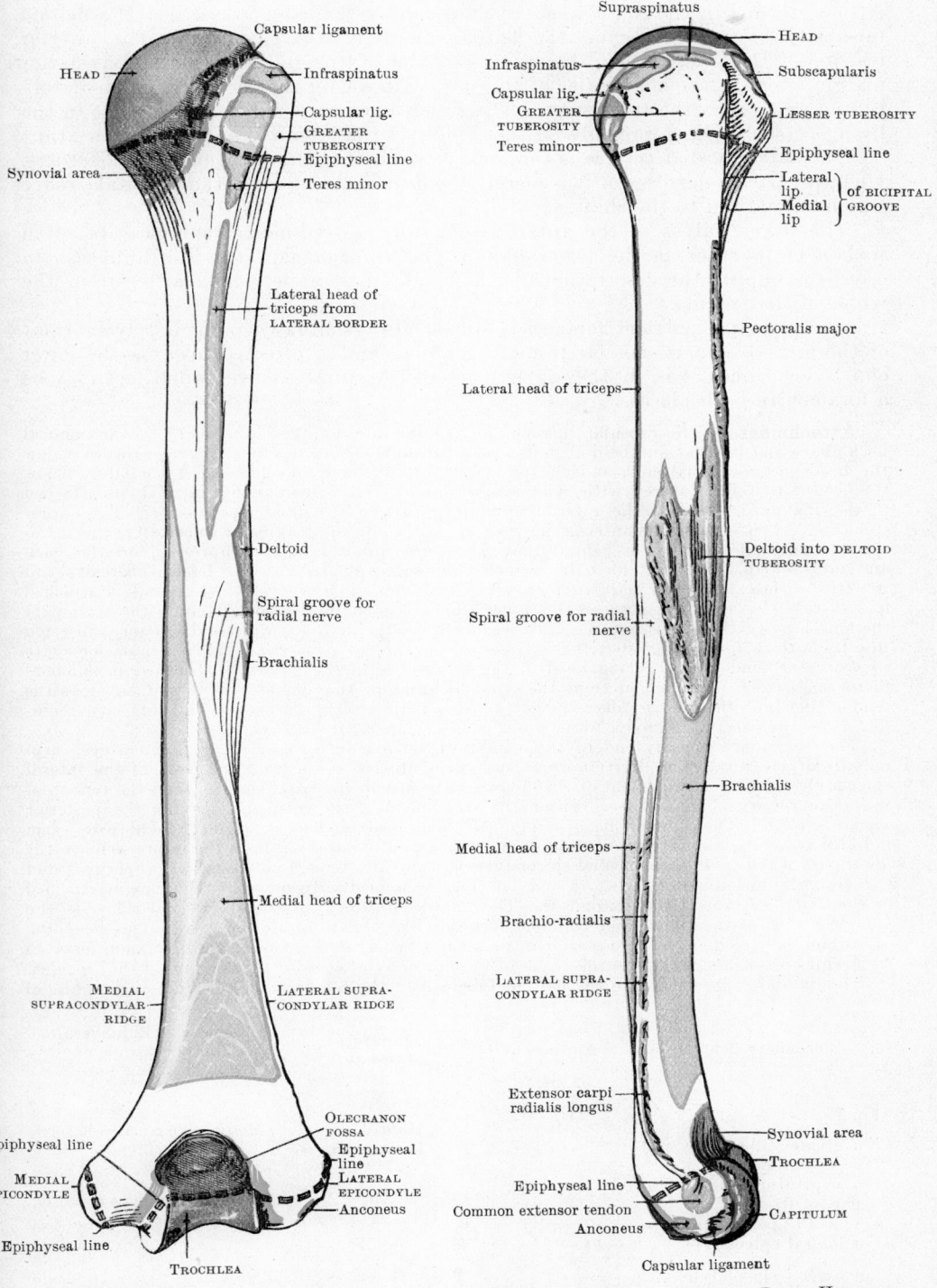

FIG. 207.—BACK OF RIGHT HUMERUS.

FIG. 208.—LATERAL ASPECT OF RIGHT HUMERUS.

the back of the bone and is directed downwards and forwards on to the front; the radial nerve, winding round the humerus, lies in it along its posterior or lower margin.

The **posterior surface** is the area between the lateral and medial borders.

The **antero-lateral surface** is the area between the anterior and lateral borders. Its proximal part is continuous with the lateral surface of the greater tuberosity. About its middle it is occupied by a rough, V-shaped mark called the **deltoid tuberosity**—so named because the deltoid muscle is inserted into it. The anterior margin of the V is part of the anterior border of the humerus, and its posterior margin is one of the boundaries of the spiral groove, for that groove is immediately behind and below the tuberosity. The tuberosity can usually be made out in the living person by deep pressure on the middle of the lateral side of the upper arm.

The **antero-medial surface** is the area between the anterior and medial borders. Its upper part is narrow, for it is merely the floor of that part of the bicipital groove which extends on to the shaft.

The lower halves of the antero-lateral and antero-medial surfaces are often spoken of together as the lower half of the anterior aspect of the humerus, in order to simplify the description of the brachialis muscle, which arises from the whole of that region.

The principal **nutrient foramen** is almost always situated immediately in front of the medial border—not far from its middle—and is directed towards the lower end. Sometimes it is in the upper part of the spiral groove; and there may be a foramen in both places.

Attachments.—The capsular ligament of the shoulder joint is attached to the **anatomical neck** above and in front and behind, but is attached to the bone nearly a finger's breadth below the head on the medial side, and the part of the medial side of the bone immediately below the head is therefore covered with synovial membrane; the coraco-humeral ligament is attached to the anatomical neck at the anterior and upper part of the greater tuberosity. The supra-spinatus is inserted into the anterior impression on the top of the **greater tuberosity**, the infra-spinatus into the impression behind that, the teres minor into the impression on the back and into a strip below that for half an inch; the subscapularis into the **lesser tuberosity** and into the surface below for half an inch. The transverse ligament of the humerus is attached to *both tubercles*, and bridges across the upper end of the **bicipital groove**, holding the tendon of the long head of the biceps in place; farther down—on the shaft—the pectoralis major is inserted into the *lateral lip* of the groove, the teres major into the *medial lip*, and the latissimus dorsi into *its floor*; the tendon of the long head of the biceps lies in the groove, ensheathed in synovial membrane which is prolonged from the synovial lining of the shoulder joint and envelops the tendon and lines the groove; deep to that sheath a little artery, a branch of the anterior circum-flex, runs upwards in the groove to the joint.

The common extensor tendon (the combined tendons of origin of the extensores carpi radialis brevis, digitorum, digiti minimi and carpi ulnaris) arises from the *front* of the **lateral epicondyle**; the lateral ligament of the elbow is attached to its *distal margin*; and the tendon of the anconeus arises immediately behind the attachment of the ligament, leaving the posterior surface smooth. The common flexor tendon (the combined tendons of origin of the flexores carpi radialis, palmaris longus, digitorum sublimis and carpi ulnaris) arises from the impressions on the lower part of the *front* of the **medial epicondyle**, the pronator teres from the flatter, upper part and the adjoining lower end of the supracondylar ridge; the medial ligament of the elbow is attached to the *distal margin* of the epicondyle. The anterior ligament of the elbow is attached to the *upper margins* of the **radial** and **coronoid fossæ** and to the front of the epicondyles near the capitulum and trochlea. The posterior ligament is attached to the *floor* of the **olecranon fossa**, to its margins on each side, and to the backs of the epicondyles close to the margins of the trochlea.

The deltoid is inserted into the **deltoid tuberosity**; the coraco-brachialis into the middle of

Secondary Centre	Appears at	Epiphysis fuses at	Relation of Epiphyseal Line to Capsule of Neighbouring Joint.
For head	Birth, or soon after	⎰ Male 21 ⎱ Female 18	⎰ Medial part inside, re- ⎱ mainder outside.
For greater tuberosity	3 years (F. 2)		
For lesser tuberosity	5 „		
For capitulum and lateral part of trochlea	1-1½ „	⎰ M. 19 ⎱ F. 14–15	⎰ Lateral extremity outside, ⎱ remainder inside.
For medial part of trochlea	10 „		
For lateral epicondyle	14 „	M. 17–18. F. 14–15	
For medial epicondyle	⎰ M. 8–9 ⎱ F. 5–6	M. 18–21. F. 14–15	Outside.

the **medial border**. The medial intermuscular septum is attached to the *edge* of the **medial supracondylar ridge**; the lateral intermuscular septum to the *edge* of the **lateral supracondylar ridge**; the brachio-radialis arises from the upper two-thirds of the *anterior aspect* of the lateral ridge, and the extensor carpi radialis longus from its lower third. The lateral head of the triceps arises from the *upper third* of the **lateral border**; the medial head from the *whole width* of the **posterior surface** below the spiral groove; the brachialis from the distal half or two-thirds of the **anterior aspect** of the shaft.

Ossification.—The **primary** centre appears at the eighth week of intra-uterine life. At birth only the ends are cartilaginous.

The centres for the head and the tuberosities coalesce in the sixth year to form **one** epiphysis, which fits like a cap on the end of the diaphysis. Radiograms show a separate centre for the greater tuberosity in only 50 per cent. of cases (Paterson), and seldom show one for the lesser tuberosity; and though the overlap of shadows may account for their apparent absence in some

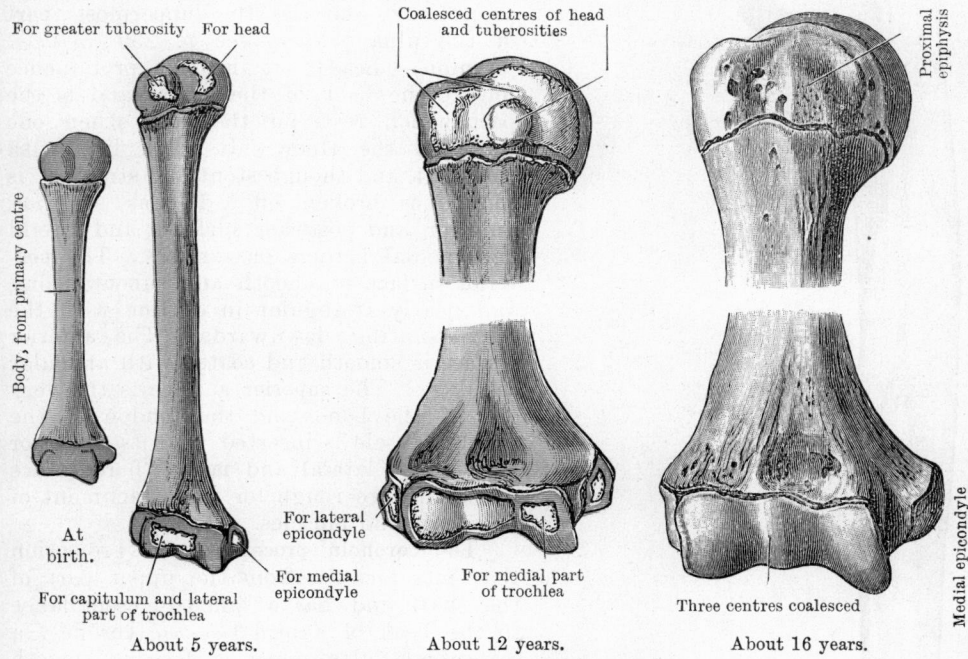

FIG. 209.—OSSIFICATION OF THE HUMERUS.

cases, yet it may be that the tuberosities are often ossified by extensions from the head. The centres for the capitulum and the trochlea coalesce to form **one** epiphysis at 15 in boys and **13** in girls. The lateral epicondyle usually joins the shaft independently (Paterson), but it may fuse with the capitulum before doing so; and in 30 per cent. of cases it appears to have no separate centre but to be ossified by extension from the capitulum.

Structure and Variations.—The structure is that of a typical long bone; the walls of the medullary cavity are thickest immediately below the middle of the bone. *Vascular foramina* are most numerous at the upper end—where most of the growth takes place. The chief nutrient canal runs a course of over two inches before it reaches the medullary cavity.

In women the head is relatively smaller than in men. Occasionally—more often in lower races—the bone above the trochlea is perforated. In rare cases a small projection (*supra-condylar process*) is found about two inches above the medial epicondyle, with which it is connected by a fibrous band; the median nerve and brachial vessels—taking an unusual course—pass under cover of the band. The humerus normally appears twisted, so that while the articular surface at the upper end looks mainly in a medial direction, the articular surfaces at the lower end look backwards and forwards; the twist is more marked in adults than in children and fœtuses, in men than in women, and in modern Europeans than in more primitive races or in prehistoric Europeans.

Ulna

The **ulna** is the medial and longer bone of the forearm [from ὠλένη (ōlenē) = forearm or elbow]. It is easily felt on the back of the forearm in its whole length. It is a long bone, about one-sixth of the body length, and has a **shaft** and two ends.

The **upper** end is the larger end, and has two large projections that give it a resemblance to a spanner and enable the beginner to pick the ulna out from among other bones.   The wide, deep concavity between those two projections is

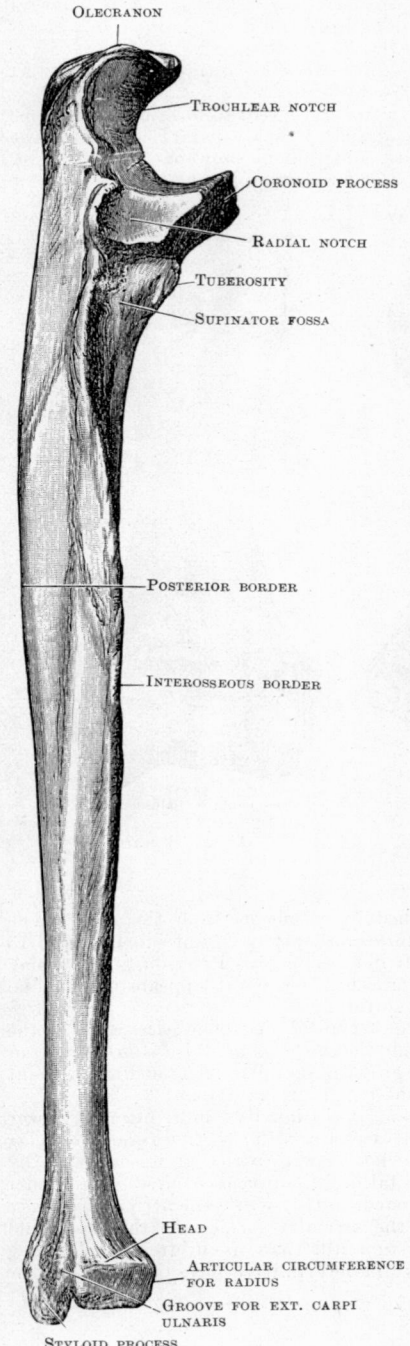

OLECRANON

TROCHLEAR NOTCH

CORONOID PROCESS

RADIAL NOTCH

TUBEROSITY

SUPINATOR FOSSA

POSTERIOR BORDER

INTEROSSEOUS BORDER

HEAD

ARTICULAR CIRCUMFERENCE FOR RADIUS

GROOVE FOR EXT. CARPI ULNARIS

STYLOID PROCESS

FIG. 210.—LATERAL SIDE OF RIGHT ULNA.

directed **forwards**.   The lateral side can be distinguished from the medial because the **lateral** border of the shaft is the sharpest and most outstanding of the three borders.

The **upper end** includes the olecranon, the coronoid process, the trochlear notch, the radial notch, and the tuberosity of the ulna.

The **olecranon** is the larger of the two projections and is the uppermost part of the ulna [ὠλένη—see p. 239; κρανίον (cranion) = head]; it is the prominence felt at the back of the elbow, and is the part which rests on the table when one leans on the elbow.   It is in line with the shaft, and though stout and strong it is sometimes broken off.   It has superior, anterior, and posterior surfaces, and lateral and medial borders or surfaces.   The **posterior** surface is smooth and subcutaneous, and nearly triangular in outline with the apex pointing downwards.   The **anterior** surface is smooth and coated with articular cartilage.   The **superior** surface is the very end of the bone, and the tendon of the triceps muscle is inserted into its posterior part.   The **lateral** and **medial** borders are thick, and are rough for the attachment of ligaments and muscles.

The **coronoid process** is the projection that juts forward from the upper part of the shaft and has a fancied resemblance to the beak of a bird [κορώνη (corōnē) = a sea crow].   Its *upper* surface is smooth and coated with articular cartilage; its *anterior* surface is rough for the insertion of a muscle called brachialis; on its *medial* side there is a rounded tubercle for the attachment of part of the medial ligament of the elbow joint; the tubercle can be felt about a thumb's breadth below the medial epicondyle of the humerus, and the ulnar nerve, as it passes into the forearm, can be felt and rolled over the tubercle by the finger.

The **radial notch** is the shallow, smooth hollow on the lateral surface of the coronoid process; it is coated with articular cartilage and articulates with the side of the head of the radius.   Immediately below the notch—on the shaft—there is a rough, shallow hollow, triangular in outline with its base at the notch; it is named the *supinator fossa*, and its posterior margin, which is often a strong ridge, is named the *supinator crest*, for the supinator muscle arises from both.

The **trochlear notch** [incisura semilunaris] is the wide concavity between the coronoid process and the olecranon. The trochlea of the humerus fits into it; therefore both olecranon and coronoid process articulate with the trochlea, and their articular surfaces are the reverse of a pulley, being elevated in the middle and sloping to the sides—the medial slope being the more pronounced. If the humerus and the ulna are placed together properly, the olecranon fits into the olecranon fossa when the bones are in line, *i.e.*, when the forearm is extended; and the coronoid process comes into relation with the coronoid fossa when the two bones make an acute angle, *i.e.*, when the forearm is fully flexed. Where the olecranon and the coronoid process join each other the trochlear notch has little rough patches at its sides; those patches may meet, forming a rough narrow strip across the notch, separating the front of the olecranon from the upper surface of the coronoid process.

The **tuberosity** of the ulna is a rough mark at the distal end of the anterior surface of the coronoid process, and is continuous with that surface; but it is on the shaft rather than on the upper end.

The **lower end** of the ulna is small, and includes the head and the styloid process.

The **head** is the larger, rounded part. Note that in the ulna the part called the *head* is at the *lower* end. When the hand is held with the palm looking downwards, the head of the ulna can be seen as a knob on the back of the forearm immediately above the wrist on the ulnar side (that is, the side in line with the little finger). The *front* and *lateral side* of the head are smooth and convex, and articulate with the lower end of the radius—the radius articulating with the lateral side when the limb is in the position in which the thumb points away from the body, and with the front when the thumb points medially. The *lower surface* also is smooth; it articulates not with a bone but

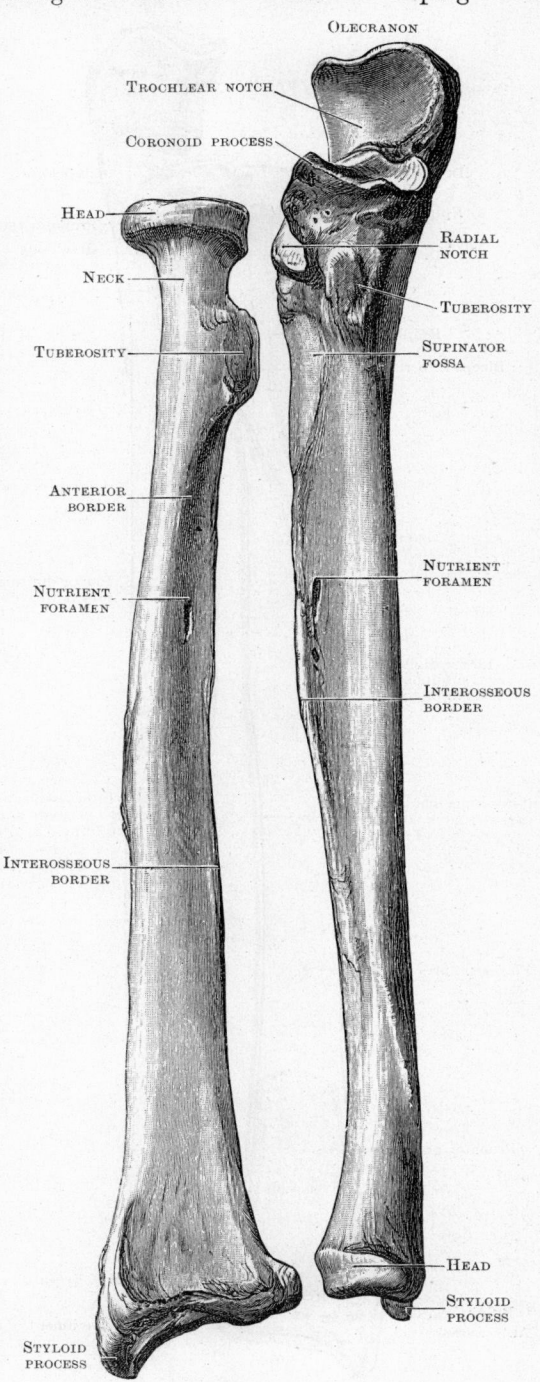

FIG. 211.—FRONT OF RIGHT RADIUS AND ULNA.

with a triangular plate of fibro-cartilage, called the *articular disc*, which separates the head from the bones of the wrist.

The **styloid process** is the small, conical projection that juts downwards towards

16

the wrist from the postero-medial part of the lower end. Between the base of the styloid process and the lower surface of the head there is a small, rough patch to which the apex of the articular disc is attached. On the *back of the bone*, between the styloid process and the head, there is a well-marked **groove** which lodges the tendon of a muscle called the *extensor carpi ulnaris.*

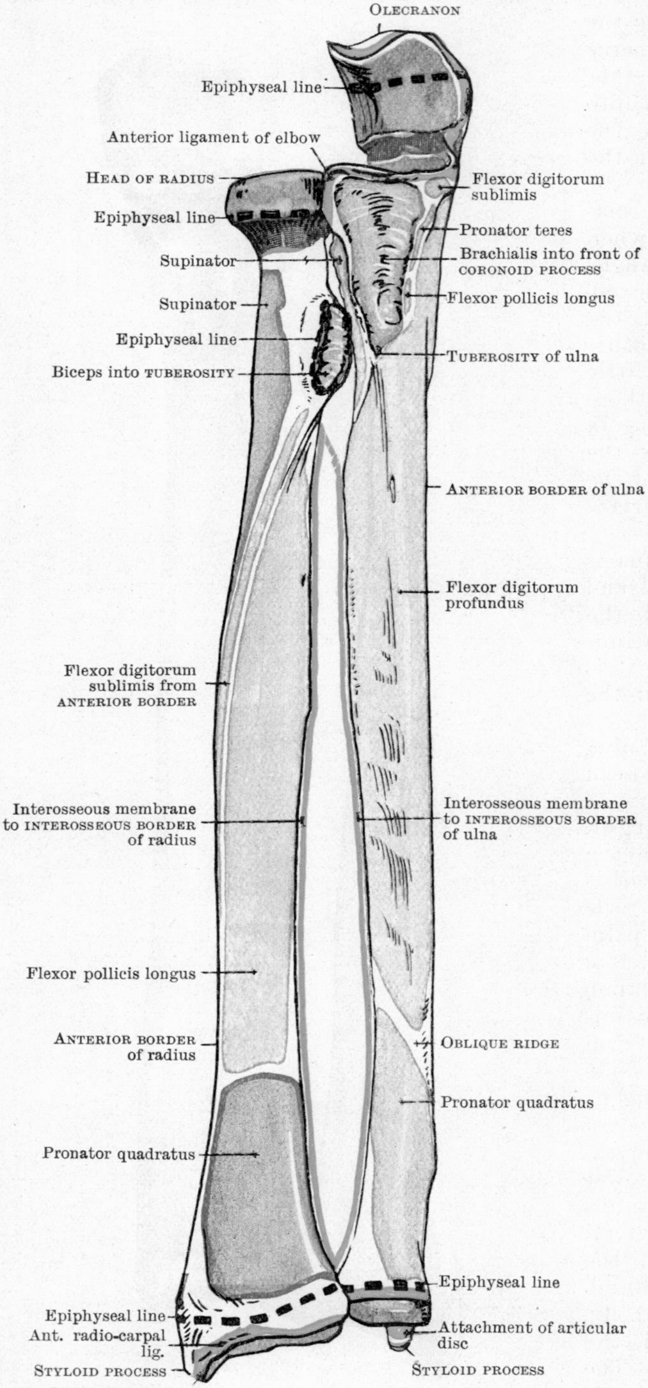

FIG. 212.—FRONT OF RIGHT RADIUS AND ULNA.

Labels (top to bottom, left then right):
OLECRANON
Epiphyseal line
Anterior ligament of elbow
HEAD OF RADIUS
Epiphyseal line
Supinator
Supinator
Epiphyseal line
Biceps into TUBEROSITY
Flexor digitorum sublimis from ANTERIOR BORDER
Interosseous membrane to INTEROSSEOUS BORDER of radius
Flexor pollicis longus
ANTERIOR BORDER of radius
Pronator quadratus
Epiphyseal line
Ant. radio-carpal lig.
STYLOID PROCESS
Lateral lig. of wrist
Flexor digitorum sublimis
Pronator teres
Brachialis into front of CORONOID PROCESS
Flexor pollicis longus
TUBEROSITY of ulna
ANTERIOR BORDER of ulna
Flexor digitorum profundus
Interosseous membrane to INTEROSSEOUS BORDER of ulna
OBLIQUE RIDGE
Pronator quadratus
Epiphyseal line
Attachment of articular disc
STYLOID PROCESS

When the hand is in the position in which the palm looks towards the shoulder (the elbow being bent) the styloid process, along with the tendon of the extensor carpi ulnaris, can be felt as a ridge on the ulnar border of the back of the forearm, but the head of the ulna is scarcely palpable. When the hand is held palm downwards the head of the ulna appears as a round knob at the ulnar border of the back of the forearm, and the styloid process is then felt on the ulnar surface of the limb. The apparent differences in position are not due to movements of the ulna, but to movements of the radius called *supination* and *pronation* (p. 248).

The **shaft** of the ulna diminishes in thickness from above downwards. It has three **borders**, named anterior, posterior, and interosseous, and three **surfaces**, named posterior, anterior, and medial.

The **anterior border** [margo volaris] is smooth and rounded. It begins at the tuberosity and ends at or near the root of the styloid process.

The **posterior border** begins at the lower angle of the back of the olecranon, extends sinuously along the shaft, and fades away near the distal end. It is felt as a sharp subcutaneous ridge on the back of the forearm.

The **interosseous border** is a sharp, salient ridge on the lateral side. It is so named because a strong, wide fibrous sheet, called the *interosseous* membrane, stretches across from it to the radius. It begins at the lower angle of the supinator fossa, becomes very prominent in the middle of the bone, and fades away near the lower end.

The **anterior surface** [facies volaris] is between the anterior and interosseous borders; and the tuberosity of the ulna is situated at its upper end. It is usually hollowed out longitudinally in its upper two-thirds or more, and the lower end of the hollow is limited by an oblique ridge from which a part of the pronator quadratus muscle arises. The ridge begins about two inches above the lower end and winds spirally towards the root of the styloid process.

The **posterior surface** is between the posterior and interosseous borders. In a well-marked bone an oblique ridge runs from the back of the radial notch to a point on the posterior border about an inch below the lower end of the back of the olecranon. A muscle called the anconeus is inserted into the area above the ridge. Below the ridge a vertical line maps off a long, flat strip between itself and the posterior border. The strip does not give attachment to any muscle, but the extensor carpi ulnaris lies on it; nearly all the rest of the posterior surface is mapped out by faint oblique ridges into areas for the origin of muscles.

The **medial surface** is the smooth, slightly convex surface between the anterior and posterior borders. Its upper part is covered with muscle, but its lower third is subcutaneous and therefore easily felt.

The **nutrient foramen** is on the anterior surface about the junction of the upper and middle thirds, and is directed towards the upper end.

Attachments.—The tendon of the triceps is inserted into the posterior part of the *superior surface* of the **olecranon** ; the posterior ligament of the elbow joint is attached to the anterior edge of the surface ; and a small *bursa* lies between them on the intervening part. The posterior ligament is attached also to the *lateral surface*, and the anconeus is inserted into that surface behind the ligament ; the posterior band of the medial ligament of the elbow joint is attached to the *medial surface*, and fibres of the flexor carpi ulnaris and of the flexor digitorum profundus arise from it behind the ligament.

The anterior band of the medial ligament is attached to the *tubercle* on the *medial border* of the **coronoid process** ; some fibres of the flexor digitorum sublimis arise from it ; slips of the pronator teres and flexor pollicis longus arise from the ridge which descends from the tubercle, and fibres of the flexor profundus from the hollow behind that ridge ; the anterior ligament of the elbow joint is attached to the *anterior margin* of the process, and the brachialis is inserted into the *anterior surface* and also into the **tuberosity** immediately below. The annular ligament which surrounds the head of the radius is attached to the *anterior* and *posterior margins* of the **radial notch**, and the quadrate ligament to its *lower margin*.

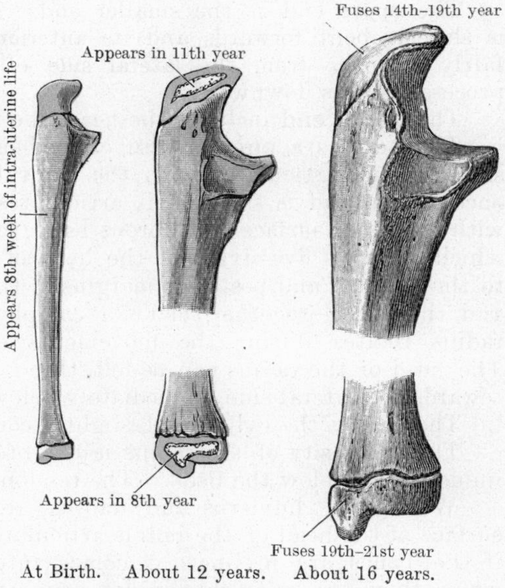

The capsule of the inferior radio-ulnar joint is attached to the *front* and *back* of the **head** ; a septum of the extensor retinaculum [lig. carpi dorsale] to the radial border of the **groove** on the back ; the medial ligament of the wrist joint to the tip of the **styloid process,** and the apex of the articular disc to the small, rough mark between its root and the head.

Appears in 11th year

Fuses 14th–19th year

Appears 8th week of intra-uterine life

Appears in 8th year

Fuses 19th–21st year

At Birth. About 12 years. About 16 years.

FIG. 213.—THE OSSIFICATION OF THE ULNA

On the **shaft,** the oblique cord, as well as part of the brachialis, is attached to the **tuberosity.** The supinator arises from the **supinator crest** and **fossa.** The interosseous membrane is attached to the **interosseous border.** The flexor carpi ulnaris arises by a wide aponeurosis from the upper three-fourths of the *posterior border*, besides having a small origin from the lateral surface of the olecranon. By means of the same aponeurosis part of the extensor carpi ulnaris arises from the middle third of the posterior border. The anconeus is inserted into the upper part of the *posterior surface* ; parts of the abductor pollicis longus, extensor pollicis longus, and extensor indicis arise from the lateral part of the posterior surface—in that order from above downwards. The pronator

16 *a*

quadratus arises from the lower fourth of the *anterior surface* (including the ridge above that fourth); the flexor digitorum profundus arises from the two-thirds or three-fourths of the *anterior* and *medial surfaces*—extending up to the medial surfaces of the coronoid process and olecranon.

Ossification.—The **primary centre** appears at the eighth week of intra-uterine life, and from it the shaft, the coronoid process, and nearly the whole of the olecranon are ossified, though at birth a great part of the olecranon—as well as the lower end—is cartilaginous.

Secondary Centre.	Appears at	Epiphysis joins at	Relation of Epiphyseal Line to Capsule of Neighbouring Joint.
For lower end	8th year	M. 21. F. 19-20	Outside.
For top of olecranon	11th ,,	{ M. 18-19 { F. 14-15	Outside; anterior part sometimes inside (Fig. 212).

The olecranon may have an additional centre, or more than one, in its body; and its epiphysis varies in size.—See Figs. 212, 213.

Structure and Variations.—The structure resembles that of the humerus and other long bones. The medullary canal extends from the root of the coronoid process to the distal fifth of the bone, and its posterior wall is the thicker. The weakest parts are at the junction of the olecranon and the coronoid process, and the junction of the middle and lower thirds of the shaft.

In rare cases the ulna is incompletely developed or is absent. In one recorded case the olecranon was a separate bone.

Radius

The **radius** is shaped like the spoke of a wheel—hence its name. It is the lateral and shorter bone of the forearm, and can be felt in all its length, though deep pressure is necessary at its middle. It is a long bone with a **shaft** and **two ends**.

The **upper** end is the smaller end. The lower end is a block of bone; it is slightly bent forwards, and its **anterior** surface is broad, slightly concave, and fairly smooth; from the **lateral side** of the lower end a short, thick pointed process projects downwards.

The **upper end** includes the head, the neck, and the tuberosity.

The **head** is a circular disc, cupped on its upper surface, and that surface is smooth and articulates with the capitulum of the humerus. The circumference of the head is smooth; it articulates with the radial notch of the ulna and with the inner surface of a fibrous band, called the *annular ligament* of the radius, which encircles five-sixths of the head of the radius and is attached by its ends to the anterior and posterior margins of the radial notch of the ulna; the ligament and the notch, together, make a complete ring within which the head of the radius rotates during the movements of supination and pronation (p. 248). The head of the radius can be felt, through the ligament, on the back of the limb towards the lateral side, immediately below the lateral epicondyle of the humerus.

The **neck** is the cylindrical, slightly constricted part that supports the head.

The **tuberosity** of the radius is the broad, low prominence on the medial side, immediately below the neck. The tendon of the biceps is inserted into it.

When the humerus and radius are fitted together properly the upper surface of the head of the radius articulates with the lower part of the capitulum if the bones are in line; it comes into full articulation with the capitulum when they are at right angles; and its edge comes into relation with the radial fossa of the humerus in extreme flexion. The radius only touches the capitulum, while the trochlear notch of the ulna grips the trochlea; the ulna is therefore much the more important constituent of the elbow joint, and the stability of the joint depends on it—the radius offering no bar to dislocation. The grip of the ulna is least secure when the forearm is extended, *i.e.* in line with the arm; the ulna can then slip backwards off the humerus. But the olecranon is a positive bar to forward dislocation until the forearm is becoming acutely flexed.

The **lower end** of the radius has five surfaces and a styloid process. The surfaces are anterior, posterior, medial, lateral, and distal or carpal.

The **anterior surface** is broad and slightly concave; at its lower margin there is a broad, rough ridge that can be felt on the front of the forearm about an inch above the ball of the thumb; it indicates the position of the distal epiphyseal line, and is also a guide to the position of the wrist joint, which is immediately distal to it.

The **posterior surface** is more uneven, being occupied by grooves and ridges. The most prominent ridge is about the middle of the surface; it is called the **dorsal tubercle**, and can usually be felt in the living limb. On the lateral side of the tubercle there is a shallow groove, more than half an inch wide, on which two thick tendons lie; they are the tendons of the extensor carpi radialis longus and brevis muscles, and when the closed fist is bent slightly backwards they can be seen as they pass off the radius on to the back of the wrist. On the medial side of the tubercle there is a narrow, oblique, clean-cut groove for the tendon of the extensor pollicis longus, which can be seen reaching almost to the thumb nail when the thumb is outstretched. The rest of the surface—the part medial to the narrow groove—is a wide, shallow groove that lodges the tendons of the extensor digitorum and extensor indicis (Fig. 214).

The **lateral surface** is less than half an inch wide; it is occupied by a shallow groove for the tendons of the abductor pollicis longus and extensor pollicis brevis, and is separated from the anterior surface by a sharp ridge that is easily felt in the living limb.

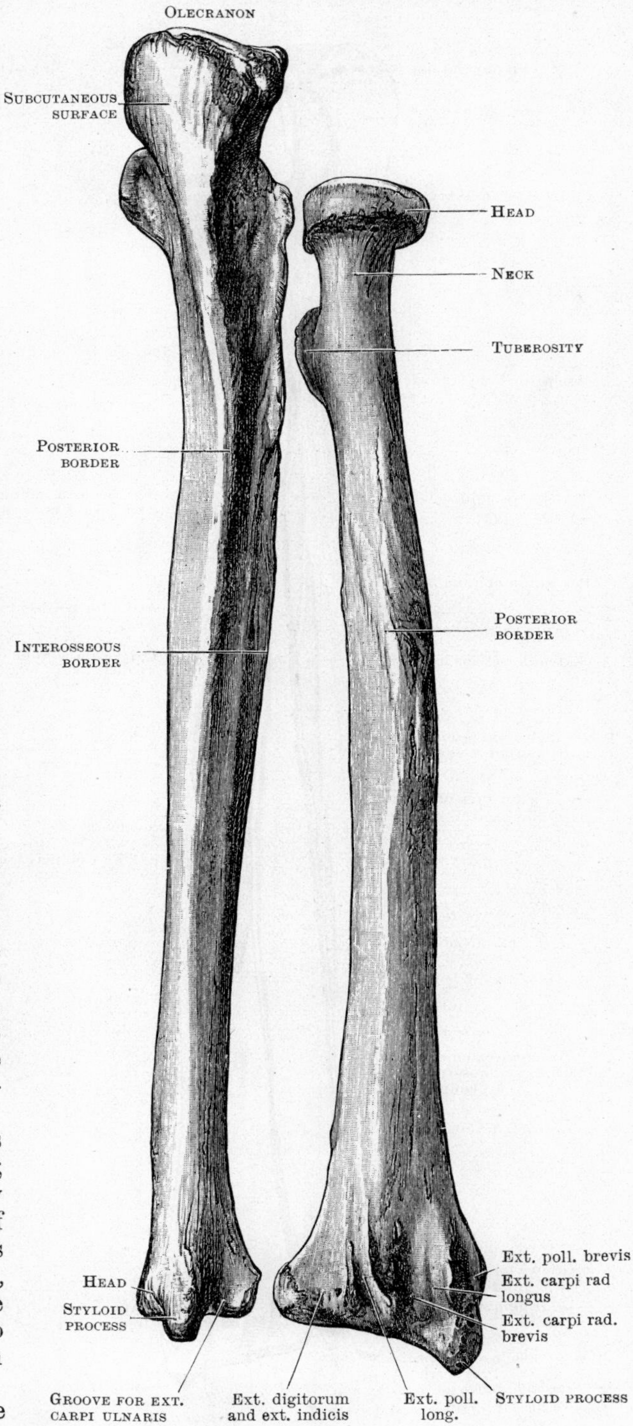

The lateral part of the lower end of the radius is prolonged downwards as the short, thick **styloid process**. When the thumb is outstretched a hollow is seen on the radial side of the wrist, called by the French the *anatomical snuff-box*

FIG. 214.—BACK OF RIGHT RADIUS AND ULNA.

16 b

(tabatière anatomique); its posterior boundary is the tendon of the extensor pollicis longus; its anterior boundary is the tendons of the abductor pollicis longus and

extensor pollicis brevis, which lie close together and make a ridge between the front of the wrist and its lateral surface; the styloid process is the bone felt in the proximal part of the floor of the hollow. Its position should be compared with that of the styloid process of the ulna; the radial styloid process is at a lower level than that of the ulna; in the common variety of fracture of the lower end of the radius that relationship may be reversed.

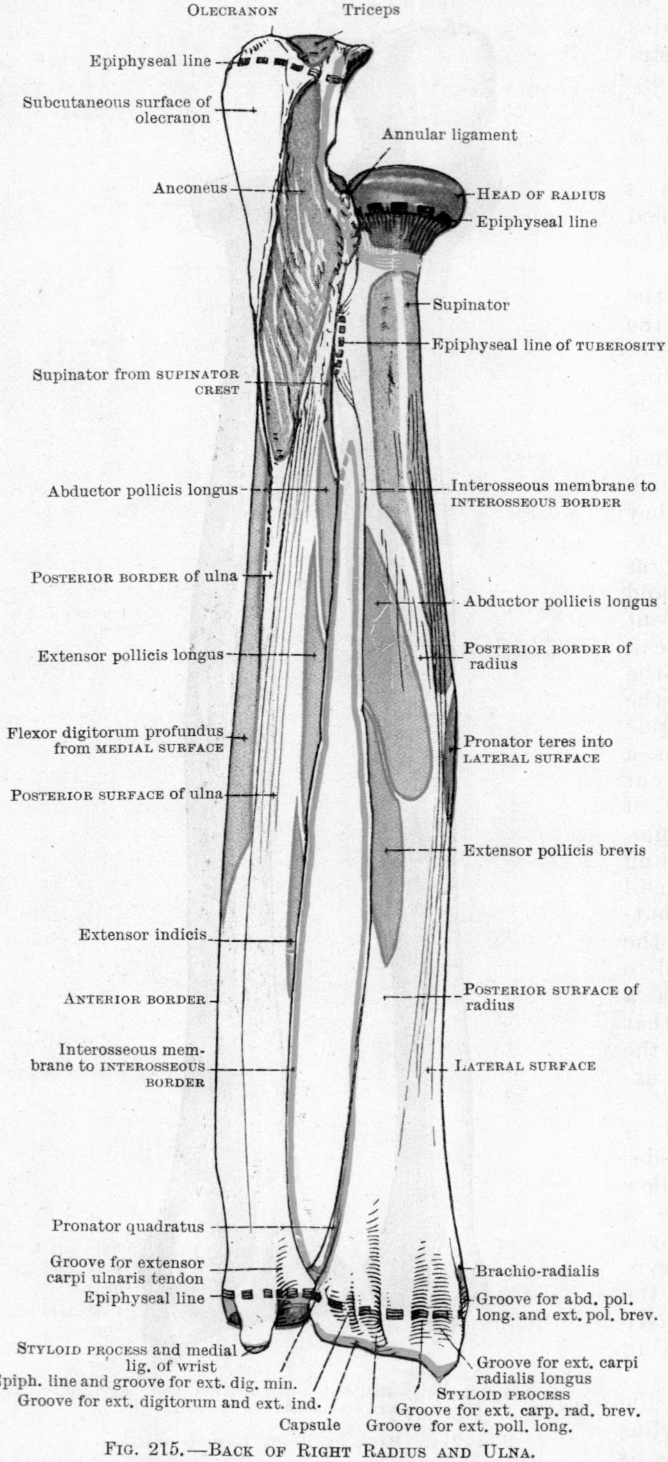

The **medial surface** is small, smooth and concave—the concavity being called the **ulnar notch**. It articulates with the head of the ulna and rotates round it during the rotatory movements of the forearm and hand (pronation and supination).

The *distal* or **carpal surface** is concave and smooth, and articulates with bones of the wrist or carpus. It is divided into two areas: a medial area nearly quadrilateral, and a lateral area nearly triangular, the apical part of which extends on to the styloid process. Between the carpal surface and the medial surface there is a sharp edge to which the base of the articular disc is attached. The posterior and lateral boundaries of the surface reach lower down than the others, and

FIG. 215.—BACK OF RIGHT RADIUS AND ULNA.

in a fall on the hand the posterior and lateral part of the lower end is liable to be chipped off.

The **shaft** increases in girth from above downwards, but is most often broken near the lower end; it has three borders and three surfaces. The **borders** are anterior, posterior and interosseous; the **surfaces** are posterior, anterior, and lateral.

The **interosseous border** is on the medial side and is the sharpest and most definite of the three; the interosseous membrane is attached to it. It begins near the tuberosity; towards its lower end it divides into two ridges which diverge slightly and become continuous with the margins of the ulnar notch.

The **anterior border** begins at the tuberosity and ends at the ridge between the anterior and lateral surfaces of the lower end of the bone. Its upper part is well marked and oblique; its lower part is rounded and indistinct (Fig. 211).

The **posterior border** is distinct in the middle third of the bone (Fig. 214); the upper part is an indistinct line that leads from the middle third obliquely towards the back of the tuberosity; the lower part—a smooth, indistinct ridge—runs from the middle third to the dorsal tubercle on the distal end.

The **anterior** and **posterior surfaces** separate the interosseous border from the anterior and posterior borders.

The **lateral surface** is between the anterior and posterior borders. It is roughened at its middle for the insertion of the pronator teres muscle. Its upper part encroaches greatly on the front and back of the bone owing to the obliquity of the upper parts of the anterior and posterior borders; the lower part of the surface also encroaches on the back, and is continuous not only with the lateral surface of the lower end but also with the lateral part of the back.

The **nutrient foramen** is on the anterior surface about the junction of its upper and middle thirds, and it is directed towards the upper end.

Attachments.—The lower margin of the annular ligament and the lateral margin of the quadrate ligament are attached round the **neck**—*loosely*, so as not to interfere with the rotatory movements of the radius. The posterior part of the **tuberosity** is roughened for the insertion of the tendon of the biceps, but the anterior part is smooth for the *bursa* that separates it from that tendon.

At the **lower end,** the anterior radio-carpal ligament is attached to the distal margin of the *anterior surface*; the lateral ligament to the **styloid process**; the posterior ligament to the distal edge of the *posterior surface*; the capsule of the inferior radio-ulnar joint to the anterior and posterior margins of the **ulnar notch**; the base of the articular disc to the border between the notch and the *carpal surface*; the lateral end of the extensor retinaculum [lig. carpi dorsale] to the *sharp border* between the lateral and anterior surfaces, and its septa to the ridges that bound the grooves on the *posterior surface*; the tendon of the brachio-radialis is inserted into the upper part of the *lateral surface*.

On the **shaft,** the oblique cord is attached to the bone immediately below the tuberosity; the interosseous membrane to the **interosseous border** and to the hinder of the two ridges into which the lower end of the border divides. Part of the flexor digitorum sublimis arises from the upper half of the *anterior border*, and the flexor pollicis longus from the upper three-fourths of the *anterior surface*; the pronator quadratus is inserted into the lower fourth of the anterior border and anterior surface, into the anterior surface of the lower end, and into the narrow triangular area above the ulnar notch. The pronator teres is inserted into the rough mark on the middle of the *lateral surface*; the supinator into the upper third, including its encroachments on the front and back. Parts of the abductor pollicis longus and extensor pollicis brevis arise from the *posterior surface*—the abductor immediately above the middle of the bone, and the extensor immediately below.

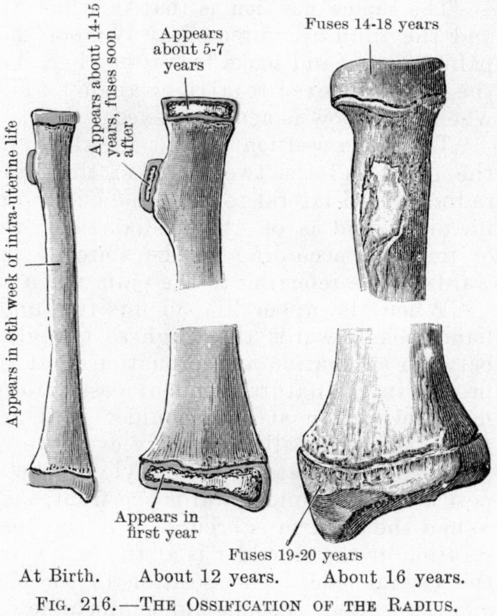

The radius has a slight double curve—convex in a medial direction in its upper quarter, and in a lateral direction in the lower three-quarters. The biceps and the pronator teres are inserted into the maximum points of the curves, and their value as supinator and pronator, respectively,

FIG. 216.—THE OSSIFICATION OF THE RADIUS.

Appears about 14-15 years, fuses soon after

Appears in 8th week of intra-uterine life

Appears about 5-7 years

Fuses 14-18 years

Appears in first year

Fuses 19-20 years

At Birth. About 12 years. About 16 years.

16 c

is thus increased. The medial side of the head is deeper and flatter from above downwards than the rest of its circumference. The lower part of the lateral surface of the shaft does not give attachment to any muscle; but it is overlain by the tendons of the brachio-radialis and the radial extensors of the carpus. Occasionally there is a small tubercle on the posterior lip of the groove on the lateral side of the lower end for the attachment of the most lateral septum of the extensor retinaculum. The slight ridge between the two areas on the carpal surface is best marked at its ends; and at those ends there may be slight notches on the anterior and posterior margins of the carpal surface.

Ossification.—The **primary centre** appears at the eighth week of intra-uterine life. At birth only the lower end, the head, and the tuberosity are cartilaginous.

Secondary Centre.	Appears at	Epiphysis fuses at	Relation of Epiphyseal Line to Capsule of Neighbouring Joint.
For lower end	M. 1-1½ yr. F. 1	M. 21. F. 19-20	Outside.
For head	M. 6-7. F. 5-6	M. 18-19. F. 14-15	Inside.
For tuberosity (occasional)	Puberty	Shortly after puberty	Outside.

Structure and Variations.—The medullary canal reaches the neck but does not reach the lower part of the shaft; its walls are thick compared with the size of the bone; the thickness is especially marked along the interosseous border—imparting rigidity to the curve of the bone. The neck is the most slender part of the bone, but the commonest seat of fracture is near the lower end, for that part of the bone bears the impact of a fall on the hand. The nutrient canal traverses the bone for half an inch before it reaches the medullary cavity.

Absence of the radius has been recorded more than once, and in some of those cases the thumb also was absent.

Supination and Pronation

The terms *supination* and *pronation* refer to position and movements of the forearm and hand, though in ordinary circumstances supination and pronation of the forearm are always supplemented by rotation of the upper arm.

The **supine position** is that in which the two bones of the forearm are parallel and the thumb is directed away from the side of the body; in that position the palm of the hand looks forwards when the limb hangs by the side, upwards when the elbow is flexed to a right angle [*supinus* = lying on the back], and backwards when the elbow is acutely flexed.

The **prone position** is that in which the thumb is directed towards the side of the body, and the two bones of the forearm are crossed; the upper end of the radius is still lateral to the ulna, but the radius is crossed in front of the ulna and its distal end is on the medial side; the palm looks backwards or downwards or forwards according to the state of the elbow joint [*pronus* = inclined downwards—here referring to the palm when the elbow is flexed to a right angle].

When the upper limb hangs free and naturally by the side the palm of the hand looks towards the thigh as though the forearm were in a position midway between supination and pronation; but it is nearer the supine position than the prone; in the natural pendent position of the limb the whole limb is rotated in a medial direction at the shoulder joint, and that makes the forearm appear more prone than it really is; ready evidence of the rotation at the shoulder joint is afforded by the lateral epicondyle of the humerus; the epicondyle is felt, in that position, well round towards the front, instead of on the lateral side of the limb. When the forearm is brought into the position of complete supination, the medial rotation at the shoulder is at the same time undone, and the epicondyle is felt on the lateral side. The position of complete supination is, however, an unnatural one, and soon becomes uncomfortable; none the less, the structures are all described on the assumption that the limb is in the supine position, because, the radius and ulna being then parallel, the relations of all the other structures in the forearm can be more simply stated.

The **movement of supination** is the movement by which the forearm and hand are rotated from the position of pronation, or from the intermediate position, into the position of supination; and the **movement of pronation** is the reverse. The movement of supination is the stronger; and screws and screwing instruments are made so as to be manipulated by supination of the right forearm.

When the upper arm is rotated the forearm rotates with it, but in the movements of simple supination and pronation the ulna remains practically stationary. It is the radius that is moved, and the hand is moved with the radius. The head of the radius rotates within the ring composed of the annular ligament and the radial notch of the ulna, and the lower end of the radius rotates round the head of the ulna and carries the hand with it. The actual movements in the living limb are not only greatly supplemented by rotation of the humerus at the shoulder joint, but are also slightly added to by movement at the wrist joint and intercarpal joints. In pronation the tuberosity of the radius comes into close relation with the lower part of the supinator fossa of the ulna.

Carpus

The skeleton of the **carpus** or **wrist** consists of *eight* small bones closely held together by ligaments, and arranged in two rows—a proximal and a distal. From lateral to medial side, the names of those in the **proximal row** are: scaphoid, lunate, triquetrum, pisiform; and in the **distal row**: trapezium, trapezoid, capitate, hamate.

The **pisiform bone** is the hard knob at the medial border of the front of the wrist. It is rather loosely attached and can be moved slightly from side to side if the hand is held slack; the sinew seen and felt descending to it, along the medial border of the forearm, is the tendon of the flexor carpi ulnaris muscle.

The **other bones** of the wrist are so tightly bound together that, until the ligaments are cut, they form **one compact mass** with *six* surfaces—palmar, dorsal, medial, lateral, proximal, and distal. (See Fig. 310, p. 351.)

The *proximal surface* is smooth and convex, and measures much more from side to side than from before backwards; it articulates with the radius and the articular disc to form the radio-carpal or wrist joint. The *distal surface* is uneven, and its transverse measurement also is much greater than the antero-posterior; it articulates with the bases of the five metacarpal bones to form the carpo-metacarpal joints. The *medial surface* is small, and can be felt on the medial side of the wrist. The *lateral surface* also is small; it is partly palpable in the " anatomical snuff-box," and is partly hidden by the tendons in the anterior boundary of that hollow; an artery, called the radial artery, crosses it obliquely, under cover of those tendons.

The *dorsal surface* is large and rough; it is convex from side to side, and is to a large extent concealed by tendons. The *palmar surface* is large, and is concave from side to side; the concavity is greatly deepened by, and, indeed, is largely owing to, the shape and position of the bones at the sides. On the medial side there is the prominence made by the pisiform bone, and, distal to that, a hook-like process projects forwards from the hamate bone [*hamatus* = hooked]. On the lateral side a tubercle on the scaphoid bone and a thick crest on the trapezium project forward. The deep concavity is called the **carpal groove**; it is bridged across and converted into a **carpal canal** or tunnel by a very strong, flattened, fibrous band that holds the flexor tendons proceeding to the thumb and fingers in their place in the groove; this band is named, therefore, the *flexor retinaculum* [lig. carpi transversum].

Those projections can all be felt in the living hand. The **pisiform bone** has been referred to already. The **hook of the hamate bone** can be felt if deep pressure is made by the thumb of the other hand on the ball of the little finger—*i.e.* the fleshy eminence on the medial side of the palm. The pressure should be made at a point 15-25 mm. from the pisiform bone and on a line drawn from the pisiform towards the centre of the palm. A nerve can often be felt slipping from side to side on the hook; that is the superficial branch of the ulnar nerve.

The **tubercle of the scaphoid bone** can always be felt and is often a visible projection. The guide to its position is a tendon. In the lower half of the front of the forearm, about midway from side to side, the tendons of the palmaris longus and the flexor carpi radialis can be seen, close together, extending to the wrist; the tendon of the flexor carpi radialis is the more lateral of the two, and sometimes, of the two, it alone is present. Where it passes out of sight at the wrist the tubercle of the scaphoid bone can be felt—partly under cover of the tendon and partly lateral to it—immediately above the ball of the thumb.

The **crest on the trapezium** is not so easily felt. It is immediately distal to the tubercle of the scaphoid in the medial edge of the ball of the thumb, and pressure should be made there with the hand bent backwards; the bony resistance encountered there is the crest; it may be felt as a prominence separate from the tubercle of the scaphoid, but the two often are felt as one continuous bony resistance.

If the student has a skeleton of the hand in which the carpal bones are strung or wired together he will be able to identify them from their position. If they are separate he may require the aid of a demonstrator, but should try himself to identify them by means of their chief characters—beginning with those that are more easily recognised.

The **pisiform bone** is the smallest of all. It resembles a large pea with a slice cut off [*pisum* = a pea].

The **hamate bone** has a large, compressed, curved process that juts forwards from its palmar surface.

The **capitate bone** is usually the largest. Its proximal surface or end is smooth and rounded—resembling a head.

The **scaphoid bone** [os naviculare manus] is one of the larger bones. It bears a slight resemblance to a comma—the tubercle being the bent, narrower end of the comma. Of its *articular* surfaces two are convex and one is concave in each direction, fitting the tip of a finger. The bone is called the "scaphoid" from a far-fetched resemblance to a boat given to it by that concave surface. [σκάφη (scaphē) = anything dug out—a boat].

The **lunate bone** is one of the smaller bones. Its distal surface is markedly concave in one direction and fits the tip of a finger. On another surface (the lateral) it has an articular facet, shaped like a crescent moon, which gives the bone its name.

The **trapezium** [os multangulum majus] is medium in size. One of its articular surfaces is saddle-shaped; one of its non-articular surfaces has the thick crest—mentioned before—with a groove alongside the crest.

The triquetrum and the trapezoid are the only two left. The **triquetrum** is more or less pyramidal in shape [*triquetrus* = three-cornered] and on one of its surfaces it has a circular, flat facet which occupies a great part of that surface but not the whole of it. The **trapezoid** [os multangulum minus], though very unlike the others, has no outstanding characters. It has four definite articular surfaces set almost at right angles to one another, and two non-articular surfaces, one of which is considerably larger than the other; when it is placed on that larger surface it has a fanciful resemblance to a Chinese boot.

Each of the carpal bones has six surfaces—proximal, distal, palmar, dorsal, lateral, and medial.

Scaphoid Bone.—The *proximal surface* is the larger of the two convex articular surfaces; it articulates with the lower end of the radius. The *distal surface* is the smaller of the two convex surfaces, and articulates with the proximal surfaces of the trapezium and trapezoid. The *dorsal surface* is the narrow strip between the proximal and the distal surface, and is rough for the attachment of ligaments. The *medial surface* has a smooth area—concave in each direction—for articulation with the lateral surface of the head of the capitate bone, and above that there is a semilunar strip that articulates with the lateral surface of the lunate bone. The *lateral surface* is greatly reduced and is represented by the **tubercle**. The *palmar surface* is concave in one direction and is the concave side of the comma; the concavity lodges the tendon of the flexor carpi radialis.

Lunate Bone.—The *distal surface* is the concave surface and articulates with the top of the head of the capitate. The *proximal surface*, directly opposite, is convex, and articulates with the lower end of the radius and with the articular disc. The *lateral surface* is the one shaped like a crescent moon, and it articulates with the scaphoid bone. The *medial surface*, directly opposite, is flat and nearly quadrilateral and articulates with the base or lateral surface of the os triquetrum. Between the medial and the distal surface there is usually a narrow strip that articulates with the upper edge of the hamate. The *palmar* and *dorsal surfaces* give attachment to ligaments; the palmar surface is convex and is larger and smoother than the dorsal surface.

Triquetrum.—The *palmar surface* is nearly flat; its medial two-thirds is covered with a flat, circular facet that articulates with the pisiform bone. The *distal surface* is concavo-convex or undulating, and articulates with the medial surface of the hamate bone. The *lateral surface* is the base of the pyramid and articulates with the lunate bone. The *medial surface* is greatly reduced—being only the apex of the pyramid—and can be felt on the side of the wrist distal to the styloid process of the ulna and behind the pisiform bone. The *proximal* and *dorsal surfaces* are confluent, making one uneven convex surface; its lateral part has a facet that articulates with the medial ligament of the wrist joint, and, during adduction of the wrist, with the articular disc.

Pisiform Bone. — The *dorsal surface* is oval or circular, and is covered with a flat or slightly concave facet for articulation with the triquetrum. It is marked off by a very narrow, circular groove that gives attachment to the capsular ligament of the joint. The other five surfaces are non-articular, and run into one another. The student should not waste time by trying to distinguish among them, but they can be identified. The *distal surface* differs from the others in that it bulges beyond the level of the facet. The *proximal surface* is the one opposite that. The *palmar surface* is opposite the facet. It slopes to each side; its lateral slope is the part of the bone related to the ulnar nerve, but it is not in close enough contact to be grooved by the nerve. The *medial surface* is rounded. The *lateral surface* is slightly concave from before backwards, for it forms the upper part of the medial wall of the carpal tunnel; it is related to the flexor synovial sheath and the ulnar edge of the flexor profundus; it is separated from the palmar surface by a low, overhanging ridge that gives attachment to the upper part of the flexor retinaculum.

Trapezium.—The *distal surface* is saddle-shaped and articulates with the base of the first

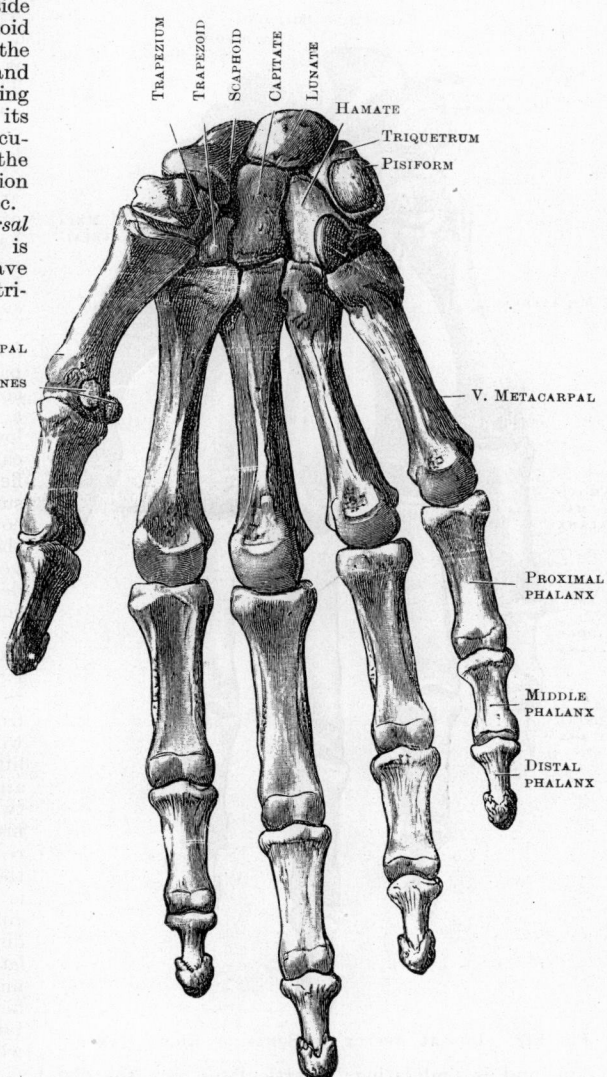

FIG. 217.—PALMAR ASPECT OF BONES OF RIGHT HAND.

metacarpal bone. The *proximal surface* is the small, smooth, concave surface opposite; it articulates with the scaphoid bone. The *medial surface* has a large facet which is separated by a smooth ridge from the proximal surface, and articulates with the lateral surface of the trapezoid; lower down there is a small facet for articulation with the base of the second metacarpal bone. The *palmar, dorsal,* and *lateral surfaces* are non-articular. The palmar surface is distinguished from the other two by having the thick *crest* along its lateral margin, and a well-defined, narrow groove along the medial side of the crest; the groove lodges the tendon of the flexor carpi radialis. The lateral surface is continuous with the lateral side of the crest, and the dorsal surface is directly opposite the palmar.

Trapezoid.—Beginners find difficulty in identifying its surfaces. The *dorsal* and *palmar surfaces* are both non-articular; the palmar surface is much the smaller. The other four surfaces are articular. The *distal surface* is the largest of those four; it is concave from before backwards and convex from side to side; it articulates with the base of the second metacarpal bone. From the palmar surface a rough strip, which may be V-shaped, passes backwards between the distal and lateral surfaces, and so the *lateral surface* can be identified; it articulates with the trapezium. The *proximal surface*, opposite the distal, articulates with the scaphoid bone. The *medial surface* articulates with the lateral surface of the capitate.

Capitate Bone.—The *proximal surface* is the rounded top of the head, and articulates with the concave surface of the lunate bone. The *distal surface* is the base; its greater part articulates with the base of the third metacarpal bone, but at the edges it articulates also with the second and the fourth. The *palmar surface* is rough and protuberant. The *dorsal surface* also is non-articular, but is nearly flat. The *lateral surface* of the head is convex and articulates with the concave facet of the scaphoid bone; lower down, on the lateral surface of the body, there is a facet for articulation with the medial surface of the trapezoid. The *medial surface* has a large, nearly flat facet, which includes the medial side of the head, for articulation with the lateral surface of the hamate bone.

Hamate Bone.—The *hook* juts forwards from the distal and medial part of the palmar surface. The concave side of the hook looks in a lateral direction; it forms the lower part of the medial wall of the carpal tunnel and is lined with the flexor synovial sheath. The medial surface and the tip of the hook are covered with muscles and ligaments; the superficial branches of the ulnar vessels and nerve cross the tip; the deep branches cross the medial surface, and the nerve may groove it. The body of the bone is shaped like a wedge. The base of the wedge is the *distal surface*; it is concave from before backwards and convex from side to side; it articulates with the bases of the fourth and fifth metacarpal bones, and usually an indication of subdivision into two corresponding parts can be made out. The *proximal surface* is reduced to a blunt border between the medial and lateral surfaces and is the edge of the wedge; it articulates with the lunate bone. The distal and anterior part of the *lateral surface* is rough; the remainder is covered with a large facet for articulation with the capitate bone. The *medial surface* is wholly articular except at its distal

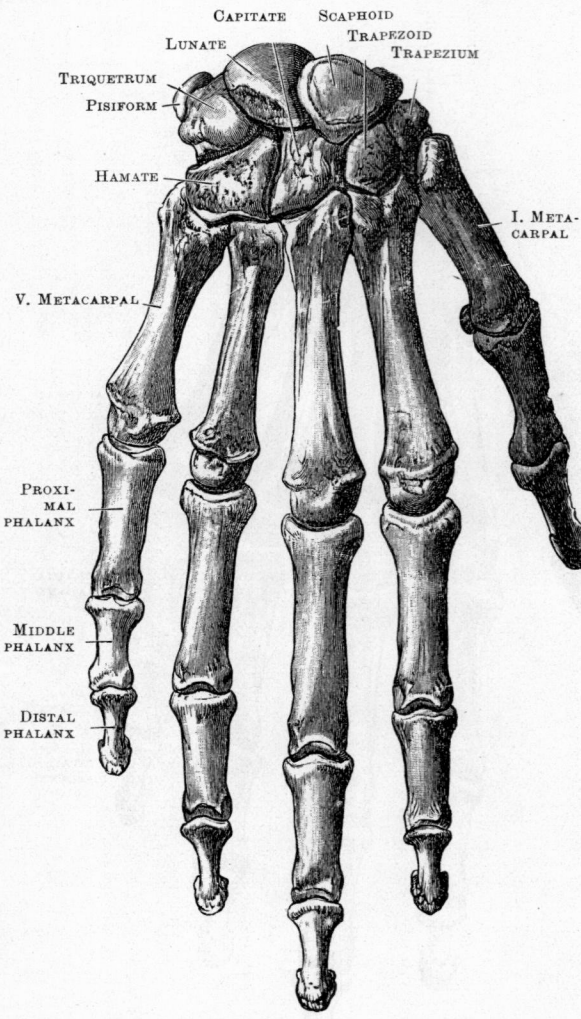

CAPITATE SCAPHOID
LUNATE   TRAPEZOID
                    TRAPEZIUM
TRIQUETRUM
PISIFORM

HAMATE

                                    I. META-
                                    CARPAL

V. METACARPAL

PROXI-
MAL
PHALANX

MIDDLE
PHALANX

DISTAL
PHALANX

Fig. 218.—Dorsal Aspect of Bones of Right Hand.

margin, and is undulating; it articulates with the distal surface of the triquetrum, which is correspondingly concavo-convex. The *dorsal surface* is non-articular and fairly flat. The *palmar surface*, also non-articular, bears the hook.

Attachments.—The pisiform is attached to the front of the triquetrum by a capsular ligament. The other seven bones are closely bound together by ligaments attached (1) to their *palmar* and *dorsal* surfaces, (2) to the rough areas and edges of *contiguous surfaces*, and (3) to the surfaces on the *ulnar and radial borders of the wrist*. The medial and lateral ligaments of the wrist joint also are attached to those surfaces, while the anterior radio-carpal ligament is attached to the palmar surfaces of the *scaphoid* and *lunate bones*, and the posterior ligament to the dorsal surfaces of the *scaphoid, lunate*, and *triquetrum*. The *distal row* of bones is closely bound to the bases of the medial four metacarpal bones by dorsal and palmar carpo-metacarpal ligaments, but the *trapezium* is more loosely attached to the base of the first metacarpal bone by a separate capsular ligament.

One end of the flexor retinaculum [lig. carpi transversum] is attached to the *pisiform* bone and the *hook* of the hamate, and the other end to the *tubercle of the scaphoid* bone and the palmar surface of the *trapezium*. The extensor retinaculum [lig. carpi dorsale] stretches obliquely from the lower end of the radius to the *triquetrum* and the *pisiform*.

The tendon of the flexor carpi ulnaris is inserted into the front of the *pisiform bone,* leaving the proximal surface of the bone in relation to the fatty, fibrous tissue behind the tendon ; but many of the tendinous fibres are continued onwards to the *hook* of the hamate and the base of the

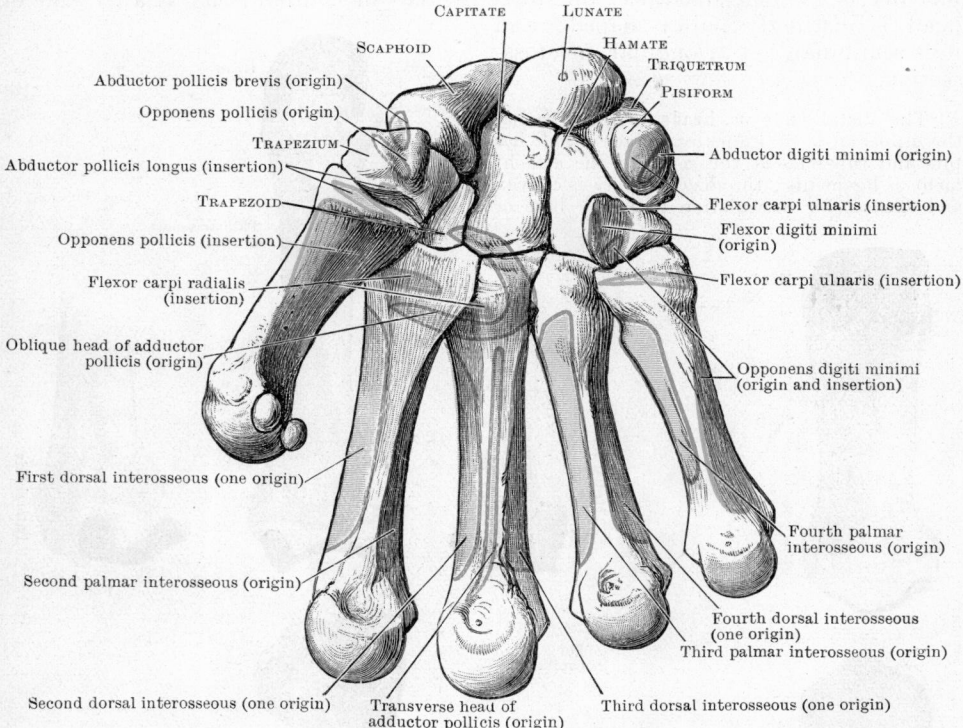

Capitate   Lunate

Scaphoid   Hamate

Triquetrum

Pisiform

Abductor pollicis brevis (origin)

Opponens pollicis (origin)

Trapezium

Abductor pollicis longus (insertion)

Trapezoid

Opponens pollicis (insertion)

Flexor carpi radialis (insertion)

Oblique head of adductor pollicis (origin)

First dorsal interosseous (one origin)

Second palmar interosseous (origin)

Second dorsal interosseous (one origin)

Transverse head of adductor pollicis (origin)

Abductor digiti minimi (origin)

Flexor carpi ulnaris (insertion)

Flexor digiti minimi (origin)

Flexor carpi ulnaris (insertion)

Opponens digiti minimi (origin and insertion)

Fourth palmar interosseous (origin)

Fourth dorsal interosseous (one origin)

Third palmar interosseous (origin)

Third dorsal interosseous (one origin)

FIG. 219.—Front of Right Carpus and Metacarpus with Attachments marked.

fifth metacarpal in two distinct strong bands called the piso-hamate and piso-metacarpal ligaments. The abductor digiti minimi arises partly from the *pisiform bone.* The flexor and opponens digiti minimi arise partly from the *hook* of the hamate. The abductor pollicis brevis arises in great part from the *tubercle of the scaphoid* and the *crest* on the *trapezium*; portions of the flexor pollicis brevis and opponens pollicis also arise from that crest ; and, distal to the crest the trapezium often receives a slip from the abductor pollicis longus. A portion of the oblique head of the adductor pollicis arises from the palmar surfaces of the *trapezium, trapezoid,* and *capitate*.

Metacarpus

The **metacarpus** is the skeleton of the hand proper [μετά (meta) = next after ; καρπός (carpos) = wrist]. It consists of five separate bones, called **metacarpal bones,** one corresponding to each digit. They are named by number, *first, second,* etc., beginning with the one that corresponds to the thumb. Each of them is a miniature long bone, and has a **shaft** and **two ends.** Each is slightly concave lengthwise on the **palmar** surface ; the **distal end** is the rounded end and is called the *head* ; the **proximal end** is called the *base.* The lateral surface can be distinguished from the medial after the base is examined.

The corresponding bones of the **foot** are called *metatarsal bones* ; they are not at all unlike the metacarpals, and a beginner may mistake the one for the other if they are loose and mixed. The metacarpals are between two and three inches long, and are rather shorter than the metatarsals, but are relatively thicker and less compressed ; the dorsal surface is an elongated, nearly flat, triangular area with its base at the distal end of the bone, and the proximal parts of the lateral and medial surfaces therefore encroach on the dorsum; the distal end is larger—conforming to the larger size of the finger. Those distinctions do not apply to the first metacarpal and metatarsal, but the first metacarpal is the shortest of all those bones, and the first metatarsal is the thickest. A beginner may also mistake the *proximal phalanx* of a finger for a metacarpal bone. But the phalanx is smaller, smoother, and more regular in contour; its smaller end or head is distinctly pulley-shaped; and it is semilunar, not triangular, in cross-section.

The **distal ends** or **heads** are familiar as the upper row of knuckles. Each head has pits and tubercles at the *sides* for the attachment of ligaments; the *distal surface* is convex and smooth for articulation with the base of

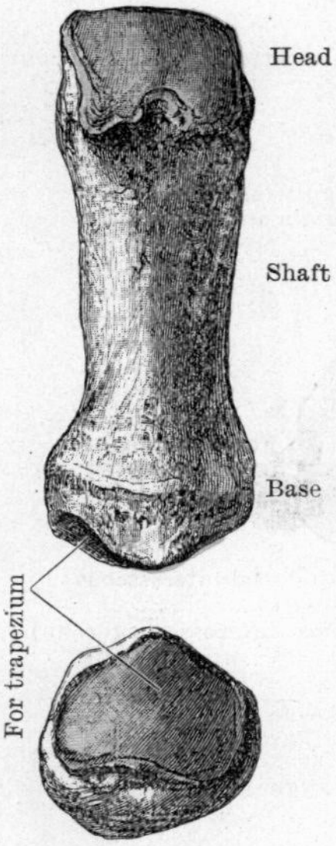

FIG. 220.— FIRST RIGHT METACARPAL BONE.

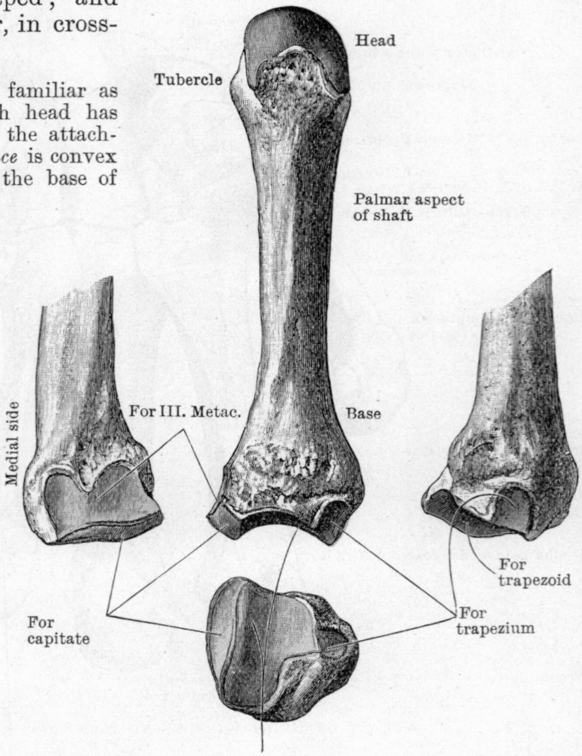

FIG. 221.—SECOND RIGHT METACARPAL BONE.

the proximal phalanx when the digit is straightened; the articular surface extends much farther on to the palmar surface than on to the dorsal, for when a digit is *flexed*, as when the hand is closed, the phalanx articulates with the palmar surface of the head. When a finger is *extended* it is in straight line with the hand, and the phalanx articulates with the distal surface of the head. The degree to which the finger can be *dorsiflexed*, *i.e.*, bent backwards beyond the straight line, varies considerably in different people, and the greater the degree of dorsiflexion possible the more does the articular surface extend on to the back of the head of the metacarpal bone. The edge of the palmar articular surface is notched in the middle, especially in the first and second; the margins of the notch end proximally in prominent tubercles, which may be grooved if sesamoid bones have been present.

The **shaft** is thinnest in the middle. It is slightly curved—being concave forwards to provide room for the structures in the palm. It has a *dorsal surface* which can be felt on the back of the hand, and a *medial* and a *lateral surface*. The blunt *palmar border*, which separates the lateral and medial surfaces, broadens out into a surface near each end.

The **proximal end** or **base** of a metacarpal bone articulates with the carpus by its *proximal surface*, which is therefore smooth; the bases of the medial four articulate with each other by their *sides*, and the sides therefore have articular facets. The readiest means of identifying the individual metacarpal bones is found in the base, and in the medial four the base provides the means of distinguishing the lateral surface from the medial surface.

The **first** metacarpal bone is shorter than the others, and is placed farthest forwards; it is set obliquely—diverging from the others, and with its dorsal surface looking laterally rather than backwards. Were it not for that position and obliquity, it would not be possible to oppose the thumb to the other digits. The bone is slightly compressed from before backwards, and the surfaces of the **shaft** are therefore usually regarded as two—a *dorsal* and a *palmar*; but the palmar surface is divided by a blunt ridge into a radial and an ulnar half, of which the radial or *lateral* half is slightly the larger; the dorsal surface is of equal width from end to end. The base has no facets on its *sides*; its *proximal surface* is saddle-shaped and articulates with the distal surface of the trapezium—that surface also being saddle-shaped. The *palmar surface* of the head has two shallow grooves which articulate with the sesamoid bones (p. 259).

The **second** is the longest of the metacarpal bones and its base is the largest. It has a wide groove or *notch* on the *proximal surface* of its base. The notch articulates with the trapezoid. The ridge that bounds the notch medially articulates with the capitate bone; the pointed tubercle on the *lateral side* articulates with the trapezium. There is a facet on the *medial side* of the base for articulation with the lateral surface of the base of the third metacarpal.

The **third** metacarpal has a thick, pointed projection, called its **styloid process**, which juts upwards from the junction of the *dorsal* and *lateral* surfaces of the **base**, and by that the **lateral** side can be recognised. The *proximal surface* of the base articulates with the capitate bone, and on the sides there are facets for articulation with the second and fourth metacarpals.

The **fourth** is usually the most slender of the metacarpal bones. It has a cubical **base**. Its *proximal surface* is nearly flat and articulates chiefly with the hamate bone and slightly with the capitate. There are two nearly circular facets on the *lateral surface* of the base for articulation with the third metacarpal, and a single facet on the *medial surface* for articulation with the fifth.

The **fifth** is the shortest metacarpal bone, except the first; the dorsal surface reaches the base, and is wide enough there to exclude the medial surface from the dorsum. Being the bone on the side of the hand, it has a facet on only one side of the **base**, and that is on the *lateral surface* for articulation with the fourth; there is a tubercle on the *medial surface*; the *proximal surface* is convex from before backwards and slightly concave from side to side, and articulates with the hamate bone.

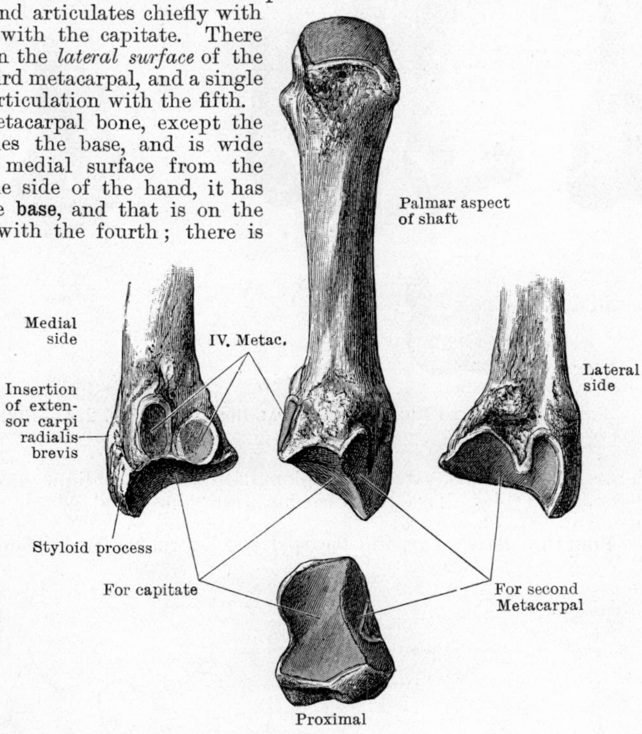

Attachments.—The **base** of the *first metacarpal* is attached to the trapezium by a capsular ligament. The *other four* are bound to the carpus by ligaments attached to their palmar and dorsal surfaces; they are bound to each other by palmar and dorsal ligaments and by interosseous ligaments attached to the rough parts of their sides; the **base** of the *fifth* has two additional ligaments—the piso-metacarpal attached to the palmar surface, and the medial ligament of the carpus stretching to the tubercle on its medial side. The **head** of each metacarpal is attached to the

FIG. 222.—THIRD RIGHT METACARPAL BONE.

proximal phalanx by a capsular ligament; this ligament is thickened at the sides to form radial and ulnar collateral ligaments, which are attached to the *sides* of the head, and it is greatly thickened in front to form the palmar ligament, which is attached loosely to the *palmar surface* immediately above the smooth articular part; on the back, the capsular ligament is fused with the extensor tendon that overlies the joint.

The abductor pollicis longus is inserted into the radial and palmar surfaces of the **base** of the *first*; the flexor carpi radialis into the palmar surface of the base of the *second* and slightly into the base of the *third* also; the extensor carpi radialis longus into the radial part of the back of the base of the *second*; the extensor carpi radialis brevis into the radial part of the base of the *third* at the root of the *styloid process*, and slightly also into the base of the *second*; the extensor carpi ulnaris into the back and ulnar side of the *fifth*. The first palmar interosseous arises from the ulnar side of the base of the *first*; part of the oblique head of the adductor pollicis from the palmar surfaces of the *second*, *third*, and *fourth*.

The opponens pollicis is inserted into the radial half of the palmar surface of the **shaft** of the *first*; the opponens digiti minimi into the ulnar surface of the *fifth*. The four dorsal interosseous muscles lie between the metacarpal bones and are attached to *all* of them; each arises by two heads which spring from the adjacent sides of the two metacarpal bones between which the muscle lies. The medial three palmar interosseous muscles lie in front of the dorsal interosseous; they arise by single heads from the *second*, *fourth*, and *fifth*. The transverse head of the adductor pollicis arises from the palmar border of the *third*.

The structures attached to each individual metacarpal bone are as follows :—

First Metacarpal Bone.—Base : Capsular ligament; abductor pollicis longus; first palmar interosseous. **Shaft** : Opponens pollicis; first dorsal interosseous. **Head** : Capsular ligament.

Second.—Base: Carpo-metacarpal and intermetacarpal ligaments; flexor carpi radialis, extensor carpi radialis longus and brevis; oblique head of adductor pollicis. **Shaft:** First and second dorsal interosseous, second palmar interosseous. **Head:** Capsular ligament.

   Third.—Base: Carpo-metacarpal and intermetacarpal ligaments;

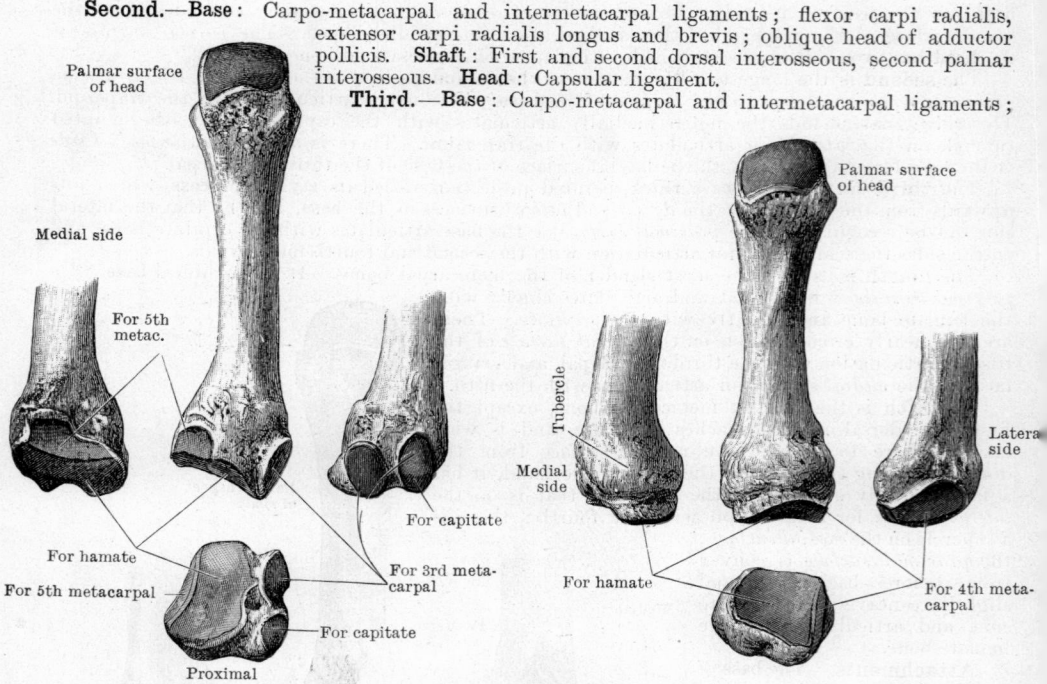

   Fig. 223.—Fourth Right Metacarpal Bone.   Fig. 224.—Fifth Right Metacarpal Bone.

flexor carpi radialis, extensor carpi radialis brevis; oblique head of adductor pollicis. **Shaft:** Second and third dorsal interosseous, transverse head of adductor pollicis. **Head:** Capsular ligament.

  Fourth.—Base: Carpo-metacarpal and intermetacarpal ligaments; oblique head of adductor

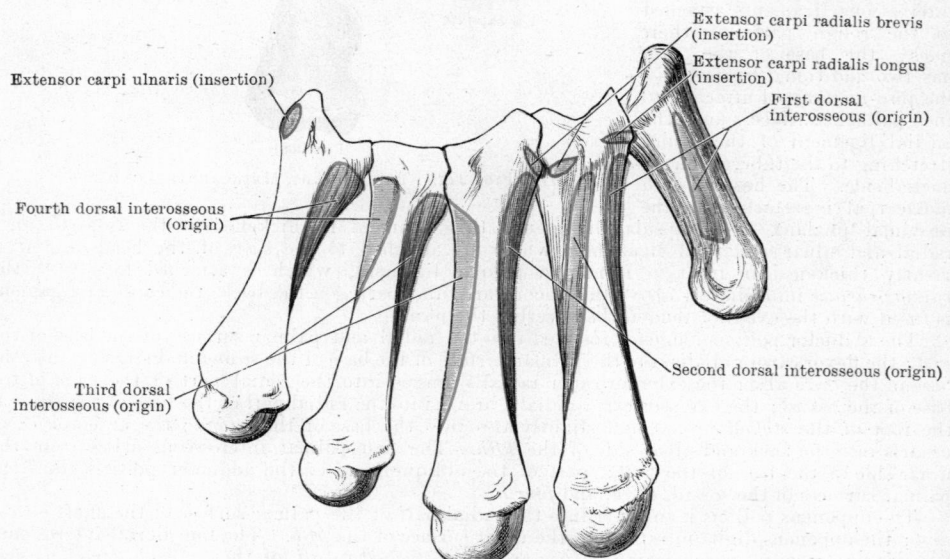

   Fig. 225.—Back of Right Metacarpus with Attachments marked.

pollicis. **Shaft:** Third and fourth dorsal interosseous, third palmar interosseous. **Head:** Capsular ligament.

  Fifth.—Base: Carpo-metacarpal (including piso-metacarpal) and intermetacarpal ligaments; extensor carpi ulnaris. **Shaft:** Fourth dorsal and palmar interosseous; opponens digiti minimi. **Head:** Capsular ligament.

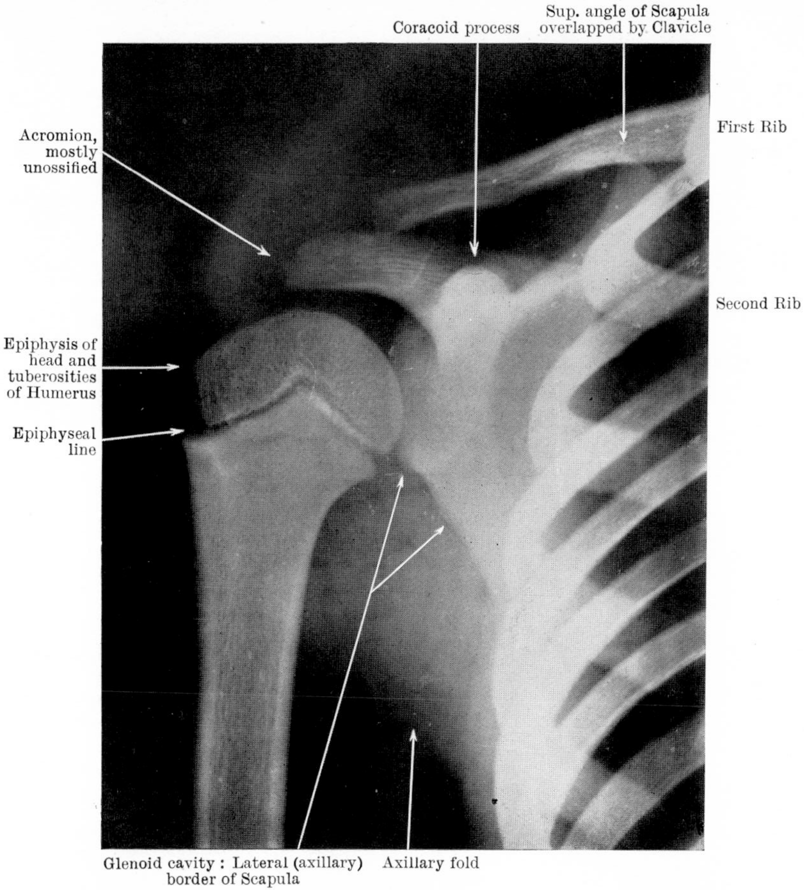

PLATE III

Fifth
Metacarpal

Hamate

Triquetral

Pisiform

Styloid
process

Epiphysis
of Ulna

Epiphysis of
base of First
Metacarpal

Trapezium
and
Trapezoid

Scaphoid

Styloid
process

Epiphysis
of Radius

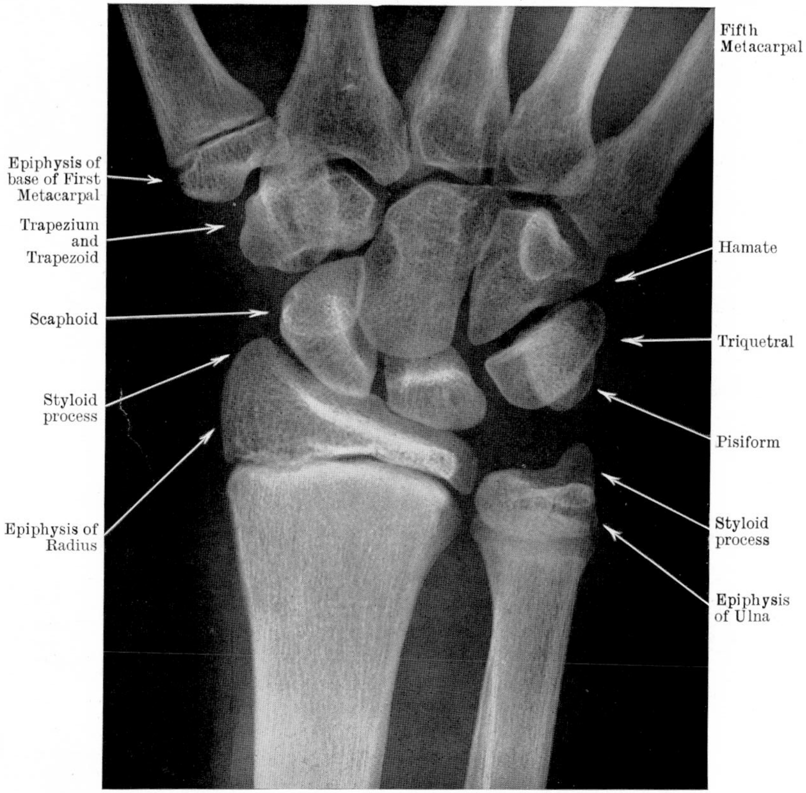

Fig. 2.—Radiograph of Wrist of Girl aged 14, to show the Distal
Epiphyses of Radius and Ulna.

Coracoid process

Sup. angle of Scapula
overlapped by Clavicle

First Rib

Second Rib

Acromion,
mostly
unossified

Epiphysis of
head and
tuberosities
of Humerus

Epiphyseal
line

Glenoid cavity : Lateral (axillary)   Axillary fold
border of Scapula

Fig. 1.—Radiograph of Shoulder Region of Boy aged 7.   (Dr. J. Duncan White.)

Note that the proximal epiphysis of the Humerus (formed by union of centres for head,
greater (and sometimes lesser) tuberosity) fits like a cap on the end of the shaft.

PLATE X

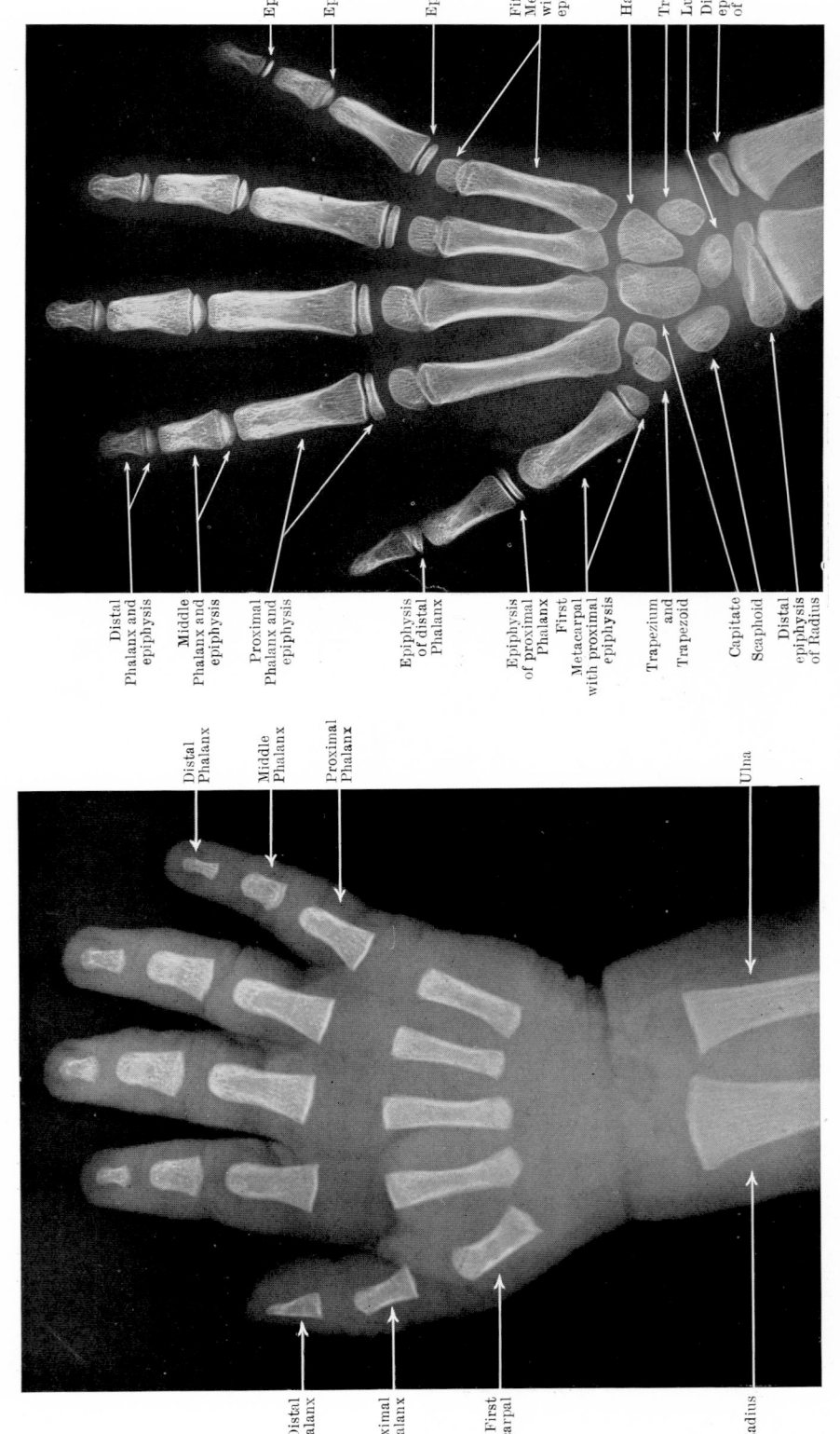

Distal Phalanx and epiphysis
Middle Phalanx and epiphysis
Proximal Phalanx and epiphysis

Epiphysis of distal Phalanx
Epiphysis of proximal Phalanx
First Metacarpal with proximal epiphysis
Trapezium and Trapezoid
Capitate
Scaphoid
Distal epiphysis of Radius

Epiphysis
Epiphysis
Epiphysis
Fifth Metacarpal with distal epiphysis
Hamate
Triquetral
Lunate
Distal epiphysis of Ulna

Fig. 2.—Radiograph of Wrist and Hand of Girl aged 7. (Dr. J. Duncan White.)

Note the relative position of the ossifying carpal bones—the pisiform centre has not yet appeared, and compare with Plate XIX. (Cf. also Plate XVI,

Distal Phalanx
Middle Phalanx
Proximal Phalanx
Ulna

Distal Phalanx
Proximal Phalanx
First Metacarpal
Radius

Fig. 1.—Radiograph of Hand of Full-time Fœtus.

Note the absence of centres of ossification for the carpal bones.

[Facing p. 257

Phalanges of Digits of Hand

Each **phalanx** is a miniature long bone having a **shaft** and **two ends** [φάλαγξ (phalanx)=a round log or roller]. The **proximal** end is the larger end and is called the *base*; the **distal** end is called the *head*. The **shaft** is markedly *convex* from side to side on its *dorsal* surface and nearly flat on the *palmar* surface. There is little distinction between the lateral and medial margins of a phalanx.

The **proximal** phalanx of a digit is the largest; the proximal surface of its **base** is hollowed out as a single concavity, and its **head** is pulley-shaped. The **head** of the **middle** phalanx also is pulley-shaped, but its **base**, since it articulates with the head of the proximal phalanx, is the reverse of a pulley, having two shallow concavities with a low intervening ridge; that distinguishes the middle phalanx of a large hand from the proximal phalanx of a small hand. The **base** of the **distal** phalanx also is the reverse of a pulley, but it is the smallest phalanx and its **head** is non-articular.

The **thumb** has only *two* phalanges. They are shorter and broader than those of the fingers; the **proximal** resembles the proximal phalanx of a finger, and the **distal** resembles the distal phalanx of a finger.

The middle finger is the longest; the little finger is the shortest; the other two fingers are nearly equal in length, the ring finger being usually slightly longer than the index. But the relative lengths of the phalanges are such that the finger-tips come into line when the interphalangeal joints are bent.

The phalanges of the toes should not be mistaken for those of the fingers. The proximal phalanx of a toe is about the same length as the middle phalanx of a finger, but its body is much thinner and its base is relatively large. Both of the phalanges of the big toe are so thick, and the middle and distal phalanges of the other toes are so short, that they cannot be mistaken.

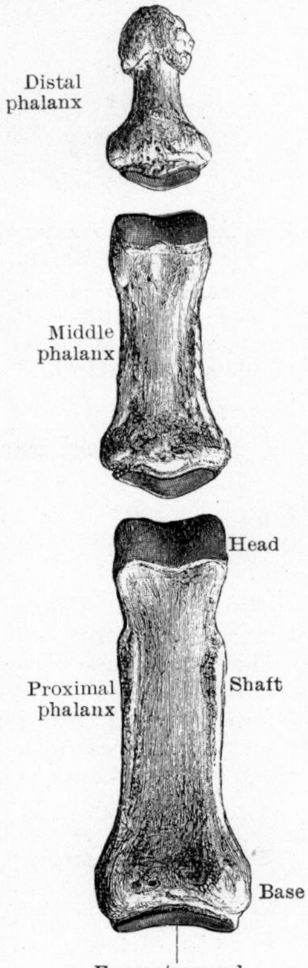

The **proximal phalanx** of a finger measures 35-45 mm. in length, and is slightly curved lengthwise, with the concavity on the palmar surface. The *proximal surface* of its **base** is concave, and articulates with the head of the metacarpal; the *sides* of the base are slightly enlarged and give attachment to ligaments. The *dorsal surface* of the **shaft** is markedly convex sideways. The *palmar surface* is nearly flat from side to side, and is separated from the dorsum by sharp margins. The **head** articulates with the base of the middle phalanx; the articular surface extends much farther on to the front than on to the back, just as on the head of a metacarpal bone and for the same reason. The *sides* of the head show shallow pits for the attachment of ligaments.

FIG. 226.—PHALANGES OF A FINGER (Palmar View).

The **middle phalanx** is 25-30 mm. Its **shaft** and **head** resemble those of a proximal phalanx, but the **base** differs in the way already mentioned. The **distal phalanx** is very small and is not curved. Its **base** is relatively large, and resembles that of a middle phalanx. The **shaft** is short. The **head** is expanded sideways, is non-articular, and is very rough on its palmar surface.

Attachments.—The **base** of the *proximal* phalanx is attached to the metacarpal bone by a capsular ligament, the characters of which are briefly indicated in the account of the metacarpals; the palmar ligament is attached firmly to the palmar surface of the base, and the collateral ligaments to its sides. The *middle* phalanx is attached to the first and the third by similar capsules. Each of the four tendons of the extensor digitorum spreads out on the back of a proximal phalanx to form an *extensor expansion* which is inserted into the back of the base of the middle and distal phalanges of a finger; the tendon of the extensor indicis joins the tendon of the digitorum for the forefinger, and the tendon of the extensor digiti minimi joins that for the little finger; the tendons of the interossei and of the lumbricales are inserted into the extensor tendon of a finger; therefore each *extensor expansion* is made up of several tendons. Each of the four tendons of the flexor digitorum sublimis is inserted into the margins of the **shaft** of a *middle* phalanx. Each of the four tendons of the flexor digitorum profundus is inserted into the palmar surface of the **base** of a *distal* phalanx. The abductor and flexor digiti minimi are inserted into the ulnar side of the **base** of the proximal phalanx of the *little finger*.

17

The tendons of the long flexors of a digit are held in place along its palmar surface by a fibrous strap, called the fibrous flexor sheath, the edges of which are attached to the margins of the **shaft** of the *proximal* phalanx of the *thumb* and of the *proximal* and *middle* phalanges of the *fingers*, and its distal extremity is attached to the palmar surface of the *distal* phalanx, immediately beyond the insertion of the flexor tendon.

The structures attached to the individual phalanges are as follows :—

Fingers.—To **proximal phalanx** :—Capsular ligaments; flexor sheath; and, in little finger, the abductor and flexor digiti minimi. To **middle phalanx** :—Capsular ligaments; flexor sheath; extensor expansion, flexor digitorum sublimis. To **distal phalanx** :—Capsular ligament; flexor sheath; extensor expansion; flexor digitorum profundus.

Thumb.—The extensor pollicis brevis is inserted into the *dorsal* surface of the **base** of the **proximal phalanx**; the flexor brevis and abductor brevis together into the *radial* side of the base; the first palmar interosseous and transverse head of adductor into the *ulnar* side; oblique head of adductor into both sides. The extensor longus into the *dorsum* of the **base** of the **distal phalanx**; and the flexor longus into the *palmar* surface. The fibrous flexor sheath is attached to the *margins* of the **shaft** of the **proximal phalanx** and the *palmar surface* of the **distal**. Capsular ligaments, like those of the fingers, connect the proximal phalanx with the metacarpal bone and the distal phalanx.

Ossification of Bones of Hand.—The **carpus** is cartilaginous at birth. Each carpal bone has **one** centre; ossification is completed between 20 and 25.

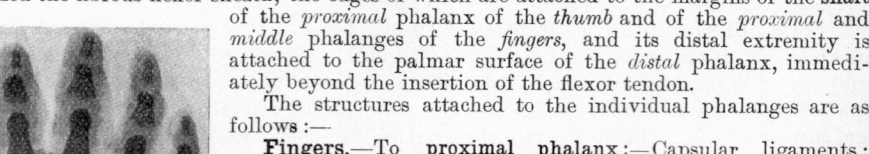

FIG. 227.—RADIOGRAPH OF THE HAND AT BIRTH.

Metacarpus and phalanges well ossified; carpus still cartilaginous. Compare with tarsus at birth, p. 309 and Plate XVI.

	Capitate.	Hamate.	Triquetrum.	Lunate.	Scaphoid.	Trapezium.	Trapezoid.	Pisiform.
Centre appears	6 month	6 month	M. 3-4 yr. F. 2-3 yr.	M. 4-5 yr. F. 3-4 yr.	M. 6 yr. F. 4 yr.	M. 6 yr. F. 4-5 yr.	M. 6 yr. F. 4-5 yr.	M. 13-14 yr. F. 9-10 yr.

Metacarpus.—The *primary* centre, one for each metacarpal bone, appears in the ninth week of intra-uterine life. The metacarpal bones are well ossified at birth.

The **first** differs from the other in having the epiphysis at the base instead of at the head, possibly because movement is more free at the carpo-metacarpal joint of the thumb than at the metacarpo-phalangeal joint, while the reverse is the case at the joints of the other metacarpal bones. In rare cases the first has an epiphysis at its head also; and, still more rarely, the second or one of the others has an epiphysis at its base.

Secondary Centre.	Appears at	Epiphysis joins at	Relation of Epiphyseal Line to Capsule of Neighbouring Joint.
For base of first	M. $3\frac{1}{2}$ yr. F. $2\frac{1}{2}$	{ M. 19 yr. F. 17 yr.	Outside.
For head of others	M. 3 yr. F. 2		Outside.

Phalanges.—The *primary* centre for each appears between the eighth and the twelfth week of intra-uterine life. At birth the phalanges are well formed.

Secondary Centre.	Appears at	Epiphysis fuses at	Relation of Epiphyseal Line to Capsule of Neighbouring Joint.
For base	{ M. 3rd yr. F. 2nd yr.	{ M. 19 F. 17	Outside.

The **distal phalanges** are the first bones of the hand to ossify, and their primary centres appear near their distal ends instead of in the middle.

In rare cases the proximal phalanx has an epiphysis at its head as well as at its base.

It is possible that "double epiphysis" in metacarpals and phalanges is hereditary.

Structure and Variations of Bones of Hand.—**Carpal bones** have the typical structure of short bones. **Metacarpal bones** and **phalanges** have the structure of long bones. The walls of the medullary cavity are thick compared with the size of the bone; that is especially the case in the dorsal wall in a phalanx. The *nutrient foramen* of a metacarpal is near the palmar margin; it is directed towards the head in the first, and towards the base in the others. There are usually two on each phalanx. They are on the palmar surface, and are directed towards the head.

Variation in the number of carpal bones may arise from the fusion of two carpal bones or the division of one; but fusion is caused usually by disease. The hook of the hamate bone may be separate; the **os centrale**, though normally a separate bone in the carpus of most mammals, and represented by a separate cartilage in the earlier months of intra-uterine life, is almost always fused with the scaphoid bone, but sometimes it is a separate ossicle on the back of the carpus between the scaphoid, capitate, and trapezoid. Radiographs sometimes reveal what appear to be small additional nodules in the carpus. The *styloid process* of the third metacarpal bone may have an epiphyseal centre, and may be a separate bone, or may be fused with the capitate bone or the trapezium, instead of with the metacarpal.

Sometimes a *distal phalanx* is bifurcated. The thumb may have three phalanges. Occasionally a phalanx is very short, or is absent or has been absorbed by another phalanx.

Sesamoid Bones

The **sesamoid bones** of the hand are two very small nodules that lie in the tendons of insertion of the flexor pollicis brevis and the adductor pollicis. They are blended with the palmar ligament of the metacarpo-phalangeal joint, and play against the palmar surface of the head of the metacarpal bone. Occasionally little nodules are found also in the palmar ligament of the other metacarpo-phalangeal joints and in the interphalangeal joint of the thumb.

The sesamoid bones of the hand are cartilaginous in childhood; they begin to ossify after 13, and may have more than one centre for each.

BONES OF THE LOWER LIMB

The parts of the **lower limb** [extremitas inferior] are the hip and buttock, the thigh, the leg, and the foot (Figs. 113, 114, pp. 99 and 100).

The **hip** (*coxa*), above and at the side, and the **buttock** (*natis*), below and behind, make up the **gluteal region**, which extends from the waist and the small of the back down to the level of the horizontal crease that limits the buttock below; the crease is called the *fold of the buttock*; the interval between the buttocks is called the *natal cleft* [γλουτός (glūtos) = *natis* = buttock]. The lower end of the trunk, between the thighs and between the buttocks, is called the *perineum* [περίνεος (perineos) = the perineum: derivation uncertain].

The skeleton of the hip and buttock of each side is a single bone called the **hip bone** (os coxæ). It is part of the framework of the trunk also, for the right and left hip bones, together with the sacrum and the coccyx, form the bony walls of the pelvis; and the hip bone is sometimes referred to as the *pelvic girdle*. (The sacrum and coccyx are the lowest subdivisions of the backbone; the pelvis is the lower subdivision of the abdomen or belly, and the perineum is included in the pelvis.)

The **thigh** (*femur*) extends from the gluteal region to the knee. On the lateral [1] side it is continuous with the hip; posteriorly it joins the buttock at the fold of the buttock; on the medial side it joins the perineum, which separates it from the other thigh; anteriorly it joins the anterior wall of the abdomen and reaches a higher level than it does behind; the depression between the front of the thigh and the front of the abdomen is the *groin* or *inguinal region* [inguen = groin, from inquinare = to stain].

The bone of the thigh is called the **femur**. At its upper end the femur articulates with the hip bone to form the *hip joint*. At the knee joint the distal end of the femur articulates (1) with the tibia or shin bone, which is the larger of the two bones of the leg, and (2) with the patella or knee cap—the small bone that lies in the front of the knee joint. The ham is the back of the knee and the lower part of the back of the thigh, and the hollow of the ham is called the *popliteal fossa* [poples = the hough; the ham of the knee].

The term **leg** (*crus*) is often applied to the whole free part of the lower limb, but in Anatomical Text-books it is limited strictly to the segment between the knee joint and the ankle joint. The two bones of the leg are called the **tibia**

[1] Definitions of terms are given on pp. 3, 94.

17 a

and the **fibula**. They articulate with each other at their upper and lower ends, and the joints so formed are called the *tibio-fibular joints*. The tibia articulates with the femur at the *knee joint*, but the fibula does not do so; the tibia and fibula both articulate with one of the bones of the foot, called the talus, to form the *ankle joint*.

The **foot** (*pes*) is joined to the leg at the ankle joint, and is divided into foot proper and the toes. The **foot proper** is all the region from the point of the heel to the roots of the toes. Its upper surface is called the *dorsal surface* or *dorsum* of the foot; the *sole* is often called the *plantar surface* [*planta* = the sole]. The foot proper is divided into—(1) the *tarsus*, which is the hinder half of the foot proper, and corresponds to the carpus or wrist, and (2) the *metatarsus*, which is the half next the toes, and corresponds to the metacarpus or hand proper.

The bones of the **tarsus** are seven in number; they are named collectively the **tarsal bones**, and each has its own name besides; they articulate with one another, forming *inter-tarsal joints*. They are arranged in two rows—two bones in the first row and four bones in the second row—and an intermediate bone between the rows. The bones of the second row are placed side by side; the bones of the first row are placed one above the other, and the upper one—the talus—articulates with the bones of the leg at the *ankle joint*.

The bones of the **metatarsus** are called **metatarsal bones**. There are five of them, placed side by side, one corresponding to each toe. They are named by number: **first** metatarsal, **second**, etc., beginning with the one that corresponds to the big toe. The posterior ends of the metatarsal bones articulate (1) with the second row of tarsal bones, forming *tarso-metatarsal joints*, and (2) with one another, side by side, forming *inter-metatarsal joints*.

Toes or **Digits**.—The big toe is called the **hallux** [probably from *allex* = thumb or big toe]. The other toes are usually designated by number—**second, third**, etc.

The bones of the toes are called **phalanges**. The big toe has two phalanges, named the **proximal** phalanx and the **distal** phalanx. Each of the other toes has three phalanges—**proximal, middle**, and **distal**. The distal phalanx is sometimes called the *ungual phalanx*, because the nail (*unguis*) is associated with it. The proximal phalanx of a digit articulates with the distal end of the corresponding metatarsal bone to form a *metatarso-phalangeal joint*; and the middle phalanx articulates with the other two, forming *interphalangeal joints*.

Hip Bone

The **hip bone** is the broadest bone in the skeleton. It is large, expanded, and unevenly compressed. On one side of it there is a deep cup or cavity with a broken rim; the cavity is called the **acetabulum**, and near it there is a large aperture called the **obturator foramen**.

The hip bone lies in the side wall and the anterior wall of the pelvis. In the anterior wall it articulates with its fellow of the opposite side to form a joint called the *pubic symphysis*. Posteriorly the hip bone articulates with the side of the sacrum, which lies in the back wall of the pelvis between the two hip bones; and the joint is called the *sacro-iliac joint*.

The hip bone is made up of three originally distinct bones which in the adult are fused together at the acetabulum. The three bones or parts are named the *ilium, ischium*, and *pubis*.

The **ilium** is the largest and broadest of the three parts. It is the uppermost part of the hip bone; and the bone should be held in the hand so that this broad part is uppermost, and the deficient side of the acetabulum looks directly downwards. The **ischium** is the thick, three-sided part below and behind the acetabulum and behind the obturator foramen; from the lower end of the ischium a broad, fairly flat bar of bone, called the *ramus of the ischium*, projects forwards; it is the lower boundary of the obturator foramen, and joins the pubis. The **pubis** is the remaining part of the hip bone, and forms the other boundaries of the obturator foramen. The pubis has three main parts: (1) an expanded part in front, called the *body* of the pubis ; (2) a compressed bar of bone, called the *inferior ramus* of the pubis, which extends backwards from the body and fuses with the ramus of the ischium ; (3) a thicker bar, called the *superior ramus*, which extends from the body to the acetabulum.

The position of parts is roughly as follows : the ilium is the upper part ; the ischium is the lower and posterior part ; the pubis is the lower, anterior, and

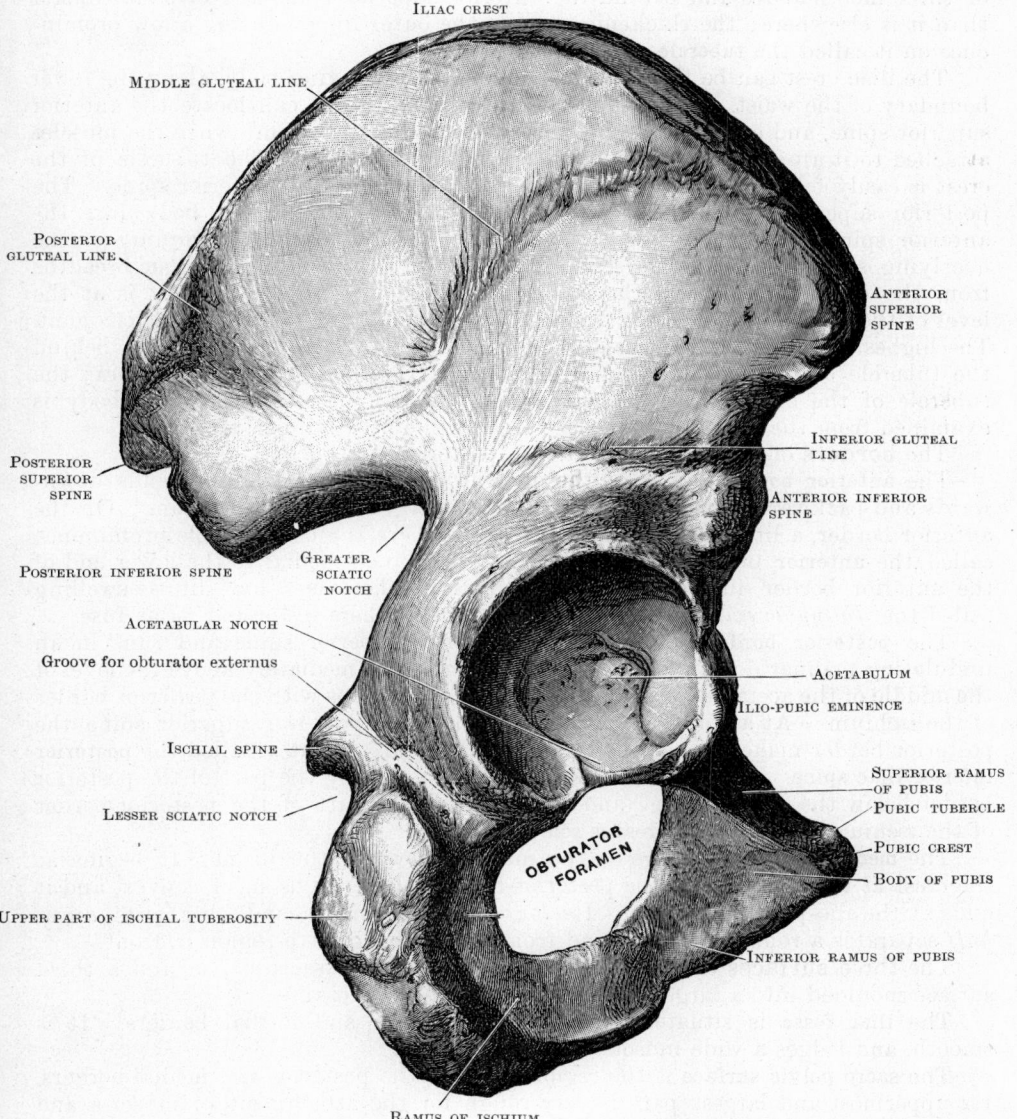

ILIAC CREST

MIDDLE GLUTEAL LINE

POSTERIOR GLUTEAL LINE

ANTERIOR SUPERIOR SPINE

POSTERIOR SUPERIOR SPINE

INFERIOR GLUTEAL LINE

ANTERIOR INFERIOR SPINE

POSTERIOR INFERIOR SPINE

GREATER SCIATIC NOTCH

ACETABULAR NOTCH

Groove for obturator externus

ACETABULUM

ILIO-PUBIC EMINENCE

ISCHIAL SPINE

SUPERIOR RAMUS OF PUBIS

PUBIC TUBERCLE

LESSER SCIATIC NOTCH

OBTURATOR FORAMEN

PUBIC CREST

BODY OF PUBIS

UPPER PART OF ISCHIAL TUBEROSITY

INFERIOR RAMUS OF PUBIS

RAMUS OF ISCHIUM

FIG. 228.—THE RIGHT HIP BONE SEEN FROM THE LATERAL SIDE.

medial part ; the acetabulum is on the lateral surface ; the obturator foramen is below and medial to the acetabulum.

The **ilium** (os ilium) is the bone of the flank [*ilia* (plural) = the flank]. It lies below the waist in the uppermost part of the hip. It is large, compressed, and fluted, and has two ends, three borders, and three surfaces.

The two **ends** are upper and lower. The **lower end** forms the upper part of the acetabulum, and is fused there with the ischium and the pubis.

The **upper end** is scarcely recognisable as an end, for the ilium in Man is so expanded that the upper end is drawn out like the wide end of an open fan and resembles a border; it is called the **iliac crest**. The crest is curved like the *italic letter f*; the curve of the anterior half is convex in the lateral direction, and the curve of the posterior half is convex in the medial direction. The anterior and posterior ends of the crest are named the **anterior superior iliac spine** and the **posterior superior iliac spine**. The margins of the crest are called its *outer* and *inner lips*; the interval between the lips is called the *intermediate area*. Two or three inches above and behind the anterior superior spine the crest is thicker than it is elsewhere; the thickening affects the outer lip, producing a low prominence on it called the **tubercle of the crest**.

The iliac crest can be felt from end to end in the living body, along the lower boundary of the waist. By tracing the crest forwards one can locate the anterior superior spine, and can almost grip it between finger and thumb when the muscles attached to it are relaxed—as they are when one is sitting. The tubercle of the crest is easily felt, two or three inches behind and above the anterior spine. The posterior superior spine is not distinctly palpable in the living body like the anterior spine, but its position can always be recognised by a dimpling of the overlying skin; the dimple is seen above the buttock about two finger-breadths from the median plane, and the spine is the bone felt in its floor; it is at the level of the second spine of the sacrum and the middle of the sacro-iliac joint. The highest point of the crest is about its middle point, one or two inches behind the tubercle of the crest, and is at the level of the fourth lumbar vertebra; the tubercle of the crest is the highest point that can be seen when the body is examined from the front, and is at the level of the fifth lumbar vertebra.

The **borders** of the ilium are anterior, posterior, and medial.

The **anterior border** begins at the anterior superior spine and extends downwards and backwards to end at the anterior margin of the acetabulum. On the anterior border, a little above the acetabulum, there is a considerable prominence called the **anterior inferior iliac spine**. About an inch medial to the lower end of the anterior border, in front of the acetabulum, there is a low, diffuse swelling called the *ilio-pubic eminence*; it marks the region where ilium and pubis fuse.

The **posterior border** begins at the posterior superior spine and runs in an undulating manner downwards and forwards to end immediately above the level of the middle of the acetabulum, where it becomes continuous with the posterior border of the ischium. At a point about an inch below the posterior superior spine, the posterior border makes an abrupt bend forwards; that point is called the **posterior inferior iliac spine**. The wide notch which is bounded by the part of the posterior border below the inferior spine and by the adjoining part of the posterior border of the ischium is called the **greater sciatic notch**.

The **medial border** is a ridge on the medial aspect of the ilium. It begins at the crest at the point where the posterior half of the crest is most convex, and it ends at the ilio-pubic eminence. Its *lower half* is smooth and blunt; its *upper half* separates a rough region behind from a smooth, concave region in front.

The three **surfaces** of the ilium are the gluteal, the sacro-pelvic, and a third surface moulded into a large concavity called the iliac fossa.

The **iliac fossa** is situated between the anterior and medial borders. It is smooth, and lodges a wide muscle called the iliacus.

The **sacro-pelvic surface** is the region between the posterior and medial borders. Its uppermost and largest part is very rough for the attachment of muscles and ligaments, and is called the **iliac tuberosity**. The middle part usually has a sharply defined outline, and is called the **auricular surface**, because its shape resembles that of an ear (though turned the wrong way); it articulates with a corresponding "auricular" surface on the sacrum to form the *sacro-iliac joint*, but though it is an articular surface it is uneven and rather rough; the lobe of the "ear" is the posterior inferior iliac spine. The lowest part of the sacro-pelvic surface is smooth; it is the area between the lower, smooth part of the medial border and the bottom of the greater sciatic notch; it forms part of the side wall of the true pelvis, which is the basin-like, lower part of the pelvis. By far the thickest, strongest, and oldest part of the ilium is the part in the neighbourhood of the auricular surface; for it is the part that bears the weight of the trunk.

The **gluteal surface** of the ilium is the wide, concavo-convex or undulating surface above the acetabulum, between the anterior and posterior borders; it looks laterally and backwards, and is sometimes called the **dorsum ilii**. It is divided into areas by three curved ridges, called gluteal lines, which vary in distinctness with the muscularity of the subject. The *inferior gluteal line* is the least distinct;

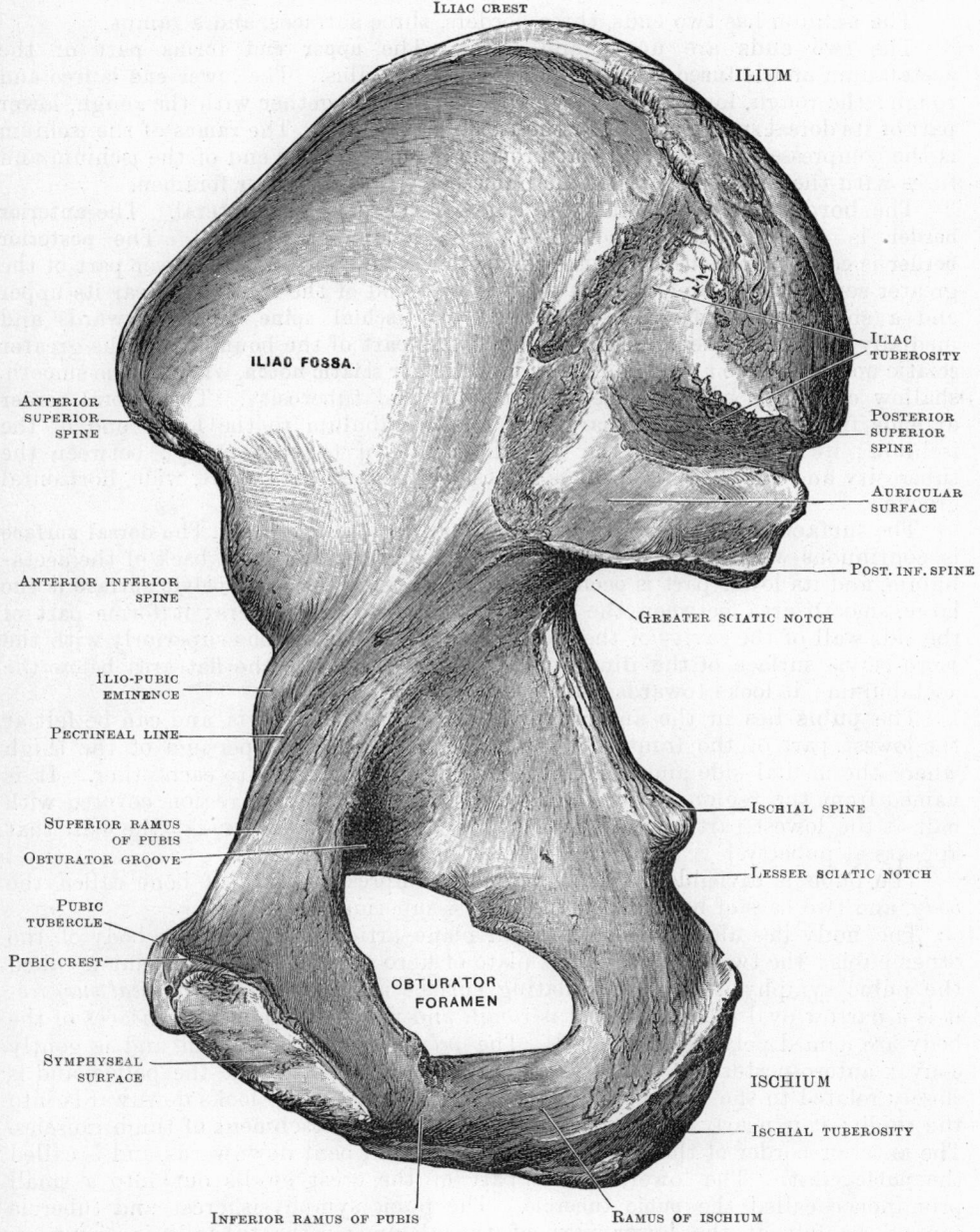

ILIAC CREST

ILIUM

ILIAC FOSSA.

ANTERIOR
SUPERIOR
SPINE

ANTERIOR INFERIOR
SPINE

ILIO-PUBIC
EMINENCE

PECTINEAL LINE

SUPERIOR RAMUS
OF PUBIS
OBTURATOR GROOVE

PUBIC
TUBERCLE

PUBIC CREST

SYMPHYSEAL
SURFACE

ILIAC
TUBEROSITY

POSTERIOR
SUPERIOR
SPINE

AURICULAR
SURFACE

POST. INF. SPINE

GREATER SCIATIC NOTCH

ISCHIAL SPINE

LESSER SCIATIC NOTCH

OBTURATOR
FORAMEN

ISCHIUM

ISCHIAL TUBEROSITY

INFERIOR RAMUS OF PUBIS

RAMUS OF ISCHIUM

FIG. 229.—THE RIGHT HIP BONE SEEN FROM THE MEDIAL SIDE.

it begins at the anterior border above the anterior inferior spine and curves backwards, about an inch above the acetabulum, towards the greater sciatic notch. The *middle gluteal* line begins at the crest an inch or more behind the anterior superior spine and arches across the middle of the surface towards the greater sciatic notch. The *posterior gluteal line* begins at the crest two or three inches

17 *b*

in front of the posterior superior spine and curves downwards to the greater sciatic notch.

The **ischium** is the thick, prismatic part of the hip bone below and behind the acetabulum. In the upright sitting posture the body rests on the two ischia [ἰσχίον (ischion) = buttock. The adjective *ischiadic* has been reduced by time to *sciatic*].

The ischium has two ends, three borders, three surfaces, and a ramus.

The two **ends** are upper and lower. The **upper end** forms part of the acetabulum and is fused with the ilium and the pubis. The **lower end** is free and rough; the rough, lower extremity of the ischium, together with the rough, lower part of its dorsal surface, is called the **ischial tuberosity**. The **ramus** of the ischium is the compressed bar of bone that projects from the lower end of the ischium and fuses with the inferior ramus of the pubis below the obturator foramen.

The **borders** of the ischium are anterior, posterior, and lateral. The **anterior border** is one of the boundaries of the obturator foramen. The **posterior border** is continuous with the posterior border of the ilium at the lower part of the greater sciatic notch and extends to the lower end of the ischium; near its upper end a sharp, triangular process, called the **ischial spine**, juts backwards and medially from it. The spine forms the lowest part of the boundary of the greater sciatic notch and the upper boundary of the **lesser sciatic notch**, which is the smooth, shallow concavity between the ischial spine and tuberosity. The **lateral border** extends from the posterior margin of the acetabulum to the lower end of the ischium; its lower part is the lateral margin of the tuberosity; between the tuberosity and the acetabulum it is almost obliterated by a short, wide, horizontal groove.

The **surfaces** of the ischium are dorsal, pelvic, and femoral. The **dorsal surface** is continuous with the gluteal surface of the ilium across the back of the acetabulum, and its lower part is occupied by the tuberosity. The **pelvic surface** is the large, smooth area between the anterior and posterior borders; it forms part of the side wall of the cavity of the true pelvis, and is continuous superiorly with the sacro-pelvic surface of the ilium. The **femoral surface** is the flat area below the acetabulum; it looks towards the thigh.

The **pubis** lies in the anterior or lower wall of the pelvis, and can be felt at the lowest part of the front of the abdomen and at the upper end of the thigh where the medial side and the front of the thigh merge into each other. It is named from the region in which it lies. [The *pubis* is the region covered with hair at the lowest part of the front of the abdomen: from *pubes* = the hair that appears at puberty.]

The pubis is divisible into an expanded, compressed piece of bone called the *body*, and two bars of bone called the *rami*—superior and inferior.

The **body** lies alongside the median plane, articulating with the body of the other pubis; the two are joined by a plate of fibro-cartilage, and the joint is called the pubic symphysis; the articulating surface is called the *symphyseal surface*; it is a narrow oval in outline, and is rough and ridged. The other surfaces of the body are named pelvic and femoral. The *pelvic surface* is smooth, and is gently convex antero-posteriorly; it looks upwards into the cavity of the pelvis, and is closely related to the urinary bladder. The *femoral surface* looks downwards into the thigh; it is nearly flat, but is roughened for the attachment of thigh muscles. The anterior border of the body is thick, rough, and bent downwards, and is called the **pubic crest**. The lower, lateral part of the crest swells out into a small prominence called the **pubic tubercle**. The pubic symphysis, crest, and tubercle can all be felt at the lower part of the abdomen; the tubercle is about an inch from the median plane, and is often referred to as a landmark. When the hip bone is held in the position it occupies in the erect body, the pubic tubercle and the anterior superior iliac spine lie in one vertical plane; the hip bone is therefore in its proper position when it is placed against a wall with only those two points touching, and the defective side of the acetabulum looking straight downwards. A fibrous band called the *inguinal ligament* stretches between the pubic tubercle and the anterior superior iliac spine. It can be felt in the living groin as a tense, resisting cord along the floor of the curved groove that extends between those two bony points. Though called a "ligament" it is the lower edge of the aponeurosis of the external oblique muscle of the wall of the abdomen; it lies along the line where the front of the thigh joins the abdomen, and is encountered in the first steps of the dissection of the lower limb. [An *aponeurosis* is a tendon or sinew in the form of a wide sheet: ἀπό (apo) = from; νεῦρον (neuron) = *nervus* = a sinew (though now both *neuron* and *nervus* always signify *nerve*).]

The **inferior ramus** is the short, compressed bar which begins at the posterior part of the body of the pubis, and passes backwards, downwards, and in a lateral direction to meet and fuse with the ramus of the ischium; the position of their junction may be marked by a thickening or a ridge, but is often difficult to make out in an adult bone. The two fused rami form a bar of bone called the **conjoined rami** of ischium and pubis. The bar has two surfaces and two borders. The *inner surface* is divided lengthwise by a ridge into an upper and a lower part; the upper part looks into the pelvis; the lower part looks into the perineum and gives attachment to the crus of the penis or of the clitoris. The *outer surface* is directed towards the thigh and gives attachment to thigh muscles. The *upper border* is the lower boundary of the obturator foramen. The *lower border* can be felt in the boundary between the medial side of the thigh and the anterior part of the perineum. The conjoined rami of the right and left hip bones constitute the sides of an archway called the **pubic arch**.

The **superior ramus**, though named merely a "ramus," is the true pubic bone. It has two ends, three borders, and three surfaces.

The **ends** are medial and lateral. The **medial end** is wide and compressed, and is described above as the "body" of the pubis. The **lateral end** is expanded to form part of the acetabulum, and it fuses there with the ilium and the ischium. The *ilio-pubic eminence*, in front of the acetabulum, marks the position of its union with the ilium.

The **borders** are anterior, posterior, and inferior. The *anterior border* is a sharp edge called the **pectineal line** [*pecten* = a crest or comb]. It begins at or near the pubic tubercle and extends to the upper part of the ilio-pubic eminence, where it is continuous with the lower, smooth part of the medial border of the ilium. The *inferior border* is a strong ridge called the **obturator crest**. It begins near the pubic tubercle and runs to the acetabulum to end at the anterior part of the gap in its rim. The **posterior border** is seen best from the pelvic side. It is the anterior boundary of the obturator foramen as seen from that point of view.

The **surfaces** of the superior ramus are named pectineal, pelvic, and obturator. The **pectineal surface** is the triangular area between the pectineal line and the obturator crest; the pectineus muscle arises from it; the femoral artery crosses its lateral end, but is separated from the bone by a muscle called psoas major. The **pelvic surface** is continuous with the pelvic surface of the body. The **obturator surface** forms the floor of a broad, oblique groove in the anterior boundary of the obturator foramen; through that groove the obturator vessels and nerve pass out of the pelvis into the thigh.

The **acetabulum** is the large, cup-shaped cavity on the lateral side of the hip bone [*acetabulum* = a vinegar cup]. It looks not only in a lateral direction, but also forwards and downwards. It articulates with the head of the femur to form the *hip joint*. The lower part of its wall is deficient, and the gap is called the **acetabular notch**; a fibrous band, called the *transverse ligament*, bridges across the notch and completes the rim. The floor of the acetabulum above the notch shows a large, rough depression called the **acetabular fossa**. The rest of the inside of the cup is smooth and articular. The pubis forms about one-fifth of the acetabulum, the ischium rather more than two-fifths, and the ilium rather less than two-fifths.

The **obturator foramen** is bounded by the ischium and the pubis and their rami. It is almost completely closed up with a thin, strong membrane called the *obturator membrane*, from which the foramen gets its name [*obturare* = to close up]. The outer and inner surfaces of the membrane are directed, respectively, towards the thigh and towards the cavity of the pelvis.

Ossification.—From *three* **primary** centres and several secondary centres.

| **Primary Centre** appears for | **Ilium,** above greater sciatic notch, early in 3rd month. | **Ischium,** below acetabulum, in 4th month. | **Pubis,** in superior ramus, in 5th month. |

At birth the larger part of each bone is ossified, including a portion of its acetabular end, but a great deal is still gristle, viz. : upper part of ilium, greater part of acetabulum, lower end of ischium, medial part of body of pubis, and the conjoined rami. By the tenth year most of the cartilage is ossified, that between the three bones at the *acetabulum* being reduced to a triradiate strip ; and the *conjoined rami* are completely ossified and fused together. Secondary centres appear in the acetabulum at twelve, and in the other parts at puberty.

Secondary Centre.	**Appears at**	**Epiphysis unites at**	**Relation of Epiphyseal Line to Capsule of Neighbouring Joint.**
Two or three for triradiate strip	12th year	17	Inside laterally, outside medially.
One or two for iliac crest including superior spines	Puberty	20-25	None.
For anterior inferior spine	Puberty	20-25	Outside.
For ischial tuberosity	Puberty	20-25	None.
For symphyseal part of pubis	Puberty	20-25	No joint cavity.

Occasionally small epiphyses, which appear and fuse at the same times as those in the list above, are present for the ends of the pubic crest, and the ischial spine. The portions ossified from the centres in the acetabulum fuse with the nearest bone ; *os acetabuli* is the name given to the part that joins the pubic bone.

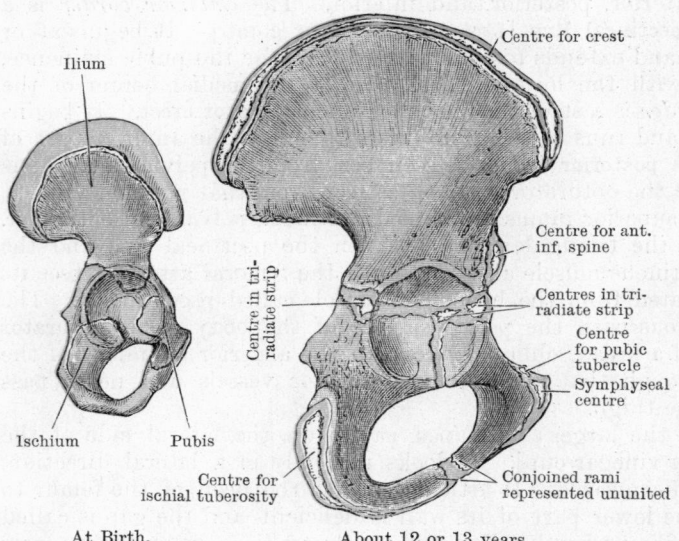

Ilium

Centre for crest

Centre in triradiate strip

Ischium   Pubis

Centre for ischial tuberosity

Centre for ant. inf. spine

Centres in triradiate strip

Centre for pubic tubercle

Symphyseal centre

Conjoined rami represented ununited

At Birth.   About 12 or 13 years.

FIG. 230.—OSSIFICATION OF THE HIP BONE.

Structure and Variations.—The hip bone is composed of spongy substance enclosed in compact substance. Spongy bone is, however, absent in the centre of the iliac fossa and the floor of the acetabulum, and those parts are therefore translucent ; occasionally the compact bone also is absent in one or other of those two situations. The compact bone is thick on the gluteal side of the ilium, and more so at and near the medial border. The whole bone is thickest and strongest above the acetabulum, between it and the auricular surface, for through that part the weight of the trunk is transmitted from the sacrum to the femur. The ischium is wider at its upper end than at its lower end, and is widest at the ischial spine. The *nutrient foramina* are scattered here and there.

The obturator foramen varies in outline from oval to triangular ; and it is relatively wider in women than in men. The **anterior obturator tubercle** is a small spur occasionally present on the posterior border of the superior ramus of the pubis. The **posterior obturator tubercle,** more often present, is a little, rough protuberance on the free edge of the acetabular fossa at or near the junction of the pubis and the ischium. The thickened upper part of the obturator membrane stretches across between the tubercles and converts the groove for the obturator nerve and vessels into a tunnel called the *obturator canal* ; in rare cases it is ossified. The *os acetabuli* may

remain a separate bone; the acetabular notch may be absent. A separate articular facet may
be present above the auricular surface, for articulation with a small facet on the back of the
sacrum lateral to the first sacral foramen (Derry). The ischial and pubic rami sometimes fail to
unite.

Attachments.—*See* p. 270.

Pelvis

The **pelvis** is the lower subdivision of the abdomen [*pelvis* = a basin], and the
large crate that constitutes its bony framework is also called the pelvis. The
bony pelvis is made up of the two hip bones and the portions of the backbone or
vertebral column which are called the sacrum and the coccyx. The two hip bones
form the sides of the pelvis and its ventral wall, the right and left pubic bones
being joined together by the symphysis at the median plane in front; the
sacrum and coccyx form its dorsal wall, the sacrum being wedged in between
the hip bones and held in place by strong ligaments, while the coccyx lies
below the sacrum between the hip bones and also is attached to them by
ligaments.

The pelvis provides a large surface for the attachment of muscles, especially
those which move the lower limb; it contains and protects the urinary bladder,
some of the organs of reproduction, and part of the alimentary canal; but
the chief use of the bony pelvis is to serve as a firm, unyielding base for the
trunk resting on the thighs. The curved or ring-like construction of the pelvic

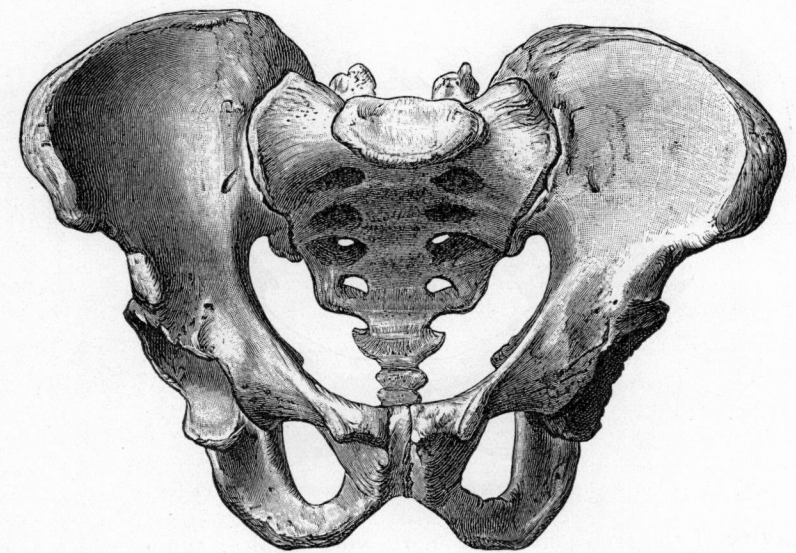

Fig. 231.—The Male Pelvis seen from the Front.

framework prevents its collapse under the weight of the body, which is borne
at only two points on the framework—where the thigh bones articulate with
the pelvis.

The pelvis does not occupy the position in the body which is suggested by its
stance when it is set on a table. Its upper part is tilted forwards, so that when
the body is in the erect posture the pubic tubercles and the anterior superior iliac
spines are all in one vertical plane, and the tip of the coccyx is on a level with the
upper margin of the pubic symphysis; the ventral wall is therefore largely
inferior, and the dorsal wall is largely *superior*.

A wide interval separates the lower part of the hip bone from the coccyx
and the lower part of the sacrum. The interval is crossed by two fibrous bands
named the *sacro-tuberous* and *sacro-spinous ligaments*. They are such important parts of the pelvis that in many prepared skeletons they are preserved.
The **sacro-tuberous ligament** is a long, strong band which stretches from the

sacrum and coccyx to the ischial tuberosity. The **sacro-spinous ligament** is a shorter, flatter band that stretches across the pelvic surface of the sacro-tuberous ligament from the sacrum and coccyx to the ischial spine. Those two ligaments convert the sciatic notches of the hip bone into foramina, named the **greater sciatic foramen** and the **lesser sciatic foramen**, through which muscles, nerves, and vessels pass between the pelvis and the gluteal region. The dissector of the lower limb encounters both the ligaments and the foramina during the dissection of the gluteal region. (See Figs. 312, 313, pp. 355, 357, in the chapter on Joints.)

The **pubic arch** is the arch formed by the conjoined rami of ischium and pubis of the two sides. The apex of the arch is the posterior end of the pubic symphysis. The archway is to a large extent filled in by a fibrous sheet, called the *perineal membrane,* which is comparable to the obturator membrane.

The bony pelvis as a whole is divisible into two parts—false and true. The **false pelvis** [p. major] is the upper part; it is the skeleton of the lower part of the abdomen proper, and bounds the iliac fossæ.

The **true pelvis** [p. minor] is more important. When reference is made to " the pelvis " in the description of muscles, viscera, etc., it is usually the true pelvis only that is meant. The bones that enclose it are the sacrum and coccyx and the lower half of the hip bone—the pubis, the ischium, and the lower part of the sacro-pelvic surface of the ilium.

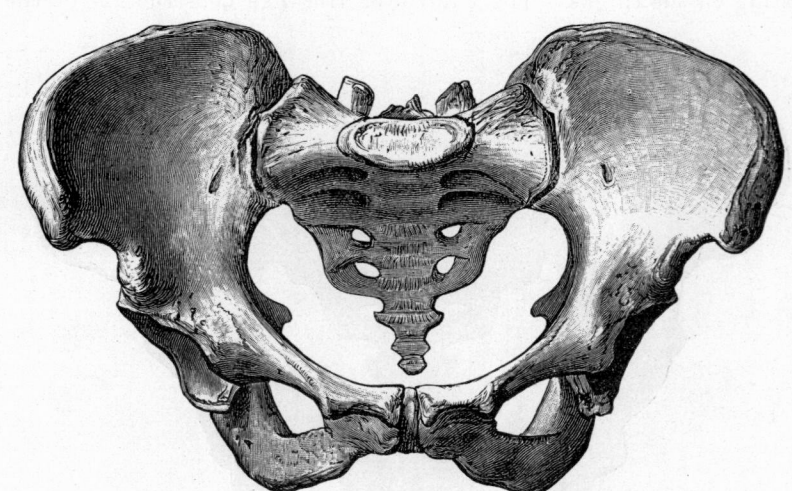

FIG. 232.—THE FEMALE PELVIS SEEN FROM THE FRONT.

The **cavity** of the true pelvis is a short, wide canal or tunnel which is curved in general conformity with the curve of the sacrum and coccyx; in length it measures five or six inches along the sacrum and coccyx, but only one and a half or two inches along the pubic symphysis. The cavity is continuous with that of the abdomen proper at the **inlet** of the pelvis. The inlet looks forwards and slightly upwards, and its boundary is the **brim** of the pelvis. The brim is formed by a pair of curved bony edges, called the **arcuate lines**, each divided into sacral, iliac, and pubic parts. The *sacral part* of the arcuate line is the sacral promontory and the lower margin of the ala; the *iliac part* is the lower half of the medial border of the ilium; the *pubic part* is the pectineal line and the pubic crest and symphysis. The **outlet** is *bounded* by: (1) the coccyx in the median plane *behind*; (2) the pubic symphysis in the median plane *in front*; and, *on each side* from behind forwards, (3) the sacro-tuberous ligament, (4) the lower end of the ischium, and (5) the side of the pubic arch. These are also the boundaries of the region called the *perineum,* which is shut off from the cavity of the pelvis by (1) a sheet of muscle, called the sphincter urethræ, that lies in the pubic archway on the upper surface of the perineal membrane; and (2) a pair of thin, curved sheets of muscles called the levatores ani, which are placed farther back—between the ischia.

Planes and Axes of the Pelvis.—The **plane of the inlet** forms an angle of about 60° with the horizontal. The **plane of the outlet** forms an angle of only 10° to 15° with the horizontal, because the symphysis is much shorter than the sacrum and coccyx. The **planes of the cavity** are a plane that passes through the middle of the third sacral vertebra and the middle of the pubic symphysis, and any number of planes set between that plane and those of the inlet and outlet. The **axis of the inlet** is a line drawn at right angles to the centre of its plane; the line, if continued, would pass through the umbilicus and through the tip of the coccyx. The **axis of the outlet** is a line drawn at right angles to the centre of its plane; if continued upwards the line would strike the sacral promontory. The **axis of the pelvis** is a line drawn through the centres of all the planes; it is therefore parallel to the curve of the sacrum and coccyx.

Diameters of the Pelvis.—The **intercristal diameter** is the distance between the outer lips of the two iliac crests where they are farthest apart. The **interspinous diameter** is the distance between the two anterior superior iliac spines. The **external antero-posterior diameter** is the distance between the first sacral spine and the anterior (upper) margin of the pubic symphysis. Those three diameters are slightly longer in a man than in a woman.

The **diameters of the true pelvis** are of more importance.

Diameters of Inlet.—*Antero-posterior* or conjugate: from the middle of the sacral promontory to the anterior (upper) margin of the symphysis. *Transverse*: across the aperture where it is widest. *Oblique*: from one sacro-iliac joint to the ilio-pubic eminence of the other side.

Diameters of Cavity.—*Antero-posterior*: from the centre of the pelvic surface of the middle piece of the sacrum to the middle of the pelvic surface of the pubic symphysis. *Transverse*: across the cavity where it is widest. *Oblique*: from the posterior end of one sacro-iliac joint to the centre of the obturator membrane of the other side.

Diameters of Outlet.—*Antero-posterior*: from the tip of the coccyx to the posterior (lower) margin of the pubic symphysis; it varies in the same pelvis, especially in the female, owing to the mobility of the coccyx. *Transverse*: across the aperture where it is widest. *Oblique*: from the point where the sacro-tuberous and sacro-spinous ligaments cross each other to the junction of the pubic and ischial rami of the other side.

All the diameters of the true pelvis are longer in a woman than in a man. Measurements vary in individuals of the same sex. In the following table the smaller figures are average measurements in inches and correspond to those given in Quain's *Anatomy*, 10th edition; the large figures are millimetres—not the exact equivalents of the inches, but the nearest to them in round numbers (25 mm. is very slightly less than 1 inch).

	FEMALE.			MALE.		
Intercristal . . .	11 ; 275			11¼ ; 280+		
Interspinous . . .	9¼ ; 230+			9½ ; 235+		
External antero-posterior . . .	7 ; 175			7¼ ; 180+		
True Pelvis.	Inlet.	Cavity.	Outlet.	Inlet.	Cavity.	Outlet.
Antero-posterior . .	4½ 110+	5 125	4-5 100-125	4 100	4¼ 105+	3¼ 80+
Transverse . . .	5¼ 130+	5 125	4¾ 120-	5 125	4¾ 120-	3½ 85+
Oblique . . .	5 125	5¼ 130+	4½ 110+	4¾ 120-	4½ 110+	4 100

Sexual Differences.—The pelvis of a woman differs from that of a man in many particulars, because the female pelvis is modified for the function of child-bearing. Distinctive sex characters are present in the fœtal pelvis—appearing as early as the third or fourth month of intra-uterine life. They are less marked in childhood; they become fully developed after puberty. The essential differences between male and female pelves are in the true pelvis. In the female it is absolutely wider in all the diameters; this is especially marked in those of the outlet, and the cavity is therefore less funnel-shaped. But the cavity is shorter. Nearly all the differences in detail are due to the fact that the cavity of the **true pelvis** in the **female** is *roomier, less funnel-shaped,* and *shorter*. Most of the differences cannot be appreciated by a beginner unless he has at hand both a male and a female pelvis which he can compare; but the following single difference will enable him to decide whether the specimen of pelvis or of hip bone which he is using for study is male or female : the **pubic arch** in the **female** is *wide* and its *apex is rounded*; it is usually wide enough to accommodate a right angle; in the male it is less than a right angle, and the apex is rather pointed.

The differences in detail are very numerous. The chief of them are that **in the female**— The bones are lighter and thinner, and muscular markings are less evident. The *ilium* is less everted and the *iliac fossa* is shallower. The **inlet** is larger, and is kidney-shaped rather than heart-shaped; its *plane* forms a wider angle with the horizontal, for the tilt of the pelvis is greater (the anterior superior iliac spines being even farther forward than the pubic tubercles); the *sacral promontory* projects less, and the *pubic tubercles* are wider apart. The **cavity** is less funnel-shaped, is shorter, but is much roomier. The *sacrum* is shorter and wider, and its curve is less uniform—being flatter above and more sharply turned forwards below. The **outlet** is much larger. The *pubic arch* is wider and more rounded. The *coccyx* is more movable. The *sciatic notches* are wider and shallower; the *ischial spine* is less inturned. The *obturator foramen* is smaller and may be triangular in outline rather than oval. The *acetabula* are farther apart and are smaller, especially relatively, for the head of the femur is smaller in a woman while the hip bone is larger. A pre-auricular sulcus is present immediately in front of the convex margin of the auricular surface of the ilium.

Growth of the Pelvis.—At birth, in both sexes, the pelvis is relatively small; the ilium is relatively narrow and is more upright than in the adult; the iliac fossa is shallower and looks more forwards. The pubic arch is more acute, the ischia are closer together, and the cavity is consequently more funnel-shaped. The sacrum is narrow, more upright and less curved, and its promontory projects less. The lower limbs also are relatively small—being only about a quarter of the length of the body. After birth the lower limbs grow much more rapidly than the rest of the body, especially after the first year when the child begins to learn to walk. The whole pelvis keeps pace with the lower limbs; it gives origin to a great number of the muscles that move the limbs, and grows concurrently with them to provide them with adequate attachments. At birth the true pelvis is not big enough to hold the pelvic organs; the greater part of the urinary bladder and, in the female, the uterus and ovaries are in the abdomen proper. By the sixth year the pelvis has grown large enough to contain the greater part of them, but the pelvic organs are not wholly pelvic in position till puberty. The rate and manner of growth are similar in boys and girls till puberty, when the growth is modified to produce the distinctive sex characters of the adult pelvis.

Besides mere relative increase of size, there are other changes in the pelvis when the child, learning to walk, straightens out the lower limbs and adopts the erect attitude. The principal changes are : (1) The upper part of the pelvis is tilted forwards so that the sacro-vertebral angle becomes less obtuse. (2) The basal part of the sacrum, now bearing the weight of the trunk obliquely, sinks more deeply between the two hip bones, and that further accentuates the sacro-vertebral angle. (3) The sacrum becomes more curved also, for, while the weight of the trunk bends the basal part downwards, the apical part is held down and prevented from tilting up by the sacro-tuberous and sacro-spinous ligaments. (4) At the same time the hip bone, where it bounds the true pelvis, becomes curved outwards, and thus the true pelvis is widened; for those parts of the two hip bones, at that time, resemble the limbs of the letter V, the apex being at the symphysis; the sacrum lies between the upper ends of the limbs of the V, and the weight of the trunk is transmitted to them through the sacrum; they are fastened to the sacrum at their upper ends and to each other at the apex, *i.e.* at the symphysis, and therefore, under the weight of the trunk, have to bend outwards in the middle. (5) The acetabulum (which is relatively shallower at birth than it is at the sixth month of intra-uterine life) becomes deeper to make the hip joint more stable, especially after the third year, when the child begins to run about more actively and to jump. (6) The part of the ilium between the acetabulum and the auricular surface, which transmits the weight of the trunk from sacrum to femur, grows stronger, and in consequence of its growth the iliac part of the arcuate line becomes better defined.

Attachments.—(A) **Of Structures encountered in the Dissection of the Lower Limb.**— The lateral end of the inguinal ligament is attached to the **anterior superior iliac spine**. The sartorius arises from that spine and from part of the notch below; the tensor fasciæ latæ from the spine and the adjoining two inches of the outer lip of the **iliac crest**. The lateral part of the fascia lata is attached to the whole length of the outer lip of the crest, its ilio-tibial tract being attached to the **tubercle of the crest**; the ilio-femoral ligament to the lower part of the **anterior inferior spine**; the straight head of the rectus femoris from its upper part; the reflected head from the rough depression on the **gluteal surface** immediately above the acetabulum; the gluteus minimus from the area between the *inferior* and *middle gluteal lines*; the gluteus medius from the area between the *middle* and *posterior gluteal lines*; the gluteus maximus from the upper, rough part of the area behind the *posterior line* and from the *back* of the **sacrum** and *sacro-tuberous ligament*; the iliacus from the floor of the **iliac fossa**; the piriformis from the *pelvic surface* of the middle three pieces of the **sacrum**, and from the upper margin of the **greater sciatic notch** and the sacro-tuberous ligament as the muscle emerges from the pelvis through the *greater sciatic foramen*; the obturator internus from the side wall of the cavity of the pelvis, viz. the inner surface of the **obturator membrane**, the bone around the obturator foramen, especially the wide, flat area between the foramen and the greater sciatic notch, and the fibres converge on the tendon, which leaves the pelvis through the *lesser sciatic foramen*; the superior gemellus from the **ischial spine** where it forms the upper boundary of the lesser sciatic foramen; the inferior gemellus from the **ischial tuberosity** where it forms the lower boundary.

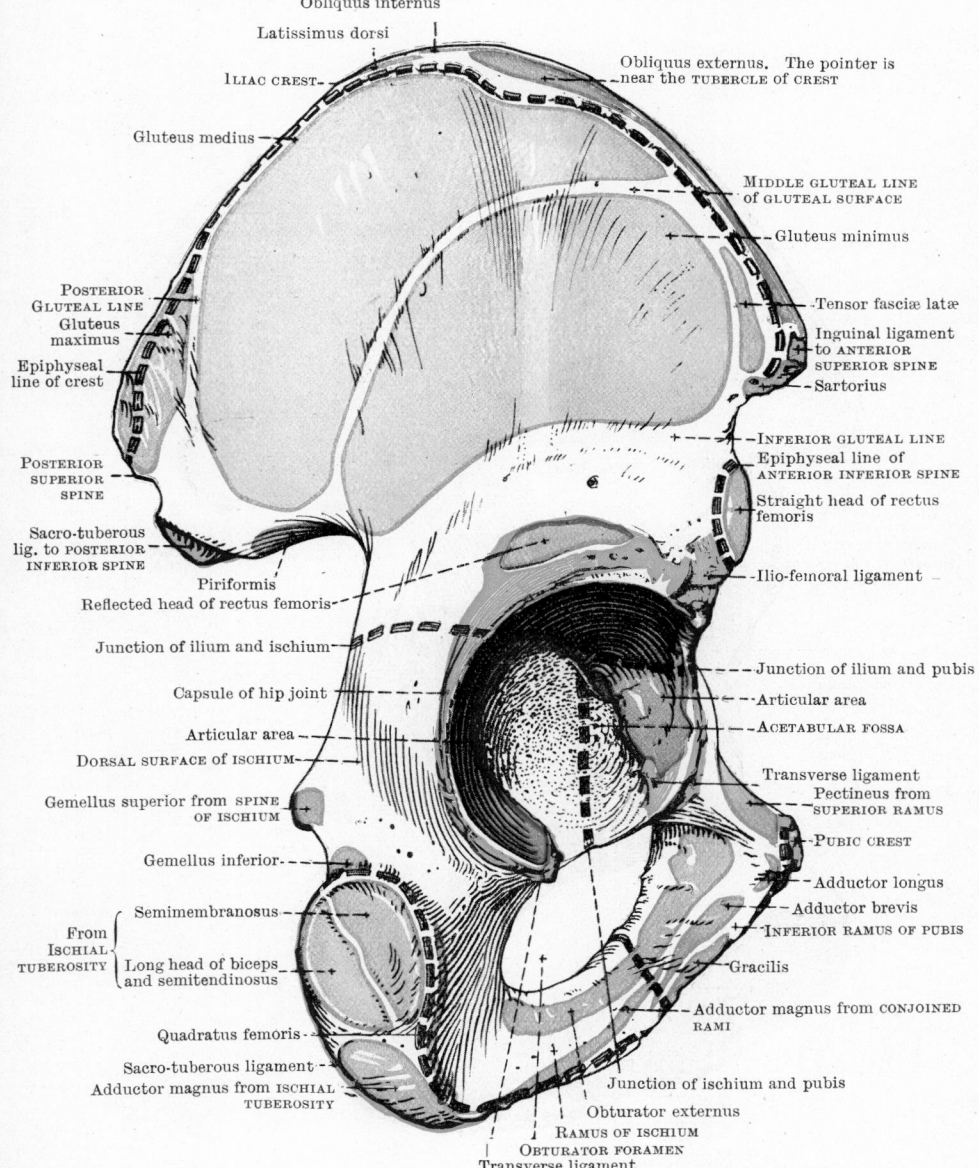

FIG. 233.—LATERAL ASPECT OF RIGHT HIP BONE.

The sacro-spinous ligament stretches from the tip of the *ischial spine* to the side of the last piece of the *sacrum* and first piece of the *coccyx*. The sacro-tuberous ligament covers the dorsal surface of the medial and larger part of the sacro-spinous ligament; its upper end widens out to be attached to the side of the *coccyx* and *sacrum* and to the **posterior superior** and **posterior inferior iliac spine**; its lower end widens out to be attached to the medial margin and lower medial area of the **ischial tuberosity**, and sends a prolongation, called its *falciform process*, forwards along the inner surface of the *ischial ramus*. The quadratus femoris arises from the *lateral margin* of the **ischial tuberosity**. The surface of the tuberosity is divided by a transverse line into an upper and a lower part, and each of those is divided into a lateral and a medial part. The tendon of the semimembranosus arises from the *upper lateral* area; the tendons of the semitendinosus and the long head of the biceps conjointly from the *upper medial* area ; the adductor magnus muscle from the *lower lateral* area and from the lower part of the outer surface of the *conjoined rami*, the sacro-tuberous ligament being attached to the *lower medial* area.

The medial end of the inguinal ligament is attached to the **pubic tubercle**, and its pectineal part [lig. lacunare] to the medial inch of the **pectineal line**. The pectineus muscle arises from the *pectineal line* and *pectineal surface* of the **pubis**; the tendon of the adductor longus from

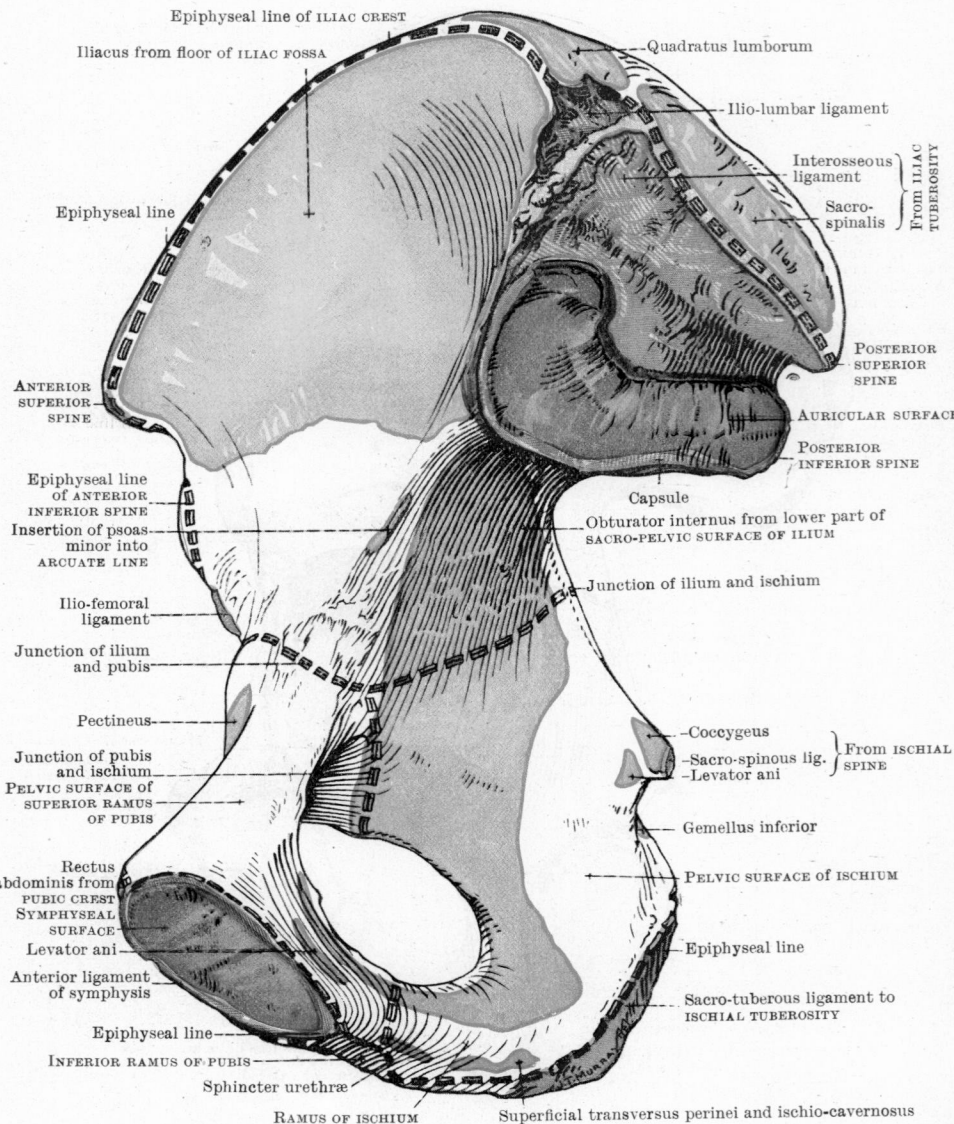

Epiphyseal line of ILIAC CREST

Iliacus from floor of ILIAC FOSSA

Quadratus lumborum

Ilio-lumbar ligament

Epiphyseal line

Interosseous ligament

Sacro-spinalis

}From ILIAC TUBEROSITY

ANTERIOR SUPERIOR SPINE

Posterior SUPERIOR SPINE

AURICULAR SURFACE

POSTERIOR INFERIOR SPINE

Epiphyseal line of ANTERIOR INFERIOR SPINE

Capsule

Obturator internus from lower part of SACRO-PELVIC SURFACE OF ILIUM

Insertion of psoas minor into ARCUATE LINE

Junction of ilium and ischium

Ilio-femoral ligament

Junction of ilium and pubis

Pectineus

Coccygeus

Sacro-spinous lig.

Levator ani

}From ISCHIAL SPINE

Junction of pubis and ischium

PELVIC SURFACE of SUPERIOR RAMUS OF PUBIS

Gemellus inferior

PELVIC SURFACE OF ISCHIUM

Rectus abdominis from PUBIC CREST

SYMPHYSEAL SURFACE

Levator ani

Epiphyseal line

Anterior ligament of symphysis

Sacro-tuberous ligament to ISCHIAL TUBEROSITY

Epiphyseal line

INFERIOR RAMUS OF PUBIS

Sphincter urethræ

RAMUS OF ISCHIUM

Superficial transversus perinei and ischio-cavernosus

FIG. 234.—MEDIAL ASPECT OF RIGHT HIP BONE.

the *femoral surface* of the body of the pubis, in the angle between the crest and the symphysis; the gracilis muscle from the margin of the *symphysis* and of the **inferior ramus**; the adductor brevis muscle from a broad strip lateral to the gracilis and below the adductor longus; the obturator externus muscle from the area below and in front of the obturator foramen and from the adjoining half of the **obturator membrane**, and as it winds backwards below the neck of the femur it lies in the wide groove below the acetabulum.

The fascia lata has a continuous attachment to the inguinal ligament, the lower lip of the pubic crest, the margin of the pubic symphysis, the lower margin of the conjoined rami, the medial margin of the ischial tuberosity, the medial margin of the sacro-tuberous ligament, the back of the sacrum and coccyx, and the whole length of the outer lip of the iliac crest.

The transverse ligament bridges across the *acetabular notch* and completes the rim of the

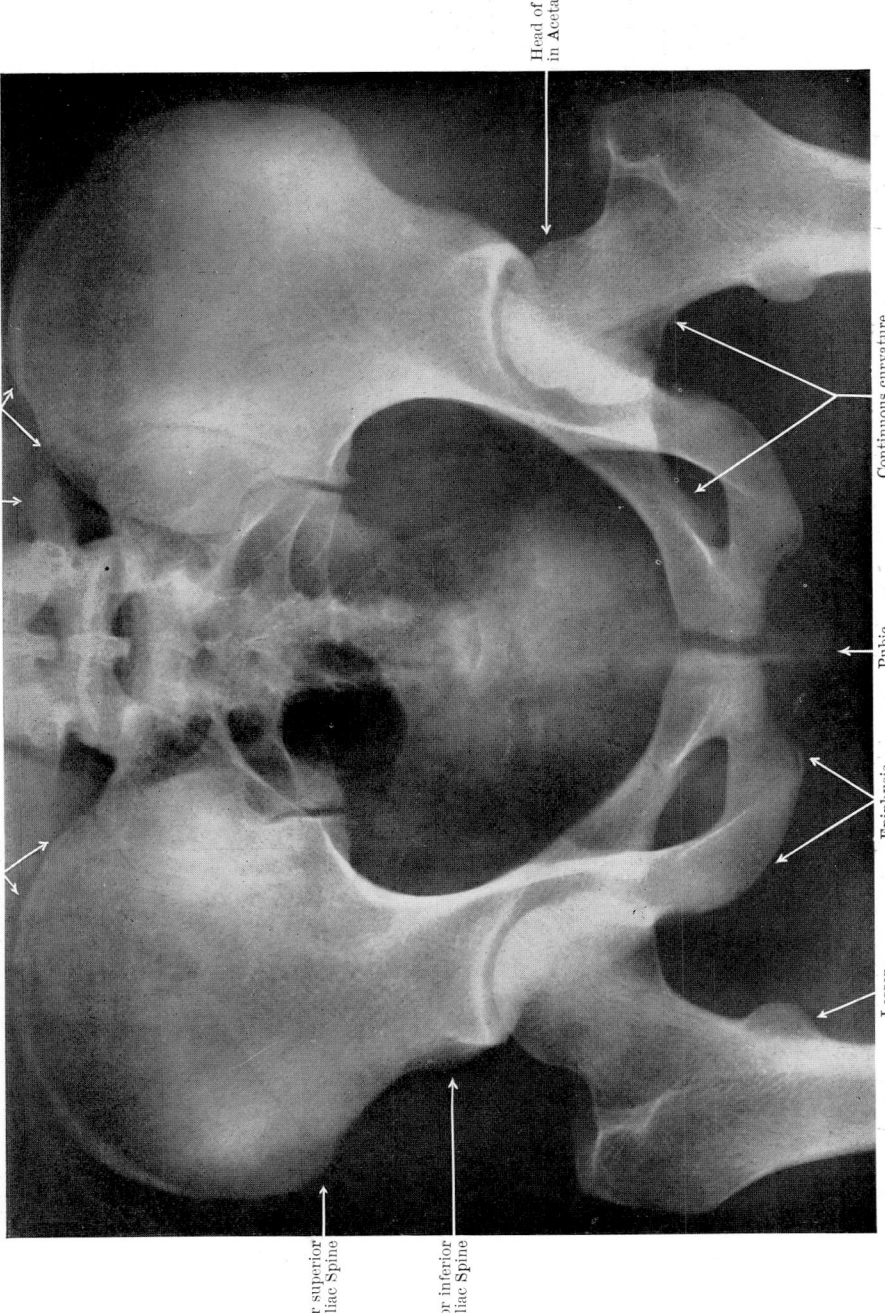

Head of Femur
in Acetabulum

Continuous curvature
of Superior Pubic Ramus
and Neck of Femur
(Shenton's line)

Pubic
Arch
and
Symphysis

Epiphysis
of Ischial
Tuberosity
and Ramus

Lesser
Trochanter

Epiphysis of Iliac Crest,

transverse process

Iliac Crest

Anterior superior
Iliac Spine

Anterior inferior
Iliac Spine

PLATE XIII.—RADIOGRAPH OF LIVING FEMALE PELVIS (GIRL AGED 17).
(Dr. J. Duncan White.)

Compare with Fig. 232, p. 268, and with Plate XII. For the Sexual Differences in the Pelvis see p. 269. Note
the presence of uniting epiphyses of the Iliac Crests and the Ischial Tuberosities (cf. Fig. 230, p. 266).

PLATE XIV

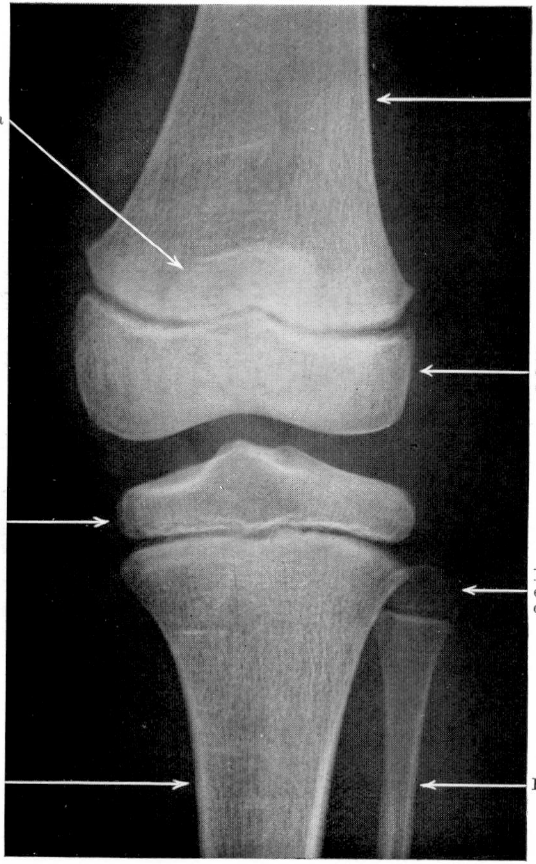

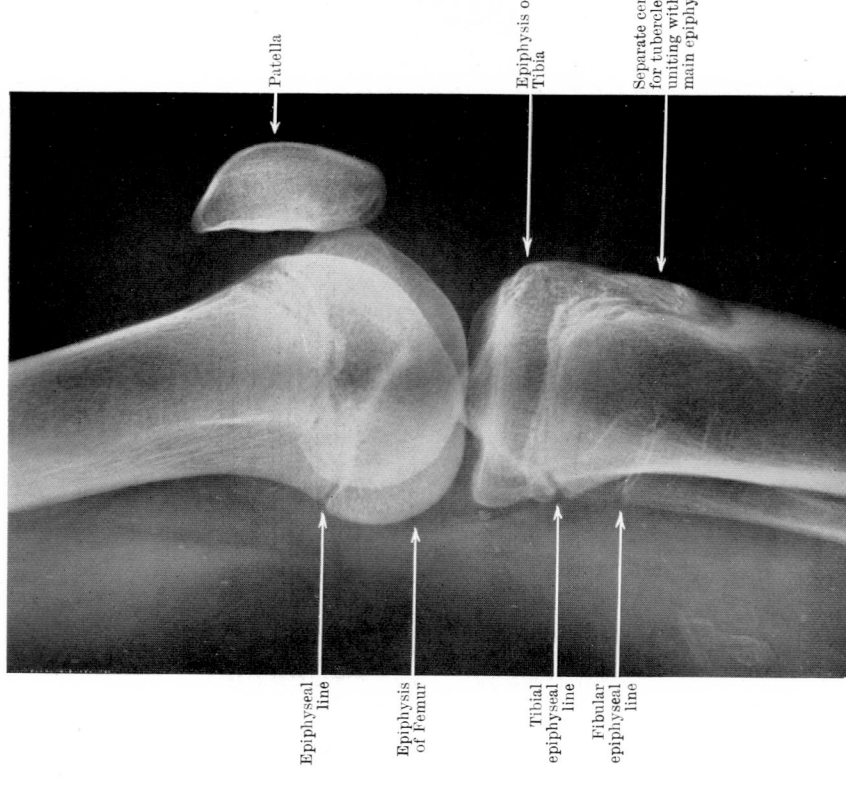

Patella

Epiphysis of
Tibia

Separate centre
for tubercle
uniting with
main epiphysis

Epiphyseal
line

Epiphysis
of Femur

Tibial
epiphyseal
line

Fibular
epiphyseal
line

FIG. 2.—OBLIQUE LATERAL RADIOGRAPH OF SLIGHTLY FLEXED KNEE
OF GIRL AGED 12. (Dr. J. Duncan White.)

Note the apparent doubling of the femoral epiphyseal line, and the extension of the tibial

Femur

Distal
epiphysis
of Femur

Proximal
epiphysis
of Fibula

Fibula

Patella

Proximal
epiphysis
of Tibia

Tibia

FIG. 1.—ANTERO-POSTERIOR RADIOGRAPH OF KNEE OF GIRL
AGED 7. (Dr. J. Duncan White.)

Note the form of the Epiphyses, and compare with Plate XXV, Fig. 2.

acetabulum. The ligament of the head of the femur [lig. teres femoris] spreads out to be attached to the transverse ligament and the margins of the **acetabular notch** and **fossa**. A fibro-cartilaginous ring, called the labrum acetabulare, is attached to the *rim* and serves to deepen the cavity of the acetabulum and narrow its mouth. The capsular ligament of the hip joint is attached to the labrum below and in front, to the bony rim above and behind, and to the rough strip above the acetabulum. The thickened parts of the capsule are attached as follows: the ilio-femoral ligament to the lower part of the *anterior inferior iliac spine*; the pubo-femoral ligament to the lateral end of the *obturator crest*; the ischio-femoral ligament to the *ischium* below the acetabulum.

(B) **Of Structures encountered in the Dissection of other Parts.**—The iliacus arises from the upper and larger part of the floor of the **iliac fossa**. The fascia iliaca and part of the transversalis fascia are continuous with each other at the *inner lip* of the **iliac crest** above the iliac fossa and are loosely attached to that part of the lip. Part of the transversus abdominis arises from the anterior half of the inner lip; part of the quadratus lumborum from the inner lip immediately behind the transversus, above the posterior part of the iliac fossa; a slip of the latissimus dorsi from the corresponding part of the *outer lip*. Part of the external oblique is inserted into the anterior half of the outer lip, and part of the internal oblique arises from the anterior half of the *intermediate area*. The ilio-lumbar ligament is attached to the upper end of the **medial border** of the ilium; the anterior ligament of the sacro-iliac joint to the convex margin of the **auricular surface**; the interosseous and short posterior sacro-iliac ligaments to the lower half of the **iliac tuberosity**; the lower part of the sacro-spinalis arises from the upper half, and from the back of the *sacrum*. The long posterior sacro-iliac ligament stretches from the **posterior superior iliac spine** to the side of the back of the sacrum half-way down; the sacro-tuberous ligament stretches from both *posterior spines* and from the side of the sacrum and coccyx to the lower part of the **ischial tuberosity** and the *ischial ramus*. The sacro-spinous ligament stretches from the tip of the **ischial spine**, across the pelvic surface of the sacro-tuberous ligament, to the side of the last piece of the sacrum and the first piece of the coccyx; the coccygeus muscle lies on the front of the sacro-spinous ligament and has the same attachments—the ligament being merely the degenerated dorsal fibres of the muscle. The piriformis muscle arises from the *pelvic surface* of the second, third, and fourth pieces of the **sacrum**, from the upper margin of the *greater sciatic notch*, and from the sacro-tuberous ligament; the obturator internus from the side wall of the pelvic cavity; the posterior fibres of the levator ani from the *ischial spine*, its anterior fibres from the *pelvic surface* of the **body of the pubis** below its middle, and the rest of the muscle from the fascia that covers the obturator internus. The pubo-prostatic ligaments are attached to the pubis above the levator ani.

The fibro-cartilage of the pubic symphysis is attached to the **symphyseal surface**; the superior, anterior, posterior, and inferior pubic ligaments to the *margins* of that surface, and the inferior ligament curves backwards on to the inferior pubic ramus.

Part of the fascia transversalis is attached to the upper lip of the **pubic crest** and to the medial half of the **pectineal line**. The rectus abdominis arises from the crest below the fascia and from the anterior pubic ligament; the pyramidalis from the crest below the rectus. The conjoint tendon [falx aponeurotica inguinalis] is attached to the anterior ligament of the *symphysis* below the rectus, to the *crest* below the pyramidalis, and to the *pectineal line* below the fascia transversalis; the lower medial part of the external oblique aponeurosis to the lower lip of the pubic crest and to the anterior ligament of the pubis, below the conjoint tendon.

The inguinal ligament stretches from the anterior superior iliac spine to the **pubic tubercle** and, by means of its pectineal part [lig. lacunare], to the medial inch of the *pectineal line*, below the conjoint tendon. One end of the loops of the cremaster muscle is attached to the pubic tubercle behind the inguinal ligament. The tendon of the psoas minor is inserted partly into the **arcuate line** and **ilio-pubic eminence**.

The membranous layer of the superficial fascia of the perineum is attached to the lower margin of the **ischial ramus**. The crus penis or crus clitoridis is attached to the lower half of the *inner surface* of the **conjoined rami**, the lower half usually being grooved lengthwise for the lodgment of the crus. The ischio-cavernosus and superficial transversus perinei arise from the posterior end of the groove. The deep transversus and sphincter urethrae are attached to the ridge between the upper and lower halves of the surface. The same ridge gives attachment to fibrous structures:—(1) the perineal membrane immediately below these muscles; (2) the falciform process of the sacro-tuberous ligament and the prolongation of the inferior pubic ligament immediately above the muscles. Fibres of the obturator internus arise from the upper half of the surface, *i.e.* the strip between the ridge and the obturator foramen, and the fascia that covers that muscle blends with the falciform process.

Femur

The **femur** or thigh-bone is the longest and strongest and heaviest bone in the skeleton, and is between a third and a fourth of the length of the body. It has a **shaft** and **two ends**. It is so thickly covered with muscles that, in the living body, it can be palpated only at and near the ends. The beginner should at once proceed to distinguish the upper end from the lower end, the front of the bone from the back, and the medial side from the lateral side. The larger end of the bone is the **lower end**, and it is partially divided into two, the wide notch between the two parts being on the **posterior** aspect; the globular head at the upper end is on the **medial** side.

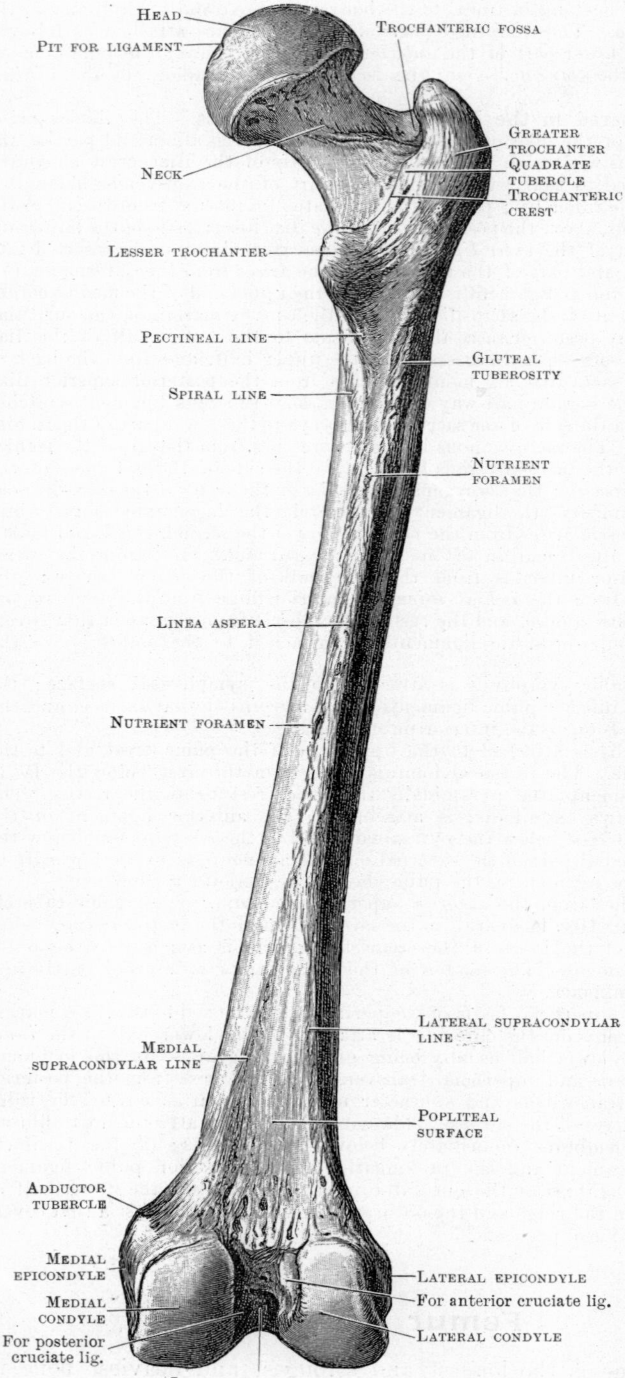

The **upper end** includes the head, the neck, the greater trochanter and the lesser trochanter.

The **head** is smooth and is about two-thirds of a sphere. It fits into the acetabulum to form the *hip joint*. On its medial aspect there is a rough, shallow pit to which the apex of a triangular fibrous band is attached.

The **neck** is the thick bar that connects the head with the shaft in the region of the trochanters. It is nearly two inches long, is thinnest in the middle and widens towards each end, especially the end which joins the shaft, and the lower border is therefore more oblique than the upper. The neck joins the shaft at an angle and is therefore liable to be broken; but a long neck joined to the shaft at an angle enables the femur to be moved freely and extensively, even though the head is deeply and stably socketed in the side of the pelvis.

The **greater trochanter** is the large, square prominence on the lateral side where the neck joins the shaft; its upper part stands up above the level of the adjacent part of the neck; its root is marked off from the shaft by a more or less horizontal ridge. It is the

FIG. 235.—THE RIGHT FEMUR SEEN FROM BEHIND.

bone felt in front of the hollow on the side of the hip, and the body falls on it in a fall sideways; its upper border is at the level of the upper border of the pubic symphysis and the centre of the hip joint. Many of the muscles of the gluteal region are inserted into the greater trochanter [τροχαντήρ (trochantēr) = a runner]. The rough pit on the medial side of the trochanter, where it joins the back of the neck, is called the **trochanteric fossa.**

The **lesser trochanter** is the rounded, conical projection on the postero-medial aspect of the bone where the lower part of the neck joins the shaft.

The ridge connecting the lesser trochanter with the back of the greater trochanter is called the **trochanteric crest.** The low, rounded swelling on or alongside the crest, on the back of the trochanter major, is called the **quadrate tubercle** because part of the quadratus femoris muscle is inserted into it. The **trochanteric line** is the rough, broad line which extends from the upper part of the front of the greater trochanter towards the lesser trochanter, and marks the union of the front of the neck with the front of the shaft; it does not reach the lesser trochanter, but becomes continuous with a faint ridge, called the *spiral line*, which winds to the back of the bone below the lesser trochanter.

The **lower end** of the femur is made up of two large masses called *condyles*, separated posteriorly by a wide, deep interval called the *intercondylar notch.*

Anteriorly the **condyles** are nearly in line with the front of the shaft,

FIG. 236.—THE RIGHT FEMUR SEEN FROM THE FRONT.

but they bulge backwards considerably beyond the shaft. The anterior, lower, and posterior surfaces of each condyle are confluent, smooth, and articular. The *anterior parts* of the two are joined together, forming a wide surface for articulation with the patella. This **patellar surface** is deeply concave from side to side and slightly convex from above downwards; its lateral part is more prominent than the medial, and extends farther up, and the upper margin of the surface is therefore sloping. The tibia articulates with the *lower surfaces* when the knee is extended, and with the *posterior surfaces* when the knee is flexed. The surfaces that form the sides of the intercondylar notch are rough for the attachment of strong fibrous bands, called the cruciate ligaments, which lie inside the knee joint and bind the femur and tibia together.

On the *lateral surface* of the **lateral condyle** there is a prominence, called the *lateral epicondyle*—much nearer the back of the bone than the front. Above the epicondyle there is a pit or impression for the origin of the lateral head of the large muscle, called the gastrocnemius, that forms the superficial part of the fleshy mass of the calf. Below the epicondyle there is a pit for the origin of the tendon of the popliteus muscle; a groove, in which the tendon lies when the knee is acutely flexed, runs upwards and backwards from the pit close alongside the articular margin.

The **medial condyle** stands farther away from the shaft than the lateral condyle does. Its medial surface is rough and convex; its most prominent part is called the *medial epicondyle*. On the uppermost part of the condyle there is a small, sharp prominence, called the **adductor tubercle** because the tendon of the adductor magnus is inserted into it.

The condyles can be felt as large prominences at the sides of the knee; the adductor tubercle can be felt at the uppermost part of the medial condyle, and is often used as a landmark; if the knee is bent to a right angle, the tendon of the

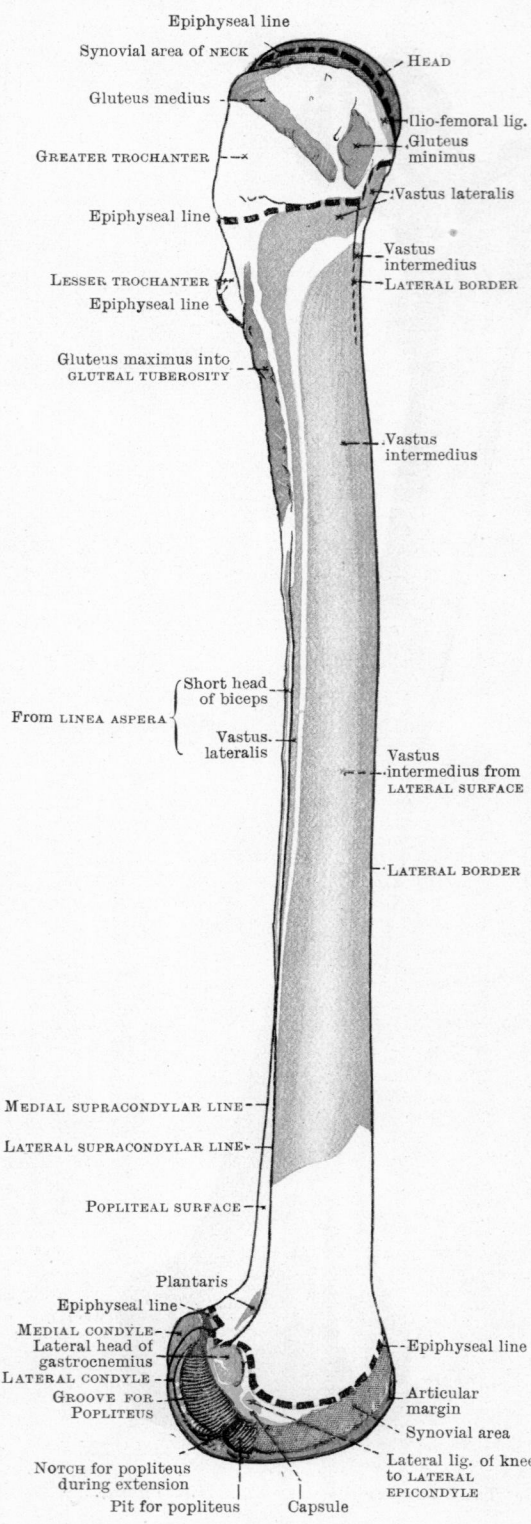

Epiphyseal line
Synovial area of NECK
HEAD
Gluteus medius
Ilio-femoral lig.
Gluteus minimus
GREATER TROCHANTER
Vastus lateralis
Epiphyseal line
Vastus intermedius
LATERAL BORDER
LESSER TROCHANTER
Epiphyseal line
Gluteus maximus into GLUTEAL TUBEROSITY
Vastus intermedius
Short head of biceps
From LINEA ASPERA
Vastus lateralis
Vastus intermedius from LATERAL SURFACE
LATERAL BORDER
MEDIAL SUPRACONDYLAR LINE
LATERAL SUPRACONDYLAR LINE
POPLITEAL SURFACE
Plantaris
Epiphyseal line
MEDIAL CONDYLE
Lateral head of gastrocnemius
LATERAL CONDYLE
GROOVE FOR POPLITEUS
Epiphyseal line
Articular margin
Synovial area
Lateral lig. of knee to LATERAL EPICONDYLE
NOTCH for popliteus during extension
Pit for popliteus   Capsule

FIG. 237.—LATERAL ASPECT OF RIGHT FEMUR.

adductor magnus can usually be felt as it descends to the tubercle (but it is not the only tendon that can be felt at the medial side of the knee.) When the knee is flexed, the patellar surface of the femur can be felt (or, at any rate, its lateral and medial margins), for the patella is drawn off it when the knee is bent; and a portion of the distal surface of each condyle can be felt at the side of the *ligamentum patellae*—which is the thick broad band felt between the patella and the tibia.

The **shaft** is thinnest in its middle third and widens sideways towards each end, especially the lower end.

The **middle third** has three surfaces and three borders. The *surfaces* are anterior, medial, and lateral; the *borders* are posterior, lateral, and medial.

The *lateral* and *medial borders* are blunt and ill-defined, so that the *anterior surface* is not sharply marked off from the *lateral* and *medial surfaces*; but the *posterior border*, which separates the medial surface from the lateral surface, is well-defined and rough, and is called the linea aspera.

The **linea aspera** is the rough ridge on the back of the femur, and it is limited to the middle third of the bone. Its margins are called its *lips*—*lateral* and *medial*; the lateral lip is the sharper and better defined of the two. At the upper and lower ends of the linea aspera the lips diverge from each other and become continuous with ridges, bearing different names, on the upper and lower thirds of the femur.

At the **upper third** the *medial* lip becomes continuous with a narrow ridge, called the **spiral line**, which winds obliquely round the medial side of the femur on to the front of the bone and becomes continuous with the trochanteric line. The *lateral* lip becomes continuous with a long, broad, rough mark, called the **gluteal tuberosity**, which is situated on the back of the upper third of the shaft towards the lateral

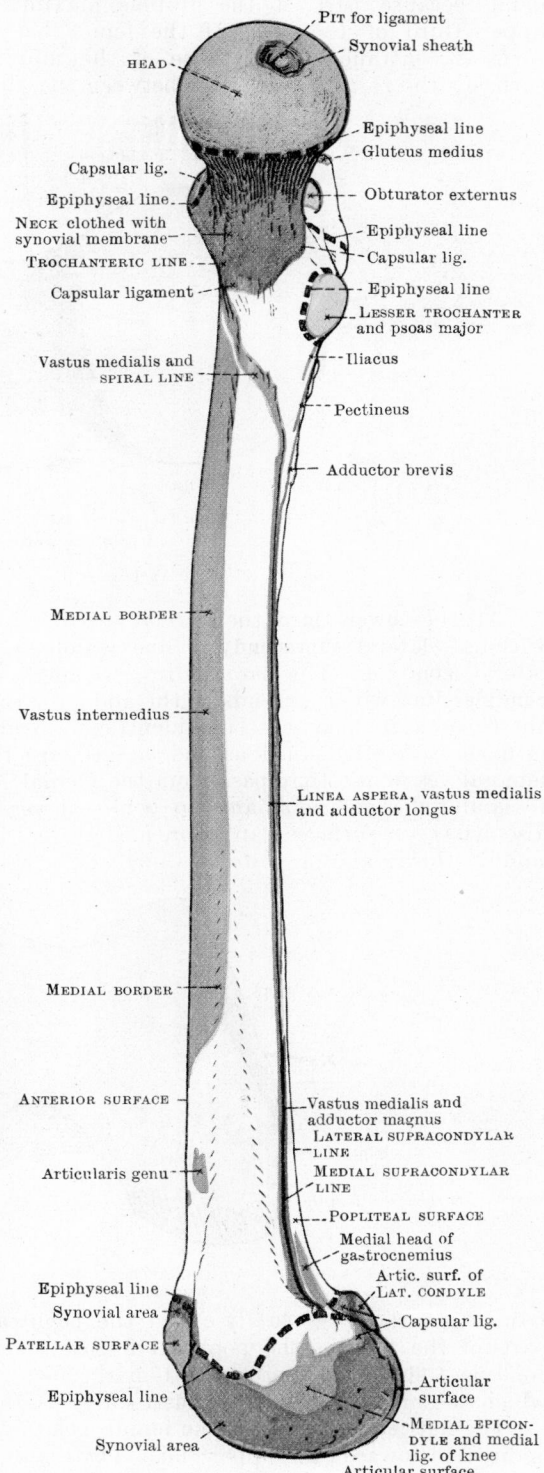

FIG. 238.—MEDIAL ASPECT OF RIGHT FEMUR.

18 a

side, and extends from the linea aspera to the greater trochanter; it receives its name because part of the gluteus maximus muscle is inserted into it. The upper third of the body of the femur has therefore *four* surfaces: the three surfaces continuous with those of the middle third, and an additional, fourth surface—the *posterior surface*—between the gluteal tuberosity and the spiral line.

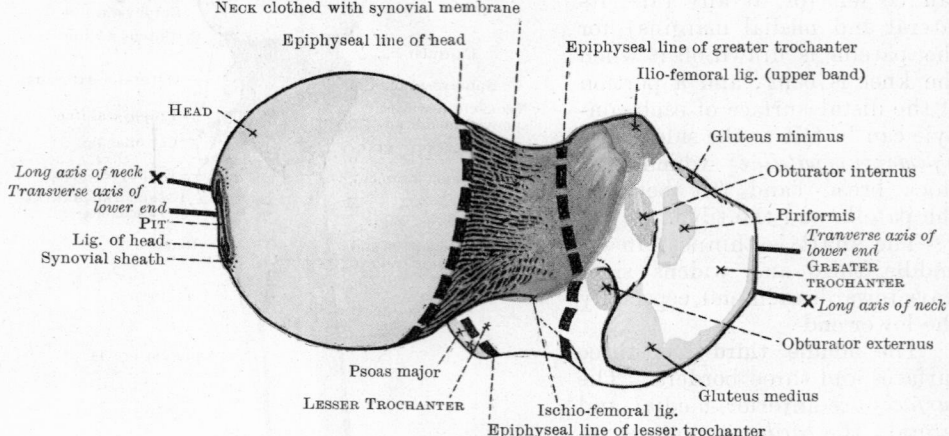

NECK clothed with synovial membrane

Epiphyseal line of head

Epiphyseal line of greater trochanter

Ilio-femoral lig. (upper band)

HEAD

Gluteus minimus

Long axis of neck **X**
Transverse axis of lower end
PIT
Lig. of head
Synovial sheath

Obturator internus

Piriformis

Tranverse axis of lower end
GREATER TROCHANTER

X *Long axis of neck*

Obturator externus

Psoas major

LESSER TROCHANTER

Ischio-femoral lig.

Epiphyseal line of lesser trochanter

Gluteus medius

FIG. 239.—UPPER ASPECT OF UPPER END OF RIGHT FEMUR.

At the **lower third** the *lateral* lip of the linea aspera becomes continuous with the **lateral supracondylar line**, which extends as a well-defined line to the lateral condyle. The *medial* lip becomes continuous with the **medial supracondylar line**, which extends to the adductor tubercle, and may serve as a guide to the tubercle if it has not been identified already. The medial supracondylar line is never so well defined as the lateral, largely because it is worn down by the femoral vessels as they pass from the medial side of the thigh into the popliteal fossa and change their name to popliteal vessels. The lower third of the shaft also has *four* surfaces: anterior, medial, and lateral, continuous with those of the middle third, and ⟨a *posterior surface* between the supracondylar lines. The

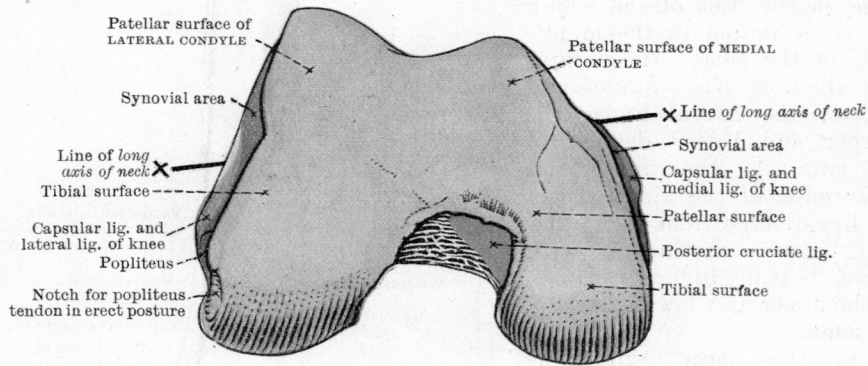

Patellar surface of
LATERAL CONDYLE

Patellar surface of MEDIAL
CONDYLE

Synovial area

X Line *of long axis of neck*

Synovial area

Line *of long axis of neck* **X**
Tibial surface

Capsular lig. and
medial lig. of knee

Patellar surface

Capsular lig. and
lateral lig. of knee
Popliteus

Posterior cruciate lig.

Notch for popliteus
tendon in erect posture

Tibial surface

FIG. 240.—DISTAL ASPECT OF LOWER END OF RIGHT FEMUR.

posterior surface is usually called the **popliteal surface**, because it forms a great part of the floor of the popliteal fossa; on its lower part, above the medial condyle, there is a rough, raised mark, about half an inch wide each way, from which the medial head of the gastrocnemius muscle arises.

The **nutrient foramen** of the femur is situated on or near the linea aspera, and is directed towards the upper end. There may be two nutrient foramina.

The **head** usually looks upwards and slightly forwards as well as medially. It is relatively smaller in women than in men. The pit for the ligament of the head of the femur is situated below and behind the centre of the head; blood-vessels from the ligament enter through it, and the head thus obtains a double blood supply; sometimes the pit is absent, as in the orang.

The articular margin is undulating and is sharper behind than in front.

The **neck** extends laterally, downwards and slightly backwards from the head. Its antero-posterior diameter is less than the vertical. Its posterior surface is concave lengthwise and convex from above downwards; usually a shallow, horizontal groove can be seen on it, leading into the trochanteric fossa; the tendon of the obturator externus lies in the groove. Its anterior surface is nearly flat, and nearly in the same plane as the head and shaft. Near the head it often presents a smooth patch, produced by pressure against the iliofemoral ligament. The neck is joined to the shaft at an angle which varies, but averages 125°. The angle is less in the adult than in the child, and less in short-limbed people, especially in women; the upper ends of the shafts are separated by the width of the pelvis and by the length of the two necks, but the lower ends are in contact; the shaft is therefore oblique; the obliquity is more marked in short-limbed men, and still more so in women, for the pelvis is wider; and the greater the obliquity, the less is the angle. At the upper end of the **trochanteric line** there is often a little tubercle for the attachment of the stronger part of the iliofemoral ligament.

The **greater trochanter** is under cover of the aponeurotic insertion of the gluteus maximus into the ilio-tibial tract during extension, but slips under the fleshy part of the muscle during flexion. The highest point or tip of the trochanter is the angle between its upper and posterior borders, and it overhangs the trochanteric fossa.

Sometimes part of the **gluteal tuberosity** is so raised that it makes a prominent excrescence, easily felt in the living person, comparable to the **third trochanter** which is always present on the thighbone of a horse. Sometimes the tuberosity is represented by a depression.

The **shaft** of the femur is slightly twisted, making the

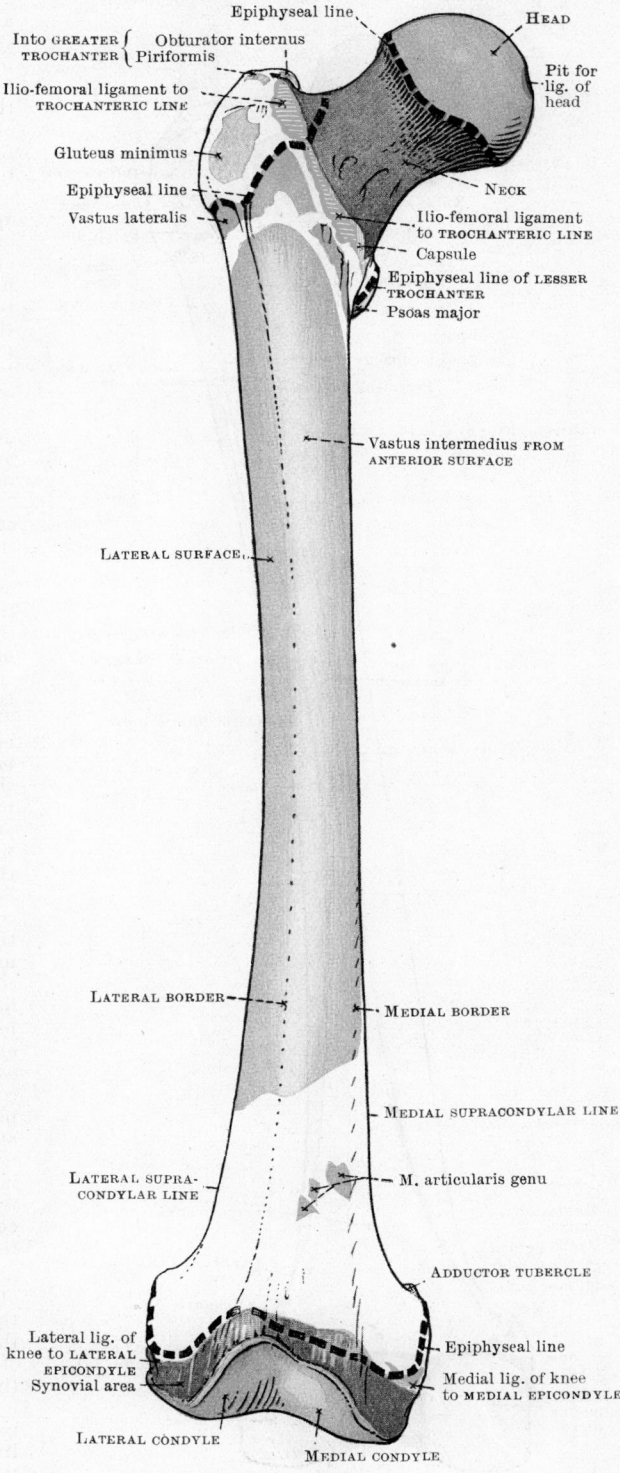

FIG. 241.—FRONT OF RIGHT FEMUR.

transverse diameter of the condyles and the long axis of the neck lie in two vertical planes that intersect each other—the neck plane being a little in front of the condylar plane medially. The acute angle between the planes is the **angle of torsion** of the femur. The shaft is also curved, with the convexity forwards, and that partly accounts for the fulness of the front of the thigh; the degree of curvature varies considerably, and is usually most pronounced at the upper part. The **linea aspera** may be a prominent keel; or it may be absent, as it is in apes. Sometimes a small tubercle on the lateral supracondylar line, about two inches above the condyle, marks the lower limit of the lateral intermuscular septum; and above that there is a shallow groove for a muscular artery. The upper and lower parts of the shaft are rather compressed from before backwards; a femur showing an exaggerated degree of compression is called **platymeric**; this condition is more common in the femora of prehistoric races.

The articular surfaces of the **condyles** are spirally curved. Their tibial parts articulate partly with the upper end of the tibia and partly with the semilunar cartilages that lie within the knee joint between the femur and tibia; faint grooves, made by the anterior edges of these cartilages, separate the *distal* articular surfaces from the *patellar* surface. The distal surfaces are on the same horizontal plane when the femur is held in its proper oblique position; the lateral condyle is then the one more directly in line with the shaft, and, since it thus receives the body weight more directly, it is stronger than the medial condyle; when the bone is perpendicular the medial condyle reaches a lower level than the lateral. The medial condyle is narrower than the lateral, is more curved, and its central side is more hollowed out. The semilunar area for articulation with the patella in extreme flexion of the knee can sometimes be seen on the medial condyle where it bounds the anterior part of the intercondylar notch. The anterior margin of the intercondylar notch is opposite the centre of the lateral condyle; and the floor slopes upwards and backwards to the **intercondylar line**, which separates it from the popliteal surface.

Attachments. — The ligament of the head [lig. teres] is attached to the *pit* on the **head**. The capsule of the hip joint is attached to the back of the **neck** a finger's-breadth from the trochanter, to the upper and lower borders of the neck near the trochanters, and to the **trochanteric line**; the part of the neck within the capsule is clothed with synovial membrane. The uppermost fibres of the vastus medialis arise from the lower half of the trochanteric line;

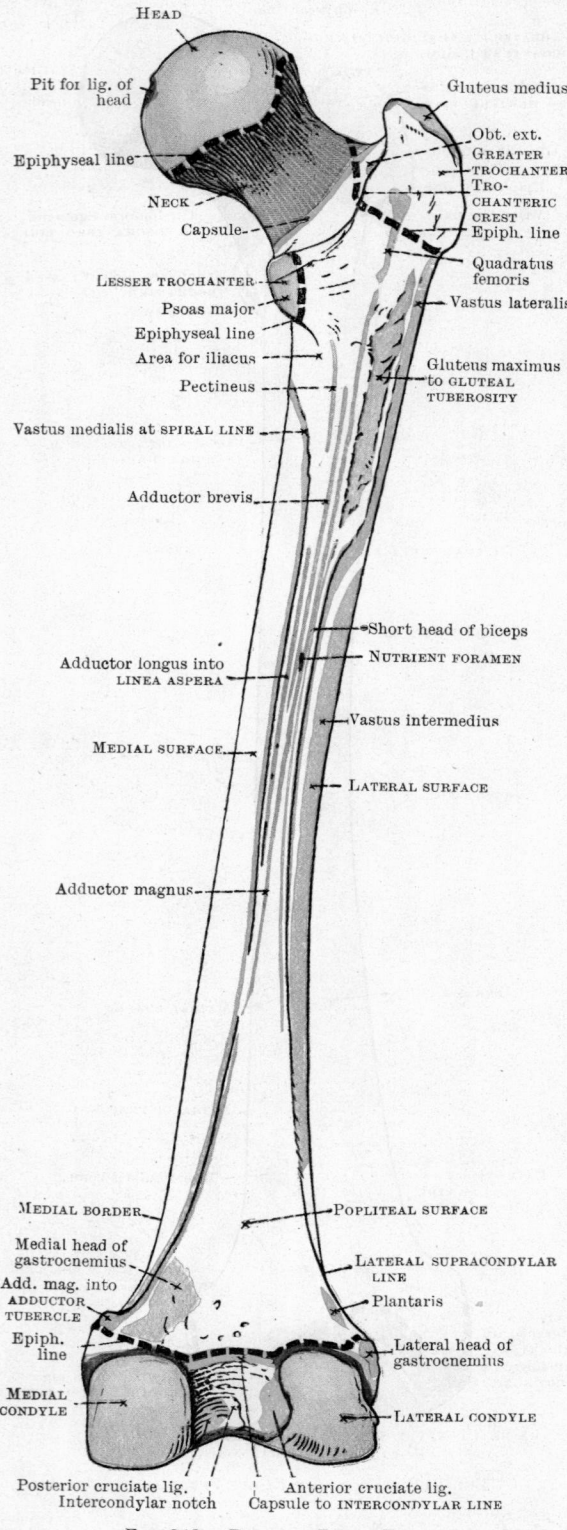

FIG. 242.—BACK OF RIGHT FEMUR.

HEAD

Pit for lig. of head

Epiphyseal line

NECK

Capsule

LESSER TROCHANTER

Psoas major

Epiphyseal line

Area for iliacus

Pectineus

Vastus medialis at SPIRAL LINE

Adductor brevis

Adductor longus into LINEA ASPERA

MEDIAL SURFACE

Adductor magnus

MEDIAL BORDER

Medial head of gastrocnemius

Add. mag. into ADDUCTOR TUBERCLE

Epiph. line

MEDIAL CONDYLE

Posterior cruciate lig.
Intercondylar notch

Gluteus medius

Obt. ext.
GREATER
TROCHANTER
TRO-
CHANTERIC
CREST
Epiph. line

Quadratus femoris

Vastus lateralis

Gluteus maximus to GLUTEAL TUBEROSITY

Short head of biceps
NUTRIENT FORAMEN

Vastus intermedius

LATERAL SURFACE

POPLITEAL SURFACE

LATERAL SUPRACONDYLAR LINE

Plantaris

Lateral head of gastrocnemius

LATERAL CONDYLE

Anterior cruciate lig.
Capsule to INTERCONDYLAR LINE

the uppermost fibres of the vastus lateralis from the upper half of the line, and from the front and lateral side of the root of the **greater trochanter**. The gluteus minimus is inserted into the *front* of the greater trochanter, and is partly separated from it by a *bursa*; the gluteus medius into its *lateral surface* on a broad, oblique ridge that extends downwards and forwards from the postero-superior angle; the surface in front of the ridge is separated from the gluteus medius by a *bursa*, and another *bursa* intervenes between the gluteus maximus and the surface behind the ridge; the piriformis into the *upper border*; the obturator internus and the gemelli into the *medial surface* above the neck; the obturator externus into the **trochanteric fossa**; the quadratus femoris into the **quadrate tubercle** and into a strip leading down from the tubercle for an inch; the psoas major into the **lesser trochanter**; the iliacus into the tendon of the psoas, the lesser trochanter, and the area below and in front of the trochanter.

Part of the gluteus maximus is inserted into the **gluteal tuberosity**, and part of the vastus lateralis arises from its lateral edge; part of the vastus medialis from the **spiral line**. The surface between the spiral line and the gluteal tuberosity gives insertion to four muscles: (1) part of the iliacus (see above); (2) the pectineus into a strip which begins lateral to the back of the root of the lesser trochanter and runs down to the linea aspera; (3) the upper part of the adductor brevis into the same strip, lateral to the pectineus; (4) the uppermost fibres of the adductor magnus between the attachment of the adductor brevis and the gluteal tuberosity.

The **linea aspera** gives attachment to the following structures, named from medial to lateral side : the origin of part of the vastus medialis; the medial intermuscular septum; the insertion of the adductor longus, in the whole length of the line or in the lower two-thirds only; the insertion of the lower part of the adductor brevis, in the upper third of the line; the insertion of a part of the adductor magnus; the posterior intermuscular septum; the origin of the greater part of the short head of the biceps femoris; the lateral intermuscular septum; the origin of part of the vastus lateralis from the upper half of the line, and of part of the vastus intermedius from the lower half.

From medial to lateral side the following structures are attached to the **supracondylar lines**: part of the vastus medialis from the upper two-thirds of the **medial** line; the medial septum and part of the adductor magnus into the whole length, except where interrupted for the passage of the femoral vessels; the lower parts of the short head of the biceps, the lateral septum, and the vastus intermedius from the upper two-thirds of the **lateral** line.

The greater part of the vastus intermedius arises from the upper two-thirds or three-fourths of the **anterior** and **lateral surfaces** of the shaft; the articularis genu muscle (as slender bundles) from the lower part of the anterior surface. The medial surface is covered by vastus medialis, but does not give attachment to any muscle.

The medial head of the gastrocnemius arises from the rough patch on the **popliteal surface** above the medial condyle; the plantaris from a small area above the lateral condyle; the lateral head of the gastrocnemius from an impression on the lateral surface of the **lateral condyle** and the adjoining lower end of the lateral supracondylar line; the tendon of the popliteus from the anterior end of the **popliteal groove**, and when the knee is extended it crosses the lower lip of the groove, which bears therefore a shallow notch near its anterior end. The lateral ligament of the knee is attached to the *lateral epicondyle*; the anterior cruciate ligament to the posterior part of the *lateral wall* of the **intercondylar notch**; the posterior cruciate ligament to the anterior part of the *medial wall*; the medial ligament of the knee to the *medial epicondyle*. The tendon formed by the posterior part of the adductor magnus is inserted into the **adductor tubercle**.

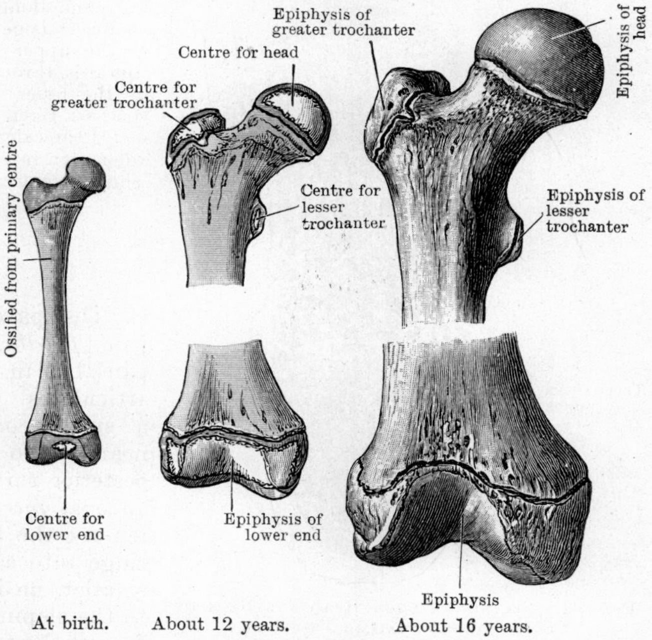

The fascia lata blends with the periosteum of both condyles at the sides of the knee. The capsular ligament of the knee joint is attached to the **intercondylar line**, to the bone immediately above the posterior parts of the condyles, to the lateral condyle between the popliteal groove and the epicondyle, and to the medial condyle immediately below the medial

FIG. 243.—OSSIFICATION OF THE FEMUR.

epicondyle. There is no definite capsular ligament in front, and the synovial membrane is reflected off the quadriceps on to the femur about a finger's breadth above the patellar surface; but, by means of a wide communication with a large *bursa* that lies under cover of the quadriceps, the cavity of the knee joint extends upwards to a point at least three finger-breadths above the patella. The apex of the infra-patellar synovial fold is attached to the anterior margin of the intercondylar notch.

Ossification.—The **primary** centre for shaft and neck appears at the seventh week of intra-uterine life. At birth the shaft is ossified; ossification extends into the neck after birth.

Secondary Centre.	Appears at	Epiphysis fuses at	Relation of Epiphyseal Line to Capsule of Neighbouring Joint.
For lower end	9th month of *intra-uterine* life	**M.** 18; **F.** 16-17	Outside.
For head	**M.** ½-1 yr.; **F.** ½ yr.	**M.** 18; **F.** 17	Inside.
For greater trochanter	**M.** 5 yr.; **F.** 4 yr.	**M.** 18; **F.** 16-17	Outside (inside superiorly).
For lesser trochanter	9-11 yr.	**M.** 18; **F.** 16-17	Outside.

The presence of the centre in the cartilage at the lower end in a new-born child found dead is accepted as proof that the child had come to full time. The epiphyseal line at the lower end passes through the adductor tubercle, and immediately above the patellar surface, and along the intercondylar line.

Structure.—As in other long bones, the ends are composed of spongy substance enclosed in a shell of compact substance; the arrangement of the lamellæ in the upper end of the femur is a classical example of the functional orientation of the architecture of bone. The shaft is a thick tube of compact bone enclosing a medullary cavity; the cavity begins opposite the lesser trochanter and ends about a handbreadth from the distal articular surface. The walls of the cavity are thickest above the middle of the bone and along the linea aspera. A sheet of compact tissue branches off the posterior wall of the upper end of the cavity and extends upwards, through the spongy tissue under cover of the lesser trochanter, to blend with the compact tissue of the back of the neck; it is called the **calcar femorale**, from its appearance when seen in section; it strengthens the neck. The **nutrient canal** is two inches long.

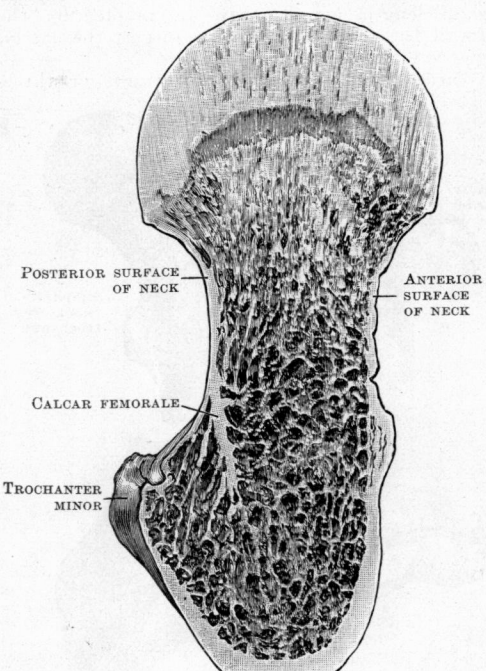

POSTERIOR SURFACE OF NECK

ANTERIOR SURFACE OF NECK

CALCAR FEMORALE

TROCHANTER MINOR

FIG. 244.—SECTION THROUGH HEAD AND NECK OF FEMUR TO SHOW CALCAR FEMORALE.

Patella

The **patella** or knee cap or knee pan [*patella*, diminutive of *patina* = a pan] lies in the front of the knee, and articulates with the femur. It is a small, compressed bone, measuring nearly two inches each way. The **posterior surface** is largely occupied by an oval *facet* for articulation with the femur; the facet is divided by a blunt ridge into a larger, lateral part, and a smaller, medial part, which correspond to the sloping sides of the patellar surface of the femur. The **anterior surface** is slightly convex, and is triangular in outline; the *apex* of the triangle points towards the leg, and is on a level immediately above the plane of the knee joint; the base of the triangle is the anterior margin of the *base of the patella*, *i.e.* its thick, upper border; the *lateral* and *medial borders* are convex.

The **patella** is the largest of the *sesamoid* bones; it lies in the tendon of the quadriceps femoris and, playing against the patellar surface of the femur, it increases the leverage of the muscle when it contracts to move the leg. The lower part of the quadriceps tendon is the *ligamentum patellae*—a strong band that stretches from the patella to the tibia, and on which the body partly rests in the kneeling posture.   When the knee is extended and the muscles are relaxed, the patella can be moved from side to side fairly freely, and to some extent also downwards ; when the knee is flexed the quadriceps muscle, including the ligamentum patellæ, is put on the stretch, the patella is jammed hard against the femur and is immovable. The anterior surface has a vertically striated or fibrous appearance. The lateral part of the articular surface is concave in both directions; the medial part is slightly concave from above downwards and is flat or slightly convex from side to side. The vertical ridge lies in the intercondylar notch in extreme flexion. When the cartilage is in place

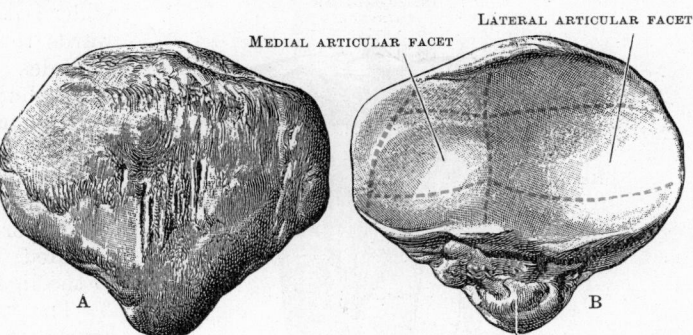

FIG. 245.—THE RIGHT PATELLA.

A. Anterior Surface.   B. Posterior Surface.

a vertical strip along the medial margin for articulation with the lateral margin of the medial condyle in extreme flexion can be seen ; and the rest of the surface is faintly subdivided into six areas (see Fig. 245).   The medial, vertical strip can sometimes be seen in the macerated bone.

Attachments.—The three vasti and the rectus femoris are inserted into the upper border ; the vastus lateralis and medialis, into the lateral and medial margins also.   A transverse line or groove divides the upper border into an anterior part for muscular insertion and a posterior part covered with fat and synovial membrane.   There is often a well-defined area at the supero-lateral angle for part of the vastus lateralis.   Some tendinous fibres of the quadriceps are continued downwards over the front of the patella to the ligamentum patellæ, and, in infancy, they can easily be stripped off the cartilaginous patella.   The ligamentum patellæ is attached to the apex and to the adjoining part of the posterior surface, but the greater part of the rough surface below the articular facet is related to fat and the synovial membrane of the knee.

Ossification.—The patella is cartilaginous at birth.   Ossification, usually from a single centre, begins about the fifth year, and is completed about puberty.   Separate epiphyseal nodules have been found in the lateral margin of the patella.

Structure and Variations.—The patella is composed of spongy tissue enclosed in a shell of compact tissue, which is thickest in front and at the vertical elevation behind.   Small *vascular foramina* are present on the anterior surface.   The patella may be absent ; its absence is said to be hereditary and transmitted by the female.   In one recorded case the patella was divided into a large, upper part and a smaller, lower part imbedded in the ligamentum patellæ.   The facets on the articular surface are modified in people who habitually squat.

Tibia

The **tibia** or shin-bone [*tibia* = shin-bone] comes next in size after the femur, and is between a fourth and a fifth of the length of the body. It is the medial and larger of the two bones of the leg, and can be felt through the skin in all its length. It is a long bone, having a **shaft** and **two ends.** The most outstanding border of the shaft is the **anterior** border; the lower end is the smaller end; and on the **medial** side of

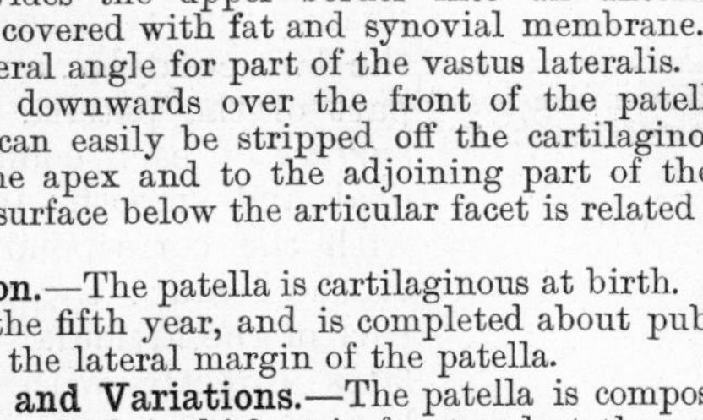

FIG. 246.—PROXIMAL SURFACE OF RIGHT TIBIA.

the lower end there is a stout, blunt projection called the *medial malleolus.*

The **upper end** is large and expanded to support the lower end of the femur; its transverse diameter is the wider; it is bent slightly backwards to overhang the shaft; it includes two imperfectly separated condyles and a tubercle.

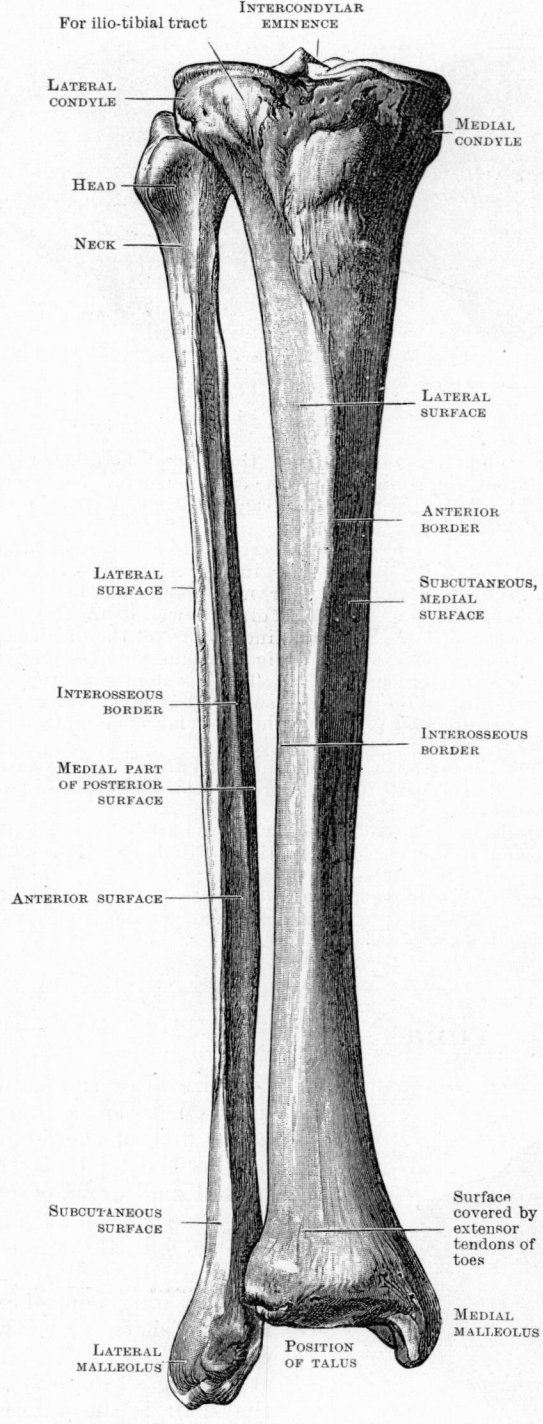

The **tubercle** is the low elevation on the front where the upper end joins the anterior border of the shaft; its lower part is rough; its upper part is smooth and rounded, and gives attachment to the ligamentum patellæ.

The two **condyles** make up nearly the whole of the upper end; they are separated *posteriorly* by a wide, shallow depression or notch; *anteriorly*, above the tubercle, they are united by a more or less flattened surface concealed behind the ligamentum patellæ. In the **kneeling posture** the body rests on the rough part of the tubercle, the ligamentum patellæ, the front of the two condyles, and the lower part of the patella. The *upper surface* of each condyle is large, oval and smooth; it articulates with the corresponding condyle of the femur; the more central part of the articular area articulates directly with the femur, but the more peripheral part is separated from the femur by a *semilunar fibro-cartilage* [meniscus, from μηνίσκος = a crescent]. Between the articular surfaces of the two condyles there is a rough **intercondylar area**, rising near its middle into a prominence called the **intercondylar eminence**.

On the back of the **medial condyle** there is a rough, horizontal groove for the insertion of part of the tendon of the semimembranosus muscle. The **lateral condyle** stands more abruptly away from the shaft than the medial does—so much so that it has a *distal surface*. This distal surface is separated from the lateral surface by a curved ridge to which the thick fascia of the antero-lateral side of the leg is attached; on the posterior part of the distal surface there is a flat, circular **facet** for articulation with the head of the fibula. On the anterior part of the *lateral surface* there is usually a well-marked impression for the attachment

FIG. 247.—THE RIGHT TIBIA AND FIBULA SEEN FROM THE FRONT.

of the strong, posterior part of a thick band of fascia called the *ilio-tibial tract.*
Both the condyles can be felt at
the sides of the knee.

The **lower end** of the tibia has
five surfaces—anterior, posterior,
lateral, medial, and distal.

The **anterior surface** is smooth
and rounded, and can be felt
indistinctly through the skin and
the tendons that descend from
the front of the leg to the foot.

The **medial surface** is subcutaneous, and from it there juts
downwards a short, broad, thick
projection, called the **medial malleolus**, which is the well-known
prominence, both felt and seen,
on the medial side of the ankle
[*malleolus* = a small hammer]. The
distal border of the malleolus is
pointed anteriorly and notched
posteriorly; it gives attachment to
an exceedingly strong fibrous band
named, from its shape, the *deltoid
ligament* [Δ = the Greek capital
letter *delta*]. The lateral surface
of the malleolus is smooth, and
articulates with the medial surface
of the talus or ankle bone.

The **posterior surface** lies deeply
under cover of a pad of fat and the
tendo calcaneus — *i.e.* the stout
sinew felt above the heel. The
surface is on the same plane as the
back of the malleolus, which can
be felt. Where it merges into
the back of the malleolus there
is a distinct vertical groove which
lodges the tendons of the tibialis
posterior and flexor digitorum
longus; nearer the lateral side
there is an indistinct groove which
lodges the tendon of the flexor
hallucis longus.

The **lateral surface** is occupied
by a wide, triangular depression;
the apical part of the depression
extends on to the shaft and is
shallow and rough, but the basal
part is smoother and is deeper—
being bounded in front and behind
by prominent ridges or tubercles.
It is called the **fibular notch** because the lower part of the fibula
lies in it; the fibula is usually in
actual contact with the lower
part, but is bound to the upper
part by a very short but very thick interosseous ligament.

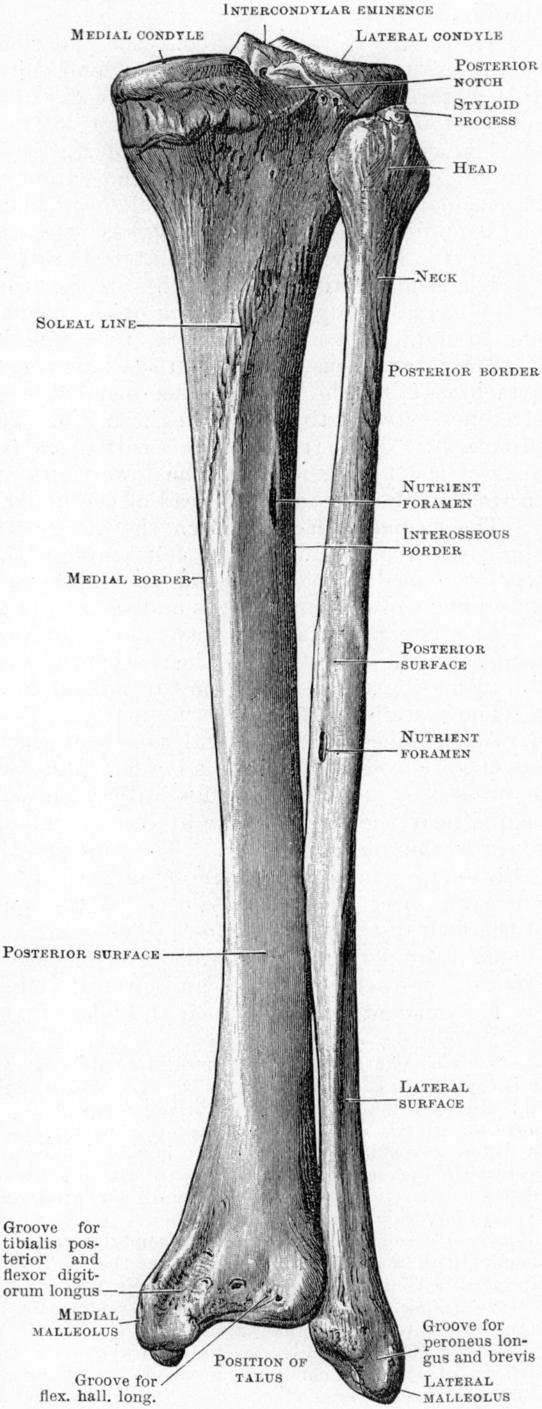

The **distal surface** is square and smooth, concave from before backwards,

FIG. 248.—THE RIGHT TIBIA AND FIBULA SEEN FROM
BEHIND.

slightly convex from side to side, and broader in front than behind; it articulates with and rests upon the upper surface of the talus, which is the highest bone of the tarsus.

The **shaft** is thinnest about the junction of the middle and lower thirds; it becomes thicker towards the lower end and still more so towards the upper end. It has three borders and three surfaces. The *borders* are anterior, medial, and interosseous; the *surfaces* are posterior, lateral, and medial.

The **anterior border** is the shin of the leg. It is the most prominent of the borders; it begins at the tubercle and extends sinuously to the anterior margin of the medial malleolus; it can be felt from end to end in the living leg. Everyone is familiar with it; small notches—the result of accidental impacts—may be felt in it. Its lower third is blunter than the rest of it.

The **medial border** is a smooth, blunt margin that extends from near the back of the medial condyle to the back of the medial malleolus; it also can be felt from end to end, but it is best marked in the middle third of the bone.

The **interosseous border** is on the lateral side, and is so named because it gives attachment to the interosseous membrane—a strong, wide fibrous sheet that stretches between the tibia and the fibula. It is a distinct, sharp line, but is not prominent. It is traced more easily from below upwards; it extends from the apex of the fibular notch to the lower part of the lateral condyle, some distance in front of the facet for the head of the fibula.

The **medial surface**, between the anterior and medial borders, is smooth and slightly convex, and can be felt through the skin; it is continuous inferiorly with the medial malleolus; at its upper part it is slightly roughened for the attachment of certain tendons and ligaments that overlie it.

The **lateral surface** is between the anterior and interosseous borders, and, owing to the direction of the lower parts of those borders it turns forwards to become continuous with the front of the lower end of the tibia.

The **posterior surface** is between the medial and interosseous borders; its upper part encroaches on the lateral aspect of the bone owing to the position of the upper part of the interosseous border. The upper third of the posterior surface is crossed by an oblique ridge called the **soleal line** [linea poplitea]; the line begins near the facet for the head of the fibula and runs downwards and medially towards the medial border. The line is the chief bony origin of a muscle called the soleus that lies deeply in the calf; the part of the surface above the line gives insertion to a muscle called the popliteus which lies in the lower part of the floor of the popliteal fossa. The part of the surface below the soleal line is usually imperfectly subdivided into medial and lateral parts by a more or less *vertical line*—which is blunt and often ill-defined.

The **nutrient foramen** is near the soleal line and is directed downwards.

The articular surface of the **medial condyle** is ovoid, with its long axis antero-posterior; it [is concave in each direction. The superior articular surface of the **lateral condyle** is rounder and slightly smaller. It is slightly concave from side to side; from before backwards, its posterior part is convex, but its anterior part varies from slightly convex to slightly concave in different specimens. Its margin is well defined anteriorly and laterally, but is rounded off posteriorly, increasing the convexity of the posterior part. The parts of a condylar articular surface that articulate with the semilunar cartilage and with the femur may be indicated by a difference in texture or in colour. The sides of the **intercondylar eminence** stand up prominently and are named the **intercondylar tubercles**; the articular cartilage extends on to them, and they are separated by a groove that runs obliquely from in front backwards and in a lateral direction. The medial tubercle is the higher and blunter, and sends backwards an oblique ridge that bounds the groove posteriorly, and gives attachment to the posterior horn of the lateral semilunar cartilage.

On the front of the bone, the area above the tubercle, composed of the united anterior surfaces of the two condyles, is covered with fat and is related to the deep infrapatellar bursa, which sometimes also overlaps the upper edge of the tubercle. The **tubercle of the tibia** is divided into two parts—an upper and a lower. The *lower part* is subcutaneous, but is rough; and its upper edge is often raised as a rough ridge that receives the superficial fibres of the ligamentum patellæ; but there may be no ridge, or there may be a depression in place of a ridge. The *upper part* is smooth and rounded, and is the chief insertion of the ligamentum patellæ; its upper edge is sharply defined, and is often bounded by a narrow, shallow, arched groove.

The posterior surface of the **shaft** is variable in contour, but usually its upper part is rounded and its lower part flat. The lower parts of the posterior and lateral surfaces are free from muscular attachments, but are overlain by muscles and tendons.

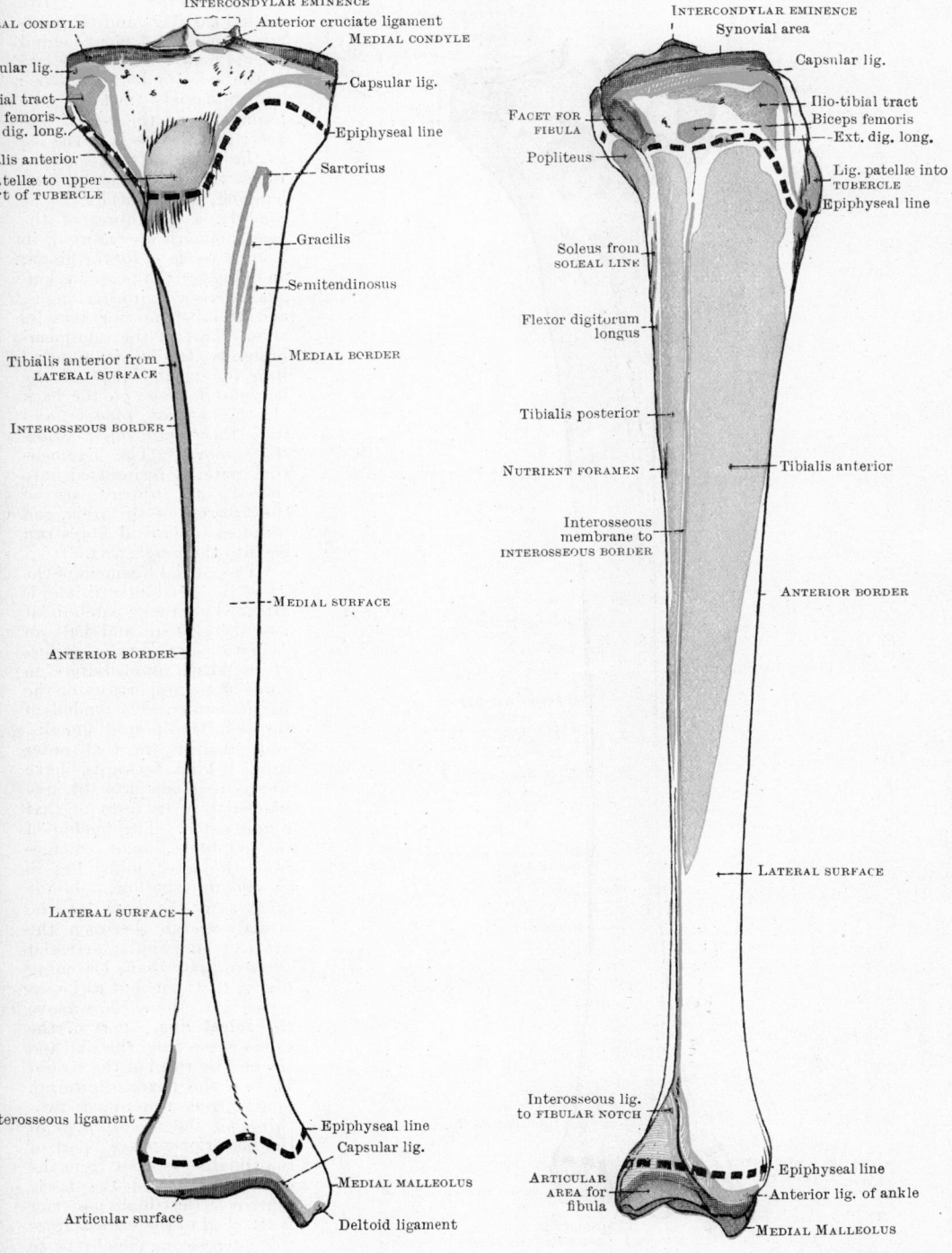

FIG. 249.—ANTERIOR ASPECT OF RIGHT TIBIA.   FIG. 250.—LATERAL ASPECT OF RIGHT TIBIA.

Attachments.—The capsular ligament of the knee joint is attached to the circumference of the **condyles** a little below the margins of the articular surface ; the capsule of the upper tibio-fibular joint to the margins of the **facet for the fibula** ; the cruciate ligaments and the horns of the semilunar cartilages to the **intercondylar area** in the following order from before backwards: anterior horn of medial cartilage and anterior cruciate ligament in front of the intercondylar eminence, the horns of the lateral cartilage to the front and back of the eminence,

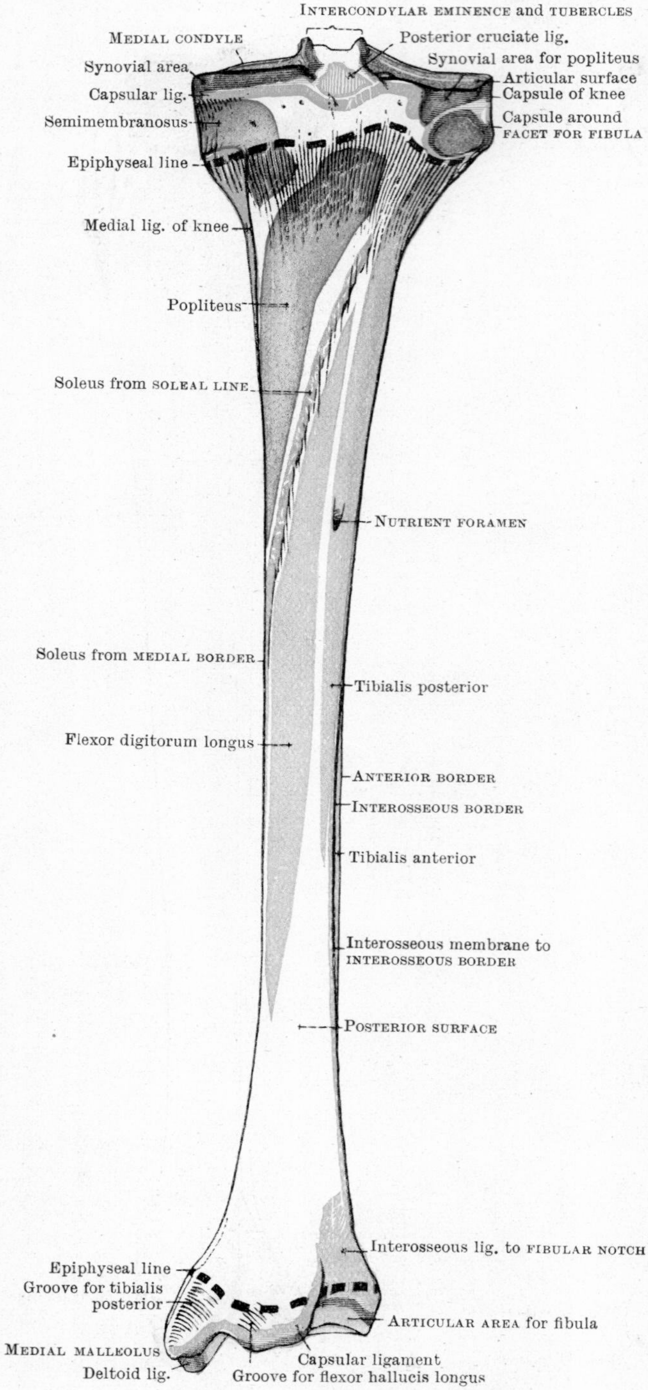

FIG. 251.—POSTERIOR ASPECT OF RIGHT TIBIA.

Labels on figure:
INTERCONDYLAR EMINENCE and TUBERCLES
MEDIAL CONDYLE
Posterior cruciate lig.
Synovial area
Synovial area for popliteus
Capsular lig.
Articular surface
Capsule of knee
Semimembranosus
Capsule around FACET FOR FIBULA
Epiphyseal line
Medial lig. of knee
Popliteus
Soleus from SOLEAL LINE
NUTRIENT FORAMEN
Soleus from MEDIAL BORDER
Tibialis posterior
Flexor digitorum longus
ANTERIOR BORDER
INTEROSSEOUS BORDER
Tibialis anterior
Interosseous membrane to INTEROSSEOUS BORDER
POSTERIOR SURFACE
Interosseous lig. to FIBULAR NOTCH
Epiphyseal line
Groove for tibialis posterior
ARTICULAR AREA for fibula
MEDIAL MALLEOLUS
Deltoid lig.
Capsular ligament
Groove for flexor hallucis longus

the posterior horn of the medial cartilage and the posterior cruciate ligament behind the eminence. The fascia lata to the sides of both *condyles*; its ilio-tibial tract to the impression on the *lateral condyle*; and the fascia of the leg to the ridge on that condyle. Below that ridge, on the overhanging, distal surface of the condyle, a few fibres of the biceps femoris are inserted, in front of the facet for the fibula, and fibres of the peroneus longus, extensor digitorum longus, and tibialis anterior muscles arise. Part of the semimembranosus tendon is inserted into the medial part of the horizontal *groove* on the back of the *medial condyle* and into the rough area below the groove. The ligamentum patellæ is inserted into the smooth, upper part of the **tubercle** of the tibia, and its most superficial fibres run on into the rough part.

The medial ligament of the knee [lig. collaterale tibiale] is attached to a rough patch about two inches long and half an inch wide on the *medial surface of the* **shaft**, immediately in front of the upper part of the medial border. The tendons of the semitendinosus, gracilis, and sartorius, in that order from behind forwards, have linear insertions into the area immediately in front of that rough patch. The tendon of the popliteus, as it emerges from the knee joint, lies in a smooth, shallow, oblique groove on the back of the lateral condyle between the superior and fibular articular surfaces, and then, becoming fleshy, it widens out to be inserted into the surface above the **soleal line.** Part of the soleus arises from the line and the middle third of the *medial border*; the flexor digitorum longus from the upper two-thirds of the *medial area* of the **posterior surface**; part of the tibialis posterior from the *lateral area*; and the fascia that covers the tibialis posterior is attached to the *vertical line*; the interosseous membrane to the *interosseous border*; the fascia of the leg to the *medial* and *anterior borders*; the superior extensor retinaculum [lig. transversum cruris] to the lower part of the anterior border.

The inferior extensor retinaculum [lig. cruciatum cruris] is attached to the *anterior* border of

PLATE XV

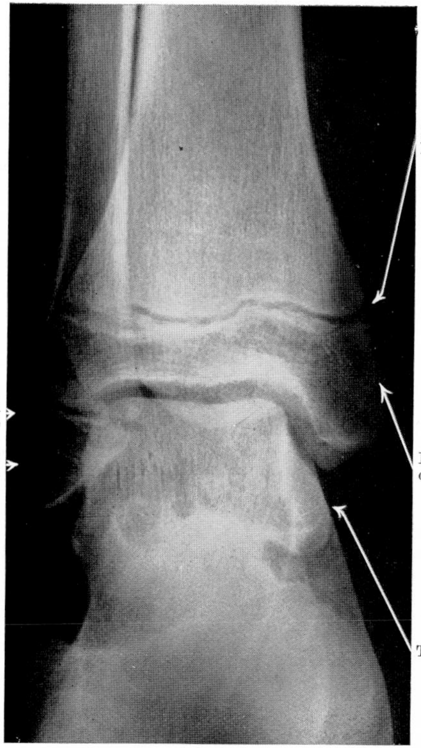

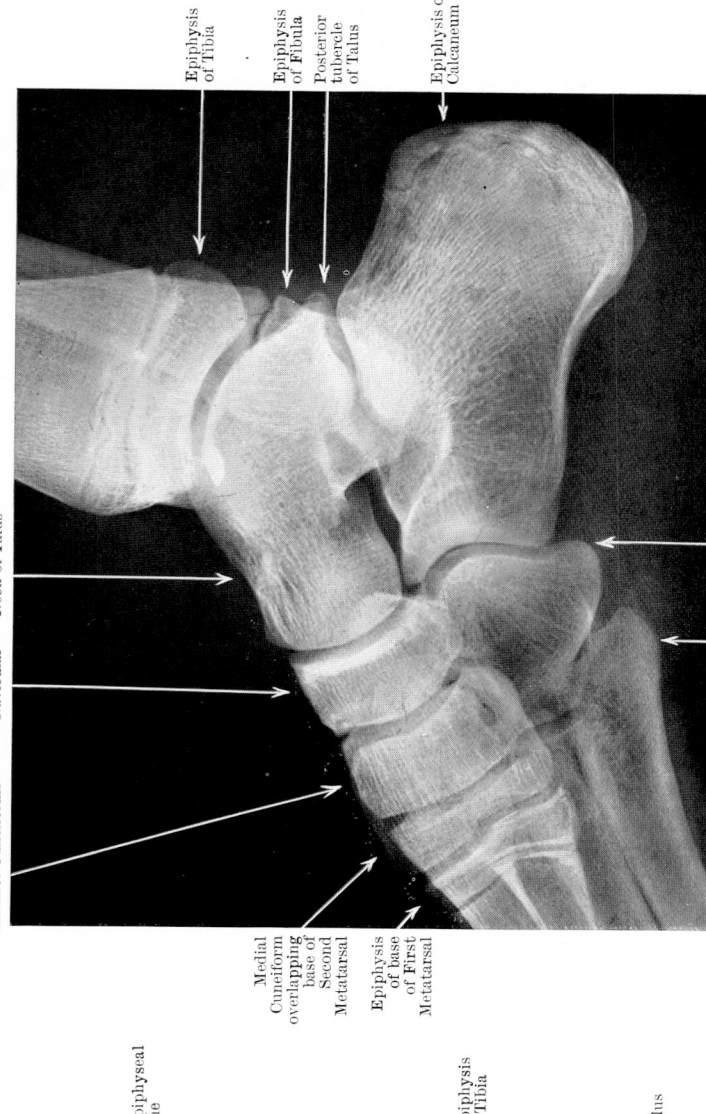

Medial and Inter-
mediate Cuneiforms

Navicular   Neck of Talus

Epiphysis
of Tibia

Epiphysis
of Fibula

Posterior
tubercle
of Talus

Epiphysis of
Calcaneum

Medial
Cuneiform
overlapping
base of
Second
Metatarsal

Epiphysis
of base
of First
Metatarsal

Base of   Cuboid
Fifth Metatarsal

Fig. 2.—Lateral Radiograph of the same Ankle and Foot (Girl aged 12).

Cf. Plate XXVII, Fig. 2, and note that the epiphysis of the Calcaneum is almost united.

Epiphyseal
line

Epiphysis
of Tibia

Talus

Epiphyseal
line

Epiphysis
of Fibula

Fig. 1.—Antero-posterior Radiograph of
Ankle of Girl aged 12.

Cf. Plate XXVII, Fig. 1, and note the relation
of the epiphyses of Tibia and Fibula to the Malleoli
and to the Ankle Joint.

PLATE XVI

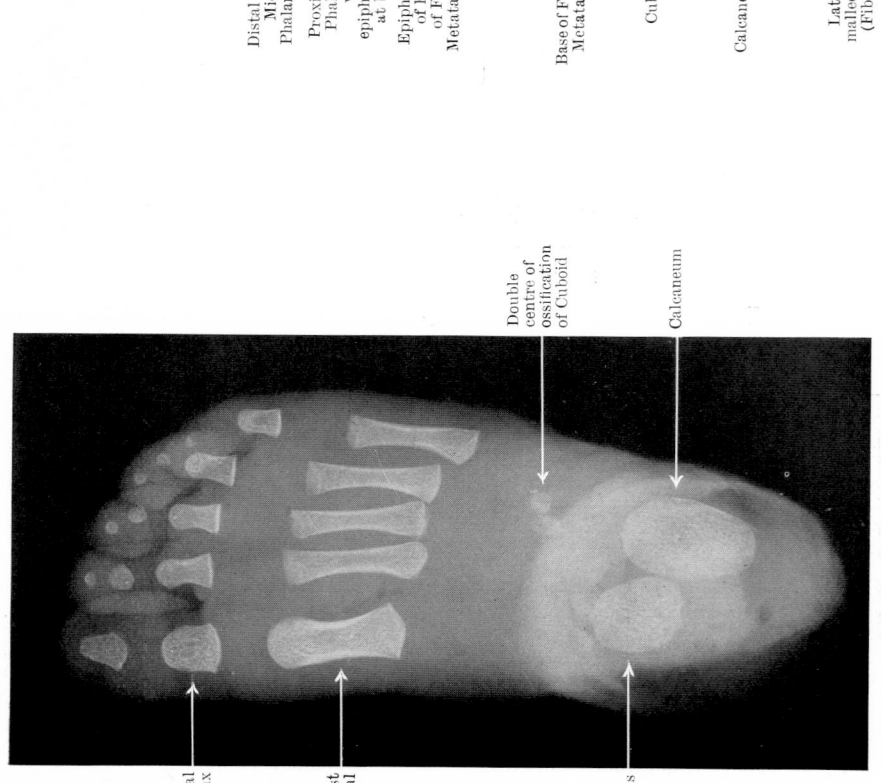

Distal Phalanx with epiphysis at base

Proximal Phalanx with epiphysis at base

Epiphysis at base of First Metatarsal

Medial Cuneiform

Intermediate and Lateral Cuneiforms

Navicular

Talus

Medial malleolus (Tibia)

Distal and Middle Phalanges

Proximal Phalanx with epiphysis at base

Epiphysis of head of Fifth Metatarsal

Base of Fifth Metatarsal

Cuboid

Calcaneum

Lateral malleolus (Fibula)

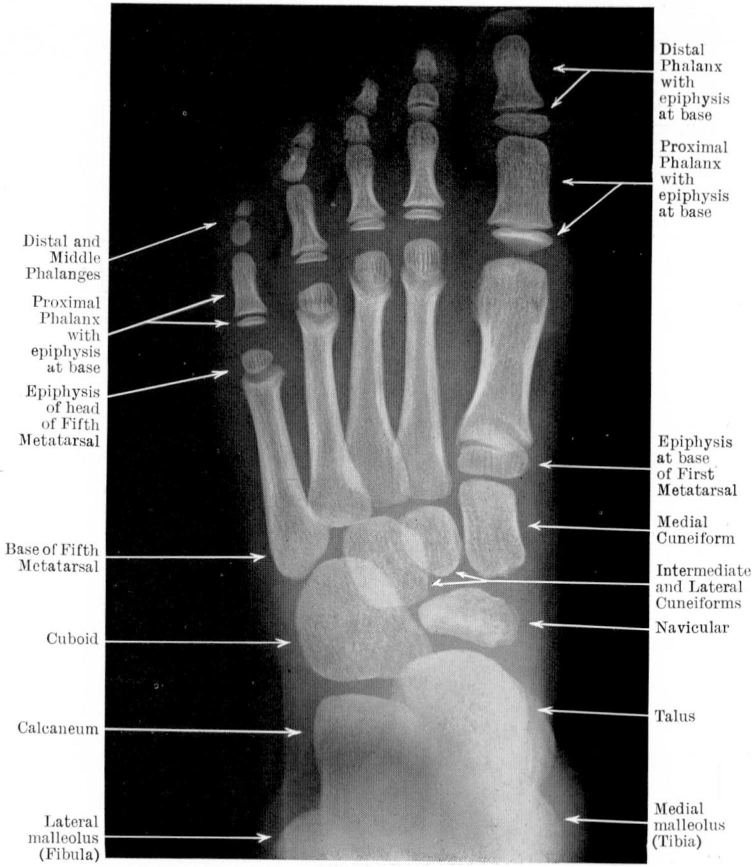

FIG. 2.—RADIOGRAPH OF FOOT OF BOY AGED 7. (Dr. J. Duncan White.)

Cf. Plate X, Fig. 2, noting that the Tarsus is more advanced in ossification than the Carpus, but that the Phalanges of the Toes are less advanced than those of the Fingers.

Double centre of ossification of Cuboid

Calcaneum

Proximal Phalanx

First Metatarsal

Talus

FIG. 1.—RADIOGRAPH OF FOOT OF FULL-TIME FŒTUS.

Cf. Plate X, Fig. 1, and note (1) the presence of centres of ossification for tarsal bones, (2) that the phalanges of the Foot are less advanced than those of the Hand.

the **medial malleolus**; the deltoid ligament to the *distal* border; the flexor retinaculum [lig. laciniatum] to the *posterior* border; the posterior ligament of the ankle joint and transverse tibio-fibular ligament to the *posterior* border of the **lower end**; the anterior ligament to the *anterior* border; the interosseous tibio-fibular ligament to the floor of the **fibular notch**; the anterior inferior and posterior inferior tibio-fibular ligaments to the anterior and posterior *margins* of the lower part of the notch.

Ossification.—The **primary** centre appears at the seventh week of intra-uterine life. At birth only the ends are cartilaginous.

The *upper* epiphyseal centre appears shortly after birth and sometimes shortly before birth. The *epiphyseal line* extends downwards in front to include the greater part of the tubercle. The downward spread of ossification to include the tubercle begins at the end of the tenth year; and that is the last part of the epiphysis to unite with

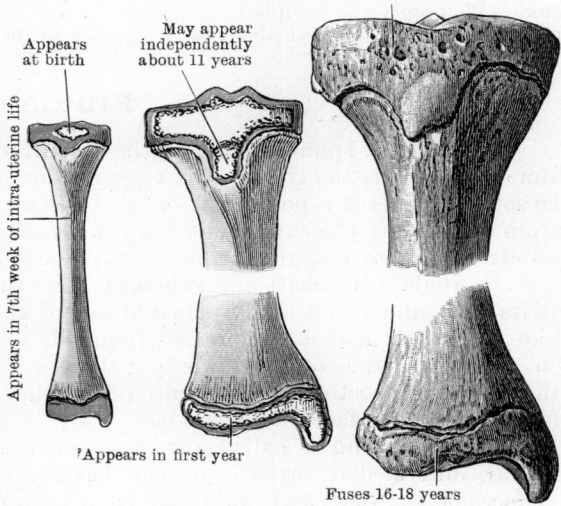

FIG. 252.—OSSIFICATION OF THE TIBIA.

Secondary Centre.	Appears at	Epiphysis fuses at	Relation of Epiphyseal Line to Capsule of Neighbouring Joint.
For upper end	Birth	M. 18–19; F. 16–17	Outside.
For lower end	6 mo.–1 year	M. 18; F. 16	Outside.

the shaft. The medial malleolus is cartilaginous till the eighth year, when ossification begins to extend into it from the lower epiphysis. Occasionally there are additional epiphyseal centres for the tubercle and the medial malleolus.

Structure and Variations.— The structure is like that of the other long bones. The medullary cavity falls short of each end by two or three inches. The cavity is narrow in the middle, for its walls are thickest there. The posterior wall is thicker than the side walls, and the anterior wall is thicker still, owing to the heaping up of dense bone at the shin. The compact bone is much thicker in the tubercle and the intercondylar eminence than elsewhere at the upper end. The **nutrient canal** extends through the compact bone obliquely for two inches before reaching the medullary cavity.

Tibiæ that show compression from side to side are called **platyknemic**; the condition is more common in prehistoric and savage people than among modern Europeans. Exaggerated *retroversion* of the upper end is said to be due to the habit that some people have of walking with the knees slightly bent. The anterior margin of the

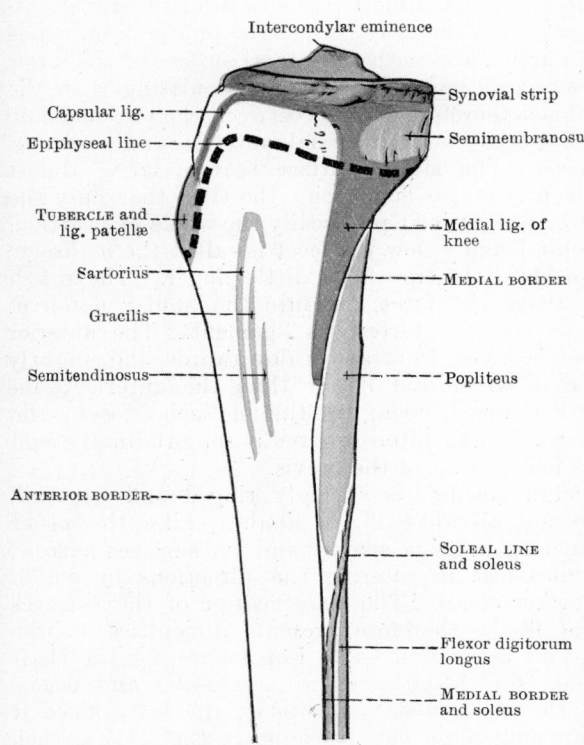

FIG. 253.—MEDIAL ASPECT OF UPPER HALF OF RIGHT TIBIA.

19

lower end is often grooved transversely for the attachment of the anterior ligament of the ankle. In people who habitually squat rather than sit there may be a "pressure" facet on that margin, due to contact with the neck of the talus in the squatting posture.

Fibula

The **fibula** or splinter bone is the lateral and smaller bone of the leg. It is almost as long as the tibia but is very slender, and it has slightly expanded ends. In some animals it is pointed at one end—hence its name [*fibula* (from *figibula*) = a pin or skewer; the equivalent word in Greek is περόνη (peronē), hence the names *peroneus* and *peroneal* given to muscles, vessels, and nerves related to the fibula].

The fibula has a **shaft** and **two ends**; it is thickly covered with muscles except at its ends, and is not easily palpated except at the ends. The **upper** end is knob-like; the lower end is compressed from side to side and is triangular in outline; on the **medial** side of the lower end there is a large, nearly flat, triangular facet; the **posterior** aspect can be recognised from the fact that there is a pit *behind* the lower part of the facet.

The **upper end** is called the *head* of the fibula. The anterior, posterior, lateral, and medial surfaces of the **head** are identified more easily after the surfaces of the shaft and lower end have been recognised; the medial part of the *proximal surface* bears a *facet* of considerable size for articulation with the lateral condyle of the tibia; a stunted projection, called the **styloid process** [apex capituli], stands up from the junction of the *lateral* and *posterior* surfaces. The head is felt as a hard knob well back on the lateral side of the leg, at the level of the tubercle of the tibia. If the finger is passed round to its posterior surface, a big nerve, called the *lateral popliteal nerve* [n. peronæus communis], can be felt and rolled between the finger and the bone; it is felt most easily when the knee is bent to a right angle and the muscles are relaxed. The part of the shaft immediately adjoining the head is called the **neck** of the fibula, and it also can be felt; the nerve inclines downwards and forwards from the back of the head and ends on the lateral side of the neck, and is most liable to injury there.

The **lower end** is called the *lateral malleolus*. It is the outstanding prominence on the lateral side of the ankle. It articulates with the lateral surface of the lower end of the tibia, but projects downwards beyond the tibia, articulating with the lateral surface of the talus; the talus is therefore gripped between the two malleoli.

The **lateral malleolus** has four surfaces—lateral, medial, anterior, and posterior. The **lateral surface** is subcutaneous. The **medial surface** bears a large, almost flat, articular *facet*; the malleolus projects so far beyond the tibia that only the upper edge of the facet articulates with the tibia; practically the whole of it articulates with the talus. The pit behind and below the facet is called the *malleolar fossa*, and is big enough to accommodate the tip of the little finger. The rough mark on the shaft, immediately above the facet, fits into the fibular notch of the tibia and is bound to its floor by an interosseous ligament. The **anterior surface** is narrow from side to side, convex from above downwards, and slightly roughened. The **posterior surface** is wider and flatter than the anterior; the width of its lower part is greatly reduced, owing to the malleolar fossa; the tendon of the peroneus brevis lies on it and often grooves it longitudinally, and the tendon of the peroneus longus lies on that of the brevis.

The **shaft** of the fibula, though slender, is strongly ridged and grooved, but the ridges and grooves are not all alike in all fibulæ. Like the other long bones, the fibula is twisted, but, as it is slender and its surfaces narrow, the torsion has a greater apparent effect in altering the directions in which the surfaces look than it has in thicker bones. The identification of the surfaces and borders of the shaft of the fibula therefore presents difficulties to the beginner and takes up time out of all proportion to its importance, for the shaft of the fibula is merely a stanchion for the attachment of muscles and fasciæ and the interosseous membrane; the fibula does not support the body, since it does not articulate with the femur, and, being closely bound to the tibia at each end, it does not serve independently as a lever in the movements of the leg.

The **shaft** of the fibula has three borders and three surfaces; but one of the surfaces—the posterior—is divided into two parts by a sharp, outstanding crest that resembles a border. The

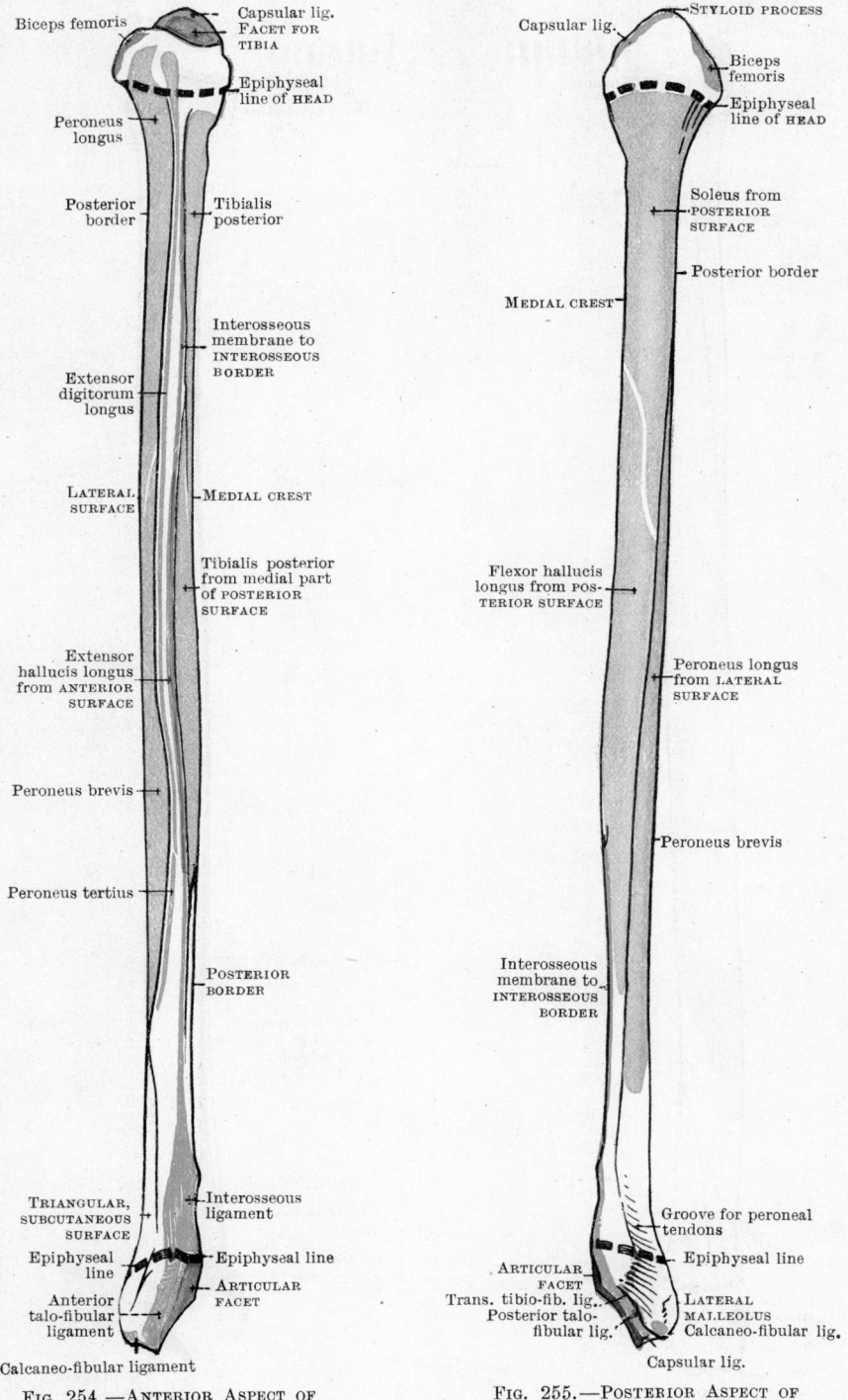

Biceps femoris

Capsular lig.
FACET FOR TIBIA

Epiphyseal line of HEAD

Peroneus longus

Posterior border

Tibialis posterior

Interosseous membrane to INTEROSSEOUS BORDER

Extensor digitorum longus

LATERAL SURFACE

MEDIAL CREST

Tibialis posterior from medial part of POSTERIOR SURFACE

Extensor hallucis longus from ANTERIOR SURFACE

Peroneus brevis

Peroneus tertius

POSTERIOR BORDER

TRIANGULAR, SUBCUTANEOUS SURFACE

Interosseous ligament

Epiphyseal line

Epiphyseal line

Anterior talo-fibular ligament

ARTICULAR FACET

Calcaneo-fibular ligament

FIG. 254.—ANTERIOR ASPECT OF RIGHT FIBULA.

Capsular lig.

STYLOID PROCESS

Biceps femoris

Epiphyseal line of HEAD

Soleus from POSTERIOR SURFACE

Posterior border

MEDIAL CREST

Flexor hallucis longus from POSTERIOR SURFACE

Peroneus longus from LATERAL SURFACE

Peroneus brevis

Interosseous membrane to INTEROSSEOUS BORDER

Groove for peroneal tendons

Epiphyseal line

ARTICULAR FACET

Trans. tibio-fib. lig.

Posterior talo-fibular lig.

LATERAL MALLEOLUS

Calcaneo-fibular lig.

Capsular lig.

FIG. 255.—POSTERIOR ASPECT OF RIGHT FIBULA.

borders are anterior, posterior, and interosseous. The *surfaces* are posterior, anterior, and lateral; and there is an additional, small "triangular, subcutaneous surface" not included in any of the three surfaces named above.

The **triangular, subcutaneous surface** should be identified first. It is a narrow, triangular area, about two inches long, on the lower part of the shaft; its base is continuous with the lateral

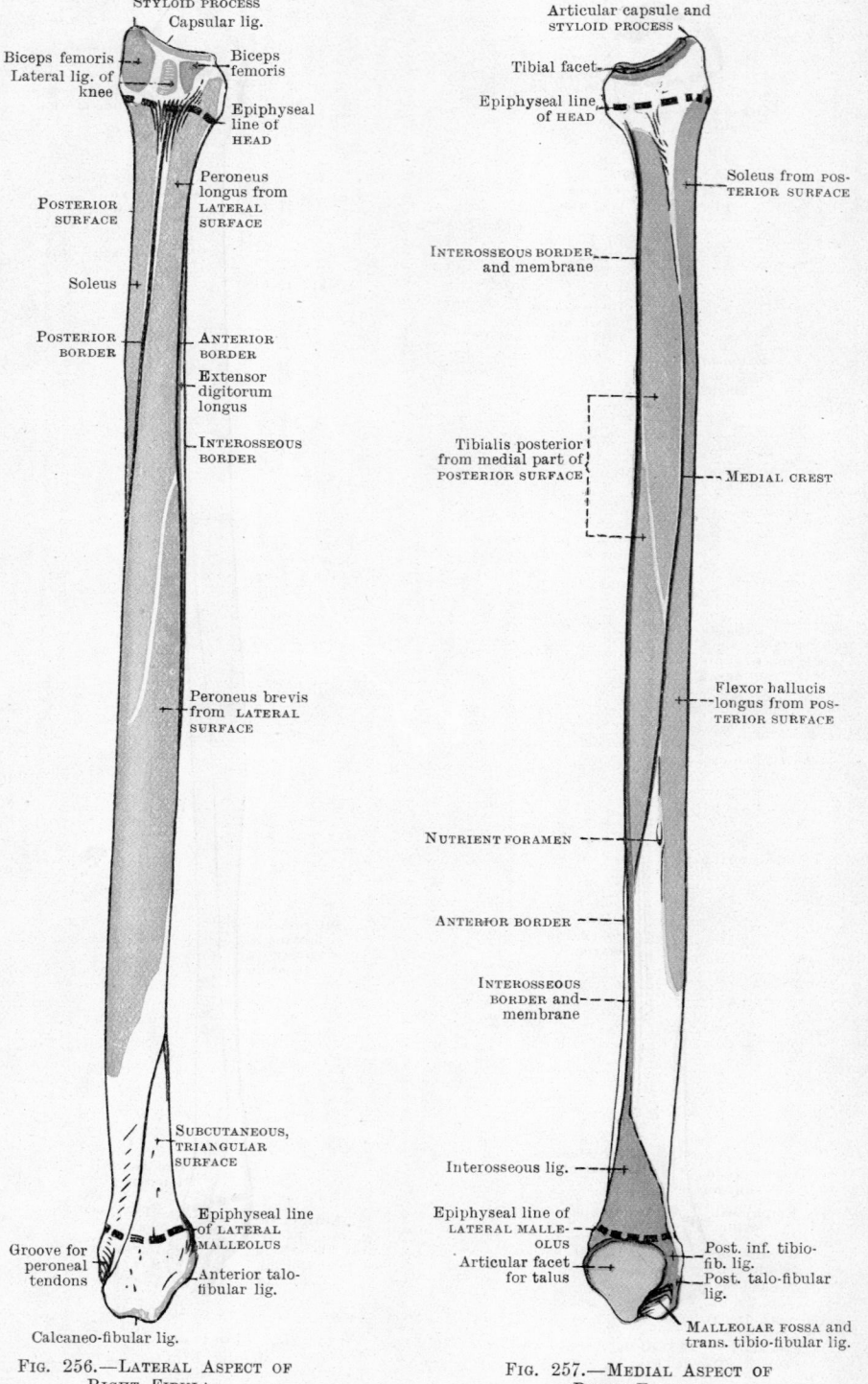

STYLOID PROCESS
Capsular lig.

Biceps femoris
Lateral lig. of
knee

Biceps
femoris

Epiphyseal
line of
HEAD

POSTERIOR
SURFACE

Peroneus
longus from
LATERAL
SURFACE

Soleus

POSTERIOR
BORDER

ANTERIOR
BORDER

Extensor
digitorum
longus

INTEROSSEOUS
BORDER

Peroneus brevis
from LATERAL
SURFACE

SUBCUTANEOUS,
TRIANGULAR
SURFACE

Groove for
peroneal
tendons

Epiphyseal line
of LATERAL
MALLEOLUS

Anterior talo-
fibular lig.

Calcaneo-fibular lig.

FIG. 256.—LATERAL ASPECT OF
RIGHT FIBULA.

Articular capsule and
STYLOID PROCESS

Tibial facet

Epiphyseal line
of HEAD

Soleus from POS-
TERIOR SURFACE

INTEROSSEOUS BORDER
and membrane

Tibialis posterior
from medial part of
POSTERIOR SURFACE

MEDIAL CREST

Flexor hallucis
longus from POS-
TERIOR SURFACE

NUTRIENT FORAMEN

ANTERIOR BORDER

INTEROSSEOUS
BORDER and
membrane

Interosseous lig.

Epiphyseal line of
LATERAL MALLE-
OLUS

Articular facet
for talus

Post. inf. tibio-
fib. lig.
Post. talo-fibular
lig.

MALLEOLAR FOSSA and
trans. tibio-fibular lig.

FIG. 257.—MEDIAL ASPECT OF
RIGHT FIBULA.

surface of the lateral malleolus, and both the malleolus and the triangular surface are easily dientified through the skin.

The **anterior border** is located most easily at the *apex* of the triangular, subcutaneous surface, where it bifurcates to enclose that surface; from that point it passes upwards to the neck as a sharp, even line.

The **interosseous border** should be located next. It is medial to the anterior border, and should be looked for first in the lower third of the shaft, where there is nearly always an interval of a quarter of an inch or so between it and the anterior border. Its lower end runs into the rough, triangular patch above the medial surface of the malleolus. When traced towards the neck it is apt to be lost, for in many fibulæ it approaches the anterior border so closely that the two almost merge into one, and even when the two borders remain quite distinct there is seldom more than a twelfth of an inch interval between their upper parts. The interosseous border is never a strongly marked line, though the interosseous membrane is attached to it.

The *medial crest* should be looked for next; it is medial to and behind the interosseous border, and in some fibulæ it is the most outstanding ridge on the bone. It begins at the neck, but, instead of running the whole length of the shaft like the borders, it joins the interosseous border three or four inches above the lower end; it should be located there first and traced upwards.

The **posterior border** is the remaining ridge on the fibula, and is usually well defined. It begins at the neck and ends at the posterior margin of the medial surface of the malleolus.

The **lateral surface** is that which is mainly between the posterior border and the anterior border, but its lower fourth or fifth is between the posterior border and the subcutaneous triangle, and, owing to the twist of the fibula, it becomes continuous with the *posterior* surface of the malleolus. The **anterior surface** is the strip between the anterior and interosseous borders. Its upper part is very narrow, and may be a mere line; but it usually widens to about a quarter of an inch towards the lower end.

The **posterior surface** is all the remainder, and is wider than the other two surfaces together. It is bounded by the interosseous and posterior borders, and is divided into two distinct parts by the medial crest. Since the medial crest does not reach the lower end, the part between it and the interosseous border is restricted to the upper two-thirds of the shaft; though this part looks medially, it is included in the posterior surface because it is behind the interosseous membrane, which separates the back of the leg from the front; its upper part is crossed by an oblique ridge that begins at the interosseous border near the neck and runs downwards and backwards, and may be mistaken for the upper part of the medial crest. The rest of the posterior surface extends the whole length of the shaft, and, owing to the twist of the bone, its lower part is continuous with the *medial* surface of the malleolus.

The *anterior* surface gives origin to muscles of the front of the leg; the *lateral* surface to muscles of the lateral side; and the *posterior* to muscles of the back of the leg.

The **nutrient foramen** is usually on the posterior surface, about the junction of the upper and middle thirds, and is directed downwards; it may be near the lower third.

Attachments.—The tendon of the biceps is inserted into the **head**—the main slip on the lateral side of the styloid process, and a small slip farther forwards. The lateral ligament of the knee is attached to the head between the slips of the biceps tendon; the capsular ligament of the superior tibio-fibular joint to the margins of the *facet*; the deep fascia to the *lateral side* of the head. The muscles that arise from the upper part of the shaft take origin also from the adjoining surfaces of the head.

The peroneus longus arises from the head and the upper two-thirds of the *lateral surface* of the **shaft**; the peroneus brevis from the lower two-thirds, overlapping the longus anteriorly in the middle third. Part of the tibialis posterior from the head and the part of the *posterior surface* between the medial crest and the interosseous border; part of soleus from the head and the upper third of the remainder of the surface, and the flexor hallucis longus from the lower two-thirds. The extensor digitorum longus from the head and the upper two-thirds of the *anterior surface*; the peroneus tertius from the lower third; and, medial to those two, the extensor hallucis longus from the middle three-fifths. The interosseous membrane is attached to the *interosseous border*; the fascia covering the tibialis posterior to the *medial crest*; the posterior intermuscular septum to the *posterior border*; the anterior intermuscular septum to the greater part of the *anterior border*; the deep fascia of the leg to the *margins of the subcutaneous surface* (including the superior extensor retinaculum attached to its anterior margin); the interosseous ligament to the rough area above the facet at the lower end.

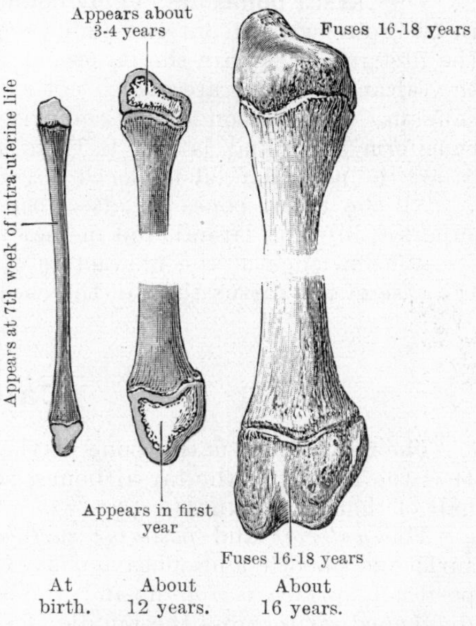

Appears about 3-4 years

Fuses 16-18 years

Appears at 7th week of intra-uterine life

Appears in first year

Fuses 16-18 years

At birth.   About 12 years.   About 16 years.

FIG. 258.—OSSIFICATION OF FIBULA.

The anterior inferior and posterior inferior tibio-fibular ligaments are attached to the **lateral malleolus** at the anterior and posterior margins of its articular facet; the anterior talo-fibular ligament to the *anterior surface* of the malleolus near its tip; the calcaneo-fibular ligament to the *tip*; the posterior talo-fibular ligament and the transverse tibio-fibular ligament to the **malleolar fossa**; the superior peroneal retinaculum to the margins of the *posterior surface* of the malleolus.

Ossification.—The **primary** centre appears at the seventh week of intra-uterine life. Only the ends are cartilaginous at birth.

Secondary Centre.	Appears at	Epiphysis fuses at	Relation of Epiphyseal Line to Capsule of Neighbouring Joint.
For lower end	M. 1 yr. F. 1 yr.	M. 18; F. 16	Medial part inside, lateral part outside.
For upper end	M. 3-4 yr. F. 3 yr.	M. 18; F. 16	Outside.

At the third month of intra-uterine life the fibula is nearly half as thick as the tibia, and its lower end is either at the same level as the tibial malleolus or only a very little lower. At birth it is still, compared with the tibia, much thicker relatively than in the adult; its lower end has not yet reached the adult level, and does not do so until ossification has begun in it. The fibular malleolus reaches lower than the tibial in only a few vertebrates besides Man, *e.g.* elephant, leopard, walrus; and Man vies with the Elephant in that respect. Its importance in the construction of the ankle joint accounts for its downward extension, and probably accounts also for ossification beginning in it sooner than in the upper end.

Structure and Variations.—The structure is like that of other long bones. The medullary canal extends from the neck to a point about three inches from the tip of the malleolus; its lateral wall is thicker than the medial. The *nutrient canal* is one inch in length.

The fibula is occasionally absent or incompletely developed. The facet on the head may be double or may be absent.

Tarsus

The term **tarsus** originally included nearly the whole foot [ταρσός (tarsos) = the part of the foot between the toes and the heel], but it is now applied only to the posterior half of the foot, the skeleton of which consists of seven bones called tarsal bones.

The **tarsal bones** are closely bound together by ligaments. They are arranged in two rows, with an intermediate bone between the rows. There are two bones in the first row; they are the largest of the tarsal bones and are named the **talus** and the **calcaneum**; they are placed not side by side, but the talus on the top of the calcaneum. The second row comprises four bones placed side by side—three **cuneiform** bones and, lateral to them, the **cuboid** bone. The intermediate bone is called the **navicular**; it is placed between the talus and the three cuneiform bones.

All the tarsal bones are described as having six surfaces—anterior, posterior, superior, inferior, lateral, and medial.

A knowledge of the characters of the individual bones is more necessary in the case of the tarsus than in the case of the carpus.

Calcaneum

The **calcaneum** is the bone of the heel [*calcaneum* (allied to calx) = the heel]. It is the largest of the tarsal bones, being nearly three inches in length and about half of that in thickness.

The *anterior* and *posterior surfaces* are the ends of the bone. The anterior surface is smooth and concavo-convex, and articulates with the cuboid bone; the posterior surface is rough, and the tendo calcaneus is inserted into a specially roughened strip across the middle of the surface.

The *superior surface* is distinguished from the others because it has a large, oval, smooth facet about its middle; the facet is for articulation with the body of the talus. In front of the facet there is a rough groove for the attachment of a strong interosseous ligament that binds the talus and calcaneum together. In front of the lateral part of that groove there is a rough, fairly flat area, and at the anterior and medial corner of the area there is usually a small facet for articulation with the head of the talus. In front of and medial to the medial part of the groove there is a projecting shelf of bone, called the **sustentaculum tali** because part of the

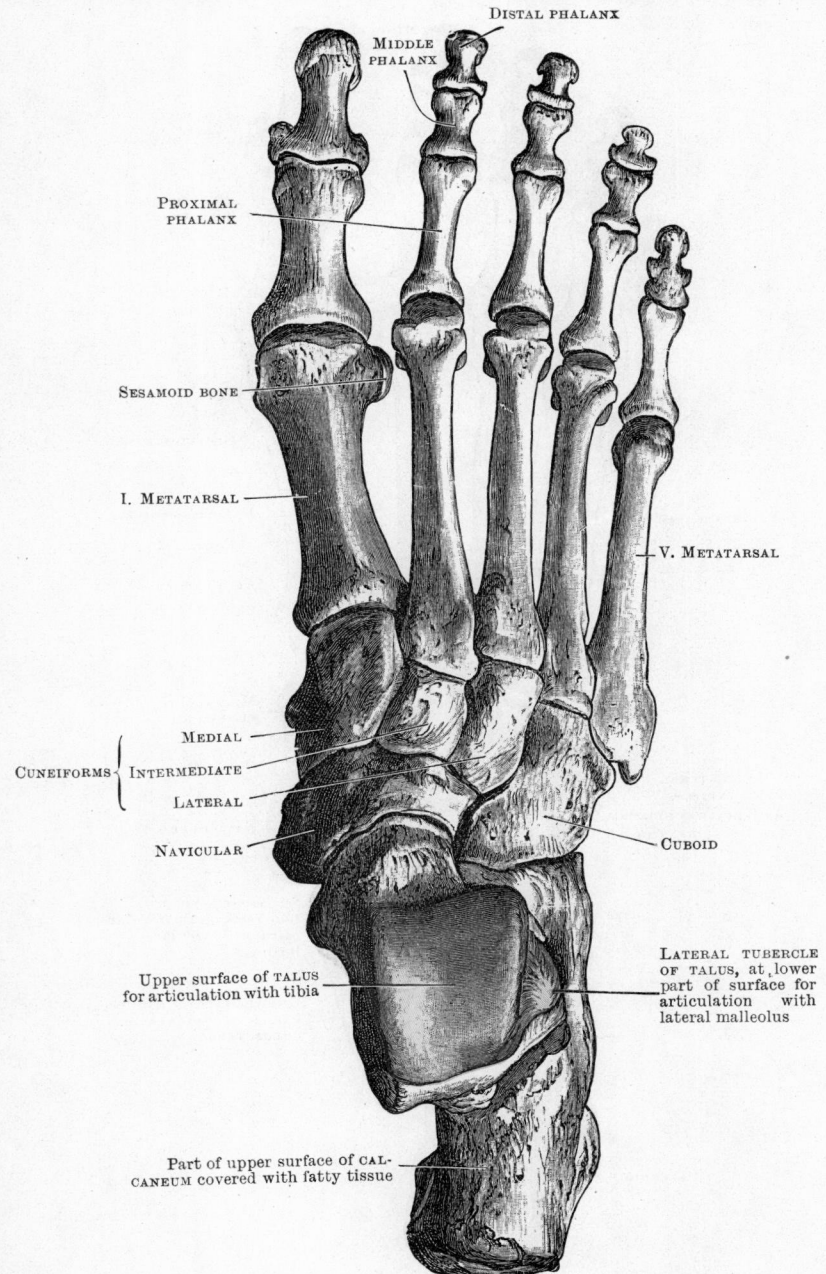

DISTAL PHALANX

MIDDLE
PHALANX

PROXIMAL
PHALANX

SESAMOID BONE

I. METATARSAL

V. METATARSAL

MEDIAL

CUNEIFORMS { INTERMEDIATE

LATERAL

NAVICULAR

CUBOID

Upper surface of TALUS
for articulation with tibia

LATERAL TUBERCLE
OF TALUS, at lower
part of surface for
articulation with
lateral malleolus

Part of upper surface of CAL-
CANEUM covered with fatty tissue

FIG. 259.—UPPER OR DORSAL SURFACE OF BONES OF RIGHT FOOT.

talus rests on it; the upper surface of the sustentaculum is smooth for articulation with the talus; its lower surface is occupied by a shallow groove in which the tendon of the flexor hallucis longus is lodged as it runs forwards into the sole of the foot; the thick, rough medial border of the sustentaculum can be felt in the living body as an ill-defined bony resistance directly below the medial malleolus.

19 c

The *inferior surface* is rough. At its anterior part there is a low, rounded eminence called the **anterior tubercle** of the calcaneum. At its most posterior part there are two blunt, rounded prominences called the **lateral** and **medial tubercles** of the calcaneum; the medial tubercle is the larger of the two. When the calcaneum

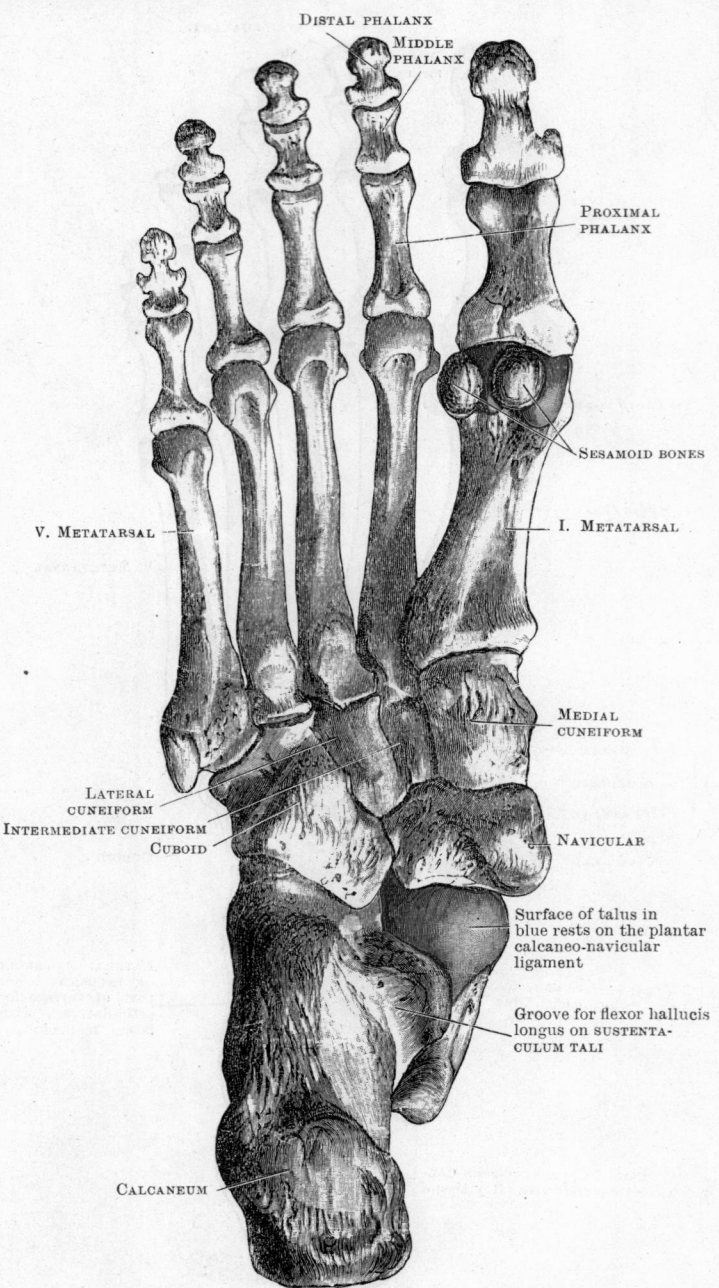

FIG. 260.—LOWER OR PLANTAR SURFACE OF BONES OF RIGHT FOOT.

is laid on the table it rests on the three tubercles. But that is not its position in the foot: when the sole is on the ground the long axis of the calcaneum is directed forwards, upwards and slightly laterally; the bone rests on the backs of the lateral and medial tubercles, *i.e.* on the lower, sloping part of the posterior surface; and the anterior part of the bone is raised up from the ground.

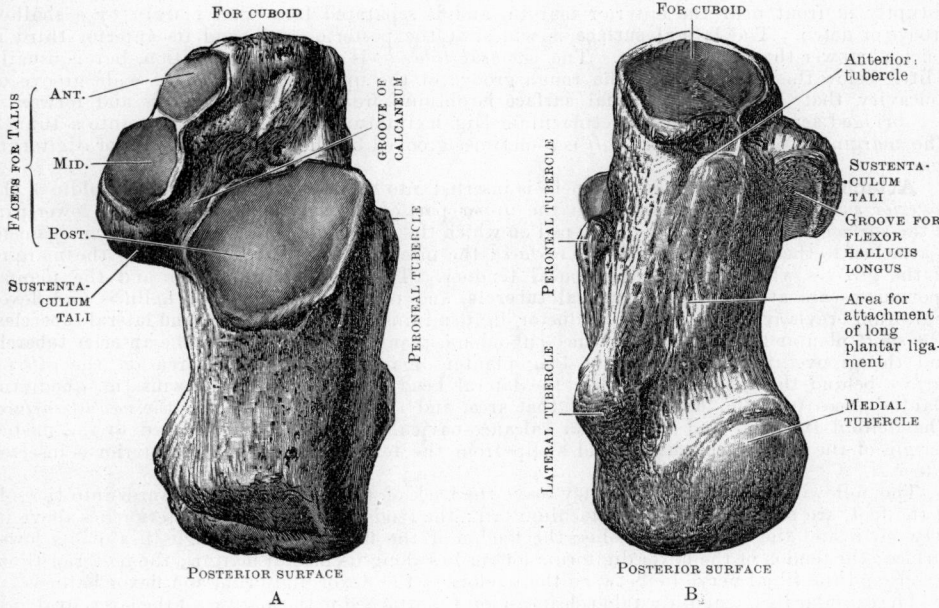

FIG. 261.—RIGHT CALCANEUM. A, seen from above ; B, seen from below.

The *medial surface* is markedly concave owing to the projection of the medial tubercle and the sustentaculum. The *lateral surface* is slightly convex and is rough. On the anterior half of the surface, in some specimens, there is a small but well-marked tubercle called the **peroneal tubercle** [processus trochlearis] ; the tendons of the peroneus longus and brevis cross the surface obliquely — the longus below the tubercle, the brevis above it—and produce shallow grooves on the bone. Except for the strips covered by those two tendons, the whole of the lateral surface is sub-cutaneous and can be felt in the living foot.

The **anterior surface** is concave from above downwards, and convex sideways ; its margins are sharp, except medially. The **posterior surface** widens from above downwards ; the upper of its three areas is cres-centic in outline ; the lower has a striated appearance. The wide, saddle-shaped area behind the large facet on the **superior surface** is covered with the fatty, fibrous tissue that lies deep to the tendo calcaneus ; and it varies in length with the degree of pro-jection of the heel. The **inferior surface** is slightly concave from behind forwards, and is convex from side to side. The *anterior tubercle* fades away posteriorly, but ends

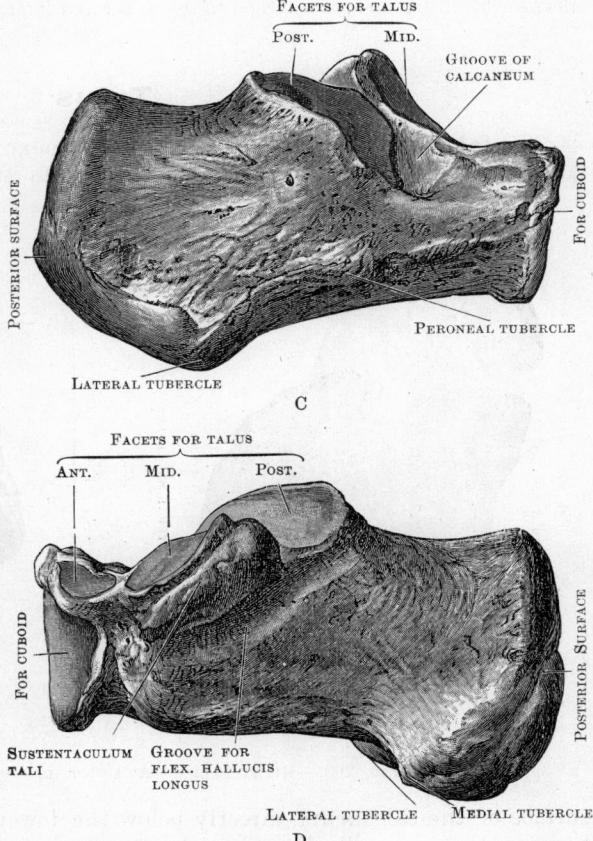

FIG. 262.—RIGHT CALCANEUM. C, Lateral side ; D, Medial side.

abruptly in front near the anterior margin, and is separated from that margin by a shallow groove or notch. The **lateral surface** is widest at the posterior end; and its anterior third is much narrower than the rest of it. The *peroneal tubercle* is variable in position, but is usually a little below the lateral end of the rough groove of the upper surface. The wide groove or concavity that occupies the **medial surface** is oblique from above, downwards and forwards; it is bridged across by the flexor retinaculum [lig. laciniatum], which converts it into a tunnel. The margin of the *sustentaculum tali* is sometimes grooved by the tendon of the flexor digitorum longus.

Attachments.—The tendo calcaneus is inserted into the rough strip across the middle of the *posterior surface*, and is separated from the upper part of the surface by a *bursa*; the lower part of the surface is covered with the fatty pad on which the heel rests. The calcaneo-fibular ligament is attached to the middle of the *lateral surface*; the inferior peroneal retinaculum to the margins of the grooves which lodge the peroneal tendons. The flexor retinaculum and the plantar aponeurosis are attached to the **medial tubercle**, and parts of the abductor hallucis and flexor digitorum brevis arise from it; the abductor digiti minimi from both **medial and lateral tubercles**. The short plantar ligament [lig. calcaneo-cuboideum plantare] is attached to the **anterior tubercle** and the groove in front of it; the long plantar ligament to the wide area on the *inferior surface* behind the anterior tubercle; the lateral head of the flexor accessorius [m. quadratus plantæ] arises from the lateral edge of that area, and the medial head from the *medial surface*. The deltoid ligament and the plantar calcaneo-navicular ligament are attached to the medial margin of the **sustentaculum tali**, and a slip from the tendon of the tibialis posterior is inserted into it.

The following structures, after they leave the back of the leg and turn forwards into the sole of the foot, are related to the sustentaculum tali: the tendon of the tibialis posterior lies above it, between it and the medial malleolus; the tendon of the flexor hallucis longus lies on its lower surface; the tendon of the flexor digitorum longus lies along its medial margin; the posterior tibial vessels and the tibial nerve lie between the tendons of the flexor digitorum and flexor hallucis.

The capsular ligament of the talo-calcanean joint is attached to the margins of the large, oval *facet* on the *upper surface*; the groove in front of the facet gives attachment to the interosseous talo-calcanean ligament; the rough flat area in front of the lateral end of the groove gives attachment to the stem of the bifurcated ligament, the stem of the inferior extensor retinaculum [lig. cruciatum cruris], and some fibres of origin of the extensor digitorum brevis; and the dorsal calcaneo-cuboid ligament is attached to the upper and lateral margins of the *anterior surface*.

Talus

The **talus**, or witch bone, or ankle bone, is next to the calcaneum in size, and has large smooth articular facets on several of its surfaces. It rests on the upper

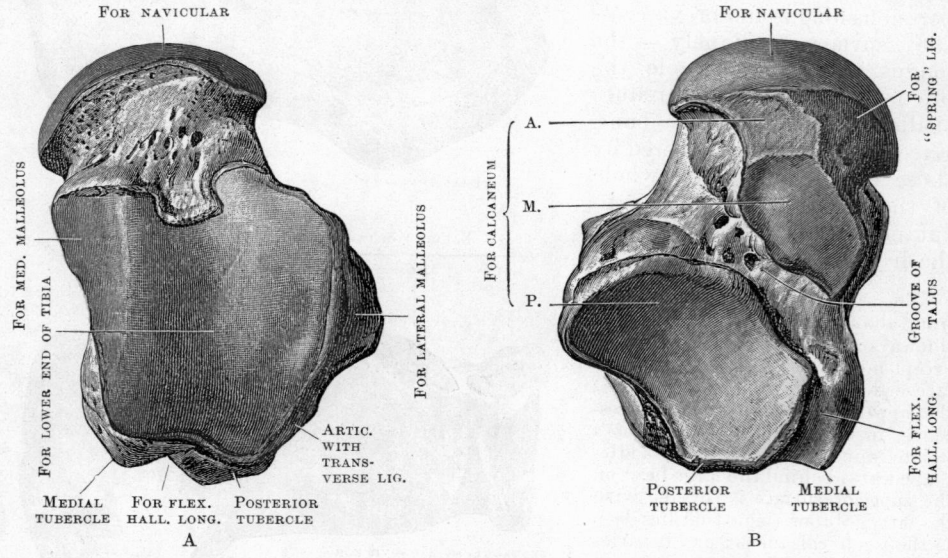

FIG. 263.—RIGHT TALUS. A, Upper surface; B, Lower surface.

surface of the calcaneum, directly below the lower end of the tibia; it is gripped between the two malleoli, and with them and the lower end of the tibia it forms the *ankle joint* [*talus* = the ankle bone].

The bulkier part of the talus is called the *body*; the smooth and rounded end is the anterior part of the bone, and is called the *head*; the rough, slightly constricted part between the head and the body is called the *neck*.

The *superior surface* of the **body** is a large face for articulation with the lower end of the tibia. It is convex from before backwards, slightly concave from side to side, and is narrower behind than in front. The superior and lateral surfaces and the articular part of the medial surface are sometimes, together, called the **trochlea** of the talus. The *inferior surface* has two facets with a deep groove between them. The one farther back is large, concave, and oval, with the long axis oblique, and it articulates with the large, oval facet on the upper surface of the calcaneum. The one in front is on body, neck, and head; it articulates with the sustentaculum tali, and with the facet on the anterior part of the upper surface of the calcaneum; it varies in its extent, and the part on the head may be separate from the rest.

The *medial surface* can be distinguished from the lateral surface because it is nearly all rough, and is flush with the medial side of the neck. Near the upper margin there is a comma-shaped facet for articulation with the medial malleolus.

The *lateral surface* stands away from the neck, and is nearly all occupied by a large facet for articulation with the lateral malleolus. The posterior part of the facet is united to the upper surface by an ill-defined, narrow, triangular facet which articulates with the transverse tibio-fibular ligament.

The *posterior surface* is very small. It is crossed by a fairly broad, oblique groove that lodges the tendon of the flexor hallucis longus. When the talus and calcaneum are placed together properly, that groove is continuous with the groove for the same tendon on the lower surface of the sustentaculum tali. The projection on the lateral side of the groove is called the **posterior tubercle** of the talus, and that on the medial side is called the **medial tubercle**.

The *anterior surface* is the convex, smooth surface of the **head**; it articulates with the navicular bone. The facet on the lower surface of the head for articulation with the anterior part of the upper surface of the calcaneum is usually continuous with the facet that articulates with the sustentaculum tali. The lower part of the medial side of the head articulates not with a bone but with a ligament called the plantar calcaneo-navicular or "spring" ligament, which stretches between the sustentaculum tali and the plantar surface of the navicular bone; a faint ridge often marks off that area from the rest of the articular surface of the head.

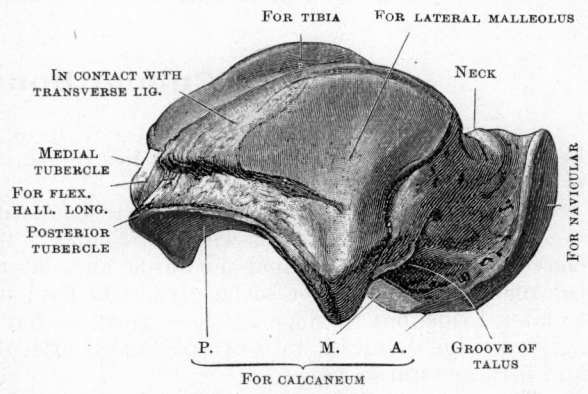

Lateral side.

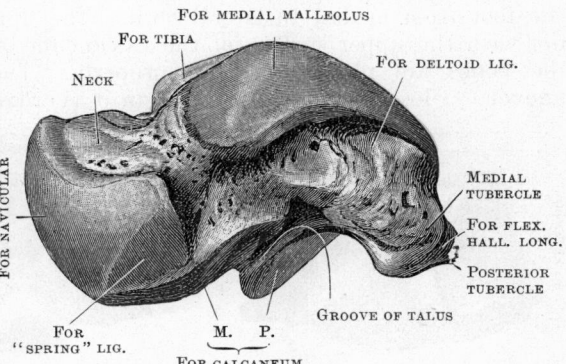

Medial side.

FIG. 264.—RIGHT TALUS.

When the talus and the calcaneum of the same foot are placed together properly, their anterior surfaces are almost in the same transverse vertical plane, and the anterior surface of the talus is medial to that of the calcaneum as well as above it; the anterior surfaces of the talus and the calcaneum articulate respectively with the navicular and the cuboid, and the two joints are spoken of together as the *transverse tarsal joint*. The movements of inversion and eversion of the foot take place largely at the transverse tarsal joint. **Inversion** is the movement whereby the medial border of the foot is lifted up, and the sole looks towards the median plane. **Eversion** is the movement whereby the lateral border of the foot is lifted up, and the sole looks in a lateral direction. When the foot is extended so that it is almost in line with the leg, and is inverted, the head of the talus can be both felt and seen as a distinct prominence about an inch in front of and below the ankle joint, and the body of the talus also may be felt near the lateral malleolus.

When the talus and calcaneum are placed together, the grooves which give attachment to the interosseous ligament form a tunnel called the **sinus tarsi**. The head of the talus looks in a medial direction as well as forwards. The articular facet on the lateral surface of the body is concave from above downwards; at its lower angle the bone projects laterally to form the **lateral tubercle**. On the medial surface, below the tail of the articular comma, there may be a circular or oval impression for the attachment of part of the deltoid ligament.

Attachments.—The anterior ligament of the ankle joint and the dorsal talo-navicular ligament are attached to the *upper surface* of the **neck**; the anterior talo-fibular ligament to the *lateral surface*; a part of the deltoid ligament to the *medial surface* of both neck and **body**; the capsular ligament of the talo-calcanean joint to the margins of the large, oval facet on the *lower surface* of the body; the interosseous ligament to the *groove* in front of that facet; the posterior ligament of the ankle joint to the upper part of the *posterior surface*; the posterior talo-fibular ligament to the **posterior tubercle**. No muscle or tendon is attached to the talus.

Cuboid Bone

The **cuboid** bone may be picked out from the other smaller tarsal bones because of its more cubical shape. It lies in the lateral margin of the foot in front of the calcaneum.

The *anterior* and *posterior surfaces* can be distinguished from the other surfaces because each of those two is wholly articular. The posterior surface is concavo-convex, slopes from behind forwards and laterally, and articulates with the calcaneum. The anterior surface is nearly flat; it slopes backwards from medial to lateral side, but its slope is not so great as that of the posterior surface; a faint, vertical ridge divides it into two parts that articulate with the bases of the fourth and fifth metatarsal bones.

The *superior surface* is distinguished from the others because it is nearly flat and is rough—having no articular facet. Owing to the slope of the dorsum of the foot from medial to lateral border, the upper surface of the cuboid is flush not with the upper surface of the calcaneum but with the lateral surface, when the bones are placed together properly. The *inferior surface* is rough and uneven. Close to its anterior margin it is crossed by a fairly deep groove which lodges the tendon of the peroneus longus as it crosses the sole of the foot; the posterior boundary of the groove is a broad, prominent ridge, the lateral end of which is called the **tuberosity**.

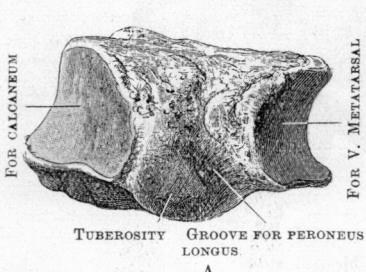

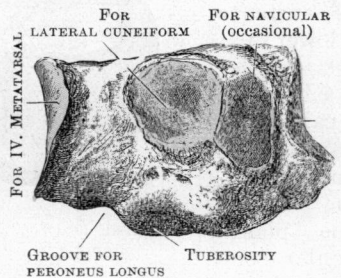

FIG. 265.—RIGHT CUBOID BONE. A, Lateral Side; B, Medial Side.

The *lateral surface* is the smallest of all the surfaces, owing to the slope of the other surfaces, and it looks downwards as well as in a lateral direction. It is occupied by the tuberosity and the lateral end of the groove seen on the plantar surface. On the antero-lateral aspect of the tuberosity there is often a smooth facet produced by contact with a sesamoid bone or cartilage which lies in the substance of the peroneus longus tendon as the tendon turns into the sole. The *medial surface* is large and rather uneven; about its middle there is a facet for articulation with the lateral cuneiform bone; and behind that facet, and continuous with it, there may be another, smaller facet for articulation with the navicular bone.

The long peroneal tendon traverses the whole length of the groove on the lateral and lower surfaces; and the groove is lined throughout with the synovial sheath of the tendon. The facet for the peroneal sesamoid is, however, not in line with the groove; but the tendon, as it enters the groove, expands, so that the part of it containing the sesamoid articulates with the facet while its upper edge lies in the groove. The sesamoid glides obliquely on the facet during the movements of eversion and inversion; during inversion the tendon is partly drawn off the facet, and occupies the lateral end of the groove more completely.

Attachments.—Dorsal, plantar, and interosseous ligaments that bind the **cuboid** to neighbouring bones are attached to the rough parts of its surfaces. The long plantar ligament is attached to both *lips* of the **groove** on the *plantar surface* and holds the peroneus longus tendon in place. A slip from the tendon of the tibialis posterior is inserted into the medial part of the groove; and a slip of the flexor hallucis brevis arises from the medial part of the area behind the ridge.

Navicular Bone

The **navicular bone** is readily identified because one of its two large surfaces is markedly concave—hence its name, from a fancied resemblance to a boat. It lies in the medial side of the foot in front of the talus; and it is compressed from before backwards.

The *posterior surface* is the large, smooth, concave surface, and articulates with the head of the talus. The *anterior surface* also is smooth, but it is slightly convex, and it is mapped out by faint ridges into three areas for articulation with the three cuneiform bones. The *superior surface* is rough and is convex

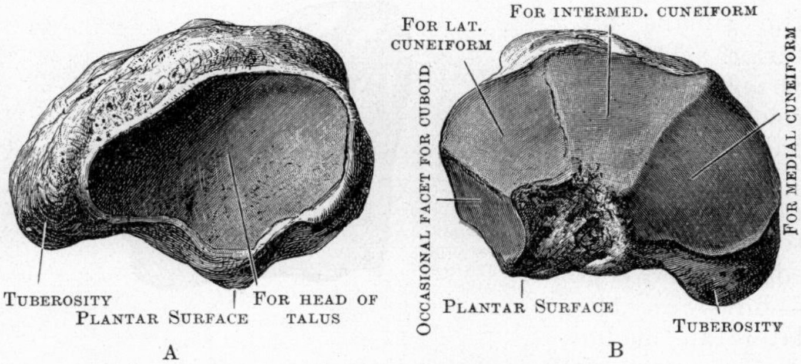

FIG. 266.—RIGHT NAVICULAR BONE.

A, Posterior aspect; B, Anterior aspect.

in its longer measurement. The *inferior surface* also is rough, but it is much smaller than the dorsal surface and is very uneven.

The *medial surface* is modified into a rough projection called the **tuberosity** of the navicular bone. This tuberosity is an important landmark. It can be felt on the medial side of the foot about an inch below and in front of the medial malleolus; when shoes are worn the tuberosity is felt at the lip of the shoe. Close to the tuberosity, on the plantar surface, there is a shallow, oblique groove that lodges the smaller, deeper part of the tendon of the tibialis posterior as it runs forwards in the sole. The *lateral* surface is not marked off from the superior surface by any definite line; it is small and usually rough, but may be faceted to articulate with the cuboid bone.

Attachments.—Dorsal and plantar ligaments are attached to the rough parts and bind the **navicular** bone to adjacent bones. The most important is the plantar calcaneo-navicular ligament (or " spring " ligament), which stretches from its *plantar surface* to the sustentaculum tali. The anterior fibres of the deltoid ligament are attached to the **tuberosity**, which receives also a great part of the tendon of the tibialis posterior.

Cuneiform Bones

The three **cuneiform** bones are wedge-shaped [*cuneus* = a wedge]. They lie side by side in front of the navicular bone, and separate it from the medial three metatarsal bones. Their anterior and posterior surfaces are occupied by smooth articular facets. The medial cuneiform is the largest and most important; the intermediate one is the smallest and is the most definitely wedge-shaped.

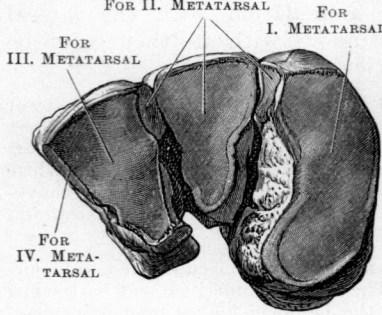

FIG. 267.—ANTERIOR ASPECT OF CUNEI- FORM BONES OF RIGHT FOOT.

The **medial cuneiform** lies in the medial side of the foot and is the bone felt in front of the tuberosity of the navicular bone. The *anterior surface* is kidney-shaped in outline, the concave edge being its lateral margin; it articulates with the base of the first metatarsal bone. The *posterior surface* is concave and pear-shaped, with the stalk of the pear upwards; it articulates with the navicular bone. The *lateral surface* is uneven and slightly concave; it has facets near its posterior and upper margins for articulation with the intermediate cuneiform and with the medial side of the base of the second metatarsal bone. The *medial surface* is the largest of the surfaces and is rough, and, in conformity with the shape of the medial side of the foot, it is convex from above downwards. At the most anterior and lowest part there is a smooth impression, resembling a facet, for the insertion of the greater part of the tendon of the tibialis anterior. The *inferior surface* is rough and is the base of the wedge. The *superior surface* is reduced to a border—the edge of the wedge—between the lateral and medial surfaces, and it

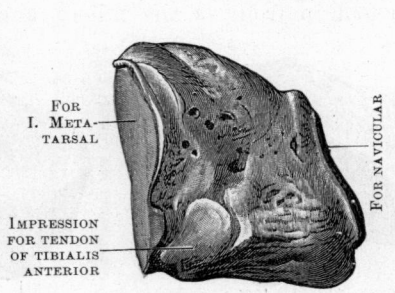

FIG. 268.—RIGHT MEDIAL CUNEIFORM (Medial Side).

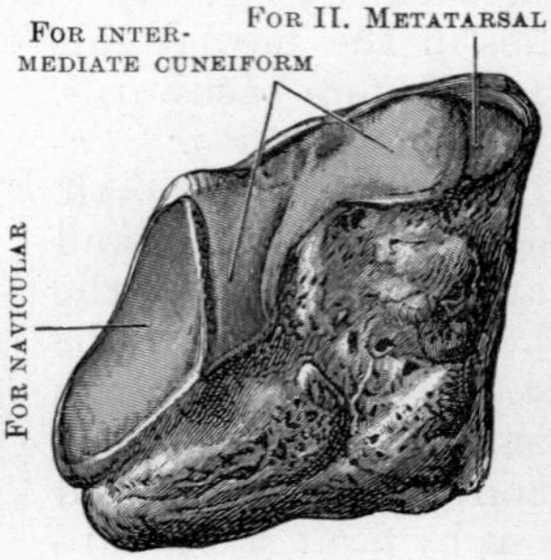

FIG. 269.—RIGHT MEDIAL CUNEIFORM (Lateral Side).

slopes downwards and backwards, because the posterior surface is smaller than the anterior.

The **intermediate cuneiform** is the smallest of the tarsal bones. Its *superior surface* is square in outline, rough and slightly convex, and is the base of the wedge. The *inferior surface* is reduced to a rough border between the medial and lateral surfaces, and is the edge of the wedge. The *anterior* and *posterior surfaces* are triangular in outline; the anterior is slightly convex and articulates with the base of the second metatarsal bone; the posterior is slightly concave and articulates with the navicular bone. The *medial surface* has a facet along its upper border and another along its posterior border, both for articulation with the medial cuneiform; the rest of the surface is rough. The *lateral surface* has a facet along its posterior border for articulation with the lateral cuneiform, and the rest of it is rough. The facet along the upper border distinguishes the medial surface from the lateral surface; the facets along the posterior borders enable one to distinguish the posterior surface from the anterior, if that has not been done already.

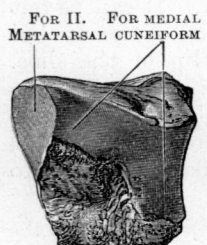

FIG. 270. — RIGHT INTERMEDIATE CUNEI- FORM (Medial Side).

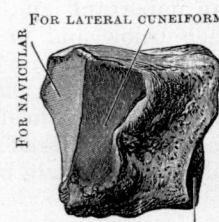

FIG. 271. — RIGHT INTERMEDIATE CUNEI- FORM (Lateral Side).

The **lateral cuneiform** is larger than the intermediate cuneiform—if both specimens come from the same skeleton. A beginner may have difficulty in distinguishing the lateral cuneiform of a small foot from the intermediate of a large foot, for the two bones are not unlike in general appearance.

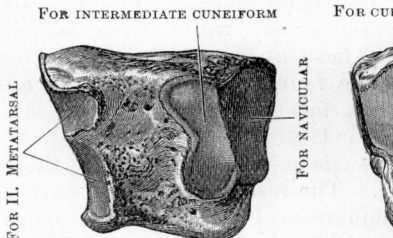

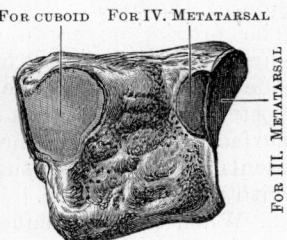

For intermediate cuneiform
For II. Metatarsal
For navicular
Fig. 272.—Right Lateral Cuneiform (Medial Side).

For cuboid
For IV. Metatarsal
For III. Metatarsal
Fig. 273.—Right Lateral Cuneiform (Lateral Side).

The *superior surface* is oblong in outline, rough and nearly flat, and is the base of the wedge; its anterior part turns medially, so that its long axis is slightly bent. The *inferior surface* is reduced to a rough, thick border between the medial and lateral surfaces, and is the edge of the wedge. The *anterior surface* is all covered with a facet for articulation with the base of the third metatarsal bone,

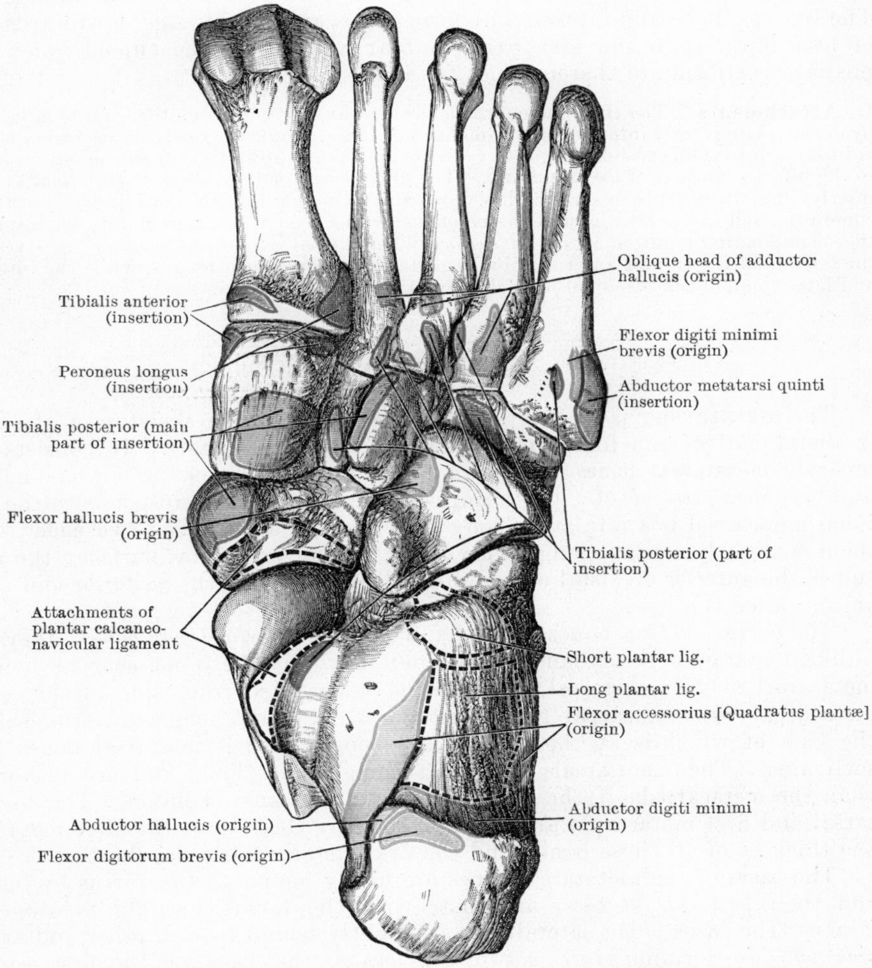

Tibialis anterior (insertion)
Peroneus longus (insertion)
Tibialis posterior (main part of insertion)
Flexor hallucis brevis (origin)
Attachments of plantar calcaneo-navicular ligament
Abductor hallucis (origin)
Flexor digitorum brevis (origin)
Oblique head of adductor hallucis (origin)
Flexor digiti minimi brevis (origin)
Abductor metatarsi quinti (insertion)
Tibialis posterior (part of insertion)
Short plantar lig.
Long plantar lig.
Flexor accessorius [Quadratus plantæ] (origin)
Abductor digiti minimi (origin)
Fig. 274.—Muscle-Attachments to Left Tarsus and Metatarsus (Plantar Aspect).

and is nearly triangular in outline. The upper and larger part of the *posterior surface* is covered with a quadrangular facet for articulation with the navicular bone, and the small, lower part is rough. The *medial surface* has a narrow facet along its posterior border for articulation with the intermediate cuneiform, and usually two small facets along its anterior border for articulation with the lateral side of the base of the second metatarsal bone; the rest of the surface is rough. The *lateral surface* is usually wider from before backwards than the medial surface; it has a small facet at its anterior border for articulation with the medial side of the base of the fourth metatarsal bone, and a large facet in its upper posterior corner. That facet distinguishes the lateral surface from the medial surface, distinguishes the lateral cuneiform from the intermediate, and enables one to identify the posterior surface, for it lies close to the posterior border; it articulates with the cuboid bone. The rest of the lateral surface is rough.

When the three cuneiform bones are fitted together their posterior surfaces are nearly flush, for they all articulate with the front of the navicular bone. The intermediate cuneiform is shorter than the other two; a gap is left therefore between the medial and the lateral and in front of the intermediate one. (*See* Fig. 259.) The base of the second metatarsal bone fits into the gap; it therefore articulates posteriorly with the intermediate cuneiform, and at the sides with the medial and the lateral—an arrangement which increases the stability of the foot, but adds to the difficulty of amputating the foot at the tarso-metatarsal joints. The intermediate and lateral cuneiform bones are placed edge downwards and are of less depth than the first; the plantar surfaces of the cuboid bone and the medial cuneiform are therefore not far apart.

Attachments.—The three cuneiform bones are united to one another and to adjacent bones by dorsal, plantar, and interosseous ligaments. A large part of the tendon of the tibialis posterior is inserted into the posterior part of the *inferior surface* of the **medial** cuneiform, and it sends slips to the inferior surfaces of the **other two.** The greater part of the tendon of the tibialis anterior is inserted into an impression situated low down and far forward on the *medial surface* of the **medial** cuneiform, and the smaller part of the peroneus longus tendon is inserted into an impression at the corresponding point on its *lateral surface.* The medial cuneiform therefore receives parts of the tendons of the tibialis anterior, tibialis posterior, and peroneus longus, while the intermediate and lateral cuneiform bones get only slips from the tibialis posterior.

Metatarsus

The **metatarsus** is in front of the tarsus, and is the skeleton of the anterior or distal half of the foot proper [μετά (meta) = next after]. It consists of five separate **metatarsal bones**—one corresponding to each toe. They are named by number—*first, second,* etc., beginning with the one that corresponds to the big toe. Each metatarsal is a miniature long bone, having a **shaft** and **two ends**. Each of them is slightly concave lengthwise on its inferior or plantar surface; the rounded end is the **anterior** or distal end, and is called the *head*; the **posterior** end is larger, and is called the *base*.

The corresponding bones of the hand are called *metacarpal bones*; they are not unlike metatarsal bones, and a beginner may mistake a metacarpal bone for a metatarsal. The metatarsal bones are more flattened from side to side than the metacarpals; a metacarpal has on its dorsal surface a long, flat, triangular area, the base of which is at the head of the bone, but the metatarsal bones have no such area. The metatarsals are about three inches long, and are rather longer than the metacarpals, if the bones are from the same skeleton. The first metatarsal and first metacarpal are distinguished by their size: the first metatarsal is the thickest of all those bones, and the first metacarpal is the shortest.

The **bases** of the metatarsal bones are firmly bound to the tarsus by ligaments, and their *posterior surfaces* articulate with the tarsus, forming *tarso-metatarsal joints.* The bases of the lateral four are tightly bound to each other and articulate *side by side,* forming *inter-metatarsal joints*; the base of the first sometimes articulates with that of the second, but is usually free.

The **heads** articulate with the proximal row of phalanges, forming *metatarso-phalangeal joints.* The sides of the heads have grooves and tubercles for the attachment of the collateral ligaments of those joints. The articular part extends much farther on to the plantar surface than on to the dorsum, because when the toe is *flexed* (*i.e.* moved towards the sole) the base of the phalanx articulates with the plantar surface of the head of the metatarsal; when the toe is *extended* it is in a straight line with the metatarsal, and the base of the phalanx articulates with the distal surface of the head. *Dorsiflexion* or *hyper-extension* is the movement of bending the toe upwards out of line with the metatarsal; the degree to which it is possible varies in different people but is never great, and therefore the articular surface of the head extends very little on to the dorsum.

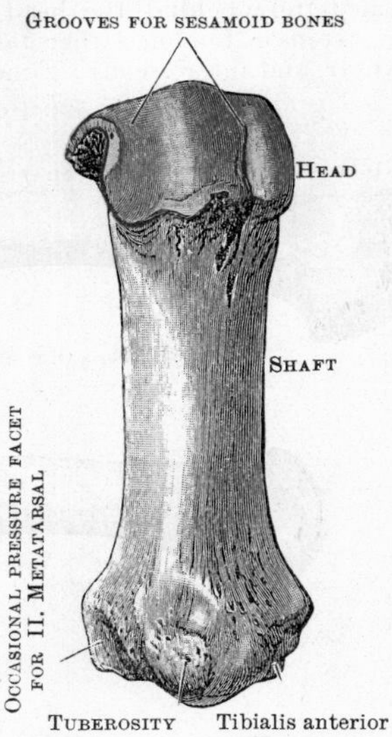

The **first metatarsal bone** can be felt in all its length in the medial side of the foot. Its **base**—looked at end on—is kidney-shaped, with the long axis vertical, and the notched or concave side is the *lateral* side. It articulates with the medial cuneiform bone. The **head** is slightly compressed from above downwards, and has two well-marked grooves on its lower or *plantar* surface, for articulation with two small sesamoid bones. The **shaft** is three-sided; its surfaces are dorsal, plantar, and lateral, and can be identified by reference to the head and base.

The **fifth metatarsal bone** is easily distinguished from the others because it is compressed from above downwards, has a relatively small **head**, and has a large **tubercle** on the *lateral* side of the **base**. The whole length of the bone can be felt in the lateral border of the foot, and the tubercle makes the prominence—seen as well as felt—about midway between the heel and the little toe. The posterior surface of the base articulates with the cuboid.

GROOVES FOR SESAMOID BONES

HEAD

SHAFT

OCCASIONAL PRESSURE FACET FOR II. METATARSAL

TUBEROSITY   Tibialis anterior

FIG. 275.—RIGHT FIRST METATARSAL BONE (Plantar Aspect).

A line drawn from the base of the first metatarsal to the tubercle of the fifth slants backwards, and corresponds fairly closely to the position of the tarso-metatarsal joints. Those joints and the posterior surfaces of the bases of the lateral four metatarsals therefore slope backwards from medial to lateral side; consequently, the lateral surface of a metatarsal is longer than the medial surface and can be distinguished from it at a glance.

The **second** and **third metatarsal bones** are very much alike. They are compressed from side to side in all their length; the posterior surface of the base is nearly triangular in outline and articulates with a cuneiform bone. But they can be distinguished if the *lateral* surface of the base is examined: the lateral surface of the **second** has two facets—an upper and a lower—separated by a horizontal groove, and one or both of the facets are double; for the base of the second metatarsal fits in between the lateral and medial cuneiform bones, articulating with them, and the lateral surface articulates also with the base of the third metatarsal.

FOR IV. METATARSAL

For CUBOID

TUBERCLE

FIG. 276. — RIGHT FIFTH METATARSAL BONE (Dorsal Aspect).

The **head** and **shaft** of the **fourth metatarsal bone** resemble those of the second and third, but the base is more irregular, is more cuboidal in shape, and its posterior surface, which articulates with the cuboid, is more nearly square in outline. The *lateral surface* of the **base** has a large facet bounded by an oblique groove; in that respect it resembles the lateral surface of the third, but the medial surfaces are quite different: the *medial surface* of the **third** has two small facets, an upper and a lower; the *medial surface* of the **fourth** has a large facet which is usually subdivided, for it articulates not only with the base of the third metatarsal but also with the lateral surface of the lateral cuneiform bone.

The articular surface of the head is bounded, on the sides and superiorly, by a groove—better marked in the smaller metatarsals than in the first. On each side the upper part of the groove is bounded posteriorly by a smooth tubercle. The edge of the plantar part of the articular surface is notched in the middle. The boundaries of the notch end posteriorly as pointed tubercles. The groove on the first for the medial sesamoid is usually the wider. (Fig. 274.)

Attachments.—In the case of *each metatarsal*, collateral ligaments pass from the sides of the **head** to the sides of the base of the proximal phalanx, and the plantar ligament closes in the metatarso-phalangeal joint below, being attached loosely to the plantar surface of the metatarsal immediately behind the head, and firmly to the plantar surface of the base of the phalanx; the extensor tendon either takes the place of a dorsal ligament or is fused with it. Dorsal, plantar, and interosseous ligaments bind the **bases** to one another and to the tarsus.

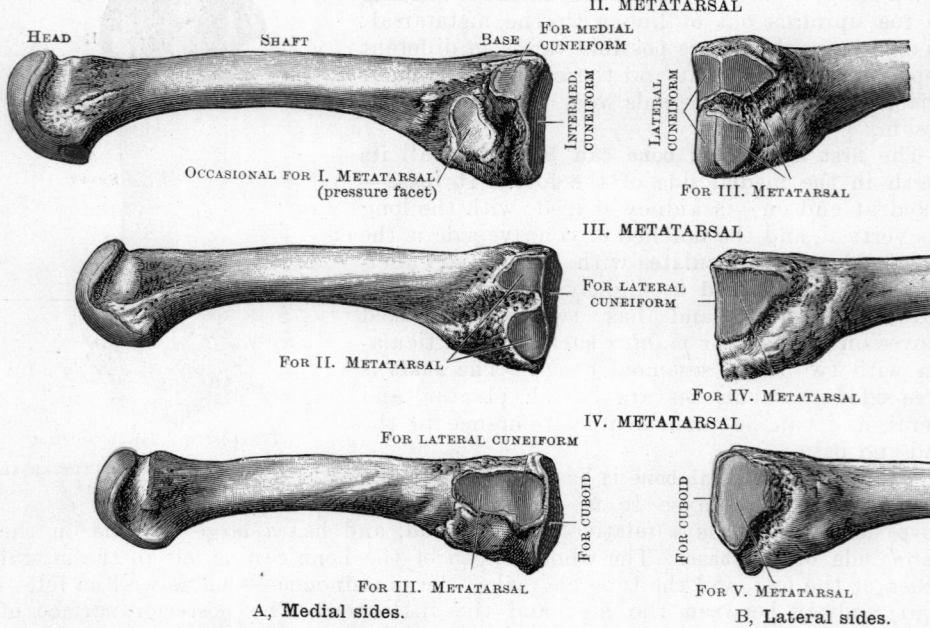

FIG. 277.—VIEW OF THE BASES AND SHAFTS OF THE SECOND, THIRD, AND FOURTH METATARSAL BONES OF THE RIGHT FOOT. NOTE THAT THE SECOND IS THE LONGEST.

Slips of the long plantar ligament are attached to the plantar surfaces of the **bases** of the *second*, *third*, and *fourth* metatarsals; slips of the tibialis posterior tendon are inserted into those bases, and the oblique head of the adductor hallucis arises from them. One head of a dorsal interosseous muscle arises from each side of the **shaft** of each of those three bones, and the first and second plantar interosseous muscles arise respectively from the third and fourth.

The smaller part of the tendon of the tibialis anterior is inserted into an impression on the medial side of the **base** of the *first* metatarsal bone near the sole, and the greater part of the peroneus longus tendon into a smooth impression on the prominent, lowest part of the lateral side; one head of the first dorsal interosseous muscle arises from the lateral surface of the **shaft**.

The peroneus brevis and tertius are inserted into the dorsum of the **base** of the *fifth* metatarsal; part of the flexor digiti minimi brevis arises from the plantar surface. The abductor metatarsi quinti (when present) and a strong band of the plantar fascia are inserted into the *tubercle*. The third plantar interosseous muscle arises from the plantar surface of the **shaft**, and one head of the fourth dorsal interosseous from the medial surface.

Phalanges of Toes

Each **phalanx** is a miniature long bone, possessing a **shaft** and **two ends** [φάλαγξ (phalanx) = a round log or roller]; the **proximal** or posterior end is the larger end and is called the *base*; the **distal** end is called the *head*. The proximal phalanx of a toe is about the same length as the middle phalanx of a finger, but it can be picked out from among phalanges of fingers because its base is larger, and its shaft is relatively more attenuated; the proximal phalanx of the big toe, on the contrary, is thicker than any other phalanx. The middle and distal phalanges of the toes are so short that they cannot be mistaken either for the proximal phalanges of toes or for the phalanges of fingers.

The **proximal phalanx** of a toe is a little more than an inch in length, and is slightly concave lengthwise on its inferior or *plantar surface*. The **base** is expanded and is concave on its proximal surface for articulation with the

head of the metatarsal.   The **shaft** is thin—being compressed from side to side near
the base, and from above downwards near the head.   The **head** is pulley-shaped and
articulates with the base of the middle phalanx ; the arti-
cular part extends on to the plantar surface but scarcely
at all on to the dorsum, for dorsiflexion is a limited movement, while flexion is free, and the middle joint of the toes
in many people who have worn boots since infancy is in
a permanent position of flexion.

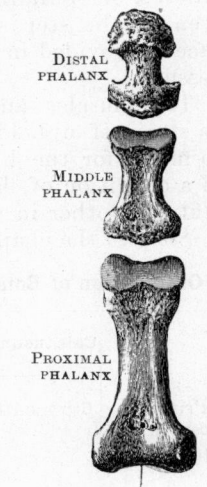

DISTAL
PHALANX

MIDDLE
PHALANX

PROXIMAL
PHALANX

FOR METATARSAL

FIG. 278.—PHALANGES OF
A TOE (Plantar Aspect).

The **middle phalanx** is very short—usually less than half an inch
in length—and it may be a mere nodule of bone.   The **base** articulates
with the head of the proximal phalanx and is therefore the reverse of
a pulley : it has two concave smooth areas with a low, vertical, smooth
ridge between them.   The **shaft** is convex on its dorsal surface and
either flat or concave on its plantar surface ; but it may be difficult
to distinguish the surfaces if the phalanx is stunted.   The articular
part of the **head** is a shallow pulley, and as it extends some distance
on to the plantar surface it is a guide to the surfaces.

The **distal phalanx** also is very small.   The **base** articulates with
the head of the middle phalanx and is relatively expanded.   The
shaft is constricted ; the **head** is expanded and is very rough on its
plantar surface.

The **big toe** has only two phalanges.   The **proximal** resembles
the proximal phalanx of the other toes and the **distal** resembles the
distal ; but they are much larger in every way than the phalanges of
other toes.   In an adult big toe the medial side of the base of a
phalanx is larger than the lateral side, and the big toe inclines therefore towards the other toes ; the inclination is not an abnormality
due to wearing pointed boots, but it may be exaggerated by the use of boots that do not fit.

Owing to the slant of the joints between the tarsus and metatarsus and to the fact that the toes
are progressively shorter from the second to the fifth, the nail of the little toe is about the level
of the root of the big toe ; the root of the little toe or fifth metatarso-phalangeal joint is the
yielding prominence on the lateral border of the widest part of the foot, and usually bulges out
the side of the shoe a little in front of the middle, and, being so far back, is apt to be mistaken for
the base of the metatarsal bone if the foot is shod.

Attachments.—The plantar and the collateral ligaments of the metatarso-phalangeal
joints and interphalangeal joints are attached to the **bases** and the **heads** ; the fibrous flexor
sheaths are attached to the margins of the **shafts** of the proximal and middle phalanges, and to
the base of the distal phalanx in front of the insertion of the long flexor tendon.

The abductor hallucis is inserted into the medial side of the **base** of the **proximal phalanx**
of the *big toe* ; the adductor hallucis into the lateral side ; the flexor hallucis brevis into both sides ;
the medial tendon of the extensor digitorum brevis into the dorsum.   The flexor brevis and
abductor digiti minimi are inserted into the lateral side of the base of the proximal phalanx of the
little toe.

The **base** of the **distal phalanx** of the *big toe* receives the insertion of the tendons of the
long flexor and extensor on the plantar and dorsal surfaces respectively.   A tendon of the flexor
digitorum brevis is inserted into the margins of the **shafts** of the **middle phalanx** of each of the
other toes, and a slip of the extensor expansion into the dorsum of its base.   The **base** of each **distal
phalanx** gives insertion to a tendon of the flexor digitorum longus on its plantar surface, and the
rest of the extensor expansion on its dorsal surface.

Columns of the Foot.—The bones of the foot as a whole are arranged in two
columns.   The **lateral column** consists of the calcaneum, the cuboid, the fourth and
fifth metatarsal bones, and the phalanges of the corresponding digits.   The **medial
column** consists of the talus, the navicular, the three cuneiform bones, the medial
three metatarsal bones, and the phalanges of the corresponding digits.

Arches of the Foot.—The bones of the tarsus and metatarsus do not lie in a
horizontal plane, but are arranged in the form of a half-dome, with longitudinal
and transverse arches ; the foot therefore rests posteriorly on the lower part of the
back of the calcaneum, anteriorly on the heads of the metatarsal bones, and at the
lateral border slightly on the fifth metatarsal bone, while at the medial border it
is raised well away from the ground.

The dome and its arches are due primarily to the shape of the bones with
which the framework of the foot is built, and they are maintained by the
ligaments that bind the bones together and by the muscles, tendons, and fasciæ
of the foot, their chief support being the tendons of the tibialis posterior and
peroneus longus, which cross the sole obliquely from opposite sides.

The advantages given by the arches of the foot are that the weight of the body is distributed over the foot (compare the use of arches above windows in the wall of a big building), the height of the body is slightly increased, springiness is given to the step, shocks received in running and jumping are broken ; and a space is provided in which the soft parts of the sole of the foot may lie free from pressure.

The muscles and tendons may become inefficient owing to malnutrition ; the strain of upholding the arches under the weight of the body then becomes too much for the ligaments ; they stretch, and the arches sink down gradually, till a condition of flat-foot or splay-foot is established, the bones altering in shape to fit each other in their modified positions in the flattened arch.

See also the chapter on JOINTS, in which the arches are described more fully.

Ossification of Bones of Foot.—Tarsus.   Each tarsal bone has one *primary* centre.

	Calcaneum.	Talus.	Cuboid.	Lateral Cuneiform.	Navicular.	Intermed. Cuneiform.	Medial Cuneiform.
Primary centre appears at	6th month	8th month	Birth or soon after	1st year	3rd year	M. 4 yr. F. 3 yr.	M. 4 yr. F. 3 yr.

The centres for the navicular may be double (or even multiple) at first, but they rapidly fuse. The calcaneum alone has a *secondary* centre.   The part of the bone that bears the medial and lateral tubercles is ossified from it ; it appears at 8 in girls and 10 in boys, and unites at 15 and 18 respectively.   Ossification of all the tarsal bones is completed after puberty.   Part of the posterior tubercle of the talus may have a separate centre, and that portion of it may develop as an independent bone called the *os trigonum*.

Metatarsus.—A *primary* centre for each metatarsal appears in the ninth week of intra-uterine life.   They are well ossified at birth.   A *secondary* centre for each appears as follows, that for the first being a few months earlier than the others :—

Secondary Centre.	Appears at	Epiphysis fuses at	Relation of Epiphyseal Line to Capsule of Neighbouring Joint.
For *base* of first	M. 3 yr.; F. 2 yr.	M. 18 ; F. 15	Outside.
For *head* of others	M. 3 yr.; F. 2 yr.	M. 18 ; F. 15	Outside.

Epiphyses have been seen in the bases of the lateral metatarsals instead of in the heads.

Phalanges.—Each has a *primary* centre for shaft and head, and a secondary centre for the base.

Primary Centre for	Distal Phalanx.	Proximal Phalanx.	Middle Phalanx.
Appears	At end of 3rd month	At end of 4th month	6th month—birth

Secondary Centre.	Appears at	Epiphysis fuses at	Relation of Epiphyseal Line to Capsule of Neighbouring Joint.
For base	M. 3 yr. F. 2 „	M. 18 F. 15	Outside.

Structure and Variations.—The *tarsal* bones have the structure of short bones ; their non-articular surfaces are pierced by numerous *nutrient vessels*.   The *metatarsal* bones and the *phalanges* have the structure of long bones.   The medullary cavity is relatively narrow, and may be absent in the distal two phalanges.   The *nutrient foramen* of a metatarsal is on or near the plantar surface ; it is directed towards the head in the first, towards the base in the others. In the phalanges, when it is present, it is on the plantar surface and is directed towards the base.

The **calcaneum** occasionally articulates with the navicular.   The sustentaculum tali may be a separate bone, and so may be the peroneal tubercle   The articular surface for the medial malleolus on the **talus** extends on to the neck in an infant.   Occasionally in an adult talus there is a small facet for the tibia on the medial part of the upper surface of the neck, probably due to the ankle joint being often in a state of extreme flexion.   The *os trigonum*, when present, may be quite separate, or joined to the body of the talus by cartilage. An ossicle may be present between the talus and dorsal surface of navicular, and another on the dorsum between the talus, calcaneum, navicular, and cuboid. The tuberosity of the **navicular** is sometimes a separate bone. The metatarsal articular surface of the **medial cuneiform bone** may be divided into a dorsal and a plantar part, and the whole bone may be so divided ; in both cases there is similar subdivision of the tarsal surface of the first metatarsal. In rare cases a little separate ossicle is found between the posterior parts of the dorsal surfaces of the medial and intermediate cuneiform bones. Division of the

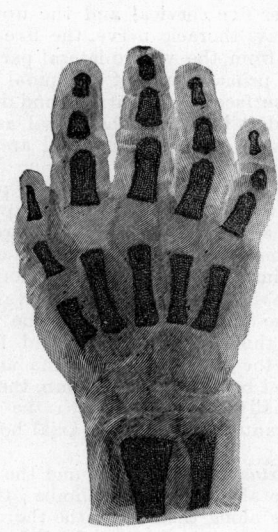

Fig. 279.—Radiograph of the Hand at Birth.

The metacarpus and phalanges are well ossified, but the carpus is still entirely cartilaginous. (Compare with Fig. 280, and see also Plates X and XVI).

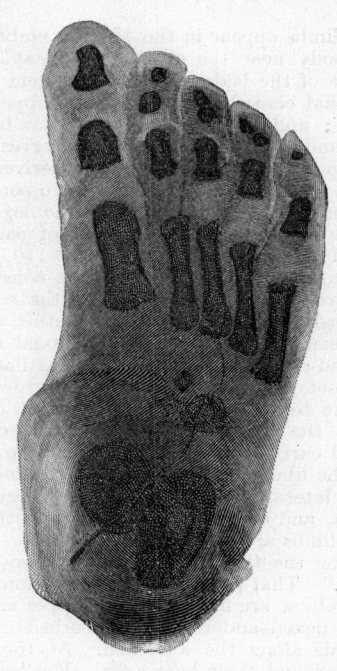

Fig. 280.—Radiograph of the Foot at Birth.

Calcaneum and talus are well ossified ; the cuboid is quite distinct, and in this instance the lateral cuneiform is already beginning to ossify.

cuboid has been recorded ; in rare cases there is a very small facet for the lower part of the head of the talus on the medial side of the projecting angle of its posterior surface. The tubercle of the **fifth metatarsal** may be separate ; as also the part of the base of the **first** into which the peroneus longus is inserted. A separate ossicle may be found between the bases of the first and second metatarsals. Fusion of **phalanges** is not uncommon, especially in the little toe.

Sesamoid Bones

Sesamoid bones are imbedded in tendons, but there is usually one surface free and smooth for articulation. The largest sesamoid bone is the **patella**. The *flexor hallucis brevis* has two little sesamoid bones in its tendons of insertion. They are about the size of half of a marrowfat pea, and, being compressed and oval, should not be mistaken for the pisiform bone. They play against the grooves on the plantar surface of the head of the first metatarsal bone, and they add to the size and firm consistence of the medial part of the ball of the foot ; the medial sesamoid may be divided transversely, and sometimes there is a minute nodule between the two. Occasionally there are minute sesamoid bones at the *other metatarso-phalangeal joints* and at the *interphalangeal joint* of the big toe and other interphalangeal joints. A sesamoid bone or cartilage is usually present in the tendon of the *peroneus longus* as it crosses the lateral side of the cuboid bone to enter the sole. The tendon of the *tibialis posterior* is thickened at the point where it glides over the spring ligament ; the thickening has sometimes the character of a sesamoid cartilage. More seldom, a sesamoid bone is present—in the *tibialis anterior* near its insertion; in the *psoas major* as it passes over the pubic bone; in the lateral head of the *gastrocnemius* as it crosses the lateral condyle of the femur; and in the *gluteus maximus* as it overlies the greater trochanter.

DEVELOPMENT AND MORPHOLOGY OF THE LIMBS

The limbs appear in the Human embryo about the third week as small buds on the sides of the body near the cephalic and caudal ends of the trunk. They are derived from several segments of the body, for each of them contains branches of several spinal nerves; the spinal nerves that contribute fibres to the upper limb are the lower five cervical and the upper two thoracic; and the lower limb contains branches from the last thoracic nerve, the five lumbar nerves, and the upper four sacral nerves. The buds arise from the ventro-lateral part of the trunk, and the nerves of a limb are derived from the anterior primary rami of the spinal nerves.

Each bud has two surfaces and two borders. At first the surfaces look ventrally and dorsally; the ventral aspect corresponds to the flexor surface of the adult limb, and the dorsal aspect to the extensor surface; the borders of each bud look headward and tailward, and are named pre-axial and post-axial. (Figs. 105-110, pp. 86, 87.)

During the second month slight constrictions appear in the elongating buds at positions that correspond to the elbow and the wrist, the knee and the ankle; and grooves appear on the dorsal surfaces of the extremities of the buds—indicating the subdivision into digits. At the same time, the central or axial mesoderm of the bud passes through a pro-cartilage stage, and chondrifies to form the cartilage models of the limb bones. Chondrification begins in the roots of the limbs and spreads towards the digits, leaving unchondrified intervals where joints are to be formed. The cartilage developed along the pre-axial border of the forearm becomes the radius, and the pre-axial digit becomes the thumb; in the leg and foot the pre-axial cartilage and digit become the tibia and the big toe; similarly, the ulna and little finger, the fibula and little toe are developed at the post-axial borders. The thumb, the radius, and the lateral epicondyle of the humerus are therefore serially homologous with the big toe, the tibia, and the medial epicondyle of the femur, if it is granted that the pre-axial borders of the two limbs are serially homologous.

During the third month the embryo—now called the *fœtus*—begins to assume the "fœtal position." That position is one of flexion at all the joints, notably those of the limbs; the wrist and the elbow are flexed and the upper arm is bent tailwards along the side of the thorax; the ankle is flexed and the foot is turned medially, the knee is flexed and the thigh is inclined headwards along the abdomen. At the same time the upper and lower limbs begin to be rotated around their long axes. The *lower limb* is rotated through an angle of 90°; the pre-axial border, which originally looked headwards, now looks towards the median plane; but the rotation is not completed till after birth. The *upper limb* is rotated in the opposite direction, the pre-axial border being turned away from the median plane; the flexor surface is therefore the anterior surface of the upper limb, but is the posterior surface of the lower limb. The movement is not so complete in the upper limb as in the lower; for it is only in the supine position—an unnatural position—that the flexor surface of the upper limb looks straight forwards. The rotation takes place partly at the shoulder joint and the hip joint, and partly in the shafts of the bones; some assert and others deny that the rotation involves also the dorsal part of the limb girdles.

Homologies.—The homology between the limb bones of Man and those of other animals, and the serial homology or homo-dynamy between the bones of the two limbs in Man, are fairly clear except in the limb girdles.

Limb Girdles.—The homologies of the parts of the girdles have become obscured owing to the structural alterations that have occurred in order to adapt the two limbs to their different functions. Even in four-footed animals the functions of the fore limbs and hind limbs are not quite the same, though both are used for support and locomotion; the fore limb is at the same time adapted for *pull* and the hind limb for *push*; the pelvic girdle is therefore more consolidated than the shoulder girdle. The modifications from the primitive type are more varied and more profound in the shoulder girdle, and began so long ago in phylogenetic development that in Man there is no evidence in ontogenetic development of how they came about.

The primitive, fundamental limb girdle is a curved bar of cartilage imbedded in the muscular substance of the side of the trunk at right angles to the long axis of the trunk. The cartilage is divisible into a dorsal part and a ventral part by means of an articulation of the middle of its lateral surface with the cartilage of the free portion of the limb.

In higher vertebrates the *ventral part* of the developing cartilage of the pelvic girdle is divided into two bars—a cephalic and a caudal; the cephalic bar corresponds to the pubis, the caudal bar to the ischium. The *dorsal part* is undivided and corresponds to the ilium.

The shoulder girdle does not show such a uniform arrangement. The *dorsal part*, however, does not undergo grave modification; it corresponds to the blade of the scapula and may be regarded as homologous with the ilium.

The *ventral part* is subdivided to a varying extent in different vertebrates; and the homo-dynamy of its subdivisions with the ischium and pubis is difficult to establish.

Attempts have been made to demonstrate homologies between the several parts of the scapula and ilium. Flower's scheme is the most generally accepted. It assumed a primitive or ideal type bone with dorsal and ventral *ends*, pre-axial, post-axial, and vertebral or medial *surfaces*, postero-medial, antero-medial, and lateral *borders*; and it postulated that the rotation of the limbs involved the scapular and iliac parts of the limb girdles in the directions indicated by the arrows in the diagram. In the scapula, the dorsal end is the medial border; in the ilium it is the iliac crest. The ventral end is the glenoid cavity of the scapula and the acetabular end of the ilium. The diagram indicates the homologies of the surfaces and borders under Flower's scheme.

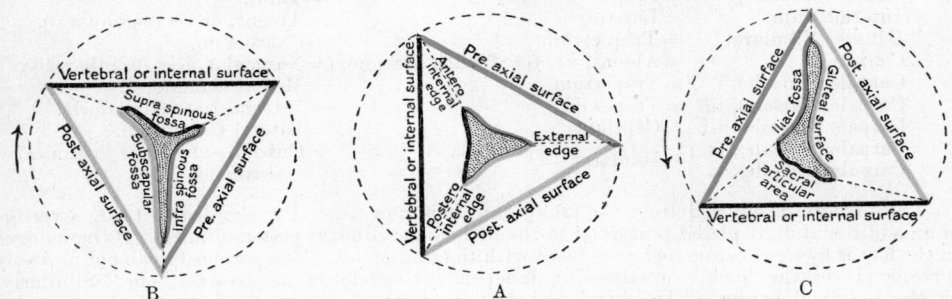

FIG. 281.—DIAGRAM OF HOMOLOGOUS PARTS OF SCAPULA AND ILIUM, ACCORDING TO FLOWER.

A : Ideal type ; three-sided rod.   B : Scapula rotated forward through a quarter of a circle (90°), and the primitive medial or vertebral surface is now directed forwards.   C : Ilium rotated backwards through a quarter of a circle and the primitive medial surface is now directed backwards.

Humphry assumed that the girdles were not involved in the rotation of the limbs; and the second diagram expresses the homologies which he ascribed to the scapula and ilium. In that diagram the anterior border of the ilium (between gluteal surface and iliac fossa), which gives origin to the rectus femoris, corresponds to the crest of the scapular spine (between the supraspinous and infraspinous fossæ) and not to the lateral border of the scapula (between the subscapular and infraspinous fossæ), which gives origin to the homologous muscle—the long head of the triceps. But Humphry explained that those muscles arose from the lateral surface of the bone (an attachment partly retained by the human rectus femoris) and in the rotation of the free part

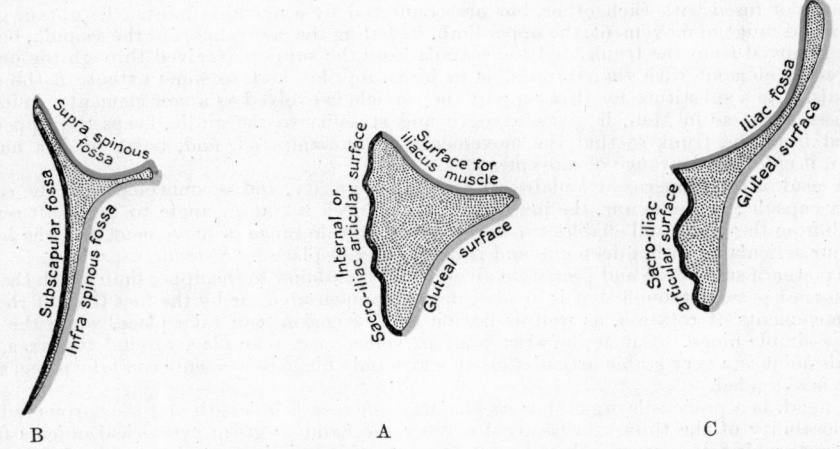

FIG. 282.—DIAGRAM OF HOMOLOGOUS PARTS OF SCAPULA AND ILIUM, ACCORDING TO HUMPHRY.

A : Primitive rod-like ilium of kangaroo, prismatic on section.   B : Scapula.   C : Ilium.
The corresponding surfaces are similarly coloured.

of the limb, the rectus femoris attachment was turned forward on to the anterior border, while the triceps was turned on to the posterior border (the lateral border in Man is the posterior or caudal border in quadrupeds).

Humerus and Femur.—Owing to the rotation of the limbs in opposite directions, the greater tuberosity, the posterior surface of the shaft and the lateral epicondyle of the humerus correspond respectively to the lesser trochanter, the anterior surface, and the medial epicondyle of the femur.

Bones of Forearm and Leg.—The radius corresponds to the tibia, and the ulna to the fibula. There is nothing in the lower limb, however, to correspond to the olecranon, and nothing in the upper limb to correspond to the patella. Those two parts are not homologous; but they are analogous, for each of them gives insertion to the extensor tendon and gives the extensor muscle more leverage for its action.

In the **hand and foot** the homology of metacarpus with metatarsus, thumb and fingers with toes, is obvious—the radial side of the hand corresponding with the tibial side of the foot.

The homologies of the carpal and tarsal bones are not so clear ; they are given in the following table, together with the more generalised type from which they are evolved :—

Type.	Hand.	Foot.
Radiale (Tibiale)	= Scaphoid (body)	= Talus.
Intermedium	= Lunate	= Absent, or Os trigonum (?).
Ulnare (Fibulare)	= Triquetrum	= Calcaneum.
Centrale	= Absent, or fused with Scaphoid	= Navicular, less its tuberosity.
Carpale (Tarsale), i.	= Trapezium	= Medial Cuneiform.
Carpale (Tarsale), ii.	= Trapezoid	= Intermediate Cuneiform.
Carpale (Tarsale), iii.	= Capitate	= Lateral Cuneiform.
Carpale (Tarsale), iv. } Carpale (Tarsale), v. }	= Hamate	= Cuboid, plus the peroneal sesamoid.

The pisiform is omitted from the table, since it is now generally regarded as being a vestige of an additional digit placed post-axial to the little finger (digitus post-minimus). Its homologue in the foot is by some considered to be fused with the calcaneum. The peroneal sesamoid probably corresponds to the hook (sometimes an independent ossicle) of the hamate bone. Similarly, on the pre-axial border of the hand and foot, vestiges of a suppressed digit (prepollex and prehallux) may occasionally be met with. The tuberosity of the navicular bone of the foot may be the homologue of the pre-axial sesamoid in the hand, which probably fuses with the scaphoid to form its tubercle. The frequent occurrence of an increase in the number of digits seems to indicate that phylogenetically the number of digits was greater than at present, and included a prepollex or prehallux, and a digitus post-minimus.

In Man the lower limbs have been modified for the whole office of support and locomotion and the upper limbs have undertaken more varied and specialised functions, including that of prehension. The lower limbs are increased in strength and length and are constructed with the view of stability ; mobility is the aim achieved in the upper limb. The elements of the lower limb girdle are welded into one bone which is firmly jointed to its fellow and to the backbone, and, with the adoption of the erect attitude, it assumes the special human characteristic of wide expansion of the ilia to support the abdominal viscera.

In order to be free and movable, the shoulder girdle is not built into the wall of the body cavity. The scapula is only loosely connected with the axial skeleton by muscles ; the clavicle is joined to the sternum by a freely movable joint ; and, further, those two constituents of the girdle are not fused with each other, but are connected by a movable joint. To obtain greater freedom and range of movement, the upper limb, including the ventral part of the scapula, becomes farther removed from the trunk, and the scapula loses the support received through the union of the coracoid element with the sternum, as in birds, reptiles, and, to some extent, in the lowest mammals. As a substitute for that support the clavicle is evolved as a new element ; in its most specialised form, as in Man, it gives strength and stability to the girdle, keeps the upper limb removed from the trunk so that the movements are unhampered, and, being itself a movable fulcrum, it enlarges the range of movement.

The head of the humerus articulates with a shallow cavity, and is connected with the scapula by a lax capsule ; in the femur, the presence of a long neck set at an angle to the shaft removes the limb from the trunk and enables the limb to have a wide range of movement, but the head of the femur articulates with a deep cup and is held firmly in place by a strong capsule.

The power of supination and pronation gives a varied mobility to the upper limb which the lower limb does not possess, though that is in some degree compensated for by the fact that, at the knee joint, movements of rotation, as well as flexion and extension, can take place, while the elbow joint is a simple hinge. But at the wrist joint movement can take place around two axes, while the ankle-joint is a very stable articulation at which only hinge movements can take place, except when it is extended.

The hand, as a prehensile organ, has its phalanges increased in length and the carpus reduced ; the opposability of the thumb metacarpal enables the hand to grasp cylindrical objects firmly, and the opposable fifth metacarpal enables it to grasp spherical objects. In the foot, strength and stability are required ; the tarsal bones are large, and, having to sustain the weight of the body, the tarsus and metatarsus are built in the form of an arch ; the foot does not have the prehensile function which it discharges in Apes, and therefore the digits are short and none of them is opposable.

MEASUREMENTS AND INDICES EMPLOYED IN PHYSICAL ANTHROPOLOGY

(1) Craniometry

Craniology is the study of the skull, and includes the consideration of the differences in the skull in the various groups of Mankind. Accurate measurements are required for the estimation of the differences, and the name *craniometry* is given to the methods of measurement.

Capacity of the Cranium.—The size of the skull varies considerably in the different races of Men. Apart from individual differences and the proportion of head-size to body-weight, the size is generally greater in the more highly civilised races than in the lower types.   The size of the head is closely correlated with the size of the brain ; and an estimate of the size of the brain can be formed from the dimensions of the cranial cavity.   To determine the capacity of the cavity, fill it with some suitable material and then measure the cubage of the amount of material required.   Various materials have been employed, each of which has its advantage.   Liquids would be the most accurate, but the foramina make them useless, without special precautions. In practice, seeds, glass beads, and leaden shot have been found to be sufficiently serviceable.

There is a wide range of variation in the capacity of different crania, but, owing to the varying thickness of bone and size of sinuses, the capacity is not directly proportional to the size of the skull as a whole.   For purposes of classification and comparison, skulls are grouped according to their **cranial capacity** into the following varieties :—

Microcephalic skulls are those with a capacity below 1350 c.c., and include those of Andamanese, Veddahs, Australians, Bushmen, Tasmanians, etc.   [μικρός (micros)= small ; κεφαλή (cephalē) = head.]

Mesocephalic skulls range from 1350 c.c. to 1450 c.c., and embrace examples of the following races : American Indians, Chinese, and some African Negroes.   [μέσος (mesos)=middle.]

Megacephalic skulls are those with a capacity over 1450 c.c., and are most commonly met with in the more highly civilised races : Mixed Europeans, Japanese, etc.   [μέγας (megas)=big.]

Form of the Cranium.—The shape, as well as the size, has been used as a means of classifying skulls ; but, in the past, undue emphasis may have been laid on differences in shape.   These differences are expressed by the comparison of measurements between given points.   The more important points from which measurements are taken are included in the subjoined table :—

Akanthion.—The point of the anterior nasal spine.

Alveolar Point or Prosthion.—The lower end of the intermaxillary suture.

Asterion is the region of the postero-lateral fontanelle, where the lambdoid, parieto-mastoid, and occipito-mastoid sutures meet.

Basion.—The middle of the anterior margin of the foramen magnum.

Bregma.—The point of junction of the coronal and sagittal sutures.

Dacryon.—The point where the vertical lacrimo-maxillary suture meets the fronto-maxillary suture at the medial angle of the orbit.

Glabella.—A point midway between the two superciliary arches.

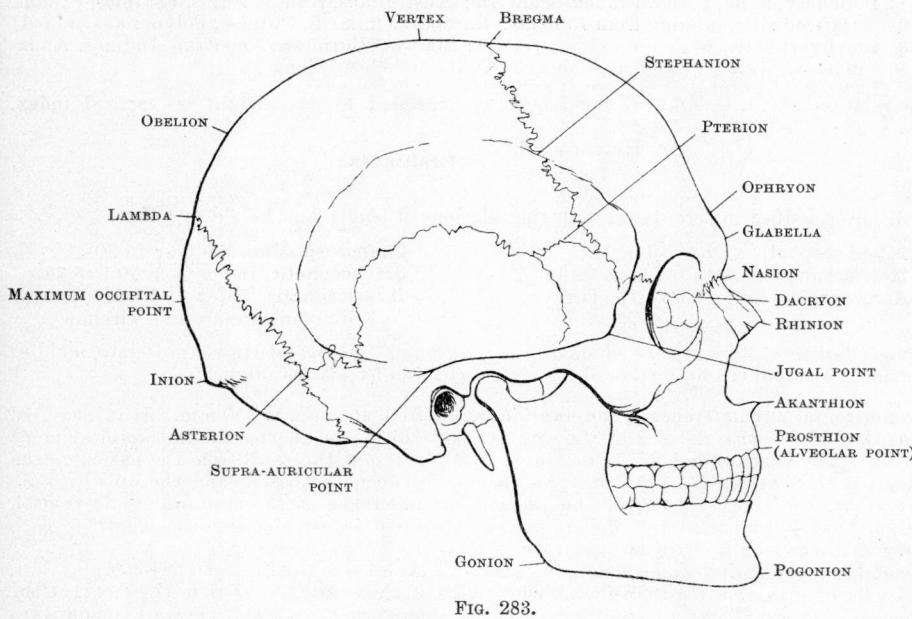

FIG. 283.

Gonion.—The lateral side of the angle of the mandible.   [γωνία (gōnia)=a corner.]

Inion.—The centre of the external occipital protuberance.

Jugal Point.—The junction of the frontal and temporal processes of the zygomatic bone.

Lambda.—The meeting-point of the sagittal and lambdoid sutures.

Maximum Occipital Point.—The point on the squamous part of the occipital in the sagittal plane most distant from the glabella.

Nasion.—The middle of the naso-frontal suture.

Obelion.—A point on the sagittal suture, between the parietal foramina.

Ophryon.—The mid point between the temporal lines at the narrowest part of the forehead.

Opisthion.—The middle of the posterior margin of the foramen magnum.

Pogonion.—The most prominent point of the chin as represented on the mandible. [πώγων (pōgōn)=the beard.]

Pterion.—The region of the antero-lateral fontanelle, where the frontal, parietal, squamous temporal, and greater wing of sphenoid meet. As a rule, the sutures are arranged like the letter Η, the parietal and the greater wing separating the frontal from the squamous temporal. In some skulls the form of the suture is like an Χ; and in a third variety the frontal and the squamous temporal meet—separating the greater wing from the parietal.

Rhinion.—The lower end of the internasal suture.

Stephanion.—The point where the coronal suture crosses the temporal line.

Subnasal Point.—The middle of the inferior border of the anterior bony aperture of the nose [apertura piriformis] at the root of the anterior nasal spine.

Supra-auricular Point.—A point immediately above the middle of the orifice of the external auditory meatus close to the edge of the posterior root of the zygoma.

Vertex.—The summit of the cranial vault

The measurements of the length of the skull may be taken between a variety of points—the nasion, the glabella, or the ophryon in front, and the inion or the maximum occipital point behind. Or the maximum length alone may be taken without reference to any fixed points. In all cases, state where the measurement is taken. The widest part of the skull is very variable in position ; note whether it occurs above or below the parieto-squamosal suture. The width of the skull may also be measured from one asterion to the other (**bi-asterionic width**) or from one stephanion to the other (**bi-stephanic width**). The height measurement usually taken is the distance from the basion to the bregma.

The relation of the breadth to the length of the skull is expressed by the **cephalic index**, which gives the proportion of the maximum breadth to the maximum length of the skull, assuming the latter equal 100, or—

$$\frac{\text{Max. breadth} \times 100}{\text{Max. length}} = \text{Cephalic index.}$$

The results are classified into three groups :—

1. **Dolichocephalic**, with an index below 75 : Australians, Kaffirs, Zulus, Eskimos, Fijians.
2. **Mesaticephalic**, ranging from 75 to 80 : Europeans (mixed), Chinese, Polynesians (mixed).
3. **Brachycephalic**, with an index over 80 : Malays, Burmese, American Indians, Andamanese. [βραχύς (brachys)=short ; δολιχός (dolichos)=long.]

The relation of the height to the length is expressed by the **height** or **vertical index**, thus—

$$\frac{\text{Height} \times 100}{\text{Length}} = \text{Vertical index.}$$

Skulls are classified in accordance with the relations of length and height as follows :—

Tapeinocephalic, index below 72.		**Chamæcephalic**, index up to 70.
Metriocephalic, index between 72 and 77.	or	**Orthocephalic**, index from 70·1 to 75.
Acrocephalic, index above 77 (Turner).		**Hypsicephalic**, index 75·1 and upwards (Kollmann, Ranke, and Virchow).

[ταπεινός (tapeinos)=low ; χαμαί (chamai)=on the ground. μέτριος (metrios)=moderate, middle ; ὀρθός (orthos)=straight, right. ἄκρος (akros)=highest ; ὔψι (hypsi)=on high.]

The **horizontal circumference** of the cranium ranges from 450 mm. to 550 mm. It is measured by a line that crosses the glabella or the ophryon anteriorly and the maximum occipital point posteriorly. The **longitudinal arc** is measured over the top of the skull from the nasion to the opisthion ; if the basi-nasal length and the distance between the basion and the opisthion are added to that, we have a record of the median circumference of the cranium. The frontal, parietal, and occipital portions of the arc may be measured separately, and the length of each compared with the length of the arc and with each other.

Facial Measurements.—The measurements of the skeleton of the face are more complex, but, on the whole, of greater value than the measurements of the cranium. It is in the *face* that the characteristic features of race are seen best ; and its skeleton most accurately records the outward form and proportions of the living.

The form of the face varies, like that of the cranium, in the relative proportions of its length and breadth. Generally speaking, a dolichocephalic cranium is associated with a long face, and the brachycephalic with a rounder and shorter face. This rule is, however, not universal.

The determination of the facial index varies according to whether the measurements are made with or without the mandible in position. When the mandible is in place the length is measured from the ophryon (or the nasion) to the mental tubercle, and it is compared with the maximum bi-zygomatic width. This is called the **total facial index**, and is obtained by the formula—

$$\frac{\text{Ophryo-mental length} \times 100}{\text{Bi-zygomatic width}} = \text{Total facial index.}$$

More usually, however, owing to the loss of the mandible, the proportions of the face are expressed by the **superior facial index**, that is, the ophryo-alveolar or naso-alveolar length compared with the bi-zygomatic width, thus—

$$\frac{\text{Ophryo-alveolar length} \times 100}{\text{Bi-zygomatic width}} = \textbf{Superior facial index.}$$

The terms **dolichofacial** or **leptoprosope** and **brachyfacial** or **chamæprosope** have been employed to express the differences thus recorded. [λεπτός (leptos)=thin, delicate, refined; πρόσωπον (prosōpon)=the face.] Uniformity in these measurements is, however, far from complete, since many anthropologists compare the width with the length=100.

The proportion of the face-width to the width of the calvaria is roughly expressed by the use of the terms **cryptozygous** and **phænozygous**. When cryptozygous skulls are viewed from above the zygomatic arches are concealed by the bulging of the sides of the cranial box; in phænozygous skulls the calvaria is narrow enough for the zygomatic arches to be visible. [κρυπτός (cryptos)= hidden; φαίνω (phainō), in passive=appear.]

The projection of the face, so characteristic of certain races (Negroes, for example), may be estimated on the living by measurement of the angle formed by two straight lines—the one passing from the middle of the external auditory meatus to the lower margin of the septum of the nose; the other drawn from the most prominent part of the forehead to the incisor teeth. The angle between those two lines is called the **facial angle** (Camper), and ranges from 62° to 85°. The smaller angle is characteristic of a muzzle-like projection of the lower part of the face. The larger angle is the concomitant of a more vertical profile. The degree of projection of the maxilla in the macerated cranium is most commonly expressed by the **gnathic** or **alveolar index** of Flower. This records the relative proportions of the basi-alveolar and basi-nasal lengths, the latter being regarded as=100, thus—

$$\frac{\text{Basi-alveolar length} \times 100}{\text{Basi-nasal length}} = \textbf{Gnathic index.}$$

The results are conveniently grouped into three classes :—

Orthognathous, index below 98: including mixed Europeans, ancient Egyptians, etc.
Mesognathous, index from 98 to 103: Chinese, Japanese, Eskimos, Polynesians (mixed).
Prognathous, index above 103: Tasmanians, Australians, Melanesians, various African
Negroes. [γνάθος (gnathos)=the jaw.]

Unfortunately, however, little reliance can be placed on the results obtained by this method, since it takes no account of the proportion of the third or facial side of the gnathic triangle.

The form of the anterior bony aperture of the nose in the macerated skull is of much value from an ethnic standpoint, as it is so intimately associated with the shape of the nose in the living. The greatest width of the aperture is compared with the nasal height (measured from the nasion to the lower border of the aperture) and the **nasal index** is thus determined :—

$$\frac{\text{Nasal width} \times 100}{\text{Nasal height}} = \textbf{Nasal index.}$$

Skulls are—

Leptorrhine, with a nasal index below 48: as in mixed Europeans, ancient Egyptians, American Indians, etc.
Mesorrhine, with an index ranging from 48 to 53: as in Chinese, Japanese, Malays, etc.
Platyrrhine, with an index above 53: as in Australians, Negroes, Kaffirs, Zulus, etc.
[πλατύς (platys)=wide, flat; ῥίς (rhis)=nose.]

The form of the orbit varies considerably in different races, but is of much less value from the standpoint of classification. The **orbital index** expresses the proportion of the orbital height to the orbital width, and is obtained by the following formula :—

$$\frac{\text{Orbital height} \times 100}{\text{Orbital width}} = \textbf{Orbital index.}$$

The orbital height is the distance between the upper and lower margins of the orbit at the middle; the orbital width is measured from the point where the ridge that forms the posterior boundary of the lacrimal groove meets the fronto-lacrimal suture (Flower), or from the dacryon (Broca), to the most distant point on the lateral margin of the orbital opening.

The form of the orbital aperture is referred to as—

Megaseme, if the index is over 89 ;
Mesoseme, if the index is between 89 and 84 ;
Microseme, if the index is below 84. [σῆμα (sēma)=a sign or signal.]

The variations met with in the form of the palate and dentary arcade may be expressed by the **palato-maxillary index** of Flower. The length is measured from the alveolar point to a line drawn across the posterior borders of the maxillæ; the width is taken between the outer borders of the alveolar arch immediately above the middle of the second molar tooth. To obtain the index, the following formula is employed :—

$$\frac{\text{Palato-maxillary width} \times 100}{\text{Palato-maxillary length}} = \textbf{Palato-maxillary index.}$$

For purposes of classification Turner introduced the following terms :—

Dolichuranic, index below 110.
Mesuranic, index between 110 and 115.
Brachyuranic, index above 115. [οὐρανός (uranos)=the vault of heaven, any vault, the roof of the mouth.]

The size of the teeth has an important influence on the architecture of the skull. Considered from a racial standpoint, the relative size of the teeth to the length of the cranio-facial axis has been found by Flower to be a character of much value. The dental length is taken as the distance between the anterior surface of the first premolar and the posterior surface of the third molar of the upper jaw.

To obtain the **dental index** the following formula is used :—

$$\frac{\text{Dental length} \times 100}{\text{Basi-nasal length}} = \textbf{Dental index.}$$

The dental indices may be divided into three series—

Microdont, index below 42 : including the so-called Caucasian or white races.
Mesodont, index between 42 and 44 : including the Mongolian or yellow races.
Megadont, index above 44 : comprising the black races, including the Australians.

Many complicated instruments have been devised to take the various measurements, but for all practical purposes the calipers of Flower or the *compas glissière* of Broca are sufficient.

In calculating indices, time is saved by the use of—the tables in the *Osteological Catalogue of the Royal College of Surgeons of England*, Part I., Man ; *Index-Tabellen zum anthropometrischen Gebrauche*, C. M. Fürst, Jena, 1902 ; or the index calculator invented by Waterston.

(2) Indices and Measurements of other Parts of the Skeleton

In addition to the indices employed to express the proportions of the cranial measurements, there are others similarly made use of to convey an idea of the proportions of different parts of the skeleton. The following may be mentioned as those in most common use :—

Scapula.—At birth the human scapula more closely resembles the mammalian type in that its breadth, measured from the glenoid cavity to the medial border, is greater in comparison with its length than in the adult. This proportion is expressed as follows :—

$$\frac{\text{Breadth from glenoid cavity to medial border} \times 100}{\text{Length from superior to inferior angle}} = \textbf{Scapular index.}$$

The index ranges from 87 in African pygmies (who therefore have proportionately broader scapulæ) to 61 in Eskimos. The average European index is about 65.

Hip Bone.—The relation of its breadth to its height is computed as follows :—

$$\frac{\text{Iliac breadth} \times 100}{\text{Ischio-iliac height}} = \textbf{Hip bone index.}$$

Man, as compared with the apes, has proportionately broader and shorter hip bones. The index in man ranges from 74 to 90.

Pelvis.—The human pelvis is characterised by an increased proportionate width and a reduced proportionate height or length. The relation of these diameters is expressed by the formula—

$$\frac{\text{Ischio-iliac height} \times 100}{\text{Greatest breadth between the outer lips of the iliac crests}} = \textbf{Pelvic breadth-height index.}$$

The average index for white races is 73.

Pelvic Cavity.—The measurements usually taken are those of the inlet. In man there is a proportionate increase in the transverse diameter as compared with lower forms :—

$$\frac{\text{Antero-posterior (conjugate) diameter} \times 100}{\text{Greatest transverse width across the inlet}} = \textbf{Pelvic or brim index.}$$

Turner has classified the indices into three groups :—

Dolichopellic, index above 95 : Australians, Bushmen, Kaffirs.
Mesatipellic, index between 90 and 95 : Negroes, Tasmanians, New Caledonians.
Platypellic, index below 90 : Europeans and Mongolians. [πέλλα (pella)=a bowl or pail.]

Vertebral Column.—A characteristic feature of the human vertebral column is the pronounced lumbar curve associated with the erect posture in the living. The curve is due partly to the shape of the intervertebral discs, but the bodies of the lumbar vertebræ contribute to it owing to the greater depth of the front of most of them. Endeavours have been made to reconstruct the lumbar curve from the dried and macerated bones, but it must be borne in mind that habitual posture or increased range of movements may yield results that are misleading. Thus, there is reason for believing that the squatting position, when habitually adopted, may give rise to a compression of the anterior parts of the bodies of the vertebræ, suggesting an absence of or flattening of the lumbar curve that in fact did not exist during life.

The curve is estimated from the macerated bones by an index computed as follows :—

$$\frac{\text{Sum of posterior vertical diameters of the five bodies} \times 100}{\text{Sum of anterior vertical diameters}} = \text{General lumbar index.}$$

The results are classified as follows :—

Kyrtorrhachic, index below 98, indicating a forward convexity : includes Europeans generally, and Chinese. [κυρτός (kyrtos) = curved, convex ; ῥάχις (rhachis) = the lower part of the back.]
Orthorrhachic, index between 98 and 102, the column being practically straight : includes examples of Eskimos and Maoris.
Koilorrhachic, index above 102, indicating a forward concavity : includes Australians, Negroes, Bushmen, and Andamanese. [κοῖλος (koilos) = hollow, concave.]

Sacrum.—Man's sacrum is characterised by its great breadth in proportion to its length. Those relations are expressed as follows :—

$$\frac{\text{Greatest breadth of base of sacrum} \times 100}{\text{Length from middle of promontory to middle of anterior inferior border of fifth sacral vertebræ}} = \text{Sacral index.}$$

The diverse forms are grouped as follows :—

Dolichohieric, index below 100, sacra longer than broad : includes Australians, Tasmanians, Bushmen, Hottentots, Kaffirs, and Andamanese.
Platyhieric, index above 100, sacra broader than long : includes Europeans, Negroes, Hindoos, North and South American Indians. The average European index is 112·4 for males, 116·8 for females. [ἱερός (hieros) = sacred.]

Thorax.—The diameters are taken at the level of the xiphi-sternal joint.

$$\frac{\text{Transverse diameter} \times 100}{\text{Antero-posterior diameter}} = \text{Thoracic index.}$$

The index is usually lower in the female—the form of the thorax being more rounded.

Limb Bones.—The proportionate length of the limb bones to one another and to the body height is of practical interest. It is a matter of common knowledge that the forearms of Negroes are proportionately longer than those of Europeans. Great differences, too, are met with in the absolute and proportionate length of the lower limbs ; nor must the relation of these to body height be overlooked. An enumeration of the more important of these indices, and the manner of their computation, will suffice.

The proportion of the lengths of the *radius* and *humerus* is expressed as follows :—

$$\frac{\text{Length of radius} \times 100}{\text{Length of humerus}} = \text{Radio-humeral index.}$$

Subdivided into three groups :—

Brachykerkic, index less than 75 : includes Europeans, Lapps, Eskimos. [κερκίς = κνήμη—see below ; but also meant *radius*.]
Mesatikerkic, index between 75 and 80 : Chinese, Australians, Polynesians, Negroes.
Dolichokerkic, index above 80 : Andamanese, Negritoes and Fuegians, Simiidæ in general.

The proportion of the length of the *tibia* to the *femur* is computed by the formula—

$$\frac{\text{Length of tibia from surface of condyle to articular surface for talus} \times 100}{\text{Oblique length of femur}} = \text{Tibio-femoral index.}$$

Subdivided into two groups :—

Brachyknemic, index 82 and under : includes Europeans and Mongolians generally.
Dolichoknemic, index 83 and over : includes Australians, Negroes, Negritoes, American Indians. [κνήμη (knēmē) = the leg.]

The proportion of the length of the *upper limb* to that of the *lower limb* is obtained thus :—

$$\frac{\text{Lengths of humerus + radius} \times 100}{\text{Lengths of femur + tibia}} = \text{Intermembral index.}$$

A comparison between the relative lengths of the upper segments of the limbs is obtained by the following formula :—

$$\frac{\text{Length of humerus} \times 100}{\text{Length of femur}} = \text{Humero-femoral index.}$$

Platymeria (see p. 280) [μηρός (mēros) = thigh].—The degree of compression of the femur is estimated as follows :—

$$\frac{\text{Sagittal diameter of shaft immediately below lesser trochanter} \times 100}{\text{Transverse diameter of shaft immediately below lesser trochanter}} = \textbf{Platymeric index.}$$

Platyknemia (see p. 289).—The degree of compression of the tibia is estimated by the formula—

$$\frac{\text{Transverse diameter of shaft at level of nutrient foramen} \times 100}{\text{Antero-posterior diameter of shaft at level of nutrient foramen}} = \textbf{Platyknemic index.}$$

The index ranges between 60 in a Maori tibia and 80 to 108 in modern French tibiæ.

For further information relating to the measurements and indices used by physical anthropologists, the reader is referred to Topinard's *Éléments d'anthropologie* ; Sir W. Turner's *Challenger Memoirs*, Part 47, vol. xvi. ; Duckworth's *Morphology and Anthropology* ; Rudolf Martin's *Lehrbuch der Anthropologie.*

ARTHROLOGY

Originally written by the late DAVID HEPBURN, C.M.G., M.D.
Professor of Anatomy, University College, Cardiff

Rewritten by D. M. BLAIR

Arthrology is that branch of Anatomy which deals with the manner in which the individual bones of the skeleton are joined together. These **joints** or **articulations** between the bones vary in structure and function: some are immovable; others permit movement of varying extent and complexity. The chief kinds of joints have also developmental differences, with some relation to the different modes of origin of the conjoined bones.

To begin with, the skeleton in any region exists as a continuous thickening of mesoderm. Where next a cartilaginous phase intervenes, the cartilaginous precursors of the bones may still be continuous, as in the cartilaginous base of the skull, or may remain separate as in the limbs and be joined by zones of persisting membranous tissue. When ossification occurs, the bones are all formed separately, and therefore joints are found between their contiguous parts. Bones formed in membrane are connected by the intervening membranous tissue, and so become united by fibrous joints; bones formed in cartilage are connected either by cartilage or by membranous tissue according to the continuous or discrete formation of the preceding cartilages. The membranous connexion between bones formed from separate cartilages may persist and give rise to a fibrous joint, or may become chondrified and give rise to a cartilaginous joint; but in most cases the connecting membranous tissue undergoes a special development, forming a thickened pad called the *primitive joint plate,* in which further striking changes occur. A cavity appears, by absorption, in the joint plate, while the periphery of the plate becomes a fibrous sleeve, with a specialised lining, connecting the contiguous bones and bounding the joint cavity now existing between them.

Classification of Joints.—Bones are ultimately joined, therefore, in one of three ways :—

(1) By **fibrous joints,** where the bones have arisen in membrane or where they were preceded by discrete cartilaginous models and the primitive membranous connexion has persisted.

(2) By **cartilaginous joints,** either of a primary type where the uniting cartilage is the remains of a preceding continuous cartilaginous formation, or of a secondary type where the membranous tissue between bones ossifying from discrete cartilages is subsequently chondrified.

(3) By a more elaborate type of joint having a cavity between the bone ends surrounded by fibrous ligaments lined with a specialised membrane. This lining membrane secretes a fluid called *synovia* into the joint cavity, and is therefore itself called the *synovial membrane.* As the synovial fluid and membrane are characteristic of joints of this type, these are called **synovial joints.**

These three kinds of joints will now be considered in detail and the varieties of each described.

319

FIBROUS JOINTS

Fibrous joints are of two types—suture and syndesmosis.

Suture.—A suture is a fibrous joint in which the opposed bone surfaces are closely bound together by an extremely thin layer of intervening white fibrous tissue (Fig. 284). So close is the union that no movement between the united bones can take place. Sutures are found only between bones of the skull, and tend to become obliterated in the later years of life by ossification across the joint lines —a process called *synostosis.*

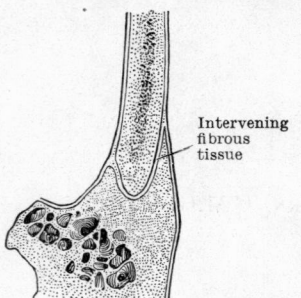

Intervening fibrous tissue

FIG. 284.—VERTICAL SECTION THROUGH A SUTURE.

Varieties of Suture.—Different varieties of suture are named from the ways in which the opposed parts of the bones are fitted to one another. Sutures between bones joined edge to edge are commonly strengthened by toothed projections from the one bone fitting between similar processes on the other; such a suture is called **serrate** when the projections are pointed like the teeth of a saw (Fig. 285), or **denticulate** when the projections broaden towards their free ends like human teeth, and the bones are dovetailed together. In a **limbous** suture, serrate or dentate edges of the opposed bones alternately overlap one another in addition. Where plane overlapping bevelled edges of bone are united, a **squamous** suture is formed. When relatively flat surfaces of bone are joined together, as in the joint between the maxilla and the vertical plate of the palatine bone, a **flat** suture results [sutura harmonia]. In a **wedge and groove** suture a crest on one bone fits into a groove on another, as the rostrum of the sphenoid fits into the groove between the alæ of the vomer. A **peg and socket** suture resembles the union between the fang of a tooth and its socket; but the only example in the skeletal system is the insertion of the styloid process in the temporal bone.

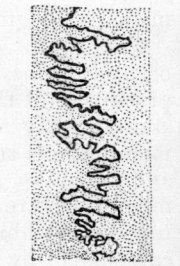

FIG. 285.—SERRATE SUTURE.

Syndesmosis.—A syndesmosis is a fibrous joint in which the uniting fibrous tissue, much greater in amount than in a suture, forms an interosseous membrane or ligament. The inferior tibio-fibular joint is a syndesmosis where the bones are joined by an interosseous ligament; the attachment of the shaft of the radius to that of the ulna may be regarded as an example of syndesmosis in which an interosseous membrane unites the bones. Movement may be permitted at a syndesmosis by the flexibility of an interosseous membrane or the stretching or twisting of an interosseous ligament. This last occurs to an extremely small extent unless the ligament is composed largely of elastic fibrous tissue, as in the case of the ligamenta flava between the laminæ of adjacent vertebræ.

CARTILAGINOUS JOINTS

In a **cartilaginous joint** [synchondrosis] the bones are united by an intervening plate of cartilage. The sides of the plate are directly fused to the joint surfaces of the two bones, and the perichondrium clothing its periphery is continuous with the periosteum covering the bones. As already indicated, cartilaginous joints are of two types, primary and secondary, which differ in development, structure, and function.

Primary Cartilaginous Joint.—The cartilage of the **primary** type of joint (Fig. 286) is a remnant of the continuous cartilaginous mass in which the articulating bones are formed, and it retains its original hyaline nature. This is the most rigid kind of cartilage; hence no movement is permitted at this type of joint unless, as in the solitary example of the union between the first rib and the sternum, the uniting cartilage is a bar long enough to allow an appreciable degree of bending or twisting. Most of the primary cartilaginous joints become obliterated by synostosis before the age of twenty-five; only two pairs of joints escape this fate—the petro-basilar and the first costo-sternal.

Secondary Cartilaginous Joint.—The **secondary** type of cartilaginous joint is more specialised. It arises by chondrification of a primitive membranous plate between separate cartilaginous rudiments. It is permanent in character. In the chondrified joint plate, a thin layer adjoining each of the two uniting bones remains hyaline in nature, but the intervening zone, of much greater thickness, becomes fibro-cartilaginous. Such a joint is that between the bodies of adjacent vertebræ. Fibro-cartilage is less rigid than hyaline cartilage; a slight amount of bending or twisting of the one bone upon the other may therefore take place at this type of joint, the amount depending on the thickness of the fibro-cartilaginous plate and the degree to which fibrous tissue is formed in it. In some such joints the centre of the fibro-cartilaginous plate is modified either by the formation of an irregular slit-like cavity, as in the pubic symphysis, or by the presence of a core

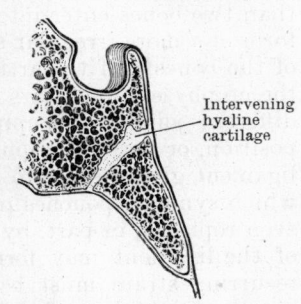

Intervening hyaline cartilage

FIG. 286. — SECTION THROUGH THE PRIMARY CARTILAGINOUS JOINT BETWEEN THE OCCI- PITAL AND SPHENOID BONES.

of soft, pulpy tissue, as in an intervertebral disc; these modifications increase the possibility of slight movement. In most fibro-cartilaginous joints, if not in all, additional strength is secured by the presence of ligaments surrounding the joint, which may be regarded as exaggerations of the perichondrio-periosteal sheath which encloses the simpler primary cartilaginous joint.

SYNOVIAL JOINTS

The **synovial joint** [diarthrosis] (Fig. 287) is the most highly developed form of all: it is specialised to permit free movement. The joint surfaces of the articulating bones—separated by the **joint cavity** and each provided with a special bearing surface of hyaline cartilage—are free to move upon each other; the connexion between the bones is by means of flexible ligaments attached chiefly round about the bone ends to form a **capsular ligament** around the joint cavity. Lining this capsular ligament and bounding the cavity is the **synovial membrane** which produces the synovial fluid within the cavity.[1]

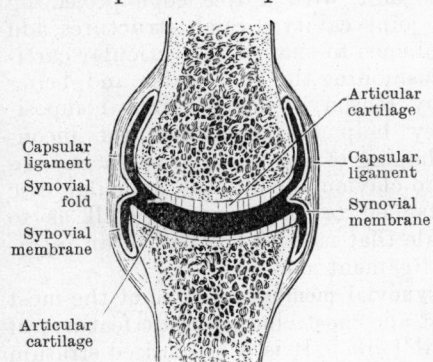

Articular cartilage

Capsular ligament
Synovial fold

Synovial membrane

Articular cartilage

Capsular ligament

Synovial membrane

FIG. 287.—DIAGRAM OF A SYNOVIAL JOINT.

The part of a bone that enters into the formation of a synovial joint—usually enlarged or expanded in the case of the extremity of a long bone—is composed of spongy tissue with a thin superficial layer of particularly dense bone. The *articular surface*—that area of the bone which comes into contact during movement with the other bone of the joint—is covered with a layer of hyaline cartilage called the **articular cartilage.** This presents a firm, perfectly smooth, free surface, devoid of perichondrium. By its slight elasticity the articular cartilage lessens jarring shocks at the joint. Having no nerves, it is insensitive. It is avascular, and is nourished to some extent by permeation of fluid from the vascular ring in the synovial membrane at its periphery and from the vessels in the underlying bone, but principally by the synovial fluid itself (Strangeways, *B.M.J.*, 1920).

The connecting structures of the synovial joint are the *articular ligaments.* These are arranged in various ways, but are always composed of dense white fibrous tissue which by its flexibility permits movement at the joint, but by its

[1] The conventional term "joint cavity" is inexact. There is normally no real "cavity," but only a solution of continuity between surfaces in contact. A true cavity may arise pathologically, if the joint be-comes distended with an abnormal amount of fluid.

great tensile strength resists disruption.   Every synovial joint is provided with a
capsular ligament.   This usually takes the form of a sleeve, each end of which
is firmly attached in a continuous line around the articular extremity of one of the
bones at a variable distance from the edge of the articular cartilage.   Where more
than two bones enter into the formation of the joint, the capsular ligament has the
form of a more irregular sac with openings tightly filled by the articulating parts
of the bones.   If the articular end of a bone is ossified from an epiphyseal centre,
the epiphyseal line bears no constant relation to the line of capsular attachment in
different joints: the epiphyseal line may be intracapsular or extracapsular in
position, or partly the one and partly the other.   Small apertures in the capsular
ligament give passage to nerves and vessels; there may be larger openings through
which synovial pouches protrude.   The capsular ligament may be strengthened or
even replaced, in part, by adjacent muscle tendons or their expansions.   The fibres
of the ligament may form a dense felt-work; but where, during movement, any
recurring strain must be resisted, the fibres there become arranged in parallel
bundles in the line of the straining force; such specialised portions of the capsular
ligament are usually thickened and distinguished by special names.   Besides
the capsular ligament with its possible special bands, other ligaments, standing
apart from it, may join the bones.   These **accessory ligaments** may be extracapsular,
like the costo-clavicular and coraco-clavicular ligaments of the clavicular joints, or
intracapsular, like the cruciate ligaments of the knee joint.

   Inside some synovial joints, pads of fibro-cartilage lie between the articular
surfaces and blend peripherally with the capsular ligament.   Such a fibro-cartilage
may form a complete **articular disc** attached to the capsule all round, so as to divide
the joint cavity into two separate compartments (Fig. 288); the mandibular and
sterno-clavicular joints are made bi-cameral in this way.   Or the intra-articular
fibro-cartilage may be wedge-shaped as in the
acromio-clavicular joint, or crescentic as in
the knee joint, with a free edge projecting
into the joint cavity.   Such structures add
their resilience to that of the articular cartilage in cushioning the bone ends; and, being
pliable by reason of their fibrous composition, they help to compensate for incon-
gruous shaping of the articular surfaces.   In
the sterno-clavicular joint the articular disc
is so attached to the bones as well as to
the capsule that it plays the part of an intracapsular ligament also.

   The **synovial membrane** is one of the most
important and most characteristic features of
a synovial joint.   It is a specialised stratum
of delicate connective tissue—highly vascular
and velvety in appearance in the living—

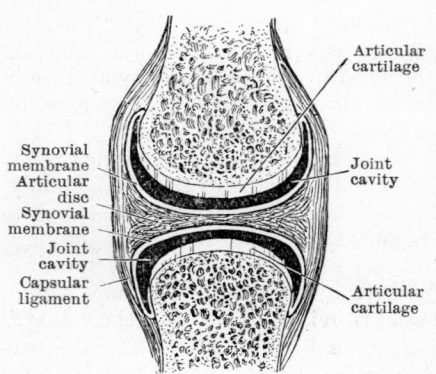

Articular
cartilage

Synovial
membrane
Articular
disc
Synovial
membrane
Joint
cavity
Capsular
ligament

Joint
cavity

Articular
cartilage

Fig. 288.—Diagram of a Synovial Joint
with Articular Disc dividing the Joint
Cavity into two Compartments.

which lines the capsular ligament, and, with it, forms the capsule of the joint.
At the attachments of the capsular ligament the synovial membrane is
reflected on to the bones to clothe them as far as the edge of the articular
cartilage.   Thus, all intra-articular bony surfaces are covered with hyaline
cartilage on the articular areas and with synovial membrane on the non-
articular areas.   The transition between the two coverings is fairly abrupt;
the junction goes obliquely from the free surface so that the membrane
slightly overruns the bevelled edge of the cartilage.   Often a redundant fold of
the membrane from just beyond the junction overlaps the cartilage in addition.
A varying amount of fatty or areolar tissue may intervene between the membrane
and the ligament or bone which it covers.   The fatty tissue, when large in
amount, bulges the synovial membrane into the joint cavity, forming soft
and highly compressible pads or folds; these serve to fill up irregularities of
the intra-articular surfaces, such as the fossæ at the lower end of the humerus,
but permit projections on the other moving member of the articulation to

occupy the fossæ in certain positions of the joint. The synovial membrane is also folded over intracapsular tendons, ligaments, or cartilages, which usually are thus excluded from the joint cavity. But it must be remembered that although the synovial stratum can be traced continuously over most intra-articular surfaces except those covered with articular cartilage, it is not everywhere recognisable as a

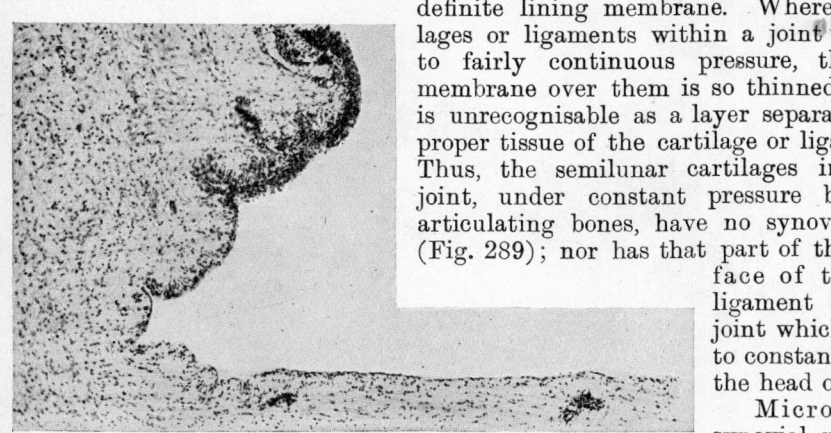

definite lining membrane. Where fibro-cartilages or ligaments within a joint are exposed to fairly continuous pressure, the synovial membrane over them is so thinned out that it is unrecognisable as a layer separate from the proper tissue of the cartilage or ligament itself. Thus, the semilunar cartilages in the knee joint, under constant pressure between the articulating bones, have no synovial covering (Fig. 289); nor has that part of the deep surface of the capsular ligament of the hip joint which is exposed to constant pressure of the head of the femur.

FIG. 289.—SECTION FROM HUMAN KNEE JOINT.

The section is at the angle between the *semilunar cartilage* (below) and the *capsular ligament* (on left). Note that the *synovial membrane* forms a folded lining over the ligament, but disappears on the surface of the cartilage. (Photomicrograph × 50.) (D.M.B.)

Microscopically, synovial membrane is composed of a collagenous ground-work, showing delicate fibres and containing connective tissue cells of different kinds. Its thickness and cell content vary in different situations: it is thickest where separated from underlying ligaments by a layer of areolar tissue, is very thin when covering fatty pads, and, as already described, thins out to disappearance in areas under pressure. Towards its free surface the cells become rather flattened, but no complete endothelial lining is formed. From the surface, *synovial villi* may project into the joint cavity, each a tuft, sessile or pedunculated, of the fibrous ground-work with cells embedded in it and arranged irregularly around its surface. *Synovial folds* are projections on a larger scale, involving a folding of the whole thickness of the membrane (Fig. 290); secondary folds may arise from primary ones, and for localised collections of these folds, covered in turn with villi, the term **synovial fringes** is apt.

The function of the synovial membrane is to secrete the **synovia**—a colourless, glairy fluid deriving its name from its likeness in appearance and consistence to white of egg. It is in amount sufficient only to cover with a thin film all surfaces within the joint. Its function is threefold: it serves to lubricate the joint surfaces; it appears to be the main source of nourishment for the articular cartilage; and the cells it contains—constantly migrating from the synovial membrane, circulating in the fluid and entering the membrane again—remove by phagocytic action microorganisms and the debris of joint wear and tear.

It will be clear that the synovial cavity of the joint, bounded by synovial membrane and articular cartilage, is completely closed. Where an opening in the ligamentous layer of the capsule allows the synovial layer to protrude, the imperforate continuity of the synovial layer is always maintained. But the synovial cavity is not completely closed in a histological sense: the synovial membrane, unlike the pleura or the peritoneum of the coelomic cavities, has no complete epithelial lining as a barrier between the joint cavity and the tissue spaces around. The joint cavity is itself, in effect, an enormously enlarged tissue space; that is how it was developed. This has a bearing on the rapid absorption which can take place from an acutely infected joint cavity.

Bursæ.—Closely akin to synovial membrane are the walls of certain closed sacs, known as **synovial bursæ**, that are found in many situations in the body. The bursæ contain fluid resembling synovia, and they serve to facilitate the play of one structure upon another. **Subcutaneous bursæ** are found between the skin and underlying bony prominences such as the olecranon and the patella. **Subfascial bursæ** are similarly placed beneath the deep fascia. **Subtendinous bursæ** are found where one tendon overlies another tendon or a projection of

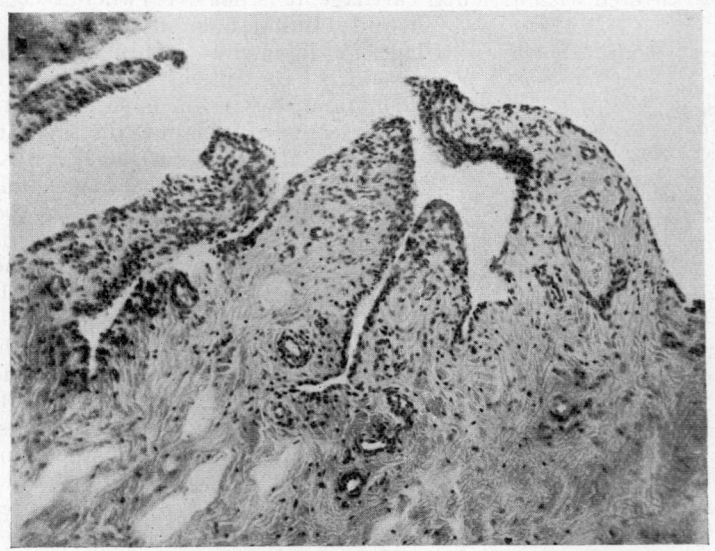

FIG. 290.—SYNOVIAL FOLDS FROM HUMAN KNEE JOINT.

The *capsular ligament* (just appearing at base of photograph) is separated from the *synovial membrane* by loose areolar tissue. Note numerous blood-vessels in the synovial membrane. (Photomicrograph × 100.) (D.M.B.)

bone; the walls of such a bursa in the neighbourhood of a joint may be continuous with the synovial membrane of the joint through an aperture in the capsular ligament.

Of the same nature are the **synovial sheaths** that surround tendons running in osteo-fascial tunnels, as in the case of the tendons passing behind the flexor retinaculum [lig. carpi transversum] at the wrist and of the flexor tendons lying on the front of the fingers.

Development of a Synovial Joint.—As already mentioned, a synovial joint has a special developmental history. The primary rudiment is the **primitive joint plate**, which arises by a separate thickening of the mesenchyme between the thickenings that foreshadow the bones to be joined. Later, a cavity appears in the joint plate; and when the bone rudiments become chondrified their ends are at first excluded from the primitive joint cavity by its mesenchymatous wall. This perichondrial layer afterwards disappears from the areas that correspond to the future **articular surfaces**. Meantime the persisting circumferential part of the joint plate, extending sleeve-like between the bones, is differentiated into two layers—an *outer*, which becomes the **capsular ligament**, and an *inner*, which becomes the **synovial membrane**. *Intra-articular ligaments* and *fibro-cartilages* arise from thickenings that project inwards from the wall of the primitive joint cavity. A complete *articular disc* arises from a transverse mesenchymatous septum between double cavities which appear in the joint plate. *Extra-capsular ligaments* may arise independently of the joint plate, from separate membranous bands.

Morphology of Ligaments.—Certain articular ligaments and fibro-cartilages, whether or not arising ontogenetically after the common manner just described, have been credited with interesting phylogenetic histories, sometimes in different versions. Thus, a muscle tendon that originally stretches over a joint to the farther bone may acquire a new attachment on the nearer bone, leaving the original terminal portion of the tendon to become a ligament fixed to both bones. Or the altered functioning of a joint in phylogeny may cause an earlier ligament or cartilage to be married into changed relations in the later type of joint. In the knee joint the medial and lateral [collateral] ligaments are examples of stranded tendons, while the attachment of the lateral semilunar cartilage to the posterior cruciate ligament is a reminder of the different mechanism of an earlier vertebrate knee.

Such morphological points will be mentioned with the structures concerned, but it must be remembered that they are of interest rather than importance from the standpoint of present function.

Joint Approximation Forces.—It is useful to consider the factors concerned in maintaining the integrity of the union between the bones in synovial joints, in which, for the sake of a joint cavity to assist free movement, structural continuity of the united bones is given up. Two minor factors common to all such joints are the **force of cohesion** and **atmospheric pressure**—the cohesion because of the smooth joint surfaces in perfect contact with each other except for an intervening capillary layer of fluid, and the pressure because the atmosphere is excluded from the closed synovial cavity. A third factor of very different value in different joints is **interlocking of the co-apted bones**; this is well marked in the hip joint, but is completely absent in plane joints.

The most important factors are the **strength of the articular ligaments** and the **tension of the muscles** around the joint. These two act together in varying proportions; in, for example, the shoulder joint, with its relatively lax capsule, the ligamentous factor is small, while in the hip joint, with well developed ligamentous bands in its capsule, it is of more importance. But it must be emphasised that white fibrous tissue ligaments cannot resist continuous strains without lengthening permanently, so that they must ever be supported by the contractile tension of muscle. Whether at rest or in contraction, the muscles around a joint are ever exerting by their active tonicity a force of joint approximation. Their efforts may be relieved considerably by suitably disposed ligaments, but no ligament will for long resist stretching under constant strain if unaided by muscular action. Thus, in flatfoot deformity, while the bone displacement is permitted by over-stretched ligaments, this in turn is due to diminished support from muscles deficient in tone. In the knee joint, where the capsular ligament is largely formed of tendinous expansions from muscles acting on the joint, a beautiful example is seen of close structural and functional co-operation of muscle and ligament.

Limitation of Movement.—Four factors are concerned in the limitation of movement at synovial joints: the locking of the articulating bones; the apposition of soft parts; the tightness of ligaments; and the tension of fully stretched muscles. **Locking of the bones** probably occurs only exceptionally; thus, in the elbow joint, in a few cases pressure facets at the sides of the olecranon fossa of the humerus indicate that extension must have been limited by actual contact of the olecranon with the humerus, but in the majority of cases tension of the muscles and ligaments in front of the joint is the limiting factor. **Apposition of soft parts** obviously limits movement in such examples as flexion of the elbow when the front of the forearm is pressed against the front of the upper arm, and flexion of the knee when the back of the leg meets the back of the thigh. The **tension of ligaments** undoubtedly limits movement in certain instances, such as the action of the ilio-femoral ligament limiting extension at the hip joint and the alar ligaments of the odontoid process checking rotation of the head. But in most cases **muscular tension** reinforces the restraint on movement imposed by the ligaments, if it does not actually check movement before the ligaments are fully stretched. This effect of the muscles is called their *passive insufficiency* or *ligamentous action*. A good example of limitation of movement purely by muscular tension is the check imposed on flexion of the hip by the tension of the hamstrings while the knee is fully extended; flexion of the knee lessens the tension of these muscles, and further flexion of the hip can then take place. The effect of muscles in limiting movement in the ordinary person can be appreciated when one considers the greater range of movement possessed by acrobats, who by constant practice conserve or even increase the full extensibility of muscle possessed by all in early life. Admittedly in such cases ligaments and joint surfaces also are modified to allow the extreme movements; but that muscles normally exert a restraint on movement beyond that exercised by ligaments is shown by the extreme movements sometimes produced in the convulsions of tetanus or epileptic fits, when the safeguarding muscular restraint operating in ordinary voluntary action is withdrawn.

CLASSIFICATION OF SYNOVIAL JOINTS

Synovial joints may be subdivided for further consideration in terms of the shape of the articulating surfaces and the movements performed at the joint;

these two factors being related can be used together in a system of classification. From the point of view of form only, a distinction can be made between **homomorphic** and **heteromorphic** joints. The articular surfaces in a homomorphic joint are similar in conformation; those in a heteromorphic joint are dissimilar. Combining further consideration of shape with an analysis of movement, we distinguish *plane* and *saddle* joints of homomorphic pattern, and *hinge, pivot, ball-and-socket, condyloid* and *ellipsoid* joints in the heteromorphic division.

Plane Joint [Arthrosis].—In a typical plane joint the opposed surfaces are flat, and are equal in extent; but in many cases the term is a relative one, as the surfaces are slightly curved. Such curvature, however, is never sufficient to bring the joint into one of the other subdivisions, and has little influence on the movement that takes place. This is a simple **gliding**, in any direction, or twisting, of the one bone on the other within the narrow limits permitted by a slight laxity of the capsular ligament. Such joints are found between the individual carpal and tarsal bones, and between the articular processes of adjacent vertebræ.

Saddle Joint.—Here the concavo-convex articular surface of the one bone is reciprocally homomorphic with the convexo-concave surface of the other. Movements are permitted around two principal axes at right angles to each other, and to a less extent around intermediate axes. The only good example is the carpo-metacarpal joint of the thumb.

Hinge Joint (Ginglymus).—In this, the articulating surfaces are arranged to permit movement around only one axis—and that a transverse one—as in the hinge of a box lid. The elbow and interphalangeal joints are good examples. Usually the articulating bones are in line in the normal anatomical position; movement around the transverse axis causing the bones to become increasingly angulated is termed **flexion**, while movement in the reverse direction is called **extension**. In cases where the normal position is angular, as at the ankle joint, suitably modified terms may describe the movements with less ambiguity, as *dorsi-flexion* and *plantar flexion* in the example quoted. Two features in the disposition of the ligaments are common to all hinge joints. In the first place, the capsular ligament must be of sufficient length in front and behind to permit movement; of these parts one will be taut and the other lax in full flexion or full extension. But in the second place, strong ligaments are placed at the sides of the joint, one end of each ligament being attached in the axis of the hinge; these therefore can be taut in all positions of the joint without restricting its movement.

Pivot Joint (Artic. trochoidea).—Here also movement can take place around only one axis, but a vertical one, as in the hinge of a gate. A more or less cylindrical articular surface **rotates** within a ring formed partly by bone, partly by ligament, as in the superior radio-ulnar joint; or, conversely, the ring may rotate around the cylindrical surface, as in the joint between the odontoid process and the anterior arch and transverse ligament of the atlas.

Ball-and-socket Joint (Artic. cotylica).—Here, as for example in the hip and shoulder joints, a "ball" formed by a spheroidal surface on the one bone rotates in a "socket" provided by a concavity in the other. This is the most completely movable form of joint, for movement can take place around an almost infinite number of axes passing through the centre of the "ball." For descriptive convenience three principal axes at right angles to one another are specially considered. Around a transverse axis, movements of **flexion** and **extension** take place, as in a hinge joint. Movements sideways around an antero-posterior axis are named **abduction** in the case of a limb raised laterally, away from the middle line of the body, and **adduction** when the limb is brought towards or across the middle line. Around a vertical axis in the centre line of the limb, the limb **rotates medially** or **laterally**. **Circumduction** is a composite movement around a number of axes whereby the limb describes the side of a cone, the apex of which corresponds to the centre of the "ball." The stability of such a joint depends on the depth of the "socket," but greater depth of socket proportionately limits movement.

Condyloid Joint.—In this variety the articular surfaces are of the ball-and-socket type; but, owing to the disposition of the ligaments and muscles, the movement of rotation around a vertical axis is absent. **Flexion** and **extension**, **abduction** and **adduction**, and **circumduction** take place. The metacarpo-phalangeal joints of the fingers (but not of the thumb) are condyloid joints.

Ellipsoid Joint.—This is a further modification of the ball-and-socket type of joint; in it the articular surfaces, instead of being spheroidal, are ellipsoidal. The curvature in the long axis of the joint surfaces has a greater radius than in the short axis. Movement takes place around two principal axes at right angles, corresponding to the greatest and least diameters of the joint, and to a slight extent around intermediate axes. Circumduction also is allowed, but the ellipsoidal surfaces prevent rotation.

JOINTS OF THE TRUNK AND HEAD

INTERVERTEBRAL JOINTS

The joints between the free vertebræ are arranged on a common plan, with the exception of the specialised joints between the atlas and axis. The bodies of adjacent vertebræ are joined together and also the vertebral arches, but on each side, between these connexions, the pedicles remain free, being separated by the intervertebral foramina (Fig. 291).

Joints between Vertebral Bodies.—These joints are cartilaginous joints of the secondary type; for the bodies are united mainly by *fibro-cartilages*, though these are supplemented by *longitudinal ligaments*.

Intervertebral Discs.—The under surface of one body is united to the upper surface of the succeeding body by a fibro-cartilaginous **intervertebral disc** (Fig. 291). The peripheral part of this disc is called the *annulus fibrosus*, and

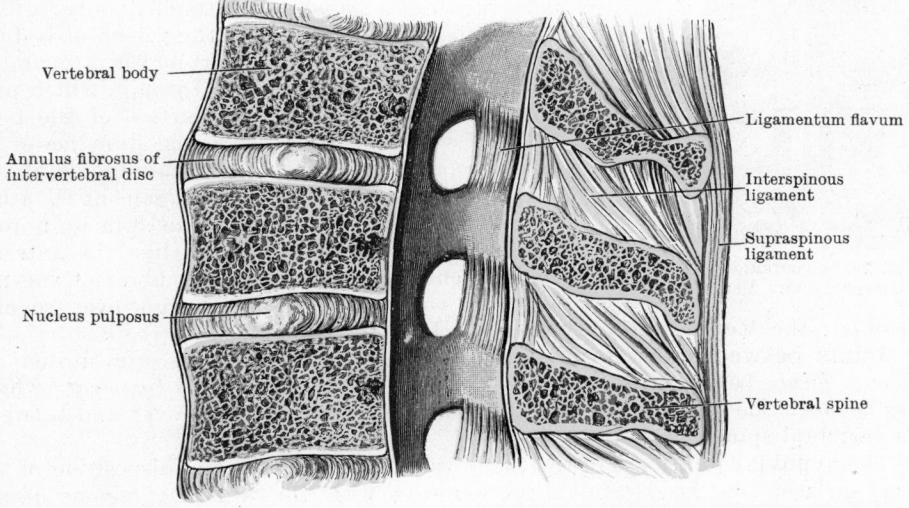

Vertebral body

Annulus fibrosus of intervertebral disc

Nucleus pulposus

Ligamentum flavum

Interspinous ligament

Supraspinous ligament

Vertebral spine

Fig. 291.—Median Section through a Portion of the Lumbar Part of the Vertebral Column.

is composed of fibro-cartilage so densely fibrous that the cartilaginous element is appreciated with difficulty in a section. The fibres run obliquely between the two vertebræ and are arranged in concentric rings, the fibres in successive rings having opposite obliquities. The central part of the disc is called the *nucleus pulposus*. It is soft and elastic, and is composed of a pulpy, fibrous material containing branched cells; it is thought to be derived from the notochord and its sheath. On each surface of the disc, above and below, there is a thin layer of hyaline cartilage, in the marginal part of which the annular epiphysis of the vertebral body develops. The discs between the cervical vertebræ do not extend quite to the lateral edges of the vertebral bodies, where, between the lipped edge of the body below and the bevelled edge of the one above, there is a small synovial joint. The thickness of the discs varies in different parts of the column, being least in the upper thoracic region and greatest in the lumbar region. The discs are also slightly wedge-shaped, in conformity with the curvature of the vertebral column in their neighbourhood; this is particularly marked in the cervical and lumbar regions, where the anterior convexity is due chiefly to the greater thickness of the discs in front than behind.

Longitudinal Ligaments.—The anterior and posterior longitudinal ligaments also help to unite the bodies of the vertebræ. The **anterior ligament** (Fig. 299) is a broad band of some thickness that runs up and down the front of the column over the anterior surfaces of the vertebral bodies. It is narrowest at its upper end, where it has a pointed attachment to the anterior tubercle of the atlas; it becomes wider as it descends, and ends below by spreading on to the pelvic surface of the sacrum. It is firmly attached to the intervertebral discs and adjacent parts of the vertebral bodies; the superficial fibres pass over several vertebræ, the deepest join adjacent bones. The **posterior longitudinal ligament** (Fig. 292) is constructed on a similar plan. It is placed on the back of the vertebral bodies, in the anterior wall of the vertebral canal. Unlike the anterior ligament, it is broader above than below. Its upper end is continued into the membrana tectoria, which covers the odontoid process and its ligaments and is attached to the occipital bone. Opposite the bodies of the thoracic and lumbar vertebræ it narrows markedly, but remains broader opposite the intervertebral discs, so that each edge presents a series of pointed dentations. Its narrow, lower end passes on to the anterior wall of the sacral canal. The posterior ligament is attached only to the discs and adjoining edges of the vertebral bodies; opposite the middle of each vertebra it is separated from the bone by an interval through which pass thin-walled veins. The free surface of the ligament is separated from the spinal dura mater by loose areolar tissue with veins running in it; in the lower part of the canal the ligament is rather more intimately connected to the dura by fibrous bands. The posterior ligament, like the anterior one, is composed of longitudinal fibres of varying length: the most superficial run over several

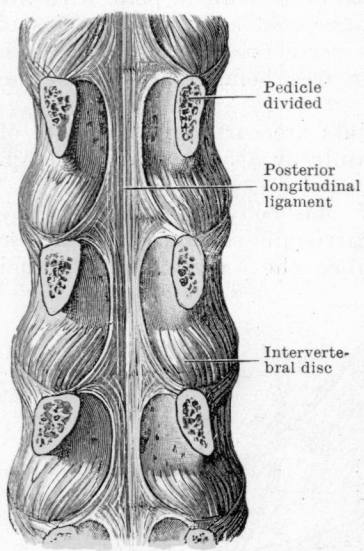

Pedicle divided

Posterior longitudinal ligament

Intervertebral disc

FIG. 292.—POSTERIOR LONGITUDINAL LIGAMENT OF THE VERTEBRAL COLUMN.

vertebræ; the deepest pass only from one bone to the next.

Joints between Vertebral Arches.—The vertebral arches are united by *synovial joints* between the articular processes, and by *accessory ligaments* which pass between the laminæ, between the transverse processes, and over and between the vertebral spines.

The **synovial joints** are of the plane variety; the shape and disposition of the joint surfaces on the articular processes vary in the different regions of the column, as already described in the section on Osteology. Each joint is surrounded by a thin **capsular ligament** lined with **synovial membrane.** The joint capsules are lax, particularly in the cervical region, so that slight gliding movements can take place between the bones.

The **accessory ligaments** are the supraspinous and interspinous, the intertransverse, and the ligamenta flava. The **interspinous ligaments** are relatively weak bands that run between the lower border of one vertebral spine and the upper border of the next below; they are longest and strongest in the loin (Fig. 291). The **supraspinous ligament** runs over the tips of the spines and is fused with the posterior edges of the interspinous ligaments; short fibres in the ligament join adjacent spines; longer ones connect spines several vertebræ apart.

In the neck, the supraspinous ligament merges into the triangular **ligamentum nuchæ.** This, in Man, is merely a fibrous partition between the muscles of the two sides of the back of the neck; it is attached above to the external occipital

PLATE XIX

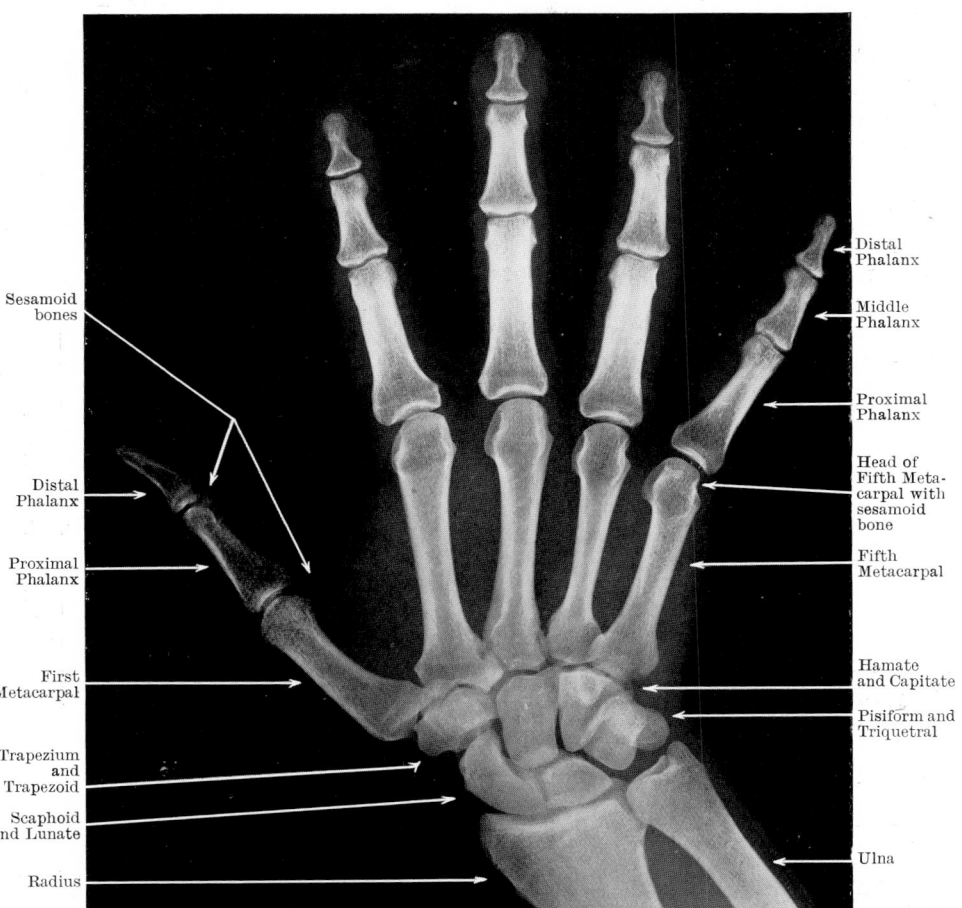

Sesamoid
bones

Distal
Phalanx

Proximal
Phalanx

First
Metacarpal

Trapezium
and
Trapezoid

Scaphoid
and Lunate

Radius

Distal
Phalanx

Middle
Phalanx

Proximal
Phalanx

Head of
Fifth Meta-
carpal with
sesamoid
bone

Fifth
Metacarpal

Hamate
and Capitate

Pisiform and
Triquetral

Ulna

PLATE XIX.—RADIOGRAPH OF WRIST AND HAND OF MAN AGED 25.
(Dr. J. Duncan White.)

Compare with Plate X, Fig. 2, for the identification and relative position of the carpal bones.

PLATE XX

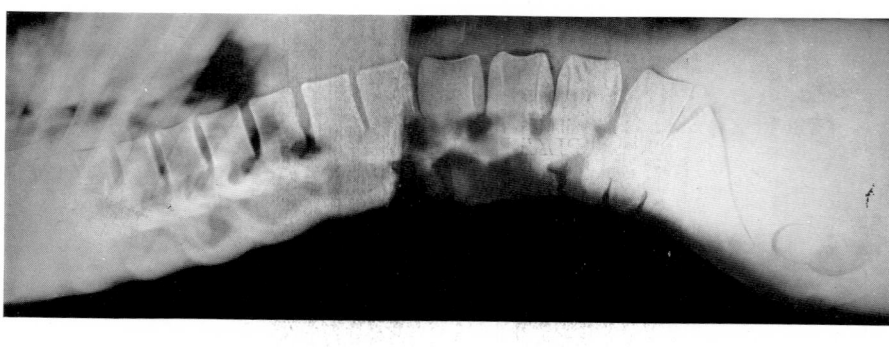

FIG. 1.—FORWARD BEND (FLEXION).

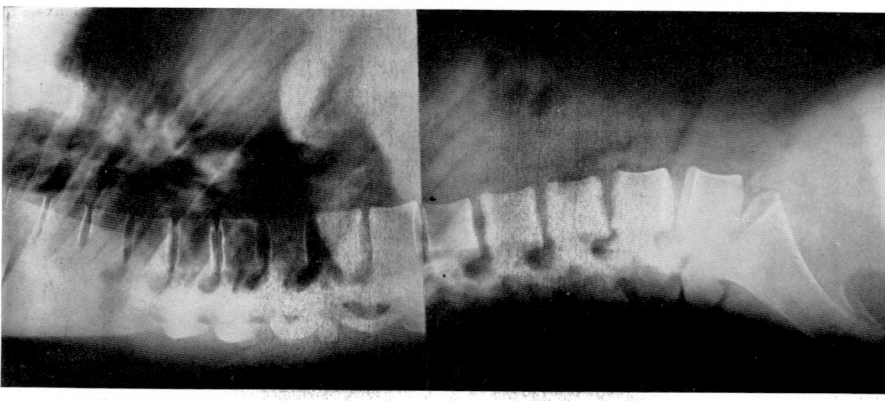

FIG. 2.—ERECT POSITION.

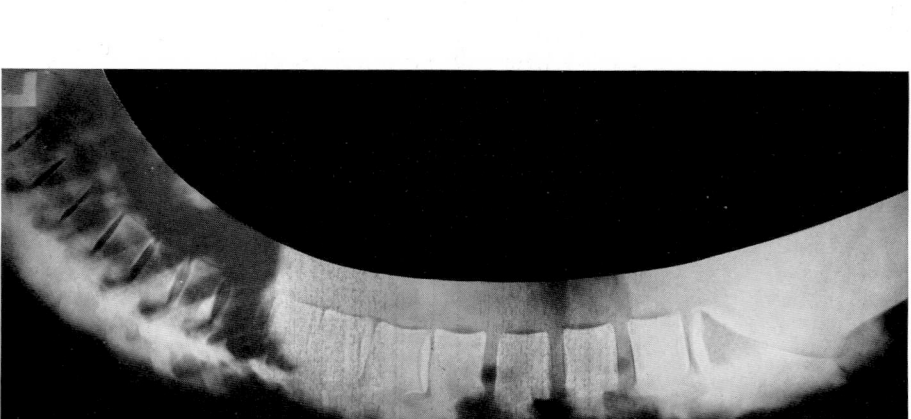

FIG. 3.—BACKWARD BEND (EXTENSION).
(Cf. Plate XVII, Fig. 2.)

PLATE XX.—THREE LATERAL RADIOGRAPHS ILLUSTRATING THE EXTENT OF THE NORMAL ANTERO-POSTERIOR MOVEMENTS OF THE VERTEBRAL COLUMN IN THE THORACIC AND LUMBAR REGIONS. (P.P.L.)

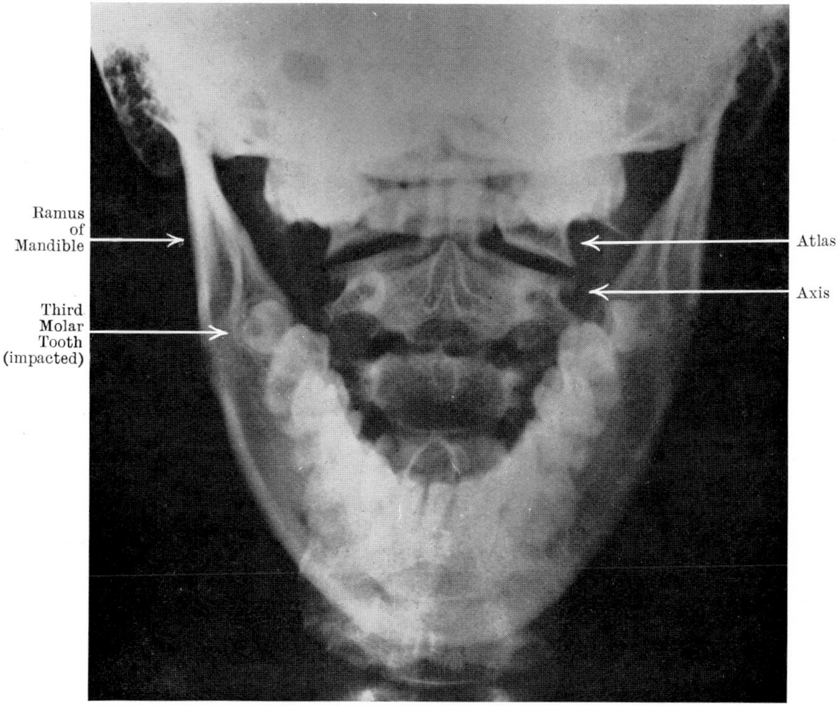

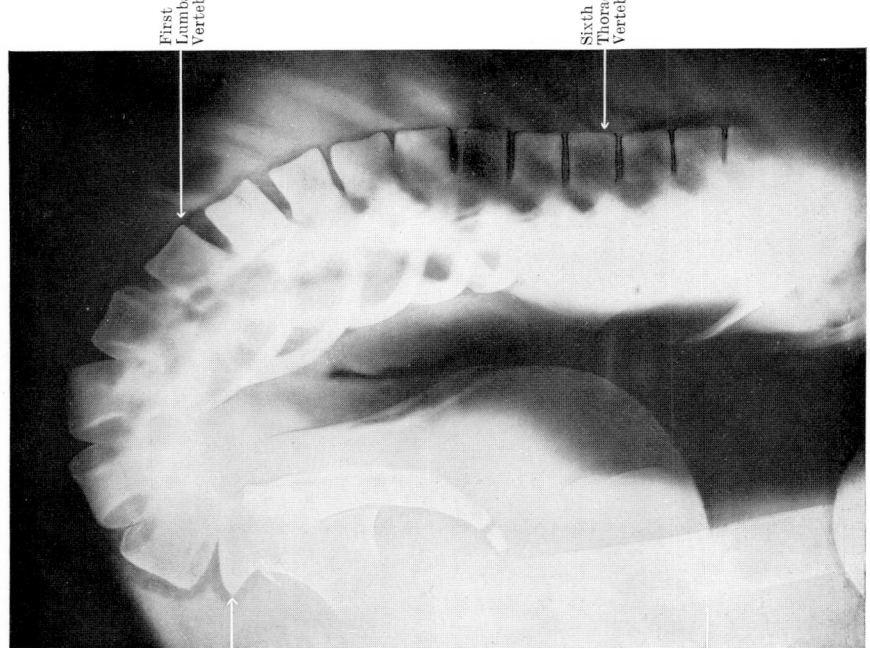

First Lumbar Vertebra

Sixth Thoracic Vertebra

Occiput

FIG. 2.—LATERAL RADIOGRAPH ILLUSTRATING EXTREME HYPER-EXTENSION OF VERTEBRAL COLUMN IN A TRAINED ACROBAT. (R. D. L.)

Note the apparent rotation of the lumbar vertebræ, due partly to the obliquity of the X-Rays in that area.

Promontory of Sacrum

Femur

Atlas

Axis

FIG. 1.—RADIOGRAPH TAKEN THROUGH OPEN MOUTH, SHOWING THE POSITION OF THE CERVICAL VERTEBRÆ IN RELATION TO THE JAWS AND THE MOUTH CAVITY. (D. M. B.)

Ramus of Mandible

Third Molar Tooth (impacted)

PLATE XVIII

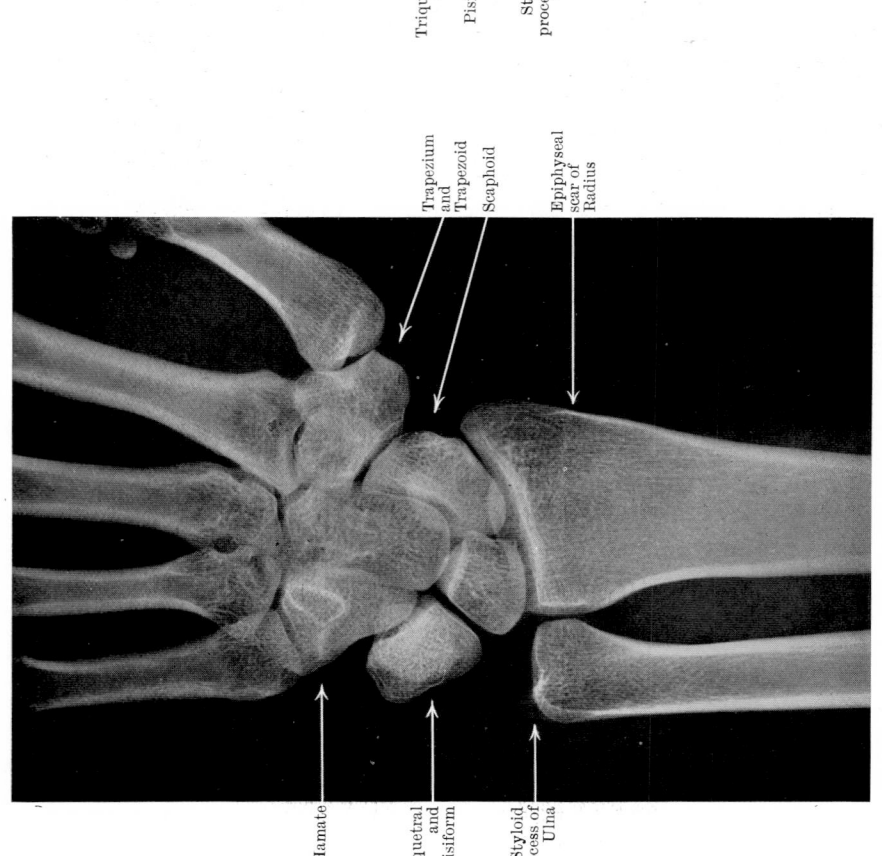

Trapezium and Trapezoid

Scaphoid

Epiphyseal scar of Radius

Triquetral

Pisiform

Styloid process of Ulna

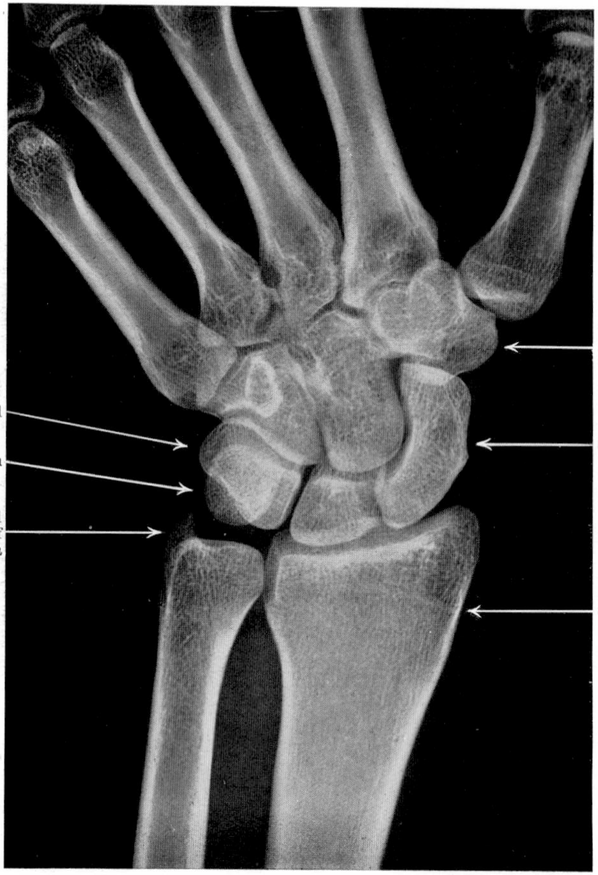

Fig. 2.—Radiograph of the same Wrist in Extreme Ulnar Flexion (Adduction) at the Radio-carpal Joint. (D. M. B.)

Note the alteration in the relation of the Carpus to the Radius and the movement that has taken place between the proximal and distal rows of carpal bones. The space between the Triquetral, the Ulna and the Pisi-

Trapezium and Trapezoid

Scaphoid

Epiphyseal scar of Radius

Hamate

Triquetral and Pisiform

Styloid process of Ulna

Fig. 1.—Radiograph of Wrist showing the relation of the Carpus to the Radius and Ulna in Extreme Radial Flexion (Abduction) at the Radio-carpal Joint. (D. M. B.)

Note the wide space between the head of the Ulna and the Triquetral bone.

crest and deeply to the cervical spines, while its superficial border runs between the external occipital protuberance and the spine of the last cervical vertebra. In quadrupeds the ligamentum nuchæ is a well-developed elastic ligament which relieves the muscles in supporting the head.

The intervals between the laminæ of adjacent vertebræ are filled by the **ligamenta flava,** so called because of their yellowish colour due to the presence of much elastic tissue.   Each is attached above to the front of the lower border of a lamina, and below to the back of the upper border of the succeeding lamina (Fig. 293).   There are two—a right and a left—in each vertebral interval;

their medial borders are separated by a narrow, median chink through which pass veins that connect the venous plexus within the vertebral canal to the posterior vertebral plexus; laterally, they extend to the capsules of the intervertebral synovial joints, but do not blend with them. The ligamenta flava are the only markedly elastic ligaments in Man. By their elasticity they can accommodate themselves to separation of the laminæ in forward flexion of the vertebral column without falling, on extension of the column, into folds which might press upon the dura mater or be caught between the laminæ they

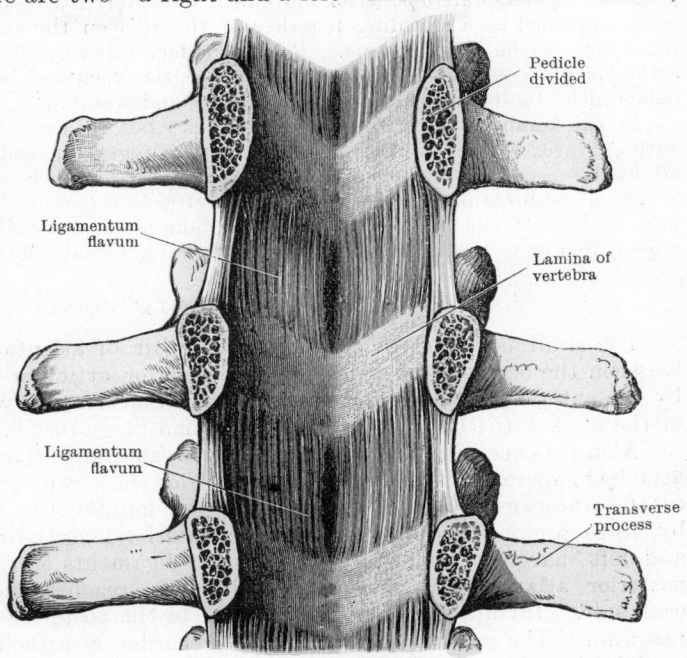

Fig. 293.—Ligamenta Flava seen from the front after Removal of the Bodies of the Vertebræ by saw cuts through the Pedicles.

connect; and their elastic tension assists the posterior vertebral muscles in maintaining the erect attitude.

The *intertransverse ligaments* are insignificant bands between the transverse processes. They are generally absent in the cervical region; they are marked only in the lumbar region. In the upper part of the column they tend to be replaced by the intertransverse muscles.

Movements of Vertebral Column

Movement between any two successive vertebræ is very slight; but the sum total of movement in the whole column is considerable (Pl. XX). The possibility of movement is due to the slight flexibility of the intervertebral discs coupled with the laxity of the capsules and the incomplete apposition of the articular surfaces of the intervertebral synovial joints. Where the discs are thick or numerous, movement is likely to be more free, though the arrangement of the fibres in the discs strictly limits movement between adjacent vertebræ in any direction; the elasticity of the nucleus pulposus tends to equalise pressure within each disc in the bending movements. The shape and set of the articular processes in the different regions affect the degree of movement permitted at the synovial joints.

Movement in each region and in the column as a whole can be analysed in terms of forward **flexion,** backward **extension, lateral flexion,** and **rotation.**

In the neck, where the discs are relatively preponderant for the length of that part of the column, all movements are, on this score, more extensive than elsewhere. The articular surfaces, set obliquely in a transverse plane, facilitate *flexion* and *extension* but cause *lateral flexion* and *rotation* to be accompanied each by some degree of the other movement. Thus, when the neck is bent to one side, each lower articular process on that side glides downwards and backwards on the upper process of the vertebra below, while on the other side each lower process mounts upwards and forwards upon the superior process below it; hence bending to one side is accompanied by a slight rotation to that side.

In the thorax, the small proportion of the fibro-cartilage relative to the length of the thoracic region, the presence of the ribs and sternum and the imbrication of the long, sloping spines all tend to limit movement. The vertical disposition of the articular processes hinders *antero-posterior* movement but interferes less with *lateral flexion*, which is accompanied by a crowding together of the ribs on the side of flexion and a spreading apart on the opposite side. *Rotation* is facilitated by the centre of curvature of the articular processes being near the centre of the vertebral body; but this is counterbalanced by the restraint imposed by the ribs and sternum.

In the lumbar region the discs are thick; but the articular processes, vertically set with curvatures centred behind the vertebræ altogether, tend to restrict movements of all kinds—especially rotation. Fairly free *antero-posterior* and *lateral* movements do occur; a combination of these brings about *circumduction* of the trunk as a whole; some pure *rotation* of the lumbar vertebræ does take place, especially in the lower part of the region, thanks to the laxity of the intervertebral synovial joints.

ATLANTO-OCCIPITAL JOINTS

The skull is joined to the atlas by a pair of **atlanto-occipital synovial joints** between the occipital condyles and the superior articular facets of the atlas, and by the **anterior** and **posterior atlanto-occipital membranes**, which connect the arches of the atlas with the margins of the foramen magnum (Fig. 294).

Atlanto - occipital Membranes.—The **anterior atlanto-occipital membrane** is attached superiorly to the anterior margin of the foramen magnum, and inferiorly to the anterior arch of the atlas; in the middle, the membrane is thickened by fibres prolonged upwards from the anterior longitudinal ligament; the right and left margins blend with the capsular ligaments of the synovial joints. The **posterior atlanto-occipital membrane** likewise reaches the capsular ligament at each side. Its upper border is attached to the posterior margin of the foramen magnum. The median part of its lower border is attached to the posterior arch of the atlas; but the lateral part, on each side, arches over the vertebral artery and the first cervical nerve as they cross the posterior arch of the atlas; this part of the lower edge of the membrane is thickened and is sometimes ossified.

Atlanto-occipital Joint.—Each of the pair of synovial joints is enclosed by a **capsular ligament** which is attached at the margins of the articular surfaces and is lined with **synovial membrane.** The atlantal articular surface is concave; the occipital surface is convex. But the corresponding surfaces of the joints of the two sides are really segments of one ellipsoidal surface whose transverse diameter is the longer, and functionally the joints act together as a single ellipsoidal articulation. Movement therefore takes place around two principal axes—nodding or bending the head forwards and backwards around a transverse axis, and bending the head sideways around an antero-posterior axis. The antero-posterior axis is inclined upwards and forwards; therefore, as the head is bent to one side, the face is slightly turned towards the opposite side. No rotation takes place between the skull and the atlas beyond a little slipping of the occipital condyles, the one forwards the other backwards, on the atlantal facets, giving the face a slight oblique tilt; the joint surfaces are then in better apposition, and this is the natural pose of greatest ease and stability.

ATLANTO-AXIAL JOINTS

The **atlas** and the **axis** have *bilateral synovial joints* between their opposed articular processes, and a *median synovial joint* formed by the articulation of the odontoid process with the anterior arch of the atlas and with the transverse ligament; in addition, various *accessory ligaments* connect the axis to the atlas, and the odontoid process to the occipital bone.

Lateral Atlanto-axial Joint.—Each of the paired joints is of the plane variety, enclosed by a **capsular ligament** with **synovial lining**. The joint surfaces are flat, and are inclined laterally and downwards. Applied to the back of the capsule is an accessory atlanto-axial ligament which runs obliquely downwards and medially from the back of the lateral mass of the atlas to the back of the body of the axis (Fig. 295).

The anterior arch of the atlas is connected to the front of the body of the axis by a membranous expansion from each side of the pointed upper part of the anterior longitudinal ligament as it descends from the anterior tubercle of the

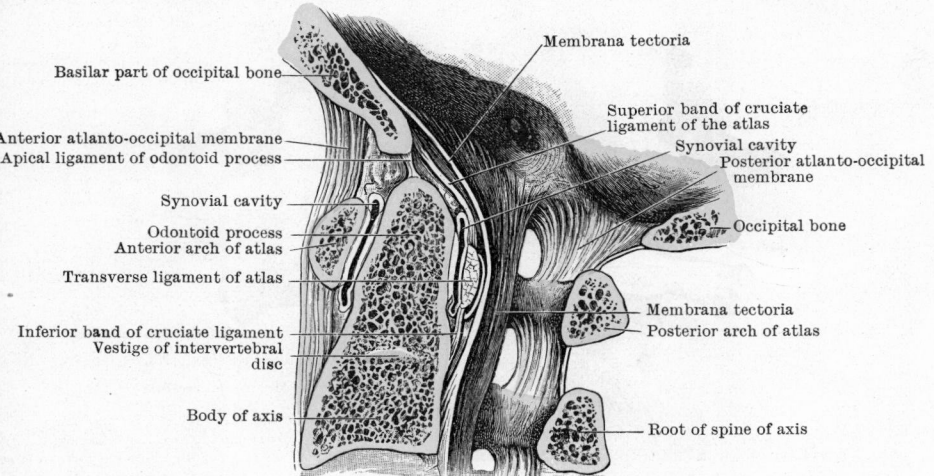

FIG. 294.—MEDIAN SECTION THROUGH THE ATLANTO-OCCIPITAL AND ATLANTO-AXIAL REGION.

atlas. The gap between the posterior arch of the atlas and the arch of the axis is bridged by a membrane, in series with the ligamenta flava, which is pierced at each side by the second cervical nerve. The position of this nerve behind the atlanto-axial joint bespeaks the different morphological value of this joint compared with other intervertebral joints; it is held to be homologous with the small synovial cavity at the side of each cervical intervertebral disc.

Median Atlanto-axial Joint.—The **articulation of the odontoid process with the atlas** is a pivot joint provided with two little synovial cavities (Fig. 294). The smaller of these cavities is between the facet on the front of the odontoid process and the facet on the back of the anterior arch of the atlas; the larger cavity is between the posterior facet on the odontoid process and the transverse ligament of the atlas; each cavity is enclosed by a thin capsular ligament lined with synovial membrane.

The transverse ligament of the atlas is a stout band that passes behind the odontoid process, between the tubercles on the medial sides of the lateral masses of the atlas (Fig. 295). From the middle of the transverse ligament a small band of longitudinal fibres passes upwards to the anterior edge of the foramen magnum, and another passes downwards to the back of the body of the axis. These bands, together with the transverse ligament, constitute a cruciform structure known as the **cruciate ligament** of the atlas.

OCCIPITO-AXIAL LIGAMENTS

The axis is connected with the occipital bone indirectly by the longitudinal bands of the cruciate ligament, and, more directly, by the apical and alar ligaments of the odontoid process and by the membrana tectoria.

Ligaments of Odontoid Process.—Lying immediately in front of the upper band of the cruciate ligament, there is a slender cord which stretches from the apex of the odontoid process to the anterior edge of the foramen magnum: this is the **apical ligament** of the odontoid process, a structure developed from the rudiment of a supra-atlantal disc and the segment of notochord passing from the first cervical centrum to the cranial base. The **alar ligaments** of the odontoid process are short, stout bands that run, one from each side of the apex of the odontoid process, upwards and laterally to the medial side of each occipital condyle (Fig. 295).

Membrana Tectoria.—The odontoid process and the cruciate and alar ligaments are covered over posteriorly by the **membrana tectoria**, a broad sheet continuous

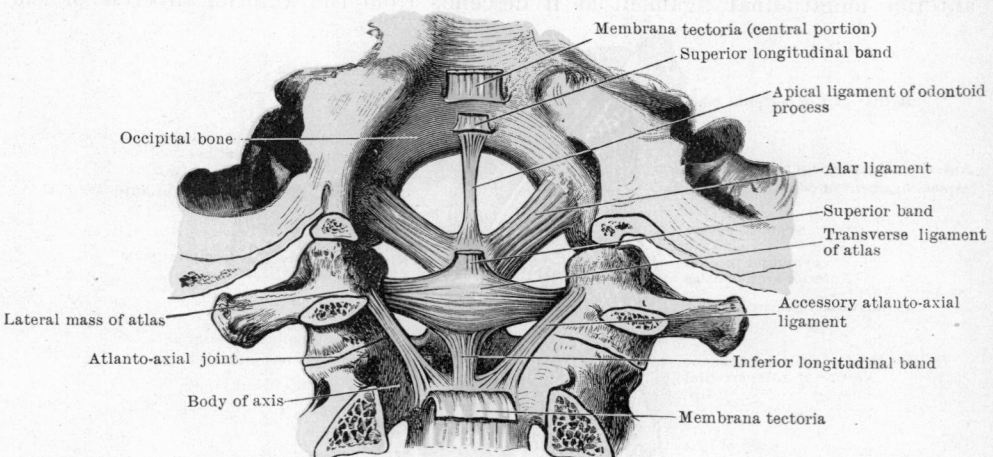

Fig. 295.—Dissection from behind of the Ligaments connecting the Occipital Bone, the Atlas, and the Axis with one another. (The capsular ligaments of the atlanto-occipital and atlanto-axial joints have been removed.)

below with the upper end of the posterior longitudinal ligament, and attached above to the occipital bone within the anterior edge of the foramen magnum between the anterior condylar canals. The margin of the membrana tectoria overlies and blends with the accessory atlanto-axial ligament. The upper end of the spinal dural tube is closely attached in front to the posterior surface of the membrana tectoria, and behind, to the anterior surface of the posterior atlanto-occipital membrane (Figs. 294, 295).

Movements of the Head

The movements of the head at the **atlanto-occipital joints** have been referred to in the description of those joints.

The combined movements at the three **atlanto-axial joints** serve to effect rotation of the head around a vertical axis, the skull and the atlas moving as one. While the ring formed by the anterior arch and transverse ligament of the atlas pivots round the odontoid process, the lateral masses of the atlas glide, the one forwards and the other backwards, on the upper articular facets of the axis. Owing to the oblique disposition of these lateral joint surfaces, rotation of the head to one side is accompanied by a slight vertical descent of the head, so that the median pivot-joint around the odontoid process resembles in action a rising butt hinge. Excessive rotation is checked by the alar ligaments and to a less extent by the accessory atlanto-axial ligaments. But the descent of the head, by approximating the attachments of the alar ligaments, serves to delay their check action, and this action can be obviated during a further degree of extreme lateral rotation by tilting the head backwards and to the opposite side. When the face looks straight forward the lateral joint surfaces are not fully in apposition ; slight rotation to one side secures better apposition and a pose more easily maintained.

MANDIBULAR JOINT

The **mandibular joint** is formed by the articulation of the **head of the mandible** with the **articular fossa** and the **articular tubercle** of the temporal bone. It is a synovial joint possessing a complete articular disc of fibro-cartilage which divides the joint cavity into two separate compartments—an upper one between the disc and the articular surface on the temporal bone, and a lower one between the disc and the head of the mandible.

The **temporal articular surface** is concavo-convex from behind forwards, extending from the squamo-tympanic fissure over the articular fossa and tubercle to the anterior border of the tubercle (Fig. 297). The **head** of the **mandible** is a narrow ellipsoidal bar of bone directed medially and slightly backwards, markedly convex from before backwards but only slightly convex from side to side.

The **capsular ligament** is loosely arranged around the joint. It is attached superiorly around the limits of the articular surface, and inferiorly to the neck of the mandible. Each compartment of the joint has its separate **synovial membrane**,

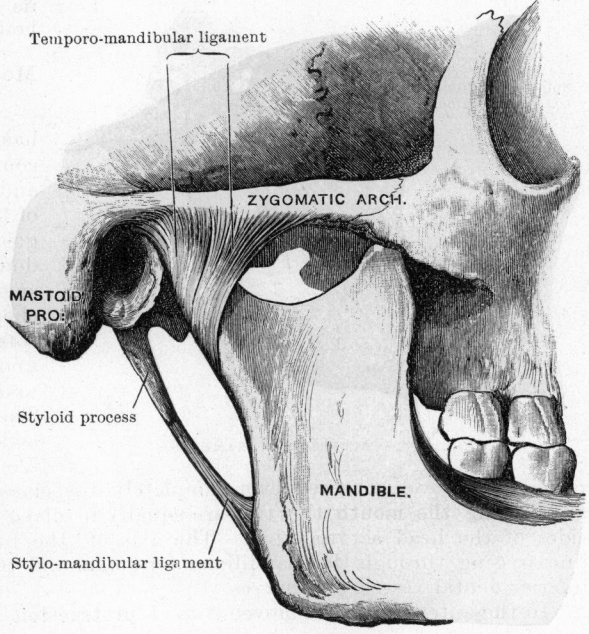

Temporo-mandibular ligament

ZYGOMATIC ARCH.

MASTOID PRO...

Styloid process

MANDIBLE.

Stylo-mandibular ligament

FIG. 296.—MANDIBULAR JOINT.

which lines the capsular ligament, but disappears over the surface of the disc. The capsular ligament is thickened laterally by a strengthening band, called the **temporo-mandibular ligament**, which is directed downwards and backwards from the lower border and tubercle of the zygoma to the lateral and posterior aspect of the neck of the mandible (Fig. 296). Anteriorly the capsular ligament receives part of the insertion of the lateral pterygoid muscle.

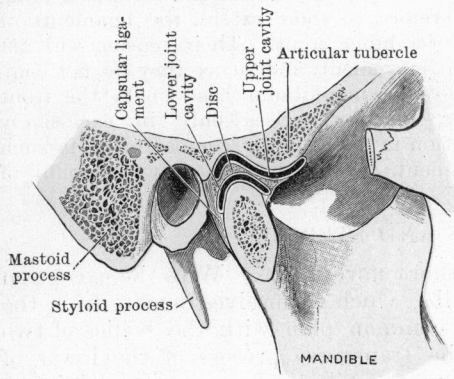

Capsular ligament

Lower joint cavity

Disc

Upper joint cavity

Articular tubercle

Mastoid process

Styloid process

MANDIBLE

FIG. 297.—ANTERO-POSTERIOR SECTION THROUGH THE MANDIBULAR JOINT.

The **articular disc** separates the highly incongruent joint surfaces and is moulded upon them in different positions of the joint; it is therefore concave below and concavo-convex above (Fig. 297). It is attached all round to the capsular ligament, and, anteriorly, through the capsule, to the lateral pterygoid tendon. The disc is thick anteriorly and in the middle; between these thickenings it is thin, and the posterior half of the disc thins out as it passes down behind the head of the mandible.

Accessory Ligaments. — Two other ligaments in the vicinity of the mandibular joint may be mentioned here. The **spheno-mandibular ligament** is a thin band that runs from the spine of the sphenoid bone and the adjacent medial end of the squamo-tympanic fissure downwards and forwards to the lingula and the adjoining part of the deep surface of the ramus of the mandible (Fig. 298). It lies a little medial to the capsule of the mandibular joint; intervening between the two, there are the maxillary artery and the first parts of its middle meningeal and inferior dental branches, the auriculo-temporal and inferior dental nerves, and a process of the parotid gland. This ligament is of some interest from its developmental relation to the part of the cartilage of the mandibular arch (Meckel's cartilage) that lies between the base of the skull and the mandibular foramen. The **stylo-mandibular ligament** is merely a thickened band of deep cervical fascia between the styloid process and the lower part of the posterior border of the ramus of the mandible (Figs. 296, 298).

Nerve-Supply.—The mandibular joint is supplied from the **mandibular** nerve by twigs from its **auriculo-temporal** and **masseteric** branches.

Movements at the Mandibular Joints

Movement at the mandibular joint has two components. In the upper compartment the head of the mandible and the disc, acting as one by virtue of the attachment of the lateral ptery-goid muscle to both, glide forwards and downwards round the postero-inferior surface of the articular tubercle. In the lower compartment a hinge-like rotation of the head of the mandible under the concave surface of the disc takes place around a transverse axis. The upper part of the joint therefore acts like a plane joint, the lower part like a hinge joint; but the two com-

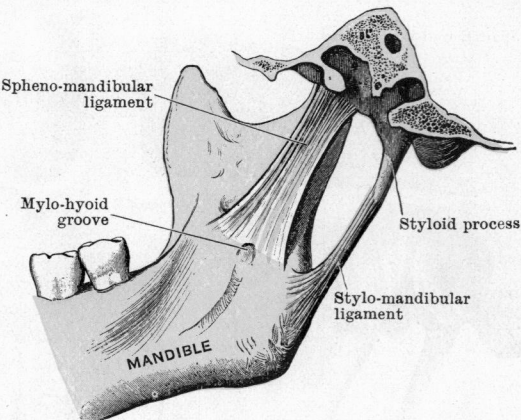

Fig. 298.—Accessory Ligaments.

[Labels on figure: Spheno-mandibular ligament; Mylo-hyoid groove; MANDIBLE; Styloid process; Stylo-mandibular ligament]

ponents of movement are never completely dissociated. In the movements of **opening** and **closing the mouth** the two are equally involved; and, of course, the joints on both sides of the head act together. The axis of the total movement is approximately a line passing through the mandibular foramina, and therefore no tension is put upon the inferior dental vessels and nerves.

In the antero-posterior movements of **protraction** and **retraction** of the lower jaw, it is mainly the gliding action in the upper compartment which is involved, the joints of both sides acting together. The oblique **grinding** movements of chewing are brought about by alternate or opposite movements in the upper compartments of the two joints, combined with associated hinge movements in the lower compartments.

It is worth noting that the upper attachment of the main (anterior) band of the temporo-mandibular ligament is on the axis of the curved downward and forward gliding movement in the upper compartment, and therefore, to some extent, the ligaments of the two sides resemble the collateral ligaments of a hinge joint. Their tension will not vary much throughout this upper-compartment movement, and hence they do not completely prevent the possibility of dislocation of the mandibular head on to the front of the articular tubercle. As this danger, however, arises only in excessively wide opening of the mouth, the associated rotation in the inferior compartment in such a position, by putting a strain upon the ligament, brings about a certain amount of safeguarding tension.

JOINTS OF THE RIBS AND STERNUM

The ribs articulate posteriorly with the thoracic vertebræ. With the exception of the first rib and the last two or three ribs, which themselves deviate from the common form, each rib articulates after a common plan with the bodies of two adjacent vertebræ by its head and with the transverse process of the lower of these vertebræ by its tubercle. Anteriorly, the ribs end in costal cartilages, which, with the exception of the last two, make further connexions with the sternum or with one another.

Costo-Vertebral Joints

Joints of Heads of Ribs (Fig. 299).—The **head** of each typical rib has two articular facets—superior and inferior—separated by a horizontal crest. Between the bodies of each two typical thoracic vertebræ, there is situated, postero-laterally, a little cupped depression bottomed by the edge of the intervertebral disc and completed above and below by slightly concave facets on the sides of the adjacent vertebræ. Into this depression the rib head is fitted, its crest being bound to the intervertebral disc by a short, thick **intra-articular ligament**. The facets on the head articulate with the facets on the vertebral bodies, of which the lower is in numerical correspondence with the rib.

The whole articulation is surrounded by a **capsular ligament**, within which the intra-articular ligament forms a complete horizontal septum between upper and lower joint cavities provided with synovial membranes. The anterior part of the capsular ligament is specially thickened to form the **radiate ligament** of the head of the rib, which passes medially from the front of the rib head to the adjacent parts of the disc and vertebral bodies, spreading fanwise upon them, under cover of the edge of the anterior longitudinal ligament. Three radiating bands are often to be seen, especially in the middle joints of the series, a central one blending with the intervertebral disc, and upper and lower bands attached to the vertebral bodies. The back of the joint capsule is connected to the adjacent denticulation of the posterior longitudinal ligament.

The intra-articular ligament and the connexion between the capsular ligament and the denticulation of the posterior longitudinal ligament are said to be related to the *conjugal*

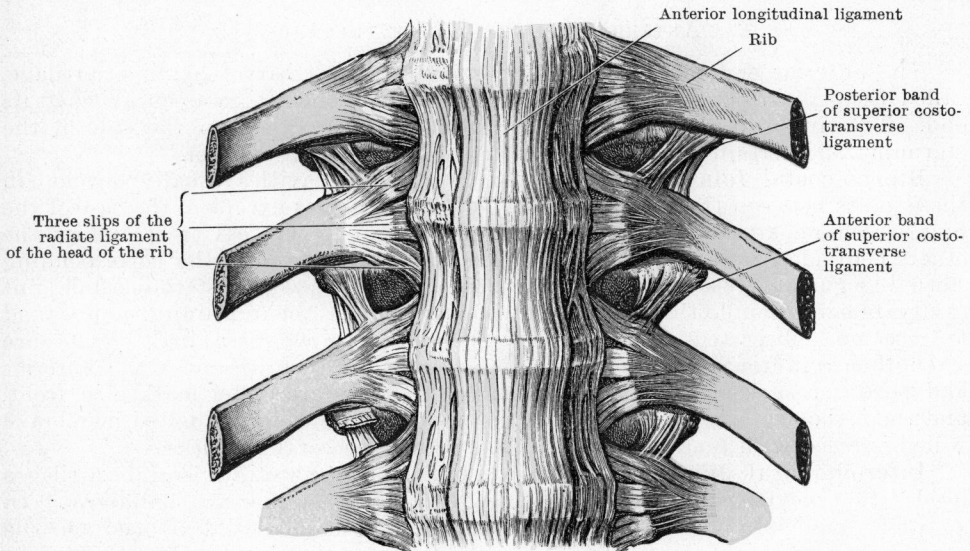

Anterior longitudinal ligament

Rib

Posterior band of superior costo-transverse ligament

Three slips of the radiate ligament of the head of the rib

Anterior band of superior costo-transverse ligament

FIG. 299.—ANTERIOR LONGITUDINAL LIGAMENT OF THE VERTEBRAL COLUMN, AND THE COSTO-VERTEBRAL JOINTS AS SEEN FROM THE FRONT.

ligament which in certain mammals connects the heads of a pair of ribs across the back of the intervertebral disc. Conjugal ligaments are present in the human fœtus, but disappear later except for the formation of the above-mentioned structures from their lateral ends.

Costo-transverse Joints.—Each typical rib further articulates by its **tubercle** with the transverse process of the lower of the two vertebræ to which its head is joined; and it is attached to the transverse processes of both vertebræ by certain accessory ligaments. A little costo-transverse synovial joint surrounded by a thin **capsular ligament** is formed between the medial part of the costal tubercle and a circular facet on the anterior surface of the corresponding transverse process near the tip. Strengthening this joint, on its postero-lateral aspect, there is the **lateral costo-transverse ligament** [lig. tuberculi costæ]—a stout band running between the rough, lateral part of the costal tubercle and the tip of the transverse process. It is in contact with, but is not fused with, the capsular ligament of the costo-transverse joint.

The **inferior costo-transverse ligament** [lig. colli costæ] also binds the rib to the same transverse process; it is composed of very short fibres that bridge the narrow interval between the back of the neck of the rib and the front of the transverse process.

Finally, the rib is attached to the transverse process of the vertebra above by the **superior costo-transverse ligament** (Fig. 299). This ligament consists of an anterior and a posterior band that spring from the upper border of the neck of the rib, and are separated laterally by the posterior fibres of the external intercostal muscle. The anterior band has medially a thickened free border, but laterally it blends with the posterior intercostal membrane; its fibres pass upwards and laterally to the lower border of the transverse process above. The posterior band ascends vertically, or with a medial inclination, to the medial part of the lower border of the transverse process above, and in some cases extends medially on to the inferior articular facet of the vertebra above.

The vertebral connexions of the **first rib** and of the **last two or three ribs** are atypical. The head of each of these ribs has a single facet that articulates with an impression on the side of only the corresponding vertebra. The intra-articular ligament is therefore absent in each case, and there is a **single synovial cavity**; the radiate ligament is incompletely developed. The superior costo-transverse ligament of the first rib is represented by feeble bands attached to the seventh cervical transverse process. The tubercles of the lowest ribs do not form synovial joints with the transverse processes; their costo-transverse ligaments are progressively less well defined: those of the last rib may be absent altogether.

ANTERIOR CONNEXIONS OF THE RIBS

The anterior end of each rib is continuous with a bar of hyaline cartilage, called the *costal cartilage*, which is solidly united to the rib in a concavity at its end. The first seven costal cartilages articulate with facets on the side of the sternum; and certain of the cartilages articulate with one another.

Sterno-costal Joints (Fig. 300).—Little synovial cavities usually develop in these joints between the sternum and the costal cartilages except in the case of the first, which remains a continuous cartilaginous joint. The cavity of each of the others is divided into two by an **intra-articular ligament,** until the corresponding sternal segments fuse together; in most cases the second sterno-costal joint cavity remains double throughout life; the cavities in the remaining joints tend to become obliterated in old age. The **capsules** of these little joints are strengthened in front and behind by fibres that spread fanwise over the anterior and posterior surfaces of the sternum. These fibres are better marked in front, and there they interlace with those of the opposite side to form a felted membrane which is fused with tendinous fibres of the greater pectoral muscles.

Inter-chondral Joints.—The tips of the eighth and ninth costal cartilages form little **synovial joints**, each with the lower border of the cartilage above. In addition, synovial joints are formed between slight bosses developed on the contiguous margins of the fifth to the eighth or ninth cartilages. All these joints between cartilages are enclosed by short **articular capsules** strengthened in front and behind by oblique ligamentous bands. The terminal part of the tenth cartilage is united to the ninth by a syndesmosis.

The last two costal cartilages are short conical structures ending freely amongst the muscles of the flank.

STERNAL JOINTS

The manubrium sterni is united to the body of the sternum by a **manubrio-sternal joint** of secondary cartilaginous type which is only exceptionally obliterated by synostosis in old age. Special longitudinal fibres and the neighbouring sterno-costal ligaments strengthen this joint in front and behind. The cartilaginous **xiphi-sternal joint** between the body of the sternum and the xiphoid process is usually ossified in early adult life.

Movements of the Ribs and Sternum

The active movements of the ribs and sternum are those associated with respiration. The capitular and costo-transverse joints of each rib together form a hinge with a horizontal axis passing through the two joints; owing to the backward tilt of the transverse process of the typical thoracic vertebra, this axis is directed from before backwards and in a lateral direction. Thus hinged posteriorly, the anterior part of the rib is raised during inspiration and lowered during expiration. As the anterior end of the rib is below the level of the posterior end, raising the rib in inspiration causes the anterior end to travel forwards as well as upwards and, owing to the obliquity of the axis of the hinge, a little laterally as well. The sternum, attached to the anterior ends of the upper ribs, is also made to travel upwards and forwards, and the lateral deviation of the anterior ends of the ribs causes an opening out of the angles between the sternum and the costal cartilages. The obliquity of the axis of movement is most marked in the case of the middle ribs, which possess long, inclined cartilages, and therefore the greater lateral movement of the anterior ends of these ribs can readily take place. But in the upper ribs, where the axis is almost transverse, the lateral movement is slight or absent ; shorter cartilages therefore suffice, set almost at right angles to the sternum. As the first rib is so much shorter than those which succeed it, the upward and forward excursion of its anterior end is less in extent, and the upper border of the sternum is only slightly raised and is carried forward hardly at all. The greater travel—especially in the forward direction—imposed upon the rest of the sternum by the longer ribs causes a bending of the breastbone at the manubrio-sternal joint. The result of all this on the capacity of the thorax is to increase its antero-posterior diameter. But its transverse diameter also is increased, for the following reason. The sternal attachments of the ribs to some extent hamper the movements of their anterior ends and to that extent "fix" the anterior ends, so that the raising of the ribs is in part translated into a twisting of the anterior parts of the costal arches, causing torsion of the cartilages and rotation at the sterno-costal joints. But to begin with, each costal arch is so disposed that the middle part is below the level of a line joining its two ends —like a bucket handle hanging down below the rim of the bucket. Hence this longi-tudinal twisting of the costal arch causes the middle part of the rib to rise upwards and outwards, so increasing the transverse width of the thorax.

Expiration is accompanied by reverse movements whereby the antero-posterior and transverse diameters of the thorax are diminished. Although it is convenient thus to describe the respiratory movements of the thorax as taking place in alternate opposite directions between the extreme inspiratory and expiratory positions, it should be explained that the "resting" position of the thorax is midway between these extremes. This is the position of balance between the elastic tension of the costal arches tending upwards and the muscular and mechanical pull of the abdominal wall and contents tending downwards. The first half of the complete movement in either direction between full expiration and inspiration represents a recoil to this mean position; beyond this point, the second half of the movement is the result of positive muscular effort.

Apart from respiratory movements, the ribs move passively with changes in the thoracic part of the vertebral column. Flexion of the column causes a crowding together of the ribs ; extension causes a spreading apart ; bending of the column to one side brings about crowding of the ribs on that side of the trunk, and spreading on the opposite side.

JOINTS OF THE UPPER LIMB

JOINTS OF THE SHOULDER GIRDLE

In order to promote freedom of movement of the arm, the shoulder girdle remains relatively independent of the skeleton of the trunk ; only one joint, and a freely movable one—the *sterno-clavicular*—exists between the two. The scapula is attached to the axial skeleton by muscles only. The bones of the girdle are them-selves movably united to each other at the *acromio-clavicular joint*.

STERNO-CLAVICULAR JOINT

At the **sterno-clavicular joint** the medial end of the clavicle articulates with the sternum (an articular disc intervening), and with the first costal cartilage. The clavicular surface is more extensive than the sternal, but the medial joint surface is prolonged a little way over the upper surface of the cartilage of the first rib. The bony surfaces are reciprocally concavo-convex, being convex vertically and concave horizontally on the clavicular side. But the curvatures are slight and not fully congruent. and the clavicular and sternal sur-faces are separated by the articular disc, so that the joint cannot function as a saddle-joint. It is rather, in its movements, of the ball-and-socket type. The articular cartilage in this joint is partly fibrous.

A **capsular ligament** surrounds the whole joint and is attached around the clavicular and the sterno-chondral articular surfaces. The epiphysis at the sternal end of the clavicle is intra-capsular. The inferior part of the capsular ligament, passing between the costal cartilage and the clavicle, is weak, as it is put to little

22

strain. The other parts of the ligament are strong, being reinforced in front, behind, and above, by thickened bands called the *anterior* and *posterior sterno-clavicular ligaments* and the *interclavicular ligament*.

The **anterior** and **posterior sterno-clavicular ligaments**, of which the anterior is the stronger, run downwards and medially from bone to bone (Fig. 300). The origin of the sterno-hyoid muscle extends across the posterior ligament; this muscle and the sterno-thyroid separate the back of the left joint from the left innominate vein and the left common carotid artery, and the right joint from the innominate artery. The **interclavicular ligament** is formed by fibres from the strengthening band on the upper aspect of the capsular ligament that pass across the floor of the suprasternal notch to join similar fibres from the joint of

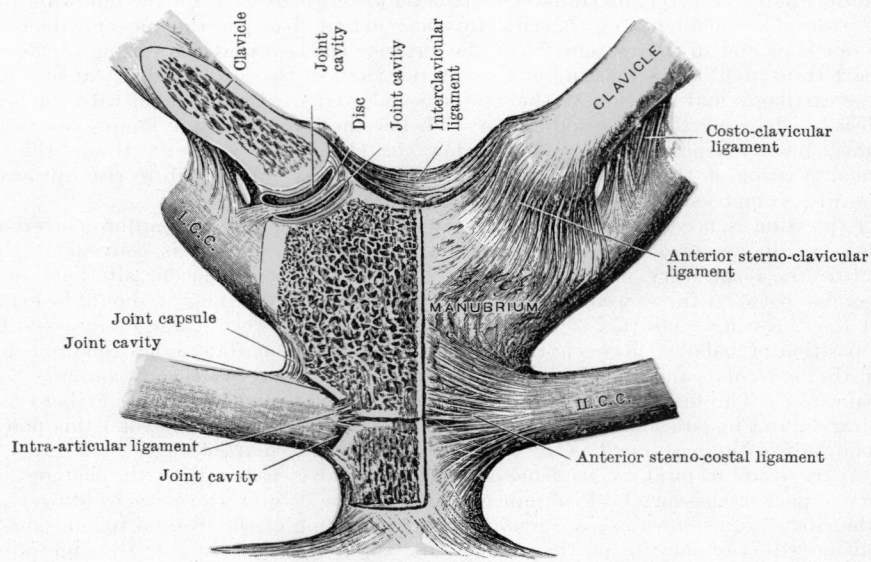

FIG. 300.—STERNO-CLAVICULAR AND STERNO-COSTAL JOINTS.

the opposite side. The interclavicular ligament is thought to be a derivative of the embryonic episternal band.

Within the joint there is a complete fibro-cartilaginous **articular disc**, which blends with the capsular ligament in front and behind, but has its firmest attachment above to the clavicle and below to the first costal cartilage, just wide of the sternal articular surface. Hence the disc, in addition to cushioning the joint surfaces from shocks transmitted along the clavicle from the shoulder, has an important ligamentous action in preventing such forces from driving the sternal end of the clavicle upwards and medially along the sloping chondro-sternal surface. Also, when the clavicle is depressed, as by a heavy weight carried in the hand, any tendency for the medial end of the bone to start up out of its sternal socket is resisted by the disc, supported by tension of the upper part of the capsular ligament and of the obliquely disposed anterior and posterior bands.

There are two separate **synovial cavities** within the sterno-clavicular joint, save when, exceptionally, the thinner central part of the articular disc is perforated.

The **costo-clavicular ligament** is an accessory ligament placed on the lateral side of this joint. It ascends from the upper surface of the first costal cartilage near its lateral end to a rough tubercle on the under aspect of the medial part of the clavicle. The ligament is related anteriorly to the tendon of the subclavius muscle, and posteriorly to the innominate vein, on the right side, and, on the left side, to the subclavian or the innominate vein or to both. It limits elevation of the clavicle, and, by its strength in this connexion, compensates for the weakness of the adjacent inferior part of the sterno-clavicular joint capsule; to a lesser extent it limits antero-posterior clavicular movement also.

Nerve Supply.—The sterno-clavicular joint is supplied by twigs from the most medial supra-clavicular nerve.

ACROMIO-CLAVICULAR JOINT

The **acromio-clavicular joint** is a small synovial joint, of the plane type, between oval facets on the lateral end of the clavicle and on the medial border of the acromion (Fig. 302). The joint surfaces, covered with fibrous articular cartilage, slope downwards and medially so that the clavicle tends to override the acromion.

A **capsular ligament**, of no great strength, encloses the joint cavity; it is stoutest above, and is there reinforced by fibres from the trapezius. A wedge-shaped, fibro-cartilaginous **articular disc**, attached to the upper part of the capsule, partially subdivides the joint cavity in most cases. Only rarely does it form a complete partition; and sometimes it is absent altogether.

Nerve Supply.—The acromio-clavicular joint is supplied by the **pectoral, suprascapular** and **circumflex** nerves.

Coraco-clavicular Ligament.—The real strength of the union between clavicle and scapula depends on the powerful **coraco-clavicular ligament** (Fig. 302), which anchors the lateral end of the clavicle over the coracoid process. It is divided into two parts, called from their shape the conoid and trapezoid ligaments, which form anteriorly a re-entrant angle occupied by a synovial bursa.

The **conoid ligament** passes upwards and slightly backwards from an apical attachment at the angle between the two parts of the bent coracoid process to a wider insertion on the conoid tubercle on the under surface of the clavicle. The **trapezoid ligament** bears antero-laterally from the conoid ligament. Its lower attachment is to a short ridge on the posterior part of the upper surface of the coracoid process; its upper end is wider, and is attached to the trapezoid ridge on the under side of the acromial end of the clavicle. The attached borders of the trapezoid ligament are slightly askew, and its surfaces so oblique as to be more nearly horizontal than vertical.

The conoid ligament is so set as to restrain backward movement of the acromial end of the clavicle without similar movement of the scapula, the trapezoid ligament to restrain forward movement. Both ligaments, but more particularly the trapezoid, prevent the acromion from being carried medially below the lateral end of the clavicle when blows fall upon the lateral surface of the shoulder.

Movements of the Shoulder Girdle

Movements of the shoulder girdle serve to increase the range of movement at the shoulder joint by suitable alteration in the position of the socket for the head of the humerus, brought about by movement of the scapula upon the chest wall. Thus, forward movement of the scapula round the chest causes the glenoid cavity to be directed more forwards; backward movement causes the cavity to look laterally; upward movement of the scapula, combined with rotation so that the inferior angle passes forwards and upwards, causes the fossa to be turned increasingly upwards; and sinking of the scapula with medial rotation of the inferior angle turns the cavity slightly downwards. But in all these changes of position the shoulder is kept boomed out from the trunk by the thrust of the clavicle upon the acromion, thus further to secure freedom of shoulder movement. The medial part of the scapular blade, in its ambit, is held close to the chest wall by the muscles, and must therefore travel in a curve whose radius—the radius of the thoracic curvature—is shorter than the length of the clavicle, to which the lateral part of the scapula is attached. Hence, the set of the scapula relative to the clavicle must be capable of modification, and this is brought about by alteration, at the acromio-clavicular joint, of the angle between the clavicle and the scapular spine: that is the function of this gliding joint. One particular result of the different arc of travel of the acromion and lateral angle of the scapula from that of the medial part of the blade is to obviate, in forward movement of the shoulder, any marked change in direction of the glenoid cavity which would diminish the power of forward thrusting movement of the arm.

The clavicle is pivoted at its sternal end, while its acromial end moves, in association with the scapula, forwards, backwards, upwards, downwards, and, of course, in intermediate directions. A small amount of rotation around the long axis of the bone (not more than 45°) also can take place at the sterno-clavicular joint, but only in association with other movements of the acromial end. This rotation occurs particularly with elevation and depression, when scapular rotation also takes place.

SCAPULAR LIGAMENTS

The following ligaments attached wholly to the scapula are not connected with any joint.

The **suprascapular ligament** bridges the suprascapular notch, and so continues the line of the superior border of the scapula laterally to the root of the coracoid process. Sometimes it is partly or completely ossified. Fibres of the inferior belly of the omo-hyoid are attached to its medial portion. The suprascapular nerve enters the supraspinous fossa through the foramen completed by the ligament, while the suprascapular vessels pass over the ligament to reach the fossa.

The **spino-glenoid ligament** is a weak band that stretches between the lateral border of the scapular spine and the back of the neck of the bone, over the suprascapular nerve and vessels. It may be regarded as formed from a fusion of the fasciæ over the contiguous supraspinatus and infraspinatus muscles.

The **coraco-acromial ligament** is functionally related to the shoulder joint, with which it will be described.

SHOULDER JOINT

The **shoulder joint** is a synovial joint of ball-and-socket type in which freedom of movement is developed at the expense of stability. The spheroidal

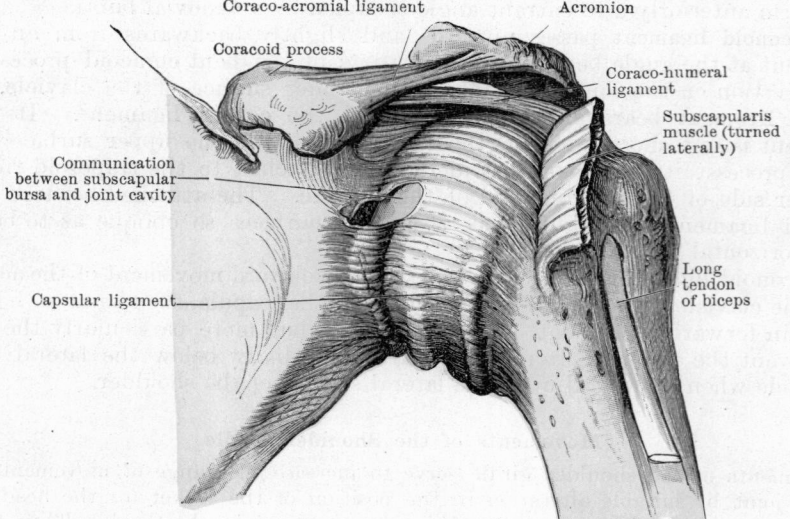

FIG. 301.—CAPSULE OF THE SHOULDER JOINT FROM THE FRONT.

surface of the head of the humerus articulates with the shallow glenoid cavity of the scapula, each surface being covered with articular cartilage. The area of the scapular "socket" is little more than a third of that of the humeral "ball," so that the co-aptation of these surfaces contributes very little to the security of the joint. Nor does the capsular ligament play a great part, for it is of necessity lax enough to permit the required freedom of movement. The real strength of the joint lies in the muscles which surround it. They are attached close up to the articular areas and are intimately related to the joint capsule; hence they are admirably disposed for the purpose of keeping the joint surfaces in firm contact in all positions, although at the sacrifice of the greater power that would be obtained were they inserted farther from the centre of movement in the joint.

Labrum Glenoidale (Fig. 302).—The labrum glenoidale is a fibro-cartilaginous rim, triangular in cross section, attached to the edge of the glenoid cavity, which is slightly deepened by it. At the notch above the middle of the anterior edge of the cavity the labrum is less solidly attached to the bone and a synovial fold intervenes between the two. The long tendon of the biceps, arising within the joint from the apex of the glenoid cavity, is there fused to the labrum glenoidale.

Capsular Ligament.—The capsular ligament forms a cylindrical sleeve

attached close to the articular area of each bone.   On the scapular side it is
attached external to the labrum glenoidale and partly to the labrum itself,
especially above and behind.   On the humeral side the ligament is attached above
to the anatomical neck immediately medial to the tuberosities; but below, it
extends on to the medial surface of the shaft of the bone some way from the
articular head.   The upper epiphyseal line of the humerus is therefore chiefly
extracapsular, but comes within the joint on the medial side.   The anterior part
of the capsular ligament is immediately related to the tendons of the subscapularis
muscle, the superior part to the supraspinatus tendon, and the posterior part to
the tendons of the infraspinatus and teres minor muscles.   All these tendons blend
with the ligament towards their insertion.   The inferior part of the capsular
ligament, which is also the weakest, is relatively unsupported by muscles, but as

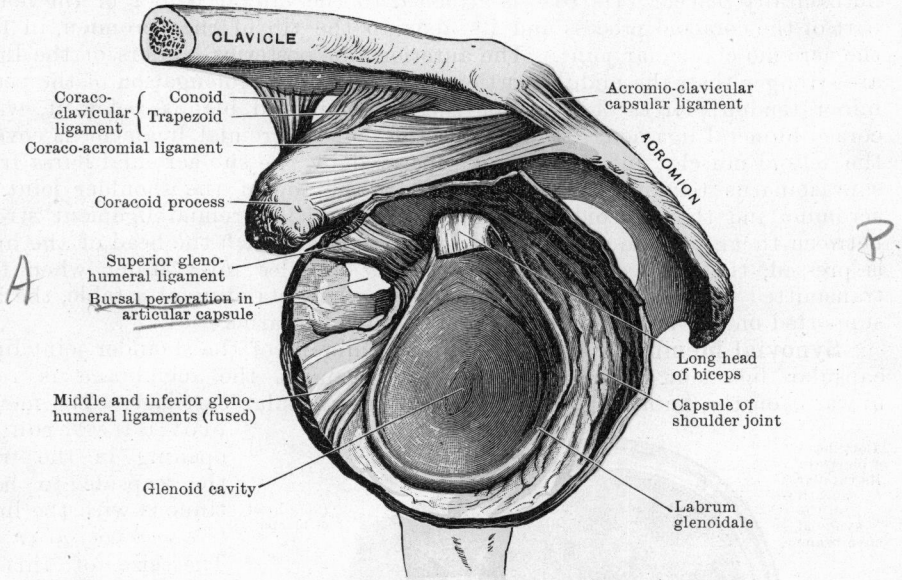

FIG. 302.—CAPSULE OF SHOULDER JOINT CUT ACROSS AND HUMERUS REMOVED.

the arm is raised from the side the long head of the triceps and the teres major
are increasingly applied to this surface of the joint.
     There are two **openings** in the capsular ligament (Fig. 301).   One is an
interruption in its attachment to the humerus at the upper end of the bicipital
groove; the long tendon of the biceps escapes through the aperture so formed.
The other opening is in the front of the capsular ligament under cover of the
subscapularis tendon, and through it the subscapular bursa communicates with
the synovial cavity of the joint.
     The fibres of the capsular ligament run for the most part longitudinally from
bone to bone.   In addition to longitudinal fibres, a few fibres run transversely
round the capsular ligament.   The **transverse humeral ligament** is a special bundle
of transverse fibres that arch over the opening through which the biceps tendon
leaves the joint and bridge the upper end of the bicipital groove.

Three slightly thickened bands of longitudinal fibres are to be seen on the internal surface
of the anterior part of the capsule, although not visible on the outside of the joint.   These are
the *superior, middle,* and *inferior gleno-humeral ligaments* (Fig. 302).   The **superior gleno-
humeral ligament** is attached to the upper part of the labrum glenoidale immediately anterior
to the long tendon of the biceps, and passes laterally, alongside the tendon, to reach the humerus
near the upper surface of the lesser tuberosity.   It has been considered homologous with the
ligament of the head of the femur, but has also been regarded, possibly with more likelihood,
as representing the base of the synovial fold by which, in the foetus, the long tendon of the
biceps is attached to the upper part of the joint capsule.   The **middle gleno-humeral ligament**
is attached to the scapula close to the superior band and reaches the humerus at the front of the
lesser tuberosity.   The opening in the capsular ligament under the subscapularis tendon is

between the superior and middle bands.   The **inferior gleno-humeral ligament**, usually the best marked of the three, is attached to the scapula immediately below the notch in the anterior border of the glenoid cavity and to the humerus on the under surface of the neck.

Accessory Ligaments.—The **coraco-humeral ligament** is an accessory ligament on the upper aspect of the joint (Fig. 301).   It springs from the lateral side of the root of the coracoid process and runs laterally upon the capsular ligament as a raised band which gradually flattens as it blends laterally with the upper and posterior part of the capsular ligament; it reaches the neck of the humerus opposite the greater tuberosity.   This band greatly strengthens the upper part of the capsular ligament, which is under tension when the arm hangs by the side.

Arching over the upper aspect of the shoulder joint, but not connected to its capsule, is the **coraco-acromial ligament** (Figs. 301, 302).   It is triangular, and horizontally placed.   Its base is attached to the lateral border of the horizontal part of the coracoid process and its apex to the tip of the acromion, in front of the acromio-clavicular joint.   The anterior and posterior borders of the ligament are stronger than the middle portion.   Sometimes a prolongation of the pectoralis minor tendon pierces the base of the ligament and blends, below it, with the coraco-humeral ligament.   Superiorly, the coraco-acromial ligament is covered by the deltoid muscle; inferiorly, it is separated by the sub-acromial bursa from the supraspinatus tendon, which is applied to the top of the shoulder joint.   The acromion and the coracoid process, with the coraco-acromial ligament stretching between them, provide an accessory socket against which the head of the humerus is pressed, the joint capsule and overlying muscles intervening, when force is transmitted upwards along the humerus as when, standing at a table, the body is supported on the table edge by the down-stretched arms.

Synovial Membrane.—The synovial membrane of the shoulder joint lines the capsular ligament.   From the capsular ligament the membrane is reflected upwards on the humerus to the edge of the articular cartilage.   The membrane protrudes through the opening in the front of the capsule to be continuous with the lining of the *subscapular bursa*.   The size of this bursa varies; when large it may be wrapped round the upper border of the subscapularis tendon underneath the coracoid process, but this upper, *sub-coracoid* extension may be represented by a separate bursa of that name, not communicating with the joint.   Occasionally the synovial membrane protrudes through an opening in the back of the capsular ligament to form a small bursa beneath the infraspinatus tendon.

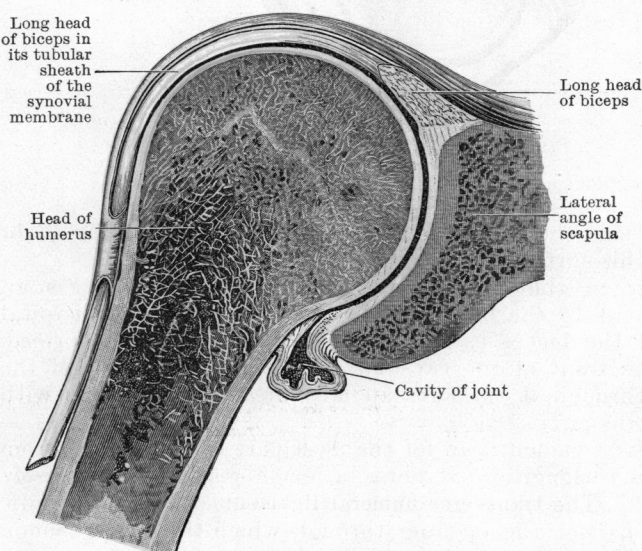

Long head of biceps in its tubular sheath of the synovial membrane

Head of humerus

Long head of biceps

Lateral angle of scapula

Cavity of joint

FIG. 303.—CORONAL SECTION THROUGH THE SHOULDER JOINT.

In this neighbourhood there is always a large *sub-acromial bursa* which separates the coraco-acromial arch and the deltoid muscle from the upper and lateral aspect of the shoulder joint and the tendons lying upon it; this bursa does not communicate with the interior of the joint.

The relation of the *long tendon of the biceps* to the synovial membrane is important (Fig. 303).   The intracapsular part of the tendon is covered with a sheath of synovial membrane which is continued along the tendon in the upper part of the bicipital groove.   The synovial sheath is then reflected upwards as a

PLATE XXI

Acromio-clavicular
joint

Coracoid process
overlapping
Spine of Scapula

Superior angle
of Scapula

Acromion

Anatomical
Neck of
Humerus

Greater
Tuberosity

Surgical
Neck

First Rib

Second Rib

Clavicle

Medial
(vertebral)
border of
Scapula

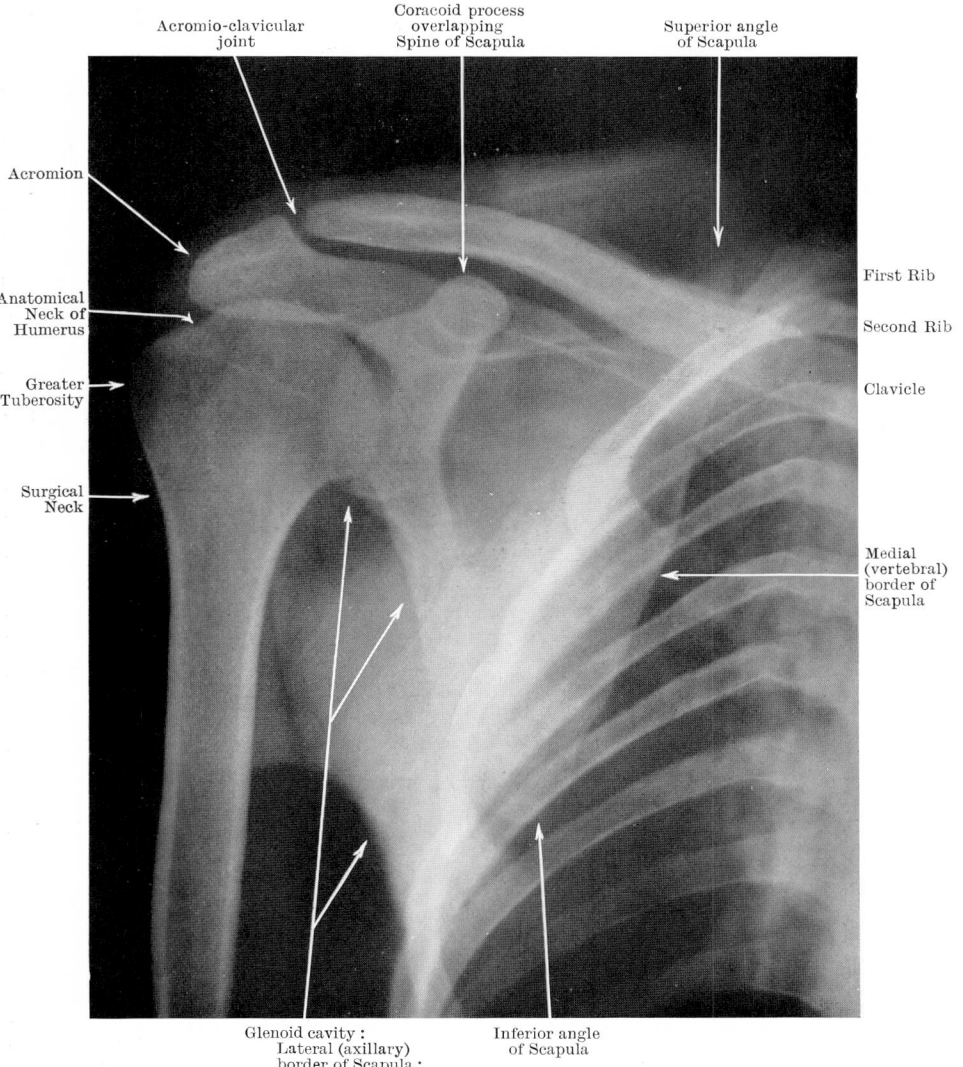

Glenoid cavity :
Lateral (axillary)
border of Scapula :
Axillary fold

Inferior angle
of Scapula

PLATE XXI.—RADIOGRAPH OF SHOULDER REGION OF MAN AGED 29.

For alterations in the relative positions of the Humerus and the Scapula during movements of the Upper Limb,
see Plate XXII.

[Facing p. 342

PLATE XXII

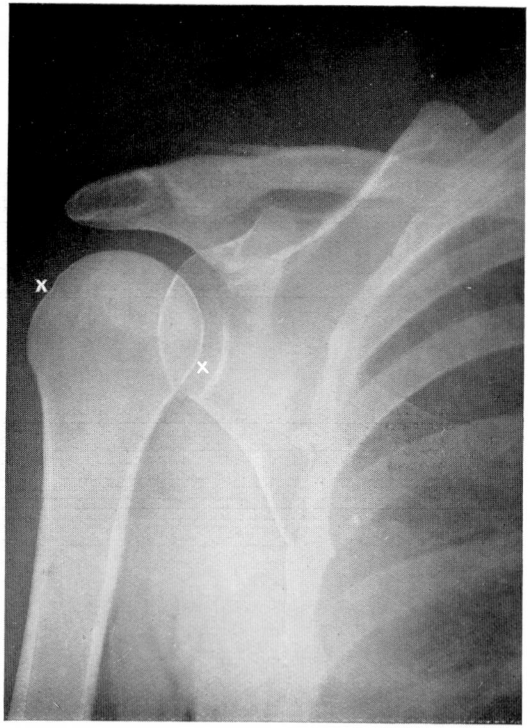

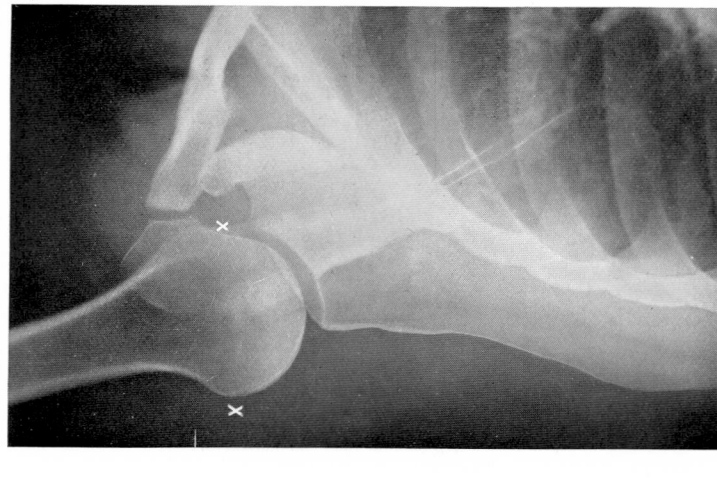

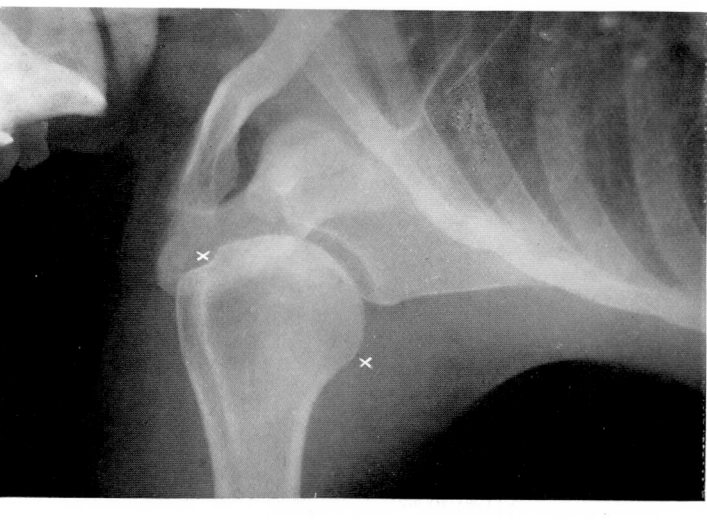

Fig. 1.—With the Arm Dependent. Note the position of the Anatomical Neck of the Humerus (indicated by the white crosses) and of the Scapula.

Fig. 2.—With the Arm raised to the Horizontal Position. Note that Scapular as well as Gleno-humeral Movement has taken place.

Fig. 3.—With the Arm Vertical. In addition to further Scapular Movement, Gleno-humeral Movement has continued until the Shaft of the Humerus is in line with the Spine of the Scapula.

PLATE XXII.—Three Radiographs of the Shoulder to demonstrate the Mechanism of Abduction and Elevation of the Arm. (R. D. L.). (See p. 459).

Note that in addition to movement of the scapula on the chest wall, and of the humerus at the shoulder joint, lateral rotation of the humerus also takes place.

lining to the osteo-fascial tunnel in which the tendon runs and so passes into continuity with the synovial lining of the capsular ligament. As the tendon runs over the upper part of the articular head of the humerus, it has a steadying influence upon movements of the shoulder joint.

In the embryo the long tendon of the biceps at first lies outside the developing joint capsule; this is the persisting relationship in some lower mammals. But later in human development the tendon sinks through the capsular ligament and is attached to its deep surface by a mesentery-like fold of synovial membrane; this condition persists in most higher mammals. Normally, in man, the "mesentery" breaks down before birth, leaving the tendon unattached to the capsule but surrounded by a sheath of synovial membrane.

Nerve-Supply.—The shoulder joint is supplied by branches from the **suprascapular, circumflex,** and **subscapular nerves.**

Movements at the Shoulder Joint

This being a ball-and-socket joint, movement can take place around an infinite number of axes intersecting in the centre of the globular head of the humerus. The principal axes of descriptive convenience are: (1) a transverse axis around which the arm moves forwards in **flexion** and backwards in **extension**; (2) an antero-posterior axis around which occur the movements of **abduction** (away from the side of the trunk) and **adduction** (towards the side of the trunk); and (3) a vertical axis around which the arm **rotates medially** and **laterally**. **Circumduction** is a combination of antero-posterior and sideward movements around successive axes, when the arm swings round the side of a cone whose apex is the point of intersection of the various axes in the head of the humerus.

Since in the normal position, with the arm by the side, the glenoid cavity looks slightly forwards as well as laterally, and the humeral head is turned slightly backwards as well as medially, the strict transverse and antero-posterior axes of the joint are set obliquely to frontal and sagittal planes of the trunk. Thus, for example, the true transverse axis of the joint runs medio-laterally and slightly forwards, and, in flexion-extension movements around this axis, the arm swings forwards and medially, backwards and laterally. But in common practice, when movement is considered simply as movement of the arm upon the trunk, flexion and extension are thought of as movements directly forwards and backwards, and abduction and adduction as movements directly laterally and medially.

The range of movement at the shoulder joint is greatly increased by associated movements of the shoulder girdle. The total apparent movement of the humerus is made up of its real movement upon the scapula plus movement of the scapula upon the chest wall, with associated changes at the clavicular joints: the effective mobility of the ball-and-socket shoulder joint is increased by mobility of the socket itself. And not only the range but also the power of movement is increased by this means. It has already been shown that as the muscles acting upon the shoulder joint are attached close to the centre of movement in the joint, their force is thereby lessened; the muscles acting on the scapula, however, have the advantage of much greater leverage, and therefore the scapular movements add greatly to the total force of arm movements from the shoulder.

The adjuvant effect of scapular movements is strikingly illustrated in those in whom the scapulo-humeral joint is completely fixed as the result of disease or of surgical treatment to combat disease. Provided that care has been exercised to secure fixation in such a position as will allow full advantage to be taken of scapular movement, these patients may retain a considerable degree of mobility of the arm upon the trunk. Nevertheless it must be realised that, normally, movements at the shoulder joint and movements of the scapula are not dissociated but take place together. Thus, in raising the arm from the side to a vertical position above the head, although gleno-humeral action is more concerned in the first half of the movement and scapular rotation in the second half, yet the scapula slides on the chest from the beginning and the head of the humerus moves upon the glenoid cavity to the very end of the movement (Lockhart, *Journal of Anatomy*, 1930). (See also p. 459, and Pl. XXII).

ELBOW JOINT

The **elbow joint** is a large synovial joint, of the hinge type, in which the forearm bones articulate with the lower end of the humerus. The upper ends of the radius and ulna are tied together by the annular ligament of the radius, but in such a way as to permit movement between these two bones at what is described separately as the superior radio-ulnar joint; the cavity of this joint is freely continuous with that of the elbow joint. The annular ligament plays a part in the structure of both, but it will be described later with the superior radio-ulnar joint.

Articular Surfaces.—The **humeral articular surface** at the elbow comprises the grooved *trochlea* and the spheroidal *capitulum*, together with the sulcus between them. This composite surface is covered with a continuous layer of articular cartilage. The capitulum is limited to the anterior and distal aspects of the bone, while the trochlea extends from the lower edge of the coronoid fossa on the front of the humerus round to the lower edge of the olecranon fossa on the back (Fig. 203). The **ulnar surface** of the elbow joint (Fig. 307) is the *trochlear notch*, covered with articular cartilage interrupted along a transverse line across the deepest part of the notch; this surface articulates with the trochlea of the humerus. The **radial surface** is the slightly cupped upper surface of the *head* of the radius, covered with articular cartilage continuous with that round the sides of the head in the radio-ulnar joint; the concave part of the upper surface of the head articulates with the capitulum, and the raised margin with the capitulo-trochlear groove. The radial and ulnar surfaces are not strictly congruent with the corresponding humeral surfaces, and the degree of accurate apposition varies slightly in different positions of the joint. The articular surfaces are most fully in contact when the forearm is in a position midway between full pronation and full supination and is flexed to a right angle.

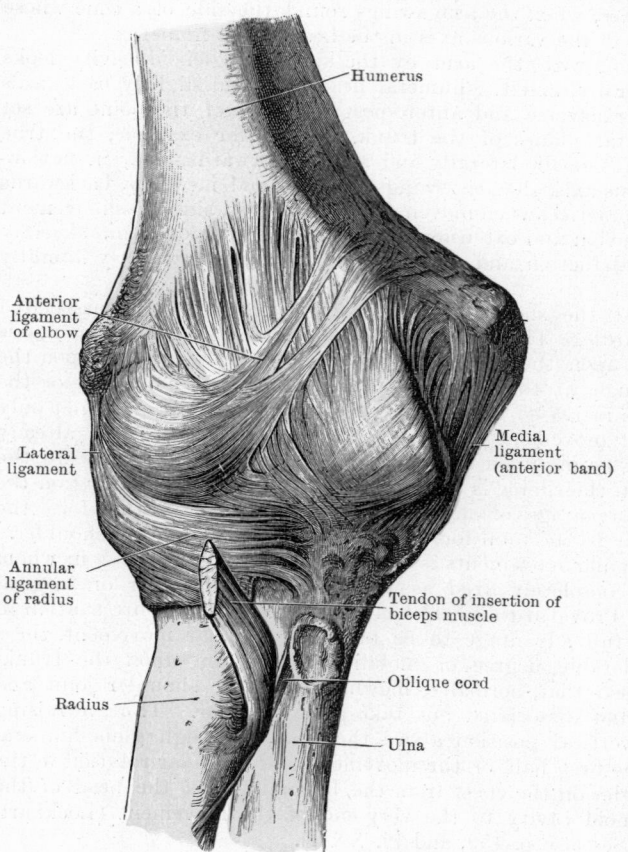

FIG. 304.—FRONT OF ELBOW JOINT.

Labels on figure: Humerus; Anterior ligament of elbow; Lateral ligament; Annular ligament of radius; Radius; Medial ligament (anterior band); Tendon of insertion of biceps muscle; Oblique cord; Ulna

Capsular Ligament.—A capsular ligament completely invests the joint. Following the usual arrangement in a hinge joint, this ligament is relatively weak in front and behind, but is specially strengthened at the sides. The parts in front and behind are called the *anterior* and *posterior ligaments* of the elbow joint; the anterior is taut only in extension and the posterior only in flexion. The strong portions at the sides of the capsular ligament constitute the *lateral* and *medial ligaments*; these, being attached to the humerus in the axis of movement at the joint, remain tense in all positions.

The **anterior ligament** (Fig. 304) is composed of fibres that run for the most part longitudinally, but also transversely and obliquely; it is thicker in the middle than at the sides. Proximally, it is attached to the front of the humerus immediately above the radial and coronoid fossæ; distally, it is attached to the anterior border of the coronoid process of the ulna and to the anterior part of the annular ligament of the radius; at the sides it blends with the medial and lateral ligaments. The brachialis muscle covers the greater part of the anterior ligament, and some deep fibres are inserted into the ligament, which is therefore drawn upwards when the muscle contracts to flex the joint.

The **posterior ligament** is very weak in its medial part, but is here closely attached to the overlying tendon of the triceps, which affords ample support to the joint capsule and draws it upwards in extension. The fibres in that part of the ligament run mainly from the sides of the olecranon fossa to the margin of the olecranon ; some fibres stretch across the fossa above the olecranon as a transverse band with a free upper edge which falls short of the upper margin of the fossa. Beneath these transverse fibres a few longitudinal strands pass to the upper part of the fossa and afford slight support to the synovial pouch within it. The lateral part of the posterior ligament is a stronger band that runs from the back of the lateral epicondyle to the ulna at the posterior border of the radial

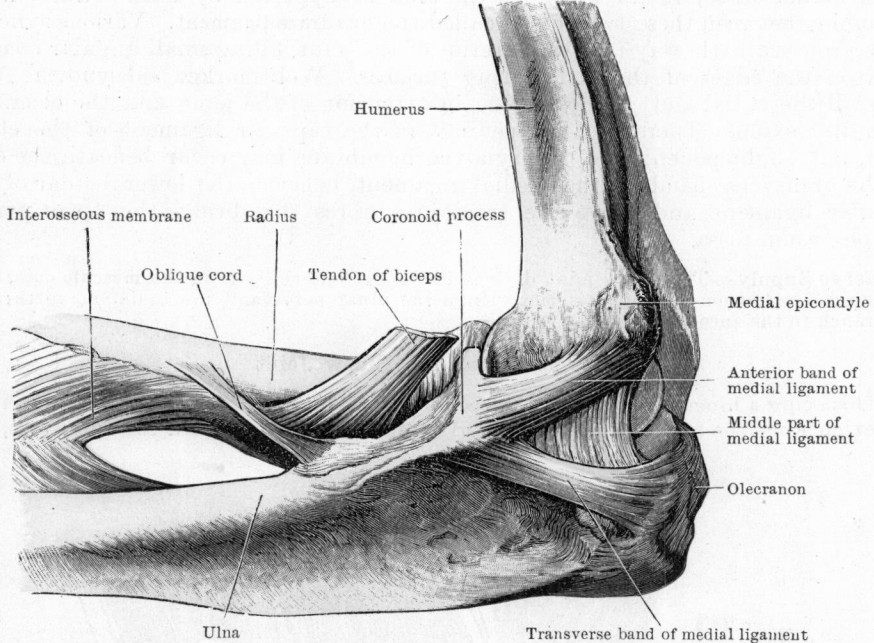

FIG. 305.—MEDIAL ASPECT OF DISSECTION OF ELBOW JOINT, WITH ANTERIOR AND POSTERIOR LIGAMENTS REMOVED.

notch. The posterior ligament blends at the sides with the medial and lateral ligaments.

The **lateral ligament** [lig. collaterale radiale] (Fig. 304) is a strong, triangular band whose apex is attached above to the antero-inferior aspect of the lateral epicondyle of the humerus in close relation to the overlying common origin of the extensor muscles. Distally, the middle part of the base of the ligament blends with the annular ligament of the radius, and the slightly thicker portions in front and behind sweep forwards and backwards to be attached to the margins of the radial notch on the ulna.

The **medial ligament** [lig. collaterale ulnare] (Fig. 305) is composed of three fairly distinct bands, continuous with one another. An *anterior band* passes from the fore part of the medial epicondyle of the humerus to the medial edge of the coronoid process of the ulna ; it is closely associated with the common origin of the superficial flexor muscles and gives rise to fibres of the flexor digitorum sublimis. A *posterior band* is attached above to the back of the medial epicondyle and below to the medial edge of the olecranon. Between these bands there is a middle, thinner part of the ligament, triangular in shape, and presenting a grooved external surface which is crossed by the ulnar nerve as it passes from upper arm to forearm ; its upper end is attached to the under surface of the medial epicondyle, and its base is fixed distally to the upper border of a *transverse band* which stretches between the attachments of the anterior and posterior bands on the coronoid process and the olecranon. The lower edge of this transverse ligament is free, and through the narrow gap between this edge and the bone the synovial membrane protrudes slightly during movement of the joint.

Synovial Membrane.—The synovial membrane of the elbow joint lines the capsular ligament and is reflected on to the humerus to line the radial and coronoid fossæ in front and the olecranon fossa behind (Fig. 306). Distally, it is prolonged downwards on the deep surface of the annular ligament and is then reflected on to the neck of the radius. This reflection is supported by a few loose fibres which pass from the lower border of the annular ligament to the neck of the radius. The synovial membrane passing from the medial side of the radial neck to the lower border of the radial notch on the ulna is supported by a lax band of fibres stretching between these two points, called the **quadrate ligament**. Various synovial folds project a little way into the interior of the joint, filling small angular recesses between the edges of the articulating surfaces. Well-marked subsynovial fatty pads fill the radial and coronoid fossæ in extension of the joint, and the olecranon fossa in flexion. There are no openings in the capsular ligament of the elbow joint, but slight pouching of the synovial membrane may occur beneath the edge of the transverse band of the medial ligament, beneath the lower border of the annular ligament, and above the transverse fibres that bridge the upper part of the olecranon fossa.

Nerve-Supply.—The elbow joint derives its supply anteriorly from the **musculo-cutaneous**, **median** and **radial** nerves, and posteriorly from the **ulnar** nerve and the radial nerve through its **branch to the anconeus** muscle.

Movements at the Elbow Joint

This being a hinge joint, movement occurs only around a transverse axis—a movement of **flexion** when the forearm makes anteriorly a diminishing angle with the upper arm, and

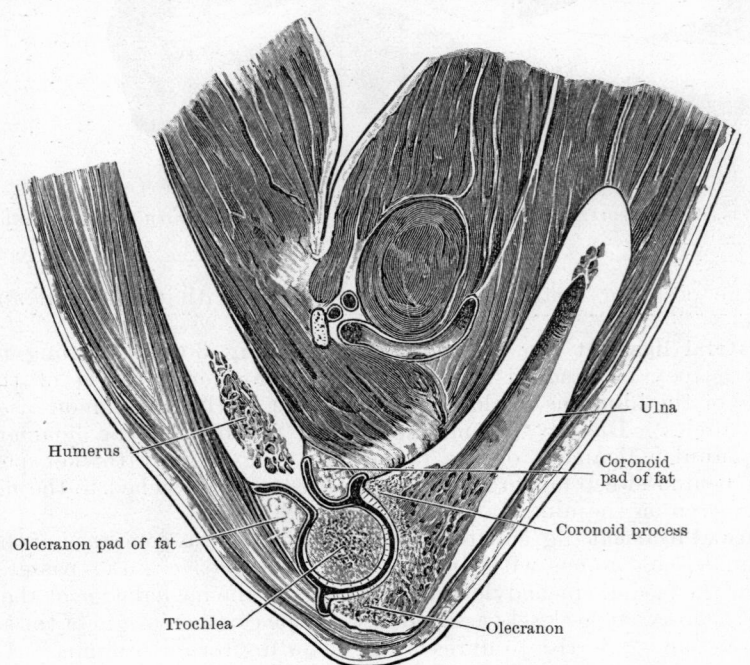

Humerus

Olecranon pad of fat

Trochlea

Ulna

Coronoid pad of fat

Coronoid process

Olecranon

FIG. 306.—VERTICAL SECTION THROUGH THE HUMERO-ULNAR PART OF THE ELBOW JOINT.

of **extension** when this angle is opened out again. The axis of movement passes through the humeral epicondyles and is not at right angles with either the humerus or the fore-

PLATE XXIII

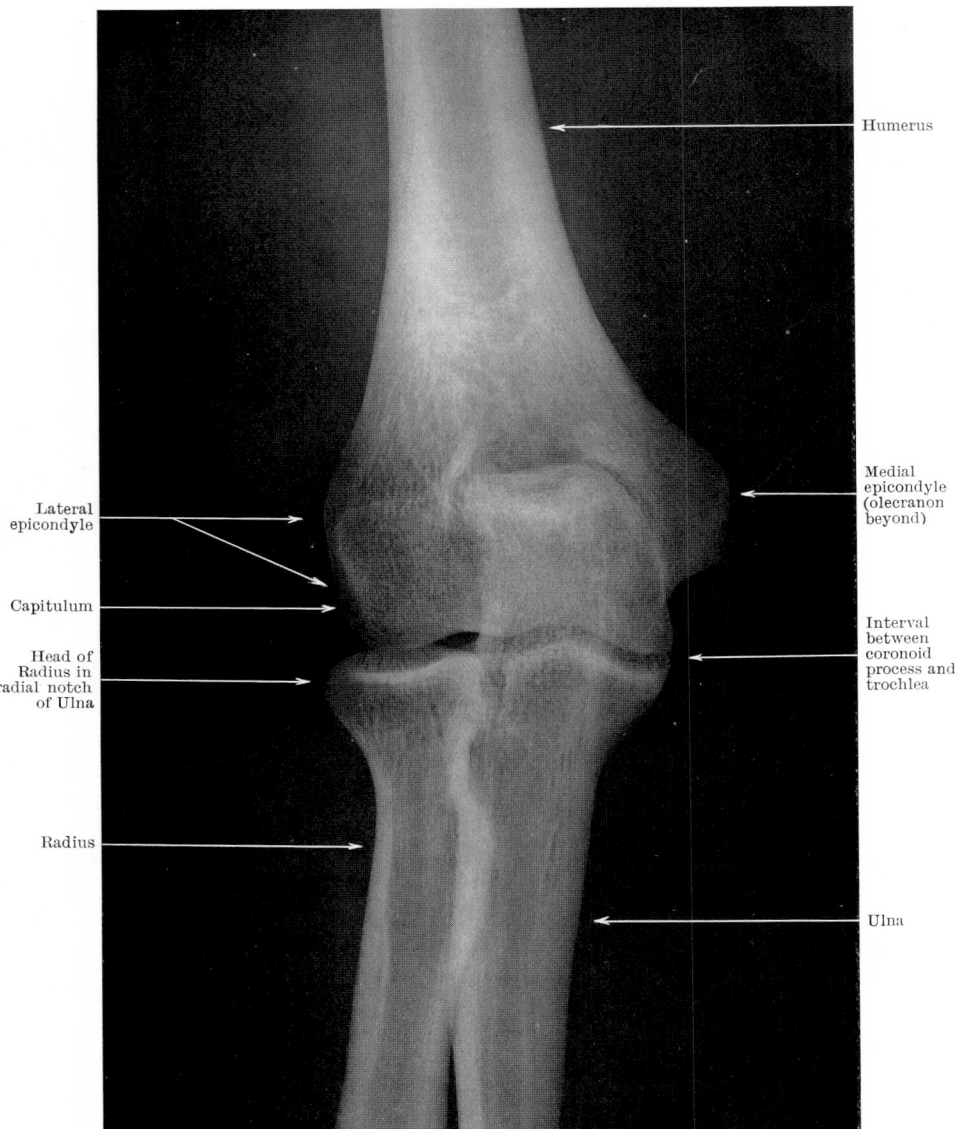

Humerus

Medial
epicondyle
(olecranon
beyond)

Lateral
epicondyle

Capitulum

Interval
between
coronoid
process and
trochlea

Head of
Radius in
radial notch
of Ulna

Radius

Ulna

PLATE XXIII.—ANTERO-POSTERIOR RADIOGRAPH OF ELBOW OF YOUNG WOMAN
AGED 19.

For lateral radiographs of the same elbow, see Plate XXIV. Cf. also Plate VI, and Plate VII, Fig. 1.

PLATE XXIV

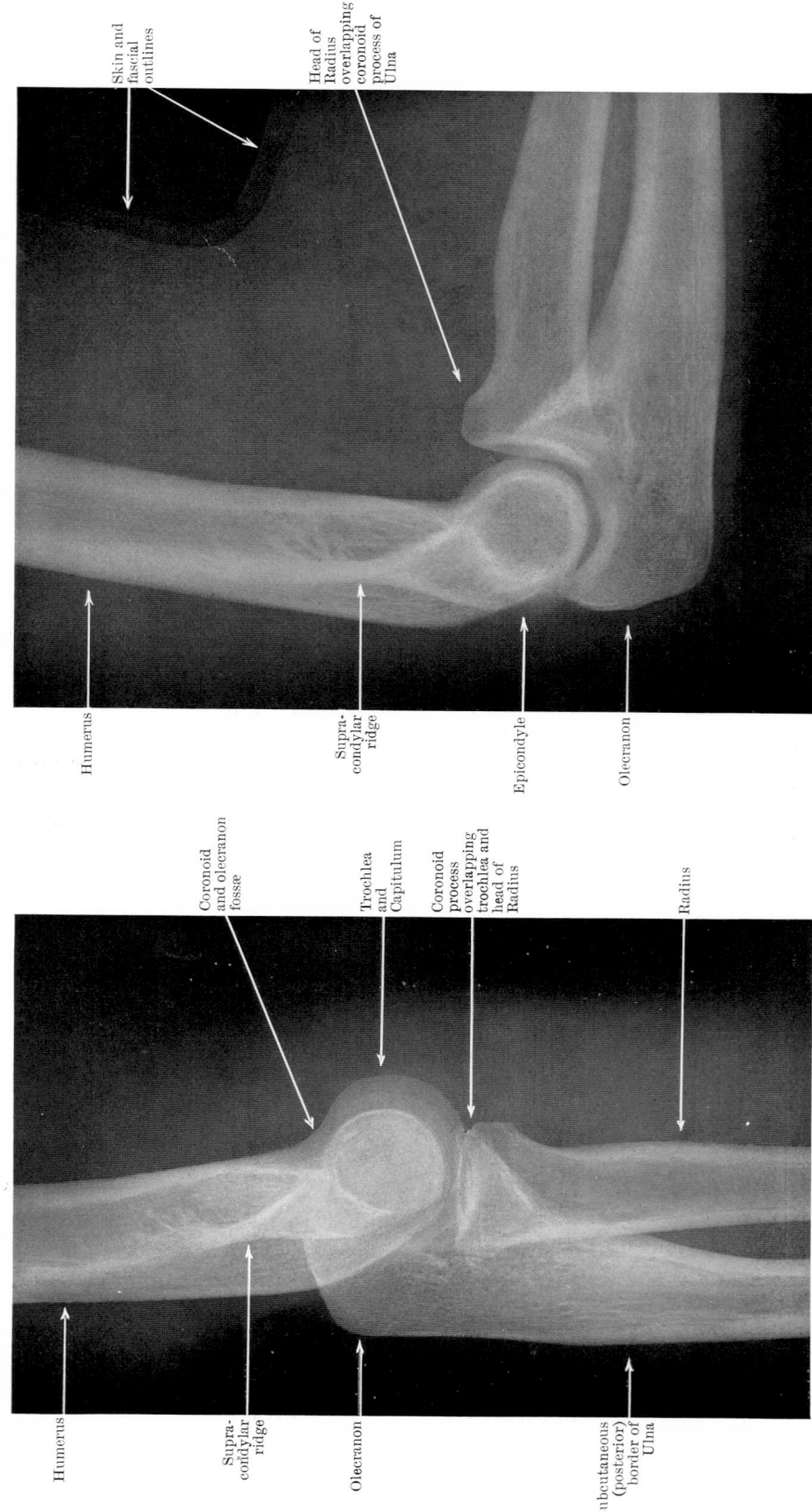

Skin and
fascial
outlines

Head of
Radius
overlapping
coronoid
process of
Ulna

Humerus

Supra-
condylar
ridge

Epicondyle

Olecranon

Fig. 2.—Lateral Radiograph of the same Elbow, Half-flexed.
Compare with Fig, 1, and note the relative positions of Epicondyle and Olecranon.
Cf. also Plate VII, Fig. 2.

Coronoid
and olecranon
fossae

Trochlea
and
Capitulum

Coronoid
process
overlapping
trochlea and
head of
Radius

Radius

Humerus

Supra-
condylar
ridge

Olecranon

Subcutaneous
(posterior) border of
Ulna

Fig. 1.—Lateral Radiograph of the same Elbow as in Plate XXIII
(Young Woman aged 19) Fully Extended.
Note the tip of the Olecranon in the olecranon fossa of the Humerus.

arm bones.   In full extension, with the forearm supinated, the upper arm and forearm form an angle opening laterally, more pronounced in women than in men.   The axis of elbow joint movement bisects this angle; hence in full flexion the forearm comes up in line with the upper arm.

Flexion can proceed until checked by apposition of upper arm and forearm and by the tension of the posterior muscles and ligament.   Extension cannot occur beyond the straight position of the limb; it is then limited by the tension of the anterior muscles and ligament.   The lateral and medial ligaments are fairly tense in all positions, the anterior part of each being specially tight in extension and the posterior part in flexion.

Limitation of movement by locking of the bones seldom occurs.   That it does take place in some persons is shown by the occasional presence of small cartilage-covered facets at the bottom of the coronoid fossa and at the sides of the olecranon fossa which obviously must have made contact during life with the coronoid and olecranon processes.

As already mentioned, the joint surfaces are in closest contact in a position of right-angled flexion, with the forearm midway between pronation and supination.   This is therefore the position of greatest stability and is the position naturally assumed when the hands are engaged in fine manipulations.

RADIO-ULNAR JOINTS

The bones of the forearm are united at their upper and lower ends by synovial joints which act together to provide movement of the radius on the ulna around a vertical axis; these joints are therefore of the pivot type.   In addition, the shafts of the two bones are connected by fibrous interosseous bands in the manner of a syndesmosis.

SUPERIOR RADIO-ULNAR JOINT

At the **superior radio-ulnar joint** the discoidal head of the radius rotates within the ring formed by the radial notch on the ulna and the annular ligament of the radius.   The notch on the ulna is lined with articular cartilage continuous with that on the lower half of the trochlear notch in the elbow joint; the surface of the radial notch is concave antero-posteriorly but is flat vertically and is inclined slightly laterally below (Fig. 307).   The head of the radius is covered with a continuous layer of cartilage above and around the sides.   The upper surface is slightly cupped and rotates under the capitulum of the humerus, while the sides of the head bear on the annular ligament and radial notch.

Annular Ligament of Radius.—The annular ligament of the radius is a strong, well-defined curved band attached by its ends to the anterior and posterior margins of the radial notch on the ulna so as to form nearly four-fifths of a ring which is completed by the notch itself. This ring is slightly narrower at its lower border than above, forming a segment of a hollow cone; and the radial head, enclosed by the ring, is reciprocally bevelled all round.   This arrangement tends to prevent the radius from being pulled downwards through the ring.   The annular ligament is supported above by its firm fusion with the lateral ligament and lateral parts of the anterior and posterior ligaments of the elbow

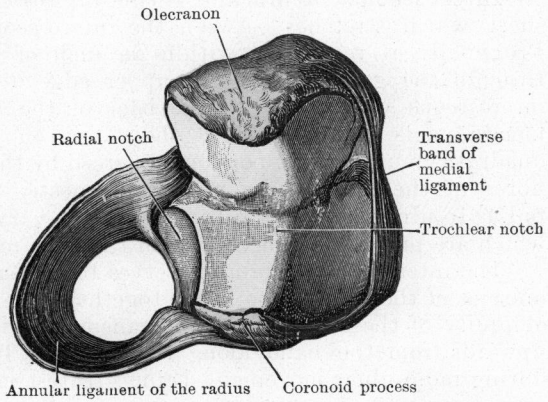

Olecranon

Radial notch

Transverse
band of
medial
ligament

Trochlear notch

Annular ligament of the radius   Coronoid process

FIG. 307.—ANNULAR LIGAMENT OF THE RADIUS.

joint (Fig. 304).   Below, it is only feebly attached to the neck of the radius, distal to the epiphyseal line, by fibres which are too loose to interfere with movement.

As already explained, the annular ligament is lined with **synovial membrane** which is carried down from the elbow joint and is reflected on to the upper part of the neck of the radius and carried across to the lower border of the notch on the ulna by the quadrate ligament.   The synovial cavities of the two joints are thus freely continuous with each other.

INFERIOR RADIO-ULNAR JOINT

The **inferior radio-ulnar joint** is formed between the head of the ulna and the ulnar notch on the radius.   The bony surfaces are covered with articular cartilage; the lateral and distal ulnar surfaces are continuous with each other over a rounded border.

Articular Disc.—The chief uniting structure is the fibro-cartilaginous, triangular **articular disc**, which is attached by its base to the sharp edge on the radius between the ulnar and carpal surfaces and by its apex to the lateral side of the root of the ulnar styloid process (Fig. 308).   This disc provides an additional joint surface, for its upper surface articulates with the distal aspect of the head of the ulna.   Thus the joint cavity is ∟-shaped in vertical section, with a vertical limb between the ulna and the radius and a horizontal limb between the ulna and the articular disc (Fig. 310).   The distal surface of the disc forms part of the proximal articular surface of the wrist joint; but the two joint cavities do not communicate except in some cases where the disc is perforated.

Capsular Ligament.—The capsular ligament is represented only by transverse bands of no great strength which stretch from radius to ulna across the front (Fig. 309) and back of the joint.   The distal edges of these bands blend with the margins of the articular disc, but proximally they are separated from each other by a pouch of the synovial lining of the joint, called the *recessus sacciformis*, which extends upwards a little way between the radius and ulna.

Nerve-Supply.—The inferior radio-ulnar joint is supplied by twigs from the **anterior** and **posterior interosseous** nerves.

CONNEXION BETWEEN SHAFTS OF RADIUS AND ULNA

The shafts of the radius and ulna are connected by the oblique cord and the interosseous membrane of the forearm.

Oblique Cord.—The oblique cord is a slender fibrous band which passes from the lateral border of the tuberosity of the ulna downwards and laterally to the radius just distal to its tuberosity; it is possibly a degenerated portion of the flexor pollicis longus (Figs. 304, 305).

Interosseous Membrane.—The interosseous membrane is a strong fibrous sheet which stretches between the interosseous borders of the radius and ulna. Proximally, it reaches to within an inch of the level of the radial tuberosity.; through the gap between its upper edge and the oblique cord the posterior interosseous vessels pass to the back of the forearm.   Distally, the interosseous membrane is continued into the fascia on the dorsal surface of the pronator quadratus muscle; this portion is pierced by the anterior interosseous vessels.   The fibres of the interosseous membrane mostly run medially and downwards from radius to ulna; but on the back there are varying bands of an opposite obliquity, which are probably connected with the long muscles of the thumb.

The interosseous membrane serves to increase the surfaces of origin of the deep muscles of the forearm, to brace together the radius and ulna, and, because of the obliquity of the main fibres, to transmit to the ulna part of any force passing upwards from the hand along the radius.   The tension of the membrane varies during radio-ulnar movement, being greatest in semi-pronation.

Movements at the Radio-ulnar Joints

Movement at the radio-ulnar joints takes place around an axis that passes through the centre of the head of the radius above and the apical attachment of the articular disc below.   The movement is chiefly on the part of the radius ; its upper end rotates under the humeral capitulum and within the ring formed by the annular ligament and the radial notch on the ulna, while its lower end, bearing the hand, travels round the lower end of the ulna, to which it is tethered by the articular disc.   Starting from the supine position, in which the forearm bones are parallel and the palm is directed forwards (if the forearm is extended at the elbow), in the movement of **pronation** the lower end of the radius is carried forwards and medially round the lower end of the ulna until the palm is turned backwards and the shafts of the radius and ulna cross each other. Movement in the reverse direction is termed **supination.** These movements cannot be dissociated from slight accompanying rotation at the shoulder joint—medially with pronation and laterally with supination. But the ulna also changes position in pronation and supination. Its lower end precedes the lower end of the radius round the opposite half of the circle of excursion, moving backwards and laterally as the radius travels forwards and medially during pronation, and in the reverse direction during supination. This excursion of the lower end of the ulna is the magnified result of slight antero-posterior movements of its upper end at the elbow joint, which also cannot be dissociated from radio-ulnar movement proper.

When the upper limb is straight, the axis of humeral rotation is in the same line as the axis of radio-ulnar movement, and therefore pronation and supination can be supplemented by the full extent of rotation at the shoulder joint so that it is then possible to turn the hand through a complete circle.

WRIST (RADIO-CARPAL) JOINT

The **wrist joint** proper is formed between the distal surface of the radius and the articular disc, and the proximal row of carpal bones (except the pisiform).

Articular Surfaces.—The radius and the disc together form a concave, ellipsoidal surface of shallower curvature in its long axis from side to side than in its short axis from before backwards (Fig. 308). A similar surface, but convex, is provided distally by the proximal articular areas of the scaphoid, lunate, and triquetral bones, closely united by interosseous ligaments which are flush with the articular cartilage on the proximal surface of the bones (Fig. 310). The joint is therefore ellipsoidal in type. The *articular cartilage on the radius* is divided by a low ridge into a triangular lateral area and a quadrangular medial area. In the normal, straight position of the hand, the scaphoid bone is opposite the lateral radial area, the lunate is opposite the medial area and the disc, and the triquetral is in contact with the medial portion of the joint capsule (Fig. 310).

When the hand is bent to the ulnar side, the triquetral is then moved over to lie opposite the disc.

Capsular Ligament.—A capsular ligament surrounds the joint. It is attached close to the articular areas; its proximal attachment is distal to the inferior epiphyseal lines of the radius and ulna.

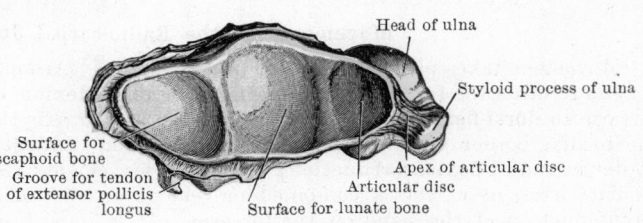

Surface for scaphoid bone
Groove for tendon of extensor pollicis longus
Head of ulna
Styloid process of ulna
Apex of articular disc
Articular disc
Surface for lunate bone

FIG. 308.—PROXIMAL ARTICULAR SURFACE OF WRIST JOINT.

The anterior part of the capsular ligament, called the **anterior radio-carpal ligament** is formed chiefly of a broad band of fibres that spread downwards, with a medial inclination, from the anterior edge of the distal end of the radius to the first carpal row—some longer fibres extending to the capitate bone in the second row (Fig. 309). From the anterior edge of the disc and the base of the ulnar styloid process some fibres pass downwards and laterally to the carpus, and others pass laterally to the radius, blending with the inferior radio-ulnar joint capsule.

On the back of the joint, the **posterior radio-carpal ligament** is composed of fibres that run mainly from the posterior edge of the lower end of the radius downwards and medially to the bones of the first carpal row, particularly the triquetral bone.

At the sides, the capsular ligament is specially strengthened to form the **lateral** and **medial ligaments** [ligg. collateralia] (Fig. 309). The lateral ligament runs from the radial styloid process to the scaphoid bone immediately lateral to its proximal articular surface; the radial artery crosses this ligament deep to the long abductor and short extensor tendons of the thumb. The medial ligament spreads downwards from the ulnar styloid process to the medial, non-articular border of the triquetral bone and to the pisiform bone.

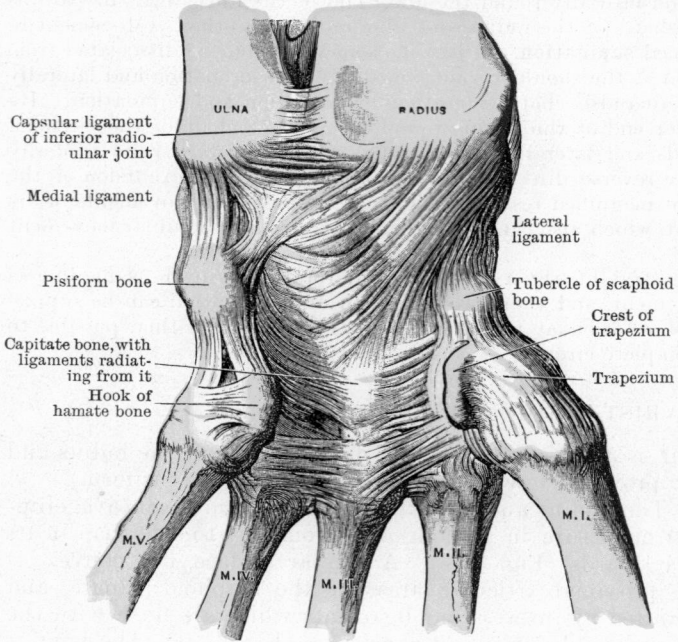

FIG. 309.—LIGAMENTS ON THE FRONT OF RADIO-CARPAL, CARPAL, AND CARPO-METACARPAL JOINTS.

Synovial Membrane.—A synovial membrane lines the capsular ligament. In exceptional cases the synovial cavity communicates with the inferior radio-ulnar joint through a perforated articular disc, or with the intercarpal joint when one of the interosseous ligaments of the proximal carpal row forms an incomplete barrier.

Nerve-Supply.—The radio-carpal joint (in common with the carpal and carpo-metacarpal joints—described later) receives its supply from all three main nerves of the upper limb :—from the median nerve, through the **anterior interosseous** branch ; from the radial nerve, through the **posterior interosseous** branch ; and from the ulnar nerve, through the **dorsal branch** and **deep (palmar) branch**.

Movements at the Radio-carpal Joint

Movement takes place around two principal axes. Around a transverse axis the hand is bent towards the front of the forearm in **palmar flexion** or towards the back of the forearm in **dorsi-flexion**. Around an antero-posterior axis the hand is deflected towards the medial border of the forearm in **ulnar flexion (adduction)** or towards the lateral border in **radial flexion (abduction)**. Oblique movements also are possible around intermediate axes, as well as a combined movement around successive axes bringing about **circumduction** of the hand on the forearm. It is important to note that slight dorsi-flexion is the position naturally assumed at the wrist when the hand is used for grasping purposes, and therefore, if the wrist joint is likely to become fixed through disease, fixation should be secured in a position of slight dorsi-flexion in order to conserve efficient grasping power.

INTERCARPAL JOINTS

The carpal bones are, in the first place, joined together in two rows—proximal and distal—in such fashion as to permit little movement between the bones in each row. The two rows are then united in a transverse intercarpal joint, at which a more appreciable degree of movement can take place. The joints between the bones are of the plane or gliding type.

Joints of the Proximal Row.—Of the bones of the proximal row, the scaphoid, the lunate, and the triquetral are tied together by palmar, dorsal, and interosseous bands.

The **palmar** and **dorsal ligaments** pass between neighbouring parts on those aspects of the bones. The **interosseous ligaments** are short bands that pass between contiguous surfaces, uniting them in their whole antero-posterior depth near their proximal margins, and leaving joint clefts between their distal parts, which are therefore coated with articular cartilage (Fig. 310).

Pisiform Joint.—The pisiform bone rests on the palmar surface of the triquetral bone, and forms with that bone a separate little synovial joint surrounded by a thin, but strong, **capsular ligament**. It is further anchored by strong bands—the **piso-metacarpal** and **piso-hamate ligaments**—to the base of the fifth metacarpal and the hook of the hamate bone : these ligaments resist the pull of the flexor carpi ulnaris muscle upon the pisiform bone, and, in effect, provide additional insertions for that muscle.

Joints of the Distal Row.—All four bones of the distal carpal row are connected by **palmar, dorsal,** and **inter-osseous ligaments**. The inter-osseous ligaments (Fig. 310) are, in general, not so extensive as those of the proximal row ; they leave joint-clefts between the bones both proximally, running into the transverse intercarpal joint, and distally, running into the carpo-meta-carpal joint. These two larger joints sometimes communicate with each other between bones of the distal row where an interosseous ligament is absent (most often that between the trapezium and trapezoid) or where it does not extend the whole way between the dorsal and palmar surfaces of the adjoining bones.

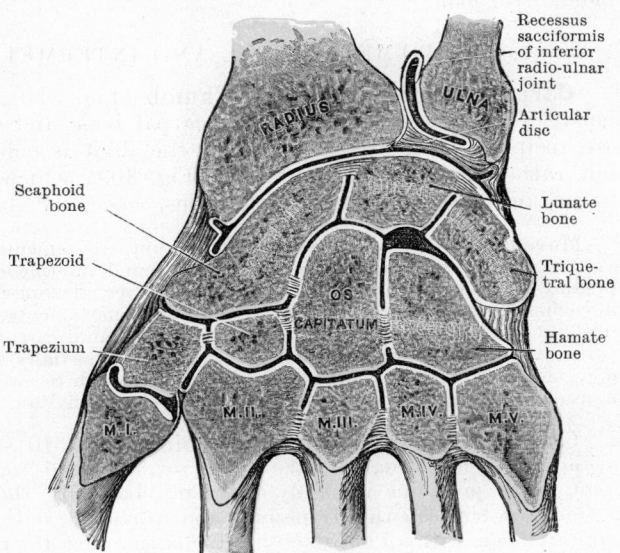

Fig. 310.—CORONAL SECTION through the radio-carpal, carpal, carpo-metacarpal, and intermetacarpal joints, to show joint cavities and interosseous ligaments (diagrammatic).

Transverse Intercarpal Joint (Fig. 310).—This is the joint between the two carpal rows. The joint line is convex distally on the lateral side, where the trapezium and trapezoid are opposed to the rounded distal surface of the scaphoid. In the medial and larger part of the joint there is a deep concavity facing distally, bounded by the triquetral and lunate bones and the medial surface of the scaphoid bone, and occupied by the rounded head of the capitate bone and the proximal angle of the hamate bone.

The joint is surrounded by a **capsular ligament** made up, in front and behind, of irregular bands which run between the two rows of bones and constitute the **palmar** and **dorsal intercarpal ligaments** ; the bands in the palmar ligament chiefly radiate from the head of the capitate bone (Fig. 309). At the sides of the transverse intercarpal joint the capsular ligament is strengthened as it passes between the scaphoid and trapezium and between the triquetral and hamate bones.

Intercarpal Synovial Cavity.—The intercarpal synovial cavity (Fig. 310) is large and complicated. The main part extends from side to side between the two rows of bones, and may be partially interrupted by an interosseous ligament connecting contiguous parts of the scaphoid and capitate bones. Offshoots of the cavity pass upwards between the three main bones of the proximal row until blocked by the interosseous ligaments ; but, in rare cases, a deficiency in one of these may permit the intercarpal joint to communicate with the radio-carpal joint. Other offshoots pass downwards between the four bones of the distal row, and not infrequently communicate with the carpo-metacarpal joint cavity, especially on one or other side of the trapezoid.

Nerve-Supply.—The intercarpal joints are supplied by twigs from the **anterior** and **posterior interosseous** nerves and the **dorsal** and **deep branches of the ulnar** nerve.

Accessory Ligaments of Carpus.—The carpus, in each of its rows, forms a transverse arch with a palmar concavity. The concavity is bridged over by the **flexor retinaculum** [lig. carpi transversum], which is attached medially to the pisiform bone and the hook of the hamate bone, and laterally to the scaphoid tubercle and the crest of the trapezium. Through the tunnel behind the retinaculum, the median nerve and the flexor tendons enter the palm, while the ulnar vessels and nerve pass in front of it. The **extensor retinaculum** [lig. carpi dorsale] is merely a thickened portion of the deep fascia covering the back of the carpus and the lower end of the radius. By its intermediate attachments to the ridges on the radius, it provides a series of tunnels for the extensor tendons of the wrist and fingers.

Movements in the Carpus.—Movement consists chiefly of palmar and dorsal flexion of the distal carpal row upon the proximal row and of a lesser amount of rocking of the distal row to either side. These movements are facilitated by slight gliding of the scaphoid and triquetral bones on the sides of the lunate bone; very little gliding movement occurs between the bones of the distal row. The result of these changes is to increase slightly the range of movements of the hand which are primarily effected at the radio-carpal joint.

CARPO-METACARPAL AND INTERMETACARPAL JOINTS

Carpo-metacarpal Joint of Thumb (Fig. 310).—This joint is self-contained between the base of the first metacarpal bone and the trapezium. The surfaces are reciprocally saddle-shaped, and the joint is completely enclosed by a strong but rather loose **capsular ligament** (Fig. 309), which is lined with synovial membrane, and is strengthened at the sides, especially at the medial side.

Movements.—This is a typical saddle-joint; movements take place around two principal axes at right angles to each other, and also around intermediate axes, and can be combined to produce circumduction. Around the main axes, **flexion-extension** and **adduction-abduction** movements are performed, but the axes of these movements are obliquely disposed in relation to the rest of the hand. Thus in flexion the thumb is carried forwards and medially across the palm; and in adduction it is carried backwards and medially against the index finger; these two movements, in varying combination, allow the thumb to meet any of the other fingers. This movement of **opposition** is peculiarly well developed in Man.

Common Carpo-metacarpal Joint (Fig. 310).—The bases of the medial four metacarpal bones form, with the distal row of carpal bones, a common carpo-metacarpal joint. The joint line is highly irregular. Laterally, the base of the second metacarpal is recessed between the trapezium and trapezoid and between the trapezoid and the capitate bone, with all of which it articulates; next, the third metacarpal articulates with the capitate bone at a small transverse segment of the joint line; the fourth metacarpal causes the line to become angular again as it articulates to a small extent with the capitate and to a greater extent with the hamate bone; finally, the fifth metacarpal articulates only with the medial, bevelled facet on the hamate bone.

The joint is surrounded by a **capsular ligament** in which various **palmar** and **dorsal carpo-metacarpal** slips can be distinguished passing from the distal carpal bones to the metacarpal bases. An **interosseous ligament** is usually present, stretching from contiguous parts of the capitate and hamate bones to the third or fourth metacarpal base or to both; this ligament may divide the joint into separate medial and lateral compartments.

The **synovial cavity** of the common carpo-metacarpal joint extends upwards between the four distal carpal bones, and there usually communicates with the transverse carpal joint. Distally, the cavity is continuous with the little joints between the bases of the medial four metacarpal bones. (Fig. 310.)

Intermetacarpal Joints (Figs. 309, 310).—These joints are formed between small articular facets on the contiguous sides of the bases of the medial four metacarpal bones. The three little joints are closed in front, behind, and below by **palmar, dorsal**, and **interosseous ligaments** that pass transversely between adjacent bones. Proximally, the joint cavities open into the common carpo-metacarpal joint.

Nerve-Supply.—The carpo-metacarpal and intermetacarpal joints are supplied by twigs from the **anterior** and **posterior interosseous** nerves and the **dorsal** and **deep branches of the ulnar** nerve.

Movements.—Very little movement is possible between the carpus and the medial four metacarpal bones. It is more appreciable in the case of the fifth metacarpal, whose articulation with the hamate bone is of a flattened saddle type; around an oblique axis, this metacarpal bone can be flexed a little way across the palm in a fashion similar to the more extensive opposition movement of the metacarpal bone of the thumb.

METACARPO-PHALANGEAL AND INTERPHALANGEAL JOINTS

Metacarpo-phalangeal Joints.—Each metacarpo-phalangeal joint (Fig 311) is formed between the slightly cupped base of the proximal phalanx and the rounded metacarpal head, which is covered with articular cartilage distally and on the front but not on the back.

Capsular Ligament.—The capsular ligament is strengthened on each side by a **collateral ligament** which radiates fanwise from the tubercle and adjacent depression on the side of the metacarpal head to the side of the base of the proximal phalanx and to the front of the joint capsule.

On the front there is a dense, fibrous pad, called the **palmar ligament**, which blends with the collateral ligaments at the sides and is firmly fixed distally to the base of the phalanx but is only weakly attached proximally to the neck of the metacarpal bone. This pad is grooved in front by the long flexor tendons. In the thumb there are two sesamoid bones embedded in it; there is usually one such sesamoid in the radial side of the pad on the index finger and occasionally in the ulnar side in the little finger.

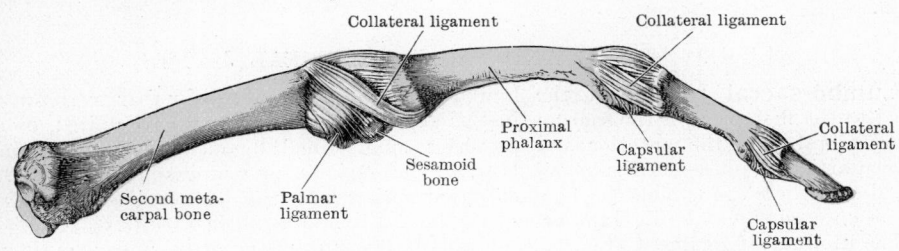

FIG. 311.—METACARPO-PHALANGEAL AND INTERPHALANGEAL JOINTS.

The capsular ligament is deficient **dorsally**, and is replaced by the expansion of the long extensor tendon, which blends at the sides with the collateral ligaments.

Deep Transverse Ligaments of the Palm.—The palmar ligaments of the medial four joints are connected by strong transverse bands, called the **deep transverse ligaments of the palm**, which indirectly bind together the heads of the medial four metacarpal bones. The interossei tendons descend behind these bands; the lumbrical tendons pass in front of them.

Nerve-Supply.—The metacarpo-phalangeal joints of the thumb, the fore-finger, and the middle finger are supplied by the **median** and **radial** nerves; those of the ring and little fingers by the **ulnar** nerve. (*See also* the last paragraph on this page.)

Movements.—The metacarpo-phalangeal joints are of condyloid type, having all the movements of a ball-and-socket joint except rotation. The proximal phalanges can be **flexed** to at least a right angle with the metacarpal bones but can be **extended** little beyond the line of the metacarpals. In the extended position the fingers can be **adducted** or **abducted** towards or away from the centre line of the middle finger. When the fingers are flexed, sideward movements become impossible because of increased tension of the collateral ligaments, which are fixed to the metacarpals nearer the distal than the palmar surface of their heads, and are also more stretched in flexion owing to the greater width of the palmar aspect of the metacarpal articular surface. The metacarpo-phalangeal joint of the thumb has much less extensive movement than the others—hardly any at all from side to side.

Interphalangeal Joints (Fig. 311).—The interphalangeal joints are constructed, as regards ligaments, in exactly the same fashion as the metacarpo-phalangeal joints. But owing to the bi-condyloid shape of the articular surfaces these are pure hinge joints, capable only of **flexion** and **extension**. Although the fingers are of unequal length, the phalanges are so proportioned that in flexion the finger-tips come into line and meet the palm simultaneously.

Nerve-Supply.—The interphalangeal joint of the *thumb* is supplied by the **median** nerve, with twigs occasionally from the **radial** also; the joints of the *fore-finger* and *middle finger* by the **median** nerve; those of the *ring finger* by the **ulnar** nerve and probably **median** also; and those of the *little finger* by the **ulnar** nerve.

The nerve-supply of the metacarpo-phalangeal and interphalangeal joints has been specially studied by Stopford (*Journ. Anat.*, 1921), whose principal findings are here summarised. Individual variation in the articular nerve-supply is closely related to variations in the cutaneous distribution of the nerves concerned. The joints of the **thumb** are supplied by the **radial** and **median** nerves—chiefly the radial in the *metacarpo-phalangeal joint*, which, however, in a few cases may be supplied by either nerve alone; and chiefly the median nerve in the *interphalangeal joint*, of which it is often the sole supply. In the **index** and **middle fingers** the *metacarpo-phalangeal joints* are supplied by both **median** and **radial** nerves—chiefly the median— but in some cases either nerve may supply the joint; the *interphalangeal joints* are supplied by the **median** only. The joints of the **ring finger** are supplied by the **ulnar** nerve, probably

23

supplemented by the **median** in most cases. The joints of the little finger are supplied by the **ulnar** nerve alone.

JOINTS OF THE PELVIS

The skeleton of the pelvic girdle is joined to the skeleton of the trunk in such a way as to provide great strength in the region of weight transference from trunk to girdle at the sacrifice of almost all mobility. The girdle, formed of a single unjointed piece—the hip-bone—is firmly but not quite immovably joined to the sacrum behind and to its fellow of the opposite side in front. These two joints, sacro-iliac and inter-pubic, with the sacro-coccygeal union and the lumbo-sacral articulation between the pelvis and the last lumbar vertebra, make up the pelvic joints.

LUMBO-SACRAL AND SACRO-COCCYGEAL JOINTS

Lumbo-sacral Joint.—At the lumbo-sacral joint the fifth lumbar vertebra is united to the first piece of the sacrum, just as any two typical vertebræ are united, by an intervertebral disc, the anterior and posterior longitudinal ligaments, synovial joints between articular processes, ligamenta flava, and interspinous and supraspinous ligaments. In addition there are two special ligaments that spring from the fifth lumbar transverse process on each side—the ilio-lumbar and the lateral lumbo-sacral ligaments.

The **ilio-lumbar ligament** (Fig. 312) spreads laterally from the fifth lumbar transverse process to the posterior part of the inner lip of the iliac crest; it is really the thickened lower border of the anterior layer of lumbar fascia lying in front of the quadratus lumborum muscle.

The **lateral lumbo-sacral ligament**—usually partly blended with the preceding ligament—consists of variable bundles that pass downwards and laterally from the lower border of the fifth lumbar transverse process to the ala of the sacrum, where they intermingle with the anterior sacro-iliac ligament; its attachments indicate its homology with the superior costo-transverse ligaments of the thoracic region.

Sacro-coccygeal Joint.—At the sacro-coccygeal joint there is an intervertebral disc between the last sacral and first coccygeal segments, reinforced all round by longitudinal strands called the **sacro-coccygeal ligaments** (Fig. 312).

SACRO-ILIAC JOINT

The **sacro-iliac joint** is formed between the auricular facets on the sacrum and on the iliac bone. Reciprocal sinuosities on these two surfaces, or even in some cases more pronounced irregularities in the form of tubercles with depressions opposite to them, cause a certain amount of interlocking between the facets. Each facet is covered with hyaline cartilage, and, before middle life at any rate, there is a complete cleft between the articular surfaces. In later life, particularly in males, it is usual to find fibrous or fibro-cartilaginous adhesions between the surfaces, with partial or complete obliteration of the joint cavity.

The anterior and posterior sacro-iliac ligaments provide a complete **capsular** investment lined on the inside with **synovial membrane**; the joint is classed as synovial, of the plane or gliding type.

The **anterior sacro-iliac ligament** is a broad band, of no great thickness, which closes the joint in front both above and below the pelvic brim. It stretches from the ala and pelvic surface of the sacrum to the adjoining surface of the iliac bone.

The **posterior sacro-iliac ligaments** present a very much stronger and thicker formation. It consists of three strata. The deepest—the **interosseous sacro-iliac ligament**—short, thick, and very strong, fills the narrow cleft between the rough areas on the bones immediately above and behind the joint surfaces (Fig. 313). Occasionally one or two small accessory joint cavities are found in the substance of this ligament, between facets near the posterior superior spine and bosses on the sacrum in the position of transverse tubercles (Jazuta, *Anat. Anzeig.*, 1929).

Superficial to the interosseous fibres, longer bands run obliquely medially and downwards between more divergent parts of the bones; these constitute the

short posterior sacro-iliac ligament (Fig. 312).   Still longer fibres, descending almost vertically from the posterior superior iliac spine to the third and fourth sacral segments, behind and lateral to the short ligament, compose the **long posterior**

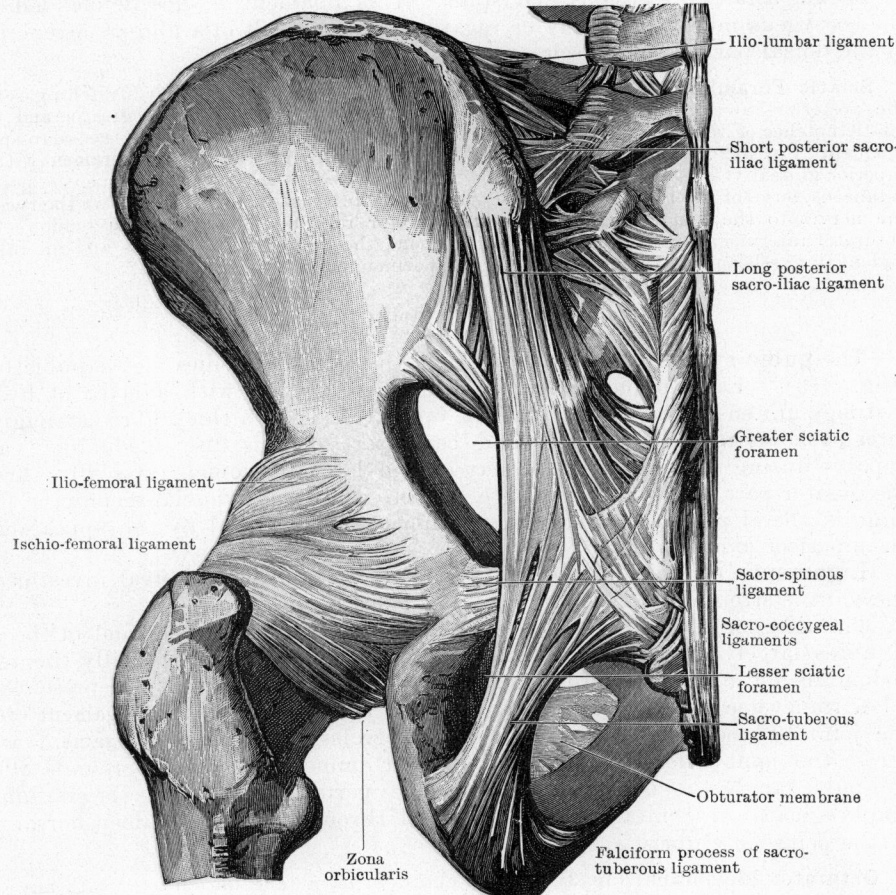

Ilio-lumbar ligament

Short posterior sacro-
iliac ligament

Long posterior
sacro-iliac ligament

Greater sciatic
foramen

Ilio-femoral ligament

Ischio-femoral ligament

Sacro-spinous
ligament

Sacro-coccygeal
ligaments

Lesser sciatic
foramen

Sacro-tuberous
ligament

Obturator membrane

Zona
orbicularis

Falciform process of sacro-
tuberous ligament

FIG. 312.—POSTERIOR VIEW OF THE PELVIC LIGAMENTS AND OF THE HIP JOINT.

sacro-iliac ligament.   The lateral part of the long ligament is indistinguishable from the sacro-tuberous ligament.

Nerve-Supply.—The sacro-iliac joint is supplied (1) by twigs directly from the **sacral plexus** and the **posterior primary rami of the first two sacral** nerves, and (2) by branches from the **superior gluteal** and **obturator** nerves.

Accessory Ligaments.—The gap left in the bony pelvis between the sacrum and the ischial part of the hip-bone is bridged by a system of widespread fibres that form accessory ligaments of the sacro-iliac joint called the sacro-tuberous and sacro-spinous ligaments (Figs. 312, 313).

The **sacro-tuberous ligament** has an extensive attachment to the posterior superior and posterior inferior iliac spines, the back and side of the lower part of the sacrum and the side of the upper part of the coccyx.   Thence the fibres converge towards the ischial tuberosity, but, twisting upon themselves, they diverge again to be attached to the medial margin of the ischial tuberosity and the lower margin of the ramus of the ischium.   The fibres to the ramus form a sickle-shaped extension of the ligament called the **falciform process**.

The superficial fibres attached to the tuberosity are intimately associated with the long head of the biceps femoris muscle ; the whole ligament, indeed, is usually regarded as a stranded proximal portion of this muscle.

The **sacro-spinous ligament** lies on the pelvic surface of the sacro-tuberous ligament. It is triangular in outline. Its base is attached to the edge of the lower sacral and upper coccygeal segments, in front of the sacro-tuberous ligament; its apex is attached to the ischial spine. This ligament is closely blended with the coccygeus muscle, and may be regarded as the result of a fibrous degeneration of the dorsal part of the muscle.

Sciatic Foramina.—The sacro-tuberous ligament, by its lateral border stretching between the posterior inferior iliac spine and the ischial tuberosity, converts the greater and lesser sciatic notches of the hip-bone into foramina separated by the apical part of the sacro-spinous ligament (Fig. 312). The piriformis muscle runs out through the **greater foramen** with the superior gluteal vessels and nerve above the muscle, and below it the sciatic nerve, the posterior cutaneous nerve of the thigh, the inferior gluteal and internal pudendal vessels and nerves, and the nerves to the quadratus femoris and obturator internus muscles. The tendon of the obturator internus emerges from the **lesser foramen**; the nerve to that muscle and the internal pudendal vessels and pudendal nerve enter the perineum above the tendon.

PUBIC SYMPHYSIS

The **pubic symphysis** is a median joint between the bodies of the pubic bones (Fig. 313). Each pubic articular surface is covered with a layer of hyaline cartilage united to the cartilage of the opposite side by a thick fibro-cartilaginous **inter-pubic disc**. In the upper and back part of this disc a slit-like cavity appears during early life, and it may extend later, in women especially, through the greater part of the fibro-cartilage. There is no true synovial membrane. The joint is therefore of secondary cartilaginous type, modified by the appearance of an imperfect joint cavity.

Ligaments of Pubic Symphysis.—The perichondrio-periosteal investment of the joint is strengthened all round by the **pubic ligaments**.

The **anterior ligament** is an interlaced decussation across the front of the joint of fibres largely derived from tendons of adjacent muscles, especially the rectus abdominis and external oblique muscles. The **posterior ligament** is represented by a few transverse fibres across the back of the joint. The **superior ligament** crosses the joint between the pubic crests and tubercles. The **inferior ligament** arches across the joint below, between the inferior pubic rami, and so rounds off the sub-pubic angle; it is separated from the perineal membrane [fascia inferior diaphragmatis urogenitalis] by an interval through which the deep dorsal vein of the penis (or clitoris) enters the pelvis.

Obturator Membrane (Fig. 314).—The obturator membrane, unconnected with any pelvic joint, is an interlacement of ligamentous bundles that close the obturator foramen save in its antero-superior part. It is attached to the margin of the foramen all round except in the neighbourhood of the **obturator canal**. This aperture is bounded above by a rounded part of the margin of the foramen and completed below by the short, free edge of the membrane; it transmits the obturator vessels and nerve. The obturator muscles arise from the surfaces of the membrane.

Pelvic Mechanics

The primary skeletal function of the pelvis is to provide for stable transference of body weight from the vertebral column to the thigh bones. From the last lumbar vertebra the weight is transmitted through the upper part of the sacrum and the adjoining part of each iliac bone to the head of the femur; these parts constitute a pelvic arch of thickened bone, the concave border of which corresponds to the posterior half of the pelvic brim. The ventral pelvic bar formed by the superior rami and bodies of the pubic bones acts as a horizontal tie-beam connecting the bases of the pillars of the arch. The relation of the sacrum to the iliac components of the arch is that of a keystone. Owing to the sinuous nature of the sacro-iliac joint surfaces and the inclination of the long axis of the joint downwards and medially, the direction of the joint line varies in sections cut in different planes. But a coronal section (see Fig. 313), in the plane of weight transference in the upright position, shows the sacrum to be wedged between the hip bones with the base of the wedge uppermost.

The body weight tends to displace the sacrum downwards into the pelvis, with separation of the hip bones. This downward displacement and separation is resisted by the strong ligaments behind the sacro-iliac joints. Any tendency to flattening of the arch, with opening out of the sacro-iliac joints below and in front, is resisted by the tie-beam action of the ventral pelvic bar. The body weight, superimposed on the upper end of the obliquely placed sacrum, tends to drive that end downwards and to tilt the lower end upwards and backwards; this is prevented by the strong sacro-tuberous ligaments holding down the lower part of the sacrum. The ilio-lumbar ligaments help to prevent the last lumbar vertebra from slipping forwards on the oblique upper surface of the body of the first sacral segment. A slight amount of separation or gliding movement is possible at the sacro-iliac joints and the pubic symphysis; the cartilaginous plates in those joints have a cushioning action against jarring shocks. In these ways the pelvic joints provide that element of controlled resilience necessary to perfect function.

The **female pelvis** is modified in association with the requirements of child-bearing. Differences are seen in the joints as in the bones. At the sacro-iliac joint there is less

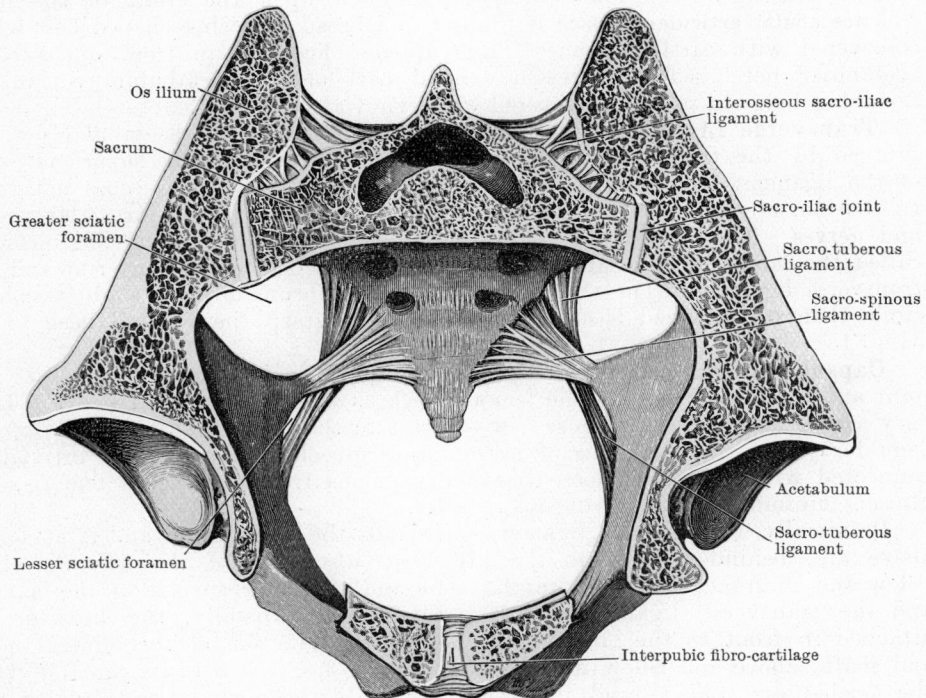

Os ilium
Sacrum
Greater sciatic foramen
Lesser sciatic foramen
Interosseous sacro-iliac ligament
Sacro-iliac joint
Sacro-tuberous ligament
Sacro-spinous ligament
Acetabulum
Sacro-tuberous ligament
Interpubic fibro-cartilage

Fig. 313.—Coronal Section of Pelvis.

interlocking by reciprocal irregularity of the bones, and more movement is permitted than in the male pelvis; the limitation of movement by fibrous ankylosis in later life is not nearly so marked in women as in men. The larger cavity in the interpubic disc, characteristic of the female joint, allows greater separation of the bones. The coccyx, which in men is usually fused to the sacrum by synostosis in later life, is more mobile and preserves its mobility longer in women.

Above all, during the later months of pregnancy, a softening of the pelvic ligaments occurs to such an extent as to allow, at term, more than double the normal movement. During childbirth the pelvic diameters can then be increased to an appreciable extent by yielding of the pelvic joints.

JOINTS OF THE LOWER LIMB

HIP JOINT

At the **hip joint** the globular head of the femur articulates with the cup-like acetabulum of the hip bone, and provides the most striking example in the body of a ball-and-socket joint.

The mechanical requirements at this joint are severe. It must be capable not merely of supporting the entire weight of the body—as in standing on one leg—but of stable transference of that weight even during movement of the trunk upon the femur such as occurs with rapid alternation at the two hip joints during walking and running. The joint must therefore possess great strength and stability even at the expense of limitation of range of movement. To this end, the deep socket securely holding the contained ball, the strong, tense capsular ligament, the insertion of the controlling muscles at some distance from the centre of movement, are all in marked contrast to the conditions at the shoulder joint.

Articular Surfaces.—The **femoral articular surface** forms nearly two-thirds of a spheroid. The covering cartilage is interrupted at the pit on the head, and it ends at the commencement of the neck of the femur along a sinuous line which sometimes makes a scalloped excursion upon the front of the neck. The **acetabular articular surface** is limited to a broad horseshoe-shaped belt which is covered with cartilage and is interrupted below and in front opposite the acetabular notch. The depressed central part of the acetabulum within the horseshoe lodges a pad of fat covered with synovial membrane.

Transverse Ligament and Labrum Acetabulare.—The acetabular notch is bridged by the **transverse ligament** of the acetabulum. The superficial edge of the ligament is flush with the acetabular rim; its deep edge does not reach the bottom of the notch but bounds an aperture which admits articular vessels and nerves. The acetabulum is deepened all round by a fibro-cartilaginous lip, called the **labrum acetabulare**, which is firmly attached to the bony rim and the transverse ligament. The thin, free edge of the labrum forms a slightly smaller circle than its attached base, and so is able to grasp the femoral head (Figs. 314, 315).

Capsular Ligament (Figs. 312, 314).—The capsular ligament encloses the joint and the greater part of the femoral neck as with a cylindrical sleeve. It is very strong and uniformly tense—in contrast to the thin and lax capsule of the shoulder joint. The tendons of surrounding muscles are much less intimately connected with it, but it does receive expansions from the rectus femoris, the gluteus minimus, and the piriformis muscles.

Proximally, the capsular ligament surrounds the acetabulum and is attached above and behind directly to the hip bone just wide of the labrum, while below and in front it is fixed to the bone and the outer surface of the labrum and the transverse ligament of the acetabulum. Distally, the ligament is attached in front to the trochanteric line at the junction of the femoral neck and shaft; above and below it is attached to the neck close to its junction with the trochanters; but, behind, it extends over only the medial two-thirds of the neck. Thus, the whole of the neck of the femur is intracapsular in front, but the lateral third is extracapsular behind. The epiphyseal line of the head is intracapsular; the trochanteric epiphyseal lines are extracapsular.

The fibres of the capsular ligament run for the most part longitudinally from pelvis to femur. Some deeper fibres pass circularly round the joint, constituting the **zona orbicularis**; this is marked only on the back of the capsule, where it appears on the surface, winding round behind the femoral neck (Fig. 312).

Some of the deepest longitudinal fibres, on reaching the neck of the femur, turn upwards upon the neck towards the articular margin; these reflected fibres form bundles, best marked on the upper and lower surfaces of the neck, called *retinacula* or cervical ligaments (Fig. 315).

The main longitudinal fibres of the capsular ligament are massed to form certain thickened bands developed to resist particular stresses to which the joint capsule is subjected. These bands are specially named after the regions of the acetabulum (iliac, pubic, and ischial) from which they arise—the ilio-femoral, pubo-femoral, and ischio-femoral ligaments.

The **ilio-femoral ligament**, of great strength and considerable thickness, is a triangular band attached proximally by its apex to the lower part of the anterior inferior iliac spine and adjoining part of the acetabular rim, and distally by its base to the trochanteric line. It occupies all the front of the capsule except at the medial side above. Usually the sides of this triangular ligament are stronger than the middle part, so that the stronger bands, diverging below from a common stem above, resemble an inverted Y (⅄). The upper or lateral of the two diverging bands is attached distally to a special tubercle on the front of the greater trochanter at the upper end of the trochanteric line (Fig. 314).

The ilio-femoral ligament resists the strain put upon the anterior part of the capsular ligament in the standing position, when the incidence of body weight tends to roll the pelvis backwards on the femoral heads.

The **pubo-femoral ligament** arises from the pubic part of the acetabular rim, with additional fibres from the superior pubic ramus overhanging the obturator groove, and loses itself distally in the general capsular ligament. Some fibres, however, reach the under part of the femoral neck. This ligament helps the adductor muscles in checking excessive abduction of the thigh.

The **ischio-femoral ligament**, less well defined than the others, springs from the ischial wall of the acetabulum on the hinder and lower aspect of the joint (Fig. 312). The upper fibres pass out horizontally across the back of the joint, the lower ones ascend spirally; and both sets of fibres, converging on the upper and lateral part of

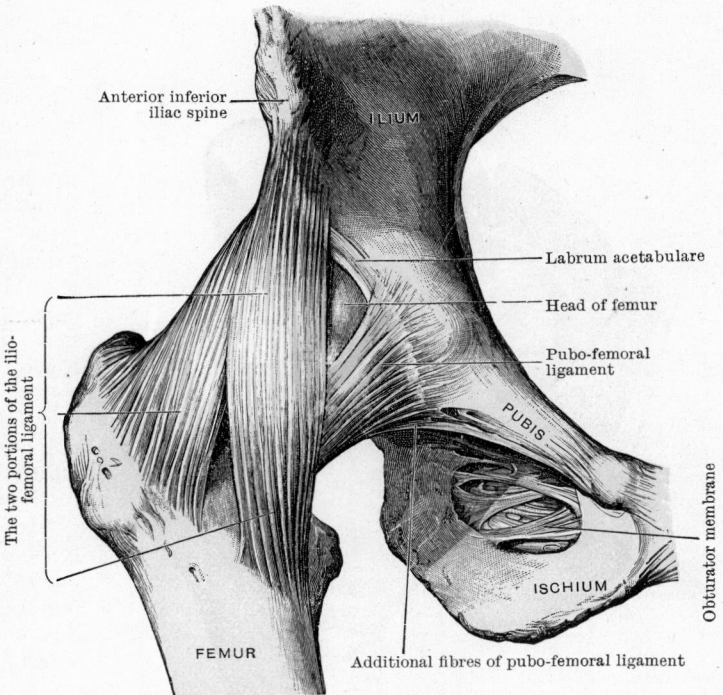

FIG. 314.—DISSECTION OF THE HIP JOINT FROM THE FRONT.

the femoral neck, are attached to the neck, medial to the root of the greater trochanter, close behind the upper band of the ilio-femoral ligament. The general spiral course of the ischio-femoral ligament upwards and laterally across the back of the joint causes the femoral head to be " screwed home " in extension, and the ligament thereby aids the ilio-femoral band in promoting increased stability when standing.

Ligament of Head of Femur.—In the hip joint there is also an intra-articular ligament of flattened triangular shape, known as the **ligament of the head of the femur** [lig. teres] (Fig. 315). Its base is attached within the joint to the lower border of the transverse ligament and to the margins of the acetabular notch, especially the lower or ischial margin. It then narrows to its apical attachment in the upper part of the pit on the head of the femur. Between those attachments the ligament runs free within the joint cavity, surrounded by a synovial sheath. It passes round the head of the femur between it and the non-articular part of the acetabular floor (Fig. 315).

The ligament of the head of the femur varies in size, and in rare cases is absent. Its function is uncertain. It is stretched when the flexed thigh is adducted or rotated laterally, but in many cases it is too weak to have any definite ligamentous action. No appreciable disability results from its rupture or absence. Morphologically, it has been reckoned a relic of the avian *ambiens* muscle or a detached portion of the pectineus. A more feasible ontogenetic explanation of its appearance in Man is that it represents a part of the capsule as first developed which is subsequently included within the joint by the wing-like extension of the femoral head round each side of its femoral attachment and by the increasing size of the ischial contribution to the acetabulum. These developmental changes are associated with provision for increased rotation in the human joint, which is much specialised in comparison with the simple hinge-like type of joint in lower vertebrates.

Synovial Membrane.—The synovial membrane of the hip joint lines the capsular ligament and covers the labrum acetabulare. At the acetabular notch it passes over the inner face of the transverse ligament to cover the fatty tissue in the non-articular part of the acetabulum, and extends as a funnel-shaped sheath upon the ligament of the head of the femur to the edge of the pit on the femoral head. Distally, at the femoral attachment of the capsular ligament, the synovial membrane is reflected upwards on the neck of the femur as far as the edge of the articular cartilage on the head. The retinacula raise this reflected part into prominent folds (Fig. 315), within which blood-vessels run upwards to the head of the bone. At the back of the joint a fold of synovial membrane may protrude beneath the lateral border of the capsular ligament, which is here composed mainly of fibres passing circularly round the femoral neck ; the few longitudinal fibres that reach the back of the neck afford some slight support to the synovial protrusion.

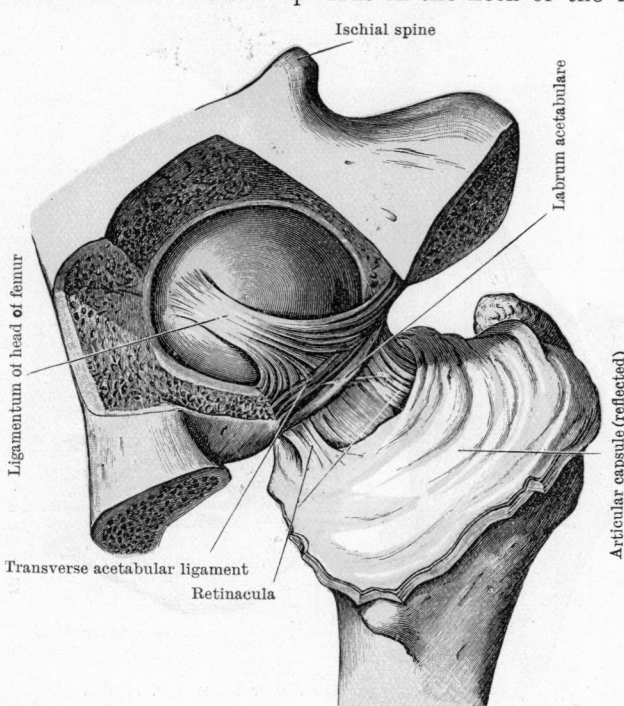

In this joint, where the tense ligaments are, in places, closely applied to the femoral head, the synovial lining is not recognisable as a definite membrane in areas under constant pressure, as on the deep surface of the front of the capsule. The

FIG. 315.—DISSECTION OF THE HIP JOINT.
Bottom of the acetabulum removed, and capsule of the joint thrown laterally towards the trochanters.

excursion of articular cartilage on to the front of the neck of the femur, already referred to, is probably a reaction to the pressure of the overlying ilio-femoral ligament.

There may be one extra-articular extension of the synovial membrane : the psoas tendon passes over a thin portion of the capsule between the upper ends of the ilio-femoral and pubo-femoral ligaments, with a small bursa intervening ; sometimes there is an opening in the capsular ligament under the tendon, and the bursa is then continuous with the synovial membrane of the joint.

Nerve-Supply.—The hip joint is supplied (1) from the lumbar plexus by twigs from the femoral and obturator nerves, and (2) from the sacral plexus by twigs from the nerve to the quadratus femoris muscle.

Movements at the Hip Joint

The movements are those typical of a ball-and-socket joint. They can be analysed as : (1) **flexion** and **extension** around a transverse axis ; (2) **abduction** and **adduction** around an antero-posterior axis ; (3) **medial** and **lateral rotation** around a vertical axis ; with movements compounded of these around intermediate axes. In the movement of **circumduction**, the limb swings round the side of a cone the apex of which is in the hip joint. All axes intersect at the centre of the head of the femur.

Flexion is limited by the tension of the hamstring muscles while the knee joint is extended ; but those are relaxed when the knee is bent, and the thigh can then be brought against the anterior abdominal wall.   All parts of the capsular ligament are relaxed in flexion, and dislocation is therefore most liable to occur then.   Extension takes place very little beyond the vertical position with the limb in line with the trunk ; the movement is then checked by the ilio-femoral ligament and the tension of the muscles in front of the joint. A perpendicular line through the centre of gravity of the trunk falls behind a line joining the centres of the femoral heads ; hence, in the erect position the pelvis, bearing the trunk, tends to roll backwards on the femora, but is prevented from so doing by this check imposed on extension at the hip joints.   All parts of the capsular ligament are taut in extension—the position in which the body weight is normally borne by the limbs. Abduction is limited by tension of the adductor muscles and the pubo-femoral ligament ; adduction, by tension of the abductors and the lateral part of the ilio-femoral ligament. Rotation is termed medial or lateral according to the direction in which the toes are turned ; it is rather more free when combined with flexion than in the extended position of the hip. Medial rotation is limited by tension of the lateral rotator muscles and the ischio-femoral ligament ; lateral rotation, by the medial rotators and the ilio-femoral ligament.

The difference between average mobility and the extreme mobility possessed by trained contortionists is nowhere more marked than at the hip joint.   The greater limitation of movement in the ordinary person is probably largely due to muscle shortening. The final limitation imposed by locking of the femoral neck on the rim of the acetabulum does not arise in the ordinary use of the joint.

KNEE JOINT

The **knee joint** is the largest joint in the body, and is structurally the most complicated.   It is, in the main, a hinge joint ; but, even as such, it is modified in some ways, and, in addition, it is capable of rotation.   The human knee joint must possess great stability, especially in extension, and it must at the same time permit full freedom of movement.   In joint mechanism in general, stability and mobility are to some extent incompatible qualities, and most joints secure one of these at the expense of the other.   At the knee joint both are secured to a remarkable degree by such an alliance of muscle and ligament in controlling the joint as prevails nowhere else.   Here, to a large extent, the muscles *are* the ligaments.

Articular Surfaces.—Functionally, as well as phylogenetically, the knee joint is compounded of three articulations—an intermediate one between the patella and the patellar surface of the femur, and lateral and medial articulations between the femoral and tibial condyles.

The **articular surface of the femur** comprises: the *condylar areas*, which are opposed to the tibia and are separated behind by the intercondylar notch; and the *patellar surface*, which unites the condyles in front and is opposed to the patella. Each condylar surface is delimited from the patellar surface by a shallow groove on the articular cartilage.   On the lateral condyle this groove is almost transverse and is emphasised at each end.   On the medial condyle the groove begins farther forward medially, and, passing obliquely backwards across the condyle, disappears before reaching the lateral edge, where a narrow crescentic facet is marked off which engages with the patella in acute flexion.   The axis of the medial condylar surface turns laterally in its anterior part; the whole surface is made up of a posterior part which lies parallel to the lateral condylar surface and is equal to it in extent, and an additional wedge-shaped part in front, where the axis turns laterally, which has no corresponding part on the lateral condyle.   Each condylar surface is convex from side to side and from before backwards, the antero-posterior curve being much flatter in front than behind.   The patellar surface is grooved vertically between two prominent borders—the lateral the more salient (Fig. 316).

The **articular surface of the patella** is broadly oval, and is divided into a larger lateral area and a smaller medial area by a rounded vertical ridge apparent even on the macerated bone.   The cartilaginous covering reveals a further sub-division of the surface: on each side of the vertical ridge two faint tranverse ridges separate three facets paired with the facets on the other side, and another

faint vertical ridge delimits a medial perpendicular facet adjoining the medial
border of the articular surface. In acute flexion the medial facet rests on the
crescentic facet on the medial femoral condyle; the other facets engage in succession from above downwards with the patellar surface of the femur, as the joint
moves towards full extension.

The **articular surfaces of the tibia** are the cartilage-covered areas on the upper
surface of each tibial condyle. These areas are separated by a non-articular intercondylar area formed by the intercondylar eminence in the middle, and rough,
triangular depressions in front and behind. The medial articular area is oval and
concave. The lateral area, smaller and more circular, is concave from side to side
and concavo-convex from before backwards; posteriorly it is prolonged downwards

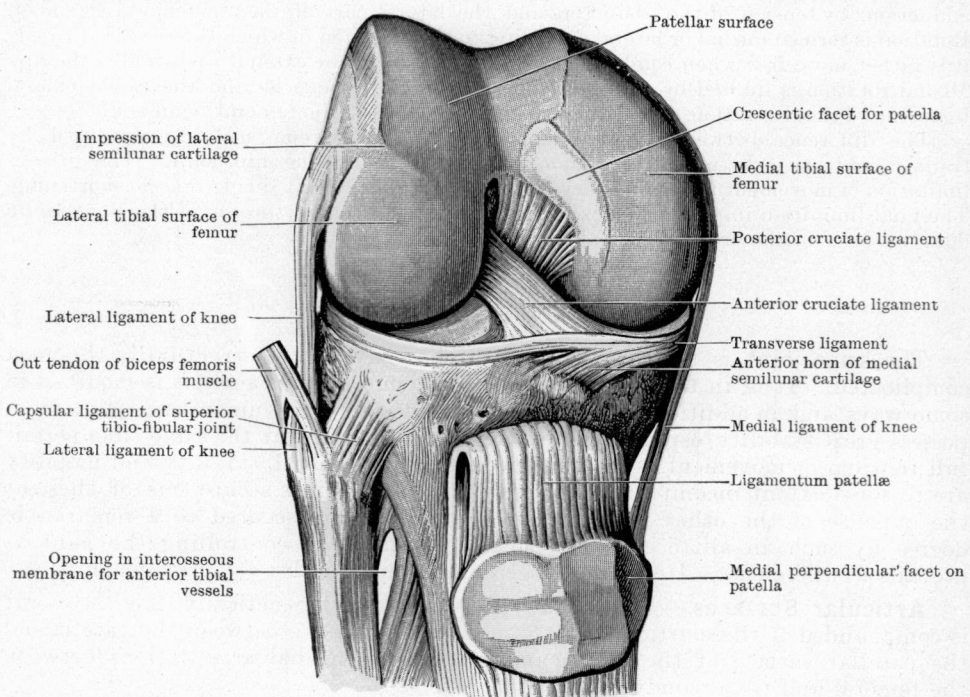

Patellar surface
Crescentic facet for patella
Medial tibial surface of femur
Posterior cruciate ligament
Anterior cruciate ligament
Transverse ligament
Anterior horn of medial semilunar cartilage
Medial ligament of knee
Ligamentum patellæ
Medial perpendicular facet on patella

Impression of lateral semilunar cartilage
Lateral tibial surface of femur
Lateral ligament of knee
Cut tendon of biceps femoris muscle
Capsular ligament of superior tibio-fibular joint
Lateral ligament of knee
Opening in interosseous membrane for anterior tibial vessels

FIG. 316.—DISSECTION OF THE KNEE JOINT FROM THE FRONT: PATELLA THROWN DOWN.

over the back of the condyle in relation to the popliteus tendon (Fig. 318). A
peripheral flattened strip on each condyle underlies a semilunar fibro-cartilage.
The tibial articular surfaces are far from congruent with the femoral condyles,
which rest upon them; but the effect of this incongruence is lessened by the
interposition of the semilunar cartilages.

Articular Capsule.—The capsule of the joint is a complicated structure.
There is no complete, independent capsular ligament uniting the bones. Instead,
the joint is surrounded by a thick ligamentous formation constructed chiefly of
muscle tendons or expansions from them; only here and there is it composed of
true capsular fibres running between the articulating bones. Inside the capsule,
the synovial lining of the joint is in places separated from the ligamentous stratum
by wide intervals occupied by fatty pads or special intra-articular structures.

At the **front of the joint** this ligamentous formation is built up mainly of the
fused tendons of insertion of the rectus femoris and vasti muscles. These descend
on the patella from above and from each side to a marginal insertion round the
upper half of the bone. Superficial tendinous fibres are continued downwards over
the front of the bone into the **ligamentum patellæ**. This thick band securely anchors
the patella to the tibia, and is in reality the distal part of the quadriceps insertion;
it is attached to the apex and the posterior surface of the patella below the arti-

cular area, and to the tubercle of the tibia. Other thinner bands pass down from the sides of the patella, diverging slightly, to the front of each tibial condyle; these constitute the **medial** and **lateral patellar retinacula.** Tendinous fibres of the vasti muscles pass obliquely downwards across the patella into the retinaculum of the other side. Other deeper fibres from each side of the patella pass across to the anterior part of each femoral epicondyle.

Superficial to all these bands there are strong expansions of the fascia lata. The ilio-tibial tract descends across the antero-lateral aspect of the joint to be inserted into the lateral tibial condyle. A strong band diverges anteriorly from this tract to be attached to the upper part of the lateral edge of the patella, forming a *superior patellar retinaculum.* Less definite fascial expansions sweep down over the patella, and on each side of it, towards the upper part of the tibia; some fibres form U-shaped loops in front of the ligamentum patellæ.

The whole of this anterior covering of the knee joint, with the patella inset on its deep aspect, is kept tense by the tonicity of the extensor muscles, and is tightly braced up when these muscles contract in extension. In the ordinary type of hinge joint the extensor portion of the capsule must be loose in the extended position to permit the possibility of flexion. But at the knee this part of the capsule is, as it were, continued into muscle above, instead of being attached directly to the proximal bone, and can be kept taut in all positions.

The **back of the joint** is covered over by a ligamentous feltwork of intersecting bands which form a **posterior ligament.** True *capsular fibres* descend over the upper part of the joint from a femoral attachment along the base of the popliteal surface and invest the back of each condyle with a thin covering overlain by the corresponding head of the gastrocnemius, which in part arises from it. Distally, other capsular fibres ascend from the posterior border of the proximal end of the tibia, leaving an opening laterally for the escaping popliteus tendon. The stronger central portion of the posterior ligament is formed by a well-marked expansion from the semi-membranosus tendon which turns obliquely upwards and laterally to blend with the general capsular fibres over the lateral condyle of the femur. This expansion is called the **oblique posterior ligament.** The lower lateral part of the back of the joint is strengthened by the **arcuate ligament of the knee**, which springs from the back of the head of the fibula, arches upwards and medially over the popliteus tendon as it emerges from the joint, and spreads out on the back of the capsule. Sometimes the most lateral fibres of the arcuate ligament are specially developed as a separate band that runs from the top of the fibula to the back of the lateral femoral condyle (Fig. 317).

At the **sides of the joint** there are true capsular fibres which descend from the sides of the femoral condyles to the sides of the tibial condyles. They blend posteriorly with the ligamentous feltwork, and anteriorly with the various tendinous expansions already described. Here are found the special *medial* and *lateral ligaments* characteristic of hinge joints, but the ligaments of the two sides differ greatly in form and relations.

The **medial ligament** [lig. collaterale tibiale] is a broad, flat band in the true capsular plane. Its upper end has an extensive attachment on the medial epicondyle of the femur; some fibres may be traced upwards into the adductor magnus tendon, and the ligament has been regarded as formed, in part at least, from an original tibial insertion of this muscle. Distally, the ligament is attached to the medial surface of the tibia: the superficial fibres descend to below the level of the tibial tubercle; deeper fibres have a shorter course from femur to tibia, the deepest of all having an intermediate attachment to the medial semilunar cartilage. Posterior to the upper part of the main band, shorter fibres reach the edge of the tibial condyle immediately above the principal insertion of the semimembranosus tendon. A downward expansion from this tendon reaches the shaft of the tibia, partly under cover of the posterior border of the main band (the medial inferior genicular vessels and nerve running forwards between them) and partly blending with this border of the ligament.

The **lateral ligament** [lig. collaterale fibulare] (Figs. 316, 317), round and cord-like, stands altogether clear of the capsular ligament, and is wrapped round by an expansion of the fascia lata. It is attached above to the lateral epicondyle of the femur; below, it reaches the head of the fibula in front of its highest point, splitting the tendon of the biceps as it does so. As in the specimen drawn in Fig. 317, the ligament is sometimes partly continued into the upper end of the peroneus longus muscle, and may be regarded as a stranded femoral tendon of this muscle.

On the lateral side of the joint the true capsular fibres are short and weak; they bridge the interval between the femoral and tibial condyles, and are separated

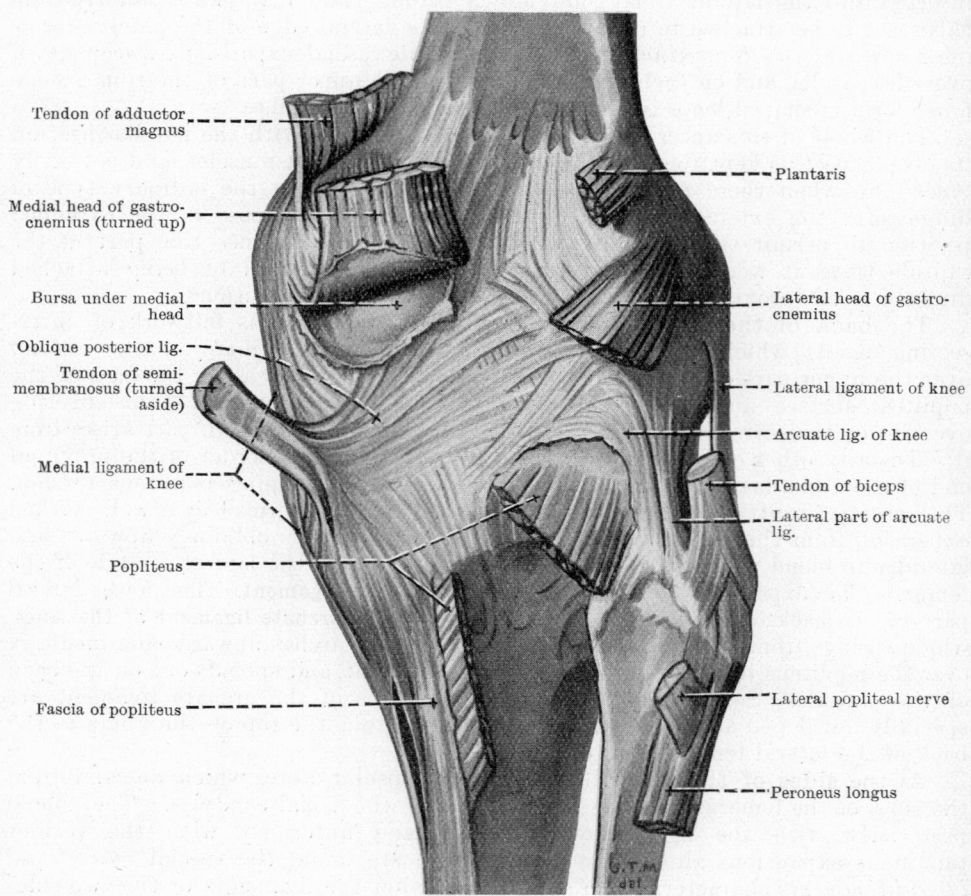

Tendon of adductor magnus
Plantaris
Medial head of gastro-cnemius (turned up)
Lateral head of gastro-cnemius
Bursa under medial head
Oblique posterior lig.
Tendon of semi-membranosus (turned aside)
Lateral ligament of knee
Arcuate lig. of knee
Medial ligament of knee
Tendon of biceps
Lateral part of arcuate lig.
Popliteus
Lateral popliteal nerve
Fascia of popliteus
Peroneus longus

FIG. 317.—THE KNEE JOINT FROM BEHIND.

In the specimen the lateral part of the *arcuate ligament* was present as a separate band; and the continuity between the lateral ligament of the knee and the peroneus longus muscle was specially well marked.

from the lateral semilunar cartilage by the popliteus tendon. There is a distinct interval between these capsular fibres and the lateral ligament of the knee; through the interval the lateral inferior genicular vessels and nerve run forwards.

The medial and lateral ligaments prevent disruption of the joint at the sides. They are most tightly stretched in extension, and then their direction—the fibular ligament downwards and backwards, the tibial downwards and forwards—is such as to prevent rotation of the tibia laterally or of the femur medially.

Intra-articular ligaments (Figs. 316, 318, 319).—In addition to the capsular ligamentous formation, there are two intra-articular ligaments that stretch between the tibia and femur. These are the **cruciate ligaments**—strong, rounded bands named from the way in which they cross each other between their attachments, and distinguished as **anterior** and **posterior** from their relative positions on the tibia, from which they ascend to the sides of the intercondylar notch of the femur. The **anterior cruciate ligament** extends obliquely upwards and backwards from the rough, non-articular area in front of the intercondylar eminence of the tibia to the back part of the medial side of the lateral femoral condyle. The **posterior cruciate ligament** passes upwards and forwards on the medial side of the other; it extends from the sloping, non-articular surface behind the eminence to the lateral side of the medial condyle. The cruciate ligaments are fairly tense in all positions, the

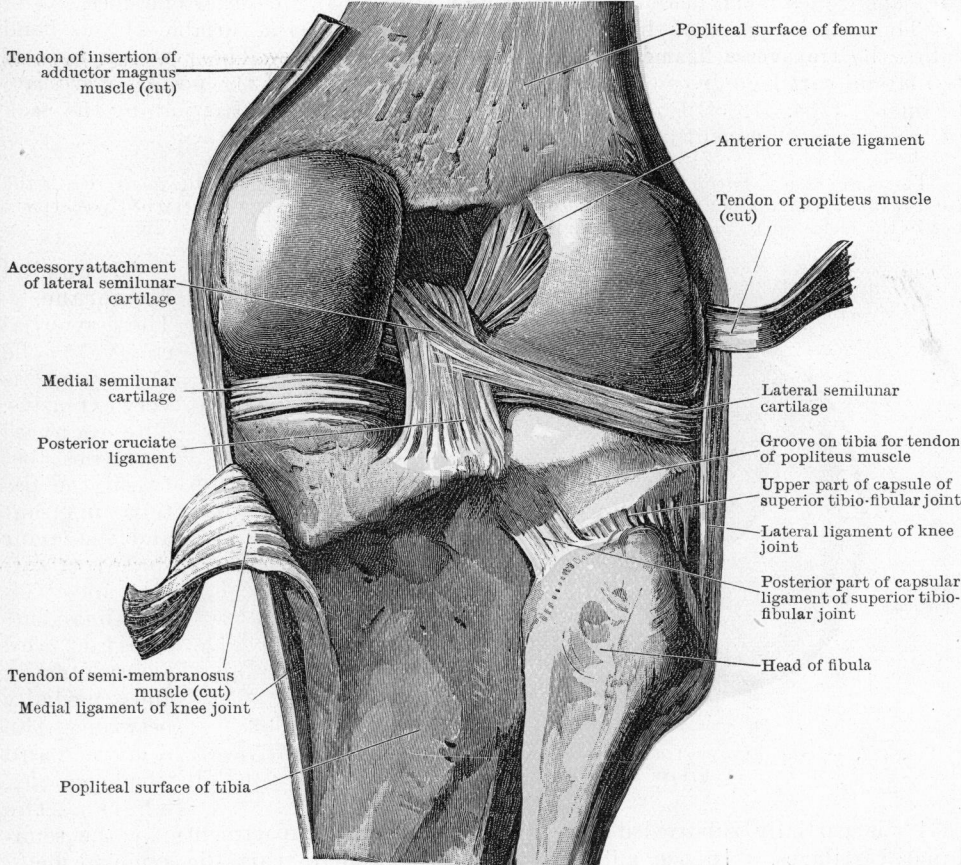

Tendon of insertion of adductor magnus muscle (cut)

Accessory attachment of lateral semilunar cartilage

Medial semilunar cartilage

Posterior cruciate ligament

Tendon of semi-membranosus muscle (cut)
Medial ligament of knee joint

Popliteal surface of tibia

Popliteal surface of femur

Anterior cruciate ligament

Tendon of popliteus muscle (cut)

Lateral semilunar cartilage

Groove on tibia for tendon of popliteus muscle

Upper part of capsule of superior tibio-fibular joint

Lateral ligament of knee joint

Posterior part of capsular ligament of superior tibio-fibular joint

Head of fibula

FIG. 318.—THE KNEE JOINT OPENED FROM BEHIND BY THE REMOVAL OF THE POSTERIOR LIGAMENT.

anterior more so in extension, the posterior in flexion. They prevent antero-posterior displacement of the tibia and limit medial rotation of the tibia or lateral rotation of the femur.

The Semilunar Cartilages (Figs. 316, 318, 319).—Two **semilunar cartilages** [menisci] also are found within the joint, interposed between the femoral and tibial condyles so as to compensate for their incongruence. Each is a flattened, crescentic slip of fibro-cartilage, wedge-shaped in cross section, with the edge of the wedge at the concave border.

The thick, convex border of each cartilage is bound down to the peripheral margin of the tibial condyle by short ligamentous fibres, and is also fused to the deep surface of the capsular ligament. This means that the **medial cartilage** is much more firmly anchored, for through its capsular attachment it is fixed to the medial ligament of the knee, while the **lateral cartilage** is attached only to the weak fibres which represent the capsular ligament on the lateral side of the joint and not at all to the lateral ligament of the joint. At one point—where it is crossed by the popliteus tendon—the peripheral edge of the lateral cartilage is quite free from capsular attachment.

The extremities of each cartilage are prolonged into fibrous horns which are firmly attached to the intercondylar area on the top of the tibia (Fig. 319). The *anterior horn* of the **medial semilunar cartilage** is fixed to the fore part of this area, in front of the anterior cruciate ligament; its *posterior horn* is fixed towards the back, between the posterior cruciate ligament and the posterior horn of the lateral cartilage. The *two horns* of the **lateral semilunar cartilage** are attached close together, in front of and behind the intercondylar eminence, so that this cartilage comes much nearer to completing a circle than the other one does.

The anterior parts of the two cartilages are joined by a variable fibrous band called the **transverse ligament** of the knee (Figs. 316, 319). The posterior horn of the lateral cartilage gives off a ligamentous slip which joins the posterior cruciate ligament (Figs. 318, 319); this slip may split into two, one part joining the back of the cruciate ligament and the other joining the front.

The connexion between the lateral cartilage and the posterior cruciate ligament recalls the typical lower mammalian condition where the lateral semilunar cartilage is attached posteriorly not to the tibia but to the medial femoral condyle behind the posterior cruciate ligament.

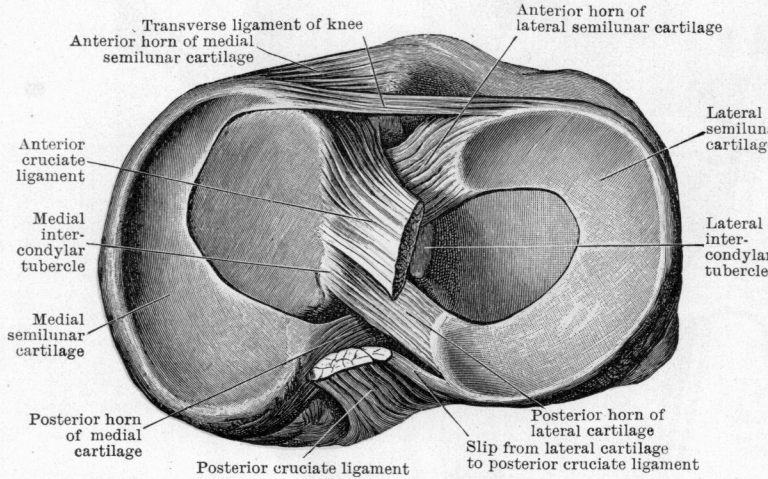

Synovial Membrane. — The synovial cavity of the knee joint is very extensive. The central part lies between the patella in front and the femur (patellar surface) and cruciate ligaments behind, and passes laterally and medially between the femoral and tibial condyles, where the

FIG. 319.—UPPER END OF TIBIA WITH SEMILUNAR CARTILAGES AND ATTACHED PORTIONS OF CRUCIATE LIGAMENTS.

cavity is partially subdivided into upper and lower compartments by the semilunar cartilages. In the anterior wall of this central part the synovial membrane passes from the edges of the articular surface of the patella in all directions on the deep aspect of the anterior wall of the joint. Below the patella, the membrane is carried towards the tibia over a mass of fatty, fibrous tissue, called the **infrapatellar pad of fat**, which fills up the angle between the deep surface of the patellar ligament and the front of the tibia above the tubercle. From the synovial surface of this pad a vertical, crescentic fold of synovial membrane, called the **infrapatellar fold**, runs towards the cruciate ligaments. Similar folds, called the **alar folds**, run horizontally across the fatty pad, one from each side of the vertical fold. These synovial folds are vestiges of the original partitions that separated the three components of the cavity of the knee joint.

Three recesses open off the central part of the joint cavity. One is median, and is called the **suprapatellar synovial pouch**. It lies above the level of the patella between the quadriceps muscle and the lower part of the shaft of the femur; it develops as a bursa separate from the joint, with which it eventually communicates. The articularis genu muscle, composed of fleshy slips that arise from the femur above the pouch, is inserted into its wall and draws it upwards in extension of the joint. The other recesses lie one behind the posterior part of each femoral condyle; in this situation the capsular ligament is overlain by the gastrocnemius muscle, and there is usually a bursa between the muscle and the ligament, especially on the medial side, where the bursa sometimes communicates with the joint cavity through an opening in the capsule (Fig. 317). These posterior recesses are separated from each other by a thick, median septum which projects into the joint cavity from behind and is formed by the cruciate ligaments carrying forward a broad, vertical fold of synovial membrane which clothes them in front and at the sides.

The **synovial relations of the popliteus tendon** are important. As the tendon passes backwards from its origin deep to the lateral part of the capsular ligament, the synovial membrane is wrapped round its medial side, separating it from the edge of the lateral semilunar cartilage. When the tendon leaves the joint through the opening in the posterior part of the capsule, a *synovial pouch* is carried down on its deep surface across the back of the superior tibio-fibular joint. In some cases the cavity of this joint communicates with the bursa-like pouch accompanying the tendon, and therefore also with the cavity of the knee joint.

Additional Bursæ.—In addition to the bursæ mentioned, numerous others are found in the vicinity of the knee joint. The more constant of these others are : the *subcutaneous prepatellar bursa*, under the skin over the lower part of the patella ; the *subfascial prepatellar bursa*, between the fascial and tendinous expansions in front of the patella ; the *subtendinous prepatellar bursa*, between the superficial and deep layers of the tendinous fibres that cross the patella ; the *deep infrapatellar bursa*, between the upper part of the tibia and the lower part of the ligamentum patellae, separated from the knee joint by the infrapatellar pad of fat ; a bursa between the medial ligament of the knee and the overlying tendons of the sartorius, gracilis and semitendinosus ; bursæ between the semi-membranosus tendon and the medial ligament of the knee and between that tendon and the medial head of the gastrocnemius ; and a bursa between the biceps tendon and the lateral ligament of the knee.

Nerve-Supply.—The knee joint is supplied by several branches from the **femoral** nerve and from both divisions—**medial** and **lateral popliteal**—of the sciatic nerve, and by a filament from the **obturator** nerve.

Movements of the Knee Joint

These are primarily **flexion** and **extension** around a transverse axis as in an ordinary hinge joint, but with these differences: that the axis changes its position during movement owing to the different curvature of different parts of the femoral condyles, and that the end of extension or beginning of flexion is accompanied by a special **rotatory movement**.

As the joint passes from flexion to extension the femoral condyles roll or glide upon the tibia until, just before full extension is reached, the tibial surface of the lateral femoral condyle is almost exhausted, although the anterior, oblique part of the surface on the medial condyle has still to be brought into play. While the lateral condyle completes its forward roll, the medial condyle rolls forward equally but at the same time glides backwards—until the oblique part in front is exhausted—in a horizontal arc centred in the lateral condyle, which is therefore twisted vertically and a medial rotation of the femur results. This terminal rotatory movement tightens the medial and lateral ligaments of the knee and the joint is then, as it were, "screwed home." Before flexion can take place the rotatory movement must be undone. At the end of extension, before the terminal rotation takes place the anterior cruciate ligament is at its tightest ; the rotation lessens its tension sufficiently to prevent it checking the initial opposite (*i.e.* lateral) rotation of the femur at the beginning of flexion. These rotations have been described as of the femur on the tibia ; this is what occurs when the tibia is fixed during the movement at the knee, as in rising up or sitting down with the feet planted on the floor. But if, as in the extension movement of kicking, the foot is not thus fixed, the rotation is of the tibia on the femur—laterally at the end of extension, medially at the beginning of flexion.

When the body is erect, the axis of gravity of the body falls in front of a line uniting the knee joints ; gravity therefore tends to produce hyper-extension, which is prevented by the tension of the hamstring muscles, the oblique posterior ligament (itself an expansion of one of the hamstrings), and the cruciate and medial and lateral ligaments. This effect of gravity, together with the resistance offered to rotation by the tight medial and lateral and cruciate ligaments, keeps the knee-joint "locked" in extension with the minimum of muscular effort. Indeed, the quadriceps extensor muscle is then actually relaxed, and the patella can be moved from side to side.

The relation of the patella to the femur during flexion-extension movement has already been mentioned.

In addition to the hinge movements of flexion and extension, some **rotation** of the leg around a vertical axis can take place except when the joint is fully extended. In full extension, apart from the special, small rotatory movements already described, all rotation is prevented by the tension of the medial and lateral and cruciate ligaments. Rotation is most free when the knee is flexed to about a right angle; for neither cruciate ligament is then very tight and the tension of the medial and lateral ligaments, slightly reduced by the special rotatory movement at the beginning of flexion, is further lessened during flexion by descent of their femoral attachments.

The **semilunar cartilages**, as already explained, compensate for the incongruity of the opposed femoral and tibial surfaces and, by slight movement, accommodate themselves to the differently shaped parts of the femoral condyles that rest upon them in different positions of the joint. They shift slightly forwards in extension and open out their curve under the "flatter" anterior parts of the condyles then opposed to them. In flexion they shift backwards and curl in upon the more rounded posterior parts of the femoral condyles. The attachment of the medial cartilage to the medial ligament causes this cartilage to be drawn medially when the ligament tightens in extension. In a sudden, unguarded movement, the cartilage may at that moment be pinned between femur and tibia before its normal opening out has occurred. The pull of the medial ligament may then split the cartilage in its long axis, producing one form of the commonest derangement of the knee joint—torn medial semilunar cartilage.

TIBIO-FIBULAR JOINTS

The fibula is closely bound to the tibia by a joint at each end; and the shafts of the two bones are connected by an interosseous membrane.

Superior Tibio-fibular Joint (Figs. 316, 318).—This is a small synovial joint, of plane type, between a flat, circular or oval facet on the head of the fibula and a similar facet on the tibia placed postero-laterally on the under aspect of the overhanging lateral condyle. The **capsular ligament** surrounding the joint is strengthened in front and behind by fibres directed upwards and medially from the fibula to the adjoining part of the tibia.

The tendon of the popliteus muscle is intimately related to the postero-superior aspect of the joint; and the pouch of synovial membrane prolonged under the tendon from the knee joint sometimes communicates with the synovial cavity of the tibio-fibular joint through an opening in the upper part of the capsule.

Nerve-Supply.—The superior tibio-fibular joint is supplied by twigs from the **lateral popliteal nerve** and from the branch of the **medial popliteal nerve** to the popliteus muscle.

Inferior Tibio-fibular Joint (Figs. 320, 323).—This is a fibrous joint. The rough, triangular, opposed surfaces of the bones are united by a strong **interosseous ligament**. In addition, the joint is strengthened in front and behind by longer bands called the **anterior** and **posterior inferior tibio-fibular ligaments** [ligg. malleoli lateralis]. These bands stretch from the lower border of the tibia, in front and behind, to the back and front of the distal end of the fibula, each inclined laterally and downwards. Under cover of the posterior ligament there is a longer band, called the **transverse tibio-fibular ligament**, which is attached to the whole length of the posterior edge of the inferior surface of the tibia and to the upper end of the malleolar fossa on the fibula. This band closes the posterior angle between the tibia and fibula and articulates with the bevelled posterior half of the lateral border of the trochlea tali (Fig. 320).

A recess of the cavity of the ankle joint usually extends upwards between the tibia and fibula for about a quarter of an inch. It is blocked above by the base of the interosseous ligament and is occupied by a fold of synovial membrane of the ankle joint. Sometimes the articular cartilage on the lower ends of the tibia and fibula extends upwards for a little way on the walls of this recess.

Nerve-Supply.—The inferior tibio-fibular joint is supplied by twigs from the **anterior** and **posterior tibial nerves**.

Interosseous Membrane.—The interosseous membrane of the leg is tightly stretched between the interosseous borders of the two bones; its fibres in great part run downwards and laterally from tibia to fibula. The membrane reaches up to the under aspect of the superior joint and downwards to blend with the upper edge of the interosseous ligament of the inferior joint. There is an oval aperture near the upper end of the membrane through which pass the anterior tibial vessels (Fig. 316), and a smaller one at the lower end for the perforating peroneal vessels (Fig. 320).

Movement at the tibio-fibular joints is slight and entirely passive. It is occasioned by changes in the ankle joint, with which it will be described.

ANKLE JOINT

The **ankle joint** is a synovial joint of typical hinge pattern. The lower ends of the tibia and fibula provide a socket in which the upper part of the talus rocks

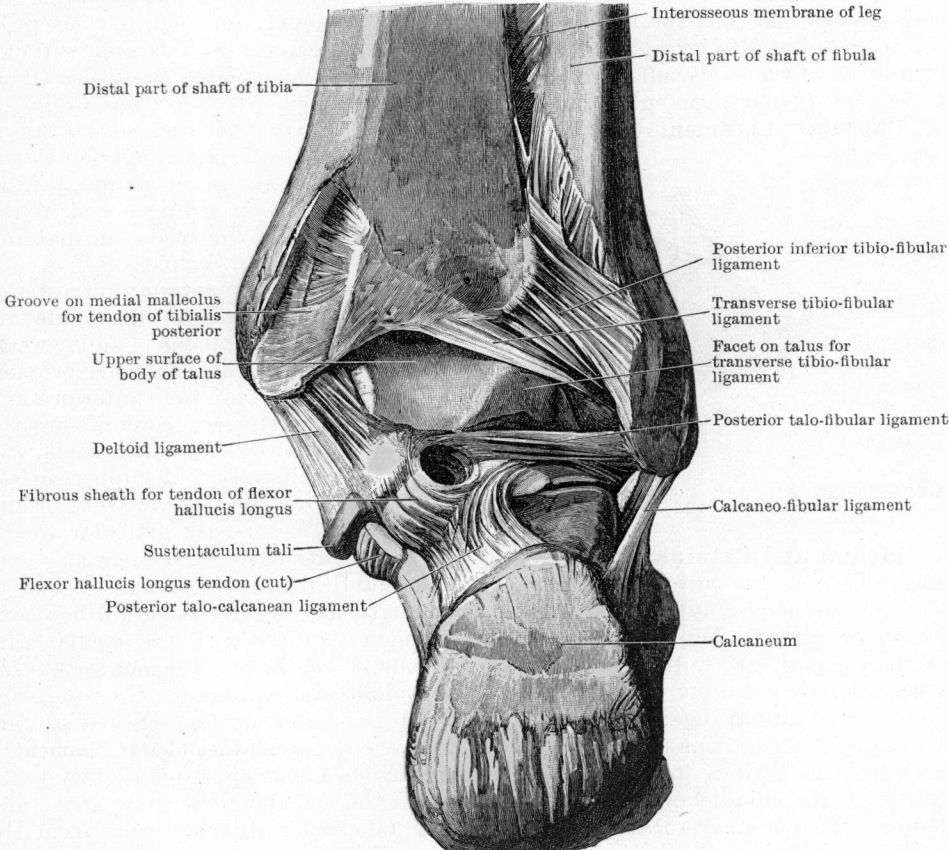

Interosseous membrane of leg

Distal part of shaft of fibula

Distal part of shaft of tibia

Posterior inferior tibio-fibular ligament

Groove on medial malleolus for tendon of tibialis posterior

Transverse tibio-fibular ligament

Facet on talus for transverse tibio-fibular ligament

Upper surface of body of talus

Deltoid ligament

Posterior talo-fibular ligament

Fibrous sheath for tendon of flexor hallucis longus

Calcaneo-fibular ligament

Sustentaculum tali

Flexor hallucis longus tendon (cut)

Posterior talo-calcanean ligament

Calcaneum

FIG. 320.—ANKLE JOINT DISSECTED FROM BEHIND WITH PART OF THE ARTICULAR CAPSULE REMOVED.

around a transverse axis. The only special feature of the hinge is an arrangement whereby the sides of the socket come to exercise a positive "grip" upon the moving member of the joint as an aid to increased stability.

Articular Surfaces.—The **proximal articular surface** provides the socket (Fig. 321). It is formed by the cartilage-covered areas on the lower ends of the leg bones. The roof of the socket, wider in front than behind, is the *distal surface of the tibia*, concave from before backwards and slightly convex from side to side. The medial wall is the *lateral surface of the medial malleolus*, the cartilage here being continuous with that on the roof at a rounded angle. The lateral wall is the triangular facet on the fore part of the *medial side of the lateral malleolus*. The angle between this wall and the roof corresponds to the narrow cleft between

24

the tibia and fibula distal to the interosseous ligament between these bones; but, posteriorly, this angle is filled up by the *transverse tibio-fibular ligament.*

The **distal articular surface** is formed entirely by the upper part of the body of the talus—the *trochlea tali*—which is shaped like the upper part of a short cylinder placed transversely. The cylinder is square cut medially, but obliquely cut laterally, in such a way that the cylindrical surface is broader in front than behind. This surface articulates with the distal surface of the tibia—the roof of the socket—which also is broader in front. A shallow, wide antero-posterior groove on the upper trochlear surface corresponds to the convexity on the tibial surface. The cartilage on top of the trochlea is continued on to its sides—the "ends" of the cylinder. The medial articular surface or "end" is vertically set, and is shaped like a comma laid on its side, tail backwards; it is opposed to the medial malleolar wall of the proximal joint surface. The lateral articular area or "end" of the trochlea is triangular, corresponding to the opposed facet on the lateral malleolus; it is obliquely set, inclining laterally below and medially behind. The angle between the upper and lateral surfaces of the trochlea is bevelled off posteriorly where it articulates with the transverse tibio-fibular ligament (Fig. 320).

Capsular Ligament.—The capsular ligament surrounds the joint. As is usual in a hinge joint, it is weak in front and behind but is strengthened at the sides by special medial and lateral ligaments.

The **anterior** and **posterior ligaments of the ankle** are membranous and weak. They are attached proximally to the anterior and posterior borders of the lower end of the tibia, and distally to the upper surface of the talus in front of and behind the articular area.

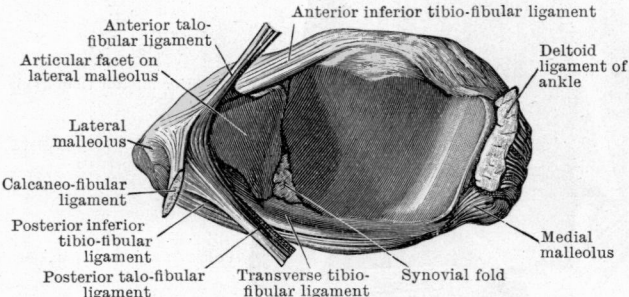

Anterior talo-fibular ligament
Articular facet on lateral malleolus
Lateral malleolus
Calcaneo-fibular ligament
Posterior inferior tibio-fibular ligament
Posterior talo-fibular ligament
Anterior inferior tibio-fibular ligament
Deltoid ligament of ankle
Transverse tibio-fibular ligament
Synovial fold
Medial malleolus

FIG. 321.—ARTICULAR SURFACES OF TIBIA AND FIBULA WHICH ARE OPPOSED TO THE TALUS IN THE ANKLE JOINT.

Medial and Lateral Ligaments.—These ligaments have in common an upper attachment to the corresponding malleolus, a middle band descending thence to the calcaneum, and anterior and posterior bands to the talus; the medial ligament has other parts in addition. The medial ligament is fused with the medial part of the capsule; the anterior and posterior bands of the lateral ligament are fused with the lateral part of the capsule, but the middle band is not.

In the **lateral ligament** (Figs. 320, 323) the three bands referred to are quite distinct from one another. The middle one—the **calcaneo-fibular ligament**—runs from in front of the tip of the lateral malleolus downwards and slightly backwards to the middle of the lateral surface of the calcaneum, a little above and behind the peroneal tubercle. The **anterior talo-fibular ligament** runs from the anterior border of the lateral malleolus forwards and medially to the neck of the talus. The **posterior talo-fibular ligament** is attached to the fibula at the bottom of the malleolar fossa and passes medially and slightly backwards to the upper surface of the posterior tubercle of the talus.

The **medial ligament** (Figs. 320, 322) is made up of several bands which, however, are differentiated only by their distal attachments. They are fused in a strong ligamentous formation usually called, from its triangular shape, the **deltoid ligament**. The apical part of this structure is attached to the pit on the lower border of the medial malleolus. Its thick base has a continuous attachment—to the rounded upper and medial part of the navicular bone (*tibio-navicular fibres*), to the medial part of the neck of the talus (*anterior talo-tibial fibres*), to the medial border of the sustentaculum tali and the plantar calcaneo-navicular ligament (*calcaneo-tibial fibres*), and to the medial side of the talus, under the "tail" of the comma-shaped facet (*posterior talo-tibial fibres*). The talo-tibial fibres are on a

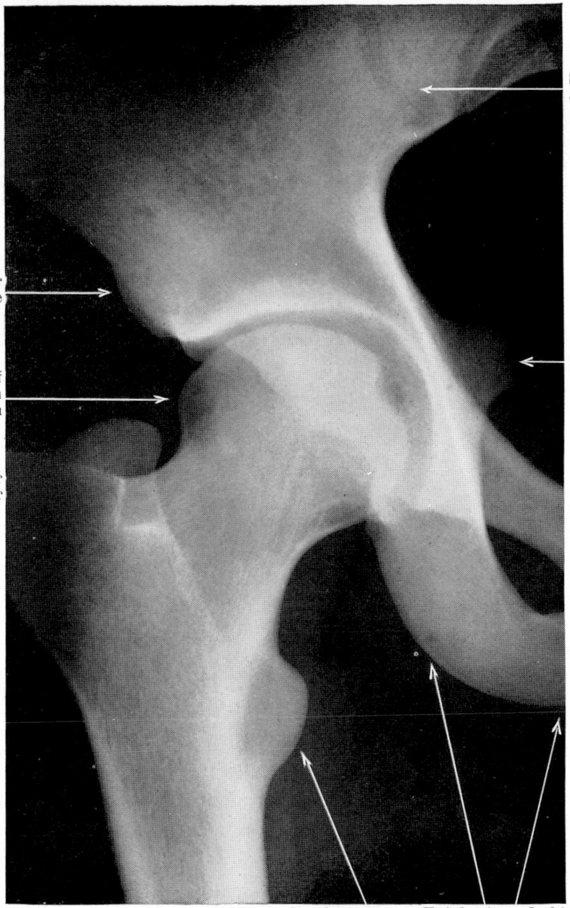

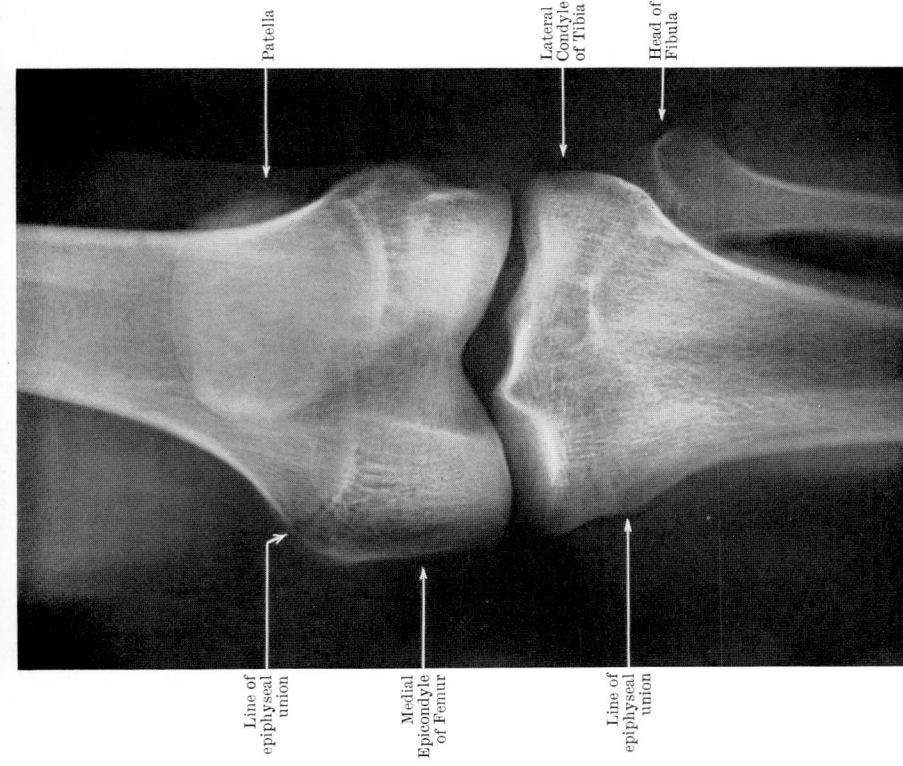

Patella

Lateral
Condyle
of Tibia

Head of
Fibula

Line of
epiphyseal
union

Medial
Epicondyle
of Femur

Line of
epiphyseal
union

FIG. 2.—RADIOGRAPH OF LEFT KNEE OF YOUNG MAN AGED 22.

The union of the epiphysis of the Femur is not quite complete.
Cf. Plate XIV, Fig. 1.

Sacro-iliac
Joint

Ischial
Spine

Superior
Pubic Ramus

Obturator
Foramen

Ramus of
Ischium

Epiphysis on Ischial
Tuberosity and Ramus

Lesser Trochanter

Anterior inferior
Iliac Spine

Head of
Femur in
Acetabulum

Greater
Trochanter

FIG. 1.—RADIOGRAPH OF HIP OF YOUTH AGED 17. (Dr. J. Duncan White.)

All three epiphyses of the Femur are united. Note the continuity
of the lines of the lower borders of the Superior Pubic Ramus and the
Neck of the Femur (Shenton's line), seen also in Plate XIII.

[Facing p. 370

PLATE XXVI

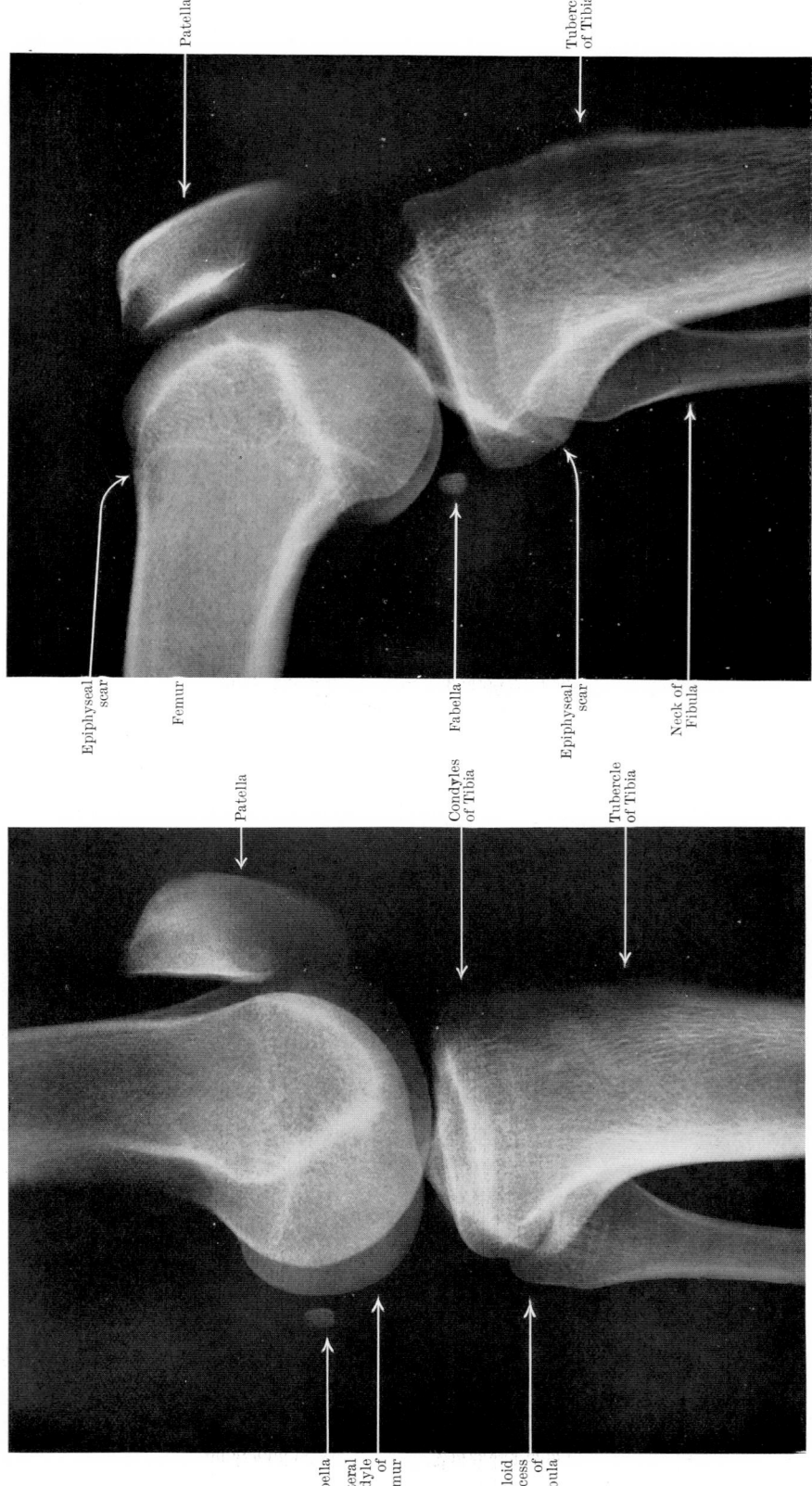

Patella

Tubercle
of Tibia

Epiphyseal
scar

Femur

Fabella

Epiphyseal
scar

Neck of
Fibula

FIG. 2.—LATERAL RADIOGRAPH OF THE SAME KNEE, SEMI-FLEXED.
Compare with Fig. 1, and note the change in the areas of contact of the
F ... 'th (l D t'll   1 T'b.

Patella

Condyles
of Tibia

Tubercle
of Tibia

Fabella
Lateral
condyle
of
Femur

Styloid
process
of
Fibula

FIG. 1.—LATERAL RADIOGRAPH OF THE SAME KNEE AS IN PLATE XXV, IN EXTENSION.
Note the areas of contact of the Femur with the Patella and Tibia ; also the
sesamoid bone (Fabella) in the lateral head of the gastrocnemius muscle

deeper plane than the others; the tibio-navicular and calcaneo-tibial portions are continuous over the superficial aspect of the anterior talo-tibial fibres.

Synovial Membrane.—The synovial membrane of the joint lines the capsular ligament and covers well-marked fatty pads that lie in relation to the anterior and posterior ligaments. A synovial fold (Fig. 321) occupies the cleft between the tibia and fibula below the base of the interosseous tibio-fibular ligament; the sides of this cleft may be covered in part by an extension of the articular cartilage on the tibia and fibula.

Nerve-Supply.—The ankle joint is supplied by twigs from the **anterior** and **posterior tibial** nerves.

Movements at the Ankle Joint

Movement takes place around a transverse axis on a level with the tip of the lateral malleolus and slightly below the level of the medial malleolus. In the normal, standing

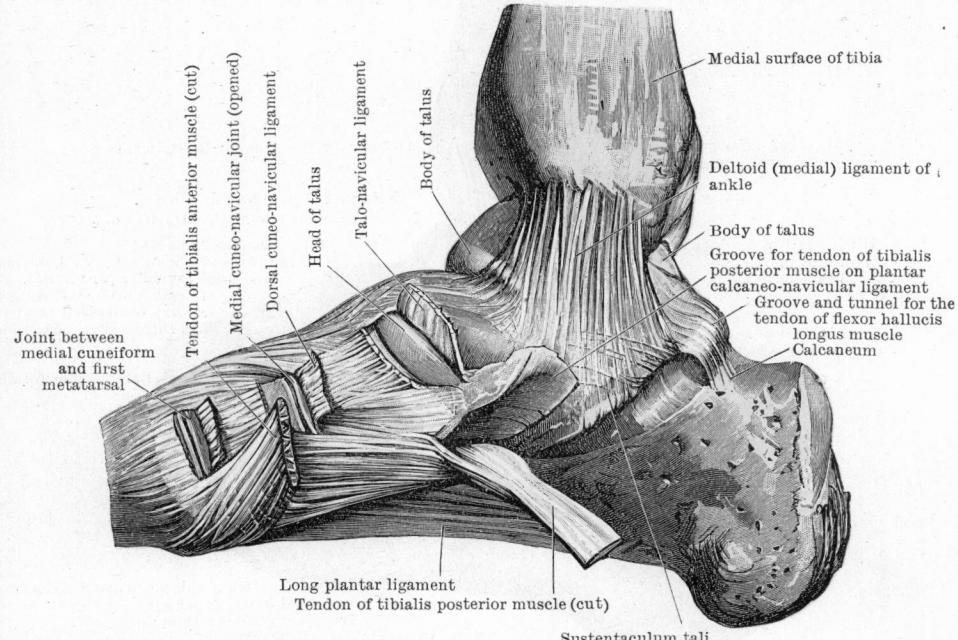

FIG. 322.—ANKLE AND TARSAL JOINTS FROM THE TIBIAL SIDE.

position the foot makes a right angle with the leg. In *flexion* the foot is drawn upwards, the trochlea tali turning backwards in its socket. Movement from the right angle position in the opposite direction is *extension*. As similar terms are used of movements of the toes in reverse directions, confusion is avoided if flexion at the ankle joint is called **dorsi-flexion** and extension called **plantar-flexion.** There is considerable individual variation in the range of these movements.

In **dorsi-flexion,** the broader, anterior part of the trochlea tali is forced back into the narrower, posterior part of the tibio-fibular socket; this causes slight separation of the tibia and fibula, with increased tension of the interosseous and transverse tibio-fibular ligaments. The talus is then most securely held between the malleoli. In **plantar-flexion,** as the narrower part of the trochlea turns forward into the broader part of the socket, the malleoli spring together again, so retaining up to a point their grasp upon the sides of the talus; but in full plantar-flexion a little side play can be demonstrated in the joint. The maintenance of this positive grasp upon the talus is the function of the inferior tibio-fibular joint, the strong ligaments of which provide the spring mechanism involved. The superior tibio-fibular joint permits slight gliding movement in association with the displacement of the lower ends of the leg bones.

When the body is erect, muscular effort is needed to prevent falling forwards, owing to the incidence of body weight in front of the ankle joints. But this effect of gravity is minimised in so far as the feet are usually turned a little laterally, and the axes of the two ankle joints are inclined to each other so as to make an angle pointing forwards.

The ankle joint is strongly supported by the tendons of the leg muscles which descend in close relation to it. In front, the tendons of tibialis anterior, extensor hallucis longus, extensor digitorum longus and peroneus tertius pass over the anterior ligament in that order medio-laterally; posteriorly and medially are the tibialis posterior and flexor digitorum longus tendons; posteriorly is the tendon of the flexor hallucis longus; and posteriorly and laterally are the tendons of the peroneus longus and peroneus brevis.

JOINTS OF THE FOOT

The joints between the tarsal bones, between metatarsal bases and between tarsus and metatarsus, are all functionally of the plane or gliding type. Only a slight amount of gliding movement can occur at any one joint, but the total movement

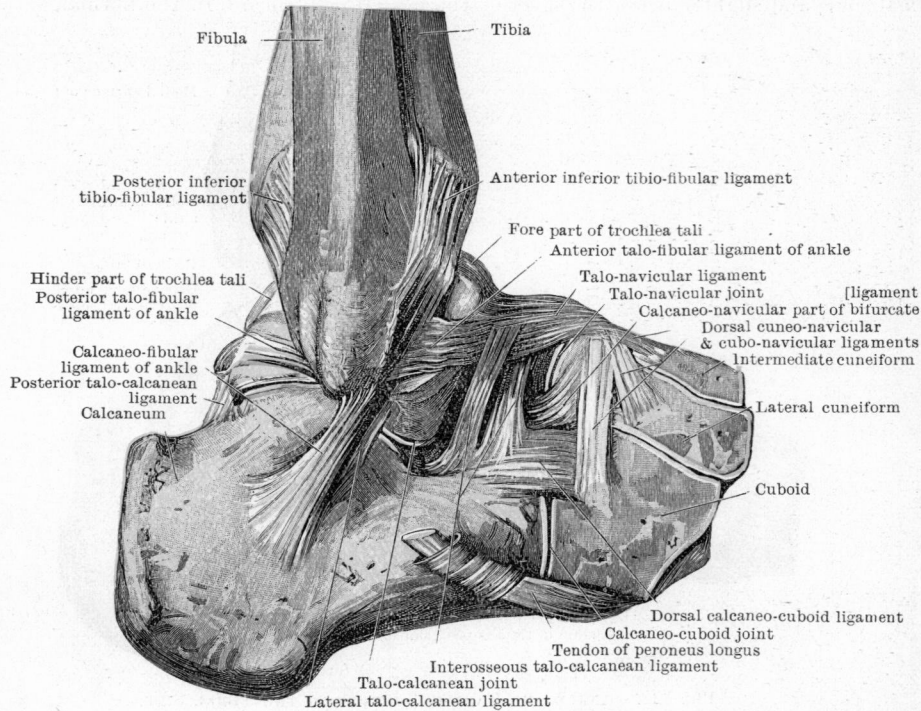

FIG. 323.—LIGAMENTS ON THE LATERAL SIDE OF THE ANKLE JOINT AND ON THE DORSUM OF THE TARSUS.

in the whole system is considerable. These joints are very intricate; and the systematic details of their individual structure are unedifying unless they are considered in the light of the architecture of the foot as a whole.

Arches of the Foot

The foot acts as a spring platform for the support of the body. This effect is achieved by the presence of a series of resilient arches, convex above, which become slightly flattened by the incidence of the body weight in standing or during progression, and resume their original curvature when the pressure on them is relieved. The arches are formed by the tarsal and metatarsal bones, and are disposed both longitudinally and transversely.

Longitudinally there are two arches, one on each side of the foot, which share a common posterior pillar in the posterior part of the calcaneum. The **lateral arch** proceeds from this through the anterior part of the calcaneum, which forms a joint with the cuboid bone; the arch is continued through the cuboid into the lateral two metatarsal bones, which articulate with the cuboid. This arch is

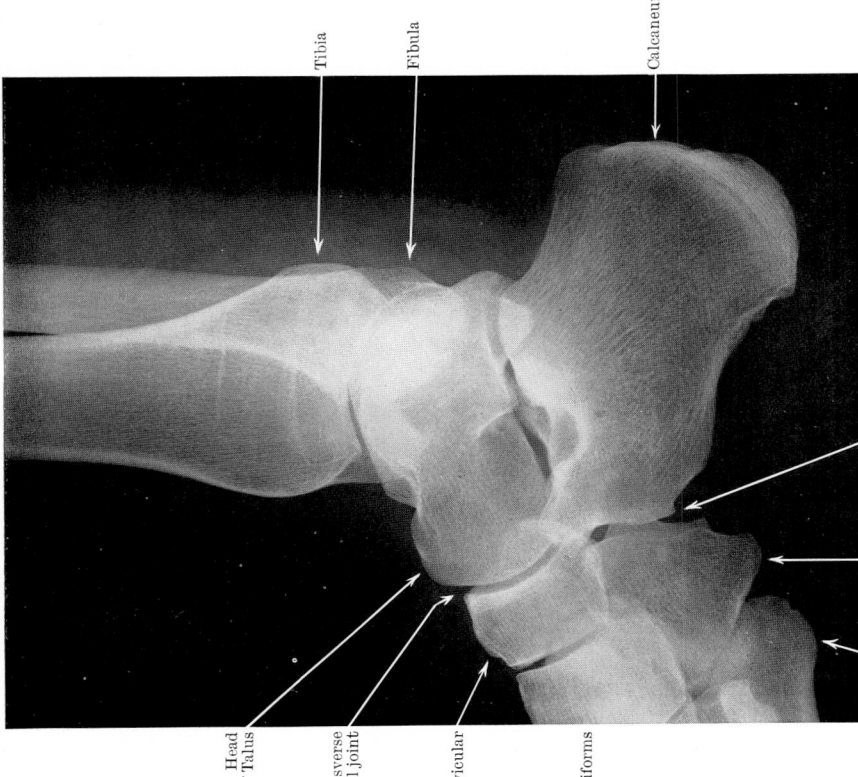

Tibia

Fibula

Calcaneum

Base of Fifth   Cuboid│   Transverse
Metatarsal   tarsal joint

Fig. 2.—Lateral Radiograph of the same Ankle and Tarsus. (Dr. J.
Duncan White). Cf. Plate XXVIII, noting the change in the relation of the
articular surfaces of Tibia and Talus during movements of the Ankle.

Head
of Talus

Transverse
tarsal joint

Navicular

Cuneiforms

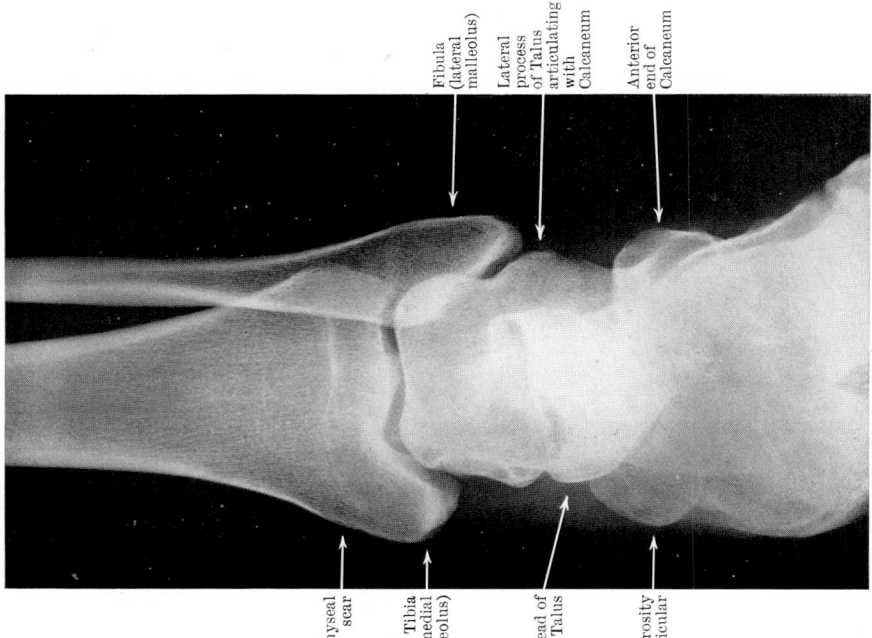

Fibula
(lateral
malleolus)

Lateral
process
of Talus
articulating
with
Calcaneum

Anterior
end of
Calcaneum

Fig. 1.—Antero-posterior Radiograph of Ankle and
Tarsus of Young Man aged 22. (Dr. J. Duncan White).
Note that the superimposition of the shadows of the tarsal
bones makes it difficult to distinguish them.

Epiphyseal
scar

Tibia
(medial
malleolus)

Head of
Talus

Tuberosity
of Navicular

PLATE XXVIII

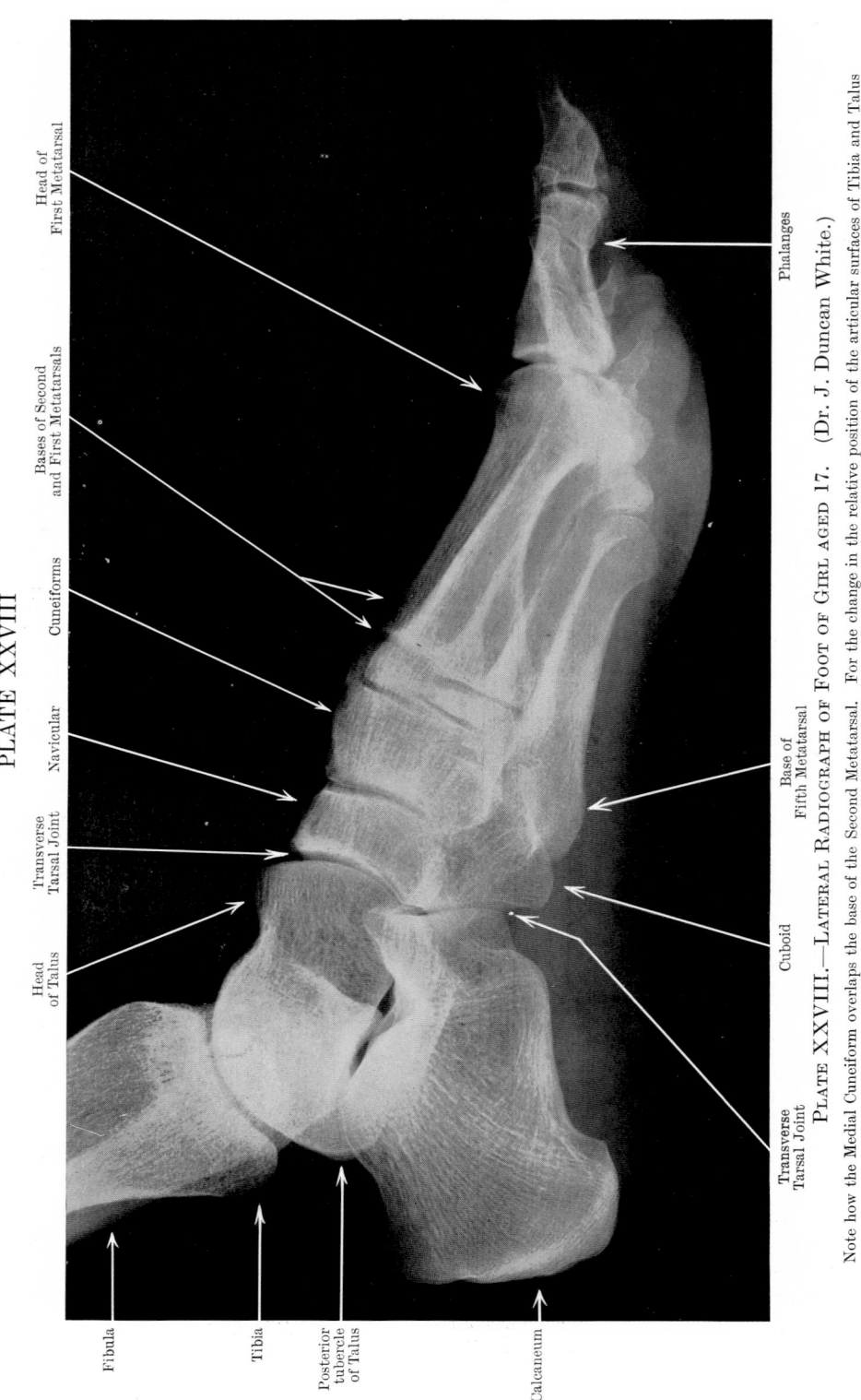

Fibula

Tibia

Posterior
tubercle
of Talus

Calcaneum

Head
of Talus

Transverse
Tarsal Joint

Navicular

Cuneiforms

Bases of Second
and First Metatarsals

Head of
First Metatarsal

Phalanges

Transverse
Tarsal Joint

Cuboid

Base of
Fifth Metatarsal

PLATE XXVIII.—LATERAL RADIOGRAPH OF FOOT OF GIRL AGED 17.   (Dr. J. Duncan White.)

Note how the Medial Cuneiform overlaps the base of the Second Metatarsal. For the change in the relative position of the articular surfaces of Tibia and Talus
during movements of the Ankle, compare Plate XXVII, Fig. 2.

a very low one, and receives the body weight through the talus at the talo-calcanean joint. The **medial arch** is higher and more important. The posterior pillar is continued into the sustentaculum tali, and the summit or keystone of the arch is then formed by the head of the talus placed above and between the sustentaculum tali and the navicular bone. The anterior pillar is formed by the navicular bone, the three cuneiform bones, and the medial three metatarsal bones.

The **transverse arch** is placed across the anterior part of the tarsus and the posterior part of the metatarsus, being best marked along the line of the tarso-metatarsal joints.

For the preservation of these arches the integrity of the tarsal, tarso-metatarsal, and inter-metatarsal joints is important, for at them the bones are held in their proper relationship as segments of the arches. For this purpose certain ligaments of the joints are much more important than others. The important ligaments are specially strengthened to resist undue yielding of the joints and consequent collapse of the arches; they are therefore found on the plantar aspect of the joints (that is, on the concave side of the arches) or, especially in the joints of the transverse arch, in interosseous positions. But it must be emphasised once more that unsupported ligaments will, in time, stretch under continuous strain, and the arches of the foot are in every case supported by muscles as well. Proper tonus of these muscles is, indeed, the primary factor in maintaining the arches.

The body weight is transmitted from the leg bones to the longitudinal arches through the talus. The talus forms two joints with the rest of the tarsus (Fig. 324), each being more particularly concerned in weight transference to one of those arches. The more posterior joint—the *talo-calcanean*—is specially associated with the lateral arch. At the more anterior joint—the *talo-calcaneo-navicular*—the weight is transmitted to the medial arch, and the head of the talus there takes up its position as keystone of that arch. At both joints the talus rests on the calcaneum, and between the joints a ligament common to both—the *interosseous talo-calcanean ligament* — is of special importance in binding the two bones together.

INTERTARSAL JOINTS

Talo-calcanean Joint (Figs. 323, 324).—This joint is formed between the facet on the under surface of the body of the talus and the posterior facet on the upper surface of the calcaneum; each facet is approximately cylindrical in curvature—that on the talus concave, the other convex.

The **capsular ligament** surrounding the joint is made up of short fibres attached close to the articular surfaces all round. Slightly stronger portions, specially named the *anterior, posterior, medial*, and *lateral talo-calcanean ligaments*, are situated in corresponding parts of the capsule.

The **interosseous talo-calcanean ligament**, the main band of union between the bones, is situated on the antero-medial aspect of the capsular ligament and is in great part fused with it. This very strong ligament is attached to the roof and floor of the tarsal tunnel (*sinus tarsi*), which is formed by the wide, deep grooves on the talus and calcaneum that run obliquely forwards and laterally in front of the articular facets of this joint (Fig. 324).

The calcanean parts of the medial and lateral ligaments of the ankle joint act as accessory ligaments of the talo-calcanean joint.

The articular capsule is lined with **synovial membrane**; the synovial cavity does not communicate with any other joint.

Talo-calcaneo-navicular Joint (Fig. 324).—The talo-calcaneo-navicular joint is of great importance in the medial longitudinal arch. Here the head of the talus is received as keystone between the anterior and posterior pillars, and therefore articulates in front with the navicular bone, and behind and below with the sustentaculum tali of the calcaneum. But these two bones are braced together by a strong ligament that passes between them under the head of the talus, and this ligament—the plantar calcaneo-navicular—also articulates with the talus.

The tibialis posterior tendon turns down into the sole under this ligament and acts as a sling to it and to the head of the talus (Figs. 322, 325).

The rounded head of the talus has a continuous covering of **articular cartilage** marked off into a facet for the navicular bone in front, one for the sustentaculum tali below, and, between these, a third for the plantar calcaneo-navicular ligament. The navicular bone presents an oval concave articular surface in the joint. The elongated articular surface on the sustentaculum tali, slightly concave, is often partially or completely divided by a constriction across the middle.

Capsule.—The joint cavity is closed by a capsular fusion of special, strong ligaments on all sides except above, where there is only a weak dorsal ligament.

The **plantar calcaneo-navicular ligament** closes the joint below and medially (Figs. 322, 324, 325). It is a fibro-cartilaginous band of great strength, sometimes

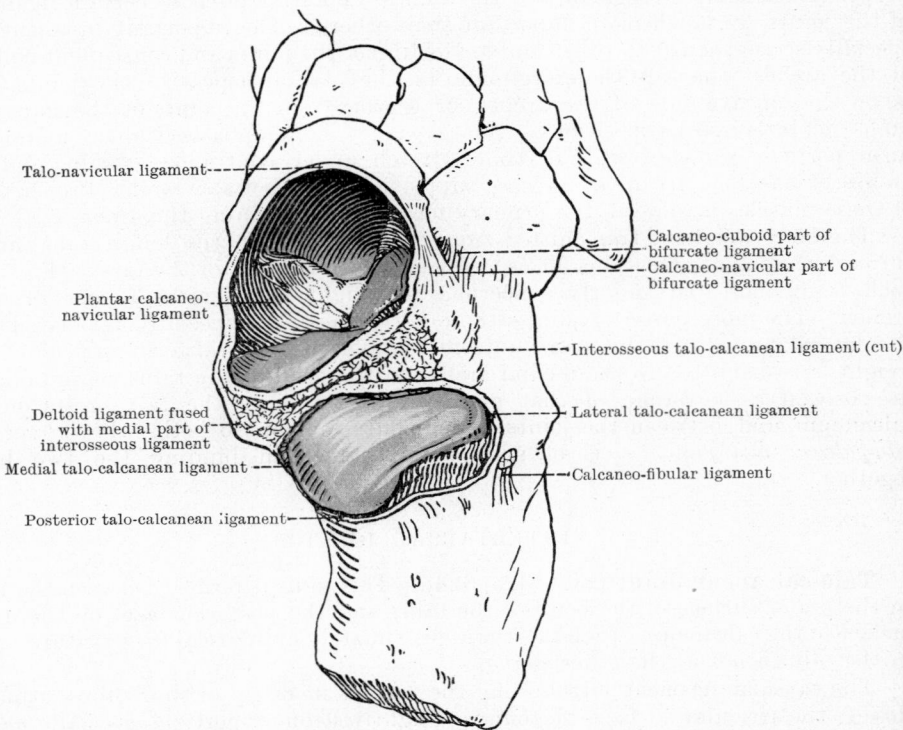

Talo-navicular ligament

Plantar calcaneo-navicular ligament

Deltoid ligament fused with medial part of interosseous ligament

Medial talo-calcanean ligament

Posterior talo-calcanean ligament

Calcaneo-cuboid part of bifurcate ligament
Calcaneo-navicular part of bifurcate ligament

Interosseous talo-calcanean ligament (cut)

Lateral talo-calcanean ligament

Calcaneo-fibular ligament

FIG. 324.—THE LIGAMENTS OF THE TALO-CALCANEAN AND THE TALO-CALCANEO-NAVICULAR JOINTS (seen from above after removal of the Talus).

ossified in the part against which the tibialis posterior tendon plays. It is attached behind to the anterior end and medial border of the sustentaculum tali; in front it spreads out on to the plantar and medial surfaces of the navicular bone; its medial part is joined and supported by fibres of the deltoid ligament of the ankle joint. The tension of the plantar calcaneo-navicular ligament, supported by the tibialis posterior muscle, resists the tendency of the weight of the body to drive the head of the talus downwards between the bones which it braces together, and the resilience it imparts to the medial arch is recognised in its common appellation—the *spring ligament*.

Laterally, the joint is closed by another calcaneo-navicular band composed of short fibres from the upper surface of the anterior end of the calcaneum to the adjacent lateral surface of the navicular bone. This band is the **calcaneo-navicular part of the bifurcate ligament** (Fig. 323), whose other limb goes to the cuboid bone. Sometimes the part of the articular head of the talus in contact with this band is faceted by it.

Posteriorly, behind the talo-sustentacular part of the joint, the cavity is closed by the **interosseous talo-calcanean ligament**, which separates this joint from the talo-calcanean articulation (Fig. 324).

The capsular ligament is completed round the dorsal aspect of the joint, between the two calcaneo-navicular bands, by a thin sheet, called the **talo-navicular ligament** (Figs. 322, 324), which extends from the neck of the talus to the dorsal surface of the navicular bone. It blends medially with the anterior fibres of the deltoid ligament that go to the navicular bone.

The **synovial cavity** of this joint makes no communications with neighbouring articulations (Fig. 322).

Calcaneo-cuboid Joint (Figs. 323, 324).—The calcaneo-cuboid joint is the highest point in the lateral longitudinal arch, which, as already mentioned, is formed by the calcaneum, the cuboid bone, and the lateral two metatarsal bones.

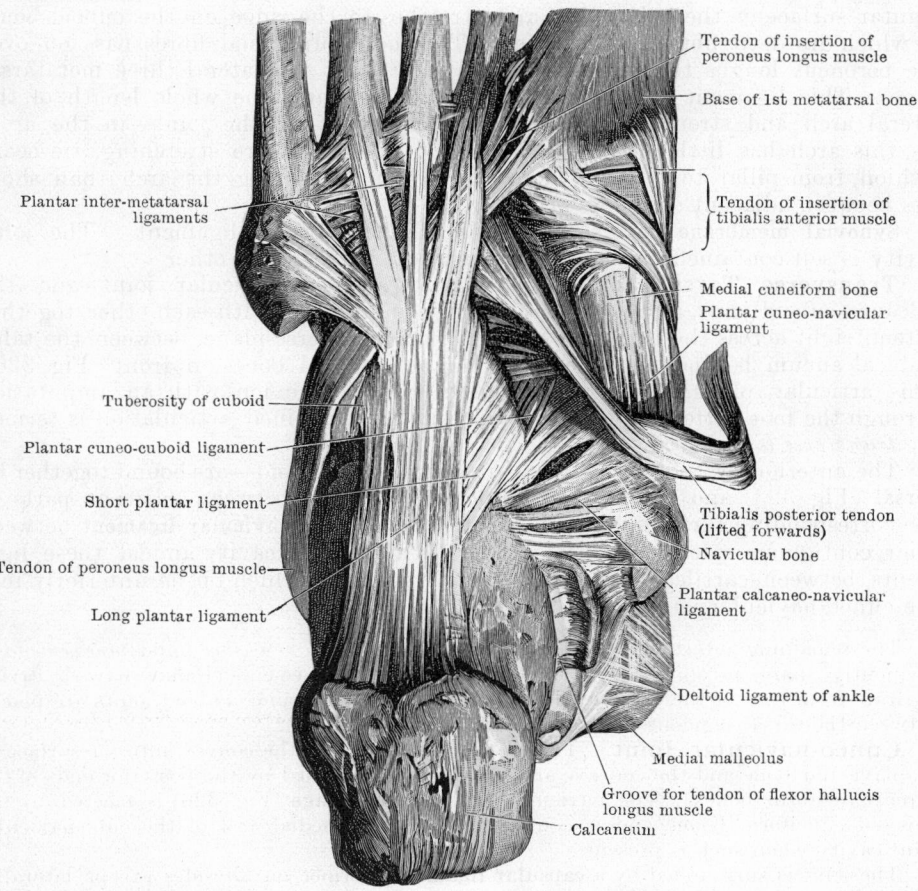

Tendon of insertion of peroneus longus muscle

Base of 1st metatarsal bone

Tendon of insertion of tibialis anterior muscle

Plantar inter-metatarsal ligaments

Medial cuneiform bone

Plantar cuneo-navicular ligament

Tuberosity of cuboid

Plantar cuneo-cuboid ligament

Short plantar ligament

Tendon of peroneus longus muscle

Long plantar ligament

Tibialis posterior tendon (lifted forwards)

Navicular bone

Plantar calcaneo-navicular ligament

Deltoid ligament of ankle

Medial malleolus

Groove for tendon of flexor hallucis longus muscle

Calcaneum

FIG. 325.—PLANTAR ASPECT OF TARSAL AND TARSO-METATARSAL JOINTS.

The body weight falls on this arch behind its summit, at the talo-calcanean joint, and the strain is most felt at the joint immediately in front of the calcaneum— the calcaneo-cuboid joint. This joint, like the talo-calcaneo-navicular joint at the summit of the medial arch, must therefore be specially reinforced on its under aspect, and here are placed the strong bands called the long and short plantar ligaments. In addition, the tendon of the peroneus longus, passing under the cuboid bone in front of the articulation, acts as a sling after the manner of the tibialis posterior tendon under the medial arch.

The **articular facets** on the opposed surfaces of the calcaneum and cuboid bone are quadrilateral and reciprocally concavo-convex.

24 *b*

Capsule.—An articular capsule completely surrounds the joint, and certain special ligaments are to be described in connexion with it.

Applied to the dorso-medial aspect of the joint is the **calcaneo-cuboid part of the bifurcate ligament**, which springs from the upper and fore part of the calcaneum in common with the calcaneo-navicular part of the ligament, and is attached to the adjacent dorso-medial angle of the cuboid bone (Fig. 324).

On the plantar aspect of the joint are two special ligaments, superficial and deep, separated by areolar tissue (Fig. 325). The deep one is the **short plantar ligaments** [lig. calcaneo-cuboideum plantare]. It is a broad band of short fibres immediately applied to the joint; it runs from the anterior part of the inferior surface of the calcaneum to the cuboid bone behind the ridge that bounds the peroneal groove. The superficial and much longer band is the **long plantar ligament**. It arises from the whole length of the rounded, keel-like ridge on the plantar surface of the calcaneum and stretches to the ridge on the cuboid bone, to which its deep fibres are attached. The more superficial fibres pass on over the peroneus longus tendon to the bases of at least the lateral three metatarsal bones. This ligament therefore stretches under nearly the whole length of the lateral arch and strengthens the plantar aspect of all the joints in the arch. As this arch has little height, a long band of this nature stretching, tie-beam fashion, from pillar to pillar is more effective in preserving the arch than short ties between adjacent segments of the arch.

Synovial membrane covers the inside of the capsular ligament. The joint cavity is self-contained, making no communication with any other.

Transverse Tarsal Joint.—The talo-calcaneo-navicular joint and the calcaneo-cuboid joint, although they do not communicate with each other, together extend right across the tarsus in an irregular transverse plane, between the talus and calcaneum behind and the navicular and cuboid bones in front (Fig. 326). This articular plane is of surgical interest in connexion with an amputation through the foot performed at this level, and the combined articulation is termed the *transverse tarsal joint*.

The anterior two bones involved—navicular and cuboid—are bound together by **dorsal** (Fig. 323) and **plantar cubo-navicular ligaments** between adjacent parts of the corresponding surfaces, and by an **interosseous cubo-navicular ligament** between their contiguous sides. Sometimes there is a synovial cavity amidst these ligaments, between cartilage-covered facets on the bones, which opens anteriorly into the cuneo-navicular joint (Fig. 326).

The remaining intertarsal joints—*cuneo-navicular*, *inter-cuneiform*, and *cuneo-cuboid*—frequently share a common synovial cavity, but the cuneo-cuboid may have a cavity separate from that of the others. The inter-cuneiform and cuneo-cuboid joints are placed between the tarsal segments of the transverse arch of the foot.

Cuneo-navicular Joint.—This is the joint between the convex anterior surface of the navicular bone and the concave articular surface provided by the posterior ends of the three cuneiform bones. The navicular **articular cartilage** (Fig. 326) is faceted by the opposed cuneiform bones, and is continued on to the medial wall of the cubo-navicular joint cavity when such is present.

The joint is surrounded by a **capsular ligament** distinct on all sides except laterally, towards the cuboid bone, where the joint may communicate with the cuneo-cuboid joint and always with a cubo-navicular joint when present. Distally, the joint cavity forms recesses between the cuneiform bones (Fig. 326). In the upper and medial parts of the capsule there are short bands, relatively weak, passing from the navicular to each cuneiform bone; these are the **dorsal cuneo-navicular ligaments** (Figs. 322, 323). Similar stronger bands on the under aspect of the joint, inseparable from slips of insertion of the tibialis posterior tendon, constitute the **plantar cuneo-navicular ligaments**.

Inter-cuneiform Joints.—At the inter-cuneiform joints the three cuneiform bones are bound together by weak, transverse **dorsal ligaments** and much stronger **interosseous** and **plantar ligaments**. The last two limit, in front, small joint cavities between articular facets placed behind and above on the contiguous surfaces of the bones. These cavities are continued from that of the cuneo-navicular joint (Fig. 326), and usually the medial inter-cuneiform joint extends forwards over the interosseous ligament to open into the middle tarso-metatarsal joint.

Cuneo-cuboid Joint.—This is a joint between oval or circular facets on the lateral cuneiform bone and the cuboid bone. It is surrounded by a weak **dorsal cuneo-cuboid ligament** between the dorsal surfaces of the bones, by a **plantar cuneo-cuboid ligament** (Fig. 325) between their adjacent plantar borders, and by a strong **interosseous cuneo-cuboid ligament** (Fig. 326) which closes the cavity anteriorly. Posteriorly, the joint may or may not open into the cuneo-navicular joint.

The cuboid and cuneiform bones, placed side by side across the distal part of the tarsus, form the tarsal side of the *transverse arch of the foot*. The strong interosseous and plantar inter-cuneiform and cuneo-cuboid ligaments maintain the segments of the arch in position, and additional strength is obtained from the peroneus longus tendon as it passes across the foot between the two pillars of the arch (Fig. 325).

Nerve-Supply.—The tarsal joints are supplied on the dorsal aspect by the **anterior tibial** nerve, and on the plantar aspect by the **medial** and **lateral plantar** nerves.

Movements in the Tarsus

Apart from the more passive changes that accompany slight flattening of the arches under pressure and their recoil again when freed from weight-bearing, active movement between the tarsal bones, very slight between any two, produces in summation the characteristic changes of inversion and eversion of the foot.

In **inversion**, the foot is adducted and twisted so that the medial border is raised and the lateral border depressed until the sole is turned slightly medially. In **eversion**, the foot is abducted, the lateral border raised and the medial border lowered so that the sole is turned slightly laterally. These changes are mainly brought about at the transverse tarsal joint. Inversion is accompanied by dorsi-flexion at the ankle joint, and eversion by plantar-flexion.

TARSO-METATARSAL AND INTER-METATARSAL JOINTS

Tarso-metatarsal Joints (Fig. 326).—The anterior members of the tarsus —the cuboid and three cuneiform bones—articulate with the bases of the meta-tarsal bones along an irregular line which " presents the outline of an indented parapet both on its tarsal and its metatarsal aspects " (Hepburn).

The *first* metatarsal bone articulates only with the anterior surface of the medial cuneiform bone. The *second* metatarsal articulates in a socket with all three cuneiform bones—the lateral side of the medial bone, the anterior end of the intermediate, and the medial side of the lateral bone. The *third* metatarsal articulates with the lateral cuneiform bone. The *fourth* metatarsal articulates with the cuboid and to a small extent with the lateral cuneiform bone. The *fifth* metatarsal articulates with the cuboid bone only.

The articulations are all synovial joints of gliding type, closed over by dorsal and plantar ligaments. In addition there are certain interosseous ligaments which delimit three separate synovial cavities.

The **dorsal tarso-metatarsal ligaments** are short slips that pass between the adjoining dorsal surfaces of the tarsal and metatarsal bones, each metatarsal bone receiving a slip from each tarsal bone with which it articulates.

The **plantar tarso-metatarsal ligaments** are similar bands on the under aspect of the joints, but are less regularly disposed. Those for the medial two metatarsal bones are the strongest, but the lateral tarso-metatarsal joints are strengthened underneath by fibres from the long plantar ligament. The tarso-metatarsal joint of the big toe is strengthened below by the insertion of the tibialis anterior into the articulating bones medially and the peroneus longus laterally. Slips from the tibialis posterior tendon are applied to the under aspect of the joints of the middle three metatarsal bones. (*See* Fig. 325.)

Two strong **interosseous tarso-metatarsal ligaments** are always present (Fig. 326). One passes from the anterior and lateral part of the medial cuneiform bone to the contiguous medial side of the second metatarsal base. The other passes from the anterior and lateral angle of the lateral cuneiform to the adjacent medial surface of the fourth metatarsal base. These two ligaments separate **three tarso-metatarsal synovial cavities.**

The **medial** cavity is entirely confined to the joint between the first metatarsal and medial cuneiform bones. The **intermediate** cavity separates the second and third metatarsals from the intermediate and lateral cuneiform bones ; this cavity is prolonged forwards for a little way between the second and third, and third and fourth metatarsal bases; posteriorly, it usually communicates, between the medial and intermediate cuneiform bones, with the cuneo-navicular joint. The lateral joint cavity separates the cuboid from the fourth and fifth metatarsal bones, and is prolonged forwards between these two metatarsal bases. Sometimes the intermediate cavity is partially subdivided by a third interosseous ligament that passes between the adjacent angles of the lateral cuneiform and second metatarsal bones; this band was absent in the specimen drawn in Fig. 326.

The indented nature of the tarso-metatarsal joint line adds strength to the *transverse arch* of the foot. This arch is built of two spans placed side by side,

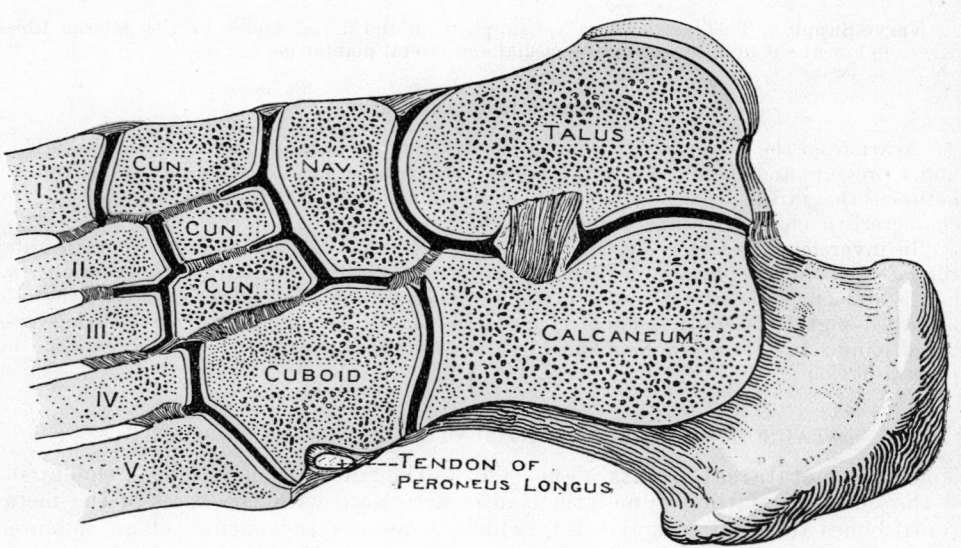

FIG. 326.—OBLIQUE SECTION OF FOOT TO SHOW THE SYNOVIAL CAVITIES OF THE TARSAL
AND TARSO-METATARSAL JOINTS.

The communication usually present between the cuneo-navicular and intermediate tarso-metatarsal joints
is not revealed at the level of section. An unusually large cubo-navicular joint cavity was present.

the one formed by the cuboid and cuneiform bones, the other formed by the metatarsal bases. These two spans are interlocked by the indentations and tied together by the ligaments of the tarso-metatarsal joints.

Inter-metatarsal Joints.—The inter-metatarsal joints are small synovial joints between cartilage-covered facets on the contiguous sides of the bases of the lateral four metatarsal bones. The joint cavities (Fig. 326) are prolonged from the tarso-metatarsal cavities—that between the fourth and fifth bones from the lateral tarso-metatarsal joint, those on each side of the third bone from the intermediate joint.

Above, below, and in front, the little joints are closed by **dorsal**, **plantar**, and **interosseous inter-metatarsal ligaments**, composed of short, transverse fibres between corresponding surfaces of the bases of the metatarsal bones. The interosseous ligaments are very strong, and play an important part in holding together the metatarsal bases as segments of the metatarsal span of the transverse arch of the foot.

The first metatarsal bone is connected to the second by interosseous fibres only. Sometimes a bursal sac is formed amidst these fibres, between indistinct facets on the bones; its cavity may communicate with the medial tarso-metatarsal joint.

Nerve-Supply.—The tarso-metatarsal and inter-metatarsal joints are supplied by twigs from the anterior tibial and the lateral and medial plantar nerves.

Metatarsal Movements.—The interlocking of the bones at the tarso-metatarsal joints and the inter-metatarsal interosseous ligaments preclude anything beyond small gliding movements of the metatarsal bones, by which they contribute very slightly to the inversion and eversion movements of the foot. The fourth and, more particularly, the fifth, owing to the oblique line of their basal joints, have a slight capability of flexion, accompanied by adduction.

METATARSO-PHALANGEAL AND INTERPHALANGEAL JOINTS

Metatarso-phalangeal Joints.—These joints closely resemble the metacarpo-phalangeal joints in the shape of the articular surfaces and the disposition of the ligaments. At the base of each toe the cupped posterior end of the proximal phalanx is applied to the rounded metatarsal head.

The **capsular ligament,** lined with synovial membrane, is formed at the sides by strong, fan-shaped **collateral ligaments** attached to neighbouring parts of the bones, and, on the plantar aspect, by a thick, pad-like **plantar ligament ;** dorsally, the capsule is completed by an expansion of the extensor tendon.

The plantar ligament is grooved by the flexor tendons. In the big toe, this ligament has two fairly large sesamoid bones developed in it ; they are covered with cartilage on their upper surfaces, which articulate with grooves scored on the under surface of the head of the first metatarsal bone. The plantar ligaments of all the joints are connected by the **deep transverse ligaments of the sole,** which are arranged like the deep transverse ligaments of the palm, except that while in the hand this connexion does not involve the joint of the thumb, in the foot the joint of the big toe is linked up with the others.

Nerve-Supply.—The metatarso-phalangeal joints are supplied on their **dorsal** and **plantar** aspects by the corresponding **digital** nerves.

Movements.—The movements of these condyloid joints are similar to the movements at the corresponding joints in the hand but are less extensive. In the foot, however, **extension** of the proximal phalanges can be carried beyond the line of the metatarsal bones ; and **abduction** and **adduction** are centred on the second toe because of the slightly different arrangement of the interossei muscles. In **flexion** the toes are at the same time drawn together ; in **extension** they are spread apart and inclined slightly in the lateral direction.

Interphalangeal Joints.—The interphalangeal joints also are similar to the corresponding joints in the hand. At each articulation the proximal bone presents a double convexity within the joint and the distal bone a double concavity.

Collateral ligaments at the sides, a thick **plantar ligament** and the expansion of the extensor tendon dorsally complete the **articular capsule,** lined with synovial membrane. The second interphalangeal joint of the little toe is often obliterated by synostosis.

Nerve-Supply.—These joints are supplied by the **dorsal** and **plantar digital** nerves.

Movements.—These are hinge joints. Movement is limited to **flexion** towards the sole of the foot and **extension** in the opposite direction, around a transverse axis.

Mechanism of the Foot

The foot is specialised to support the body in the erect position, alike in standing and in progression. Its skeletal parts are arranged in arches, longitudinal and transverse, in the manner already described. These arches do not merely support the body weight statically as arches of masonry support a bridge : the presence of the joints in the arches introduces a spring mechanism, so that the arches resemble the half-elliptical springs of a carriage. They yield slightly when weight is put upon them, and recoil when it is removed. The medial longitudinal arch, having more joints in its construction, is better sprung than the lateral arch.

Attention has been drawn to the ligaments which specially support the arches, and to the prime importance of the muscles in safeguarding the ligaments from overstretching. The tendon of the tibialis posterior muscle passes as a sling below the summit of the medial arch, and, because of the insertion of that tendon on the plantar aspect of nearly all the tarsal and metatarsal bones, the contraction of the muscle must tend to increase the general concavity of the sole. The peroneus longus acts similarly as a sling beneath the lateral arch and also as a contractile tie-beam between the extremities of the transverse arch. The tibialis anterior and peroneus tertius muscles pull upon the medial and lateral arches from above. The long flexors of the toes act as contractile ties to the longitudinal arches. The muscles of the sole help to brace all the arches, according to their disposition.

In walking, the weight is first applied to the common posterior pillar of the two longitudinal arches as the heel strikes the ground. As the body moves forward the weight falls on the lateral border of the foot along the lateral arch,

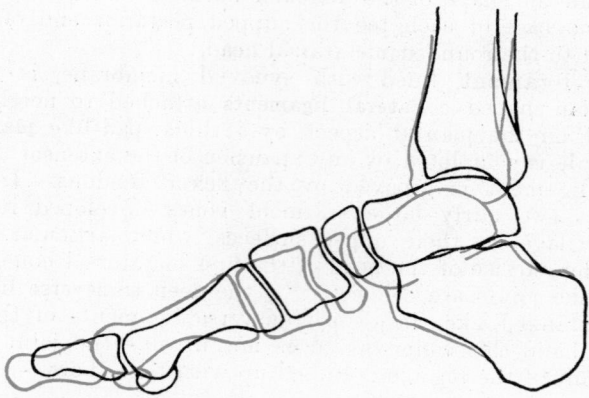

Fig. 327.—Tracing of Radiographs (Pl. XXIX. Figs. 2 and 3). Superimposed to show the position of the Longitudinal Arch of the Foot during Relaxation (red) and Contraction (black) of the muscles. (See also Fig. 442, Footprints 2 and 3.) (R. D. L.)

is rapidly transferred across the transverse arch to the medial arch as the heel leaves the ground, and a final propulsive thrust is obtained by flexion of the joints of the big toe. In running, the weight reaches the ground at the distal ends only of the longitudinal arches, which then act as quarter-elliptical springs, and, by their recoil, reinforce the final thrust derived from flexion of the medial toes.

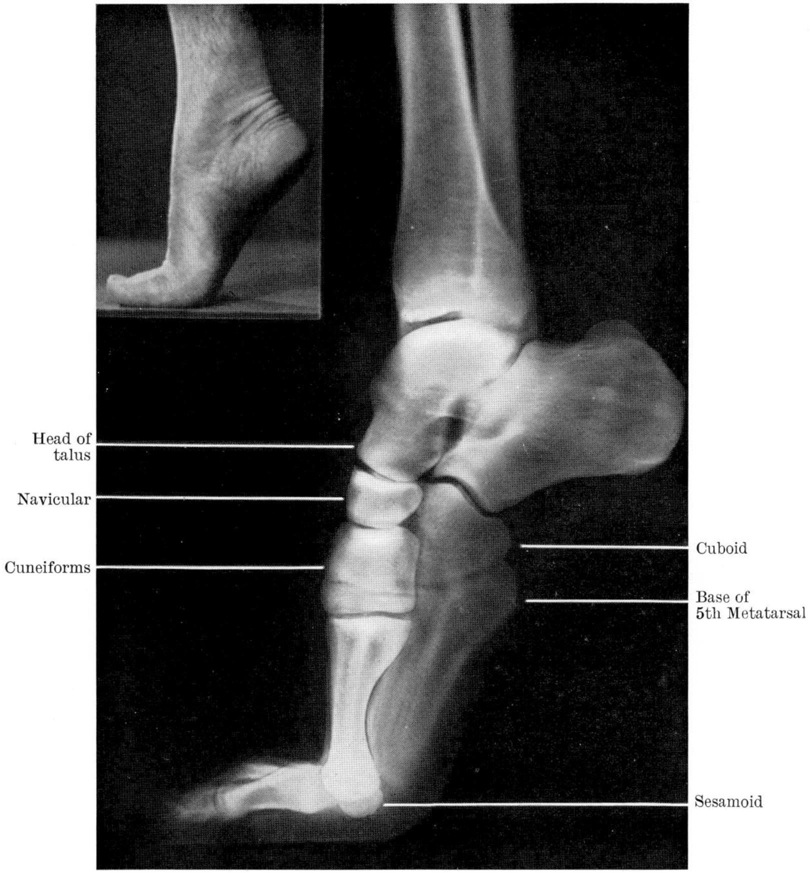

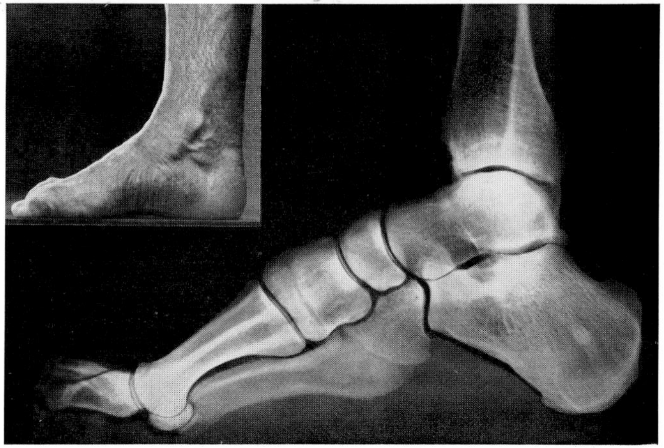

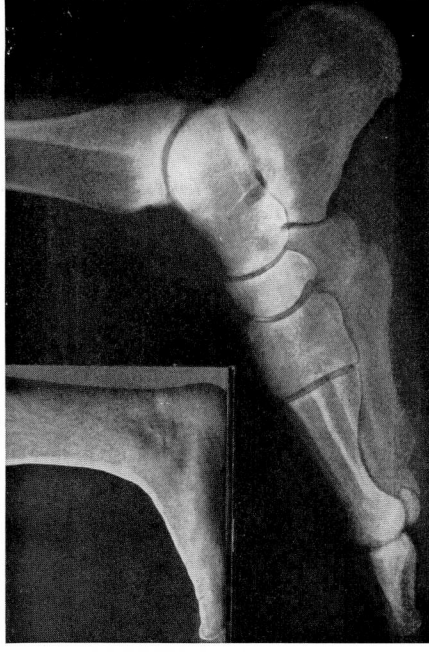

Fig. 2.—Radiograph of Right Foot of Subject standing with Muscles Contracted. (See Fig. 442, footprint 2 and contrast with footprints 1 and 3.)

Fig. 3.—Radiograph of Right Foot of Subject standing with Muscles relaxed as fully as possible. (For footprint see Fig. 442, 3, p. 520.)

Cuboid

Base of 5th Metatarsal

Sesamoid

Head of talus

Navicular

Cuneiforms

Fig. 1.—Radiograph of Right Foot of Subject standing on Toes (see inset).

Plate XXIX.—Photographic and Radiographic Illustrations of the Weight-bearing Areas of the Foot. (R. D. L.)

(See pp. 520-521 and Fig. 442, p. 520.)

[Facing p. 380

PLATE XXX

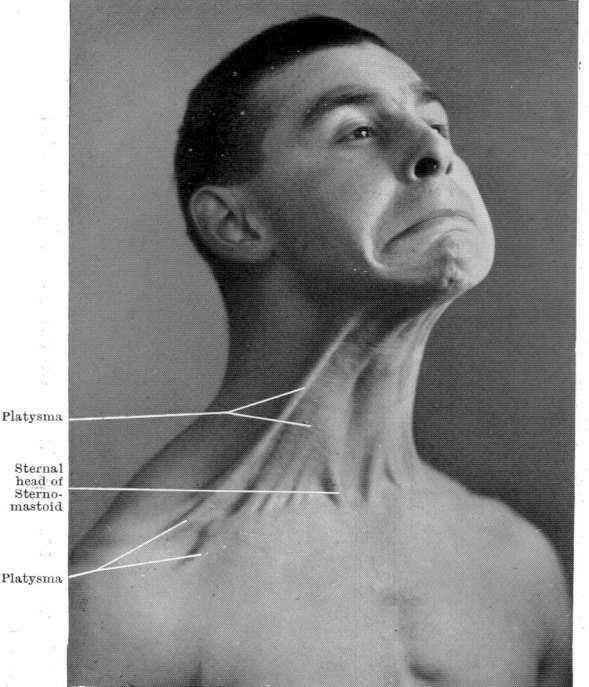

Platysma

Sternal
head of
Sterno-
mastoid

Platysma

FIG. 1.—THE PLATYSMA IN ACTION.

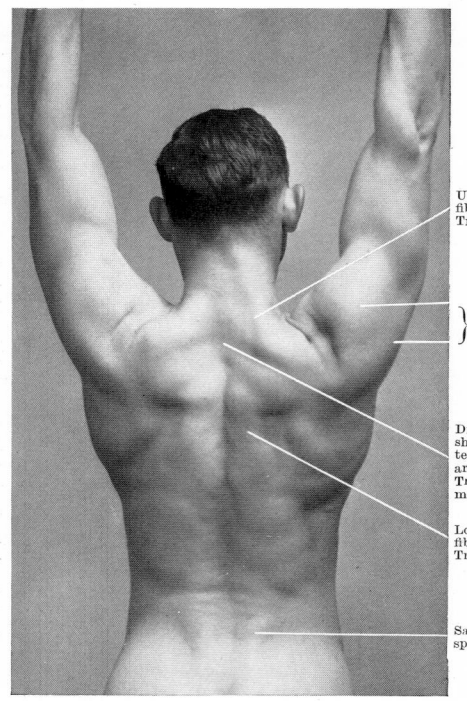

Up
fibr
Tra

Dis
sha
ter
are
Tra
mu

Lov
fibr
Tra

Sac
spir

FIG. 2.—ACTION OF TRAPEZIUS AND DELTOID MUSCLES
IN ELEVATION OF THE UPPER LIMB.

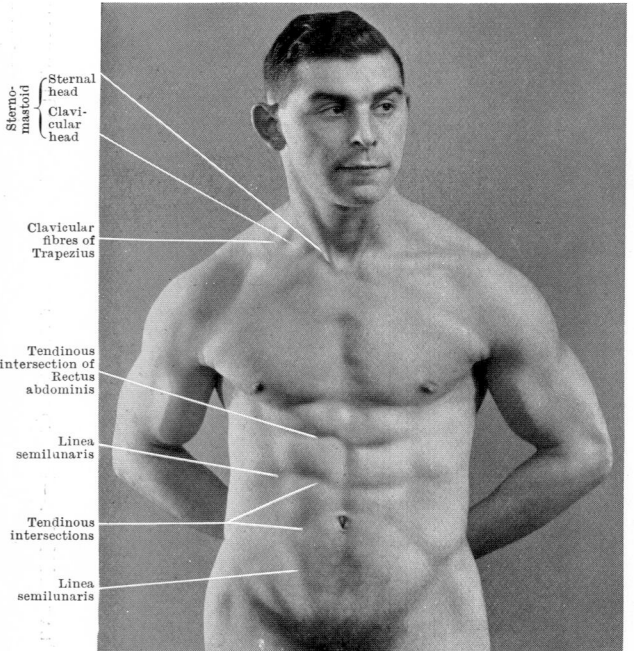

Sterno-
mastoid {
Sternal
head
Clavi-
cular
head

Clavicular
fibres of
Trapezius

Tendinous
intersection of
Rectus
abdominis

Linea
semilunaris

Tendinous
intersections

Linea
semilunaris

FIG. 3.—THE RECTUS ABDOMINIS IN ACTION.

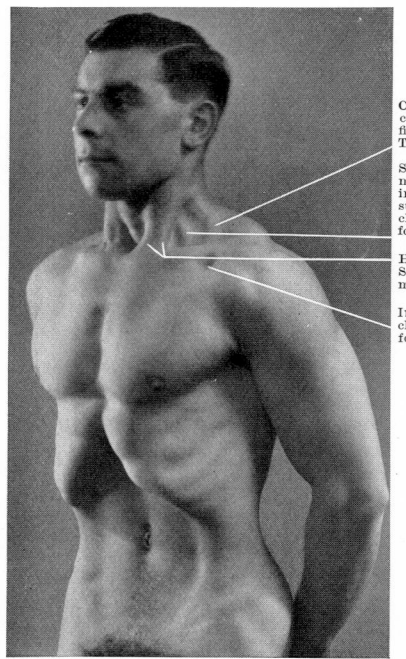

Cla
cul
fibr
Tra

Sca
mus
in g
sup
clav
foss

Hea
Ster
mas

Infr
clav
foss

FIG. 4.—EXPULSIVE ACTION OF ABDOMINAL
MUSCLES IN FORCED EXPIRATION. Note the
fixation action of sterno-mastoid and scalene
muscles, and the retraction of tissues in the
suprasternal, greater supraclavicular and
infraclavicular fossæ.

PLATE XXX.—PHOTOGRAPHIC ILLUSTRATIONS OF MUSCLES IN ACTION. (R. D. L.)

MYOLOGY

Originally written by the late A. M. PATERSON, M.D., F.R.C.S.
Professor of Anatomy, University of Liverpool

Revised by R. D. LOCKHART

THE **skeletal muscles** alone are considered in this section. They constitute the "red flesh" of the body, and account for forty-two per cent. of its weight in the male, thirty-six in the female. They execute movements initiated by the will, for which reason the tissue concerned is known as voluntary muscle. On account of its characteristic histological feature, it is known also as **striated** muscle. It differs from the other two varieties of muscle tissue, namely, **unstriated** or **plain** muscle found in the walls of viscera, blood-vessels, ducts of glands, and elsewhere; and the distinctive type of striated muscle confined to the heart, and hence termed **cardiac** muscle. Both these varieties are under the control of the involuntary nervous system.

All three varieties of muscle tissue are derived from mesoderm, the cells of which acquire the characteristic power of contractility and become specialised to form muscle fibres.

A **typical skeletal muscle** consists of a number of *fasciculi* or muscle bundles, enveloped in a fibrous tissue sheath termed *fascia*, and usually connected, at one or both extremities, with bundles of white fibrous tissue which constitute some variety of *tendon*.

Each fasciculus is surrounded and bound to its neighbours by areolar tissue called the **perimysium externum**; and each consists of a number of elongated muscle fibres, held together in their turn by areolar tissue called the **perimysium internum**. The perimysium internum is connected on the one hand to the **sarcolemma** (or cell-wall of the muscle fibre) and on the other to the perimysium externum, by which it is brought into connexion with some part of a tendon.

Attachments.—In order that a muscle may effectively exercise its power of contractility, it must possess (1) a relatively fixed point of attachment, termed the **origin**, usually nearer the median plane of the body, or proximal in a limb, and (2) a movable point of attachment, termed the **insertion**, usually farther from the median plane, or distal in a limb. Skeletal muscles are usually attached at both ends to bone, not directly by contractile muscle substance but by intervening non-contractile fibrous tissue. Some muscles have extensive attachments to bands of deep fascia and thereby to the bones, while such varied structures as tendons, cartilages, fibrous raphes, ligaments, and skin may also be the site of origin or insertion.

Muscular attachments show marked individual variation in their extent and character and may be (1) fleshy, (2) tendinous, or (3) a combination of both. In the first case, *e.g.* vastus intermedius, the fleshy fibres appear to spring directly from the bone, but the actual union is by perimysium to periosteum. In the second case, a varying extent of white fibrous tissue is interposed between the attachment and the fleshy belly. This intermediary is termed a **tendon**, and the shape and appearance of tendons vary greatly, the extremes being represented by the narrow ribbon-like tendon of the palmaris longus and the broad sheet-like tendon of the obliquus externus abdominis. A sheet-like tendon is usually referred to as an **aponeurosis**.

In some cases a muscle consists of two bellies connected by an *intermediate tendon*. Such muscles are termed "digastric" or "biventral." The fleshy bellies may be set at an angle to each other (*e.g.* digastric and omo-hyoid), and in that event the intermediate tendon is anchored to some part of the skeletal system by a fascial sling. On the other hand, the two bellies may be placed in the same line.

The tendon, whether of origin or insertion, usually sends prolongations into the substance of the muscle—an arrangement which is not only efficient, but is also economical in the use of highly specialised tissue such as muscle, since it obviates the need for long muscle fibres when the required movement may be produced by short fibres.

Muscular Form.—The phylogeny and the function of a muscle determine its general form, and its detailed structure depends upon the number, arrangement, and length of its fibres. The more powerful a muscle the greater is the number and the shorter the length of its fibres; and the more extensive also is the use of tendinous fibres for their attachment. The greater the range of movement produced the longer are the fibres in the muscle concerned. (The sartorius has the longest fibres and they do not exceed 15 cm.)

In some muscles the fibres run parallel (or nearly parallel) to the long axis. They are termed **fusiform**. When the points of attachment of a fusiform muscle are widely separated, a long tendon of insertion is provided—again an efficient arrangement economical of muscle tissue.

When power is a prime consideration, a different arrangement of the fibres is adopted, and the various **penniform** types result. In **unipenniform** muscles, the fibres are placed parallel to one another but not to the long axis. This arrangement provides the necessary increase in the number of fibres by increasing the length of the muscular belly (*e.g.* vastus medialis). In **bipenniform** (*e.g.* rectus femoris) and **multipenniform** muscles (*e.g.* deltoid) still greater power is obtained by modifications of the same arrangement.

Nomenclature of Muscles.—Muscles have received their names from a variety of circumstances, such as—their shape, *e.g.* trapezius, quadratus; their structure, *e.g.* triceps, digastric; their situation, *e.g.* pectoralis, tibialis; their points of attachment, *e.g.* sterno-mastoid, pubo-coccygeus; their direction, *e.g.* rectus, obliquus; or their function, *e.g.* flexor, abductor, etc. The names of most muscles combine two characteristics, *e.g.* pronator teres, flexor digitorum sublimis. It is an interesting (and instructive) exercise for the student, as he proceeds with his study of Myology, to note the reasons for the names of individual muscles.

Variations.—The muscular system is remarkable for the numerous variations in its members. Individual muscles may possess additional heads of origin, *e.g.* the biceps brachii; some muscles are remarkable for the frequency with which they are absent, *e.g.* palmaris longus; while, in addition to the variations of muscles which we speak of as "normal," a large number of "abnormal" muscles or muscular slips have been described. Many of the latter, on account of the regularity of their position and attachments, have received special names. In a students' text-book it is not possible to deal with this aspect of Myology; but references to a few of these anomalous muscles will be found at the appropriate places in the description of the "normal" muscles.

Types of Muscle Fibres.—Human muscles and the muscles of all other vertebrates are composed of several kinds of fibres :—(1) Pale, thin, rapidly contracting, easily fatigued, and metabolically expensive fibres—the first to be called upon in the production of active movements; (2) red, thick, slowly contracting, difficult to fatigue, and metabolically inexpensive fibres, that are harnessed in the work to increase and maintain the effort; (3) several intermediate types of fibres. Invertebrates and some vertebrates (*e.g.* the rabbit) possess muscles composed exclusively of either the first or second types of fibre; but in man the fibres are mixed, though the red kind are considered to predominate in certain muscles, for example, the soleus, and the pale in others, for example, the gastrocnemius. Fibres of the same speed of contraction usually form separate groups. The deeper heads of a muscle are said to have more of the slowly contracting fibres.

PLATE XXXI

posterior
part of
Deltoid

ng head
Triceps

es major
and
tissimus
dorsi

Rhom-
boideus
major

Serratus
anterior

tissimus
dorsi

FIG. 1.—ACTION OF LATISSIMUS DORSI AS DEPRESSOR AND
ADDUCTOR OF UPPER LIMB, SUBJECT PULLING ON A ROPE.

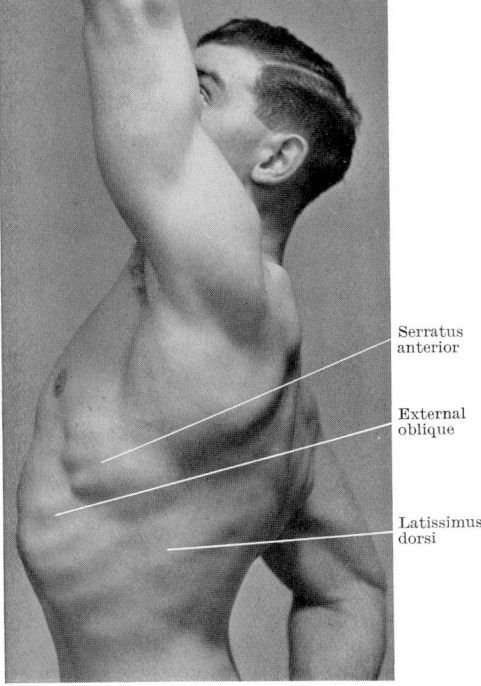

Serratus
anterior

External
oblique

Latissimus
dorsi

FIG. 2.—ACTION OF SERRATUS ANTERIOR IN
ELEVATION OF UPPER LIMB.

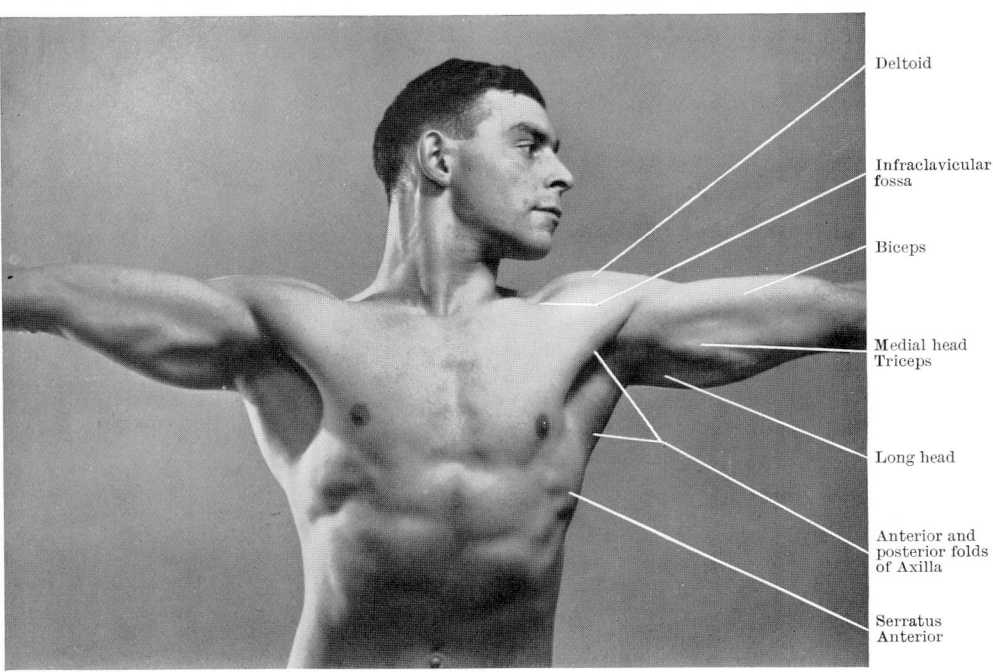

Deltoid

Infraclavicular
fossa

Biceps

Medial head
Triceps

Long head

Anterior and
posterior folds
of Axilla

Serratus
Anterior

FIG. 3.—FOLDS OF THE AXILLA AND THE MEDIAL ASPECT OF THE UPPER ARM, SHOWING THE POSITION
OF THE LONG AND MEDIAL HEADS OF THE TRICEPS.

PLATE XXXI.—PHOTOGRAPHIC ILLUSTRATIONS OF MUSCLES IN ACTION. (R. D. L.)

PLATE XXXII

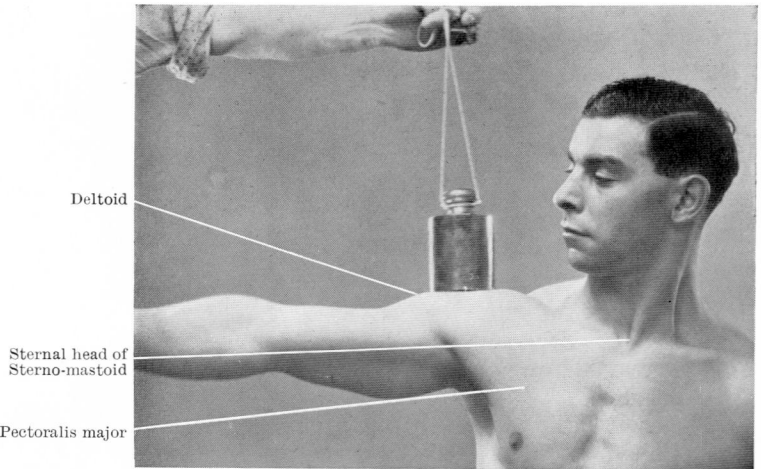

Deltoid

Sternal head of
Sterno-mastoid

Pectoralis major

FIG. 1.—ACTIVITY OF DELTOID IN CONTROLLING GRAVITATIONAL DESCENT OF UPPER LIMB,
SHOWN BY WEIGHT RIDING UPON THE MUSCLE. Cf. Fig. 2.

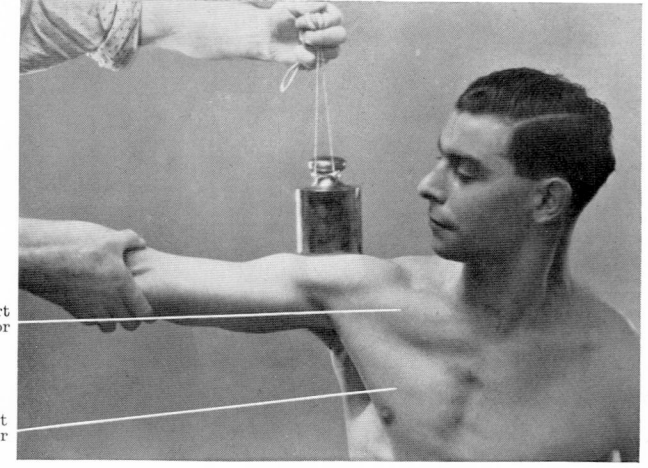

Clavicular part
of Pectoralis major

Sterno-costal part
of Pectoralis major

FIG. 2.—FLACCIDITY OF DELTOID WHEN ANTAGONISTS PULL ON THE LIMB AGAINST RESISTANCE, SHOWN BY WEIGHT
SINKING INTO THE MUSCLE. Note the activity of the pectoralis major in contrast with its passive state in Fig. 1.

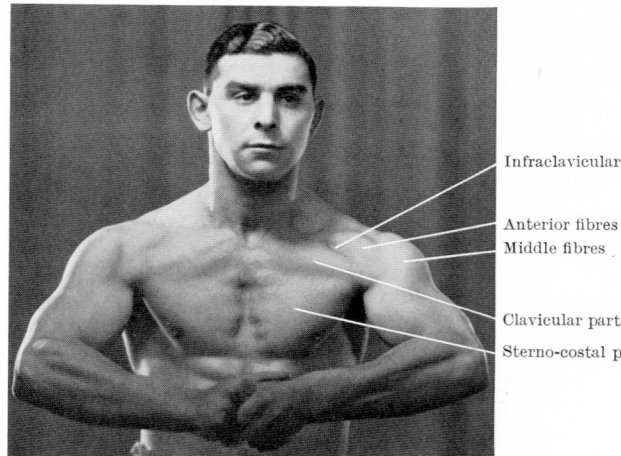

Infraclavicular fossa

Anterior fibres ⎫
Middle fibres ⎭ Deltoid

Clavicular part ⎫ Pectoralis
Sterno-costal part ⎭ major

FIG. 3.—ACTIVITY OF THE PECTORAL MUSCLES AS ADDUCTORS AGAINST RECIPROCAL RESISTANCE OF HANDS.

PLATE XXXII.—PHOTOGRAPHIC ILLUSTRATIONS OF MUSCLES IN ACTION. (R. D. L.)

Slight stimuli (for example, a stretching of the muscle) conveyed by its sensory nerves to the central nervous system produce a reflex state of muscle contraction or tone *via* the motor nerves to the muscle. Red and pale fibres both function in this respect in maintaining *tone* and *posture*. There is no example of a purely postural muscle in Man. The greater the stimulus, the more fibres are called to function; and there is no basic difference in the production of the contraction maintaining postural tone, and that causing any active voluntary movement.

Contraction of Muscle Fibres.—The amount of shortening which any muscle undergoes is directly proportional (nearly 1:2) to the length of its constituent fibres. Haines (*Journal of Anatomy*, 1934) states that a muscle fibre contracts by about fifty-seven per cent. of its length when fully stretched. If all the fibres of a given muscle are the same length and run from the tendon of origin to the tendon of insertion, then the extent of the muscle's contraction may be associated with the range of movement possible at a joint or joints; Haines considers that in movements not habitual, such as full flexion at the knee with full extension at the hip, the fibres of certain muscles, *e.g.* the long head of the biceps femoris, are too short to perform the dual movements fully, and consequently that such muscles can act fully on only one joint at a time.

Muscular Action.[1]—The essential virtue of muscle—its contractility—is displayed in producing movements of the body. Muscular action is therefore the basis of physical culture, an underlying principle of treatment in orthopædic surgery, and very frequently the secret of diagnosis in affections of the nervous system when the muscles are made to yield tell-tale evidence of the condition of their nerve supply. Physical fitness may be assessed by the general tone of the muscular system; for example, the poise of the shoulders, which depends mainly on the trapezius muscles, is a good general indication of the well-being of an individual. Great emphasis must therefore be placed on the value of practical and experimental study of the function of muscles in the living human body. The following paragraphs dealing with the action of muscles should, indeed, be frequently consulted throughout the study of Myology.

Most skeletal muscles function by producing movements at the joint or joints over which they pass on their way from origin to insertion; and it is important to note that the muscles most powerfully concerned may act either by contraction or by relaxation, according to whether the movement is made against gravity or resistance, or with gravity in the absence of resistance. For example, the deltoid contracts when the arm is raised, but in Fig. 1, Pl. XXXII, the lengthening muscle is still firm and active, as shown by the weight riding upon it, while the arm is being lowered. The deltoid thus controls the gravitational descent of the arm, as a crane would pay out rope in lowering a girder, but when the arm is being lowered against resistance, as in Fig. 2, Pl. XXXII, such activity of the deltoid is useless; other muscles, antagonists to the deltoid, such as the pectoralis major and the latissimus dorsi, have to pull the arm downwards, and the deltoid itself becomes flaccid, as is shown by the weight sinking into it. It is therefore essential to consider the influence of gravity and resistance in determining muscular action, and to note that the relaxation of muscles is as important as their contraction; modern physical training methods exercise both functions to obtain harmony in development. Muscular relaxation may be the important feature in certain exercises. For example, the hip joint may be fully flexed, and then again the knee joint may be fully extended, but not both together unless the " hamstring " muscles acquire a special power of relaxation through practice; extreme relaxation of the hamstrings is essential for the accomplishment of the " high kick," and a lesser degree is required in touching the toes without bending the knees.

Muscles may be voluntarily contracted without movements occurring and without appreciable shortening. This condition is known as **isometric contraction**, and occurs, for example in the quadriceps femoris, when the knee joint is held extended against a flexing force.

---

[1] The detailed yet engrossing works of Duchenne (*Physiologie des mouvements*, 1861, Trans. New Sydenham Society, 1883) and Beevor (Croonian Lectures, 1904) are recommended for considerations beyond the scope of this text.

The more powerful the action of a muscle the greater is the number of fibres stimulated to function. It is not necessary for all the fibres of a muscle to contract at the same time for gentle movements; indeed, muscle fibres work in group relays to avoid fatigue. When examining a patient, the physician, in order to bring more fibres into play, adopts the method of **reinforcing** muscular action by opposing the patient's movements; this is a practice which will afford the student of anatomy also, as he carefully palpates living limbs, valuable practical information concerning muscles.

When a muscle contracts, its insertion is, as a general rule, approximated to its origin, but when both attachments are movable, the insertion may on occasion be relatively more fixed than the origin. Thus, in Fig. 1, Pl. XXXI, in which the subject pulls down a weighted rope towards the body, the insertion of the latissimus dorsi into the arm is brought towards its origin from the trunk; but if the subject were to raise the body by means of the rope, the origin would be approximated to the insertion.

Most skeletal muscles utilise the bones as levers, and in the limbs the muscles are usually attached just beyond the joint upon which they mainly act; one advantage of this is that a small movement of the knee or elbow joint, for instance, produces, with economy of muscle contraction, a much wider excursion of the foot or hand. The particular action of any muscle is a problem in mechanics, depending on the position of the two attachments and the relation of the muscle to the axes of the movements which are possible at the joint, or joints, over which it passes. Thus, in the case of the elbow joint where movements occur around a transverse axis only, all muscles which pass anterior to the joint can act as flexors, and all muscles which pass posterior to the joint can act as extensors. But such questions are not of great importance.

Movements, and not individual muscles, are represented in the cerebral cortex— that is, we are aware of the execution of a movement but not of the executive muscles. In fact, we may hardly even be aware of certain movements that initiate or are accessory to the chief movement. Even the simplest movements require the co-ordinated action of many muscles in different functional capacities to ensure precision of performance.

Although some persons may appear to have the power to contract a particular muscle at will, probably other muscles are also employed, and it is justifiable to say that, from a functional point of view, there is no such thing as the isolated action of a muscle. The control of the muscles producing any given voluntary movement is an automatic function of the central nervous system.

The different capacities in which individual muscles may function in any given movement are as follows:—1. Prime movers; 2. Antagonists; 3. Fixation muscles; 4. Synergists; but the same muscles appear in different capacities for different movements.

The **prime movers**, as the term implies, are the muscles which by their active contractions, and the consequent approximation of their attachments, are responsible for the actual movements which take place. When the fist is clenched, for example, the prime movers are the flexors of the fingers and the thumb.

The **antagonists** in any movement are those muscles which are capable by contraction of producing the reverse movement, and by their relaxation enable the movement to be effected. The extensors of the fingers and thumb, for example, would prevent the clenching of the fist, but for the law of reciprocal innervation between two groups which causes antagonists to relax as prime movers contract. It has been shown experimentally that the same areas of the motor cortex of the brain are responsible for the contraction of the one and the inhibition or relaxation of the other. The term "antagonists" belies the function of muscles in that capacity, for they do everything to secure harmony in the movement, "paying out" just as much as, and no more than, is required, thus securing guidance and precision. For example, the deltoid remains taut when the arm is lowered against slight resistance, but becomes flaccid when severe resistance is encountered.

Precision in the performance of any desired movement, or effective action against resistance, is possible only if the muscles concerned have a stable basis from which to act. It is the function of **fixation muscles** to provide this stable basis by steadying a part or a joint. For example, if the scapula is not adequately steadied and guided by the trapezius and serratus anterior muscles, disharmony in elevation of the arm by the deltoid will result. The trapezius and serratus anterior are prime movers in securing the rotation of the scapula upon the chest wall necessary for elevation of the arm, but are also fixation muscles in providing a firm base upon which the humerus is turned by muscles of the arm. During the exercise, in the supine position, of raising both legs from the floor, the rectus abdominis, though it does not act upon the limbs, soon becomes painfully cramped, because of the heavy and exhausting work required of it in fixing the pelvis for the pull of the limb muscles, and the support of the weight of the limbs.

Synergists [σύν (syn) = together, ἔργειν (ergein) = to work] might well be classed as special examples of fixation muscles, since they control the position of intermediate joints so that prime movers which pass over several joints may exert their power in a desired movement of a distal joint. In clenching the fist the synergists are the extensors of the wrist. If the wrist were not held extended, then the flexors of the fingers would be powerful enough to produce flexion of the wrist. Now, flexion of the wrist added to flexion of the fingers stretches the tendons of the extensors of the fingers until they can yield no more, when the continued flexion at the wrist causes the fingers to open out and the grip to slacken. This is the explanation of the success of the common trick of forcibly flexing an opponent's wrist to compel him to drop a weapon from his hand. Similarly the synergic action of the flexor carpi ulnaris and the extensor carpi ulnaris, acting together as adductors of the wrist, is essential for the apparently simple movement of abducting the thumb.

Group Actions of Muscles and Association of Muscles and of Movements.— Most of the muscles are arranged in groups with common sources of nerve-supply and common or related actions. Appreciating this fact, surgeons endeavour to mitigate the disability that results from paralysis of one muscle by transplanting another to act as a substitute. The transplanted muscle should, if possible, belong to the same team. But a muscle transferred from a rival team may be trained to play a new part among its former antagonists—more efficiently in the upper limb than in the lower. In the lower limb, individualism is suppressed in the well-nigh automatic group actions of locomotion, and such a practice as replacing a paralysed tibialis anterior by an antagonist—the peroneus longus—is usually unsatisfactory. In the upper limb, however, with its universal movements and more diverse and refined functions, muscles are more accustomed to the need for varied uses and individual specialisation, and an extensor can be educated to take the part of a flexor (a normal action of the extensors upon the pronated forearm, p. 464) much more easily than in the lower limb (cf. Dunn, *Journ. Orthopaedic Surgery*, 1920).

Muscles of one region may act in harmony with remote muscle-groups; in walking, the post-vertebral muscles of one side can be felt contracting to maintain the balance of the body as the opposite foot leaves the ground; and every large movement is preceded and accompanied by movements of which we are not aware until we study the principal movement with attention and analyse the preliminary and accessory movements as each merges into its successor. Owing to these associations, paralysis of a single muscle affects the general co-ordination as well as the chief movement in which it is concerned. The defect resulting from paralysis of a muscle is not necessarily a full indication of its action as a component of the movement.

Dual Action of Muscles.—The involuntary actions of muscles are not invariably lost when they are paralysed: a point of clinical importance, in certain kinds of paralysis, is the retention of function for involuntary *bi-lateral* acts—*e.g.* a paralysed upper limb is moved with its fellow in the stretching that accompanies a yawn, and a latissimus dorsi, paralysed for voluntary unilateral movement, contracts in the instinctive bilateral act of coughing (Beevor). Further, a muscle which participates in more than one voluntary movement (*e.g.* biceps, flexor and supinator), may suffer from a paralysis that affects the one movement and not the other, as the movements are not represented in the same part of the cerebral cortex.

Ligamentous action of Muscles.—The ligaments of a joint would require to be much stronger and bulkier were it not for the aid given by muscles. All the activities of muscles, from gentle muscle-tone to vigorous contraction, prevent undue strain being thrown on the ligaments; and, indeed, ligaments stretch rapidly when the muscular safeguard is removed or diminished. But muscles have a more truly ligamentous effect through their inability to relax sufficiently to allow free movement of a joint in all circumstances. For example, when the knee is straight the hamstring muscles, unable to relax enough to permit full flexion of the hip joint, play the part of restraining ligaments at that joint (cf. pp. 502, 516).

Nerve-Supply.—Each muscle is supplied by one or more nerves, which in their course through it separate into smaller and smaller branches. Ultimately their terminal filaments (axons) give off numerous collaterals, each of which forms a special end-organ in relation to a muscle cell.

It has been estimated that of the fibres contained in a nerve of supply to a muscle three-fifths are motor and two-fifths are sensory; the reciprocal action of these has already been described under muscle fibres. In addition, all muscles receive sympathetic nerve fibres, which have been shown to diminish and delay the occurrence of fatigue in skeletal muscle, but the details of their action are not yet fully determined.

Vascular-Supply.—*Blood-vessels* enter muscles with the nerves along a line which is frequently definite enough to receive the name of *neuro-vascular hilum*. Striated muscles may be said not to possess *lymph vessels* since these are not found between the individual fibres. But a capillary network is present in the sheath of a muscle and between the fasciculi.

FASCIÆ AND SYNOVIAL SHEATHS AND BURSÆ

Beneath the skin there are two layers of connective tissue to be considered in relation to the muscular system—the superficial fascia [panniculus adiposus] and the deep fascia. The panniculus carnosus (rudimentary in man) is placed in the substance of the superficial fascia.

The cells of the mesoderm, not differentiated into muscles, vessels, and bones, are utilised to form connective tissue or fascia ensheathing these structures.

Superficial Fascia.—The superficial fascia is a continuous sheet of areolar tissue which underlies the skin of the whole body. It is closely adherent to the corium; and, except beneath the skin of the eyelids, penis, and scrotum, it is usually more or less impregnated with fat. The fat of the superficial fascia is of very small amount in the healthy adult male, but tends to increase on the abdomen, breast, and buttocks; it forms a thicker subcutaneous layer in women and children, and is thus mainly responsible for the more rounded contours of their bodies. Its relative amount is indeed a secondary sex character, since in the average it accounts for about eighteen per cent. of the body weight in men and twenty-eight per cent. in women. The cutaneous vessels and nerves ramify in this fascia; and its deep surface—membranous in character—is in loose connexion with the deep fascia. It is chiefly in this layer that dropsical effusions occur.

Deep Fascia.—Underneath the skin and superficial fascia there is a fibrous membrane, bluish white in colour, devoid of fat, and in closest relation to skeleton, ligaments, and muscles. This is the deep fascia. It covers and invests the various muscles, and in some cases is the means of their attachment. It has a special tendency to become attached to all subcutaneous bony prominences, and to be continuous with the connecting ligaments. Laminæ from its deep surface extend inwards among the deeper structures; these sheets enclose glands and viscera, provide nerves and vessels with sheaths, and form **intermuscular septa** which separate groups of muscles and individual muscles—affording them additional means of attachment.

In the distal portions of the limbs, where the various joints are close to one another, special thickenings of the deep fascia called **retinacula** are present for the purpose of retaining the tendons in position when their muscles contract. These fascial bands act as pulleys round which the tendons work and they serve to prevent waste of power. There is a further modification on the flexor aspects of the digits for the same purpose; the fibrous bands are connected to one another and to the phalanges in such a way as to form osteo-fascial tunnels in which the tendons lie.

Synovial Sheaths [Vaginæ Mucosæ]. — In the situations just described, where tendons are retained in place by localised thickenings of the deep fascia, synovial sheaths are provided to facilitate their movements. Such sheaths may be related to one or more tendons. They are always closed sacs, with a parietal layer lining the walls of the space in which the tendon lies and a "visceral" layer closely applied to the tendon itself, so that the two synovial surfaces are in apposition with each other.

In the digital synovial sheaths, continuity is established between the parietal and visceral layers by means of **vincula tendinum** (p. 468), as well as at the extremities of the sheaths. The vincula tendinum transmit small blood-vessels, and may be regarded as incomplete "meso-tendons."

Synovial Bursæ [Bursæ Mucosæ].—Simple, closed synovial sacs are placed between a tendon (or an aponeurosis) and a bony point or ligament over which it plays, or between the distal ends of two or more tendons, when they are inserted in close proximity to one another.

DESCRIPTION OF THE MUSCLES

In the study of the muscular system it is necessary to note the following characters in reference to each individual muscle: (1) The *shape* of the muscle— flat, cylindrical, triangular, rhomboidal, etc.; and the character of its extremities —membranous, tendinous, or fleshy. (2) The *attachments* of the muscle. (3) The *relations* of the surfaces and borders of the muscle to bones, joints, muscles, and other important structures. (4) Its *vascular* and *nervous supply*. (5) The *movements* in which it takes part.

The skeletal muscles may be divided into two series: axial and appendicular. The **axial muscles** comprise the muscles of the trunk, neck, head, and face; they are more or less segmental in arrangement, and are grouped around the axial skeleton. The **appendicular muscles** are the muscles of the limbs; they are grouped around the appendicular skeleton, and are not segmental in arrangement.

AXIAL MUSCLES
THE MUSCLES OF THE VERTEBRAL COLUMN

The muscles of the vertebral column are arranged in two main groups—post-vertebral and prevertebral—on the dorsal and ventral aspects of the column respectively. The post-vertebral or dorsal group is by far the more extensive and the more complex in its attachments. It extends from the sacrum to the head, forming a cylindrical fleshy column in the loin, filling up the vertebral groove in the thoracic region, and giving rise to the muscular mass at the back of the neck. It is attached not only to the vertebral column but also to the pelvic girdle below, the posterior part of the base of the skull above, and, by means of numerous slips of its component parts, to all the ribs.

The prevertebral or ventral group, on the other hand, is interrupted. It extends from the base of the skull, in front of the foramen magnum, to the upper thoracic region, and reappears again in the lumbar region as the psoas major and minor.

It is evident that the physiological antagonists of the powerful dorsal group, whose main action, taken as a whole, is to extend the vertebral column, are to be found not merely in the true prevertebral group directly in relation to the vertebral column, but also and mainly in the ventral and lateral muscles of the abdominal wall, which, through their attachments to the thorax, are in a position to bend the vertebral column forwards on the pelvis.

The muscles of the back, from the topographical point of view, may be conveniently divided into two main groups—(1) the *superficial* and (2) the *deep*.

The **superficial muscles of the back** are described with the muscles of the upper limb, which they connect to the axial skeleton.

DEEP MUSCLES OF THE BACK

The **deep muscles of the back**—the post-vertebral or dorsal group of the vertebral column—may be classified according to their attachments in three series — vertebro-costal, vertebro-cranial, and intervertebral. It is, however, more convenient to describe them as they are met with in irregular strata in the dissection of the back. On this basis, and having regard to serial repetition of attachments and the general direction taken by the muscular fibres, the greater part of this complex musculature—so bewildering at first to the student, subdivided as it has been into many parts, separately named and largely artificial—may be resolved into two main systems, a superficial, longitudinal *sacro-spinalis* system and a deeper, oblique *transverso-spinalis* system. These form the basis of the first two of the following three groups into which the deep muscles of the back may be divided: (1) the sacro-spinalis system (including the splenius muscle and the spinalis thoracis); (2) the transverso-spinalis system (semispinalis thoracis and cervicis, multifidus and rotatores) with the semispinalis capitis; and (3) the interspinal, intertransverse, and suboccipital muscles. The general regional disposition as indicated in Figs. 328, 329 should be studied, rather than the details of attachments.

It should be noted that the component parts of the more superficial group are arranged in more or less separate longitudinal columns and stretch between their attachments over many vertebræ; the component parts of the deeper muscles are shorter, passing over fewer vertebræ; and in the deepest layer the attachments of the individual parts are between contiguous vertebræ only.

In general also, the differentiation of the muscular systems described increases from below upwards. All three groups are continued to the head, and, in the cervical region, portions of each become definitely individualised in relation to the finer movements of the head and the cervical part of the vertebral column as compared with the more generalised movements of the column as a whole.

Two small muscles called the *serrati posteriores, superior* and *inferior*, situated between the superficial and the deep muscles of the back, are described with the muscles of the thorax, to which they properly belong.

First Group

This group includes the sacro-spinalis with the spinalis thoracis (usually described as its medial column), and the splenius (capitis and cervicis) muscle, which lies in a more superficial plane in the upper thoracic and cervical regions.

Splenius.—The splenius muscle is a broad, flattened band which lies in the back of the neck and the upper part of the thoracic region. It **arises** from the ligamentum nuchæ (from the level of the fourth cervical vertebra downwards) and from the spines of the last cervical and higher (four to six) thoracic vertebræ.

Its fibres extend upwards and laterally into the neck, separating in their course into an upper and a lower part. The upper part is the **splenius capitis**, which is **inserted** into the mastoid portion of the temporal bone and the lateral part of the superior nuchal line of the occipital bone (Fig. 332, p. 393). The lower part is the **splenius cervicis**, which is **inserted** into the posterior tubercles of the transverse processes of the upper three or four cervical vertebræ, under cover of the origin of the levator scapulæ.

The greater part of the muscle is concealed by the trapezius and the sternomastoid, but a portion of the splenius capitis appears between them in the floor of the posterior triangle of the neck. It is covered also by the rhomboid muscles, levator scapulæ, and serratus posterior superior, and, itself, helps to conceal the cervical prolongations of the sacro-spinalis and the semispinalis capitis.

Sacro-spinalis.—The sacro-spinalis possesses vertebral, vertebro-cranial, and vertebro-costal attachments. It is an elongated mass composed of separate slips extending from the sacrum to the skull. Simple at its origin, it becomes more and more complex as it is traced upwards towards the head, its continuity as a whole being maintained at higher levels by relays of fibres arising as the lower fibres are inserted.

Its primary origin is (1) by a strong tendinous sheet fused with the posterior layer of the lumbar fascia and continuous below, as it narrows to a pointed extremity, with the posterior sacro-iliac, the sacro-tuberous, and the sacro-coccygeal ligaments, from the iliac crest and posterior superior iliac spine, the dorsum of the sacrum, and the sacral and lumbar spines; and (2) by fleshy fibres massed beneath the lateral border of the tendon just above the posterior superior iliac spine, where they obtain a powerful direct attachment to the upper half of the iliac tuberosity and to the inner lip of the iliac crest. Below this level the tendon is spread over the underlying multifidus muscle, which is separated from it for the most part by a layer of areolar tissue containing some fat. The muscle extends upwards through the loin, in which it forms the main muscular mass posterior and lateral to the multifidus, and separates into two columns—a **lateral portion**, called the **ilio-costo-cervicalis**, derived from the lateral part of the fleshy origin, and a **medial portion**, called the **longissimus**, comprising the remaining, larger part of the muscle.

Ilio-costo-cervicalis.—The ilio-costalis [lumborum] is **inserted** by six slender slips into the lower six ribs.

Medial to the insertion of each of these slips is the origin of the **costalis** [ilio-costalis dorsi], which, **arising** from the lower six ribs medial to the ilio-costalis, is **inserted** in line with it by similar slips into the upper six ribs.

The **costo-cervicalis** [ilio-costalis cervicis] **arises** in the same way by six slips from the upper six ribs, medial to the insertions of the costalis. It forms a narrow band that extends into the neck to be **inserted** into the posterior tubercles of the transverse processes of the fourth, fifth, and sixth cervical vertebræ, behind the scalenus posterior.

The three subdivisions of the ilio-costo-cervicalis form together a continuous muscular column, and constitute the most lateral group of the component elements of the sacro-spinalis.

Longissimus.—The longissimus is the largest element in the sacro-spinalis system. Mostly tendinous on the surface at its **origin**, it becomes fleshy in the

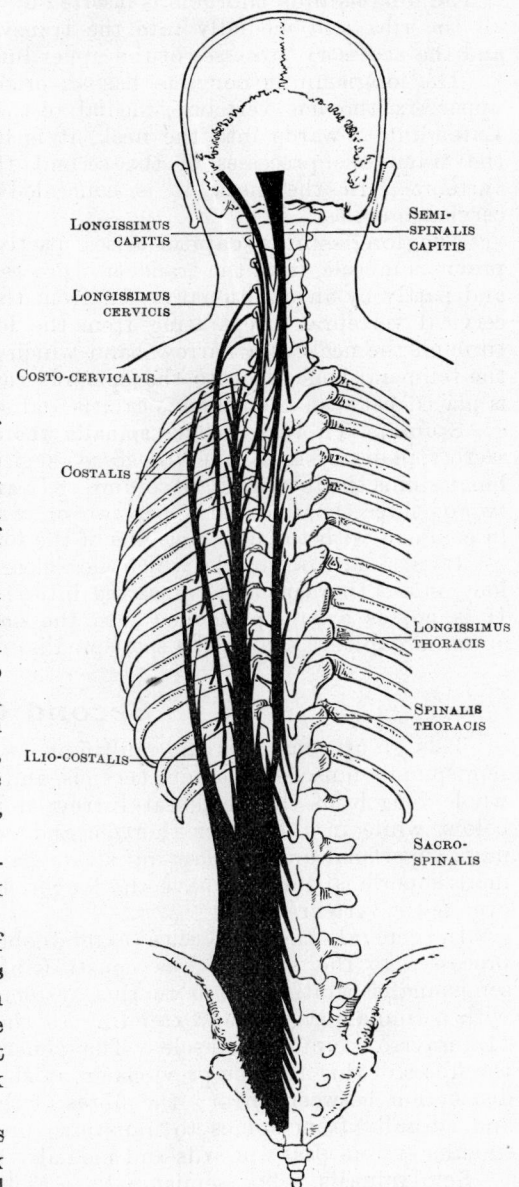

LONGISSIMUS CAPITIS

SEMI-SPINALIS CAPITIS

LONGISSIMUS CERVICIS

COSTO-CERVICALIS

COSTALIS

LONGISSIMUS THORACIS

SPINALIS THORACIS

ILIO-COSTALIS

SACRO-SPINALIS

FIG. 328.—SCHEMATIC REPRESENTATION OF THE PARTS OF THE LEFT SACRO-SPINALIS MUSCLE.

upper part of the loin. It is thickest in the loin, and becomes thinner as it passes upwards in the back, as the longissimus thoracis, between the columns formed by the ilio-costo-cervicalis laterally and the spinalis thoracis medially. It is continued up into the neck as the longissimus cervicis and longissimus capitis.

The longissimus thoracis is **inserted** by two series of slips—laterally into nearly all the ribs, and medially into the transverse processes of the thoracic vertebræ and the accessory processes of the upper lumbar vertebræ.

The longissimus cervicis has an **origin** from the transverse processes of the upper six thoracic vertebræ, medial to the insertions of the longissimus thoracis. Extending upwards into the neck, it is **inserted** into the posterior tubercles of the transverse processes of the second, third, fourth, fifth, and sixth cervical vertebræ. In the neck it is concealed by the costo-cervicalis and splenius cervicis muscles.

The longissimus capitis **arises**, partly by an origin common to it and the previous muscle, from the transverse processes of the upper six thoracic vertebræ, and partly by an additional origin from the articular processes of the lower four cervical vertebræ. Separating from the longissimus cervicis, the muscle ascends through the neck as a narrow band which is **inserted** into the mastoid portion of the temporal bone, deep to the splenius capitis muscle. In the neck the muscle is placed between the splenius capitis and semispinalis capitis.

Spinalis Thoracis.—The **spinalis thoracis** forms the medial column of the sacro-spinalis system—the ilio-costo-cervicalis being the lateral column and the longissimus the intermediate column. It **arises** by tendinous fibres from the lower two or three thoracic and upper two or three lumbar spines, the lower slips being in common with the upper origins of the longissimus dorsi.

It is a narrow muscle which lies close to the thoracic spines, medial to the longissimus thoracis, and is **inserted** into the upper (four to eight) thoracic spines. It is not as a rule prolonged into the neck, though a spinalis cervicis and a spinalis capitis (joining the semispinalis) may both be present.

Second Group

This group comprises the multifidus (with the deep-lying rotatores) and the semispinalis muscles (thoracis, cervicis, and capitis). The multifidus occupies the whole length of the vertebral furrow and is under cover of the sacro-spinalis below, while in the upper thoracic and cervical regions the semispinales form more superficial and overlapping strata partially concealed by the splenius. The more superficial muscles have the longer fibres; the fibres of the multifidus pass over fewer vertebræ.

In general, these muscles extend obliquely upwards from the transverse processes to the spines, thus constituting a "transverso-spinal" system; the semispinalis capitis, related to this system as the splenius is to the sacro-spinalis, with a similar origin, but extending to the base of the skull, is a corresponding "transverso-occipital" muscle. The general contrast between the directions of the fibres of this and the previous group should be noted as an indication of a real distinction between them; the fibres of the sacro-spinalis system pass upwards and laterally from spines to transverse processes, while those of the transverso-spinalis system pass upwards and medially from transverse processes to spines.

Semispinalis.—The semispinalis muscle extends from the loin to the skull. It is described as three muscles—the **semispinalis thoracis**, the **semispinalis cervicis**, and the **semispinalis capitis**—but the separation between S. thoracis and S. cervicis is artificial.

The **semispinalis thoracis** arises from the transverse processes of the lower six thoracic vertebræ, and is **inserted** into the spines of the first four thoracic and last two cervical vertebræ.

The **semispinalis cervicis** arises from the transverse processes of the upper six thoracic, and the articular processes of the lower four cervical vertebræ, and is **inserted** into the spines of the cervical vertebræ from the second to the fifth.

The **semispinalis capitis** is very similar in its attachments to the longissimus

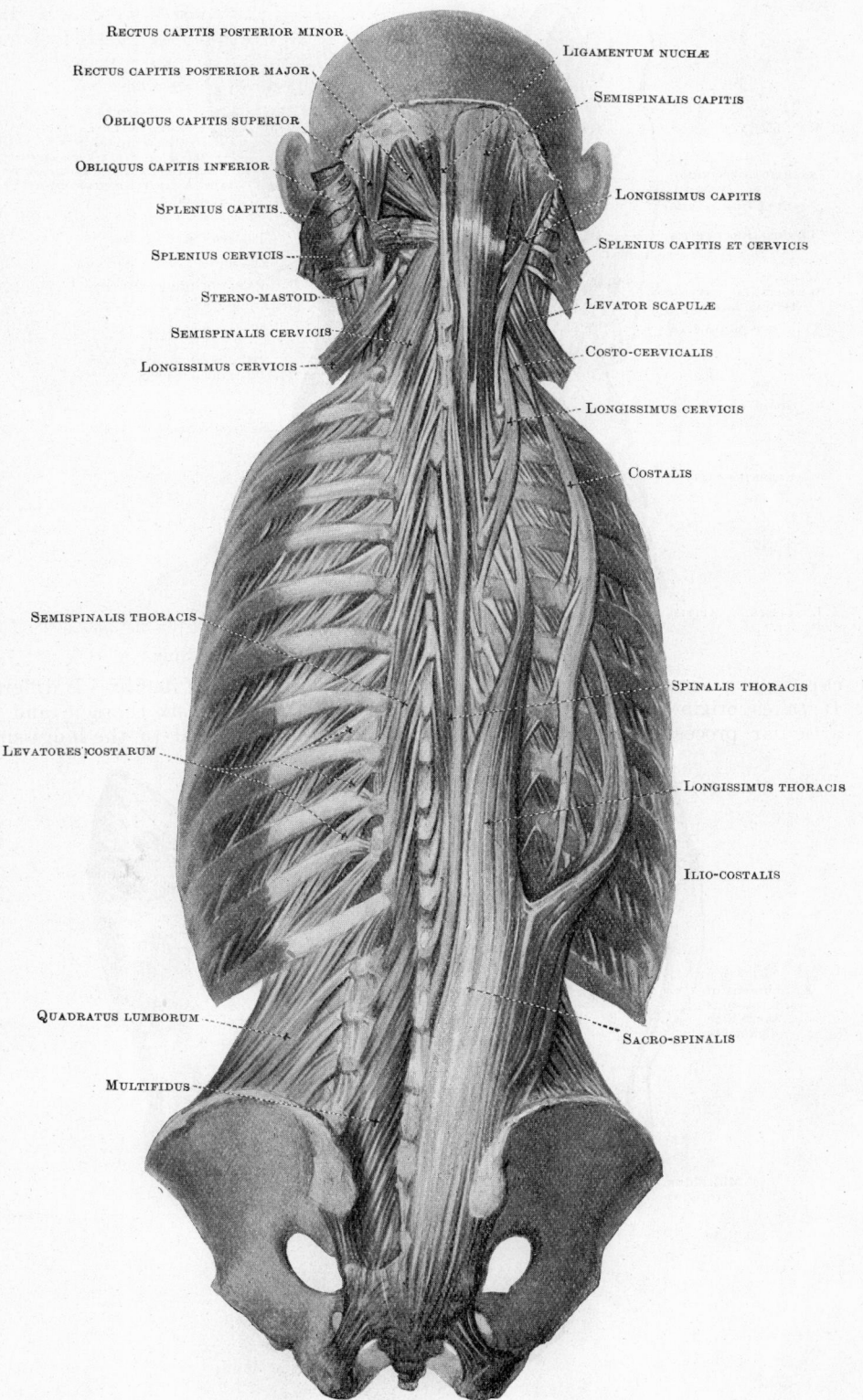

RECTUS CAPITIS POSTERIOR MINOR

RECTUS CAPITIS POSTERIOR MAJOR

OBLIQUUS CAPITIS SUPERIOR

OBLIQUUS CAPITIS INFERIOR

SPLENIUS CAPITIS

SPLENIUS CERVICIS

STERNO-MASTOID

SEMISPINALIS CERVICIS

LONGISSIMUS CERVICIS

SEMISPINALIS THORACIS

LEVATORES COSTARUM

QUADRATUS LUMBORUM

MULTIFIDUS

LIGAMENTUM NUCHÆ

SEMISPINALIS CAPITIS

LONGISSIMUS CAPITIS

SPLENIUS CAPITIS ET CERVICIS

LEVATOR SCAPULÆ

COSTO-CERVICALIS

LONGISSIMUS CERVICIS

COSTALIS

SPINALIS THORACIS

LONGISSIMUS THORACIS

ILIO-COSTALIS

SACRO-SPINALIS

FIG. 329.—THE DEEP MUSCLES OF THE BACK.

25 c

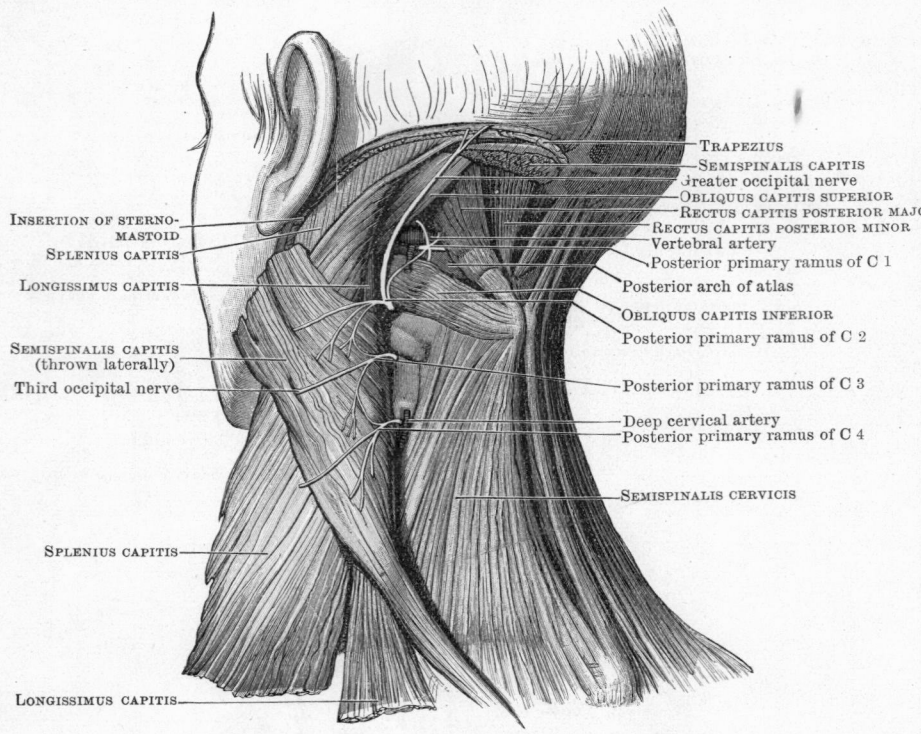

INSERTION OF STERNO-
MASTOID
SPLENIUS CAPITIS
LONGISSIMUS CAPITIS

SEMISPINALIS CAPITIS
(thrown laterally)
Third occipital nerve

SPLENIUS CAPITIS

LONGISSIMUS CAPITIS

TRAPEZIUS
SEMISPINALIS CAPITIS
Greater occipital nerve
OBLIQUUS CAPITIS SUPERIOR
RECTUS CAPITIS POSTERIOR MAJOR
RECTUS CAPITIS POSTERIOR MINOR
Vertebral artery
Posterior primary ramus of C 1
Posterior arch of atlas
OBLIQUUS CAPITIS INFERIOR
Posterior primary ramus of C 2

Posterior primary ramus of C 3

Deep cervical artery
Posterior primary ramus of C 4

SEMISPINALIS CERVICIS

FIG. 330.—THE SUBOCCIPITAL TRIANGLE OF THE LEFT SIDE.

capitis, but it is a very much larger muscle and the direction of its fibres is different. It takes **origin** from the transverse processes of the upper six thoracic and the articular processes of the lower four cervical vertebræ, medial to the longissimus

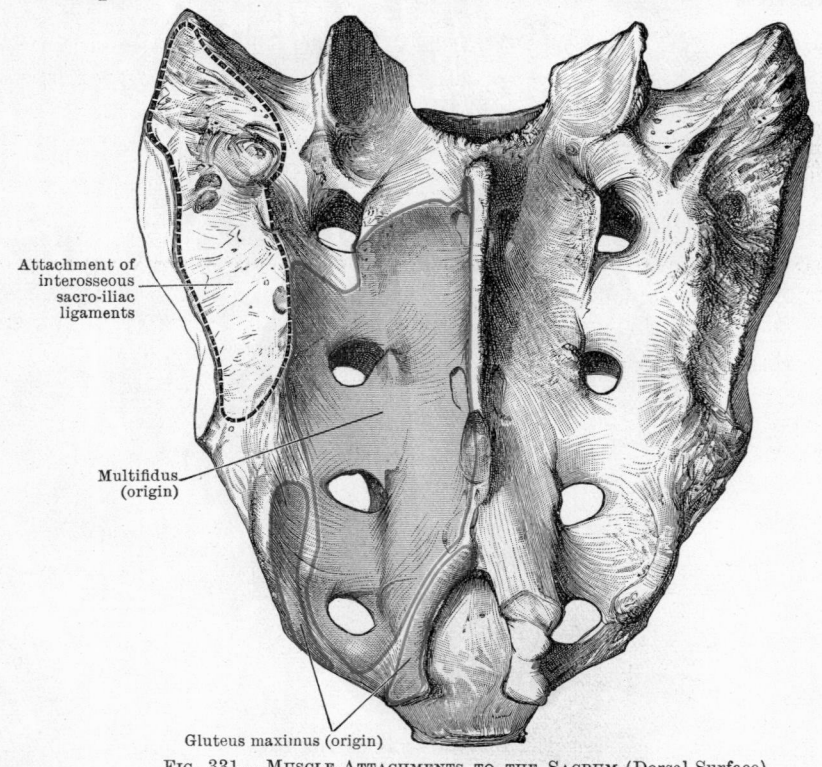

Attachment of
interosseous
sacro-iliac
ligaments

Multifidus
(origin)

Gluteus maximus (origin)

FIG. 331.—MUSCLE-ATTACHMENTS TO THE SACRUM (Dorsal Surface).

cervicis and longissimus capitis. It may have an origin also from a variable number of the spines of the lower cervical and upper thoracic vertebræ (**spinalis capitis**).

It forms a broad muscular sheet which extends upwards in the neck to be **inserted** into the medial impression between the superior and inferior nuchal lines of the occipital bone (Fig. 332). The medial portion of the muscle is separate; it consists of two fleshy bellies with an intervening tendon placed vertically in contact with the ligamentum nuchæ. The muscle is covered mainly by the splenius and longissimus capitis muscles. It conceals the semispinalis cervicis and the medial part of the suboccipital triangle, and its vertical fibres are usually visible at the upper angle of the posterior triangle of the neck above the splenius capitis.

Multifidus.—The multifidus differs from the semispinalis in extending from the sacrum to the second cervical vertebra, and in the shortness of its fasciculi, which pass over fewer vertebræ to reach their insertion.

It **arises** from the sacrum (Fig. 331) under cover of the tendon of the sacro-spinalis, from the posterior sacro-iliac ligaments, from the mamillary processes of the lumbar vertebræ, from the transverse processes of the thoracic vertebræ, and from the articular processes of the lower four cervical vertebræ. It is **inserted** into the spines up to and including the second cervical.

Lying in contact with the vertebral laminæ and, in the thoracic region, with the rotatores, the muscle is covered in the neck and back by the semispinalis, and in the loin by the sacro-spinalis muscle.

Rotatores.—The rotatores are eleven pairs of small muscles that occupy the vertebral groove in the thoracic region, deep to the multifidus, of which they form the deepest fibres. Each is a small slip which **arises** from the transverse process of one vertebra and is **inserted** into the lamina of the vertebra directly above.

Third Group

This group comprises several series of small muscles which are vertebro-cranial

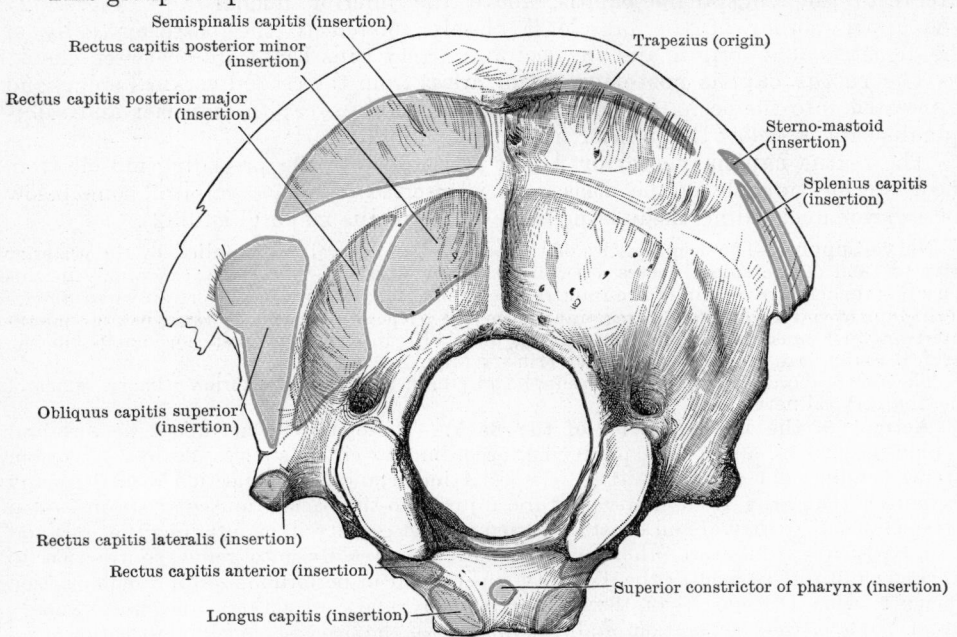

FIG. 332.—MUSCLE-ATTACHMENTS TO THE OCCIPITAL BONE.

or intervertebral in their attachments, and include the special group of suboccipital muscles.

Interspinales.—The interspinales are bands of muscular fibres that connect together the spines of the vertebræ from the second cervical downwards. They are well developed in the cervical and lumbar regions, where they lie one on each side of the corresponding interspinous ligament, but are poorly developed and may be absent in the thoracic region.

Intertransverse Muscles.—The intertransverse muscles are slender slips that extend between the transverse processes.

In the cervical region, with certain exceptions, an anterior intertransverse muscle extends from costal element to costal element, in front of the emerging anterior primary ramus of the corresponding spinal nerve, and a posterior intertransverse muscle extends from transverse element to transverse element, behind the nerve. Above the atlas, the rectus capitis lateralis is in series with the posterior intertransverse muscles, and the rectus capitis anterior may represent the anterior group. . Between the atlas and the second cervical vertebræ, the posterior muscle is well developed and is situated, like the rectus capitis lateralis, posterior to the emerging nerve, but the anterior muscle in this space is frequently absent.

In the thoracic region the intertransverse muscles are absent, except in the lower three or four intervals, where their arrangement corresponds to that found in the lumbar region.

In the lumbar region lateral and medial intertransverse muscles are present. The lateral are in series with the posterior muscles of the cervical region and pass between the extremities of the transverse processes, while the medial connect the mamillary tubercles to the accessory tubercles of the vertebræ above.

Suboccipital Muscles.—These muscles are four in number—obliquus capitis inferior and superior, and rectus capitis posterior major and minor (Fig. 330). They are concealed by the semispinalis capitis, longissimus capitis, and splenius capitis, and enclose a triangular space (the suboccipital triangle) which contains the vertebral artery, the posterior primary ramus of the first cervical nerve, the posterior arch of the atlas, and the posterior atlanto-occipital membrane.

The **obliquus capitis inferior,** the stoutest of the group, **arises** from the second cervical spine, and passes upward and laterally to be **inserted** into the transverse process of the atlas. The greater occipital nerve curls round the inferior border of this muscle.

The **obliquus capitis superior arises** from the transverse process of the atlas, and passes backwards and upwards to be **inserted** into the occipital bone deep and lateral to the semispinalis capitis, above the inferior nuchal line (Fig. 332). The upper border of the muscle is closely related to the posterior belly of the digastric at its origin, and the occipital artery runs backwards between them.

The **rectus capitis posterior major arises** from the second cervical spine, and is **inserted** into the occipital bone deep to the obliquus capitis superior and semispinalis capitis, below the inferior nuchal line (Fig. 332).

The **rectus capitis posterior minor arises** deep to the preceding muscle from the posterior tubercle of the atlas, and is **inserted** into the occipital bone below the inferior nuchal line, medial and deep to the rectus major (Fig. 332).

Nerve-Supply.—The deep muscles of the back are, in general, all supplied by the **posterior primary rami** of the **spinal nerves** according to their situation. The only exceptions to this general statement are certain of the intertransverse muscles ; the medial intertransverse muscles in the lumbar and lower thoracic region are supplied by posterior primary rami, but the lateral intertransverse muscles in the same regions, and both anterior and posterior muscles in the cervical region, are supplied by **anterior primary rami.**

The four suboccipital muscles are supplied by branches of the **posterior primary ramus** of the **first cervical nerve.**

Actions of the Deep Muscles of the Back.—These muscles act upon the vertebral column, head, ribs, and pelvis, producing, according to circumstances, flexion, extension, lateral bending and rotation. It is of special importance, in connection with the many disabilities that arise from faulty posture, injuries to the back, "muscular strains," etc., to remember that they are in constant action against gravity in maintaining the erect and sitting postures. Like all other muscles they pass readily into reflex contraction to prevent painful movements ; the difficulty experienced in performing *any* muscular action efficiently when the muscles of the back are thus in rigid contraction emphasises strongly the principle of the co-operation of all the muscles of the body in the simplest action.

The deep muscles of the back not only control the gravitational descent of the body in bending forwards (flexion), but also act powerfully in regaining the erect position (extension). The extensor muscles of the vertebral column are therefore twice as massive as the flexors—just the opposite of the proportions found in anthropoid apes (Fick). If extension is continued beyond the erect position—backward bending (Pl. XVII, Fig. 2)—the important action is the relaxation of the sterno-mastoid, abdominal, and prevertebral groups to permit and control the movement. If flexion of the column is resisted, or performed against gravity, as in getting up from the supine position, then the prevertebral muscles, to which the sterno-mastoid and the abdominal groups functionally belong, are called into action. Gravitational control is again concerned in lateral flexion. The oblique parts of the post-vertebral and prevertebral muscles, the oppositely directed fibres of the two sides working in unison, produce rotation, a movement that also occurs in the lumbar region. The muscles that produce lateral flexion act with those that produce rotation, which must also occur during side bending. Although relaxation of the post-vertebral group secures forward bending (flexion) of the body, it should be noted that the greater part of this movement is executed not so much by the vertebral column as by relaxation of the hamstring muscles allowing hip flexion.

The association of the post-vertebral muscles with the limb muscles in walking has already been mentioned (p. 385). The muscles acting upon the head, particularly those of the suboccipital group, may be associated with the muscles of the eyeballs ; for example, when the eyes are turned to one side, the head also is turned to that side.

The student will appreciate therefore that the following statement of isolated muscle actions is merely a summary of mechanical deductions and is of little clinical value.

Splenius cervicis—Extension and lateral flexion of vertebral column to the same side.

Splenius—Extension of head, and lateral flexion and rotation to the same side.

Sacro-spinalis, multifidus and semispinalis—Extension, lateral flexion, and rotation of column ; extension and lateral movement of pelvis in walking.

Longissimus capitis and semispinalis capitis—Extension, lateral flexion and rotation of the head.

Inferior oblique—Extension, lateral flexion and rotation of the atlas (with the head) on the axis.

Superior oblique—Extension, lateral movement and rotation of the head on the atlas.

Rectus capitis posterior major—Extension, lateral flexion and rotation of the head.

Rectus capitis posterior minor—Extension and lateral flexion of the head.

FASCIÆ OF THE BACK

The **superficial fascia** of the back is thick and tough, and contains a quantity of granular fat.

The **deep fascia** is attached to the superior nuchal line of the occipital bone, and in the median plane to the ligamentum nuchae, and, below this level, to the supraspinous ligaments and vertebral spines —thus extending from the skull to the back of the sacrum and coccyx. Its fibres are mainly transverse. Ensheathing the superficial muscles of the back, *e.g.* trapezius and latissimus dorsi, it becomes continuous with the fascia of the neck, axilla, thorax, and abdomen (cf. Fig. 382, p. 456). In the shoulder region it is attached to the spine and acromion of the scapula and to the clavicle, and sweeps over the deltoid into the arm. Below and laterally it is attached to the iliac crest.

In the loin, the deep fascia is specially named the **lumbar**

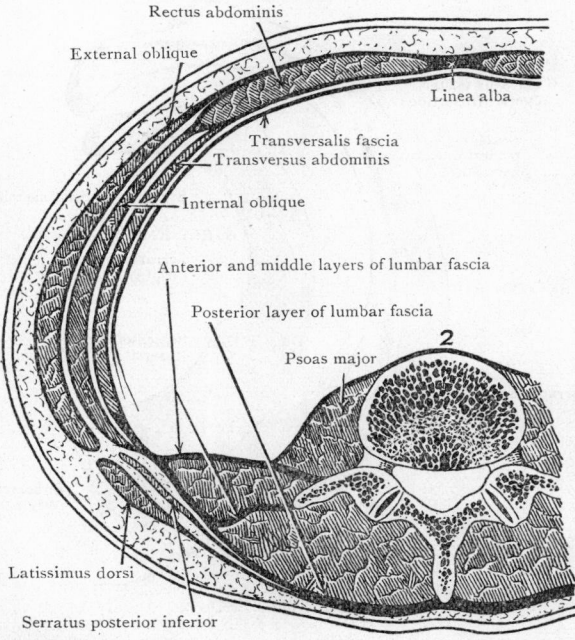

FIG. 333.—TRANSVERSE SECTION THROUGH THE ABDOMEN AT THE LEVEL OF THE SECOND LUMBAR VERTEBRA.

fascia, and is divided into three layers—posterior, middle, and anterior—which enclose muscles between them ; but the posterior layer is the only one of the three that is continuous with the deep fascia above the loin. In the course of development the deep muscles of the back, within their fascial sheaths, become covered by muscles derived from myotomes developed in other situations, for example, by the trapezius, rhomboid and latissimus dorsi muscles. The sheet that covers the posterior surface of the deep muscles of the back therefore runs upwards under the superficial muscles, becomes attached to the angles of the ribs lateral to the ilio-costo-cervicalis, and blends with the aponeurosis of serratus posterior superior in its course. In the sacral and lumbar regions, because of the interweaving of this sheath with the tendinous expansion of the latissimus dorsi and serratus posterior inferior, it becomes a strong, glistening aponeurosis termed the **posterior layer of the lumbar fascia.** This layer is attached medially to the lumbar and sacral spines and supraspinous ligaments, laterally to the iliac crest; it covers the sacrospinalis muscle, and is continuous round the lateral border of this muscular column with another fascial plane—the **middle layer of the lumbar fascia.** The middle layer is the continuation of the posterior aponeurosis of the transversus abdominis. It extends medially to be attached to the tips of the lumbar transverse processes. It covers the posterior surface of the quadratus lumborum and separates its medial part from the sacro-spinalis. The **anterior layer** is the thinnest of the three. It covers the front of the quadratus lumborum and separates its medial part from the psoas major. Medially, it is attached to the fronts of the lumbar transverse processes. Laterally, it blends with the middle layer at the lateral margin of the quadratus to form a narrow band that stretches from the last rib to the iliac crest.

MUSCLES AND FASCIÆ OF THE HEAD AND NECK

Deep Lateral and Prevertebral Muscles of the Neck

There are three series of muscles in this group: (1) vertebro-costal (scalenus anterior, medius and posterior), (2) vertebro-cranial (longus capitis and rectus capitis anterior and lateralis), and (3) intervertebral (longus cervicis). They clothe the antero-lateral borders of the cervical portion of the vertebral column, and are in relation anteriorly with the pharynx and œsophagus, and the large vessels and nerves of the neck.

Scalenus Anterior. — The scalenus anterior **arises** from the anterior tubercles of the transverse processes of the third, fourth, fifth, and sixth cervical vertebræ. It runs downwards and laterally to be **inserted** into the scalene tubercle and ridge on the first rib (Figs. 334, 335, 353).

The phrenic nerve is formed at the upper part of the lateral border of the scalenus anterior and runs vertically downwards on its

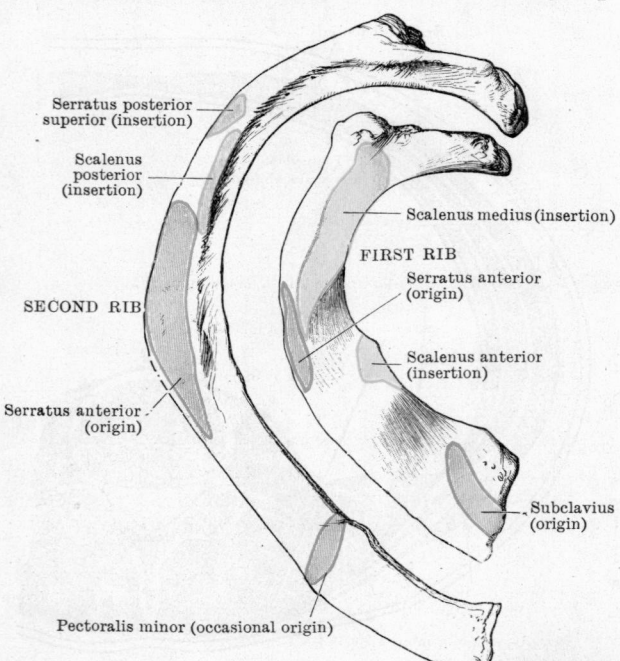

Serratus posterior superior (insertion)

Scalenus posterior (insertion)

Scalenus medius (insertion)

FIRST RIB

Serratus anterior (origin)

SECOND RIB

Scalenus anterior (insertion)

Serratus anterior (origin)

Subclavius (origin)

Pectoralis minor (occasional origin)

FIG. 334.—MUSCLE-ATTACHMENTS TO UPPER SURFACE OF FIRST RIB AND OUTER SURFACE OF SECOND RIB (RIGHT SIDE).

anterior surface, leaving its medial border a little above its insertion. The prevertebral fascia covers the muscle and binds down the phrenic nerve to its surface.

With the exception of its insertion, which lies behind the clavicle, the muscle is completely covered by the sterno-mastoid, but the inferior belly of the omo-hyoid and the internal jugular vein intervene between them. It is separated posteriorly from the scalenus medius by the roots of the brachial plexus and the subclavian artery.

Scalenus Medius.—The scalenus medius **arises** from the posterior tubercles of the transverse processes of all the cervical vertebræ—occasionally omitting the first or the seventh. It descends in the posterior triangle, behind the brachial plexus and the subclavian artery, to be **inserted** into the rough impression on the first rib behind the subclavian groove (Fig. 334). The muscle is pierced by the nerve to the rhomboids and the nerve to the serratus anterior, which descend on its lateral aspect, under cover of the fascia.

Between these scalene muscles laterally and the longus cervicis medially, there is a pyramidal space into the base of which the pleura projects, capped by a fascial membrane that may be strengthened by a few slips from the scalene muscles and their fascial sheaths. The vertebral vessels run to the apex of this pyramid.

Scalenus Posterior.— The scalenus posterior **arises**, behind the scalenus medius, from the posterior tubercles of the fourth, fifth, and sixth cervical transverse processes. It is **inserted** into an impression on the outer side of the second rib.

At first completely hidden by the scalenus medius, the scalenus posterior appears in the lowest part of the floor of the posterior triangle in the angle between the scalenus medius and the levator scapulæ muscles.

Longus Capitis.—The longus capitis **arises** from

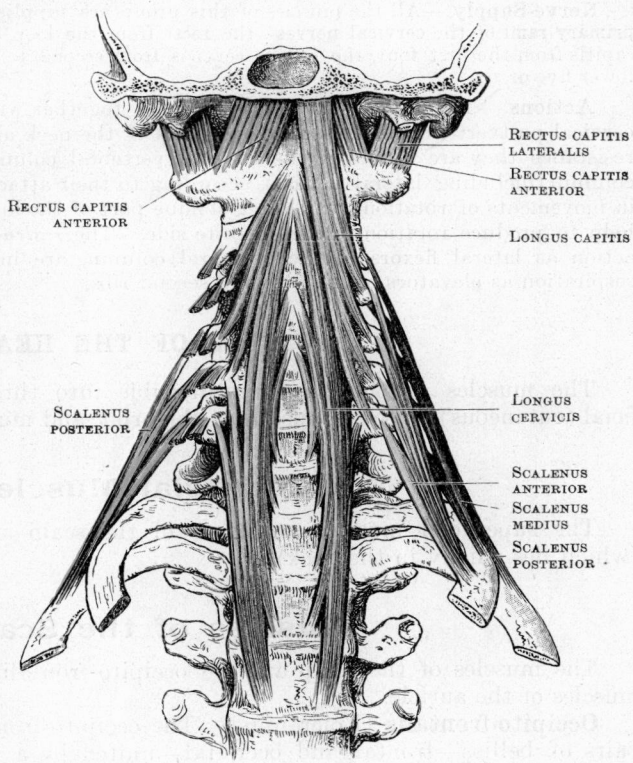

FIG. 335.—THE PREVERTEBRAL MUSCLES OF THE NECK.

the anterior tubercles of the transverse processes of the third, fourth, fifth, and sixth cervical vertebræ. It is a flat, triangular muscle which is directed upwards, behind the carotid sheath, and overlapping the upper oblique part of the longus cervicis muscle, to be **inserted** into an impression on the inferior surface of the basilar part of the occipital bone, anterior and lateral to the pharyngeal tubercle (Fig. 332, p. 393).

Rectus Capitis Anterior.—The rectus capitis anterior **arises**, under cover of the longus capitis, from the lateral mass of the atlas. It is **inserted** into the basilar part of occipital bone between the longus capitis and the occipital condyle (Fig. 332, p. 393).

Longus Cervicis.—The longus cervicis is a flattened muscular band which extends from the third thoracic vertebra to the atlas. It is divisible into three portions—a vertical, an inferior oblique, and a superior oblique portion. The **vertical portion** of the muscle **arises** from the bodies of the first three thoracic and the last three cervical vertebræ. Passing vertically upwards, it is **inserted**

into the bodies of the second, third, and fourth cervical vertebræ (Fig. 335). The **inferior oblique portion arises** from the bodies of the first three thoracic vertebræ, and is **inserted** into the anterior tubercles of the transverse processes of the fifth and sixth cervical vertebræ. The **superior oblique portion arises** from the anterior tubercles of the transverse processes of the third, fourth, and fifth cervical vertebræ, and is directed upwards to be **inserted** into the anterior tubercle of the atlas.

Rectus Capitis Lateralis.—The rectus capitis lateralis, in series with the posterior intertransverse muscles in the neck, **arises** from the transverse process of the atlas, and is **inserted** into the inferior surface of the jugular process of the occipital bone. It is placed alongside the rectus capitis anterior, separated from it by the anterior primary ramus of the first cervical nerve, and is covered anteriorly by the internal jugular vein.

Nerve-Supply.—All the muscles of this group are supplied by branches from the **anterior primary rami of the cervical nerves**—the recti from the loop between the first two, the longus capitis from the first four, the longus cervicis from second to eighth, and the scaleni from the lower five or six.

Actions.—The muscles of this group act together with, and as antagonists to, the cervical postvertebral muscles in movements of the neck and head. Against gravity and resistance they are flexors of the cervical vertebral column and of the head upon the column (including lateral flexion), according to their attachments. They also take part in movements of rotation; the lower oblique part of the longus cervicis, for example, may help to produce rotation to the opposite side. The *scalene* muscles, in addition to their action as lateral flexors of the vertebral column, are important accessory muscles of respiration as elevators of the first and second ribs.

MUSCLES OF THE HEAD

The muscles of the head are divisible into three separate groups: superficial (cutaneous) muscles, muscles of the orbit, and muscles of mastication.

Superficial Muscles

The superficial muscles are those of the scalp and face, and the platysma (which lies chiefly in the neck).

Muscles of the Scalp

The muscles of the scalp are the occipito-frontalis muscle and the extrinsic muscles of the auricle.

Occipito-frontalis [Epicranius].—The occipito-frontalis is a muscle with two pairs of bellies—frontal and occipital—united by a tendinous sheet, called the epicranial aponeurosis, which stretches uninterruptedly across the median plane of the cranium. Each **occipital belly arises** as a broad flat band from the lateral two-thirds of the superior nuchal line of the occipital bone. Each **frontal belly** has no bony attachments; **arising** from the epicranial aponeurosis about the level of the coronal suture, it passes downwards to the supra-orbital arch, where it interlaces with the orbicularis oculi muscle and is inserted into the skin. The two frontal bellies extend across the full width of the forehead and blend with each other in the median plane.

The **epicranial aponeurosis**, extending between the frontal and the occipital fleshy bellies, caps the dome of the skull, and has been termed the galea aponeurotica (from *galea*, a leather helmet). Posteriorly, it is attached to the superior nuchal line—its medial part directly, and its lateral part indirectly through the occipital bellies. Anteriorly, it joins the frontal bellies, sending a short slip between them; and a fascial layer beneath that is fixed to the supra-orbital margin. Laterally, it gives origin to the superior and anterior auricular muscles, and is continued downwards as a thin sheet that blends with the temporal fascia a short distance above the zygomatic arch. The superficial surface is bound to the skin of the scalp by dense fibrous strands with enmeshed fatty granules, but the deep surface is connected with the pericranium only by loose areolar tissue.

The attachments of the aponeurosis limit effusions beneath it which may extend forwards to the supra-orbital margin and downwards almost to the zygomatic arch. The mobility of the scalp as a whole accounts for the readiness with which it may be torn away from the pericranium and for the scalp-hunter's dexterity in removing his victim's scalp by cutting through the aponeurosis.

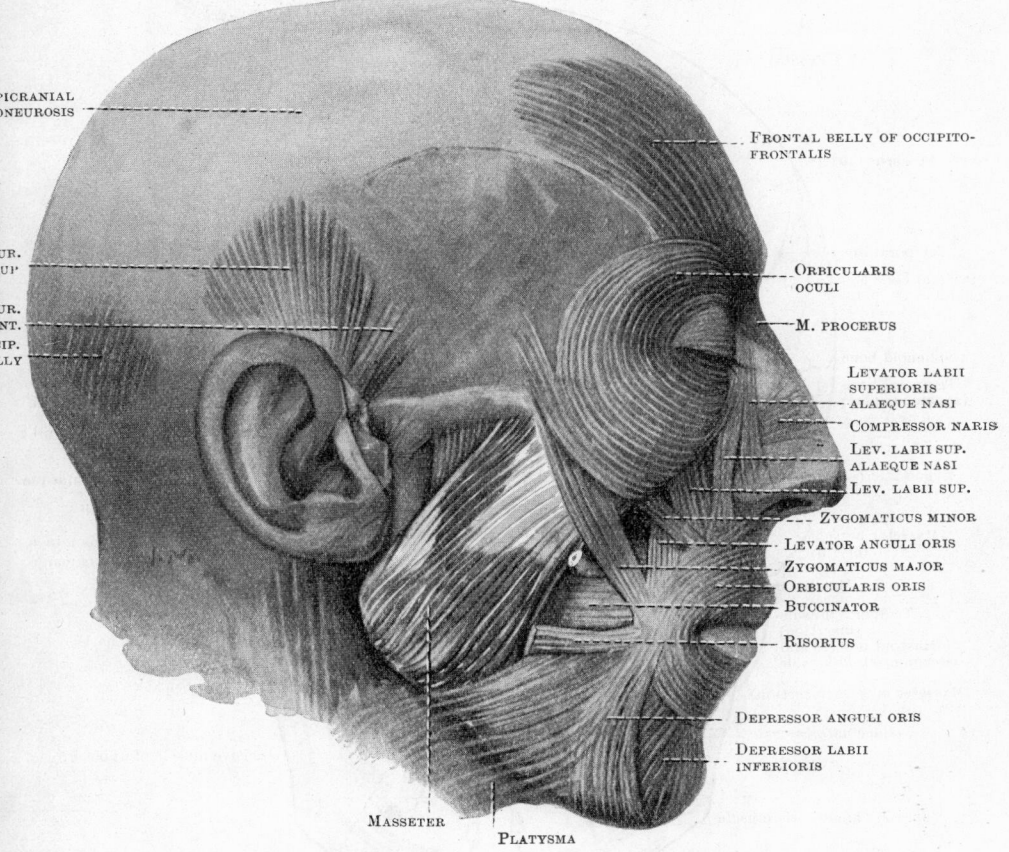

FIG. 336.—MUSCLES OF THE FACE AND SCALP (Muscles of Expression).

The **extrinsic muscles of the auricle** are three in number: posterior, superior, and anterior. They are rudimentary and usually functionless, though variable in development and capable of training.

The **auricularis posterior** is a narrow fleshy slip which **arises** from the surface of the mastoid part of the temporal bone and is **inserted** into the cranial surface of the auricle. It bridges across the groove between the mastoid part of the temporal bone and the auricle, and conceals the posterior auricular vessels and nerve.

The **auricularis superior** is a fan-shaped muscle, and is the largest of the three. It **arises** from the epicranial aponeurosis and the temporal fascia, and descends to be **inserted** into the medial surface of the auricle opposite the fossa of the antihelix.

The **auricularis anterior** is a small muscle placed in front of the auricularis superior; it stretches obliquely from the temporal fascia to the anterior part of the medial surface of the helix.

The intrinsic muscles of the auricle and the small muscles of the tympanic cavity (tensor tympani and stapedius) are described with the Ear as an Organ of Sense.

Muscles of the Face

The facial muscles are divided into groups associated with the eyelid, the external nose, and the mouth.

1. The **muscles of the eyelids** are the orbicularis oculi, and the levator palpebræ superioris—which is described with the orbital muscles (p. 404).

Orbicularis Oculi.—The orbicularis oculi is a transversely oval sphincter

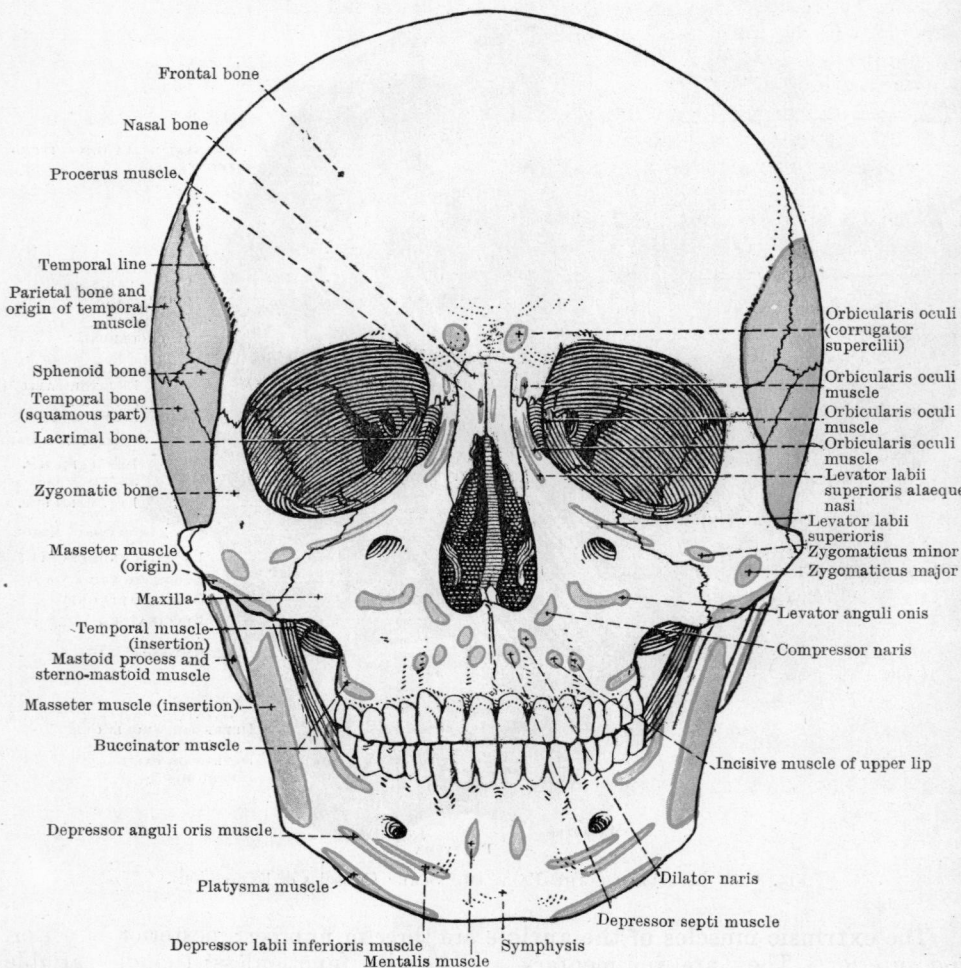

FIG. 337.—ANTERIOR VIEW OF THE SKULL, showing the muscular attachments.

muscle that surrounds and occupies the eyelids (Fig. 336). It is divisible into two parts which differ in action. The peripheral, **orbital part** has red, thick fibres, spreads on to the forehead, temple, and cheek, and closes the eyes forcibly ; the central, **palpebral part** has pale, thin fibres, is situated beneath the skin of the eyelids, and closes the eyes gently.

The **orbital part** is attached to the medial orbital margin between the supra-orbital notch and the infra-orbital foramen—the medial palpebral ligament, also a source of origin, interrupting this bony attachment. Fibres arch from the site above the ligament round the upper lid, and then return round the lower lid to the site below the ligament, without interruption laterally. (Some authors describe interlacing of the fibres of both lids laterally). A deep bundle (*corrugator super-cilii*), inseparable from the orbital fibres and arising from the medial part of the supra-orbital margin, runs, intermingling laterally with the superficial fibres, to be inserted into the skin of the medial half of the eyebrow.

The **palpebral part** has two origins—a superficial origin from the medial palpebral ligament and adjacent bone, and a deep origin from the crest of the lacrimal bone. The superficial fibres (preseptal) arch round the peripheral (septal) portions of the eyelids, while the deep fibres (pretarsal) pass across the tarsal plates; both sets interlace at the lateral angle to form the *lateral palpebral raphe*. The deep fibres, termed the *lacrimal part*, since they enclose the lacrimal canaliculi and run posterior to the lacrimal sac, are important, because their destruction, *e.g.* in operations on the lacrimal sac, results in the lower lid falling away from the eyeball (ectropion—seen also in facial paralysis). A slip of delicate fibres runs from the palpebral part along the free margin of each lid.

2. The **muscles of the nose**, small and feeble, are the procerus, compressor naris, dilator naris, and depressor septi.

Procerus.—The muscles of the two sides are united. **Arising** from the fascia covering the lower parts of the nasal bones, they broaden to be **inserted** into the skin between and above the eyebrows, interlace with the frontal bellies of the occipito-frontalis, and draw down the skin at the root of the nose and produce transverse wrinkling of the skin in this area.

Compressor Naris.—This muscle **arises** from the upper end of the canine eminence and is **inserted** with its fellow into an aponeurosis on the cartilaginous part of the nose. It compresses the nostril in the production of certain sounds, and its action is well seen in the crying infant.

Dilator Naris.—The dilator naris **arises** from the maxilla above the lateral incisor tooth and is **inserted** into the lateral part of the lower margin of the ala of the nose. It dilates the nostril.

The **depressor septi** is a flat quadrangular muscle that **arises** with the medial fibres of the dilator, and is **inserted** into the mobile part of the nasal septum. It draws the septum downwards and narrows the nostril.

3. The **muscles of the mouth** are bilaterally placed, except for orbicularis oris. They are :—(1) orbicularis oris ; (2) levator labii superioris alæque nasi; (3) levator labii superioris ; (4) zygomaticus minor ; (5) levator anguli oris ; (6) zygomaticus major ; (7) risorius ; (8) depressor anguli oris ; (9) depressor labii inferioris ; (10) mentalis ; (11) buccinator. With them may be considered the platysma, as it is a prolongation downwards into the neck of the same superficial sheet.

Orbicularis Oris.—The orbicularis oris is a sphincter formed by contributions from muscles converging on the mouth ; it arches round the two lips, its constituent fibres partly interlacing at the angles of the mouth, thereby forming a nodule that may be felt in the living subject. Lying between the skin and mucous membrane of the lips, it is limited superiorly by the nose, and inferiorly by the junction of the lower lip and chin. The deeper fibres in the upper lip are derived from the buccinator muscle, reinforced by the *superior incisive* bundles. This pair of little bands arises from the nasal septum and from the maxilla above the lateral incisor teeth, and each passes laterally towards the angle of the mouth. The more superficial fibres are continued upwards from the depressor anguli oris and are inserted into the skin of the central part of the lip. A similar arrangement is found in the orbicularis oris in the lower lip. The deeper fibres are derived from the buccinator, but they are reinforced on each side by an *inferior incisive* bundle, which runs laterally from the mandible below the canine tooth. The more superficial fibres are continued downwards from the levator anguli oris to be inserted into the skin of the median part of the lip.

Levator Labii Superioris Alæque Nasi.—With the dual action implied in its name, this is a narrow band that **arises** from the root of the frontal process of the maxilla, and descends along the side of the nose to be **inserted** partly into the ala of the nose and partly into the skin of the naso-labial groove, blending with the orbicularis oris.

Levator Labii Superioris.—The levator labii superioris **arises** from the maxilla immediately above the infra-orbital foramen, and is **inserted** into the skin of the naso-labial groove ; it conceals the infra-orbital vessels and nerve.

26

Zygomaticus Minor.—This slender slip **arises** from the zygomatic bone, and is often continuous near its origin with the orbicularis oculi; it is **inserted** into the skin of the naso-labial groove and upper lip.

In the B.N.A., the last three muscles are named the angular, infra-orbital, and zygomatic heads of the quadratus labii superioris.

Levator Anguli Oris [M. Caninus].—The levator anguli oris **arises** from the maxilla below the infra-orbital foramen and under cover of the zygomaticus minor. It is directed laterally and downwards, to be **inserted** into the orbicularis oris and the skin at the angle of the mouth, some fibres arching into the lower lip.

Zygomaticus Major [M. Zygomaticus].—This narrow muscular band **arises** from the zygomatic portion of the zygomatic arch, and passes to the angle of the mouth, to be **inserted** partly into the skin, partly into the orbicularis oris.

Risorius.—The risorius is a thin flat muscle which is in part a continuation of the platysma on the face, and in part a separate muscle, with an **origin** from the parotid fascia. It passes transversely forwards to be **inserted** into the skin at the angle of the mouth.

Depressor Anguli Oris [M. Triangularis].—This muscle **arises** from the oblique line of the mandible and is continuous with the platysma (Fig. 336, p. 399). It is triangular in form, its fibres converging on the angle of the mouth, where they are **inserted** into the orbicularis oris and the skin. Some of the fibres reach the upper lip through the orbicularis muscle.

Depressor Labii Inferioris [Quadratus Labii Inferioris].—The depressor of the lower lip **arises** from the lateral surface of the mandible deep and medial to the depressor anguli oris (Fig. 337, p. 400). It is quadrilateral in form, and is directed upwards to be **inserted** into the orbicularis oris and the skin of the lower lip. Its lateral fibres are overlapped by the depressor anguli oris, and its medial fibres join with those of the opposite muscle.

Mentalis.—This small muscle **arises** from the mandible below the incisor teeth, and passes downwards to be **inserted** into the skin of the chin.

Buccinator.—The buccinator muscle lies in the side wall of the mouth, and is in series posteriorly with the constrictor muscles of the pharynx. It **arises** from the outer surfaces of the maxilla and mandible opposite the sockets of the molar teeth (Fig. 337), and from the pterygo-mandibular ligament. Its fibres are directed forwards to the angle of the mouth, where they blend with the corresponding (upper and lower) portions of the orbicularis oris muscle. The *middle fibres* of the muscle decussate at the angle of the mouth—the lower set passing to the upper lip, the upper set to the lower lip (cf. orbicularis oris, p. 401). The buccinator is covered on its deep surface with the mucous membrane of the mouth. Towards its insertion it is concealed by the muscles which converge on the angle of the mouth; and it is covered behind by the masseter, from which it is separated by the buccal pad of fat. It is pierced by the duct of the parotid gland, and by branches of the buccal nerve. A small gap between the fibres arising from the maxilla and those arising from the pterygo-mandibular ligament transmits the tendon of the tensor palati as it twists round the pterygoid hamulus to gain the soft palate.

Platysma.—The platysma is a thin, quadrilateral sheet that **arises** in the upper pectoral and deltoid regions by scattered bundles from the superficial fascia and the skin, and extends from the chest over the side of the neck between the superficial and deep fasciæ to the face (Fig. 336 and Pl. XXX, Fig. 1).

It is directed upwards and forwards, and is partly **inserted** (by its intermediate fibres) into the lower border of the mandible, becoming connected with the depressor labii inferioris and depressor anguli oris muscles (Figs. 336, 337). The more anterior fibres pass across the median plane and decussate, for a variable distance below the chin, with those of the opposite side. The posterior fibres sweep over the angle of the jaw and become continuous with the risorius muscle.

Nerve-Supply.—The facial and scalp muscles are all innervated by the **facial nerve.** The *posterior auricular branch* supplies the posterior auricular muscle and the occipital belly of occipito-frontalis; the branches into which the facial nerve breaks up in the parotid gland supply the frontal belly, the superior and anterior auricular muscles, the several muscles associated with the apertures of the orbit, nose, and mouth (including the buccinator), and the platysma (cervical branch). The facial nerve conveys motor fibres to these muscles, and sensory fibres from them which gain the nucleus of the fifth nerve (Edgeworth and Wakeley) ; there is a similar arrangement in the innervation of the ocular muscles (p. 406) and probably also for the muscles of mastication and the muscles of the tongue.

Actions.—The almost infinite variety of facial expression is produced partly by the action of these muscles, partly by their inactivity, or by the action of antagonising muscles (antithesis). Joy is betrayed by the action of one set of muscles, while grief is accompanied by the contraction of an opposing set. Determination or eagerness is accompanied by a fixed expression due to a combination of muscles acting together ; and despair is expressed by a relaxation of muscular action.

The frontal belly of **occipito-frontalis** raises the eyebrows as in surprise ; alternate contraction of the occipital and frontal bellies moves the scalp backwards and forwards. The **auricular** muscles may be capable of moving the auricle upwards and backwards.

The **procerus,** assisting the upper deep part of the orbital portion of orbicularis oculi in wrinkling the skin at the root of the nose and adjacent part of the forehead, is so habitually in use in some people as to be almost involuntary in its action. The **orbicularis oculi** contracts in protecting the eye from intense light and injury. The **orbital part** closes the lids firmly ; the **palpebral part** closes the lids gently, but it acts also reflexly—contracting periodically to moisten and clean the eye. The importance of the *lacrimal part* has been considered (p. 401). The levator palpebræ superioris and occipito-frontalis are antagonists of the orbicularis oculi. The **muscles of the nose** take part in contraction and dilatation of the nostrils. Their tonic action supports the alæ nasi, which do not move during ordinary respiration ; but in deep and laboured respiration a visible movement of elevation and expansion takes place with each inspiration. In enfeebled states, on the other hand, owing to the diminution of the tonic action, the alæ nasi are drawn in with each inspiration giving a characteristic "sharp" appearance to the nose. Of the muscles of the mouth, the **orbicularis oris** has a complex action, depending on the degree of contraction of its component parts, producing compression, contraction, and protrusion. The **zygomaticus major** and **risorius** are associated with mirth, the **depressor anguli oris** with grief, while the **mentalis** raises the skin of the chin and protrudes the lower lip.

The muscles of the lips are concerned in the production of speech, and they have an important function in retaining food during mastication. The delicate co-ordination between the **buccinator** and the tongue muscles in keeping food poised between the grinding teeth may be appreciated by the infrequency of the accident of biting either the inside of the cheek or the tongue. Apart from retracting the angles of the mouth as antagonists of the orbicularis oris, the buccinators control the expulsion of air from the distended cheeks (*buccinator*—a trumpeter). With the orbicularis protruding the lips the buccinators cave in the cheeks, producing a suctorial action. The **platysma** (Pl. XXX, Fig. 1). retracts and depresses the angle of the mouth. Its contraction when the head is extended produces longitudinal ridging of the skin, well seen in violent stages of athletic effort, and the view has been advanced that its contraction prevents the retraction of the soft tissue at the root of the neck which would press on the veins and impede the return of blood to the heart in violent inspiratory effort. Its action is evident in sudden fear. It depresses the mandible, but only against resistance.

When the muscles of one side of the face are paralysed because of injury to the facial nerve (peripheral paralysis) the face is twisted to the opposite side by the active muscles of that side, the lines of the features are smoothed out, the eye cannot be closed and tears run down the cheeks because the lacrimal puncta are not kept close to the eyeball through the lower lids falling away (p. 401). The lips are open upon the active side and slightly closed towards the affected side. Food and saliva cannot be retained by the affected cheek and escape from between the lips on that side.

For further information, see Lightoller, *Journ. Anat.* 1925 ; Huber on the *Evolution of Facial Musculature ;* and Darwin on the *Expression of the Emotions in Man and Animals.*

Fasciæ and Muscles of the Orbit

The eyeball, with its muscles, vessels, and nerves, is lodged in a mass of soft and yielding fat within the cavity of the orbit. The eyeball is surrounded by a fascial cup called the **fascial sheath of the eyeball**, which is loosely connected with the sclera by easily cleft *episcleral tissue.* The fascial cup accompanies the eyeball in its wider excursions, but there is a slight play of the eyeball within the cup. Anteriorly the sheath is adherent to the overlying conjunctiva, while more

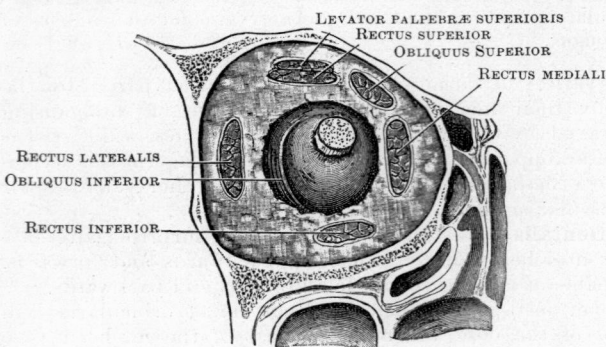

posteriorly it is pierced by the muscles, vessels, and nerves of the eyeball. The fascial cup is thickened at the points where the muscles pierce it, and is reflected backwards over them as tightly-adherent sleeves, so that the fascial sheath swings at anchor by the fascial expansions or *check ligaments* that extend from the muscle sheaths to the orbital walls; the strongest of these ligaments extend from the lateral and medial

FIG. 338.—CORONAL SECTION THROUGH THE LEFT ORBIT BEHIND THE EYEBALL TO SHOW THE ARRANGEMENT OF MUSCLES.

rectus towards the medial and lateral palpebral ligaments. In the case of the inferior rectus, these expansions, sweeping towards the medial and lateral palpebral ligaments, form a hammock that holds the eyeball up in position and must therefore be preserved in surgical removal of the floor of the orbit. The fascial sheath helps to form a socket for an artificial eye when the eyeball is removed, and

after this operation the muscles cannot retract far because of their tight adherence to the fascial sleeves.

The muscles of the orbit (Figs. 338-341) are seven in number: one, the levator palpebræ superioris, belongs to the upper eyelid; the other six are extrinsic muscles of the eyeball.

Levator Palpebræ Superioris.—The levator palpebræ superioris lies immediately beneath the roof of

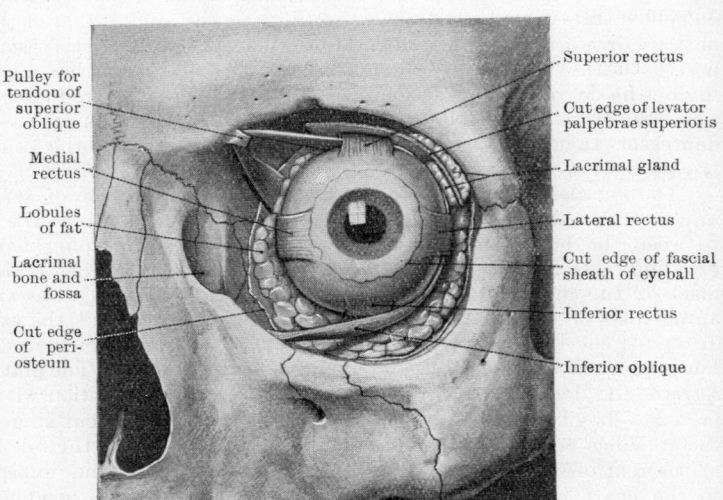

FIG. 339.—DISSECTION OF ORBIT FROM THE FRONT. (R.D.L.).

the orbit and covers the superior rectus muscle. It has a narrow origin from the roof of the orbit in front of the optic foramen. It expands as it passes forwards to be inserted, in relation to the upper lid, into a membranous expansion. This aponeurosis has the following attachments: (1) arching from side to side over the eyeball, its ends, or horns, are fixed to the mid points of the medial and lateral orbital margins; (2) a superficial layer of fibres from the anterior edge of the aponeurosis runs downwards into the eyelid to become attached to the front of the tarsus, and into the skin of the eyelid with the orbicularis; (3) a layer of non-striated (involuntary) muscle fibres **arises** from the deep surface of the aponeurosis and is **inserted** into the upper border of the tarsus of the upper eyelid. The muscle has an additional attachment through its fascial sheath; anteriorly, the sheath is thickened by fusion with the sheath of the rectus superior, and is then attached to the superior fornix of the conjunctiva, so that the fornix also is pulled up when the lid is elevated.

Non-striated muscle is present in the eyelids of land mammals, but in the seal striated slips run from the recti to the eyelids, a condition partly represented by the striated elevator of the upper lid.

Mm. Recti.—The recti muscles are four in number—**superior, inferior, medial, and lateral**—and they all arise from a *common tendinous ring.* Medially and superiorly the ring is attached around the optic foramen; laterally it bridges across the superior orbital fissure to be fixed to a tubercle on its lower margin. The part of the ring that gives origin to the rectus lateralis transmits the two divisions of the oculo-motor nerve, the naso-ciliary nerve, and the abducent nerve. Forming flattened bands which lie in the fat around the optic nerve and eyeball, the four muscles end in tendons which pierce the fascial sheath and are **inserted** into the sclera about eight millimetres behind the margin of the cornea.

The **superior** and **inferior recti** are inserted in the vertical plane slightly medial to the axis of the eyeball; the **lateral** and **medial recti** in the transverse plane of the eyeball; and all are attached in front of the equator of the eyeball.

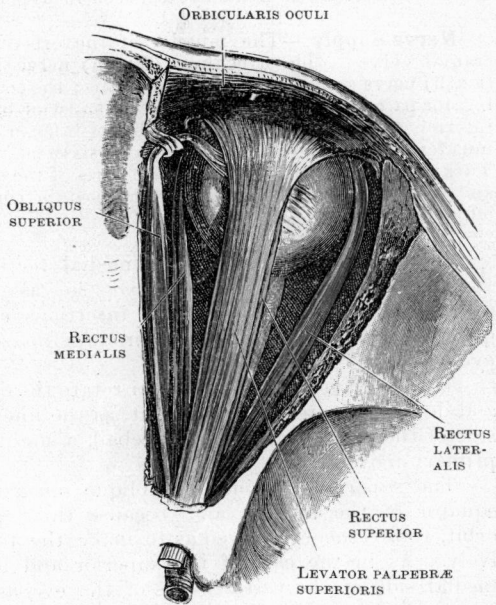

FIG. 340.—MUSCLES OF THE RIGHT ORBIT (from above).

Superior Oblique.—The superior oblique arises from the margin of the optic foramen between the rectus superior and rectus medialis. It passes forwards, as a narrow muscular band, medial to the rectus superior, and at the anterior part of the orbit it forms a narrow tendon which passes through a special fibro-cartilaginous pulley (trochlea) attached to the roof of the orbit. Its direction is then altered, and, passing laterally between the tendon of the superior rectus and the eyeball, it is **inserted** into the sclera between the superior and lateral recti, midway between the margin of the cornea and the entrance of the optic nerve.

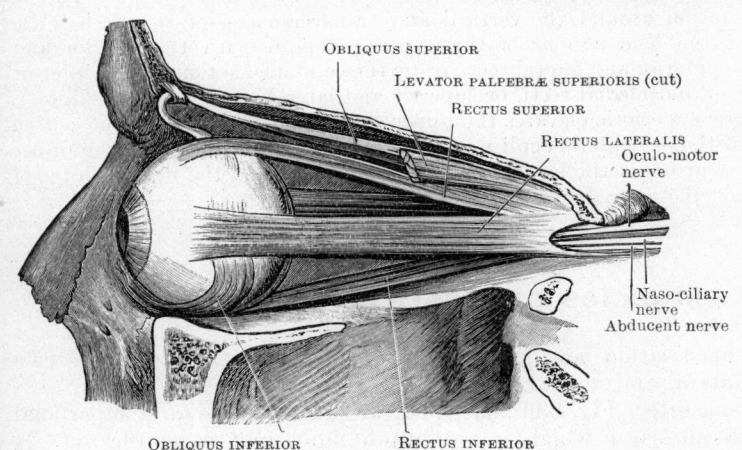

FIG. 341.—MUSCLES OF THE LEFT ORBIT (from lateral aspect).

Inferior Oblique.—The inferior oblique **arises** from the floor of the orbit immediately lateral to the naso-lacrimal canal. It is a slender, rounded slip which passes laterally below the inferior rectus tendon, and curves upwards between the lateral rectus and the eyeball, to be **inserted** into the sclera between the superior and lateral recti, and farther back than the superior oblique muscle.

The superior oblique muscle occasionally arises from the site of the pulley. This is normal in lower vertebrates, where the muscle is the counterpart of the inferior oblique; in mammals, a posterior belly develops ; the two bellies join, and the pulley and tendon are the remains of the original anterior belly.

M. orbitalis is a rudimentary bundle of non-striated muscular fibres that bridges across the inferior orbital fissure and infra-orbital groove. It is supplied by sympathetic fibres, and it has been suggested that contraction of the muscle compresses the veins, producing congestion that causes the protrusion of the eyeball seen in hyperactivity of the sympathetic system.

Nerve-Supply.—The muscles of the orbit are supplied by the third, fourth, and sixth cranial nerves. The **trochlear (fourth) nerve** supplies the obliquus superior ; the **abducent (sixth) nerve** supplies the rectus lateralis ; the **oculo-motor (third) nerve** supplies the others—the levator palpebræ superioris and rectus superior by its superior division ; the rectus medialis and inferior, and the obliquus inferior by its inferior division. The afferent fibres from the ocular muscles run in the third, fourth, and sixth nerves to the nucleus of the fifth nerve (Woollard ; Turkhan). The non-striated muscle fibres of the eyelids are supplied by the sympathetic system, and the upper lid is retracted or dropped in conditions that stimulate or paralyse this system (cf. p. 403).

Actions.—The lateral and medial recti, by virtue of their insertions in front of the equator, rotate the eyeball so as to make the pupil look laterally or medially, respectively. As their insertions extend equally on to the upper and lower quadrants of the sclera, they produce no rotation around the transverse axis of the eyeball.

The superior and inferior recti rotate the eyeball so as to make the pupil look upwards and downwards, respectively ; but, as the line of pull of each muscle passes to the medial side of the vertical axis of the eyeball, a slight degree of medial rotation accompanies the primary movement.

The superior and inferior oblique muscles, by virtue of their insertion behind the equator of the eyeball and because their pull is exerted from the forepart of the orbit, rotate the eyeball so as to make the pupil look downwards and upwards, respectively. As in the case of the superior and inferior recti, the lines of pull pass to the medial side of the vertical axis of the eyeball, but, as the pull is exerted from in front instead of from behind, the opposite effect—viz. lateral rotation—is added to the primary movement.

When the eyeball is rotated so as to make the pupil look directly downwards, the superior oblique and the inferior rectus act together and the lateral rotation caused by the obliquus is counteracted by the medial rotation caused by the rectus. In a similar way the inferior oblique and the superior rectus act together to produce a purely upward direction of the pupil.

Combinations of rotation around the vertical and transverse axes of the eyeball are brought about by the combined actions of the superior oblique with the inferior and medial recti, or with the inferior and lateral recti, or by the combined actions of the inferior oblique with the superior and medial recti, or superior and lateral recti.

The levator palpebræ superioris elevates the upper eyelid and antagonises the action of the palpebral part of the orbicularis oculi muscle. The unstriped muscle of the upper lid attached to the aponeurosis of the levator palpebræ superioris and the upper border of the tarsus raises the lid involuntarily.

Muscles of Mastication

The muscles of mastication are the masseter, the temporal, and the two pterygoid muscles—lateral and medial.

Masseter.—The masseter (Fig. 336), flat, quadrangular and the most superficial of these muscles, has an origin which is partly tendinous and partly fleshy. It **arises** in two parts : (1) superficially from the lower border of the zygomatic arch in its anterior two-thirds, and (2) more deeply from the deep surface of the zygomatic arch in its whole length. The superficial fibres are directed downwards and backwards towards the angle of the mandible ; the deeper fibres are directed vertically downwards. The muscle is **inserted** by fleshy and tendinous fibres into the lateral surfaces of the coronoid process, ramus and angle of the mandible. The deepest fibres blend with the subjacent fibres of the temporal muscle.

The muscle is partially concealed by the parotid gland, the accessory parotid gland, and the parotid duct (which may be rolled under the finger against the contracted muscle as the duct turns round the anterior border of the masseter to pierce the buccinator) ; by the anterior facial vein ; by the branches of the facial nerve ; and by the zygomaticus major and platysma muscles. It conceals the ramus of the mandible, and, anteriorly, is separated from the buccinator muscle by the buccal pad of fat. The masseteric nerve and vessels reach its deep surface through the mandibular notch.

Temporal Muscle.—This is a fan-shaped muscle that **arises** from the whole of the floor of the temporal fossa and also from the temporal fascia, which covers it. Although thin at its origin, its converging fibres form a thick tendon as they pass medial to the zygomatic arch — the anterior fibres vertically, the posterior horizontally and then curved—to be **inserted** into the apex and deep surface of the coronoid process, and into the anterior border of the ramus of the mandible, almost as far as the last molar tooth, its lower fibres becoming continuous with the buccinator.

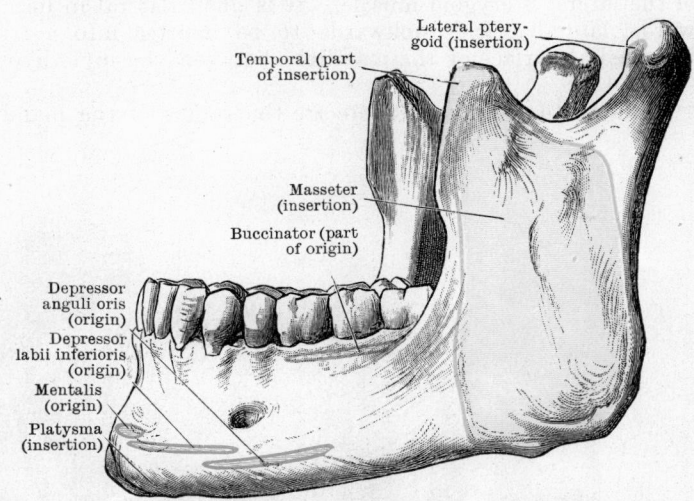

FIG. 342.—MUSCLE-ATTACHMENTS TO THE LATERAL SURFACE OF MANDIBLE.

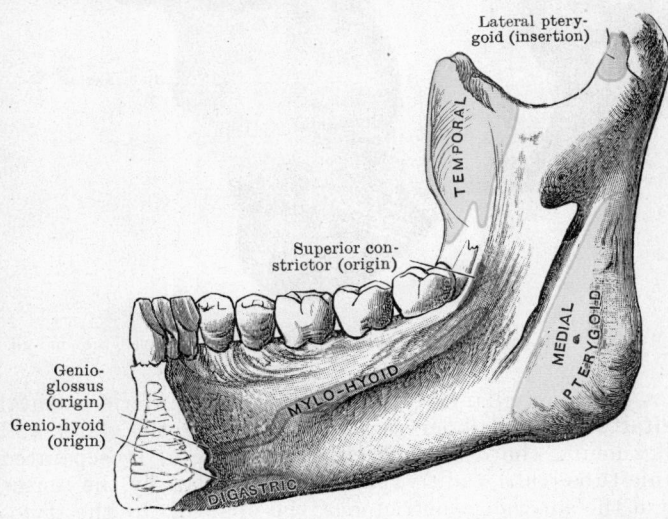

FIG. 343.—MUSCLE-ATTACHMENTS ON THE MEDIAL SIDE OF MANDIBLE.

As the muscle passes to its insertion it is concealed by the zygomatic arch, the masseter muscle, and the coronoid process of the mandible. The maxillary artery usually passes between it and the lateral pterygoid muscle. The masseteric nerve and vessels appear at its posterior border; the buccal nerve and vessels at its anterior border.

Lateral Pterygoid Muscle. — The lateral pterygoid muscle is deeply placed in the infra-temporal fossa. It **arises** by two heads —upper and lower. The *upper head* is attached to the infra-temporal surface of the greater wing of the sphenoid; the *lower head* takes origin from the lateral surface of the lateral pterygoid plate. The muscle is directed laterally and backwards to be **inserted** into the front of the neck of the mandible (Figs. 342 and 343), and the capsule of the mandibular joint.

This muscle is covered by the lower part of the temporal muscle and the coronoid process of the mandible, and its lower head is usually crossed by the maxillary

26 a

artery. It conceals the mandibular branch of the trigeminal nerve, the pterygoid origin of the medial pterygoid muscle, and the spheno-mandibular ligament.

Medial Pterygoid Muscle.—The medial pterygoid muscle has a double **origin** —(1) from the medial surface of the lateral pterygoid plate and the posterior surface of the tubercle of the palatine bone, and (2) by a small slip from the tuberosity of the maxilla. Its two heads of origin embrace the inferior fibres of the lateral pterygoid muscle. It is quadrilateral in form, and is directed downwards, laterally, and backwards to be **inserted** into a triangular impression on the medial surface of the mandible between the mylo-hyoid groove and the angle (Fig. 343).

Lateral to the muscle there are the ramus of the mandible, the temporal and

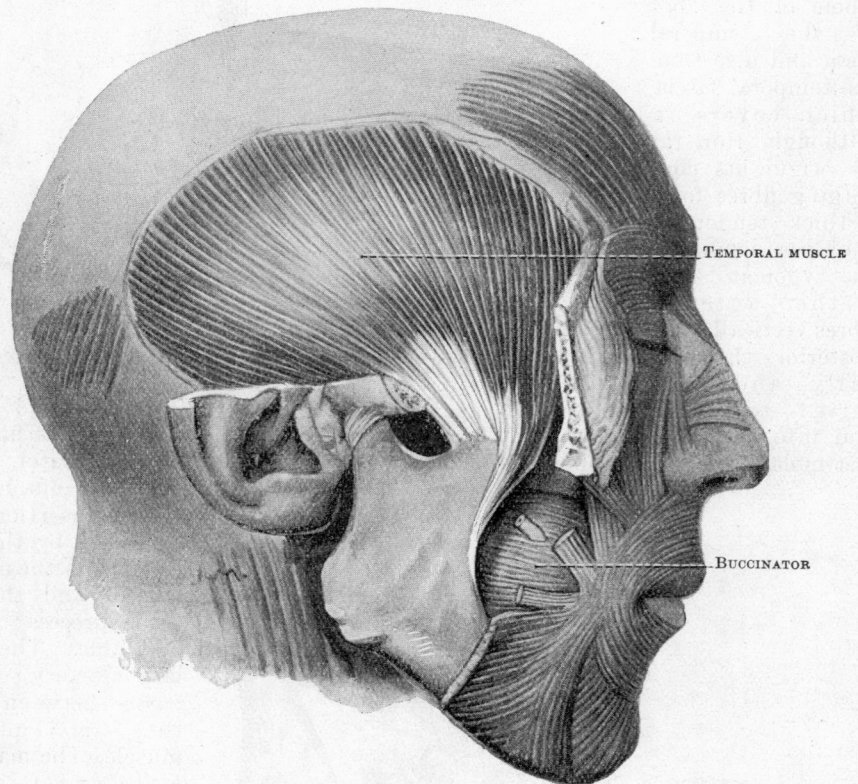

FIG. 344.—THE RIGHT TEMPORAL MUSCLE. (The Zygomatic Arch and the Masseter Muscle have been removed.)

lateral pterygoid muscles, the maxillary vessels with their inferior dental branches, the inferior dental and lingual nerves, part of the parotid gland, and the spheno-mandibular ligament; the deep surface, at its origin, is separated from the pharyngo-tympanic tube [tuba auditiva] and levator palati by the tensor palati, and, lower down, from the superior constrictor of the pharynx by the stylo-glossus and stylo-pharyngeus.

Nerve-Supply.—The **mandibular division of the trigeminal (fifth cranial) nerve** supplies all the muscles of mastication. The medial pterygoid muscle is supplied by the nerve before it divides; the other muscles are innervated by the anterior division.

Actions.—The temporal, masseter, and medial pterygoid muscles raise the jaw and have great power in keeping the teeth clenched. (But it is important to note that in the dislocated jaw their contraction increases the opening of the mouth). The mouth opens by the relaxation of these muscles and the weight of the mandible, and, against resistance, by the contraction of the suprahyoid and infrahyoid groups and the platysma, and the lateral pterygoids. When the teeth are tightly clenched, the hyoid bone will be found firmly fixed. (See action of hyoid muscles p. 412).

The lateral pterygoids protrude the jaw and pull the articular discs forward; the temporal muscles retract the jaw.

The co-ordinated alternate action of the right lateral pterygoid with the elevators of the left side, and of the left one with the elevators of the right side, produces chewing movements.

MUSCLES OF THE NECK

In addition to the muscles included among those of the vertebral column (p. 387), the following muscles lie wholly or chiefly in the neck: (1) sterno-(cleido-)mastoid; (2) the muscles of the hyoid bone (suprahyoid and infrahyoid) (3) the muscles of the tongue (extrinsic and intrinsic); (4) the muscles of the pharynx and soft palate; and (5) the intrinsic muscles of the larynx. The last group is described with the larynx itself.

Sterno - (cleido-) mastoid. —The sterno-mastoid muscle lies obliquely in the side of the neck between the

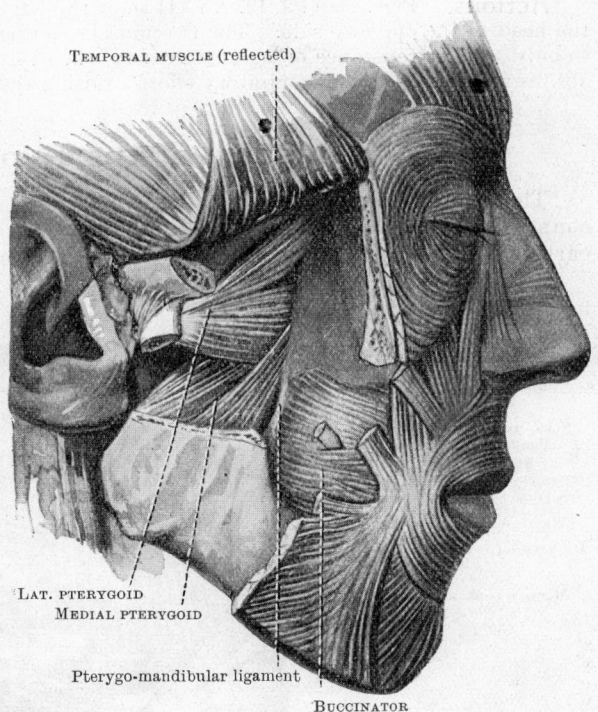

FIG. 345.—THE PTERYGOID MUSCLES OF THE RIGHT SIDE.

anterior and posterior triangles, and stands out prominently when thrown into action (Pl. XXX, Figs. 3, 4; Pl. XXXI, Fig. 3). It arises by two heads— (1) a narrow, tendinous, *sternal* head from the anterior surface of the manubrium sterni (Fig. 377, p. 451), and (2) a broader, *clavicular* head, partly tendinous, partly fleshy, from the upper surface of the clavicle in its medial third. The clavicular head ascends to blend with the deep surface of the sternal head forming a thick belly which is inserted by a short, strong tendon into the anterior border and tip of the mastoid process, and the lateral surface of the mastoid portion of the temporal bone, and by a thin tendinous expansion into the lateral half of the superior nuchal line of the occipital bone (Fig. 322, p. 393)

The careful dissection of the relations of this muscle provides a good guide to the disposition of most of the structures in the neck. It is seen and felt superficially throughout its extent, but its upper part is overlapped anteriorly by the parotid gland; the external jugular vein descends over its surface; and, curving round its posterior border, there are the lesser occipital nerve, the great auricular nerve, the anterior cutaneous nerve of the neck, and the medial and intermediate supraclavicular nerves—all, except the first two, covered by the platysma. Its deep surface is related to a large number of structures. Its lower third is in relation with the scalenus anterior, the phrenic nerve, the transverse cervical and suprascapular arteries, and, at its posterior border, with the brachial plexus; farther forward, the infrahyoid muscles (along with the anterior jugular vein, which crosses them superficially above the clavicle) separate the muscle from the common carotid artery, the subclavian artery and the internal jugular vein, the lower part of the vein being opposite the depression between the two heads of the muscle. The middle third is in relation with the internal jugular, the common facial and lingual veins, the external and internal carotid arteries (with the vagus posteriorly), the descending branch of the hypoglossal nerve, the nervus descendens cervicalis, and deep cervical lymph glands. The upper third is related to the cervical plexus, the scalenus medius, the levator scapulae, the posterior belly of the digastric, and, near its insertion, to the splenius capitis and longissimus capitis. The occipital artery runs upwards and backwards along the lower border of the digastric; and the accessory nerve, escaping from under cover of that muscle, descends to sink into the sterno-mastoid. A group of lymphatic glands is chained along its posterior border.

Nerve-Supply.—The muscle is innervated by the accessory nerve, and also by branches from the second cervical nerve which are said to be afferent.

Actions.—Figs. 1 and 2, Pl. XXXII show the left sterno-mastoid in action as it turns the head to the opposite side. The two muscles acting together can flex the head, but do so only against resistance or against gravity when the subject is supine. They function also as muscles of forced inspiratory effort—raising the thorax when the head is fixed.

Muscles of the Hyoid Bone

There are two groups of these muscles: (1) infrahyoid muscles, which connect the hyoid bone to the scapula, the wall of the thorax, and the thyroid cartilage; (2) suprahyoid muscles, which connect it to the mandible, cranium,

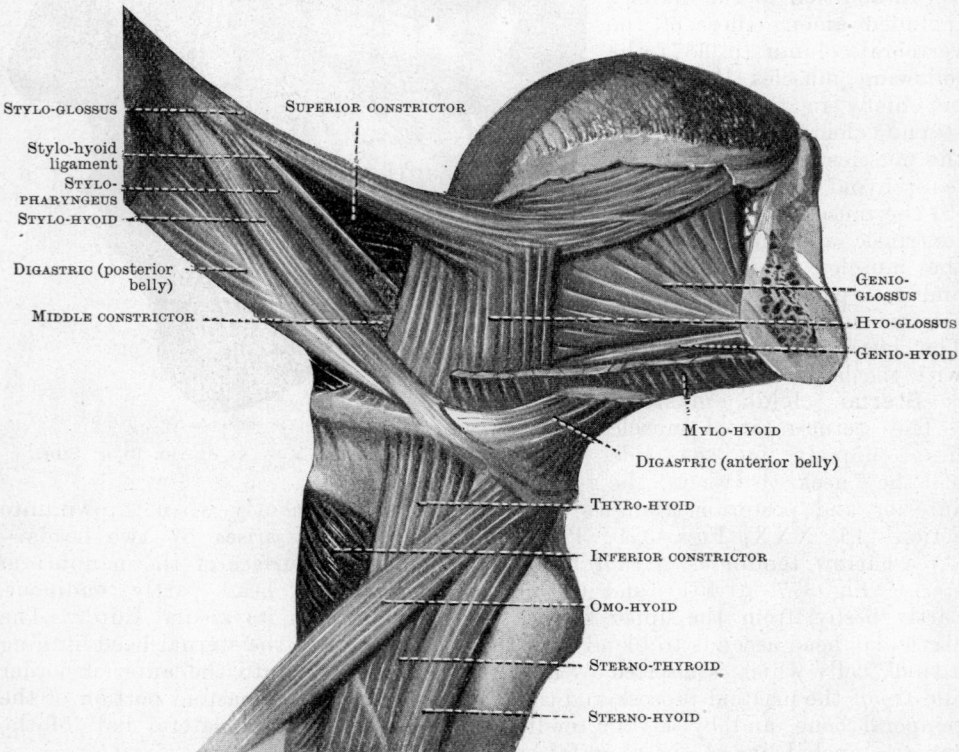

FIG. 346.—THE MUSCLES OF THE TONGUE AND HYOID BONE (right side).

and tongue. The middle constrictor muscle of the pharynx also is attached to the hyoid bone.

The **infrahyoid muscles** are the omo-hyoid, sterno-hyoid, sterno-thyroid, and thyro-hyoid.

Omo-hyoid.—The omo-hyoid is a muscle with two bellies—superior and inferior. The *inferior belly* arises from the upper margin of the scapula and the supra-scapular ligament (Fig. 191, p. 227). It is a narrow muscular band which passes obliquely forwards and upwards across the scalene muscles to end in an intermediate tendon under cover of the sterno-mastoid muscle. From this tendon the *superior belly* proceeds upwards across the carotid sheath, to be **inserted** into the lower border of the body of the hyoid bone, lateral to the sterno-hyoid. A process of the deep cervical fascia binds down the tendon and the inferior belly to the clavicle and the first rib.

Sterno-hyoid.—The sterno-hyoid muscle **arises** from the posterior surface of the manubrium and from the posterior sterno-clavicular ligament. Converging slightly towards its fellow it ascends along the medial border of the omo-hyoid and superficial to the sterno-thyroid muscle, to be **inserted** into the medial part of the body of the hyoid bone. Near its origin it is covered by the sternum, clavicle, and sternal head of the sterno-mastoid, but the greater part of the muscle is superficial.

Sterno-thyroid.—The sterno-thyroid muscle **arises** from the back of the manubrium and first costal cartilage. Broader than the preceding muscle, and diverging from its fellow, it passes upwards in front of the trachea and thyroid gland, and deep to the sterno-mastoid, omo-hyoid, and sterno-hyoid muscles. It is **inserted** into the oblique line of the thyroid cartilage. The muscle is marked by an oblique tendinous intersection in the middle of its length.

Thyro-hyoid.—The thyro-hyoid muscle continues the line of the preceding muscle to the hyoid bone. Short and quadrilateral, it **arises** from the oblique line of the thyroid cartilage. Passing over the thyro-hyoid membrane, deep to the omo-hyoid and sterno-hyoid, it is **inserted** into the body and greater horn of the hyoid bone.

The **levator glandulæ thyreoideæ** is an occasional unpaired slip that stretches between the hyoid bone and the isthmus or the pyramidal lobe of the thyroid gland.

The **suprahyoid muscles** are the digastric, stylo-hyoid, mylo-hyoid, and genio-hyoid; and also two muscles—the genio-glossus and hyo-glossus—which will be described along with the extrinsic muscles of the tongue.

Digastric Muscle.—The digastric muscle, as its name implies, has two bellies —anterior and posterior. The *posterior belly* **arises** from the mastoid notch of the temporal bone. It is directed forwards and downwards, in company with the stylo-hyoid muscle, to end in an intermediate tendon which passes through the stirrup-like insertion of the stylo-hyoid, and is connected by a pulley-like band of fascia to the body of the hyoid bone. The *anterior belly* is directed forwards and slightly upwards from the tendon and often from the body of the hyoid bone, and is **inserted** into the lower border of the mandible close to the symphysis (Fig. 343).

The muscle forms the inferior boundary of the space occupied by the submandibular gland. The posterior belly, in company with the stylo-hyoid, crosses lateral to the transverse process of the atlas, the accessory nerve, the internal jugular vein and carotid arteries. The occipital artery runs backwards along its lower margin, and the parotid gland covers its upper border. The hypoglossal nerve emerges from under cover of the muscle. The anterior belly lies on the lower surface of the mylo-hyoid muscle.

Stylo-hyoid.—The stylo-hyoid muscle **arises** from the posterior border of the styloid process of the temporal bone. Extending downwards and forwards, along with the posterior belly of the digastric muscle, it is **inserted** into the body of the hyoid bone by two slips which enclose the tendon of the digastric muscle.

Mylo-hyoid.—The mylo-hyoid muscle forms with its fellow a diaphragm in the floor of the mouth. It **arises** from the mylo-hyoid ridge of the mandible (Fig. 343). It is directed downwards and medially to be **inserted** into the body of the hyoid bone, and, more anteriorly (along with the opposite muscle), into a median raphe that extends from the hyoid bone nearly to the chin.

The muscle is in contact, on its superficial surface, with the digastric muscle, the submandibular gland, the mandible, and the mylo-hyoid vessels and nerve. Its deep surface is partially covered by the mucous membrane of the floor of the mouth, and is separated from the muscles of the tongue by the submandibular duct and the deep part of the gland, the sublingual gland, the lingual and hypoglossal nerves and the vena comitans of the hypoglossal nerve.

Genio-hyoid.—The genio-hyoid muscle **arises** from the inferior genial tubercle of the mandible (Fig. 343). It is directed backwards and slightly downwards, between the mylo-hyoid and the genio-glossus (Fig. 346), to be **inserted** into the body of the hyoid bone. The muscles of opposite sides are often fused together.

Nerve-Supply.—The sterno-hyoid, sterno-thyroid, and omo-hyoid are supplied by the *ansa hypoglossi*, through which the muscles are innervated by fibres ultimately derived from the first

three cervical nerves. The ramus descendens hypoglossi is derived from the loop between the first two cervical nerves, and the ramus descendens cervicalis springs from the second and third. These two trunks combine to form the ansa. The thyro-hyoid muscle is innervated (through the hypoglossal) from the loop between the **first** and **second cervical nerves.**

Three cranial nerves are concerned in the supply of the suprahyoid muscles — an indication of their diverse developmental origins. The posterior belly of the digastric and the stylo-hyoid are supplied by branches from the trunk of the **facial nerve** ; the anterior belly of the digastric and the mylo-hyoid by the **trigeminal** through the mylo-hyoid branch of the inferior dental nerve ; and the genio-hyoid is supplied by the **hypoglossal nerve.** From the point of view of nerve-supply, the genio-hyoid is a link between the infrahyoid muscles and the muscles of the tongue, since its nerve can be traced back to an origin from the communication between the first two cervical nerves and the hypoglossal.

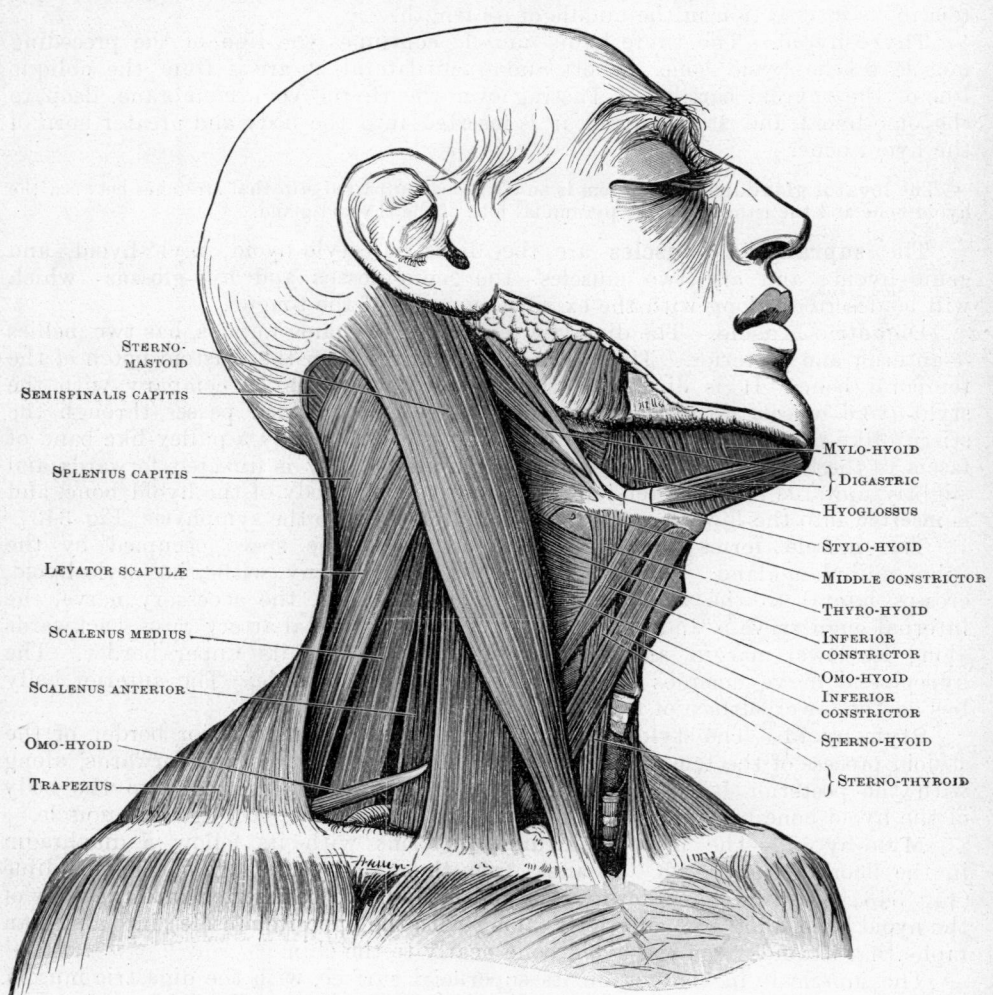

STERNO-MASTOID

SEMISPINALIS CAPITIS

SPLENIUS CAPITIS

LEVATOR SCAPULÆ

SCALENUS MEDIUS

SCALENUS ANTERIOR

OMO-HYOID

TRAPEZIUS

MYLO-HYOID

} DIGASTRIC

HYOGLOSSUS

STYLO-HYOID

MIDDLE CONSTRICTOR

THYRO-HYOID

INFERIOR CONSTRICTOR

OMO-HYOID INFERIOR CONSTRICTOR

STERNO-HYOID

} STERNO-THYROID

FIG. 347.—THE MUSCLES OF THE SIDE OF THE NECK (anterior and posterior triangles).

Actions.—The hyoid bone is steadied by the suprahyoid and infrahyoid muscles, as a ship rides when anchored fore and aft. The hyoid bone, through its muscles, provides a fulcrum for the action of the tongue, and plays a part in mastication, deglutition, and phonation—with the associated muscle groups. The suprahyoid and infrahyoid groups act in concert, and, whether the bone is being raised by one group or lowered by the other, the opposing group steadies the bone like a guy rope. Descent of the hyoid is not usually an active movement. Both hyoid groups relax slightly as the jaws are closed against resistance ; but, when the teeth are forcibly clenched, the hyoid bone will be found firmly fixed—irrespective of the position of the tongue in the mouth. In the first stage of swallowing, the mylo-hyoid and genio-hyoid raise the hyoid bone and the floor of the mouth (the digastric and stylo-hyoid assisting, while the infrahyoid group steadies the bone) ; the tongue is pressed against the palate and the food is forced backwards ; the hyoid bone then regains its resting position.   Though not attached to the hyoid bone, the sterno-thyroid, in concert with the thyro-hyoid, depresses the bone.   When the upper end of the thyro-hyoid is fixed, the muscle pulls the larynx upwards in the production of high notes ; the sterno-thyroid pulls down the larynx markedly when low notes are produced. During high and low notes, the hyoid bone is relatively fixed by the action of the appropriate muscles.   During deglutition, the thyro-hyoid pulls the larynx upwards and slightly backwards, probably assisting the synchronous sphincteric action of the laryngeal muscles as they approximate the arytenoid cartilages and the tubercle of the epiglottis.

Muscles of the Tongue

The substance of the tongue consists mainly of muscular fibres arranged symmetrically on each side of a median fibrous septum, and interlacing with one another in three main directions—longitudinal, transverse, and vertical.   They belong to two sets of muscles—(1) the **intrinsic** muscles, proper to the tongue itself; and (2) the **extrinsic** muscles, arising outside the tongue (from the mandible, the hyoid bone, and the styloid process) and inserted into it.

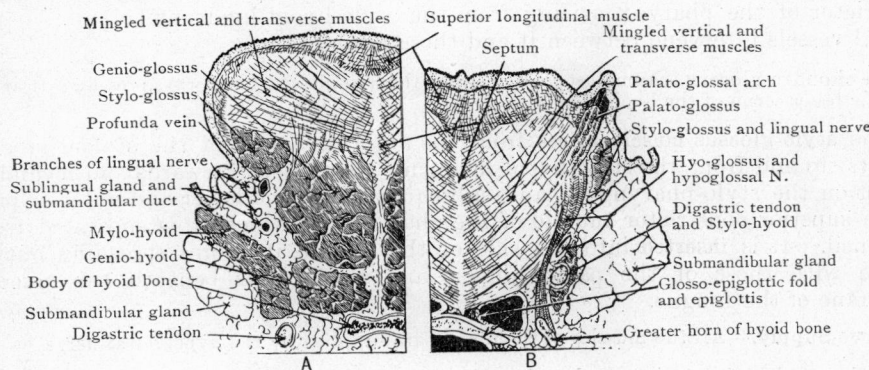

Mingled vertical and transverse muscles — Superior longitudinal muscle

Septum — Mingled vertical and transverse muscles

Genio-glossus — Palato-glossal arch

Stylo-glossus — Palato-glossus

Profunda vein — Stylo-glossus and lingual nerve

Branches of lingual nerve — Hyo-glossus and hypoglossal N.

Sublingual gland and submandibular duct — Digastric tendon and Stylo-hyoid

Mylo-hyoid —

Genio-hyoid — Submandibular gland

Body of hyoid bone — Glosso-epiglottic fold and epiglottis

Submandibular gland —

Digastric tendon — Greater horn of hyoid bone

A   B

FIG. 348.—A. SECTION THROUGH TONGUE AND BODY OF HYOID BONE.
B. SECTION THROUGH TONGUE AND GREATOR HORN OF HYOID BONE.

Intrinsic Muscles of the Tongue.—There are four pairs of intrinsic muscles —the superior and inferior longitudinal, the transverse and vertical muscles.

The **superior longitudinal muscle** extends from the back of the tongue to its tip, and is united to its fellow of the opposite side.   It is placed immediately under the mucous membrane, into which many of its fibres are inserted.   The **inferior longitudinal muscle** is a cylindrical band of muscular fibres that lies in the lower part of the tongue, in the interval between the genio-glossus and the hyo-glossus.   Posteriorly, some of its fibres extend to the hyoid bone.   The **transversus linguæ** arises from the median septum and radiates to the dorsum and sides of the tongue, intermingling with the extrinsic muscles and the fibres of the vertical muscle.   The **verticalis linguæ** arises from the mucous membrane of the dorsum of the tongue, and sweeps downwards and laterally to its sides, intermingled with the fibres of the transversus and the extrinsic muscles.   The transverse and vertical muscles form a very considerable part of the muscular substance of the organ.

Extrinsic Muscles of the Tongue.—There are three pairs of these muscles : genio-glossus, hyo-glossus, and stylo-glossus.   The palato-glossus, also attached to the tongue, is described with the muscles of the soft palate (p. 417).

The **genio-glossus muscle** (Fig. 346) is an extrinsic muscle of the tongue as well as a suprahyoid muscle.   It is a fan-shaped muscle that **arises** by its apex from the upper genial tubercle of the mandible (Fig. 343, p. 407), and radiates into the tongue ; the lowest fibres are directed downwards and backwards, to be **inserted** into the body of the hyoid bone; the highest fibres curve forwards, to be attached to the tip of the tongue; the intermediate fibres end in the substance of the tongue in its whole length. The muscles of opposite sides are separated only by the median septum of the tongue. Laterally, each is related to the inferior longitudinal muscle, the stylo-glossus, the hyo-glossus, the lingual artery, and the sublingual gland.

The **hyo-glossus muscle** also is an extrinsic muscle of the tongue as well as a supra-hyoid muscle. It is a quadrilateral sheet that **arises** from the body and greater horn of the hyoid bone, and is directed upwards and forwards to be **inserted** into the side of the tongue, its fibres interlacing with the fibres of the longitudinalis inferior medially, and the stylo-glossus laterally (Fig. 346).

With the exception of its posterior portion, the muscle is hidden by the mylo-hyoid and the structures that lie on its surface partly between the two muscles. A little above the greater horn of the hyoid bone the tendon of the digastric, the hypoglossal nerve and its accompanying vein lie on the muscle; at a higher level there are the submandibular duct, the deep part of the submandibular gland, the submandibular ganglion, and the lingual nerve. The uppermost part of the hyo-glossus is separated from the mylo-hyoid by the mucous membrane of the floor of the mouth. The deep surface of the hyo-glossus is in contact with the genio-glossus in front, and with the glosso-pharyngeal nerve and the middle constrictor of the pharynx arising from the stylo-hyoid ligament behind, but the lingual vessels intervene between it and those muscles.

The **chondro-glossus** is a small separated slip of the hyo-glossus, not always present. It arises from the lesser cornu of the hyoid bone.

The **stylo-glossus muscle arises** from the anterior border of the styloid process near its tip and from the stylo-hyoid ligament. It sweeps forwards and medially, at first on the stylo-pharyngeus, and subsequently on the lower and anterior part of the superior constrictor muscle of the pharynx, by which it is separated from the tonsil. It is **inserted** into the side of the tongue, its fibres spreading out to mingle with those of the palato-glossus and hyo-glossus beneath the mucous membrane of the tongue.

Nerve-Supply.—All the muscles of the tongue are supplied by the **hypoglossal nerve.**

Actions.—The intrinsic muscles alter the shape of the tongue. The extrinsic muscles alter the shape and also produce changes in its position. The tongue is protruded by the action of the posterior fibres of the genio-glossus, retracted by the anterior fibres aided by the stylo-glossus. The stylo-glossus and palato-glossus are elevators of the tongue, while the genio-glossus and hyo-glossus are depressors. The tongue is active during speech, and in the mastication and swallowing of food.

Muscles of the Pharynx

The muscular wall of the pharynx is composed of two strata. The *external* or *circular layer* consists of the three constrictor muscles; the *internal* or *longitudinal layer* consists of the fibres of the stylo-pharyngeus and palato-pharyngeus muscles. (The palato-pharyngeus is described with the muscles of the soft palate.) The outer surface of the muscular wall is covered with a thin layer of fascia, called the *bucco-pharyngeal fascia*, which extends forwards to cover the buccinator also. The inner surface is lined with the *pharyngo-basilar fascia*, which is very thin inferiorly but thickens as it approaches the skull.

Superior Constrictor.—The superior constrictor muscle **arises** successively from the lower half of the posterior border of the medial pterygoid plate, from the pterygo-mandibular ligament, from the mylo-hyoid line of the mandible, and from the musculature of the side of the tongue and adjacent mucous membrane of the mouth.

The muscular fibres radiate backwards and medially, and are **inserted**, for the most part, into a median raphe in the posterior wall of the pharynx; the highest fibres are attached to the pharyngeal tubercle of the occipital bone (Fig. 332).

A band of fibres from the anterior and lateral part of the palatine aponeurosis sweeps backwards round the levator palati to blend with the pharyngeal surface of the superior constrictor near its upper border. This band is highly developed in cases of complete cleft palate. Between the upper border of the muscle and the base of the skull there is a crescentic interval which is occupied by the pharyngo-basilar fascia and transmits the levator palati muscle and the pharyngo-tympanic tube [tuba auditiva].

Posteriorly and laterally it is overlapped from below by the middle constrictor. Anteriorly it is continuous with the buccinator through the pterygo-mandibular ligament. A triangular gap filled with fibrous tissue is seen between its lower border, the posterior border of the hyo-glossus and the upper border of the middle constrictor. Here, the stylo-pharyngeus insinuates itself between the superior and middle constrictors; and the glosso-pharyngeal nerve and the stylo-hyoid ligament cross the gap.

Middle Constrictor.—The middle constrictor muscle **arises** from the lower part of the stylo-hyoid ligament and from both horns of the hyoid bone, and spreads fanwise backwards and medially to be **inserted** into the median raphe. The upper fibres overlap the superior constrictor; the lower fibres are concealed posteriorly by the inferior constrictor muscle. Between its lower border and the upper border of the inferior constrictor there is a triangular gap. This gap is bounded in front by the thyro-hyoid muscle, and is occupied by the posterior part of the thyro-hyoid membrane and the lower part of the stylo-pharyngeus.

Inferior Constrictor.—The inferior constrictor muscle **arises** from the oblique line of the thyroid cartilage, from the area behind that line,

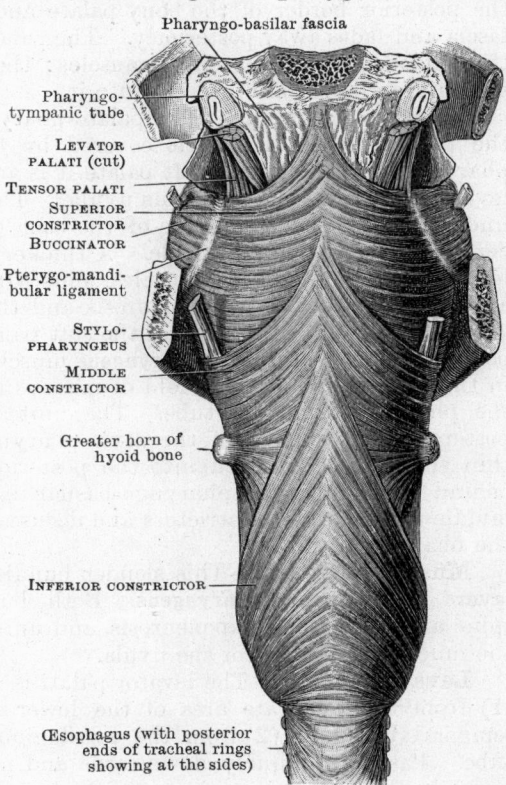

Pharyngo-basilar fascia

Pharyngo-tympanic tube

LEVATOR PALATI (cut)

TENSOR PALATI

SUPERIOR CONSTRICTOR

BUCCINATOR

Pterygo-mandibular ligament

STYLO-PHARYNGEUS

MIDDLE CONSTRICTOR

Greater horn of hyoid bone

INFERIOR CONSTRICTOR

Œsophagus (with posterior ends of tracheal rings showing at the sides)

FIG. 349.—POSTERIOR VIEW OF THE PHARYNX AND CONSTRICTOR MUSCLES.

from the side of the cricoid cartilage, and from the fascia on the posterior part of the crico-thyroid muscle.

Its fibres curve backwards and medially to be **inserted** into the median raphe of the pharynx. The upper fibres incline markedly upwards and overlap the middle constrictor; the lowest fibres are horizontal, and blend with the circular muscular fibres of the œsophagus. Under cover of the lower border of the muscle, the inferior laryngeal artery and recurrent laryngeal nerve pass up behind the crico-thyroid joint to enter the larynx.

Stylo-pharyngeus.—The stylo-pharyngeus **arises** from the root of the styloid process on its medial side, and passes downwards between the external and internal carotid arteries. It enters the wall of the pharynx in the interval between the superior and middle constrictor muscles. Spreading out internal to the middle constrictor muscle, the greater horn of the hyoid bone, and the thyro-hyoid membrane, it is **inserted** into the superior and posterior borders of the thyroid cartilage and into the wall of the pharynx itself, becoming continuous posteriorly with the palato-pharyngeus.

Muscles of the Soft Palate

The soft palate and uvula consist of a fold of mucous membrane enclosing a fibrous aponeurosis and several muscles. The fold hangs down from the hard palate between the pharynx and the mouth.

The muscular substance is composed of five pairs of muscles—the palato-pharyngeus, musculus uvulæ, levator palati, tensor palati, and palato-glossus. In its anterior part the fold contains the **palatine aponeurosis**, which is attached in front to the posterior border of the bony palate and on each side to the pharyngo-basilar fascia and fades away posteriorly. The palatine aponeurosis is derived mainly from the tendons of the two tensor muscles; the other muscles, with the exception of the palato-glossus, are inserted into it.

Palato-pharyngeus.—The palato-pharyngeus extends from the soft palate to the pharyngeal wall, and is covered by the mucous membrane of the palato-pharyngeal arch. In the soft palate it is arranged in two layers which enclose the levator palati and the musculus uvulæ. The postero-superior layer is thin; it lies under the mucous membrane of the back of the soft palate, and blends with its companion of the opposite side. A thicker, antero-inferior layer lies between the levator and tensor palati muscles, joins with its fellow in the median plane and **arises** from the palatine aponeurosis and the posterior border of the bony palate. At the postero-lateral border of the soft palate the two layers blend and are joined posteriorly by the **salpingo-pharyngeus** muscle, which is a slender slip that descends in the salpingo-pharyngeal fold of mucous membrane from the pharyngeal end of the pharyngo-tympanic tube. The united muscles run downwards along the postero-medial margin of the stylo-pharyngeus, and their fibres spread out in a thin sheet to be **inserted** into the posterior border of the thyroid cartilage, and, behind that, into the pharyngo-basilar fascia. The muscle is covered by the middle and inferior constrictors and decussates with its fellow in the lower part of the pharyngeal wall.

Musculus Uvulæ.—This slender bundle lies alongside its fellow, between the layers of the **palato-pharyngeus**. Both bundles **arise** from the posterior nasal spine and the palatine aponeurosis, and unite as they proceed backwards to end in the mucous membrane of the uvula.

Levator Palati.—The levator palati is a rounded muscle with a double **origin**: (1) from the quadrate area of the lower surface of the petrous portion of the temporal bone, and (2) from the cartilaginous portion of the pharyngo-tympanic tube. Passing obliquely downwards and medially, across the medial side of the upper border of the superior constrictor muscle, it descends in front of the salpingo-pharyngeus, and enters the soft palate between the two layers of the palato-pharyngeus muscle to be **inserted** by its anterior fibres into the palatine aponeurosis, but mainly by its posterior fibres becoming continuous with those of the opposite muscle.

It is separated from the tensor palati muscle (1) by the pharyngo-tympanic tube, (2) by the upper fibres of the superior constrictor, and (3) by the deeper layer of the palato-pharyngeus muscle.

Tensor Palati.—The tensor palati is a flat, triangular muscle which **arises** (1) from the scaphoid fossa and the spine of the sphenoid bone, and (2) from the lateral side of the cartilaginous part of the pharyngo-tympanic tube.

Tapering by the vertical descent of its anterior border, and the oblique descent of its posterior border, the muscle ends in a tendon which hooks round the pterygoid hamulus, and passes through a gap in the origin of the buccinator muscle (p. 402), to enter the soft palate. The tendon spreads out below the lower layer of the palato-pharyngeus, to be inserted into the posterior border of the hard palate, and into the palatine aponeurosis. It is related *medially* to the medial pterygoid plate, the pharyngo-basilar fascia, the pharyngo-tympanic (auditory) tube, and the upper origin of the superior constrictor. Its lateral surface is related to the otic ganglion, the mandibular and chorda tympani nerves, the middle meningeal vessels and the medial pterygoid muscle.

Palato-glossus.—The palato-glossus arises as a thin sheet of muscle in continuity with its fellow, above the mucous membrane of the antero-inferior surface of the soft palate. The fibres become roped together and pass downwards, forwards, and laterally in front of the tonsil forming the substance of the palato-glossal arch, to be **inserted** into the dorsum and side of the tongue by scattered fibres that blend with the stylo-glossus and the transversus linguæ.

Nerve - Supply. — All the muscles of the pharynx and soft palate, except the tensor palati and the stylopharyngeus, are innervated by the **vagus (tenth cranial) nerve**, through the pharyngeal plexus, but the principal motor fibres of the pharynx are derived mainly from the cranial root of the accessory nerve. The tensor palati receives its supply from the mandibular division of the **trigeminal** by a branch from the nerve to the pterygoid muscle through the otic ganglion. The stylo-pharyngeus is supplied by the **glossopharyngeal** nerve. The inferior constrictor receives additional supply from the external and recurrent laryngeal nerves.

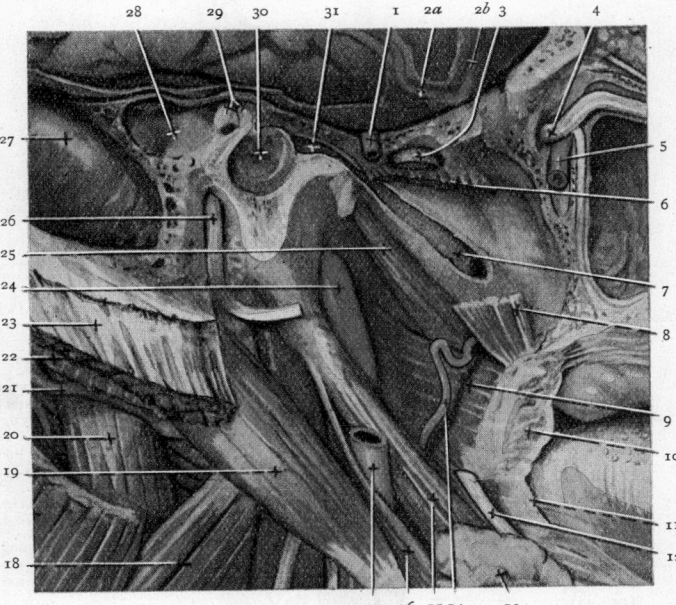

FIG. 350.—REGION OF PHARYNGO-TYMPANIC TUBE AND TYMPANIC ANTRUM

1. Middle meningeal artery in the foramen spinosum.
2a, 2b. Posterior and anterior branches of middle meningeal artery.
3. Mandibular nerve.
4. Maxillary nerve.
5. Maxillary artery.
6. Upper part of tensor palati muscle.
7. Cavity of pharyngo-tympanic tube.
8. Lower part of tensor palati muscle.
9. Superior constrictor muscle.
10. Buccinator muscle.
11. Mucous membrane of mouth.
12. Lingual nerve.
13. Submandibular gland.
14. Ascending palatine artery.
15. Stylo-glossus muscle.
16. Stylo-hyoid muscle.
17. External carotid artery.
18. Levator scapulæ and scalenus medius.
19. Posterior belly of digastric muscle.
20. Longissimus capitis muscle.
21. Occipital artery.
22. Splenius capitis muscle.
23. Sterno-mastoid muscle.
24. Internal carotid artery.
25. Levator palati muscle.
26. Facial nerve.
27. Sigmoid sinus.
28. Tympanic antrum.
29. Malleus and incus.
30. Tympanic membrane.
31. Bony part of pharyngo-tympanic tube.

Actions of the Muscles of the Pharynx and Soft Palate.—The muscles of the pharynx and soft palate are concerned in **the act of swallowing**. This act is divided into a *voluntary stage*, in which the bolus lies in front of the oro-pharyngeal isthmus, and an *involuntary stage*, during which the food passes from the mouth through the pharynx. The movements that occur during the passage of food through the mouth are as follows : the cheeks are compressed by the action of the buccinator muscles ; the tongue, hyoid bone, and thyroid cartilage are successively raised by the action of the muscles which close the mouth and elevate the hyoid bone. By these means the food is pushed backwards between the palatine arches.

At this time, by the contraction of the palato-glossus and palato-pharyngeus, the oro-pharyngeal isthmus is narrowed, while the levators raise the soft palate, and by bringing it into contact with the posterior wall of the pharynx, shut off the nasal portion of the cavity—thereby preventing the regurgitation of food into the naso-pharynx that occurs in paralysis of the palate. The elevation of the tongue, hyoid bone (p. 412), and larynx causes the elevation of the epiglottis and the inlet of the larynx, which is closed by the approximation of the arytenoid cartilages to the tubercle of the epiglottis by the combined sphincteric action of the laryngeal muscles (arytenoid, thyro-arytenoid, and thyro-epiglottic). The food thus slips over the posterior surface of the epiglottis and the closed inlet of the larynx into the pharynx. When the bolus of food enters the pharynx, it is clasped by the constrictor muscles, which, by their contractions, force it down into the œsophagus—their constriction at one level being accompanied by their relaxation at the level immediately below. The contraction of the constrictor muscles results in a flattening of the pharynx and elevation of its anterior attachments ; and, as the larynx ascends, the pharynx also is pulled up by the palato-pharyngeus and stylo-pharyngeus.

During the act of swallowing, it is generally thought that the pharyngo-tympanic tube is opened by the contraction of the tensor palati muscle, which arises from it. On the other hand, it has been held that the tube is closed during swallowing by contraction of the levator palati compressing its wall.

Throughout the **production of speech** (Wardill, *Brit. Jour. Surg.*, 1928; *cf.* Browne, *B.M.J.*, 7th December 1935) the upper part of the superior constrictor (chiefly by means of its palatine bundle) forms a ridge (Passavant, 1869) to or from which the soft palate moves in occluding or opening the pharyngeal isthmus. Occlusion is complete for most consonants, but not complete for vowels. (Occlusion, as by a "cold in the head," is therefore not such a serious defect for speech as is the patency in cleft palate). The muscles which pull the palate away from the ridge are the palato-pharyngeus, the palatoglossus, and the tensor palati, while the levators close the isthmus—as may be seen by the dimples that appear at their insertion in the soft palate when they contract during the saying of "ah."

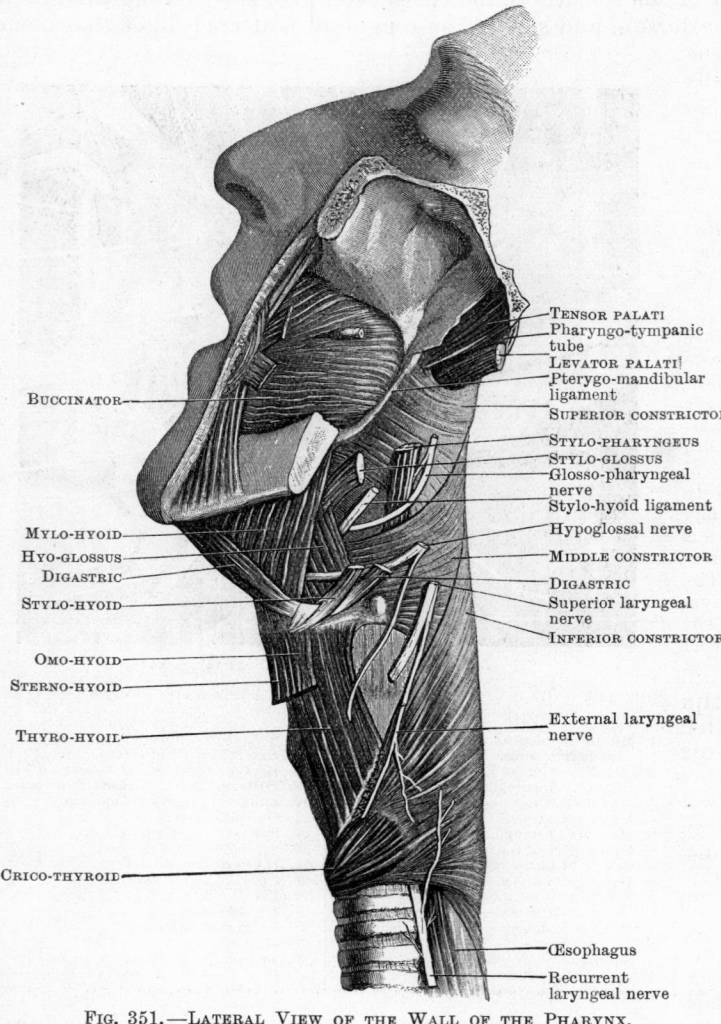

BUCCINATOR

TENSOR PALATI
Pharyngo-tympanic tube
LEVATOR PALATI
Pterygo-mandibular ligament
SUPERIOR CONSTRICTOR
STYLO-PHARYNGEUS
STYLO-GLOSSUS
Glosso-pharyngeal nerve
Stylo-hyoid ligament
Hypoglossal nerve

MYLO-HYOID
HYO-GLOSSUS
DIGASTRIC
STYLO-HYOID

MIDDLE CONSTRICTOR
DIGASTRIC
Superior laryngeal nerve
INFERIOR CONSTRICTOR

OMO-HYOID
STERNO-HYOID

THYRO-HYOID

External laryngeal nerve

CRICO-THYROID

Œsophagus
Recurrent laryngeal nerve

FIG. 351.—LATERAL VIEW OF THE WALL OF THE PHARYNX.

FASCIÆ OF THE HEAD AND NECK

The **superficial fascia** of the head and neck possesses certain features of special interest. In the scalp, it is closely adherent to the skin and the epicranial aponeurosis, and it contains the superficial vessels and nerves. In the eyelids it is loose and thin and contains no fat. In the face and in the side of the neck, it is separated from the deep fascia by the facial muscles and the platysma. Between the buccinator and the masseter, it is continuous with the *buccal pad of fat*, which lies in the interval between those muscles.

The **deep fascia** of the head and neck presents remarkable characters in certain areas, but in studying the various planes described, it is well to remember in general that the fascia is a packing material that ensheaths more highly differentiated structures and fills the spaces between them.

In the scalp, it is replaced by the **epicranial aponeurosis**. *In the temple*, the **temporal fascia** is a stout layer that extends from the superior temporal line to the zygomatic arch, and covers the temporal muscle. Near the zygomatic arch, it separates into two layers to enclose a quantity of fat and some small vessels. *On the face*, the deep fascia is practically non-existent anteriorly in relation to the facial muscles. Posteriorly it forms the **parotid fascia**; this fascia is thin where it covers the masseter, but it thickens to cover and ensheath the parotid gland.

In the neck, the deep fascia invests the muscles, and forms fascial coverings for the pharynx, trachea, œsophagus, glands, and large vessels, making, in brief,

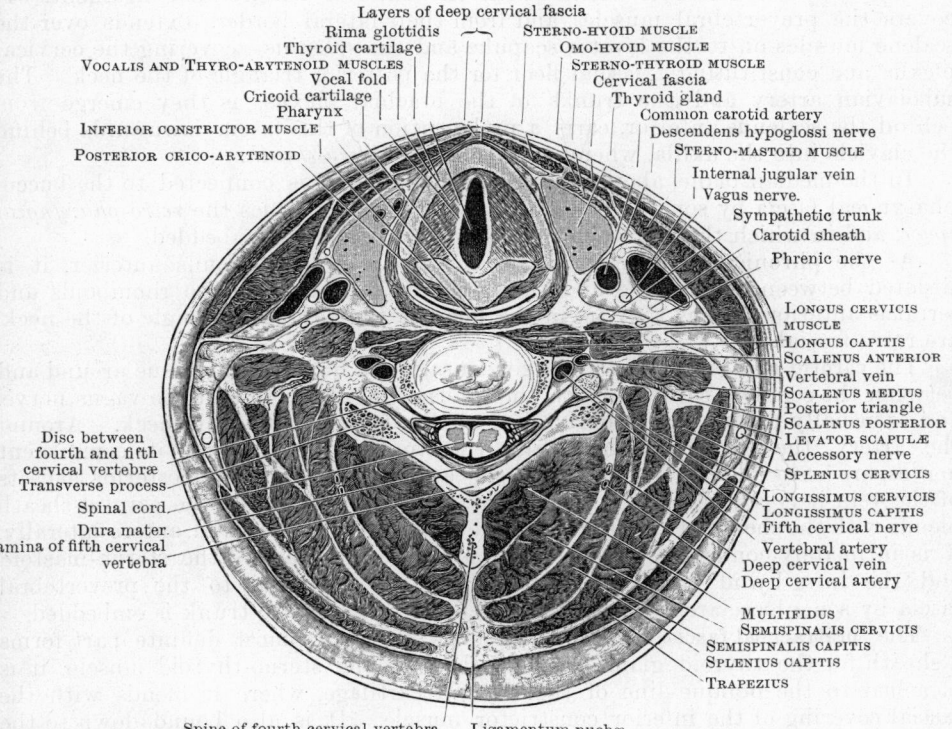

Layers of deep cervical fascia
Rima glottidis — STERNO-HYOID MUSCLE
Thyroid cartilage OMO-HYOID MUSCLE
VOCALIS AND THYRO-ARYTENOID MUSCLES STERNO-THYROID MUSCLE
Vocal fold Cervical fascia
Cricoid cartilage Thyroid gland
Pharynx Common carotid artery
INFERIOR CONSTRICTOR MUSCLE Descendens hypoglossi nerve
POSTERIOR CRICO-ARYTENOID STERNO-MASTOID MUSCLE
Internal jugular vein
Vagus nerve
Sympathetic trunk
Carotid sheath
Phrenic nerve
LONGUS CERVICIS MUSCLE
LONGUS CAPITIS
SCALENUS ANTERIOR
Vertebral vein
SCALENUS MEDIUS
Posterior triangle
SCALENUS POSTERIOR
LEVATOR SCAPULÆ
Accessory nerve
SPLENIUS CERVICIS
Disc between fourth and fifth cervical vertebræ
Transverse process
Spinal cord
Dura mater
Lamina of fifth cervical vertebra
LONGISSIMUS CERVICIS
LONGISSIMUS CAPITIS
Fifth cervical nerve
Vertebral artery
Deep cervical vein
Deep cervical artery
MULTIFIDUS
SEMISPINALIS CERVICIS
SEMISPINALIS CAPITIS
SPLENIUS CAPITIS
TRAPEZIUS
Spine of fourth cervical vertebra   Ligamentum nuchæ

FIG. 352.—TRANSVERSE SECTION IN THE CERVICAL REGION (between the fourth and fifth cervical vertebræ).

a superficial collar or tube that gives off various intermuscular septa; but most of the deep septa are condensations of areolar tissue rather than definite membranes. The superficial or **investing** layer is usually less dense where it is covered by the platysma; it encloses the sterno-mastoid muscle, and extends backwards to enclose the trapezius; it can be traced forwards over the anterior triangle to the median plane, where it is continuous with the fascia of the other side.

In the upper part of the neck, this layer is bound down to the body and greater horn of the hyoid bone, and then extends upwards over the digastric muscle and the submandibular gland to be attached to the lower border of the mandible. At the angle of the mandible it blends with the fascial sheath of the parotid gland. Through this intermediary the investing layer gains attachment to the zygoma, the posterior boundary of the squamo-tympanic fissure, the styloid process, and the lower border of the tympanic plate. Behind the parotid gland, the line of attachment of this layer follows the line of attachment to the skull of the sterno-mastoid and trapezius muscles—so reaching the external occipital protuberance. A specially thickened portion of the parotid sheath extends between

27 *a*

the styloid process and the posterior border of the mandible, separating the lower part of the parotid gland from the submandibular gland. This is termed the **stylo-mandibular ligament**.

Below the cricoid cartilage, the investing layer separates into anterior and posterior lamellæ which are continuous on each side with the layers that invest the sterno-mastoid muscle. At the suprasternal notch, the lamellæ are attached to the anterior and posterior surfaces of the manubrium sterni; the posterior lamella, which covers the infra-hyoid muscles, is attached also to the interclavicular ligament. The **suprasternal space** is enclosed between these two lamellæ, and contains the *jugular arch*, which connects the right and left anterior jugular veins.

The **prevertebral fascia** extends from the basilar part of the occipital bone into the thorax, where it blends with the anterior longitudinal ligament. It covers the prevertebral muscles, and from their lateral borders extends over the scalene muscles on to the levator scapulæ and the splenius—covering the cervical plexus and constituting a fascial floor for the posterior triangle of the neck. The subclavian artery and the trunks of the brachial plexus, as they emerge from behind the scalenus anterior, carry a prolongation of this fascia downwards behind the clavicle into the axilla, where it forms the *axillary sheath*.

In the median plane, above, the prevertebral fascia is connected to the bucco-pharyngeal fascia by some loose areolar tissue which occupies the *retro-pharyngeal space*, and in which the retro-pharyngeal lymph glands are embedded.

As the phrenic nerve descends on the front of the scalenus anterior, it is situated between the muscle and the fascia. The nerves to the rhomboids and serratus anterior also, as they lie in the floor of the posterior triangle of the neck, are retro-fascial.

The **carotid sheath** is formed by a condensation of fibro-areolar tissue around and between the common carotid artery, the internal jugular vein and the vagus nerve, and is usually regarded as a derivative of the deep fascia of the neck. Around the artery, the sheath is thick, and the ansa hypoglossi and its constituent nerves are embedded in it; but over the anterior, lateral, and posterior aspects of the vein it is reduced to a very thin layer. Antero-medially the carotid sheath blends with the sheath of the thyroid gland (pretracheal fascia), and, antero-laterally, it is intimately connected to the fascia on the deep surface of the sterno-mastoid and the infra-hyoid muscles. Posteriorly, it is connected to the prevertebral fascia by some loose areolar tissue in which the sympathetic trunk is embedded.

The **pretracheal fascia** is a very ill-defined layer; its most definite part forms a sheath for the thyroid gland. Placed deep to the sterno-thyroid muscle, it is attached to the oblique line of the thyroid cartilage, where it blends with the fascial covering of the inferior constrictor muscle. It is also bound down to the cricoid cartilage anteriorly; and, on the postero-lateral aspect of the lobe of the thyroid gland, it blends with the carotid sheath. From the isthmus of the thyroid gland it is carried downwards in front of the trachea, and blends with the fascial sheaths of the great vessels in the thorax.

MUSCLES OF THE THORAX
Muscles of Respiration

The muscles which complete the boundaries of the thorax are: (1) The external and internal intercostal muscles (Figs. 353, 354); (2) the transversus thoracis; (3) the levatores costarum; (4) the serrati posteriores: and (5) the diaphragm.

Intercostal Muscles.—In each intercostal space there are two intercostal muscles—an external and an internal. Deep to the middle part of the internal intercostal there is a thin and variable layer called the innermost intercostal muscle (intercostalis intimus), which is part of the transversus thoracis.

Each **external intercostal muscle arises** from the lower border of a rib, and its fibres are directed downwards and forwards to be **inserted** into the upper border of the rib below. It extends from the tubercle of the rib almost to the costal cartilages, gradually thinning to become continuous with the *anterior intercostal membrane*. This membrane extends onwards to the margin of the sternum and is attached above and below to the costal cartilages. In the lower spaces, the muscular fibres may merge into the external oblique muscle, which is the abdominal representative of this sheet.

Each **internal intercostal arises** from the costal cartilage and the upper edge of the costal groove, and is directed downwards and backwards to be **inserted** into

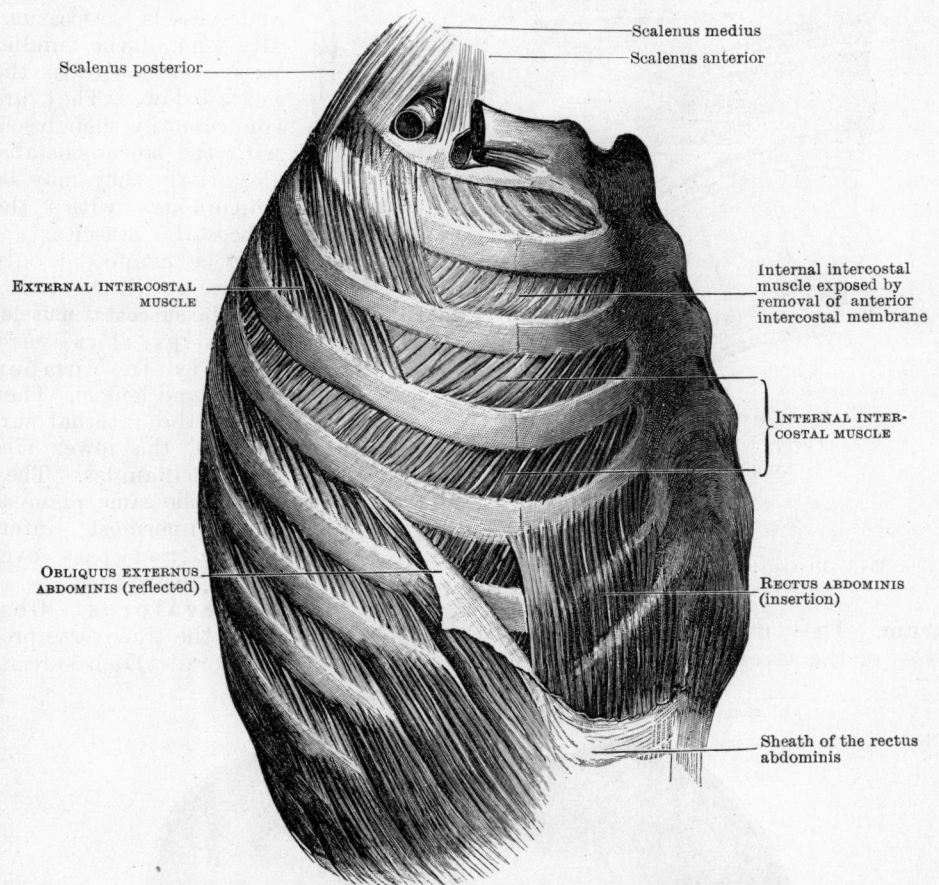

FIG. 353.—THE MUSCLES OF THE RIGHT SIDE OF THE THORACIC WALL.

the upper border of the costal cartilage and rib below. It is thicker anteriorly than posteriorly and extends from the side of the sternum to the angle of the rib, where it is replaced by the *posterior intercostal membrane*, which extends to the tubercle of the rib. The internal intercostal lies external to the intercostal vessels and nerves, and in the lower two spaces is continuous with the internal oblique muscle of the abdominal wall.

Transversus Thoracis.—This muscular sheet is divided into three parts, named the sterno-costalis, the innermost intercostals and the subcostals.

The **sterno-costalis** is the *transversus thoracis* of the B.N.A.; it is the most constant part of the muscle, and lies on the back of the anterior wall of the thorax. It **arises** from the back of the xiphoid process and the body of the sternum as high as the level of the third costal cartilage, and is **inserted** into the costal cartilages from the sixth to the second. The lowest fibres are horizontal, and are continuous with the uppermost part of the transversus abdominis; the other fibres pass obliquely upwards and laterally to their insertion. The internal mammary artery descends in front of the muscle; the pleura is behind it.

The **innermost intercostal** muscles are incomplete and variable layers that pass from rib to rib, deep to the internal intercostal. The fibres have the same direction as those of the internal muscle, and often cannot be distinguished from it except where they are separated by the intercostal nerve and vessels. Occasionally some of the bundles pass over a rib to the next below. They are connected by their fascia with the sterno-costalis. Posteriorly they may be continuous with the subcostal muscles, or may be connected only by fascia with them also.

The **subcostal muscles** are slips that vary greatly in number, width, and length. They lie on the internal surface of the lower ribs near their angles. They are in the same plane as the innermost intercostals, and pass over one or two spaces.

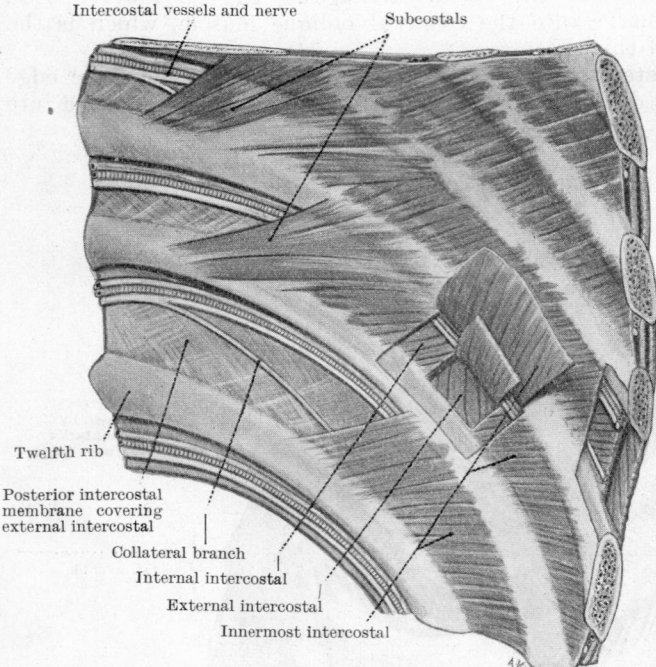

FIG. 354.—DISSECTION OF INNER SURFACE OF CHEST WALL to show intercostal muscles, vessels, and nerves. (R. D. L.)

Levatores Costarum.—These muscles are twelve small slips that arise from the transverse processes of the seventh cervical and upper eleven thoracic vertebræ. Each spreads

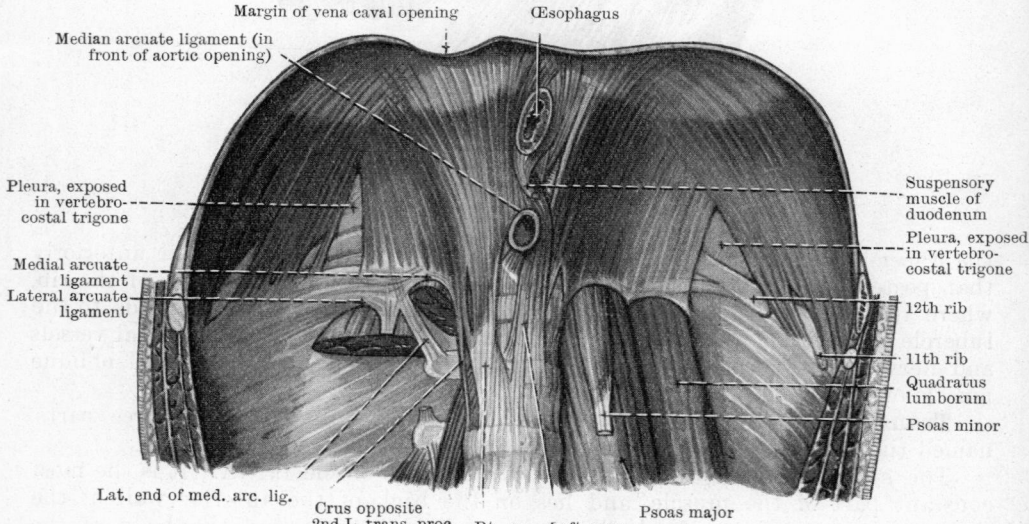

FIG. 355.—DISSECTION SHOWING THE POSTERIOR ORIGIN OF THE DIAPHRAGM. (J. C. B.)

out in a fan-like manner as it descends to the external surface of the rib immediately below, into which it is **inserted** medial to the angle.

Serrati Posteriores.—These are two thin and fairly wide muscles that lie on the outer aspect of the ribs between the superficial and deep muscles of the back. The **serratus posterior superior** has a membranous **origin** from the ligamentum nuchæ and the spines of the last cervical and upper three or four thoracic vertebræ. It is directed obliquely downwards and laterally to be **inserted** by separate slips into the second, third, fourth, and fifth ribs. The muscle is concealed by the vertebro-scapular muscles, and crosses obliquely over the splenius, sacro-spinalis, and semispinalis capitis. Its aponeurosis is blended with the deep fascia that extends upwards from the lumbar fascia.

The **serratus posterior inferior** has a membranous **origin**, through the medium of the lumbar fascia, from the last two thoracic and first two lumbar spines. It forms four muscular bands which pass almost horizontally to an **insertion** into the last four ribs. The muscular slips overlap one another from below upwards. The muscle is concealed by the latissimus dorsi.

The Diaphragm

The **diaphragm** is the great muscular and membranous partition that separates the cavities of the thorax and abdomen. A peripheral muscular portion completely surrounds a central aponeurotic membrane, and together they form a thin but strong lamella which arches over the abdominal cavity, and is clothed on that surface, for the most part, with peritoneum. It is related, on its inferior, concave surface to the liver, stomach, and spleen, the kidneys and suprarenal glands, and the inferior vena cava. Its superior, convex surface bulges into the thoracic cavity, rising higher on the right side than on the left, and is related to the pericardium and pleuræ, and, along its margin, to the chest wall. The œsophagus and thoracic aorta are in contact with this surface posteriorly.

The diaphragm as a whole has an extensive peripheral attachment to the inner surface of the lower margin of the thorax and to the lumbar vertebræ. Its muscular fibres, springing from sternum, ribs, and vertebræ, arch upwards and inwards, with varying degrees of curvature, to end in tendinous fibres which by their interlacement constitute the central tendon.

The **central tendon** is a dense felted aponeurosis, resembling a trefoil, since it is incompletely subdivided into three lobes or leaflets. As a whole, it is crescentic in outline, with an antero-lateral, convex border which receives the muscular fibres that spring from the thoracic margin, and a posterior, concave border that receives the fibres from the vertebral column. The central tendon is not "central," but is placed nearer the front than the back : the anterior muscular fibres (from the xiphoid process) are consequently the shortest; and the crural fibres (from the vertebral column) are the longest. The middle or anterior lobe of the central tendon is rounded, and projects forwards from the convex border towards the sternum; by contrast, the lateral or posterior lobes appear to be narrowed from side to side. Nor is the central tendon symmetrical; the right lobe is the largest, the middle is intermediate in size, and the left is distinctly the smallest.

The central tendon is made up of interlacing tendinous bundles which are continuous at each end with portions of the muscular sheet. The main bundles are related to the margins of the large opening for the inferior vena cava at the posterior part of the junction between the middle and right lobes; and the most obvious interlacement is found, in the densest part of the central tendon, in the median plane to the left of that opening. In that situation the interlacing tendinous bundles are arranged more or less regularly in the form of a St. Andrew's cross; in the right concavity of this X-shaped figure the vena caval opening is situated, and it has been shown that there is frequently a small venous foramen in the corresponding situation on the left side, so that the whole arrangement is in reality symmetrical (Blair).

The fleshy portion of the diaphragm is naturally divided, into two portions—

a sterno-costal and a vertebral (distinguished in the classical descriptions as the *greater* and the *lesser* muscles of the diaphragm)—which are not only distinct developmentally but are separated on one or both sides of most bodies by a hiatus in the muscular sheet termed the *vertebro-costal trigone*. The sterno-costal portion is subdivided, according to the attachment of its fibres, into sternal and costal parts.

The **sternal part** consists of a pair of short narrow slips that arise from the back of the xiphoid process and pass backwards and slightly upwards to be **inserted** into the central tendon.

The **costal part** arises from the deep surfaces of the lower six costal cartilages on each side by fleshy bands which interdigitate with those of the transversus abdominis. It is **inserted** into the whole length of the antero-lateral border of the central tendon.

The **vertebral part** arises from the lumbar vertebræ—directly from the bodies of the first three by the crura, and indirectly from the transverse processes of the first or second (or both) by means of the medial and lateral arcuate ligaments. It is **inserted** into the posterior border of the central tendon.

The **crura** are a pair of elongated musculo-tendinous bundles which arise, at the sides of the aorta, from the anterior surfaces of the bodies of the lumbar vertebræ—the right crus from the first three, the left crus from the first two. They are partly separated from the vertebral bodies by the upper lumbar arteries, but are firmly attached, with the anterior longitudinal ligament, to their margins and to the intervertebral discs.

The **right crus** is, as a rule, much the larger. It spreads out to form a thick triangular sheet which is directed upwards to its insertion into the middle part of the concave border of the central tendon on both sides of the median plane. Its left margin is directed obliquely upwards and to the left in front of the aorta, and splits as it approaches the central tendon to form an elliptical opening for the passage of the œsophagus; the muscular fibres usually meet again and decussate to form the anterior margin of that opening, which is thus separated from the central tendon and surrounded by a sphincter-like arrangement of the muscle. From the right crus, below the œsophageal opening (from both sides of which it may spring), a narrow, detached band of muscle passes forwards and downwards to the left of the cœliac artery; this is the upper portion of the **suspensory muscle of the duodenum**.

The **left crus** is very variable in its size and attachments, but usually it is much smaller and arises higher up and farther from the median plane than the right crus. The main part of its muscular fibres is directed upwards to the left of the œsophageal opening, from which it is separated by the left margin of the right crus. Frequently a separate bundle passes to the right, between the aortic and œsophageal openings behind the fibres of the right crus, to be inserted into the central tendon in the neighbourhood of the vena caval opening; but as a general rule this bundle takes no part in the formation of the œsophageal opening.

The crura are frequently subdivided into two or three distinct portions in relation to the passage of the splanchnic nerves and the sympathetic trunk. The medial part of each crus forms at its origin a characteristic tendinous funnel; the mouth of the funnel is limited above by a spiral edge that runs downwards and laterally from the aortic opening, and from it the muscular bundle emerges; it is connected with its fellow of the opposite side by a tendinous band, called the **median arcuate ligament**, which arches between them, in front of the aorta, and gives origin to fibres which join the right crus as it splits to encircle the gullet. The splanchnic nerves pierce the crus between the medial and intermediate parts. The most lateral part of the crus is continuous with the medial end of the medial arcuate ligament. The sympathetic trunk sometimes pierces the crus between the intermediate and lateral parts.

Between the crus and the medial edge of the costal portion of the diaphragm the origin of the lateral part of its vertebral portion is associated with the tendinous structures known as the medial and lateral arcuate ligaments; by means of these the origin of the diaphragm is carried across the upper parts of the psoas major and quadratus lumborum muscles. Both of these arches have frequently been described as mere thickenings of the fascial covering of those two muscles, but one of them is in reality an independent structure with which the fascia is fused. The medial arch is an essential tendinous origin of the diaphragm itself, while the lateral is a thickened portion of the anterior lamella of the lumbar fascia from which muscular fibres of the diaphragm may secondarily arise. It may be compared with the *arcuate line* formed by the aponeurosis of the internal oblique muscle in the lower part of the posterior wall of the sheath of the rectus abdominis.

The **medial arcuate ligament** [arcus lumbo-costalis medialis] springs from the side of the body of the second (or first) lumbar vertebra, where it is continuous with the lateral part of the crus, and arches obliquely over the upper part of the psoas muscle, behind the lateral border of which it passes downwards and medially to be attached to the transverse process of the first (or second) lumbar vertebra near the tip. The lateral end of the ligament furnishes a direct tendinous origin of the diaphragm from the transverse process to which it is attached, and the part of the arch which lies in front of the psoas gives rise to a thin sheet of muscle which fills the interval between that origin and the crus.

The **lateral arcuate ligament** [arcus lumbo-costalis lateralis] stretches from the transverse

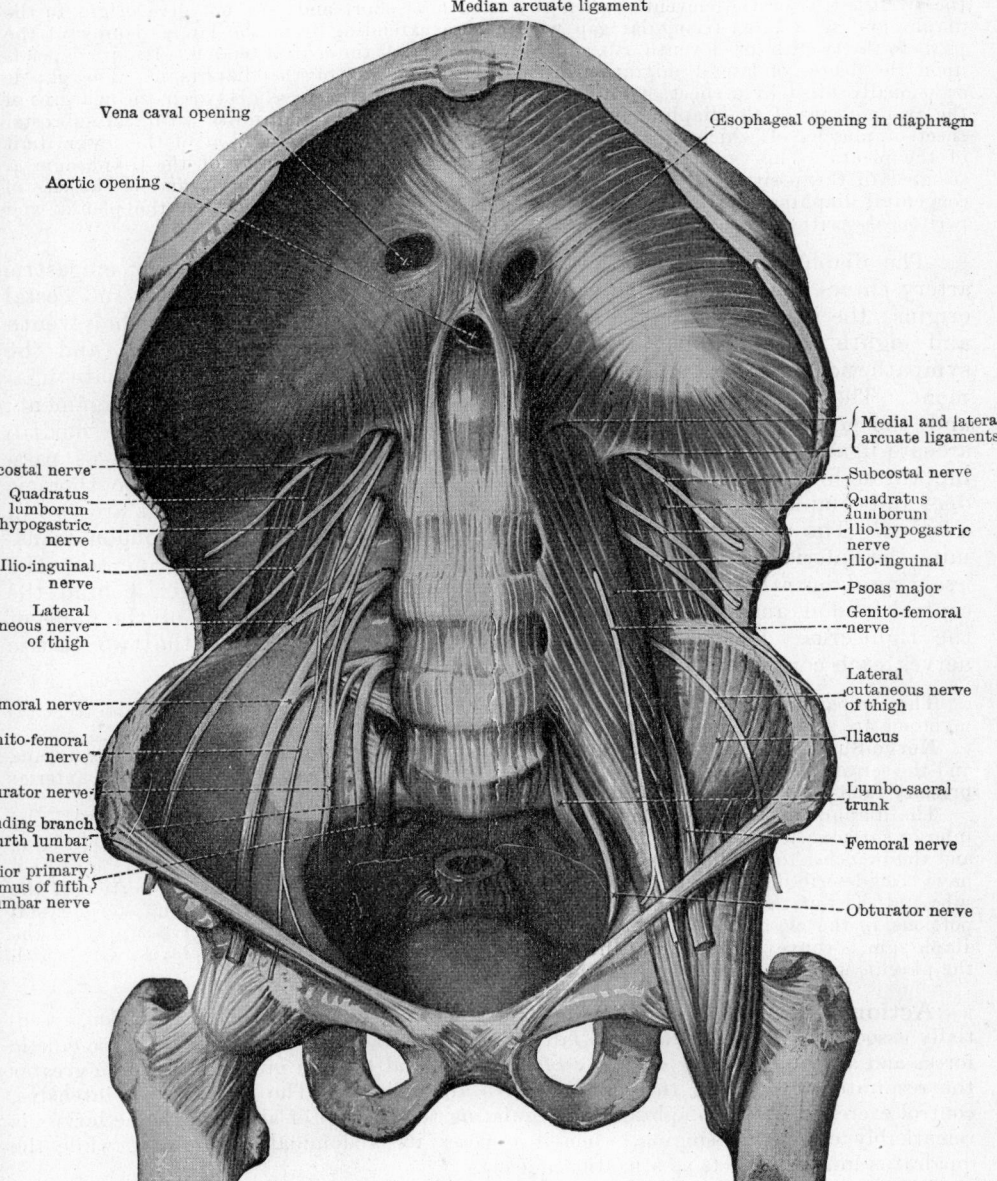

FIG. 356.—THE DIAPHRAGM AND POSTERIOR WALL OF ABDOMEN.

process of the first (or second) lumbar vertebra across the upper part of the quadratus lumborum to be attached laterally to the twelfth (or eleventh) rib. Between the lateral margin of the quadratus and the costal attachment the ligament is continuous below with the posterior aponeurosis of the transversus abdominis, and it corresponds to similar, smaller arches which exist between the ends of the twelfth and eleventh, and of the eleventh and tenth ribs. A broad band of muscular fibres sweeps upwards from this ligament to be inserted into the medial and posterior border of the lateral portion of the central tendon. This band is overlapped towards its insertion by the edge of the costal portion of the diaphragm, and it may or may not completely fill the interval between the edge of the psoas and the last rib.

The **vertebro-costal trigone** may be defined as the interval between the medial margin of the vertebro-costal part and the lateral margin of the vertebral portion of the diaphragm. A muscular hiatus is present in this situation on one or both sides in at least 80 per cent. of bodies, disclosing to a considerable extent the lower limit of the pleura, with which the kidney may thus be intimately related ; it is more frequent, and (when bilateral) usually larger, on the left side. It varies in size from a slight separation of the muscular fibres just medial to the twelfth rib (or the eleventh when the twelfth is short and does not give origin to the diaphragm) to a large triangular gap with a base extending from the lateral border of the psoas to the twelfth (or eleventh) rib, and an apex reaching the central tendon. Its size depends upon the degree of lateral migration of the vertebral part of the diaphragm. The gap is occasionally filled by a sheet of muscle whose fibres arch *transversely* between the margins of the two portions of the diaphragm ; this sheet is sometimes in continuity with the subcostal sheet of muscle, of which it appears to be a portion displaced in *front* of the lower limit of the pleura. The vertebro-costal hiatus in the muscular continuity of ·the diaphragm is situated in the position of the pleuro-peritoneal opening of the embryo, and is the site of congenital diaphragmatic hernia (more common on the left side) in which the pleural and peritoneal cavities are continuous.

The diaphragm is pierced by numerous structures. The superior epigastric artery enters the sheath of the rectus abdominis between its sternal and costal origins ; the musculo-phrenic artery passes between its attachments to the seventh and eighth costal cartilages. The splanchnic nerves pierce the crus, and the sympathetic trunk descends behind the medial end of the medial arcuate ligament. The subcostal nerve and vessels pass behind the lateral arcuate ligament ; and the aorta and thoracic duct pass between the crura, behind the median arcuate ligament (*aortic opening*). The azygos vein is usually described as passing through the aortic opening, but it is placed postero-lateral to the thoracic duct and completely under cover of the right crus. The special openings are two in number. The *vena-caval opening* in the right half of the central tendon transmits the inferior vena cava and small branches of the right phrenic nerve. The *œsophageal opening* is in the muscular substance of the diaphragm, behind the central tendon, and is surrounded by a sphincter-like arrangement of the fibres of the right crus. Besides the œsophagus, this opening transmits the two gastric nerves, each containing fibres from both the right and the left vagus.

The comparative morphology of the diaphragm and its derivation from the fourth cervical myotome are summarised on p. 527.

Nerve-Supply.—The intercostal muscles, the transversus thoracis, the levatores costarum, and the serrati posteriores (superior, Th., 1-4 ; inferior, Th. 9-11) are all supplied by the **anterior primary rami** of the **thoracic nerves.**

The diaphragm receives its motor supply from the **phrenic nerve** (C. 3. 4. 5.), mainly on its inferior surface after the nerves have pierced it. The phrenic nerves contain afferent fibres also, and the branches to the diaphragm from the lower intercostal nerves (9th, 10th, and 11th), which have been described, may be of this nature, or they may supply motor fibres to a portion of the subcostal sheet if that is incorporated in the diaphragm, between its lumbar and sterno-costal portions, in the closure of the vertebro-costal trigone. The sympathetic nerve-supply to the diaphragm is conveyed to it from the cœliac ganglion through the phrenic plexus, with which the phrenic nerve communicates.

Actions.—The opposite respiratory movements of expiration and inspiration, essentially associated with the rise and fall of the diaphragm, are effected by antagonistic forces and are supported by an array of accessory and fixation muscles ; and the greater the respiratory excursions, the more reserves are enlisted. The delicate, yet intensive, control exercised by the diaphragm in regulating the outflow of air through the larynx is remarkably evident in singing, when it opposes its abdominal antagonists, while the quadratus lumborum acts as a fixation muscle.

Before considering the details of these movements, points of clinical value regarding the position of the diaphragm as affected by posture in the living subject during expiration and inspiration may be considered with reference to the radiographs on Plates XXXIV and XXXV. With the subject standing (Fig. 1) the diaphragm occupies a lower level than in the supine position (Fig. 3), in which the abdominal weight presses against the diaphragm instead of pulling it downwards, and this level is lower even when the abdominal muscles are securing full expiration. Breathless patients breathe more easily, therefore, when propped up in bed. When the subject lies prone the diaphragm rises markedly on the right side. The diaphragm occupies the same level in sitting as in standing (Pls. XXXIV and XXXV, Figs. 1 and 2).

When the subject lies on one side (Figs. 4 and 5), apart from the fact that corresponding side of the diaphragm, owing to the pressure of the abdominal viscera, reaches a higher level than in other positions, the costo-diaphragmatic recess [phrenico-costal sinus] is narrowed and deepened, while on the opposite side the diaphragm reaches a low level and the recess becomes wider and shallow. The same effect is secured in bending to the side while in the erect position (Pl. XXXIV, Fig. 6), and this exercise has been used clinically to prevent or stretch pleuritic adhesions. Fig. 4, Pl. XXX, shows the expulsive action of the abdominal muscles in forced expiration. Such abdominal retraction in a normal person is capable of raising the central part of the diaphragm one and a half vertebræ, after either expiration or inspiration (Pl. XXXV, Fig. 6).

Costal breathing, more pronounced in the female, has been considered to be adventitiously produced ; but in a series of students recently examined, the costal type was markedly evident in the female in contrast with the abdominal type in the male.

The **movement of inspiration** results in an increase in the capacity of the thorax which is partly brought about by muscles acting on the ribs, sternum, and vertebral column, and partly by the diaphragm. The transverse diameter of the thorax is increased by elevation and eversion of the ribs, and these movements are produced, during quiet respiration, by the external and internal intercostals, the serratus posterior superior, and the levatores costarum. As a result of the elevation of the ribs the sternum is thrust forwards, particularly in its lower part, thus increasing the thoracic capacity in an antero-posterior direction.

In **forced inspiration**, the transverse and antero-posterior diameters of the thorax are further increased by elevation of the first rib, elevation and forward movement of the upper part of the sternum, and diminution of the concavity of the curve of the thoracic part of the vertebral column, accompanied by further elevation and eversion of the ribs (2-8). Elevation of the first rib is produced by the scalenus anterior and medius muscles, and by the sterno-mastoid (acting through the sternum, the sterno-clavicular joint, and the costo-clavicular ligament). Elevation and forward movement of the upper part of the sternum necessarily accompany this movement. Extension of the vertebral column by the sacro-spinalis makes further elevation of the ribs possible, and this is produced by the action of the serratus anterior and pectoralis minor. For this purpose it is necessary that the scapula should be fixed by the trapezius, the rhomboids, and the levator scapulæ. When the arm is raised above the head and fixed, the pectoralis major also comes into action as an accessory muscle of respiration. In fact, there is a remarkable co-ordination of almost the whole muscular system of the body when respiration is difficult.

The effect of the contraction of the diaphragm is threefold. (1) When relaxed, the fibres of the diaphragm curve upwards over the liver, stomach, and spleen, and the flattening of this curve, when the muscle contracts, provides a great increase in the depth of the thorax. (2) The central tendon descends to a slight extent. As a result of (1) and (2) the abdominal viscera are thrust downwards and the relaxed abdominal parietes are bulged outwards. (3) The eighth, ninth, tenth, and eleventh ribs are slightly elevated by the diaphragm, and the lower ribs as a whole tend to be thrust outwards by the abdominal viscera ; the serratus posterior inferior steadies the lower ribs, and the twelfth rib is fixed by the quadratus lumborum.

In the **movement of expiration**, diminution of the transverse and antero-posterior diameters is effected by the elastic recoil of the costal cartilages and the weight of the thoracic walls. The elasticity of the thoracic skeleton tends to produce the inspiratory position, but in the resting or mid position, the abdominal muscles and gravity are antagonists that effect a balance. The depth of the thorax is diminished by the reproduction of the concavity of the cupolæ of the diaphragm. This result is brought about by the contraction of the abdominal muscles. The transversus abdominis, assisted by the other abdominal muscles, can produce a remarkable concavity of the anterior abdominal surface and a binder-like effect upon the abdominal contents (Pl. XXX, Fig. 4). In **forced expiration** these muscles are assisted by the latissimus dorsi (p. 455), which exerts a powerful compressing effect ; and the vertebral column is flexed, thus allowing the ribs to be still further approximated.

The external and internal intercostal muscles elevate the ribs. The members of the transversus thoracis are depressors.

MUSCLES AND FASCIÆ OF THE ABDOMINAL WALL

The abdominal wall is composed of muscular sheets covered externally and internally with fascia.

MUSCLES OF THE ABDOMINAL WALL

The muscles of the abdominal wall are in three series—lateral, anterior, and posterior. The lateral muscles comprise the obliquus externus abdominis, obliquus internus abdominis, and transversus abdominis. The anterior muscles are the rectus abdominis and the pyramidalis. Those situated posteriorly are the quadratus lumborum, and three muscles included among the muscles of the lower limb, namely, the psoas major, psoas minor, and iliacus.

Obliquus Externus Abdominis.—The external oblique muscle is a broad, thin sheet of muscle, with an **origin** from the outer surfaces of the lower eight ribs by slips which interdigitate with the serratus anterior and latissimus dorsi muscles. This disposition may be seen in the well-developed living subject (Pl. XXXI, Fig. 2). The muscular fibres radiate downwards and forwards, the lowest fibres passing vertically downwards.

The muscle fibres of the lower and posterior part of the muscle are **inserted** into the anterior half of the outer lip of the iliac crest (Fig. 357). The rest of the fleshy fibres of the muscle do not extend forwards as far as the linea semilunaris, which marks the lateral border of the rectus abdominis muscle, nor downwards below the level of the anterior superior iliac spine (Fig. 357), but are inserted into an extensive triangular aponeurosis which forms part of the anterior abdominal wall. This aponeurosis is broader below than above; it is united with part of the aponeurosis of the internal oblique in the upper three-fourths of its extent, and with the whole aponeurosis of that muscle as well as with that of the transversus abdominis in its lower fourth, thus forming the anterior wall of the sheath of the rectus muscle. It gains attachments, below to the pubic bone and symphysis, above to the xiphoid process, and by its intermediate decussating fibres to the **linea alba.**

The muscle is superficial in almost its whole extent. It is overlapped posteriorly by the latissimus dorsi, but is often separated from it immediately above the iliac crest by an angular interval called the **lumbar triangle.** The uppermost part of the aponeurosis covers the insertion of the rectus abdominis on the chest wall, and gives origin to fibres of the pectoralis major; its lower border is folded slightly backwards upon itself, between the anterior superior iliac spine and the pubic tubercle, to form the inguinal ligament; and immediately above the pubic tubercle there is a cleft in the aponeurosis, called the superficial inguinal ring, which transmits the spermatic cord or the round ligament of the uterus.

The **linea alba** is a band of interlacing fibres, narrow below the umbilicus but increasing to about half an inch in width in its upper part. It occupies the median plane of the anterior abdominal wall in its whole extent, is pierced by the umbilicus and forms the greater part of the ultimate insertion of all the lateral abdominal muscles.

The **umbilicus** or navel is a little below the middle of the linea alba, opposite the disc between the third and fourth lumbar vertebrae. It is a puckered scar in the skin and the linea alba, and it results from the closure of the *umbilical orifice* of the fœtus. The orifice transmits the umbilical vein and arteries and the connexion between the allantois and the urachus. After birth the derivatives of those structures remain attached to the umbilicus—the round ligament of the liver derived from the vein, the lateral umbilical ligaments from the arteries, and the median umbilical ligament from the urachus. The deep surface of the umbilicus is related also to the extraperitoneal tissue; and a fibrous band may connect it with the diverticulum ilei when the diverticulum is present.

The **inguinal ligament** is a tendinous band that extends from the anterior superior iliac spine to the pubic tubercle across the iliacus, psoas major and pectineus. From ilium to pubis, it passes with a curve which is convex towards the thigh, and the convex surface gives attachment to the fascia lata. It is the lower margin of the external oblique aponeurosis folded back on itself, and its upper surface is therefore grooved. In its lateral part, this surface gives partial origin to the internal oblique and the transversus, and receives the attachments of the fascia transversalis and fascia iliaca; in its medial part it forms the gutter-like floor of the inguinal canal. This portion includes the **pectineal part** of the ligament [lig. lacunare], which is a triangular expansion that spreads *backwards* from the most medial part of the ligament to the pectineal line. Some of these fibres are reflected from the pectineal line obliquely through the linea alba to mingle with the aponeurosis of the other side; this **reflected part** of the inguinal ligament [lig. inguinale reflexum], sometimes described as an additional insertion of the opposite external oblique aponeurosis, is seldom well marked.   The inguinal ligament is related posteriorly to the femoral nerve and to the femoral vessels enclosed in the femoral sheath : the nerve is between the iliacus and the psoas major ; the artery is on the psoas ; the vein is partly on the psoas and partly on the pectineus.   The lateral margin of the pectineal part of the ligament is the medial boundary of the *femoral ring* (p. 505 and Fig. 363, p. 435).

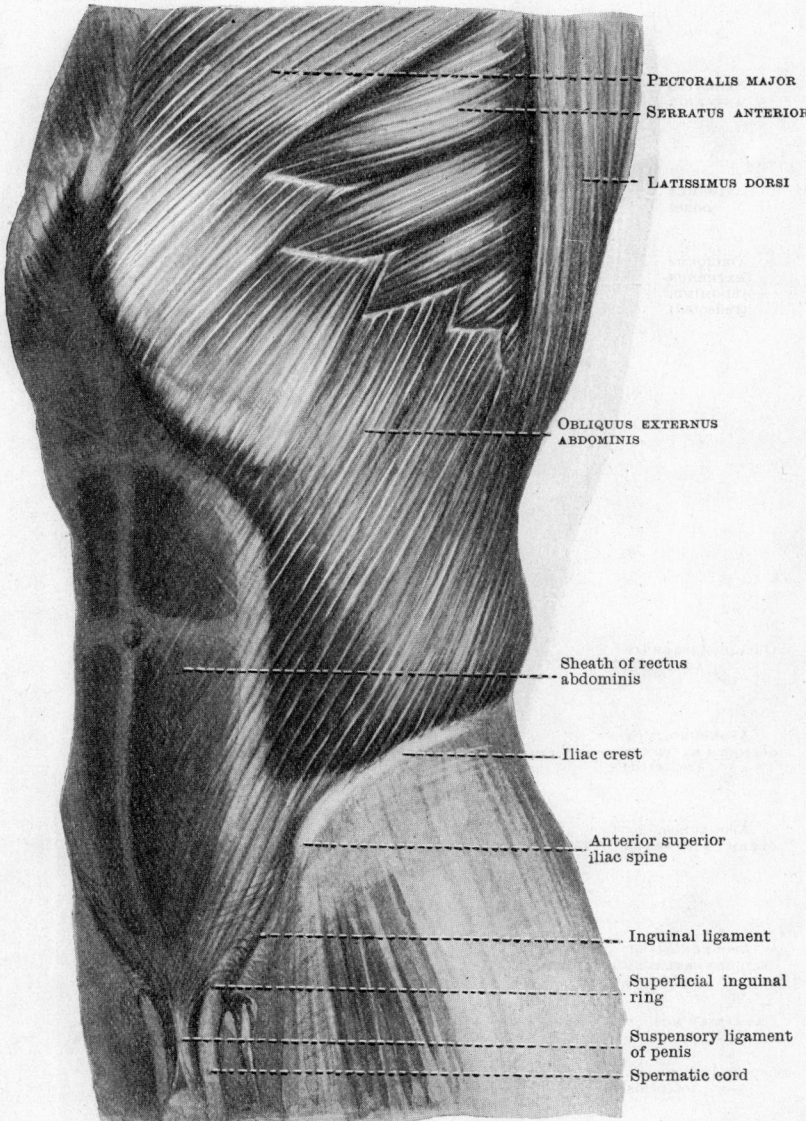

PECTORALIS MAJOR

SERRATUS ANTERIOR

LATISSIMUS DORSI

OBLIQUUS EXTERNUS
ABDOMINIS

Sheath of rectus
abdominis

Iliac crest

Anterior superior
iliac spine

Inguinal ligament

Superficial inguinal
ring

Suspensory ligament
of penis

Spermatic cord

FIG. 357.—THE LEFT OBLIQUUS EXTERNUS ABDOMINIS.

The **superficial inguinal ring** [annulus inguinalis subcutaneus] is the place of exit of an inguinal hernia.   It is a cleft in the external oblique aponeurosis immediately above the pubic tubercle.   In the male it transmits the spermatic cord, enclosed in the internal spermatic fascia and the cremaster muscle and fascia ; in the female it transmits the round ligament of the uterus.   The opening is variable in width and is triangular in outline ; its edges are drawn together by a thin fascia, strengthened superficially by a number of arched and horizontal fibres, called the **intercrural fibres** (Fig. 364), which arise from the inguinal ligament and sweep medially across the cleft in the aponeurosis; but the margins of the opening are readily felt in the living subject if the finger is passed upwards over the spermatic cord, invaginating the overlying skin, till it is opposite the ring, and is then pressed backwards.

The margins of the ring are called its crura. The **inferior crus** is narrow, and is formed from that part of the aponeurosis which is fixed to the pubic tubercle, and constitutes the medial end of the inguinal ligament. The **superior crus**, flat and

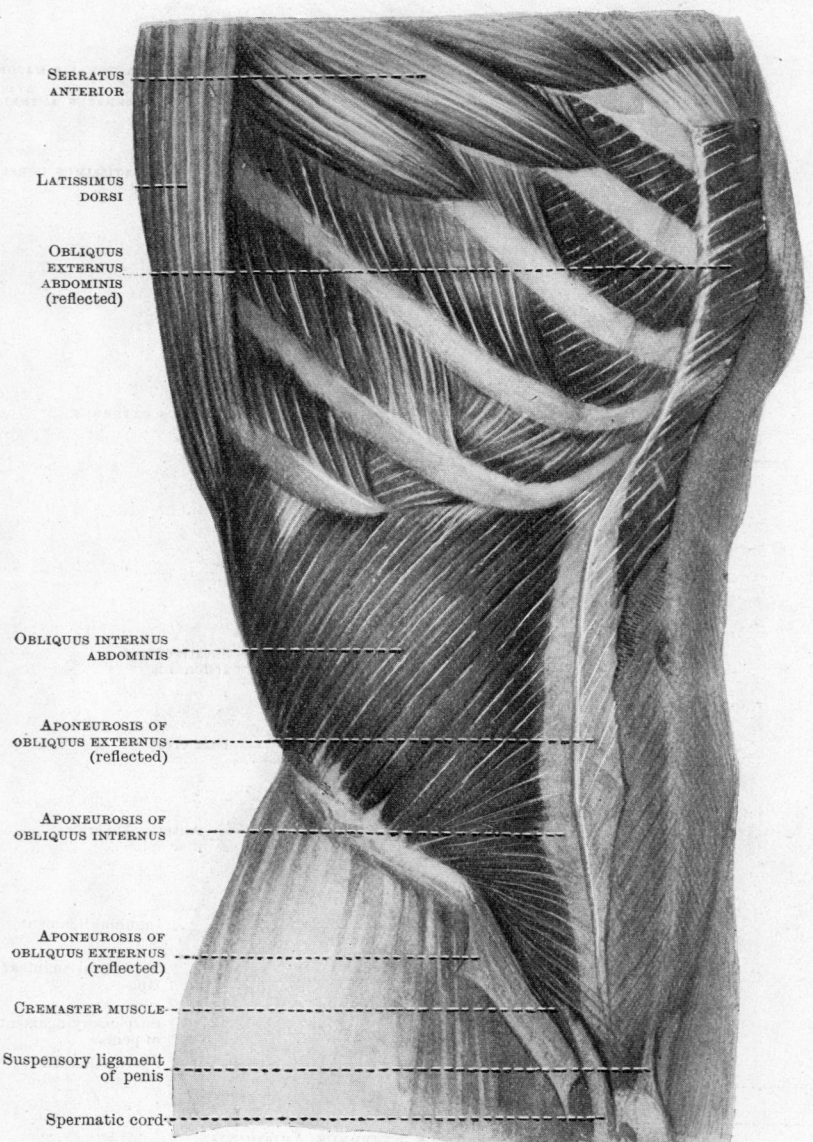

SERRATUS
ANTERIOR

LATISSIMUS
DORSI

OBLIQUUS
EXTERNUS
ABDOMINIS
(reflected)

OBLIQUUS INTERNUS
ABDOMINIS

APONEUROSIS OF
OBLIQUUS EXTERNUS
(reflected)

APONEUROSIS OF
OBLIQUUS INTERNUS

APONEUROSIS OF
OBLIQUUS EXTERNUS
(reflected)

CREMASTER MUSCLE

Suspensory ligament
of penis

Spermatic cord

FIG. 358.—THE RIGHT OBLIQUUS INTERNUS ABDOMINIS.

broad, is the part of the aponeurosis which is attached to the pubic crest and symphysis.

The intercrural fibres and the crura of the superficial inguinal ring are continuous with a thin tubular sheath, called the **external spermatic fascia**, which forms an envelope for the spermatic cord (or for the round ligament) after it has passed beyond the abdominal wall; and it must be noted that the ring is not apparent until the external spermatic fascia has been removed from its edges.

Obliquus Internus Abdominis.—The internal oblique muscle is a broad, thin sheet situated between the external oblique and the transversus. It arises from (1) the lumbar fascia, (2) the anterior two-thirds of the intermediate area of the iliac crest, and (3) the lateral two-thirds of the inguinal ligament.

It runs, for the most part, upwards and forwards, and its highest and most posterior fibres are inserted directly into the cartilages of the last three ribs in line with the internal intercostals. The rest of the muscular fibres spread like a fan and become an aponeurosis, the change taking place along a line that extends downwards and medially from the tenth costal cartilage to the pubic bone. The

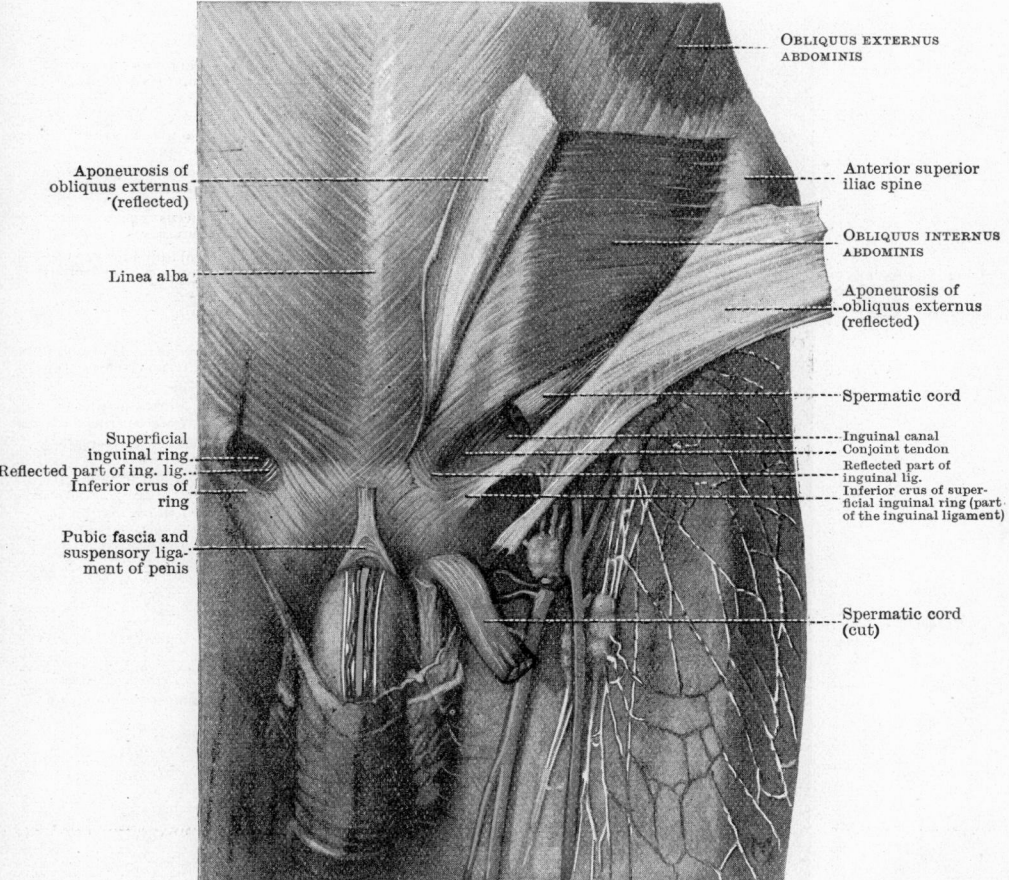

Fig. 359.—The Left Inguinal Canal. Structures seen on reflexion of the Obliquus Externus.

principal insertion of the aponeurosis is the whole length of the linea alba, but it does not reach its insertion as an undivided sheet. The lower fourth passes in front of the rectus abdominis, and, spreading downwards and medially, reaches the pubic bone as well as the linea alba. The upper three-fourths splits at once into two layers which enclose the rectus as they pass to their insertion into the linea alba and the xiphoid process; the posterior layer is attached also to the margins of the ninth, eighth and seventh costal cartilages, and above that level the rectus abdominis muscle is therefore in direct contact with the chest wall. The part which passes undivided in front of the rectus is derived from the fleshy fibres that arise from the inguinal ligament. It fuses with the part of the transversus aponeurosis that has a like origin to form a sheet called the conjoint tendon. The **conjoint tendon** [falx aponeurotica inguinalis] meets its fellow at the linea alba, and also extends downwards to be attached to the pubic crest and the pectineal line.

The internal oblique is limited above by the inferior margin of the thorax. Its lower fibres, arching over the spermatic cord, assist in forming, laterally, the anterior wall of the inguinal canal; medially, by means of the conjoint tendon, they help to form the posterior wall.

Its lowest fibres are continued into the **cremaster muscle**, which is prolonged along the spermatic cord through the inguinal canal.

The **cremaster muscle** and its **fascia** form an investment for the testis and spermatic cord deep to the external spermatic fascia. In the female it is more largely represented by fascia than by muscular fibres. It may be said to have an **origin** from

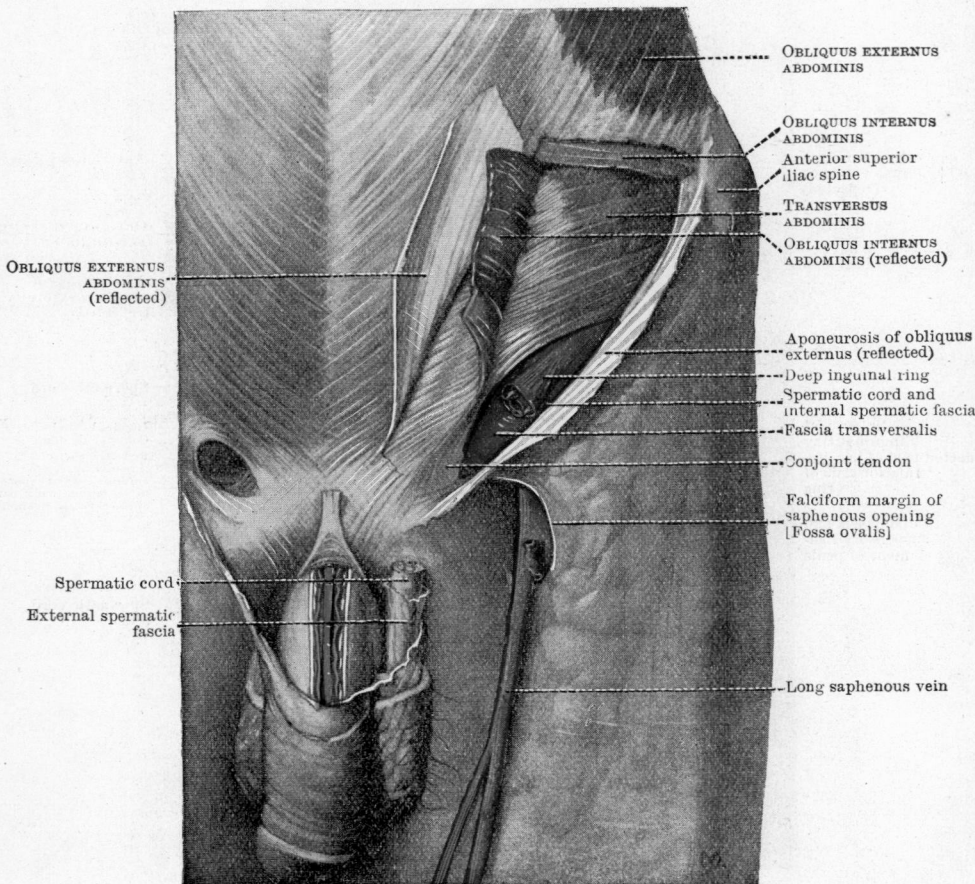

FIG. 360.—THE DISSECTION OF THE INGUINAL CANAL.

the inferior edge of the internal oblique and the adjacent part of the inguinal ligament. Its fibres form loops over the spermatic cord and testis, the highest fibres getting an **insertion** into the pubic tubercle

Transversus Abdominis.—The transversus abdominis muscle **arises** (1) from the deep surfaces of the costal cartilages of the lower six ribs, interdigitating with the origins of the diaphragm; (2) from the transverse processes of the lumbar vertebræ through the middle layer of the lumbar fascia; (3) from the anterior two-thirds of the inner lip of the iliac crest; and (4) from the lateral third of the inguinal ligament.

The muscular fibres run, for the most part, horizontally forwards, and end in an aponeurosis which has a twofold **insertion**. (1) After taking part in the formation of the sheath of the rectus, the aponeurosis is attached to the xiphoid process, the whole length of the linea alba, and the pubic symphysis. (2) The fibres that arise from the inguinal ligament are joined by the lower part of the internal oblique to form the larger part of the conjoint tendon.

The aponeurosis of the transversus abdominis is widest opposite the interval between the last rib and the iliac crest, and gradually becomes narrower above and below. Near the xiphoid process it is barely 3 cm. wide, and in this situation

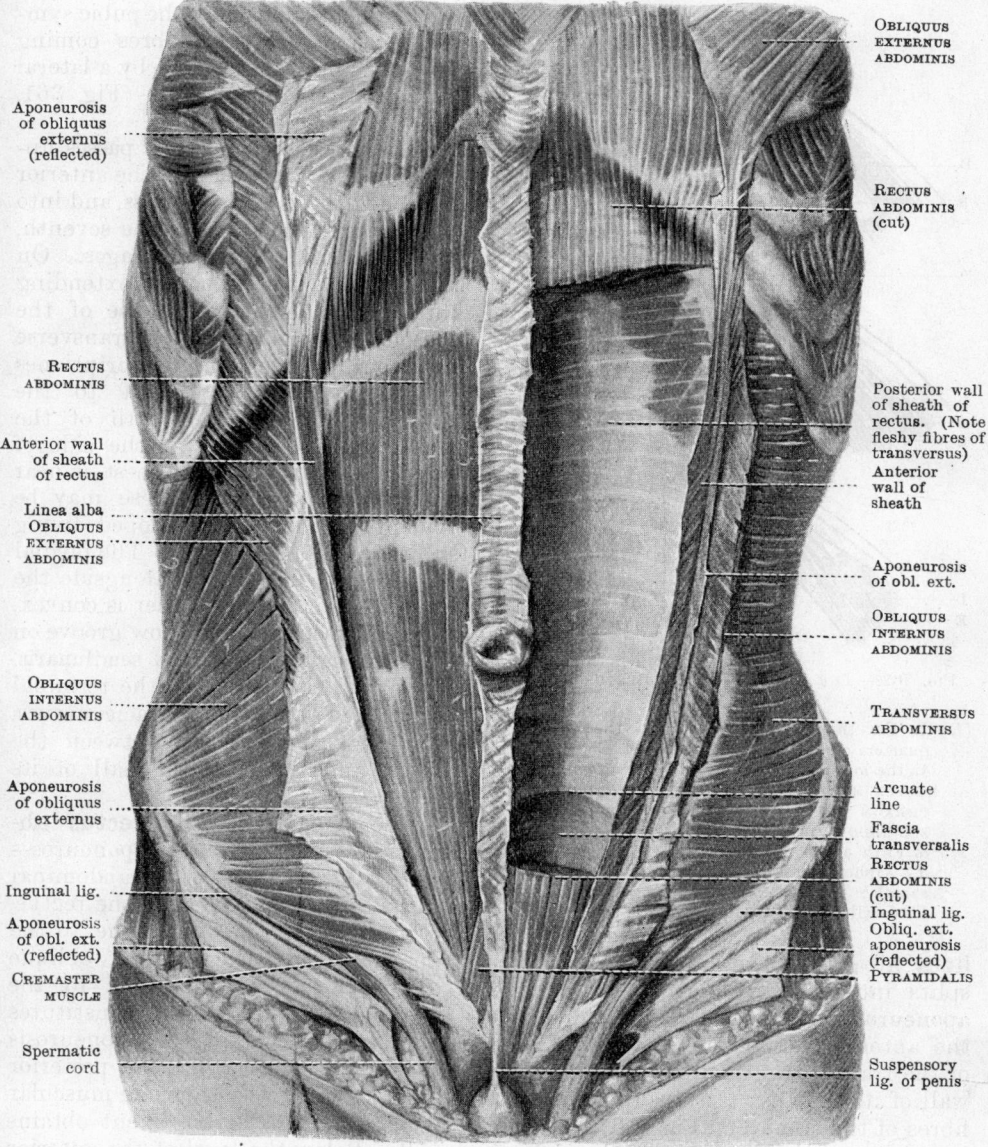

Aponeurosis of obliquus externus (reflected)

Rectus abdominis

Anterior wall of sheath of rectus

Linea alba
OBLIQUUS EXTERNUS ABDOMINIS

OBLIQUUS INTERNUS ABDOMINIS

Aponeurosis of obliquus externus

Inguinal lig.

Aponeurosis of obl. ext. (reflected)

CREMASTER MUSCLE

Spermatic cord

OBLIQUUS EXTERNUS ABDOMINIS

RECTUS ABDOMINIS (cut)

Posterior wall of sheath of rectus. (Note fleshy fibres of transversus)

Anterior wall of sheath

Aponeurosis of obl. ext.

OBLIQUUS INTERNUS ABDOMINIS

TRANSVERSUS ABDOMINIS

Arcuate line

Fascia transversalis

RECTUS ABDOMINIS (cut)

Inguinal lig. Obliq. ext. aponeurosis (reflected)

PYRAMIDALIS

Suspensory lig. of penis

Fig. 361.—Deep Dissection of the Abdominal Wall. The Rectus Muscle and its Sheath.

fleshy fibres of the muscle are separated from the rectus abdominis only by the posterior lamella of the aponeurosis of the internal oblique (Fig. 361).

The lower intercostal nerves lie between the internal oblique muscle and the transversus muscle, which is lined on its deep surface by the fascia transversalis. Its inferior border forms a concave edge, separated from the inguinal ligament by a semilunar interval in which the fascia transversalis appears, and through which the spermatic cord emerges at the deep inguinal ring, under cover of the internal oblique muscle and the aponeurosis of the external oblique.

28

Pyramidalis.—The pyramidalis is a small triangular muscle that lies on the front of the lower part of the rectus abdominis. It arises from the pubic crest lower down than the origin of the rectus. It is directed obliquely upwards, for a variable distance, to be **inserted** into the linea alba. The muscle is often absent.

Rectus Abdominis.—The rectus abdominis muscle is long and strap-like, and arises by a medial head from the ligaments in front of the pubic symphysis, many of the fibres coming from the opposite side, and by a lateral head from the pubic crest (Fig. 361, p. 433).

The muscle widens as it passes upwards, and is **inserted** into the anterior surface of the xiphoid process, and into the superficial surfaces of the seventh, sixth, and fifth costal cartilages. On its anterior surface, but not extending through the entire substance of the muscle, are three or more transverse **tendinous intersections** [inscriptiones tendineæ], firmly adherent to the anterior wall of the sheath of the muscle; the lowest is at the side of the umbilicus, and the highest is near the xiphoid process. These may be evident in the well-developed living subject (Pl. XXX, Fig. 3). The medial border of the muscle lies alongside the linea alba; its lateral border is convex, and corresponds to a shallow groove on the skin called the **linea semilunaris.** The muscle is pierced by the terminal branches of the lower thoracic nerves, after they have passed between the muscle and the posterior wall of its sheath.

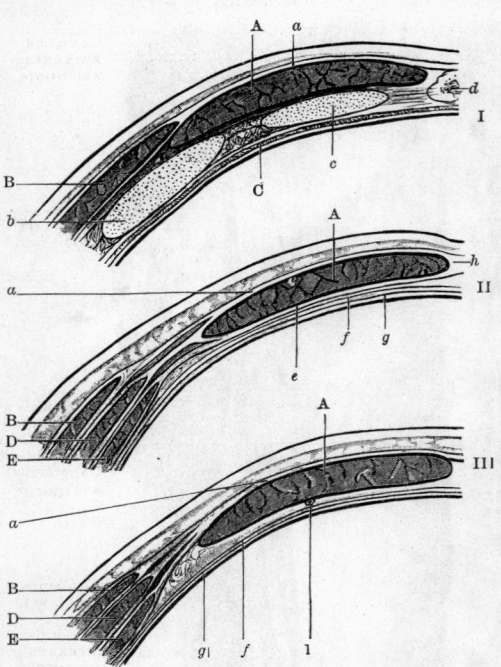

FIG. 362.—THE SHEATH OF THE RECTUS ABDOMINIS MUSCLE.

(I.) In the thoracic wall; (II.) In the upper three-quarters of the abdominal wall, cf. Fig. 361; (III.) In the lower fourth of the abdominal wall.

A, RECTUS MUSCLE; B, OBLIQUUS EXTERNUS; C, DIA-PHRAGM; D, OBLIQUUS INTERNUS; E, TRANSVER-SUS ABDOMINIS. *a*, Anterior wall of rectus sheath; *b*, Fifth costal cartilage; *c*, Sixth costal cartilage; *d*, Xiphoid process; *e*, Posterior wall of rectus sheath; *f*, Fascia transversalis; *g*, Peritoneum; *h*, Linea alba. 1, Inferior epigastric artery.

The **sheath of the rectus abdominis** is derived from the aponeuroses of the lateral muscles of the abdominal wall, which, after enclosing the rectus, give rise, in the median plane, to the linea alba. At the linea semilunaris, the aponeurosis of the internal oblique splits into anterior and posterior layers. The anterior layer, joined by the aponeurosis of the external oblique, passes in front of the rectus and constitutes the anterior wall of the sheath. The posterior layer, joined by the aponeurosis of the transversus muscle, passes behind the rectus and constitutes the posterior wall of its sheath. (In the uppermost part of the posterior wall there are muscular fibres of the transversus as well as aponeurotic fibres). This arrangement obtains in the upper three-fourths of the abdominal wall. Below the level of the anterior superior iliac spine, the sheath of the muscle is deficient posteriorly, and a crescentic border, called the **arcuate line** [linea semicircularis], marks the lower limit of the posterior wall. In consequence, the rectus in the lower fourth of the abdominal wall rests directly on the fascia transversalis. Close examination, however, usually reveals a thin layer behind the muscle in continuity with the arcuate line, and merging below with the fascia transversalis. In this region the rectus is covered anteriorly by the aponeuroses of the external oblique, internal oblique, and transversus (Fig. 362). The upper part of the rectus, lying directly on the chest wall (because the posterior wall of the sheath ascends no higher than the costal margin), is covered anteriorly by only a single layer of aponeurosis derived from the external oblique, which in that situation is giving origin to the pectoralis major muscle.

Inguinal Canal.—The spermatic cord in the male (or the round ligament in the female), in its passage through the lower part of the abdominal wall, traverses the **inguinal canal**, which is bounded by these abdominal muscles. The canal begins at the *deep inguinal ring*, which is an opening in the fascia transversalis, half an inch or less above the inguinal ligament, and midway between the anterior superior iliac spine and the pubic symphysis. It ends at the *superficial inguinal ring*, which is an opening in the external oblique aponeurosis immediately above the pubic tubercle and the medial end of the inguinal ligament. The *anterior wall* of the canal is formed by the aponeurosis of the external

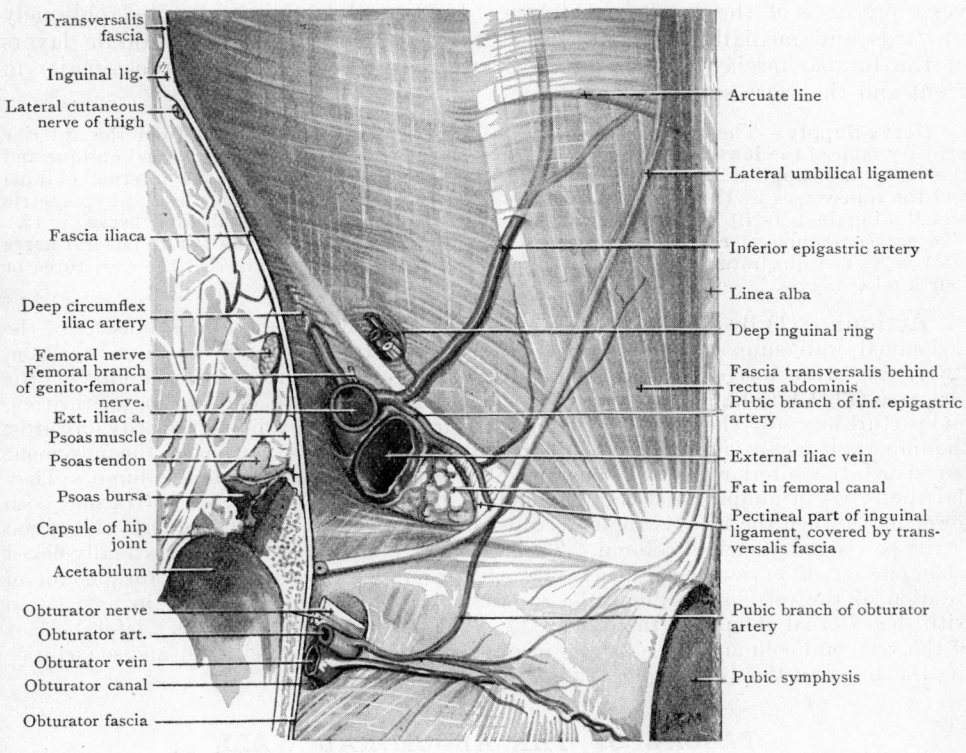

Transversalis fascia

Inguinal lig.

Lateral cutaneous nerve of thigh

Fascia iliaca

Deep circumflex iliac artery

Femoral nerve
Femoral branch of genito-femoral nerve.
Ext. iliac a.
Psoas muscle
Psoas tendon

Psoas bursa

Capsule of hip joint

Acetabulum

Obturator nerve

Obturator art.

Obturator vein

Obturator canal

Obturator fascia

Arcuate line

Lateral umbilical ligament

Inferior epigastric artery

Linea alba

Deep inguinal ring

Fascia transversalis behind rectus abdominis
Pubic branch of inf. epigastric artery

External iliac vein

Fat in femoral canal

Pectineal part of inguinal ligament, covered by transversalis fascia

Pubic branch of obturator artery

Pubic symphysis

FIG. 363.—DEEP INGUINAL RING, FEMORAL RING, AND OBTURATOR CANAL
SEEN FROM INSIDE THE ABDOMEN.

oblique, and in its lateral part by the muscular fibres of the internal oblique; the *posterior wall* of the canal is formed by the fascia transversalis, and in its medial part by the conjoint tendon and by the reflected part of the inguinal ligament when that structure is well developed. Thus, the anterior wall is strongest opposite the deep inguinal ring, and the posterior wall opposite the superficial ring. The *floor* of the canal is formed by the inguinal ligament, and, medially, by its pectineal part. The spermatic cord, evaginating the transversalis fascia, enters the inguinal canal at the deep inguinal ring, and is there invested by its *first envelope*—the **internal spermatic fascia**—a sheath of fascia derived from the margins of the ring and continuous with the fascia transversalis. The cord then passes obliquely medially, downwards, and forwards, and escapes below the lower border of the internal oblique muscle, from which it carries off a *second investment*, partly fascial, partly muscular—the **cremaster muscle** and **fascia**. Continuing its course, in front of the conjoint tendon, it emerges through the superficial inguinal ring, from the edges of which the **external spermatic fascia** is derived, *i.e.* the *third* or *external investment* of the cord.

The **inguinal triangle** (Hesselbach) is the site of one form of inguinal hernia. It is bounded below by the inguinal ligament, medially by the rectus abdominis muscle, and laterally by the inferior epigastric artery coursing upwards and medially behind the fascia transversalis. The spermatic cord passes over the base of the triangle, covered over by the aponeurosis of the external oblique. Behind the cord, and forming the floor of the triangle, is the fascia transversalis, partially covered, in the medial portion of the triangle, by the conjoint tendon.

Quadratus Lumborum.—The quadratus lumborum lies alongside the tips of the lumbar transverse processes, and extends between the iliac crest and the last rib. It arises from the posterior part of the iliac crest, from the ilio-lumbar ligament, and from the transverse processes of the lower lumbar vertebræ. It is inserted into the medial part of the lower border of the last rib and the transverse processes of the lumbar vertebræ. Its lateral border is directed obliquely upwards and medially. It is enclosed between the anterior and middle layers of the lumbar fascia (p. 396), and is overlapped, medially, by the psoas major in front and the sacro-spinalis behind.

Nerve-Supply.—The nerve-supply of the foregoing muscles is derived from the anterior primary rami of the **lower six thoracic** and **upper four lumbar nerves.** The external oblique and the rectus are supplied by the lower five intercostal nerves (T. 7.-11.), the internal oblique and the transversus by the lower five intercostal, the subcostal (T. 12.), and the ilio-hypogastric and ilio-inguinal (L. 1.). The pyramidalis muscle is innervated by the **subcostal nerve** (T. 12.). The cremaster muscle receives its supply from the **genital branch of the genito-femoral nerve** (L. 1. 2.). The quadratus lumborum is supplied by the subcostal nerve and the first three or four lumbar nerves.

Actions.—(1) By virtue of their normal tone, the anterior and lateral muscles of the abdominal wall support the abdominal viscera and help to retain them in position. (2) Acting with but against the diaphragm they can compress the contents of the abdomen (Pl. XXX, Fig. 4), and are powerful agents in vomiting, defæcation, micturition, and parturition. (3) They take part in forced expiration. (4) In bending the body forwards, the important factor is relaxation of the post-vertebral muscles ; but, when the movement is resisted, the anterior muscles come into play as flexors of the vertebral column. They flex the pelvis in jumping and climbing and act powerfully in the exercise of raising both lower limbs when the body is supine because of their rôle (an exhausting one) of fixation of the pelvis and vertebral column. The vertebral column and pelvis are laterally flexed when one set of muscles acts alone. The oblique muscles produce a certain amount of rotation of the vertebral column, the internal oblique of one side acting in association with the external oblique of the other side. The quadratus lumborum is a lateral flexor of the vertebral column, and assists in inspiration by fixing the twelfth rib and so facilitating the action of the diaphragm.

FASCIÆ OF THE ABDOMINAL WALL

The fasciæ of the abdominal wall are—*externally*, the superficial and deep fasciæ, *internally*, the fascia transversalis. The fascia transversalis clothes the deep surface of the anterior and lateral walls of the abdominal cavity, is continuous with the diaphragmatic, lumbar, psoas, iliac, and pelvic fasciæ, and is lined by the **extraperitoneal tissue.** In this way a fascial envelope is formed which encloses the abdominal and pelvic cavities, the viscera, and the great vessels.

The **superficial fascia** of the abdomen is liable to contain a large quantity of fat. In the groin it is separated into *two layers* : a superficial, **fatty layer** continuous over the inguinal ligament with the fascia of the anterior surface of the thigh (p. 503), and a deeper, **membranous layer** attached to the medial half of the inguinal ligament, and more laterally to the fascia lata of the thigh distal to the inguinal ligament. The two layers are separated by the lymph glands and the superficial vessels of the groin. Higher up in the abdominal wall the two layers blend together. In the median plane the membranous layer is adherent to the linea alba, from the lower part of which it descends as the *fundiform ligament* to the dorsum of the penis and makes a sling continuous with the superficial fascia of the penis. From the front of the symphysis the fascia descends as a triangular band—the *suspensory ligament*—to be attached to the deep fascia of the penis. As the layers pass downwards over the spermatic cord, they arer eplaced by the fascia and dartos muscle of the scrotum. The attachment of the fascia to the groin prevents the passage into the thigh of fluid extravasated beneath the membranous layer of the abdominal wall (p. 442 and Fig. 368). The membranous layer represents the elastic tunic which supports the abdominal wall and inguinal mammæ in such animals as the cow.

The **deep fascia** of the abdominal wall resembles similar fasciæ in other situations. It forms an investment for the external oblique muscle, and becomes thin and almost imperceptible in relation to the aponeurosis of that muscle.

The **fascial lining** of the abdominal cavity is a continuous layer of membrane

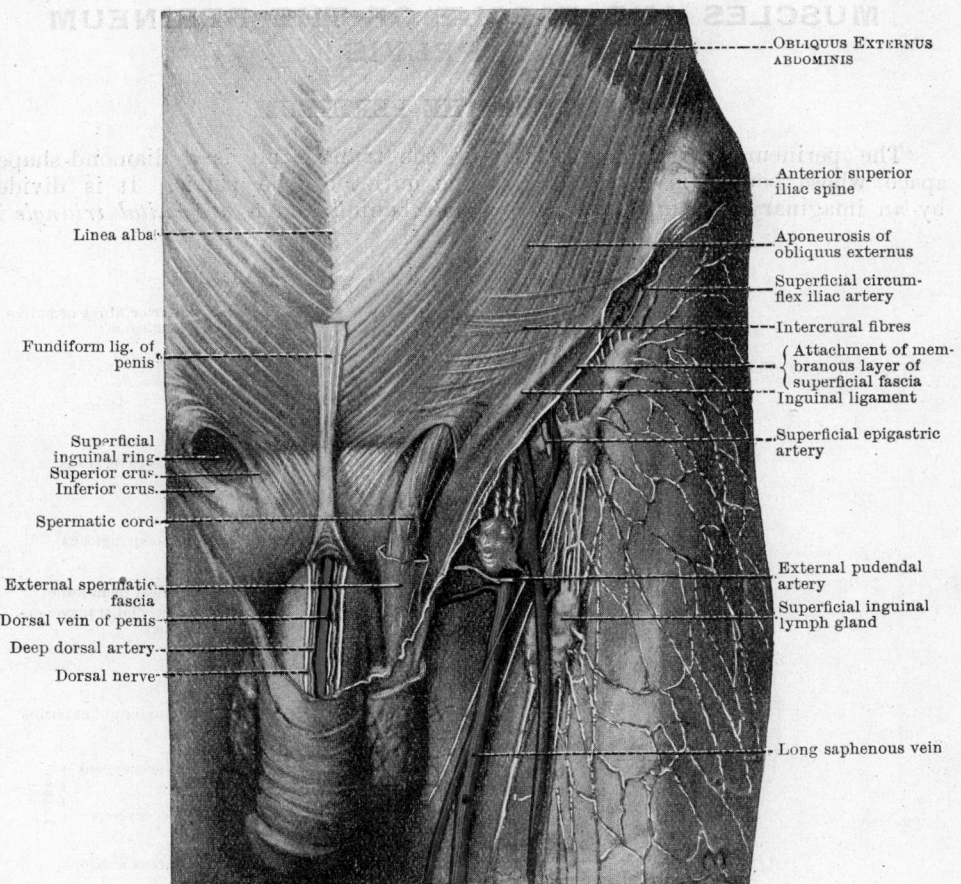

OBLIQUUS EXTERNUS ABDOMINIS

Anterior superior iliac spine

Aponeurosis of obliquus externus

Superficial circumflex iliac artery

Intercrural fibres

Attachment of membranous layer of superficial fascia

Inguinal ligament

Superficial epigastric artery

External pudendal artery

Superficial inguinal lymph gland

Long saphenous vein

Linea alba

Fundiform lig. of penis

Superficial inguinal ring
Superior crus.
Inferior crus.

Spermatic cord

External spermatic fascia
Dorsal vein of penis
Deep dorsal artery
Dorsal nerve

FIG. 364.—SUPERFICIAL ANATOMY OF THE GROIN.

which receives different names in different parts of its extent. The **transversalis fascia** covers the deep surface of the transversus muscle, and is continuous medially with the fasciæ of the quadratus lumborum and the psoas muscles. It is continuous above with the fascia of the diaphragm, and below with the **fascia iliaca** at the iliac crest and the inguinal ligament (see p. 504). Along with the fascia iliaca it forms the **femoral sheath**. It is evaginated by the spermatic cord, or by the round ligament of the uterus, at the deep inguinal ring, and its prolongation into the inguinal canal around the cord forms the **internal spermatic fascia**. Internally, it is lined with the peritoneum, from which it is separated by a layer of extraperitoneal tissue.

The **extraperitoneal tissue** is usually loaded with fat; it envelops the kidneys, ureters, suprarenal glands, abdominal aorta, and inferior vena cava and their branches, and forms sheaths for the vessels and ducts (ureter, vas deferens, etc.). It is continued upwards into the posterior mediastinum of the thorax through the aortic opening in the diaphragm, and is in continuity with the extra-peritoneal tissue in the pelvis. It not only completely invests the kidneys and suprarenal glands, but also becomes insinuated between the layers of peri-toneum that uphold and envelop the intestines. On the anterior wall, below the level of the umbilicus, it contains the inferior epigastric vessels, the lateral and median umbilical ligaments, and the upper part of the bladder when it is dis-tended. This tissue is absent in relation to the diaphragm, on the under surface of which there is no fat.

MUSCLES AND FASCIÆ OF THE PERINEUM AND PELVIS

MUSCLES OF THE PERINEUM

The perineum is the lowest part of the trunk, and is a diamond-shaped space whose boundaries are those of the outlet of the pelvis. It is divided by an imaginary line into an *anal triangle* behind and a *urogenital triangle* in

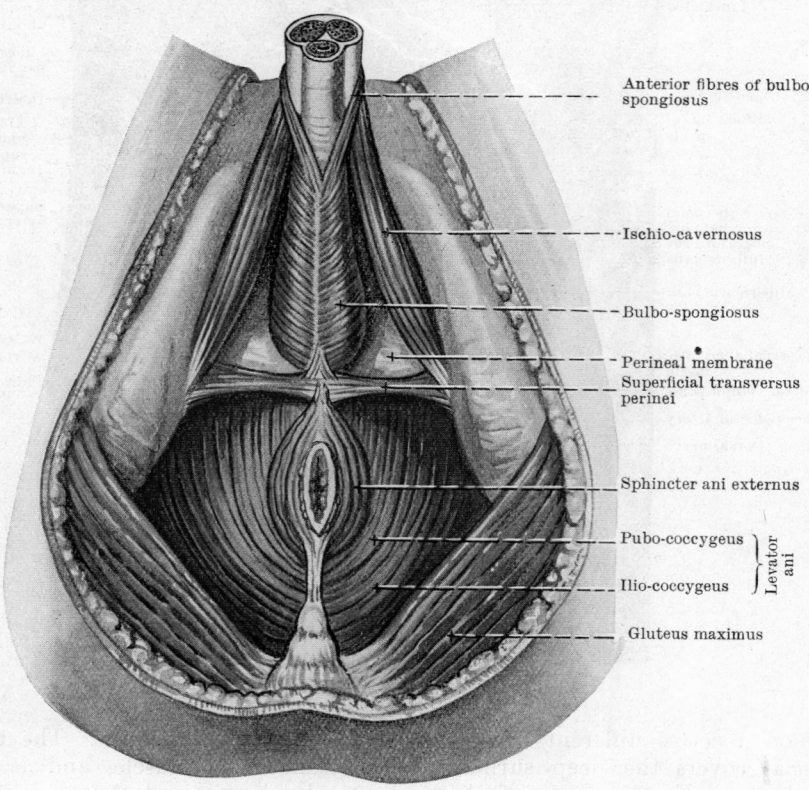

FIG. 365.—MUSCLES OF THE MALE PERINEUM. (J. C. B.)

front. In the anal triangle there is only one perineal muscle—the external sphincter ani. A fibrous sheet called the *perineal membrane* stretches across the pubic arch and divides the urogenital triangle into an upper and a lower part. The lower part contains three pairs of muscles—ischio-cavernosus, bulbo-spongiosus, and the superficial transversus perinei. The upper part contains the sphincter urethræ and a pair of deep transverse perineal muscles.

Sphincter Ani Externus.—This muscle is fusiform in outline, flattened, and obliquely placed around the anus and anal canal. It can be separated into three layers—subcutaneous, superficial, and deep. (1) The most superficial lamina consists of subcutaneous fibres decussating posterior and anterior to the anus, but without bony attachments. (2) The main portion of the muscle is attached posteriorly to the coccyx, and anteriorly to the perineal body. (3) The deepest fibres form, for the most part, a complete sphincter for the anal canal—encircling its lower two-thirds and blending anteriorly with the perineal body and the superficial transversus perinei muscle.

Superficial Transversus Perinei.—The superficial transversus perinei, not always present, is a feeble bundle of fibres that arises from the fore part of the medial side of the ischial tuberosity and passes medially below the posterior border of the perineal membrane to be inserted into the perineal body.

Bulbo-spongiosus [Bulbo-cavernosus].— *In the male,* the right and left bulbo-spongiosus muscles are united together by a fibrous median raphe, and they cover the bulb of the penis and the adjoining part of the corpus spongiosum. They arise from the raphe and the perineal body, and their fibres, curving upwards and forwards round the sides of the bulb, have a triple insertion: from behind forwards, (1) into the lower surface of the perineal membrane; (2) into the dorsal surface of the corpus spongiosum

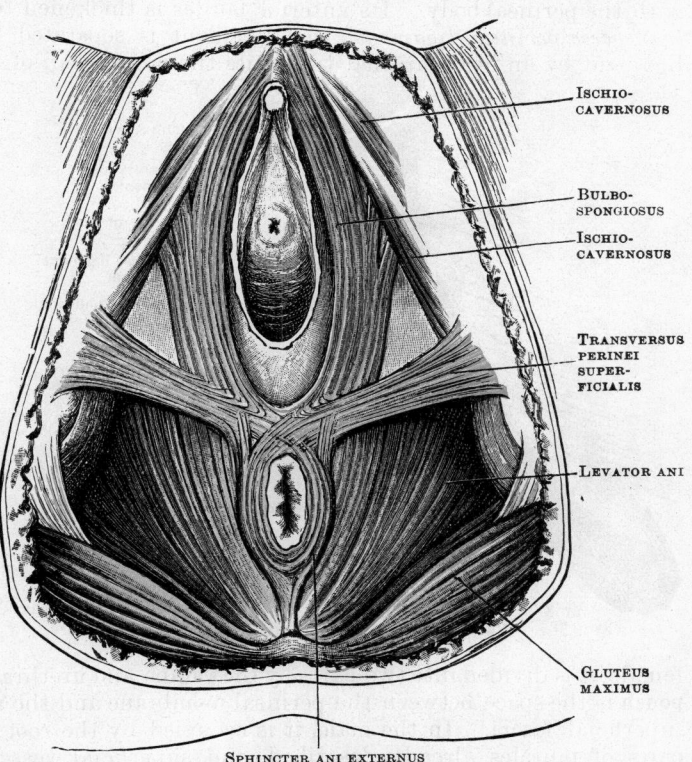

FIG. 366.—THE MUSCLES OF THE FEMALE PERINEUM. (After Peter Thompson.)

penis; and (3), after encircling the corpora cavernosa penis, into the deep fascia on the dorsum of the penis.

In the female, the bulbo-spongiosus muscles are separate. Each is a thin layer that lies at the side of the lower part of the vagina and covers the bulb of the vestibule. It arises from the perineal body, and, passing forwards, its fibres separate to be inserted into the side of the pubic arch and into the root and dorsum of the clitoris.

Ischio-cavernosus.—The ischio-cavernosus, partly fleshy, partly tendinous, covers the crus of the penis or of the clitoris. It arises from the medial side of the ischial tuberosity, and passing forwards over the crus, it is inserted into the margin of the pubic arch on each side of the crus and into the corpus cavernosum.

Perineal Body.—(Central point of perineum.) The perineal body is a fibro-muscular node of considerable importance in the anatomy of the perineum, especially in the female, for it may be torn during child-birth. It is placed between the anal canal and the perineal membrane: it is inseparably blended with the membrane (and, in the male, with the fascial sheath of the prostate), and both striped and unstriped muscle fibres enter into its constitution. The superficial and deep transverse perineal muscles, the bulbo-spongiosus, the external sphincter ani and the levator ani all contribute to it; and, in addition, prolongations of the longitudinal fibres of the gut (superior and inferior recto-urethralis muscles) are continued into it.

Perineal Membrane [Fascia Diaphragmatis Urogenitalis Inferior].—This membrane stretches across the pubic arch. In the male, it almost completely fills the archway, but in the female it is defective in the middle to give passage to the vagina and the urethra. Its posterior border is fused with the posterior borders of (1) the membranous layer of the superficial fascia of the perineum, and (2) the layer of fascia that covers the upper surface of the sphincter urethræ and deep transversus perinei. In the median plane this border is thickened, and is united with the perineal body. Its anterior border is thickened to form a band called the *transverse perineal ligament*; this ligament is separated from the inferior pubic ligament by an oval gap that transmits the dorsal vein of the clitoris or the deep dorsal vein of the penis; and this border also is fused with the fascia that covers the sphincter urethræ. The space between the membrane and that fascia is therefore closed; it is called the **deep perineal pouch**, and contains the sphincter urethræ and the deep transversus perinei, the internal pudendal vessels and the dorsal nerve of the penis or of the clitoris, the vessels of the bulb; in the male, it contains, also, the membranous part of the urethra and the bulbo-urethral glands; and, in the female, it is divided into two parts by the vagina and urethra.

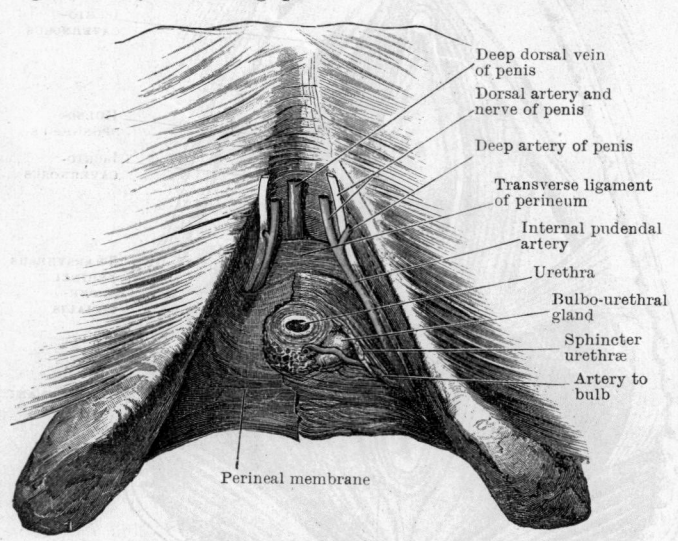

Deep dorsal vein of penis
Dorsal artery and nerve of penis
Deep artery of penis
Transverse ligament of perineum
Internal pudendal artery
Urethra
Bulbo-urethral gland
Sphincter urethræ
Artery to bulb
Perineal membrane

FIG. 367.—PERINEAL MEMBRANE AND SPHINCTER URETHRÆ.

The **superficial perineal pouch** is the space between the perineal membrane and the membranous layer of the superficial fascia. In the male, it is occupied by the root of the penis, the three pairs of muscles already described, and superficial vessels and nerves. In the female, the vagina divides it into halves; each half contains the corresponding muscles, vessels and nerves, the crus of the clitoris, the bulb of the vestibule and the greater vestibular gland. The perineal membrane is pierced, in the male, by the urethra, the artery to the bulb, the internal pudendal vessels and the dorsal nerves of the penis, in the female, by corresponding vessels and nerves and the vagina and urethra.

Sphincter Urethræ.—The sphincter of the urethra **arises** from the inferior pubic ramus, and is directed medially—its fibres radiating towards the urethra.

In the male, it is **inserted** into a median raphe, partly in front of the urethra, but for the most part behind it. The fibres most intimately related to the urethra form a muscular sheath for the canal, and have no bony attachments. *In the female*, it encloses the urethra, but, together with the deep transversus perinei, it is also attached to the side of the vagina. The **deep transversus perinei** is a small muscular slip closely connected with the posterior fibres of the sphincter; *in the male*, it is inserted into the perineal body.

Nerve-Supply.—All the muscles of the perineum are supplied from the **anterior primary rami** of the **third** and **fourth** sacral nerves. The external sphincter of the anus has three nerves of supply—from the perineal and inferior hæmorrhoidal nerves (branches of the pudendal nerve S. 3. 4.), and the perineal branch of the fourth sacral nerve. All the other muscles are supplied by the **perineal nerve**.

Action of the Perineal Muscles.—The sphincter ani externus keeps the anal orifice firmly closed by its tonic contraction—which may be voluntarily increased. The bulbo-spongiosus in the male, relaxed during the course of micturition, contracts to expel the last drops of urine ; it acts also as an accessory muscle in erection of the penis by compressing the bulb and impeding the venous return ; in the female, it compresses the bulb of the vestibule, and constricts the vaginal orifice—forming with the pubo-coccygeus a kind of sphincter.   The ischio-cavernosus, by compressing the crus and impeding venous return, is the chief muscular agent in erection of the penis or the clitoris.   The sphincter urethræ compresses the urethra at the end of micturition.   The deep transversus perinei assists other muscles attached to the perineal body in fixing that body and in supporting the prostate.

FASCIÆ OF THE PERINEUM

The **superficial fascia** of the perineum possesses certain special feature (Figs. 368, 372, 373).   It is continuous with the superficial fascia of the abdominal

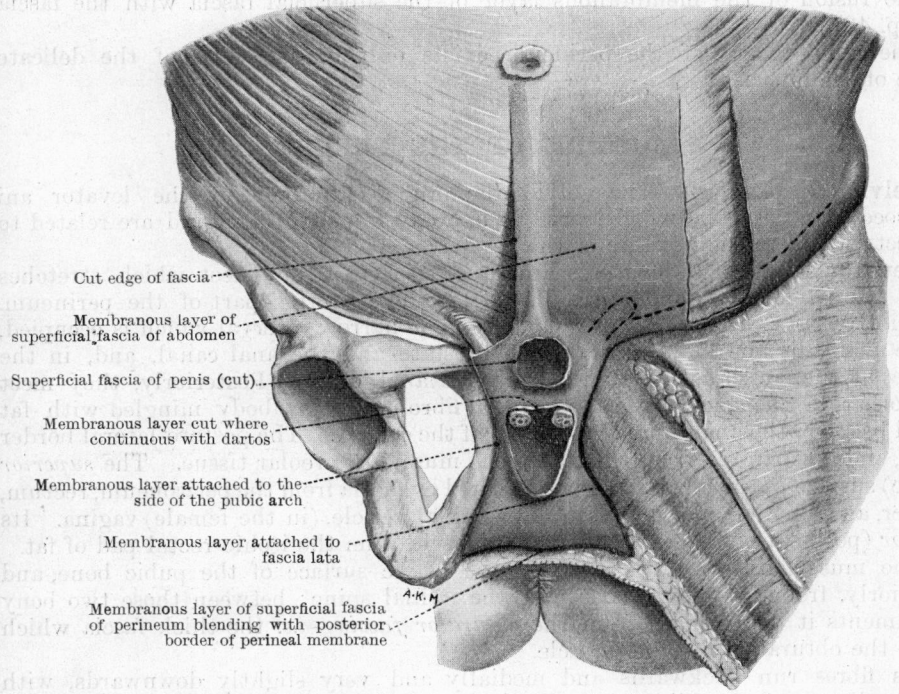

Cut edge of fascia

Membranous layer of superficial fascia of abdomen

Superficial fascia of penis (cut)

Membranous layer cut where continuous with dartos

Membranous layer attached to the side of the pubic arch

Membranous layer attached to fascia lata

Membranous layer of superficial fascia of perineum blending with posterior border of perineal membrane

Fig. 368.—Diagram showing Continuity of Membranous Layer of the Superficial Fascia of Abdominal Wall and Perineum.   (R. D. L.)

wall, thigh, and buttock, and is prolonged on to the penis and scrotum.   In the penis, it is devoid of fat and consists only of areolar tissue.   In the scrotum, it is intermingled with involuntary muscular fibres, and constitutes the **dartos muscle**, which assists in suspending the testes and corrugates the skin of the scrotum.   This fascia also forms the **septum of the scrotum**, which, extending upwards, incompletely separates the two testes and their coverings.   In the female, the superficial fascia, in which there is a considerable quantity of fat, takes a large share in the formation of the mons pubis and the labia majora.

The superficial fascia over the posterior part of the perineum fills up the ischio-rectal fossæ, in the form of a pair of **ischio-rectal pads of fat**, at the sides of the rectum and anal canal.   Over the ischial tuberosities the fat is intermingled with bands of fibrous tissue closely adherent to the subjacent deep fascia.

The fascia in the anterior part of the perineum closely resembles the same fascia in the groin.   It is divisible into a superficial, **fatty layer** and a deep, **membranous layer**.   The **fatty layer** is continuous with the same layer in the thigh, and with the fat of the ischio-rectal fossa. The **membranous layer** is attached on each side to the deep fascia on the front of the pubis and to the side of the pubic arch, posteriorly to the posterior border of the perineal membrane, and in the median plane to the median raphe of the bulbo-spongiosus muscles and to the septum of the scrotum. Anteriorly the fascia invests the scrotum and gives a tubular covering to the penis. Finally it is continued over the spermatic cords to the anterior abdominal wall. The importance of this fascia lies in relation to the extravasation of urine from a rupture of the urethra in the perineum. By the fascial attachments the fluid is prevented from passing backwards into the ischio-rectal fossa, or sideways into the thigh. It is directed forwards—invading the subcutaneous tissues of the scrotum (the septum of the scrotum being incomplete, the fluid can pass across the median plane to the opposite half of the perineum and scrotum) and gravitating into the fascial covering of the penis as far as the glans, and lastly mounting upwards around the spermatic cord to the anterior abdominal wall, where it is kept from entering the front of the thigh by the fusion of the membranous layer of the superficial fascia with the fascia lata (p. 437).

The **deep fascia** of the perineum exists only in the form of the delicate fasciæ of the muscles.

MUSCLES OF THE PELVIS

Pelvic Diaphragm.—The pelvic diaphragm is formed by the levator ani and coccygeus muscles, which serve to uphold the pelvic floor, and are related to the rectum and to the prostate or the vagina.

Levator Ani.—The levatores ani muscles form a thin sheet which stretches across the pelvic cavity and separates it from the posterior part of the perineum. Anteriorly, the two muscles are separated by a narrow interval which is occupied, in the male, by the lower part of the prostate and the anal canal, and, in the female, by the urethra, the vagina, and the anal canal. Posteriorly, they meet each other in the **ano-coccygeal body**—a fibro-muscular body mingled with fat placed between the anal canal and the tip of the coccyx. The postero-lateral border is free, and is separated from the coccygeus muscle by areolar tissue. The *superior* (pelvic) surface of the levator ani is separated by fascia from the peritoneum, rectum, bladder, and (in the male) prostate and seminal vesicle, (in the female) vagina. Its *inferior* (perineal) surface is separated by fascia from the ischio-rectal pad of fat.

The muscle **arises** anteriorly from the pelvic surface of the pubic bone, and posteriorly, from the pelvic surface of the ischial spine; between those two bony attachments it takes origin from the *obturator fascia—i.e.* the thick fascia which covers the obturator internus muscle.

Its fibres run backwards and medially and very slightly downwards, with varying degrees of obliquity, and are **inserted** (1) into the perineal body, (2) into the ano-coccygeal body, and (3) into the front and sides of the coccyx. In addition, some of the fibres form a sling around the upper end of the anal canal.

The levator ani is divisible into two distinct portions, namely, the **ilio-coccygeus** and the **pubo-coccygeus**, and the latter can be subdivided into three parts, imperfectly separated from one another, viz.—the *pubo-coccygeus proper*, the *pubo-rectalis*, and the *levator prostatae.*

The **ilio-coccygeus** is the posterior part of the levator ani, and its origin extends as far forwards as the obturator canal. It is usually a thin sheet in which the muscular fibres are feebly developed and often separated by membranous intervals. The strong fascia from which it arises represents the upward continuation of the muscle to reach the arcuate line of the pelvis, and has, secondarily, become blended with the obturator fascia. This attachment to the arcuate line is the primitive origin of the ilio-coccygeus and is the normal condition in many mammals. The fibres run medially to be inserted into the side of the coccyx and the ano-coccygeal body, but, at their insertion, they are covered on their pelvic aspect by the backward-running fibres of the pubo-coccygeus (Figs. 369, 370).

The **pubo-coccygeus** is composed of those fibres of the levator ani which arise in front of the obturator canal. The most anterior (medial) fibres pass backwards in contact with the side of the prostate or of the vagina and are inserted into the perineal body, where they mingle with the deeper fibres of the sphincter ani externus.

The fibres which have a more lateral origin from the pubic bone form the *pubo-rectalis*. This muscle sweeps backwards over the side of the prostate (or vagina) and the upper part of the anal canal, behind which it becomes directly continuous with the corresponding muscle of the opposite side. The pubo-rectales form therefore a U-shaped sling for the ano-rectal junction (Figs. 370, 371), and they can constrict the anal canal in the male, and the vagina and anal canal in the female. Together, they constitute the most highly developed part of the pelvic diaphragm.

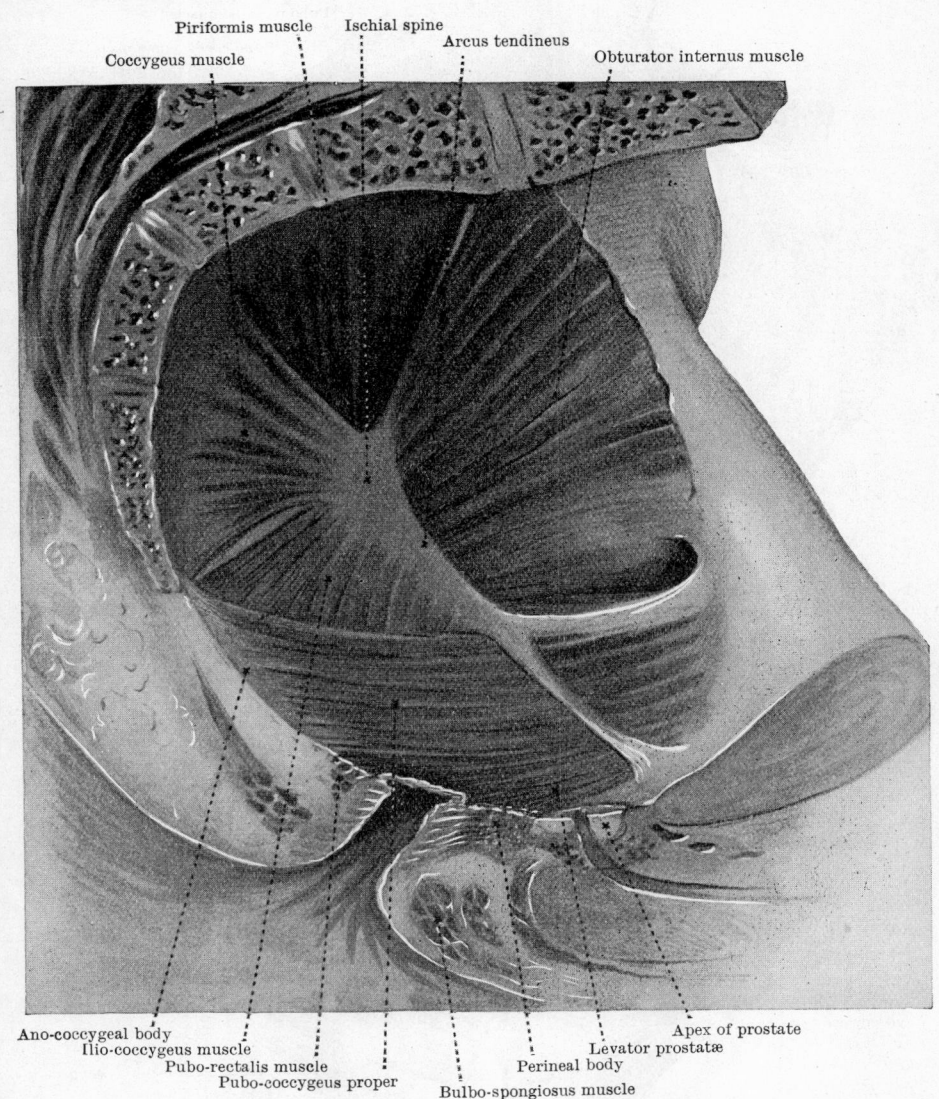

FIG. 369.—THE LEFT LEVATOR ANI MUSCLE. (T. B. J.)

The *pubo-coccygeus proper* is the remainder of this part of the levator ani muscle. Its fibres run backwards and medially, above the fibres of the ilio-coccygeus, and are inserted (1) into the ano-coccygeal body, where they meet the fibres of the opposite side, and (2) into the sides and front of the coccyx.

The **coccygeus** (ischio-coccygeus), which lies on the same plane as the ilio-coccygeus, is a fan-shaped muscle. It **arises** from the pelvic surface of the ischial spine and is **inserted** into the margin of the lower two pieces of the sacrum and the upper two pieces of the coccyx.

Nerve-Supply.—The pelvic diaphragm, like the perineal muscles, is supplied from the anterior primary rami of the **third** and **fourth sacral nerves**. Direct branches enter the levator ani and the coccygeus on their pelvic surfaces, and in addition the anterior part of the levator ani is supplied on its perineal surface by the perineal branch of the pudendal nerve.

Actions.—Both these muscles play a very important part in retaining the pelvic viscera in position, especially in the female. In addition, the pubo-rectales reinforce the sphincters of the vagina and anal canal, and the fibres which are inserted into the perineal

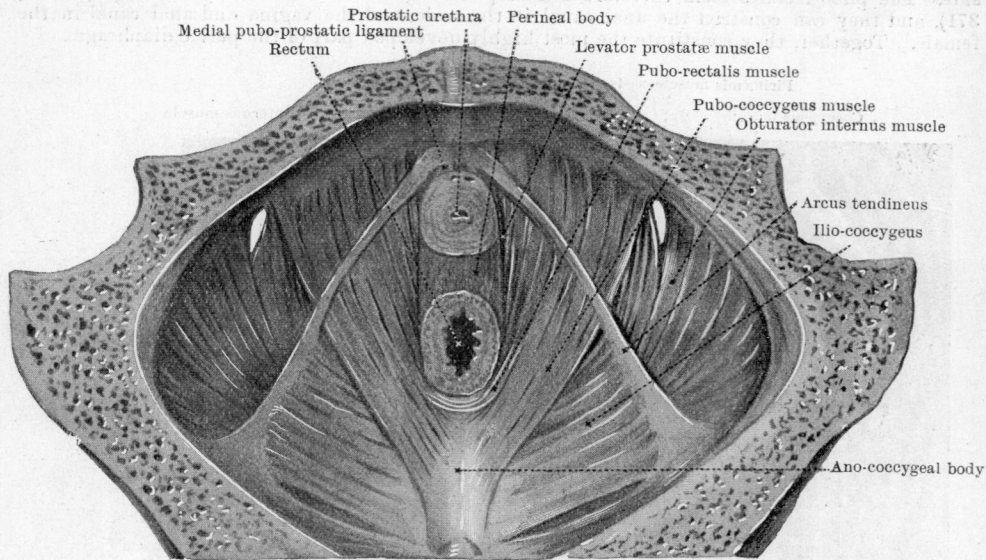

FIG. 370.—THE LEVATOR ANI MUSCLE VIEWED FROM ABOVE. (T. B. J.)

body draw it upwards and forwards. This latter action assists in the later stages of expulsion during defæcation and parturition.

Comparative Morphology.—In pronograde mammals, the ilio-coccygei and pubo-coccygei are inserted into the caudal vertebræ and act, respectively, as abductors and flexors of the tail.

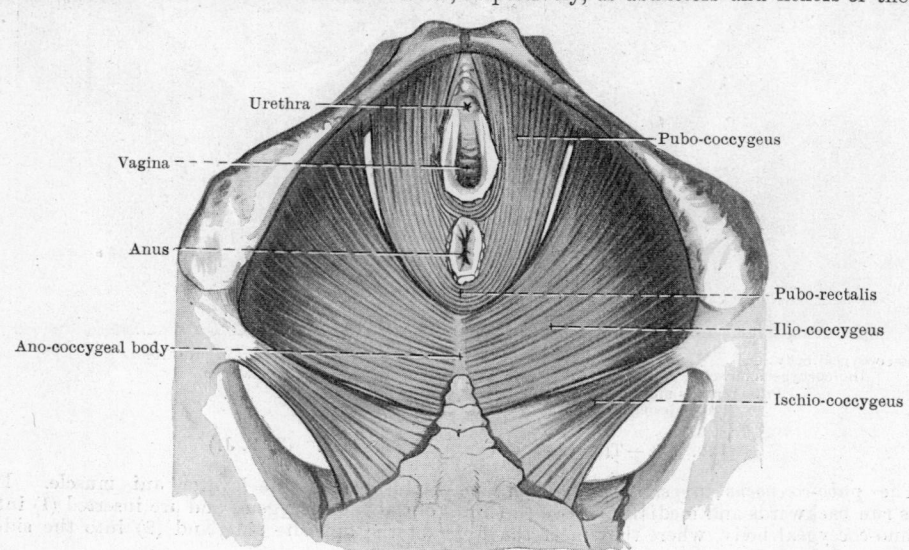

FIG. 371.—DISSECTION OF FEMALE PELVIC DIAPHRAGM FROM BELOW. (After Peter Thompson.)
By permission of the Editors of the *Journ. of Anatomy.*

The ischial origin of the ilio-coccygeus in Man is secondary; the true ischio-coccygeus is the "abductor caudæ" of tailed mammals. Although the pubo-coccygei may have a compressing effect on the vagina and rectum, such action is purely secondary. In pronograde animals there is not the same need for a muscular pelvic diaphragm, and, consequently, the two muscles are separated from each other both dorsal and ventral to the rectum.

The adoption of the erect attitude necessitates the provision of a strong, but elastic, pelvic floor, to maintain the pelvic viscera in position and to permit the downward passage of the fœtus. This function is assumed by the ilio- and the ischio-coccygei, which are no longer needed to act on a tail; and the pubo-coccygei become specialised in relation to the anal and vaginal canals. [Consult *The Myology of the Pelvic Floor*, by P. Thompson.]

Ischio-rectal Fossæ.—The ischio-rectal fossæ are the pair of wedge-shaped spaces that occupy the lateral parts of the anal triangle of the perineum. The lateral wall of each fossa is the obturator fascia; the medial wall is the fascia that covers the perineal surface of the levator ani; the edge of the wedge is at the junction of these fasciæ; and the base is the skin of the perineum. The fossa is filled with the plug of fat known as the ischio-rectal pad. It is crossed transversely by the inferior hæmorrhoidal nerve and the inferior rectal vessels; the perineal branch of the fourth sacral nerve appears in its posterior part, and the posterior scrotal (or labial)

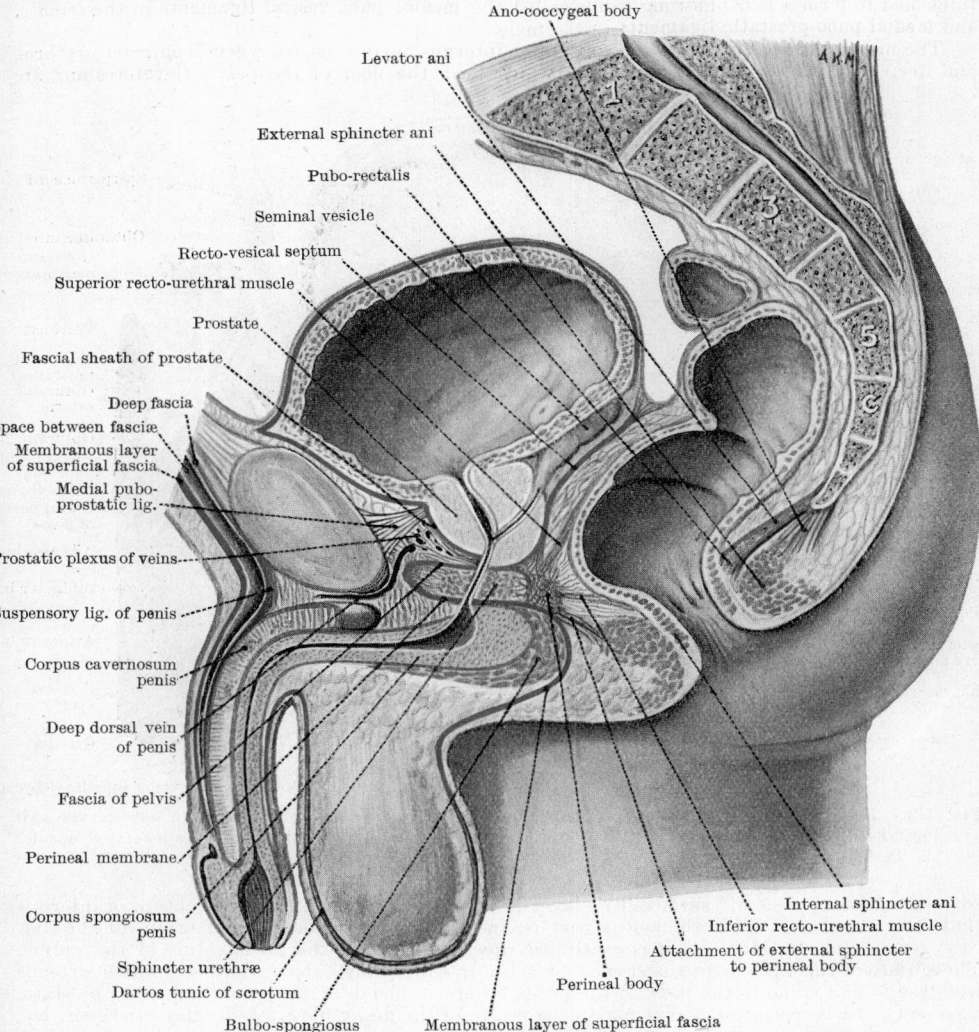

FIG. 372.—SAGITTAL SECTION OF MALE PELVIS SHOWING FASCIÆ IN BLUE.   (R. D. L.)

nerves and vessels in its anterior part; the internal pudendal vessels, the perineal nerve, and the dorsal nerve of the penis (or clitoris) traverse the pudendal canal in its lateral wall. Posteriorly, it extends backwards for a little distance above the sacro-tuberous ligament and the gluteus maximus. Anteriorly, it sends forward a "diverticulum" (Fig. 373) above the deep perineal pouch as far as the pubis; this extension retains the lateral and medial boundaries of the fossa—the fascia of the obturator internus and levator ani—and is occupied by loose, vascular fatty tissue.

FASCIÆ OF THE PELVIS

The extraperitoneal tissue in the pelvic cavity is of great importance. The internal iliac [hypogastric] vessels and their branches, the visceral nerves and plexuses, the ureters, and vasa deferentia, lie in this tissue. It forms in relation to **the rectum** a thick sheath, for the most part devoid of fat, which completely encloses the lower part of the rectum. It forms a kind of packing for the parts of **the bladder** that are not covered with peritoneum, and it surrounds the prostate with a strong sheath. In the female it forms, in addition, the fibrous basis of the **broad ligament**, and also occurs as a layer, devoid of fat, which loosely connects the anterior surface of the **cervix uteri** with the base of the bladder.

The **pelvic fascia** covers the free surfaces of the muscles, and is condensed around the viscera, vessels, and nerves to ensheath them ; and between the pubis and the neck of the bladder, it is thickened to form a pair of strong bands called the **medial pubo-vesical ligaments** in the female, and **medial pubo-prostatic ligaments** in the male.

The muscles which line the walls (obturator internus, piriformis, coccygeus, sphincter urethræ, and deep transversus perinei) and those which form the floor of the pelvis (levatores ani) are

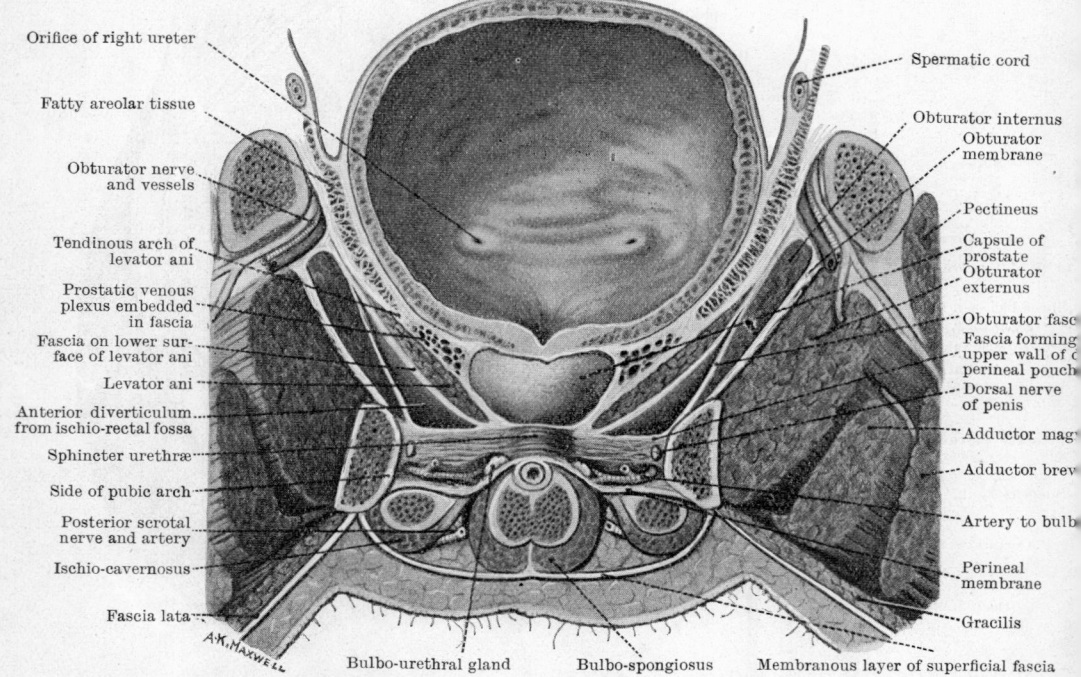

Orifice of right ureter
Fatty areolar tissue
Obturator nerve and vessels
Tendinous arch of levator ani
Prostatic venous plexus embedded in fascia
Fascia on lower surface of levator ani
Levator ani
Anterior diverticulum from ischio-rectal fossa
Sphincter urethræ
Side of pubic arch
Posterior scrotal nerve and artery
Ischio-cavernosus
Fascia lata

Spermatic cord
Obturator internus
Obturator membrane
Pectineus
Capsule of prostate
Obturator externus
Obturator fasc
Fascia forming upper wall of deep perineal pouch
Dorsal nerve of penis
Adductor mag
Adductor brev
Artery to bulb
Perineal membrane
Gracilis

Bulbo-urethral gland   Bulbo-spongiosus   Membranous layer of superficial fascia

A·K·MAXWELL

FIG. 373.—DISSECTION OF MALE PELVIS IN A CORONAL PLANE TO SHOW THE FASCIÆ OF PELVIS AND PERINEUM. The fascial sheath of the prostate has been removed in front to show the prostatic capsule. (R. D. L.)

covered on their "visceral" surfaces by a layer of fascia which is thicker over the obturator internus than it is elsewhere. This thickened part is, in reality, the aponeurosis of origin of the ilio-coccygeus muscle (p. 442), and it is continued upwards to reach the arcuate line of the pelvis. The surface of this aponeurosis is crossed by a linear thickening (*arcus tendineus*) which extends from the ischial spine to the body of the pubis, where it blends with the medial pubo-prostatic ligament. In its posterior part it marks the origin of the fleshy fibres of the ilio-coccygeus, but its anterior part crosses the pelvic surface of the pubo-coccygeus at least 1·5 cm. below its origin from the bone. The anterior portion of the arcus tendineus may represent an additional tendon of origin for the ilio-coccygeus.

A strong fascial sheath is provided for the prostate. The **fascial sheath of the prostate** is largely derived from the fibrous tissue which is condensed around the prostatic venous plexus. It is continuous inferiorly with the roof of the deep perineal pouch (Fig. 373), on each side with the fascia of the levator ani, and superiorly with the fascia condensed around the vesical plexus of veins on the infero-lateral surfaces of the bladder. Anteriorly it is attached to the pelvic surface of the pubic bones near the symphysis by the **medial pubo-prostatic ligaments**. These two strong bands and the fascia which connects them to each other and to that covering the levatores ani contain a number of plain muscle fibres.

The posterior part of the sheath of the prostate differs from the rest of the sheath in its mode of formation, and is a definite layer easily demonstrated by dissection. In a four months' fœtus the recto-vesical peritoneal pouch is very much deeper than it is in the adult, and the subsequent alteration in level is brought about by the occlusion of the lower part of the pouch.   The fused walls of the occluded portion persist as a fairly strong sheet, called the **recto-vesical septum**, which extends from the perineal body to the floor of the recto-vesical pouch—thus retaining its primitive connexion with the peritoneum.   It is separated by areolar tissue from the prostate, seminal vesicles, and vasa deferentia anteriorly and from the ampulla of the rectum posteriorly.

In enucleating the prostate, the surgeon endeavours to leave the fascial sheath of the prostate (and also the capsule of the gland) *in situ.*

APPENDICULAR MUSCLES

THE MUSCLES OF THE UPPER LIMB

The muscles of the upper limb are divisible into the following series and groups, according to their regional arrangement and their functions.   1. Muscles connecting the limb to the trunk—Dorsal Group (superficial muscles of the back), and Ventral Group (Muscles of the Pectoral Region).   2. Muscles of the Shoulder. 3. Muscles of the Upper Arm (flexor and extensor groups).   4. Muscles of the Forearm (flexor and extensor groups).   5. Short muscles of the Hand.

THE MUSCLES CONNECTING THE UPPER LIMB TO THE TRUNK

Two groups of muscles connect the upper limb to the trunk—a dorsal group arising primarily from the vertebral column, and a ventral group arising mainly from the thoracic skeleton.   With two exceptions (one in each group), all the muscles are inserted into the shoulder girdle (clavicle and scapula).   The exceptions are the latissimus dorsi and the pectoralis major, which are inserted into the humerus; and each of them has an additional origin from the shoulder girdle itself—the pectoralis major from the clavicle and the latissimus dorsi from the scapula.

The Superficial Muscles of the Back

The dorsal group comprises the first two layers of the muscles of the back—(1) trapezius and latissimus dorsi ; (2) levator scapulæ and rhomboidei (major and minor).

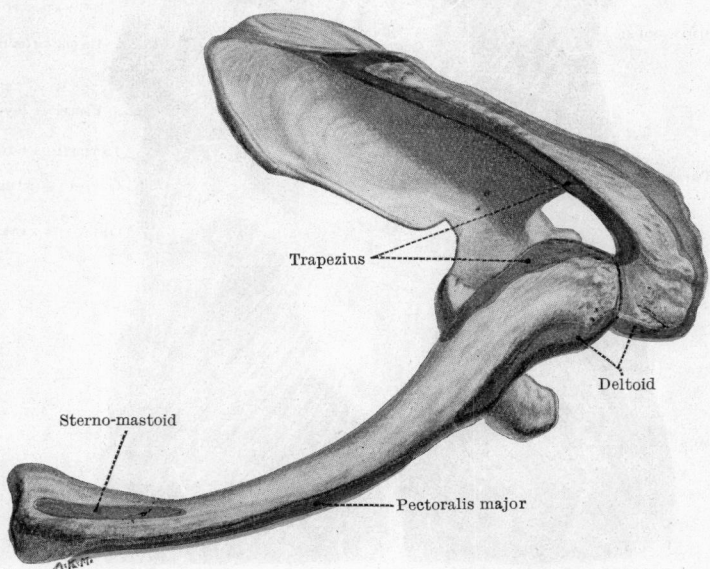

FIG. 374.—SHOULDER GIRDLE FROM ABOVE SHOWING MUSCLE ATTACHMENTS.   (R. D. L.)

Trapezius.—The trapezius is a large, triangular muscle situated in the upper part of the back and the back of the neck.   It **arises** from the medial third of the superior nuchal line of the occipital bone, from the external occipital protuberance

(Fig. 375), from the ligamentum nuchæ, from the spines of the seventh cervical and all the thoracic vertebræ, and the intervening supraspinous ligaments. The

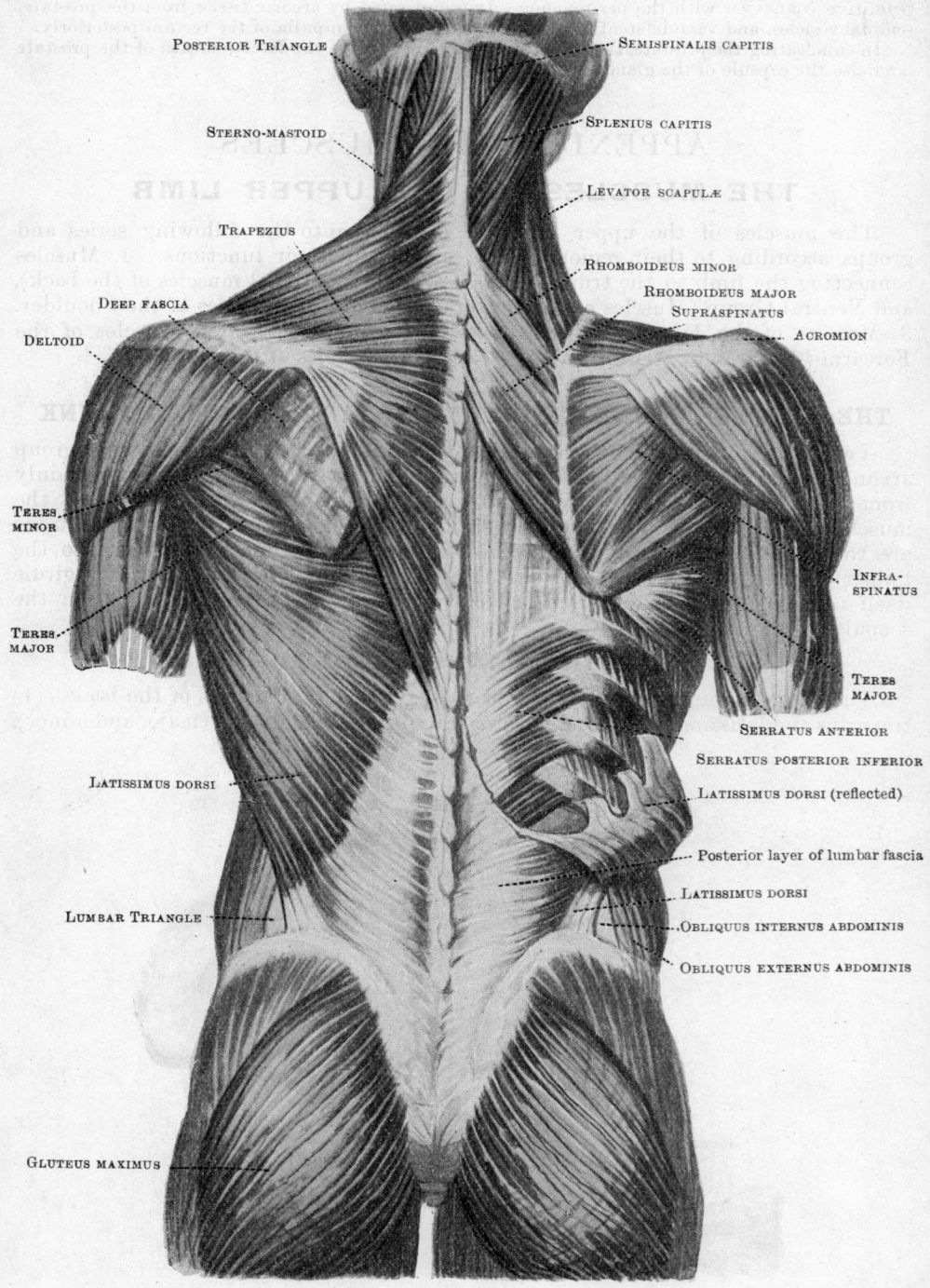

POSTERIOR TRIANGLE

SEMISPINALIS CAPITIS

STERNO-MASTOID

SPLENIUS CAPITIS

TRAPEZIUS

LEVATOR SCAPULÆ

DEEP FASCIA

RHOMBOIDEUS MINOR

RHOMBOIDEUS MAJOR

DELTOID

SUPRASPINATUS

ACROMION

TERES MINOR

INFRA-SPINATUS

TERES MAJOR

TERES MAJOR

SERRATUS ANTERIOR

SERRATUS POSTERIOR INFERIOR

LATISSIMUS DORSI

LATISSIMUS DORSI (reflected)

Posterior layer of lumbar fascia

LATISSIMUS DORSI

LUMBAR TRIANGLE

OBLIQUUS INTERNUS ABDOMINIS

OBLIQUUS EXTERNUS ABDOMINIS

GLUTEUS MAXIMUS

FIG. 375.—SUPERFICIAL MUSCLES OF THE BACK, AND VERTEBRO-SCAPULAR MUSCLES.

origin is by tendinous fibres which are mainly short, but in the lower part of the neck the tendinous fibres extend towards the shoulder to afford a larger area of origin for the thickest part of the muscle; between the two muscles there is thus formed a characteristic, irregular, diamond-shaped tendinous area which surrounds the seventh cervical spine, and forms the floor of a shallow depression seen in the living subject (Pl. XXX, Fig. 2).

The muscular fibres converge towards the bones of the shoulder to be **inserted** continuously from before backwards as follows : (1) The occipital and upper cervical fibres—into the posterior border of the lateral third of the clavicle (Figs. 374, 375); (2) the lower cervical and upper thoracic fibres—into the medial border of the acromion, and the upper border of the crest of the spine of the scapula ; and (3) the lower thoracic fibres, by a triangular, flat tendon, separated by a small *bursa* from the smooth area at the root of the spine—into the tubercle of the crest of the scapula.   The fibres inserted into the clavicle, acromion, and the upper border of the spine of the scapula spread over the adjacent subcutaneous surfaces of those bones for a variable distance.   The occipital portion of the muscle may be in the form of a separate slip, or may be absent.

The trapezius is superficial in its whole extent.   Its upper lateral border forms the posterior limit of the posterior triangle of the neck.   The lower lateral border, passing over the upper edge of the latissimus dorsi and the medial margin of the scapula, forms a boundary of the so-called *triangle of auscultation*, which is completed below by the latissimus dorsi, and laterally by the rhomboideus major ; that space is increased when the arms are folded to pull the scapula forwards.   The trapezius overlaps the upper margin of the latissimus dorsi, and covers the rhomboidei, levator scapulæ, splenius capitis, semispinalis capitis, and the deeper axial muscles of the back, along with the superficial and the deep branches of the transverse cervical artery, the accessory nerve, and muscular branches from the cervical plexus.

Latissimus Dorsi.—The latissimus dorsi is a wide triangular muscle which lies in the lower part of the back. The greater part of the muscle **arises**—(1) from the spines of the lower six thoracic vertebræ, and, through the posterior layer of the lumbar fascia, from the spines of the lumbar and sacral vertebræ and the iliac crest. Its lateral border also arises directly by tendinous fibres from the posterior part of the outer lip of the iliac crest. From this main origin the muscle is directed upwards and laterally, its fibres converging towards the lower border of the axilla. In relation to its lateral and upper borders additional fibres arise. (2) *Along the lateral border* muscular slips arise from the lower three or four ribs, inter-digitating with the slips of origin of the obliquus externus abdominis. (Fig. 375 and Pl. XXXI, Figs. 1, 2.) (3) As *the superior border* of the muscle passes horizontally over the inferior angle

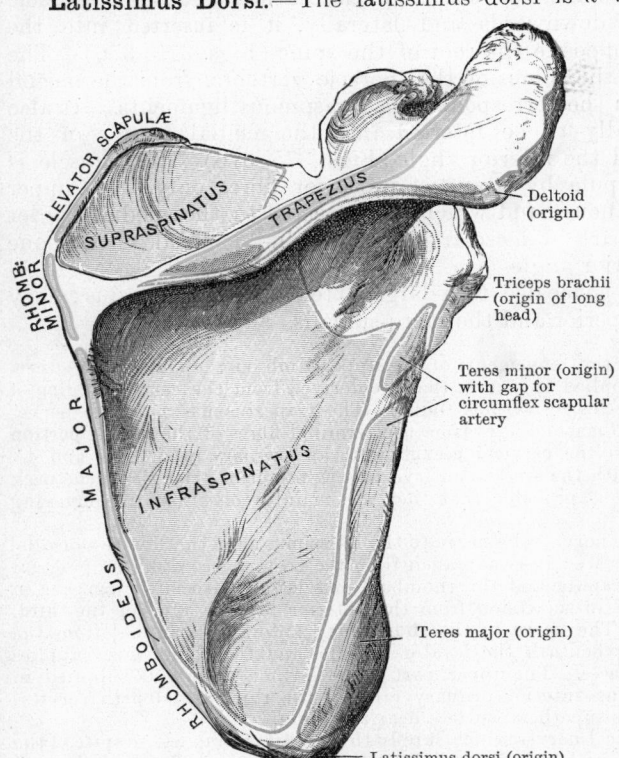

FIG. 376.—MUSCLE-ATTACHMENTS TO THE RIGHT SCAPULA
(Dorsal Surface).

Deltoid (origin)

Triceps brachii (origin of long head)

Teres minor (origin) with gap for circumflex scapular artery

Teres major (origin)

Latissimus dorsi (origin)

LEVATOR SCAPULÆ

SUPRASPINATUS

TRAPEZIUS

RHOMB. MINOR

INFRASPINATUS

MAJOR

RHOMBOIDEUS

of the scapula, an additional fleshy slip usually takes origin from that part of the bone and joins the muscle on its deep surface (Fig. 376).

Beyond the inferior angle of the scapula the latissimus dorsi, greatly narrowed.

29

curves spirally round the teres major muscle, forming the prominence of the posterior axillary fold. It ends in a ribbon-like tendon which is closely adherent at first to the teres major, and is **inserted** into the floor of the bicipital groove of the humerus [sulcus intertubercularis] (Fig. 385). It is placed behind the axillary vessels and nerves, and in front of the insertion of the teres major—a *bursa* intervening. Because of the spiral turn, the anterior surface of the tendon of insertion is continuous with the posterior surface of the rest of the muscle.

In the back the latissimus dorsi is superficial, except that its upper part is concealed by the trapezius. It covers part of the lumbar fascia, the serratus posterior inferior, the lower ribs, and the inferior angle of the scapula. At its upper border is the *triangle of auscultation*; at its lateral border is the *lumbar triangle*—a small space bounded by the iliac crest, the latissimus dorsi, and the obliquus externus abdominis. That space is sometimes the site of a lumbar hernia.

Levator Scapulæ.—This strap-like muscle **arises** by tendinous slips from the posterior tubercles of the transverse processes of the first three or four cervical vertebræ, between the attachments of the scalenus medius in front and the splenius cervicis behind. It is directed downwards to be **inserted** into the medial margin of the scapula, from the upper angle to the spine (Figs. 375, 376).

It is concealed in its upper third by the sterno-mastoid muscle. Its middle third forms part of the floor of the posterior triangle of the neck and is related to the accessory nerve. Its lower third is hidden by the trapezius, and conceals the nerve to the rhomboids and the deep branch of the transverse cervical artery.

Rhomboidei.—The **rhomboideus minor** may be regarded as a separated slip of the rhomboideus major, with which it is often continuous. It **arises** from the *ligamentum nuchæ* and the spines of the seventh cervical and first thoracic vertebræ. Passing obliquely downwards and laterally, it is **inserted** into the medial border of the scapula opposite the root of the spine (Figs. 375, 376). The **rhomboideus major arises** from the spines of the thoracic vertebræ from the second to the fifth inclusive, and from the corresponding supraspinous ligaments. It also passes downwards and laterally to be **inserted** into the medial border of the scapula, between the spine and the inferior angle (Figs. 375, 376). The muscle is inserted directly into the scapula by means of its lower fibres only. Its upper part is attached to a membranous band which is connected to the medial border of the scapula, for the most part by loose areolar tissue, but is fixed to the bone near the spine and at the inferior angle.

The rhomboid muscles are concealed to a large extent by the trapezius; they cover the serratus posterior superior and the sacro-spinalis.

Nerve-Supply.—Associated in the movements of the upper limb on the trunk, the superficial muscles of the back are all supplied by nerves that are derived from the cervical region of the spinal cord but reach the muscles by various routes. The trapezius has a double nerve-supply, similar to that of the sterno-mastoid : (1) from the terminal fibres of the **spinal portion** of the **accessory** nerve and (2) from the **cervical plexus** (anterior primary rami, C. 3. and 4.). The cervical nerves communicate with the accessory nerve in the posterior triangle of the neck and beneath the trapezius; and it is probable that they are mainly concerned in conveying afferent impulses from the muscle.

The latissimus dorsi has a single nerve—the **nerve to the latissimus dorsi** [n. thoraco-dorsalis] —which supplies it on its deep surface; it is a branch from the posterior cord of the brachial plexus (C. (6.) 7. 8.). The levator scapulæ and the rhomboid muscles are associated together in their nerve supply, which is derived in succession from the anterior primary rami of the third, **fourth, and fifth cervical** nerves. The **nerve to the rhomboids** [n. dorsalis scapulæ] from the brachial plexus (C. (4.) 5.), passing beneath the levator scapulæ and the rhomboids, supplies all three muscles on their deep surfaces. The upper part of the levator scapulæ is supplied in addition by small branches from the anterior primary rami of the third and fourth cervical nerves which enter the muscle on its superficial surface near its origin.

It should be noted that the cervical nerves which supply this group of muscles, in spite of the fact that it is situated mainly in the back, are derived through the cervical and brachial plexuses from the *anterior* primary rami of the spinal nerves concerned ; the explanation is to be found in the developmental origin of the muscles from the ventro-lateral sheet of musculature and their subsequent migration to obtain secondary attachment to the vertebral column (pp. 526, 528).

MUSCLES AND FASCIÆ OF THE PECTORAL REGION

Muscles of the Pectoral Region

The ventral group of muscles connecting the upper limb to the trunk comprises the pectoralis major, pectoralis minor, subclavius, and the serratus anterior. The sterno-(cleido-)mastoid, by virtue of its attachment to the clavicle, may be considered a member of this group; it has already been described (p. 409).

Pectoralis Major.—The pectoralis major is a large fan-shaped muscle **arising** in two main portions—a small clavicular and a large sterno-costal—separated by a distinct interval. (1) The *clavicular part* arises from the front of the clavicle in its medial half or two-thirds (Figs. 374, 378, 379). (2) The *sterno-costal part* is larger, and arises from the anterior surface of the manubrium and body of the sternum by tendinous fibres that decussate with those of the opposite muscle (Fig. 378); more deeply, from the cartilages of the first six ribs; and by a small slip, sometimes separate (*abdominal part*), from the aponeurosis of the external oblique muscle of the abdominal wall.

The fibres converge towards the proximal part of the arm, and are inseparably blended at a point half an inch from their **insertion** into the lateral lip of the bicipital groove of the humerus.

The arrangement of the fibres of the muscle at its insertion is peculiar. The clavicular part is attached to the humerus in front of the sterno-costal part and blends, inferiorly, with the tendinous insertion of the deltoid, the lateral fibres of origin being inserted proximal to the medial fibres. The upper sterno-costal fibres disappear under cover of the clavicular part near its insertion and are blended with the deep surface of its tendon. The lower sterno-costal fibres and the abdominal part curve upwards behind the upper sterno-costal fibres; the abdominal part has the highest attachment to the shaft of the humerus, and helps to form a fascial expansion which extends upwards over the biceps tendon to the capsule of the shoulder joint. In this way a bilaminar tendon is produced, united along its inferior border. The superficial lamina is formed by the upper sterno-costal fibres blended for the most part with the tendon of the clavicular part; and the deep lamina, by the twisted, lower sterno-costal and abdominal fibres.

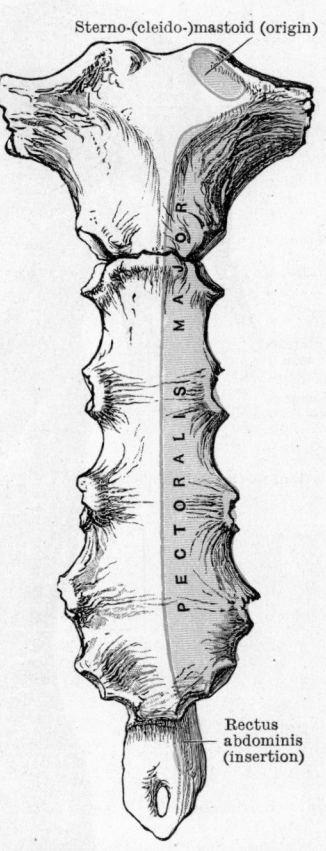

Sterno-(cleido-)mastoid (origin)

PECTORALIS MAJOR

Rectus abdominis (insertion)

Fig. 377.—Muscle-Attachments to the Front of the Sternum.

Placed superficially, the pectoralis major lies in the anterior wall and anterior fold of the axilla (Pl. XXXI, Fig. 3, and Fig. 382, p. 456). Its upper border is separated from the edge of the deltoid muscle by an interval called the *infra-clavicular fossa* (Pl. XXXII, Fig. 3), in which lie the cephalic vein and the deltoid branches of the acromio-thoracic artery. Its deep surface is in relation with the ribs and intercostal muscles, the clavi-pectoral fascia and the structures piercing it, the pectoralis minor, the biceps and coraco-brachialis, the axillary vessels, and the nerves of the brachial plexus.

Sternalis Muscle.—The sternalis is an occasional muscle (4·4%) that lies parallel to the sternum on the origin of the pectoralis major. It has variable attachments to the costal cartilages, sternum, rectus sheath, sterno-mastoid, and pectoralis major. Its **nerve-supply** is from one or both of the pectoral nerves. In certain rare cases it has been said to be innervated by intercostal nerves.

Chondro-epitrochlearis, Dorso-epitrochlearis, Axillary Arches, Costo-coracoideus.—
One or other of the above-named slips is occasionally present, crossing the floor of the axilla

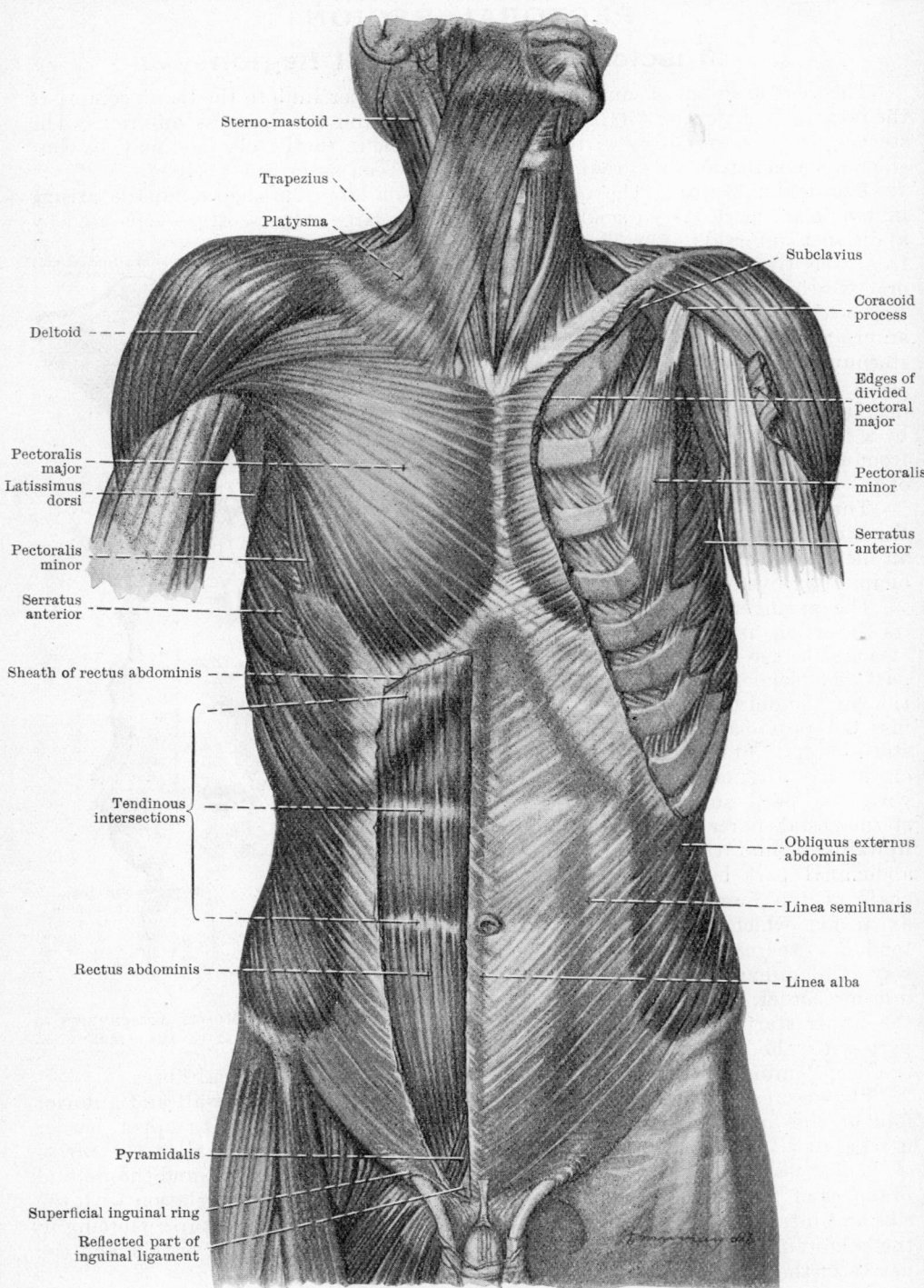

Sterno-mastoid

Trapezius

Platysma

Subclavius

Coracoid process

Deltoid

Edges of divided pectoral major

Pectoralis major

Pectoralis minor

Latissimus dorsi

Serratus anterior

Pectoralis minor

Serratus anterior

Sheath of rectus abdominis

Tendinous intersections

Obliquus externus abdominis

Linea semilunaris

Rectus abdominis

Linea alba

Pyramidalis

Superficial inguinal ring

Reflected part of inguinal ligament

FIG. 378.—MUSCLES OF THE ANTERIOR WALL OF THE TRUNK.

in the interval between the latissimus dorsi and the pectoralis major. They take **origin** from
the costal cartilages, ribs, or borders of the pectoralis major (*chondro-epitrochlearis, axillary
arches, costo-coracoideus*), or from the border of the latissimus dorsi (*dorso-epitrochlearis, axillary*

arches, costo-coracoideus). Their **insertion** is variable. The *chondro-epitrochlearis* and *dorso-epitrochlearis* are inserted into the fascia of the arm, the medial intermuscular septum, or the medial epicondyle of the humerus. The *axillary arches* are inserted into the border of the pectoralis major, the fascia of the arm, or the coraco-brachialis or biceps muscle. The *costo-coracoideus*, arising from the ribs or the aponeurosis of the external oblique, or detaching itself from the border of the pectoralis major or latissimus dorsi, is attached to the coracoid process, alone or along with one of the muscles attached to that bone. These variable slips of muscle are supplied by the medial pectoral nerve, the medial cutaneous nerve of the arm, or the intercosto-brachial nerve.

Pectoralis Minor.—The pectoralis minor (Fig. 378) is a narrow, flat, triangular muscle that lies in the anterior wall of the axilla behind the pectoralis major. It **arises**, under cover of the pectoralis major, from the third, fourth, and fifth ribs near their anterior ends, and from the fascia of the corresponding intercostal spaces. It may have an additional origin from the second rib (Fig. 334, p. 396); and that from the fifth rib is often absent. Directed upwards and laterally, it is **inserted** by a short, flat tendon into the anterior half of the medial border and upper surface of the coracoid process (Fig. 381, p. 455), and usually also into the conjoint tendon of the biceps and coraco-brachialis.

It crosses the axillary vessels and the cords of the brachial plexus, and is pierced

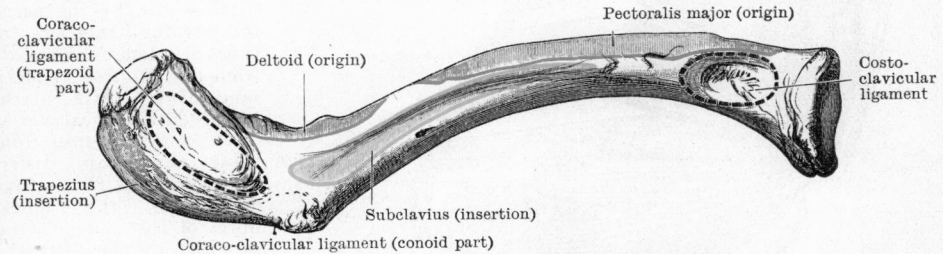

Coraco-clavicular ligament (trapezoid part)

Deltoid (origin)

Pectoralis major (origin)

Costo-clavicular ligament

Trapezius (insertion)

Subclavius (insertion)

Coraco-clavicular ligament (conoid part)

Fig. 379.—Muscle-Attachments to the Right Clavicle (Inferior Surface).

by the medial pectoral nerve. Its fascial sheath is continuous above with the clavi-pectoral fascia and below with the axillary fascia.

Either in part or wholly, the pectoralis minor may pass over the coracoid process (separated from it by a *bursa*), to pierce the coraco-acromial ligament, and be attached to the capsule of the shoulder joint.

Subclavius.—This small muscle **arises** from the first rib and its cartilage (at their junction) in front of the costo-clavicular ligament, and passes upwards and laterally to be **inserted** into the floor of an elongated groove on the lower surface of the clavicle. It is concealed by the clavicle and the pectoralis major; and the clavi-pectoral fascia splits to enclose it.

Serratus Anterior.—The serratus anterior is a large, curved, quadrilateral muscle that lies on the side of the chest and in the medial wall of the axilla. It **arises** by fleshy slips from the outer surfaces of the upper eight (or nine) ribs. The first slip is a double one, arising from the first two ribs and the fascia of the intervening space (Fig. 380).

The **insertion** of the muscle is threefold. (1) The first slip is directed backwards to be inserted into the costal surface of the scapula at the superior angle. (2) The next three slips are inserted into the medial border of the scapula. (3) The last four slips are directed obliquely upwards and backwards, to be inserted on the costal surface of the scapula at the inferior angle (Fig. 381).

The lateral surface of the muscle is partly superficial (Pl. XXXI, Fig. 2) below the axilla, where its slips of origin interdigitate with those of the obliquus externus abdominis. Higher up, it forms the medial wall of the axilla and is covered by the infero-lateral part of the mammary gland. It is in contact with the pectoral muscles anteriorly and the subscapularis posteriorly. Its upper border appears in the floor of the posterior triangle of the neck, and over it the axillary artery and the cords of the brachial plexus enter the axilla. The lower border is oblique, and is in contact with the latissimus dorsi muscle. The muscle is sometimes continuous, in the neck, with the levator scapulæ.

Nerve-Supply.—The muscles of the pectoral region are all supplied by branches from the nerves of the brachial plexus (C. 5. 6. 7. 8. T. 1.). The **nerve to the subclavius** is a fine branch which arises above the clavicle from the upper trunk of the brachial plexus (C. 5. 6.), and descends in front of the subclavian artery to reach the muscle.

The pectoral muscles are each supplied by both pectoral nerves [nn. thoracici anteriores]. The **lateral pectoral nerve**, derived from the lateral cord of the brachial plexus (C. 5. 6. 7.), divides into two branches, both of which pierce the clavi-pectoral fascia to supply respectively the clavicular and the upper portion of the sterno-costal part of the pectoralis major; the lower branch communicates over the axillary artery with the **medial pectoral nerve.** This nerve, a derivative of the medial cord (C. 8. T. 1.), likewise divides into two branches which supply the pectoralis minor and, piercing that muscle (the lower may wind round its inferior border), terminate in the lower part of the pectoralis major.

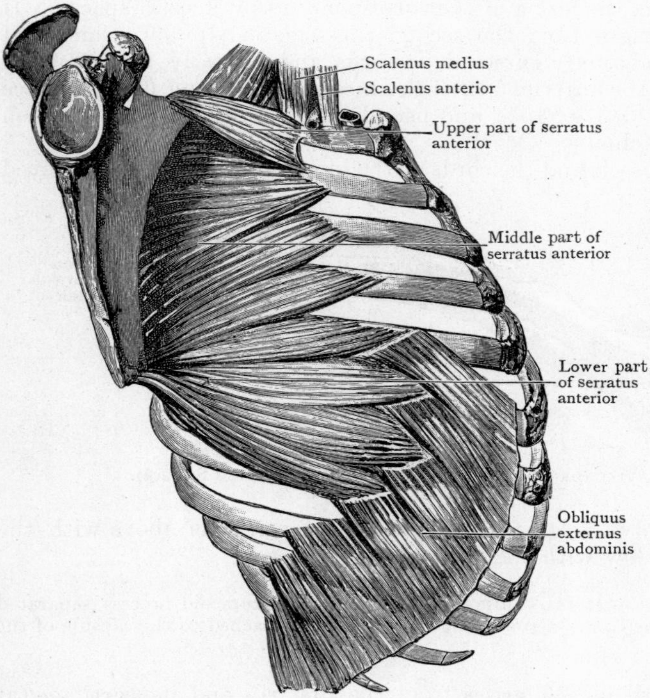

FIG. 380.—SERRATUS ANTERIOR AND ORIGIN OF EXTERNAL OBLIQUE.
The Scapula is drawn away from the side of the Chest.

The serratus anterior is supplied, on its superficial aspect, by the **nerve to serratus anterior** [n. thoracicus longus], a branch from the anterior primary rami of the fifth, sixth, and seventh cervical nerves. The contributions from those nerves are distributed in order from above downwards — the highest fibres of the muscle being supplied by the fifth, the lowest by the seventh.

The Actions of Muscles in the Movements of the Shoulder Girdle. —The great range of action of the upper limb is due to a combination of free movements of the arm at the shoulder joint with movements of the shoulder girdle on the trunk. The action of the muscles which connect the limb to the trunk is most readily appreciated with reference to the movements of the scapula. From the position of rest with the arm hanging by the side, the scapula is freely movable on the chest wall in three directions by (1) elevation, (2) forward translation, and (3) lateral rotation (the inferior angle passing forwards and laterally). Those movements are normally combined, and may be readily observed as the arm is raised above the head; they then occur as associated movements of the girdle as a whole at the sterno-clavicular joint, and as compensating or adapting movements between clavicle and scapula at the acromio-clavicular joint. All the muscles which act from the trunk upon the limb are so arranged that they tend to produce or to antagonise this combination of three movements of the scapula.

The **trapezius** muscles, by their tonic action alone, keep the shoulders braced, and thus help to suspend the upper limbs—drooping shoulders are an outward sign of diminished nervous and muscular tone. When a weight is shouldered, the muscle has to work harder to maintain the position of the shoulder.

The lever afforded by the spine of the scapula is like a winged nut for the grip of this muscle in rotating the scapula during elevation of the upper limb (Fig. 189, p. 225; and Pl. XXX, Fig. 2). The lateral angle is then raised, the superior angle lowered, and the inferior angle directed laterally; and the various fibres, converging on the spine, cooperate in producing this movement (cf. Pl. XXII, and Fig. 374, p. 447).

The **levator scapulae** and the **rhomboids** act in concert with their antagonist, the trapezius, in pulling the shoulders backwards—the movement being the resultant of their opposed forces.   In the rotatory movement of shrugging the shoulders, the trapezius and the serratus anterior, followed by the levator and the rhomboids, act in sequence, first one group predominating, then the other, with at times the opposed action of both groups securing a resultant movement—the approximation of the scapulæ.   When the trapezius is paralysed the lateral angle of the scapula is lower than on the unaffected side, and the other angles are higher ; this tilting is brought about by the levator and the rhomboids—assisted by the weight of the limb.

The **serratus anterior** is a powerful factor in steadying the scapula, in pulling it forwards, and, acting with the trapezius, in raising its inferior angle as the limb is elevated (Pl. XXXI, Fig. 2).   When the limb is raised forwards to the horizontal, the serratus gives the extra forward thrust as in fencing, and is brought into use in pushing movements.   It acts from its insertion in forced inspiration, or in hand balance exercises ("standing on the hands")—in which most of the muscles of the arm reverse their actions.   In paralysis of the serratus anterior, the medial border of the scapula stands farther away from the chest wall ("winged scapula") than it does in paralysis of the trapezius, and the patient has difficulty in raising his arm much beyond the horizontal position, whereas the arm may be completely raised (though clumsily) in trapezius paralysis.   As a rule, when abduction of the arm begins, its weight causes a slight medial movement of the inferior angle of the scapula, but in a few cases it moves immediately lateralwards.   The muscles that rotate the scapula are active throughout elevation of the arm, and so also are the muscles that produce this movement at the shoulder joint (cf. Actions, p. 459).

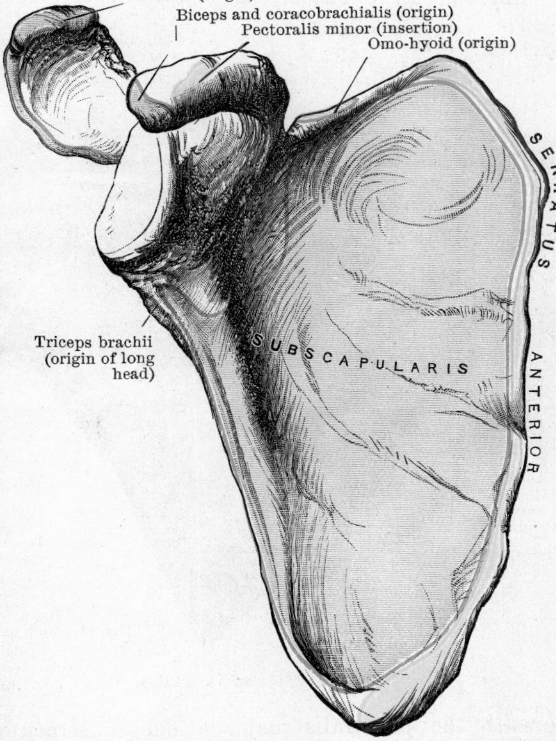

The **pectoralis minor** assists in drawing the shoulder forwards, and is an opponent of the trapezius by depressing the shoulder and rotating the scapula medially.   Its action is very difficult to appreciate in the living subject, since it lies under cover of the pectoralis major and is never paralysed alone.

FIG. 381.—MUSCLE-ATTACHMENTS TO THE RIGHT SCAPULA
(Anterior Aspect).

The **subclavius** is a depressor of the lateral end of the clavicle, and by drawing the bone medially towards the sternum it steadies it in movements of the shoulder girdle.

Two of the muscles that attach the upper limb to the trunk (**latissimus dorsi** and **pectoralis major**) act primarily at the shoulder joint, but also take part indirectly in the movements of the shoulder girdle.   The latissimus dorsi (Pl. XXXI, Fig. 1) assists in backward movements of the girdle, the pectoralis major in forward movement (Pl. XXXII, Fig. 3), and together they take part in the movement of depression of the shoulder (Pl. XXXII, Fig. 2).   Both these muscles can act, from their insertions, upon the trunk : (1) they are the chief climbing muscles—drawing the body upwards when the arms are fixed ; (2) when the shoulders are elevated and fixed they act as accessory muscles of respiration (p. 427).   The pectoralis major, with the minor, assists violent inspiratory efforts by raising the upper ribs, and the costal slips of the latissimus dorsi raise the lower ribs.   The latissimus dorsi muscles appear also to assist the abdominal muscles in violent expiratory efforts by their general compressing effect on the thorax (p. 427).

FASCIÆ OF THE PECTORAL REGION

The **superficial fascia** of the chest usually contains a quantity of fat in which the mammary gland is embedded. The fibres of the platysma muscle lie beneath its upper part, and many of them pierce it to take origin from the skin.

The **deep fascia** is attached above to the clavicle, and medially to the sternum. It invests the pectoralis major, and is continuous below with the fascia of the abdominal wall. At the lateral border of the great pectoral muscle it is thickened, and forms the floor of the axillary space **(axillary fascia)**—continued posteriorly on to the posterior fold of the axilla and laterally into connexion with the deep fascia of the upper arm.

Clavi-pectoral Fascia [F. coraco-clavicularis] (Costo-coracoid membrane).—

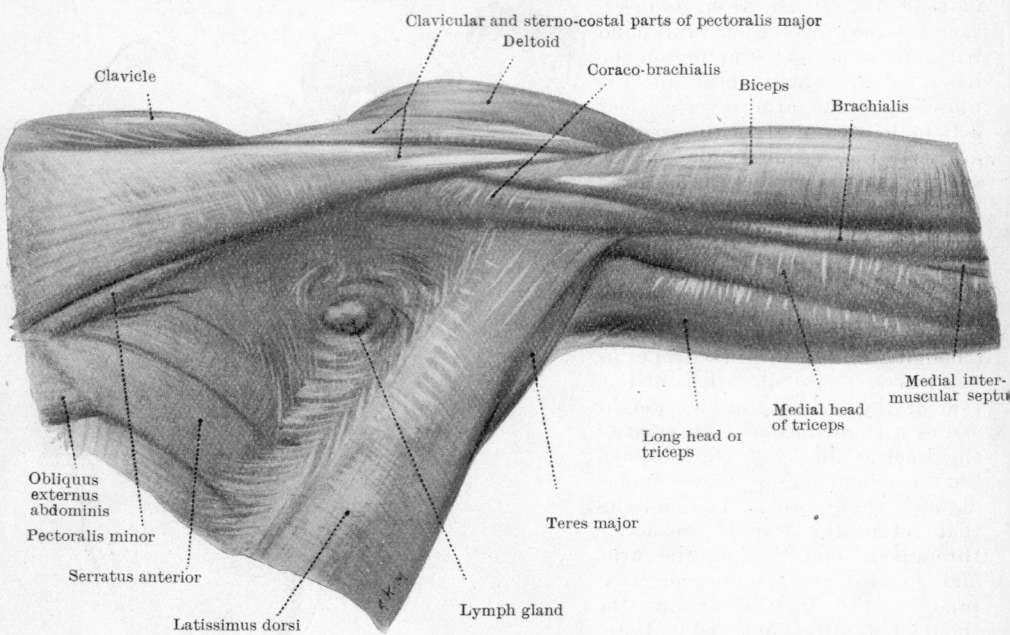

FIG. 382.—FASCIA AND MUSCLES OF LEFT AXILLA. (R.D.L.)

Beneath the pectoralis major a deeper stratum of fascia invests the pectoralis minor muscle. At the supero-medial border of that muscle it forms the clavi-pectoral fascia, which passes upwards to the inferior border of the subclavius muscle, where it splits into two layers, attached in front of and behind that muscle to the borders of the inferior surface of the clavicle. The membrane, traced medially along the subclavius muscle, is attached to the first costal cartilage; passing laterally along the pectoralis minor, it reaches the coracoid process and the coraco-clavicular ligament; and the part of the membrane that extends directly between the first costal cartilage and the coracoid process is thicker than the rest of it. The clavi-pectoral fascia is pierced by the cephalic vein, acromio-thoracic artery, and branches of the lateral pectoral nerve. Its deep surface is connected with the sheath of the axillary vessels.

At the infero-lateral border of the pectoralis minor there is a further extension of the deep fascia beneath the pectoralis major. It passes downwards to join the fascia of the floor of the axilla, and is continued laterally into the fascia that covers the biceps and coraco-brachialis muscles.

MUSCLES AND FASCIÆ OF THE SHOULDER

Muscles of the Shoulder

The **muscles** proper to the shoulder are the deltoid, supraspinatus, infraspinatus, teres minor, teres major, and subscapularis.

Deltoid Muscle.—The deltoid, a coarsely fasciculated, multipennate muscle, has an extensive **origin** from : (1) the front of the clavicle in its lateral third (Fig. 374); (2) the lateral border of the acromion; (3) the lower lip of the crest of the spine of the scapula and the fascia of the infraspinatus muscle. Its origin embraces the insertion of the trapezius.

The fibres of the muscle converge on the lateral surface of the shaft of the humerus to be **inserted** into the deltoid tuberosity. The insertion is partly united with the tendon of the pectoralis major (Fig. 388, p. 463).

The most anterior part of the deltoid muscle is formed of parallel fibres, not uncommonly separate from the rest of the muscle at their origin. Those fibres may be continuous across the clavicle with the trapezius. The most posterior fibres have a membranous origin, and converge on the main tendon. The middle fibres are multipennate, being attached above and below to three or four septal tendons which extend for a variable distance downwards and upwards from the origin and insertion of the muscle—an arrangement that increases the number of the fibres and consequently the power of the deltoid. The increased power is necessary owing to the obvious mechanical disadvantage at which the muscle acts, and the fact that its action is usually exerted against the force of gravity.

The deltoid is superficial in its whole extent. It is spread out over the greater tuberosity of the humerus and so forms the prominence of the shoulder. Its anterior border is separated from the pectoralis major by a narrow interval occupied by the cephalic vein and deltoid branch of the acromio-thoracic artery. The deep surface of the muscle is related to—(1) the *coracoid process*, associated with which are the coraco-acromial ligament, and the attachments of the pectoralis minor, the coraco-brachialis, and the short head of the biceps muscle; (2) the subscapularis, supraspinatus, infraspinatus, and teres minor which cover the capsule of the shoulder joint; and (3) the proximal part of the lateral surface of the *shaft of the humerus* and the posterior circumflex humeral vessels and the circumflex nerve [n. axillaris]. The *sub-acromial bursa* separates the middle fibres of the deltoid, the acromion and the coraco-acromial ligament from the supraspinatus, infraspinatus, and subscapularis tendons.

Supraspinatus.—The supraspinatus **arises**, by fleshy fibres, from the walls of the supraspinous fossa (except near the neck of the bone) and from the deep fascia. It is directed forwards and laterally under the trapezius muscle, the acromion and coraco-acromial ligament, to be **inserted** by a broad thick tendon into the anterior facet on the top of the greater tuberosity of the humerus, and into the capsule of the shoulder joint.

Infraspinatus.—The infraspinatus **arises** from the walls of the infraspinous fossa (excepting near the neck of the bone and the flat surface along the lateral margin) and from the thick fascia over it. The fibres of the muscle converge on the neck of the scapula, and are **inserted** by tendon into the middle facet on the greater tuberosity of the humerus, and into the capsule of the shoulder joint. The *bursa of the infraspinatus muscle* separates the muscle from the neck of the scapula, and occasionally communicates with the cavity of the shoulder joint.

The supraspinatus and the upper part of the infraspinatus muscles are covered by the trapezius, acromion, and deltoid and, in turn, conceal the neck of the scapula, the suprascapular vessels and nerve, and the capsule of the shoulder joint.

Teres Minor.—This small muscle **arises**, by fleshy fibres, from the upper two-thirds of the flat area on the dorsal surface of the scapula along the lateral border, and from fascial septa that separate it from the infraspinatus and teres major muscles. Lying alongside the lateral border of the infraspinatus, it is inserted, under cover of the deltoid, by a thick flat tendon, into the lowest of the three facets on the greater tuberosity of the humerus and into the capsule of the shoulder joint, and, by fleshy fibres, into the back of the humerus below the tuberosity for about an inch.

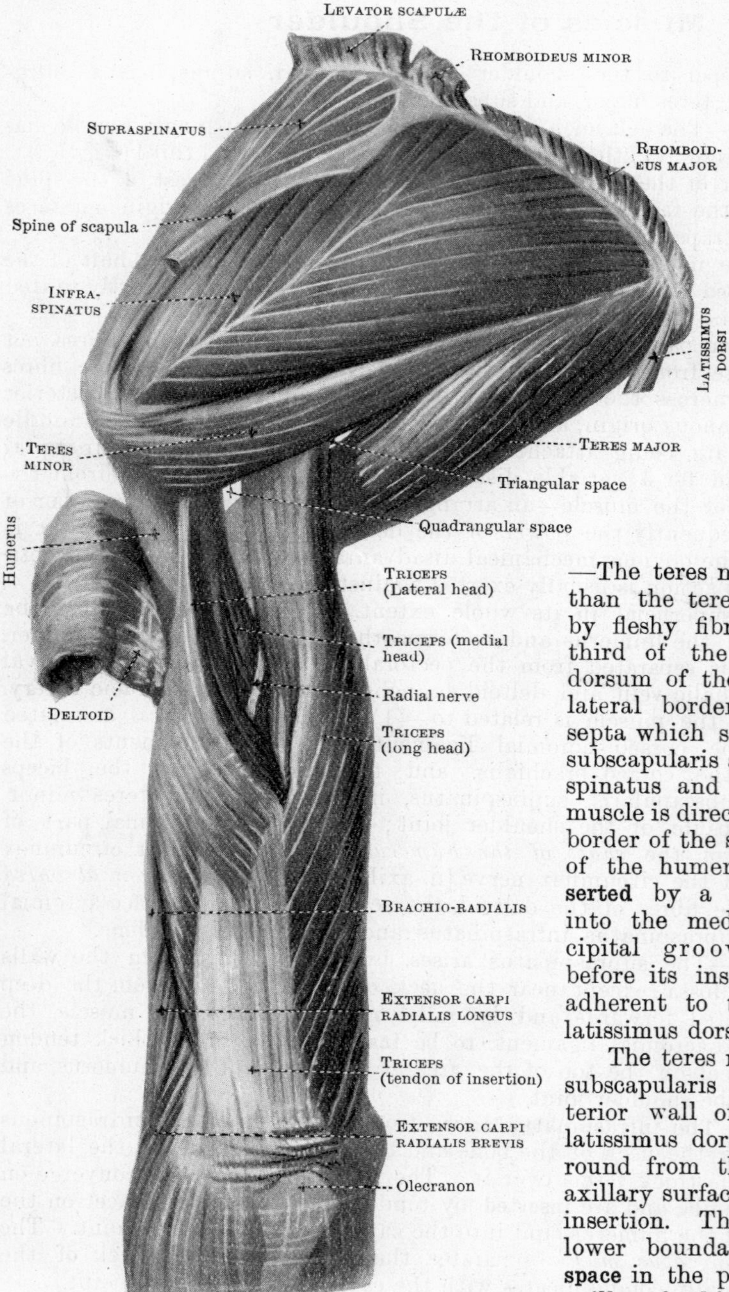

FIG. 383.—LEFT SCAPULAR MUSCLES AND TRICEPS.

It is separated from the teres major by the long head of the triceps, and by the posterior circumflex humeral vessels and the circumflex nerve. At its origin it is pierced by the circumflex scapular artery. The muscle is invested by the fascia of the infraspinatus, and is sometimes inseparable from that muscle.

Teres Major.—The teres major is much larger than the teres minor. It arises by fleshy fibres from the lower third of the flat area on the dorsum of the scapula along the lateral border, and from fascial septa which separate it from the subscapularis and from the infraspinatus and teres minor. The muscle is directed along the lateral border of the scapula to the front of the humerus, where it is inserted by a broad, flat tendon into the medial lip of the bicipital groove. Immediately before its insertion it is closely adherent to the tendon of the latissimus dorsi.

The teres major lies below the subscapularis muscle in the posterior wall of the axilla. The latissimus dorsi muscle, sweeping round from the back, covers its axillary surface on its way to its insertion. The muscle forms the lower boundary of a triangular space in the posterior wall of the axilla, of which the other boundaries are, above, the borders of the subscapularis and teres minor muscles, and laterally the surgical neck of the humerus. That space is subdivided by the long head of the triceps, which passes behind the teres major muscle, into (a) a quadrangular space laterally, for the passage of the circumflex nerve and posterior humeral circumflex artery; and (b) a smaller triangular space medially, for the circumflex scapular artery.

Subscapularis.—The subscapularis is a large triangular muscle which covers the costal surface of the scapula. It **arises**, by fleshy fibres, from the whole of the floor of the subscapular fossa and the groove along the lateral border, excepting the surfaces at the angles of the bone. Several fibrous septa that spring from ridges in the fossa project into the substance of the muscle, and increase the extent of its attachment. Converging on the upper end of the humerus, the muscular fibres are **inserted** by a broad, thick tendon into the lesser tuberosity of the humerus and into the capsule of the shoulder joint, and, by fleshy fibres, into the front of the humerus below the tuberosity for about an inch, under cover of the coraco-brachialis and short head of the biceps.

This muscle forms the greater part of the posterior wall of the axilla. Its medial or anterior surface is in contact with the serratus anterior and the axillary vessels and nerves. It is separated from the neck of the scapula by the *subscapular bursa*.

Nerve-Supply.—All muscles of the shoulder are supplied by the anterior primary rami of the **fifth** and **sixth cervical nerves** through branches of the brachial plexus. The supraspinatus and infraspinatus are supplied by the **supra-scapular nerve**, which takes origin from the upper trunk of the plexus; the remaining muscles by branches from the posterior cord. The deltoid is supplied by the terminal branches of the **circumflex nerve** [n. axillaris]; that nerve supplies also the teres minor by a branch which is distinguished by a fibrous swelling or "pseudo-ganglion" on its trunk. The subscapularis is supplied by the two **subscapular nerves**; the upper subscapular is often double, and the lower subscapular, after supplying the lower lateral portion of the subscapularis, ends in the teres major.

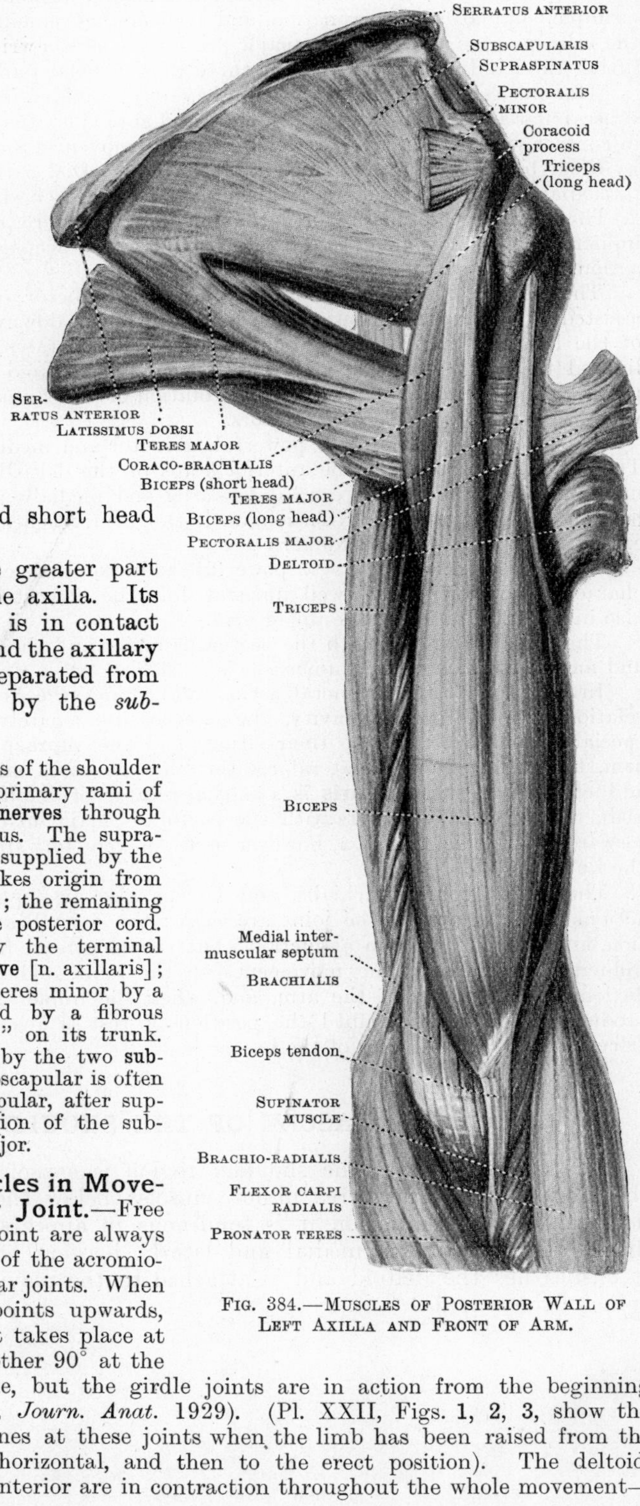

The Actions of Muscles in Movements at the Shoulder Joint.—Free movements at the shoulder joint are always accompanied by movements of the acromio-clavicular and sterno-clavicular joints. When the limb is raised till it points upwards, about 90° of the movement takes place at the shoulder joint and the other 90° at the

FIG. 384.—MUSCLES OF POSTERIOR WALL OF LEFT AXILLA AND FRONT OF ARM.

joints of the shoulder girdle, but the girdle joints are in action from the beginning (Cathcart, 1882; Lockhart, *Journ. Anat.* 1929). (Pl. XXII, Figs. 1, 2, 3, show the relative positions of the bones at these joints when the limb has been raised from the dependent position to the horizontal, and then to the erect position). The deltoid, trapezius, and the serratus anterior are in contraction throughout the whole movement—

during which a certain amount of lateral rotation of the humerus occurs (Duchenne, 1861 ; Martin, *Journ. Anat.* 1935). With the humerus fixed, the shoulder muscles, reversing their action, assist in forced respiration. The shoulder joint is called into use also in many of the movements carried out mainly at joints lower down in the limb, for example, supination and pronation, and even fine movements of the fingers. Paralysis of the infraspinatus and the teres major prevents a person writing a continuous line without lifting the hand along every two or three words or else pulling the paper to the left.

The muscles of the shoulder joint have been divided into functional groups : 1. The subscapularis, infraspinatus, teres minor, and supraspinatus keep the head of the humerus in contact with the glenoid cavity during all movements at the joint executed not only by them but also by other muscles of the arm. Dislocation occurs when these muscles (articular muscles, Winslow) are taken off their guard or when their strength is overcome. 2. The deltoid, pectoralis major, latissimus dorsi, and teres major are the chief effectors of humero-glenoid movement. 3. The deltoid, triceps, biceps and coraco-brachialis, by tonic action, assist in sustaining the weight of the limb.

The **deltoid muscle** is the most powerful abductor of the shoulder joint, and is assisted by the **supraspinatus**, which helps to prevent downward displacement of the head of the humerus during strong deltoid action. In paralysis of the deltoid abduction is limited to about 45°. The anterior fibres of the deltoid assist the clavicular part of pectoralis major in flexion and medial rotation of the humerus ; the posterior fibres act with the extensors and lateral rotators.

The **pectoralis major** is a powerful adductor and medial rotator of the upper arm. The clavicular part assists the anterior fibres of the deltoid to flex the humerus, a movement in which the limb is carried forwards and medially ; the sterno-costal part takes part in flexion from full extension until the arm reaches the side, but is a powerful extensor of the fully flexed humerus.

The **latissimus dorsi** is a powerful adductor and extensor of the humerus, its characteristic action being well illustrated in the downstroke in swimming. It assists also in medial rotation of the upper arm.

The **teres major** acts with the pectoralis major and the latissimus dorsi in adduction and medial rotation of the humerus.

In addition to their general action of keeping the head of the humerus in close relation with the glenoid cavity, the muscles immediately surrounding the joint have special actions according to their situation. The **supraspinatus** is an abductor of the arm, the **infraspinatus** a lateral rotator, and the **teres minor** a lateral rotator and an adductor. The **subscapularis** is a medial rotator of the humerus, and when the arm is abducted through 90° it acts with the pectoralis major in drawing the arm horizontally forwards. Its chief function, however, is to prevent forward displacement of the head of the humerus.

The biceps, coraco-brachialis, and triceps also act upon the shoulder joint. The actions of the **biceps** on the joint are weak ; the short head helps in flexion and adduction, and the long head in abduction ; but the long head has an additional, mechanical influence in steadying the movements at the joint. The **coraco-brachialis** assists in flexion and adduction of the arm, and, when the humerus is rotated laterally, it can produce medial rotation until the position of rest is reached. The long head of the **triceps** acts as an adductor of the humerus.

FASCIÆ OF THE SHOULDER

The **deep fascia** of the shoulder region is especially strong where it covers the infraspinatus and teres minor muscles below the posterior border of the deltoid. In that situation it is tendinous in appearance and character, and is firmly attached to the medial and lateral borders of the scapula. Superiorly it ensheathes the deltoid and is attached to the clavicle, the acromion, and the spine of the scapula.

MUSCLES AND FASCIÆ OF THE UPPER ARM

MUSCLES OF THE UPPER ARM

The muscles of the upper arm are the biceps, coraco-brachialis, and brachialis on the front, and the triceps on the back. Except at its ends, the biceps is superficial, and forms a rounded fleshy mass on the front of the arm. The coraco-brachialis is visible in the proximal half of the upper arm on its medial side, particularly when the limb is raised. The brachialis is concealed by the biceps. The triceps is the thick mass of muscle on the back of the upper arm.

Coraco-brachialis.—The coraco-brachialis **arises,** under cover of the deltoid, from the tip of the coracoid process, by fleshy fibres, in common with the short head of the biceps. The fleshy belly is pierced by the musculo-cutaneous nerve, and ends in a flat tendon which is **inserted** into a faint linear impression about an inch in length on the middle of the medial border of the shaft of the humerus (Fig. 385). Some fibres are often continued into the medial intermuscular septum.

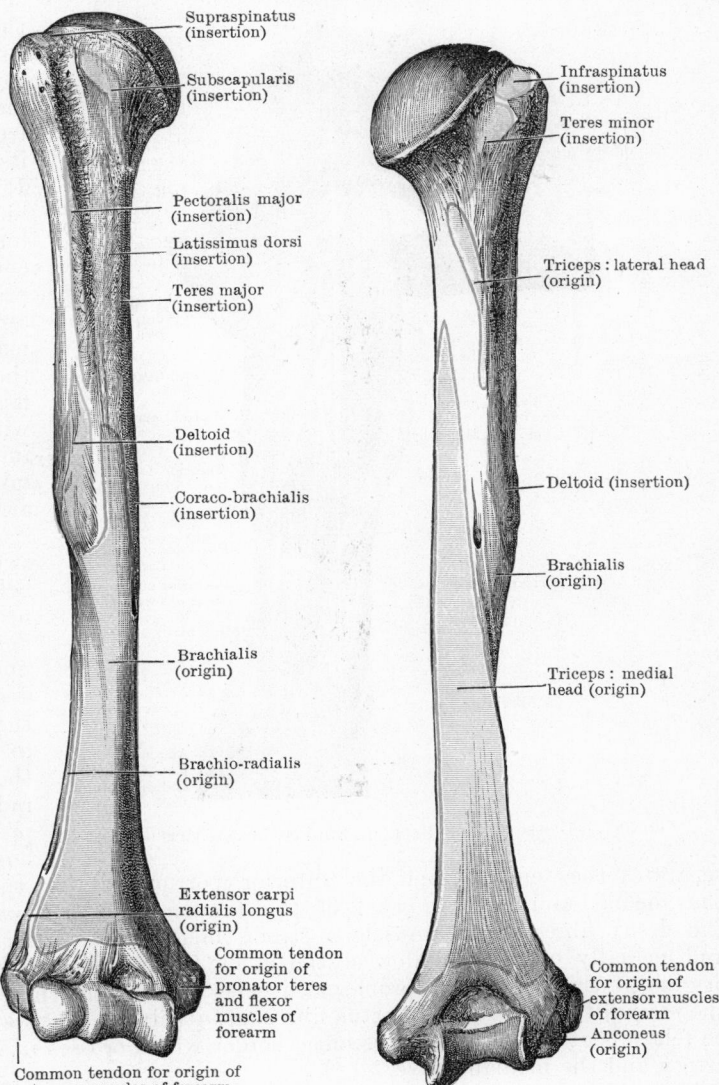

Supraspinatus (insertion)

Subscapularis (insertion)

Infraspinatus (insertion)

Teres minor (insertion)

Pectoralis major (insertion)

Latissimus dorsi (insertion)

Teres major (insertion)

Triceps : lateral head (origin)

Deltoid (insertion)

Coraco-brachialis (insertion)

Deltoid (insertion)

Brachialis (origin)

Triceps : medial head (origin)

Brachialis (origin)

Brachio-radialis (origin)

Extensor carpi radialis longus (origin)

Common tendon for origin of pronator teres and flexor muscles of forearm

Common tendon for origin of extensor muscles of forearm

Anconeus (origin)

Common tendon for origin of extensor muscles of forearm

FIG. 385.—MUSCLE-ATTACHMENTS TO FRONT OF RIGHT HUMERUS.

FIG. 386.—MUSCLE-ATTACHMENTS TO BACK OF RIGHT HUMERUS.

The **coraco-brachialis** is the remains of a *threefold muscle*. Usually only two elements are present in man, but in anomalous cases all the parts may be more or less fully developed. The passage of the musculo-cutaneous nerve through the muscle is an indication of its separation into the persisting middle and distal elements. In the commonest variation the more superficial part of the muscle (*coraco-brachialis inferior* or *longus*) extends farther down than usual, so as to be inserted into the medial intermuscular septum, or even into the medial epicondyle of the humerus. A third slip (*coraco-brachialis superior* or *brevis*) may more rarely be present; it springs from the root of the coracoid process and is inserted into the medial side of the humerus immediately below the capsule of the shoulder joint.

Biceps [Brachii].—The biceps muscle **arises** by two tendinous *heads*. The **short head** is attached in common with the coraco-brachialis to the tip of the coracoid process of the scapula (Fig. 381, p. 455). Concealed by the deltoid and tendinous at first, this head forms a separate fleshy belly which is united to the long head by an investment of the deep fascia. The **long head** arises by a round tendon from the supraglenoid tubercle and from the labrum glenoidale.

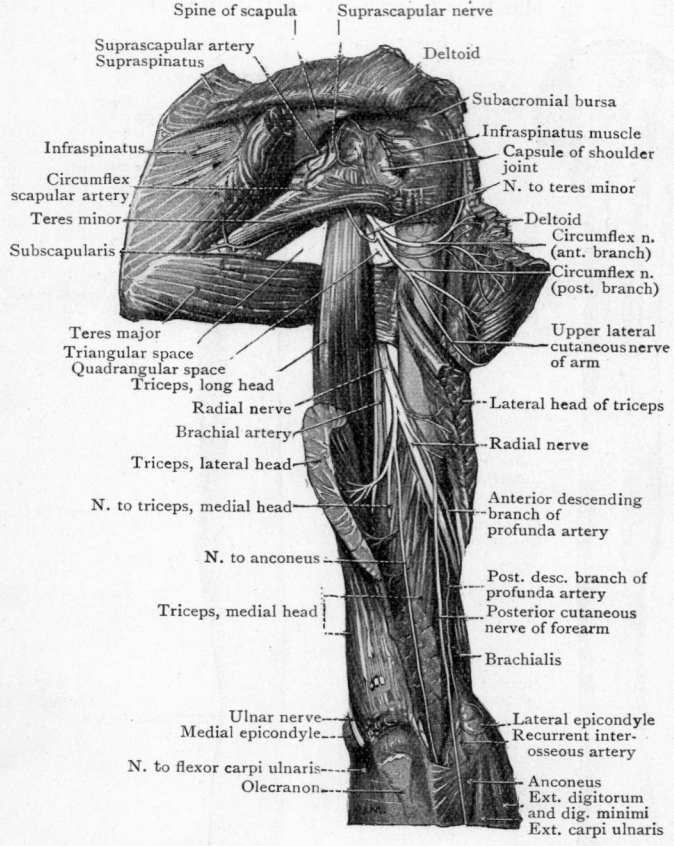

Spine of scapula Suprascapular nerve
Suprascapular artery
Supraspinatus
Deltoid
Subacromial bursa
Infraspinatus
Infraspinatus muscle
Capsule of shoulder joint
Circumflex scapular artery
N. to teres minor
Teres minor
Deltoid
Subscapularis
Circumflex n. (ant. branch)
Circumflex n. (post. branch)
Teres major
Upper lateral cutaneous nerve of arm
Triangular space
Quadrangular space
Triceps, long head
Radial nerve
Lateral head of triceps
Brachial artery
Radial nerve
Triceps, lateral head
N. to triceps, medial head
Anterior descending branch of profunda artery
N. to anconeus
Post. desc. branch of profunda artery
Triceps, medial head
Posterior cutaneous nerve of forearm
Brachialis
Ulnar nerve
Medial epicondyle
Lateral epicondyle
Recurrent interosseous artery
N. to flexor carpi ulnaris
Olecranon
Anconeus
Ext. digitorum and dig. minimi
Ext. carpi ulnaris

FIG. 387.—DISSECTION OF BACK OF SHOULDER AND UPPER ARM

Its tendon passes through the cavity of the shoulder joint, and (invested by a prolongation of the synovial membranè) emerges from the joint beneath its transverse ligament. It then occupies the bicipital groove of the humerus, where it is covered by a fascial prolongation of the tendon of the pectoralis major; emerging from the groove, it forms a fleshy belly which unites with the short head immediately below the middle of the upper arm.

The **insertion** also is twofold. (1) The united bellies become connected to a strong *tendon*, which is twisted upon itself as it passes deeply in the hollow of the elbow to be attached to the posterior part of the tuberosity of the radius (Figs. 391, 393, pp. 467, 469. A small bursa (*bicipito-radial*) separates the tendon from the anterior portion of the tuberosity. (2) From the medial and anterior part of the tendon, and partly in continuity with the fleshy fibres of the muscle, a strong membranous band spreads downwards and medially over the hollow of the elbow to join the deep fascia covering the origins of the flexor and pronator muscles of the forearm. This band is called the *bicipital aponeurosis* [lacertus fibrosus]; its upper part is thickened and can be felt subcutaneously as a crescentic border which crosses in front of the brachial artery and the median nerve.

The biceps conceals the brachialis muscle and the musculo-cutaneous nerve. Its medial border is the guide to the position of the brachial artery and median nerve.

A **third** (or humeral) **head** is a common variation of the biceps (10 per cent.); its usual site of origin is at the insertion of the coraco-brachialis, and it is inserted mainly with the bicipital aponeurosis. Two or even three additional heads may be present in the same subject. The long head of the muscle may be absent, or may take origin from the bicipital groove. The muscle may have an additional insertion into the medial epicondyle of the humerus, or into the fascia of the forearm.

Brachialis.—This large muscle **arises** from the distal two-thirds of the front of the shaft of the humerus and from the intermuscular septum on each side (Fig.

385, p. 461).   Clasping the insertion of the deltoid proximally, it ends distally in a strong tendon which is **inserted** into the lower surface of the coronoid process and into the tuberosity of the ulna (Fig. 393).   Some fleshy fibres are inserted

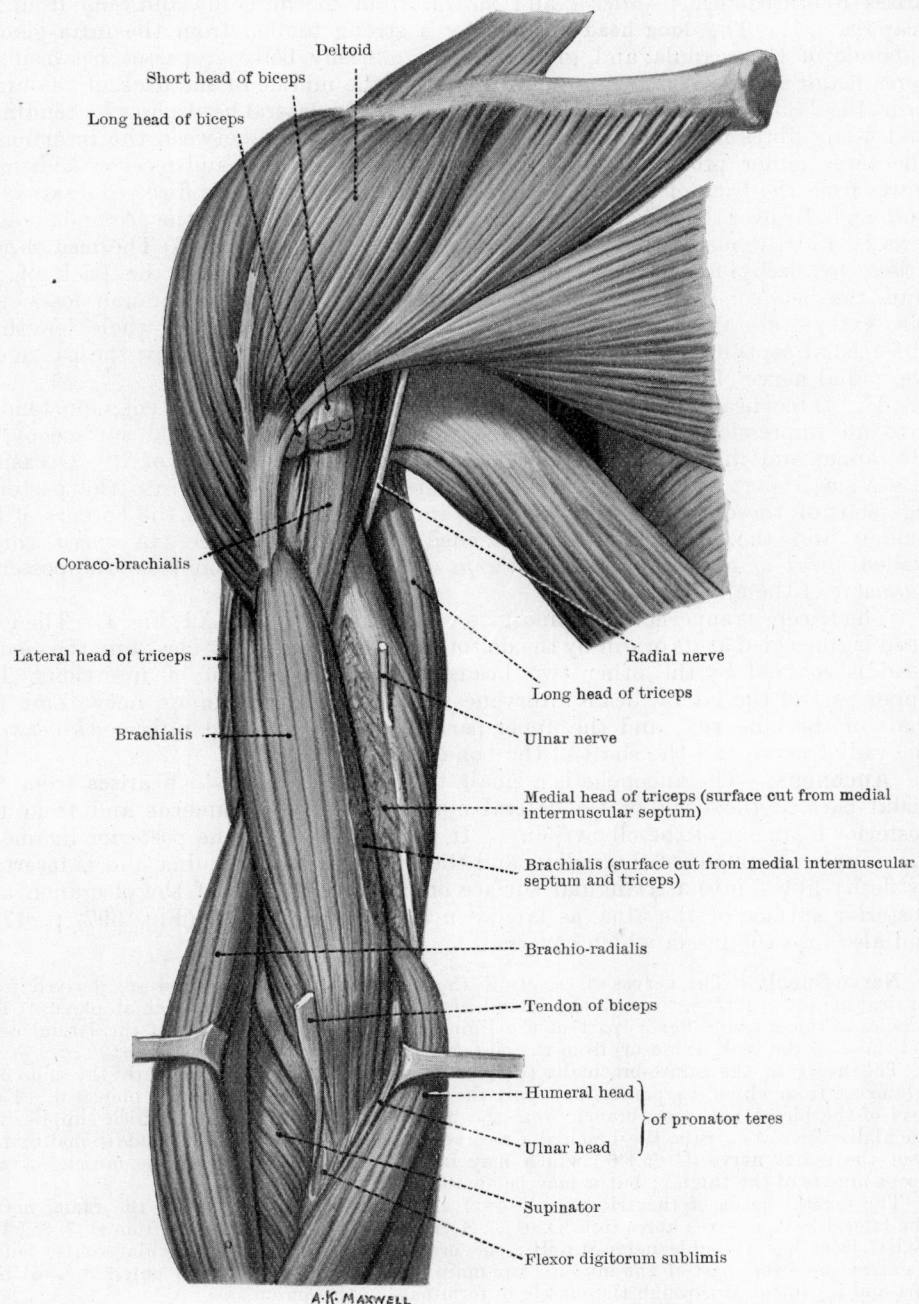

Deltoid

Short head of biceps

Long head of biceps

Coraco-brachialis

Lateral head of triceps

Brachialis

Radial nerve

Long head of triceps

Ulnar nerve

Medial head of triceps (surface cut from medial intermuscular septum)

Brachialis (surface cut from medial intermuscular septum and triceps)

Brachio-radialis

Tendon of biceps

Humeral head ⎱
                  ⎰ of pronator teres
Ulnar head   ⎰

Supinator

Flexor digitorum sublimis

A·K· MAXWELL

Fig. 388.—Dissection of Muscles of the Front of Upper Arm. The biceps has been removed to show the brachialis.   (R. D. L.)

into the anterior ligament of the elbow joint ; and the lateral part of the muscle, arising from the lateral supracondylar ridge and lateral intermuscular septum, forms a slip, more or less separate, which may be partially fused with the brachio-radialis muscle.

It is concealed for the most part by the biceps in the upper arm. Its distal part lies on the front of the elbow joint and in the floor of the cubital fossa.

Triceps.—The triceps is the only muscle on the back of the upper arm. It **arises** by three heads—*lateral* and *medial* from the humerus, and *long* from the scapula. (1) The **long head** springs by a strong tendon from the infra-glenoid tubercle of the scapula, and, giving rise to a fleshy belly, it passes between the teres major and teres minor muscles to occupy the middle of the back of the upper arm (Fig. 383, p. 458, and Fig. 387, p. 462). (2) The **lateral head** arises by tendinous and fleshy fibres from the lateral border of the humerus between the insertion of the teres minor proximally and the spiral groove distally, and receives additional fibres from the back of the lateral intermuscular septum; it is directed downwards and medially over the spiral groove—concealing the radial nerve, the profunda brachii vessels, and the medial head of the muscle (Figs. 386, 387). (3) The **medial head** arises, by fleshy fibres, from an elongated triangular area on the back of the humerus between the insertion of the teres major and the olecranon fossa, and also extensively from the back of the intermuscular septa—the whole length of the medial septum, and from the part of the lateral septum below the passage of the radial nerve (Fig. 388).

The three heads of origin are **inserted**, by a broad, flattened common tendon, into an impression occupying the posterior part of the proximal surface of the olecranon, and into the deep fascia of the forearm on each side of it. Occasionally a small part (**subanconeus**) of the medial head is inserted into the posterior ligament of the elbow joint. The long and lateral heads join the borders of the tendon, and the medial head is attached to its deep surface. A small, thick-walled *bursa of the tendon of the triceps* separates the tendon from the posterior ligament of the elbow joint.

The triceps is superficial in almost its whole extent (Pl. XXXI, Fig. 3). The long head is concealed at its origin by the deltoid and teres minor muscles; and the medial head is covered by the other two heads, and by the tendon of insertion. The upper part of the lateral head intervenes between the circumflex nerve and the shaft of the humerus; and the upper part of the medial head intervenes between the radial nerve and the shaft of the bone.

Anconeus.—The anconeus is a small, triangular muscle which **arises** from the distal part of the back of the lateral epicondyle of the humerus and from the posterior ligament of the elbow joint. It partially conceals the posterior ligament, the annular ligament of the radius, and the upper part of the ulna, and is **inserted**, by fleshy fibres, into a triangular surface on the lateral side of the olecranon and posterior surface of the ulna, as far down as the oblique line (Fig. 397, p. 473), and also into the fascia which covers it.

Nerve-Supply.—The nerves of supply to the muscles of the upper arm are derived from cervical nerves, 5, 6, 7, 8, through the lateral and posterior cords of the brachial plexus. The muscles in the anterior (flexor) part of the limb are supplied by branches of the lateral cord, and those on the back (extensor) from the posterior cord through the radial nerve.

The **nerve to the coraco-brachialis** (C. (6.) 7.) is usually incorporated with the musculo-cutaneous, from which it separates to supply the muscle before the latter nerve pierces it. Each head of the biceps receives a branch from the **musculo-cutaneous** (C. 5. 6.), which supplies the brachialis also. As a rule, the brachialis receives at its lateral border a fine, additional branch from the **radial nerve** (C. (5.) 6.) which may indicate a double origin of the muscle (cf. the biceps muscle of the thigh); but it may be an afferent nerve.

The several heads of the triceps are supplied separately by branches of the **radial nerve**. The lateral head receives fibres from C. (6.) 7. 8., the long and medial heads from C. 7. 8. The medial head has a double nerve-supply: one branch has a long extra-muscular course before it enters the distal part of the muscle; the main nerve to the medial head enters its proximal part and is continued through the muscle to terminate in the anconeus.

The Actions of Muscles in Movements at the Elbow Joint.—The **biceps** and the **brachialis** act together in flexion of the forearm, and are assisted in that action by the **brachio-radialis** and the **pronator teres**, and in lesser degrees by members of the flexor and extensor groups of the forearm that arise from the medial and lateral epicondyles of the humerus; for example, the radial extensors of the carpus may also assist in flexion at the elbow (see p. 385). It is of clinical interest to note that the biceps may retain its power of flexion when its supinating action is lost (Beevor). The brachialis, a pure flexor, is the most powerful flexor at the elbow, while the biceps acts also in flexion of the shoulder joint, and on the radio-ulnar joints as a supinator. The brachio-radialis is primarily a flexor of the elbow joint. It may also act as a semi-pronator and semi-supinator of the forearm, bringing the limb from a supine or prone position into an intermediate position.

The **triceps**, assisted by the **anconeus**, is the extensor of the elbow joint.

FASCIÆ OF THE UPPER ARM

The **superficial fascia** presents no features of importance. It is separated from the back of the olecranon by a subcutaneous *bursa,* and occasionally by others from the epicondyles of the humerus.

The **deep fascia** forms a strong tubular investment for the muscles on the front and back of the humerus. It is continuous above with the deep fascia of the shoulder and axilla, and is strengthened by fibres derived from the insertions of the pectoralis major, latissimus dorsi, and deltoid muscles. At the elbow it gains attachment to the epicondyles of the humerus and the olecranon; and becomes continuous with the deep fascia of the forearm. It is strengthened also by important bands associated with the insertions of the biceps anteriorly and the triceps posteriorly. About the middle of the upper arm on the medial side, it is perforated by the basilic vein and the medial cutaneous nerve of the forearm.

The **intermuscular septa** are processes of the deep fascia attached to the supracondylar ridges of the humerus. The **medial septum** [of the upper arm] is the stronger. It is placed between the brachialis and the medial head of the triceps and gives origin to both (Fig. 388, p. 463). It extends up to the insertion of the coraco-brachialis (which is often continued into it), and its upper part is pierced by the ulnar nerve and ulnar collateral vessels. The **lateral septum** separates the brachialis and brachio-radialis from the medial and lateral heads of the triceps and gives origin to all of them. It extends up to the insertion of the deltoid, and is pierced by the radial nerve and profunda brachii vessels.

MUSCLES AND FASCIÆ OF THE FOREARM AND HAND

MUSCLES ON THE FRONT AND MEDIAL SIDE OF THE FOREARM

The muscles on the front and medial side of the forearm are the pronators and the flexors of the wrist and fingers. In the forearm they are arranged in three strata: (1) A superficial layer of four muscles which radiate from a common tendon attached to the medial epicondyle of the humerus. They are named, from radial to ulnar side, pronator teres, flexor carpi radialis, palmaris longus, and flexor carpi ulnaris. They conceal the muscle which by itself constitutes (2) the middle stratum—the flexor digitorum sublimis. That in turn conceals, for the most part, (3) the deep layer of muscles, comprising the flexor digitorum profundus on the ulna, the flexor pollicis longus on the radius, and the pronator quadratus, which is more deeply placed, and stretches across the forearm between the distal portions of the radius and ulna.

I. Superficial Layer

Pronator Teres.—The pronator teres, the shortest muscle of this group, has a double **origin**. The **humeral head** forms almost the whole muscle; it arises by fleshy and tendinous fibres from the lowest part of the medial supracondylar ridge and medial intermuscular septum, from the medial epicondyle of the humerus, from the fascia over it, and from the fascial septum between it and the flexor carpi radialis (Fig. 391). The **ulnar head** is a slender slip that springs from the coronoid process of the ulna and joins the humeral head on its deep surface (Fig. 391). The median nerve passes between the two heads.

The muscle passes downwards and laterally to be **inserted** by a flattened tendon into an oval impression on the middle of the lateral surface of the shaft of the radius (Figs. 391, 393)—the most superficial humeral fibres passing to the distal part of the tendon of insertion.

The pronator teres forms the medial boundary of the *cubital fossa*. It is superficially placed except near its insertion, where it is covered by the brachio-radialis muscle and by the radial vessels.

Flexor Carpi Radialis.—The flexor carpi radialis muscle takes **origin** from the medial epicondyle of the humerus by the common tendon, from the fascia over it, and from the fascial septum on each side. About the middle of the

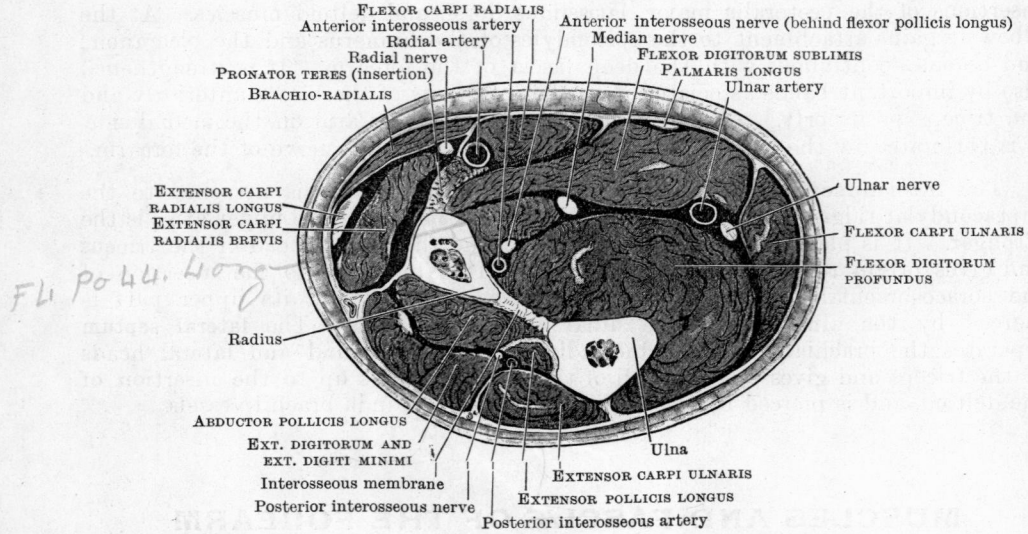

FLEXOR CARPI RADIALIS
Anterior interosseous artery
Radial artery
Radial nerve
PRONATOR TERES (insertion)
BRACHIO-RADIALIS
Anterior interosseous nerve (behind flexor pollicis longus)
Median nerve
FLEXOR DIGITORUM SUBLIMIS
PALMARIS LONGUS
Ulnar artery

EXTENSOR CARPI
RADIALIS LONGUS
EXTENSOR CARPI
RADIALIS BREVIS

Ulnar nerve
FLEXOR CARPI ULNARIS
FLEXOR DIGITORUM
PROFUNDUS

Radius

ABDUCTOR POLLICIS LONGUS
EXT. DIGITORUM AND
EXT. DIGITI MINIMI
Interosseous membrane
Posterior interosseous nerve
Ulna
EXTENSOR CARPI ULNARIS
EXTENSOR POLLICIS LONGUS
Posterior interosseous artery

FIG. 389.—DISTAL SURFACE OF A SECTION ACROSS THE RIGHT FOREARM IN THE MIDDLE THIRD.

forearm, the fleshy belly gives place to a flattened tendon which becomes more cord-like as it approaches the wrist. Passing into the hand, the tendon enters a special compartment in the lateral border of the flexor retinaculum, which it appears to split into two layers as it lies in the groove on the trapezium surrounded by a synovial sheath. Finally, it is **inserted** into the base of the second metacarpal bone and usually into the base of the third.

The muscle is superficial except near its insertion. Its tendon, in the distal half of the forearm, is an important guide to the radial vessels, which are placed to its radial side. After passing through the flexor retinaculum [lig. carpi transversum] the tendon is concealed by the origins of the short muscles of the thumb, and is crossed, from medial to lateral side, by the tendon of the flexor pollicis longus. Besides the synovial sheath that envelops the tendon on the trapezium, a synovial *bursa* is placed behind the tendon at its insertion.

Palmaris Longus.—The palmaris longus also **arises** from the medial epicondyle of the humerus by the common flexor tendon, from the deep fascia, and the septum on each side. The fleshy belly is short and fusiform, and ends at the middle of the forearm in a long, flat tendon. The tendon passes superficial to the flexor retinaculum, and is **inserted** (1) into the surface of that band and (2) into the apex of the palmar aponeurosis. A tendinous slip is frequently sent to the short muscles of the thumb and the fascia covering them.

The palmaris longus is the most slender of the muscles of the front of the forearm. In the distal part of the forearm, the median nerve is behind its tendon, at the radial border of the tendons of the flexor digitorum sublimis.

The palmaris longus is the most variable muscle in the body, and is often absent (about 11 per cent.). It represents a flexor of the proximal phalanges, but in man it has become very much reduced, owing to differentiation of the other digital flexors and to finer control of the movements of the fingers by the lumbricals and interossei.

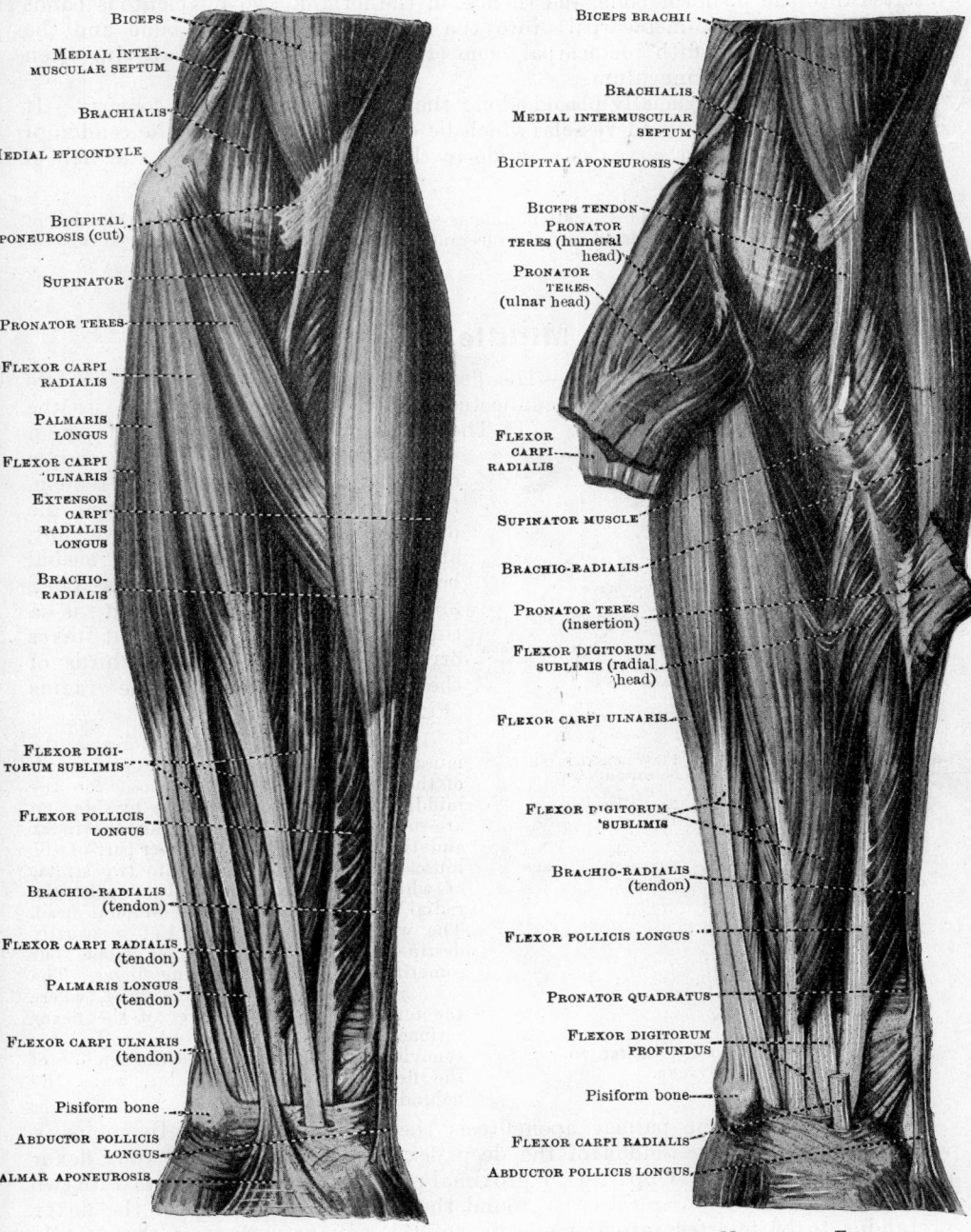

FIG. 390.—SUPERFICIAL MUSCLES OF FRONT OF LEFT FOREARM.

FIG. 391.—DEEPER MUSCLES OF FRONT OF LEFT FOREARM.

Flexor Carpi Ulnaris.—The flexor carpi ulnaris muscle **arises** by two heads—humeral and ulnar—joined by a tendinous arch, under cover of which the ulnar nerve enters the forearm. (1) The **humeral head** springs from the medial epicondyle of the humerus by the common tendon, from the covering fascia, and from a lateral intermuscular septum. (2) The **ulnar head**, by means of the deep fascia of the forearm, obtains an origin from the medial border of the olecranon and the posterior border of the ulna in its upper three-fifths. The fleshy fibres join a tendon which runs down the anterior border of the distal half of the muscle to be **inserted** into the pisiform bone, and thence, in the form of two ligamentous bands (piso-hamate and piso-metacarpal), into the hook of the hamate bone and the proximal end of the fifth metacarpal bone (Fig. 400, p. 477); a small slip often passes to the flexor retinaculum.

The muscle is superficially placed along the medial border of the forearm. It conceals the ulnar nerve and vessels (which lie on the lateral side of the tendon of insertion). The tendon serves as a guide to these structures in the distal half of the forearm.

M. **Epitrochleo-anconeus.**—This small muscle is seldom present; it **arises** from the back of the medial epicondyle and is **inserted** into the olecranon; it is usually represented by a band of transverse fibres in the fascia.

2. Middle Layer

Flexor Digitorum Sublimis.—The flexor digitorum sublimis **arises** by two heads—humero-ulnar and radial—connected by a fibrous bridge that crosses the median nerve and ulnar vessels. (1) The **humero-ulnar head**—the chief origin —springs from the medial epicondyle of the humerus by the common tendon, from adjacent fascial septa, from the medial ligament of the elbow joint, and by a slender slip from the medial border of the coronoid process (Fig. 393). (2) The **radial head** is a thin fibro-muscular sheet that takes origin from the upper two-thirds of the **anterior border** of the radius (Fig. 393).

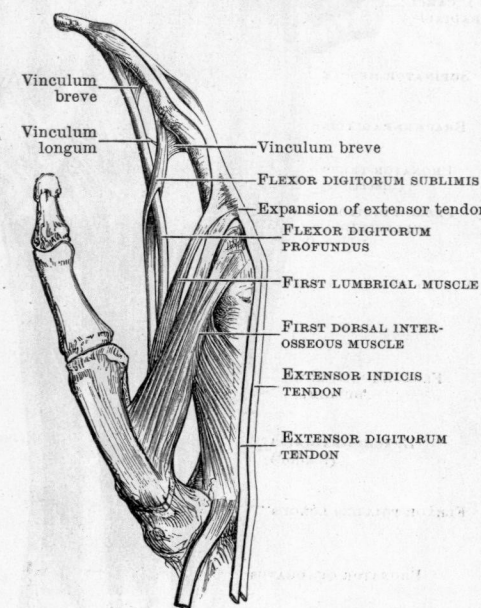

Vinculum breve
Vinculum longum
Vinculum breve
FLEXOR DIGITORUM SUBLIMIS
Expansion of extensor tendon
FLEXOR DIGITORUM PROFUNDUS
FIRST LUMBRICAL MUSCLE
FIRST DORSAL INTER-OSSEOUS MUSCLE
EXTENSOR INDICIS TENDON
EXTENSOR DIGITORUM TENDON

FIG. 392.—THE TENDONS ATTACHED TO THE INDEX FINGER.

In the distal third of the forearm the muscle gives rise to four tendons, one for each of the medial four digits. Those for the middle and ring fingers lie side by side and are superficial to the tendons for the index and the little finger. The upper part of the muscle is similarly divisible into two strata, of which the more superficial comprise the radial head and part of the humeral head. The whole of the radial head is usually destined for the middle finger alone, but sometimes also acts on the ring finger. The same arrangement holds at the wrist, where the tendons pass under cover of the flexor retinaculum and are enclosed in a large synovial sheath together with the tendons of the flexor digitorum profundus, which lie behind them.

Under cover of the palmar aponeurosis the tendons diverge. In company with the corresponding tendon of the deep flexor, each enters the fibrous flexor sheath of its own digit. Opposite the proximal phalanx each tendon splits into two parts which pass, with a spiral twist, round the sides of the tendon of the flexor profundus to be **inserted** into the margins of the palmar surface of the middle phalanx. The reversed edges of the two portions of the split tendon are partially reunited by decussating fibres behind the tendon of the flexor profundus; the oblique, tubular passage thus made in the tendon of the flexor sublimis, for the passage of the profundus tendon, is such that it cannot be obliterated by tension.

The **vincula tendinum** form additional attachments of the tendons, to which they also convey small blood-vessels. They are delicate bands of fibrous tissue enveloped in folds of the synovial sheath, and are known as the **vincula longa** and

brevia. Each vinculum breve is a triangular band of fibres containing yellow elastic tissue; it occupies the interval between the tendon and the digit for a short distance close to the insertion. It is attached to the front of the interphalangeal joint and the distal part of the proximal phalanx. The vinculum longum is a variable, narrow, double band that extends from the back of the tendon to the proximal part of the palmar surface of the proximal phalanx.

The upper part of the muscle lies deep to the brachio-radialis, pronator teres, flexor carpi radialis, palmaris longus and flexor carpi ulnaris; the lower part lies between the flexor carpi radialis and flexor carpi ulnaris, and is overlapped by the palmaris longus alone. It is crossed by the radial vessels and crosses the ulnar vessels and nerve. At the wrist, the tendons are medial to the tendon of flexor pollicis longus and the median nerve. In the hand, the tendons are superficial to the tendons of the flexor digitorum profundus and the lumbrical muscles, and deep to the superficial palmar arch and the digital branches of the median and ulnar nerves.

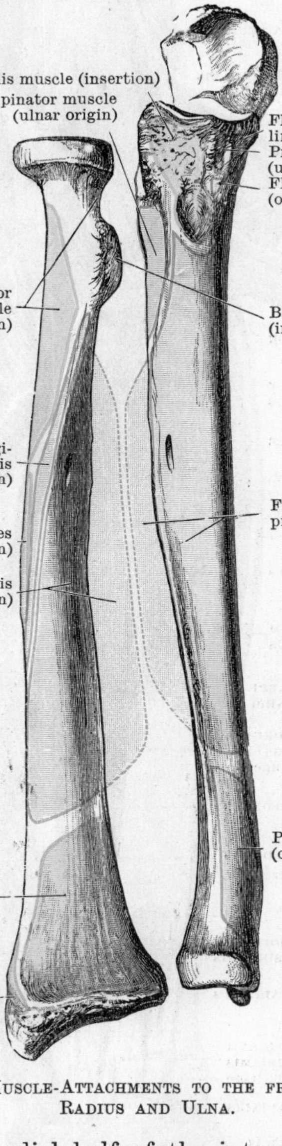

3. Deep Layer

Flexor Digitorum Profundus.—The flexor digitorum profundus is a large muscle that arises from the ulna, the interosseous membrane, and the deep fascia of the forearm, under cover of the flexor digitorum sublimis and the flexor carpi ulnaris. The ulnar origin is the upper two-thirds of the medial and anterior surfaces of the ulna—reaching the medial side of the olecranon and embracing the insertion of the brachialis at the upper end and extending almost to the pronator quadratus

FIG. 393.—MUSCLE-ATTACHMENTS TO THE FRONT OF RIGHT RADIUS AND ULNA.

below. It arises also, laterally, from the medial half of the interosseous membrane in its middle third (Figs. 393, 394), and medially from the deep fascia which attaches the flexor carpi ulnaris to the posterior border of the ulna.

The muscle becomes a broad thick tendon which lies behind the tendons of the flexor digitorum sublimis, and is enveloped with them in the common flexor synovial sheath; with them it descends behind the flexor retinaculum into the palm, where it divides into separate tendons for insertion into the distal phalanges of the four fingers. The tendon for the forefinger is, however, usually separate in its whole length, and is mainly derived from those fibres which arise from the interosseous membrane.

Each tendon enters the fibrous flexor sheath of the finger, deep to the tendon of the flexor digitorum sublimis, which it pierces opposite the proximal phalanx, and is finally inserted into the base of the distal phalanx. Like the tendons of the flexor sublimis, those of the deep flexor are provided with vincula, viz. **vincula brevia** attached to the capsule of the second interphalangeal joint and **vincula longa** connected to the tendons of the flexor digitorum sublimis and their vincula brevia.

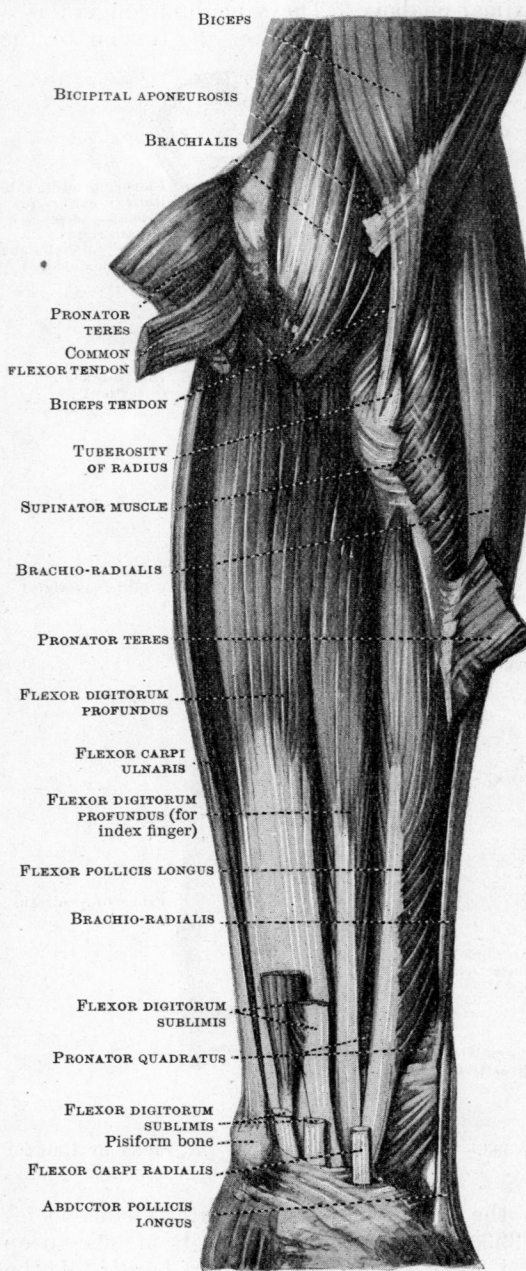

FIG. 394.—THE DEEPEST MUSCLES OF THE FRONT OF LEFT FOREARM.

Lumbricals.—The lumbricals are four small, cylindrical muscles associated with the tendons of the flexor digitorum profundus in the palm of the hand. *The lateral two muscles* arise, each by a single head, from the radial sides of the tendons of the flexor digitorum profundus destined respectively for the fore and middle fingers; *the medial two muscles* arise, each by two heads, from the adjacent sides of the tendons between which they lie (viz. the tendons of the middle, ring, and little fingers).

Each lumbrical becomes a slender, flattened tendon which passes obliquely backwards across the lateral side of the corresponding metacarpo-phalangeal joint and, becoming connected with the expansion of the extensor tendon, is **inserted** with the tendon of an interosseous muscle, into the base of a terminal phalanx. The lumbricals may be increased to six or diminished to two.

Flexor Pollicis Longus.—The flexor pollicis longus **arises**, by fleshy fibres, from the anterior surface of the shaft of the radius between the radial tuberosity and the upper border of the pronator quadratus, and also from a corresponding portion of the interosseous membrane. Usually it has a slip that arises in common with the flexor digitorum sublimis from the medial border of the coronoid process or medial epicondyle, or from both.

Distally, the muscle is placed between the brachio-radialis laterally, the overlapping flexor carpi radialis medially, and the radial vessels anteriorly, while the anterior interosseous nerve and vessels descend on the interosseous membrane between the flexor pollicis longus and flexor digitorum profundus.

The muscle ends above the wrist in a tendon which passes in front of the pronator quadratus into the hand behind the flexor retinaculum, enveloped in a special synovial sheath.

In the palm, the tendon, directed downwards along the medial side of the thenar eminence, between the flexor brevis and adductor muscles of the thumb, and between the two sesamoid bones of the metacarpo-phalangeal joint, enters a fibrous sheath, to be **inserted** into the base of the distal phalanx of the thumb on its palmar surface.

Pronator Quadratus.—The pronator quadratus is a quadrilateral fleshy muscle that lies deeply in the distal part of the forearm behind the flexor tendons and the radial vessels. It **arises** from the distal fourth of the anterior border and surface of the ulna, and its fibres run transversely to be **inserted** into the distal fourth of the anterior surface of the radius, and into the narrow triangular area on its medial side in front of the attachment of the interosseous membrane (Fig. 215, p. 246).

The pronator quadratus is subject to considerable variations. It frequently consists of two strata, separated by the terminal part of the anterior interosseous nerve; it may be increased in size, having an additional origin from radius or ulna, or from both bones, and an insertion into the carpus; it may even be absent. (In most of the lower mammals the two pronators form one muscle).

MUSCLES ON THE BACK OF THE FOREARM

The muscles at the lateral side of the elbow and on the back of the forearm and hand are the supinator muscles of the forearm and the extensors of the wrist and digits, and they are divisible into a **superficial** and a **deep layer.**

The muscles of the **superficial layer** —seven in number and named from radial to ulnar side—are the brachio - radialis, the two radial extensors of the carpus, the extensor digitorum and extensor digiti minimi, the extensor carpi ulnaris, and the anconeus. With the exception of the brachio - radialis, extensor carpi radialis longus and the anconeus, they share a common tendon of origin, which is attached to the front of the lateral epicondyle of the humerus (Fig. 385, p. 461).

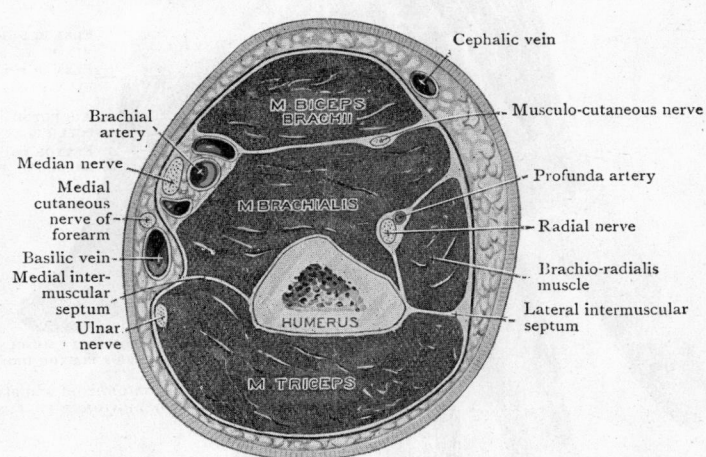

Fig. 395.—Section through the Distal Third of the Right Upper Arm.

Five muscles make up the **deep layer:** one—the supinator—extends between the proximal parts of the ulna and radius; the others are the special extensors of the thumb and forefinger, viz., the abductor pollicis longus, extensor pollicis longus and extensor pollicis brevis, and extensor indicis. They cover the posterior surface of the bones of the forearm and the interosseous membrane, and are wholly concealed by the superficial muscles, with the exception of the abductor pollicis longus and the extensor pollicis brevis, which emerge between the radial extensors of the carpus and the extensor digitorum and become superficial in the distal part of the forearm.

Superficial Layer

Brachio-radialis.—The brachio-radialis **arises**, by fleshy fibres, from the proximal two-thirds of the front of the lateral supracondylar ridge of the humerus and the adjoining part of the lateral intermuscular septum—the radial nerve and anastomosing vessels intervening between it and the brachialis. Descending along the lateral border of the forearm, the muscle bounds the cubital fossa laterally, and ends about the middle of the forearm in a narrow flat tendon which is **inserted**, under cover of the tendons of the abductor pollicis longus and extensor pollicis brevis, into the lateral side of the lower end of the radius (Figs. 393, p. 469, and 397, p. 473).

Extensor Carpi Radialis Longus.—The extensor carpi radialis longus **arises**, by fleshy fibres, from the distal third of the front of the lateral supra-condylar ridge of the humerus, and from the adjoining part of the lateral inter-muscular septum (Figs. 385 and 398).

In its upper part, the muscle lies close to the lateral side of the elbow joint, overlapped by the brachio-radialis and the extensor carpi radialis brevis, between which it descends into the forearm. About the middle of the forearm it ends in a flat tendon which, throughout, is closely applied to the lateral side of the extensor carpi radialis brevis; and as the two tendons descend they are crossed obliquely by the abductor pollicis longus and extensor pollicis brevis. Still side by side

FLEXOR CARPI ULNARIS
FLEXOR DIGITORUM SUBLIMIS
FLEXOR CARPI RADIALIS
PALMARIS LONGUS
Pisiform bone
ABDUCTOR POLLICIS LONGUS
FLEXOR RETINACULUM
ABDUCTOR DIGITI MINIMI
ABDUCTOR POLLICIS BREVIS
FLEXOR DIGITI MINIMI
FLEXOR POLLICIS BREVIS
ADDUCTOR POLLICIS
FLEXOR POLLICIS LONGUS
LUMBRICAL MUSCLES
TENDONS OF FLEXOR DIGITORUM SUBLIMIS
FLEXOR DIGITORUM SUBLIMIS
FLEXOR DIGITORUM PROFUNDUS

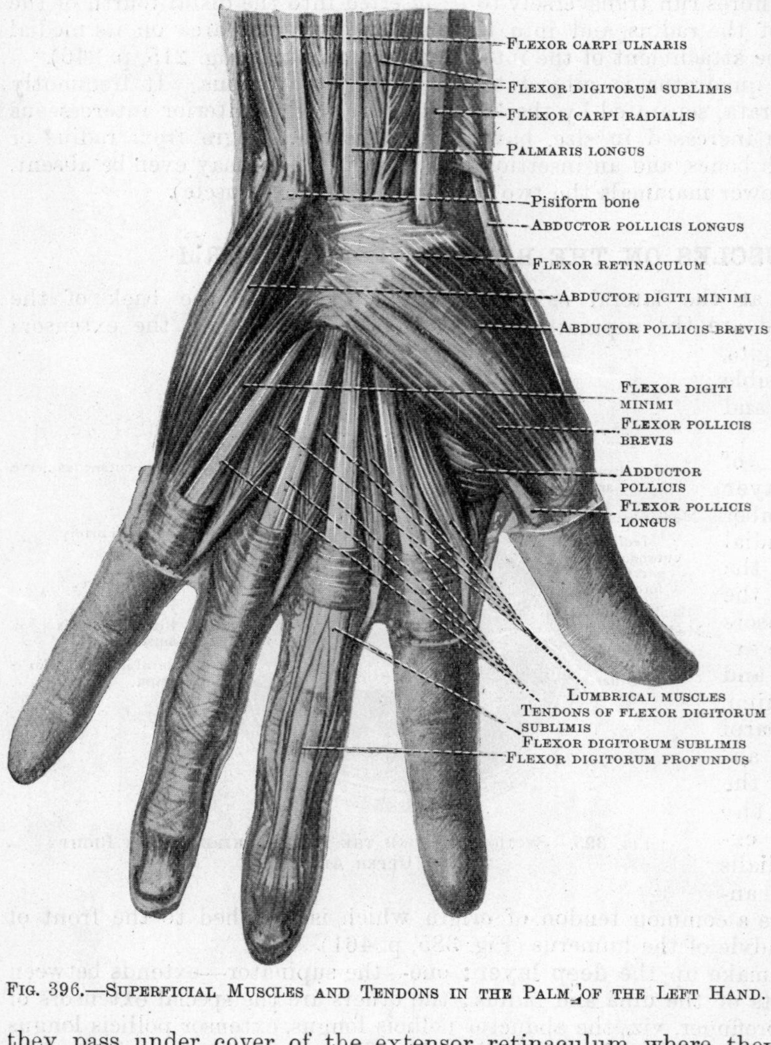

FIG. 396.—SUPERFICIAL MUSCLES AND TENDONS IN THE PALM OF THE LEFT HAND.

they pass under cover of the extensor retinaculum, where they are enclosed in a single synovial sheath and groove the distal end of the radius, and there are crossed obliquely by the extensor longus pollicis; finally, the long extensor is inserted into the dorsal surface of the base of the second metacarpal bone on its radial side. A small *bursa* may be found under the tendon close to its insertion.

Extensor Carpi Radialis Brevis.—The extensor carpi radialis brevis **arises** from the common tendon, from the lateral ligament of the elbow joint, from the covering fascia, and from the intermuscular septum on each side. Accompanied by its long companion (the two are represented by one muscle in the lower mammals), it descends as just described, to be inserted, by a tendon, into the base of the third metacarpal bone—a small *bursa* lying between the tendon and the styloid process of the metacarpal bone. The tendons of the long and short radial extensors of the wrist may split and both be attached to the second and third and sometimes the fourth metacarpal bones.

Extensor Digitorum.—The extensor digitorum [communis] lies between the extensors of the carpus and the extensor of the little finger (Fig. 398). It arises from the common tendon, from the fascia over it, and from intermuscular septa at its sides.

Extending along the back of the forearm, it ends above the wrist in four tendons of which the most lateral often has a separate fleshy belly. After passing deep to the extensor retinaculum, surrounded by a synovial sheath in the same compartment as the extensor indicis, the tendons separate on the back of the hand, where the most medial three tendons are joined together by two obliquely placed bands. One band passes downwards and laterally, and connects together the third and second tendons; the other is a broader and shorter band which also passes downwards and laterally, and joins the fourth to the third tendon. A band sometimes passes downwards and medially from the first to the second tendon; and, frequently, the tendon for the little finger is joined to the tendon for the ring finger, and separates from it only a short distance above the distal end of the metacarpal bone.

The tendons are **inserted** in the following manner: On the finger each tendon spreads out to form a membranous expansion over the knuckle and on the dorsum of the proximal phalanx. The border of the tendon is indefinite over the metacarpo-phalangeal joint, the dorsal ligament of which it replaces. On the back of the proximal phalanx the tendon receives at its sides the tendons of the interosseous and lumbrical muscles. At the distal end of the proximal phalanx it appears to split into ill-defined middle and collateral slips which

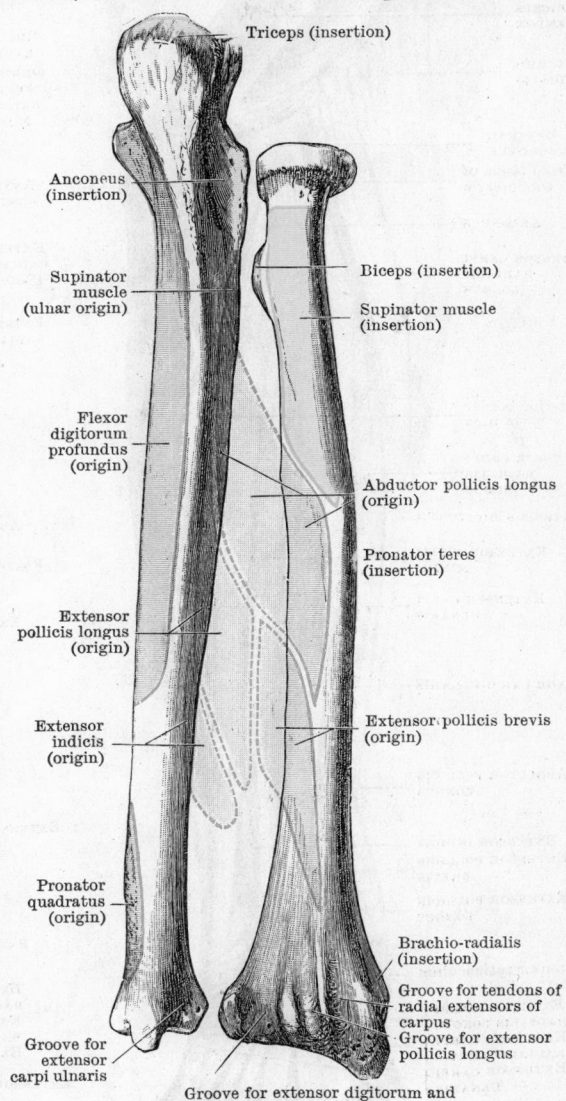

FIG. 397.—MUSCLE-ATTACHMENTS TO THE BACK OF RIGHT RADIUS AND ULNA.

pass over the back of the first interphalangeal joint, where they replace the dorsal ligament. The middle slip, which is directly continuous with the extensor tendon itself, is inserted into the dorsum of the base of the middle phalanx. The two collateral pieces are continuous with the tendons of the lumbrical muscles and the interossei; they all become united to form a membranous tendon on the back of the middle phalanx, which, after passing over the second interphalangeal joint, is inserted into the base of the distal phalanx.

Extensor Digiti Minimi.—The extensor digiti minimi arises, like the preceding muscle, from the common tendon, the fascia over it, and from intermuscular septa. It descends as a narrow fleshy slip between the extensor digitorum and the extensor carpi ulnaris, and ends in a tendon which occupies a groove between the radius and ulna in a special compartment of the extensor retinaculum, and is enveloped in a long synovial sheath. On the back of the hand, the tendon

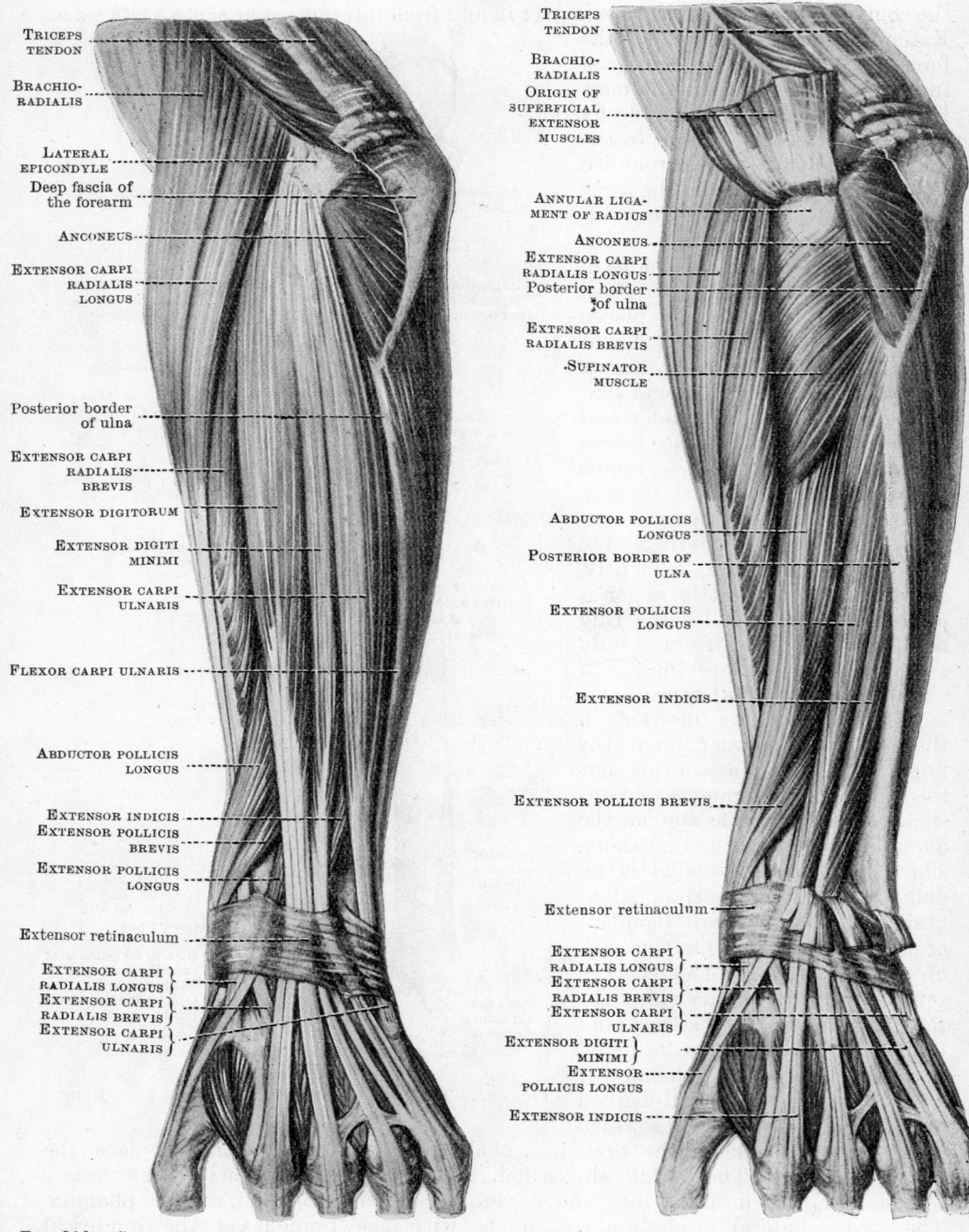

FIG. 398.—SUPERFICIAL MUSCLES ON THE DORSUM OF THE LEFT FOREARM.

FIG. 399.—DEEP MUSCLES ON THE DORSUM OF THE LEFT FOREARM.

is split into two parts, of which the more lateral is joined by the most medial tendon of the extensor digitorum, and both are **inserted** into the expansion of the extensor tendon on the back of the proximal phalanx of the little finger.

Extensor Carpi Ulnaris.—The extensor carpi ulnaris has a double **origin**:

(1) from the lateral epicondyle of the humerus by the common tendon, from the fascia over it, and from the intermuscular septa; and (2), through the medium of the deep fascia, from the posterior border of the ulna in its middle two-fourths.

Lying in the forearm on the medial part of the posterior surface of the ulna, it ends in a tendon which is enclosed in a synovial sheath and traverses a groove on the back of the lower end of the ulna in a special compartment of the extensor retinaculum, and is **inserted** into the medial side of the base of the fifth metacarpal bone (Fig. 403, p. 480).

Deep Layer

Supinator.—The supinator muscle is the highest of the deep layer, and is almost wholly concealed by the superficial muscles. It has a complex **origin** —(1) from the lateral epicondyle of the humerus; (2) from the lateral ligament of the elbow joint and the annular ligament of the radius; and (3) from the supinator crest and fossa of the ulna (Fig. 393, p. 469).

From that origin the muscle, spreading laterally and downwards behind the upper third of the radius, which it envelops almost completely, is **inserted** into the lateral and anterior surfaces of the bone. The attachment extends as far forwards as the tuberosity of the radius, as far upwards as the neck, and as far downwards as the oblique part of the anterior border and the insertion of the pronator teres (Figs. 393, p. 469, and 397, p. 473).

The muscle is divisible into *superficial* and *deep layers*, with humeral and ulnar origins, between which the posterior interosseous nerve passes in its course to the back of the forearm.

Abductor Pollicis Longus.—The abductor pollicis longus **arises**, by fleshy fibres, distal to the supinator muscle, from the uppermost of the narrow impressions on the lateral half of the posterior surface of the ulna; from the middle third of the posterior surface of the radius, and from the intervening portion of the interosseous membrane (Fig. 397, p. 473).

The muscle passes obliquely downwards and laterally, and emerges between the radial extensors of the wrist and the extensor of the fingers to become superficial in the distal part of the forearm. With the extensor pollicis brevis tendon closely applied to its medial side, the tendon covers the insertion of the brachioradialis and passes through the most lateral compartment of the extensor retinaculum in a synovial sheath which communicates with that of extensor pollicis brevis. Then, covering the styloid process of the radius and the lateral ligament of the wrist joint, but separated from the ligament by the radial artery, it is **inserted** into the lateral side of the base of the first metacarpal bone (Fig. 400, p. 477). Close to its insertion, a tendinous slip passes from it to the abductor pollicis brevis and the fascia over the thenar eminence, and frequently another is attached to the trapezium.

Extensor Pollicis Brevis.—The extensor pollicis brevis, an essentially human muscle, is a specialised portion of the abductor longus. It **arises** from a rhomboid impression on the posterior surface of the radius, and from the interosseous membrane, distal to the abductor pollicis longus (Fig. 397, p. 473). It is closely adherent to that muscle, and accompanies it, deep to the extensor retinaculum and over the radial artery, to the thumb. Its tendon is then continued along the back of the first metacarpal bone, to be **inserted** into the dorsal surface of the base of the proximal phalanx of the thumb. Before reaching its insertion the tendon helps to form the capsule of the metacarpo-phalangeal joint.

Extensor Pollicis Longus.—The extensor pollicis longus **arises** from the lateral part of the posterior surface of the ulna, in its middle third, and from the interosseous membrane, distal to the abductor pollicis longus and overlapping the extensor pollicis brevis. Its tendon is enclosed in a synovial sheath and grooves the posterior surface of the radius as it descends through a special compartment of the extensor retinaculum (Figs. 397, 399). Extending obliquely across the back of the hand, the tendon crosses the tendons of the radial extensors of the carpus and the radial artery, helps to form the capsule of the first metacarpo-phalangeal joint, and is **inserted** into the dorsal surface of the base of the distal phalanx of the thumb.

At the wrist, the tendons of the muscles of the thumb—the abductor pollicis longus and extensor pollicis brevis laterally, and the extensor pollicis longus medially—bound a hollow (the "anatomical snuff-box") seen best when the thumb is extended. In this situation the pulsation of the radial artery can readily be felt.

Extensor Indicis.—The extensor indicis [proprius] **arises**, distal to the extensor pollicis longus, from the lowest impression on the posterior surface of the ulna, and sometimes also from the interosseous membrane (Fig. 397). Its tendon passes through a compartment of the extensor retinaculum enclosed with the tendons of the extensor digitorum in a common synovial sheath. On the back of the hand the tendon lies on the ulnar side of the tendon of the extensor digitorum destined for the forefinger, and is **inserted** into the membranous expansion of that tendon on the back of the proximal phalanx.

Nerve-Supply.—The muscles on the front (flexor surface) of the forearm are supplied, through the **median** and **ulnar nerves**, by the anterior—*i.e.* lateral and medial—cords of the brachial plexus ; and those on the back (extensor surface) by the posterior cord, through the **radial nerve** and its **posterior interosseous** branch. The pronator teres (C. 6.), flexor carpi radialis (C. 6.), palmaris longus and flexor digitorum sublimis (C. 7. 8. T. 1.) are all supplied by direct branches from the median nerve ; the flexor pollicis longus and the pronator quadratus by its anterior interosseous branch (C. (7). 8. T. 1.), and the flexor carpi ulnaris by the ulnar nerve (C. 8. T. 1.). The flexor digitorum profundus and the associated lumbricals are supplied in a corresponding manner by nerves derived from the two main sources. The lateral part of the deep flexor is supplied by the interosseous branch of the median nerve (C. (7). 8. T. 1.) and the lateral two lumbricals by twigs from digital branches of the median nerve (C. (7). 8. T. 1.) in the hand ; the medial part of the deep flexor is supplied by the ulnar nerve (C. 8. T. 1.) and the medial two lumbricals by twigs from the deep branch of the same nerve in the hand. The branches to the brachio-radialis (C. (5). 6.) and the extensor carpi radialis longus (C. (5). 6. 7. (8.)) are given off by the radial nerve itself above the elbow ; the extensor carpi radialis brevis (C. (5). 6. 7. (8.)) and the supinator (C. (5). 6.) are supplied by branches of the posterior interosseous nerve before it pierces the supinator ; all the remaining muscles are supplied by the posterior interosseous nerve (C. (6). 7. (8.)).

The Actions of Muscles in Movements at the Radio-ulnar Joints : Pronation and Supination.—The movement of pronation is performed by the **pronator** muscles—**teres** and **quadratus**—and of supination by the **biceps** and the **supinator** ; other muscles which pass obliquely across the forearm from the ulnar to the radial side take part in these actions when they are performed against resistance—the **flexor carpi radialis** and **palmaris longus** assisting in pronation and the **extensors of the thumb** in supination. Both sets of muscles act at best advantage when the elbow is flexed to a right angle. The brachio-radialis also may act as a semi-pronator and semi-supinator as already mentioned. See also p. 464.

The Actions of Muscles in Movements at the Wrist Joint.—The movements at the wrist joint are flexion and extension, abduction and adduction of the hand. The **radial and ulnar flexors and extensors of the carpus** are the muscles primarily concerned in these movements—abduction and adduction being performed by the combined action of the flexors and extensors of the radial and ulnar sides respectively. Other muscles of the forearm also assist in those actions.

The **flexores carpi radialis** and **ulnaris** act primarily to flex the wrist, assisted by the **palmaris longus** and by the **flexors of the fingers** (**sublimis** and **profundus**) when the movement is effected against strong resistance. The **abductor pollicis longus** also is an important flexor of the wrist, being capable of performing this movement when the other flexors are paralysed.

The muscles primarily concerned in extension at the wrist are the **radial extensors of the carpus** (**longus** and **brevis**) and the **extensor carpi ulnaris**. The extensors of the fingers also act at the wrist joint.

Abduction of the hand is produced by the co-operation of the **flexor carpi radialis** with the **radial extensors of the carpus**, assisted by the **long abductor** and the **extensors of the thumb**. Adduction of the hand is similarly produced by the co-operation of the **flexor** and the **extensor carpi ulnaris**.

The flexor and extensor muscles of the carpus have, in addition to the actions just detailed, important synergic actions at the wrist joint. The flexor carpi radialis and flexor carpi ulnaris together steady the wrist during the extension of the fingers, *i.e.* they are synergic muscles for the extensors of the digits. The flexor carpi ulnaris also steadies the pisiform bone during contractions of the abductor digiti minimi. The radial extensors of the carpus in association with the extensor carpi ulnaris are similarly synergic muscles for flexion of the fingers, as they counteract the effect which the digital flexors would otherwise produce at the wrist (cf. p. 385).

SHORT MUSCLES OF THE HAND

The short or intrinsic muscles of the hand (in addition to the lumbrical muscles, and a subcutaneous muscle called the palmaris brevis) are the four short muscles of the thumb which form the thenar eminence, the three short muscles of the little finger which form the hypothenar eminence, and the interosseous muscles which are placed between the metacarpal bones.

Short Muscles of the Thumb

The abductor pollicis brevis, the opponens pollicis, the flexor pollicis brevis, and the adductor pollicis constitute the short muscles of the thumb.

Abductor Pollicis Brevis.—The abductor pollicis brevis **arises**, by fleshy fibres, mainly from the anterior surface of the flexor retinaculum but also from the

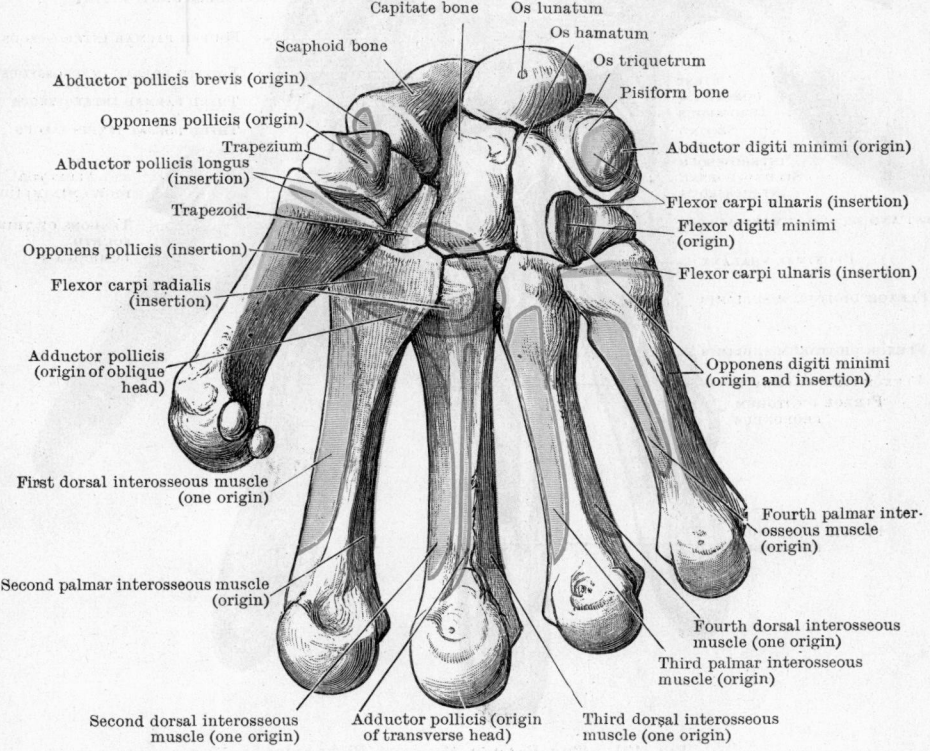

FIG. 400.—MUSCLE-ATTACHMENTS TO THE FRONT OF THE CARPUS AND METACARPUS.

tubercle of the scaphoid bone, the crest of the trapezium and from tendinous slips derived from the insertions of the palmaris longus and abductor pollicis longus muscles (Fig. 396, p. 472). Strap-like in form, and superficial in position, it is **inserted** by a short tendon into the radial side of the proximal phalanx of the thumb at its upper end, and into the lateral border of the tendon of the extensor pollicis longus muscle.

Opponens Pollicis.—The opponens pollicis is partially concealed by the abductor, and is united with the flexor pollicis brevis, which lies along its medial side. It **arises**, by fleshy and tendinous fibres, from the anterior surface of the flexor retinaculum and from the crest on the trapezium, and is **inserted** into the whole

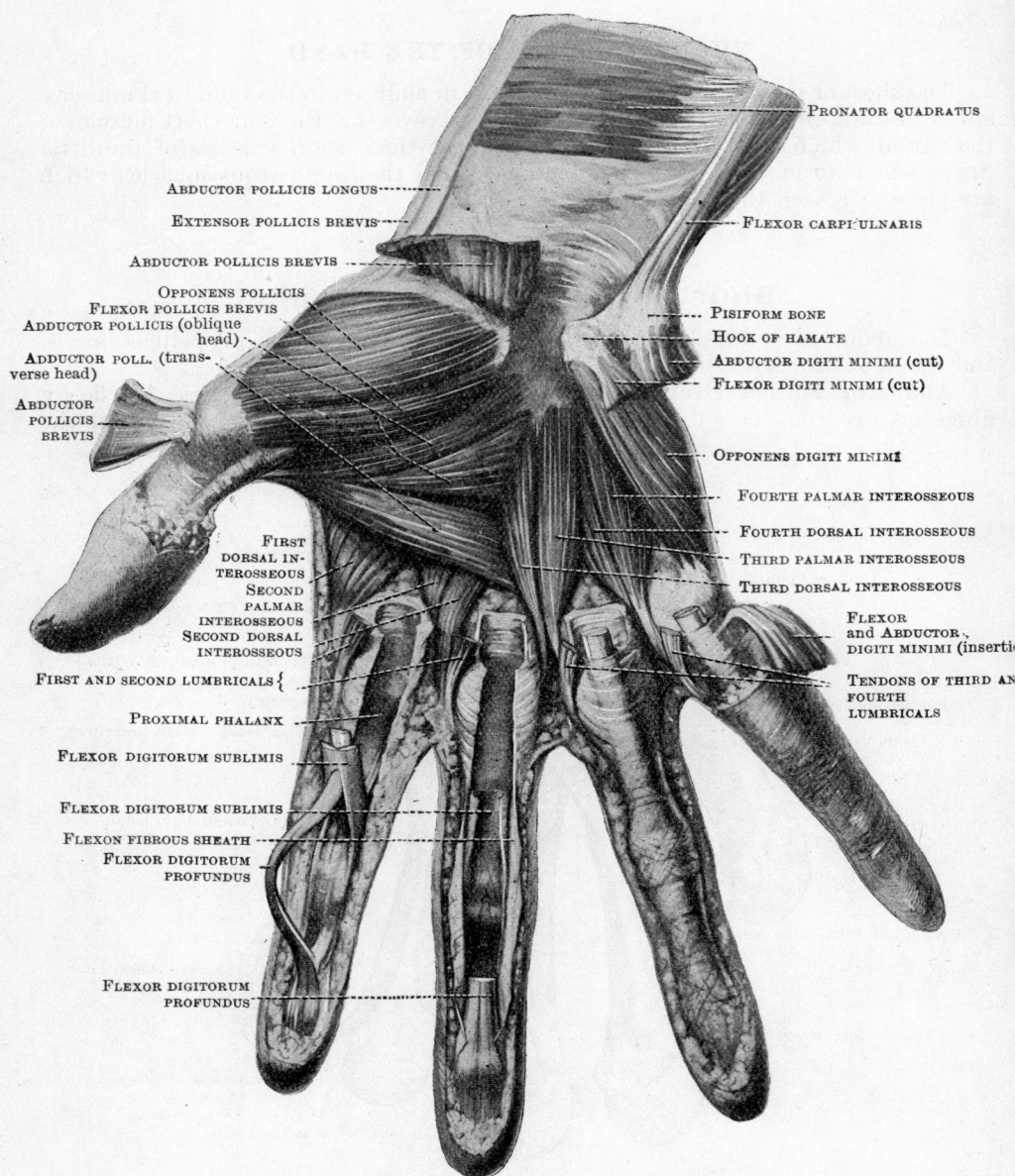

FIG. 401.—THE PALMAR MUSCLES (Right Side).

length of the radial border and the radial half of the anterior surface of the first metacarpal bone.

Flexor Pollicis Brevis.—The flexor pollicis brevis, also partly concealed by the abductor, **arises** by fleshy and tendinous fibres from the distal border of the flexor retinaculum, and sometimes from the crest of the trapezium. It is **inserted** into the radial side of the base of the proximal phalanx of the thumb, a *sesamoid bone* being present in the tendon of insertion.

Adductor Pollicis.—The adductor pollicis has two heads—oblique and transverse—separated at their origins by a gap that transmits the radial artery, but inserted together by a tendon (in which a sesamoid bone is developed) into the ulnar side of the base of the proximal phalanx of the thumb. Both heads lie deep in the palm behind the long flexor tendons.

The *oblique head* arises by fleshy fibres from the sheath of the tendon of the flexor carpi radialis, from the front of the trapezium, trapezoid and capitate bones and the bases of the second, third, and fourth metacarpal bones, and from the palmar ligaments that connect these bones. Usually a slip separates from its upper border, and, passing deep to the tendon of the flexor pollicis longus, is inserted with the flexor brevis into the radial side of the proximal phalanx. The *transverse head* arises from the longitudinal ridge on the front of the shaft of the third metacarpal bone, and its fibres converge on the common tendon of insertion.

Short Muscles of the Little Finger

The short muscles of the little finger are the abductor, opponens, and flexor digiti minimi.

Abductor Digiti Minimi.—The abductor digiti minimi, the most superficial, arises from the pisiform bone and from the tendon of the flexor carpi ulnaris and its ligamentous continuations (Figs. 396, 400). It is inserted by tendon into the medial side of the base of the proximal phalanx of the little finger—sending a slip to the extensor tendon.

Opponens Digiti Minimi.—The opponens digiti minimi arises under cover of the abductor by tendinous fibres from the flexor retinaculum and from the hook of the hamate bone. It is inserted into the medial margin and medial half of the palmar surface of the fifth metacarpal bone in its distal three-fourths (Fig. 400, p. 477).

Flexor Digiti Minimi.—The flexor digiti minimi may be absent or incorporated with either the opponens or the abductor digiti minimi. It arises, by tendinous fibres, from the flexor retinaculum and from the hook of the hamate bone (Figs. 396, 400), and is inserted along with the abductor.

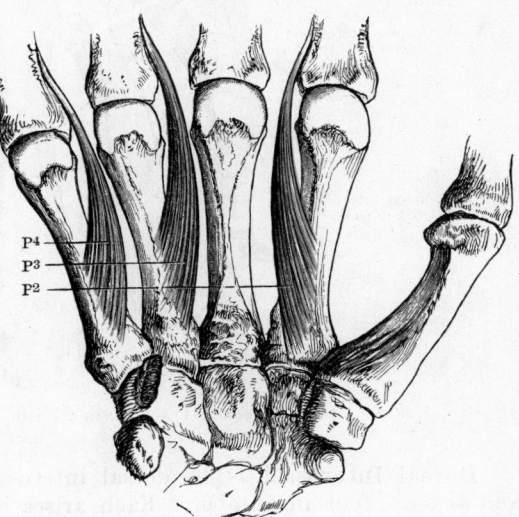

FIG. 402.—THE 2ND, 3RD, AND 4TH PALMAR INTEROSSEOUS MUSCLES (Right Side).

See fig. 404, p. 481 for 1st palmar interosseous muscle.

The Interosseous Muscles

The interosseous muscles of the hand, placed between the metacarpal bones, are arranged in two sets—palmar and dorsal—which are respectively adductors and abductors to or from a line through the middle finger.

Palmar Interossei.—The palmar interossei are four in number. Each arises by a single head from the metacarpal bone of the digit which it moves. The muscular fibres of the second, third, and fourth converge on tendons that begin a little above the metacarpo-phalangeal joint. Each tendon passes behind the deep transverse ligament of the palm, and is inserted partly into the base of the proximal phalanx and partly into the extensor tendon (the continuation of the extensor expansion to the base of the distal phalanx being formed chiefly by the tendons of the interossei and lumbricals, cf. p. 470). The **second** arises from the ulnar side of the shaft of the second metacarpal bone, the **third** and **fourth** from the radial sides of the shafts of the fourth and fifth metacarpal bones respectively, and are inserted into the corresponding sides of the fingers. Therefore, if the fingers are outspread and the middle finger is held, each muscle adducts its finger to the middle finger. That digit does not require palmar adductors because, when the index and ring fingers are held apart, the middle finger is drawn to one or the other by the alternate action of its two dorsal interossei muscles.

The **first** palmar interosseous muscle ("deep head of flexor pollicis brevis") is a slender slip that springs from the ulnar side of the base of the first metacarpal bone, passes deeply between the first dorsal interosseous muscle and the oblique head of the adductor pollicis to be inserted into the ulnar side of the base of the proximal phalanx of the thumb, in common with the adductor muscle.

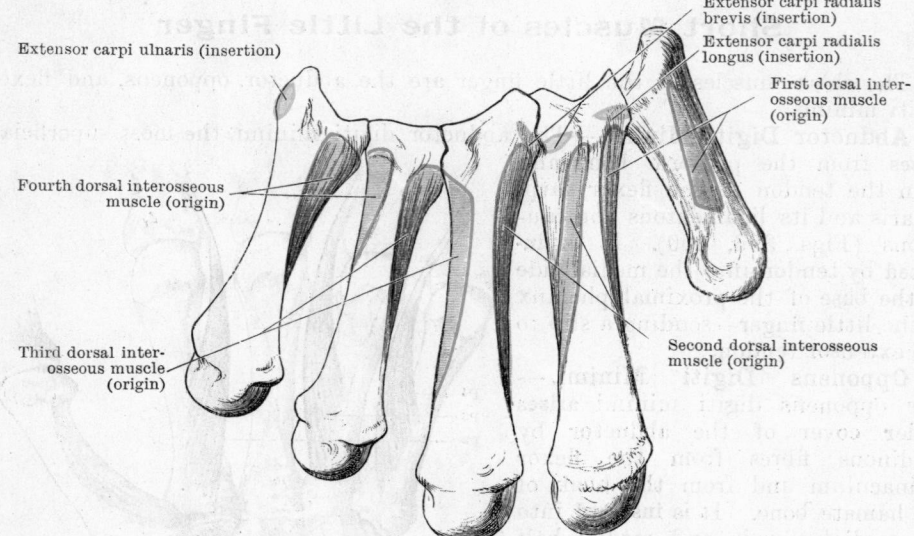

FIG. 403.—MUSCLE-ATTACHMENTS TO THE BACK OF THE RIGHT METACARPUS.

Dorsal Interossei.—The dorsal interossei are larger than the palmar group, and also are four in number. Each **arises** by two heads from the adjacent sides of its two metacarpal bones (Figs. 400, 403, 404). Their heads converge in a bipennate manner on four membranous tendons which descend to the four fingers to be **inserted** in the same way as the tendons of the palmar muscles— the medial three tendons passing behind the deep transverse ligaments of the palm. The insertion of the *first* dorsal interosseous muscle is on the radial side of the index finger; the *second* muscle passes to the radial side of the middle finger; the *third* muscle to the ulnar side of the same finger; and the *fourth* muscle to the ulnar side of the ring finger.

The first dorsal interosseous muscle is larger than the others, and there is a wider interval between its heads, through which the radial artery passes into the palm, while a perforating branch from the deep palmar arch runs between the two heads of each of the other muscles. Between the tendons of the interossei and the joints small *intermetacarpo-phalangeal bursae* are interposed. The interosseous muscles of the hand are occasionally arranged like those of the foot.

Nerve-Supply.—The intrinsic muscles of the hand, like the muscles on the flexor surface of the forearm, are all supplied by nerves derived from the anterior (*i.e.* lateral and medial) cords of the brachial plexus through the **median** and **ulnar** nerves. The ulnar nerve, however, takes a much greater part in the supply of the muscles of the hand—its deep branch extending across the palm to supply all the muscles on the ulnar side of the line of the tendon of the flexor pollicis longus (with the exception of the lateral two lumbricals).

The abductor brevis, the opponens and the flexor brevis of the thumb and the medial two lumbricals are supplied by the median (C. 6. 7.); the adductor pollicis, the short muscles of the little finger, and all the interossei are supplied by the ulnar (C. 8. T. 1.). (Clinical evidence suggests, however, that all the small muscles of the hand may receive their motor supply from T. 1.)

The Actions of Muscles in Movements of the Fingers.

—The movements of the fingers are controlled by the long flexors and extensors whose tendons pass over the wrist from the forearm, and by the series of short muscles situated in the hand itself, including the interossei, which act on the medial four fingers, and the special muscles of the thumb and little finger.

The **flexor digitorum sublimis** is a flexor of the proximal interphalangeal joints and the metacarpo-phalangeal joints of the medial four fingers; the **flexor digitorum profundus** acts primarily as a flexor of the distal phalanges, but it helps to produce flexion of the middle and proximal phalanges. The **lumbrical** and **interosseous** muscles act as flexors of the fingers at the metacarpo-phalangeal joints, and, at the same time (by their attachment to the extensor tendon and continuation to the base of the distal phalanx), they act as extensors of the fingers at both interphalangeal joints—a combined movement which

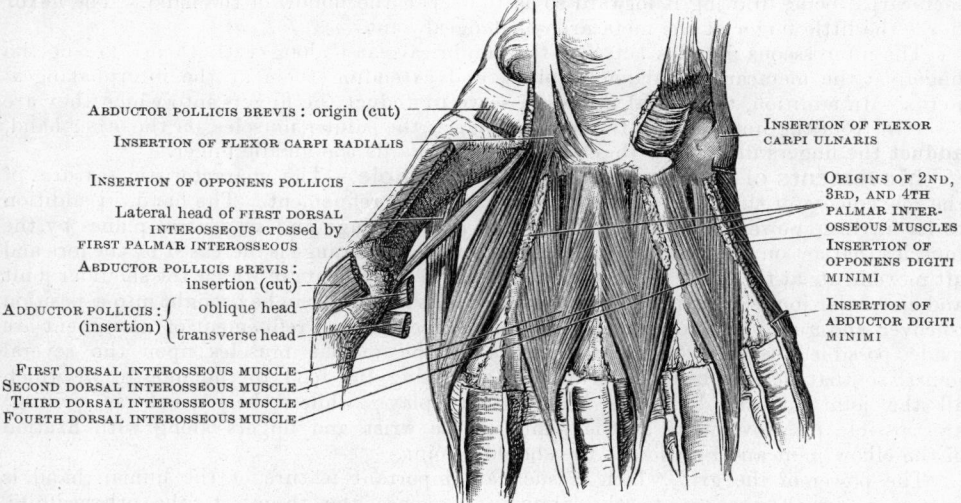

ABDUCTOR POLLICIS BREVIS : origin (cut)

INSERTION OF FLEXOR CARPI RADIALIS

INSERTION OF OPPONENS POLLICIS

Lateral head of FIRST DORSAL INTEROSSEOUS crossed by FIRST PALMAR INTEROSSEOUS

ABDUCTOR POLLICIS BREVIS : insertion (cut)

ADDUCTOR POLLICIS : (insertion) { oblique head / transverse head

FIRST DORSAL INTEROSSEOUS MUSCLE
SECOND DORSAL INTEROSSEOUS MUSCLE
THIRD DORSAL INTEROSSEOUS MUSCLE
FOURTH DORSAL INTEROSSEOUS MUSCLE

INSERTION OF FLEXOR CARPI ULNARIS

ORIGINS OF 2ND, 3RD, AND 4TH PALMAR INTEROSSEOUS MUSCLES

INSERTION OF OPPONENS DIGITI MINIMI

INSERTION OF ABDUCTOR DIGITI MINIMI

FIG. 404.—DORSAL INTEROSSEOUS MUSCLES OF THE HAND (seen from the Palmar Aspect).

is impossible when these muscles are paralysed. In that fine movement which is utilised in making the upward stroke in writing, the interossei participate as well as the lumbricals.

The **extensor digitorum**, assisted by the extensors of the index and the little finger, is the extensor of the fingers. On account of the connexion of the tendons for the third, fourth, and fifth digits with one another by means of accessory bands on the back of the hand, those three fingers cannot be fully extended separately, but extension of the index finger can take place independently. In extension of the interphalangeal joints the muscle is aided by the interossei and lumbrical muscles, but in paralysis of the lumbricals and interossei (claw hand), the intact extensor cannot extend the distal phalanges until the metacarpo-phalangeal joints have been passively flexed from the hyperextended position enforced upon them by the extensor, now freed from the antagonism of the lumbricals and interossei in its action on these joints. When the dorsal interossei are paralysed, the fingers can be abducted by the extensor digitorum—a movement always associated with hyperextension at the metacarpo-phalangeal joints.

The free movements of the thumb are of very great importance in the mechanism of the human hand; it is controlled by special muscles which are quite independent of the common flexors and extensors of the other digits. The **flexor pollicis longus** acts in flexion of the thumb on the metacarpal bone and both phalanges; the **extensor pollicis longus** acts in a similar way to extend the thumb, while the **extensor pollicis brevis** acts on the metacarpal bone and the proximal phalanx. The **abductor pollicis longus** abducts

31

and extends the metacarpal bone of the thumb; its action in assisting **flexion** of the wrist has already been noted.

The short muscles of the thumb are concerned with the movements of flexion, abduction and adduction, and the characteristic movement of opposition. The **abductor pollicis brevis** acts on all the joints of the thumb. The movement of abduction which it produces occurs at the carpo-metacarpal joint, and the thumb moves in the direction of its radial border. Owing to the fact that the first metacarpal bone is placed with its palmar surface directed medially, abduction of the thumb carries it forwards away from the palm. In addition, the muscle assists in flexion of the metacarpo-phalangeal joint and, through its insertion into the long extensor, in extension of the interphalangeal joint. The **opponens pollicis** acts solely on the metacarpal bone of the thumb, which is drawn medially and forwards, and at the same time rotated medially. As a result of the combined movements, in which the long and short flexors and the adductor pollicis participate, the thumb can be opposed to each of the other digits. The **flexor pollicis brevis** is a flexor of the thumb and assists also in the movement of opposition of the thumb. The **adductor pollicis** adducts and assists in opposition of the thumb.

The short muscles of the little finger are much less important than those of the thumb. The **abductor digiti minimi** abducts the little finger from the ring finger, and assists in flexion at the metacarpo-phalangeal joints. The **opponens** acts only on the metacarpal bone, drawing it forward so as to deepen the hollow of the hand. The **flexor** flexes the little finger at the metacarpo-phalangeal joint.

The interosseous muscles act like the lumbricals and along with them—flexing the fingers at the metacarpo-phalangeal joints, and extending them at the interphalangeal joints. In addition, the **dorsal** interossei serve to **abduct** the fingers into which they are inserted from the line through the middle finger; the palmar muscles, on the other hand, **adduct** the fingers into which they are inserted towards the middle finger.

Movements of the Upper Limb as a Whole.—The characteristic features of the movements of the upper limb are their range and refinement. The hand, in addition to its intrinsic powers, can be moved through a wide range and in several planes by the muscles that act on the wrist and radio-ulnar joints; that range is increased by the fore and aft movements at the elbow joint, and the extensive movements of which the shoulder joint and clavicular joints are capable. The result is that the hand can be brought into a position to cover and guard any portion of the body. Precision and refinement of movement are made possible by the co-ordinate actions of the various muscles upon the several joints, so that actions can be performed (as raising the food to the mouth) in which all the joints of the limb are brought into play; while others (such as writing) are possible by movements at the joints of the wrist and fingers along with fixation of the elbow joint and rotation at the shoulder joint.

The power of the grip, which is such an important feature of the human hand, is due, in no small measure, to the ability to oppose the thumb to the other digits. This movement is possible only (1) because the metacarpal bone of the thumb is set in a plane at right angles to the plane in which the other metacarpals lie, and (2) because the carpo-metacarpal joint of the thumb allows a wide range of movement. As a result of the set of the thumb, flexion carries it medially across the palm, and a very small degree of rotation of its metacarpal bone enables the movement of opposition to be effected. When the fingers encircle a small object, the grip is strengthened by the overlapping thumb, which can then be opposed to the dorsal aspect of the distal phalanges and, if the object is small enough, to the middle phalanges of the index and middle fingers.

Fasciæ of the Forearm and Hand

Superficial Fascia. — In the forearm this layer presents no exceptional features. On the back of the hand it is loose and thin, but in the palm its development into pads to assist the grip and protect underlying structures is characteristic of Man. In reflecting the palmar skin, the knife rasps through tough fibrous strands which enclose the fat in loculi and connect the palmar aponeurosis with the skin, especially along the lines of flexure. Thin and dense in the middle of the palm, and forming thicker and less fibrous pads in the thenar, hypothenar, and metacarpo-phalangeal regions, it plays an important rôle as prehensile cushions, readily adaptable to the contour of the various objects grasped. A band of transverse fibres (*superficial transverse ligament of the palm*) crosses the distal part of the palm, enclosed within the skin folds which form the webs of the fingers and connected to the palmar surfaces of the fibrous flexor sheaths.

Palmaris Brevis.—The palmaris brevis is a quadrilateral, subcutaneous muscle which lies in the hypothenar eminence under the superficial fascia. It **arises** from the medial border of the palmar aponeurosis and from the palmar surface of the flexor retinaculum, and is **inserted** into the skin of the medial border of the hand for a variable distance. It covers the ulnar artery and nerve, branches of which supply it. Its action is to wrinkle the skin of the medial border of the hand, and, by raising up the skin and superficial fascia, to deepen the hollow of the hand and prevent flattening of the hypothenar eminence by pressure — thus assisting a firm palmar grip (T. S. Kirk, *Journ Anat.*, 1924).

Deep Fascia.—The deep fascia of the forearm and hand is continuous above with the deep fascia of the upper arm. In the proximal part of the forearm it is strengthened, in front, by fibres from the bicipital aponeurosis; behind, by the fascial insertions of the triceps; and at the sides by fibres derived from the humeral epicondyles in relation to the common tendons of origin of the flexor and extensor muscles of the forearm, which in part take their origin from them. It is attached to the posterior border of the ulna, and affords increased attachment to the flexor and extensor carpi ulnaris

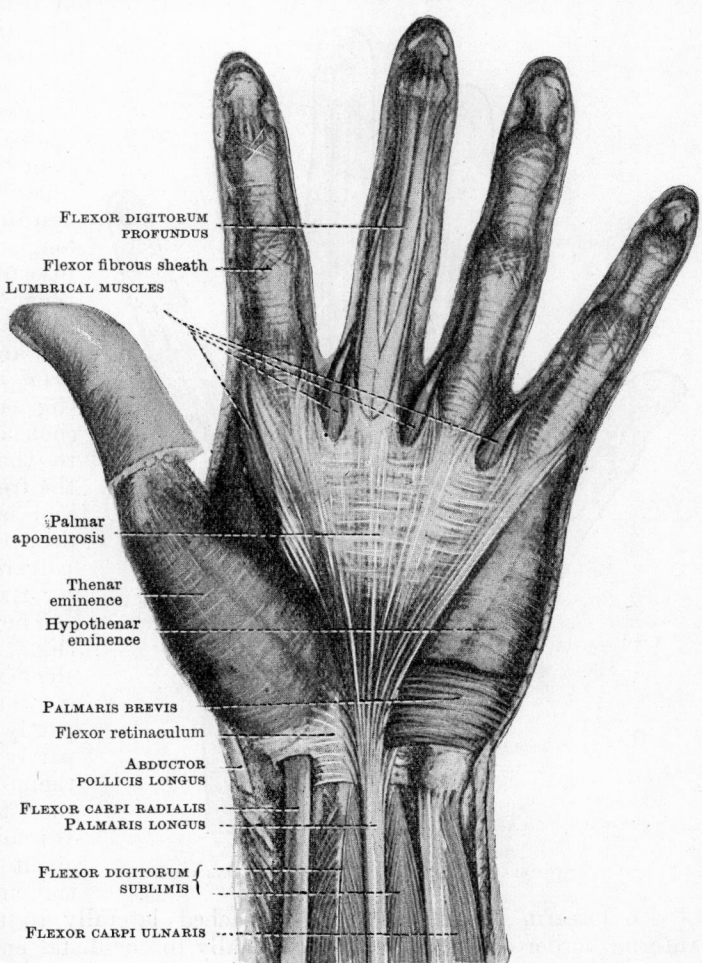

FIG. 405.—THE PALMAR APONEUROSIS.

and the flexor digitorum profundus. On the back of the wrist, the deep fascia, strengthened by a number of oblique fibres, forms the extensor retinaculum. On the front of the carpus its deep surface blends with a layer that covers the front of the flexor digitorum sublimis, and it also thickens to form the flexor retinaculum; the general fascial sheath of the forearm blends with its superficial surface and covers the tendon of the palmaris longus as the tendon descends in front of the retinaculum to merge with the peak of the palmar aponeurosis.

Flexor Retinaculum.—The flexor retinaculum [lig. carpi transversum] is a band about an inch in length and in breadth, continuous with the deep fascia of the forearm and the palm of the hand, but upon a slightly deeper plane; it is attached laterally to the scaphoid and trapezium bones, medially to the pisiform and hamate bones.   It is a fibrous restraining arch that binds down, in the hollow of the carpus, the flexor pollicis longus tendon and its synovial sheath, and the flexor tendons of the fingers and their synovial sheath, and the median nerve.   The attachment to the trapezium bone is to both lips of the groove on the front of that bone.   The fibres attached to the crest cross the groove and convert it into a tunnel which is traversed by the flexor carpi radialis tendon and its synovial sheath.   The upper border of the retinaculum is continuous with the deep fascia of the forearm; the distal border is continuous with the palmar aponeurosis in the middle, and at each side it gives origin to some fibres of the muscles of the thenar

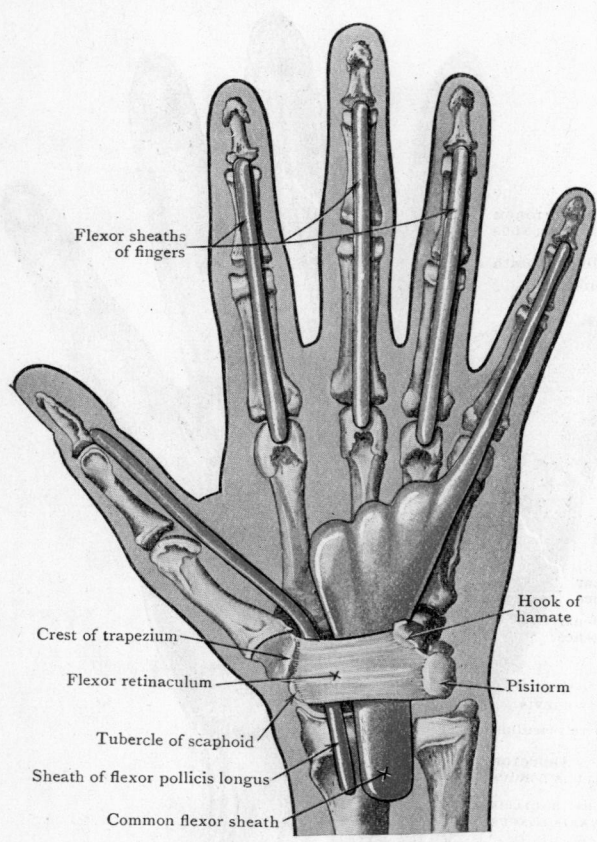

and hypothenar eminences. The anterior surface of the ligament gives further origin to those muscles, and is largely covered by them. It is also crossed by the palmar branches of the median and ulnar nerves, and by the tendon of the palmaris longus muscle, which is partly inserted into the surface; the ulnar nerve and vessels descend on to its medial part, and are crossed by the *superficial part of the retinaculum* [lig. carpi volare]. This band (not always present) passes to the pisiform bone from the front of the retinaculum and is continuous with the deep fascia that overlies the palmaris longus.

Extensor Retinaculum. —The extensor retinaculum [lig. carpi dorsale] is a thickening of the deep fascia of the back of the limb, partly on the forearm and partly on the wrist, and therefore at a higher level than the flexor retinaculum. It is an oblique band of fibres, about an inch broad, con-

Labels in figure: Flexor sheaths of fingers; Crest of trapezium; Flexor retinaculum; Tubercle of scaphoid; Sheath of flexor pollicis longus; Common flexor sheath; Hook of hamate; Pisiform

FIG. 406.—SYNOVIAL SHEATHS OF FLEXOR TENDONS OF DIGITS.

tinuous with the deep fasciæ of the forearm and hand.   It is attached laterally to the distal part of the anterior border of the radius, and medially to the distal end of the ulna (styloid process), the carpus, and the medial ligament of the wrist.   It is crossed by veins, by the radial nerve, and by the dorsal branch of the ulnar nerve.   *Six compartments* are formed deep to it by the attachment of septal bands to the distal ends of the radius and ulna.   Each compartment is provided with a synovial sheath; and they serve to transmit the extensor tendons of the wrist and fingers in the following order from lateral to medial side :—

(1) Abductor pollicis longus and extensor pollicis brevis, (2) Extensor carpi radialis longus and brevis, (3) Extensor pollicis longus, (4) Extensor digitorum and extensor indicis, (5) Extensor digiti minimi, (6) Extensor carpi ulnaris.

The deep fascia of the dorsum of the hand is arranged in two layers— superficial and deep—transmitting between them the tendons in their synovial sheaths and the branches of the radial artery.   (1) The superficial layer, very thin, and continuous with the distal border of the extensor retinaculum, descends over the tendons to fuse with them upon the fingers; (2) the deep layer is thicker and overlies the interossei—blending with the superficial layer at the clefts of the digits.

The deep fascia of the palm of the hand also is in two layers : (1) A superficial layer which displays a central, thick *palmar aponeurosis* (described below), continuous with two thin side parts on the thenar and hypothenar eminences ; (2) a deep layer spread over the interosseous muscles, and enclosing the adductor of the thumb ; certain fibres of the two layers blend between the heads of the metacarpal bones.

The flexor retinaculum, the palmar aponeurosis, and the fibrous flexor sheaths form a continuous sheet which serves to increase the efficiency of the flexor muscles of the digits and wrist and to increase the power of prehension. The fascial thickenings retain the tendons in position and provide pulleys over which they act. When the flexor muscles of the digits contract, their tendons do not produce ridges of the skin which would interfere with the efficiency of the hand as a gripping instrument ; and the extent of the movements of the phalanges is directly proportional to the amount of shortening of the muscles that act upon them.

Palmar Aponeurosis.—The palmar aponeurosis is a dense, strong triangular membrane that underlies the superficial fascia in the middle of the palm, and consists

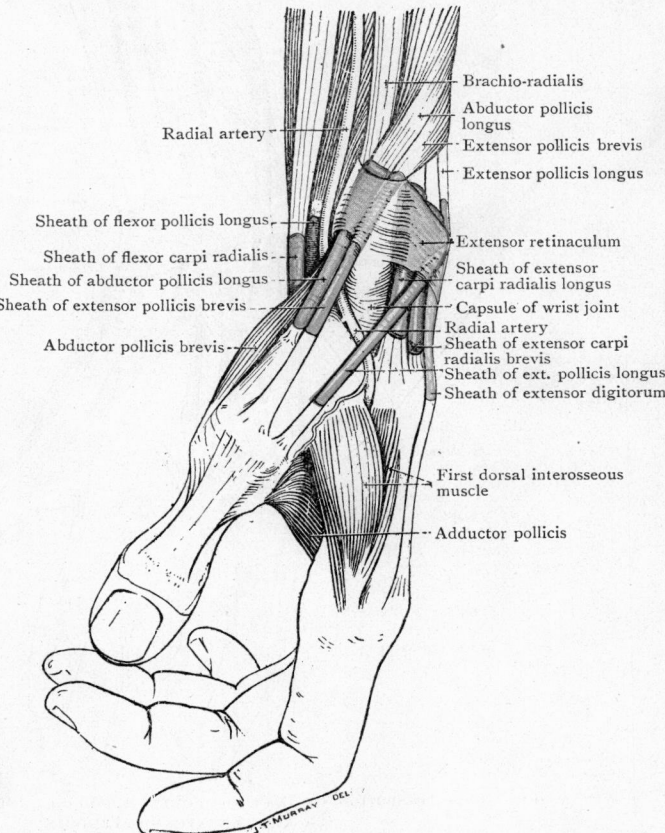

Radial artery -

Sheath of flexor pollicis longus,

Sheath of flexor carpi radialis - - -
Sheath of abductor pollicis longus - - -
Sheath of extensor pollicis brevis - - -

Abductor pollicis brevis - -

Brachio-radialis
Abductor pollicis longus
Extensor pollicis brevis
Extensor pollicis longus

Extensor retinaculum
Sheath of extensor carpi radialis longus
Capsule of wrist joint
Radial artery
Sheath of extensor carpi radialis brevis
Sheath of ext. pollicis longus
Sheath of extensor digitorum

First dorsal interosseous muscle

Adductor pollicis

FIG. 407.—DISSECTION OF THE LATERAL SIDE OF THE LEFT WRIST AND HAND SHOWING SYNOVIAL SHEATHS OF TENDONS.

mainly of longitudinal fibres. Its apex joins the lower edge of the flexor retinaculum, and, more superficially, the tendon of the palmaris longus is inserted into it. The base is scalloped into four slips—one for each finger—and the slips are connected together on their deep surfaces by transverse fibres which cross in front of the lumbrical muscles and the digital nerves and vessels. Beyond the transverse fibres, each slip separates into two parts which pass backwards to be connected to the sides of the metacarpo-phalangeal joint and the proximal phalanx of the finger, their distal edges being continuous with the proximal end of the fibrous flexor sheath. The borders of the aponeurosis are continuous with the thin fascia that covers and ensheathes the thenar and hypothenar muscles ; and the upper part of the medial border gives origin to the palmaris brevis. Further, a septum passes backwards from each border to fuse with the fascia on the interosseous muscles, and the palm is divided by them into three compartments—a *lateral* compartment containing the short muscles of the thumb and its long flexor tendon ; a *medial*, containing the short muscles of the little finger and its long flexor tendons ; and an *intermediate* compartment containing the other long flexor tendons.

Fibrous Flexor Sheaths.—The fibrous sheaths of the long flexors of the digits are arches of dense fibrous tissue that hold the tendons in place on the palmar surfaces of the digits. Each sheath is attached to the margins of the proximal and middle phalanges (in the thumb, proximal only) and interphalangeal joints and to the palmar surface of the distal phalanx; and its upper end is continuous with a divided slip of the palmar aponeurosis. Opposite the joints it is thin and loose, but opposite each phalanx it is thick and strong, and serves to keep the tendons closely applied to the bone during flexion of the digit. The canal formed

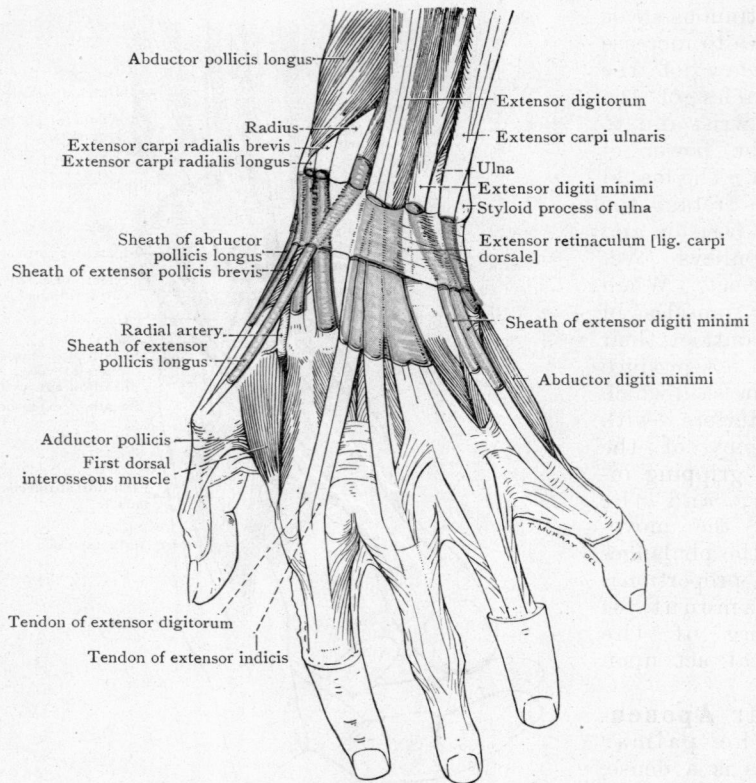

Fig. 408.—Dissection of Back of Forearm, Wrist, and Hand, showing Synovial Sheaths of Tendons.

by the phalanges and the fibrous sheath contains not only the tendons but also the synovial sheath that surrounds them.

Synovial Sheaths.—These sheaths have two layers—one around the tendon or tendons, the other applied to the walls of the spaces which the tendons occupy; and the two layers are continuous with each other at the ends of the sheath.

The **common synovial flexor sheath** is by far the largest and envelops the tendons of the flexor sublimis and flexor profundus. It begins about an inch above the flexor retinaculum and passes into the palm—the larger part of it ending at the middle of the palm, but the part related to the tendons of the little finger extends to the base of its distal phalanx. The tendons invaginate the synovial sac from the lateral side to produce the two layers, but the arrangement is complicated by a recess that passes in from the medial side to separate the tendons of the flexor sublimis from those of the profundus.

The **synovial sheaths of the flexor pollicis longus** and the **flexor carpi radialis** begin about an inch above the flexor retinaculum and extend to the insertion of the tendons. The sheath of the flexor pollicis sometimes communicates with the common sheath above the retinaculum.

The **synovial flexor sheaths of the fingers** extend as far as the insertion of the tendons. The sheath of the little finger is a prolongation from the common sheath. The sheaths of the other fingers begin at the middle of the palm at a variable distance below the common sheath (Fig. 406).

The **synovial extensor sheaths** begin at or a little above the extensor retinaculum

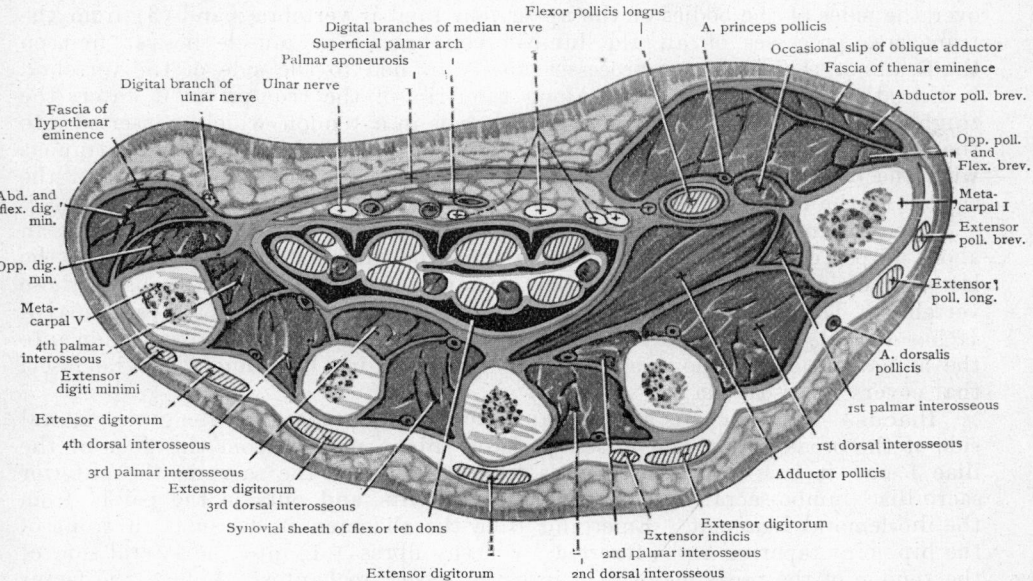

FIG. 409.—OBLIQUE CROSS SECTION THROUGH THE HAND, SHOWING THE FASCIAL COMPARTMENTS.

and extend downwards for varying distances. The tendons inserted into the metacarpus are usually ensheathed as far as their insertions; the other sheaths extend half-way down the hand.

MUSCLES OF THE LOWER LIMB

The muscles of the lower limb are divisible (according to their regional arrangement and functional uses) into series and groups corresponding in general to those of the upper limb. In contrast, however, to the freely movable shoulder girdle acted upon by the series of muscles which connect it to the trunk, the pelvic girdle is fixed to the vertebral column, and no corresponding functional series of muscles exists.

Those muscles of the lower limb which pass from the vertebral column (psoas, piriformis, and gluteus maximus) to the femur act upon the hip joint, and are included in the first two of the groups to be described: 1. Muscles of the Groin. 2. Muscles of the Hip and Buttock (Gluteal region). 3. Muscles of the Thigh (Flexor, Extensor, and Adductor Groups). 4. Muscles of the Leg (Flexor and Extensor Groups). 5. Muscles in the Sole of the Foot.

MUSCLES OF THE GROIN

The **ilio-psoas** is a compound muscle, consisting of two elements—**psoas (major and minor)**—which connects the femur and pelvic girdle to the axial skeleton; and another element—the iliacus—which extends between the hip bone and the femur. The muscles lie chiefly in the posterior wall of the abdomen; only their lower parts appear in the thigh below the inguinal ligament, in the lateral part of the femoral triangle; they are related to a large number of important structures.

31 c

Psoas Major.—The psoas major is a long, thick, fusiform muscle with an extensive origin from the lumbar part of the vertebral column. It arises by fleshy fibres—(1) from the intervertebral disc above each lumbar vertebra, and the adjacent margins of the vertebræ—from the lower border of the 12th thoracic to the upper border of the 5th lumbar; (2) from four membranous arches which pass over the sides of the bodies of the upper four lumbar vertebræ; and (3) from the transverse processes of all the lumbar vertebræ. The muscle lies at first on the fronts of the transverse processes closely applied to the side of the vertebral bodies; then, narrowing to pass along the brim of the true pelvis, it enters the thigh behind the inguinal ligament, and ends in a tendon which is **inserted** into the lesser trochanter of the femur (Fig. 410). A *bursa*, which may be continuous with the cavity of the hip joint, separates the tendon from the pubis and the capsule of the hip joint.

Psoas Minor.—The psoas minor is an inconstant muscle, being absent in about 40 per cent. of bodies. It **arises** from the intervertebral disc between the last thoracic and first lumbar vertebræ, and from the contiguous margins of those vertebræ. The muscle is closely applied to the anterior surface of the psoas major. It has a short, slender fleshy belly, and is **inserted** by a long, narrow tendon into the arcuate line and ilio-pubic eminence, its margins blending with the fascia that covers the psoas major.

Iliacus.—The iliacus is a large fan-shaped muscle that lies along the lateral side of the psoas major, and **arises**, by fleshy fibres, mainly from the floor of the iliac fossa; it has additional origins from the ala of the sacrum, the anterior sacro-iliac, lumbo-sacral, and ilio-lumbar ligaments, and, outside the pelvis, from the ilio-femoral ligament. Emerging from the abdomen, it descends in front of the hip joint tapering to be **inserted**, by fleshy fibres—(1) into the lateral side of the tendon of the psoas major; (2) into the lesser trochanter; (3) into the femur below the lesser trochanter for about an inch; and (4), by its most lateral fibres, into the capsule of the hip joint. These fibres are often separate, forming the **iliacus minor** or **ilio-capsularis.**

Nerve-Supply.—The **psoas major** is supplied directly by branches from the anterior primary rami of the **second** and **third lumbar** nerves, with additional branches in some cases from the **first** and **fourth**. The **psoas minor** receives a nerve from the **first** or **second lumbar nerve**. The **iliacus** is supplied by branches from the **femoral nerve** (L. 2. 3. 4.) within the abdomen.

MUSCLES OF THE GLUTEAL REGION

This group comprises the three gluteal muscles, the tensor fasciæ latæ, piriformis, obturator internus and gemelli, and the quadratus femoris.

The gluteus maximus and tensor fasciæ latæ muscles—both ensheathed in deep fascia—are in the same plane. The gluteus medius, partially covered by the gluteus maximus, conceals the gluteus minimus; and the piriformis, obturator internus, gemelli, and quadratus femoris intervene between the gluteus maximus and the posterior surface of the hip joint.

Gluteus Maximus.—The gluteus maximus, superficial throughout its extent, and the heaviest and most coarsely fibred muscle of the body, contributing by its weight to form the fold of the buttocks, is a peculiarly human muscle, being associated with the adoption of the erect posture. It **arises** from (1) the upper part of the area behind the posterior gluteal line of the ilium; (2) the tendon of the sacro-spinalis; (3) the dorsal surface of the sacrum and coccyx; (4) the posterior surface of the sacro-tuberous ligament; and (5) the deep fascia ensheathing it.

It extends obliquely downwards and laterally to be **inserted**, by short tendinous fibres, partly into the gluteal tuberosity of the femur (Fig. 410), but mainly, over the greater trochanter, into the ilio-tibial tract. The tract receives the insertion of the whole of the superficial fibres of the muscle and the upper half of the deep fibres, thereby enabling the muscle to obtain a powerful hold over the thigh as a whole, and a virtual insertion into the tibia (Fig. 250, p. 287). The lower half of the deep portion of the muscle is inserted, for the most part, into the gluteal tuberosity; but the lowest fibres of all are inserted into the fascia lata, and are thence connected with the lateral intermuscular septum of the thigh and the origin of the short head of the biceps.

A great part of the gluteus medius is visible at its upper border; and at its lower border the hamstring muscles and the sciatic nerve appear on their way to the thigh. This border is crossed by the fold of the buttock. In addition to the muscles already enumerated, it covers the ischial tuberosity, greater trochanter, origins of biceps femoris, semitendinosus, semimembranosus and the adductor magnus. The superficial part of the superior gluteal artery passes between the gluteus medius and the piriformis to reach its deep surface, and, between the piriformis and the superior gemellus, the inferior gluteal and internal pudendal vessels, and the sciatic, pudendal, and posterior femoral cutaneous nerves and muscular branches from the sacral plexus emerge. Three *bursæ* are deep to it: one (not always present) over the ischial tuberosity, a second over the lateral side of the greater trochanter, and a third over the vastus lateralis. The fibres of the gluteus maximus that arise from the coccyx may form a separate muscle (**coccygeo-femoralis** or **agitator caudæ**), and there may be an additional slip from the ischial tuberosity (**ischio-femoralis**).

Tensor Fasciæ Latæ. — The tensor fasciæ latæ (Pl. XXXVII, Fig. 3) arises from the outer lip of the fore part of the iliac crest and the anterior border of the ilium, and passes downwards and slightly backwards to be **inserted** into the ilio-tibial tract (p. 506) a little below the level of the greater trochanter. It is enclosed between two layers of deep fascia, of which the deep layer extends medially to fuse with the heads of the rectus

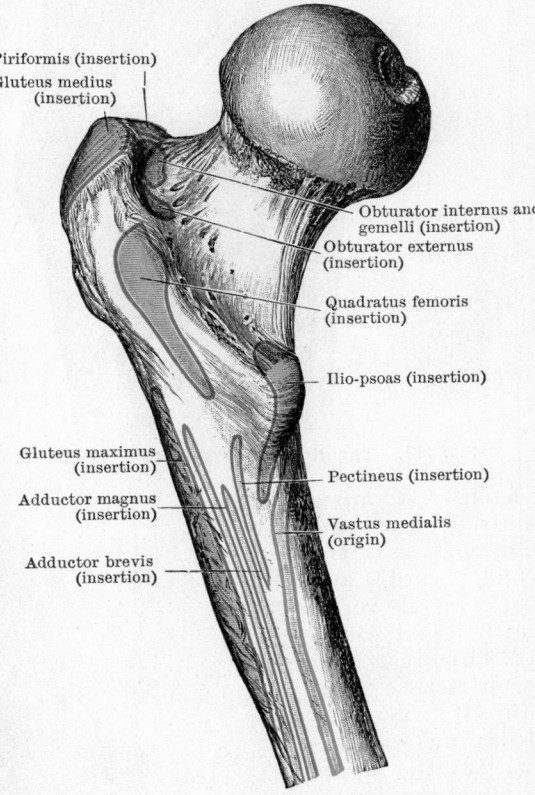

FIG. 410.—MUSCLE-ATTACHMENTS TO THE BACK OF THE UPPER PART OF THE LEFT FEMUR.

femoris and the capsule of the hip joint; and both layers blend with the ilio-tibial tract along the posterior border of the muscle. Posteriorly the muscle is related to the gluteus medius and minimus, and the vastus lateralis. Anteriorly it is closely related to the sartorius at its origin; but these two muscles diverge from each other as they descend, and the rectus femoris appears in the widening cleft between them (Fig. 417).

Gluteus Medius.—The gluteus medius **arises** from (1) the area of the ilium between the iliac crest and posterior gluteal line above and the middle gluteal line below and (2) the strong fascia that covers its anterior part. It is a fan-shaped muscle whose fibres converge on the greater trochanter to be **inserted** by a strong, short tendon into the postero-superior angle of the greater trochanter and into a well-marked diagonal line on its lateral surface—the most anterior fibres reaching the lowest level (Fig. 412). A *bursa* is placed between the tendon and the trochanter in front of the insertion. The muscle is partly superficial and partly concealed by the gluteus maximus. It covers the gluteus

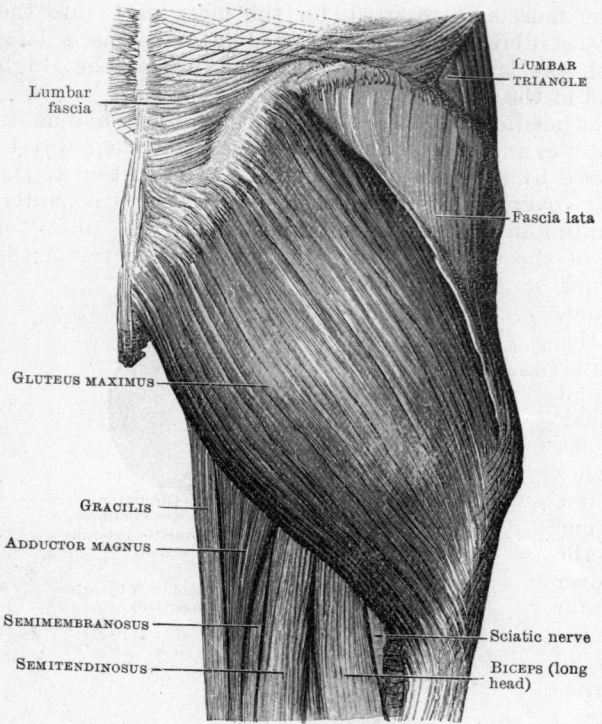

Lumbar
fascia

LUMBAR
TRIANGLE

Fascia lata

GLUTEUS MAXIMUS

GRACILIS

ADDUCTOR MAGNUS

SEMIMEMBRANOSUS

SEMITENDINOSUS

Sciatic nerve

BICEPS (long
head)

FIG. 411.—THE RIGHT GLUTEUS MAXIMUS MUSCLE.

minimus, the superior gluteal nerve and the deep branches of the superior gluteal artery.

Gluteus Minimus.—The gluteus minimus **arises** by fleshy fibres from the gluteal surface of the ilium between the middle and inferior gluteal lines. It is a fan-shaped muscle and its fibres converge on the antero-superior angle of the greater trochanter, covering the upper surface of the capsule of the hip joint. It is **inserted** into the anterior surface of the trochanter (Fig. 419). A *bursa* (trochanteric bursa of gluteus minimus) is placed deep to the tendon in front of the medial part of the anterior surface of the greater trochanter.

Piriformis.—The piriformis is one of the few muscles that connect the lower limb, to the axial

skeleton. It **arises** mainly (1) from the pelvic surfaces of the second, third, and fourth sacral vertebræ; but as it passes out through the greater sciatic foramen, it receives additional origins from (2) the upper margin of the greater sciatic notch and (3) the pelvic surface of the sacro-tuberous ligament. In the buttock it forms a rounded tendon which is **inserted**, under cover of the gluteus medius, into the upper border and medial side of the greater trochanter (Fig. 413).

The piriformis, at its origin, covers part of the inner surface of the dorsal wall of the true pelvis,

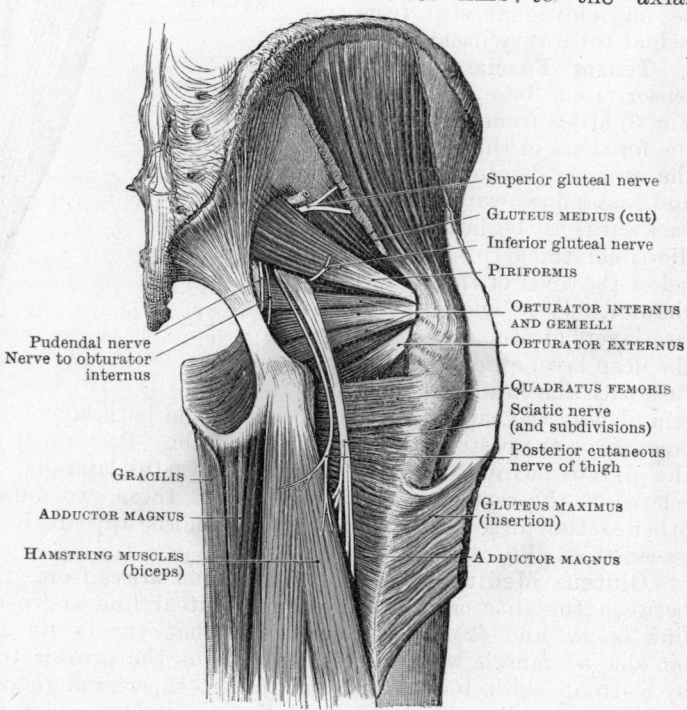

Pudendal nerve
Nerve to obturator
internus

GRACILIS

ADDUCTOR MAGNUS

HAMSTRING MUSCLES
(biceps)

Superior gluteal nerve

GLUTEUS MEDIUS (cut)

Inferior gluteal nerve

PIRIFORMIS

OBTURATOR INTERNUS
AND GEMELLI

OBTURATOR EXTERNUS

QUADRATUS FEMORIS

Sciatic nerve
(and subdivisions)

Posterior cutaneous
nerve of thigh

GLUTEUS MAXIMUS
(insertion)

ADDUCTOR MAGNUS

FIG. 412.—MUSCLES AND NERVES OF RIGHT GLUTEAL REGION.

The gluteus maximus is reflected ; and the gluteus medius is cut to show
a part of the gluteus minimus.

and is related anteriorly to the rectum and the lower part of sacral plexus. In the buttock it is covered by the gluteus maximus, and lies between the gluteus medius and superior gemellus on the back of the hip joint. It is frequently pierced by the lateral popliteal nerve [n. peronæus communis] when that nerve emerges separately from the pelvis.

Obturator Internus.—The obturator internus **arises** from (1) the whole of the margin of the obturator foramen (except the obturator groove); (2) the inner surface of the obturator membrane; (3) the whole of the pelvic surface of the hip bone behind and above the obturator foramen; and (4) the *obturator fascia* which covers it. It is a fan-shaped muscle whose fibres converge to pass through the lesser sciatic foramen. Its tendon begins on the surface next the bone as four or five separate slips; and as the muscle changes its direction at an acute angle by hooking round the margin of the lesser sciatic notch under the sacro-tuberous ligament, those tendinous slips also converge to play over corresponding grooves in the cartilage-covered, pulley-like surface of the bone—a large *bursa*, attached to the margins of the tendon and the cartilage-covered surface of the bone, facilitating this movement. The tendon, after passing over the back of the hip joint, is in-serted into the medial surface of the greater trochanter above the trochanteric fossa (Fig. 413).

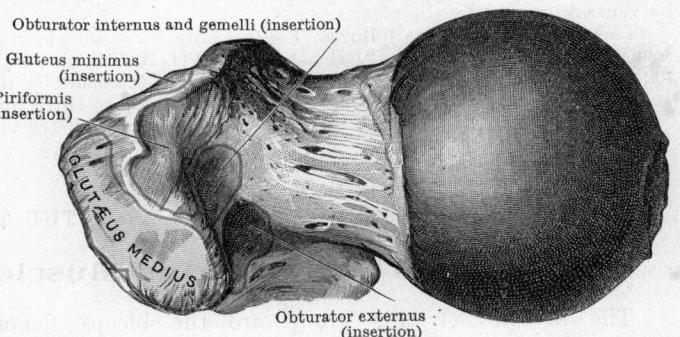

Obturator internus and gemelli (insertion)

Gluteus minimus (insertion)

Piriformis (insertion)

GLUTEUS MEDIUS

Obturator externus (insertion)

FIG. 413.—FEMUR (LOOKED AT FROM ABOVE) SHOWING MUSCLE-ATTACHMENTS TO GREATER TROCHANTER.

The fleshy part of the muscle is covered with the obturator fascia, which gives origin to a great part of the levator ani; the part above the levator is related to the cavity of the pelvis and the part below to the ischio-rectal fossa. In the buttock the tendon is embraced by the gemelli muscles which meet deep to it as it emerges from the foramen and more or less conceal its superficial surface as it passes to its insertion.

Gemelli.—The gemelli muscles form accessory portions of the obturator internus, providing it with an additional "twin" origin from the margins of the lesser sciatic notch. The superior gemellus **arises** from the gluteal surface of the ischial spine and the **inferior gemellus** from the upper part of the ischial tuberosity; each is **inserted** into the corresponding margin and the superficial surface of the tendon of the obturator internus muscle.

Quadratus Femoris.—The quadratus femoris **arises** from the lateral margin of the ischial tuberosity, and is **inserted** into the quadrate tubercle of the femur and into a line leading down from it. The posterior surface is covered by the hamstring muscles, the sciatic nerve, and the gluteus maximus; the anterior surface is related to the obturator externus muscle and to the lesser trochanter of the femur (a *bursa* intervening); its upper border meets the lower border of the inferior gemellus; and its lower border meets the upper border of the adductor magnus —fusion of these two not being infrequent.

Nerve-Supply.—The **piriformis muscle** is supplied by branches direct from the anterior primary rami of the **first and second sacral nerves**; the remaining muscles of the group are supplied by four nerves, two of which arise from the back of the sacral plexus, and the other two have corresponding origins from the front. The **superior gluteal nerve** (L. 4. 5. S. 1.) supplies the **gluteus medius and gluteus minimus** and ends in the **tensor fasciæ latæ**; the **inferior gluteal nerve** (L. 5. S. 1. 2.) is concerned solely with the supply of the **gluteus maximus**. Both those nerves arise from the back of the plexus and are associated with the roots of origin of the lateral popliteal nerve [n. peronæus communis]. The **quadratus femoris** (with the **inferior gemellus**) and the **obturator internus** (with the **superior gemellus**) are supplied by special nerves which arise respectively from the same nerves of the plexus as the gluteal nerves, but from the front of it, and are associated with the roots of origin of the medial popliteal nerve [n. tibialis]. The **nerve to the quadratus femoris** (L. 4. 5. S. 1.), after giving a twig to the inferior gemellus, enters the deep (anterior) surface of its muscle ; the **nerve to the obturator internus** (L. 5. S. 1. 2.) gives a twig to the superior gemellus and enters its muscle on its perineal surface.

MUSCLES OF THE THIGH

The muscles of the thigh are divisible into three main groups by their situation, action, and nerve-supply. On the **back** (flexor surface) of the thigh are the hamstring muscles ; on the **front** (extensor surface) of the thigh are the quadriceps femoris and the sartorius ; on the **medial side** of the thigh are the pectineus and the adductor muscles.

The muscles of the thigh, like the muscles of the upper arm, have a nerve-supply by groups, from the ventral and dorsal offsets of the nerve-plexuses concerned, according to their relation to the flexor and extensor surfaces of the thigh. The flexor and extensor surfaces of the thigh, however, are reversed in position by the developmental rotation of the limb, and become posterior and anterior respectively. There is, moreover, a special adductor group which is represented in the upper arm by the coraco-brachialis only, and is supplied (like that muscle) by ventral branches of the plexus.

The group supply is as follows : *Ventral branches of the plexus*—**Flexors** (hamstrings) by the **sciatic nerve** (medial popliteal [tibial] division) (L. 4. 5. S. 1. 2. 3.) ; **Adductors** by the **obturator nerve** (L. 2. 3. 4.). *Dorsal branches of the plexus*—**Extensors** by the **femoral nerve** (L. 2. 3. 4.). In addition to this general statement, the nerve-supply of three muscles is to be specially noted —the adductor magnus, the pectineus, and the short head of the biceps.

MUSCLES OF THE BACK OF THE THIGH

The Hamstring Muscles

The muscles of this group are the biceps femoris, semitendinosus, and semimembranosus. Morphologically, the ischio-condylar portion of the adductor magnus, as evidenced by its nerve-supply, also belongs to this group. The origins of the hamstring muscles from the ischial tuberosity are concealed by the gluteus maximus. In the back of the thigh, enveloped by the fascia lata, they are placed behind the adductor magnus—the semitendinosus and semimembranosus medially, the biceps laterally. Towards the knee they diverge to bound the popliteal fossa, the former two muscles on its medial side, the biceps on its lateral side ; behind the knee these tendons may be felt as the "hamstrings."

Biceps Femoris.—The biceps femoris has a double **origin.** (1) Its *long head* **arises**, by means of a tendon, in common with the semitendinosus, from the lower and medial impression on the ischial tuberosity (Figs. 412, 414) and from the sacro-tuberous ligament. This head, united for a distance of two or three inches with the semitendinosus, forms a separate fleshy mass which extends to the distal third of the thigh to end in a flattened tendon joined by the short head of the muscle. (2) The *short head* **arises** separately from (1) the whole length of the lateral lip of the linea aspera and the upper two-thirds of the lateral supra-condylar line of the femur, and (2) the lateral intermuscular septum ; its upper-most fibres are sometimes blended with the insertion of the lowest fibres of the gluteus maximus. The tendon of the long head, joined by the fibres of the short head, becomes rounded at the knee, and is then split into two parts by the lateral ligament of the knee joint as it is **inserted**—(1) into the head of the fibula, and by extensions, (2) forwards to the lateral condyle of the tibia, and (3) to the deep fascia on the lateral side of the leg.

There is a *bursa* between the tendon and the lateral ligament of the knee.

The short head may be absent ; there may be an additional origin from the ischium or the femur ; and the long head may send a slip to the gastrocnemius or to the tendo calcaneus (**tensor fasciæ suralis**).

Semitendinosus. — The semitendinosus **arises**, in common with the long

head of the biceps, from the lower and medial impression on the ischial
tuberosity (Fig. 414). Separating from the common tendon of origin, the muscle
forms a long band which becomes tendinous in the middle third of the thigh
and ends in the distal third in a long, cord-like tendon. Descending over the
surface of the semimembranosus and over the medial side of the knee the
tendon spreads out to be **inserted** (1) into the upper part of the medial surface of
the shaft of the tibia behind the gracilis and sartorius (Fig. 416), and (2) into
the deep fascia of the leg. A *bursa* separates it from the sartorius superficially,
and a *second bursa*, common to it and the gracilis, lies deep to its insertion.
The belly of the muscle is marked by an oblique tendinous intersection.

Semimembranosus.—The semimembranosus **arises** from the upper and

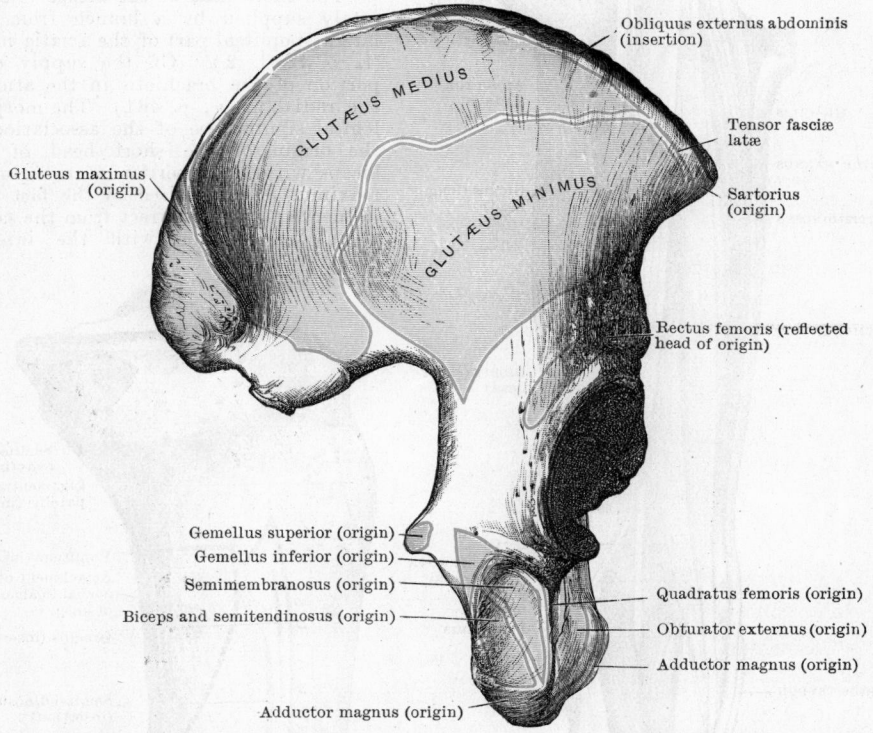

Obliquus externus abdominis
(insertion)

GLUTÆUS MEDIUS

Tensor fasciæ
latæ

Gluteus maximus
(origin)

GLUTÆUS MINIMUS

Sartorius
(origin)

Rectus femoris (reflected
head of origin)

Gemellus superior (origin)
Gemellus inferior (origin)
Semimembranosus (origin)
Biceps and semitendinosus (origin)

Quadratus femoris (origin)
Obturator externus (origin)
Adductor magnus (origin)

Adductor magnus (origin)

FIG. 414.—MUSCLE-ATTACHMENTS TO THE RIGHT DORSUM ILII AND TUBER ISCHIADICUM.

lateral facet on the ischial tuberosity (Fig. 415) by a strong membranous tendon
from which the muscle derives its name. This membranous sheet is continued
downwards along the lateral margin of the muscle, tapering to a point below
the middle of the thigh, and giving origin to the rounded fleshy belly which, in
the upper third of the thigh, lies in front of the semitendinosus and the long
head of the biceps. Inclining medially, with the semitendinosus on its posterior
surface, it ends, at the back of the knee, in a thick, flattened tendon which
is separated from the medial head of the gastrocnemius by a *bursa*, and
is **inserted** into the horizontal groove on the postero-medial surface of the
medial condyle of the tibia—another *bursa* lying deep to the tendon near its
insertion (Figs. 317, p. 364, and 416). It has three *additional membranous
insertions*: (1) a fascial band extends downwards and medially to join the posterior
border of the *medial ligament* of the knee joint; (2) another fascial band, extending downwards and laterally, forms the fascia on the popliteus muscle, and is
attached to the soleal line of the tibia; and (3) a third strong band, extending
upwards and laterally to the back of the lateral condyle of the femur, forms
the *oblique posterior ligament* of the knee joint (Fig. 317).

Nerve-Supply.—The hamstring muscles are all supplied by the **sciatic nerve**, by fibres from L. 4. 5. S. 1. 2. 3.; when there is a high division of this nerve the fact is disclosed that, with the exception of the nerve to the short head of the biceps, the supply is derived from the part which becomes the medial popliteal nerve. The **semitendinosus** receives two branches—one above and the other below its tendinous intersection.

The **ischio-condylar portion of the adductor magnus** also is supplied from the sciatic nerve by a branch which usually arises in common with the nerve to the semimembranosus.

The **short head of the biceps** is separately supplied by a branch from the lateral popliteal part of the sciatic nerve (L. 5. S. 1. 2.). (Cf. the supply of a portion of the brachialis in the arm by the radial nerve, p. 464.) The morphological significance of the association of the origin of the short head of the biceps with the insertion of the gluteus maximus is emphasised by the fact that its nerve may arise direct from the sacral plexus in common with the inferior gluteal nerve.

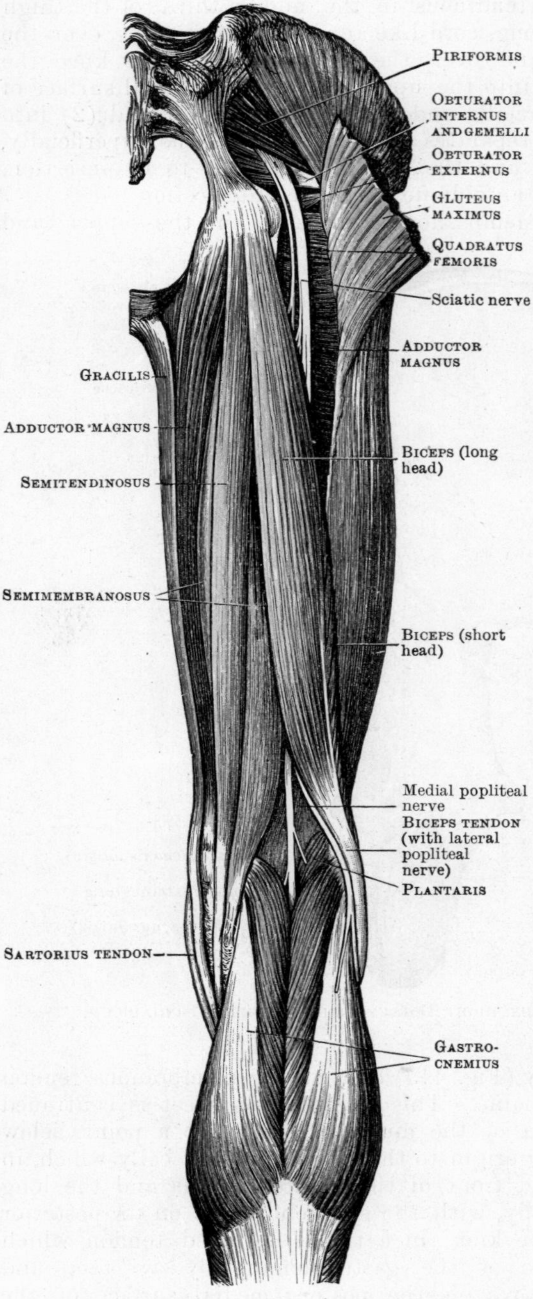

FIG. 415.—THE MUSCLES OF THE BACK OF THE RIGHT THIGH.

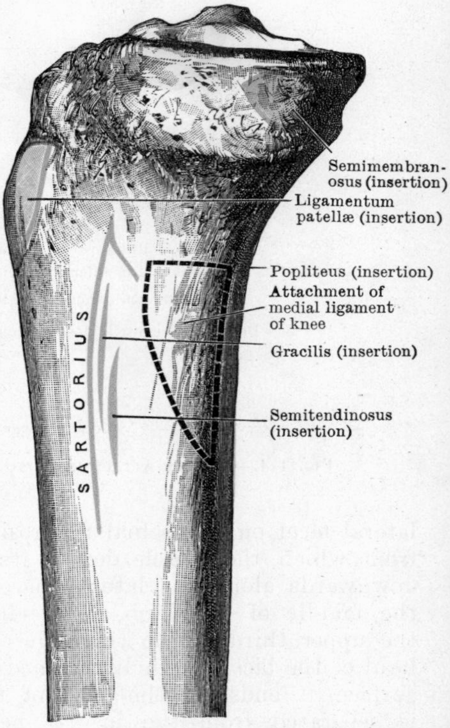

FIG. 416.—MUSCLE-ATTACHMENTS TO THE MEDIAL SURFACE OF THE UPPER PART OF THE RIGHT TIBIA.

THE MUSCLES OF THE FRONT OF THE THIGH

The chief muscle of the front of the thigh is the quadriceps femoris. The sartorius descends obliquely between the quadriceps femoris and the adductor muscles. The ilio-psoas, passing into the thigh behind the inguinal ligament, lies in the upper lateral part of the front of the thigh.

Sartorius.—The sartorius, a long strap-like muscle, **arises** from the anterior superior iliac spine and half of the margin of the notch below (Pl. XXXVII, Fig. 3). It passes obliquely across the front of the thigh, and, reaching its medial side, descends vertically across the medial side of the knee; then inclining forwards it is **inserted**, by aponeurotic fibres, into the upper part of the medial surface of the shaft of the tibia, above and in front of the insertions of the gracilis and the semitendinosus, and by its borders into fascial expansions which join the capsule and the medial ligament of the knee joint and the fascia of the leg.

The sartorius is superficial in its whole extent. Its upper third forms the lateral boundary of the femoral triangle; its middle third forms the roof of the subsartorial canal [canalis adductorius] and covers the femoral vessels; and its lower third is separated from the tendon of the gracilis muscle by the saphenous nerve and the saphenous branch of the descending genicular artery The *tibial intertendinous bursa* lies deep to the tendon at its insertion, separating it from the tendons of the gracilis and semitendinosus.

Quadriceps Femoris. — The quadriceps femoris is composed of four muscles—rectus femoris, vastus lateralis, vastus intermedius, and vastus medialis. The vastus intermedius clothes the shaft of the femur and is overlain by the rectus in front and the other vasti laterally and medially (Fig. 418).

Rectus Femoris.—The rectus femoris, a flattened spindle-shaped muscle, has a double, tendinous **origin** by a *straight head* from the anterior inferior iliac spine, and a *reflected head* from a rough groove on the ilium immediately above the acetabulum—a *bursa* lying deep to this origin. The two heads are bound together and connected to the capsule of the hip joint by the band of fascia derived from the fascia on the deep surface of the tensor fasciæ latæ, and they give rise to a single tendon. The tendon, at first deeply placed, appears in the cleft between the sartorius and the tensor

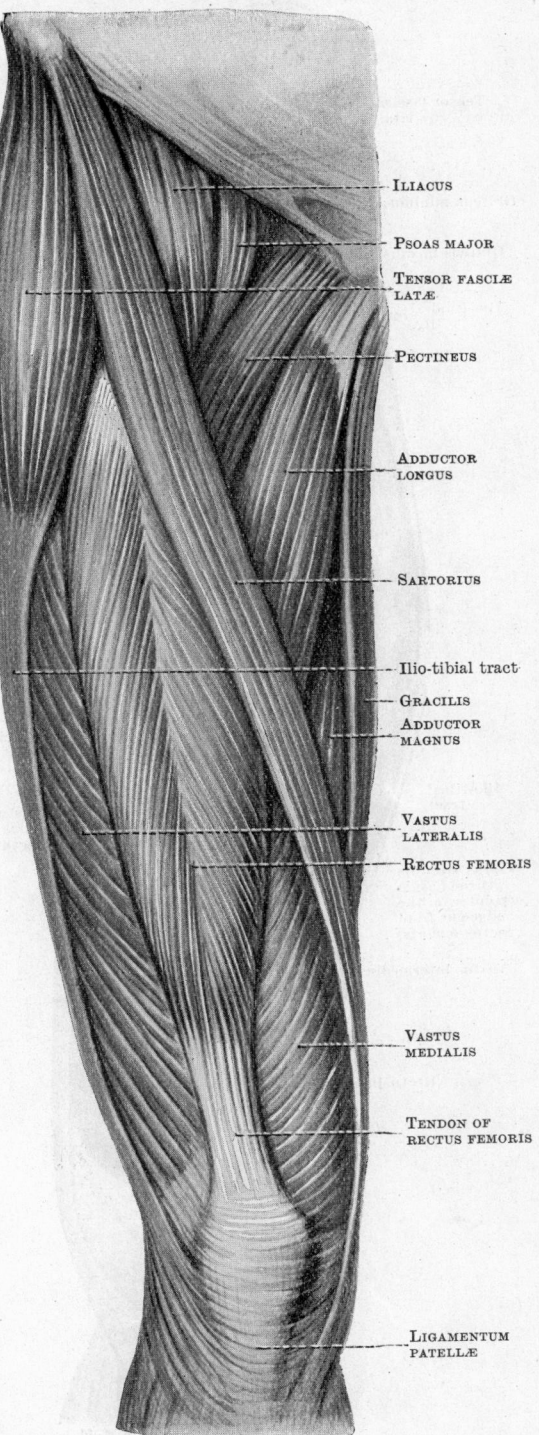

ILIACUS

PSOAS MAJOR

TENSOR FASCIÆ LATÆ

PECTINEUS

ADDUCTOR LONGUS

SARTORIUS

Ilio-tibial tract

GRACILIS
ADDUCTOR MAGNUS

VASTUS LATERALIS
RECTUS FEMORIS

VASTUS MEDIALIS

TENDON OF RECTUS FEMORIS

LIGAMENTUM PATELLÆ

FIG. 417.—MUSCLES OF FRONT OF RIGHT THIGH.

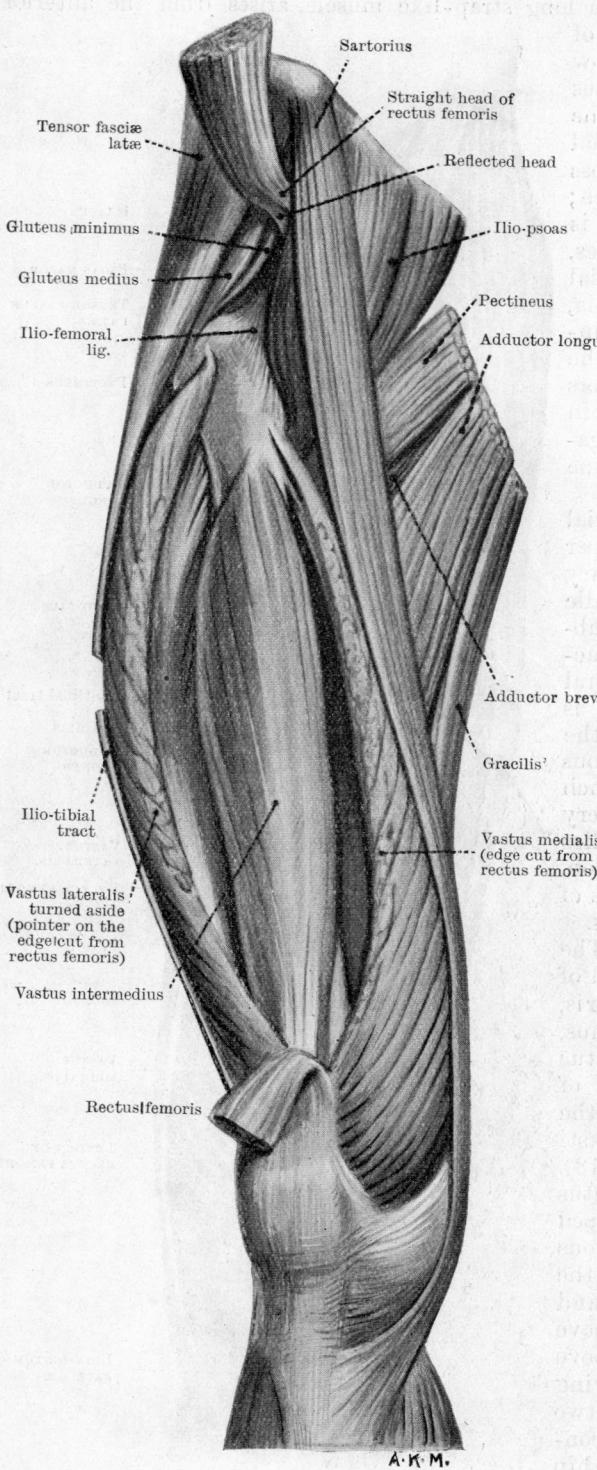

Sartorius

Straight head of rectus femoris

Tensor fasciæ latæ

Reflected head

Gluteus minimus

Ilio-psoas

Gluteus medius

Ilio-femoral lig.

Pectineus

Adductor longus

Adductor brevis

Gracilis

Ilio-tibial tract

Vastus medialis (edge cut from rectus femoris)

Vastus lateralis turned aside (pointer on the edge cut from rectus femoris)

Vastus intermedius

Rectus femoris

A·K·M·

FIG. 418.—DISSECTION OF MUSCLES OF FRONT OF RIGHT THIGH. The rectus femoris has been removed and the vastus lateralis and vastus medialis pulled apart to show the vastus intermedius. (R. D. L.)

fasciæ latæ and swells out into the fleshy belly which descends over the front of the vastus intermedius and the margins of the other two vasti. Becoming a tendon again, it is **inserted** into the upper border of the patella. The tendon of origin spreads for some distance over the front of the muscle and sends a tendinous septum into the middle of its substance as far down as the middle of the thigh. The muscle fibres arise from the tendon and the septum in a bi-penniform fashion, and end chiefly in a prolongation which extends upwards over two-thirds of the back of the muscle from the tendon of insertion. The tendon of insertion gradually narrows as it descends but widens out again near the patella; and it receives parts of the insertion of the vasti on its margins and deep surface.

Vastus Lateralis.—The vastus lateralis has an **origin**, partly fleshy, partly membranous, from (1) the capsule of the hip joint, (2) the upper part of the trochanteric line, (3) the lower border of the greater trochanter, (4) the lateral margin of the gluteal tuberosity, (5) the upper half of the linea aspera, and (6) the fascia lata and the lateral intermuscular septum (Figs. 241, 242, pp. 279, 280).

Forming a thick, broad muscle directed downwards and forwards, it is **inserted** by a broad membranous tendon into (1) the tendon of the rectus femoris, (2) the upper and lateral borders of the patella, and (3) the front of the lateral condyle of the tibia—covering, and to a large extent replacing, the anterolateral part of the capsule of the knee joint.

Vastus Medialis.—The vastus medialis is larger than the vastus lateralis; it has an extensive **origin** from (1) the lower half of the trochanteric line, the spiral line, the linea aspera, and the upper two-thirds of the medial supracondylar line; and (2) the medial intermuscular septum and the tendon of the adductor magnus (Figs. 241, p. 279, and 242, p. 280).

The muscle is directed downwards and laterally towards the knee, the lowest fibres being nearly horizontal. It is **inserted** by a strong aponeurotic tendon into (1) the rectus tendon, (2) the upper and medial borders of the patella, and (3) the front of the medial condyle of the tibia—covering and replacing the antero-medial part of the capsule of the knee joint. The muscle conceals the medial side of the shaft of the femur and the vastus intermedius, with which it is closely incorporated in its distal two-thirds.

Vastus Intermedius.—The vastus intermedius **arises** by fleshy fibres from— (1) the upper two-thirds of the shaft of the femur on the anterior and lateral surfaces —but not the medial surface; (2) the lower half of the lateral lip of the linea aspera and the upper part of the lateral supracondylar line; and (3) a corresponding portion of the lateral intermuscular septum (Figs. 241, p. 279, and 242, p. 280).

For the most part deeply placed, the muscle descends to an **insertion** into the

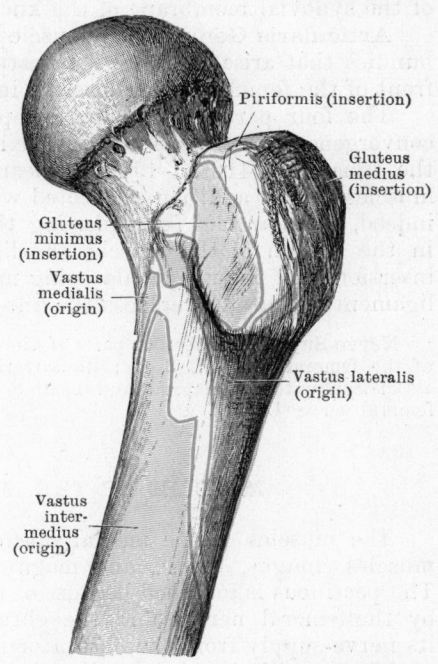

Fig. 419.—Muscle-Attachments to the Front of the Upper part of the Left Femur.

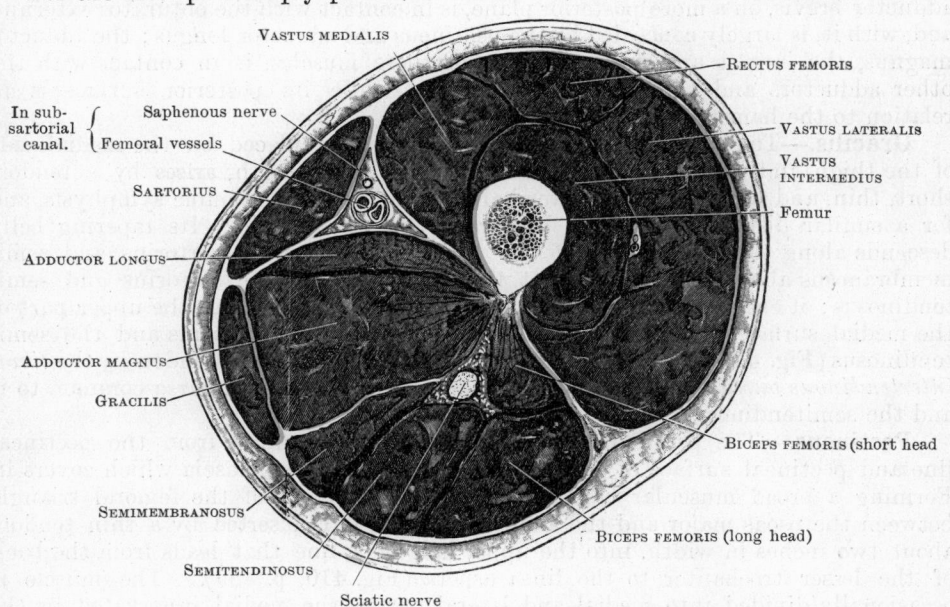

Fig. 420.—Transverse Section of the Thigh (the Subsartorial Canal).

deep surface of the tendons of the rectus and the other vasti muscles by fibres which join a membranous expansion on its surface. It is closely adherent to the vastus lateralis muscle in the middle third of the thigh, and is inseparable from the vastus medialis below the upper third. In the lower third it conceals

32

the articularis genu muscle, and the *suprapatellar bursa*—an upward prolongation of the synovial membrane of the knee joint.

Articularis Genu.—This muscle consists merely of a number of small separate bundles that **arise**, deep to the vastus intermedius, from the lower fourth of the front of the femur and are **inserted** into the synovial membrane of the knee joint.

The four parts of the quadriceps femoris muscle have been traced in their convergence to the patella. Their ultimate **insertion** is into the tubercle of the tibia (Fig. 416, p. 494), by means of the **ligamentum patellæ**; and the vasti muscles are in addition connected with the **retinacula of the patella**. The patella, indeed, is a *sesamoid bone*, playing the part of a lever and roller bearing, formed in the tendon of the muscle, the ligamentum patellæ being the real tendon of insertion, and the retinacula being membranous expansions from its borders. The ligamentum patellæ replaces the anterior part of the capsule of the knee joint.

Nerve-Supply.—The four parts of the quadriceps femoris are supplied by separate branches of the **femoral nerve** (L. 3. 4.) ; the sartorius receives its supply through two sets of nerves, in association with the lateral and medial parts of the intermediate cutaneous branch of the femoral nerve (L. 2. 3).

MUSCLES OF THE MEDIAL SIDE OF THE THIGH

The muscles of the medial side of the thigh are the pectineus, the adductor muscles (longus, brevis, and magnus), the gracilis, and the obturator externus. The pectineus is included because of its situation and action, although it is supplied by the femoral nerve; and the obturator externus because of its situation and its nerve-supply from the obturator nerve.

The gracilis is superficially placed along the medial side of the thigh. The adductor muscles, situated in the medial part of the thigh between the hip bone and the femur, are in different vertical planes. The adductor longus is in the same plane as the pectineus and lies superficially in the femoral triangle; the adductor brevis, on a more posterior plane, is in contact with the obturator externus, and, with it, is largely concealed by the pectineus and adductor longus; the adductor magnus, the largest and most posterior of these muscles, is in contact with the other adductors and the sartorius anteriorly, while its posterior surface is in relation to the hamstring muscles.

Gracilis.—The gracilis muscle, a long, flat band placed on the medial side of the thigh and knee, and superficial throughout its length, **arises** by a tendon, short, thin, and wide, from the lower half of the edge of the pubic symphysis, and for a similar distance along the border of the pubic arch. Its tapering belly descends along the medial side of the thigh to lie between sartorius and semimembranosus above the knee, and, at the knee, between the sartorius and semitendinosus; it ends in a tendon which expands to be **inserted** into the upper part of the medial surface of the shaft of the tibia between the sartorius and the semitendinosus (Fig. 416, p. 494). It is separated from the sartorius tendon by the *tibial intertendinous bursa*, and deep to its tendon there is a second *bursa* common to it and the semitendinosus.

Pectineus.—The pectineus muscle **arises** by fleshy fibres from the pectineal line and pectineal surface of the pubis and from the deep fascia which covers it. Forming a broad muscular band which lies in the floor of the femoral triangle between the psoas major and the adductor longus, it is **inserted** by a thin tendon, about two inches in width, into the upper half of a line that leads from the back of the lesser trochanter to the linea aspera (Fig. 410, p. 489). The muscle is occasionally divided into medial and lateral parts—the medial innervated by the obturator, the lateral by the femoral nerve.

Adductor Longus.—The adductor longus—a triangular muscle, lying in the floors of the femoral triangle and subsartorial canal—**arises** by a thin, strong tendon from the femoral surface of the body of the pubis in the angle between the crest and symphysis (Fig. 421). Extending downwards and laterally, it spreads out to be **inserted** by a very thin, wide tendon, into the medial lip of the linea aspera between the adductor magnus and vastus medialis. It lies between the pectineus and the gracilis, in front of the adductor brevis and magnus and the profunda vessels; superficially, its upper part is covered only with fascia and skin (but is crossed near its origin by the spermatic cord), and its lower part is related to the sartorius, the vastus medialis and the femoral vessels.

Adductor Brevis.—The adductor brevis is a large muscle which **arises** from an elongated area on the femoral surface of the body and inferior ramus of the pubis, surrounded by the other muscles of this group (Fig. 421). Directed downwards and laterally, the muscle expands to be **inserted**, by a short, aponeurotic tendon, behind the insertions of the pectineus and adductor longus, into the .

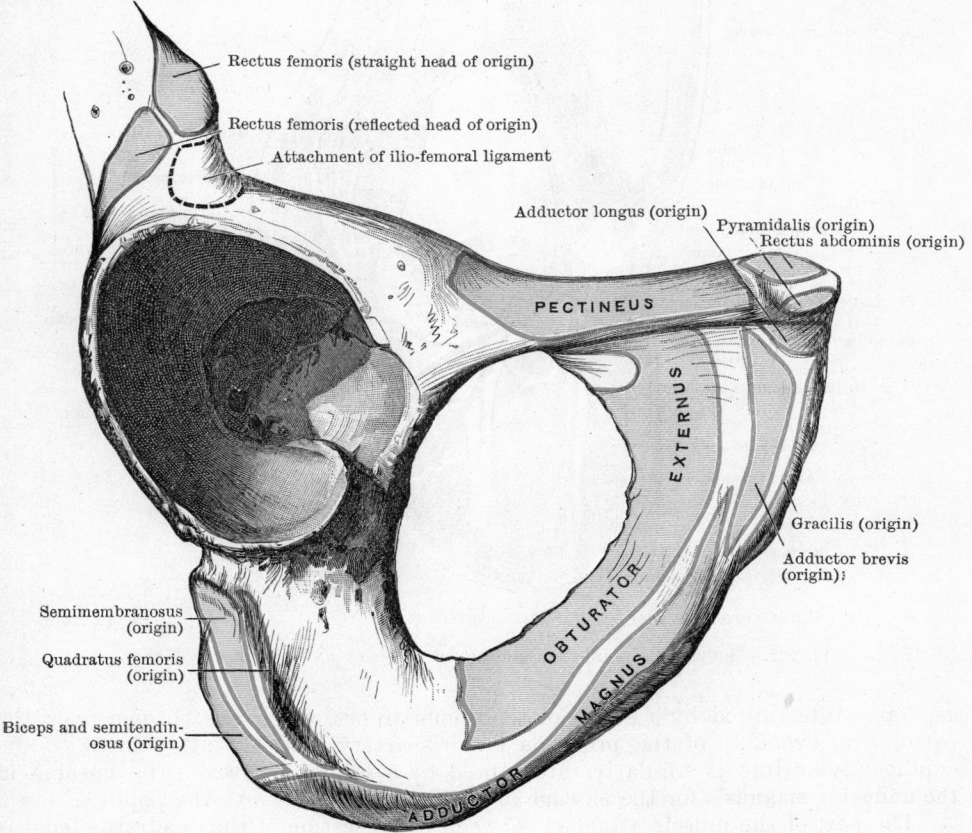

Rectus femoris (straight head of origin)

Rectus femoris (reflected head of origin)

Attachment of ilio-femoral ligament

Adductor longus (origin)

Pyramidalis (origin)

Rectus abdominis (origin)

PECTINEUS

OBTURATOR EXTERNUS

Gracilis (origin)

Adductor brevis (origin):

Semimembranosus (origin)

Quadratus femoris (origin)

Biceps and semitendinosus (origin)

ADDUCTOR MAGNUS

FIG. 421.—MUSCLE-ATTACHMENTS TO THE OUTER SURFACE OF THE RIGHT PUBIS AND ISCHIUM.

lower two-thirds of the line leading from the lesser trochanter to the linea aspera, and to the upper half of the linea aspera itself (Fig. 410, p. 489). It is in relation anteriorly with the pectineus and adductor longus, posteriorly with the adductor magnus; its upper border is crossed by the obturator externus and the tendon of the ilio-psoas; and its lower border is applied to the gracilis and adductor magnus.

Adductor Magnus.—This is the largest muscle of the adductor group and is triangular in outline. It **arises**, mainly by fleshy fibres, from the lower lateral impression on the ischial tuberosity and from the conjoined rami of the ischium and pubis—its most anterior fibres arising between the obturator externus and adductor brevis (Fig. 421). Its upper fibres are directed horizontally and laterally from the pubic bone towards the upper part of the femur; the lowest fibres descend from the ischial tuberosity to the medial condyle of the femur; and the intervening fibres radiate obliquely laterally and downwards. The muscle is **inserted** into the femur by tendinous fibres—(1) into a line extending from the insertion of the quadratus femoris, medial to the gluteal tuberosity, to the linea

32 a

aspera; (2) into the whole length of the linea aspera; (3) into the medial supracondylar line; and (4) into the adductor tubercle by a strong tendon derived from the fibres which arise from the ischial tuberosity. The tendon is bound to the medial supracondylar line by a tendinous sheet, and is partly continuous below with the medial ligament of the knee joint. The attachment to the linea

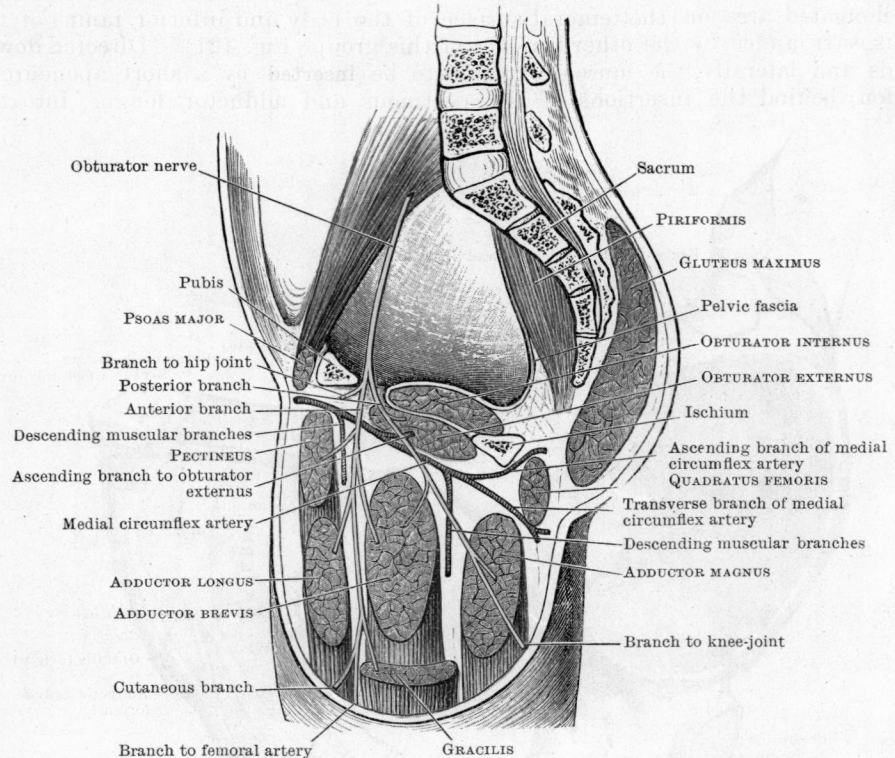

Obturator nerve

Pubis
Psoas major

Branch to hip joint
Posterior branch
Anterior branch
Descending muscular branches
Pectineus
Ascending branch to obturator externus
Medial circumflex artery

Adductor longus
Adductor brevis

Cutaneous branch

Branch to femoral artery

Sacrum
Piriformis
Gluteus maximus
Pelvic fascia
Obturator internus
Obturator externus
Ischium
Ascending branch of medial circumflex artery
Quadratus femoris
Transverse branch of medial circumflex artery
Descending muscular branches
Adductor magnus

Branch to knee-joint

Gracilis

Fig. 422.—Scheme of Adductor Group of Muscles and Obturator Nerve.

aspera is interrupted by a series of tendinous arches which are thrown over the perforating branches of the profunda femoris artery, and the attachment to the supracondylar line is similarly interrupted by a larger archway—the **opening in the adductor magnus**—for the passage of the femoral vessels into the popliteal fossa.

The part of the muscle attached between the insertion of the quadratus femoris and the linea aspera is often separated from the rest as the **adductor minimus.**

The muscle is covered anteriorly by the other adductors and by the sartorius muscle. The adductor brevis and the profunda femoris vessels lie between it and the adductor longus muscle; and the femoral vessels are in contact with it in the distal part of the subsartorial canal. The posterior surface of the muscle is in relation with the hamstring muscles and the sciatic nerve.

Obturator Externus.—The obturator externus, placed deeply, under cover of the preceding muscles, is a fan-shaped muscle that lies horizontally in the angle between the hip bone and the neck of the femur. It **arises** from the surfaces of the pubis and ischium which form the medial half of the margin of the obturator foramen, and from the corresponding portion of the superficial surface of the obturator membrane (Figs. 421, p. 499, and 233, p. 271). The fibres of the muscle converge on the wide groove below the acetabulum and end in a stout tendon which passes obliquely across the back of the neck of the femur to be **inserted** into the trochanteric fossa; in its course it overlaps the capsule of the hip joint, from which it is usually separated by the synovial *bursa of the obturator externus* (Fig. 410, p. 489).

Nerve-Supply.—The principal nerve of supply to the adductor group of muscles is the obturator (L. 2. 3. 4.); the anterior branch (L. 2. 3. (4.)) is distributed to the **gracilis**, the **adductor longus**, and the **adductor brevis**; the posterior branch (L. 3. 4.) to the **obturator externus** and the **adductor magnus**. The **adductor magnus** is, however, a double muscle and has a double nerve-supply. The *adductor* portion is supplied (on its anterior surface) by the posterior branch of the obturator: the *ischio-condylar* portion, associated with the hamstring group of muscles, is supplied (on its posterior surface) by a branch from the sciatic nerve (L. 4. 5. (S. 1.)).

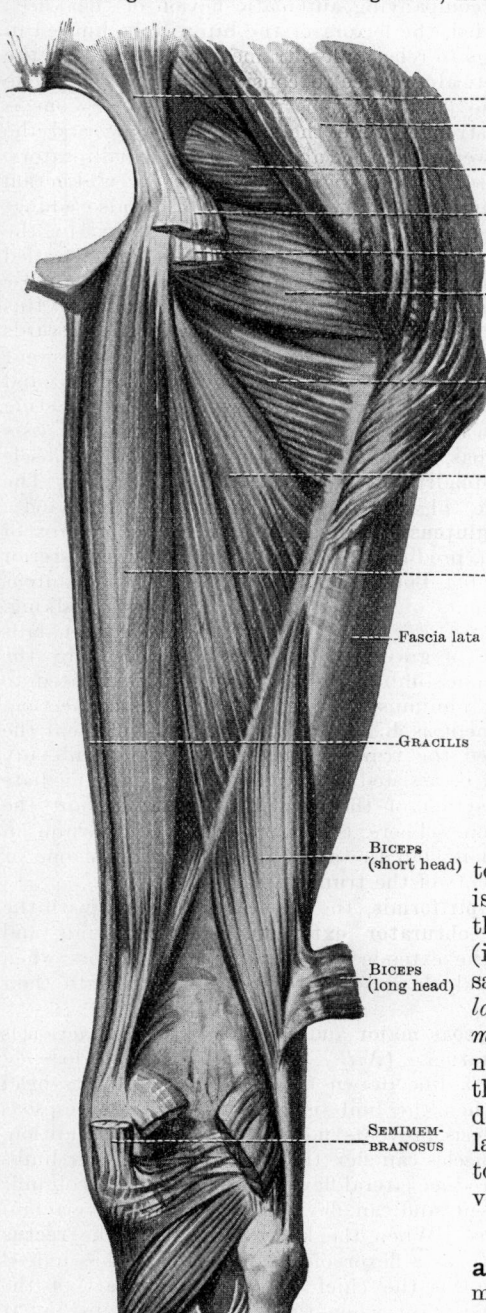

Sacro-tuber-
ous liga-
ment
Gluteus
maximus
Obturator
internus
Biceps and
semitendin-
osus
Semimem-
branosus
Quadratus
femoris

Adductor
magnus

Fascia lata

Gracilis

Biceps
(short head)

Biceps
(long head)

Semimem-
branosus

FIG. 423.—DEEP MUSCLES OF THE BACK
OF THE RIGHT THIGH.

The **pectineus**, although it belongs functionally to the adductor group on account of its situation and action, is always supplied by a branch of the **femoral nerve** (L. 2. 3.) —an indication of its morphological association with the ilio-psoas; it occasionally receives an additional nerve from the obturator, or from the accessory obturator nerve, when that nerve is present.

Femoral Triangle.—The femoral triangle is a large triangular space, in the upper third of the front of the thigh, which contains the femoral vessels in the first part of their course and the femoral nerve. It is bounded above by the inguinal ligament, laterally by the sartorius, and medially by the medial border of the adductor longus muscle. Its floor is formed laterally by the ilio-psoas, and medially by the pectineus, adductor longus, and a small part of the adductor brevis.

Sub-sartorial Canal [Canalis Adductorius (Hunteri)].—The subsartorial canal is in the middle third of the medial part of the thigh, and contains the femoral vessels (in the distal half of their course), and the saphenous nerve. It is bounded *antero-laterally* by the vastus medialis; *postero-medially* by the adductor longus and magnus; *antero-medially* (or superficially) by the sartorius; deep to the sartorius, a dense membrane, derived from the fascia lata, binds the other two boundaries together and bridges across the femoral vessels.

Action of Muscles in Movements at the Hip Joint.—In considering the muscles that move the joints of the lower limb we have to remember that they act from one end when the trunk is moved upon the limb and from the other when the limb is moved upon the trunk—conditions illustrated respectively in the supporting side and the advancing side during walking. Again, the line of the body weight transmitted through the supporting limb must be observed, for its position, say, in front of the axis of movement of a joint, will call the antagonists of that movement into action. Though the muscles may be arranged in flexor, extensor, adductor, abductor, and rotator groups, individual muscle action is not always wholly in agreement with these terms, but may merge into the action of other groups. Action of the muscles that move the hip is usually associated with action at the other joints of the limb, for the hip is seldom flexed without accompanying automatic flexion of the knee; indeed, if the knee is voluntarily kept extended, the flexors of the hip will be limited in their action by the inability of the hamstrings to relax unless trained to do so—as in the high kick. It is, therefore, largely a theoretical practice to consider the action at one joint alone : the muscular activity at all the joints must be reviewed when any one is considered. The extensors of the hip are stronger than the flexors in Man ; and the adductors and lateral rotators are far more powerful than the abductors and medial rotators.

The **gluteus maximus** is mainly an extensor of the thigh, and has a powerful action in straightening the lower limb, as in climbing or running. Its lower fibres also adduct the thigh and rotate it laterally. Acting from its insertion the muscle (assisted by the hamstring group), is a powerful extensor of the trunk on the lower limbs, and is called into play when the body is raised from the sitting or stooping position ; when these attitudes are assumed, its relaxation under tension is the main factor. The action of this muscle is all the more important in view of the fact that when the body is bent forwards flexion of the vertebral column is restricted (Pl. XX, Fig. 1) and flexion at the hip joint is the chief movement. The **tensor fasciæ latæ** assists in flexion, abduction and medial rotation of the thigh, but its most important action is exerted in counteracting the backward pull of the gluteus maximus on the ilio-tibial tract ; by this action it assists in maintaining extension of the knee, and it has, therefore, been found a suitable muscle to transplant as substitute for a paralysed quadriceps femoris (Naughton Dunn). The **gluteus medius** is a powerful abductor of the thigh for all positions of the limb, and a medial rotator of the extended thigh. The **gluteus minimus** is primarily an abductor of the thigh, but its anterior fibres, in addition, produce medial rotation, and its posterior fibres lateral rotation of the extended limb. Both the gluteus medius and gluteus minimus take an active part in the movements of the pelvis associated with walking. When one limb leaves the ground, the centre of gravity of the body no longer falls within the area of support, but the action of gravity is successfully opposed by the abductors of the opposite side. Further, as one limb advances, the pelvis is rotated to the opposite side by the gluteus medius and minimus of that side. In this connection, the muscular control of gravitational movement is highly important. The moment the abductors, acting against gravity, have poised the trunk upon, say, the right limb, any further inclination to the right (which would be assisted by gravity) results in immediate flaccidity of the abductors, and powerful action of the adductors, which permit the desired inclination by relaxing under tension. There is a position of equilibrium in which the two sets of muscles have little action ; but the alternate contraction of one or other group is readily seen in varied movements of the trunk poised on one limb.

The lateral rotators of the thigh are the **piriformis**, the **obturator internus** with the **gemelli**, the **quadratus femoris**, and the **obturator externus**. The piriformis and obturator internus act as lateral rotators of the extended thigh, and as abductors when the limb is flexed ; the quadratus femoris and obturator externus, in addition to their action as lateral rotators, are also adductors.

The chief flexors of the hip-joint are the **psoas major** and the **iliacus** ; their action is accompanied by a slight degree of medial rotation. (*N.B.*—The axis of rotation does *not* correspond to the shaft of the femur but to a line drawn from the middle of its head to the centre of the intercondylar notch when the limb is extended.) The ilio-psoas advances the limb in walking, and its paralysis prevents normal walking. In addition, acting from their insertions, the ilio-psoas muscles can flex the trunk on the lower limbs against resistance, and the psoas major can produce lateral flexion of the vertebral column. The **psoas minor** assists in the latter movement, and can flex the pelvis on the vertebral column, or the vertebral column on the pelvis. When the knee is extended the **rectus femoris** is a powerful assistant of the ilio-psoas as a flexor of the hip joint ; it has indeed been maintained that flexion of the hip joint is the chief action of that part of the quadriceps. The straight head of the rectus is taut when the movement begins, but it becomes a little relaxed and the reflected head is tightened when the thigh becomes flexed. When the body is recumbent, with the knees extended, the two recti assist the ilio-psoas muscles to flex the trunk on the hips.

In addition to their chief action, the muscles of the adductor group assist in other movements at the hip joint. The **pectineus**, while mainly an adductor, is also a flexor of the hip ; the **adductors longus** and **brevis** assist in flexion and lateral rotation ; the proximal part of the **adductor magnus** has a similar action, while the distal fibres, acting with the hamstrings, take part in extension of the femur and may assist in medial rotation.

The hamstring muscles (**long head of the biceps, semitendinosus,** and **semi-membranosus**), in virtue of their attachment to the ischial tuberosity, assist the gluteus maximus in extension of the thigh.

Action of Muscles in Movements at the Knee Joint.—In addition to the flexor and extensor groups of the thigh, the muscles of the leg which take origin from the femur are concerned in movements at the knee joint. The greater power of the flexors compared with the extensors is again a human characteristic.

The **quadriceps femoris** is the great extensor of the limb at the knee joint ; it can be felt in action both when one rises from the sitting position and when one assumes that position—taking active part in the first movement and controlling the other. The tendency for the patella to be pulled laterally as well as upwards is counteracted by the distal, horizontal fibres of the vastus medialis. The **articularis genu** draws the synovial membrane of the joint upwards during this movement.

The hamstring muscles are essentially flexors of the leg at the knee joint. When the knee is flexed the **biceps** is, in addition, a lateral rotator of the leg, and the semi-tendinosus and semimembranosus are additional medial rotators.

The **sartorius**, "the tailor's muscle," is a feeble flexor of both the hip joint and the knee joint. It also adducts the thigh and rotates it laterally, and assists in medial rotation of the tibia. The **gracilis** muscle has a similar flexing and rotating action at the knee joint.

Three muscles of the leg also act upon the knee joint. The **gastrocnemius** is a powerful flexor of the leg on the thigh (Pl. XXXVII, Fig 2), assisted by the feeble action of the **plantaris.** The **popliteus** has a special action as a medial rotator of the tibia and a flexor of the knee. It is believed that the popliteus muscle is responsible for the unlocking movement of medial rotation of the tibia which occurs immediately prior to, or synchronous with, the initial stage of flexion of the fully extended knee joint. The popliteus and the short head of the biceps are the only two flexors of the knee confined in their action to that joint. As the hip and knee are usually both flexed or both extended together, their flexors and extensors work in unison. Some muscles, *e.g.* the rectus femoris and the long head of the biceps, act upon both joints, as extensors of one and flexors of the other, and they may be unable, individually, to secure at the same time the maximum movement at both, *e.g.* the rectus femoris having extended the knee may not be able to secure full hip flexion, even if the hamstrings are relaxed, as in the high kick. The last stage of hip flexion in this exercise may be due to the momentum imparted to the limb in the initial stage of the movement. Again, the long head of the biceps (the muscular fibres of which are shorter than those of the short head), cannot flex the knee so far when the hip is extended. Quite apart from this point, the flexors of the knee do not, in the average person, secure the full flexion at this joint even when the hip is flexed, though the momentum of a slight backward kick can carry the heel into contact with the thigh, and the weight of the body may secure the full movement, as in sitting upon the heels. The main point is that the muscles are efficient for all natural movements, that their abilities are remarkably increased by training, and that contortionist movements are executed either by the aid of gravity or by pulling the limbs into place while appropriate muscles are stretched or relaxed.

FASCIÆ OF THE THIGH AND GLUTEAL REGION

The **superficial fascia** of the thigh and gluteal region is continuous above with the fascia of the abdomen and back, medially with that of the perineum, and below with that of the leg. It presents noticeable features in the gluteal region and the groin.

In the gluteal region the superficial fascia is of considerable thickness, and is usually loaded with fat, thereby contributing to the contour of the buttock and the formation of the fold of the buttock.

In the groin it is divisible into *two layers*, separated from each other by the superficial inguinal lymphatic glands and subcutaneous vessels : a superficial **fatty layer,** continuous with the similar layer on the anterior surface of the abdominal wall and in the perineum, and a deeper **membranous layer.** The deeper layer is attached medially to the pubic arch, where it is continuous

with the membranous layer of the superficial fascia of the perineum (p. 442);
lateral to the arch it blends with the deep fascia of the thigh a short distance
below the inguinal ligament; superiorly, it is continuous with the similar layer
in the abdominal wall.   Its attachments cut off the more superficial tissues
of the thigh from the perineum and the abdominal wall, preventing the passage
into the thigh of fluid collected in the perineum or beneath the fascia of the
abdominal wall.

The **deep fascia** forms a tubular investment for the muscles and vessels of the
thigh and extends upwards over the muscles of the gluteal region.   It is firmly

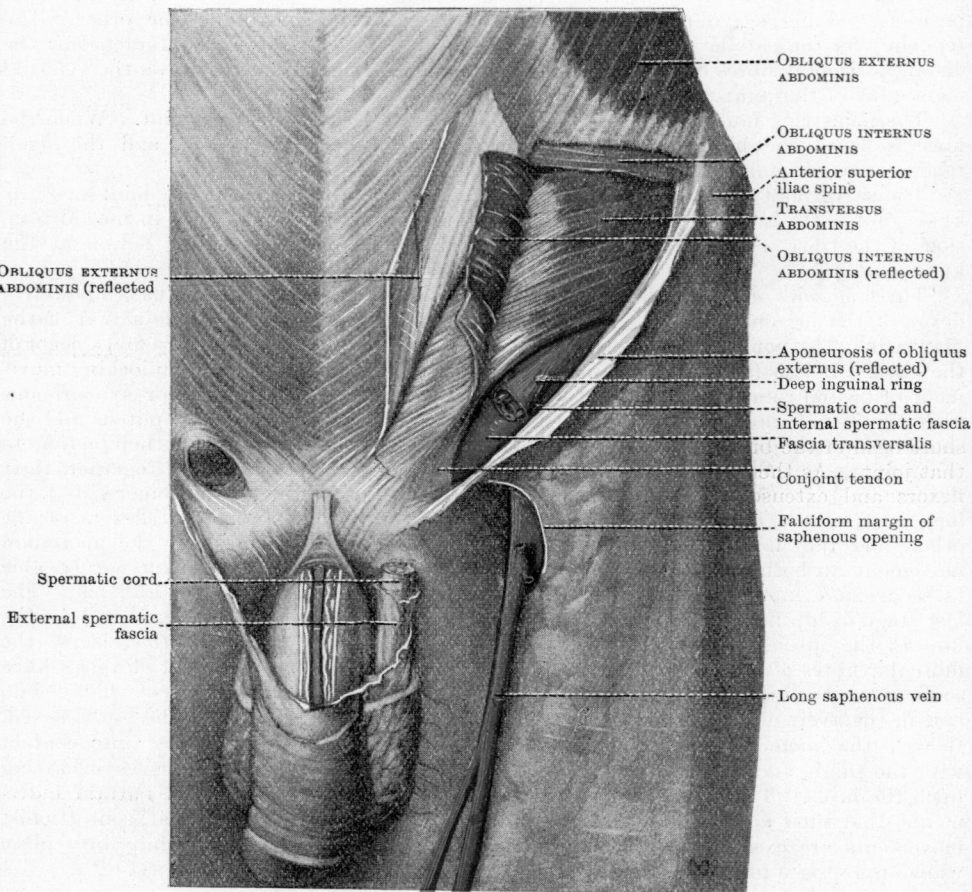

Fig. 424.—Dissection of the Left Saphenous Opening [Fossa Ovalis].

attached above to the iliac crest, the sacro-tuberous ligament, the ischium, the
pubic arch, the pubic symphysis and crest, and the inguinal ligament.   In the
distal part of the thigh the intermuscular septa are connected with its deep
surface; and in the region of the knee, it is continuous with the deep fascia of
the leg, gains attachment to the condyles of the tibia, the head of the fibula,
and the patella—forming the medial and lateral retinacula of the patella.   The
portion that invests the thigh is called the **fascia lata.**

The immediate relations of the fascia lata in its descent from the inguinal
ligament will be appreciated best if we consider first of all the disposition of
structures as they cross the inguinal border between abdomen and thigh (Figs.
425, 426.

The **transversalis fascia** and **fascia iliaca** (different names for different parts of
the same fascial sheath, p. 437) are prolonged in an oval, funnel-like tube—the

femoral sheath—upon the front and back respectively of the vessels that pass behind the inguinal ligament from the abdomen into the thigh. At the lateral side of the lip of the funnel these two layers are confluent; lateral to this point they are blended in their attachment to the inguinal ligament, and therefore are not prolonged into the thigh. At the medial side of the lip the two layers, again confluent, course past the lateral edge of the pectineal part of the inguinal ligament. Behind the inguinal ligament there are, therefore, two large compartments — a medial and a lateral. The medial compartment transmits the femoral sheath (itself divided into three compartments); the lateral transmits the ilio-psoas muscle, the femoral nerve, and the lateral cutaneous nerve of the thigh.

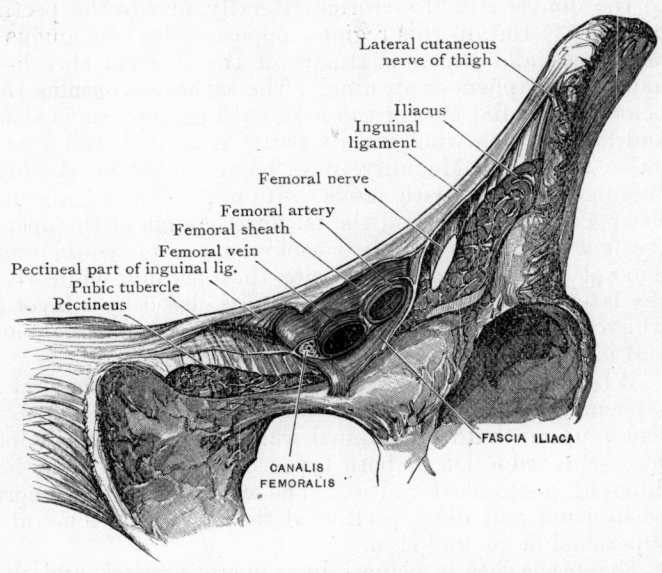

FIG. 425.—DISSECTION TO SHOW THE FEMORAL SHEATH AND THE STRUCTURE WHICH PASS BETWEEN THE INGUINAL LIGAMENT AND THE HIP BONE.

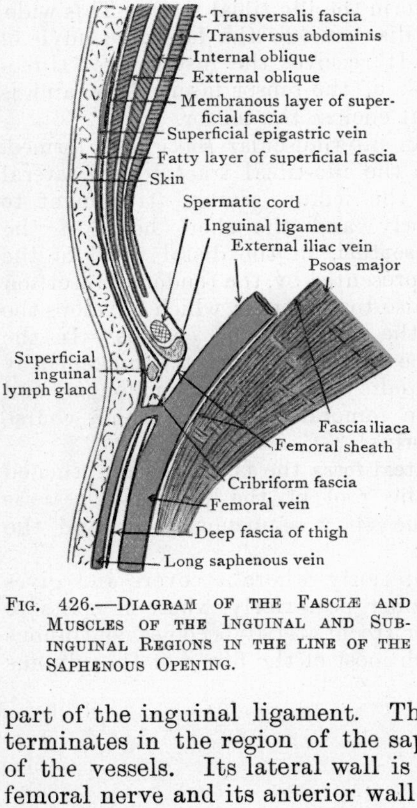

(Bearing in mind the fact that the fascia iliaca, stretching from the iliac crest to the brim of the pelvis, thus strapping down the ilio-psoas in the iliac fossa, is continuous upwards over the surface of the psoas major, it will be readily understood that inflammatory exudates from disease of the "psoas" vertebrae track down on the surface of the muscle, behind the fascia iliaca, and run behind the inguinal ligament in the muscular compartment to enter the thigh behind the fascia lata, lateral to the femoral sheath.) The femoral sheath, then, has a cover of fascia lata in front, while its bed is a muscular furrow formed by the ilio-psoas muscle and the pectineus, both covered with deep fascia—the fascia on the pectineus being tucked in behind the sheath to fuse with the capsule of the hip joint and with the fascia of the ilio-psoas in the thigh. The femoral sheath, itself, is subdivided by septa into three tubes—a lateral for the artery, an intermediate for the vein, and a medial named the femoral canal. The **femoral canal** contains some fat and a few lymph vessels; its upper end—named the **femoral ring**—covered by the peritoneum and possibly occupied by a lymph gland, is situated between the femoral vein and the lateral margin of the pectineal

FIG. 426.—DIAGRAM OF THE FASCIÆ AND MUSCLES OF THE INGUINAL AND SUBINGUINAL REGIONS IN THE LINE OF THE SAPHENOUS OPENING.

part of the inguinal ligament. The sheath is about an inch and a half long and terminates in the region of the saphenous opening, becoming lost upon the coats of the vessels. Its lateral wall is pierced by the femoral branch of the genitofemoral nerve and its anterior wall by the long saphenous vein.

On the front of the thigh, then, the fascia lata, continued from the inguinal ligament, is immediately applied to the femoral sheath in the intermediate area, to the ilio-psoas and sartorius laterally, and to the pectineus and adductor longus medially. But in this region—opposite the contiguous margins of the pectineus and psoas, and the medial part of the femoral sheath—it presents an oval gap, named the saphenous opening. The **saphenous opening** [fossa ovalis] is immediately below the medial part of the inguinal ligament; it is about an inch and a half long and half an inch wide, and its centre is an inch and a half below and lateral to the pubic tubercle. Medially, it is bounded by the sloping, anterior surface of the pectineus, covered with fascia. Its upper, lateral, and lower boundaries form one sharp, curved edge called the **falciform margin** of the opening, over whose lower part the long saphenous vein dips backwards to pierce the femoral sheath and enter the femoral vein—which is opposite the opening, while the artery is overlapped by the lateral boundary. The opening is closed by a layer of fibrous and fatty tissue which is perforated by the long saphenous vein, small arteries and lymph vessels, and is therefore termed the **cribriform fascia**.

When herniation occurs down through the femoral ring, femoral canal, and saphenous opening, the condition is termed a *femoral hernia*. This, subsequently rising up on to the abdominal wall, may be mistaken for an inguinal hernia ; the successful reduction of both types depends upon their being made to retrace their different anatomical routes. The coverings of a femoral hernia, in addition to peritoneum and extra-peritoneal tissue, are the femoral sheath, cribriform fascia, superficial fascia and skin.

The fascia lata is pierced by numerous vessels and nerves, but the largest and most important aperture is the saphenous opening just described.

On the medial side of the thigh, where it covers the adductor muscles, the fascia lata is thin. At the knee it is associated with the tendons of the vasti muscles, and forms the medial and lateral **retinacula of the patella**, attached to the borders of the patella and to the condyles of the tibia. On the lateral side of the thigh it is thickened by longitudinal fibres to form the **ilio-tibial tract**. This wide, strong band extends from the tubercle of the iliac crest to the lateral condyle of the tibia and the capsule of the knee joint. It receives the insertion of three-quarters of the gluteus maximus and the whole of the tensor fasciæ latæ, and is continuous with both of the layers of fascia that enclose the tensor.

On each side of the thigh above the knee an intermuscular septum is formed. The **lateral intermuscular septum** extends from the ilio-tibial tract to the lateral supracondylar line and the linea aspera of the femur, giving attachment to the vastus lateralis and intermedius anteriorly, and the short head of the biceps posteriorly. The **medial intermuscular septum**, in the distal third of the thigh, is associated with, and to a large extent represented by, the tendon of insertion of the adductor magnus muscle. It is related also to the fascia which envelops the adductor muscles and forms the sheaths of the sartorius and gracilis. In the middle third of the thigh the fascia under the sartorius is greatly thickened by transverse fibres and binds the vastus medialis to the adductor longus and magnus. That layer of fascia roofs over the femoral vessels in their course through the *subsartorial canal* [canalis adductorius].

On the **back of the thigh** and over the **popliteal fossa** the fascia is strengthened by transverse fibres. The fascia forming the roof of the popliteal fossa is specially thick, and is usually pierced by the short saphenous vein and the posterior cutaneous nerve of the thigh.

The **fascia of the gluteal region** is thick anteriorly, where it covers and gives origin to the gluteus medius, but is much thinner posteriorly, where it splits to enclose the gluteus maximus. Over the greater trochanter it becomes continuous with that part of the ilio-tibial tract into which most of the fibres of the gluteus maximus gain insertion.

MUSCLES AND FASCIÆ OF THE LEG AND FOOT

The muscles of the leg and foot are divisible into three series: (1) the extensor muscles on the front of the leg and dorsum of the foot; (2) the peroneal muscles

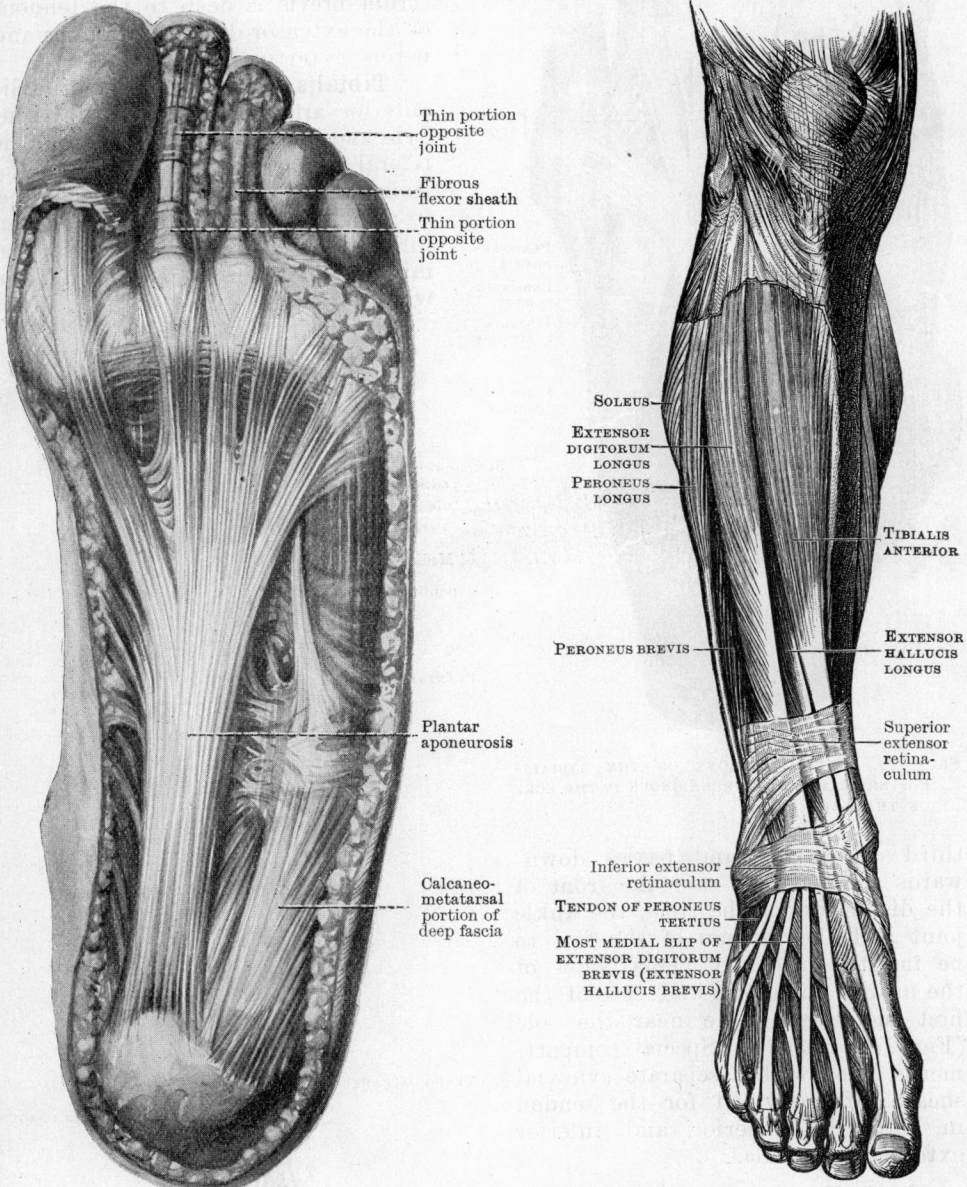

Thin portion opposite joint

Fibrous flexor sheath

Thin portion opposite joint

Plantar aponeurosis

Calcaneo-metatarsal portion of deep fascia

SOLEUS

EXTENSOR DIGITORUM LONGUS

PERONEUS LONGUS

TIBIALIS ANTERIOR

PERONEUS BREVIS

EXTENSOR HALLUCIS LONGUS

Superior extensor retinaculum

Inferior extensor retinaculum

TENDON OF PERONEUS TERTIUS

MOST MEDIAL SLIP OF EXTENSOR DIGITORUM BREVIS (EXTENSOR HALLUCIS BREVIS)

FIG. 427.—THE LEFT PLANTAR FASCIA.

FIG. 428.—MUSCLES OF FRONT OF LEG AND DORSUM OF FOOT OF THE RIGHT SIDE.

on the lateral side of the leg; and (3) the flexor muscles on the back of the leg and in the sole of the foot.

Muscles on the Front of the Leg and Dorsum of the Foot

These muscles are the tibialis anterior, the extensor hallucis longus, the extensor digitorum longus and peroneus tertius, and the extensor digitorum brevis.

On the front of the leg the tibialis anterior, extensor digitorum longus and peroneus tertius are superficially placed, and conceal the extensor hallucis longus muscle. On the dorsum of the foot, the extensor digitorum brevis is deep to the tendons of the extensor digitorum longus and peroneus tertius.

Tibialis Anterior.—The tibialis anterior **arises** from the lateral condyle and the upper two-thirds of the lateral surface of the shaft of the tibia, from the interosseous membrane, from the deep fascia, and from an intermuscular septum laterally. The muscle ends in a strong tendon which becomes free in the lower

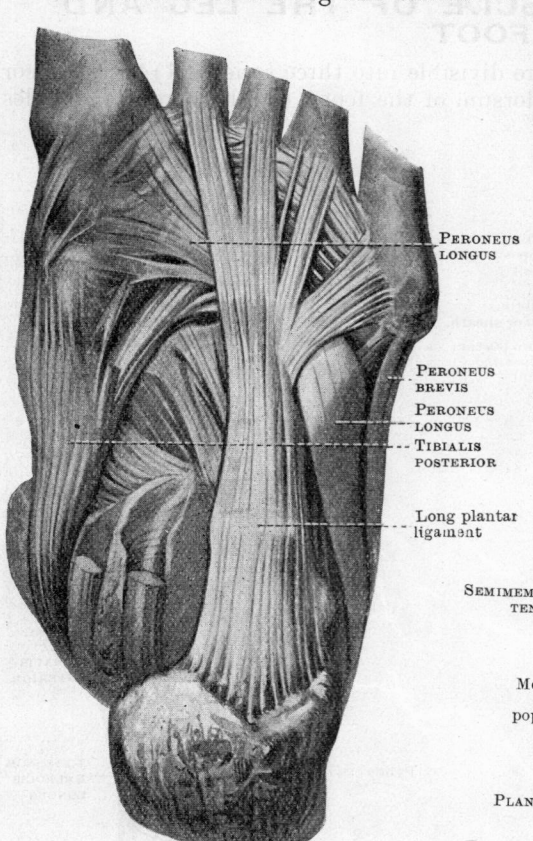

FIG. 429.—THE INSERTIONS OF THE TIBIALIS POSTERIOR AND PERONEUS LONGUS IN THE SOLE OF THE LEFT FOOT.

third of the leg, and passes downwards and medially over the front of the distal end of the tibia, the ankle joint and the dorsum of the foot to be **inserted** into the medial sides of the medial cuneiform and base of the first metatarsal bone near the sole (Fig. 274, p. 303). Special compartments, lined with a separate synovial sheath, are provided for the tendon in both the superior and inferior extensor retinacula.

The double insertion recalls the double muscle in pronograde apes.

The **tibio-fascialis anterior** is a separated portion of the muscle occasionally present, inserted into the fascia on the dorsum of the foot.

Extensor Digitorum Longus.

This is a pennate muscle which **arises**, by fleshy fibres, from the lateral side of the lateral condyle of the tibia,

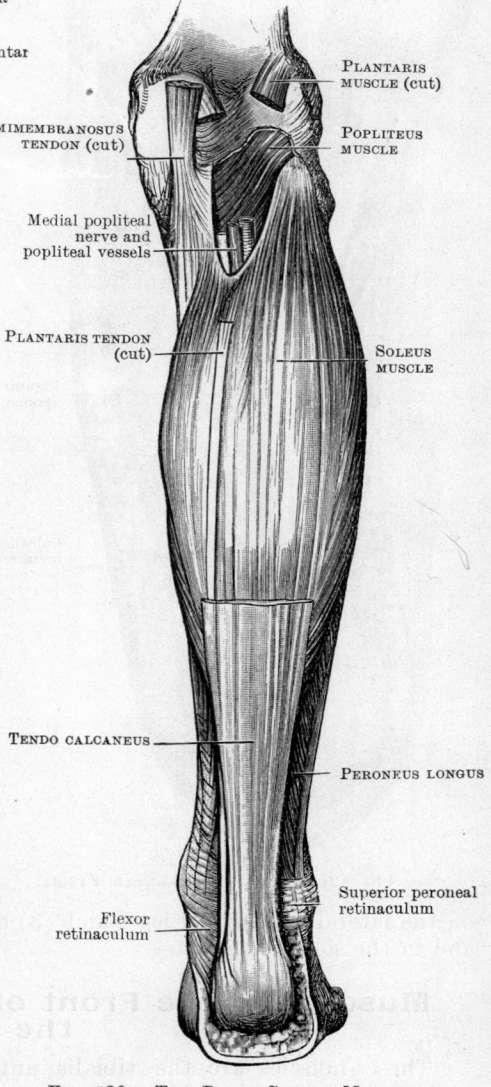

FIG. 430.—THE RIGHT SOLEUS MUSCLE.

from the upper two-thirds or more of the anterior surface of the shaft of the fibula, from the deep fascia and intermuscular septa and from the upper part of the interosseous membrane.

It gives rise to a tendon which passes deep to the superior extensor retinaculum, and subdivides into four tendons on the front of the ankle, under cover of the inferior extensor retinaculum; these tendons, together with the tendon of the peroneus tertius, are enclosed in a single synovial sheath as they lie in the most lateral compartment of this retinaculum. They are **inserted** into the lateral four toes, exactly in the same way as the corresponding tendons in the hand (see p. 473), and form membranous expansions on the dorsum of the proximal phalanx, joined by the tendons of the extensor digitorum brevis, lumbricales, and interossei, and each then separates into one middle and two collateral slips, attached respectively to the middle and distal phalanges.

Peroneus Tertius.—The peroneus tertius, very variable in its size and sometimes absent, is a partially separated portion of the extensor digitorum longus. It **arises** (inseparably from the extensor) from the lower part of the anterior surface of the fibula, and from the intermuscular septum on its lateral side. Its tendon is **inserted** into the dorsum of the fifth metatarsal bone near its base.

Extensor Hallucis Longus.—The extensor hallucis longus **arises** from the anterior surface of the fibula in its middle three-fifths, medial to the origin of the extensor digitorum longus, and for a corresponding extent from the interosseous membrane. Its tendon passes over the dorsum of the foot, to be **inserted** into the base of the distal phalanx of the big toe. As the tendon lies under cover of the superior extensor retinaculum, it occupies the same compartment as the extensor digitorum longus and the peroneus tertius, but, in the inferior extensor retinaculum, it is provided with a special compartment, lined with a separate synovial sheath.

It is occasionally inserted also by separate slips into the proximal phalanx and the metatarsal bone.

Extensor Digitorum Brevis.—The extensor digitorum brevis **arises** from the fore part of the upper surface of the calcaneum, and from the deep surface of the inferior extensor retinaculum. It usually divides into four fleshy bellies from which narrow tendons are directed forwards and medially to be **inserted** into the medial four toes. The lateral three tendons join those of the long extensor muscle to form the membranous expansions on the dorsum of the toes. The *most medial tendon* (**extensor hallucis brevis**), after crossing the dorsalis pedis artery, is inserted separately into the base of the proximal phalanx of the big toe.

Muscles on the Lateral Side of the Leg

The peroneal muscles—longus and brevis—occupy a special osteo-fascial compartment on the lateral side of the leg where they are placed between the extensor digitorum longus in front, and the soleus and flexor hallucis longus behind.

Peroneus Longus.—The peroneus longus **arises** from the lateral condyle of the tibia, from the head and the upper two-thirds of the lateral surface of the shaft of the fibula, from intermuscular septa at its sides, and from the fascia covering the muscle.

It forms a stout tendon, which lies superficial to the peroneus brevis, and hooks round the lateral malleolus deep to the superior peroneal retinaculum. Then crossing the lateral side of the calcaneum, under cover of the inferior peroneal retinaculum, it diverges from the peroneus brevis tendon, passes below the peroneal tubercle, and, finally, crosses the sole of the foot obliquely to be **inserted** into the lateral sides of the medial cuneiform and base of the first metatarsal bones (Fig. 274, p. 303). As it enters the sole of the foot a *sesamoid fibro-cartilage* (occasionally a bone) is formed in the tendon, which plays over the smooth surface of the tuberosity of the cuboid bone. In its passage across the foot the tendon traverses the groove on the cuboid, and is enclosed in a sheath derived from the long plantar ligament and the tibialis posterior tendon. A second synovial sheath invests that part of the tendon.

Peroneus Brevis. — The peroneus brevis **arises** by fleshy fibres from the lower two-thirds of the lateral surface of the shaft of the fibula, and from an intermuscular septum along its anterior border. Its tendon grooves the back of the lateral malleolus, invested by the synovial sheath common to it and the peroneus longus. Farther forwards it passes above the peroneal tubercle and is **inserted** into the dorsal surface of the base of the fifth metatarsal bone.

The peroneus longus and brevis may be fused together, or additional slips may be present which either join the tendon of the peroneus longus (**peroneus accessorius**) or are inserted into the calcaneum or cuboid ; an occasional tendinous slip of the peroneus brevis which joins the long extensor tendon of the little toe is known as the **peroneus digiti minimi.**

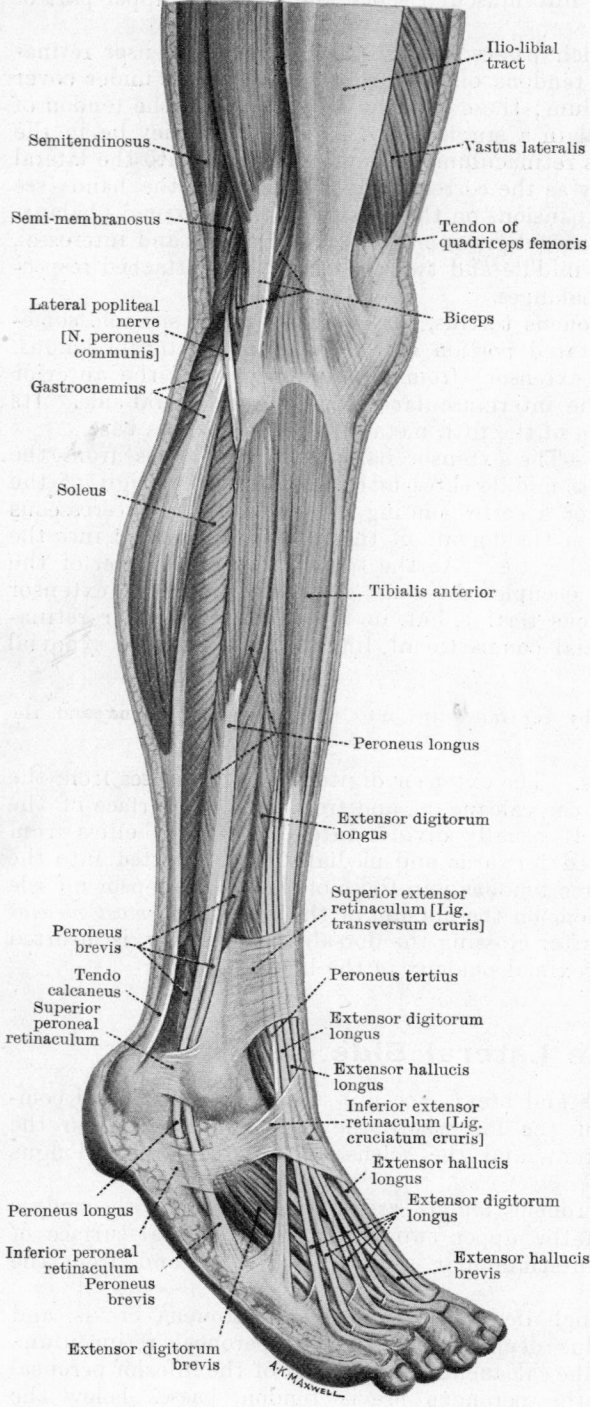

Fig. 431.—Muscles of Knee, Leg, and Dorsum of Foot seen from the Lateral Side. (R. D. L.)

Labels on figure: Ilio-tibial tract; Semitendinosus; Semi-membranosus; Vastus lateralis; Tendon of quadriceps femoris; Lateral popliteal nerve [N. peroneus communis]; Biceps; Gastrocnemius; Soleus; Tibialis anterior; Peroneus longus; Extensor digitorum longus; Superior extensor retinaculum [Lig. transversum cruris]; Peroneus brevis; Tendo calcaneus; Superior peroneal retinaculum; Peroneus tertius; Extensor digitorum longus; Extensor hallucis longus; Inferior extensor retinaculum [Lig. cruciatum cruris]; Extensor hallucis longus; Extensor digitorum longus; Peroneus longus; Inferior peroneal retinaculum; Peroneus brevis; Extensor hallucis brevis; Extensor digitorum brevis; A.K.MAXWELL

Muscles on the Back of the Leg

The muscles on the back of the leg are in two groups—superficial and deep.

The **superficial muscles** are the gastrocnemius, soleus, and the plantaris. The gastrocnemius and the soleus, by their bulk, form the calf of the leg, the massiveness of which is peculiar to man, and is associated with his ability to maintain the erect position while walking and running. The gastrocnemius is superficial except at its origin, where two bellies, forming the boundaries of the popliteal fossa, are overlapped by the tendons of the hamstring muscles. The soleus muscle is partially concealed by the gastrocnemius and plantaris, and becomes superficial in the distal part of the leg on each side of the common tendon (tendo calcaneus).

Gastrocnemius [γαστήρ (gaster) = belly ; κνήμη (knēmē) = leg]—The gastrocnemius **arises** by *two heads*, medial and lateral, by strong tendons which are prolonged over the surface of the muscle. The **lateral head** arises from an impression on the upper and posterior part of the lateral surface of the lateral condyle of the femur, and from the distal end of, the lateral supracondylar line ; at its origin it may contain a sesamoid bone. The **medial head** arises from a rough mark on the popliteal surface of the femur above the medial epicondyle. Each head has an additional origin from the back of the capsule of the knee joint. A *bursa* lies deep to each tendon of origin. The bursa of the medial head frequently communicates with the cavity of the knee joint and also with a *bursa* which intervenes between the medial head and the tendon of the semimembranosus. The bursa of the lateral head is smaller, and rarely communicates with the knee joint.

The two fleshy bellies, of which the medial is the larger, remain separate (Pl. XXXVII, Fig. 1), and are inserted into the posterior surface of a broad, membranous tendon which **narrows** distally and fuses with the tendon of the soleus to constitute the **tendo calcaneus.**

The tendo calcaneus, about half a foot long, the strongest tendon in the body, narrows and thickens as it descends to the heel, where it again spreads out to be

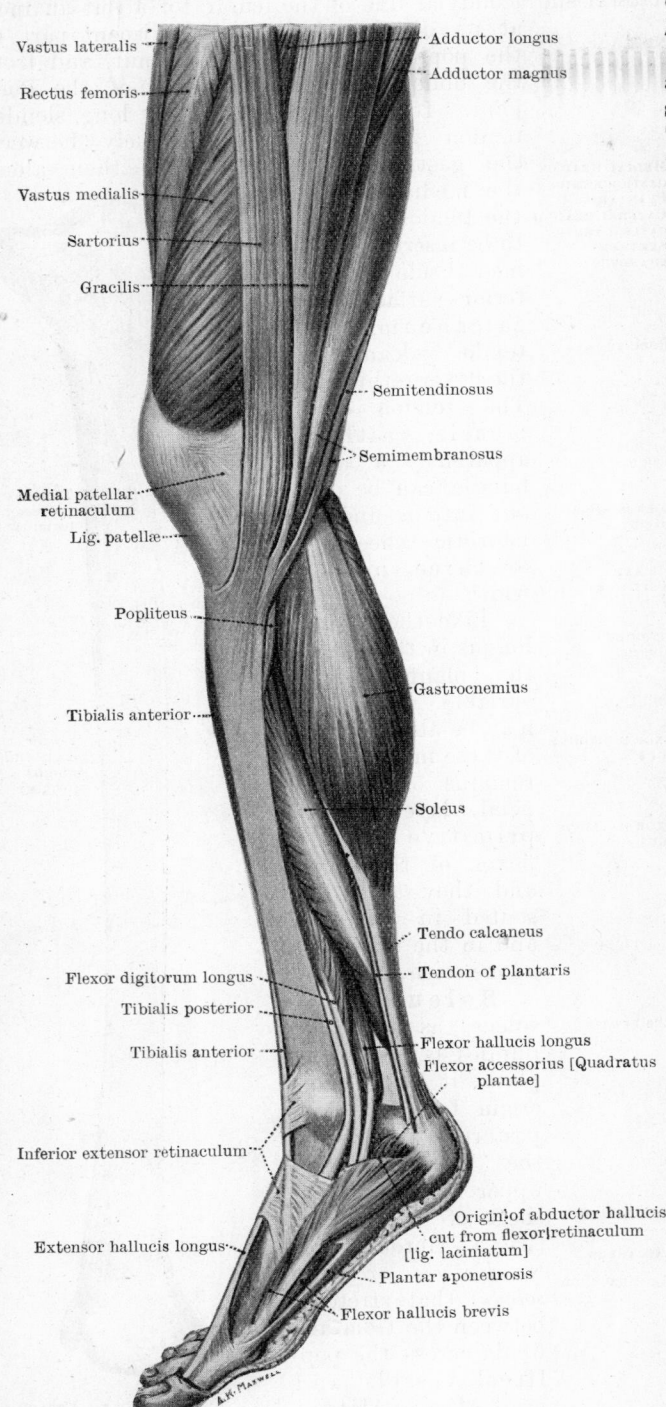

Vastus lateralis

Rectus femoris

Vastus medialis

Sartorius

Gracilis

Medial patellar retinaculum

Lig. patellæ

Popliteus

Tibialis anterior

Flexor digitorum longus

Tibialis posterior

Tibialis anterior

Inferior extensor retinaculum

Extensor hallucis longus

Adductor longus

Adductor magnus

Semitendinosus

Semimembranosus

Gastrocnemius

Soleus

Tendo calcaneus

Tendon of plantaris

Flexor hallucis longus

Flexor accessorius [Quadratus plantae]

Origin of abductor hallucis cut from flexor retinaculum [lig. laciniatum]

Plantar aponeurosis

Flexor hallucis brevis

FIG. 432.—MUSCLES OF KNEE, LEG, AND FOOT SEEN FROM THE MEDIAL SIDE. (R. D. L.)

inserted into the middle part of the posterior surface of the calcaneum. A bursa intervenes between the tendon and the bone immediately above the insertion.

Plantaris.—The plantaris—a narrow fleshy slip, not more than four inches in length—**arises** from the lateral supracondylar line of the femur for about an inch at its distal end, from the adjacent part of the popliteal surface of the femur, and from the oblique posterior ligament of the knee joint. It ends in a remarkably long, slender tendon which descends obliquely between the gastrocnemius and soleus, then along the medial border of the tendo calcaneus to be **inserted** into the medial side of the posterior surface of the calcaneum, or the tendo calcaneus, or the flexor retinaculum. The tendon of the muscle, although apparently a narrow bundle, can be drawn out into a fine, aponeurotic sheet, two or three inches in width.

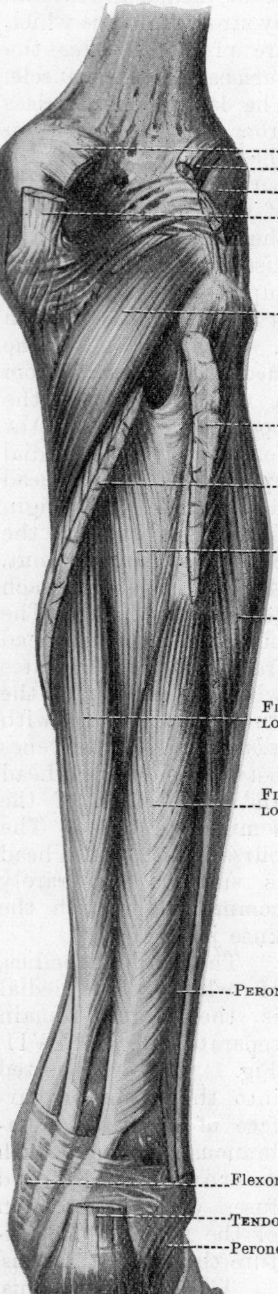

Like the palmaris longus in the forearm, the plantaris is a variable muscle and may be absent. Each of these muscles is the remains of a superficial layer of the primitive common flexor of the digits; and they are represented in the palm and in the sole by an aponeurosis.

Soleus.—The soleus, as its name implies, is a thick flat plate; it has a triple **origin** from—(1) the posterior surfaces of the head and the upper third of the shaft of the fibula; (2) a fibrous arch (*tendinous arch of soleus*) that stretches between the tibia and fibula across the popliteal vessels and medial popliteal [tibial] nerve; and (3) the soleal line of the tibia and the middle third of its medial border (Fig. 434).

From their origin the upper muscular fibres descend to join the deep (anterior) surface of a broad membranous tendon which is applied to the deep surface of

FIG. 433.—THE DEEP MUSCLES ON THE BACK OF THE RIGHT LEG.

MEDIAL HEAD OF GASTROCNEMIUS
PLANTARIS
LATERAL HEAD OF GASTROCNEMIUS
SEMIMEMBRANOSUS

POPLITEUS

SOLEUS (fibular origin)

SOLEUS (tibial origin)

TIBIALIS POSTERIOR

PERONEUS LONGUS

FLEXOR DIGITORUM LONGUS

FLEXOR HALLUCIS LONGUS

PERONEUS BREVIS

Flexor retinaculum
TENDO CALCANEUS
Peroneal retinaculum

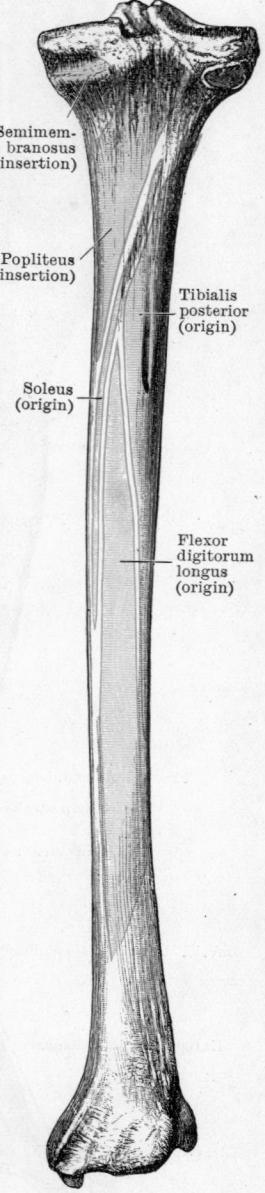

Semimembranosus insertion)

Popliteus (insertion)

Tibialis posterior (origin)

Soleus (origin)

Flexor digitorum longus (origin)

FIG. 434.—MUSCLE-ATTACHMENTS TO THE POSTERIOR SURFACE OF RIGHT TIBIA.

the similar tendon of the gastrocnemius—the two gliding upon each other above but fused below to obtain a common **insertion** through the tendo calcaneus; the lower fibres are inserted directly into the tendo calcaneus to within one or two inches of the calcaneum. The muscle is related to the lower border of the popliteus above, and is separated anteriorly by a transverse fascial septum from the posterior tibial vessels and nerve and the muscles of the following group.

The **deep muscles** of the back of the leg are the popliteus, flexor digitorum longus, flexor hallucis longus, and tibialis posterior.

The popliteus muscle is deeply placed in the distal part of the floor of the popliteal fossa, and is crossed by the popliteal vessels and medial popliteal nerve [n. tibialis]. The flexor digitorum longus lies on the tibia, the flexor hallucis longus on the fibula, and the tibialis posterior, lying between them, is related to the interosseous membrane and both bones of the leg. The four muscles are concealed by the superficial group, and are bound down to the bones by layers of the deep fascia.

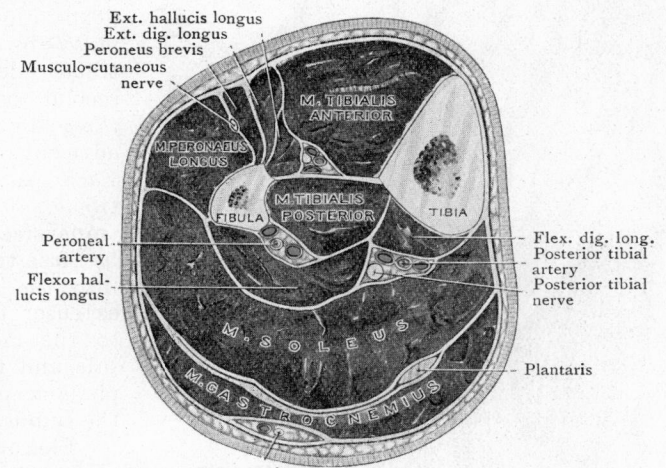

FIG. 435.—Transverse Section through the Middle of the Leg.

Popliteus.—The popliteus **arises**, by a stout tendon from a rough pit on the lateral surface of the lateral condyle of the femur, below the attachment of the lateral ligament of the knee and close to the articular margin. The tendon, grooving the lateral semilunar cartilage, passes between it and the capsule of the knee joint and emerges from under the arcuate ligament of the knee, from which it takes an additional fleshy origin. (Fig. 317, p. 364). It is **inserted**, by fleshy fibres, (1) into a triangular surface on the back of the tibia above the soleal line (Fig. 434), and (2) into the fascia which covers it.

Intracapsular at its origin, the tendon is partially invested by the synovial membrane, which protrudes along it for a short distance after it has pierced the capsule.

The pit of origin lies at the antero-inferior end of a groove on the lateral surface of the condyle; in that groove the upper margin of the tendon lies when the knee-joint is flexed, but in extension the tendon slips over the articular edge of the condyle and rests in a slight notch on the bone.

Flexor Digitorum Longus.—The flexor digitorum longus takes **origin** by fleshy fibres from the posterior surface of the shaft of the tibia in its middle three-fifths, below the soleal line and medial to the vertical line, from the overlying fascia and from an intermuscular septum on each side (Fig. 434).

Its tendon crosses obliquely behind the tendon of the tibialis posterior to lie along its lateral side on the back of the lower end of the tibia, and then passes deep to the flexor retinaculum [lig. laciniatum], where it is invested in a special synovial sheath. Escaping from the retinaculum, it passes forward over the medial margin of the sustentaculum tali and enters the sole above the abductor hallucis. As it extends forward in the sole it is above the flexor digitorum brevis and crosses below the tendon of the flexor hallucis longus, which separates it from the spring ligament; and, as the tendons cross, the flexor hallucis gives to the flexor digitorum a slip that passes into the medial two of the four subordinate tendons into which the tendon of the flexor digitorum longus finally divides. These four tendons are **inserted** into the lateral four toes in precisely the same manner

33

as the flexor digitorum profundus is inserted in the hand (p. 470). Each tendon enters the fibrous flexor sheath of the toe, perforates the tendon of the flexor digitorum brevis, and is inserted into the base of the distal phalanx. **Vincula tendinum (longa** and **brevia)** are present as in the hand.

Associated with the tendons of the flexor digitorum longus in the sole of the foot are the lumbrical muscles and the flexor digitorum accessorius.

Lumbricals. — The lumbricals are four slender muscles which are inserted into the lateral four toes; they **arise** from the tendons of the flexor digitorum longus—the *first muscle* by a single origin from the tibial side of the tendon for the second toe, and each of the *other three* by two heads from the adjacent sides of two tendons. Each passes forwards on to the tibial side of its toe, below a deep transverse ligament of the sole, to be **inserted** by tendinous fibres into the dorsal expansion of the extensor tendon; it is also bound to the metatarso-phalangeal capsule and the base of the proximal phalanx, precisely as in the case of the lumbrical muscles of the hand.

Flexor Digitorum Accessorius [M. quadratus plantæ].—The flexor digitorum accessorius **arises** by two heads: (1) the lateral, tendinous head, sometimes absent, springs from the lateral border of the plantar surface of the calcaneum and from the lateral border of the long plantar ligament; (2) the medial head, which is fleshy, arises from the medial surface of the calcaneum in its whole extent, and from the medial border of the long plantar ligament—a portion of the long plantar ligament being exposed between the two origins. The two heads unite to form a flattened band which is **inserted** into the tendons of the flexor digitorum longus—usually into those destined for the second, third, and fourth toes.

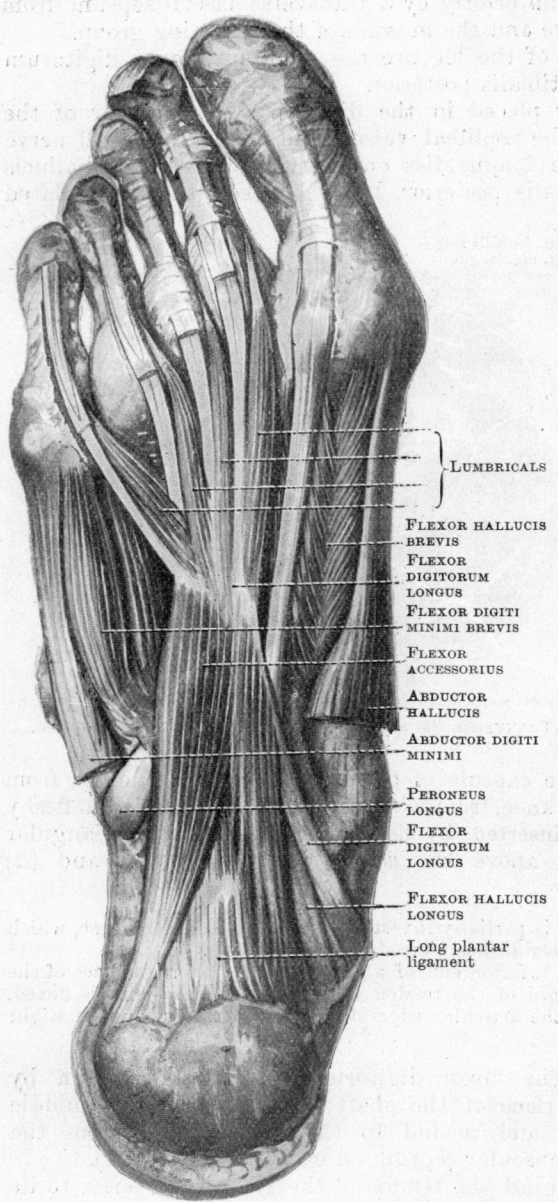

LUMBRICALS

FLEXOR HALLUCIS BREVIS

FLEXOR DIGITORUM LONGUS

FLEXOR DIGITI MINIMI BREVIS

FLEXOR ACCESSORIUS

ABDUCTOR HALLUCIS

ABDUCTOR DIGITI MINIMI

PERONEUS LONGUS

FLEXOR DIGITORUM LONGUS

FLEXOR HALLUCIS LONGUS

Long plantar ligament

FIG. 436.—THE MUSCLES OF THE RIGHT FOOT (Second Layer).

In the sole of the foot the tendons of the flexor digitorum longus, along with the lumbricales and flexor accessorius and the flexor hallucis longus tendon, constitute the second layer of muscles, which lies between the abductors of the big and little toes and the flexor digitorum brevis superficially, and the flexor brevis and adductor of the big toe more deeply.

Flexor Hallucis Longus.—The flexor hallucis longus **arises** from the lower two-thirds of the posterior surface of the shaft of the fibula, from the covering fascia and from intermuscular septa at its sides, overlapping the tibialis posterior considerably. Its tendon, passing deep to the flexor retinaculum, enclosed in a special synovial sheath, grooves the posterior surface of the distal end of the tibia, the talus, and the plantar surface of the sustentaculum tali (to which it is strapped by a fibrous sheath lined with the synovial sheath), and is directed forwards in the sole of the foot, to be **inserted** into the base of the distal phalanx of the big toe after transversing a fibrous sheath under the proximal phalanx.

Tibialis Posterior.—The tibialis posterior, the deepest muscle on the back of the leg, has a fourfold fleshy origin. It **arises**—(1) from the posterior surface of the shaft of the fibula between the medial crest and the interosseous border ; (2) from the lower part of the lateral condyle of the tibia, and from the upper two-thirds of its shaft, below the soleal line and between the vertical line and the interosseous border; (3) from the interosseous membrane; and (4) from the covering fascia and the septum on each side. The muscle ends in a strong tendon which is invested with a special synovial sheath. The tendon grooves the back of the medial malleolus, and then, turning forwards below the malleolus between the flexor retinaculum and the deltoid ligament, it passes below the plantar calcaneo-navicular ("spring") ligament and spreads out to be **inserted** by three bands into (1) the tuberosity of the navicular bone and the plantar surface of the medial cuneiform bone, (2) the plantar surfaces of the bases of the second, third, fourth (and some-times fifth) metatarsal bones, the intermediate and lateral cuneiform bones and the floor of the groove on the cuboid, and (3) into the medial border of the sustentaculum tali of the calcaneum (Fig. 274, p. 303). As it crosses the spring ligament, a sesamoid cartilage or bone is developed in its substance.

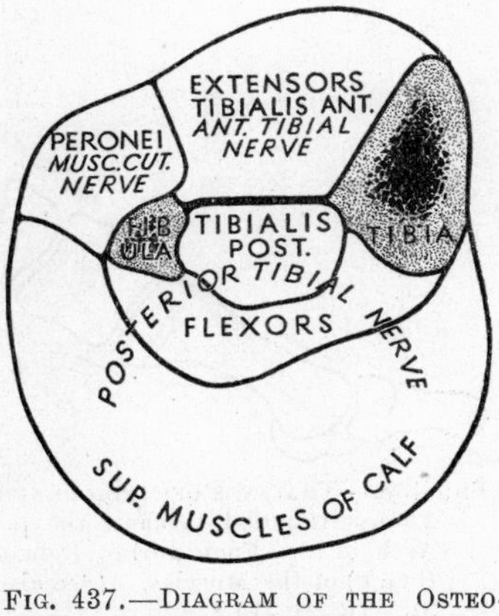

FIG. 437.—DIAGRAM OF THE OSTEO-FASCIAL COMPARTMENTS OF THE LEG.

An occasional separate slip (**peroneo-calcaneus**) arises from the lower end of the fibula, and is **inserted** into the calcaneum, or may join the tendon of the flexor hallucis longus.

Nerve-Supply.—The muscles of the front and lateral side of the leg and those on the back of the leg are all supplied by nerves derived respectively from the lateral popliteal (n. peronæus communis) and medial popliteal (n. tibialis) branches of the **sciatic nerve**, the first derived from the dorsal offsets, the second from the ventral offsets of the nerves of the sacral plexus, the extensor and flexor aspects of the leg having been reversed during the developmental rotation of the limb.

The **tibialis anterior, extensor digitorum longus, peroneus tertius, extensor hallucis longus,** and **extensor digitorum brevis** are all supplied by the *anterior tibial nerve* [n. peronæus profundus] (L. 4. 5. S. 1.); the **peroneus longus** and **peroneus brevis** by the *musculo-cutaneous nerve* [n. peronæus superficialis] (L. 4. 5. S. 1.).

The following muscles are all supplied by branches of the *medial popliteal* or its continuation—the *posterior tibial nerve* : **gastrocnemius**, by two branches, one to each head (S. 1. 2.); **plantaris** (L. 4. 5. S. 1.); soleus, by two branches, one arising in the popliteal fossa and entering its superficial surface (S. 1. 2.), the other in the back of the leg and entering its deep surface (L. 5. S. 1. 2.); **popliteus** (L. 4. 5. S. 1.), by a branch which winds round the lower border of the muscle and enters its deep surface ; **flexor digitorum longus** (L. 5. S. 1.); **flexor hallucis longus** (L. 5. S. 1. 2.); and **tibialis posterior** (L. 5. S. 1.). The *posterior tibial nerve*, through its plantar branches, supplies also the muscles associated with the tendons of the flexor digitorum longus in the sole of the foot; the **first lumbrical** is supplied by the *medial plantar nerve* (L. (4). 5. S. 1.), the other three by the *lateral plantar nerve* (S. 1. 2.), which supplies the flexor digitorum accessorius also.

Action of Muscles in Movements at the Ankle and Intertarsal Joints.—

The terms which are least liable to be misunderstood in the description of movements at the ankle-joint are **dorsi-flexion** (produced by muscles on the anterior (extensor) aspect of the leg), and **plantar-flexion** (produced by muscles on the posterior (flexor) aspect of the leg). In addition, important movements of **inversion** and **eversion** of the foot take place at the intertarsal joints.

The dorsi-flexors of the ankle are: the **tibialis anterior, extensor digitorum longus, peroneus tertius,** and **extensor hallucis longus.** The plantar-flexors of the ankle are : the **gastrocnemius** and **soleus** with the feeble **plantaris** ; the **flexor digitorum longus, flexor hallucis longus** and **tibialis posterior**; and the **peroneus longus** and **brevis.**

Most of those muscles have some action also at the intertarsal joints; but the **invertors** of the foot, in the order of their strength, are first the tibialis posterior, then the tibialis anterior, acting together, while the chief **evertors** are the two **peroneal** muscles, **longus** and **brevis**. The peroneus tertius also is associated with the movement of eversion, which is a characteristic movement of the human foot (it raises the lateral border of the foot, for example, in the action of skating or dancing).

It is to be noted that the muscles whose tendons pass into the sole have the additional, important function of maintaining the arches of the foot. The tibialis posterior is perhaps the most important muscle in that respect because of the direct relation of its tendon to the plantar calcaneo-navicular ("spring") ligament and of its numerous secondary insertions. The flexor hallucis longus also has an important share in this function because of its position in relation to the tarsus and the spring ligament. The peroneus longus by its passage across the sole keeps the transverse arch of the foot up, as a taut string maintains the bend of a bow. The arches of the foot are girders con-

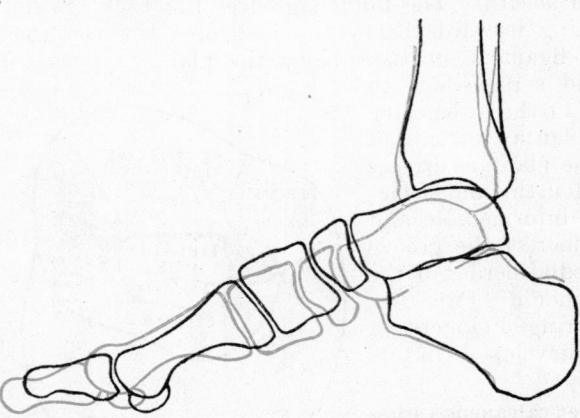

(FIG. 438.—TRACINGS OF RADIOGRAPH (Pl. XXXIII, Figs. **2** and **3**, superimposed to show the position of the Longitudinal Arch of the Foot during Relaxation (red), and Contraction (black) of the Muscles. (See also Fig. 442, footprints **2** and **3**). (R. D. L.)

structed of mobile segments which interplay as the muscles lever them into position (Pl. XXXIII, Fig. 438); and the phrase "supporting the arch" may refer to a direct pull upon its segments, such as is exerted by the tibialis anterior, or an indirect effect upon these segments by the approximation of the pliable pillars as in the action of the flexor hallucis longus.

As the line of the body weight in the erect attitude lies in front of the axis of the ankle joint, the plantar flexors are required to be far more powerful than the plantar extensors — again, a feature distinctive of man.

As the function of the limb is to support and propel the body in movement, it is essential to consider the **reversed action** of the muscles as in pulling upon the free foot from the leg. In the **standing position** the muscles of the tendo calcaneus pull from the heel, but **in walking** they pull up the heel. Again, in standing on one foot the **tibialis anterior** and **posterior** pull the leg medially while the **peroneal** muscles pull it laterally to secure a balance. Now, the movement induced by any one muscle at the joints is never pure flexion, extension or version, and accordingly the synergic action of all groups is necessary. One can readily feel this in all the muscles of the leg in poising the body on the toes of one foot, when the tibialis anterior, though a dorsi-flexor, must act as an invertor to counteract the everting pull of the peroneal muscles. The student will appreciate the co-operative action of such direct antagonists as the tibialis posterior (flexor) and the tibialis anterior (extensor) in producing inversion.

The **gastrocnemius** requires special consideration, not only because it is a powerful plantar flexor, but also because of the necessity for its relaxation during dorsi-flexion of the ankle in walking. The condition of this muscle varies considerably, and a slight shortening is so common that it can hardly be considered abnormal. Its "ligamentous action" (see p. 386) thus hampers dorsi-flexion at the ankle joint, and an endeavour is made to call in the transverse tarsal joint to supplement the ankle joint in that movement during walking. Now, at this joint, dorsi-flexion does not take place in the sagittal plane : the fore part of the foot is moved laterally as well as upwards ; the walk becomes "out-toed" and the medial longitudinal arch is depressed—predisposing to flat foot.

The power of the flexor muscles in their tie-beam action on the foot is well illustrated where the tibialis anterior is paralysed and the gastrocnemius and soleus are weak. In using the flexors powerfully to overcome the drooping of the heel caused by the weakness of their companions, the fore part of the foot is gradually pulled towards the heel, until a marked concavity is produced.

Muscles in the Sole of the Foot

The muscles in the sole of the foot are arranged in four layers :—

First layer : the abductor hallucis, flexor digitorum brevis, and abductor digiti minimi. *Second layer* : the lumbricales and flexor digitorum accessorius, together with the tendons of the flexor hallucis longus and flexor digitorum longus. *Third layer* : the flexor hallucis brevis, adductor hallucis, and flexor digiti minimi brevis. *Fourth layer* : the interossei (plantar and dorsal), placed between the metatarsal bones ; and the tendons of insertion of the tibialis posterior and peroneus longus.

FIRST LAYER

Abductor Hallucis.—The abductor hallucis arises by a short tendon from the medial side of the medial tubercle of the calcaneum and by fleshy fibres from the flexor retinaculum, the plantar aponeurosis and the intermuscular septum between it and the flexor digitorum brevis. The muscle lies superficially along the medial border of the sole, and its tendon is **inserted** into the medial side of the base of the proximal phalanx of the big toe and partly with the medial head of flexor hallucis brevis into the medial sesamoid bone.

Flexor Digitorum Brevis.— The flexor digitorum brevis is situated above the plantar aponeurosis, between the two abductors, and is separated from the second layer of muscles by their fascia and the lateral plantar vessels and nerve. It **arises** from the medial tubercle of the calcaneum, the plantar aponeurosis, and the intermuscular septa at its sides. Passing forwards, it gives rise to four slender tendons which are **inserted** into the middle phalanges of the lateral four toes, after having been perforated by the

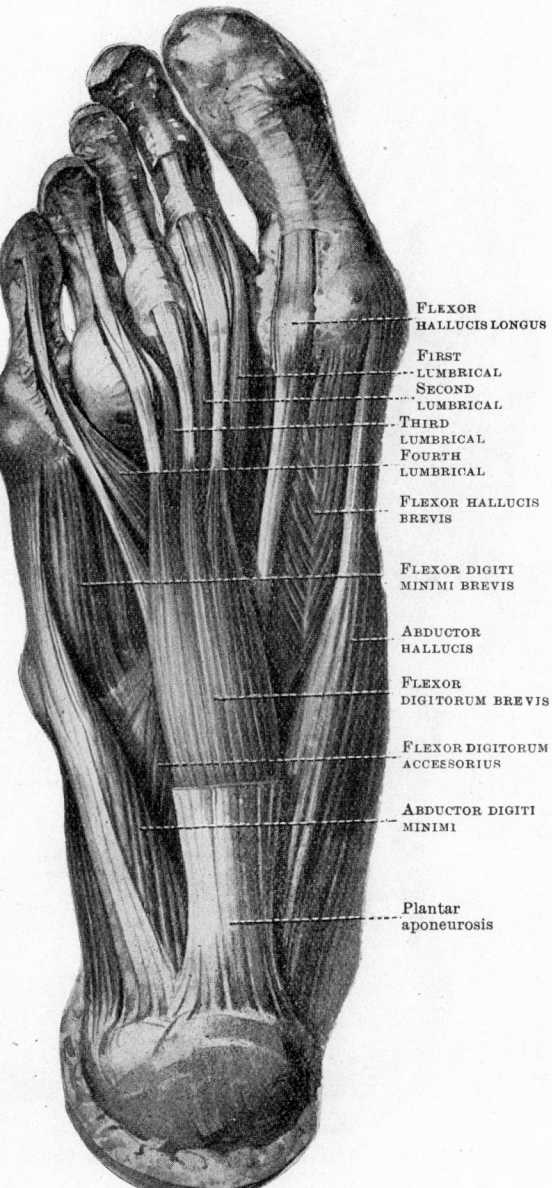

FIG. 439.—SUPERFICIAL MUSCLES OF THE RIGHT FOOT.

FLEXOR HALLUCIS LONGUS

FIRST LUMBRICAL
SECOND LUMBRICAL
THIRD LUMBRICAL
FOURTH LUMBRICAL

FLEXOR HALLUCIS BREVIS

FLEXOR DIGITI MINIMI BREVIS

ABDUCTOR HALLUCIS

FLEXOR DIGITORUM BREVIS

FLEXOR DIGITORUM ACCESSORIUS

ABDUCTOR DIGITI MINIMI

Plantar aponeurosis

long flexor tendons just, as in the case of the tendons of the flexor digitorum sublimis of the hand (p. 468).

Abductor Digiti Minimi.—The abductor digiti minimi **arises** by fleshy and tendinous fibres from both tubercles of the calcaneum (partly concealed by the flexor digitorum brevis) and by fleshy fibres from the fascia on its surface and the intermuscular septum between it and the flexor digitorum brevis. Its tendon, gliding over a smooth depression on the inferior surface of the base of the fifth metatarsal bone, runs along the bone to be **inserted** into the lateral side of the base of the proximal phalanx of the little toe. The most lateral fibres usually obtain an additional insertion into the lateral part of the plantar surface of the fifth metatarsal bone, and may constitute a small separate muscle called the **abductor ossis metatarsi quinti**.

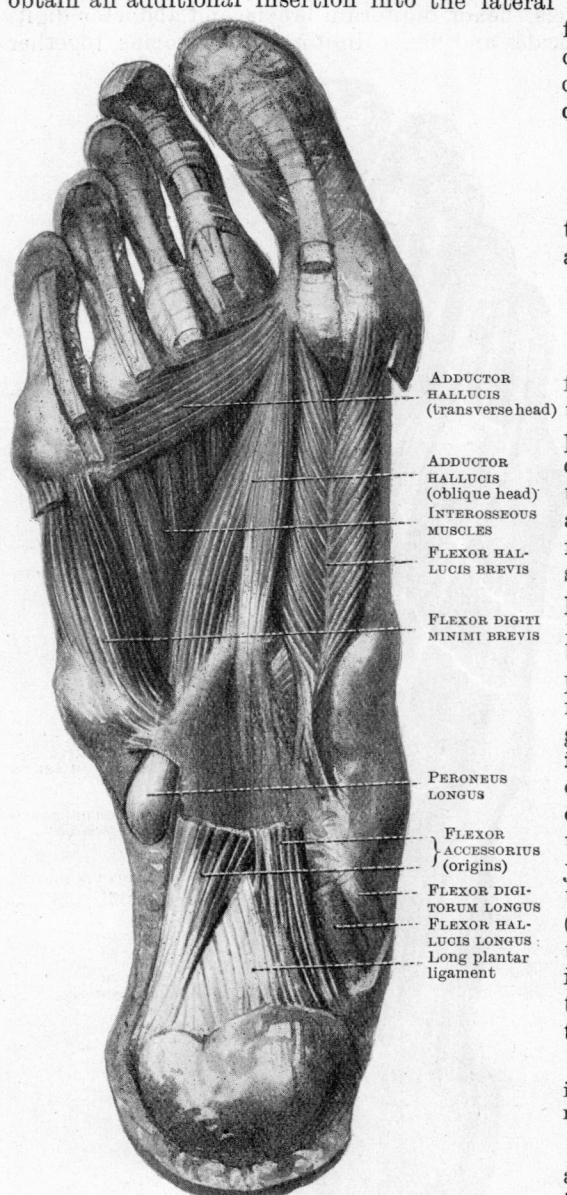

FIG. 440.—DEEP MUSCLES OF THE SOLE OF THE FOOT.

ADDUCTOR HALLUCIS (transverse head)

ADDUCTOR HALLUCIS (oblique head)

INTEROSSEOUS MUSCLES

FLEXOR HALLUCIS BREVIS

FLEXOR DIGITI MINIMI BREVIS

PERONEUS LONGUS

FLEXOR ACCESSORIUS (origins)

FLEXOR DIGITORUM LONGUS

FLEXOR HALLUCIS LONGUS

Long plantar ligament

SECOND LAYER

The muscles and tendons of this layer have been described already (pp. 513, 514).

THIRD LAYER

Flexor Hallucis Brevis.—The flexor hallucis brevis **arises** by tendinous fibres from (1) the medial part of the plantar surface of the cuboid bone (behind the groove for the peroneus longus), and from the adjacent part of the lateral cuneiform bone and (2) from the expansions of the tendon of the tibialis posterior in this area. Directed forwards over the first metatarsal bone, the muscle separates into two parts which escort the tendon of the flexor hallucis longus. Each portion gives rise to a tendon which is **inserted** into the corresponding side of the base of the proximal phalanx of the big toe; in each tendon, under the metatarso-phalangeal joint, a *sesamoid bone* is developed to play the part of a roller bearing (Fig. 438 and Pl. XXXIII). The tibial tendon is united with the insertion of the abductor muscle of the big toe, the fibular tendon with the insertion of the adductor.

An occasional insertion of some fibres into the shaft of the metatarsal bone represents an **opponens hallucis**.

Adductor Hallucis.—The adductor hallucis has two heads. The *oblique head* **arises** (1) from the sheath of the peroneus longus, and (2) from the plantar surfaces of the bases of the second, third, and fourth metatarsal bones (Fig. 274, p. 303). It lies in the hollow of the foot, on a deeper plane than the long flexor tendons and lumbricals, and on the fibular side of the flexor hallucis brevis, with which it is frequently fused; and it runs obliquely, medially and forwards, to be **inserted** on the fibular side of the base of the proximal phalanx of the big toe along with the transverse head and the flexor brevis.

The *transverse head* **arises** from the capsules of the lateral four metatarso-phalangeal joints and the deep transverse ligaments of the sole. Running transversely medially under cover of the flexor tendons and lumbricals and crossed by the digital nerves, it is **inserted,** along with the oblique head, into the fibular side of the base of the proximal phalanx of the big toe.

 Flexor Digiti Minimi Brevis.—The flexor digiti minimi brevis **arises** from the sheath of the peroneus longus and the base of the fifth metatarsal bone. Partially concealed by the abductor digiti minimi, the muscle passes along the fifth metatarsal bone, to be **inserted,** in common with that muscle, into the fibular side of the base of the proximal phalanx of the little toe.

 A frequent insertion of some fibres into the metatarsal bone represents an **opponens** digiti minimi.

FOURTH LAYER

 Interosseous Muscles.—The interosseous muscles of the foot resemble those of the hand except in one respect. In the hand the line from and to which they

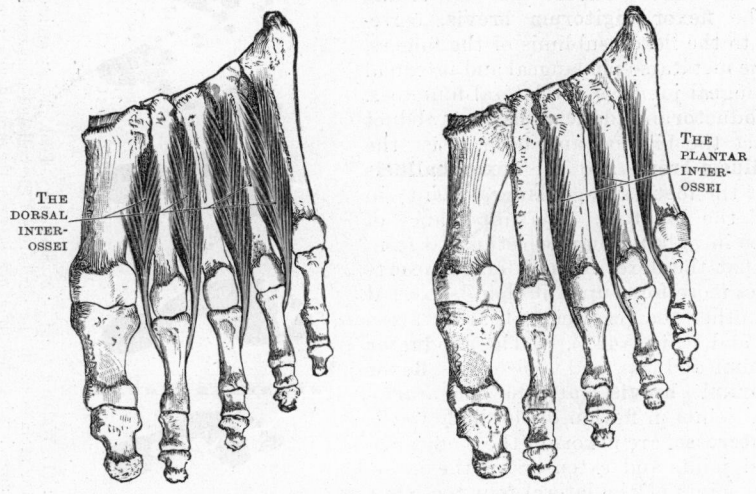

THE
DORSAL
INTER-
OSSEI

THE
PLANTAR
INTER-
OSSEI

FIG. 441.—INTEROSSEOUS MUSCLES OF THE RIGHT FOOT.

move the digits is the middle line of the middle digit, whereas, in the foot, it is the middle line of the second digit.

 There are four dorsal and three plantar muscles; they occupy the four interosseous spaces, and bulge into the hollow of the foot.

 The **four dorsal muscles** lie in the intermetatarsal spaces, and as each **arises** by two heads from the adjacent bones their fibres have a bipennate arrangement. Their tendons pass forwards above the deep transverse ligaments of the sole, and each is **inserted,** on the dorsum of the foot, into the side of the proximal phalanx, the metatarso-phalangeal capsule, and the dorsal expansion of the extensor tendon. The *first* and *second muscles* are inserted respectively into the tibial and fibular sides of the proximal end of the proximal phalanx of the second toe. The *third* and *fourth muscles* are inserted into the fibular sides of the third and fourth toes. The dorsalis pedis artery enters the sole of the foot through the cleft between the heads of the first muscle; the perforating arteries gain the dorsum of the foot through the corresponding intervals in the other three muscles.

 The **three plantar muscles** lie in the lateral three interosseous spaces. They **arise,** each by a single head, from the medial side of the third, fourth, and fifth metatarsal bones respectively. Their tendons pass forwards above the deep transverse ligaments, and each is **inserted,** in the same manner as the dorsal muscles, into the tibial sides of the third, fourth, and fifth toes.

 Nerve-Supply.—The muscles of the sole of the foot are supplied by the two *plantar nerves*; the abductor hallucis, flexor hallucis brevis, flexor digitorum brevis, and the first lumbrical by the *medial plantar nerve* (L. (4.) 5. S. 1.); the abductor digiti minimi, the flexor digiti minimi brevis, the lateral three lumbricals, the flexor digitorum accessorius, and *all* the **interossei** by the *lateral plantar nerve* (S. 1. 2.). (Branches from the anterior tibial nerve to the dorsal interossei are probably afferent).

Action of Muscles in Movements of the Toes.

—The **extensor hallucis longus** extends the big toe, the **extensor digitorum brevis** extends the medial four toes, and the **extensor digitorum longus** the lateral four toes. The **flexor digitorum longus** flexes the lateral four toes : the **lumbrical muscles** have a similar action to those of the hand ; they flex the metatarso-phalangeal joints of the lateral four toes and extend their inter-phalangeal joints. The **flexor digitorum accessorius**, as its name implies, is an accessory flexor of the toes, assisting the long flexor, and tending to draw the tendons into which it is inserted into the middle of the sole of the foot. The **flexor digitorum brevis**, corresponding to the flexor sublimis of the fingers, acts on the metatarso-phalangeal and proximal interphalangeal joints of the lateral four toes.

The **abductor** and **adductor hallucis** abduct and adduct the big toe, and both assist the **flexor hallucis brevis** and the **flexor hallucis longus** (at the metatarso-phalangeal joint) in flexion of the big toe. The importance of the big toe in walking may be estimated from the fact that the flexor hallucis longus exerts three times more force upon it than is exerted upon any other toe (cf. weight-bearing areas of foot and Fig. 442). The **abductor digiti minimi** abducts, and assists the **flexor digiti minimi brevis** (at the metatarso-phalangeal joint) in flexion of the little toe.

The **interossei** are flexors of the metatarso-phalangeal joints and extensors of the inter-phalangeal joints of the lateral four toes (but the opinion is also held that they do not extend these joints). The dorsal interossei **abduct** the toes into which they are inserted from the middle line of the *second toe* ; the plantar interossei **adduct** the lateral three toes towards the *second toe*. The small muscles of the foot also have an important tie-beam action in maintaining the arches of the foot.

Weight-bearing Areas of the Foot.

—The function of the arches of the foot and the activity of the muscles of the leg and foot in maintaining these arches (pp. 516 and 520) are indicated in some measure by the footprints, which vary considerably in different people and alter remarkably in the early years of life. In the average person (Fig. 442, **1**), the weight of the posterior pillar is taken by the heel pad, that of the anterior pillar by the metatarsal pad—particularly in the region of the ball of the big toe —while under the lateral longitudinal arch there is an area of contact (very frequently absent, Fig. 442, **6**, **10**), and not usually a weight-bearing area. (It has been said that the feet of primitive races are broad and flat, but this is not borne out in Fig. 442, **10**, which shows the foot of an Australian aboriginal

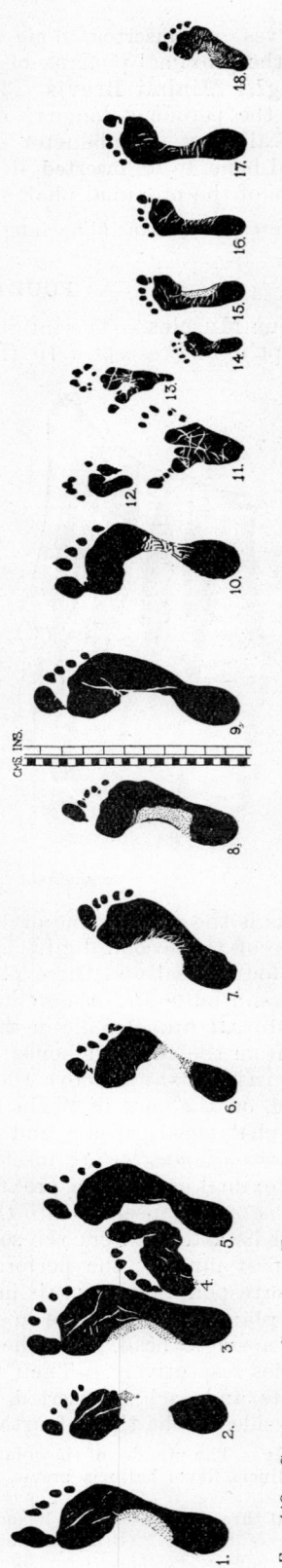

FIG. 442.—COMPARATIVE SERIES OF FOOTPRINTS. 1, 2, 3, 4. Footprints of a Man : (1) Walking Print ; (2) Stationary, Foot, highly arched ; (3) With the Muscles relaxed as much as possible (see Pl. XXXIII, Figs. 2 and 3) ; (4) Walking on the Toes. Note the prominence of the bar between the ball and phalangeal pad of the big toe. 5. Footprint of Male Athlete. 6. Athletic Girl. 7. Ballet Dancer in Attention Attitude. 8. The same showing the difference between the arched and relaxed state of the foot, the increased area of contact indicated by the dotted area. 9. Negro, Male. 10. Australian Aboriginal Woman. 11. Chimpanzee, Female, 3½ years of age, walking-print. 12. Hamadryas Baboon, Female. 13. Rhesus Macacus Monkey. (Observe the narrow heel, 11, 12, and 13). 14. Infant before walking, at 3 months old. 15. The same child after walking at 2 years, 9 months old. 16. The same child at 3 years, 7 months old. 17. The same child at 7½ years old. 18. This infant, after beginning to walk, was confined to bed through illness, and lost the art. The footprint is taken from a series while the art of walking is being learned anew. The eminence in front of the heel on the medial side is caused by the impression of the area under the head of the navicular bone. (R. D. L.).

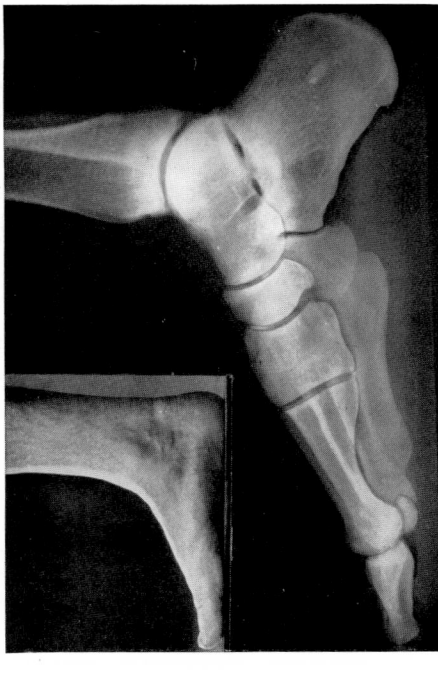

Fig. 2.—Radiograph of Right Foot of Subject standing with Muscles Contracted. (See Fig. 442, footprint **2** and contrast with footprints **1** and **3**.)

Fig. 3.—Radiograph of Right Foot of Subject standing with Muscles relaxed as fully as possible. (For footprint see Fig. 442, **3**, p. 520.)

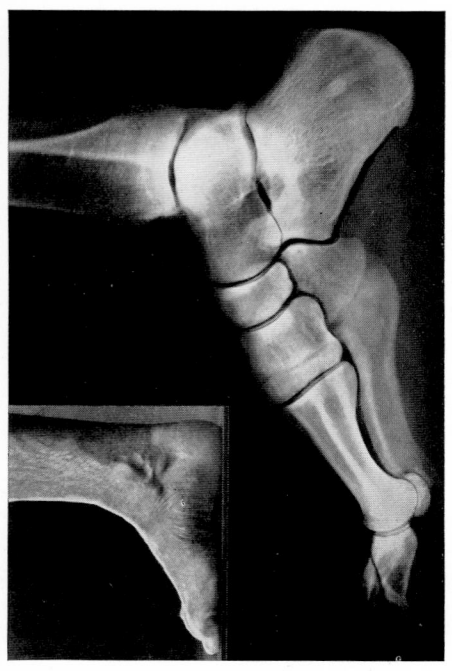

Cuboid

Base of
5th Metatarsal

Sesamoid

Head of
Talus

Navicular

Cuneiforms

Fig. 1.—Radiograph of Right Foot of Subject standing on Toes (see inset).

Plate XXXIII.—Photographic and Radiographic Illustrations of the Weight-bearing Areas of the Foot.   (R. D. L.)

(See pp. 520-521 and Fig. 442, p. 520.)

[Facing p. 520

PLATE XXXVI

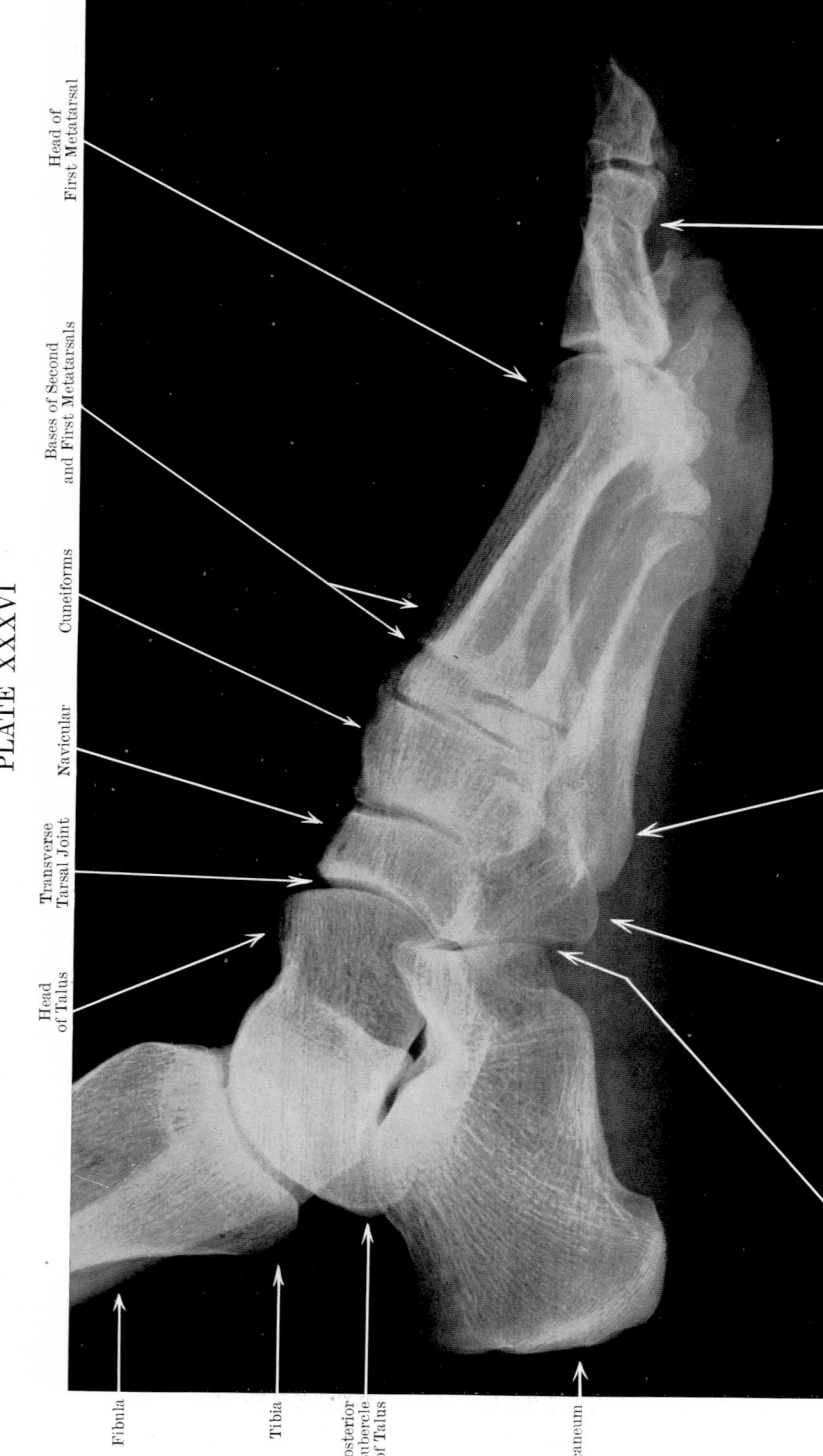

Fibula

Tibia

Posterior
tubercle
of Talus

Calcaneum

Head of
First Metatarsal

Bases of Second
and First Metatarsals

Cuneiforms

Navicular

Transverse
Tarsal Joint

Head
of Talus

Phalanges

Base of
Fifth Metatarsal

Cuboid

Transverse
Tarsal Joint

PLATE XXXVI.—LATERAL RADIOGRAPH OF FOOT OF GIRL AGED 17. (Dr. J. Duncan White.)
Note how the Medial Cuneiform overlaps the base of the Second Metatarsal. For the change in the relative position of the articular surfaces of Tibia and Talus
during movements of the Ankle, compare Plate XXVII, Fig. 2.

woman). The weight-bearing areas are merely roughly and not adequately represented by footprints; a well-worn shoe is one of the best and readiest sources of information. **In the usual method of walking,** as (say) the left heel comes down, pressure is light, for the weight is still borne mainly by the right foot; but pressure on the left heel increases as the weight is transferred, and the left heel rolls forward until the ball of the foot now makes contact. In the forward movement, the heel pressure decreases as the ball pressure increases; then the ball pressure decreases as the toe pressure increases, and this diminishes as the right foot comes forward—the left toes alone exerting pressure as the weight is being transferred to the right foot. **Most people walk slightly "toeing-out"**—the pressure being marked on the lateral side of the heel, and then transferred to the medial side of the ball of the foot. In those who walk "**toeing-in,**" the medial side of the heel bears the greater pressure, and this is transferred to the lateral side of the ball. The net result in both cases is that the line between the areas of pressure is parallel to the line of progress (Elftman). In the last part of the movement it will be noted that there is metatarso-phalangeal flexion (Pl. XXXIII, Fig. 1) and that the toes are extended while their flexors are exerting their full power of propulsion. The bar between the metatarsal pad and the phalangeal pad is evident in the case of the big toe (Fig. 442, 1, 4), but is prevented by the metatarsal pad from appearing, though the toes are extended, in the case of the others. The angle of gait, usually about 15 degrees between the two feet, varies individually and becomes less the quicker the walk (Morton). The footprint at birth is flat and the heel narrow (Fig. 442, 14) (cf. Fig. 442, 17), and is very variable as the child begins to learn to walk, as is seen by the impression in front of the heel caused by the area under the navicular bone in Fig. 442, 18. As the child grows the heel broadens out and the raising of the longitudinal arch begins.

Movements of the Lower Limb as a whole

The characteristic features of the lower limb are stability and strength, and its muscles and joints are subservient to the functions both of transmission of weight and of locomotion. In the standing position the centre of gravity of the trunk falls between the heads of the femora, and is located about the middle of the body of the last lumbar vertebra. The weight of the body is transmitted from the sacrum through the sacro-iliac joints to the hip bone, and through the femur and tibia to the arch of the foot, where the talus distributes it backwards through the calcaneum to the heel, and forwards through the tarsus and metatarsus to the ball of the foot.

Locomotion.—The three chief means of progression are walking, running, and leaping.

In **walking,** the body and its centre of gravity are inclined forwards, the trunk oscillates from side to side as it is supported alternately by each foot (the activity of the sacro-spinalis can be felt on the side of the foot leaving the ground—controlling the inclination of the trunk to the opposite side), the upper limb swings alternately with the corresponding lower limb, and one foot or the other is always on the ground. The act of progression is performed by the lower limb aided by gravity. The movements of the lower limb occur in the following way. At the beginning of a step, one lower limb, so to speak, "shoves off"; the heel is raised and the limb is extended. By the action of the muscles that flex the hip and knee joints, and extend the ankle joint and toes, the limb is raised sufficiently to clear the ground, and passes forwards by the action of gravity, aided by the force given to the movement by the extensor muscles. After passing the line of the centre of gravity the flexion of the joints ceases, the muscles relax, and the limb gradually returns to the ground. The other limb then passes through the same cycle, the weight of the body now resting on the limb which is in contact with the ground.

In **running,** the movements are all exaggerated. The time of each movement is diminished, and the force and distance are increased. Both feet are off the ground at one time; the action of flexors and extensors alternately is much more powerful, so that, on the one hand, the knees are drawn upwards to a greater extent in the forward movement, and not the whole foot but only the toes reach the ground in the extension of the limb. The attempt is made to bring the foot to the ground in front of the line of the centre of gravity. At the same time the trunk is sloped forwards much more than in walking.

In **leaping,** the actions of the limbs are still more exaggerated. The movements of flexion of the limb are still more marked, and the foot reaches the ground still farther in front of the line of the centre of gravity.

FASCIÆ OF THE LEG AND FOOT

The **superficial fascia** of the leg and foot presents no special features except in the sole, where it is greatly thickened by pads of fat, particularly at the heel and in the ball of the foot and the pads of the toes. These pads are important in weight-bearing, and they protect deeper structures. Their distribution and the flexure lines of the sole show characteristic changes during the evolution of the arches of the foot (cf. p. 520 and Fig. 442, 3, 9, 11, 15). In the webs of the toes it contains some transverse fibres that form a weak band called the *superficial transverse ligament of the sole.*

The **deep fascia** is continuous with the fascia lata and is strengthened around the knee by expansions from the tendons of the sartorius, gracilis, semitendinosus, and biceps femoris. Anteriorly, it is attached to the patella, the ligamentum patellæ, and the tubercle of the tibia; medially and laterally, it is connected to the condyles of the tibia and the head of the fibula, and helps to form the **patellar retinacula**—broad membranous bands which pass obliquely from the sides of the patella to the condyles of the tibia, and are joined by fibres of the vasti muscles.

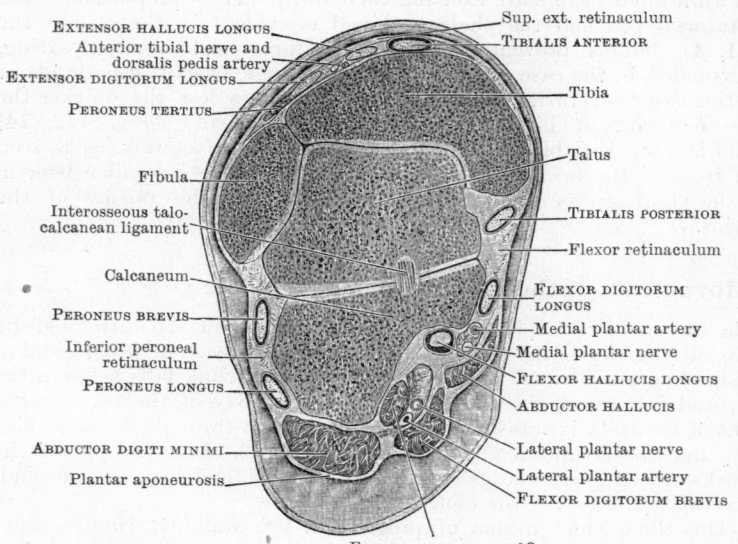

FIG. 443.—FRONTAL SECTION THROUGH THE LEFT ANKLE JOINT, TALUS, AND CALCANEUS.

Passing into the leg, the fascia blends with the periosteum of the medial surface of the tibia, and extends round the lateral side of the leg from the anterior border of the tibia to its medial border, binding the muscles together and giving origin to them, and gaining an attachment to the lower part of the shaft of the fibula. Two septa pass from its deep surface—anterior and posterior. The **anterior intermuscular septum** is attached to the anterior border of the fibula; it encloses the musculo-cutaneous nerve, and separates the peroneal muscles from the extensors; the **posterior intermuscular septum** is attached to the posterior border of the fibula, and separates the peroneal muscles from the flexors. The muscles are thus partitioned into three functional groups—extensors anteriorly, flexors posteriorly, and evertors laterally. From the posterior septum another septum extends across the back of the leg, forming a partition between the superficial and deep flexor muscles, and enclosing the posterior tibial vessels and nerve. This septum gives rise to subordinate septa which are attached to the vertical line of the tibia and the medial crest of the fibula, and separate the tibialis posterior from the flexors of the toes. It is attached above to the soleal line, whence a strong fascia is prolonged over the popliteus muscle, reinforced by an expansion from the semimembranosus.

At the ankle the deep fascia is strengthened by additional transverse fibres, and forms thickened bands named the flexor retinaculum, extensor retinacula, and peroneal retinacula.

The **flexor retinaculum** [lig. laciniatum] stretches between the medial malleolus and the medial tubercle of the calcaneus. The space which it bridges is divided into four tunnels by fibrous septa that pass from its deep surface to the back of the lower end of the tibia and to the capsule of the ankle joint. Its upper border is continuous partly with the investing deep fascia of the leg, but chiefly with the septum that covers the deep muscles of the calf. Its lower border is continuous with the deep fascia of the sole, and gives origin to the abductor hallucis muscle. It is pierced by the calcanean vessels and nerve. The four tunnels, enumerated from the medial malleolus laterally, contain (1) The tendon of the tibialis posterior, (2) the flexor digitorum longus, (3) the posterior tibial vessels and nerve, and (4) the flexor hallucis longus; and each of the tendons is enclosed in a separate synovial sheath.

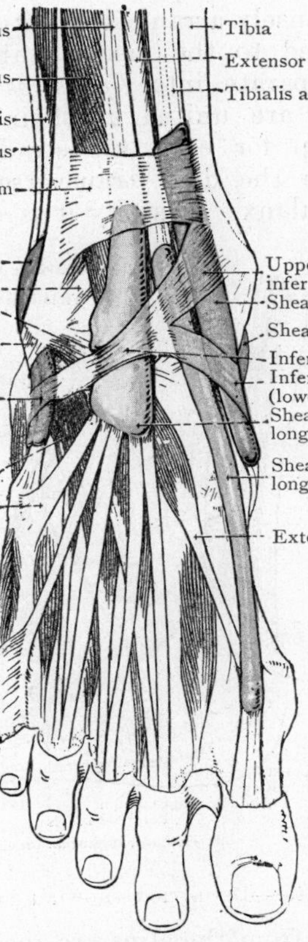

The **superior peroneal retinaculum** binds down the tendons of the peroneus longus and brevis as they pass together, invested by a single synovial sheath, behind the malleolus; the **inferior peroneal retinaculum**, attached by a septum to the peroneal tubercle, holds them separately to the lateral surface of the calcaneum, each with its own prolongation from their common synovial sheath.

The **superior extensor retinaculum** [lig. transversum cruris], broad and undefined at its proximal and distal borders, stretches across the front of the leg be-

Fig. 444.—Synovial Sheaths of the Dorsum of the Foot.

tween the distal parts of the shafts of the tibia and fibula. It binds down the tendons of the tibialis anterior and extensor muscles of the toes—of which only the tibialis has a synovial sheath at that level.

The **inferior extensor retinaculum** [lig. cruciatum cruris] is a better-defined, thickened band of deep fascia that binds down the tendons as they enter the dorsum of the foot. In shape it resembles the letter Y laid on its side. The stem is attached to the anterior part of the upper surface of the calcaneum; extending medially, it forks into two bands, the upper of which is attached to the medial malleolus, while the lower arches over the medial side of the foot and is lost in the deep fascia near the sole.

Deep to the stem of the Y, the peroneus tertius and extensor digitorum longus occupy one compartment, in a common synovial sheath. The upper limb runs superficial to the anterior tibial vessels and nerve, splits to enclose the tendon of the extensor hallucis longus, and then runs deep to the tibialis anterior, though it may sometimes split to enclose that tendon; the lower limb crosses superficial to the tendons of the extensor hallucis longus and tibialis anterior, the dorsalis pedis artery and the terminal branches of the anterior tibial nerve. There are three synovial sheaths related to the retinaculum—one for the peroneus tertius and extensor digitorum longus, and one each for the flexor hallucis longus and tibialis anterior. A band of fibres from the deep surface of the stem loops the extensor digitorum longus to become attached to adjoining parts of the calcaneum and the neck of the talus; occasionally an additional band connects the upper border of the stem with the lateral malleolus.

In the sole the deep fascia is an unbroken layer which joins the fascia of the dorsum at the borders of the foot; it is greatly thickened in the middle part and also on the surface of the abductor digiti minimi between the lateral tubercle of the calcaneum and the base of the fifth metatarsal bone. The thick portion in the middle is called the **plantar aponeurosis**, whose thickness and strength is due chiefly to densely arranged longitudinal fibres.

It is attached to the medial tubercle of the calcaneum and spreads out anteriorly to separate into *five slips* which are directed forwards to the bases of the toes and are united at their origin by ill-defined bands of transverse fibres. The slip for each toe straddles the flexor tendons and is attached on each side to the deep transverse ligaments of the sole and the base of the proximal phalanx. Distally it is continuous with the fibrous flexor sheath.

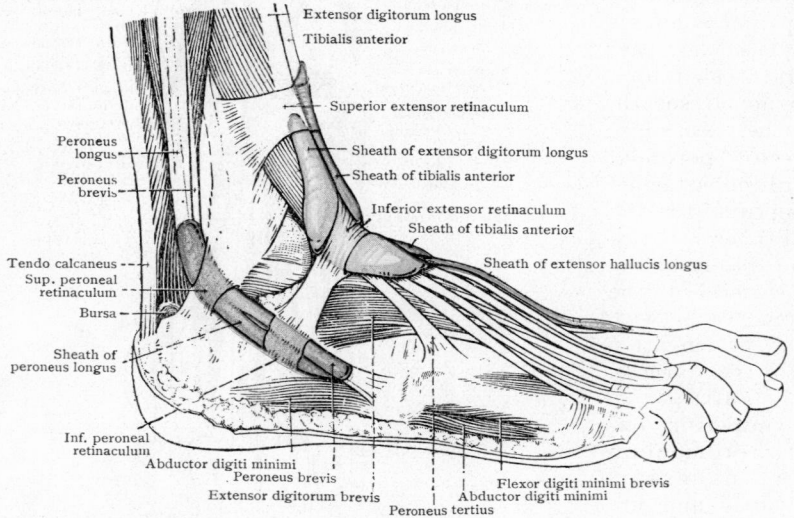

FIG. 445.—DISSECTION SHOWING SYNOVIAL SHEATH OF TENDONS OF FOOT.

Superficial fibres from the slips are inserted into the skin of the furrow between the toes and the sole. From the margins of the plantar aponeurosis strong septa are sent upwards between the flexor digitorum brevis and the two abductors; they give origin to the muscles between which they lie, and they fuse with the fascia on the deep surface of the flexor brevis, thus enclosing it in a separate sheath.

On the toes, the deep fascia is thickened to form the **fibrous flexor sheaths**, which, though smaller, are similar to those of the fingers (p. 486).

Synovial Sheaths [Vaginæ mucosæ].—The synovial sheaths facilitate the play of the tendons upon the ankle and tarsal regions. They are not so numerous as those at the wrist and in the hand, nor are they so liable to injury; and they do not communicate with the synovial sheaths in the fibrous flexor sheaths, as do those of the thumb and little finger. **On the front of the ankle and dorsum of the foot** there are three separate sheaths: one for the tendon of the tibialis anterior, one for that of the extensor hallucis longus, and a third which is common to the tendons of the extensor longus digitorum and peroneus tertius.

1. The sheath of the **tibialis anterior** begins near the upper border of the superior retinaculum and reaches almost to the insertion of the tendon.

2. The sheath of the **extensor hallucis** begins between the extensor retinacula and extends to the proximal phalanx of the big toe.

3. The sheath of the **extensor digitorum longus and peroneus tertius,** narrow above and wider below, begins at the lower border of the superior retinaculum and ends about the middle of the dorsum of the foot.

On the lateral side of the ankle and foot, the common sheath of the peroneus longus and brevis begins at the back of the lateral malleolus and bifurcates as it approaches the peroneal tubercle; one part is prolonged on the peroneus brevis almost to its insertion; the other ensheathes the peroneus longus (with or without interruption at the lateral side of the foot) across the sole to its attachment.

On the medial side of the ankle and foot there are three synovial sheaths.

1. The sheath of the **tibialis posterior** begins about 2 inches (50 mm.) above the tip of the medial malleolus, and ends at the insertion into the navicular bone.

2. The sheath of the **flexor digitorum longus** begins immediately below the previous one, but extends farther forwards—reaching the middle of the foot.

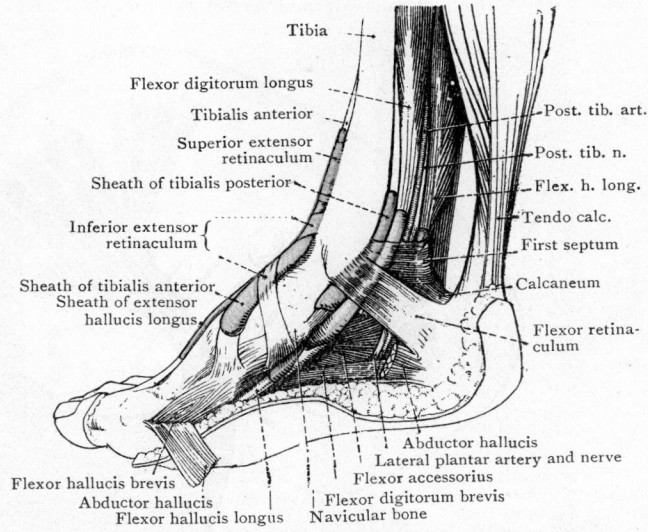

Fig. 446.—Dissection of Leg and Foot showing Synovial Sheaths.

3. The sheath of the **flexor hallucis longus** begins immediately below the last one, and may extend to the middle of the first metatarsal bone.

Within the fibrous flexor sheaths the tendons, as in the fingers, are accompanied by short synovial sheaths—that of the big toe running backwards as far as the shaft of its metatarsal bone, while the others do not extend backwards farther than the heads of the metatarsal bones.

DEVELOPMENT AND MORPHOLOGY OF SKELETAL MUSCLES

The mesoderm on each side of the neural tube separates primarily into mesodermal somites, intermediate cell mass (nephrotome), and the lateral plate. Afterwards each mesodermal somite divides into two parts—a medial portion called the **scleratogenous segment**, and a lateral portion called the **muscle plate** (myotome). The lateral plate divides into an outer layer called the **somatic mesoderm** and an inner layer called the **splanchnic mesoderm.**

The skeletal muscles are derived from the muscle plates of the mesodermal somites. The limb muscles, however, appear to be formed in the mesenchymal core of the limb-bud, probably from cells that have migrated from the muscle plates into the core; and the visceral muscles of the head and neck are derived from the mesoderm of the pharyngeal arches. Each **mesodermal somite** is at first a quadrilateral mass which rests against the neural tube and notochord. Its cavity represents a diverticulum of the cœlomic cavity. In the early stages of embryonic life the growth of the **mesodermal somite** is rapid. From its scleratogenous segment, masses of cells arise which grow medially and surround the neural tube and notochord to form the rudiment of the vertebral column. On its lateral side, cells appear to be given off which participate in the formation of the corium of the skin. At the same time the dorsal and ventral borders of the muscle plate continue to extend, and present extremities (growing points) which have an epithelial structure for a considerable period. *On the dorsal side,* it overlies the neural tube as the "dorso-lateral sheet," which gives rise to the muscles of the back; its *ventral extension* traverses the somatic mesoderm in the body wall, and produces the "ventro-lateral sheet," which gives rise to the lateral and ventral muscles of the body-wall and, by a medial prolongation, the pre-vertebral muscles of the neck. The cells of the medial layer of the muscle plates are responsible for the formation of the muscle fibres. The innervation of a muscle plate or of a pre-muscle mass is determined at a very early stage of development, and the nerve-supply of a muscle is consequently the best guide to its morphology. The dorso-lateral sheet is innervated by the posterior primary rami of the spinal nerves, the ventro-lateral by the anterior primary rami.

Portions of two or more neighbouring muscle plates may fuse to form a skeletal muscle, and that is the common mode of origin, as it is only in a few groups that the individual muscles can be referred to single muscle plates.

In the course of growth and development a muscle may become widely separated from the skeletal elements which are derived from the same somites as its myotomic constituents. The diaphragm (C. 3. 4. and 5.) is an excellent example of "muscle migration." In the same way muscles derived from the mesodermal core of the limb-buds may spread to the trunk and there

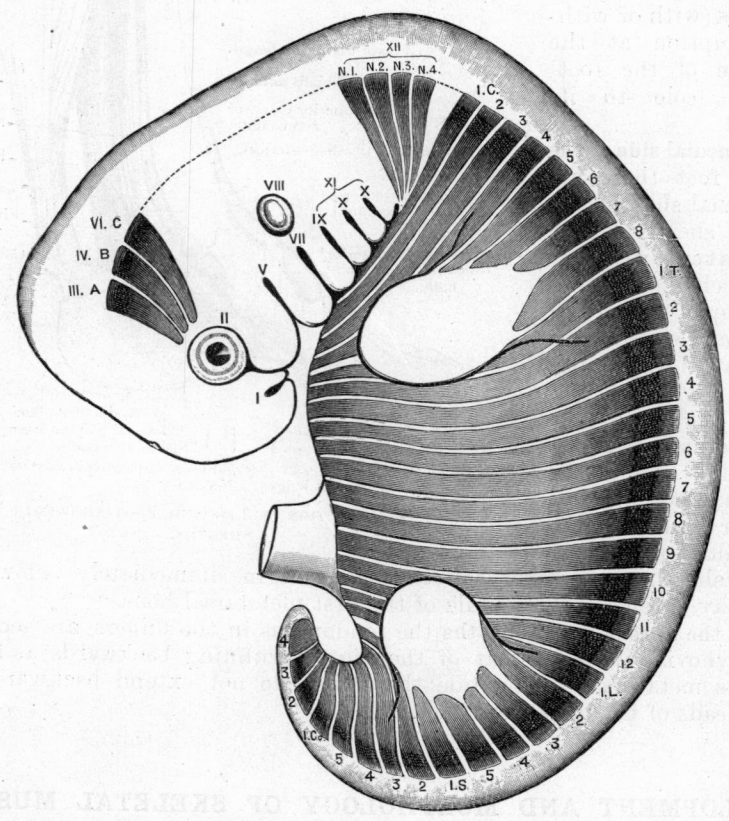

Fig. 447.—Scheme to illustrate the Disposition of the Myotomes in the Embryo in relation to the Head, Trunk, and Limbs.

A, B, C, First three cephalic myotomes; N, 1, 2, 3, occipital myotomes (it is probable that three only are represented in the human embryo); C., T., L., S., Co., The myotomes of the cervical, thoracic, lumbar, sacral, and caudal regions; I., II., III., IV., V., VI., VII., VIII., IX., X., XI., XII., refer to the cranial nerves and the structures with which they may be embryologically associated.

obtain attachments to skeletal elements at a considerable distance. The latissimus dorsi is an outstanding example of such "migration."

Musculature of the Trunk.—The **dorsal portion** of each muscle plate becomes separated off and becomes continuous with the corresponding portions of neighbouring myotomes; a longitudinal pre-muscle column is thus formed, to which the posterior primary rami of the spinal nerves are distributed. That column gives rise to the muscles of the back of the neck and the back of the trunk, and they become differentiated from one another by the formation of longitudinal fibrous septa. The deeper parts of the dorsal portions of the muscle plates remain separate in certain regions and constitute the rotatores and interspinales.

The **ventral portion** of each muscle plate carries off the anterior primary ramus of the corresponding nerve and spreads ventrally into the somatic mesoderm dorso-lateral to the derivatives of the intermediate cell mass. (a) The dorsal portion of this strip separates off from the rest and fuses with the corresponding portions of neighbouring segments. The column so formed persists in man only in the cervical region, where it gives rise to the longus cervicis, longus capitis, and the crura of the diaphragm. (b) The ventral ends of this extension into the somatic mesoderm behave in a similar way—giving rise, in man, to the rectus abdominis, the pyramidalis, the sterno-costal portions of the diaphragm, and, probably, the infra-hyoid group of muscles. (c) The intermediate portions of these strip-like extensions into the somatic mesoderm become fused and then, in some vertebrates, are delaminated into as many as five layers. In man, only three such layers are formed, viz. the obliquus externus, the obliquus internus, and the transversus abdominis. Dorsally, the quadratus lumborum, with its enclosing layers of the lumbar fascia, is derived from the same source. In the thoracic region, however, the fusion of the individual myotomic derivatives is carried out only in the case of the transversus thoracis. The more superficial derivatives constitute the external and internal intercostal muscles, which retain their segmental characters. It appears probable that in the cervical region the corresponding myotomic derivatives in part disappear and in part form the scalene muscles and the remaining portion of the diaphragm.

The ventral portions of the lumbar myotomes (with the exception of the first) and the upper sacral myotomes disappear in man ; but they persist in the third and fourth sacral somites and give rise to the levator ani and the coccygeus.

The occipital myotomes form the muscles of the tongue.

The diaphragm, which may justly be termed the most essential of all the skeletal muscles in man, is derived to a very large extent, if not entirely, from the ventral portion of the fourth cervical muscle plate. The crura are on the same morphological plane as the longus cervicis, the sterno-costal portions as the rectus and transversus abdominis. The phylogenetic history of the diaphragm shows that it represents the detached cervical portion of the transversus sheet. In Amphibia and Reptilia there is no separation of the pleural and peritoneal cavities, and the whole transversus sheet functions as a compressor of the cœlom and so as a muscle of expiration. In Mammalia, on the other hand, the diaphragm intervenes between the pleural and the peritoneal cavities, and its action as a cœlomic compressor is restricted to the latter. At the same time, its new position makes it a powerful inspiratory muscle, and in man it is of very much greater importance than all the other muscles which, primarily or secondarily, help to increase the capacity of the thorax. In pronograde mammals, on the other hand, inspiration depends much more on elevation of the ribs by the external respiratory muscles, and the principal action of the diaphragm in those animals would seem to be its primitive action as a compressor of the cœlom.

The **branchial musculature** is formed in the mesoderm of the pharyngeal arches and is quite distinct from the musculature derived from the occipital and cervical myotomes, not only in its source but also in its innervation, which is obtained from certain of the cranial nerves. Although laid down in the substance of the arches, the branchial muscles may undergo extensive "migration." This change of position is best exemplified by the muscles of the second arch (vide infra).

The sterno-mastoid and trapezius have a special morphological history, as is clearly indicated by the peculiarity of their supply from the accessory nerve. They arise from a special common rudiment, believed to be branchial in origin, situated in the embryo over the hinder part of the branchial region ventral to the last two occipital myotomes and first two cervical myotomes, from which situation they spread to their attachments to the head and shoulder-girdle. The accessory part of the vagal complex which supplies these muscles extends into the cervical part of the spinal cord, and this extension is perhaps to be associated with their afferent supply from that region (C. 2. 3. 4.) ; if any motor fibres reach the muscles through these cervical nerves, this is to be looked upon as a secondary supply from the same source by an alternative route and not as an indication of myotomic origin.

The accompanying table indicates the muscles derived from the individual pharyngeal arches with their nerves of supply :—

Arch.	Nerve.	Muscles.
First (mandibular)	Trigeminal (mandibular division)	Muscles of mastication Tensor tympani Tensor palati
Second (hyoid)	Facial	Muscles of facial expression (including muscles of scalp and platysma) Stylo-hyoid Posterior belly of digastric Stapedius
Third	Glosso-pharyngeal	Stylo-pharyngeus (Constrictors of pharynx ?)
Fourth Fifth ? Sixth	Vagus-Accessory	Constrictors of pharynx Muscles of soft palate Muscles of larynx Sterno-mastoid and trapezius

Muscles of the Orbit.—It has not been possible to identify cephalic muscle plates in the human embryo. The muscles of the orbit can be distinguished in the embryo as a single pre-muscle mass, closely related to the optic vesicle, and receiving the terminations of the third, fourth, and sixth cranial nerves. Muscle plates have been demonstrated in the head region of elasmobranch fishes : the precise number is uncertain, but probably there are at least nine, of which the last four are occipital. The first three cephalic muscle plates form the muscles of the orbit—the first giving rise to the group supplied by the oculo-motor nerve, the second to the superior oblique, and the third to the lateral rectus muscle. The fourth and subsequent myotomes disappear, but three occipital muscle plates persist to form the muscles of the tongue.

Musculature of the Limbs.—The developing limb-bud consists of an ectodermal envelope enclosing a mass of mesoderm from which both the skeletal elements and the musculature of the limb are derived. Ventral and dorsal sheets of muscle are laid down, and they are at first continuous with each other along the pre-axial and post-axial borders of the bud. The anterior primary rami of the spinal nerves which eventually enter into the formation of the limb plexus are at first arranged segmentally in the developing limb, and each gives ventral and dorsal branches to exactly corresponding portions of the muscle sheets. It will therefore be found that the muscles which develop along the pre-axial border, whether ventral or dorsal, are innervated by the highest nerve of the plexus, while those which develop along the post-axial border are innervated by the lowest nerve of the plexus. The early subdivision of the limb musculature into ventral and dorsal sheets, and the innervation of portions of both sheets by every nerve of the limb plexus, are indicated in the fully formed upper limb by the division of the trunks of the brachial plexus into anterior and posterior divisions prior to the formation of the cords ; and, in the case of the lower limb, by the similar division of the nerves that enter the lumbar and sacral plexuses.

The proximal portions of the two muscle sheets extend towards the trunk and eventually constitute the muscles which connect the limb or its girdle to the trunk (with the exception of the trapezius). Those muscles are much more numerous in the upper limb than they are in the lower limb, where their chief representative is the psoas major.

PLATE XXXVII

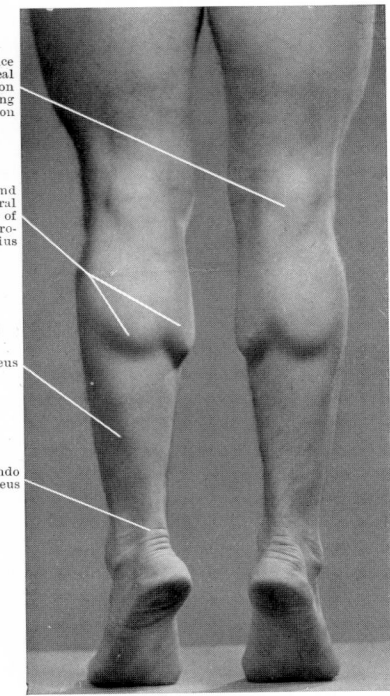

Eminence
popliteal
region
during
extension

Medial and
lateral
bellies of
Gastro-
cnemius

Soleus

Tendo
calcaneus

FIG. 1.—ACTIVITY OF THE CALF MUSCLES IN
RISING ON THE TOES.

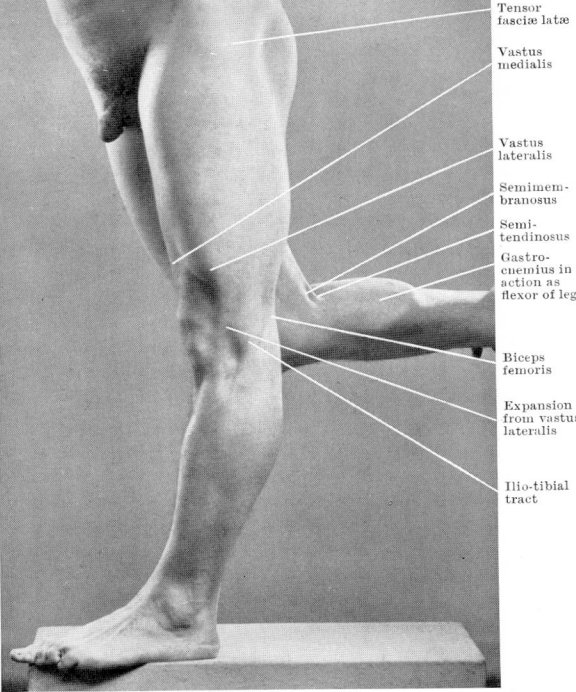

Tensor
fasciæ latæ

Vastus
medialis

Vastus
lateralis

Semimem-
branosus

Semi-
tendinosus

Gastro-
cnemius in
action as
flexor of leg

Biceps
femoris

Expansion
from vastus
lateralis

Ilio-tibial
tract

FIG. 2.—ACTIVITY OF MUSCLES IN EXTENSION AND
RESISTED FLEXION OF LEG.

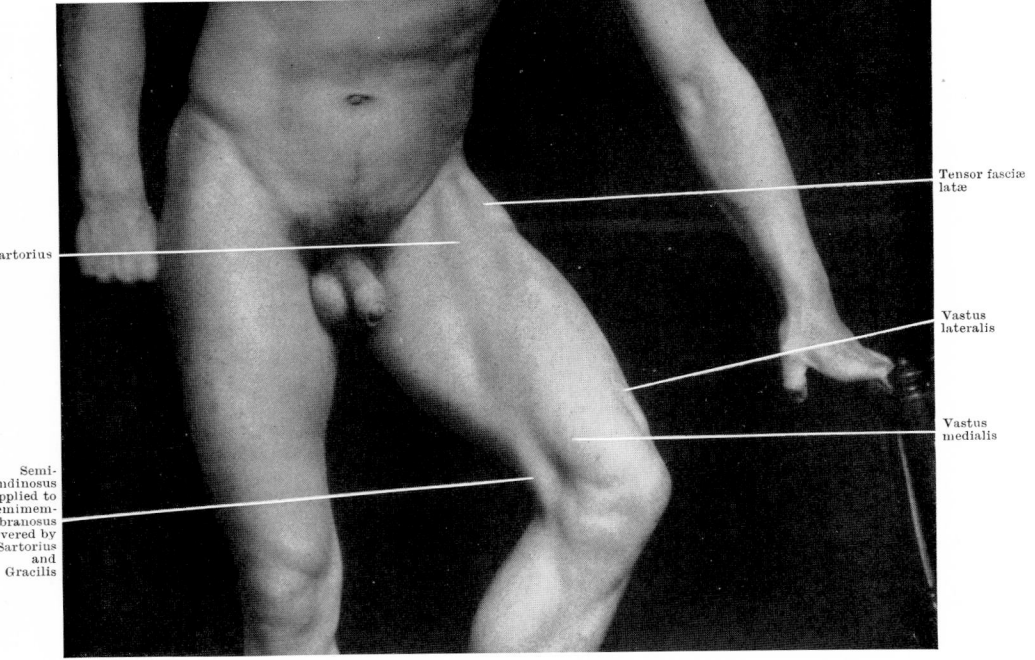

Sartorius

Tensor fasciæ
latæ

Vastus
lateralis

Vastus
medialis

Semi-
tendinosus
applied to
Semimem-
branosus
covered by
Sartorius
and
Gracilis

FIG. 3.—THE SARTORIUS IN ACTION.

PLATE XXXVII.—PHOTOGRAPHIC ILLUSTRATIONS OF MUSCLES IN ACTION.   (R. D. L.)

PLATE XXXVIII

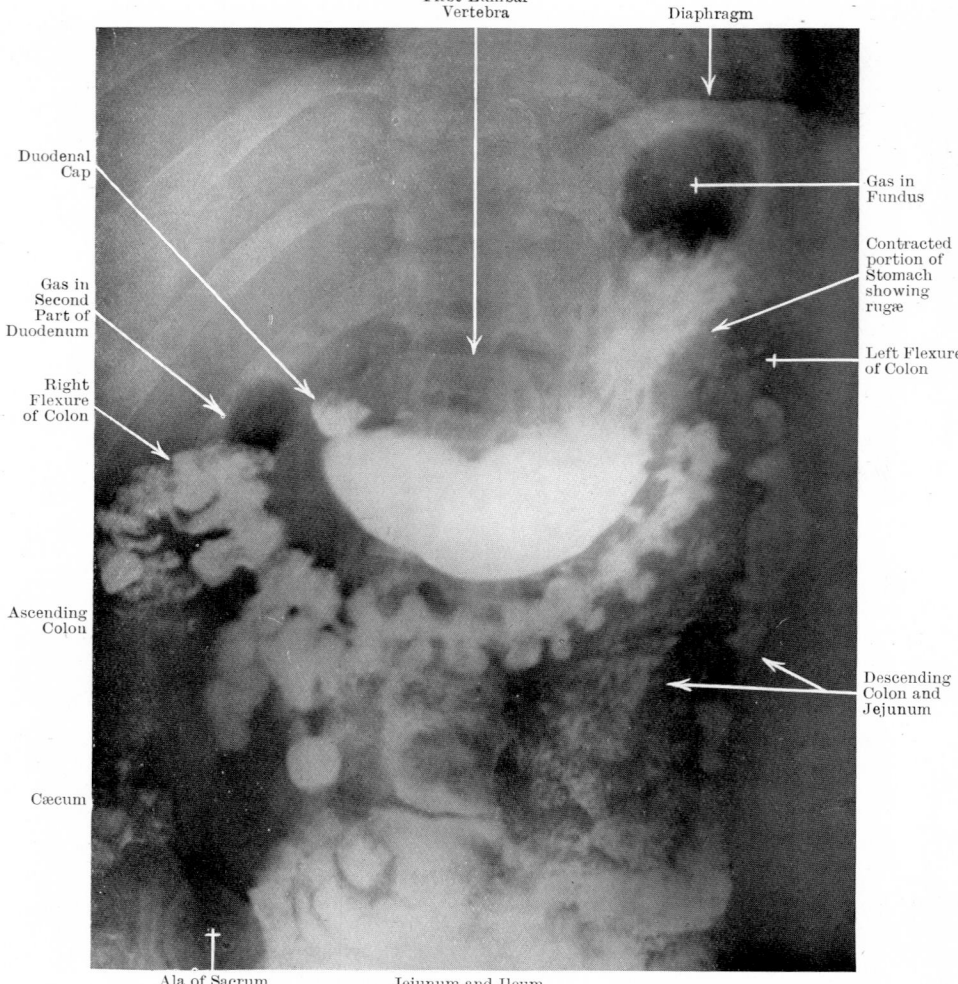

First Lumbar
Vertebra

Diaphragm

Duodenal
Cap

Gas in
Fundus

Contracted
portion of
Stomach
showing
rugæ

Gas in
Second
Part of
Duodenum

Left Flexure
of Colon

Right
Flexure
of Colon

Ascending
Colon

Descending
Colon and
Jejunum

Cæcum

Ala of Sacrum

Jejunum and Ileum

PLATE XXXVIII.—RADIOGRAPH OF ABDOMEN OF MAN AGED 28 IN THE
ERECT POSTURE, SHOWING THE APPEARANCE OF THE ALIMENTARY
CANAL AFTER ADMINISTRATION OF OPAQUE MEALS AT INTERVALS.

The contents of the Stomach and Duodenum and of the Ileum seen in Plate XLIV
(given respectively 45 and 48 hours previously) are now in the Large Intestine. The first half
of a third opaque meal (given one hour before the radiograph was taken) is in the Jejunum
and Ileum, and the Stomach is half-filled by the second half. Note the Duodenal Cap (see
p. 592) and the residue of radio-opaque material in the Cæcum and Ascending Colon. For
stages in the filling and emptying of the Large Intestine, see Plates XLI and XLVII.

DIGESTIVE SYSTEM

Originally written by the late AMBROSE BIRMINGHAM, M.D.,
Professor of Anatomy, Royal College of Surgeons, Dublin

Revised and rewritten by

DAVID WATERSTON

THE physical characters and the chemical composition of the food taken into the body are such that much of it cannot at once be utilised by the organism. Before it is absorbed and used in nutrition, it is acted upon both chemically and mechanically. The process of performing these mechanical and chemical changes is termed *digestion*.

The term **Digestive System** is applied collectively to the organs which are concerned in this process, in the reception of food into the body, and in the excretion of the unabsorbed residue.

A simple form of digestive system, found in many of the lower animals, consists of a tube that passes through the interior of the body from an anterior or mouth aperture to a posterior aperture or anal orifice.

In Man, a tube of that kind forms the basis of the digestive system. It extends from the mouth, through the neck, thorax, abdomen, and pelvis, to the anal orifice. The wall and lining membrane act mechanically and chemically upon the food in its interior, absorb products of digestion and transmit them into the adjacent blood vessels and lymph vessels.

The successive parts of this tube are the *mouth, pharynx, œsophagus, stomach, small intestine,* and *large intestine*. The mouth and pharynx are used for respiration as well as for digestion, and the **alimentary canal** proper begins at the upper end of the œsophagus. In addition, there are several glandular organs whose ducts open into the mouth—the *salivary glands*—and into the small intestine—*liver* and *pancreas*. These also are included in the digestive system. The general arrangement, position, and size of these various parts are shown in Fig. 448.

THE MOUTH

The **mouth**, the first part of the digestive system, is bounded externally by the lips and cheeks, and roofed in by the palate. Within it lie the teeth and greater part of the tongue ; and the ducts of the salivary glands open into it.

The aperture of the mouth or **oral fissure** is the interval between the lips, which meet at the *angles of the mouth*. In a state of rest, with the lips in apposition, the aperture forms a slightly curved line which extends transversely between the first premolar teeth at a level immediately below the middle of the upper incisor crowns. The shape of the aperture varies with every movement of the lips, from the resting linear form, curved like the conventional bow, to a circular or oval shape when the mouth is widely open, or the "pursed-up" condition produced by the contraction of the orbicularis oris muscle.

The **cavity of the mouth** is divisible into two portions—the *vestibule* and the *cavity proper*.

34

The **vestibule of the mouth** is the interval between the lips and cheeks externally and the teeth and gums of the upper and lower jaws internally.

When the oral fissure is closed and the lips and the teeth are in contact, the

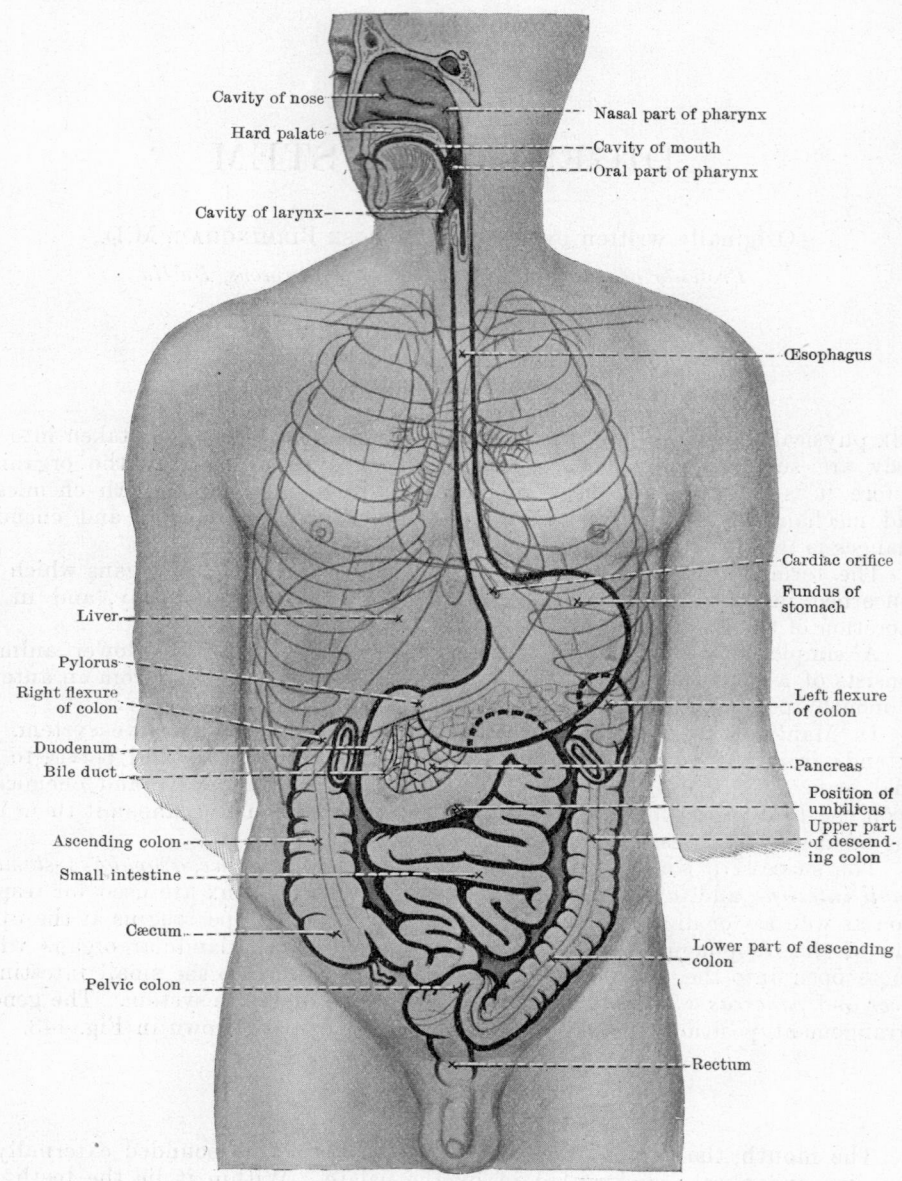

Fig. 448.—Diagram of the General Arrangement of the Digestive System.

The transverse colon is not represented, in order that the duodenum and pancreas, which lie behind it, may be seen.

vestibule is merely a slit whose narrow roof and floor are formed by the reflexion of the mucous membrane from the lips and cheeks to the maxillæ and mandible. From the back of each lip in the median plane projects a small vertical fold of mucous membrane—the **frenulum**—which connects the lip to the front of the corresponding gum. The *frenulum of the upper lip* is the larger, and is brought into view when the lip is everted. The *frenulum of the lower lip* is not always obvious.

On the outer wall of the vestibule, opposite the crown of the second upper molar, there is a slight eminence, and on its summit is the small opening of the duct of the parotid gland.

When the upper and lower teeth are in contact the vestibule communicates with the cavity of the mouth only through small and irregular spaces between opposing teeth, and, behind, by the wider but variable aperture between the last molars and the ramus of the mandible.

Advantage may be taken of that aperture for the introduction into the mouth of liquid food in certain cases—trismus, anchylosis, etc.—in which the jaws are rigidly closed.

If the finger is passed backwards in the vestibule, the anterior border of the masseter can be distinctly felt on the outer wall, when the muscle is thrown into a state of contraction. Still farther back, the front of the coronoid process, bearing the insertion of the temporal muscle, can also be made out. The spheno-mandibular ligament, which corresponds to, and is felt along with, the anterior border of the medial pterygoid muscle, is distinguishable as a pliant ridge when the finger is carried from the front of the coronoid process behind the last molar tooth into the cavity of the mouth.

In addition to the ducts of the parotid glands, those of numerous small glands, which are embedded in the lips and cheeks, open into the vestibule.

Under normal conditions the lips and cheeks lie against the teeth and gums, obliterating the cavity of the vestibule, and help, with the aid of the tongue, to keep the food between the grinding surfaces of the molar teeth during mastication. In facial palsy, however, the lips and cheeks fall away from the dental arches, owing to the paralysis of their muscles, and particularly of the buccinator muscle, and food accumulates in the vestibule.

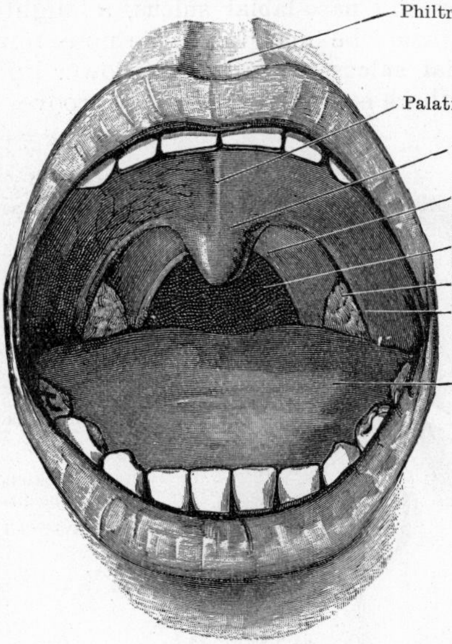

FIG. 449.—OPEN MOUTH SHOWING PALATE AND TONSILS.

It shows also the two palatine arches, the oro-pharyngeal isthmus, through which the mouth communicates with the oral part of the pharynx, and the pharyngeal isthmus or communication of the oral part of the pharynx with the nasal part.

The **cavity proper of the mouth** lies within the arches of the teeth and gums, and extends back to the palato-glossal arches. The *roof* is formed by the **hard palate** and the anterior portion of the **soft palate**, the *floor* by the anterior part of the tongue in the middle, and on each side by the reflexion of the mucous membrane from the side of the tongue to the mandible.

The term "floor of the mouth" indicates the muscular and other structures, especially the mylo-hyoid muscles, which fill in the interval between the two halves of the body of the mandible (from the symphysis menti to the body of the hyoid bone), and form the basis upon which the tongue and the mucous membrane of the sublingual space are supported.

When the tip of the tongue is raised the mucous membrane forms in the median plane a prominent fold, called the **frenulum of the tongue**, which stretches from the floor of the mouth to the inferior surface of the tongue. On each side of the frenulum, near its junction with the floor, there is a prominent soft projection, called the **sublingual papilla**, on which the **duct of the submandibular gland** opens (Fig. 450). Running laterally and backwards, on each side, from the frenulum, there is a well-marked ridge, called the **sublingual fold** (plica sublingualis), which is due to the bulging of the underlying sublingual gland. Most of the ducts of the gland open near the crest of this ridge. Another fold, called the **fimbriated fold** (plica fimbriata), lies lateral to the frenulum, on each side, on the inferior surface of the tongue (Fig. 450).

This fold represents the under-tongue of some mammals, in whom it is a sort of fringe, stated to be of service in cleaning the incisor teeth (F. Wood Jones).

34 a

Lips.—The lips are the two mobile folds, covered externally with skin, and internally with mucous membrane, which surround the oral fissure and contain the orbicularis oris muscle. Laterally, they are prolonged into the cheeks, and below into the chin. The junction of the lips and cheek is marked on the surface by the **naso-labial sulcus**, a slight groove which passes downwards and laterally from the margin of the nose towards the angle of the mouth, while the **mento-labial sulcus** separates the lower lip from the chin. At the middle of the upper lip there is a shallow vertical groove—the **philtrum**—bounded by two distinct ridges that descend from the nasal septum (Fig. 450); inferiorly the groove widens out and ends opposite a slight projection on the free edge—the *labial tubercle*. That tubercle is particularly well developed in children, and is chiefly responsible for the characteristic curve of the oral fissure. The lower lip is usually longer and more movable than the upper lip.

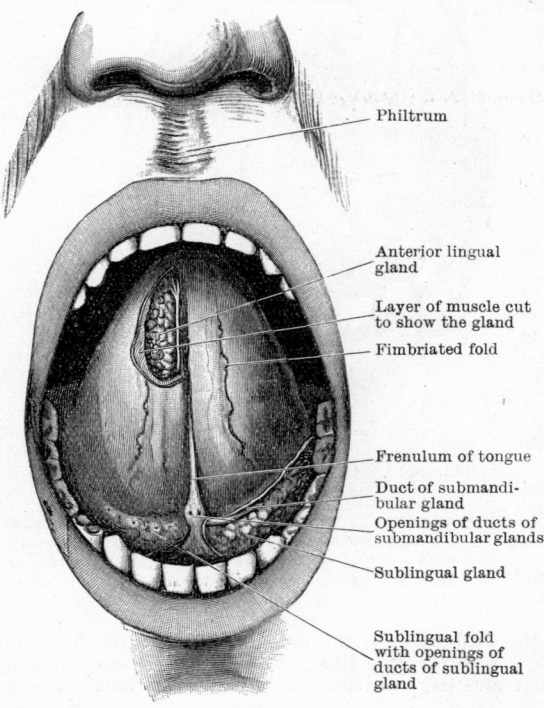

FIG. 450.—OPEN MOUTH WITH TONGUE RAISED, AND THE SUBLINGUAL AND ANTERIOR LINGUAL GLANDS EXPOSED.

The sublingual gland of the left side has been laid bare by the removal of the mucous membrane; to expose the anterior lingual gland of the right side a thin layer of muscle, in addition to the mucous membrane, has been removed. A branch of the lingual nerve is seen running on the medial side of the gland. The profunda vein also is faintly indicated on this side.

Between the inner and outer surface of each lip is an intermediate area—the free margin—which bounds the oral fissure. It is covered with a modified mucous membrane similar to that of the mouth but devoid of mucous glands and dry. It is translucent, and transmits the colour of the blood in the underlying capillaries and hence in health is reddish-pink in colour. Its size and shape vary greatly; it may be narrow and thin, occupying only a small area on the external surface of the lip, or it may be wide and pouting and, as in the negro, may occupy a wide surface externally. The surface is richly vascular and numerous nerve terminals are present in it. It is limited externally by a sharply defined line where the skin and mucous membrane meet, but the internal boundary is not easily recognisable as it merges into the mucous membrane of the mouth. In the upper lip, the external bounding line follows a curve from near the angle of the mouth to the root of the labial tubercle and there turns sharply downwards, forming with its fellow a bow-shaped figure. In the lower lip the line runs in a more uniform curve from one angle of the mouth to the other. In the child the free margin is transversely grooved and is also divided by a longitudinal groove into two zones—the outer villous, the inner smooth.

In each lip the following structures are present from the external to the internal surface:—(1) **Skin**, closely studded with hairs, small and fine in children and women, long and stout in men. (2) A layer of fatty **superficial fascia** continuous with the fascia of the face. (3) The **orbicularis oris muscle**, a number of whose fibres, or those of the muscles which join it, pass through the superficial fascia and are attached to the skin. (4) **Submucous tissue**, which is occupied by an almost continuous layer of racemose glands—the **labial glands**; they are small, nodular glands, each about the size of a grape seed, closely packed together, and lying immediately external to the mucous membrane of the upper and lower lips; each nodule is a small racemose gland, lined with mucous secretory cells, with a short duct opening through the mucous membrane. (5) **Mucous membrane** of the mouth, covered with stratified squamous epithelium.

For the various muscles which enter into the formation of the lip, see the chapter on Myology (pp. 401-403).

Vessels and Nerves.—The lips receive a free **arterial** supply from the labial branches of the *facial artery.*

The sensory **nerve** supply of the lips is derived from the *trigeminal nerve*—that of the upper through the *infra-orbital branch* of the maxillary nerve, and that of the lower from the *mental branch* of the inferior dental branch of the mandibular nerve, while the *buccal* branch of the mandibular nerve supplies the region of the angle. The **lymph vessels** of the upper lip pass with the facial artery to the *submandibular lymph glands,* while those from the lower lip pass in part to the same glands, and in part to the *submental glands.*

Movements of the Lips.—Opening and closing of the oral fissure are usually associated with elevation and depression of the mandible. Finer movements are effected by contraction of the orbicularis oris muscle as a whole or of its parts, and by those muscles of expression which are inserted into the upper and lower lips.

Ability to perform finer movements of the lips in speech or in whistling constitutes a test of the integrity of the nerve supply of these muscles.

Cheeks.—The cheeks resemble the lips in structure, and are formed of corresponding layers, but the buccinator muscle takes the place of the orbicularis oris. They are covered externally with the skin. Under the skin lies the fatty superficial fascia of the face, through which the **parotid duct** runs inwards to pierce the buccinator; it is much looser in texture than in the lips. Near the end of the duct are found four or five mucous glands, as large as hemp-seeds, known as the **molar glands**; their ducts pierce the cheek and open into the vestibule. Beneath the superficial fascia lies the *buccinator muscle,* covered by the thin bucco-pharyngeal fascia. Deeper still is the submucosa, which, like that of the lips, contains numerous racemose glands—the **buccal glands**—and finally the mucous membrane.

The **buccal pad of fat** is an encapsuled mass of fat which lies on the outer side of the buccinator, and in the recess between that muscle and the overlying part of the masseter. It gives to the cheeks their rounded contour. It is relatively larger in the child than in the adult, and strengthens the cheek to resist the effects of atmospheric pressure during the act of sucking.

Movements of the Cheeks.—The cheeks are of great importance in mastication. By their movements the cavity of the vestibule of the mouth can be obliterated, and food in the vestibule forced into the cavity of the mouth proper. Movements of the cheeks are also required in playing wind instruments. The principal agent is the buccinator muscle, but the orbicularis oris muscle and the muscles inserted into the lips also participate.

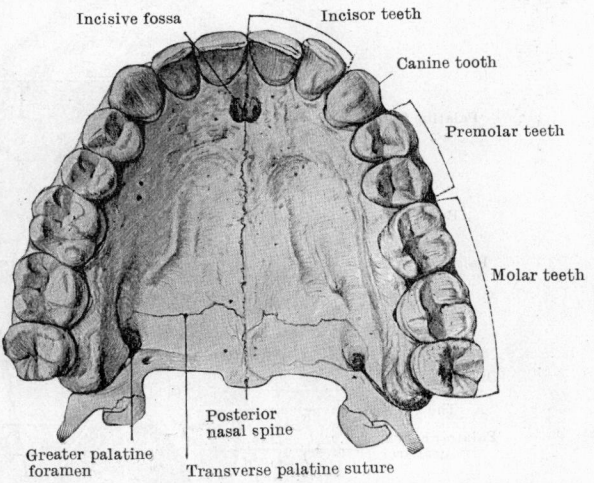

FIG. 451.—THE HARD PALATE AND UPPER PERMANENT TEETH.

Palate.—The palate forms the roof of the mouth. It separates the mouth from the nasal cavities and nasal part of the pharynx, and it extends backwards into the cavity of the pharynx, forming a partial division between the oral and the nasal parts of the pharynx.

It consists of two portions—an anterior two-thirds, with a bony foundation, and a posterior third, with a fibrous basis, termed the *hard palate* and the *soft palate* respectively. The palate is arched antero-posteriorly, and also transversely. The latter curvature is the more pronounced in the hard palate.

The **hard palate** is a horizontal plate formed by the palatine processes of the maxillæ and the horizontal plates of the palatine bones, covered on each surface, superior and inferior, with muco-periosteum. The muco-periosteum of the inferior surface is very thick, and contains in its posterior part (Fig. 452) a large number of racemose glands and the larger nerves and blood-vessels of the palate.

34 *b*

The epithelium of the muco-periosteum covering the superior surface is largely ciliated in character, and forms the floor of the nasal cavity, while that on the inferior surface is covered with stratified squamous epithelium.

The **soft palate** is attached to the posterior margin of the hard palate. Its lower or posterior margin is free, and forms an arch which extends from one side of the pharynx to the other; but the arch is interrupted in the middle by a conical projection, called the **uvula**, which shows great variation in length; in some persons it is short and blunt; in others it is long and thin and its tip may extend downwards to the dorsum of the tongue. On each side, the soft palate is connected with two folds of mucous membrane which are separated by a triangular interval occupied by the tonsil. The anterior fold is called the *palato-glossal arch* (p. 536), and descends to the side of the tongue. The posterior fold descends from the posterior edge of the soft palate and is lost on the side wall of the pharynx; it is called the *palato-pharyngeal arch* (p. 561).

The superior surface of the soft palate continues the floor of the nasal cavity backwards and downwards, and forms the floor of the nasal part of the pharynx.

Along the middle of the buccal surface of the palate, a faint median ridge—the **palatine raphe** (Figs. 449, 452)—indicates its original development from two halves; it

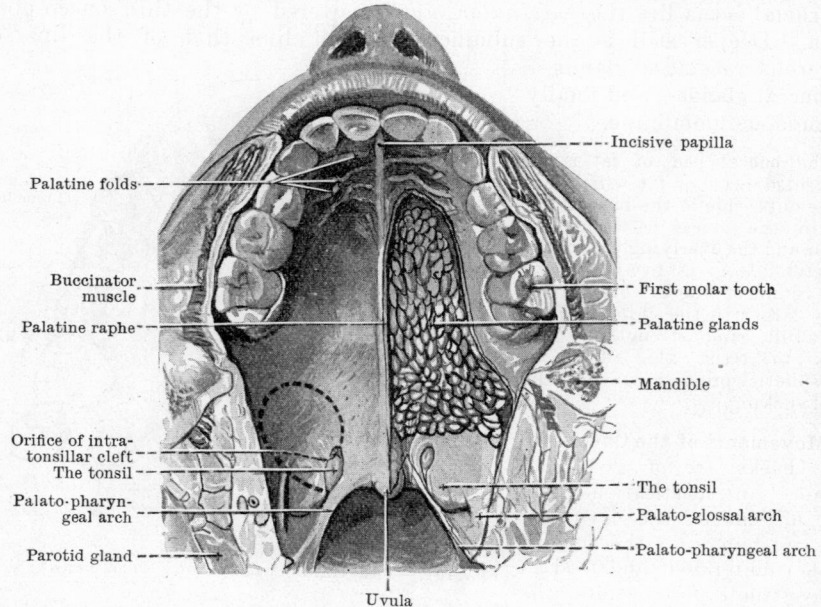

FIG. 452.—PALATE OF A CHILD OF TEN YEARS FROM BELOW. The mucous membrane has been removed over an area on the left side. The palato-glossal arch was largely adherent to the anterior surface of the tonsil, and its free margin was thus obscured. The dotted line shows the extent of the intratonsillar cleft in this specimen.

begins behind at the root of the uvula, and in front it ends in a slight elevation called the **incisive papilla**; in the fœtus, and even at birth, the papilla is continued over the edge of the gum into the frenulum of the upper lip. Sometimes a small pit, which will admit the point of a pin, is seen on each side, immediately posterior to the central incisor teeth, and about 2 mm. from the median plane. Those pits correspond to the inferior openings of the incisive canals, with which they are occasionally continuous. From the anterior part of the raphe a series of transverse ridges of mucous membrane, about six in number, run laterally, immediately behind the incisor teeth; they are known as the *palatine folds*, and are composed of dense fibrous tissues. These folds correspond to the strongly marked ridges seen in the roof of the mouth of lower animals; they are very distinct in a fœtus of five or six months, are less distinct in a child, and become more or less obliterated in old age.

The hard palate is, on the whole, horizontal in direction, both transversely and antero-posteriorly. The soft palate, during rest, as for instance in quiet nasal breathing, is very oblique in direction, and shuts off the mouth from the nasal and largely from the oral parts of the pharynx. When, however, the soft palate is raised, as in swallowing, it continues the plane of the hard palate backwards, and projects across the cavity of the pharynx, forming a nearly complete partition between its oral and nasal parts. In that position it prevents food from passing upwards into the nasal part of the pharynx and the nose.

Structure.—The framework of the soft palate is formed of a strong, thin, flat, fibrous sheet, called the *palatine aponeurosis*, which is confined to the anterior part of the soft palate, and is the expanded tendons of the tensor palati muscles. Its anterior margin is united to the posterior edge of the horizontal plates of the palatine bones. The tensor palati is continuous with its lateral part, but the other muscles do not, as a rule, reach farther forwards than 8 or 10 mm. from the posterior edge of the hard palate.

The anterior part of the soft palate contains practically no muscular fibres; it is composed of the palatine aponeurosis, covered by an extremely thick layer of glands on the inferior surface and by mucous membrane on both surfaces. The anterior portion is much less movable than the rest of the soft palate, and forms a relatively horizontal continuation backwards of the hard palate, stretching across between the two medial pterygoid laminæ. Upon that portion chiefly the tensor palati muscles act. The posterior and larger part contains muscular fibres in abundance, slopes strongly downwards, and is freely movable, and upon it the other palatine muscles act. The muscles of the soft palate (the unpaired musculus uvulæ, and four pairs, the palato-pharyngeus, palato-glossus, levator palati, and tensor palati) are described on pp. 416, 417.

The **muco-periosteum** of the inferior surface of the palate, which is covered with stratified squamous epithelium, is firmer and more closely adherent in front, near the folds, than behind, near the soft palate. In the fœtus the whole of the epithelium on the upper surface of the soft palate is ciliated, but after birth the ciliated epithelium is largely replaced by stratified squamous epithelium, except at the margins.

Mucous glands, the orifices of which can be seen as dots with the naked eye, are extremely abundant in the soft palate and in the posterior half of the hard palate, except near the raphe. The position and limits of these glands are usually clearly indicated by the smooth area of the hard palate. The glands usually extend forward as far as a line drawn behind the canine teeth.

The **uvula** is composed of a mass of racemose glands and areolar tissue covered with mucous membrane, and containing a slender prolongation of the uvular muscle in its upper part.

Vessels and Nerves of the Palate.—The principal **arteries** are the palatine branches of the maxillary artery. The largest and most important of these is the *greater palatine artery*, which reaches the palate through the greater palatine foramen, and runs forward along the lateral margin of the hard palate, near the alveolar margin, towards the incisive fossa, where it anastomoses with a minute branch of the *nasal septal branch* of the spheno-palatine artery. Some smaller *lesser palatine branches* from the maxillary artery emerge through the lesser palatine foramina and supply the soft palate and anastomose with the ascending palatine branch of the facial artery. The soft palate shares in the blood supply of neighbouring structures, and so receives a blood supply from the tonsillar branch of the facial artery, the ascending pharyngeal artery, and from dorsal lingual branches of the lingual artery.

The **sensory nerves** of the palate are all branches from the spheno-palatine ganglion. The largest of these—the *greater palatine nerve*—emerges through the greater palatine foramen, and divides in the roof of the mouth into branches which run in grooves in the hard palate and extend forward nearly to the incisor teeth. Some of them join with a small branch of the *long spheno-palatine nerve*, which reaches the palate through the median incisive foramen. The *lesser palatine nerves* emerge through the lesser palatine foramina, and are distributed to the hard and soft palate. For the **motor** nerves to the muscles of the soft palate, see p. 417.

The **lymph vessels** of the palate pass lateral to the tonsil and the palato-glossal arch to the *upper deep cervical lymph glands.*

Movements of the Soft Palate.—The hinder part of the soft palate is freely mobile, moving like a door on its hinge, near its junction with the hard palate. It can be raised so that its dorsal surface comes into contact with the posterior wall of the pharynx and so separates the oral part of the pharynx from the nasal part. This movement occurs in swallowing, in vomiting, and, to a lesser degree, in the pronunciation of the vowel "A," and is effected by the levator palati muscles. The posterior part of the soft palate can also be lowered and its under surface brought into contact with the posterior part of the upper surface of the tongue, so that the mouth is shut off from the pharynx. As a rule the tongue is elevated at the same time to meet the palate, as in swallowing. The principal agents in this movement are the palato-glossus and the palato-pharyngeus muscles.

Oro-Pharyngeal Isthmus [Isthmus Faucium].—The oro-pharyngeal isthmus is the aperture through which the mouth communicates with the oral part of the pharynx (Fig. 449). It is bounded at the sides by the palato-glossal arches, above by the inferior surface of the soft palate, and below by the dorsum of the tongue; in width it corresponds pretty closely to the cavity of the mouth.

Each **palato-glossal arch** is a fold of mucous membrane containing a palato-glossus muscle in its interior. It begins on the lower surface of the soft palate, about one third of an inch (8 mm.) in front of its posterior edge, near the root of the uvula, and, arching laterally and downwards, it descends to blend with the mucous membrane of the side of the tongue a little behind its middle.

Gums.—The gums (gingivæ) are composed of firm fibrous tissue united with mucous membrane. They are attached to the alveolar borders of the maxillæ and mandible and surround the necks of the teeth. They are richly supplied with blood-vessels, but sparsely with nerves, and are covered with stratified squamous epithelium. Around the neck of each tooth, the gum forms a free overlapping collar, and at that part particularly it is closely studded with small papillæ, visible to the naked eye. In thickness it usually measures from 1 to 2 mm.

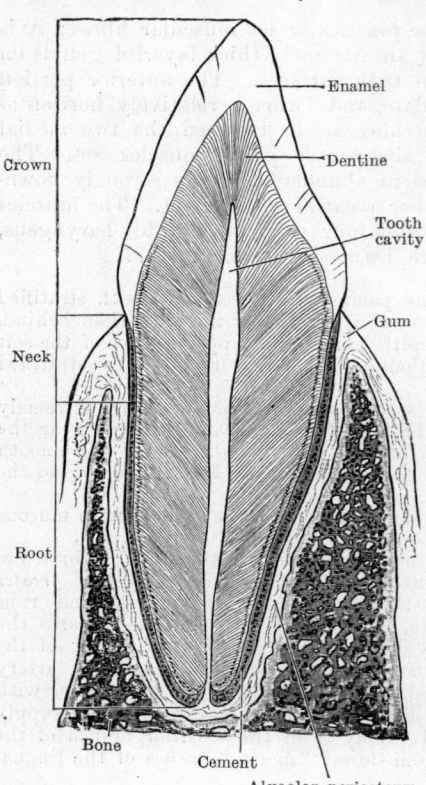

FIG. 453.—VERTICAL SECTION OF CANINE TOOTH to illustrate its various parts and its structure.

THE TEETH

The teeth, rooted in the tooth-sockets of the upper and lower jaws, are of different form and shape, and appear in two sets—a deciduous (milk teeth) and a permanent.

The deciduous teeth appear through the gums from about the sixth month of childhood. They are gradually shed, and are succeeded by the permanent teeth. Teeth of different form are found in each set.

General Form and Structure.—Each tooth has a crown, a neck, and a root (Fig. 453). The **crown** is the portion above the gum. It is of different form in the different teeth, being chisel-shaped, conical, or flattened and broad with tubercles on its masticating surface. The surface of the crown which faces outwards is termed its *labial* (or *buccal*) *surface*, that on the opposite side its *lingual surface*. The terminal surface of molars and premolars is termed the *masticatory surface*. The **neck** is the faintly constricted part which connects the crown with the **root**, which is the portion of the tooth embedded in the socket. In the majority of teeth, the root is single, or nearly so, and consists of a long, tapering, conical, or flattened piece, accurately fitting to the socket in which it lies. In the molar teeth (and in some of the others occasionally) the root is divided into two or three tapering or flattened roots or fangs. At the apex of each root there is a minute opening, called the **root foramen**, through which the vessels and nerves enter the tooth cavity.

Within each tooth there is a cavity of some size, called the **tooth cavity**, which is filled in the natural state by the loose areolar tissue with capillaries, nerves and lymph vessels; these structures collectively constitute the **tooth pulp**. The tooth cavity is prolonged into each root of every tooth as a slender tapering passage, called the **root canal**, which opens at the root foramen.

Short diverticula of the tooth cavity are prolonged into the bases of the tubercles in the molar and premolar teeth, and in the incisors also there are similar slight prolongations of the cavity towards the angles of the crown.

The roots of the teeth, embedded in the **sockets** (alveoli), are firmly united to the wall of the socket (Fig. 453) by a vascular layer of fibrous tissue—the **alveolar periosteum**—which is attached to the wall and to the root of the tooth, and above is continuous with the fibrous tissue of the gum.

So accurately are the root and the socket adapted to each other over their whole extent, and so firmly does the periosteum bind them together, that under normal conditions the tooth is quite firmly fixed in the bone, and no movement of the root within the socket can take place ; the vessels and nerves entering at the apex are thus secured against pressure or strain.

When, however, the alveolar periosteum is inflamed it becomes swollen and exquisitely sensitive ; the tooth, as a result of the swelling, is pushed partly out of its socket, its crown projects above those of its neighbours, and strikes against the opposing tooth when the mouth is closed, giving rise to much pain and discomfort.

The **neck** corresponds to the line along which the gum and alveolar periosteum meet, or along which the gum is united to the tooth ; but, as already pointed out, the gum does not stop at the neck, but forms a free fold which surrounds the base of the crown collar-wise for a short distance. The outline of the margin of the gum opposite the labial and lingual surfaces of the crown is usually concave, but opposite the contact surfaces of the tooth it is convex, and reaches much nearer to the edge of the crown than on the other surfaces.

Tartar is a hard, calcareous deposit from the saliva, often found on the teeth near their necks. It is composed of lime salts, and its deposit is largely determined by the presence of organisms (leptothrix, etc.) in the mouth.

STRUCTURE OF THE TEETH

Each tooth consists of two chief portions—namely, the **dentine** (ivory) derived from the fibrous tissue, and the **enamel** derived from the epithelial layer of the mucous membrane. The dentine constitutes the chief mass of the tooth, whilst the enamel forms a cap for the crown. A third special tissue—the **cement**—is connected with the wall of the socket by the alveolar periosteum.

The dentine and enamel, but particularly the latter, are the hardest and most resistant structures in the body.

The **enamel** [substantia adamantina] is the dense, white, glistening layer which form a cap, thickest over the tubercles, for the crown of each tooth. At the neck it ceases gradually, being there slightly overlapped by the cement.

The enamel consists of minute, solid, calcified hexagonal prisms, called the *enamel prisms*, which radiate from the surface of the dentine to the surface of the crown ; they terminate there by free ends, and most of them reach from the dentine to the surface of the crown without interruption. The prisms are held together by the smallest possible amount of calcified matrix (Tomes). In old teeth the cap of enamel is often worn away over the tubercles ; the dentine is then exposed, and can be recognised by its yellowish colour, which contrasts strongly with the whiteness of the enamel.

Whilst adjacent enamel prisms are in general parallel to one another, they do not usually take a straight course but are rather wavy, and in alternate layers they are often inclined in opposite directions, thus giving rise to certain radial striations seen by reflected light (Schreger's lines). Certain other pigmented lines, more or less parallel to the surface, are also seen in the enamel (brown striæ of Retzius). They are due to true pigmentation (Williams), and mark the lines of deposit of the enamel during its development.

The *cuticle of the tooth* is an extremely thin ($1 \cdot 5 \, \mu$) layer which covers the enamel of recently-cut teeth, and is very indestructible—resisting almost all reagents. It is produced by the outer layer of cells of the enamel organ.

Dentine or **ivory** [substantia eburnea] is the hard and elastic, yellowish-white substance which forms the greater part of every tooth (Fig. 453). Like the enamel it is highly calcified, but it differs from it in containing a very considerable amount (28 per cent.) of organic matter and water incorporated with its salts, which are chiefly phosphate and carbonate of lime (72 per cent.).

Dentine consists of a homogeneous, highly calcified, organic matrix, everywhere traversed by tubes—the **dental canaliculi**—which give to that tissue a finely striated appearance, the striæ usually running in wavy lines. The canaliculi begin by open mouths on the wall of the pulp cavity, whence they run an undulating and spiral course towards the periphery of the dentine. They give off fine anastomosing branches, and occasionally divide into two.

The dental canaliculi are generally described as being lined with special sheaths (*dentinal sheaths* of Neumann) which are composed of a most resistant material, and possibly are calcified. They are occupied by processes prolonged from the outermost cells of the pulp—called after their discoverer, *Tomes' fibrils.* The question whether they contain also neurofibrils (Mummery) cannot be said to be settled, though nerve fibres have been traced from the pulp through the odontoblast layer (see below) and some of them appear to end in fine branches which enter the mouths of the canaliculi (Lewinsky and Stewart, *Journ. Anat.,* 1936).

The concentric *lines of Schreger,* frequently seen in the dentine, are due to bends in successive canaliculi along regular lines running parallel to the periphery of the dentine. Other lines, due to imperfect calcification, are found arching across the substance of the dentine, chiefly in the crown. The **interglobular spaces** are intervals left in the dentine as a result of imperfect calcification, and are bounded by the fully calcified surrounding tissue. These interglobular spaces are very numerous in the outer or "granular layer" of the dentine.

The **cement** [subst. ossea], a layer of modified bone, encases the whole of the tooth except its crown. It begins at the neck as a very thin stratum which slightly overlaps the enamel. From there it is continued, increasing in amount, towards the apex, which is formed entirely of this substance. It is relatively less in amount in the child, and increases during life. In places the dentine seems to pass imperceptibly into the cement, the "granular layer" marking the junction of the two, and some of the dental canaliculi are continuous with the lacunæ of the cement. Like true bone, it is laminated, possesses lacunæ and canaliculi, and, when in large masses, may even contain a few Haversian canals.

The **pulp of the tooth** is composed of a number of branched fibrous tissue cells, the anastomosing processes of which form a fine network, containing in its meshes a jelly-like material, in addition to numerous blood vessels, nerves, and slender lymph vessels. The most superficial of those cells are arranged in the young tooth as a continuous layer of columnar, epithelium-like cells that lie on the surface of the tooth pulp against the dentine ; they are known as **odontoblasts**, for they are the active agents in the formation of the dentine. The vessels of the tooth pulp are numerous, and form a capillary plexus immediately internal to the odontoblasts. Fine nerve bundles run through the pulp from the root canals towards the crown of the tooth, and some of their fibres enter the odontoblast layer and may possibly supply the dentine.

The **alveolar periosteum** is a layer of fibrous tissue free from elastic fibres, but well supplied both with blood-vessels and nerves ; it fixes the root of the tooth in the socket, being firmly united by perforating fibres of Sharpey to the cement on the one hand and to the wall of the socket on the other. It establishes a communication between the bone of the jaw and the cement and it is continuous with the tissue of the gum. Its blood comes chiefly from the arteries which subsequently enter the root foramina for the supply of the tooth pulp, but in part also from the vessels of the surrounding bone and of the gum (hence the relief obtained in dental periostitis by lancing the gum).

PERMANENT TEETH

The **permanent teeth** are thirty-two in number, eight above and eight below on each side. Each set of eight consists of two incisor teeth, a medial and a lateral ; a single canine ; two premolars, first and second ; and three molars, first, second, and third, arranged in that order from the median plane. When the dentition is perfect each set is bilaterally symmetrical. The human "dental formula" showing the number of teeth of each class above and below on one side is therefore :—I. $\frac{2}{2}$, C. $\frac{1}{1}$, PM. $\frac{2}{2}$, M. $\frac{3}{3}$.

Incisor Teeth.—The **crown** is chisel-shaped, its labial surface convex, the lingual surface concave, the edge chisel-like and, when first cut, surmounted by three small tubercles separated by two grooves. Those tubercles, however, are soon worn down, and the edge becomes straight or nearly so. The upper incisors usually overlap the lower and hence the cutting edge is bevelled on the lingual aspect of the upper and on the labial aspect of the lower. The upper, and particularly the central upper incisors, are of large size, and slope slightly forwards; whilst the lower incisors, all of nearly equal size, are smaller—being the smallest of all the teeth—and are vertical. The roots of the incisors are single,

though a groove is occasionally seen on each side, suggesting a division.

The central upper incisors are very much larger than the lateral upper incisors (Fig. 455), but in the mandible the opposite is the case, the lateral incisors being slightly the larger. In all incisors the lateral angle of the crown is more rounded than the medial. The concave lingual surface of the crown in the upper incisors is usually limited towards the gum by a ∧-shaped ridge known as the **cingulum** (Fig. 456). The two limbs of the ∧ are continued up along the sides of the lingual surface, whilst the apex is turned towards the gum; and here, particularly in the lateral incisor, there is often developed a small **lingual tubercle**. The cingulum is rarely found on the lower incisors.

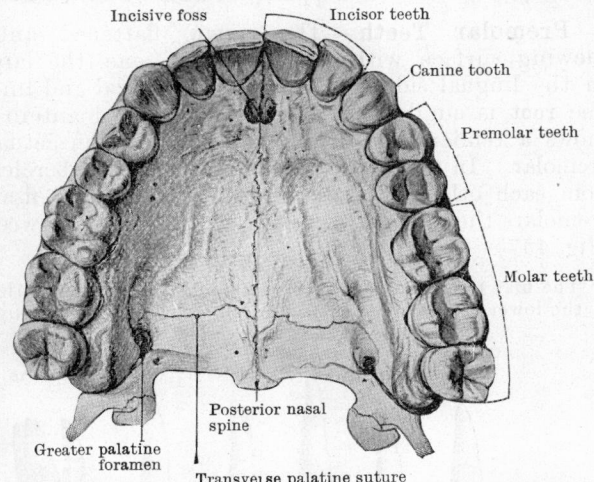

FIG. 454.—THE HARD PALATE AND THE PERMANENT TEETH OF THE SUPERIOR DENTAL ARCH.

The roots of the upper incisors and canines are conical and rounded (the lateral incisors and canines not so distinctly as the central incisors), whilst those of the mandible are flattened from side to side (medio-laterally).

Canine Teeth.—The **crown** is large and conical, and resembles in general form a very large central incisor with its angles cut away. The labial surface is convex, the lingual usually slightly concave, and both surfaces show a slight

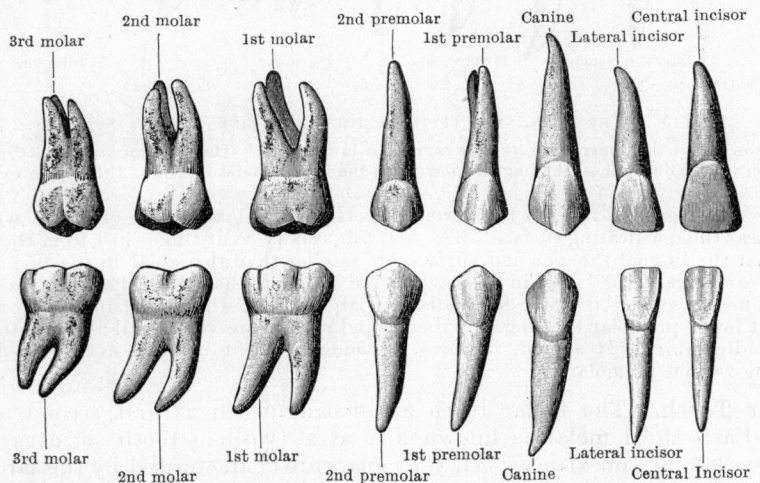

FIG. 455.—THE PERMANENT TEETH OF THE RIGHT SIDE, LABIAL OR BUCCAL SURFACES.

The upper row shows the upper teeth, the lower row the lower teeth. The wide vertical "labial ridge" is distinct on the upper canine and premolar teeth.

ridge extending from the base of the crown to the apex. The root is single and long; that of the upper canine is longer than that of any other tooth, and produces the canine eminence on the anterior surface of the maxilla. The upper canines are larger than the lower ones, and are known as the "eye teeth."

The upper canine presents on its lingual surface a well-marked cingulum, and often a distinct lingual tubercle; in addition, there is usually a median ridge (separated from the lateral part of the cingulum on each side by a slight depression) which runs from the apex of the crown to the cingulum. These features are neither so well marked, nor so constant, in the lower as in the upper canine (Fig. 456). Of the two margins sloping away from the apex of the crown, the lateral is the longer in both teeth. After it has been a little worn the lower canine is less distinctly pointed than the upper; its root also is more flattened.

Premolar Teeth.—The **crown**, flattened antero-posteriorly, shows a flat chewing surface with two tubercles—one, the larger, on the buccal, the other on the lingual side (Fig. 456). The buccal and lingual surfaces are both convex. The **root** is single, but is usually flattened antero-posteriorly and grooved, and shows a tendency to division, which is often actually present in the first upper premolar. In the upper premolars the two tubercles are large and are separated from each other by a distinct antero-posterior fissure (Fig. 454); in the lower premolars they are united by a central ridge between two dimple-like depressions (Fig. 457).

The first premolar is occasionally slightly larger than the second in the upper set but not in the lower. The labial surface of the crown is usually slightly larger than the lingual in all

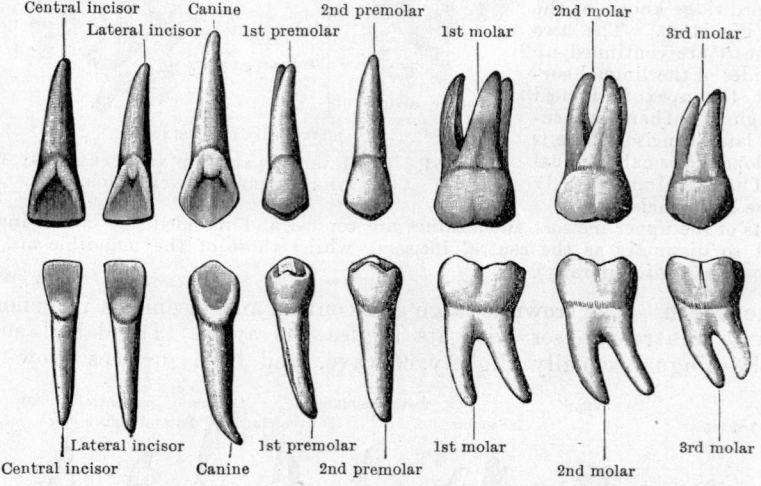

Central incisor — Canine — 2nd premolar — 2nd molar
Lateral incisor — 1st premolar — 1st molar — 3rd molar

Lateral incisor — 1st premolar — 1st molar — 3rd molar
Central incisor — Canine — 2nd premolar — 2nd molar

Fig. 456.—The Permanent Teeth of the Right Side, Lingual Surfaces.
The upper row shows the upper teeth, the lower row the lower teeth. The cingulum is distinct on the upper incisors and both canines, the lingual tubercle on the upper lateral incisor and the upper canine.

premolars. As a general rule, in the lower premolars the labial surface of the crown is sloped medially near the masticating surface. The first can usually be distinguished from the second by the fact that the lingual tubercle and surface are smaller than the labial in the first, but are of nearly the same size as the labial in the second. In addition, the root of the first upper premolar is bifid or nearly so, and it has a fairly distinct labial ridge, which is indistinct in the second. In the first lower premolar the lingual tubercle and surface are very small; in fact the tubercle is quite rudimentary. It should, however, be added that it is often extremely difficult to identify the various premolars.

Molar Teeth.—The molar teeth are distinguished as first, second, and third molars. Each third molar is known also as a "wisdom tooth" or **dens serotinus** (*serotinus* = late in appearing). All the molars are characterised by the large crown, with three or more trihedral tubercles on its masticating surface (Figs. 454 and 457). They are the largest of all the teeth and diminish in size, as a rule, from the first to the third. In shape the crown is more or less quadrangular, with convex labial and lingual surfaces. The roots are either two or three in number, but frequently in the last molars they are united to a varying degree.

The molars of the maxilla and mandible differ considerably in detail. Normally the upper molars possess three roots (Figs. 455 and 456), whilst the lower molars have two at most. The number of tubercles, though not so reliable a guide as the form of the root, is also generally sufficient to distinguish them; in the upper molars there are either three or four tubercles, whilst in the lower there are most commonly five.

In the **upper molars**, the **crown** (Fig. 454) is rhomboidal in shape (*i.e.* quadrangular with the angles not right angles). The number of **tubercles** is either four

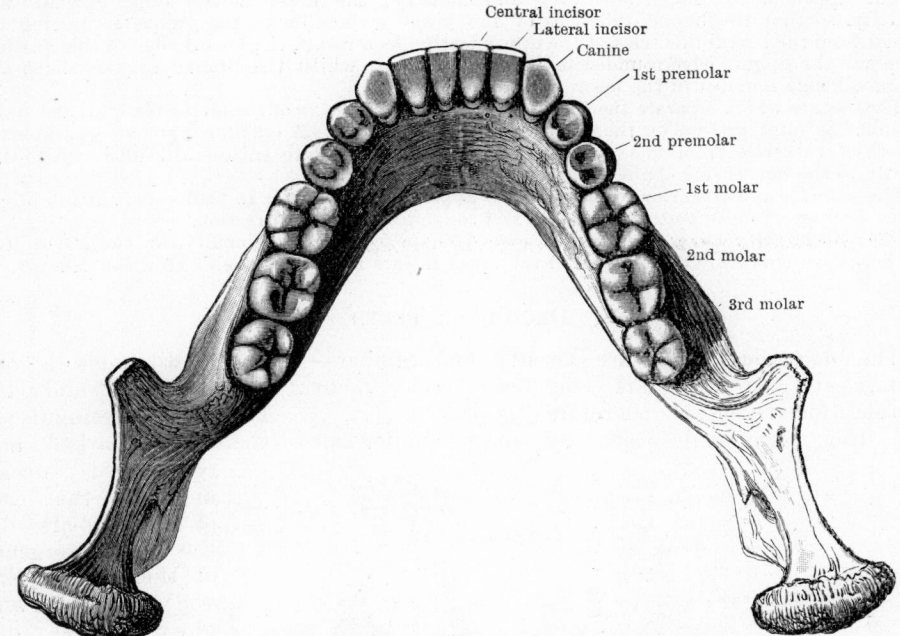

FIG. 457.—THE MANDIBLE AND THE PERMANENT TEETH OF THE INFERIOR DENTAL ARCH.

or three. On the *first* there are invariably four—two on the labial and two on the lingual side—the anterior lingual of these being connected with the posterior labial

by an oblique ridge. The *second* has either four or three tubercles in about an equal proportion; in the *third* the number is much more frequently three. The **roots** in the upper molars are three in number—two buccal, and the third lingual—but are occasionally confluent in the third molar.

In the **lower molars**, the **crown** is nearly cubical, and more massive than in the upper. The *first*, as a rule, bears five tubercles, two labial, two lingual, and the fifth behind and buccal. The *second* has usually only four tubercles; a fifth, however, is sometimes present. The *third* has either four or five, the former number more frequently than the latter. The **roots** are two in number, one anterior with two root canals, the other posterior;

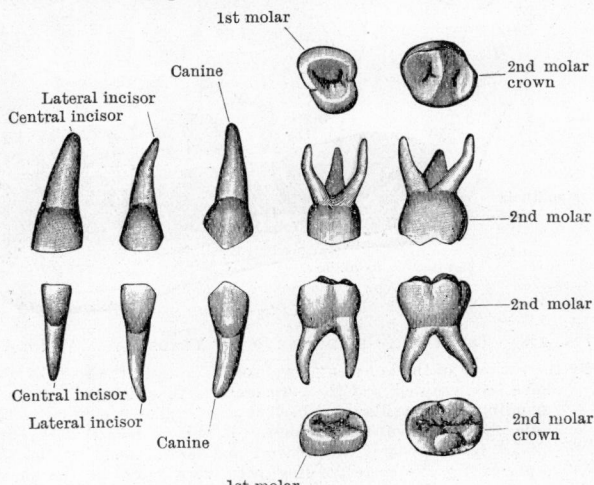

FIG. 458.—THE DECIDUOUS TEETH OF THE LEFT SIDE.

The masticating surfaces of the two upper molars are shown above. In the second row the upper teeth are viewed from the outer or labial side. In the third row the lower teeth are shown in a similar manner; and below are the masticating surfaces of the two lower molars. In the specimen from which the first upper molar was drawn the two labial tubercles were not distinctly separated, as is often the case.

they are wide roots, flattened antero-posteriorly and grooved; and both are usually recurved in their lower portions (Fig. 455). As in the corresponding teeth of the maxilla, the roots of the third lower molars are often more or less united into a single mass.

The upper molars slope downwards and laterally; the lower molars slope upwards and medially, so that the buccal tubercles of the lower molars lie in the groove separating the lingual from the buccal tubercles of the upper teeth. As a result, the buccal edge of the crown is sharp and the lingual edge rounded in the upper molars; whilst the lingual edge is sharp and the buccal edge rounded in the lower set.

The fissures which separate the cusps on the grinding surfaces of the molar teeth are generally continued as faint grooves on the labial and lingual surfaces. A cruciform groove separates the four chief tubercles from one another; it bifurcates behind to enclose the fifth, which lies slightly to the buccal side of the middle of the tooth.

The anterior and posterior surfaces of the upper molars are not in transverse but in oblique planes, sloping strongly postero-medially, and converging in that direction.

The third molar has commonly two roots like its fellows; occasionally the two are united. The backward curvature of the roots of the lower molars may make their extraction difficult.

DECIDUOUS TEETH

The **deciduous teeth** are twenty in number—namely, two incisors, one canine, and two molars, on each side, above and below; and the formula for them is therefore $i\ \frac{2}{2},\ c\ \frac{1}{1},\ m,\ \frac{2}{2}$. They are distinguished from the permanent teeth by their smaller size, their well-marked and constricted necks, and, in the case of the molars, by the wide divergence of their roots (Fig. 458). Otherwise they correspond closely to the same-named teeth of the permanent set. The first upper molar has, however, but three tubercles on its crown—two buccal and one lingual; the first lower molar has four—two buccal and two lingual—and the crowns of both are flattened from side to side. The second molars of the maxilla have four, those of the mandible five tubercles each. In every case the second are much larger than the first molars. The tubercles are sharper and are separated by deeper fissures than those of the permanent teeth, whilst the roots of the deciduous molars, except for their greater divergence, agree with those of the permanent set.

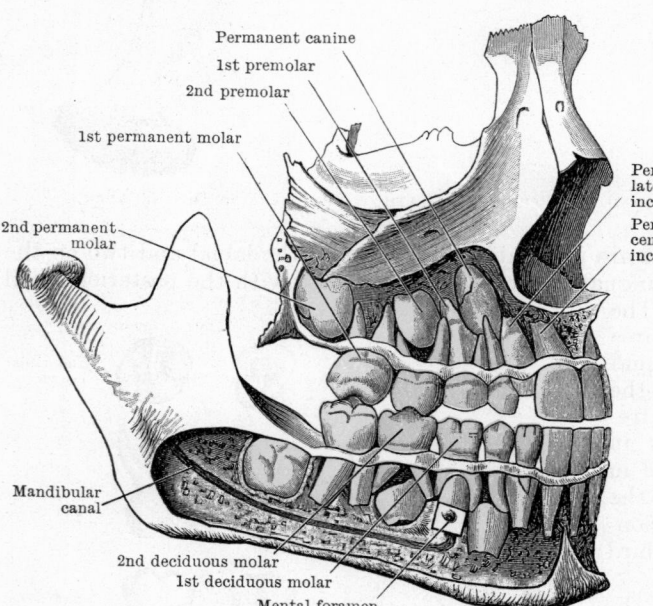

Permanent canine
1st premolar
2nd premolar
1st permanent molar
2nd permanent molar
Permanent lateral incisor
Permanent central incisor
Mandibular canal
2nd deciduous molar
1st deciduous molar
Mental foramen

FIG. 459.—TEETH OF A CHILD OVER SEVEN YEARS OLD. (Modified from Testut.)

By the removal of the bony outer wall of the alveoli, the roots of the teeth which have been erupted, and the permanent teeth which are still embedded in the mandible and maxilla, have been exposed. The deciduous teeth are coloured blue, the permanent teeth yellow. It will be seen that the first permanent molars have appeared, the central and lateral deciduous incisors have been replaced by the corresponding permanent teeth in the maxilla, but the deciduous canine and molars have not yet been shed. In the mandible the central deciduous incisor has been replaced by the permanent central; the lateral has not yet been shed, but its permanent successor is making its way up to the surface on its lingual side. In addition, the canine and two molars of the deciduous set persist. The position of the crowns of the permanent teeth between the roots of the deciduous molars, and the deep situation occupied by the permanent canines, should be noted. Observe also the absorption of the root of the lower lateral incisor.

The marked constriction at the neck of the deciduous teeth (Fig. 458) is due to a great thickening of the cap of enamel on the crown, and its abrupt termination as the neck is reached. The enamel, too, is much whiter as a rule than in the permanent teeth. It should be added that the labial surface of the canines and the buccal surface of the molars slope strongly outwards from the neck to the crown, which latter is, as a result, relatively much reduced in width.

The divergence of the roots of the deciduous molars allows the crowns of their permanent successors (premolars) to fit in between them before they are shed.

Eruption of Permanent Teeth.—The mouth of the infant at birth contains no teeth, although a number, partly developed, lie embedded in the jaws beneath the gum. Some six months later teeth begin to appear, and by the end of the second year a set, known as the **deciduous or milk teeth**, twenty in number, has been " cut." The individual teeth of that set usually appear at the following ages : the lower central incisors between six and nine months, the upper incisors between eight and ten months, lower lateral incisors and first molars between fifteen and twenty-one months, the canines between sixteen and twenty months, the second molars between twenty and twenty-four months.

Then follows a pause of about four years, during which no visible change takes place in the mouth, although active preparation for further development is going on beneath the gum.

At about the sixth year the next stage in the production of the adult condition begins. It consists in the eruption of four new teeth—the first permanent molars—one on each side above and below, behind those of the deciduous set. That eruption is followed by the gradual falling out of the twenty deciduous teeth, and the substitution for them of twenty new teeth, which take up, one by one, the vacancies created by the dropping out of each of the deciduous set in the following order :—

First, at about the age of seven the central deciduous incisors are replaced ; then the other deciduous teeth are replaced by the permanent teeth in the following order : lateral incisors, 1st premolars, 2nd premolars, canines. It will be observed that the eruption of the permanent canine is delayed until the two premolars, which succeed it in the row, are cut, so that it breaks the otherwise regular order of eruption. Finally, the adult condition is attained by the eruption of eight additional teeth—the 2nd and 3rd molars—two on each side above and below, behind those which have already appeared. All the **permanent teeth** have appeared by the end of the twelfth or thirteenth year, except the four wisdom teeth, which are usually cut between the seventeenth and twenty-fifth year, but are often delayed until a very much later period, and occasionally never appear. The 1st molar is sometimes popularly known, owing to the date of its eruption, as the " six-year-old tooth," and the 2nd molar as " the twelve-year-old tooth."

The usual dates of eruption of the lower permanent teeth may be stated as follows ; those of the upper jaw appear a little later :—

1st molars appear soon after the 6th year.
Central incisors appear soon after the 7th year.
Lateral   ,,   ,,   ,,   8th ,,
1st premolars   ,,   ,,   9th ,,
2nd   ,,   ,,   ,,   10th ,,
Canines ,,   ,,   ,,   11th ,,
2nd molars   ,,   ,,   12th ,,
3rd   ,,   ,, from the 17th ,, to 21st year, or even later.

Arrangement of the Teeth in the Jaws.—The teeth in each jaw are arranged in a curved row—the **dental arch**, upper and lower—of approximately a semi-oval form (Figs. 454 and 457). The curve formed by the upper teeth, however, is wider than that formed by the lower set, so that when the two are brought in contact the upper incisors and canines overlap the lower ones in front, and the lingual tubercles of the upper premolars and molars overlap those of the lower teeth (Fig. 138, p. 147). It will be seen also that, as a rule, the teeth in one jaw are not placed exactly opposite their fellows, but opposite the interval between two teeth, in the other jaw (Fig. 138). That arrangement is brought about largely by the great width of the upper central incisors as compared with the lower, which throws the upper canines and the succeeding teeth into a position behind that of the corresponding teeth of the lower set. But as the lower molars are larger in their antero-posterior diameter than those of the upper row—and this remark applies particularly to the third molars—the two dental arches end behind in approximately the same plane.

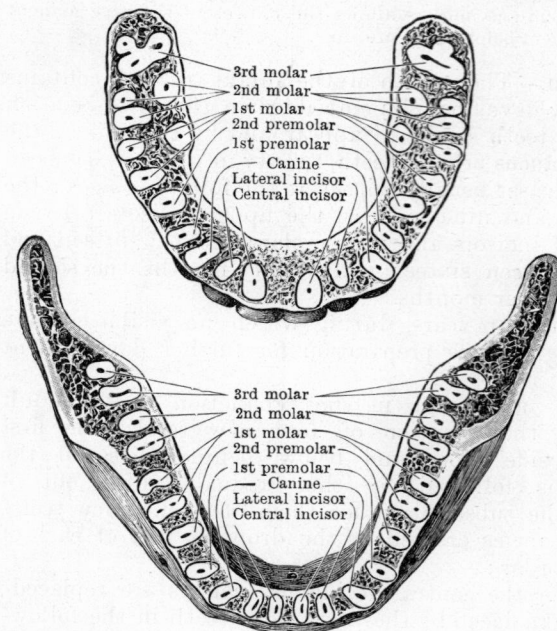

FIG. 460.—HORIZONTAL SECTIONS THROUGH BOTH THE MAXILLA AND MANDIBLE to show the roots of the teeth. The sections were carried through the bones a short distance from the edge of their alveolar borders. The upper figure shows the upper teeth, the lower figure the lower teeth. Note the flattened roots of the lower incisors, the two root-canals in the anterior root of each lower molar, and the confluence of the three roots of the upper third molars.

The upper dental arch is said to form an **elliptical**, the lower a **parabolic** curve (Fig. 460). The line formed by the masticating surfaces of the upper teeth, as seen on profile view (Fig. 138), is usually slightly convex, owing largely to the failure of the third molar to descend into line with the others. Similarly the line of the lower teeth is as a rule concave.

In both jaws the crowns of the front teeth are higher (longer) than those of the molars.

Among civilised peoples it is rare to find a perfect arrangement of the teeth. Irregularities of individual teeth and abnormal relations of the opposed dental arches are of common occurrence and give rise to "malocclusion."

Radiographic Examination of the Teeth.

—The density of healthy dentine and, especially, of enamel makes them more opaque than the surrounding tissues to the passage of X-Rays, and the shadow which they cast can be readily recognised (Pl. XXXIX, Fig. 1). In radiographs of teeth special attention should be given to the size and form of the roots, and a comparison made between them and the adjacent tissue in regard to density. The tooth cavity can also be recognised and its form and extent observed in different teeth.

THE TONGUE

The **tongue** is a mass of interlacing bundles of striped muscle mingled with fat and entirely enclosed in mucous membrane except the posterior half of its lower part, which is called its **root** and through which the extrinsic muscles, the vessels, and the nerves gain entrance into the tongue. It lies in the floor of the mouth and also forms part of the anterior wall of the pharynx; the portion in the mouth forms a mobile elevation separated from the teeth and gums by a deep groove which ends posteriorly at the palato-glossal arches.

The movements of the tongue are important and complex, for it participates in the mastication of food, it plays an important part in swallowing, and it is essential for articulate speech. Its sensory activities are two-fold, for not only does its mucous membrane possess ordinary sensation, but in addition, most, if not all, of the receptor organs for the sense of taste are placed upon its surface.

Besides its root, the tongue has an inferior surface, a dorsum, right and left margins and a tip. The **tip** and the **margins** are in relation with the teeth; the margins are blunt; the tip is pointed when the tongue is protruded, but is blunt and rounded when the tongue is at rest. The **inferior surface** belongs to the anterior half of the tongue—the part in front of the root—and is the surface seen when the living tongue is turned upwards. The **dorsum** is a highly arched surface, reaching its maximum antero-posterior curvature at the level of the palato-glossal

PLATE XXXIX

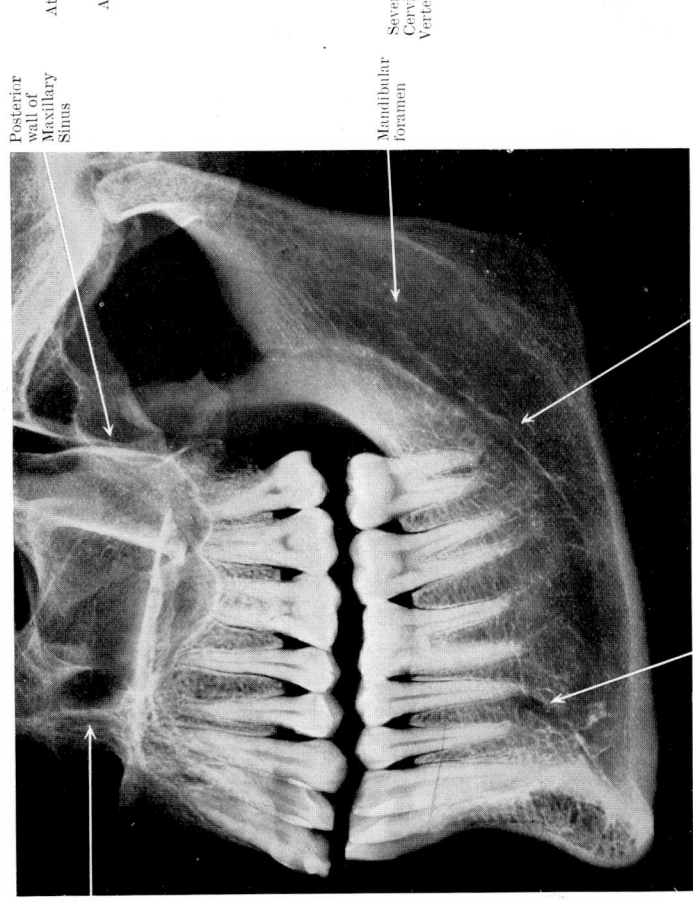

Air in Oral Part of Pharynx: and Epiglottis

Hyoid bone

Air in Laryngeal Part of Pharynx

Cricoid Cartilage (partly ossified)

Air in Trachea

Atlas

Axis

Seventh Cervical Vertebra

FIG. 2.—LATERAL RADIOGRAPH OF NECK OF MAN AGED 36.
(Dr. J. F. Brailsford.)

The positions of the Pharynx and the Trachea are shown, like air-sinuses of the head, by the relative translucency to the X-Rays of their air-filled cavities. Note the closure of the post-cricoid portion of the Laryngeal Part of the Pharynx. Cf. Plate XLIX.

Posterior wall of Maxillary Sinus

Mandibular foramen

Mandibular canal

Mental foramen

Anterior wall of Maxillary Sinus

FIG. 1.—LATERAL RADIOGRAPH OF LEFT HALF OF JAWS OF MALE SKULL WITH COMPLETE SET OF TEETH.

Note the details of the Tooth Cavities and Root Canals, and of the structure of the bone around the Tooth Sockets. The usual relation of the Roots of the Upper Teeth to the Maxillary Sinus (see p. 183) is well shown; see also Plate LIX.

PLATE XL

Right Clavicle | Left Clavicle (foreshortened)

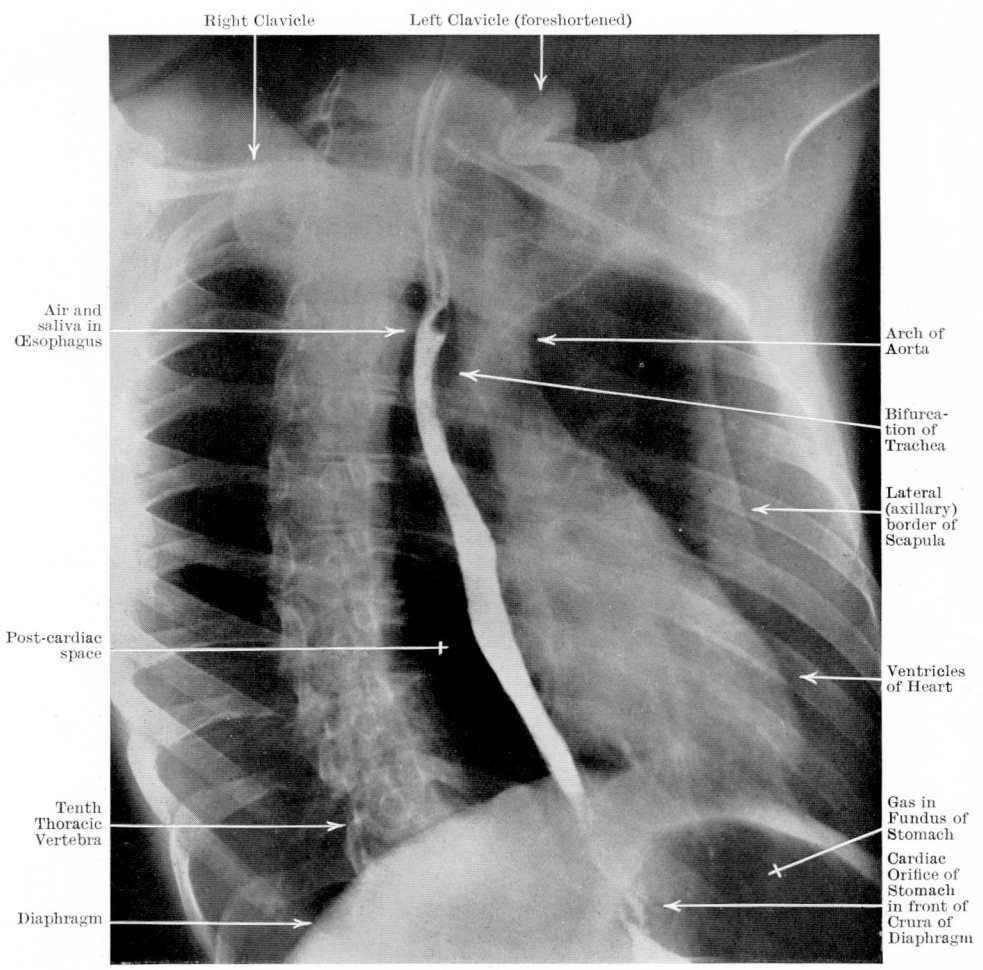

Air and
saliva in
Œsophagus

Post-cardiac
space

Tenth
Thoracic
Vertebra

Diaphragm

Arch of
Aorta

Bifurca-
tion of
Trachea

Lateral
(axillary)
border of
Scapula

Ventricles
of Heart

Gas in
Fundus of
Stomach

Cardiac
Orifice of
Stomach
in front of
Crura of
Diaphragm

PLATE XL.—OBLIQUE LATERAL RADIOGRAPH OF THORAX OF YOUTH
AGED 18, DURING THE PASSAGE OF " BISMUTH PASTE " THROUGH
THE ŒSOPHAGUS.

For the relation of the Œsophagus to the Vertebral Column and the back of the
Pericardium, see Fig. 480, D and E, p. 566 ; and note that the " post-cardiac space " is part
of the posterior mediastinum occupied mainly by the Œsophagus and the Descending Aorta.

arches. It may be conveniently divided into (1) a *palatine part* which looks upwards and is the surface seen in the open mouth, and (2) a *pharyngeal part* which looks backwards into the cavity of the pharynx and forms part of its anterior wall. These two parts are separated by a distinct V-shaped groove called the *sulcus terminalis*; the limbs of the groove diverge widely to reach the margins of

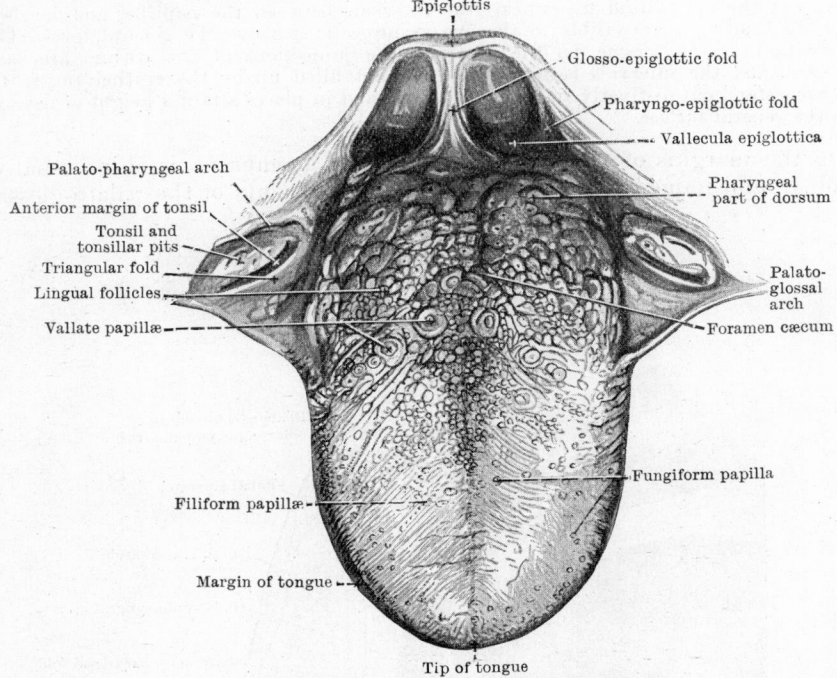

FIG. 461.—DORSUM OF TONGUE AND THE TONSILS.

the tongue; the apex of the V points backwards and is marked by a pit called the *foramen cæcum*, which indicates the position of the outgrowth of the thyroid diverticulum in the embryo.

Mucous Membrane of the Tongue.—The mucous membrane of the *palatine part of the dorsum* of the tongue is inspected in the routine examination of patients. In health, it is moist and pink in colour, showing a velvety or shaggy surface, as it is thickly studded with filiform papillæ, among which may be seen occasional larger rounded projections called the fungiform papillæ. At other times it is yellowish in colour from the accumulation of shed epithelial cells, remains of the food, and organisms. At its posterior part, immediately in front of the sulcus terminalis, there is a V-shaped row of large papillae named the vallate papillæ. The mucous membrane of the palatine part of the dorsum is firmly adherent to the underlying corium, and so affords for the filiform papillæ a firm basis, resting upon which they may rub the food against the palate.

The mucous membrane of the *pharyngeal part of the dorsum* has a smooth nodular glistening surface, and contains numerous serous glands; it is separated from the muscular substance by a submucous layer containing mucous glands and lymphoid follicles called *lingual follicles* (Fig. 473). Its surface is free from evident papillæ, but is thickly studded with rounded projections, each presenting, as a rule, a little pit, visible to the naked eye, at its centre. These nodules are produced by the follicles, which are similar to the lymph follicles found in the tonsils and collectively are called the **lingual tonsil**. At each side the mucous membrane is continuous with that covering *the* tonsil and the side wall of the pharynx. Posteriorly, it is reflected on to the front of the epiglottis, being raised up in the median plane to form a sharp ridge called the **glosso-epiglottic fold**, at each side of which there is a wide depression called the **vallecula**. The

35

vallecula is bounded laterally by a less distinct ridge of mucous membrane, called the **pharyngo-epiglottic fold**, which passes laterally and upwards from the margin of the epiglottis to blend with the mucous lining of the side wall of the pharynx.

On the pharyngeal part of the tongue there are also small papillary projections of the corium, but the epithelium fills up all the intervals between the papillæ, and levels off the surface, so that none are visible to the eye as projections above the general level. Over the anterior part of the tongue, on the contrary, the projections of the corium are large and prominent, and the intervals between them are not filled up by the epithelium, so that the projections stand out distinctly and independently, and in places attain a height of nearly 2 mm. above the general surface.

On the margins of the tongue the mucous membrane is thin, usually pink in colour, and immediately in front of the attachments of the palato-glossal arch

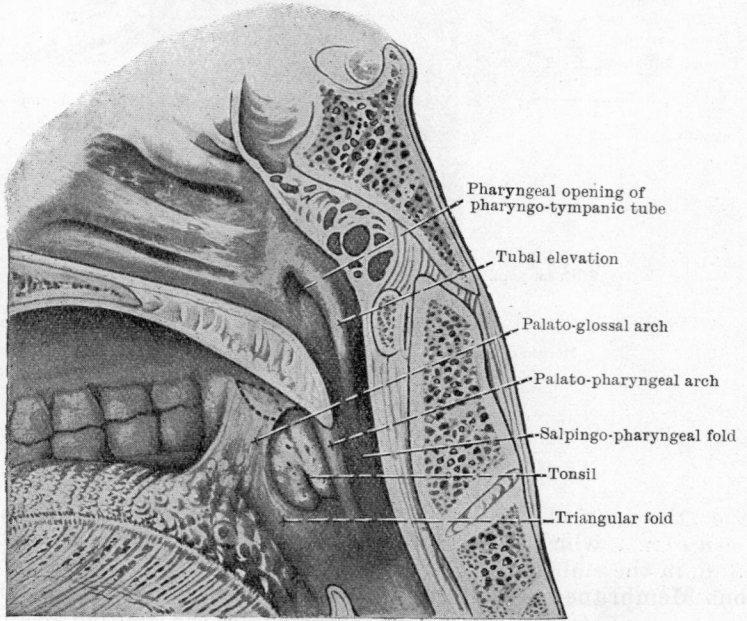

Pharyngeal opening of
pharyngo-tympanic tube

Tubal elevation

Palato-glossal arch

Palato-pharyngeal arch

Salpingo-pharyngeal fold

Tonsil

Triangular fold

Fig. 462.—Median Section of the Pharynx to show the Right Tonsil.
(From a specimen in the Anatomy Department, St. Andrews University.)

The tonsil is large and divided below by an oblique cleft. The orifice of the intratonsillar cleft lies near its upper pole and the extent of the cleft in this specimen is indicated by a dotted line.

there are five or six vertical folds of mucous membrane, termed the **folia of the tongue,** which are studded with taste-buds. They represent the foliate papillæ on the sides of the tongue in rabbits, hares, and other animals.

The *inferior surface* is covered with a smooth, thin mucous membrane devoid of papillæ. On its middle, except near the tip, there is a depression from which a fold of mucous membrane, called the **frenulum of the tongue,** passes down to the floor of the mouth and the posterior aspect of the mandible. At each side of the frenulum, and a short distance from it, the profunda linguæ vein is distinctly seen through the mucous membrane. Still farther from the frenulum, on each side, there is a fringed fold called the **fimbriated fold**; these two folds converge slightly as they are followed forwards towards the tip, near which they are lost.

Papillæ of the Tongue (Fig. 461).—The papillæ of the tongue are variously shaped projections of the corium of the mucous membrane, covered with thick caps of epithelium, and are of three main varieties: filiform, fungiform, and vallate.

The **filiform papillæ** (Fig. 463), the smallest and most numerous, form a dense crop of minute projections all over the anterior two-thirds of the dorsum of the tongue, and on the upper surface of its margins and tip. Posteriorly they lie in divergent rows that run laterally and forwards from the raphe parallel to the limbs of the sulcus terminalis. More anteriorly, the rows become nearly transverse, and near the tip irregular. Each papilla is composed of a conical projection of the corium on which there are small papillæ like those of the skin, covered by a thick long cap of stratified squamous epithelium.

In many of them the cap of epithelium is broken up into several long, slender, hair-like processes. The cap of epithelium is being constantly shed and renewed, and an excessive or diminished rate of shedding or renewal, coupled with the presence of various organisms, gives rise to the several varieties of "tongue" found in different diseases.

The filiform papillæ are highly developed and horny in carnivora.

The **fungiform papillæ** (Fig. 461), larger and redder, but less numerous than the filiform, are found chiefly near the tip and margins of the tongue,

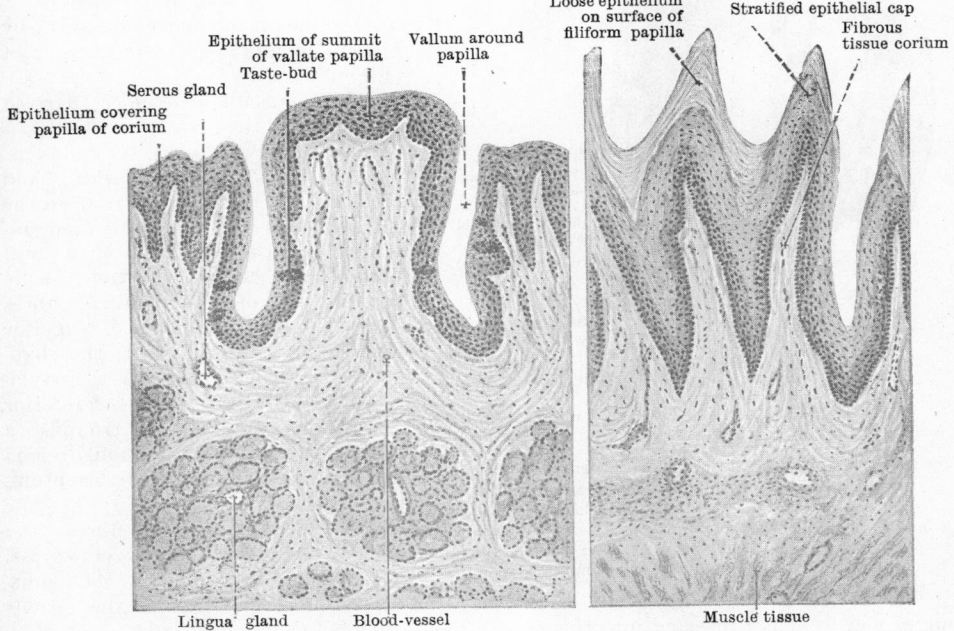

FIG. 463. A. SECTION OF A VALLATE PAPILLA OF TONGUE. B. SECTION OF FILIFORM PAPILLÆ OF TONGUE.

comparatively few being present over the dorsum generally. Each is in shape like a "puff-ball" fungus, consisting of an enlarged rounded head, attached by a narrower base. As in the filiform papillæ, the corium is studded with microscopic papillæ which are buried in the covering of squamous epithelium. Most of the fungiform papillæ, if not all, appear to be furnished with taste-buds.

The **vallate papillæ** (Fig. 463), are much the largest of all the papillæ of the tongue. Usually about nine to fourteen in number, they are arranged in the form of the letter V, with the apex posteriorly, immediately in front of and parallel to the sulcus terminalis, one or two of the papillæ being placed at the apex of the V. In appearance a vallate papilla resembles very closely the impression left by the barrel of a small pen pressed on soft wax (Fig. 461). Each is composed of a cylindrical central part (1 to 2·5 mm. wide), slightly tapering towards its base, and flattened on its crown, which projects a little above the general surface of the tongue. It is surrounded by a deep, narrow, circular fossa, the outer wall of which is known as the **vallum**. The vallum appears in the form of an encircling collar very slightly raised above the adjacent surface (Fig. 463). As in the case of the other forms, the vallate papillæ are made up of a central mass of corium, studded with numerous microscopic papillæ on the crowns (but not on the sides), and covered over by stratified squamous epithelium, as are the surfaces of the fossa and vallum. Into the fossæ open the ducts of some small serous glands (Fig. 463 A). On the sides of the vallate papillæ, as well as on the opposed surface of the vallum, are found, in considerable numbers, the structures known as **taste-buds**—the special end-organs of the nerves of taste.

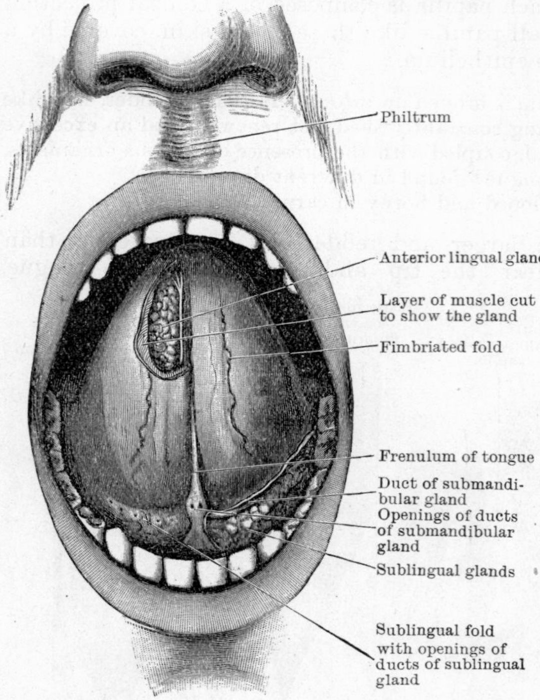

Structure of the Tongue.—

The tongue is composed chiefly of striped muscular tissue, with a considerable admixture of fine fat. A median septum of fibrous tissue occupies the central part of the organ. In addition, there are vessels, nerves, glands, and lymphoid tissue, the whole being covered over by mucous membrane, except at the root (Fig. 465).

The muscular tissue is derived partly from the extrinsic muscles—namely, the hyo-glossus, stylo-glossus, genio-glossus, palato-glossus, and chondro-glossus; and partly from the intrinsic muscles—superior and inferior longitudinal, transverse, and vertical. A **cortical portion**—made up chiefly of longitudinal fibres derived above from the superior longitudinal muscle and the hyo-glossus, at the sides from the stylo-glossus, and below from the inferior longitudinal muscle — surrounds a central or **medullary portion**, divided into two halves by the median **septum**, and formed in great part by the transverse and vertical fibres, and also by the fibres of the genio-glossi ascending to the dorsum. The muscular fibres derived from the various

FIG. 464.—OPEN MOUTH WITH TONGUE RAISED, AND THE SUBLINGUAL AND ANTERIOR LINGUAL GLANDS EXPOSED.

The sublingual gland of the left side has been laid bare by the removal of the mucous membrane ; to expose the anterior lingual gland of the right side a thin layer of muscle, in addition to the mucous membrane, has been removed. A branch of the lingual nerve is seen running on the medial aspect of the gland. The profunda vein also is faintly indicated on this side.

sources end by being inserted into the deep surface of the mucous membrane.

The detailed description of the extrinsic and intrinsic muscles will be found in the chapter on Myology (p. 413).

The **septum** is a median fibrous partition found in the medullary portion only. Anteriorly it usually extends to the apex ; whilst posteriorly it grows gradually narrower, and, expanding transversely, it passes into a broad sheet (the hyo-glossal membrane) which is united to the upper border of the hyoid bone and gives attachment to the posterior fibres of the genio-glossus. From the sides of the septum the fibres of the transverse muscle of the tongue arise.

Lingual Glands.—Numerous small racemose glands are scattered beneath the mucous membrane of the posterior third of the tongue ; and a small collection of similar glands is present at the margin, opposite the vallate papillæ. Small serous glands also are embedded in the dorsum near the vallate papillæ, into the fossæ of which their ducts open.

The chief collections of glandular tissue in the tongue, however, are found embedded in the muscle of the under surface, a little way behind the apex, on each side of the middle line (Fig. 464). They are known as the **anterior lingual glands.**

Those glands are displayed after the removal, from the under surface of the tongue a little distance behind the apex, of the mucous membrane and a layer of muscle fibres about 2 mm. thick composed of fibres of the stylo-glossus and the inferior longitudinal muscles. The anterior lingual glands are oval in shape, often partly broken up by muscular fibres, and they measure from $\frac{1}{2}$ to $\frac{3}{4}$ in. (12 to 19 mm.) in length. They are mixed serous and mucous glands, and they open by three or four very small ducts on the inferior surface of the tongue.

Vessels and nerves.—The chief **artery** is the *lingual*. It passes forwards, on each side, medial to the hyo-glossus muscle, and then is continued to the apex—between the genio-glossus on the medial side and the inferior longitudinal muscle laterally—under the name of the *profunda artery*. Anteriorly it is covered by the inferior longitudinal muscle, and lies $\frac{1}{8}$ to $\frac{1}{4}$ in. from the surface. Near the apex the arteries of opposite sides are connected by a branch which pierces the septum; but otherwise, with the exception of capillary anastomosis, they do not communicate. The *dorsales linguae* branches of the lingual artery are distributed to the pharyngeal

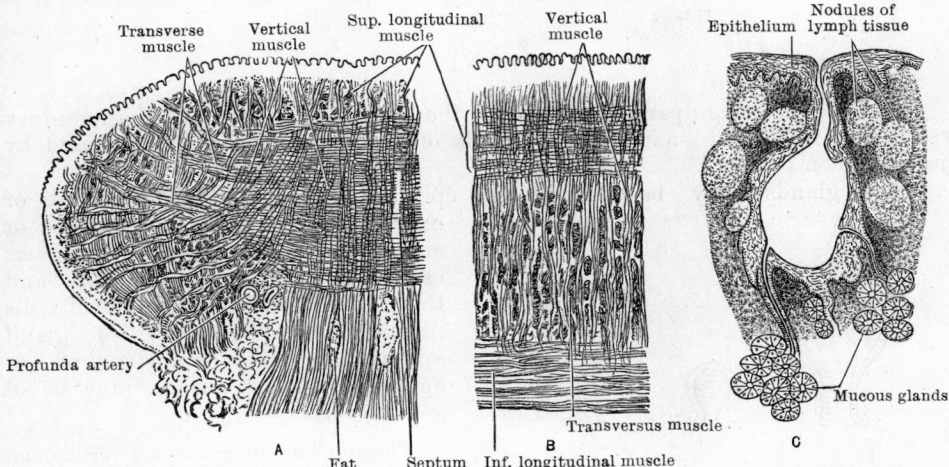

FIG. 465.—A, TRANSVERSE, AND B, LONGITUDINAL VERTICAL SECTION THROUGH THE TONGUE (Krause); C, A LYMPH FOLLICLE FROM POSTERIOR PART OF THE TONGUE. (Macalister, slightly modified.)

part of the tongue, whilst some twigs of the *tonsillar artery* (a branch of the facial) are also distributed in the same region.

The **veins** are in three sets. The chief of them is the *profunda vein*, which lies beneath the mucous membrane at the side of the frenulum, and runs backwards over the hyo-glossus with the hypoglossal nerve. The others are the two *venae comitantes* of the lingual artery and the two or more *dorsales linguae veins* from the back of the tongue. They either unite and form a common trunk, or open separately into the internal jugular vein.

The **lymph-vessels** of the tongue end in the *submental* and *submandibular glands*, and in the *deep cervical* group between and including the jugulo-digastric and the jugulo-omo-hyoid glands.

The **nerves** which supply the tongue are: (1) The *hypoglossal nerve*—the motor nerve of the tongue —which enters the genio-glossus and passes up in its substance to the intrinsic muscles, in which it ends. (2) The *lingual nerve*, which is a branch of the mandibular nerve, and is accompanied by the *chorda tympani branch* of the facial nerve. The lingual, after crossing the hyo-glossus, breaks up and enters the inferior longitudinal and genio-glossus muscles, and thus makes its way upwards to the mucous membrane of the anterior two-thirds of the tongue—the lingual itself conferring common sensation on this part, while the chorda tympani carries taste fibres and parasympathetic fibres to it.

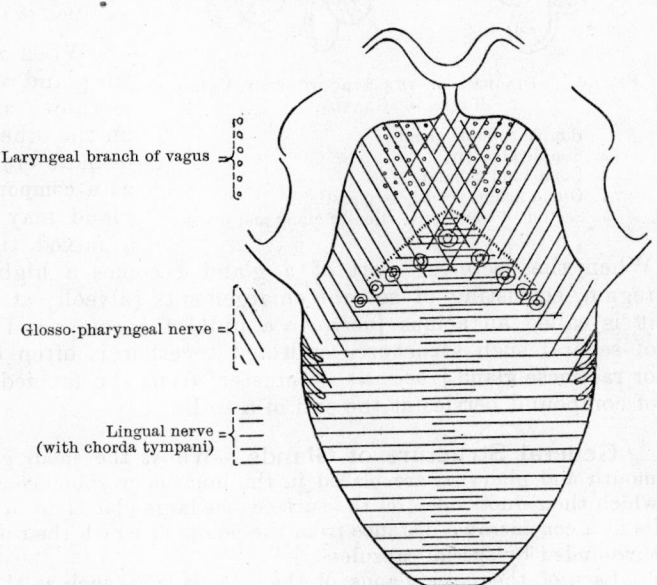

FIG. 466.—AREAS OF AFFERENT NERVE SUPPLY OF TONGUE.

(3) The *glosso-pharyngeal nerve* passes forwards beneath the upper part of the hyo-glossus muscle, and sends its terminal branches to the mucous membrane of the posterior third of the tongue, supplying the vallate papillæ, and the part of the tongue behind them,

with both gustatory and common sensory fibres. (4) The *internal laryngeal nerve* also distributes a few fibres to the posterior part of the tongue, near the epiglottis.

Movements of the Tongue.—The tongue takes an active part in mastication, in swallowing, and in the production of articulate speech (see pp. 403, 414, 417).

GLANDS

In the following paragraphs only the true glands of the alimentary system are considered—namely, the glands of epithelial origin, characterised by the possession of ducts.

Such glands may be defined as epithelial organs which secrete or excrete some particular substance or substances from the body. Their essential parts consist of cells, and there may be different kinds of cells in a gland. This type of gland appears as an involution of an epithelial surface, which may be of various forms.

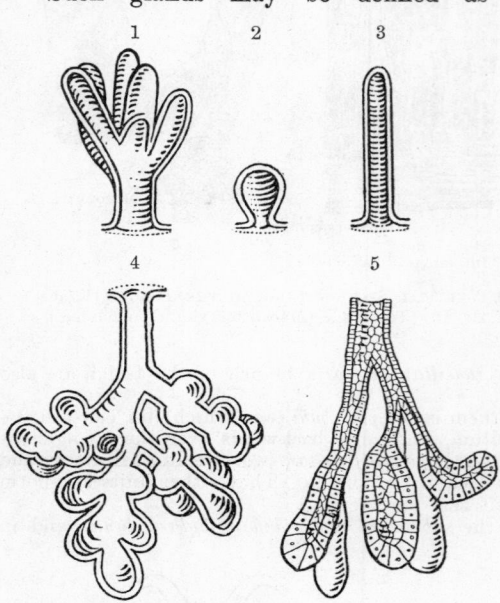

The simplest form is a single diverticulum, of uniform size throughout, forming a simple tubular gland. Of this kind are the intestinal glands in the wall of the small intestine.

The end of a tubular gland may be widened, forming a sort of pocket, called an alveolus [*alveolus*, small stomach or bag], and this type of gland is known as the simple alveolar gland. It does not exist in the alimentary canal.

In some glands the lower part or fundus of the tube does all the secretion, and the upper part forms a duct that carries the secretion to the surface.

When the outgrowth that forms the gland remains undivided, the gland is known as a **simple gland**. It may, on the other hand, break up into two or more branches, and it is then known as a **compound gland**, and a compound gland may be tubular, alveolar, or of a mixed tubular and alveolar form.

FIG. 467.—DIAGRAM OF THE STRUCTURE OF VARIOUS TYPES OF GLANDS.

1. Simple tubular gland.
2. Simple alveolar.
3. Compound tubular.
4. Gland acinus (racemose gland).
5. Section of secreting portion of gland and ducts.

When the secreting part of a gland becomes a highly differentiated saccular region, consisting of several enlargements (alveoli) at the end of a single duct, it is called an **acinus** [*acinus* = a unit of a compound berry]. A gland formed of several such structures collected together is often called a **compound acinous** or **racemose gland** [*racemus* = a cluster] from the fancied resemblance to a cluster of compound berries at the end of a stalk.

General Structure of Glands.—Whilst the small glands, such as those of the mouth and pharynx, are placed in the mucous or submucous coats close to the point at which their ducts open on the surface, the large glands form distinct masses which often lie at a considerable distance from the points at which their ducts open, and are generally surrounded by special capsules.

Each of the large glands of the acinous type, such as the parotid or submandibular, presents the following general arrangement. The gland is made up, as can be seen with the unaided eye, of a number of masses, often as large as peas, which are surrounded and held together by fibro-areolar tissue. The masses are known as lobes, and a branch of the duct passes to each. The lobes are in turn made up of a number of smaller masses—lobules —each having a special branch of the lobar duct. Those again are composed of smaller lobules, and finally the smallest are made up of a terminal branch of the duct with a cluster of acini or alveoli leading into it.

The **acini** or **alveoli** are composed of secreting epithelial cells placed on a basement membrane, often fenestrated or basket-like, formed of flattened cells, on the outer side of which the blood- and lymph-vessels lie. The secreting cells, usually polygonal in shape, almost completely fill the alveolus. A small lumen, however, is left, into which the secretion of the cells is shed ; thence it passes into the duct of the lobule, and thus to the main duct.

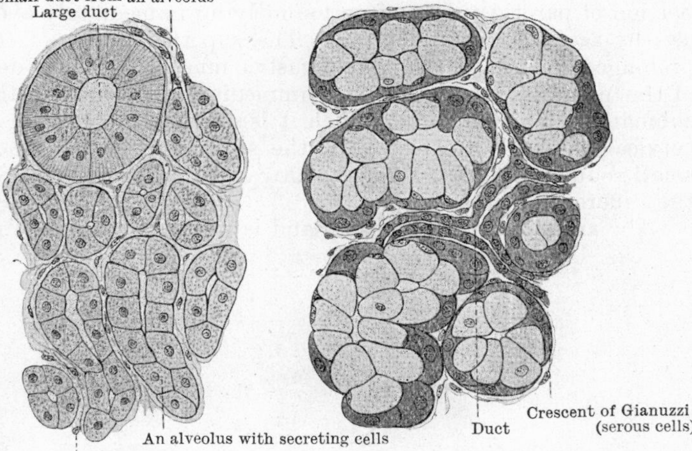

SALIVARY GLANDS

Saliva is a clear, watery fluid poured by numerous glands into the cavity of the mouth. It moistens the tongue and the walls of the mouth, and facilitates movements of the tongue in speaking. Mixed with food by mastication it helps in swallowing. It also contains a ferment which plays an important part in digestion, and can transform starch into dextrin.

FIG. 468.—SECTION OF A SEROUS GLAND ON THE LEFT, A MUCOUS GLAND ON THE RIGHT. (Böhm and v. Davidoff.)

In the serous gland the granular secreting cells and the centrally-placed nucleus should be noted. The relatively clear (mucus-secreting) cells, with the dark crescents of Gianuzzi, are distinctive in the mucous gland.

The glands which secrete it include the small glands of the lips, cheeks, and tongue, and also three large paired glands—the parotid, submandibular, and sublingual glands. The three last are the main salivary glands.

Parotid Gland.—The parotid gland, the largest of the salivary glands, lies on the side of the face, below and in front of the ear, mastoid process, and sternomastoid muscle. It is a lobulated mass, of a yellowish or light reddish-brown colour, with a large triangular superficial surface. From that mass a process of the gland passes medially behind the ramus of the mandible, almost to the side wall of the pharynx.

Shape and Relations of the Parotid Gland.—In shape the parotid gland with its deep process is three-sided (Fig. 470), the three surfaces being superficial, anterior, and posterior.

The deeper portion of the gland occupies a space of considerable size, which has two nearly vertical sides, an anterior and posterior, which converge towards each other and meet deeply at an acute angle.

A horizontal section through the head about the middle of the gland (Fig. 470) shows that the posterior wall of the space is formed, medial to the sternomastoid muscle, by the posterior belly of the digastric and the stylo-hyoid muscles, and more deeply still, by the root of the styloid process and the carotid sheath and its contents, and especially by the internal jugular vein, separating the space from the vertebral column. The anterior wall of the space is formed by the ramus of the mandible and the masseter and medial pterygoid muscles. The portion of the gland that lies in the fossa presents an anterior surface looking forwards, deeply concave, and a posterior surface, irregular in outline, directed backwards and medially. These surfaces meet at the medial angle, which may be so deep that it is in contact with the side wall of the pharynx.

The **superficial surface** is triangular in form, though irregular in outline. Its posterior border lies in front of the external auditory meatus and the

35 b

sterno-mastoid muscle, and extends down to the angle of the mandible and
the posterior belly of the digastric muscle.   Its superior border lies below
the zygomatic arch, and the inferior border passes irregularly upwards and
forwards to join it.   The apex, directed forwards, lies on the masseter muscle,
and the duct of the gland issues from it, or immediately below it.   A separate
portion of parotid tissue, often found lying immediately above the duct, is known
as the **accessory parotid gland**.   The superficial part of the gland is frequently
prolonged downwards over the digastric muscle.   It may descend beyond the angle
of the mandible, and come into immediate relation with the posterior part of the
submandibular gland, from which it is separated merely by a thin layer of the deep
cervical fascia.   Embedded in the superficial surface there are usually several
small rounded lymph glands which can be distinguished from the gland tissue by
the difference in their colour.

The **anterior surface** of the gland is wrapped round the ramus of the mandible,

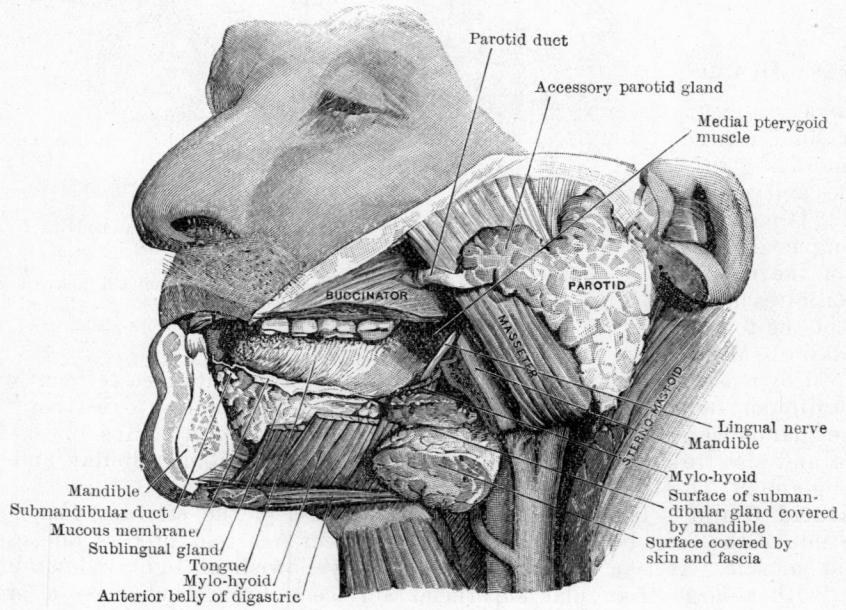

FIG. 469.—THE SALIVARY GLANDS AND THEIR DUCTS.

and extends on to the muscles—the masseter and medial pterygoid—which cover
that portion of the bone laterally and medially.

The **posterior surface** of the gland is in contact with the structures which form
the posterior wall of the space occupied by the deep portion, namely, the sterno-
mastoid muscle, the mastoid process, the external auditory meatus, the posterior
belly of the digastric muscle, the internal jugular vein, and the root of the styloid
process and the styloid muscles.   It is often deeply grooved by the posterior belly
of the digastric.

The gland is occasionally prolonged medially beyond the lower portion of
the styloid process, towards the pharynx.   In such cases the lower part of the
styloid process lies in a groove on the posterior surface of the gland.

A number of vessels and nerves are found in intimate relation to the parotid gland.   The
external carotid artery lies at first in a groove in the inferior and deep surface of the gland.   It then
enters the gland substance and lies deeply in it as far as the neck of the mandible, where it
divides into its two terminal branches.   The superficial temporal artery emerges from the
superior superficial part of the gland, and the maxillary artery turns medially and emerges from
the deep part of the anterior surface.

The transverse facial artery is given off in the substance of the gland, and emerges from
it between the zygomatic arch and the duct.

The posterior facial vein descends superficially in the substance of the gland, and divides into the two terminal branches which emerge from the inferior part of the gland.

The facial nerve enters the posterior surface of the gland, slightly below its middle, and runs forwards and laterally, dividing into its main branches within the gland, and lying superficial to the external carotid artery and posterior facial vein. Communicating branches from the auriculo-temporal and great auricular nerves to the facial also traverse the gland substance.

Parotid Fascia.—The parotid recess is lined by a layer of fascia continuous with the deep cervical fascia. It is connected above to the zygoma; posteriorly to the auditory meatus and anterior border of the sterno-mastoid; medially it is connected to the styloid process; and anteriorly it passes over the masseter and blends with the bucco-pharyngeal fascia. Together with the periosteum of the tympanic plate it forms a definite sheath which completely encloses the gland. From the lower and anterior part

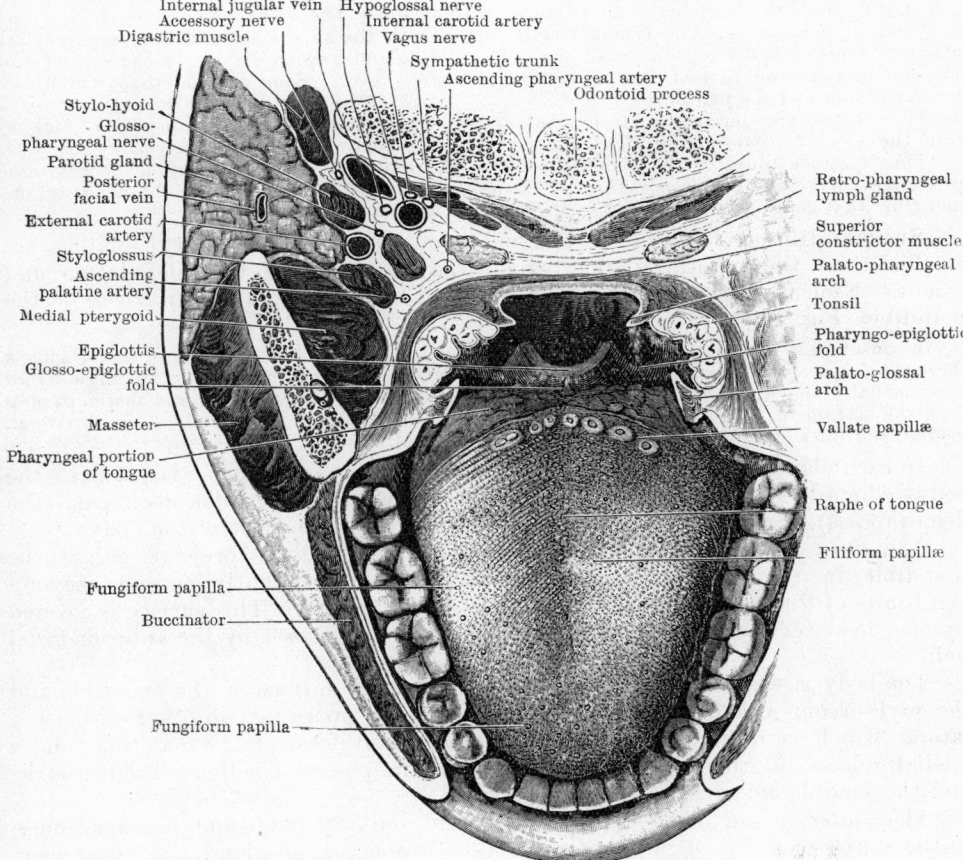

Fig. 470.—Horizontal Section through Mouth and Pharynx at the Level of the Tonsils.

The prevertebral muscles and the stylo-pharyngeus (which is shown immediately to the medial side of the external carotid artery) are not indicated by reference lines.

of this sheath a special flat band, called the **stylo-mandibular ligament**, passes downwards and laterally from the styloid process to the angle of the mandible. It separates the anterior part of the parotid gland from the posterior border of the medial pterygoid muscle and from the upper and posterior part of the submandibular gland.

Parotid Duct.—The parotid duct leaves the anterior border of the gland at its most prominent part (Fig. 469). It first runs forwards across the masseter, below the accessory parotid gland, accompanied by branches of the facial nerve and the transverse facial artery, which is commonly some distance above. The duct turns abruptly round the anterior border of the masseter and runs inwards through the fat of the cheek, practically at right angles to the first part of its course, to reach the buccinator, which it pierces. Then, passing for some distance (5 to 10 mm.) between the buccinator and the mucous membrane, it opens into the vestibule of the mouth by a very small orifice, on a variably developed papilla, opposite the crown of the second upper molar tooth.

The course of the duct can be marked by the middle third of a line from the inferior edge of the auditory meatus to a point midway between the ala of the nose and the red margin of the lip.

The duct measures from 1½ to 2½ inches (40 to 60 mm.) in length, and ⅛ inch (3 to 4 mm.) in diameter. The calibre of the duct is very much greater than that of its orifice, which admits only a fine bristle, and for that reason the duct may, to some extent, be looked upon as a reservoir for the saliva, as well as a duct for its conveyance. In the child it pierces the buccal pad of fat on its way to the mouth.

Vessels and Nerves.—The **arteries** which supply the gland arise from the *external carotid artery*, and from the branches of that artery in the gland. The **veins** join the *posterior facial vein* and its tributaries. The **lymph vessels** pass to both the superficial and the deep cervical glands; there are also a few small parotid lymph glands which lie on the surface of the superior and inferior part of the parotid beneath the sheath. Some are said to be embedded in the substance of the parotid itself.

The **nerves** are derived (*a*) from the *auriculo-temporal, great auricular*, and *facial*, and (*b*) from the *external carotid plexus*. The fibres of the sympathetic are mainly vaso-constrictor.

The secretory fibres to the gland, arising in the brain-stem, pass out through the glosso-pharyngeal nerve, and pass from it through the lesser superficial petrosal nerve to the otic ganglion, and from that ganglion to the gland in the auriculo-temporal nerve.

Submandibular Glands.—The submandibular [submaxillary] glands are smaller than the parotid glands, which they resemble in their lobulation and colour. Each is placed mainly in the submandibular triangle under cover of the mandible (Fig. 469).

In considering the relations of the gland, it is well to remark that there is in that region a three-sided space bounded laterally by the medial surface of the mandible below the mylo-hyoid line, medially and above by the mylo-hyoid muscle, and below by the skin and fascia passing from the margin of the jaw to the side of the neck. In that space the gland lies, with lateral, medial, and inferior surfaces corresponding to the walls of the space.

In each gland two portions may be recognised :—(1) a superficial, larger part (the body) which lies in the submandibular triangle, and (2) a smaller, deep part (the deep process) which springs from the middle of the deep surface of the body.

The *body* presents a superficial convex surface, which projects below the mandible in the submandibular triangle; but it frequently extends beyond the limits of that space, and overlaps the digastric muscle. This surface is covered by the deep cervical fascia and the platysma, and is crossed by the anterior facial vein.

The body is wedged upwards, between the medial surface of the mandible and the mylo-hyoid and hyo-glossus muscles. It thus presents two other surfaces, a lateral, which is in contact with the submandibular fossa of the mandible, and a medial, related to the mylo-hyoid, hyoglossus, the posterior belly of the digastric, and the stylo-hyoid muscles.

The *posterior end* of the gland is its most bulky portion and lies very close to the sterno-mastoid; it is often overlapped by the parotid gland, and is grooved by the facial artery.

The *deep process* passes around the posterior margin of the mylo-hyoid muscle, and comes to lie between the mylo-hyoid and hyo-glossus muscles.

Embedded in the substance of the gland are found a few submandibular lymph glands, which receive lymph vessels of the lip and of a portion of the tongue.

The gland is enclosed in a delicate sheath of fibrous tissue derived from the deep cervical fascia.

Submandibular Duct.—The submandibular duct leaves the deep surface of the gland about its middle, and runs forwards deep to the mylo-hyoid muscle, along the upper and medial aspect of the deep process of the gland (Fig. 471). Pursuing its course forwards beneath the floor of the mouth, on the medial side of the sublingual gland, the duct crosses the hyo-glossus and genio-glossus muscles, and finally opens on the floor of the mouth at the side of the frenulum of the tongue, on the summit of the sublingual papilla.

While running forward beneath the floor of the mouth the duct, which is about two inches long (50 mm.), is crossed on its lateral aspect by the lingual nerve near the anterior border of the hyo-glossus—that is, opposite the 2nd molar tooth. The nerve passes from the posterior end of the mylo-hyoid ridge (against which it lies) forwards and medially in order to reach the inferior surface of the tongue, and it passes below the duct at the point indicated.

As in the case of the parotid duct, the calibre of the submandibular duct is much greater than that of the orifice by which it opens ; for that reason it likewise may be looked upon as forming, to some extent, a reservoir for the saliva secreted by the gland.

Vessels and Nerves.—The **arteries** come chiefly from the *facial artery* and its *submental branch*: the **veins** accompany the arteries. The **nerves** are derived, through the *submandibular ganglion*, from the *chorda tympani, lingual,* and the *sympathetic plexus around the facial artery.* The **lymph vessels** pass to the *submandibular lymph glands.*

Sublingual Glands.—The sublingual glands, the smallest of the principal salivary glands, are situated more deeply than the others. Each lies immediately

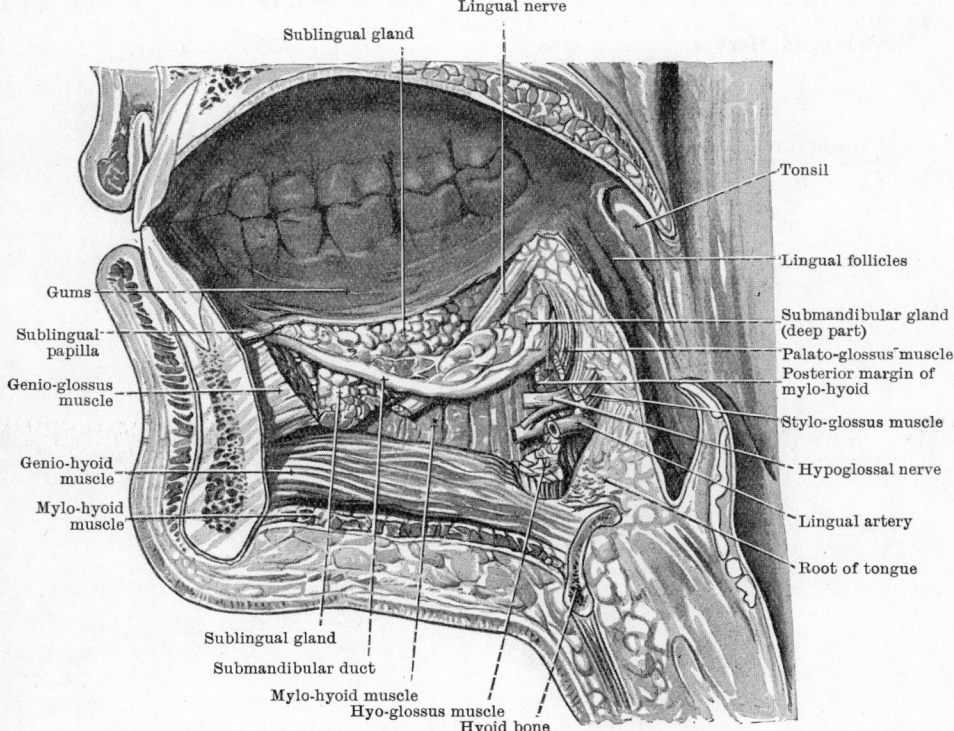

FIG. 471.—SIDE WALL AND FLOOR OF MOUTH, AFTER REMOVAL OF TONGUE AND MUCOUS MEMBRANE.

below the mucous membrane of the floor of the mouth, in the interval between the sublingual fossa (on the inner surface of the mandible above the mylo-hyoid line) and the genio-glossus muscle, which passes from the mandible to the tongue. Below, it rests upon the deep surface of the mylo-hyoid muscle.

In shape it is almond-like, flattened from side to side, but is much wider (from above downwards) anteriorly than posteriorly. It is usually from $1\frac{1}{2}$ to $1\frac{3}{4}$ inches (37 to 45 mm.) in length, whilst its bulk is about equal to that of two or three almonds.

Its detailed relations are as follows :—Its *lateral surface* rests against the inner aspect of the body of the mandible above the mylo-hyoid line. Its *medial surface* is in contact with the genio-glossus, stylo-glossus, and hyo-glossus muscles, as well as with the submandibular duct, which runs forwards between the gland and the muscles. *Below* it rests on the mylo-hyoid, and at its posterior part on the deep process of the submandibular gland ; its *upper border* is prominent and is covered only by the sublingual fold of the mucous membrane of the mouth (Fig. 464). The anterior portion of the gland is much deeper and more bulky than the posterior half, and it meets its fellow in the median plane beneath the frenulum of the tongue. The posterior part grows gradually more slender, but may extend to the posterior part of the mylo-hyoid ridge.

The **sublingual ducts** are about twelve in number and of small size; they leave the superior part of the gland, and, after a short course, open on a series of papillæ, visible to the naked eye, which are placed along the summit of the sublingual fold.

The gland is not enclosed in a distinct sheath, thus differing from the parotid and submandibular glands; but its numerous lobules, which are smaller than those of the glands just mentioned, are held together by areolar tissue, loosely, but still in such a manner as to make one more or less consolidated mass out of what was, in the embryo, a number of separate glands.

As a rule all the ducts open separately on the summit of the sublingual fold, and apparently none of them join the submandibular duct. Frequently some of those from the anterior and more bulky part of the gland are larger than the others, but the presence of a large duct running alongside the submandibular duct, and opening with or beside it, is very rare in man, although normal in the ox, sheep, and goat.

Vessels and Nerves.—The **arteries** are derived from the *sublingual artery*, a branch of

A

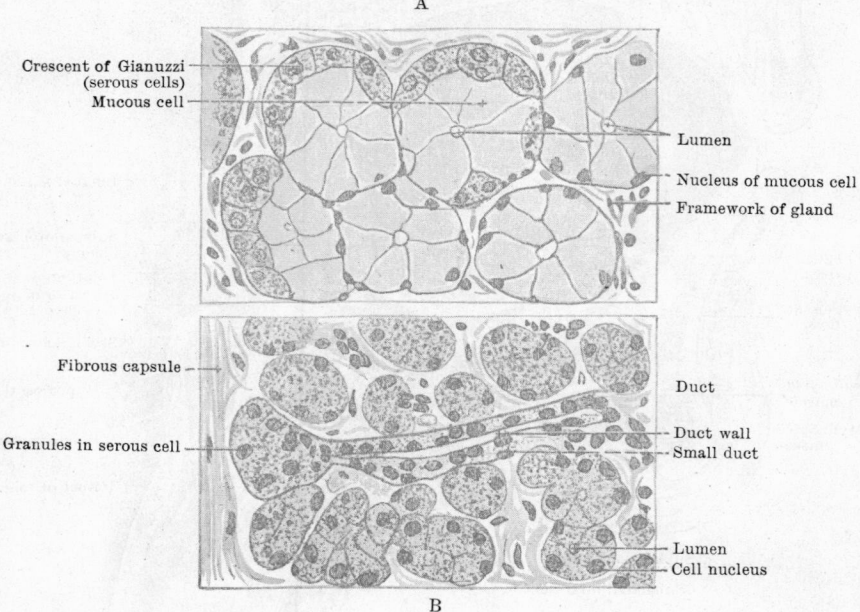

FIG 472.—A. SECTION OF HUMAN SUBMANDIBULAR GLAND. (× 400.)
B. SECTION OF HUMAN PAROTID GLAND. (× 400.)

the lingual, and from the *submental* branch of the facial. The **nerves** come from the *lingual*, the *chorda tympani*, and the *sympathetic plexus on the facial artery* through a branch of the submandibular ganglion which joins the lingual, and is conveyed by it to the gland. The secretory fibres run in the *chorda tympani nerve*, and thence through the submandibular ganglion to the gland.

The **anterior lingual gland** has been described with the tongue.

Structure of the Salivary Glands (Fig. 472).—Each of the principal salivary glands consists of a number of lobules, loosely united together by areolar tissue. From each of them one or more ducts emerge. Each duct divides into branches which terminate in a group of saccular or tubular alveoli. The epithelium lining the ducts is columnar in character, but becomes flattened at the junction with the alveoli. The epithelium lining the alveoli shows different characters in different glands. In the parotid, and in the small salivary glands of the vallate papillæ in which the secretion is watery or albuminous, the cells are uniform in character, and of small size. When the gland is at rest the cells are filled with small granules, which when the secretion is poured out are transformed into the gland ferment (ptyalin). After secretion, only the deeper parts of the cells show the presence of granules. The nuclei are rounded and lie near the margin of the cells. In the sublingual, labial, buccal, and other glands of the mouth and palate the secretion is of a mucous character and the cells are larger, and the nuclei are placed deeply. The cells appear clear and swollen unless special methods of preparation are employed, such as examination in serum ; the cells are then seen to contain large and distinct granules of mucigen which in secretion are transformed into mucus.

In the submandibular gland and the anterior lingual gland both varieties of cells are present. In those cases, the larger clear mucus cells line the cavity of the alveolus, and the smaller granular serous cells are arranged upon the basement membrane, deep to the former cells, in crescentic masses, termed the *crescents or demilunes of Gianuzzi*. They communicate with the cavity of the alveolus by small channels between adjacent mucous cells.

After secretion, the mucus cells become smaller, and stain more deeply than when loaded with mucigen before secretion.

PHARYNX

The **pharynx** lies behind the nasal cavities, the mouth, and the larynx, and communicates with them, and it is continuous inferiorly with the œsophagus or gullet (Fig. 473).

It extends from the base of the skull to the level of the sixth cervical vertebra (Fig. 473) and the lower border of the cricoid cartilage ; and in length it varies from 5 to 5½ inches (12·5 to 14·0 cm.).

In the middle part of the pharynx the pathway for respired air, between the nose and the larynx, crosses that of food and drink from the mouth to the oesophagus. The inferior portion alone, below the opening of the larnyx, is exclusively a part of the alimentary tract, and the portion above the level of the soft palate is used for respiration only. It is, however, convenient to study the structure and relations of the whole of the pharynx at once.

Structurally the pharynx is a fibro-muscular bag, lined with mucous membrane, of conical form, wide above and narrow below. The fibrous wall of the upper part of the pharynx is firmly attached to the base of the skull, especially around the posterior orifice of the nasal cavities, and hence in that part there is a permanent cavity containing air. The lower portion gradually assumes a more tubular form, and the anterior and posterior walls approach each other, so that below the level of the opening of the larynx they are in contact with each other, and the cavity is reduced to a slit, except during the passage of food.

Dimensions of the Pharynx.—From the highest part of the roof to the superior surface of the soft palate at its junction with the hard palate, it measures about 1¼ inches, or 3 cm. The vertical extent of the oral part of the pharynx is about 2¼ inches, or 6 cm., and that of the laryngeal part is about 2¾ inches, or 7 cm.

The inferior end of the pharynx is usually about 5½ to 6½ inches (14 to 16·5 cm.) from the margins of the incisor teeth, in a line passing through the cavities of the mouth and of the oral and laryngeal parts of the pharynx

The other diameters are as follows : the antero-posterior diameter (depth) of the superior segment (nasal part), from the posterior margin of the septum of the nose at its inferior part horizontally backwards, measures 15 to 18 mm., and that of the middle segment, from the palato-glossal arches to the posterior wall, about 10 mm. (two-fifths of an inch).

The **cavity of the pharynx** is partially intersected by the soft palate, which incompletely divides it into two, namely, an upper **nasal part** and a lower portion (Fig. 473). The lower portion is further subdivided into the **oral part** lying behind the mouth and tongue, and the **laryngeal part** behind the larynx.

The aperture between the margin of the soft palate and the posterior wall of the pharynx, by which the nasal part of the pharynx communicates with the lower portion of the cavity, is called the **pharyngeal isthmus.**

The pharynx presents *seven openings* by which it communicates with neighbouring cavities (Fig. 473). They are the two **posterior openings of the nose** on the anterior wall of the nasal part, and the two **pharyngeal openings of the pharyngo-tympanic tubes** on its side walls ; the **oro-pharyngeal isthmus** leading into the mouth from the oral part ; the **inlet of the larynx** on the anterior wall of the laryngeal part of the cavity ; and finally, the **opening of the œsophagus** at its inferior end.

Nasal Part (Figs. 473 and 475).—The nasal part is a portion of the true pharynx, but it is functionally part of the respiratory tract. It differs from the rest of the pharynx in that its cavity remains, under all conditions, a distinct open chamber incapable of obliteration, since all its walls, with the single exception of the floor, are practically immovable.

The cavity of the nasal part is irregular in shape, and is enclosed by *six walls*—namely, anterior and posterior, right and left, a floor and a roof or vault.

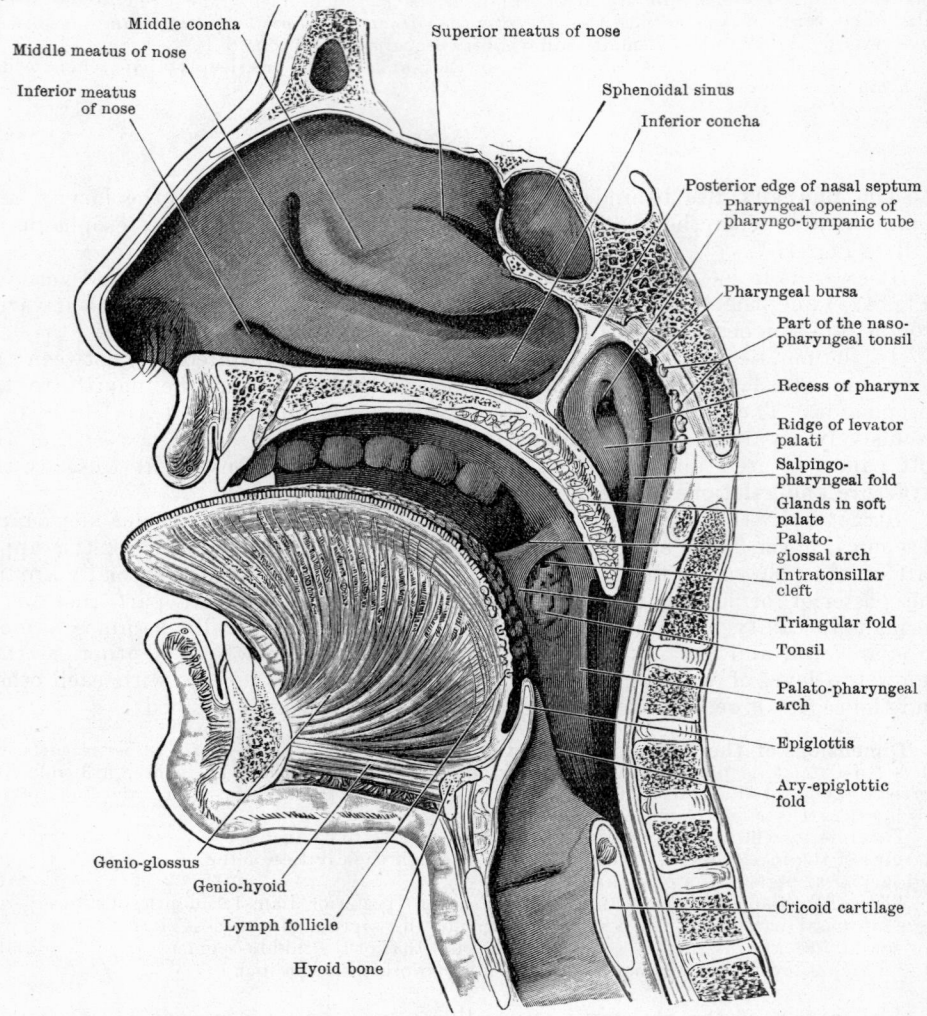

FIG. 473.—SAGITTAL SECTION THROUGH MOUTH, TONGUE, LARYNX, PHARYNX, AND NASAL CAVITY.

The section was slightly oblique, and the posterior edge of the nasal septum has been preserved.   The specimen is viewed slightly from below, hence the apparently low position of the inferior concha.

The walls all merge into one another, and the lines of separation between them are arbitrary.   Through the *anterior wall*, which slopes upwards and backwards, open the **posterior apertures of the nose**, separated from each other by the nasal septum.   The margins of the apertures form the line of separation between the nasal part and the cavity of the nose.

The *posterior wall* is nearly vertical; it corresponds in extent to the basilar part of the occipital bone and the upper two cervical vertebræ.

The *roof* lies under the posterior part of the body of the sphenoid and the basilar part of the occipital bone and slopes downwards and backwards to join the posterior wall; on each side it extends downwards to the orifice of the pharyngo-tympanic tube.

Each lateral wall is occupied by the pharyngeal opening of the pharyngo-tympanic tube and the tubal elevation, and, posterior to them, by a vertical depression that leads into a slit-like space called the **pharyngeal recess.** The *floor* is formed by the upper surface of the soft palate.

In the posterior part of the roof and upper part of the posterior wall there is a considerable accumulation of lymphoid tissue, known as the **naso-pharyngeal tonsil,** which is distinct in the child but becomes indistinct, or entirely disappears, in

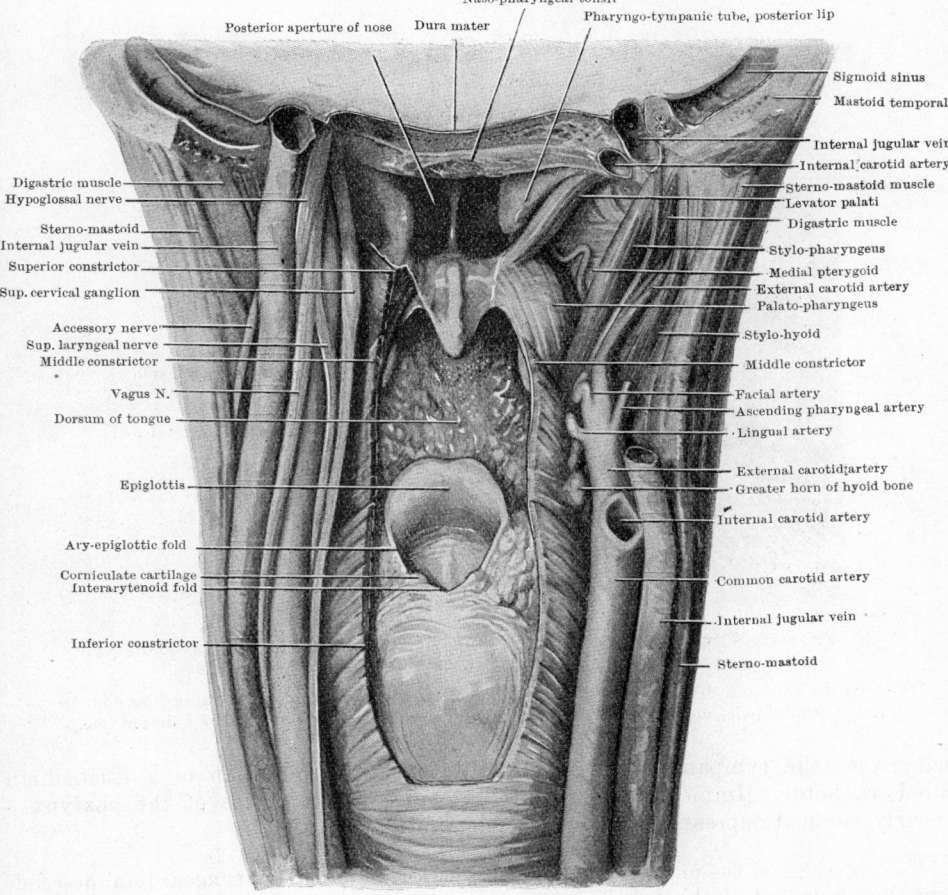

FIG. 474.—INTERIOR OF PHARYNX AND STRUCTURES IN RELATION TO ITS SIDE WALLS, VIEWED FROM BEHIND.

adult life. It extends from the body of the sphenoid down as far as the occipital bone, and, laterally, as far as the superior part of the side wall. The mucous membrane which covers it is thickened and thrown into transverse folds.

A similar collection of lymphoid tissue—a lateral prolongation of the pharyngeal tonsil—behind the mouth of the pharyngo-tympanic tube is known as the " *tubal tonsil.*"

In the inferior part of the naso-pharyngeal tonsil, there is, constantly in the child and occasionally in the adult, a small median recess, termed the **pharyngeal bursa,** which runs upwards and backwards in the wall of the pharynx for some distance (Fig. 473).

Enlargement of the lymphoid tissue in the nasal part of the pharynx occurs frequently in children, and the swollen lymph nodules are known as *adenoids.* The enlargement may be so considerable as to fill up a great part of the cavity of the nasal part of the pharynx.

The **pharyngeal opening of the pharyngo-tympanic tube,** oval or triangular, and funnel-like in appearance (Fig. 473), is situated on the side wall of the nasal part, a short distance (about $\frac{1}{3}$ to $\frac{1}{2}$ inch) behind the posterior end of the inferior concha, and immediately above the level of the hard palate (Figs. 473 and 475). It is bounded superiorly and posteriorly by a prominent rounded ridge—the **tubal elevation** (torus tubarius)—formed by the cartilage of the tube. The prominence of the posterior margin, as contrasted with the anterior margin of the orifice, and the direction of the tube itself, which runs backwards and laterally (from the

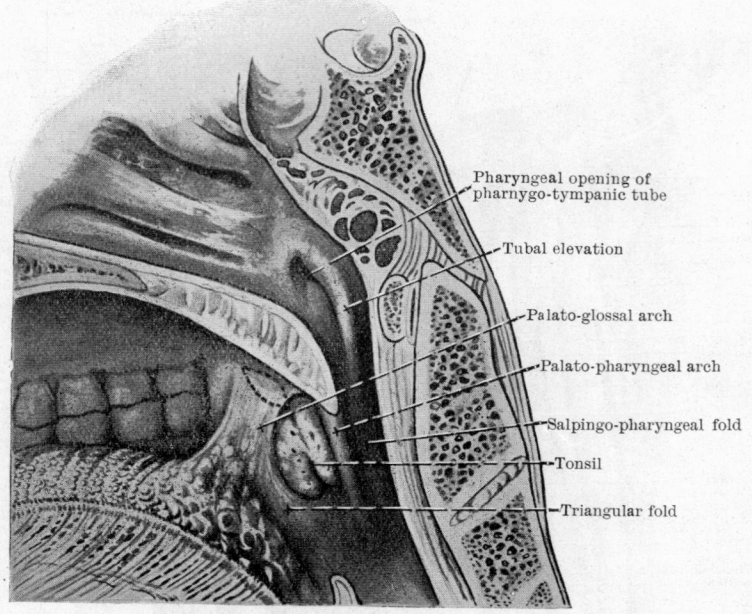

FIG. 475.—MEDIAN SECTION OF THE PHARYNX TO SHOW THE RIGHT TONSIL.
(From a specimen in the Anatomy Department, St. Andrews University.)

The tonsil is large and divided below by an oblique cleft. The orifice of the intratonsillar cleft lies near its upper pole, and the extent of the cleft in this specimen is indicated by a dotted line.

pharynx to the tympanum), greatly facilitate the introduction of a Eustachian (tubal) catheter. Immediately behind the orifice is the **recess of the pharynx**— a nearly vertical depression of considerable depth (Fig. 473).

A slight ridge of the mucous membrane, called the **salpingo-pharyngeal fold**, descends from the lower end of the tubal elevation on the side wall of the pharynx. Another less obvious ridge passes from the anterior border of the opening downwards and forwards to join the palate. In front of the latter there is an indistinct groove which indicates the division of the nasal cavity from the nasal part of the pharynx.

The levator palati runs parallel to the tube, and along its lower border. As it enters the palate, it produces, particularly when contracted, an elevation, immediately below the pharyngeal orifice of the tube (Fig. 473), which forms the base of that opening when it assumes its usual triangular shape.

The pharyngeal recess projects laterally over the superior margin of the superior constrictor, below the petrous portion of the temporal bone, and corresponds in position to the "sinus of Morgagni" on each side (cf. description of pharyngeal wall, p. 564).

Oral Part.—The oral part of the pharynx lies behind the mouth, between the soft palate above and the inlet of the larynx below. Its *posterior* boundary is the posterior wall of the pharynx, and has no distinguishing feature. *Anteriorly* it communicates with the mouth through the oro-pharyngeal isthmus, and, below that, it is bounded by the pharyngeal surface of the tongue. Each *side wall* is a triangular area named the **tonsillar sinus** because it is occupied by the tonsil. The sinus is bounded anteriorly by the palato-glossal arch (p. 536), and posteriorly by the palato-pharyngeal arch.

The **palato-pharyngeal arch** is a fold of mucous membrane containing in its interior the palato-pharyngeus muscle. It springs from the posterior edge of the soft palate, and, passing downwards and slightly backwards, ends inferiorly on the side wall of the pharynx (Fig. 473).

From the posterior surface of the palato-glossal arch a thin *triangular fold* of mucous membrane passes backwards. Its base corresponds to the palato-glossal arch, its superior border is free, and passes downwards and backwards, frequently overlapping the tonsil. Its lower border is attached to the side of the tongue. It covers, medially, the inferior part of the tonsillar sinus.

The **tonsils** are a pair of oval masses of lymphoid tissue which lie one in

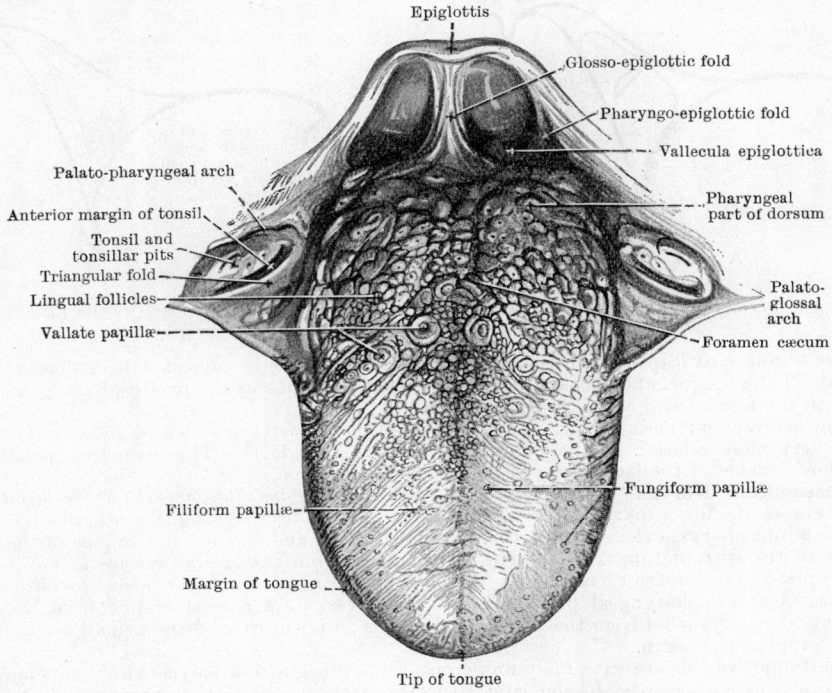

FIG. 476.—DORSUM OF TONGUE AND THE TONSILS.

each tonsillar sinus. The tonsil presents very different forms in different subjects. It may project from the sinus into the cavity of the pharynx, or it may be flat and limited to the tonsillar sinus. In some cases the triangular fold is fused with the free surface of the tonsil, and lymphoid tissue may be developed on the medial surface of that fold. It is oval in shape, with the long axis directed vertically, and it has a medial and a lateral surface, a superior and inferior pole, and an anterior and posterior margin. Its size is extremely variable, but as a rule, in early life, it measures a little under 1 inch (20 to 22 mm.) from above downwards, about ¾ inch (18 to 20 mm.) antero-posteriorly, and ½ inch (12 to 15 mm.) medio-laterally.

The medial surface is free, is covered with epithelium and is studded with deep, narrow depressions called the **tonsillar pits** or crypts (Fig. 478). On this surface there is a narrow *intra-tonsillar cleft* which penetrates the substance of the tonsil and extends upwards to the soft palate, into which it may penetrate for as much as a centimetre. The lateral, attached surface is covered by a distinct fibrous capsule which separates the tonsil from the palato-pharyngeus muscle and the superior constrictor muscle of the pharynx. At the lower part of this surface the tonsillar artery enters the tonsil and the veins leave it. The inferior pole projects downwards towards the tongue. The superior pole, rounded and blunt, presents numerous pits.

Structure of the Tonsil.—The substance of the tonsil is permeated by the tonsillar pits, each lined with stratified squamous epithelium, external to which there is a layer of lymphoid tissue 2 to 3 mm. in thickness. In this layer there are rounded germinal centres or nodules, connected together by looser tissue. The lumen of the pits is frequently filled with a cheesy material composed of epithelial cells, of lymphoid cells which have migrated through the epithelial lining, and of organisms. Each tonsillar pit with its wall forms a follicle, and the follicles are connected by loose areolar tissue.

Relations of the Tonsil.—The lateral relations of the tonsil consist of the fibrous sheath, the palato-pharyngeus and the superior constrictor muscle. Lateral to the pharyngeal wall lies the medial pterygoid muscle, and behind it a region filled with areolar tissue, containing blood-vessels and nerves. Between the capsule and the muscles lies the paratonsillar vein, either single or double, descending from the soft palate (Denis Browne).

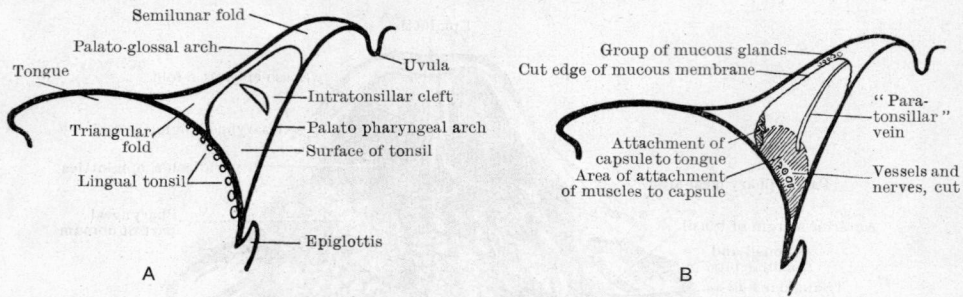

FIG. 477.—DIAGRAMS OF SURROUNDINGS OF TONSIL : A, Tonsil *in situ* ; B, After its Removal
(Denis Browne, *Journ. Anat.*, 1929).

The fibrous coat (capsule) which invests the lateral surface is connected by a fibrous band to the base of the tongue, and decussating fibres of the palato-glossus and palato-pharyngeus muscles run into the lower third of the capsule.

The nearest and most important artery is the facial artery, which, especially if tortuous, has a very close relation to the pharyngeal wall at that level. The ascending palatine and tonsillar branches of the facial artery also are in close relation.

Vessels and Nerves.—The **artery** of the tonsil is the *tonsillar branch of the facial artery*, which enters the lower part of the lateral surface close to the tongue ; other arteries from the ascending pharyngeal branch of the external carotid, and the dorsales linguæ of the lingual ramify in the surrounding tissues. The **veins** emerge from the lateral surface as two branches which pierce the superior constrictor muscle and terminate in the *common facial vein*, and connect with the pharyngeal plexus also. The **nerves** are a special branch from the glosso-pharyngeal and branches from the pharyngeal plexus ; they unite to form a small *tonsillar plexus* which supplies the organ.

The **lymph vessels** are extremely numerous. They begin in a plexus which surrounds each follicle, whence vessels pass to the lateral surface of the tonsil ; there they pierce the wall of the pharynx, and pass to a *deep cervical gland* in the neighbourhood of the greater horn of the hyoid bone, behind and below the angle of the mandible.

Laryngeal Part.—The laryngeal part of the pharyngeal cavity lies posterior to the larynx (Fig. 474). It is wide above, but at the level of the cricoid cartilage it narrows rapidly as it passes down to join the œsophagus.

Its *anterior wall* is formed throughout by the larynx, of which the following parts are seen from the pharyngeal cavity : Above, the epiglottis ; below that, the inlet of the larynx bounded at the sides by the ary-epiglottic folds ; lateral to those folds on each side, there is a deep recess called the **piriform fossa** (Fig. 553, p. 657); lower down still, the mucous membrane which covers the posterior surfaces of the arytenoid and cricoid cartilages.

Relations of the Pharynx.—1. The pharynx as a whole lies anterior to the cervical region of the vertebral column, and is separated from the bodies of the vertebræ and the intervertebral discs by the loose areolar tissue of the retro-pharyngeal space, posterior to which lie the longus capitis and longus cervicis muscles and the anterior longitudinal ligament of the vertebral column. The relations of the superior and inferior portions of the pharynx are very different.

2. The inferior portion, lying in the neck, is in contact on each side with the superior part of the thyroid gland, the carotid sheath, and especially the common and external carotid arteries, and, more posteriorly, the internal carotid artery.

The branches arising from the inferior part of the external carotid are also in close relation to the pharyngeal wall, viz. the superior thyroid and lingual arteries in the lower part, while the facial artery, as it passes under the digastric and stylo-hyoid muscles, comes into contact with the superior constrictor; and the ascending pharyngeal artery runs upwards by the side of the pharyngeal wall.

3. The relations of the superior portion are more complex. Reference to Fig. 478 will help to elucidate them. On each side lies the medial pterygoid muscle. As the medial pterygoid passes backwards and downwards to its insertion, it diverges away from the pharynx, and a triangular space is left between its medial surface and the wall of the pharynx. The styloid process, and the muscles

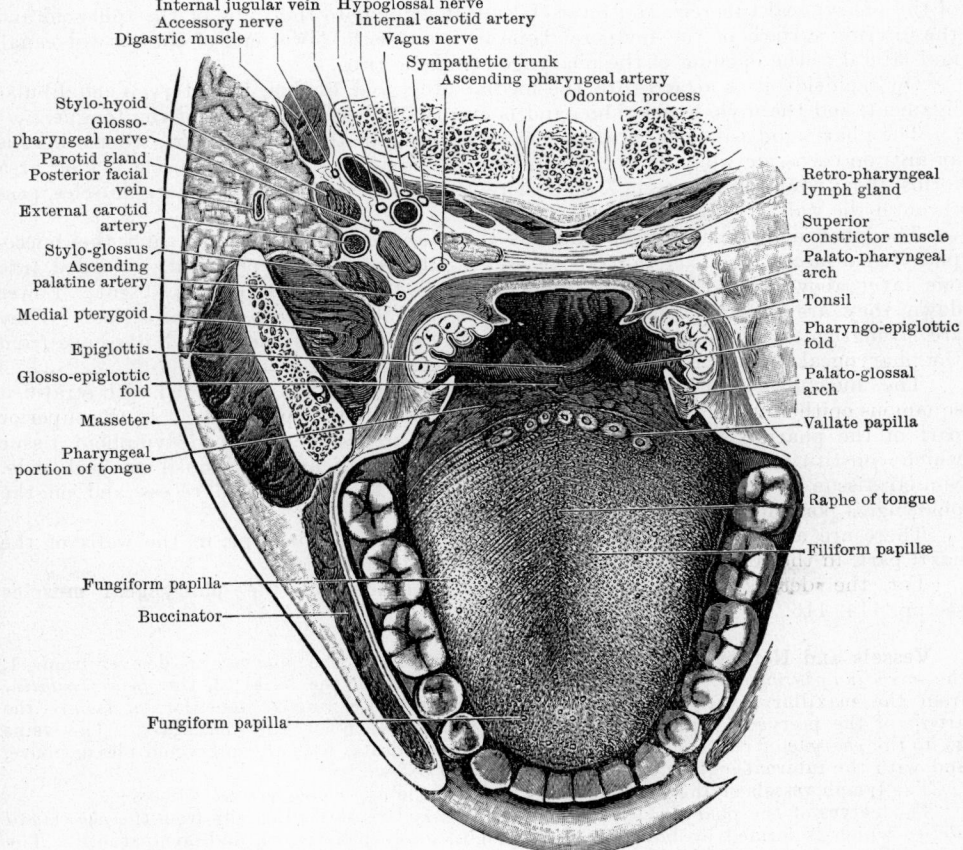

FIG. 478.—HORIZONTAL SECTION THROUGH MOUTH AND PHARYNX AT THE LEVEL OF THE TONSILS.

The stylo-pharyngeus, which is shown immediately to the medial side of the external carotid artery, and the prevertebral muscles, are not indicated by reference lines.

which arise from it, project downwards into that space, and lying beside them are numerous vessels and some nerves. Thus, the stylo-glossus and stylo-pharyngeus come into contact with the side wall, and, with the stylo-pharyngeus, the glosso-pharyngeal nerve. The ascending palatine and tonsillar branches of the facial artery ascend in close relation to the pharyngeal wall. The pharyngeal plexus of nerves and also a plexus of veins lie in contact with the side wall. The internal carotid artery lies a little farther back, with the vagus, accessory, and hypoglossal nerves. In this region the external carotid lies more superficially, and is separated by a considerable interval from the pharyngeal wall.

Structure of the Pharyngeal Wall.—The fibrous wall of the pharynx is firmly fixed above to the base of the skull, but it is not otherwise attached except to the hyoid bone and the skeleton of the larynx.

36 a

The wall is composed of a strong fibrous membrane, called the **pharyngo-basilar fascia**, lined internally with mucous membrane, and covered incompletely on its outer surface by a series of three overlapping muscles—the constrictor muscles of the pharynx.

Those muscles are covered externally by a thin layer of fascia which passes forwards, at its superior part, on to the surface of the buccinator muscle, and is called the **bucco-pharyngeal fascia.**

With the wall of the pharynx are associated several accessory muscles, viz. the muscles of the soft palate, and also the stylo-pharyngeus muscle, which blends with the wall but is also attached to the larynx (see p. 415).

The pharyngo-basilar fascia is attached to the skull as follows :—

Above, it blends with the periosteum of the basilar part of the occipital bone in front of the pharyngeal tubercle, and on each side it extends to the spine of the sphenoid and the inferior surface of the temporal bone in front of the lower end of the carotid canal, and lateral to the opening of the pharyngo-tympanic tube.

On each side it is attached to the medial pterygoid lamina, the pterygo-mandibular ligament, and the mylo-hyoid ridge, and is eventually lost on the side of the tongue.

The pharyngo-basilar fascia is particularly strong in the superior part, where there is an area on each side which is not covered by the superior constrictor muscle. That area forms the "sinus of Morgagni," and there the tensor and levator palati muscles pass through the wall.

The pharyngo-basilar fascia, which is thick above and thin below, and the bucco-pharyngeal fascia, which is thin above and stouter below, are practically blended into one layer above, near the base of the skull, where the muscular coat is absent. Lower down they are separated by the constrictors, and become two distinct sheets. They are strengthened in the median plane posteriorly by a fibrous band which descends from the pharyngeal tubercle.

The **mucous membrane** of the lower part of the pharynx is covered with stratified squamous epithelium, and that of the nasal part with ciliated epithelium. In the superior part of the pharynx and in the side wall, there are large masses of lymphoid tissue which constitute the naso-pharyngeal tonsil in the roof and *the* tonsil on each side. Similar tissue is found in considerable amount in the pharyngeal recess and on the pharyngeal portion of the dorsum of the tongue.

There are also numerous racemose glands, of the mucous type, in the walls of the nasal part, in the soft palate, and in the ary-epiglottic folds.

For the details of the attachment and relations of the **pharyngeal muscles** see pp. 414, 416.

Vessels and Nerves of the Pharynx.

Vessels and Nerves of the Pharynx.—The **arteries** of the pharynx are derived from—1, the *ascending pharyngeal ;* 2, the *ascending palatine* branch of the facial; 3, the *greater palatine* from the maxillary, with a few twigs from the dorsales linguæ, tonsillar (of facial), the artery of the pterygoid canal, and the pharyngeal branch of the maxillary. The **veins** go to the *pharyngeal venous plexus.* The plexus communicates with the pterygoid plexus above, and with the internal jugular or common facial vein below.

The **lymph vessels** of the pharynx pass chiefly to the *upper deep cervical glands.*

The **nerves** of the pharynx, both motor and sensory, are derived chiefly from the *pharyngeal plexus,* which is formed by branches of the vagus, glosso-pharyngeal, and sympathetic. The soft palate and the neighbourhood of the tonsil are supplied by the *palatine branches of the spheno-palatine ganglion.* The tonsil receives a branch from the glosso-pharyngeal direct. The vault of the pharynx, and the region around the opening of the pharyngo-tympanic tube, as well as the opening itself, are supplied by branches from the spheno-palatine ganglion. Finally, the *internal laryngeal nerve* supplies the mucous membrane of the back of the larynx.

Movements of the Pharynx.

Movements of the Pharynx.—Three different sets of movements of the pharynx or of its parts may be recognised : (1) closure of the pharyngeal isthmus, or separation of the oral part from the nasal part ; (2) closure of the oro-pharyngeal isthmus or separation of the mouth and pharynx ; and (3) movements in swallowing.

(1) This is effected by raising the posterior part of the soft palate so that its dorsal surface comes into contact with the mucous membrane on the dorsal wall of the pharynx. At the same time the uppermost fibres of the superior constrictor muscle of the pharynx contract, raising a ridge on the posterior wall known to surgeons as Passavant's ridge, in which movement they are assisted by contraction of the palato-pharyngeus muscles. In the movement of raising the soft palate the levator and tensor palati co-operate with one another.

(2) Closure of the oro-pharyngeal isthmus is effected by elevation of the posterior part of the dorsum of the tongue against the soft palate, slight lowering of the palate,

and by movement inwards of the palato-glossal folds. The palato-glossus, stylo-glossus, and tensor palati muscles participate, and also the intrinsic muscles of the tongue.

(3) The middle and inferior constrictor muscles participate in the final part of swallowing, passing the bolus of food onwards into the oesophagus. (See also p. 417).

Radiographic Examination of the Pharynx.—The form of the cavity of the pharynx during life can be shown by X-ray examination. The post-cricoid portion of the laryngeal part of the pharynx appears closed in radiographs taken under ordinary conditions (Pl. XXXIX, Fig. 2).

ŒSOPHAGUS

The **œsophagus** or **gullet** is, with the exception of the pylorus, the narrowest, and at the same time one of the most muscular parts of the whole alimentary tube.

It extends from the termination of the pharynx, at the lower border of the cricoid cartilage and opposite the sixth cervical vertebra, to the cardiac orifice of the stomach opposite the eleventh thoracic vertebra. Between those two points it traverses the lower part of the neck, the whole length of the thorax, and, having pierced the diaphragm, it enters the abdomen, and immediately afterwards joins the stomach. In its course it does not adhere to the median plane of the body, but twice leaves it, and curves to the left.

In the lower part of the neck and the upper part of the thorax, the œsophagus projects to the left beyond the margin of the trachea to the extent of $\frac{1}{6}$ or $\frac{1}{4}$ inch (4 to 6 mm.). It returns to the median plane at the level of the fourth thoracic vertebra, behind the aortic arch. Lower down, behind the pericardium, at the level of the seventh thoracic vertebra, it again passes to the left, and also forwards, in order to reach the œsophageal opening in the diaphragm, and it maintains this direction until the stomach is reached. It crosses anterior to the aorta at the level of the eighth thoracic vertebra, and traverses the diaphragm at the level of the tenth.

In addition to the curvatures just described, it is also curved in the antero-posterior direction in correspondence with the form of the vertebral column, in front of which it is situated.

In cross sections (Fig. 480) the œsophagus appears either as a flattened tube with a transverse slit-like cavity, or as an oval or rounded canal with a stellate lumen. The former condition is more common in the neck owing to the pressure of the trachea, and the latter in the thorax. When exposed in the ordinary post-mortem examination soon after death, it has rather the appearance of a solid muscular rod or band than of a hollow tube.

The œsophagus presents three distinct *constrictions*—one situated at its beginning, another at the point where it is crossed by the left bronchus, and the third where it passes through the diaphragm. The upper two constrictions are of the same size, and will admit without injury an instrument with a maximum diameter of $\frac{4}{5}$ inch (20 mm.). At each of those points the tube is flattened from before backwards.

In *length* it usually measures from ten inches (25 cm.) to twelve inches (30 cm.). Its *breadth*, where the tube is widest, varies between half an inch (13 mm.) in the empty contracted condition and an inch or more (25 to 30 mm.) in the fully distended state.

The distance from the upper incisors to the beginning of the œsophagus averages about 6 inches (15 cm.), to the level of the left bronchus 9 inches, to the opening of the diaphragm 14 to 15 inches, and to the cardiac orifice of the stomach, 16 inches.

Relations of the Œsophagus.—The relations (Fig. 480) differ so widely in different regions that they must be described separately for each of them. Three parts may be described—*cervical, thoracic,* and *abdominal*.

Cervical Part.—Anteriorly lies the trachea—to the posterior membranous wall of which the œsophagus is loosely connected by areolar tissue—and in the groove at each side, between the trachea and œsophagus, the recurrent laryngeal nerve ascends to the larynx (Fig. 480, A). Posteriorly lie the vertebral column and the longus cervicis muscles and the prevertebral layer of the cervical fascia. On each side lies the carotid sheath with its contents, the corresponding lobe of the thyroid gland and the inferior thyroid artery. Owing to the deviation of the tube to the left in the inferior part of the neck, it lies nearer to the carotid sheath and thyroid gland on the left side than on the right.

Thoracic Part.—The œsophagus passes successively through the superior and posterior mediastina, in the former lying close

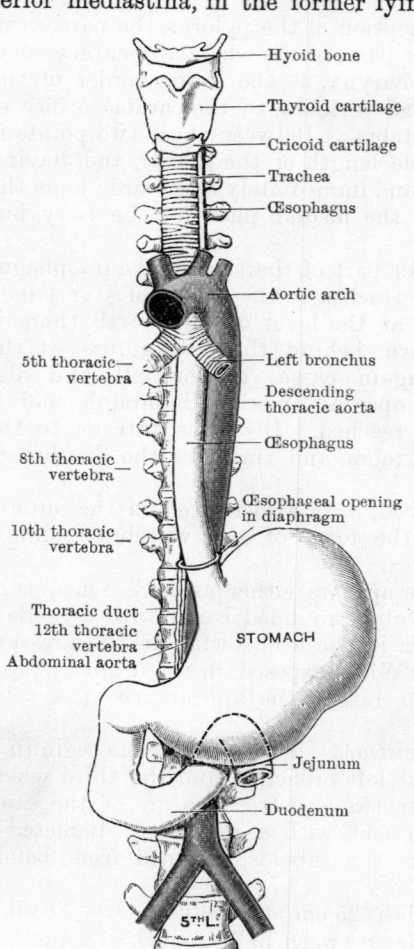

FIG. 479.—DIAGRAM TO SHOW THE COURSE OF THE ŒSOPHAGUS IN RELATION TO THE VERTEBRAL COLUMN, ETC.

to the vertebral column, but in the latter advancing into the thoracic cavity and coming into contact with the back of the pericardium. The trachea lies anterior to it as far as the fifth thoracic vertebra, where the trachea bifurcates. Immediately below that level the œsophagus is crossed by the left bronchus (Fig. 480, C), and in the rest of its thoracic course it lies in close relation to the back of the pericardium. Posteriorly,

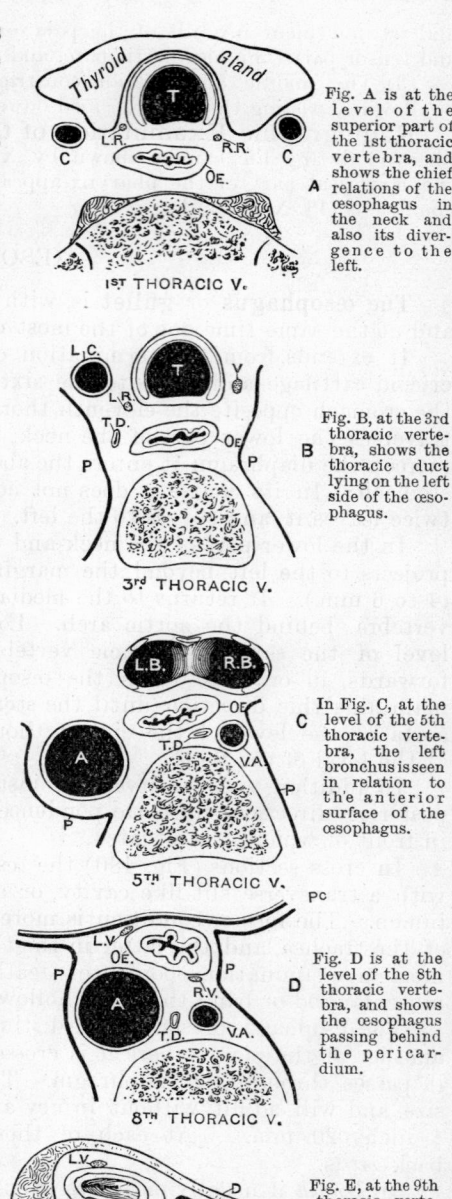

Fig. A is at the level of the superior part of the 1st thoracic vertebra, and shows the chief relations of the œsophagus in the neck and also its divergence to the left.

Fig. B, at the 3rd thoracic vertebra, shows the thoracic duct lying on the left side of the œsophagus.

In Fig. C, at the level of the 5th thoracic vertebra, the left bronchus is seen in relation to the anterior surface of the œsophagus.

Fig. D is at the level of the 8th thoracic vertebra, and shows the œsophagus passing behind the pericardium.

Fig. E, at the 9th thoracic vertebra, shows the œsophagus inclining to the left just before piercing the diaphragm.

FIG. 480.—TRACINGS FROM FROZEN SECTIONS TO SHOW THE RELATIONS OF THE ŒSOPHAGUS at the levels of the 1st, 3rd, 5th, 8th, and 9th thoracic vertebræ.

A, Aorta ; C, Common carotid artery ; D, Diaphragm ; L.B, Left bronchus ; L.C, Left subclavian artery ; L.R, Left recurrent laryngeal nerve ; L.V, Left vagus ; Œ, Œsophagus ; P, Pleura ; Pc, Pericardium ; R.B, Right bronchus ; R.R, Right recurrent laryngeal nerve ; R.V, Right vagus ; T, Trachea ; T.D, Thoracic duct ; V.A, Vena azygos.

in the upper part of the thorax, it rests on the longus cervicis muscles and the vertebral column; but below the bifurcation of the trachea, it is soon separated from the vertebral column by the vena azygos, the thoracic duct, the upper five aortic intercostal arteries of the right side, and in its lower part by the descending thoracic aorta also.

On its *left side*, in the upper part of the thorax, lie the left pleura and the left subclavian artery, with the thoracic duct posterior to the artery; in the middle region, the aorta, and lower down the left pleura again, for a little way, before the œsophagus pierces the diaphragm. On the *right side* lies the arch of the vena azygos, whilst the right pleura clothes it both below and above that level.

The two vagus nerves, after forming the posterior pulmonary plexuses, descend to the œsophagus, where they form, with each other and with branches of the sympathetic, the **œsophageal plexus.** From this plexus two nerves pass downwards, one on the front and one on the back of the oesophagus, through the opening in the diaphragm. Each of these nerves contains fibres from both vagi, and they are termed the **anterior** and **posterior gastric nerves.**

The terminal part of the thoracic part of the œsophagus, about half an inch in length (1 to 1·5 cm.), passes through the œsophageal orifice (or canal) of the diaphragm and is connected by a considerable amount of strong fibrous tissue to the boundaries of the orifice. The plane of that orifice is very oblique or almost vertical, and its abdominal opening looks forwards and to the left, and but little downwards. Above and in front, it is bounded either by the posterior edge of the central tendon or by a few decussating fibres of the muscular portion of the diaphragm. At the sides and behind, decussating bands from the right crus embrace the orifice, turn a flat surface (not an edge) towards the opening, and thus, behind and at the sides, the œsophagus is in contact with the diaphragm for a distance of 1 to 1·5 cm.

Immediately above the level at which the œsophagus passes through the diaphragm, there is a fusiform expansion of the tube, of variable length and girth, which has been called the *ampulla phrenica.* It lies in the lowest part of the posterior mediastinum, where the anterior wall is formed by the sloping posterior part of the diaphragm. Should the œsophagus be obstructed at its passage through the diaphragm, this ampulla may undergo great distension, and swallowed food may be retained in it and not pass on into the stomach.

Abdominal Part.—This part of the œsophagus is very short and funnel-shaped, widening as it approaches the stomach, and almost disappears by merging into the stomach wall when the stomach is distended. It lies against the œsophageal groove of the liver in front, with the anterior and posterior gastric nerves on its surfaces.

Relation of the Aorta to the Œsophagus.—The arch of the aorta, passing back to reach the vertebral column, crosses to the left side of the œsophagus; consequently the descending thoracic aorta lies at first to its left; lower down, however, as the aorta passes on to the front of the vertebral column, and the gullet inclines forwards and to the left, the aorta comes to lie posteriorly; and then, as the diaphragm is approached, it lies not only posteriorly, but also slightly to the right of the œsophagus (Figs. 479 and 480).

Relation of the Thoracic Duct to the Œsophagus.—The thoracic duct, lying to the right of the aorta below, is not directly related to the œsophagus (Fig. 480, E); but higher up (Fig. 480, D and E) it lies posterior to it. About the level of the aortic arch the duct passes to the left, and above that level (Fig. 480, B and A) it is found on the left side of the œsophagus, and on a plane slightly posterior to it.

Relation of the Pleural Sacs to the Œsophagus.—Above the level of the arches of the aorta and of the vena azygos, between which the œsophagus descends, the pleuræ, though not lying in immediate contact with the œsophagus, are separated from it only by a little areolar tissue, and on the left side also, behind the subclavian artery, by the thoracic duct (Fig. 480, B). There, in thin bodies, the left pleura is very close to the œsophagus, and the thoracic duct, lying on its left side, may occasionally be seen through the pleural membrane. Below the arch of the azygos vein the right pleura clothes the right side of the œsophagus—and very often even a considerable portion of its posterior surface too, thus forming a deep recess behind it—almost as low down as the opening in the diaphragm. On the left side, below the level of the aortic arch, the left pleura comes in contact with the gullet, for a short distance only, immediately above the diaphragm (Fig. 480, E).

Variations.—The chief anomalies found in the œsophagus are: (1) Annular or tubular constrictions; (2) diverticula, of which the most interesting are situated on the posterior wall close

36 c

to its junction with the pharynx ; (3) doubling in part of its course ; and (4) communications between the trachea and œsophagus.

Structure of the Œsophagus (Fig. 483).—The œsophageal wall is composed of

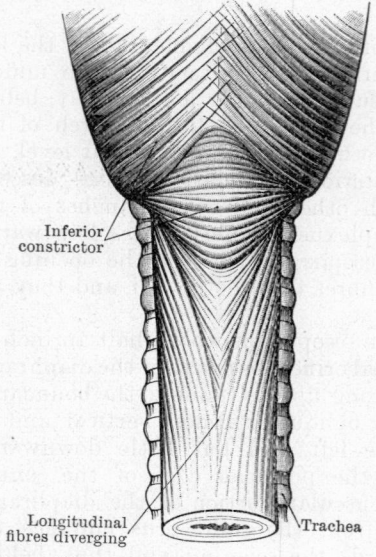

FIG. 481. — DISSECTION to show the arrangement of the muscular fibres on the back of the œsophagus and pharynx. Traced upwards, the longitudinal muscular fibres of the œsophagus are seen to separate ; passing round to the sides, they form two longitudinal bands which meet in front and are united to the cricoid cartilage, as shown in the next figure.

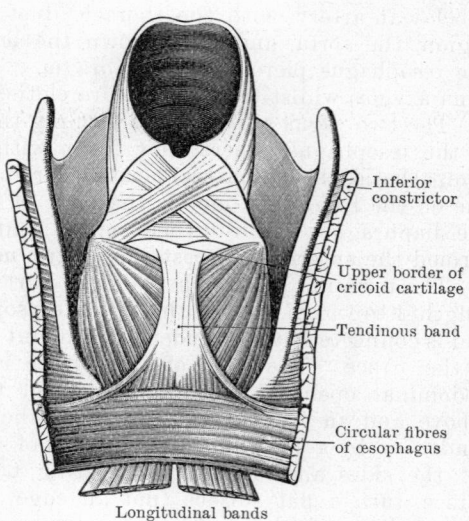

FIG. 482.—THE LOWER PART OF THE PHARYNX AND THE UPPER PART OF THE ŒSOPHAGUS have been slit up from behind, and the mucous membrane removed to show the muscular fibres. The two longitudinal bands are seen passing round to the front to be attached by a common tendon to the upper border of the cricoid cartilage. See explanation of last figure.

three proper coats—(1) *muscular coat*, (2) *submucous coat*, and (3) *mucous coat* ; in addition, it is surrounded by an outer covering of fibro-areolar tissue—(4) *adventitious coat* — by which it is loosely connected to the various structures related to it in its course. That loose covering permits of its free movement and of its increase or diminution in size, during the act of swallowing.

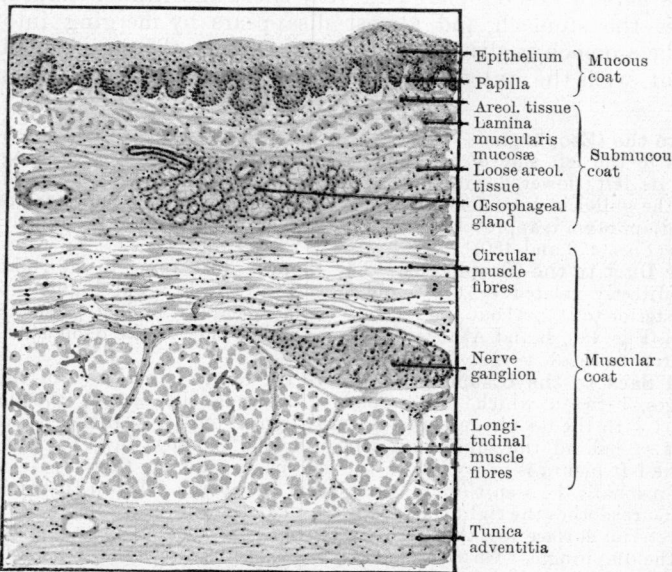

FIG. 483.—TRANSVERSE SECTION OF WALL OF HUMAN ŒSOPHAGUS.

The **muscular coat** is composed of two layers—an outer of longitudinal, and an inner of circular fibres. The *longitudinal layer* is highly developed, and, unlike the condition usually found in the digestive tube, it is as stout as the circular layer and in many places stouter. Along the greater length of the tube its fibres form an even covering outside the circular layer, and below they are continued into the longitudinal fibres of the stomach. Above, near the upper end of the œsophagus, the longitudinal fibres of each side, separating, at the back, pass round towards the anterior aspect and form two longitudinal bands (Fig. 481); these bands run up on the front of the tube, and are attached by a tendinous band to the superior part of the posterior surface of the cricoid cartilage (Fig. 482), and may extend up to the back of the arytenoid cartilages. Between these diverging muscular bands there is a thin poorly supported area on the posterior wall where a protusion of the mucous coat may occur and form an œsophageal diverticulum.

The *circular muscular fibres*, though not forming such a thick layer as the longitudinal fibres, are nevertheless well developed. Below, they are continued into both the circular and oblique fibres of the stomach. Above, they pass into the lower fibres of the inferior constrictor of the pharynx.

The longitudinal fibres for about the upper fifth of the tube are entirely striated; in the second fifth striated and unstriated are mixed; whilst in the lower three-fifths unstriated fibres alone are present. The circular fibres are entirely striated for the first inch; after that unstriated fibres appear; and in the lower two-thirds, only unstriated muscle fibres are found.

The longitudinal fibres are often joined by slips of unstriated muscle, or elastic fibres, which spring from various sources, including the left pleura (*m. pleuro-œsophageus*, constant, Cunningham), the bronchi (*m. broncho-œsophageus*), back of trachea, pericardium, aorta, etc. Those slips assist in fixing the œsophagus to the surrounding structures in its passage through the thorax, and have been aptly compared to the tendrils of a climbing plant (Treitz).

The **submucous coat**, composed of areolar tissue, is of very considerable thickness, in order to allow of the expansion of the tube during swallowing. It connects the mucous membrane loosely to the muscular coat, and admits of the former being thrown into folds when empty. In that coat are contained the numerous racemose mucous œsophageal glands which open into the cavity of the œsophagus (Fig. 483).

The **mucous coat** is of a greyish-pink colour, much paler than that of the pharynx, and of a firm and resistant texture. It is covered with a thick, stratified squamous epithelium, on the surface of which the openings of numerous glands are found. Inferiorly, its junction with the gastric mucous membrane is indicated by a distinct, irregularly dentated or crenated line which runs transversely round the tube. In carefully preserved specimens the smooth mucous membrane of the œsophagus above that line contrasts strongly with the mamillated gastric mucous membrane below.

The mucous coat is relatively inelastic, and it is but loosely connected to the muscular coat by the submucosa. Therefore it is thrown into a series of longitudinal folds when the œsophagus is empty and contracted; hence the stellate lumen often seen in sections of the gullet.

Numerous racemose mucous glands—**œsophageal glands**—large enough to be seen distinctly with the naked eye, are found in the submucous coat. They are pretty evenly distributed over the whole tube, and do not appear to be more numerous towards either end. In addition to them, other glands, resembling closely those of the cardiac end of the stomach, are found in the mucous membrane of certain portions of the œsophagus. They are entirely confined to the mucous coat, and do not extend beyond the lamina muscularis mucosæ. These glands are specially numerous at the ends of the tube.

Vessels and Nerves.—Its **arteries** consist of numerous small branches derived, in the neck from the *inferior thyroid*, in the thorax from the *bronchial arteries* and *thoracic aorta*, and in the abdomen from the *left gastric artery*, and also from the *left phrenic*.

The **veins** form a plexus on the exterior of the œsophagus from which branches pass, in the lower part of the tube, to the *left gastric vein* of the stomach, and, higher up, to the *azygos* and *thyroid veins*. There is thus established on the lower part of the œsophagus a free communication between the portal and systemic veins.

The **lymph vessels** pass to the *lower deep cervical glands*, and to the *posterior mediastinal glands*, many of which, of large size, are seen around the tube, in the thorax.

The **nerves** are derived from the *recurrent laryngeal* branches of the vagus, from the *cervical sympathetic*, and from the *vagus* and *sympathetic* nerves in the thorax.

Radiographic Examination of the Œsophagus.—The position and the movements of the œsophagus may be demonstrated by radiographic examinations made during the passage of paste opaque to X-rays (Pl. XL).

The close relation of the œsophagus to the back of the pericardium, and the interval between the œsophagus and the vertebral column at the same level, as seen in oblique lateral radiographs, are worthy of special note.

ABDOMINAL CAVITY

As the remaining parts of the digestive system lie within the abdominal cavity it is necessary first to describe that cavity, and to refer briefly to its lining membrane—the peritoneum.

The abdominal cavity is that portion of the cavity of the trunk which lies below the diaphragm. Its wall is composed in part of bones, muscles, tendons, fascia, etc., and in the cavity lie the greater part of the digestive, urinary, and genital systems of organs, as well as blood-vessels, nerves, and other structures. The greater part of the internal surface of the wall of the cavity and of the external surfaces of the viscera is clothed with a continuous smooth membrane— the peritoneum. The contained organs lie in contact with one another or with the wall, and the so-called cavity is merely a potential space between the peritoneal surfaces of adjacent viscera. When air is admitted, the viscera fall away from one another and a space is formed, in place of the capillary interval which exists under normal conditions between them.

In the following description the term **abdomen** or **abdominal cavity** is used to indicate the region enclosed by the muscular and bony walls, and the term **peritoneal cavity** the potential space inside the peritoneal membrane.

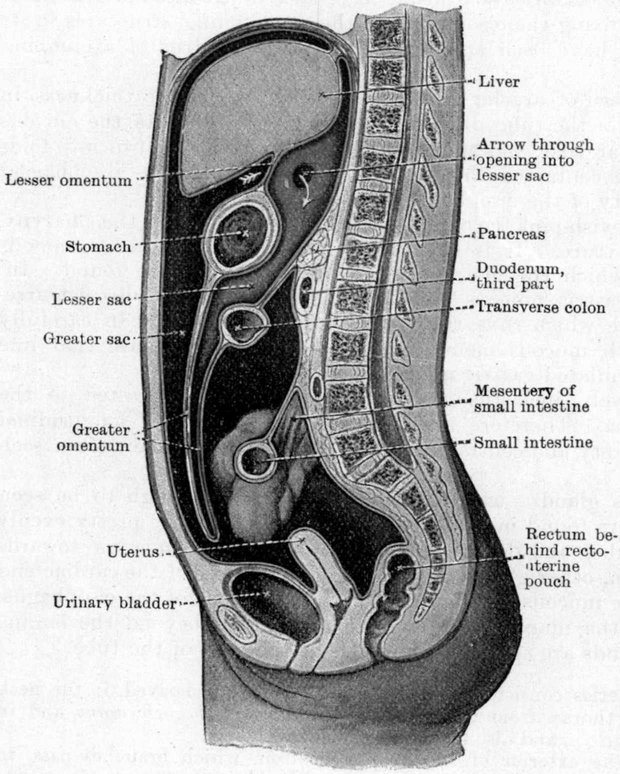

Shape.—In median section the cavity is of a more or less oval form, with the long axis vertical. The upper end is wider than the lower. In transverse section (Fig. 490) it is almost reniform, flattened from before backwards, and is encroached upon in the median plane posteriorly by the vertebral bodies to such a degree that the front of the vertebral column lies at no great distance from the back of the anterior abdominal wall (usually $2\frac{1}{2}$ to 3 inches), while on each side of the vertebral column there is a deep recess occupied by the kidneys and portions of the intestine.

The abdominal cavity is divisible into the **abdominal cavity proper** and the **pelvis**. Vertical section of the trunk shows that the **pelvis** lies below and behind the abdominal cavity, of which it forms a funnel-shaped termination.

FIG. 484.—DIAGRAMMATIC MEDIAN SECTION OF FEMALE BODY, to show the abdominal cavity and the peritoneum on vertical tracing. The greater sac of the peritoneum is blue and is represented as being much larger than in nature; the lesser sac is red; the peritoneum in section is shown as a white line.

Labels on figure: Liver; Arrow through opening into lesser sac; Pancreas; Duodenum, third part; Transverse colon; Mesentery of small intestine; Small intestine; Rectum behind recto-uterine pouch; Lesser omentum; Stomach; Lesser sac; Greater sac; Greater omentum; Uterus; Urinary bladder

The **inlet of the pelvis** (Figs. 231 and 232, p. 267), which separates these two divisions of the cavity, is bounded behind by the base of the sacrum, on each side by the arcuate line of the hip bone, and in front by the pubic crests and the upper border of the symphysis. In the erect position it makes an angle of 55 to 60 degrees with the horizontal. The two portions of the abdominal cavity meet at an angle, the abdomen proper extending almost vertically upwards from it, whilst the pelvic cavity slopes backwards and slightly downwards.

As the walls of the two regions are markedly different, the boundaries will be considered separately.

Boundaries of the Abdomen Proper.—The abdominal cavity proper is limited *above* by the concave, dome-shaped vault of the diaphragm, which presents a right and a left cupola separated by an intervening ledge. On the upper surface of each cupola is placed the base of the corresponding lung, whilst between them, above the ledge, rests the inferior surface of the heart.

During expiration, the diaphragm ascends almost to the level of the right nipple, and may reach the upper border of the fifth rib, or even the middle of the fourth intercostal space. On the left side it is half an inch to an inch (12-25 mm.) lower, and in the median plane it is opposite the xiphi-sternal joint.

Whilst the circumference of the diaphragm is attached to the lower part of the thoracic framework anteriorly and laterally, and to the lumbar vertebræ posteriorly, the central portion of the dome, formed by the central tendon, is placed high up, under cover of the ribs. As a result, the peripheral, muscular part slopes upwards and inwards from the circumference of the thoracic framework to the central tendon, and lies for a considerable distance in contact with the deep surface of the ribs; thus the diaphragm comes to form, not only the roof of the cavity, but it also enters into the formation of the sides, the posterior wall, and, to a less extent, of the anterior wall; and *almost as much of the cavity of the abdomen as of the thorax lies under shelter of the ribs.*

The *anterior wall* is formed by the aponeuroses of the three pairs of wide abdominal muscles—obliquus externus, obliquus internus, and transversus abdominis—with the pair of rectus muscles alongside the median plane. Anteriorly, below the junction of abdomen and pelvis, lies the pubic symphysis. The body of the pubis looks upwards more than backwards, and supports the viscera contained within the anterior part of the abdominal cavity.

The *side walls* are formed by the muscular portions of the obliqui and transversi muscles, and below by the iliac bones and the iliacus muscles.

The cavity is limited *posteriorly* by the lumbar portion of the vertebral column, with the crus of the diaphragm and psoas major muscle on each side, and the quadratus lumborum still more laterally. The iliac bones also enter into the formation of the inferior portion of the posterior wall.

The boundaries of the abdomen are formed chiefly of muscles which by contracting can alter the form and the size of the cavity. Its chief changes in form are due to the descent or elevation of the diaphragm, the contraction or relaxation of the anterior wall and the side walls, and the raising or lowering of the pelvic floor.

The **pelvic cavity** is bounded ventrally and at the sides by the portions of the hip bones below the level of the arcuate line, partly clothed by the obturator internus muscles and by the fascia of the pelvis as low down as the tendinous arch. The dorsal wall is formed by the sacrum and the coccyx in the middle, and on each side by the piriformis and coccygeus muscles. The floor is composed of the levatores ani covered with fascia. Those muscles pass from the side walls of the pelvis, downwards and medially towards the median plane, and present a concave superior surface towards the pelvic cavity.

The internal surfaces of the muscles immediately bounding the abdominal cavity proper and the pelvis are covered with a layer of **fascia** which separates them from the extra-peritoneal areolar tissue and the peritoneum. That fascial layer is distinguished in different localities as: (1) the *transversalis fascia*, on the anterior and side walls, lining the deep surface of the transversalis muscle and continuous above with (2) the *diaphragmatic fascia* clothing the inferior surface of the diaphragm; (3) the *iliac fascia*, on the posterior wall, covering the psoas and iliacus muscles; and (4) the *fascia of the pelvic muscles* lining the pelvis.

Apertures.—Certain apertures are found in the muscular walls of the abdomen. They are: the three openings in the diaphragm for the passage of the inferior vena cava, the œsophagus, and the aorta; the apertures in the pelvic floor through which the rectum, the urethra, and, in the female, the vagina, reach the surface; the inguinal canal, through which the spermatic cord (or the round ligament) passes;

and lastly, the femoral canal, a small passage which extends downwards from the abdomen along the medial side of the femoral vessels. The latter two, particularly, constitute weak points in the abdominal wall through which an inguinal or a femoral hernia may occur. Similar protrusions may occur at other points in the abdominal and also in the pelvic wall.

Extra-peritoneal tissue.—Between the fascia which covers the inner surfaces of the abdominal muscles and the peritoneum lies a considerable quantity of

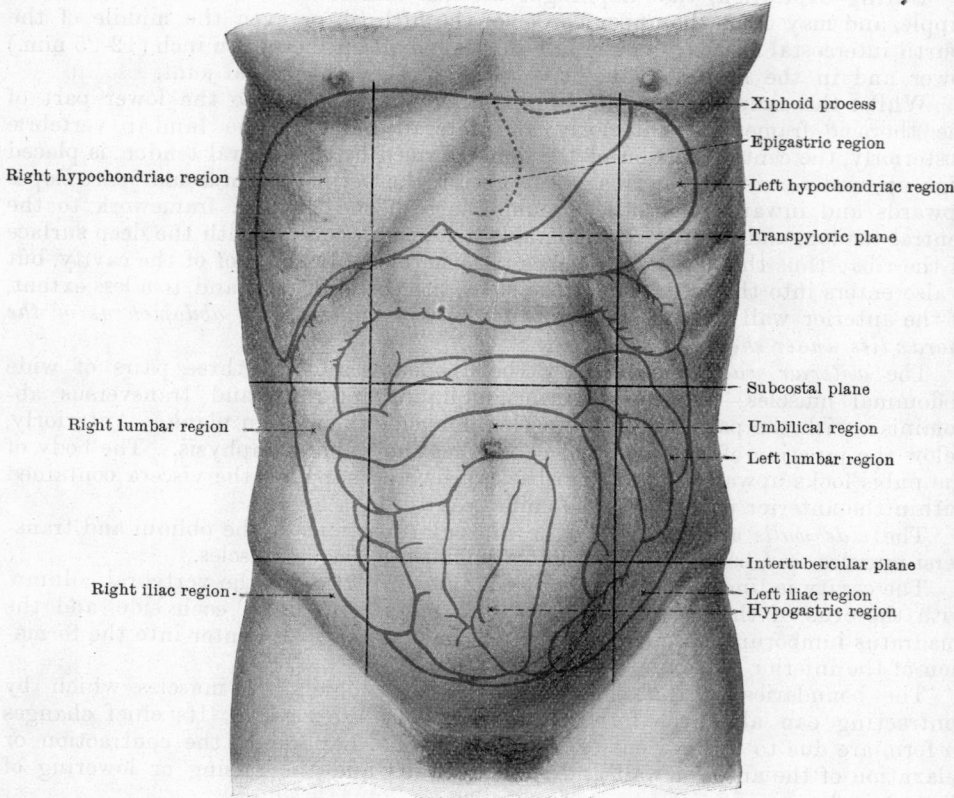

FIG. 485.—PLANES OF SUBDIVISION OF THE ABDOMINAL CAVITY, AND OUTLINE TRACING OF THE LIVER, STOMACH, AND INTESTINE IN RELATION TO THE ANTERIOR ABDOMINAL WALL.

The oblique position of the stomach and the high position of the transverse colon are largely due to the fact that the subject was fixed in the horizontal position.

extra-peritoneal areolar tissue more or less loaded with fat. It is part of an extensive layer which lines the whole of the body cavity outside the various serous sacs, and it is continued on the several vessels, nerves, and other structures which pass from the trunk into the limbs.

In the abdomen it is divisible into a parietal and a visceral portion. The former lines the walls, whilst the latter passes between the layers of the peritoneal folds to the viscera. The extra-peritoneal tissue contains a vascular plexus through which a communication is established between the vessels of the abdominal wall on the one hand and those of the contained viscera on the other, and also a network of nerve fibres derived from sympathetic and cerebro-spinal nerves.

The *parietal portion* is thin and comparatively free from fat over the roof and anterior wall of the abdomen. In the pelvis the tissue is loose and fatty, and is continued up for some inches on the anterior abdominal wall above the pubis, and so permits of the ascent of the bladder during its distension, in the interval between the peritoneum and the transversalis fascia. There also the median and lateral umbilical ligaments will be found passing up in its substance. On the posterior wall the tissue is large in amount and fatty, particularly where it surrounds the great vessels and the kidneys.

From the parietal portion the *visceral expansions* are derived in the form of prolongations around various branches of the aorta. Those expansions are connected with the areolar coats of the blood-vessels and pass with them into the mesenteries and other folds of the peritoneum, and thus reach the viscera.

The chief uses of the extra-peritoneal tissue are : (1) to unite the peritoneum to the fascial and muscular layers of the abdominal wall ; (2) to connect the viscera to those walls and to one another in such a loose manner that their distension or relaxation may not be interfered with ; (3) in addition, it is a storehouse of fat, forms sheaths for the vessels and nerves, and establishes, through its vascular plexus, communication between the parietal vessels and those distributed to the abdominal viscera.

Subdivision of the Abdomen Proper.—Owing to the large size of the cavity, and in order that the position of the various organs contained within it may be localised more exactly, the abdomen proper is artificially subdivided into nine regions by two horizontal planes (subcostal and intertubercular) and a pair of sagittal planes. The position of these nine regions and the four dividing planes is indicated in Fig. 485.

The division of the abdominal cavity and the projection of its sections on to its anterior wall provide the clinician with a chart by which he can indicate and record more precisely the exact position, for example, where a patient may indicate that he feels pain, or where a swelling may be detected in the course of examination.

The regions into which the cavity is divided have, however, only a general and not a precise relation to the position of most of the abdominal organs, and they will not be specially referred to in the following descriptions.

A particular plane which is of some practical value is the *transpyloric plane* (Addison). It is a horizontal plane which intersects the trunk at the level of the first lumbar vertebra. Its level is the mid-point of a line drawn, on the surface of the trunk, from the upper border of the sternum to the upper border of the pubic symphysis.

Contents of the Abdomen.—The following structures are found within the abdomino-pelvic cavity :—

1. The greater part of the *alimentary canal*, viz., stomach, small intestine, and large intestine.
2. *Digestive glands :* the liver and pancreas.
3. *Ductless glands :* the spleen and the suprarenal glands.
4. *Urinary apparatus :* the kidneys, ureters, bladder, and part of urethra.
5. The internal *generative organs*, according to the sex.
6. *Blood-vessels* and *lymph vessels* and *lymph glands*.
7. The abdominal portion of the cerebro-spinal and sympathetic *nervous systems*.
8. Certain *fœtal remains*.
9. The *peritoneum*—the serous membrane which lines the cavity, and is reflected over most of its contained viscera.

PERITONEUM

The **peritoneum** is the serous membrane which lines the abdominal cavity and invests most of the abdominal viscera to a greater or less degree. Like other serous membranes, it is composed of a thin layer of fibrous tissue, containing numerous elastic fibres, covered over on the side turned towards the cavity of the sac by a layer of flattened endothelial cells. Like them, also, the peritoneum in the male is a completely closed sac, but in the female the *pelvic opening* of each uterine tube is a breach in it, whilst the *uterine opening* of that tube communicates with the interior of the uterus, and thus, indirectly, with the exterior of the body. Normally the membrane secretes only sufficient moisture to lubricate its surface ; otherwise the sac is empty, and its opposing walls lie in contact, thus practically obliterating its cavity.

The serous lining of the abdomen permits of the movements of the contained viscera during any changes in size or form which they may undergo, and the stomach and intestines are free to move with a minimum of friction.

The peritoneum covering an organ is termed *visceral peritoneum*; and it is united so intimately to many of the viscera that it appears at first sight to be a superficial layer of these organs rather than a separate membrane. Peritoneum which lines the walls or forms folds connected with viscera is termed *parietal peritoneum*.

In the adult the arrangement of the peritoneum is complicated by the changes which occur in the form and position of many of the viscera during their development, and it is necessary to explain briefly some of the changes which modify its original simple arrangement.

The peritoneum represents the smooth lining membrane of the abdominal part of the body cavity or cœlom. Some of the abdominal viscera as, for example,

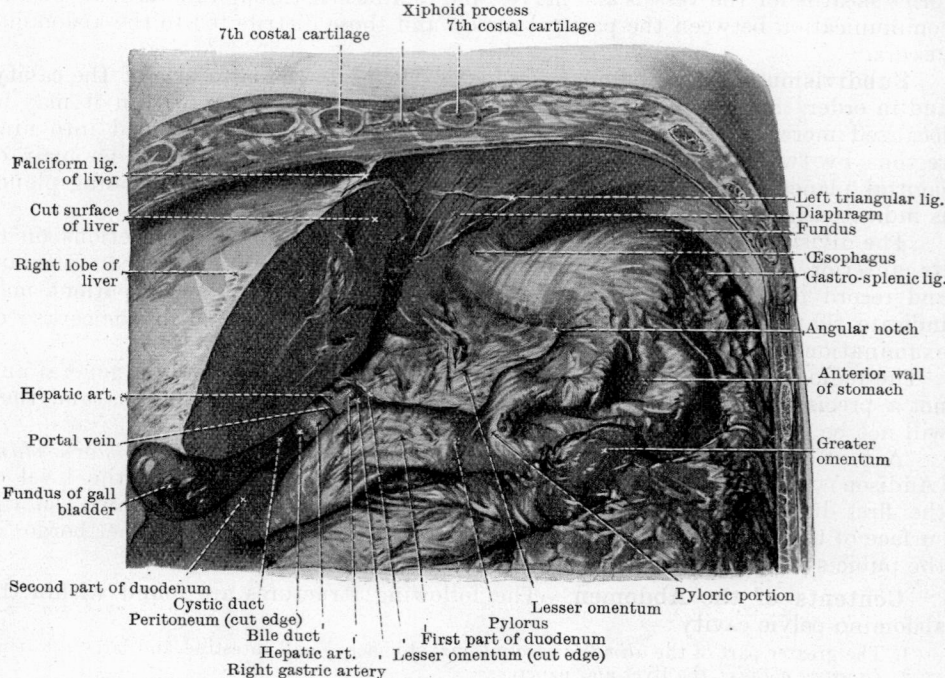

FIG. 486.—THE LESSER OMENTUM.

The left lobe of the liver has been removed, and also the anterior layer of the duodenal part of the lesser omentum. The view is taken looking upwards as well as backwards.

the kidneys, lie dorsal to the membrane on the posterior body wall, with only their ventral surfaces in contact with the lining membrane. The greater part of the intestinal tube, on the other hand, projects forwards into the body cavity, and is connected with the dorsal wall by extra-peritoneal tissue, containing nerves, and blood- and lymph-vessels, covered on each side by a thin peritoneal membrane which passes on over the intestine and invests its ventral and lateral surfaces.

Organs showing the first relationship are said to lie " behind " the peritoneum, or to be " partly invested " by it, while those of the second relationship are said to be " completely invested " and to have a " mesentery " connecting them to the abdominal wall.

The intestine originally has a continuous dorsal mesentery, and, in addition, its proximal portion is connected to the ventral wall above the level of the umbilicus by a ventral mesentery; but as it develops it alters in position and form, and the mesenteries grow or become stretched.

The liver, for example, enlarges within the ventral mesentery, and the spleen makes its appearance and grows within the original dorsal mesentery of the stomach; and so the original ventral mesentery passes from the stomach to the liver and from the liver to diaphragm, and the dorsal mesentery of the stomach passes from stomach to spleen and from spleen to left kidney.

Mesenteries are folds of extra-peritoneal tissue covered on each side by peritoneum which unite portions of the intestine to the posterior abdominal wall, and convey to them their vessels and nerves. There are several mesenteries, *e.g.* the *mesentery proper*, which connects the jejunum and ileum to the posterior abdominal wall, the *transverse mesocolon* (mesentery of the transverse colon), the *pelvic mesocolon* (mesentery of the pelvic colon), (mesentery of the appendix vermiformis), and occasionally others (see p. 576).

The term **omentum** is applied to two folds of similar structure derived from the embryonic ventral and dorsal mesenteries of the stomach respectively, which in the adult pass from the stomach, one to the liver—the *lesser omentum*— and the other to the transverse colon—the *greater omentum*.

Greater Omentum.—The greater omentum, a large apron-like fold of peritoneum, usually more or less loaded with fat, is attached to the greater curvature of the stomach, and hangs down in front of the intestines to a variable extent. When the abdomen is carefully opened without disturbing the viscera, it is rare to find the greater omentum evenly spread over the front of the intestines. More commonly it is folded in between some of the coils of intestine, or tucked into the left hypochondrium ; or perhaps it is carried upwards in front of the stomach by a distended transverse colon. The greater omentum extends between the greater curvature of the stomach above and the transverse colon below, not taking the shortest course from one of those to the other, but hanging down as a loose fold, and containing between the anterior and posterior sheets a part of the lesser sac (Fig. 484).

The greater omentum consists of two sheets, each formed of two layers of peritoneum enclosing fat and areolar tissue. The **anterior** or **descending sheet** begins at the greater curvature of the stomach, where it is formed by the meeting of the layers from the anterior and posterior surfaces of that organ. Thence it descends across the front of the transverse colon (to which it is often adherent, either in part or as a whole). Leaving the colon (see Fig. 487), the two layers proceed to the lower border of the omentum, where, turning back, they pass up as the **posterior** or **ascending sheet**, which runs upwards until it meets the transverse colon. There its two layers separate to enclose that colon—and the greater omentum, properly so called, ceases. The two layers, however, unite at the upper margin of the colon to form the **transverse mesocolon**, which is continued upwards and backwards to the lower border of the pancreas. There, the layers of the transverse mesocolon again separate—the upper running upwards over the anterior surface of the pancreas to the posterior abdominal wall behind the cavity of the lesser sac ; the lower passing downwards on the posterior abdominal wall into the pelvis.

The greater omentum is continued to the right for a short distance (one inch) along the lower border of the first part of the duodenum. At the left end it shortens very much, and is directly continued into the gastro-splenic ligament ; the spleen, as it were, being introduced between the two layers instead of the colon.

The greater omentum contains, between the two layers of its anterior sheet, the greater part of the right and left gastro-epiploic arteries and their accompanying veins, as well as lymphatic vessels and nerves. The special interest of the upper part of this sheet is that through it access may be obtained to the part of the lesser sac which is behind the stomach.

The amount of fat contained between its layers is variable, and may be very large in adipose subjects, and almost non ein spare ones. It is often fenestrated and may be a fine lace-like net. On its surface may be present milk-like spots formed by accumulations of a special variety of lymphoid cells termed *histiocytes*.

Functions of the Greater Omentum.—Numerous uses have been assigned to the great omentum ; the chief seem to be : (1) To act as a movable and easily adjustable packing material, capable of filling all spaces produced temporarily in the abdomen. In this respect it may be compared with the fatty pads in joints. (2) It probably, to some extent, prevents the passage of the small intestines up into the stomach chamber, and helps to keep them from becoming entangled there. (3) It is a storehouse of fat. (4) It is said to be " the great protector against peritoneal bacterial invasions " ; being freely movable, it can pass to almost any part of the abdomen, and there " build up barriers of exudations to check infection."

Lockwood made the interesting observation (in connection with the contents of herniæ) that in bodies under forty-five years of age the omentum can rarely be drawn down below the level of the pubic tubercle ; in older bodies the reverse is the rule.

Lesser Omentum.—The lesser omentum is a peritoneal membrane which passes from the inferior and posterior surfaces of the liver to the stomach and duodenum. Its structures and attachments are as follows :—

The portion lying to the left is thin, translucent, and sometimes fenestrated, and extends from the lesser curvature of the stomach to the left end of the porta hepatis and to the fissure for the ligamentum venosum. It contains the right and left gastric arteries and accompanying veins and lymph vessels, some lymph glands, and filaments from the anterior gastric nerve which go to the liver. The thicker strong right portion passes from the first part of the duodenum to the porta hepatis. On the right it ends in a rounded margin. Traced downwards, the layers of peritoneum which form it clothe the commencement of the duodenum on two sides. In it lie the hepatic artery, the portal vein, and the bile duct, with lymph vessels and nerves.

The lesser omentum occasionally extends still farther to the right, and forms a thin membrane that connects the gall-bladder to the transverse colon and right flexure of the colon. This portion is termed the *hepato-colic ligament*.

The **gastro-splenic ligament** is a short fold attached by one margin to the fundus and greater curvature of the stomach, and by the other to the gastric surface of the spleen immediately in front of the hilum. Between its two layers the short gastric branches of the splenic artery pass from the spleen to the stomach. Below and in front, its layers are continued into the corresponding layers of the greater omentum; above and behind, they separate at the "bare area" of the stomach (Fig. 509).

The **lieno-renal ligament** is a short fold that stretches from the front of the left kidney to the hilum on the visceral surface of the spleen (Fig. 489, p. 580). Its medial layer becomes continuous there with the medial layer of the gastro-splenic ligament; and its lateral layer is continuous with the peritoneal covering of the spleen. The splenic vessels and nerves lie between its layers.

The **gastro-phrenic ligament** is a short fold reflected from the under surface of the diaphragm on the left side of its œsophageal orifice to the posterior surface of the fundus of the stomach. It is merely a fold on the peritoneum which passes from the diaphragm to this part of the stomach.

The **mesentery** is described on p. 603.

The **mesentery of the vermiform appendix** is a small triangular fold attached by one side to the whole length of the appendix, by another to the under surface of the mesentery close to the termination of the ileum, while the third side is free. The vessels to the appendix are found in it.

The **transverse mesocolon** is a typical mesentery containing a considerable thickness of extra-peritoneal tissue, as well as the middle colic vessels and branches from the right and left colic vessels, and nerves and lymph vessels. Its root lies horizontally on the posterior abdominal wall, extending across that wall from the right to the left colic flexure, crossing the second part of the duodenum, the head of the pancreas and the lower border of the body of that organ.

The **pelvic mesocolon** is described on p. 617.

Other folds, specially named, but described elsewhere, are the right and left gastro-pancreatic folds (p. 580), and the ligaments of the liver (p. 629).

Peritoneal "Adhesions" and Variations.—In addition to the peritoneal folds which have been mentioned, many other peritoneal bands and folds are sometimes found. (1) The gall-bladder is often united to the first part of the duodenum by a dense, strong layer of fibrous tissue which blends with the lateral part of the lesser omentum. (2) The duodeno-jejunal junction is occasionally firmly joined by similar bands to the transverse meso-colon. (3) Around the cæcum, vermiform appendix, terminal part of the ileum, and lower part of the ascending colon, it is common to find bands of fairly dense tissue passing (a) from the colon to the lateral abdominal wall, (b) from the terminal portion of the ileum to the cæcum, (c) from the cæcum itself to the parietes. Such bands are usually ascribed to "peritonitis." (4) The greater omentum may be united to the anterior surface of the ascending colon. (5) Fibrous bands often pass from the left side of the lower part of the descending colon to the parietes. They have been ascribed to faults in development, to peritonitis, and to mechanical traction, but it is not possible to state definitely the exact mode and cause of their origin.

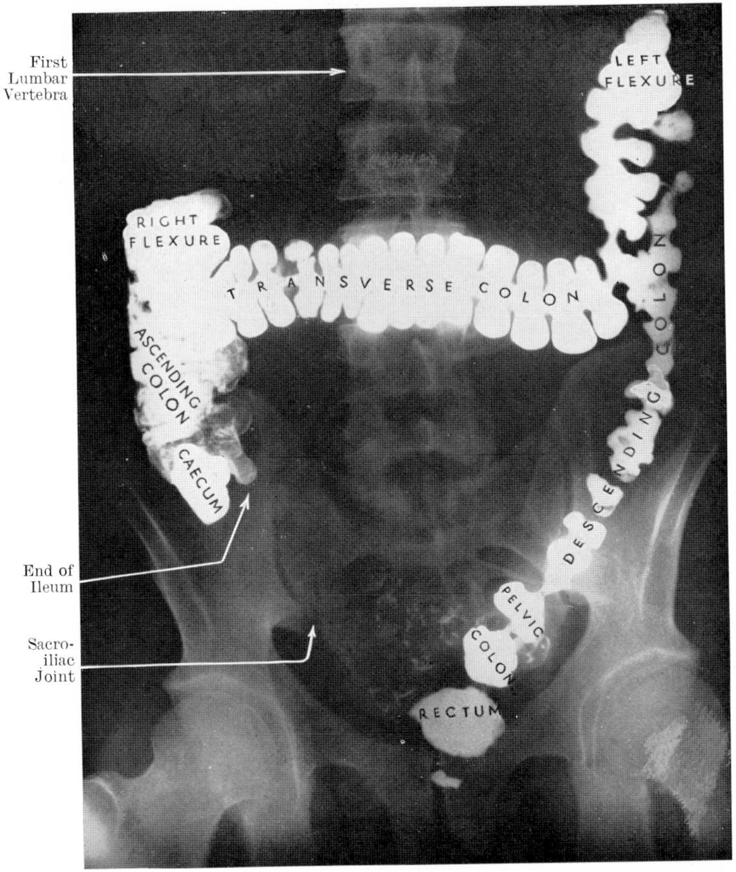

First Lumbar Vertebra

Left Flexure of Colon

Sacro-iliac Joint

TRANSVERSE COLON

ILEUM

Right Flexure of Colon

Caecum

Appendix

Terminal part of Ileum

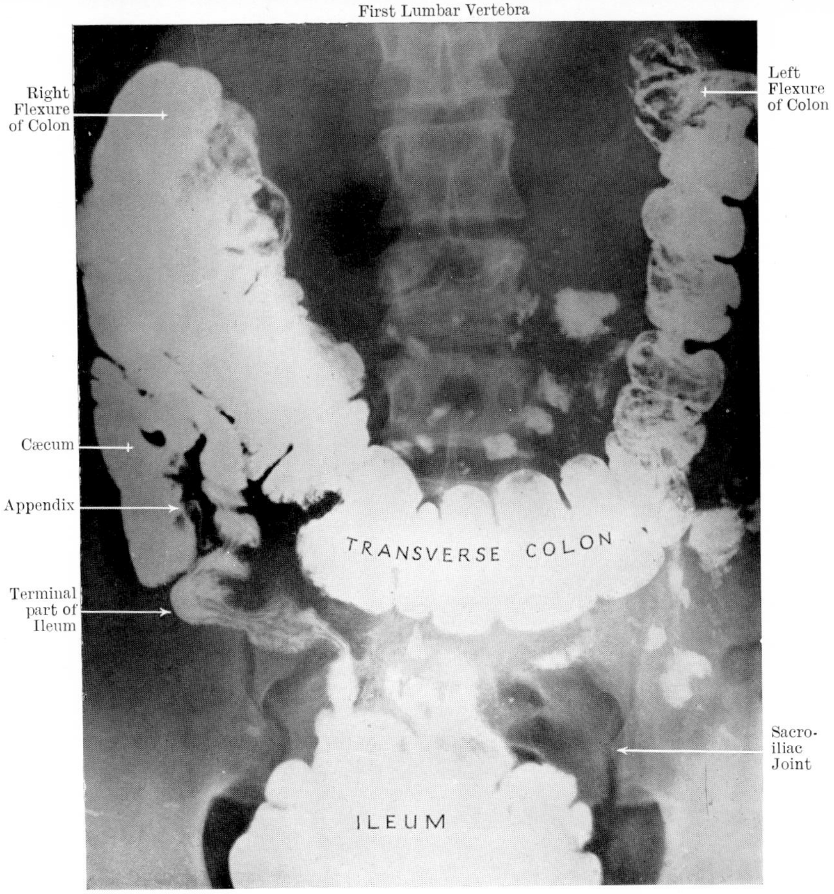

Fig. 2.—Radiograph showing Ileum and part of the Large Intestine filled by an Opaque Meal. (J. F.)

Note the high position of the Caecum (as in Fig. 1), the position of coils of the Ileum in the true pelvis, and the ascending terminal part of the Ileum. The Transverse Colon is much lower than in Fig. 1, partly because it has not contracted to pass on any of its contents to the Descending Colon.

LEFT FLEXURE

DESCENDING COLON

TRANSVERSE COLON

PELVIC COLON

RECTUM

RIGHT FLEXURE

ASCENDING COLON

CAECUM

First Lumbar Vertebra

End of Ileum

Sacro-iliac Joint

Fig. 1.—Radiograph of the Large Intestine of Man aged 31, taken 24 hours after a Barium Meal. (Dr. J. F. Brailsford.)

Note the high position of the Cæcum (cf. Plates XLII and XLVII) and that the Pelvic Colon appears very short as it contains very little barium. Cf. also Plate XXXVIII and note that there is considerable variation in the time at which an opaque meal is seen throughout the large intestine.

PLATE XLII

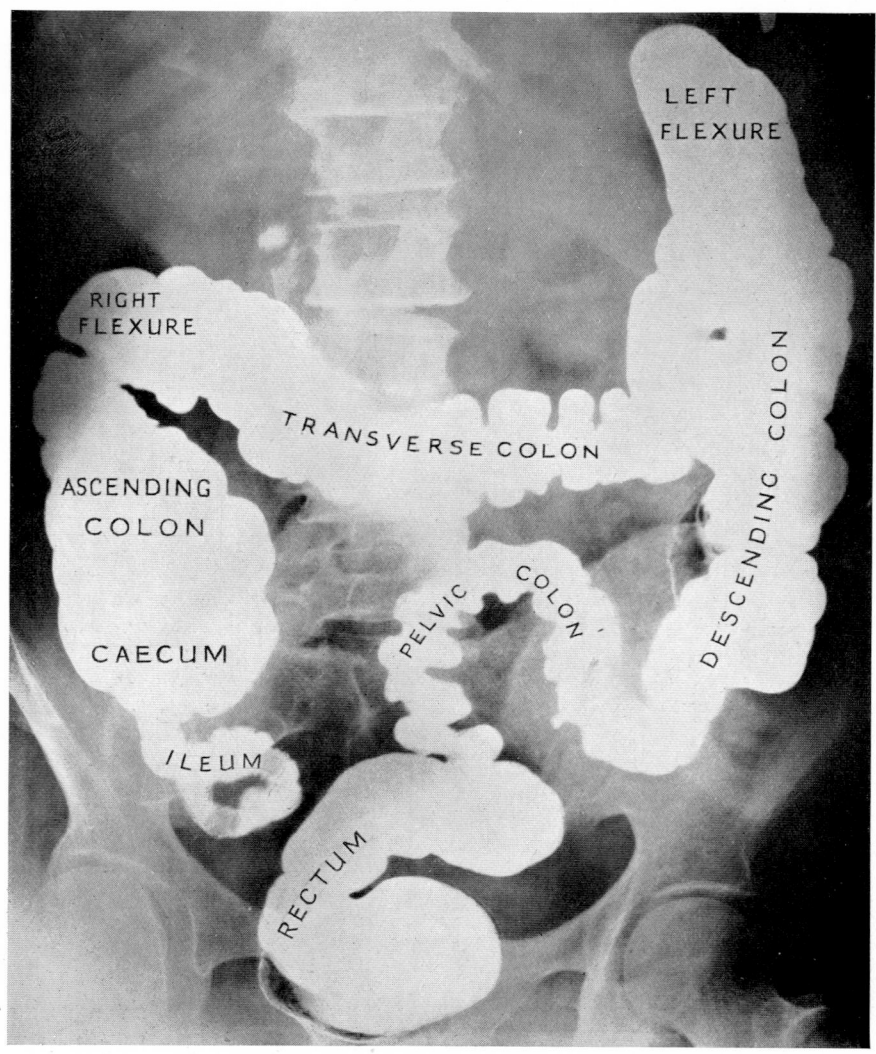

PLATE XLII.—RADIOGRAPH OF LARGE INTESTINE FILLED ENTIRELY (WITH THE EXCEPTION OF VERMIFORM APPENDIX) BY BARIUM ENEMA. (J. F.)

The position of the several parts of the Large Intestine is well shown. Note the loop of the Pelvic Colon, and that some of the barium injection has passed into the terminal part of the Ileum. Cf. Plate XLI, Figs. 1 and 2, and Plate XLVII.

[Facing p. 577

CAVITY OF PERITONEUM

The peritoneal cavity is described as consisting of two portions—the general peritoneal cavity or **greater sac** and the **lesser sac**. The greater sac is opened when the anterior abdominal wall is removed or incised; the lesser sac is chiefly behind the stomach and in the greater omentum, and is much smaller. The two sacs are not separate cavities, for the lesser sac is merely a recess of the greater sac, formed by changes that take place in the position of the viscera and their mesenteries during development. If the general peritoneal cavity is compared to a bag, the lesser sac might be represented as a pocket lying behind it, and opening into it by a narrow orifice.

Greater Sac of Peritoneum.—The general peritoneal cavity is placed between the parietes anteriorly and the abdominal viscera posteriorly. The anterior layer of peritoneum lines the anterior abdominal wall; the posterior partly covers the posterior abdominal wall, but is carried forwards by the viscera, so that the two layers come in contact.

The **anterior layer of the peritoneum** covers the anterior abdominal wall completely, from the diaphragm above to the pelvis below. Over the greater part of its extent it is connected to the wall by a small amount of fatty extra-peritoneal areolar tissue; but below, near the pubic region, the fat is more abundant, and the connexion between the two becomes much looser.

In this tissue there are five cord-like structures—one in the median plane, and two at each side. They are (*a*) the **median umbilical ligament** (*urachus*) — the remains of the allantois of the fœtus— which in the adult is a slender fibrous band connected to the umbilicus above and to the apex of the bladder below, where it usually becomes much stouter. At the sides of the median ligament, and some distance from it (Figs. 527, p. 620, and 596, p. 710), (*b*) a pair of stouter fibrous cords—the **lateral umbilical ligaments**—pass upwards and medially. They become more slender as they approach the median ligament, along with which they are connected to the umbilicus. Below, they grow thicker, and can be followed backwards along the side wall of the true pelvis to the internal iliac arteries, which they join. The lateral umbilical ligaments are obliterated portions of the **umbilical arteries**, by which in the fœtus blood passes from the internal iliac arteries to the placenta. (*c*) More laterally still, the **inferior epigastric arteries** run upwards and medially from the external iliac trunks.

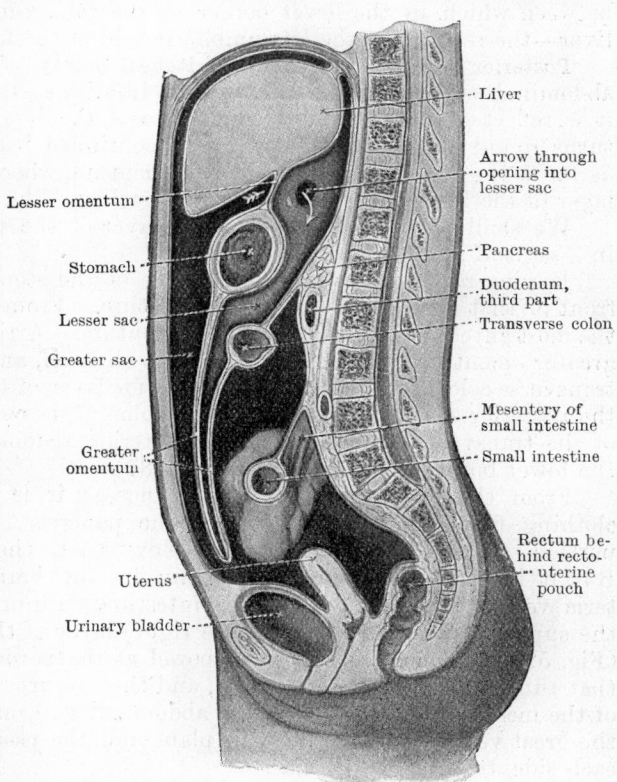

FIG. 487.—DIAGRAMMATIC MEDIAN SECTION OF FEMALE BODY, to show the abdomino-pelvic cavity and the peritoneum on vertical tracing. The greater sac of the peritoneum is blue and is represented as being much larger than in nature; the lesser sac is red; the peritoneum in section is shown as a white line.

Labels in figure: Liver; Arrow through opening into lesser sac; Pancreas; Duodenum, third part; Transverse colon; Mesentery of small intestine; Small intestine; Rectum behind recto-uterine pouch; Lesser omentum; Stomach; Lesser sac; Greater sac; Greater omentum; Uterus; Urinary bladder

When the anterior abdominal wall is examined from behind, it will be seen that the five structures form five more or less distinct peritoneal ridges, known as the *median* and *lateral umbilical folds* and the *folds of the epigastric arteries* respectively.

Three pairs of shallow peritoneal fossæ are associated with these folds—one lateral to each fold. The most lateral of them—the one lateral to the epigastric artery—corresponds to the position of the deep inguinal ring. At its bottom, a dimple-like depression of the peritoneum indicates the point from which the processus vaginalis passed down, in connection with the descent of the testis.

Between the epigastric artery laterally, the margin of the rectus abdominis muscle medially, and the inguinal ligament below, there is a small triangular region called the **inguinal triangle.** The obliterated umbilical artery, in passing upwards, crosses this triangle, and divides it into a lateral and a medial part; the intermediate one of the three fossæ mentioned above corresponds to the lateral division of the triangle.

Still another fossa of the peritoneum is seen in that region, just beneath the medial part of the inguinal ligament, corresponding to the position of the femoral ring; the vas deferens crosses its lateral part and the obliterated umbilical artery its medial part.

Near the median plane, above the umbilicus, the peritoneum is carried back from the anterior abdominal wall and diaphragm to the parietal surface of the liver in the form of a crescentic fold—the **falciform ligament** of the liver—which is described with that organ. The fold lies a little to the right of the median plane, and extends almost as low as the umbilicus. It consists of two layers of peritoneum between which, in the lower border of the fold, runs the round ligament of the liver—the remains of the left umbilical vein of the fœtus.

Posterior Wall of the General Peritoneal Cavity.—The peritoneum of the anterior abdominal wall is continued on to the inferior surface of the diaphragm. Thence it is reflected on to the superior surface of the liver, covers the anterior surface, turns round its inferior border, and is continued backwards on its inferior surface as far as the attachment of the lesser omentum, where it is reflected, as the anterior layer of the lesser omentum, to the stomach and the duodenum.

We shall now follow the posterior layer of the peritoneum downwards as seen in a sagittal section (Fig. 484).

Having reached the lesser curvature of the stomach, it passes down over the front of that organ to the greater curvature. From that curvature it descends as the most anterior layer of the greater omentum. Arrived at the lower border of the greater omentum, the membrane returns on itself, and passes upwards towards the transverse colon, forming the most posterior layer of the omentum. After covering the posterior surface of the transverse colon it is continued, as the posterior layer of the transverse mesocolon, to the posterior abdominal wall, which it reaches at the lower border of the pancreas (Fig. 487).

From the lower border of the pancreas it is continued downwards again, clothing first the lower surface of the pancreas, then the front of the third portion of the duodenum, and, below that, the posterior abdominal wall. But it is soon carried forwards again by the branches of the superior mesenteric vessels passing to the small intestine. Running out along those, it forms the superior (or, more correctly, the right) layer of the obliquely placed mesentery (Fig. 523): on reaching the small bowel at the border of the mesentery, it invests that tube, giving it its serous coat, and then returns—as the inferior, or left, layer of the mesentery—to the posterior abdominal wall, on which it runs down, covering the great vessels near the median plane and the psoas major muscle and ureter at each side, to enter the pelvis.

Pelvic Peritoneum.—The arrangement of the peritoneum in the true pelvis is different in the two sexes. and is described in connection with the pelvic viscera.

Transverse Tracing of the Peritoneum.—If the peritoneum is followed transversely around the abdomen, just above the level of the iliac crest (Fig. 490), few difficulties will be encountered. From the anterior abdominal wall it passes round on each side to the back, lining the sides and the posterior wall. Passing medially on the posterior wall, it meets the colon—ascending on the right side, descending on the left—over which it is carried, in each case covering the bowel in front and at the sides only, and leaving the posterior surface bare, as a rule. Sometimes, however, the covering is complete, and a short mesentery is formed. It is next continued *medially* over the psoas muscles, the ureters, and the great vessels, on the front of which it meets the superior mesenteric artery and vein. From both sides it passes forwards on those vessels, forming the right and left layers of the mesentery; and finally, having reached the intestine, it clothes it completely, and the two portions become continuous on the bowel.

Transverse tracings at a higher level would include the lesser sac; it will therefore be well if we describe this portion of the peritoneal cavity before directing attention to such tracings.

Lesser Sac of Peritoneum [Bursa Omentalis].—The lesser sac lies behind the stomach, lesser omentum, and part of the liver, and in the greater omentum, and it opens into the general cavity by a narrow mouth, on the right side, just below the liver, called the opening into the lesser sac. From the opening the pocket passes

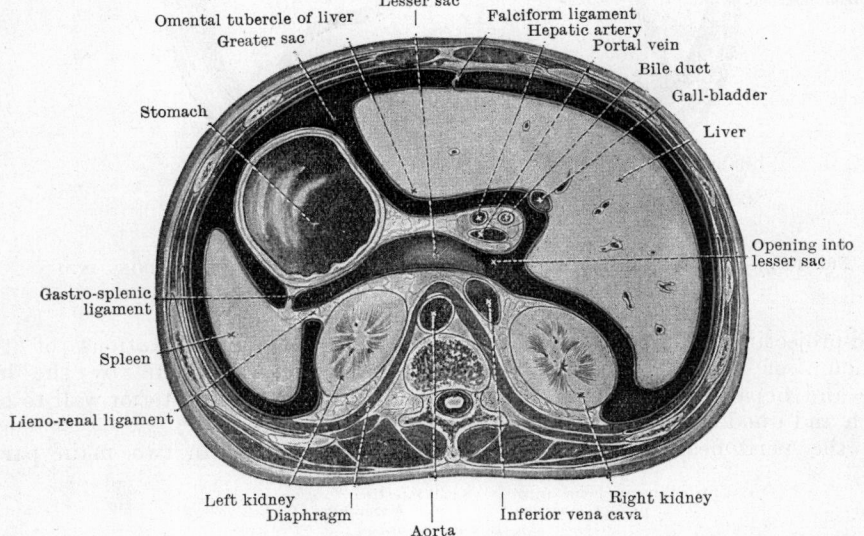

FIG. 488.—TRANSVERSE SECTION OF ABDOMEN AT LEVEL OF OPENING INTO LESSER SAC OF PERITONEUM.

to the left behind the lesser omentum and stomach, as far as the spleen, upwards behind the caudate lobe of the liver, and downwards behind the stomach and anterior sheet of the great omentum.

The **opening into the lesser sac** [foramen epiploicum] is situated just below and behind the porta hepatis. It is bounded *in front* by the right, free border of the lesser omentum passing up from the first part of the duodenum to the porta hepatis, and containing between its two layers the portal vein, hepatic artery, and bile duct. *Behind* lies the inferior vena cava, covered, of course, with peritoneum. *Above* is placed the caudate process of the liver. And *below* lies the first part of the duodenum with the hepatic artery running forwards and to the right before turning up into the lesser omentum. It should be remembered that, normally, the various boundaries of the opening lie in contact, and that its cavity can be said to exist as such only when its walls are drawn apart.

To the left of the opening, there is a small portion of the lesser sac, termed the *vestibule*, which lies below the caudate process of the liver, and above the first part of the duodenum and the head of the pancreas. The anterior wall of that portion is formed by the hepato-duodenal part of the lesser omentum, with the bile duct, hepatic artery, and portal vein. The vestibule is continued beyond a fold termed the right gastro-pancreatic fold into the true lesser sac, which presents two recesses—upper and lower. The **upper recess** passes from the vestibule upwards behind the porta hepatis and the caudate lobe, in front of the diaphragm. The **lower recess** passes in front of the pancreas and behind the stomach towards the spleen (Fig. 489).

The lower recess and the vestibule of the lesser sac communicate with each other by a rounded orifice which is constricted by the sickle-shaped,

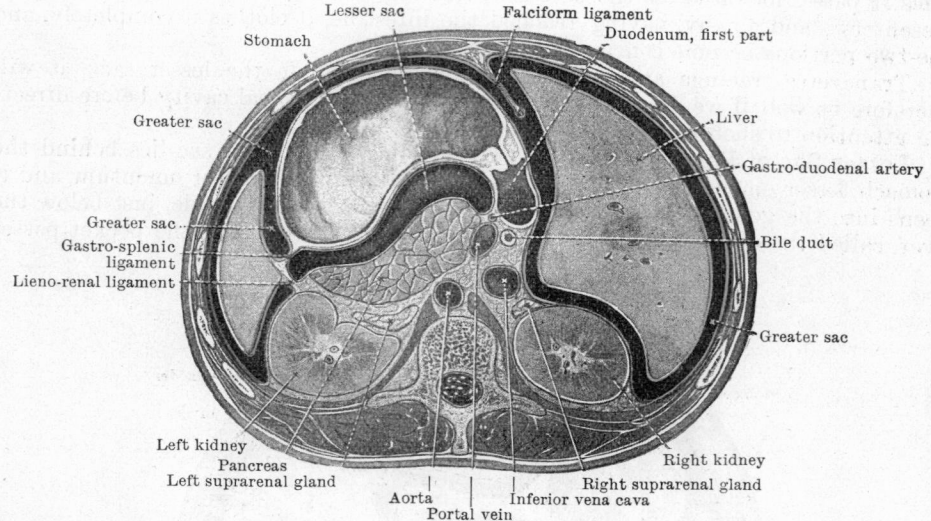

FIG. 489.—TRANSVERSE SECTION OF ABDOMEN IMMEDIATELY BELOW THE OPENING INTO LESSER SAC OF PERITONEUM.

forward-projecting *gastro-pancreatic* folds. Those folds are elevations of the peritoneum of the posterior wall of the lesser sac, raised up by the left gastric and hepatic arteries as they pass forwards from the posterior wall to the stomach and duodenum respectively.

As the peritoneal wall of the lesser sac is described in two main parts,

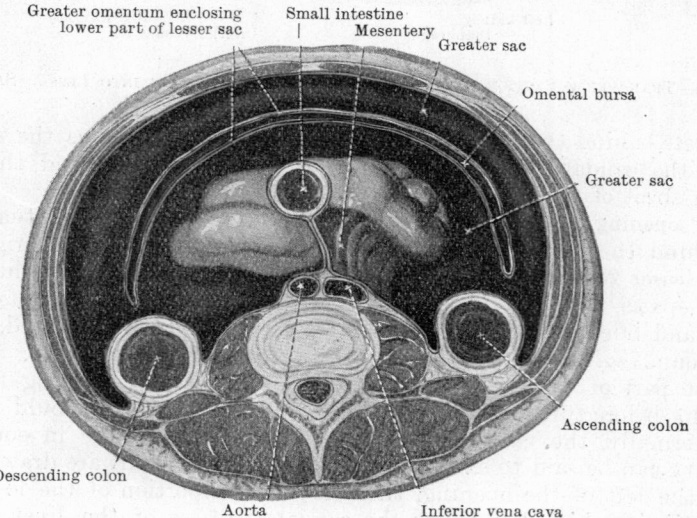

FIG. 490.—TRANSVERSE SECTION OF ABDOMEN THROUGH THE FOURTH LUMBAR VERTEBRA.

an anterior and a posterior, it will be necessary to follow each of them separately. The peritoneum which forms the **anterior wall** clothes the caudate lobe of the liver; it then passes down from the posterior margin of the porta hepatis and the fissure for the ligamentum venosum to the lesser curvature of the stomach and the duodenum as the posterior layer of the lesser omentum.   It then clothes the posterior surface of the stomach as far as the greater curvature, with the exception of the small "bare area" below and to the left of the cardiac orifice (Fig. 509).   On the left, it is reflected from the back of the stomach to the spleen as the deeper layer of the gastro-splenic ligament.   From the greater curvature of the stomach it is continued down as the posterior layer of the anterior sheet of the greater omentum, and, at the inferior part of the omentum, it meets and becomes continuous with the posterior wall of the lesser sac.

The peritoneum which forms the **posterior wall of the lesser sac** clothes the front of the inferior vena cava (Fig. 488), covers the cœliac artery, and passes upwards to cover the diaphragm behind the caudate lobe of the liver.   Passing to the left, it covers the anterior surface of the pancreas, the suprarenal gland, and a portion of the left kidney, from which it is reflected to the spleen as the deep layer of the lieno-renal ligament (Fig. 489).   From the pancreas it is prolonged downwards—as the anterior layer of the transverse mesocolon—to the transverse colon (Fig. 487).   Thence it is continued down as the anterior layer of the posterior sheet of the greater omentum, almost to its inferior border, where it becomes continuous with the anterior wall of the lesser sac already described.

Transverse tracings at the levels of the opening into the lesser sac and of the pylorus are shown in Figs. 488 and 489, and can be easily followed without any further description.

STOMACH

The **stomach** (ventriculus [gaster]) is a receptacle in which food accumulates after its passage through the œsophagus, and in it take place some of the earlier processes of digestion, resulting in the conversion of the food into a viscid fluid known as chyme.   The *chyme* escapes through the pylorus into the small intestine, where the digestive processes are continued.

The form and the position of the stomach present great variations, not only among different people but also in the same person at different times.   The degree to which it is filled, the size and position of adjacent organs, the condition of the abdominal walls, and even the assumption of the erect or the recumbent attitude can influence its shape and relations.

General Shape.—In shape, the stomach is irregularly piriform, with a wide end that lies deeply in the hollow of the left cupola of the diaphragm, and a narrow tapering extremity which passes downwards and forwards, and is bent over to the right side, in the epigastric region.

The long axis of the organ forms a spiral curve, directed downwards, forwards and to the right, and finally backwards.

The stomach has two surfaces—an anterior directed upwards and to the left, and a posterior which looks downwards and also to the right.   These surfaces meet above and to the right at the **lesser curvature**, and below and to the left at the **greater curvature**.   The œsophagus enters the stomach at the upper end of the lesser curvature, at the cardiac orifice, whilst at the lower end the stomach passes into the duodenum at the pyloric orifice.   The dome-shaped portion above and to the left of the œsophagus is the **fundus**, while the remainder of the stomach is divisible into the **body** and the **pyloric portion**.

Cardiac Orifice.—The cardiac orifice is at the upper end of the lesser curvature, to the right of the fundus, and more on the anterior than the posterior surface of the stomach.   The orifice is oval or angular rather than round, being compressed from side to side.   Around the opening the muscular walls of the œsophagus and the mucous membrane become continuous with corresponding coats of the stomach wall. The longitudinal muscular coat passes onwards into a longitudinal set of fibres, and the circular œsophageal fibres pass into the circular muscular coat.   The whitish stratified squamous epithelium of the œsophagus is continuous with the pinkish-coloured columnar epithelial wall of the stomach, and the junction is marked by a sharp irregular line around the margin of the opening.

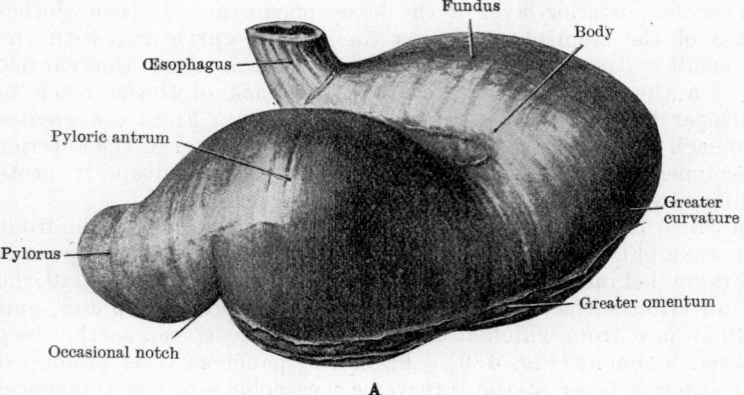

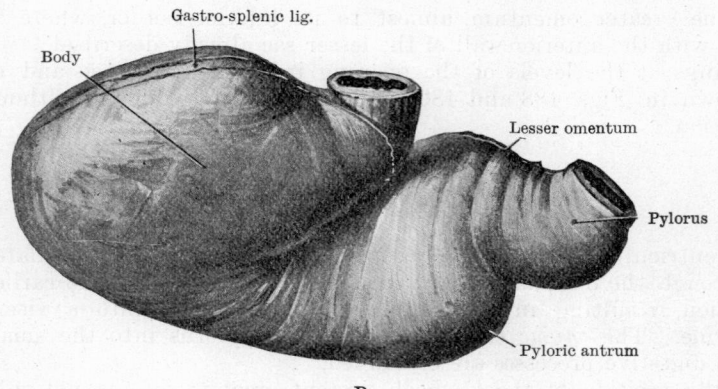

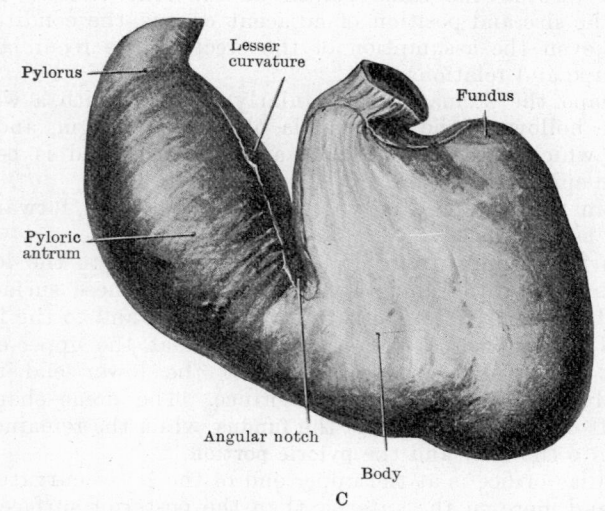

To the right of the orifice, the right margin of the œsophagus merges with a slight curve into the lesser curvature of the stomach, while on the left side there is a deep notch—**the cardiac notch**—between the end of the œsophagus and the fundus, in which lies a projecting ridge of the right crus of the diaphragm.

The cardiac notch on the outer surface produces a fold in the interior of the stomach, which may assist in closing the œsophageal opening, and that, with the decussating fibres of the diaphragm and the strengthened circular fibres of the lower end of the œsophagus, forms a kind of sphincter for this orifice which serves to prevent regurgitation from the stomach under ordinary conditions.

The cardiac orifice is very deeply placed, and lies about four inches behind the sternal end of the seventh left costal cartilage,

FIG. 491.—THREE VIEWS OF A STOMACH FIXED BY FORMALIN INJECTION *IN SITU.*

A. From the front.   B. From the back.   C. From above.

The orientation of the stomach was determined by the insertion of long pins into it in the sagittal, coronal, and transverse planes. These views show the comparatively horizontal position assumed by the stomach when the body lies supine. They also show the partial division into chambers produced by temporary constrictions of the stomach wall fixed by the action of formalin.

where that cartilage is one inch from the median line.   Posteriorly it corresponds to the level of the body of the eleventh thoracic vertebra or the intervertebral disc above it.

Owing to the fixation of the œsophagus by its passage through the diaphragm, and the close connexion between the stomach and the diaphragm near the cardiac orifice where the peritoneum is absent, this is the most fixed part of the whole stomach.

Pyloric Orifice.—By the pyloric orifice the cavity of the stomach communicates with that of the duodenum. It is placed at the distal (right) extremity

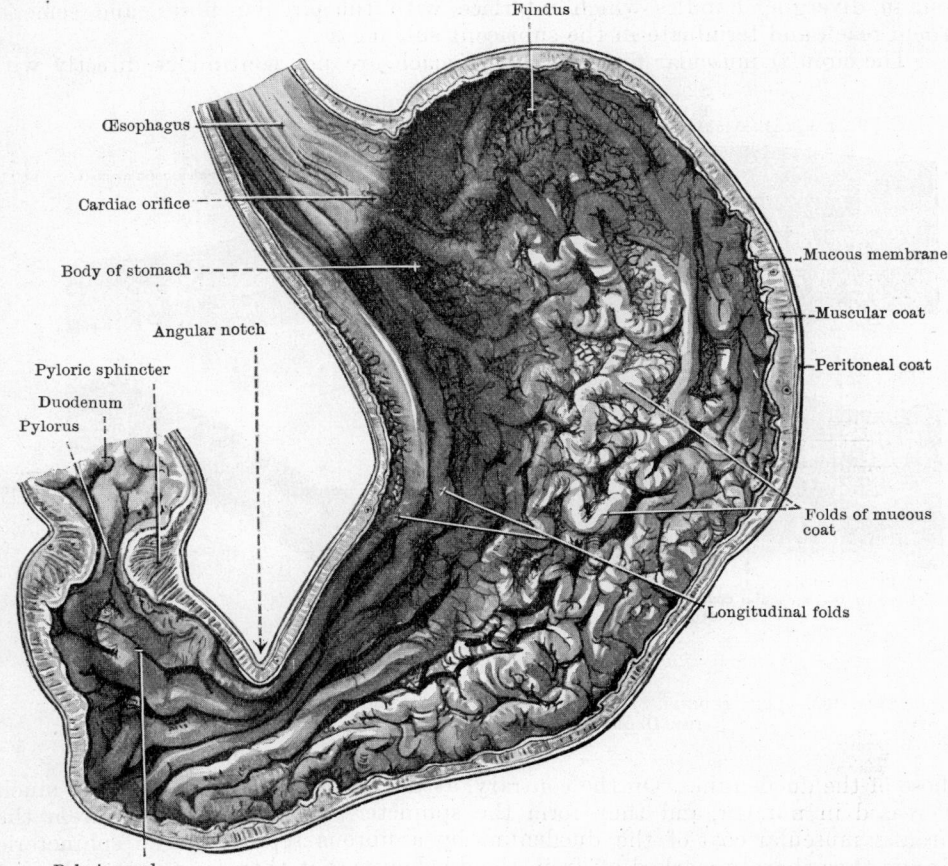

FIG. 492.—INTERIOR OF STOMACH, SHOWING THE MUCOUS COAT AND THE PARTS OF THE STOMACH IN A CONDITION OF MODERATE FILLING.

of the stomach, which is cylindrical in shape, and it is surrounded by a ring of thick muscle tissue named the **pyloric sphincter**. The term **pylorus** is applied to the area of the stomach which contains this sphincter.

The position of the pylorus is indicated to sight by a slight annular constriction on the external surface termed the *pyloric constriction*, and also by an arrangement of blood-vessels which is nearly constant. On the peritoneal surface a thick vein passes upwards from the lower side somewhat more than half-way on the anterior surface, and from the upper border a second vein (pre-pyloric vein) reaches downwards in the same line, nearly, if not quite, meeting the first (W. J. Mayo). The pylorus is also evident to touch, the thickening of the wall produced by the sphincter being readily distinguishable from the thinner wall of the pyloric canal on the proximal side and of the duodenum on the distal.

When the sphincter is in a state of contraction, the lumen of the outlet is a mere slit. A section through this part of the stomach (Fig. 492) shows that the mucous membrane which covers the sphincter slopes gradually into the lumen of the pylorus on the gastric side and abruptly or steeply at its duodenal end.

Viewed from the interior of the duodenum, the sphincter when contracted forms a dome-shaped elevation covered by the mucous coat and bulging into the duodenum, the centre of the dome being perforated by a narrow cylindrical depression—the pyloric orifice.

At the pylorus the peritoneal covering of the stomach is continued on to the first part of the duodenum, and the longitudinal fibres of the stomach are in part continued onwards into the longitudinal fibres of the duodenal coat, but many of them bend inwards into the thickened ring around the opening, and spread out in diverging bundles which interlace with the circular fibres, and some of them reach and terminate in the subjacent submucosa.

The circular muscular fibres of the stomach are not continuous directly with

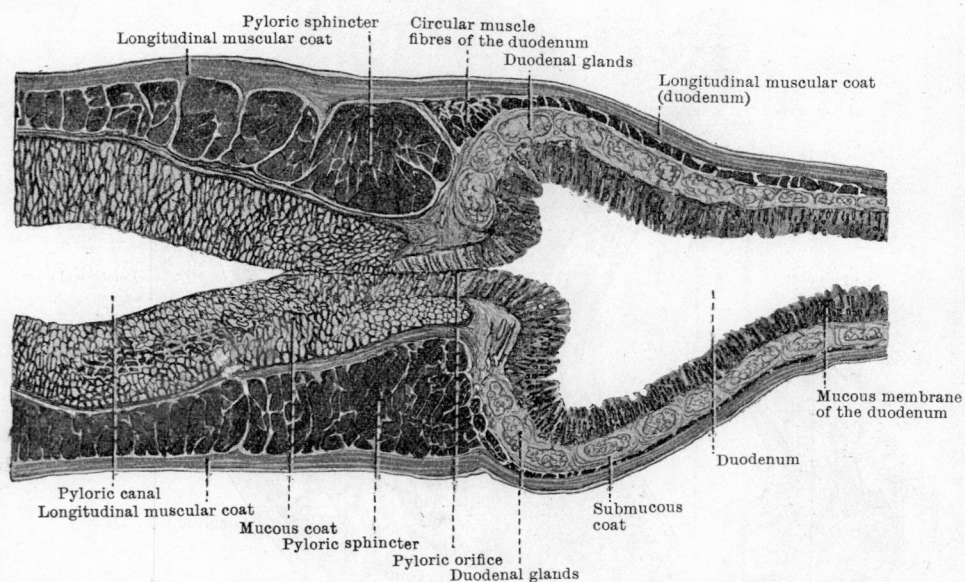

FIG. 493.—LONGITUDINAL SECTION THROUGH THE PYLORIC CANAL AND THE FIRST PART OF THE DUODENUM IN A NEW-BORN CHILD. (Stiles.)

those of the duodenum. On the contrary, at the orifice they become very much increased in number, and they form the sphincter, which is separated from the circular muscular coat of the duodenum by a fibrous septum. The sphincteric ring is thus sharply marked off from the duodenum, but there is no sharp line of demarcation on the gastric side, for it gradually merges into the circular muscular coat of the cylindrical pyloric canal.

The gastric mucous membrane (mucous coat), which is considerably thickened where it covers the sphincter muscle, is continued into the duodenum without any alteration visible to the naked eye. When examined post mortem in the ordinary way, the gastro-duodenal aperture, viewed from the duodenal side, is more or less oval in form. When seen from the opposite side, it presents a stellate appearance, owing to the fact that the rugæ of the gastric mucous membrane are continued as far as the orifice.

The orifice is directed horizontally backwards, and to the right. When the stomach is full, however, it looks almost directly backwards.

The pylorus rests on the neck of the pancreas below and posteriorly, and is overlapped by the liver above and anteriorly. When the stomach is empty the pylorus usually lies at the level of the transpyloric plane (p. 573) near (i.e. within half an inch of) the median plane, below the left lobe or sometimes below the quadrate lobe of the liver. During distension it is pushed over beneath the quadrate lobe for a variable distance, but very rarely more than $1\frac{1}{2}$ or 2 inches to the right of the median plane.

During the earlier stages of gastric digestion the pyloric sphincter is strongly contracted and the aperture firmly closed, but it opens intermittently to allow the passage of properly digested portions of the food.

As regards its size, the pylorus is stated to be about $\frac{1}{2}$ inch (12·5 mm.) in diameter, but there is no doubt that that represents neither its full size nor its calibre when at rest. Foreign bodies with a diameter of $\frac{3}{4}$ to 1 inch have been known to pass through the pylorus without giving rise to trouble, even in children. On the other hand, when at rest, with an empty stomach and duodenum, the aperture is closed.

Surfaces of the Stomach.—The **anterior surface of the stomach** is more convex and more extensive than the posterior. When the stomach is distended, it is in contact with the inferior surface of the left lobe of the liver medially, the vault

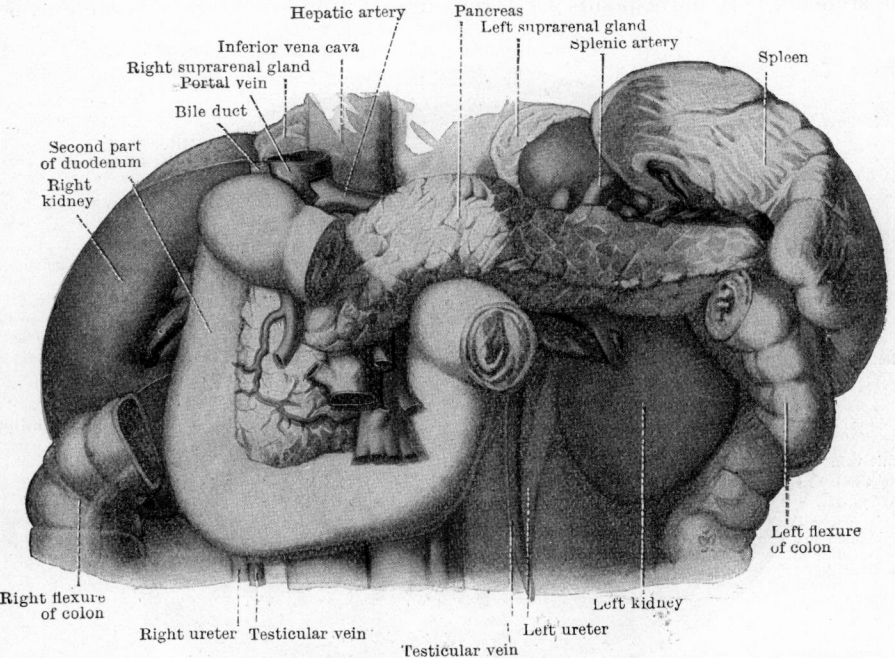

FIG. 494.—DISSECTION TO SHOW THE POSTERIOR RELATIONS OF THE STOMACH. The greater part of the stomach has been removed close to the pylorus. The transverse colon has been taken away, and the small intestine has been cut across close to the duodeno-jejunal flexure. (From a model by Birmingham.)

of the diaphragm laterally, and the anterior abdominal wall below. When the stomach is empty, on the other hand, the transverse colon may rise in front of it, and separate its anterior surface from the liver and diaphragm and abdominal wall.

The **posterior surface of the stomach** looks downwards and backwards. It is more flattened than the anterior, and is moulded by the structures upon which it rests.

Thus, on the left side, the body and fundus are in contact with the diaphragm and the spleen. To the right of the fundus the upper portion of the posterior surface is in contact with the left kidney, the suprarenal gland and the diaphragm ; and the inferior portion, more horizontal, is in contact with the pancreas, the splenic artery as it runs along the upper border of the pancreas, the transverse mesocolon and transverse colon. Those structures form what is known as the **stomach bed**, and lie immediately behind the posterior wall of the lesser sac of the peritoneum, which separates them from the stomach.

Curvatures of the Stomach.—The **lesser curvature**, directed towards the liver, and attached to it by the lesser omentum, is on the whole concave. It consists of two portions which meet at the deepest part of the concavity to form a sharp angle called the **angular notch** (incisura angularis). The upper or left portion, the longer of the two, is nearly vertical, and continues the direction of the right margin of the œsophagus; the lower or right portion may be horizontal or even directed upwards to the pylorus. The angular notch is situated at the junction of the body with the pyloric portion of the stomach; and its position, its depth and the acuteness of its angle vary with the degree of distension of the stomach. When the pyloric portion of the stomach is full, the lower portion of the lesser curvature becomes convex in outline. The lesser curvature as a whole measures some three or four inches in length.

The **greater curvature** is convex, often with indentations upon it, and is usually over three times as long as the lesser curvature. But its length depends to a greater degree than that of the lesser curvature upon the physiological state of the stomach. It corresponds to a line drawn from the cardiac notch over the

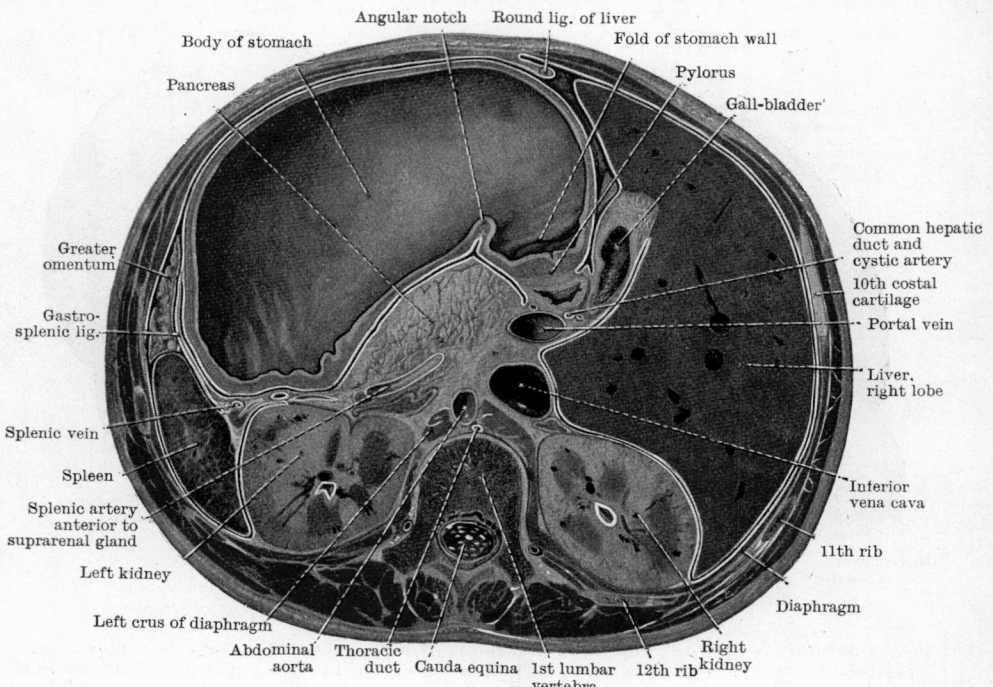

FIG. 495.—TRANSVERSE SECTION OF THE TRUNK AT THE LEVEL OF THE FIRST LUMBAR VERTEBRA.
Showing relations of stomach, pancreas, kidneys, etc. From a subject ten years old.

summit of the fundus (Fig. 491), and along the most projecting part of the stomach as far as the pylorus. It is attached to the spleen by the gastro-splenic ligament, and to the transverse colon by the greater omentum.

Divisions of the Stomach.—The stomach may be divided into a *cardiac* and a *pyloric* portion. The cardiac portion, lying to the left side, is wider in diameter than the pyloric, and comprises the *fundus* and the *body* of the stomach.

The **fundus of the stomach** is the rounded or dome-shaped portion which lies above a horizontal plane drawn through the œsophageal opening. Its shape seldom alters whatever the condition of the stomach may be, and it is usually filled with gas.

The **body of the stomach** extends from the base of the fundus along the long axis of the stomach and merges into the pyloric portion. The junction of the two parts is marked on the lesser curvature by the angular notch, but is not distinctly marked off on the greater curvature by any permanent notch. There is usually, however, on the greater curvature a slight notch due to a localised contraction of some of the circular muscular fibres which marks the junction of the two portions. The body of the stomach forms a rounded chamber, capable of great distension, but when the stomach is empty it contracts to a narrow tube-like structure. As the stomach is seldom completely empty, the body usually tapers from the fundus to the proximal end of the pyloric portion (Fig. 492).

The **pyloric portion of the stomach** extends from the angular notch in the lesser curvature, and a variable and inconstant notch on the greater curvature, as far as the pyloric orifice (Figs. 491, 492).

It differs from the body of the stomach in being more tubular in shape, and possessing thicker walls. It has been divided anatomically into the *pyloric antrum* and the *pyloric canal*.

The **pyloric canal** is the distal, short, more or less tubular portion which ends in the pyloric sphincter. The proximal portion, called the **pyloric antrum**, is more expanded. It is not clearly demarcated from the body of the stomach by any constant line of division on the greater curvature. On the lesser curvature it extends from the angular notch to the pyloric canal.

Hour-glass or Bilocular Stomach.—This is a condition of the stomach in which the organ is more or less completely separated into two divisions—a cardiac and a pyloric—the normal arrangement in certain rodents and other animals. As a rule the former division is the larger, but occasionally the two are nearly equal, or the pyloric portion may exceed the cardiac in size. Sometimes the condition is temporary, and the result of a vigorous contraction of the circular muscular fibres at the seat of constriction. In other cases it is permanent, and may be due to cicatricial contraction after gastric ulcer, or to some other pathological condition. The condition is more frequent in women than in men, and is rarely found in the foetus or child.

Size and Capacity of the Stomach.

Size and Capacity of the Stomach.—Probably no organ in the body varies more in size within the limits of health than the stomach. Moreover, as its tissues change so rapidly after death, measurements made on softened and relaxed organs are not only worthless but quite misleading.

The *length* of the stomach in the fully distended condition is about 10 to 11 inches (25 to 27·5 cm.), and its greatest *diameter* not more than 4 to 4½ inches (10 to 11·2 cm.); whilst its *capacity* in the average state rarely exceeds 40 ounces or 1 quart.

The distance in a direct line from the cardiac to the pyloric orifice varies from 3 to 5 inches (7·5 to 12·5 cm.), and that from the cardiac orifice to the summit of the fundus from 2½ to 4 inches (6 to 10·0 cm.).

As regards the *weight*, the average of twelve wet specimens freed from their omenta was found to be 4¾ oz. (135 grms.), with a maximum of 7 oz. (200 grms.) and a minimum of 3½ oz. (100 grms.). Glendinning gives the weight as 4½ oz.

In the **new-born child** the stomach is scarcely as large as a small hen's egg, and its capacity is about 1 oz. (28 grms.). In shape it corresponds fairly closely to that of the adult, and the fundus is well developed. It is vertical in position.

POSITION AND RELATIONS OF THE STOMACH

Position of the Stomach.—*In the cadaver*, lying horizontally, the stomach, if empty or nearly so, is found in the upper left quadrant of the abdominal cavity, with its fundus in the hollow of the diaphragm, its long axis lying almost horizontally and its pyloric part running to the right to join the duodenum. In that state the whole organ is narrow and tubular, particularly the pyloric part, which is contracted, and resembles a piece of thick-walled small intestine.

When the stomach is *distended*, both the cardiac and pyloric parts are full and rounded (Fig. 491). It extends down below the subcostal plane. As a result of the general increase in length which takes place during distension, the pylorus is moved a variable distance to the right beneath the quadrate lobe of the liver, and at the same time the long axis of the whole organ becomes much more vertical, running forwards, downwards, and to the right.

When the stomach has been removed, after the body has been hardened, a chamber or recess is exposed, known as the **stomach chamber** (Figs. 494 and 496). It is a space in the upper and left portion of the abdominal cavity with an arched roof, and an irregularly sloping floor. The *roof* is formed by the visceral surface of the left lobe of the liver and by the left cupola of the diaphragm.

The *floor* or "*stomach bed*" (Fig. 496) is formed behind by the upper end of the left kidney (with the suprarenal gland) and the gastric surface of the spleen; and in front by the anterior surface of the pancreas and the transverse mesocolon.

Peritoneal Relations.—The stomach is almost completely covered with peritoneum—the anterior surface being clothed with that of the general peritoneal sac, and the posterior surface by the anterior wall of the lesser sac. The layers of peritoneum that clothe the front and the back of the stomach meet at the lesser curvature and extend to the liver as the two layers of the *lesser omentum.* They meet also along the greater curvature and pass away from the stomach as a wide fold, to different parts of which different names have been given—(1) the anterior two layers of the *greater omentum,* (2) the two layers of

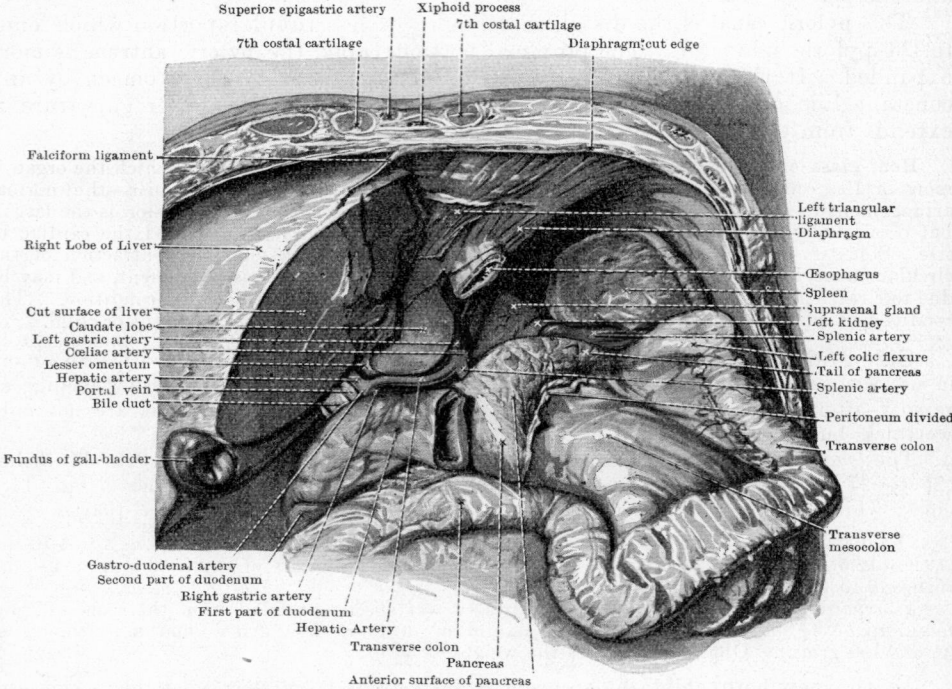

FIG. 496.—STOMACH CHAMBER VIEWED FROM THE FRONT AND FROM BELOW.
From the specimen figured in Fig. 486, after removal of the stomach.

the *gastro-splenic ligament,* and (3) a small peritoneal fold, known as the *gastro-phrenic ligament,* which runs from the stomach up to the diaphragm along the left side of the œsophagus.

A small irregularly triangular area (about 2 inches wide and 1½ inches from above downwards, during moderate distension of the stomach, on the posterior surface below and to the left of the cardia) is not covered with peritoneum, and over it the organ is in direct contact with the diaphragm, occasionally also with the upper end of the left kidney and the suprarenal gland (Fig. 509). From the left angle of that " bare area " the attachment of the gastro-splenic ligament starts ; and at the right angle a fold begins through which the left gastric artery passes to the stomach. That fold is called the *left gastro-pancreatic* fold.

The *right gastro-pancreatic* fold of peritoneum passes from the right extremity of the upper border of the pancreas to the first part of the duodenum. It encloses the hepatic artery.

STRUCTURE OF THE STOMACH

The stomach wall is composed of four coats—namely, from without inwards : (1) serous, (2) muscular, (3) submucous, and (4) mucous (Fig. 497).

The **serous coat** is formed of the peritoneum, the relations of which to the stomach have already been described. It is closely attached to the subjacent muscular coat, except near the curvatures, where the connexion is more lax.

The **muscular coat,** composed of unstriped muscle, thinnest in the fundus and body, and thicker in the pyloric portion, is responsible for the production of the gastric movements in digestion. It is made up of three complete or almost complete layers :—an external longitudinal, a middle circular, and an internal oblique layer.

The *longitudinal layer*, continuous with the longitudinal fibres of the œsophagus, sweeps from the cardiac orifice along and on each side of the curvatures particularly the lesser curvature, but is almost or entirely absent on the central parts of the anterior and posterior surfaces. On each side of the lesser curvature it forms two strong bands, many of whose marginal fibres turn aside and terminate, at intervals, in the deeper layers. Towards the pylorus the longitudinal fibres become much thicker, and also much tougher and more closely united, and they take part in the formation of the **pyloric sphincter** (see p. 584).

A specially condensed band of these can often be made out both on the front and back at the pyloric antrum, the form of which is said to be due to their presence. These bands are known as the *pyloric ligaments*.

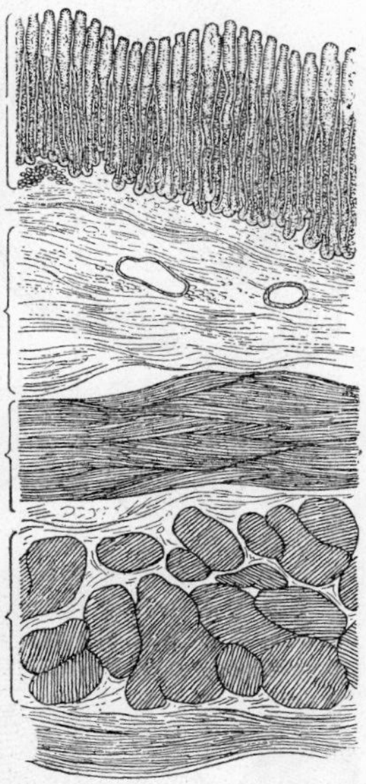

The *circular layer*, continuous with the more superficial of the circular fibres of the œsophagus (Fig. 499), is a more complete layer; its fibres encircle the body, from the lesser to the greater curvature, and are absent only from the fundus. At the pylorus they increase in thickness and pass into the pyloric sphincter.

The *oblique fibres* form the inner layer, and are continuous above with the deeper circular fibres of the œsophagus. They are arranged in U-shaped bundles which loop over the stomach immediately to the left of the cardia, and run very obliquely downwards on both surfaces of the organ as far as the angular notch (Fig. 499). The looped fibres, as they pass to the left, gradually become less oblique, and finally form circles around the wide end of the stomach as far as the fundus. These last fibres are sometimes ascribed to the circular layer.

The **submucous coat** is a layer of strong but loose areolar tissue which lies

Mucous coat

Lamina muscularis mucosae

Submucous coat

Circular muscular layer

Longitudinal muscular layer

Serous coat

FIG. 497.—TRANSVERSE SECTION THROUGH THE WALL OF A HUMAN STOMACH. × 250.

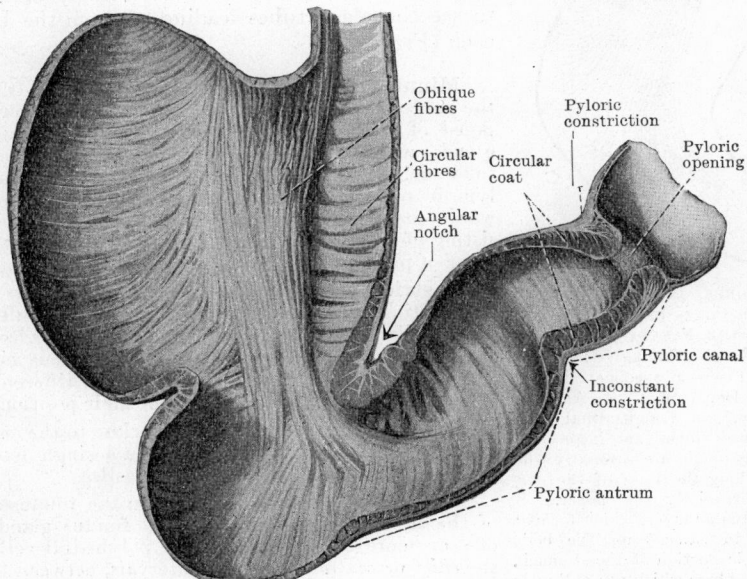

Oblique fibres

Circular fibres

Angular notch

Circular coat

Pyloric constriction

Pyloric opening

Pyloric canal

Inconstant constriction

Pyloric antrum

FIG. 498.—MUSCULAR COAT OF THE STOMACH, seen from within after removal of the mucous and submucous coats. The anterior half of the stomach is shown, viewed from behind (Cunningham).

between the muscular and mucous coats and unites them (Fig. 497). It is more loosely attached to the muscular and more closely to the mucous coat, and it forms a bed in which the vessels and nerves break up before entering the mucous membrane.

In the fresh state the **mucous coat** is of a reddish-grey colour and of moderate consistence. After death, the colour turns to a darker grey, and the whole membrane becomes softer and more pulpy. It is thicker (over 2 mm.) and firmer in the pyloric part than in the cardiac part, and is thinnest at the fundus. When the stomach is empty the mucous coat is thrown into numerous prominent folds or *rugæ* which project into the interior. They are, in general, longitudinal in direction, with numerous cross branches. They disappear when the stomach is distended. Along the lesser curvature there are three or four long, narrow, very constant ridges which pass without a break from the œsophageal orifice towards the pyloric part of the stomach (Fig. 492). They are parallel to one another, and are apparently never obliterated. Between them are deep furrows, called *gastric canals*, which lead from the cardiac orifice to the pyloric portion.

When the surface of the mucous coat is examined in a *fresh* stomach, it is seen to be marked out into a number of small, slightly elevated polygonal areas by numerous linear depressions ; the mucous membrane is consequently said to be mamillated (Fig. 500, A). These little areas, which measure from 1 to 6 mm. in diameter, show numerous small pits, about ·2 mm. wide, which are the mouths of the gastric glands, and they are so closely placed that the amount of surface separating them is reduced (particularly in the pyloric portion, where the gland mouths are widest) to a series of elevated ridges that resemble villi on section. Although the gland mouths cannot be seen with the naked eye, a very slight magnification is sufficient to show them clearly ; it is also possible to see the gland tubes leading off from the bottom of each (Fig. 500, B).

Minute Structure of the Mucous Coat.—In structure the mucous coat consists of an epithelial covering composed of long columnar cells, and of numerous tubular glands which are prolonged outwards and are enclosed in a delicate areolar tissue stroma, with some small lymph nodules. The bases of the glands reach outwards to the lamina muscularis mucosæ—a layer consisting of an external longitudinal and an internal circular layer of plain muscle fibres.

Gastric Glands.—Each gastric gland consists of a duct terminating in one or more secreting tubules. The duct is lined with columnar epithelial cells, similar to those which cover the surface of the mucous membrane. Three varieties of glands are found in different regions of the stomach, and are named from their position :—

(1) **Cardiac Glands** are situated close to the œsophageal opening. The duct of each ends in a single long tubule lined with short columnar granular cells.

(2) **Fundus Glands** are found in the fundus and body of the stomach. The duct of each fundus gland ends in one or more tubules lined with polyhedral cells termed the *chief* or *central cells*. At intervals, between that layer of cells and the basement membrane, are placed larger spheroidal cells, termed the *parietal* or *oxyntic* cells, which stain more deeply as a rule.

(3) **Pyloric glands** are found in the pyloric portion of the stomach. Each consists of a short duct which ends in a group of short but tortuous gland tubules. The tubules are lined with **short columnar** or polyhedral cells similar to the central cells of the fundus glands.

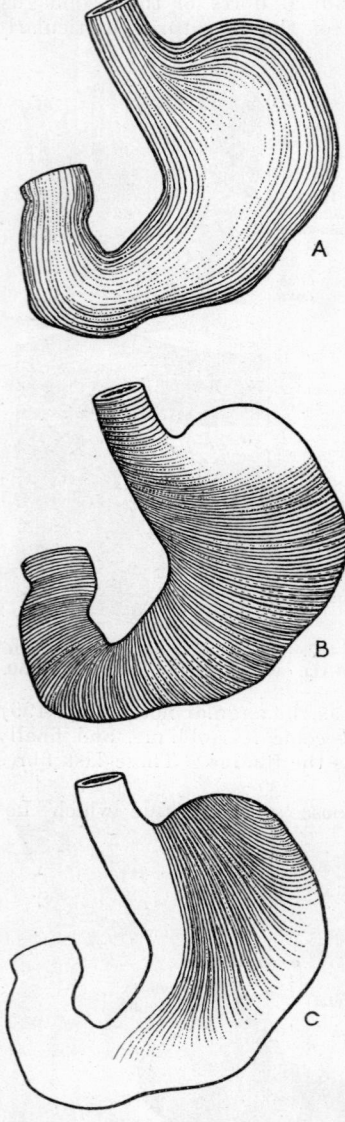

FIG. 499.—THREE DIAGRAMS OF THE MUSCULAR COATS OF THE STOMACH, TO SHOW THE EXTENT AND DIRECTION OF THE FIBRES COMPOSING THEM. (From a specimen in the Anatomy Department, St. Andrews University.) A, Longitudinal layer, whose fibres form an incomplete investment and are specially developed along the lines of the curvatures, especially the lesser. B, Middle circular layer, which forms a complete investment for the body and pyloric portion of the stomach. C, Oblique fibres which run obliquely to those of the other layers from the notch between the cardiac orifice and fundus on the anterior (and posterior) surfaces of the stomach and form an incomplete layer.

Vessels and Nerves.—The **arteries** of the stomach are all derived ultimately from the *cœliac artery.* The *left gastric artery* arises from that trunk direct. Having reached the lesser curvature and given off an œsophageal branch, it divides into two large branches which run along the front and the back of the lesser curvature, and join towards the right with two similarly disposed arteries derived from the *right gastric* branch of the hepatic. From the two arches thus formed, four or five large branches pass to each surface of the stomach, and soon pierce the muscular coat. Along the greater curvature numerous branches reach the stomach from the *right and left gastro-epiploic arteries*, which are branches respectively of the gastro-duodenal and the splenic ; they run in the greater omentum close to its attachment to the stomach. Finally, four or five *short gastric arteries*, branches of the splenic, are distributed to the fundus of the stomach, which they reach by passing forwards between the layers of the gastro-splenic ligament. At first the arteries lie beneath the peritoneum ; very soon, however, they pierce the muscular coat, which they supply, and, reaching the submucosa, break up to form a close network of vessels. From these arise numerous small branches which enter the mucous membrane and form capillary plexuses around the glands as far as the surface.

The **veins** begin in the capillary plexuses around the glands ; uniting, they form a network in the submucosa, from which arise branches that pierce the muscular coat and finally end in

the following veins: the *right gastro-epiploic*, which joins the superior mesenteric ; the *left gastro-epiploic* and four or five *short gastric veins*, which join the splenic ; the *left gastric vein*, which runs along the lesser curvature from right to left, and ultimately joins the portal vein. These veins contain numerous valves which, though competent to prevent the return of blood in the child, are rarely so in the adult.

The **lymph vessels** of the stomach arise in an extensive plexus in the mucous membrane and join a subserous plexus from which efferent vessels arise. These are arranged in three main streams which pass to numerous glands situated on the branches of the cœliac artery.

The **nerves** are derived from the *anterior* and *posterior gastric nerves*, each containing filaments from both the right and the left vagus nerve. They unite with the *sympathetic fibres* from the cœliac plexus which pass to the stomach with the branches of the cœliac artery. The nerve fibres, which are chiefly non-medullated, partly enter the myenteric plexus and the submucous plexus in the muscular and submucous coats respectively. (*See also* p. 595).

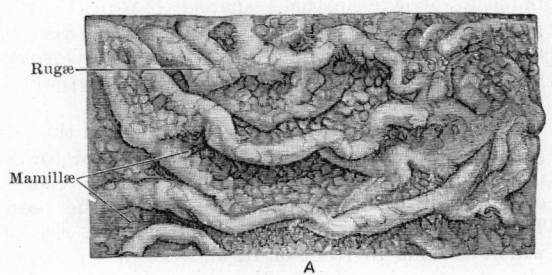

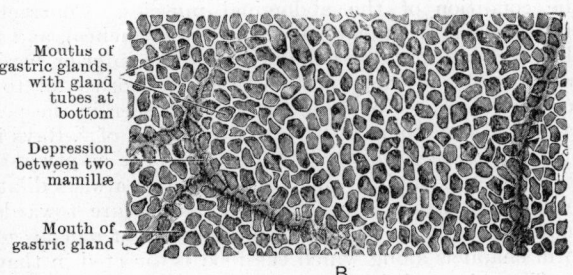

FIG. 500.—MUCOUS MEMBRANE OF THE STOMACH. A, Natural size ; B, Magnified 25 diameters. In A the rugæ and the mamillated surface are shown. In B the gland mouths with the gland tubes leading off from some of them, and the ridges separating them are seen.

Radiographic Examination of the Stomach in the Living.

—Examination of the stomach by X-Rays after a "bismuth meal" throws light upon its form and position, and also upon the action of its muscular coats. This kind of examination has shown that there are permanent differences in the form and position of the stomach—especially in the level and direction of its pyloric portion—which seem to depend on the "bodily habitus" of the individual, as well as factors such as race, age, and sex. In addition, the stomach in its form reacts to the amount and character of an ingested meal, and to emotional and general health conditions. Fatigue and mental strain produce "hypotony"—the greater curvature of the stomach showing a low position and less peristalsis (Wingate Todd). The form and position of the stomach are greatly influenced by the posture also, and are not the same when the person is standing or sitting up as when he is lying down, either supine or prone (Fig. 501).

The form and position of three well-recognised "types of stomach," as seen in the erect posture, may be studied in Plates XLIII, XLIV and XLV. It should be noted that in the filling of the stomach the bismuth meal accumulates first in the pyloric portion of the stomach, and extends thence into the body and then towards the pylorus ; the fundus remains filled with gas and therefore appears black, as it does not intercept the X-Rays.

Plate XLIII represents the J-shaped stomach, by far the commonest "type of stomach " seen on the X-ray screen. On the lesser curvature, the angular notch is distinct, and on the opposite part of the greater curvature there is a wide, shallow temporary constriction produced by contraction of the circular muscle fibres. Nearer the pylorus a peristaltic contraction is indicated by deep indentations opposite each other on the two curvatures. The position of the pyloric sphincter is shown by an abrupt interruption of the shadow of the bismuth meal. A thin streak passes through the sphincter, and leads to a shadow, higher up, produced by opaque material in the first part of the duodenum, and termed the *duodenal cap*.

Plates XLIV and XLV represent two other " types of stomach " which are much less common but equally characteristic as seen on the X-ray screen. In both of them the body and the pyloric portion exhibit a more continuous curvature, and the pyloric canal is horizontal rather than vertical. Plate XLV is a radiograph of a stomach that lies almost transversely in the abdomen even in the erect posture : it is the so-called " steer-horn " type. Plate XLIV exhibits an intermediate form.

The lowest point of the body, the pylorus and the first part of the duodenum are at a much lower level in the J-shaped than in the other types of stomach. In the former the pylorus is often as low as the third lumbar vertebra, and may be lower still ; whereas in the intermediate and steer-horn types the pylorus is frequently in the " transpyloric plane " opposite the body of the first lumbar vertebra or the disc between the bodies of the first and second.

In the horizontal posture, the form and the position of the stomach are altered. The J-shaped stomach hangs less vertically, the lowest part of the greater curvature moves upwards and forwards, and the stomach comes to resemble the other types which even in the erect posture are more in the position shown in the cadaver (Fig. 486.) The duodenal cap may be hidden by the rise of the pyloric portion of the stomach, which ascends in front of it, and the first part of the duodenum is horizontal instead of almost vertical as it is in the erect posture.

X-Ray examination shows that the position of the stomach is influenced also by the condition of the abdominal muscles. Contraction of these muscles can elevate the stomach from 5 to 13 cm. (2 to 5 inches), and the change from the horizontal to the erect posture alters the height of the inferior border from 2 to 10 cm. The sinking which occurs in the alteration from the horizontal to the erect posture accounts partly for the differences between the stomach seen in the post-mortem room or on the operating table and the stomach displayed by means of X-Rays in the living person standing erect.

Changes in form during digestion.—The empty stomach is a contracted tubular organ, except at the fundus, which appears to be always dilated. Ingested food passes from the œsophageal orifice along the lesser curvature towards the pyloric end of the stomach. It has been shown (p. 590) that the folds of mucous membrane near the lesser curvature form channels along which the food is directed in that course.

There is no definite division of the body of the stomach from the pyloric part by a permanent sphincter, but the peristaltic waves of contraction begin about the middle of the organ, and form a fleeting constriction between the two parts. As peristalsis goes on, the tubular, pyloric part begins to relax. The waves of peristalsis there become so deep that they divide that portion into chambers (Pl. XLIII). The food substances are forced through the pylorus by successive waves of peristalsis, and in the form, usually, of jets which impinge against the posterior wall of the duodenum. Should there be undigested masses, the pyloric valve relaxes to allow them also to pass into the duodenum.

That the position of the digestive organs in healthy living persons is much more variable than might be supposed from their examination in the horizontal cadaver is illustrated by the observations made by R. O. Moody and his co-workers on students in California and London. They confirm the view that in the living the form and position of the stomach vary in different people and in the same person with changes in posture, and that the individual variations which may occur are of wide range. The observations may be briefly summarised as follows :—The pylorus, for example, may lie as high as the upper half of the twelfth thoracic vertebra or as low as the upper half of the fifth lumbar vertebra, and it may lie below the " inter-iliac line " or plane of the iliac crests, when the subject is erect, supine, or prone. It may lie in the median plane, or to the right or to the left of it. Similarly the greater curvature of the stomach may lie as high as the twelfth thoracic or as low as the first sacral vertebra.

Associated with those different positions of the pylorus there is a difference in the position of the first part of the duodenum and in its relation to the head of the pancreas.

Similarly, Moody has found also that in the living subject, standing erect, " the common position of the cæcum is not in the iliac fossa, but in the cavity of the true pelvis."

He finds a similar difference in the position and form of the liver in the living person, and that its lower border extends below the inter-iliac plane in 50 per cent. of males and in 34 per

PLATE XLIII

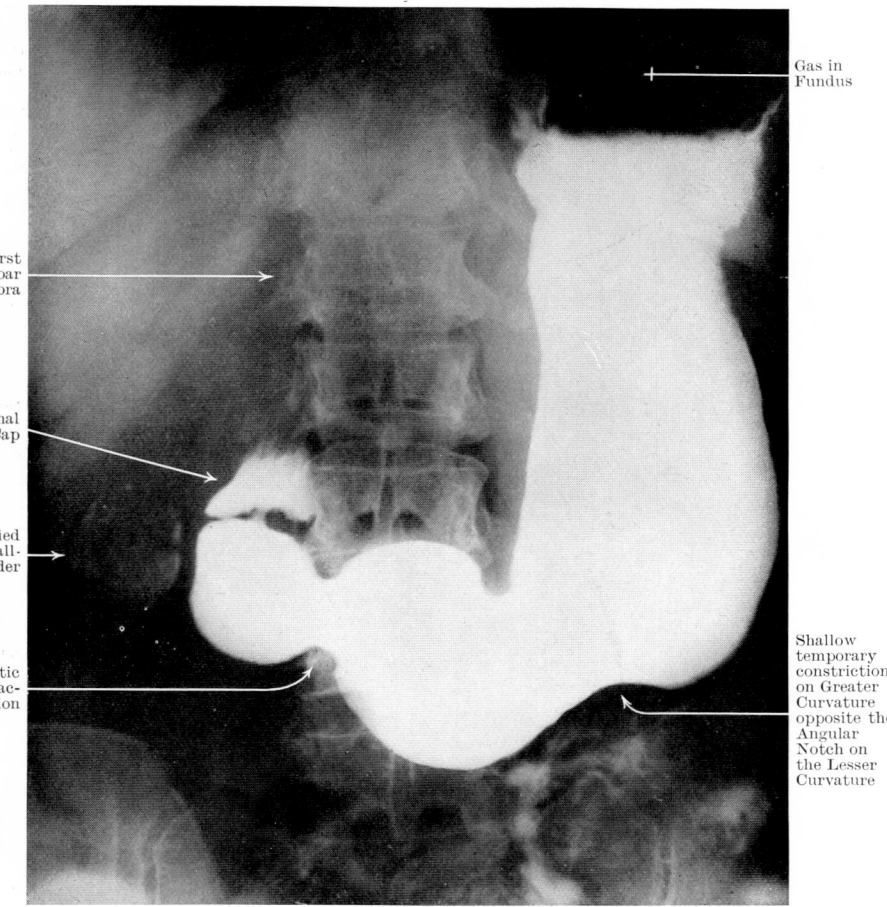

Gas in Fundus

First Lumbar Vertebra

Duodenal Cap

Calcified Gall-bladder

Peristaltic contrac-tion

Shallow temporary constriction on Greater Curvature opposite the Angular Notch on the Lesser Curvature

PLATE XLIII.—Radiograph of J-shaped Stomach of Woman aged 62, taken in the erect posture a few minutes after an Opaque Meal. (F. E. J.)

Note the low position of the Greater Curvature and of the Pylorus. Cf. Plates XLIV and XLV. The Gall-bladder, intercepting the X-Rays because of calcification in its wall, is seen in relation to the Pylorus. For the position of the gall-bladder see also Plate XLVIII.

[*Facing p.* 592

taken in the erect posture. Cf. Plates XLIII and XLIV.

PLATE XLIV

First Lumbar Vertebra

PLATE XLVI

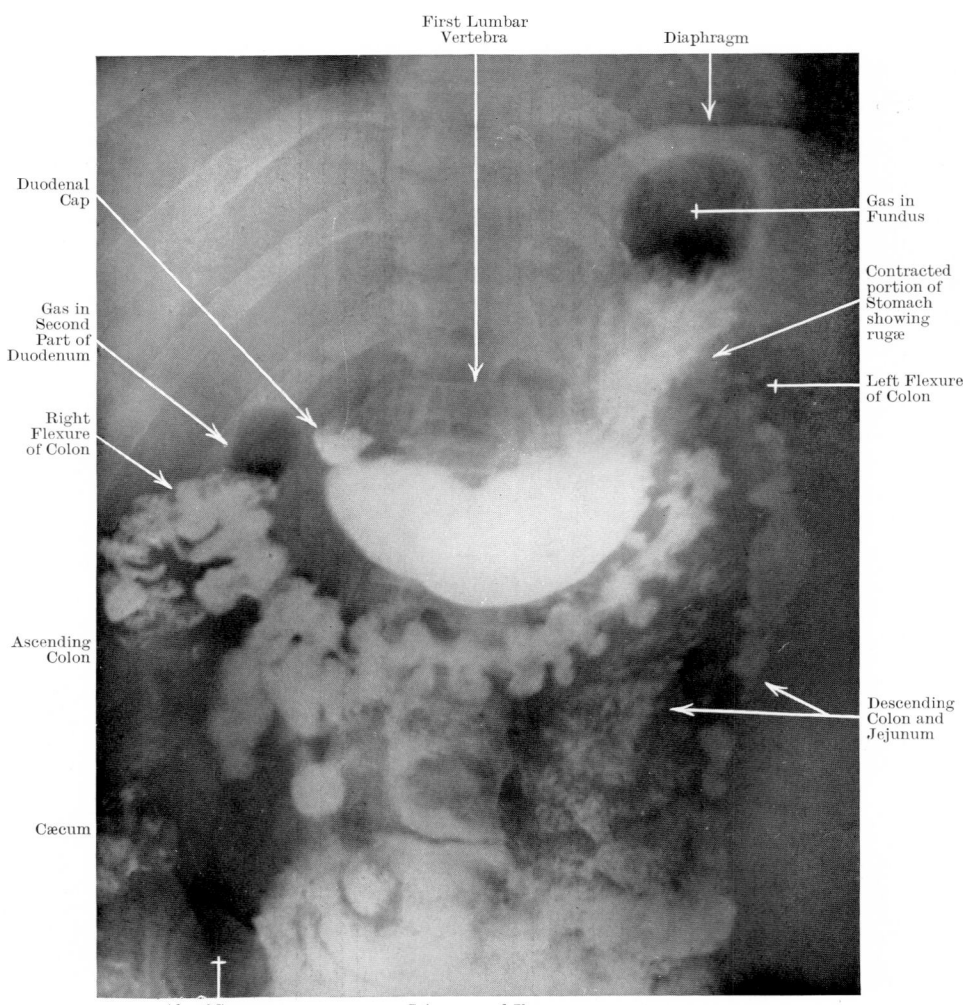

First Lumbar Vertebra

Diaphragm

Duodenal Cap

Gas in Fundus

Gas in Second Part of Duodenum

Contracted portion of Stomach showing rugæ

Right Flexure of Colon

Left Flexure of Colon

Ascending Colon

Descending Colon and Jejunum

Cæcum

Ala of Sacrum

Jejunum and Ileum

PLATE XLVI.—RADIOGRAPH OF ABDOMEN OF MAN AGED 28 IN THE ERECT POSTURE, SHOWING THE APPEARANCE OF THE ALIMENTARY CANAL AFTER ADMINISTRATION OF OPAQUE MEALS AT INTERVALS.

The contents of the Stomach and Duodenum and of the Ileum seen in Plate XLIV (given respectively 45 and 48 hours previously) are now in the Large Intestine. The first half of a third opaque meal (given one hour before the radiograph was taken) is in the Jejunum and Ileum, and the Stomach is half-filled by the second half. Note the Duodenal Cap (see p. 592) and the residue of radio-opaque material in the Cæcum and Ascending Colon. For stages in the filling and emptying of the Large Intestine, see Plates XLI and XLVII.

cent. of females. Its position and vertical dimensions are greatly influenced by posture, the "excursion" or range of movement of the lower margin with change of posture ranging from none to as much as 9 cm. and usually being from 2 to 3 cm. He finds also that "there

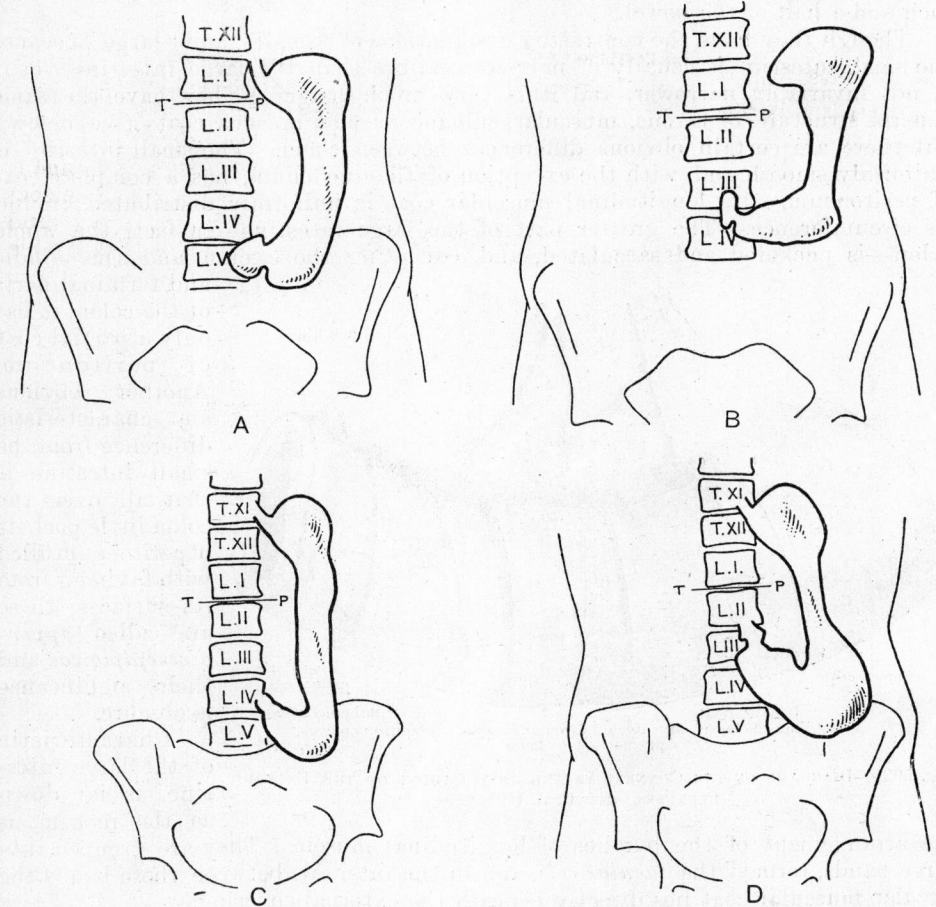

FIG. 501.—TRACINGS OF OUTLINES OF THE STOMACH AS DEFINED BY X-RAY EXAMINATION. (After Moody, Van Nuys, and Kidder.) A. Empty stomach, subject erect, the form of the stomach a "reverse L," with short horizontal arm; lowest part of the greater curvature 5 cm. below the plane of the iliac crests opposite the upper half of the first sacral vertebra. B. Same stomach, subject prone. C. Empty stomach, subject erect, pylorus opposite the fourth lumbar vertebra. D. Same stomach, subject prone, pylorus opposite the third lumbar vertebra. (From the *Anatomical Record*, by permission of the Wistar Institute.)

seems to be no definite relation between the position of the liver and that of the stomach; the liver may be low and the stomach high, or the liver high and the stomach low."

INTESTINES

The remaining portions of the alimentary canal—from the stomach to the anus—are called the *intestines*, and are divided into two main parts called the small intestine and the large intestine. The **small intestine** succeeds the stomach and is disposed in coiled loops throughout the abdomen proper and the pelvis. It is divided into three parts: the *duodenum*, which is continuous with the pylorus, the *jejunum*, and the *ileum*, which joins the large intestine in the right iliac fossa. The **large intestine** begins in that fossa, takes an arched course round the posterior wall of the abdomen, passes over the left side of the pelvic brim into the pelvis, and ends at the anus. Its commencement is called the *caecum*, to which a small worm-like structure called the *vermiform appendix* is attached;

the cæcum is succeeded by the *colon*, which is by far the longest part of the large intestine and is itself further subdivided ; it passes into the pelvis to become continuous with the *rectum*, which is succeeded by the *anal canal*—the terminal inch and a half of the bowel.

Though they have the contrasted designations of " small " and " large " because the small intestine is usually of narrower calibre than the large intestine, yet it is not invariably narrower, and it is very much longer. They have the same general structure of serous, muscular, submucous and mucous coats (see below), but there are certain obvious differences between them. The small intestine is uniformly smooth and, with the exception of the duodenum, has a complete coat of peritoneum. Its longitudinal muscular coat is uniformly distributed around its circumference. The greater part of the large intestine—in fact, the whole colon—is puckered and sacculated, and, excepting the cæcum and the middle and terminal parts of the colon, it has only a partial coat of peritoneum. Another obvious and characteristic difference from the small intestine is that all over the colon little pockets of peritoneum filled with fat hang from its surfaces; these are called *appendicesepiploicae*, and their significance is obscure.

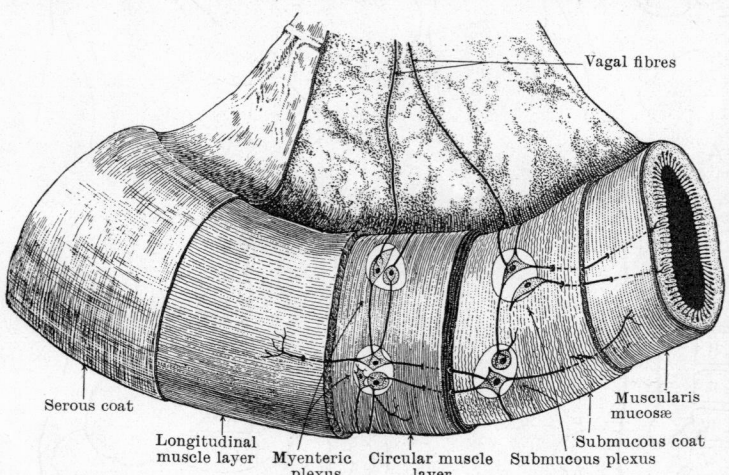

FIG. 502.—DIAGRAMS OF THE CONNEXIONS AND DISTRIBUTION OF THE ENTERIC PLEXUSES (after C. J. Hill).

Characteristic of the large intestine, as far down as the rectum, is the arrangement of the bundles of longitudinal muscle. They are grouped into three bands, termed the *taeniae coli*, and in the intervals between these bands the circular muscular coat lies directly beneath the external covering.

The sacculated appearance is often well seen in radiographs of the abdomen, when the gut is filled with material opaque to X-rays (Pls. XLI, XLII, XLVI).

Structure.—Both small and large intestines have four coats—serous, muscular, submucous, and mucous. The external *serous coat* forms a complete or a partial covering in different parts. The underlying *muscular coat*, formed of two layers of non-striped muscle—an outer longitudinal, and an inner, whose fibres are circular or ring like—is separated by the submucous coat from the mucous coat, which lines the interior of the canal. It has been stated (Eben. J. Carey, *Anat. Record*, 1921), that in the small intestine of many mammals the muscular layers are not truly circular or longitudinal, but are both spiral, the inner coat forming a close spiral and the outer a long one. In the inner coat one complete turn is made in every 0·5 to 1 mm. or less, while those of the outer coat which are spiral make a complete turn in every 200 to 500 mm. or more. The *submucous coat* consists of a layer of loosely arranged but strong areolar tissue. The *mucous coat* shows three layers of component tissue, viz. internally a layer of columnar epithelium, which may be more than one layer of cells in thickness, resting on a thin layer of loose areolar tissue, external to which there is a thin sheet of non-striped muscle called the *lamina muscularis mucosae*. The internal surface of the mucous coat shows the openings of an enormous number of *intestinal glands*—small straight tubular glands—whose closed ends lie in the deeper part of the mucous coat. The internal surfaces of the small and large intestines differ from one another in many respects, and especially in that the mucous coat of the small intestine is covered with villi, is thrown into permanent folds, and has in its substance aggregated as well as solitary lymphatic nodules.

Nerves.—The intestine has a large supply of nerves belonging to the sympathetic and parasympathetic systems. They accompany the vessels to the wall of the intestine, and are distributed to the vessels and to the walls.

The sympathetic nerves, derived from the cœliac and mesenteric plexuses, are connected with the parasympathetic from the vagi and from the second and third sacral nerves. They first mingle in the subserous tissue, traverse the outer muscular coat, and between the muscle coats form an extensive plexus, composed of interlacing fibres and ganglion cells, termed the *myenteric plexus*. From that plexus branches pierce the circular layer of the muscular coat and pass to the submucous coat, and again form a plexus, known as the *submucous plexus*, from which branches pass to the lamina muscularis mucosæ, to the muscle tissue of the villi, and to the mucous coat.

The position of these enteric plexuses and their connexions and distribution are shown diagramatically in Fig. 502. The figure shows also the connexions within the intestinal wall

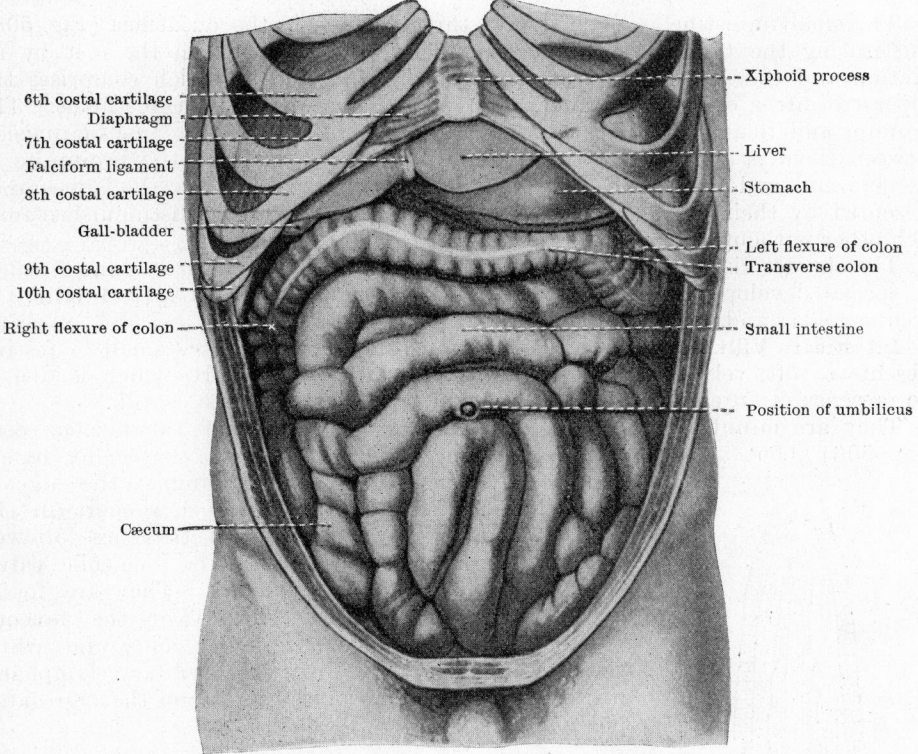

Xiphoid process

6th costal cartilage
Diaphragm
7th costal cartilage
Falciform ligament
8th costal cartilage
Gall-bladder
9th costal cartilage
10th costal cartilage
Right flexure of colon

Liver
Stomach
Left flexure of colon
Transverse colon
Small intestine

Position of umbilicus

Cæcum

FIG. 503.—THE ABDOMINAL VISCERA, AFTER REMOVAL OF THE GREATER OMENTUM.

The oblique position of the stomach and the high position of the transverse colon are largely due to the fact that the subject was fixed in the horizontal position.

of the vagal (parasympathetic) fibres. The sympathetic fibres, according to C. J. Hill, are distributed to the vessels, and few, if any, of their fibres join the plexuses.

The afferent nerve supply of the intestine is from the sympathetic system, and hence the whole intestine except the anal canal is quite insensitive to stimuli which in other parts would give rise to pain. Strong contraction, however, of the muscle coats causes severe pain which is to a large extent referred to some portion of the abdominal wall.

SMALL INTESTINE

The **small intestine** (intestinum tenue) commences at the pylorus, and ends at the ileo-colic valve by joining the large intestine. It occupies the greater portion of the abdominal cavity below the liver and stomach (Fig. 448), and may lie also in the pelvic cavity.

In *length,* the small intestine usually measures some 20 to 22 feet. In form it is cylindrical, with a *diameter* varying from nearly two inches (47 mm.) in the duodenum to a little over an inch (27 mm.) at the end of the ileum; there is thus a gradual diminution in its size from the pylorus to the ileo-colic valve.

The small intestine is relatively longer in the child than in the adult; at birth it is to the total height of the child as 7 to 1, whilst in the adult the proportion is as 4 to 1. It is generally held that the small gut is relatively longer in the male than the female.

While the entire length of the intestine in its most extended form after death, when muscular tonus has disappeared, may be 20 to 22 feet as stated, it is probable that during life the length is not so great. The muscular coats, both longitudinal and circular, are more or less contracted, and probably the total length during life may be estimated as 15 to 17 feet.

In formalin-hardened bodies the small bowel rarely measures more than 12 or 13 feet in length. Similarly its diameter is often reduced in places to $\frac{1}{2}$ or $\frac{3}{4}$ inch (12 to 18 mm.), although the greater part of the gut may retain its usual width: these narrow parts have apparently been fixed in a state of contraction.

The small intestine is divided into three parts—(1) the **duodenum** (Fig. 508), constituting the first eleven inches, distinctly marked off from the rest by its fixation and the absence of a mesentery; (2) the **jejunum**, which comprises the upper two-fifths of the remainder, and (3) the **ileum**, the lower three-fifths. The jejunum and ileum pass imperceptibly into each other, and the line of division between them is artificial. Typical parts of the two—namely, the beginning of the jejunum and the end of the ileum—differ in size and in the appearance presented by their lining mucous membrane, and they can be distinguished from each other without difficulty (see p. 605).

The characteristic features of the small intestine are found on its inner surface in special developments of its mucous coat: they are (1) intestinal villi; (2) circular folds; and (3) aggregated lymphatic nodules.

Intestinal Villi.—The mucous coat of all parts of the small intestine presents a soft, velvety, or fleecy internal surface (Fig. 505, B) which is due to the presence of an enormous number of minute processes known as villi.

They are minute, cylindrical, or finger-like projections of the mucous coat (Fig. 506) about $\frac{1}{20}$th to $\frac{1}{50}$th of an inch (0·2 to 1·2 mm.) in height, barely visible to the naked eye. Beginning at the edge of the pyloric orifice, they are broad but short in the duodenum, and grow narrower as they are followed down through the intestine to the ileo-colic valve, at the edge of which they cease. They are found not only on the general surface of the mucous membrane but also on the circular folds, and, while they are not present over the solitary lymphatic nodules, they are found on the surface of the aggregated nodules.

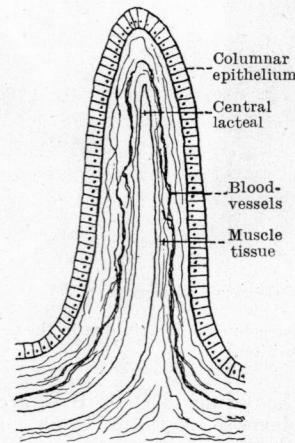

FIG. 504.—STRUCTURE OF A VILLUS.

Columnar epithelium

Central lacteal

Blood-vessels

Muscle tissue

Structure of the Villi.—Each villus is covered by a layer of columnar cells, set upon a basement membrane, and under this there is a fine layer of longitudinal non-striated muscle continuous with the lamina muscularis mucosæ.

In the interior of each villus there is a space lined with endothelium, known as the *central lacteal vessel*, which is continuous with the lymph vessels of the mucosa; there may be several lacteal vessels within the larger villi. A network of blood-vessels lies between the epithelium and the lacteal vessels.

Dilatation of those blood vessels causes enlargement of the villus, while contraction of the muscle layer diminishes its height and serves to assist in emptying the lacteal into the lymph vessels. The villi thus play an important part in the absorption of the products of digestion.

Circular Folds.—When the intestine is empty and contracted, its mucous membrane is thrown into folds which disappear on distension. In addition to those, there are in certain portions of the small intestine a series of large, permanent folds, known as circular folds (Fig. 505). They are usually more or less crescentic folds of the mucous coat, with a prolongation from the submucous coat, and resemble a series of closely placed shelves running transversely around the gut. They rarely form more than two-thirds of a circle; sometimes, however, they present a spiral arrangement, the spiral extending little more than once round the tube, as a rule. Occasionally they bifurcate at one or both ends;

sometimes, too, short irregularly directed branches pass off from them. They are usually about 2 to 3 inches (5 to 7·5 cm.) in length, and their height,

that is, their projection into the cavity, may be as much as ⅓ of an inch (8 mm.), whilst in thickness they measure about ⅛ inch (3 mm.).

They increase the amount of surface available for secretion and absorption.

Circular folds begin at a distance of from 1 to 2 inches (2·5 to 5 cm.) beyond the pylorus. At first they are small, irregular, and scattered; but they are larger lower down, and

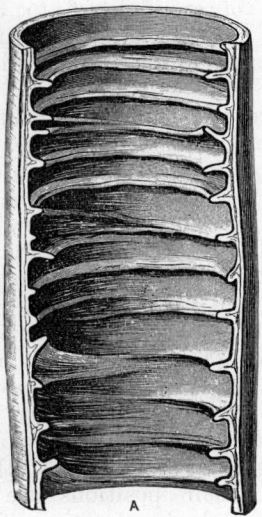

FIG. 505.—CIRCULAR FOLDS (natural size).

A, as seen in a portion of jejunum which has been filled with alcohol and hardened;
B, a portion of fresh intestine spread out under water.

at the opening of the bile duct (4 inches from the pylorus) they are distinct and prominent. In the rest of the duodenum, and in the upper half of the jejunum, they are highly developed, being large, broad, and closely set. In the lower half of the jejunum they become gradually smaller and fewer. In the ileum they become still smaller and more irregular, and, as a rule, they practically cease a little below its middle, but though much reduced in size they can be traced to within a short distance of the ileo-colic valve.

Lymphatic Nodules.—The **solitary lymphatic nodules** are minute masses of lymphoid tissue, opaque and of a whitish colour, which project on the surface of the mucous membrane throughout the whole length of both the small and the large intestine.

Isolated lymph cells are found in abundance scattered through the areolar tissue layer of the intestinal mucous membrane

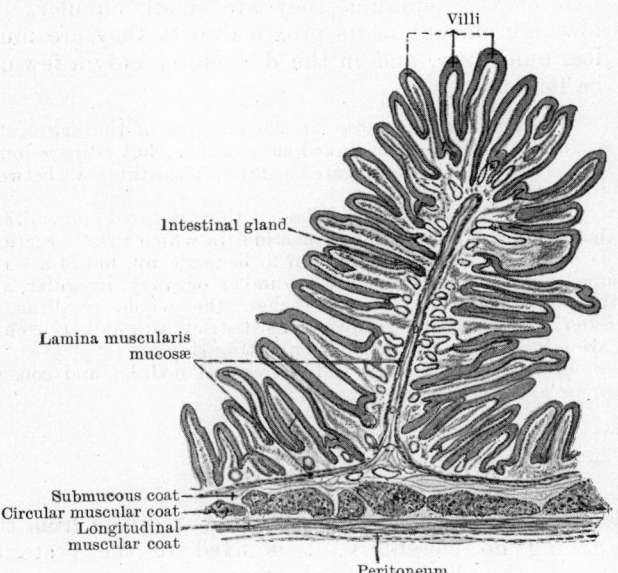

FIG. 506.—TRANSVERSE SECTION OF A CIRCULAR FOLD AND WALL OF SMALL INTESTINE.

Villi

Intestinal gland

Lamina muscularis mucosæ

Submucous coat
Circular muscular coat
Longitudinal muscular coat

Peritoneum

generally; in places those cells are gathered together to form little nodules, supported by a framework of retiform tissue, and surrounded by a lymph space which communicates externally with the lymph vessels of the submucous coat. Such a collection of lymph cells constitutes a solitary nodule. They are usually of a rounded or oval shape (Fig. 507), the deep surface resting in the submucous coat, the nodule itself piercing the lamina muscularis mucosæ, and the free surface projecting slightly above the general surface of the mucous membrane. In size they vary from $\frac{1}{40}$th to $\frac{1}{8}$th of an inch (·6 to 3·0 mm.), but their average bulk is about that of a small grain of sago, to which they bear some resemblance. They are particularly abundant in the vermiform appendix and the cæcum.

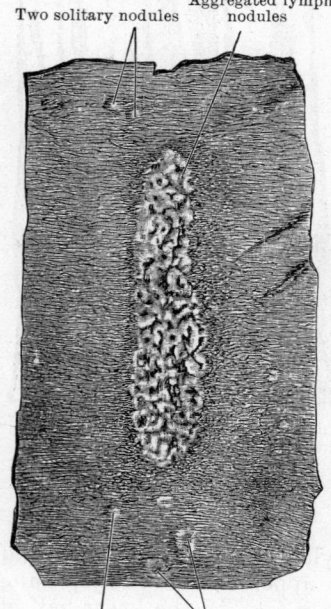

Aggregated lymph nodules

Two solitary nodules

Solitary nodule   Intermediate form

FIG. 507.—SOLITARY and AGGRE-GATED LYMPHATIC NODULES from intestine of child two years old (natural size).

Near the lower border are seen a few small patches made up of two or three lymph nodules; they are marked "intermediate form."

The **aggregated lymphatic nodules** consist of a large number of minute lymph nodules grouped closely together and forming a slightly elevated area, usually of an oblong form, on the surface of the mucous membrane (Fig. 507). In length they vary from half an inch (12 mm.), or less, to three or four inches (100 mm.), and in width they commonly measure from a third to half an inch (8 to 12 mm.). Their number is variable, but in the average condition about 20 or 30 are found. They are best marked in young subjects, where they form considerable elevations above the general surface, and may be as many as 45 in number. After middle life they atrophy, and in old age, although usually present, they are indistinct. Occasionally their positions are marked by little more than a dark discoloration of the mucous membrane. They are situated along the surface of the intestine opposite the line of mesenteric attachment, with their long axis corresponding to that of the bowel.

The aggregated nodules are confined to the small intestine, being largest and most numerous in the ileum, particularly in its distal part, where they usually assume an oblong shape; in the distal half of the jejunum they are small, circular, and few in number; in its proximal part they are much less numerous; and in the duodenum only a few can be found.

The circular folds stop at the margins of the aggregated nodules, and are not continued across them; but villi are found on the surface of the aggregated nodules, in the intervals between the individual nodules.

The chief bowel lesion in typhoid fever is found in the nodules—both aggregated and solitary.

When the surface of one of those nodules from a child's intestine (in which these structures are particularly well developed) is carefully examined, it is seen to be made up, not of a series of separate, rounded nodules grouped together, but rather of a number of wavy, irregular, and branching ridges connected with one another by cross branches, the whole recalling in miniature the appearance of a relief map of a very mountainous district in which the chief chains run irregular courses, and are joined to one another by connecting ridges.

Small patches, intermediate in form between solitary and aggregated nodules, and consisting of two or three lymph nodules, are also usually present.

DUODENUM

The **duodenum** is the first part of the small intestine, and it differs from the rest of the tube in that, having no mesentery, it is fixed to the posterior abdominal wall. The ducts of the liver and pancreas open into it, and some distinctive glands, termed the *duodenal glands*, are found in its wall.

Shape and Divisions.—The duodenum begins at the pylorus, about the level of the first lumbar vertebra, and ends at the left side of the first or the second lumbar vertebra (Fig. 508).

It forms an irregular horseshoe-shaped curve, with the opening directed upwards and to the left, and the ends reaching to within about two inches of each other. Within the concavity of the curve the head of the pancreas is placed. It is divided into four main parts: (1) the first part passes from the pylorus backwards and to the right beneath the liver, and ends at the neck of the gall-bladder by turning down and joining (2) the second part. That part begins at the neck of the gall-bladder, runs down on the posterior abdominal wall, on the right of the vertebral column, behind the transverse colon (Fig. 509), and ends opposite the third or fourth lumbar vertebra. There it turns to the left, and passes

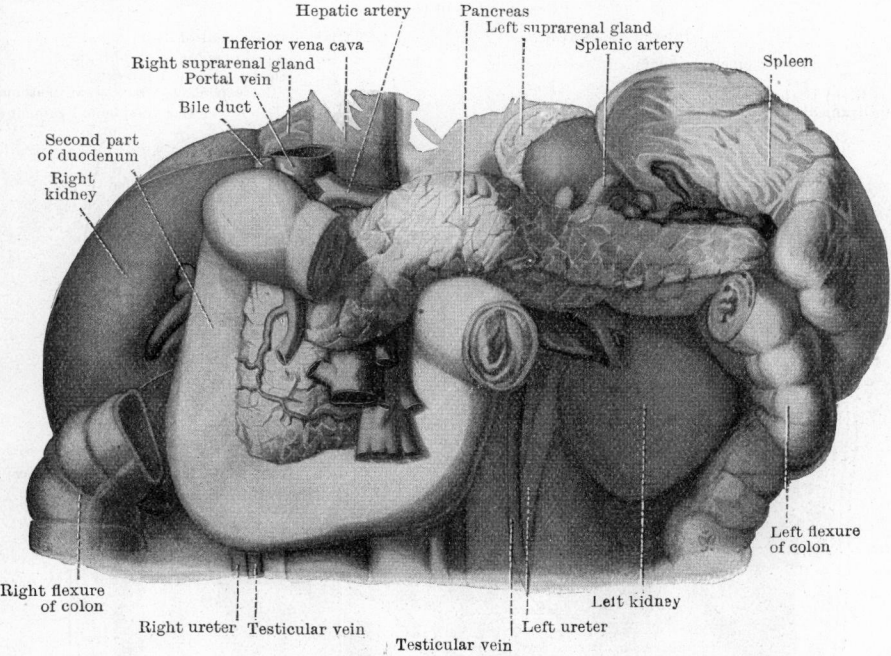

FIG. 508.—DISSECTION TO SHOW THE RELATIONS OF THE DUODENUM. The stomach (except the pylorus) has been removed. The transverse colon has been taken away, and the small intestine has been cut across close to the duodeno-jejunal flexure. (From a model by Birmingham).

into (3) the third part, which runs more or less transversely to the left, across the vena cava, aorta, and vertebral column. (4) The fourth part ascends as far as the inferior surface of the pancreas; there, at the left of the first or second lumbar vertebra, it bends abruptly forwards, forming the **duodeno-jejunal flexure** (Fig. 508), and passes into the jejunum.

Various Forms of Duodenum.—Three different types of duodenum have been described— (1) the **annular**, in which the curves separating the various parts are open, and the two extremities come fairly close to one another; (2) the U-shaped, in which the third part is very long, and the fourth part is nearly vertical; and (3) the V-shaped duodenum, in which the third part is very short or absent.

Position, Size, and Relations.—It lies on the posterior wall of the abdomen, usually opposite the upper three lumbar vertebræ, and, with the exception of the fourth part, the whole of it is to the right of the median plane.

Its length is usually about 11 inches (27·5 cm.), its first portion being the shortest and its third portion the longest. Its diameter varies considerably, and averages about 1½ inches (3·7 cm.) when empty, but it may be two inches or more in diameter when distended.

First Part [Pars superior].—The length of the first part is from about 1½ to 2 inches (3·7 to 5·0 cm.), and is said to be greater when the stomach is empty than when distended.

Above, it forms the inferior boundary of the opening into the lesser sac, and it is in relation to the caudate process of the liver. The hepatic artery is in contact for a short distance with its superior border.   Below its inferior border, which rests on the head and neck of the pancreas, there pass forwards the superior pancreatico-duodenal and the right gastro-epiploic vessels.   The quadrate lobe of the liver hangs downwards in front of the anterior (right) aspect of the first part of the duodenum.   The posterior (left) aspect is in contact with the portal vein, gastro-duodenal artery and the bile duct towards the left, and the right suprarenal gland and inferior vena cava towards the right.

Peritoneal Relations.—The first inch has the same relation to the peritoneum as the pyloric end of the stomach ; it is invested by peritoneum on the right and left aspects, and the peritoneum passes upwards from its superior border as the duodenal part of the lesser omentum.

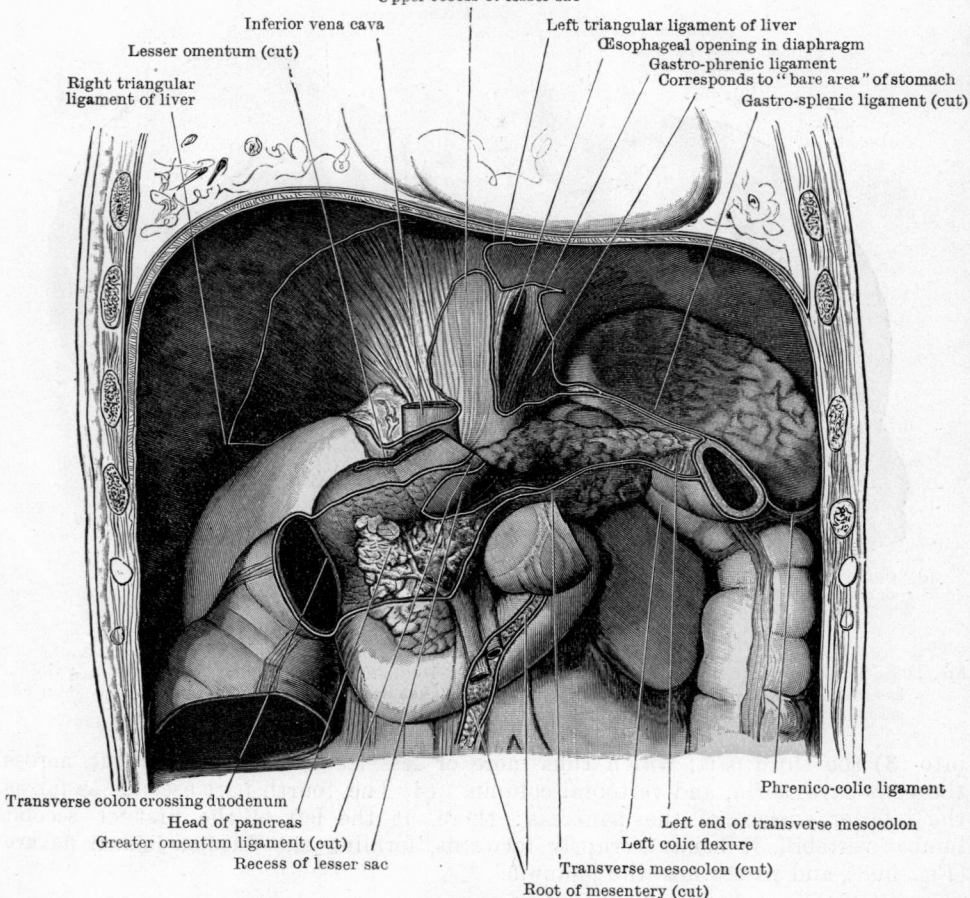

FIG. 509.—THE PERITONEAL RELATIONS OF THE DUODENUM, PANCREAS, SPLEEN, KIDNEYS, ETC.
From a body hardened by injections of formalin.   When the liver, stomach, and intestines were removed the lines of the peritoneal reflexions were carefully preserved.   The peritoneum is coloured blue.

From its inferior border the peritoneum is reflected to the left on to the pancreas and abdominal wall, and forms a fold known as the *right gastro-pancreatic fold*, while the peritoneal covering of the right side is continued downwards to invest the transverse colon (Fig. 509).

Second Part [Pars descendens].—The second part measures $3\frac{1}{2}$ to 4 inches (8·7 to 10 cm.) in length.

Its relations are as follows : It lies on the right of the vertebral column and the inferior vena cava, from the first to the third or fourth lumbar vertebra, and is anterior to the pelvis of the right ureter and the right renal vessels, and also, to a varying extent, in front of the right kidney itself ; while, below the level of those structures, it rests upon the psoas major muscle.   The anterior aspect is in contact with the inferior surface of the liver above, and with the transverse colon below.

The head of the pancreas is in contact with the left border, and occasionally overlaps it anteriorly and posteriorly ; and between the duodenum and the pancreas, both anteriorly and posteriorly, are branches of the superior and inferior pancreatico-duodenal vessels, the veins often forming a dense network on the posterior surface.

The bile duct, after passing down behind the first part of the duodenum, descends between the head of the pancreas (usually embedded in its substance) and the second part, nearly as far as its middle ; there it is joined by the pancreatic duct, and the two, piercing the wall of the duodenum obliquely, open into it by a common orifice, about 3 to 4 inches (8·7 to 10 cm.) beyond the pylorus.

Peritoneal Relations.—The anterior surface is covered with peritoneum, except about its middle, where the root of the transverse mesocolon crosses the duodenum. Not infrequently the transverse colon has no mesentery, but is itself in direct contact with the wall of the duodenum.

Third and Fourth Parts.—The third part [pars horizontalis] runs more or less transversely to the left for one or two inches, and the fourth part [pars ascendens] passes very obliquely, or even vertically, upwards. There is considerable variation in the length and form of the third and fourth parts taken together. Usually the third part is nearly horizontal and the fourth part nearly vertical (Fig. 508), but the third part may incline upwards as it passes to the left and lie in line with the fourth part (Fig. 509).

Anteriorly, the third part is crossed (about its junction with the fourth part) by the superior mesenteric vessels, and also by the root of the mesentery (Fig. 509). It is covered by coils of small intestine. *Posteriorly*, the third part lies across the inferior vena cava ; the fourth part lies on the aorta, the left renal vein and occasionally also the artery, and the left psoas major muscle, all of which separate it from the vertebral column. *Above*, it is closely applied in its whole extent to the head of the pancreas. The *left side* of the fourth part lies in contact with some coils of the small intestine.

Peritoneal Relations.—The third part of the duodenum is covered with peritoneum on its anterior surface throughout, except where it is crossed by the superior mesenteric vessels and the root of the mesentery, which contains those vessels. The fourth part also is clothed by this membrane on its left side.

The attachment of the root of the mesentery begins, above, quite close to the duodeno-jejunal flexure, on the front of the duodenum ; thence it runs down on the front of the fourth part, and finally leaves the duodenum about the union of the third and fourth parts.

Duodenal Recesses.—In the neighbourhood of the fourth part of the duodenum there may be present four peritoneal pockets—the superior and inferior duodenal, the para-duodenal, and the retro-duodenal recesses (Fig. 510).

When the fourth part of the duodenum is drawn over to the right, two triangular folds of peritoneum will generally be found passing from the duodenum to the abdominal wall (Fig. 510). Each fold is attached by one border to the duodenum, and by another to the parietal peritoneum at the left of the duodenum, whilst the third margin is free, and bounds the opening of a small pouch which lies behind the fold. Of those folds, the *upper* is situated near the termination of the duodenum, with its free margin directed down. It sometimes contains between its two layers a portion of the inferior mesenteric vein. Behind it lies the **superior duodenal recess**, whose opening looks downwards, and will usually admit the tip of a finger (Fig. 510). The second fold is placed

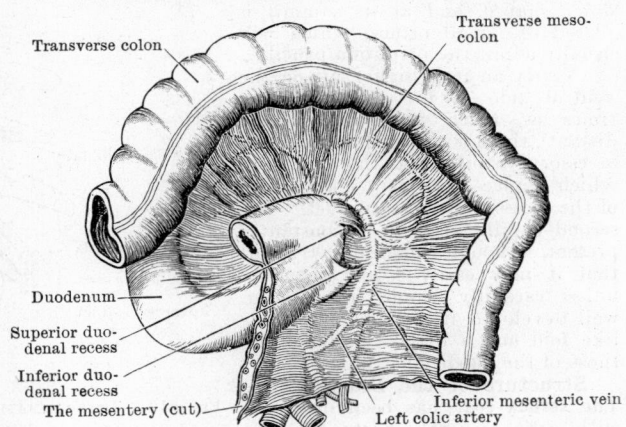

FIG. 510.—THE DUODENAL FOLDS AND RECESSES.

The transverse colon and mesocolon have been thrown up, and the mesentery has been turned to the right and cut. The para-duodenal fossa is situated to the medial side of the inferior mesenteric vein, between it and the terminal part of the duodenum. It is not shown in the illustration.

lower down. Its free border is directed upwards, as is the mouth of the **inferior duodenal recess**, which lies behind it. The inferior recess is larger and more constant than the superior, and is present in 75 per cent. of bodies, whilst the superior is present in 50 per cent. (Jonnesco).

Para-duodenal Recess.—This recess, which is seen best in the infant, is placed to the left of the fourth part of the duodenum. It is produced by the inferior mesenteric vein raising up a fold of peritoneum termed the **para-duodenal fold** as it runs along the lateral side of the recess, and then above it (see Fig. 510, where the vein, but not the fold or recess is shown). According to Moynihan, this is the only recess to the left of the duodenum capable of developing into the sac of a hernia ; and when that occurs, the inferior mesenteric vein always lies in the anterior margin of the orifice of the sac (accompanied for some distance by the ascending branch of the superior left colic artery).

The **retro-duodenal recess** is a small pocket that passes behind the fourth part of the duodenum from its left margin.

Interior of Duodenum.

—No circular folds are found in the duodenum for an inch or two beyond the pylorus. They begin as low, scattered, and irregular folds, which gradually become larger, more regular, and more numerous, and at the middle of the second part are of considerable size. In the third and fourth part of the duodenum the folds are large, prominent, and closely set.

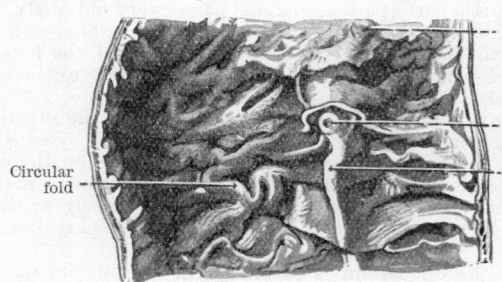

Fig. 511.—Interior of a Portion of the Second Part of the Duodenum (viewed from the front).

On the postero-medial wall of the second part, about its middle—*i.e.* 3½ or 4 inches (8·5 to 10 cm.) beyond the pylorus—there is a prominent papilla on which the bile and pancreatic ducts open by a common orifice (Fig. 512); it is known as the **duodenal papilla**.

The papilla is placed beneath, and protected by, a prominent, hood-like circular fold. From its lower margin a firm ridge of the mucous membrane, called the *longitudinal fold of the duodenum*, descends for a considerable distance and acts as a frenum which fixes the papilla and directs its apex slightly downwards (Fig. 511). The papilla is prominent and nipple or dome shaped, and at its summit is placed the small orifice, which will usually admit the point of a pencil.

Nearly an inch higher up, on the ventral side of the papilla (sometimes as much as ½ to ¾ inch distant), there is a second and smaller accessory papilla, at the point of which is placed the very small orifice of the accessory pancreatic duct. The second papilla seems to be constantly present, although sometimes so small that it may easily escape detection unless carefully sought for. When well developed it may have a hood-like fold and a little frenulum, like those of the duodenal papilla.

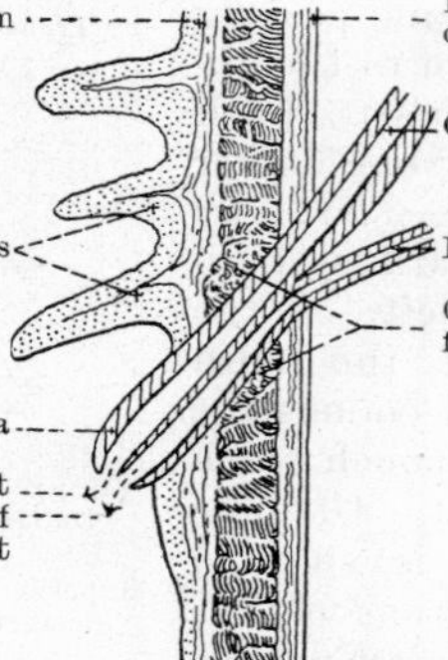

Structure of the Duodenum.

—The **serous coat** has been described with the several parts of the duodenum.

Fig. 512.—Diagrammatic Section of Wall of Duodenum through Papilla.

The **muscular coat** is well developed, and is pierced by the bile and pancreatic ducts.

As the united bile and pancreatic ducts traverse the muscular walls they are surrounded by a sphincter-like group of fibres which extends into the papilla.

The **submucous coat** differs from that of the rest of the small intestine in that it contains, especially in the upper half of the duodenum, the **duodenal glands**. They are small acino-tubular glands, closely resembling the pyloric glands of the stomach; they lie in the submucous coat, and send their ducts through the lamina muscularis mucosæ to open on the surface between the intestinal glands, or sometimes into those glands themselves (Fig. 513). To naked-eye examination they are small, round, or flattened masses of a reddish-grey colour, varying in size from $\frac{1}{50}$th to $\frac{1}{12}$th of an inch in diameter (·5 to 2·0 mm.). They form an almost continuous layer as far as the opening of the bile duct; beyond that they diminish progressively, and completely disappear near the duodeno-jejunal flexure.

The **mucous coat** is thicker in the duodenum than in any other part of the small intestine, and is covered throughout with broad, short villi.

Vessels and Nerves.

—The **arteries** are the superior and inferior pancreatico-duodenal—branches of the gastro-duodenal and superior mesenteric arteries respectively. The blood is returned by the corresponding **veins**, the superior of which opens into the superior mesenteric vein or the portal vein, and the inferior into the beginning of the portal vein.

The **lymph vessels** follow for the most part the course of the blood-vessels.

The **nerves** come from the *cœliac* and *superior mesenteric plexuses* of the sympathetic.

Duodenal Diverticula.—Occasional diverticula are found passing from the duodenal wall in different directions. Such diverticula may be hernial protrusions of the mucous and submucous coats through the muscular wall, termed "false" diverticula, or they may be "true" diverticula, in which all the coats are represented, and they may contain pancreatic tissue in their wall. They are usually situated on the aspect of the duodenum which is in contact with the pancreas, and frequently in the neighbourhood of the orifice of the bile duct. Some of them appear to be due to pressure from the interior of the duodenum, while others, including most of the true diverticula, are congenital in origin, and are possibly associated with the diverticula which give rise to the liver and pancreas.

Radiographic Examination.—The form and position of the duodenum as seen in X-ray examination after a bismuth meal are shown in Pl. XLIV. With variations in the position of the pylorus, mentioned on p. 592, there is a corresponding alteration in the position of the first part of the duodenum.

Duodeno-jejunal Flexure.—When the fourth part of the duodenum reaches the inferior surface of the pancreas, at a point opposite the left side of the first or second lumbar vertebra, it turns abruptly forwards, downwards, and to the left, and passes into the jejunum. The abrupt bend is known as the **duodeno-jejunal flexure**. Unlike the rest of the duodenum, which is subject to considerable variations in position in different individuals, the duodeno-jejunal flexure is fixed by a thin band of muscle called the *suspensory muscle of the duodenum*, which blends, at the flexure, with the muscular coat of the duodenum. Thence it passes upwards behind the pancreas, is connected with the fibrous tunic around the cœliac artery, and is continued above into the right crus of the diaphragm (p. 424).

The duodeno-jejunal flexure is occasionally directed to the right, and it lies at a variable distance from the root of the transverse mesocolon; when the attachment of the mesocolon is low, the duodeno-jejunal flexure is in contact with it.

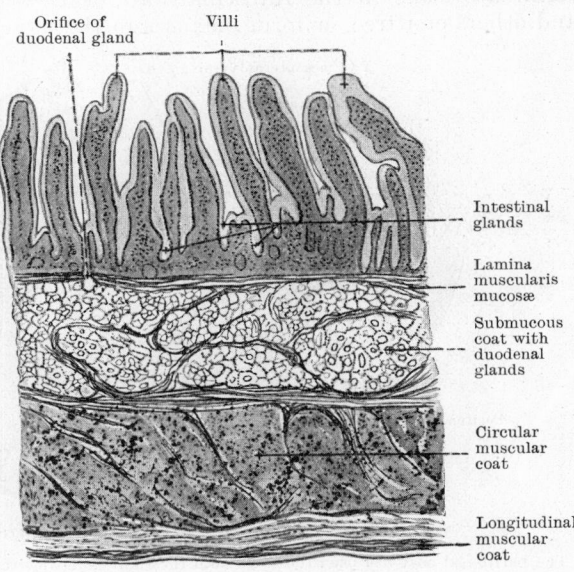

FIG. 513.—SECTION OF WALL OF DUODENUM.

JEJUNUM AND ILEUM

The **jejunum** and **ileum** are attached to the posterior wall of the abdomen by *the mesentery*, which is a lamina of fibro-areolar tissue covered on each side with peritoneum, and containing blood vessels, lymph vessels, lymph glands, and nerves.

The part of the tube to which the mesentery is connected is known as the mesenteric or attached border; the opposite side is the free border.

The **mesentery** is a broad fan-shaped fold which connects the small intestine to the posterior wall of the abdomen. The long, free border of the fold contains the intestine within it. The other, or attached border, called the **root of the mesentery**, is comparatively short, being only 6 or 7 inches long; but it is much thicker than the part near the gut, for it contains between its layers a considerable amount of fatty extra-peritoneal tissue, in addition to the large vascular trunks that supply the intestine. The root is attached to the posterior abdominal wall along an oblique line which extends approximately from the left side of the second lumbar vertebra to the right sacro-iliac joint (Fig. 523). In that course the line of attachment passes from the duodeno-jejunal flexure down over the front of the third part of the duodenum, then obliquely across the aorta, the inferior vena cava, the right ureter, and psoas major muscle, to the right iliac region.

The unattached border of the mesentery is frilled out to an enormous degree, so that, while the root measures but 6 or 7 inches, the free border is extended to some 20 feet, thus resembling a fan, one border of which may be twenty or thirty times as long as the other. The length of the mesentery, measured from its root to the attached edge of the intestine directly opposite, usually measures at its longest part about 6 inches (8 or 9 inches, Treves and Lockwood).

Its longest part goes to the portion of the small intestine situated between two points, one six feet, the other eleven feet from the duodenum (Treves).

Between the two layers of the mesentery (Fig. 514) there are: (*a*) The jejunal and ileal branches of the superior mesenteric vessels, accompanied by the mesenteric nerve plexus and lymph vessels; the nerves of the mesentery terminate some in the intestinal wall, others in blood-vessels in the mesentery, and others end free, or form plexuses in the mesentery; lamellated corpuscles also

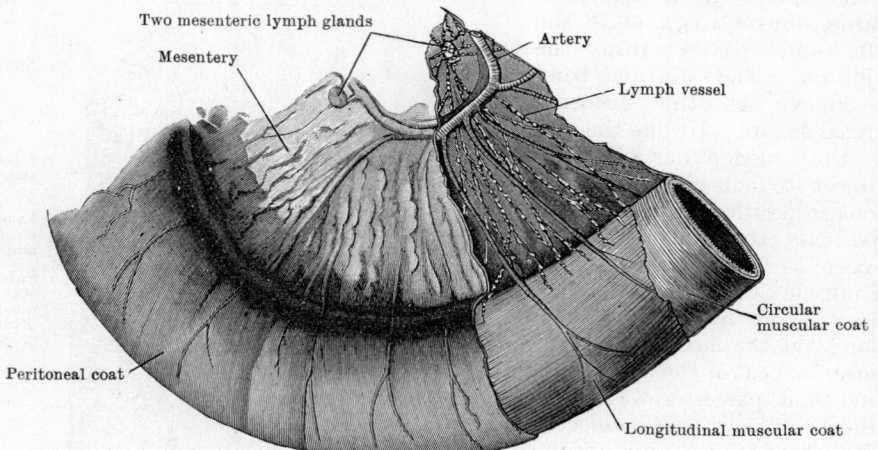

FIG. 514.—A PORTION OF SMALL INTESTINE, WITH MESENTERY AND VESSELS.

The peritoneal coat has been removed from the right half, and the two layers of the muscular coat exposed.

are occasionally present. (*b*) The mesenteric lymph glands, between 100 and 200 in number. (*c*) A considerable amount of fatty fibro-areolar tissue, continuous with the extra-peritoneal areolar tissue. (*d*) The intestine itself.

The portion of the mesentery connected to the jejunum contains less fat than that of the ileum, and near the border of the jejunum there are oval or circular areas ("windows") where fat is absent and which are translucent. The mesentery attached to the ileum is usually fat-laden and opaque up to the margin of the intestine.

The peritoneum from the right side of the mesentery passes out on the posterior abdominal wall to clothe the ascending colon, and, above, it is connected by a fold with the transverse mesocolon. That of the left side, similarly, passes across the parietes to the descending colon.

The mesentery is of such a length that the coils are able to move about freely in the abdominal cavity, and consequently the position occupied by any portion of the tube, with the exception of the beginning of the jejunum and the ending of the ileum, can never be stated with certainty. Nevertheless, it may be said that, in general, the jejunum occupies the superior and left portions of the cavity below the stomach, the ileum the inferior and right divisions, its terminal part almost always lying in the pelvis, just before it joins the large gut.

According to Mall, the most usual arrangement is to find the upper coils of the jejunum on the left side, and high up. Then the tube crosses the vertebral column below the duodenum, and a few coils are placed on the right side. It then crosses to the left side again, and several coils are formed, some of which may descend into the true pelvis. Thence it passes again to the right side, where it is coiled up, and then finally descends into the true pelvis.

Whilst the root of the mesentery pursues at its attachment an almost straight line from one end to the other, if cut across a very short distance from the posterior abdominal wall, it will there be found to form a wavy or undulating line. Farther away still that condition becomes more and more marked ; and finally, if the bowel is removed by cutting through the mesentery close to its attachment to the intestinal wall, it will be seen that its free edge is not only undulating, but is frilled or plaited to an extreme degree. When shown in that way, it is found that the plaiting or folding is not quite indiscriminate, but that the main folds, of which there are usually six, run alternately to the right and left. As a rule, the first fold runs to the left from the duodeno-jejunal flexure, and goes to a coil of jejunum which lies under the transverse mesocolon, and helps to support the stomach. The second fold passes to the right, the third to the left, and so on up to the fifth and sixth, which are usually small. From the margins of the primary folds secondary folds project in all directions, and from those again even a third series may be formed.

The order is of course by no means constant, but if the intestine is removed from a hardened body in the way suggested, without disturbing the mesentery, it will be found to be arranged with more or less regularity, on some such plan as that indicated.

Structure (Fig. 502).—The **muscular coat** is thicker in the jejunum, and grows gradually thinner as it is traced down along the ileum. The **submucous coat** contains the bases of the solitary nodules, but otherwise calls for no special remark. The **mucous coat** is thicker and redder in the jejunum, thinner and paler in the ileum. It is covered throughout by villi, which are shorter and broader in the jejunum, longer and narrower in the ileum. In its whole extent it is closely set with intestinal glands, and numerous solitary nodules are seen projecting on its surface. Aggregated lymph nodules are particularly large and numerous in the ileum ; they are fewer, smaller, and usually circular in the jejunum. Finally, the mucous membrane forms *circular folds*, which are much more prominent in the jejunum ; they are smaller and fewer in the superior part of the ileum, and usually disappear a little below its middle.

Vessels.—The **arteries**, on reaching the intestine, pass to one or other side of it and only occasionally bifurcate to give a branch to each side of the gut. They are at first under the peritoneal coat ; soon, however, they pierce the muscular coat and form a plexus in the submucous coat, from which numerous branches pass to the mucous coat, where some form plexuses around the intestinal glands whilst others pass to the villi. The **veins** are similarly disposed, and the blood from the whole of the small intestine beyond the duodenum is returned by the *superior mesenteric vein*, which joins with the splenic to form the portal vein.

The **lymph vessels** of the small intestine (known as *lacteals*) begin in the villi, and also as lymph sinuses surrounding the bases of the solitary nodules ; a large plexus is formed in the submucosa, a second between the two layers of the muscular coat, and a third beneath the peritoneum. The vessels from all these pass up in the mesentery, being connected on the way with the numerous *lymph glands of the mesentery* and finally join the *gastro-intestinal trunk*, which opens into the cisterna chyli.

Differences between Jejunum and Ileum.—If the small intestine is followed down from the duodenum to the cæcum no noticeable change in appearance will be found at any one part of its course, to indicate the transition from jejunum to ileum, for the one passes insensibly into the other. Nevertheless, a gradual change takes place, and if typical parts of the two, namely, the upper portion of the jejunum and the lower portion of the ileum, are examined, they will be found to present characteristic differences, which are set forth in the following table :—

Jejunum.	Ileum.
Wider, $1\frac{1}{2}$ to $1\frac{1}{4}$ inches in diameter.	Narrower, $1\frac{1}{4}$ to 1 inch in diameter.
Wall, thicker and heavier.	Wall, thinner and lighter.
Redder and more vascular.	Paler and less vascular.
Circular folds, well developed.	Circular folds, very small or absent.
Villi, short and broad.	Villi, slender and filiform.
Aggregated lymphatic nodules, few and small.	Aggregated lymphatic nodules, large and numerous.
Less fat in its mesentery and translucent areas present.	Mesentery, fat-laden and opaque.

The vessels of the jejunum have more numerous arches on their course in the mesentery than have those of the ileum.

Diverticulum Ilei.—This is a short protrusion which springs from the lower part of the ileum in a little over 2 per cent. of bodies. It is usually about 2 inches long, and of the same width as the intestine from which it comes off. Most commonly it is found about $2\frac{3}{4}$ feet from the ileo-colic orifice, and opposite the original termination of the superior mesenteric artery. As a rule, its end is free ; but occasionally it is adherent either to the abdominal wall, the adjacent viscera, or the mesentery, and in such cases it may be the cause of strangulation of the intestine.

The diverticulum is due to the persistence of the proximal portion of the vitello-intestinal duct, which connects the primitive intestine of the embryo with the yolk sac. In shape it may be cylindrical, conical, or cord-like, and it may present secondary diverticula near its tip in which, on microscopic examination, pancreatic tissue may sometimes be found. It arises most frequently from the free border of the intestine, but it sometimes comes off from the side. It runs at right angles to the gut most commonly, but it may assume any direction, and it is often provided with a mesentery. In 3302 bodies specially examined with reference to its existence, it was present in 73, or 2·2 per cent., and it appeared to be more common in the male than in the female. In 59 out of the 73 cases its position with reference to the end of the ileum was examined: its average distance from the ileo-colic valve was 32½ inches measured along the gut, the greatest distance being 12 feet, and the smallest 6 inches. In 52 specimens the average length was 2·1 inches, the longest being 5¼ inches, the shortest ½ inch. The diameter usually equals that of the intestine; but occasionally it is cord-like, and pervious only for a short way; on the other hand, it may attain a diameter of 3¾ inches.

LARGE INTESTINE

The ileum is succeeded by the **large intestine** (intestinum crassum), which begins on the right side, some 2½ inches below the end of the small intestine, and comprises the following parts: **cæcum** and **vermiform appendix, ascending colon,**

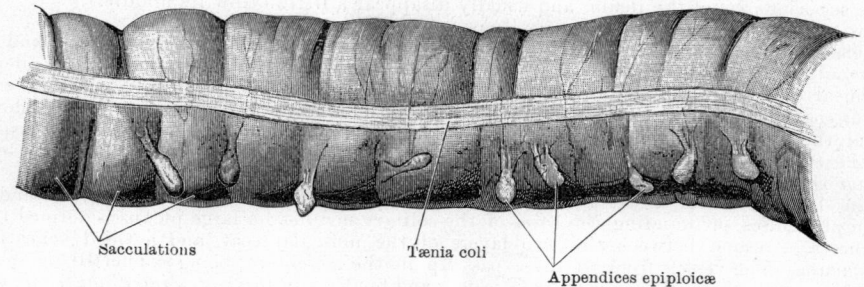

Sacculations   Tænia coli

Appendices epiploicæ

FIG. 515.—LARGE INTESTINE.

A piece of transverse colon from a child two years old. The three chief characteristics of the large intestine—appendices epiploicæ, tæniæ, and sacculations—are shown.

right flexure of colon, transverse colon, left flexure of colon, descending colon, pelvic colon, rectum, and **anal canal.** In its course the large bowel is arranged in an arched manner around the small intestine (Fig. 503 and Pl. XLVII).

In *length*, the great intestine measures about one-fifth of the whole intestinal canal, that is, 5 to 5½ feet (1-3 m.). Its *breadth* is greatest at the cæcum, which measures about 3 inches (75 mm.) in diameter when distended; and from there —with the exception of a dilatation at the rectum—it decreases to the anus. Functionally, there is a distinct difference between the ascending colon and transverse colon together and the descending colon; the descending colon is often found slightly contracted after death and measures only 1½ inches or less.

The external appearances by which the large intestine, with the exception of the vermiform appendix and the rectum, may be distinguished from the small intestine are stated on p. 594. Two structures peculiar to the large intestine and visible on its external surface require further description.

The **tæniæ coli** are about ¼ inch (6 mm.) wide, begin at the root of the vermiform appendix, and run along the surface of the large intestine at nearly equal distances from one another as far as to the rectum. There they spread out and form a layer of longitudinal muscular fibres which is continuous all round the tube (see p. 622). The tæniæ are about one-sixth shorter than the intestine to which they belong; consequently, in order to accommodate it to the length of the tæniæ, the large intestine is tucked up (Fig. 515), and three rows of **sacculations** are produced, along the length of the tube, between the tæniæ. If the tæniæ are dissected off, the sacculations largely disappear, the intestine becomes cylindrical, and at the same time about one-sixth longer.

The position of the three tæniæ on the colon is as follows : On the ascending and descending colon one tænia lies on the front of the gut, and two on the back, namely, one to the lateral side (postero-lateral) the other to the medial side (postero-medial). It is chiefly along the first of them (the anterior) that the appendices epiploicæ are found. On the transverse colon in the natural position, the anterior tænia of the ascending and descending colon becomes the posterior (or postero-inferior), the postero-lateral becomes anterior and the postero-medial becomes superior in position. The anterior and postero-lateral tæniæ of the descending colon pass below on to the front of the pelvic colon and rectum.

When the interior of a piece of distended and dried large intestine is examined, its sacculations appear as rounded pouches, separated by crescentic folds that correspond to the creases on the exterior between the saccules. These folds are made up of mucous membrane containing the muscular coats of the intestine as well as areolar tissue, and each extends over only one-third of the circumference of the intestine, between the tæniæ.

The **appendices epiploicæ** are little pouches of peritoneum, generally more or less distended with fat, which project from the serous coat along the whole length of the large intestine, with the exception of the rectum. They are rudimentary in the appendix. The appendices epiploicæ can be seen as early as the seventh month in the fœtus, but at that time they contain no fat.

In formalin-hardened bodies portions of the large intestine, but particularly of the descending colon, are often found fixed in what appears to be a state of contraction, when they are reduced to a diameter of about $\frac{5}{8}$ or $\frac{3}{4}$ of an inch (16 to 19 mm.). Under similar conditions parts of the small intestine are found correspondingly reduced.

Structure of the Large Intestine.—The serous coat is complete on the vermiform appendix, cæcum, transverse colon, and pelvic colon ; incomplete on the ascending, and descending divisions of the colon and on the rectum. It will be described in detail with each of these portions of the intestine.

The **mucous coat** is of a pale, or yellowish, ash colour in the colon, but becomes much redder in the rectum. Unlike that of the small intestine, its surface is smooth, owing to the absence of villi, but it is closely studded with the orifices of numerous large intestinal glands. Solitary lymph nodules are also numerous, particularly in the vermiform appendix (Fig. 521).

Vessels and Nerves.—The **arteries** are derived from the *mesenteric arteries*. Branches of the superior mesenteric supply the large intestine as far as the left flexure of the colon, and branches

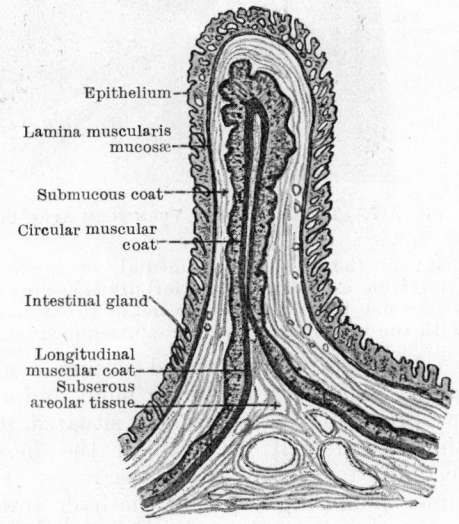

Epithelium

Lamina muscularis mucosæ

Submucous coat

Circular muscular coat

Intestinal gland

Longitudinal muscular coat

Subserous areolar tissue

Fig. 516.—Transverse Section of a Crescentic Fold of the Colon.

of the inferior supply the remainder as far as the lower part of the rectum. The cæcum and vermiform appendix receive their blood from the *ileo-colic artery* ; the ascending colon from the *right colic artery* ; and the transverse colon from the *middle colic artery*. The descending colon is supplied by the *superior and inferior left colic,* and the pelvic colon by the *inferior left colic arteries*. The rectum derives its blood from the three *rectal arteries*, which will be described with that division of the gut.

The **veins** correspond largely to the arteries, and join the *inferior* and *superior mesenteric veins*, which send their blood into the portal vein.

The **lymph vessels** of the large intestine arise from plexuses in the submucous and subperitoneal coats, as in other parts of the alimentary canal. Those from the cæcum and vermiform appendix run to the *ileo-colic glands*. The deeper vessels of the colon escape chiefly along the entering blood-vessels, those from the lateral aspects passing behind the intestine. The vessels pass first to a series of " *paracolic* " glands that lie along the medial border of the intestine; thence they pass along the lines of the main arteries to *intermediate* and *main glands* disposed at intervals about those vessels.

The **nerves** come from the *superior and inferior mesenteric plexuses*. Their arrangement is described on p. 594.

CÆCUM AND VERMIFORM APPENDIX

Cæcum.—After leaving the pelvic cavity, as already described, the terminal portion of the small intestine passes upwards, backwards, and to the right, in close contact with the cæcum, and opens very obliquely, by the ileo-colic orifice, into the large intestine some 2½ inches from its lower end. The portion of the large gut which lies below the level of this orifice is known as the **cæcum.** *In shape* (Fig. 520) it is a wide, asymmetrical cul-de-sac furnished with tæniæ and sacculations. Its lower end is directed downwards and medially, and usually rests on the right psoas major muscle, close to the brim of the true pelvis; whilst the opposite end is directed upwards and laterally, and is continued into the ascending colon.

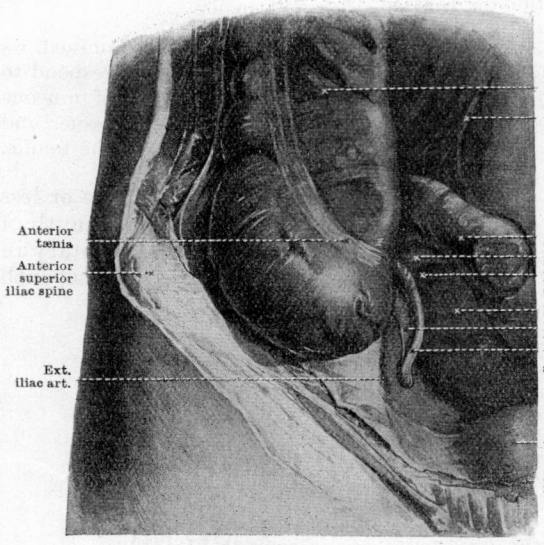

FIG. 517.—THE CÆCUM AND VERMIFORM APPENDIX FROM THE FRONT.

Its asymmetrical form is due to the fact that the lateral and medial portions of the organ undergo an unequal development in the child. The medial (or medial and posterior) section lags behind, while the lateral (or lateral and anterior) division grows much more rapidly, and, projecting downwards, soon comes to form the lower end of the cæcum. As a result the original extremity of the gut, with the vermiform appendix springing from it, is hidden on the back of the cæcum.

In *length* the distended cæcum usually measures about 2½ inches (60 mm.); whilst its *breadth* is usually more, and averages about 3 inches (75 mm.).

Position.—It is usually situated in the right iliac fossa, immediately above the lateral half or third of the inguinal ligament, but its lower end bulges medially to overlap the psoas major (Fig. 517). On the other hand, it is sometimes found high up near the liver (owing to the persistence of the fœtal position), or hanging over the pelvic brim and dipping into the pelvic cavity to a varying extent.

In most bodies the cæcum is completely covered with peritoneum on all aspects, and lies quite free in the abdominal cavity; but in 6 or 7 per cent. of bodies, the posterior surface (probably as a result of adhesions) is not completely covered, and over a greater or less portion of its extent is bound down to the posterior abdominal wall by fibro-areolar tissue.

Relations.—*Posteriorly*, the cæcum rests on the ilio-psoas muscle and the femoral nerve; generally, too, on the vermiform appendix. *Anteriorly*, it usually lies in contact with the greater omentum and anterior abdominal wall; but when the cæcum is empty, the small intestine intervenes. Its *lateral side* is placed immediately above the lateral half or third of the inguinal ligament (Fig. 517), whilst the *medial side* has the terminal part of the ileum lying in contact with it. On the medial and posterior aspects, but more on the former than the latter, the small intestine joins the cæcum. On the same aspect, and usually from 1 to 1½ inches (25 to 37 mm.) lower down, the vermiform appendix springs from the cæcum.

Types of Cæcum.—Three chief types of cæcum may be distinguished—the *fœtal type*, conical in shape and nearly symmetrical, with the inferior end gradually passing into the vermiform appendix; the *infantile*, in which the passage from the cæcum to the vermiform appendix becomes more abrupt, the lateral wall more prominent, and the whole sac more asymmetrical; and the lop-sided *adult form*, which is the condition found in 93 or 94 per cent. of adults.

PLATE XLVII

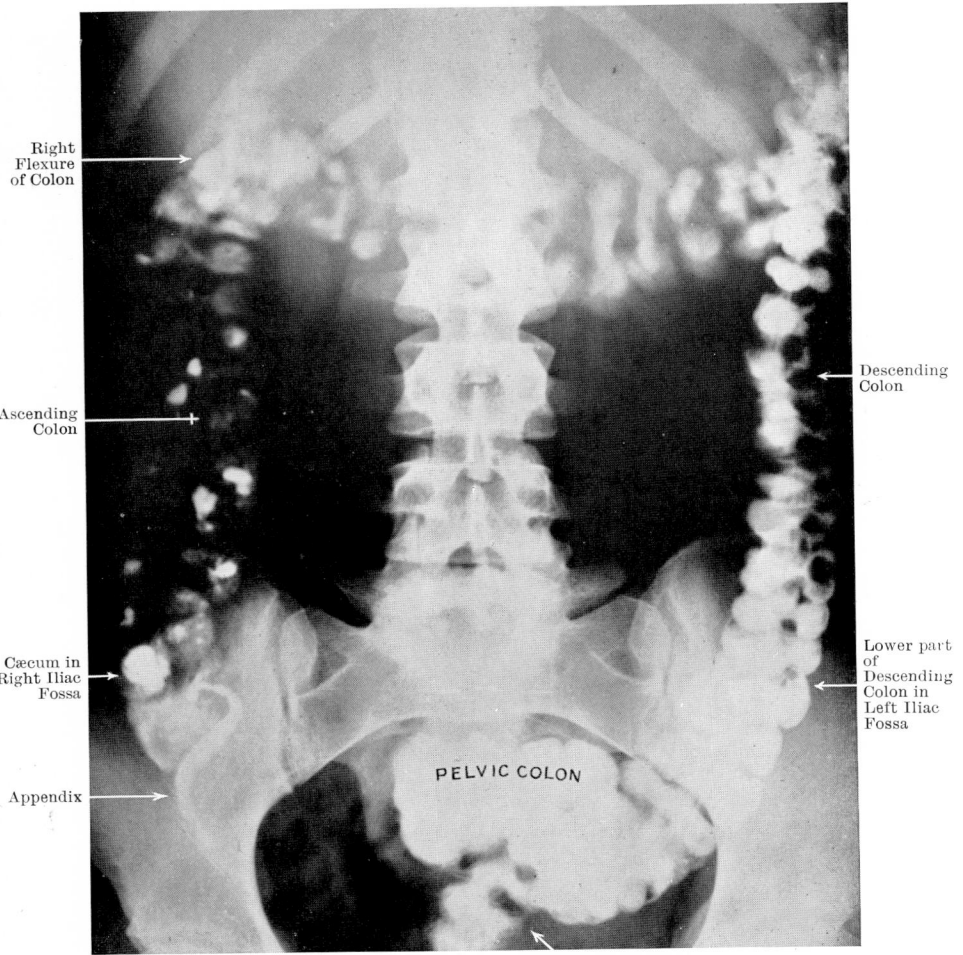

Right
Flexure
of Colon

Descending
Colon

Ascending
Colon

Cæcum in
Right Iliac
Fossa

Lower part
of
Descending
Colon in
Left Iliac
Fossa

Appendix

PELVIC COLON

Rectum

PLATE XLVII.—RADIOGRAPH SHOWING ALL THE PARTS OF THE
LARGE INTESTINE. (J. F.). MOST OF THE OPAQUE MEAL HAS
ACCUMULATED IN THE LOWER PART OF THE DESCENDING COLON,
THE PELVIC COLON AND THE RECTUM.

Note the residue of radio-opaque material in the Cæcum and Appendix, and the contraction of the Descending Colon. Compare this radiograph with Fig. 1 and Fig. 2, Plate
XLI, which represent two previous stages in the filling and emptying of the Cæcum and Colon.

PLATE XLVIII

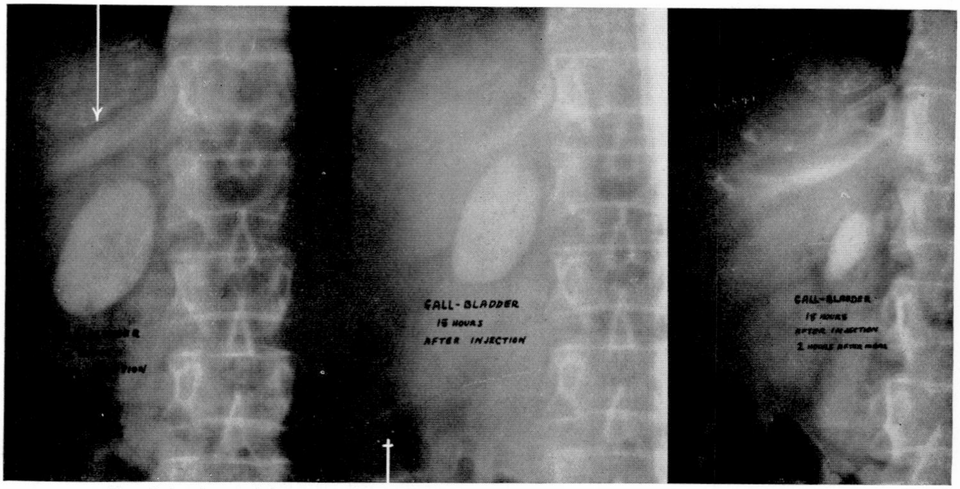

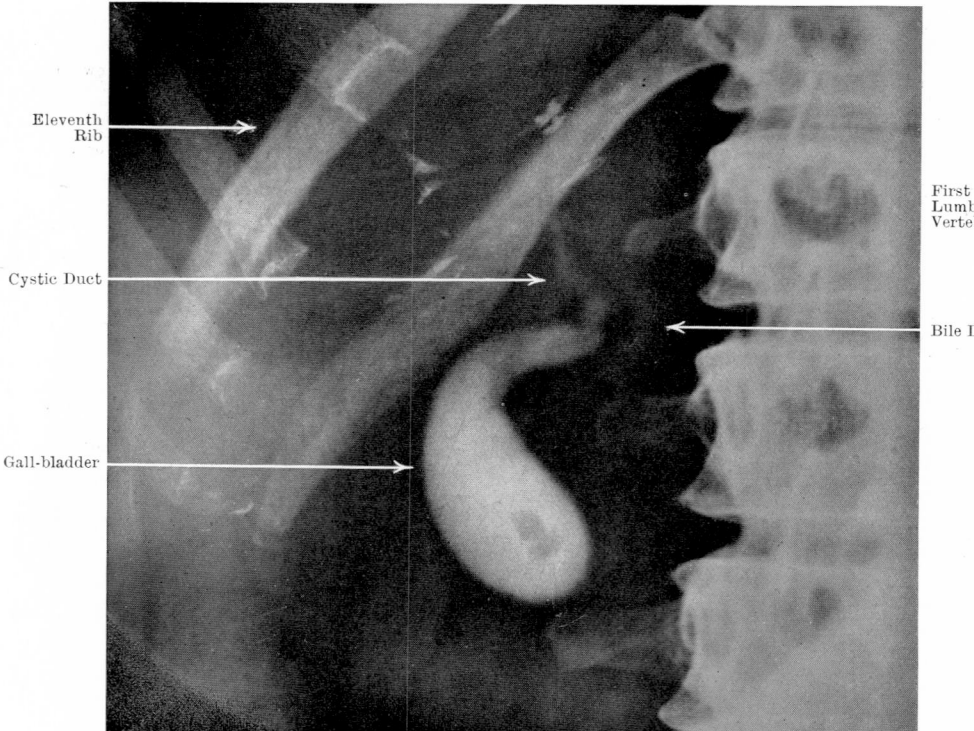

Twelfth Rib

GALL-BLADDER
15 HOURS
AFTER INJECTION

GALL-BLADDER
15 HOURS
AFTER INJECTION
2 HOURS AFTER MEAL

Fourth lumbar vertebra   Gas in Colon
A   B   C

FIG. 1.—SERIAL RADIOGRAPHS OF THE SAME GALL-BLADDER SHOWING PHYSIOLOGICAL CHANGES.
(Dr. J. F. Brailsford.)

A. 12 hours after administration of tetra-iodo-phenol-phthalein.
B. 15 hours after : Concentration of Bile.
C. 18 hours after ; 2 hours after meal : Discharge of Bile into Duodenum.

Eleventh
Rib

First
Lumbar
Vertebra

Cystic Duct

Bile Duct

Gall-bladder

FIG. 2.—RADIOGRAPH, AFTER ADMINISTRATION OF RADIO-OPAQUE DYE EXCRETED BY THE
LIVER (see p. 636), SHOWING POSITION OF THE GALL-BLADDER AND THE CYSTIC DUCT ; THE BILE
DUCT IS ALSO FAINTLY SEEN. (Dr. R. McWhirter.)

Structure.—Nothing in the arrangement of the mucous and submucous coats calls for special notice. The tæniæ all spring from the root of the vermiform appendix (Fig. 520); the anterior runs up on the front, medial to the main prominence of the cæcum; the postero-lateral runs up behind this prominence; whilst the postero-medial passes directly upwards behind the ileum (Fig. 520). The longitudinal fibres on the superior aspect of the ileum partly join the postero-medial tænia; those on the anterior and posterior aspects join the circular fibres of the large gut.

The *interior* of the cæcum corresponds in general appearance to that of the large intestine; but it presents two special features on the posterior part of its medial wall, namely, the **ileo-colic orifice**, guarded by the **ileo-colic valve**, and below that the small opening of the **vermiform appendix**.

The **position of the ileo-colic valve**, in the average condition, may be indicated on the surface of the body by the point of intersection of the intertubercular and right sagittal lines. A point 1 to 1½ inches (2·5 to 3·8 cm.) lower down would correspond to the **orifice of the vermiform appendix.**

Ileo - colic Valve [Valvula coli].— Where the ileum enters the large intestine, the end of the small gut is, as it were, thrust through the wall of the large bowel, carrying with it certain layers of that wall; these layers project into the cæcum in the form of two folds which lie one above and one below its orifice, and constitute the two segments of the valve (Fig. 519). The peritoneum and longitudinal muscular fibres of the bowel take no part in this infolding; on the contrary, they are stretched tightly across the crease produced on the exterior by the inversion, and thus serve to preserve the folds and the formation of the valve.

As seen from the interior, in specimens which have been distended and dried (Fig. 519), the valve is made up of two crescentic segments—a superior, in a more or less horizontal plane, and an inferior, which is larger, placed in an oblique plane, and sloping upwards and inwards (*i.e.* towards the cavity of the cæcum). Between the two segments is situated the slit-shaped opening, which runs in an almost antero-posterior direction, with a rounded anterior and a pointed posterior extremity. At each end of the orifice the two segments of the valve unite, and are then prolonged around the wall of the cavity as a prominent fold — the **frenulum.** It is thought that when the cæcum is distended, and its circumference thereby increased, the frenula are put on the stretch, and, pulling upon the two segments of the valve, they bring them into apposition and effect the closure of the orifice.

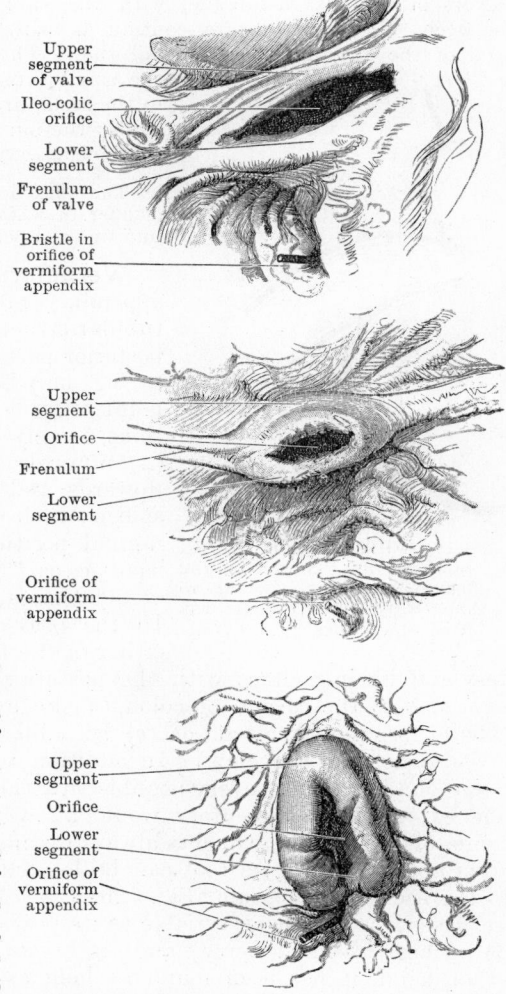

FIG. 518.—THREE FORMS OF ILEO-COLIC VALVE from bodies hardened by intravascular injections of formalin.

The hardening was not so complete in the highest of the three valves represented.

In bodies hardened with formalin the ileo-colic valve and orifice present a different appearance (see Fig. 518), suggesting, much more closely than in the dried state, the appearance of telescoping or inversion. The two segments of the valve are much thicker and shorter, but they can always be distinguished, and are found to bear the same relation to each other as in the dried condition, although this may be obscured by foldings or rugæ. The aperture may be slit-like or rounded, with sloping or funnel-shaped edges; the frenula are not so prominent in some; but the whole valve projects much more abruptly into the cavity of the cæcum than in the distended and dried specimen.

Form in the Living Body.—The ileo-colic valve has been observed, in the course of surgical operations, during life. "It is in the form of a hemispherical mamillary eminence, about 1·8 cms. in diameter, scarlet in appearance, smooth and glistening." (Rutherford.) The summit is truncated, and the orifice is of a stellate appearance, with lobulated elevations between the rays of the star. It is said also that no frenula are to be seen during life.

Structure of the Ileo-colic Valve.—Each segment of the valve consists of two layers of mucous membrane, with the submucosa and the circular muscular fibres between, all of which are continuous with those of the ileum on the one hand and of the large intestine on the other. The surface of each segment turned towards the small intestine is covered with villi, and conforms in the structure of its mucous coat to that of the ileum; whilst the mucous coat of the opposite surface resembles the mucous coat of the large bowel.

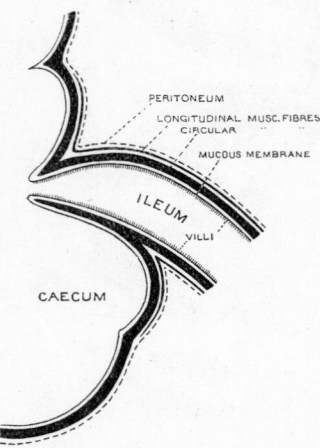

The efficiency of the valve is partly due to the oblique manner in which the ileum enters or invaginates the large intestine and partly to muscular contraction.

Vermiform Appendix (Fig. 520).—The vermiform appendix [processus vermiformis] is a worm-like tubular structure which springs from the medial and posterior part of the cæcum about 1 to 1½ inches (2·5 to 3·7 cm.) below the ileo-colic orifice. From that point it generally runs in one of three chief directions, namely—(1) over the brim into the true pelvis; (2) upwards behind the cæcum and colon; or (3) upwards and medially, thus pointing towards the spleen; each of which has been considered to be the normal position by one or more observers. It was "post-cæcal" and "retro-colic" in over 69 per cent. of 3000 cases examined by Gladstone and Wakeley. In the post-cæcal or retro-colic position, it may either (a) lie free in a recess, (b) have a short mesen-

FIG. 519.—DIAGRAMMATIC SECTION THROUGH THE JUNCTION OF THE ILEUM WITH THE CÆCUM, TO SHOW THE FORMATION OF THE ILEO-COLIC VALVE.

tery and lie in contact with the posterior surface of the cæcum or colon, (c) be adherent to the cæcum or colon, (d) lie extra-peritoneally, the peritoneal recess having been obliterated, or (e) be adherent to the posterior abdominal wall. (Gladstone and Wakeley.) In addition to the positions just mentioned, it has been found in almost every possible situation in the abdomen which its length and the extent of its mesentery would allow it to attain. Invariably the anterior tænia of the cæcum, which is always distinct, offers the surest guide to the vermiform appendix, and its root can be located with certainty if this tænia is traced to the back of the cæcum (Fig. 520).

Its *size* is almost as variable as its position. Its length may be given as about 3½ inches (92 mm., Berry), and its breadth as ¼ inch (6 mm., Berry). On the other hand, it has been found as long as 9 inches (230 mm.), and as short as ¾ inch (18 mm.). Congenital absence has been recorded, but this must be looked upon as an extremely rare occurrence.

Its *lumen* or *cavity* is variable in size, and is found to be totally or partially occluded in at least one-fourth of all adult and old bodies examined. It opens on the medial, or medial and posterior wall of the cavity of the cæcum (Fig. 518), at a point 1 to 1½ inches (25 to 38 mm.) below and slightly behind the ileo-colic orifice. Those are the relative positions of the two orifices as seen from the interior of the cæcum; viewed from the exterior, the root of the vermiform process is within ¾ inch of the lower border of the ileum. The apparent difference is due to the fact that the ileum adheres to the medial side of the cæcum for a distance of nearly 1 inch before it opens into it. The *orifice* has a crescentic fold placed at its superior border; but the fold is probably of very little functional importance.

The vermiform appendix is completely covered with peritoneum, and has a considerable **mesentery**, which extends to its tip as a rule, and connects the appendix to the inferior surface of that part of the mesentery proper which goes to the distal end of the ileum.

The vermiform appendix is longer, relative to the rest of the large intestine, in the child at birth than in the adult, the proportion being about 1 to 16 or 17 at birth and 1 to 19 or 20 in the adult. It attains its greatest length and diameter during adult and middle age, and atrophies slowly after that time. It is said to be slightly longer in the male than in the female.

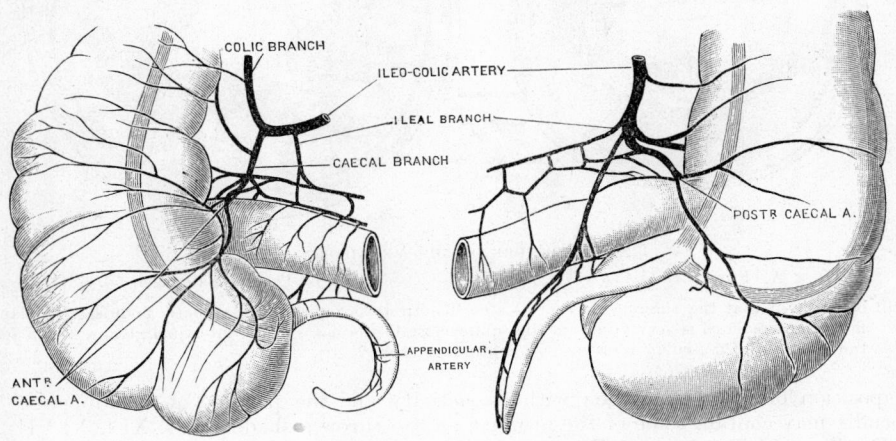

FIG. 520.—THE BLOOD-SUPPLY OF THE CÆCUM AND VERMIFORM APPENDIX.

The illustration to the left gives a front view; in that to the right the cæcum is viewed from behind. In the latter the appendicular artery and the three tæniæ coli springing from the root of the appendix, should be specially noted. (Modified from Jonnesco.)

Total occlusion of its cavity is found in 3 or 4 per cent. of bodies; it is then converted into a fibrous cord. Partial occlusion is present in 25 per cent. of adults, and in more than 50 per cent. of those over 60 years old, but it is unknown in the child. The frequency of occlusion, the physiological atrophy which takes place after middle life, the great variations in length, and other signs of instability, have been considered to point to the retrogressive character of the appendix.

A vermiform appendix is found only in man, the higher apes, and the wombat, although in certain rodents a similar arrangement exists. In carnivorous animals the cæcum is very slightly developed; in herbivorous animals (with a simple stomach) it is, as a rule, extremely large. It has been suggested that the vermiform appendix in man is the degenerated remains of the herbivorous cæcum, which has been replaced by the carnivorous form. Another and perhaps more probable view regards the appendix as a lymph organ, having the same functions as lymphatic nodules, and, like these, undergoing degeneration after middle life (Berry).

In the fœtus and child, as well as in the adult with the infantile type of cæcum, the vermiform appendix springs from the apex, not from the postero-medial wall of the cæcum.

Foreign bodies, although reputed to find their way very easily into the appendix are rarely found there after death. On the other hand, concretions or calculi, formed of mucus, fæces, and various salts, are often present (Berry).

Structure (Fig. 521).—The **serous coat** is complete, and forms a perfect investment for the appendix. The **muscular coat** unlike that of the rest of the large intestine, has a continuous and stout layer of longitudinal fibres which passes at the root of the appendix into the three tæniæ coli (Fig. 520). The layer of circular fibres is well developed. The **submucous coat** is almost entirely occupied by large masses of lymphoid tissue surrounded by sinus-like lymph spaces. Owing to the large size of those lymphatic nodules, the areolar tissue of the submucosa is compressed against the inner surface of the muscular coat, and forms a well-marked fibrous ring, which sends processes at intervals between the lymph masses towards the mucous membrane. The lymphatic nodules correspond to solitary lymphatic nodules, which, owing to their great number, have been almost completely crushed out of the mucous coat (in which they chiefly lie in the intestine) into the submucosa.

The **mucous coat** corresponds to that of the large intestine in its general characters, but the intestinal glands are fewer, and irregular in their direction; the lamina muscularis mucosæ is thin and ill-defined; it lies immediately internal to the lymphatic nodules of the submucosa, and immediately outside the base of the intestinal glands. Some few lymph nodules lie in the mucous coat also.

Radiographic Examination of the Cæcum.—The cæcum usually shows a distinct shadow when an opaque meal has passed from the ileum into the colon. The form and

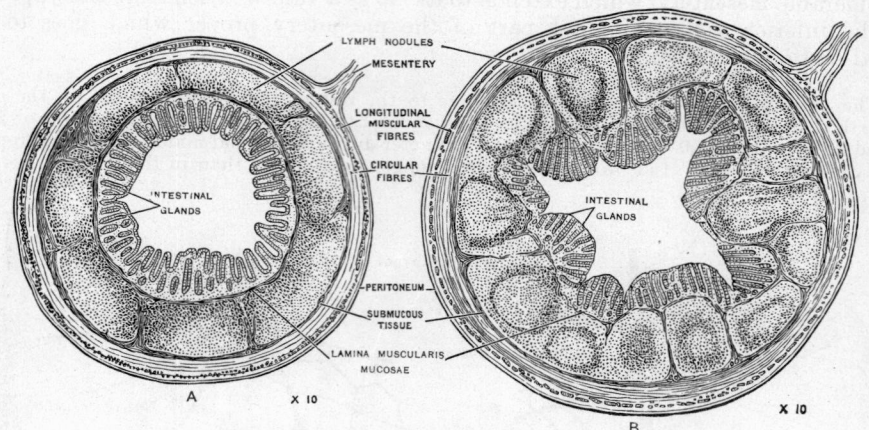

Fig. 521.—Structure of the Vermiform Appendix.

A. From a child two years old.   B. From a male, aged 56.

It will be observed that the submucous coat is almost entirely occupied by lymphatic nodules The lamina muscularis mucosæ is very faint, and lies quite close to the bases of the intestinal glands. The longitudinal layer of muscular fibres forms a continuous sheet.

the position of the cæcum vary with its activity and the position of the subject. The appendix may contain some of the bismuth and so throw a shadow (Pls. XLI, XLVII).

Peritoneal Folds and Recesses.—In the neighbourhood of the cæcum there are several peritoneal recesses, of which the most important are the superior and the inferior ileo-cæcal recesses, and the retro-cæcal recess.

If the vermiform appendix is drawn down and the finger passed towards the cæcum

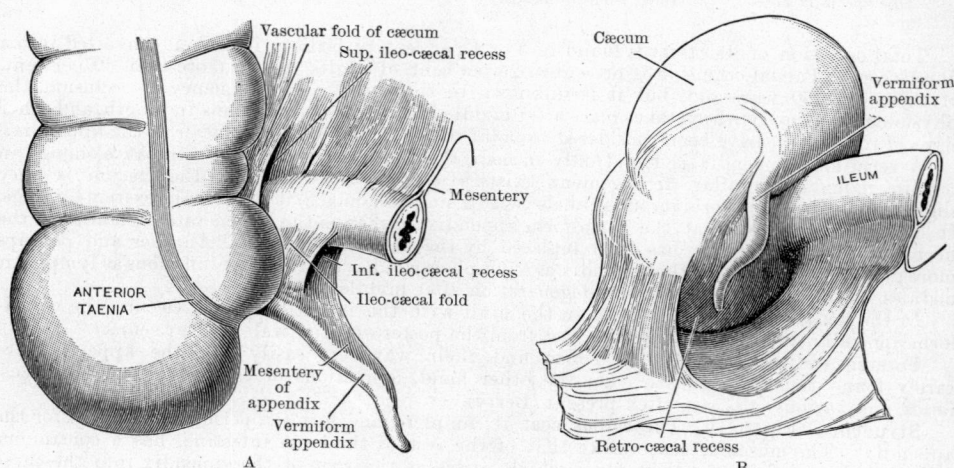

Fig. 522.—Folds and Recesses in the Ileo-cæcal Region.

In A, the cæcum is viewed from the front; the mesentery of the vermiform appendix is distinct. In B, the cæcum is turned upwards to show a retro-cæcal recess which lies behind it and behind the beginning of the ascending colon.

along the inferior border of the terminal part of the ileum, it will enter a recess between the ileum and the cæcum known as the **inferior ileo-cæcal recess**. A peritoneal fold which bounds it in front is the **ileo-cæcal fold**, often termed the " bloodless fold of Treves." It extends between the terminal part of the ileum and the front of the mesentery of the vermiform appendix. The fold contains some unstriped muscle fibres continuous with the longitudinal muscle coat of the cæcum, and some fat, especially at its free margin. The inferior ileo-cæcal recess is bounded above by the lower end of the ileum, to the right by the cæcum, in front by the ileo-cæcal fold, behind by the root of the mesentery of the vermiform appendix ; and it is open to the left or medially.

Similarly, if the finger is run along the superior border of the ileum towards the cæcum, it will usually lodge in a smaller recess—the **superior ileo-cæcal recess**—which is bounded in front by a small peritoneal fold, called the **vascular fold of the cæcum** (Fig. 522, A), which contains the junction cæcal artery. The superior ileo-cæcal recess lies at the upper margin of the junction of the ileum with the colon, and is bounded behind by the ileum, and to the right by the cæcum.

The **retro-cæcal recess** is an occasional pouch which passes upwards between the cæcum and the posterior abdominal wall. Its orifice looks downwards or to the left, and it is bounded on each side by peritoneal folds termed the **cæcal folds.**

THE COLON

Ascending Colon.—The ascending colon begins about the level of the inter-tubercular plane, opposite the ileo-colic orifice, where it is continuous with the cæcum. From there it runs upwards and slightly backwards, with a slight concavity to the left, until it reaches the inferior surface of the liver, where it bends forwards and to the left and passes into the right flexure of the colon (Fig. 523). In its course it lies in the angle between the quadratus lumborum laterally and the more prominent psoas major medially. Although it usually begins about the level of the intertubercular plane, still with a low position of the cæcum it will extend farther down.

Its *length* is extremely variable, depending upon the extent to which the cæcum has descended from the position it occupied during development, viz. in contact with the under surface of the liver. It is from 5 to 8 inches long, and it is wider and more prominent than the descending colon. It generally presents several minor curves or flexures, and it often has the appearance of being pushed into a space which is too short to accommodate it.

Relations.—*Anteriorly* it is usually in contact with the abdominal wall, but the small intestine frequently intervenes, particularly above. To its *medial side* lie the coils of the small bowel and the psoas major ; to the *lateral side* is the side wall of the abdomen. Its *posterior surface*, which is free from peritoneum as a rule, is connected by areolar tissue to the iliacus muscle as far up as the iliac crest, to the quadratus lumborum above that, and finally to the lower part of the right kidney.

In the great majority of cases only the two sides and the anterior surface are covered with peritoneum. In a small proportion of bodies, however, the ascending colon is provided with a complete peritoneal coat and a mesentery, but the mesentery is so short that it admits but a slight amount of movement of the gut. Lateral to the cæcum and colon the peritoneum forms a gutter, termed the *paracolic groove*, which is usually divided by peritoneal folds into small recesses.

Like the cæcum, the ascending colon is frequently found distended with gas or fæces after death—hence, in part, its large size and prominence as compared with the descending colon, which is generally empty.

Right Flexure of Colon.—The right flexure of the colon is the bent piece of the large intestine between the end of the ascending colon and the beginning of the transverse colon (Figs. 509 and 523). When the ascending colon reaches the inferior surface of the liver, it bends—usually acutely, sometimes obtusely—forwards and to the left on the anterior surface of the right kidney, and on reaching the front of the second part of the duodenum, passes into the transverse colon.

The flexure is placed between the duodenum medially and the anterior margin of the liver or the side wall of the abdomen, laterally ; above, it corresponds to the colic impression on the liver, and posteriorly it rests on the kidney. Its peritoneal relations are similar to those of the ascending colon.

Transverse Colon.—The transverse colon is the long and looped portion of the large intestine which lies between the right and left flexures. It begins

39 *b*

at the right flexure, and, turning to the left, crosses the second part of the duodenum (Fig. 523). It runs at first transversely to the left, and for the first few inches is comparatively fixed, being united to the front of the second part of the duodenum and the head of the pancreas either by a very short mesentery or by areolar tissue. Immediately to the left of the head of the pancreas a long mesentery is developed, which allows the colon to hang down in front of the small intestine at a considerable distance from the posterior abdominal wall. The portion of the colon so suspended is therefore very movable, and consequently its position is very variable, and is influenced by posture and by the condition of the other viscera. Towards its left extremity the mesentery shortens again, thus bringing the gut towards the body of the pancreas (Fig. 509), along which it runs upwards under cover of the stomach, as far as the lateral end of the spleen, where it passes into the left flexure (Fig. 509). Its two ends lie in or above the transpyloric plane whilst its middle portion reaches down to the level of the umbilicus, or even lower.

Its average *length* is about 19 or 20 inches (47·5 to 50·0 cm.), that is, more than twice the distance, in a direct line, between its two extremities. This great length is accounted for by the curved and somewhat irregular course which the bowel pursues.

Relations.—The greater part of the transverse colon lies behind the greater omentum, which must consequently be turned upwards in order to expose it. *Above* it is in contact, from right to left (Fig. 523), with the liver and gall-bladder (which may also descend in front of it), the stomach, and near its left end, with the body of the pancreas and the spleen (Fig. 508). *Anteriorly* are placed the omentum and the anterior abdominal wall; towards its termination the stomach also is anterior. *Posteriorly* it first lies in contact with the second part of the duodenum and head of the pancreas; farther to the left, where it hangs down, the small intestine is placed below and behind it, and it is connected to the posterior abdominal wall by the transverse mesocolon. The transverse mesocolon is described with the peritoneum, p. 576.

The transverse colon is completely covered with peritoneum, with the exception of the first few inches of its posterior surface, which are often, if not usually, uncovered.

The state of the peritoneal covering on the posterior surface of the first part of the transverse colon would seem to depend, in some degree, on the extent to which the liver passes downwards on the right side. With a small, high liver no mesentery is present, and the posterior surface is devoid of peritoneum. On the other hand, when the liver is enlarged in the vertical direction, it pushes the colon downwards before it, and the peritoneum attached to the colon is drawn out to form a mesentery. In the fœtus of three or four months every part of the colon is supplied with a long mesentery.

Left Flexure of Colon.—The terminal portion of the transverse colon runs upwards (also backwards and to the left) until the spleen is reached; there it bends sharply, forming the left flexure, and runs down into the descending colon. The flexure is placed deeply behind the stomach, and in contact with the lower part of the spleen. It lies at a slightly higher level than the right colic flexure, and is connected to the abdominal parietes by the phrenico-colic ligament, which helps to maintain it in this position on the posterior abdominal wall.

The **phrenico-colic ligament** (Fig. 509) is a triangular fold of peritoneum, with a free anterior border, which is attached medially to the left flexure and laterally to the diaphragm opposite the ninth to the eleventh rib. Owing to the fact that the spleen rests upon it, the ligament has also received the older name of " sustentaculum lienis."

The phrenico-colic ligament is formed in the fœtus from the left margin of the greater omentum (Jonnesco).

Descending Colon.—The descending colon is much narrower and less obtrusive than the ascending colon : indeed in a large number of cases it is found firmly contracted. It begins at the left flexure, passes down on the left side of the abdomen, and terminates by passing into the pelvic colon at the inlet of the pelvis on the medial side of the left psoas muscle. Its course is not quite straight, for it first curves downwards and medially along the lateral border of the left kidney, and then descends almost vertically to the iliac crest (Fig. 523). It then passes downwards and slightly medially, in the iliac fossa, lying in front of the iliacus muscle. A little way above the inguinal ligament it turns medially over the psoas major, and ends at the medial border of this muscle by dipping into the true pelvis and becoming the pelvic colon (Fig. 523).

Its *length* is usually from 9 to 12 inches (22 to 30 cm.), and its *width*, which is less than that of the ascending colon, about 1½ inches (37 mm.).

The portion of the colon formerly described as a special segment, termed the *iliac colon*, is in structure and function a part of the descending colon and is here included with it.

Relations.—The upper part of the descending colon first lies in contact with the lateral border of the left kidney; below that it is placed, like the ascending colon, in the angle between the psoas major and quadratus lumborum muscles. Posteriorly

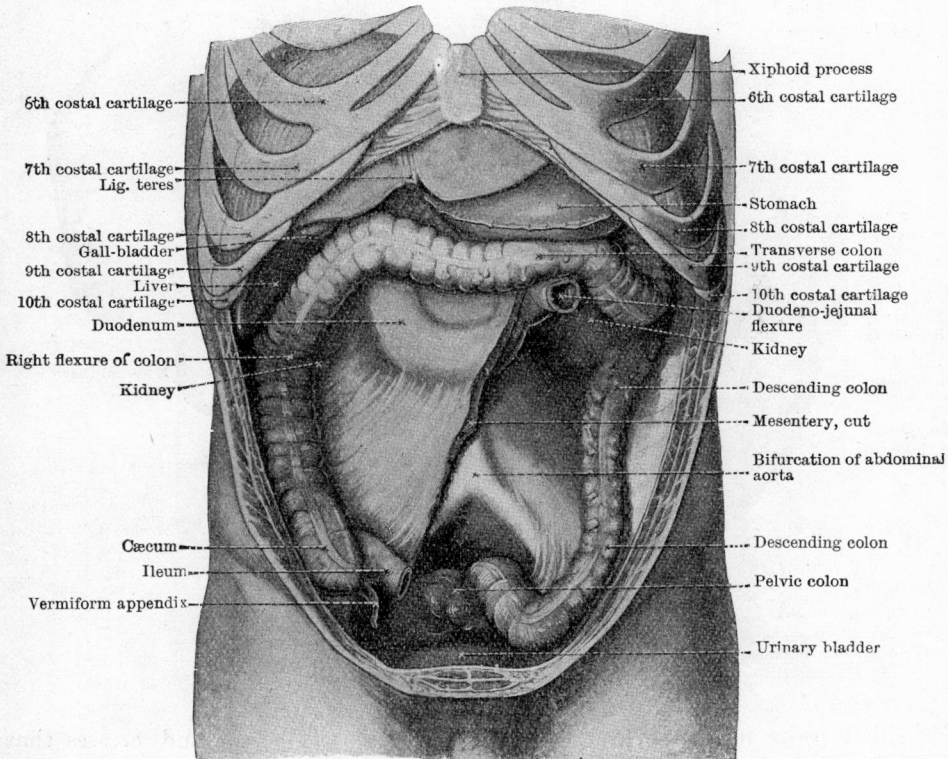

FIG. 523.—THE ABDOMINAL VISCERA AFTER THE REMOVAL OF THE JEJUNUM AND ILEUM (from a photograph of the same body as depicted in Fig. 503). The transverse colon is much more regular than usual.

it rests upon the lower part of the diaphragm above, and on the quadratus lumborum below. Anteriorly (and somewhat laterally also, except when the bowel is distended) are placed numerous coils of small intestine, which hide the colon completely from view, and compress it against the posterior abdominal wall. The lower part of the descending colon lies on the front of the ilio-psoas muscle. It also crosses the femoral and genito-femoral nerves, the left testicular (or ovarian) vessels, and the left external iliac vessels. Anteriorly it is usually covered by coils of small intestine, which hide it from view; but when distended, or when it occupies a lower position than usual, it comes into direct contact with the anterior abdominal wall.

In the great majority of bodies only the front and sides of the descending colon are covered with peritoneum; the posterior surface is connected to the posterior wall of the abdomen by areolar tissue. In a small proportion of cases, on the other hand, the serous coat is complete, and the colon is furnished with a short mesentery.

Up to the fourth or fifth month of fœtal life the descending colon has a complete investment of peritoneum and a long mesentery. After the fifth month the mesentery adheres to, and soon blends with, the parietal peritoneum on the posterior abdominal wall, and is completely lost as a rule. The persistence of the mesentery, in a greater or less degree, explains the occasional presence of a *descending mesocolon* in the adult.

Pelvic Colon.—The pelvic colon begins at the medial border of the left psoas major muscle, where it is continuous with the descending colon, and ends at the level of the third sacral vertebra by passing into the rectum. It is covered with peritoneum and has a well-developed mesentery which permits considerable movement. It forms a large and variously shaped coil which usually lies in the cavity of the true pelvis (93 per cent.).

Whilst the loop of the pelvic colon is very irregular in form, the following may be given as perhaps its most common arrangement. Beginning at the medial margin

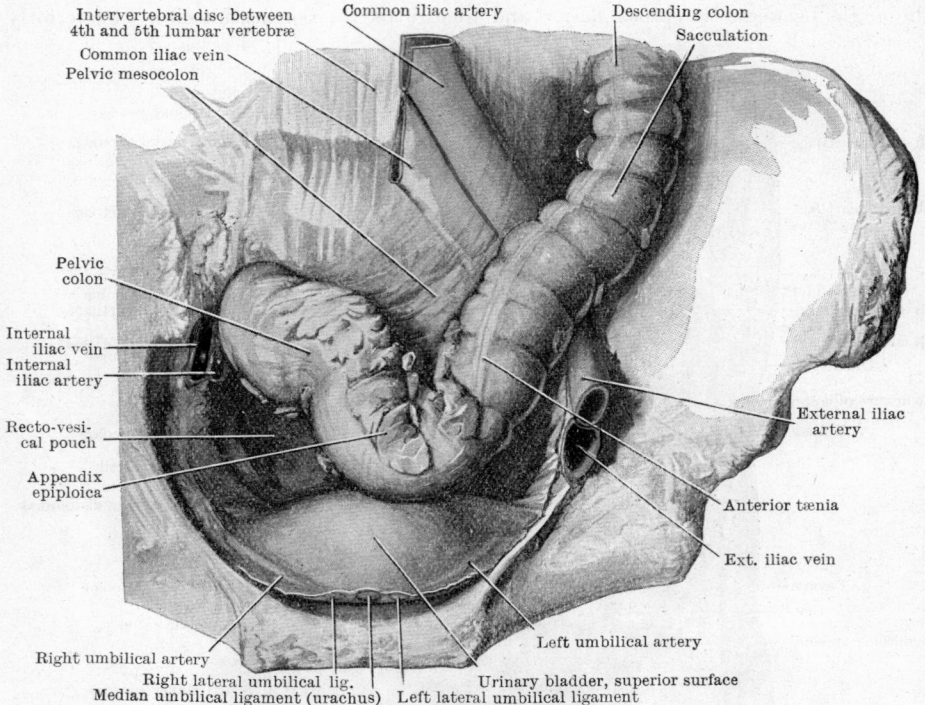

Fig. 524.—The Pelvic Colon *in situ*.

of the left psoas major, it first descends into the true pelvis, and crosses that cavity from left to right; it next bends backwards and then returns along the posterior wall of the pelvis towards the median plane, where it turns down and passes into the rectum (Figs. 523 and 524).

In *length* the pelvic colon generally measures about 16 inches (40 to 42·5 cm.), but it may be as short as 5 inches (12 cm.), or as long as 35 inches (84 cm.).

Relations.—As it passes from left to right across the cavity of the pelvis it rests on the bladder or the uterus, according to the sex, and the coils of the small intestine lie above it.

When the pelvic colon is unusually long (Fig. 523), in returning from the right side of the true pelvis it crosses the median plane, going even as far as the left wall, and then turns back a second time towards the middle of the sacrum, where it joins the rectum at the usual level, thus making an S-shaped curve within the pelvis. On the other hand, when the loop is short (a not infrequent occurrence), all its curves are abridged, and it fails to pass over to the right side, but runs more or less directly backwards after entering the pelvis.

From what has been said it will be seen that the loop of the pelvic colon is subject to considerable variations, which are dependent chiefly upon its length and that of its mesentery, and also upon the state of emptiness or distension of itself and of the other pelvic viscera. When the intestine is long the loop is more complex; when short, more simple. When the bladder and rectum are distended, or when the pelvic colon itself is much distended, it is unable to find accommodation in the pelvis and consequently it passes up into the abdomen proper, almost any part of the lower half of which it may occupy. But, as already stated, in the great majority of cases (92 per cent., according to Jonnesco) it is found after death lying entirely within the pelvis.

The **pelvic mesocolon** [mesocolon sigmoideum et meso-rectum] is a fan-shaped fold, short at each extremity and long in its middle portion (Figs. 523 and 524). Its root is attached along an inverted V-shaped line, one limb of which runs up close to the medial border of the left psoas major as high as the bifurcation of the common iliac artery (or often higher); there it bends at an acute angle, and the second limb descends over the front of the sacrum to the middle of its third piece, where the mesentery ceases and the pelvic colon passes into the rectum. When the pelvic colon ascends into the abdomen proper this mesentery is doubled up on itself, the side which was naturally posterior becoming anterior.

Recess of pelvic mesocolon.—When the pelvic colon with its mesentery is raised upwards, a small orifice will usually be found beneath the mesocolon, corresponding to the apex of the Λ-shaped attachment of its root to the posterior abdominal wall. This orifice leads into a recess which is directed upwards, and will often admit the little finger. It is known as the recess of the pelvic mesocolon [recessus intersigmoideus], and is due to the imperfect blending of the mesentery of the descending colon of the fœtus with the parietal peritoneum. The ureter is found lying behind the apex of the recess. In the fœtus the mesentery of the descending colon is well developed, and extends from the region of the vertebral column towards the descending colon. After a time it begins to unite with the underlying parietal peritoneum; but in the line of the ureter the union is rarely perfect—hence the presence of the recess.

In the **child at birth** only the terminal part of the pelvic colon lies in the pelvis. That is chiefly owing to the small size of the pelvic cavity in the infant. Beginning at the end of the descending colon, the pelvic colon generally arches upwards and to the right across the abdomen towards the right iliac fossa, where it forms one or two coils, and then passes down over the right side of the pelvic brim into the pelvis.

Structure of the Pelvic Colon.—Only the arrangement of the muscular coat need be referred to. As the tæniæ of the descending colon are followed down, it will be found that the postero-lateral band gradually passes on to the front and unites with the anterior tænia to form a broad band which occupies nearly the whole width of this bowel in its lower portion. The postero-medial tænia spreads out in a similar manner on the back; so that in the lower half of the pelvic colon the longitudinal layer of the muscular coat is complete, with the exception of a narrow part on each side; there the circular fibres come to the surface, and the intestine presents a series of small sacculations. As the rectum is approached, the sacculations disappear, and the longitudinal fibres, although thicker in front and behind, form a continuous layer all round.

Radiographic Examination of the Colon.—Some hours after a "bismuth meal" has been swallowed, the opaque matter begins to reach the colon, and gradually passes along it. The shadow is easily identified from that of other parts of the intestine by the undulating outline which corresponds to the sacculations of the colon (Pl. XXXVIII). The length and position of the different parts of the colon show a wide range of variation (Pls. XLI, XLII, XLVII. In what may be termed "a typical" condition the position and shape of the different parts as shown by this method approximate to these shown in Fig. 523, p 615. The whole of the colon and the cæcum may be filled by an opaque enema (Pl. XLII).

RECTUM

The **rectum** is the portion of the intestine between the pelvic colon and the anal canal—the slit-like passage through which it communicates with the exterior (Fig. 525).

Unlike the pelvic colon the rectum has but a partial covering of peritoneum, and has no mesentery; sacculations, too, such as are characteristic of the colon, cannot be said to be present.

The rectum begins at the termination of the pelvic mesocolon, namely, about the level of the third sacral vertebra, and ends, in the male, opposite the inferior and posterior part of the prostate, or, in both sexes, at a point 1½ inches (3·7 cm.) in front of and slightly below the tip of the coccyx. It first descends along the front of the sacrum and coccyx; it then rests for about 1½ inches on the posterior part of the pelvic floor, formed by the union of the two levatores ani; and finally, reaching the inferior part of the prostate, it bends abruptly backwards and downwards, and passes into the anal canal (Fig. 587, p. 702).

Curvatures.—The rectum is curved in both the antero-posterior and the transverse planes. Viewed *from the side* it forms a gentle curve, convex backwards, from the beginning of the rectum to the back of the prostate, and fits into the hollow of the sacrum and coccyx. At the back of the prostate a second curve is formed where the rectum joins the anal canal. The convexity of the second curve is directed forwards, whilst its concavity embraces the **ano-coccygeal body**—the mass of muscular and fibrous tissue which lies between the tip of the coccyx and the anal canal.

When *viewed from the front* the rectum is seen to be folded from side to side in a zigzag fashion, the folding being slightly marked when the rectum is empty, but becoming much more distinct with distension (Figs. 525 and 526). There are three more or less distinct lateral flexures or inflexions. Of those the

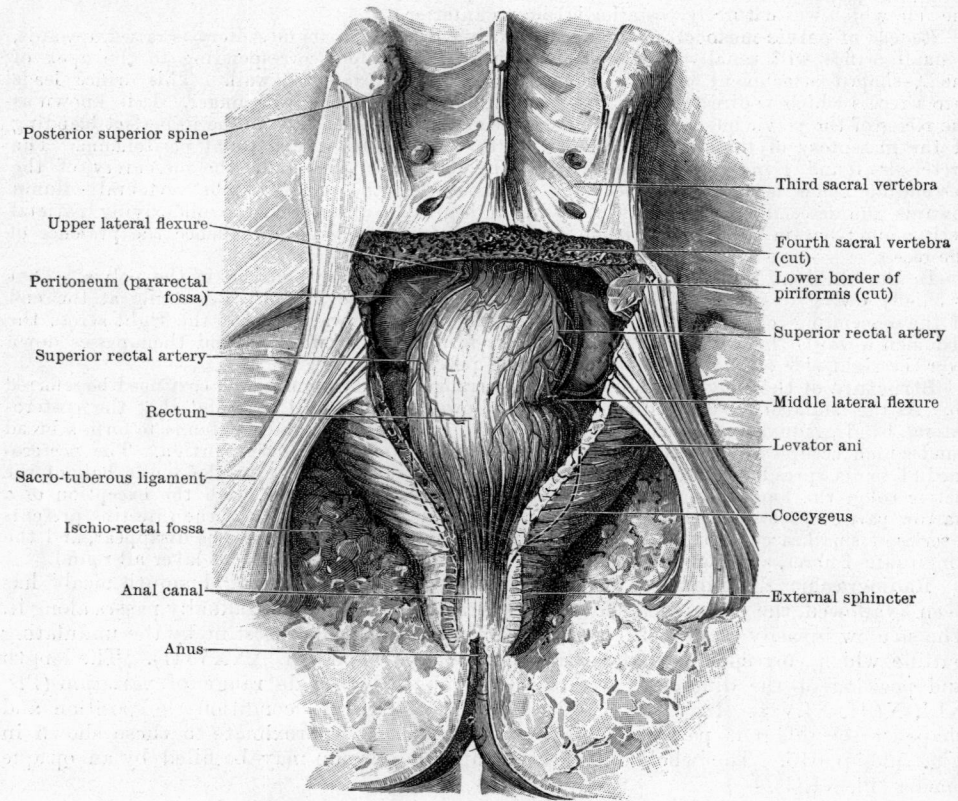

FIG. 525.—The Rectum from Behind.

The sacrum has been sawn across through the 4th sacral vertebra, and its inferior part removed with the coccyx. The posterior portions of the coccygei, levatores ani, and of the external sphincter have been cut away. The "pinching in" of the lower end of the rectum by the medial edges of the levatores ani, resulting in the formation of the flattened anal canal, is suggested in the illustration, which has been made from a formalin-hardened male body, aged 30. The lateral flexures also are shown.

upper and lower have their concavities directed to the left as a rule; the third flexure, which is the best marked, lies between the other two, but on the right side. Not infrequently, however, two are found on the right and one on the left side. The flexures are marked on the exterior by creases which appear in the interior as three prominent crescentic shelves known as the **horizontal folds of the rectum** (Fig. 528).

The folds are composed of an infolding of the mucous and submucous coats and the greater part of the circular muscular coat, and their form is preserved by the relative shortness of the anterior and posterior bands of longitudinal muscular fibres. They are produced by the projection into the interior of the bowel of the creases on the exterior which result from the lateral flexures of the rectum. Three are usually present (there may be four, five, or, it is said, even more), but often the lowest of the three is small or absent; or all the folds may be ill-developed and indistinct. They are most evident in a distended rectum which has been hardened *in situ*; they can be seen also during life, *per anum*, with the aid of a rectal speculum.

As a rule two folds are found on the left and one on the right side; this latter is generally the largest, and is situated a little above the level of the peritoneal reflexion, viz. 3 or 3½ inches (7·5 to 8·7 cm.) above the anus; the other two folds are found about 1 to 1½ inches (2·5 to 3·7 cm.) higher up and lower down respectively. The folds are distinctly marked in the fœtus, and seem to constitute an essential part of the human rectum, their use being to support the contents of the rectum, which they break up into segments, each supported by a fold. They may interfere with the introduction of an enema tube.

In *length* the rectum usually measures about 5 or 6 inches (12·5 to 15·0 cm.), but it may be much longer.

Its *diameter* is smallest above, near the junction with the pelvic colon, and

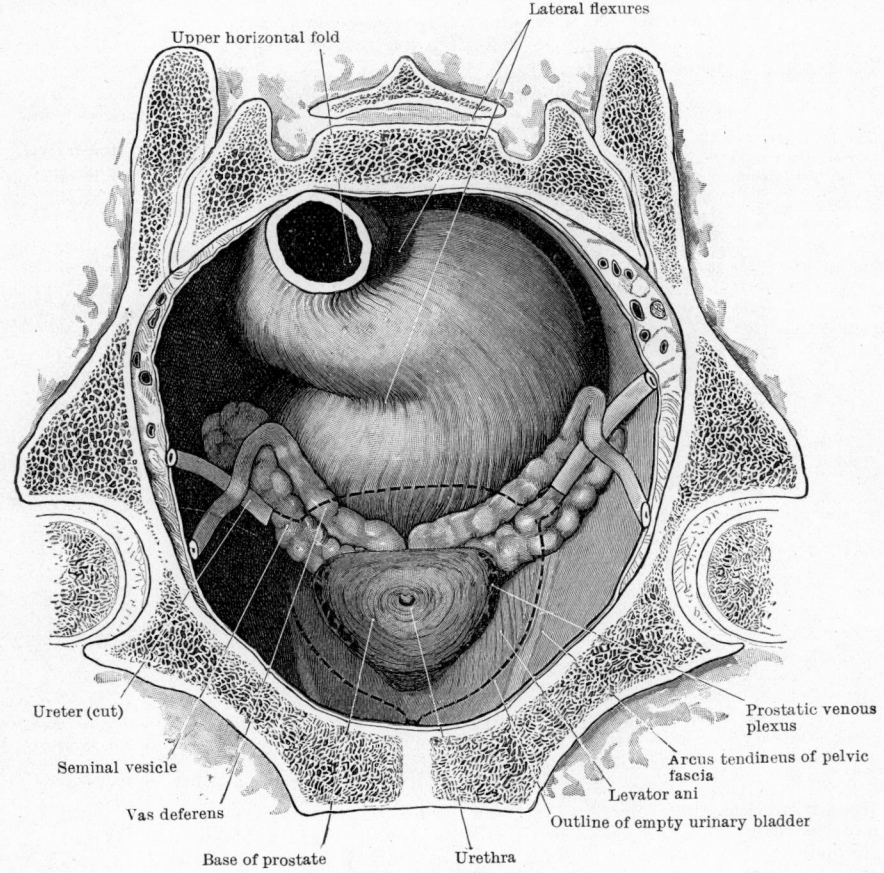

Fig. 526.—Distended Rectum *in situ*.

From a formalin-hardened male body, aged 56. The peritoneum and extra-peritoneal tissue were removed, after the pelvis had been sawn along a plane passing through the upper part of the pubic symphysis in front and the lower part of the second sacral vertebra behind. The bladder, which was empty and contracted, has also been removed, but its form is shown by a dotted line. The rectum was very much distended, and almost completely occupied the pararectal fossæ.

is greatest below, near the anal canal, where there is an enlargement known as the **ampulla of the rectum.** When empty the rectum measures little over an inch (2·5 cm.) in diameter, but in a state of extreme distension it may be as much as 3 inches (7·5 cm.) in width.

The folding is maintained by the arrangement of the longitudinal muscular fibres, the majority of which are accumulated in the form of two wide bands, one on the front of the bowel, the other on the back. The two bands, which are continuous with, and comparable in their functions to, the tæniæ of the colon, are shorter than the other coats of the rectum; hence they give rise, as in the case of the colon, to a folding or sacculation of the tube, which can be effective only at the sides where the longitudinal fibres are fewest, for the front and back are occupied by the thickened longitudinal bands.

In addition to supporting the fæces, these foldings greatly increase the capacity of the rectum without unduly dilating the tube. When the rectum is empty (Fig. 527) its course is comparatively straight, its lateral flexures being but slightly marked, and its whole calibre very much reduced. In this condition it occupies only a small portion of the posterior division of the true pelvis near the median plane, and at each side, between it and the side wall of the pelvis, there is a large fossa of the peritoneum, which, when the bowel is empty, contains a mass of small intestine or pelvic colon (Figs. 527 and 529). When the rectum is distended the lateral flexures become much more marked, and the gut, projecting alternately to each side, bulges laterally beneath the peritoneum, obliterating the pararectal fossæ (Fig. 526), and fills the greater part of the dorsal division of the pelvis.

Not uncommonly the abrupt curve at the junction of the rectum with the anal canal presents

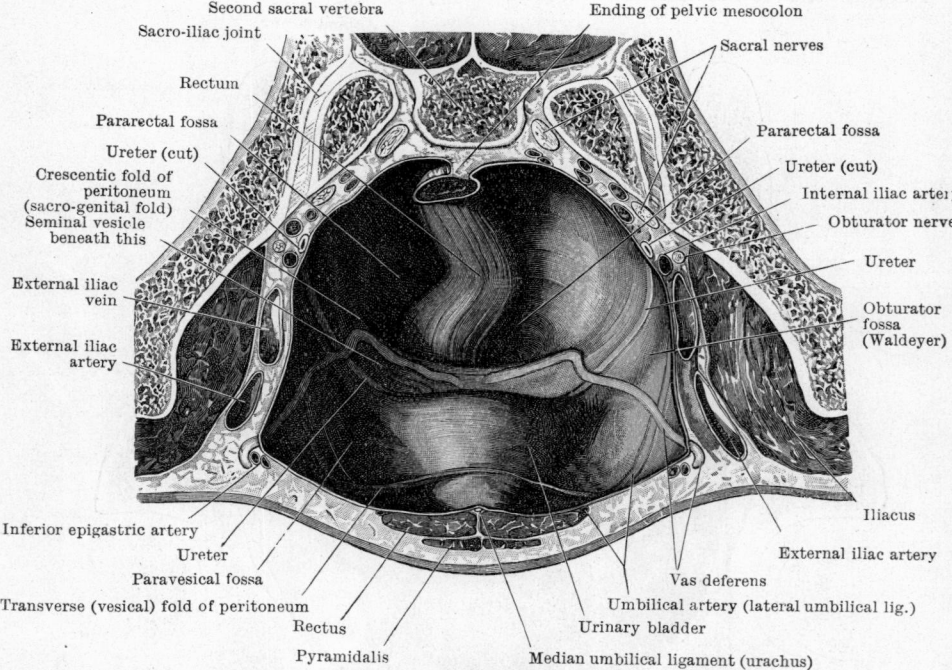

FIG. 527.—THE PERITONEUM OF THE PELVIC CAVITY.

The pelvis of a thin male subject, aged 60, was sawn across obliquely. Owing to the absence of fat the various pelvic organs were visible through the peritoneum, though not quite so distinctly as presented here. The urinary bladder and rectum are both empty and contracted; the paravesical and pararectal fossæ, as a result, are very well marked.

in front a knuckle-like projection (well seen on median section), immediately above the canal. It is most marked in females, and sometimes appears as if the bowel were doubled back upon itself at this point. The floor of the pouch thus formed may dip down in front, even below the level of the upper aperture of the anal canal. That condition is most common in multiparæ, and is evidently due to the relaxed condition of the pelvic structures, and the slight support afforded by the perineal body to this part of the gut in them, and the great capacity and shallowness of the pelvis in the female.

Peritoneal Relations of the Rectum (Figs. 525, 527).—When the mesocolon ceases at the end of the pelvic colon, its two layers separate and leave the posterior surface of the rectum destitute of peritoneum. Very soon the membrane quits its sides also, and is then found on the front only; finally it passes from the rectum on to the urinary bladder in the male (Fig. 587), and the vagina in the female; consequently the terminal part of the rectum is entirely devoid of peritoneum; the greater part of the rectum thus lies behind or beneath the pelvic peritoneum, and is capable of expanding and contracting without being in any way hampered by its partial peritoneal coat.

As the peritoneum is carried forwards to the base of the bladder in the male, it forms the floor of a recess called the **recto-vesical pouch** (Fig. 596). In the female, as it passes to the upper part of the posterior wall of the vagina, it forms the floor of the **recto-uterine** or **recto-vaginal pouch**. In both sexes it passes from the rectum on to the posterior wall of the pelvis, forming, on each side, the bottom of a large fossa, lateral to the rectum when that bowel is empty, and known as the **pararectal fossa**. As the rectum becomes distended these fossæ are encroached upon by the enlarging bowel, and are soon obliterated.

The level at which the reflexion of the peritoneum takes place from the front of the rectum is of considerable practical importance in relation to operations in this region. As a general rule it is placed at a distance of 1 inch (2·5 cm.) above the base of the prostate, or about 3 inches above the anus, but the level is subject to considerable variation, being as a rule relatively much higher in well-developed muscular or fatty subjects, whilst in emaciated bodies, owing to the thinness of the structures forming the pelvic floor, it is usually lower. In the female the floor of the recto-uterine pouch lies at a lower level and is relatively nearer the anus.

The bottom of the recto-vesical pouch may reach down in an extreme case to within an inch (2·5 cm.) of the anus, whilst it is not at all rare to find it within 2 inches (5·0 cm.) of that orifice ; on the other hand, it may be considerably higher than usual, sometimes being placed at a distance of 4 or 4½ inches (10·0 to 11·2 cm.) from the anus. It should also be added that the level is generally believed to be slightly raised by distension of the rectum and bladder, and lowered when they are empty.

In the child at birth the peritoneum extends down to the base of the prostate (Symington), and is thus lower in relation to the bladder ; but that may be partly accounted for by the high position of that organ in the child.

As a rule it will be found that 2 inches (5·0 cm.) of the front of the rectum, exclusive of the anal canal, are entirely free from peritoneum, and it is this and the adjacent portion of the bowel which, being free from the restraining influence of the peritoneum, are most distensible, and form the **ampulla of the rectum**. Including the anal canal, 3½ inches (8·7 cm.) of the rectum, *measured along the front of the tube*, have no serous covering. On the other hand, the back is free from peritoneum for 5 or 6 inches (12·5 to 15·0 cm.)—or sometimes much more—above the anus.

It is also of interest to notice that the connexion of the peritoneum to the rectum varies in its character at different parts : Above and in front it is closely adherent, and can be removed only with the greatest difficulty ; at the sides and inferiorly the connexion is much looser. As a result the peritoneum can be stripped off the rectum in its lower third or half without much difficulty, whilst in its upper portion that is not the case—an arrangement which admits of the free expansion of the rectal ampulla.

General Relations of the Rectum (Figs. 525 and 527).—*Posteriorly* the rectum rests on the front of the sacrum and coccyx, and below them upon the posterior part of the pelvic floor—formed by the meeting of the two levatores ani in the ano-coccygeal body. When much distended it also comes into relation, on each side, with the lower part of the piriformis and the sacral plexus, but is separated from them by a very considerable amount of fibro-areolar tissue. In that tissue the two chief branches of the superior rectal vessels lie behind the rectum above, but lower down they are placed on its sides.

At its sides above are the pararectal fossæ and their contents (pelvic colon, or ileum) ; below the pararectal fossæ the rectum is in contact with the coccygei and levatores ani muscles.

Anteriorly in the male the rectum is separated from the bladder to within an inch of the prostate by the recto-vesical pouch of peritoneum, which usually contains some coils of small intestine. Below the reflexion of the peritoneum the front of the rectum is in contact with the posterior surface of the bladder, the vasa deferentia, seminal vesicles, and the posterior surface of the prostate gland (Fig. 526), from all of which it is separated by the recto-vesical septum.

The lower portions of the rectum and bladder in the male are separated by the recto-vesical septum only, over a narrow triangular area which measures about an inch (2·5 cm.) in vertical height. The base of the triangle corresponds to the reflexion of the peritoneum from one organ to the other, and the apex to the union of the sides formed by the vasa deferentia, which lie very close to each other except above, near the base of the triangle, where they diverge rather abruptly (Fig. 526). Through the triangle the operation of tapping the bladder from the rectum used to be performed.

The seminal vesicles, unless when of a small size, slope laterally and backwards round the front and sides of the distended rectum (Fig. 526), which they thus embrace, as it were, within their grasp.

The ureters, as they run medially towards the base of the bladder, lie close below and in front of the vasa deferentia, and are not far separated from the distended rectum.

In the female the rectum is separated from the posterior surface of the uterus and the upper end of the vagina by the recto-uterine (recto-vaginal) pouch and the intestine which it usually contains. Below the peritoneal reflexion it is in direct contact with the posterior vaginal wall, to which it is loosely attached above, but more closely below. The portion of the rectum below the level of the peritoneal reflexion is surrounded by a layer of fascia.

In the **child** the rectum, or at least its upper part, is relatively larger, and it pursues a much straighter course than in the adult. As pointed out above, its peritoneal covering is at a lower level at birth—reaching as far as the base of the prostate.

ANAL CANAL

In order to reach the exterior, it is necessary for the lower end of the bowel to pierce the floor of the true pelvis. This it does by passing through the narrow interval left between the medial borders of the levatores ani muscles (Fig. 525). As it passes between them, the two muscles pinch in the tube, and by the apposition of its side walls obliterate its cavity, reducing it to a mere slit-like passage. The part of the large intestine through which the rectum communicates with the exterior is the "anal canal" (Symington).

Formerly this terminal portion of the tube was described as the "third part of the rectum," and, like the rest of that bowel, it was supposed to form a reservoir for the retention of the fæces. It is probable that only when the rectum is distended is the superior part of the anal canal occupied by the wedge-shaped lower end of the contained fæcal mass.

The **anal canal** [pars analis recti] *begins* where the rectum proper terminates, namely, at the level of the levatores ani muscles, opposite the inferior part of the prostate; below, the anal canal *ends* at the anus. Its *length* is usually from 1 to 1½ inches (2·5 to 3·7 cm.), and its antero-posterior diameter is from ½ to ¾ inch (12 to 19 mm.) when the canal is closed. Its *direction* is downwards and backwards.

Relations.—It is *surrounded* by the external and internal sphincters, and above also by the borders of the levatores ani, these muscles forming a muscular cylinder around it (Fig. 529). *On each side* is situated the ischio-rectal fossa with its contained fat, which allows of the distension of the canal during the passage of fæces. *Posteriorly* is placed a mass of mixed fibrous and muscular tissue, known as the **ano-coccygeal body** (Symington), which intervenes between it and the coccyx. Finally, *anteriorly* it lies close behind the perineal body and the bulb of the penis in the male, and a sound in the urethra can be easily felt by the finger introduced into the anal canal, particularly in thin bodies. In the female it is separated from the vagina by the perineal body.

Structure of the Rectum and Anal Canal.—The wall of the rectum is made up of four coats. The **outer coat** is formed in part of peritoneum (already described), and, where the peritoneum is absent, of fibrous tissue which can be dissected off in several layers. In this fibrous tissue the rectal [hæmorrhoidal] vessels run until they enter the muscular wall of the tube. In it also, at the back and sides of the rectum, are found embedded a number of rectal lymph glands.

The **muscular coat**, which is much thicker than in any other portion of the intestine, is composed of two stout layers of unstriped muscle—an outer longitudinal and an inner circular —like that of the intestine generally. The *longitudinal fibres*, although present all round, are accumulated chiefly on the front and back of the tube, where they form two broad bands; at the sides they are reduced to a thin layer, the deepest fibres of which are folded in and take part in the formation of the horizontal folds.

Where the rectum pierces the floor of the pelvis the outer layer of longitudinal fibres is united to the deeper portion of the levator ani, partly by tendinous fibres and partly by an interchange of muscular fibres between the levatores and the muscular coat of the rectum. Below, the longitudinal fibres pass between the external and internal sphincter muscles, or through the latter to join the skin around the anus.

In sagittal sections of the pelvis near the median plane there can generally be seen a distinct band of red, longitudinally arranged, muscular fibres which descends on each side from the front of the coccyx to blend with the longitudinal fibres on the back of the rectum. That band is the *recto-coccygeus muscle*. It is composed of striped fibres above, but becomes unstriped below.

Some unstriped muscular fibres which are found descending in the subcutaneous tissue of the lower part of the anal canal, to join the skin around the anus, have been described by Ellis as the *corrugator cutis ani*. The front of the rectum at the perineal flexure is, in the male, connected to the back of the membranous urethra by a band of muscle, termed the *recto-urethralis*

The *circular fibres* form, along the whole length of the tube, a continuous layer, which is doubled inwards to assist in the formation of each horizontal fold, and is thickened below to form the **internal sphincter** of the anus. The internal sphincter as just pointed out, is formed by a great, and rather sudden, increase of the circular muscular fibres, which begins at the upper end of the anal canal. It surrounds the canal for about an inch (2·5 to 3·0 cm.), and terminates opposite the junction of its mucous coat with the skin.

The **submucous coat** is composed of loose areolar tissue, which allows of a free movement of the mucous layer on the muscular coat. The rectal [hæmorrhoidal] plexus of veins is contained in this layer.

The **mucous coat** of the rectum is redder in colour than that of the colon. It is also thicker, and owing to the looseness of the underlying submucosa is thrown into numerous irregular rugæ when the rectum is empty ; these disappear when the bowel is distended. Lymphatic nodules and intestinal glands are present ; but the latter are not so numerous as in the colon, although their calibre is greater. The mucous coat of the rectum presents a characteristic punctated appearance which is due to the presence of a considerable number of rounded depressions, such as might be made by firmly pressing a finely pointed pencil against the membrane. These *rectal pits* are tubular in form, and have an accumulation of lymphoid tissue at the bottom of each, the whole appearance being such as might be produced if a small solitary nodule were drawn down from the surface into the intestinal wall.

Anal Columns and Anal Valves.

—The mucous coat of the anal canal presents a number (5 to 10) of *permanent* vertical folds, separated by grooves, and known as the **anal columns** [columnæ rectales] (Fig. 528). They are usually $\frac{1}{3}$ to $\frac{1}{2}$ inch (8 to 12 mm.) in length, $\frac{1}{8}$ to $\frac{1}{4}$ inch (3 to 6 mm.) in width, and they extend down to within $\frac{1}{2}$ or $\frac{2}{3}$ inch (12 to 20 mm.) of the anal aperture. They are formed by infoldings of the mucous coat, containing in their interior some bundles of longitudinal muscle, and also, as a rule, an artery and a vein.

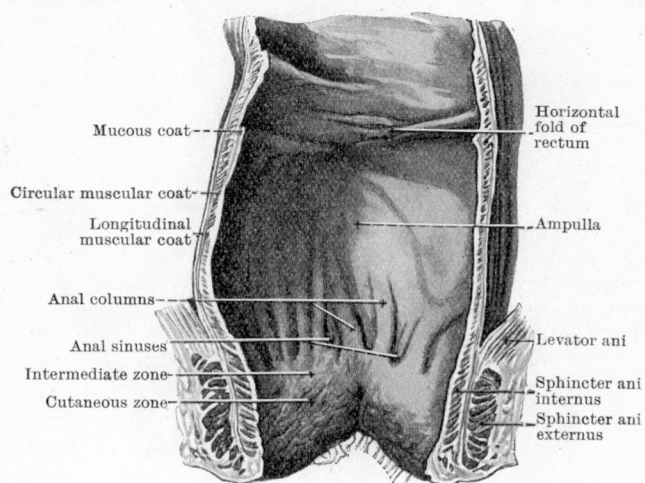

FIG. 528.—INTERIOR OF THE LOWER RECTUM AND ANAL CANAL.

Very often the contained vein presents an enlargement, or a knob-like tortuous plexus in the lower part of the column ; below this the plexus is continued down *external* to the mucous membrane of the lower zone of the anal canal into the anal veins. Dilated portions of the veins may form rounded nodular projections, known as hæmorrhoids or "piles," and this portion is therefore frequently termed the hæmorrhoidal zone of the anal canal. Sometimes the columns are very indistinct ; occasionally no trace of them can be found in the adult, although in the fœtus they are usually well marked.

If a probe is passed downwards along the groove which separates two adjacent anal columns (Fig. 528), its point will usually catch in a small crescentic fold which joins the lower ends of the two columns. The little folds, which resemble in miniature the segments of the semilunar valves of the heart are the **anal valves**. They project inwards and upwards, and behind each is found a little pocket-like **anal sinus** [sinus rectalis].

Anal Orifice.—At the inferior aperture of the anal canal, the modified skin of its lower zone passes into the ordinary skin.

The skin round the margin of the anus possesses hair follicles and glands and forms a zone, called the cutaneous zone. Above this zone there is a second, intermediate zone, not sharply marked off, but its surface is smoother and no hairs arise from it. It is lined with a stratified squamous epithelium.

The region of the lowest part of the anal columns forms a third zone lined with columnar epithelium, and clearly marked off from the intermediate zone by an abrupt sinuous line which follows the level of the anal valves and crosses the bases of the columns between the valves; this sinuous line is known as the "ano-cutaneous line" of Hermann or the "white line" of Hilton, and corresponds to the junction of epithelium derived from the rectum above and the anal pit below.

Action of the Sphincters.—Three muscles act on the anal canal, namely, the paired levatores ani, the external sphincter, and the internal sphincter.

The fibres of the **levatores ani** which arise from the pubis (pubo-coccygeus portion) pass backwards on each side of the beginning of the anal canal, and, in great part, meet behind the passage. The two muscular bands—which are but a little distance apart at their origin, and are actually united behind the bowel—are closely approximated during the contraction of the muscles, like the limbs of a clamp, and, pressing on the sides of the anal canal, they assist in closing the upper part of that passage, whilst at the same time drawing

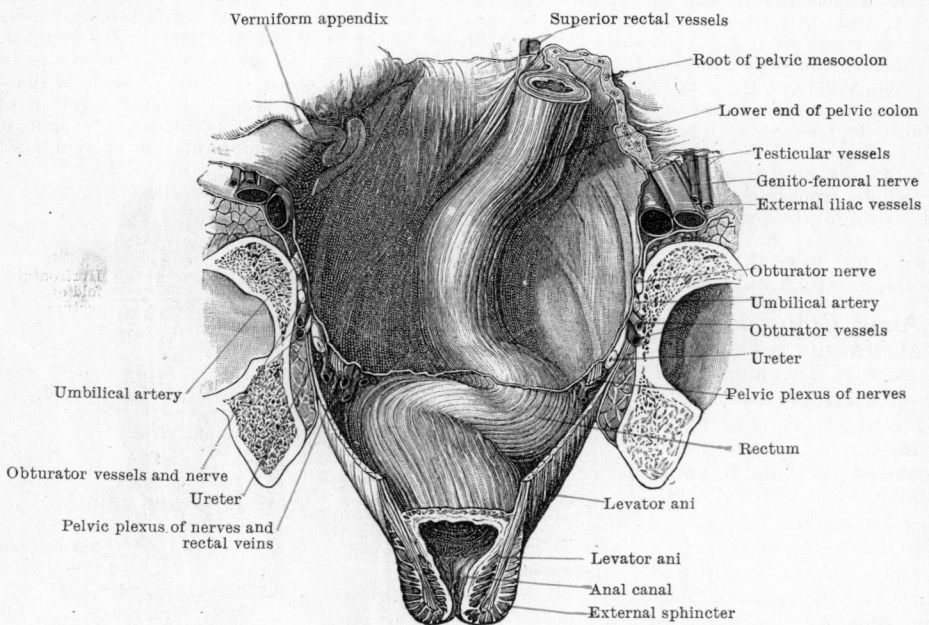

FIG. 529.—DISSECTION OF THE RECTUM AND ANAL CANAL FROM THE FRONT IN A SPECIMEN HARDENED BY FORMALIN INJECTION.

The front wall of the pelvis has been removed, and the bladder, prostate, and seminal vesicles taken away.

it towards the pubes. There is little doubt that the levator ani in that way acts as one of the chief sphincters of the bowel; and it should be noticed that it is placed where its action would be most effective, namely, opposite the point at which the rectum is narrowed or "pinched in" to form the anal canal. In addition to its sphincter action the muscle supports the expanded bowel immediately above the anal canal, and in that way sustains the weight of the fæces when the rectum is distended. It is probably relaxed during defæcation, except perhaps at the completion of the act. The muscle is under the control of the will.

The **sphincter ani externus** forms a muscular cylinder around the lower two-thirds of the anal canal, with (except in the case of some of its inner fibres) an anterior and a posterior attachment. When the muscle contracts its fibres are tightly stretched between its two attachments, and the space between them is reduced to a narrow antero-posterior slit. By that action the anal canal is flattened from side to side and closed, so that, whilst the levator ani is the sphincter of the upper aperture of the anal canal, the external sphincter closes its inferior and greater part. It is under the control of the will, but under ordinary circumstances it is in a state of tonic contraction.

The **sphincter ani internus** is continuous with the circular fibres of the gut in structure and also in action, its chief use being to empty the anal canal completely after the passage of each fæcal mass.

Vessels and Nerves.—The arteries of the rectum and anal canal are the three rectal arteries; to these, another, less important though constant, source may be added—the median sacral artery.

1. The *superior rectal* [hæmorrhoidal] *artery* is the principal artery of the rectum. It is the

prolongation of the inferior mesenteric, and at first it descends in the root of the pelvic mesocolon until the rectum is reached. There it divides into two chief branches which run downwards and forwards around the sides of the rectum—the right, usually the larger, lying more posteriorly, the left more anteriorly. From those two arteries come off secondary branches (about five to eight in all) which pierce the muscular coat about the middle of the rectum, and then descend in the submucosa as a series of longitudinal "terminal branches" as far as the anal valves, above the level of which one is usually found beneath each of the anal columns. The terminal branches give off numerous twigs which form a plexus in the submucosa by anastomosing with one another and with branches of the middle rectal artery, and also, in the lower part of the bowel, with branches of the inferior rectal artery.

2. The *middle rectal* [hæmorrhoidal] *arteries*, two in number—one on each side—are usually branches of the internal iliac or of the internal pudendal; they run on the wall of the inferior part of the rectum, and each breaks up into four or five small branches, some of which supply the muscular wall of the lower part of the rectum, whilst the others pierce the muscular coat near the upper end of the anal canal, and join in the submucosa with the plexus formed by the superior rectal artery already described.

3. The *inferior rectal* [hæmorrhoidal] *arteries*, generally two or three in number on each side, arise at variable levels from the internal pudendal. They are distributed to the levatores ani and the sphincters. Other branches pierce the sphincters and break up in the submucosa into a close network which supplies the lower part of the anal canal, and communicates above with the plexus formed by the superior and middle rectal arteries.

4. One or more small branches of the **median sacral artery** reach the posterior surface of the rectum, where they are distributed chiefly, if not solely, to the muscular coat.

The superior and middle rectal arteries anastomose freely in the plexus of the submucosa, and also by a few large branches on the exterior of the bowel: some perforating branches of the median sacral and inferior rectal arteries also join the plexus in the submucous layer at the lower part of the rectum. In addition, small branches of these several arteries unite with one another in the muscular coat. It should be remarked that the superior rectal artery supplies both the muscular and mucous coats in the superior part of the rectum, but that the muscular coats in the inferior part are supplied by the middle and inferior rectal vessels only. The inferior rectal artery is distributed chiefly on the posterior wall, and the middle rectal chiefly on the anterior wall.

The **veins** form two chief plexuses of large vessels devoid of valves, namely, an internal plexus situated in the submucous coat, and an external plexus in the outer coat. The internal plexus takes origin near the margin of the anus in a number of small (anal) veins, which are radially disposed beneath the skin of the anus, and communicate below with the rootlets of the inferior rectal vein lying lateral to the external sphincter. The anal veins are joined by others from the surrounding parts to form larger and often tortuous vessels which ascend in the anal columns. Passing upwards, the veins are known as the "terminal veins"; they communicate freely with one another, and unite into still larger vessels which pierce the muscular coat about the middle of the rectum, and join to form the superior rectal vein.

From the inferior part of the internal plexus numerous vessels pass through the external sphincter to join a venous network on the outer surface of that muscle, from which the *inferior rectal* [hæmorrhoidal] *veins* arise. The network also communicates with the internal plexus through the anal veins which descend from the latter beneath the skin of the anal canal to the exterior of the sphincter.

The various veins which pass out through the walls of the rectum unite freely on its exterior to form a rich venous plexus through which the three rectal vessels are brought into free communication with one another. Passing off from that plexus, the *superior rectal* [hæmorrhoidal] joins the left colic vein and forms with it the inferior mesenteric vein, which opens into the splenic; the middle rectal joins the internal iliac, from which the blood passes through the common iliac to the inferior vena cava; and the inferior rectal joins the internal pudendal—a tributary of the internal iliac vein. Thus, on the rectum, a free anastomosis is established between the veins of the portal and systemic circulations.

Most of the **lymph vessels** of the rectum pass to the sacral lymph glands.

The **nerves** are derived from various sources. The sympathetic fibres are derived from the *inferior mesenteric plexus*, and from the branches of the *hypogastric plexus* that accompany the superior and middle rectal arteries to the rectum. The parasympathetic fibres arise from the *second* and *third* or *third and fourth sacral nerves* soon after these leave the sacral foramina. They run forward in the pelvic areolar tissue, and, joining the pelvic plexuses, reach the side of the rectum. Fibres of the *inferior haemorrhoidal* branches of the pudendal nerve (third and fourth sacral) are distributed to the lower part of the anal canal as well as to the external sphincter.

Variations.—The best known anomalies of the rectum are those classed under the term **imperforate anus** or **atresia ani.** The atresia may be simply due to a partial or complete persistence of the anal membrane, which separates the anal pit from the hind-gut in the embryo; or the hind-gut may be deficient in its lower part when there is a considerable interval between the anal pit and the gut; or the rectum may open into the vagina, the uterus, the bladder, or the ureters, when usually no anus is evident; or finally the cloaca may persist. Other forms are also described, but the foregoing are those most commonly found.

LIVER

The **liver** (hepar) is a large glandular organ which lies immediately below the diaphragm, occupying the upper portion of the abdominal cavity mainly on the right side. It secretes a yellowish-green or brown fluid of bitter taste, called *bile* (fel). The bile is conveyed from it by two **hepatic ducts** which unite with each other to form a **common hepatic duct**. The common duct opens into the **bile duct**, which conveys the bile to the duodenum. Connected with the bile duct there is also a pear-shaped sac called the **gall-bladder** (vesica fellea), which is attached to the liver, and serves as a temporary reservoir for the bile. The bile passes to and from it through a canal, called the **cystic duct**, which unites with the common hepatic duct to form the **bile duct**.

In addition to secreting bile, the liver plays an important part in the metabolism of carbohydrate and nitrogenous materials which are absorbed from the food by the intestines and conveyed to the liver by the portal vein. The liver is associated also with the production and destruction of blood cells.

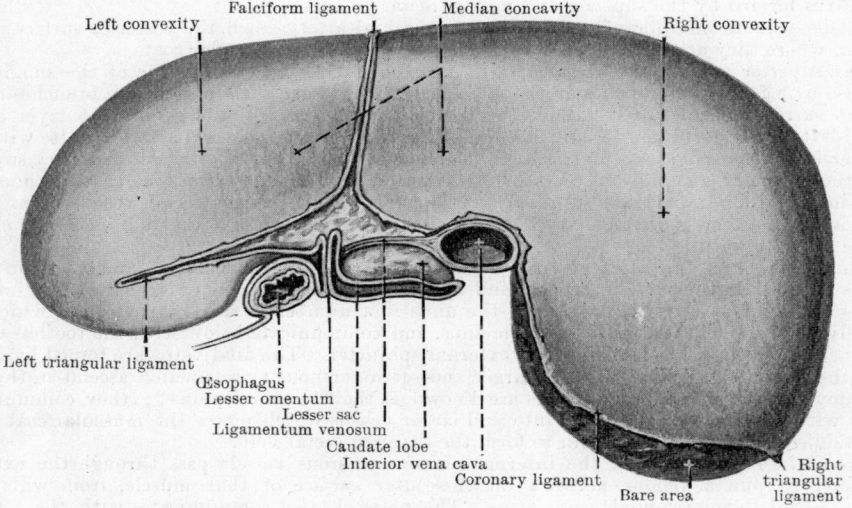

Fig. 530.—Semi-diagrammatic View of the Upper Surface of the Liver.

Physical Characters.—The liver is a large, mottled, reddish-brown mass, pliant to the touch, readily lacerated, and highly vascular. It is of uniform consistence, but the lacerated surface is granular. The granular appearance of the lacerated surface and the mottled colouring of the free surface are due to the lobules of which the liver is composed. Each lobule is polygonal or irregular in form, and measures only 1 to 2 mm. in diameter ; it is surrounded by a stroma of areolar tissue in which the vessels, nerves, and bile capillaries lie.

Size and Weight.—The average dimensions of the adult liver are seven inches across (17·5 cm.), six and a half inches vertically (16 cm.), and six inches antero-posteriorly (15 cm.) where it is thickest. It is about $\frac{1}{50}$th of the body weight, varying from 50 to 55 ounces in men, and from 43 to 48 ounces in women. The ratio to the body weight is the same in both sexes, but it varies with age. In the fœtus and child it is relatively large and heavy. At birth it occupies the greater part of the abdominal cavity, and is $\frac{1}{20}$th to $\frac{1}{18}$th of the body weight ; in a fœtus the ratio is still larger. The protuberance of an infant's abdomen is due chiefly to the liver.

Shape.—If the liver is not removed from the body until some time after death it becomes soft and flabby ; it flattens out when placed on a table and appears to have only a superior and an inferior surface separated by a circumferential border. But if it is taken out shortly after death while still firm, or if it is hardened *in situ* and then removed, its form is fairly constant ; and, although it is irregular, and varies with the position of adjacent organs and with the degree of distension of the parts of the alimentary canal which are near it, nevertheless, for descriptive purposes, it may be looked upon as an irregular four-sided pyramid laid on one side, having an edge-like apex, directed towards the left, a convex right surface, and four other surfaces—anterior, posterior, upper, and lower (or visceral)—the distinctive features of which are that the **anterior surface** is nearly flat, the **upper surface** is slightly convex on each side and slightly concave in the middle, the **posterior surface** is markedly concave from side to side, and the **lower surface** is uneven and oblique, looking to the left and backwards as well as downwards. The anterior, upper, posterior, and right surfaces merge into one another over ill-defined, rounded borders; but the lower surface is marked off

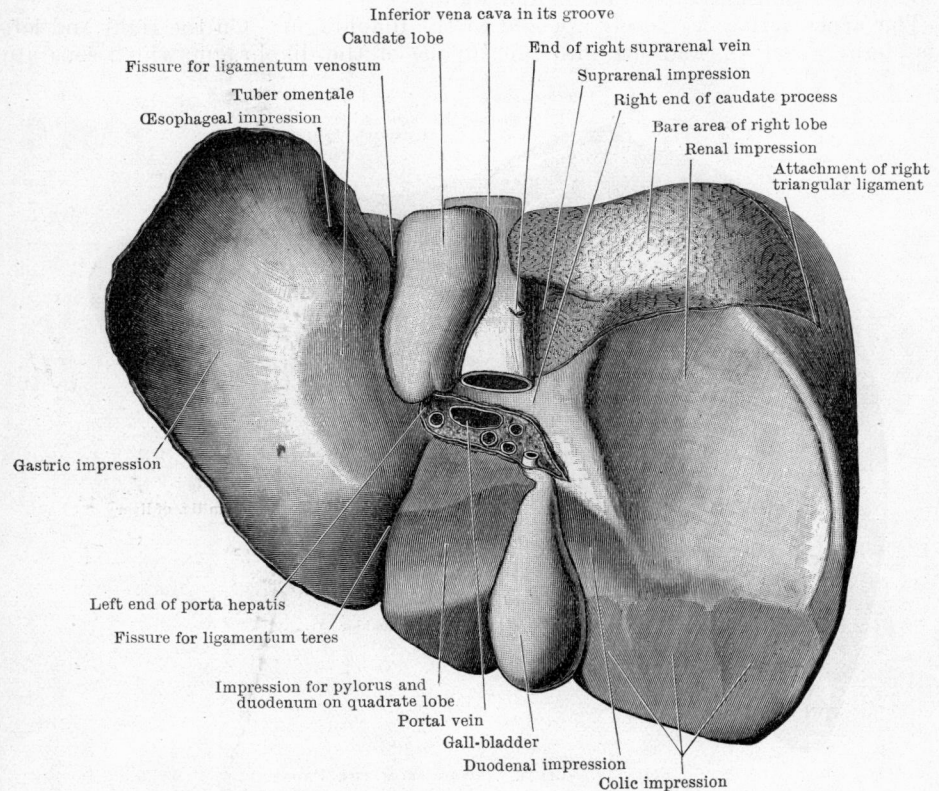

Fig. 531.—Lower (Visceral) and Posterior Surfaces of the Liver.

from the others by a definite, circumferential **lower border** of which the part which separates the anterior surface from the lower surface is the sharpest and best defined (Figs. 530-533).

Porta Hepatis.—The porta hepatis, or hilum of the liver, is a deep, wide, transverse cleft, about two inches long, situated in the posterior part of the lower or visceral surface. Part of the upper border of the lesser omentum is attached to its lips (see p. 576). The hepatic artery, the portal vein, and the nerves of the liver enter through the porta, and the common hepatic duct and the lymph vessels of the deeper parts pass out through it. These structures are surrounded by loose fibrous tissue, continuous with the fibrous (hepato-biliary) capsule of the liver.

The right and left hepatic ducts emerge from their lobes at the right and left ends of the porta, and unite near its right end to form the common hepatic duct, which unites, either inside or immediately outside the porta, with the cystic duct to form the bile duct. The hepatic artery enters the porta to the left of the common hepatic duct, and its right and left branches run to their lobes behind

the hepatic ducts. The portal vein divides similarly but at the right end of the porta
and its branches are behind those of the artery. Two or more lymph glands are
sometimes present in the porta, most commonly near its right end; if they become
enlarged they may press upon the hepatic ducts and obstruct the flow of bile.

Surfaces.—The left end of the liver is a rounded edge which lies between the
stomach and the diaphragm, and is opposite a point a little below and medial to
the left nipple.

The **right surface** of the liver is convex, and roughly quadrilateral. It is
closely related to the diaphragm, which separates it from the lower parts of the
right lung and pleura and the lower six ribs and intervening intercostal spaces.
Not uncommonly it descends below the ribs; its lowest part is then related to
the fascia and muscles of the abdominal wall.

The **upper surface** is closely apposed to the diaphragm. On the right and left
it is slightly convex, and fits into the cupolæ of the diaphragm, which separate

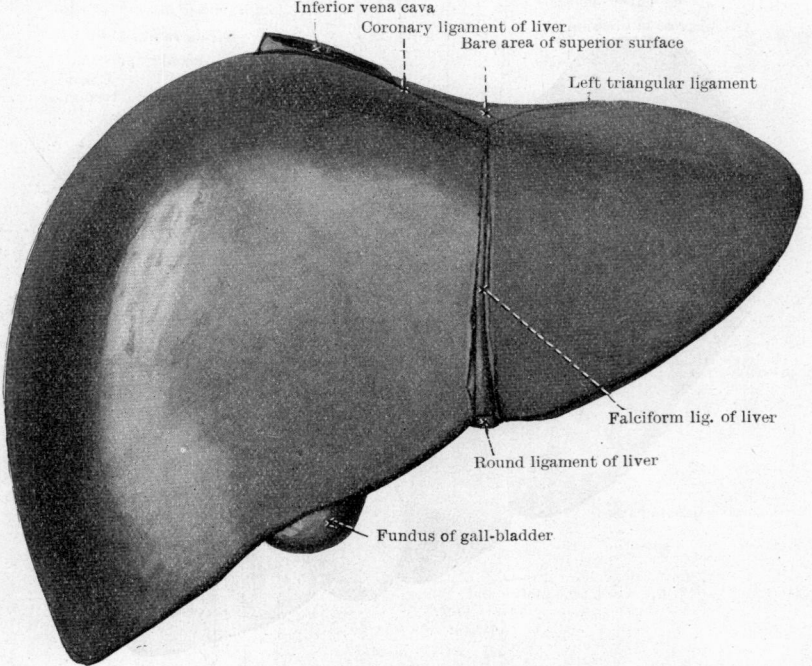

FIG. 532.—LIVER VIEWED FROM THE FRONT.

it from the pleuræ and lungs. Its middle part is slightly concave, and lies below
the pericardium and heart (Fig. 530).

The **anterior surface** is flat or slightly convex. In the infrasternal angle it is
related to the xiphoid process, the linea alba, and the sheaths of the recti muscles,
and to the falciform ligament, which lies between it and the abdominal wall
with its left surface in contact with the left lobe of the liver and its right
with the anterior abdominal wall. The smaller part of the anterior surface that
lies to the left, and the larger part to the right, are under shelter of the ribs
and costal cartilages, in contact with the diaphragm.

The **lower** or **visceral surface** (Fig. 531) is in relation (*a*) with the right kidney
posteriorly, (*b*) with the right flexure of the colon anteriorly, (*c*) with the second
part of the duodenum to the left of the kidney, then (*d*) with the gall-bladder in
its shallow fossa, and (*e*) near the apex, with the lesser omentum and the stomach.

The **posterior surface** (Fig. 533) is curved round the front of the vertebral
column. On the right, a large convex part of it is in direct contact with the
diaphragm, which separates it from the right pleura and lung, and the lower
ribs of the right side. Next, passing to the left, it is intimately attached to the

upper part of the inferior vena cava, which is embedded in the liver in a deep **groove for the vena cava.** On the right of this groove there is an area which is in contact with the right suprarenal gland. To the left of the inferior vena cava, an oblong area of the surface lies on the front of the crura of the diaphragm, which separate it from the lower part of the descending thoracic aorta; that portion is called the **caudate lobe**; it is separated from the crura by the upper recess of the lesser sac (see p. 630 and Fig. 530), and is bounded on the left by a deep, vertical cleft called the **fissure for the ligamentum venosum.** To the left of that, the surface is grooved vertically for the abdominal portion of the œsophagus, which produces the **œsophageal impression.**

Relation to Peritoneum.—The peritoneum covers the surfaces of the liver and adheres to its fibrous capsule, with the exception of (*a*) an area of the

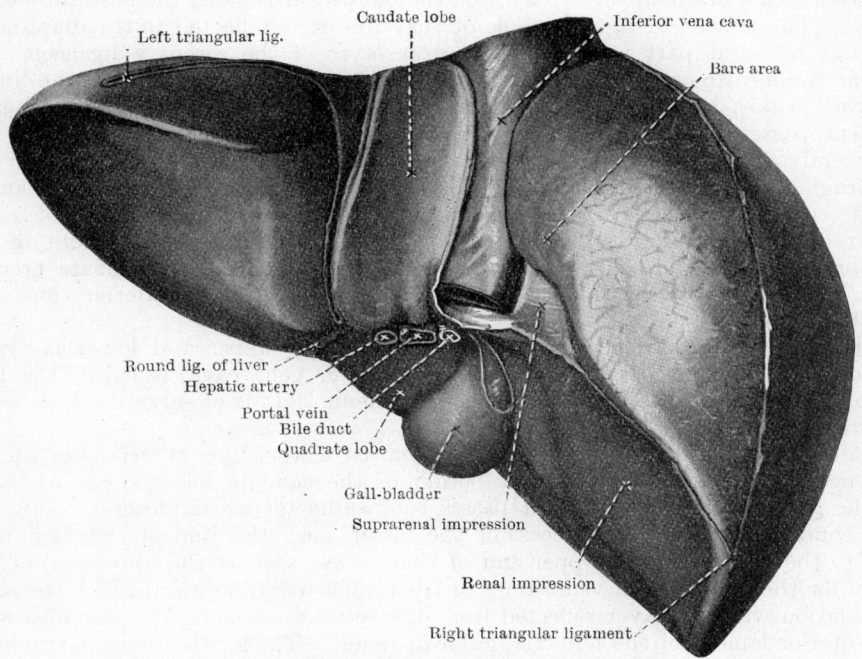

Left triangular lig.   Caudate lobe   Inferior vena cava

Bare area

Round lig. of liver
Hepatic artery
Portal vein
Bile duct
Quadrate lobe
Gall-bladder
Suprarenal impression
Renal impression
Right triangular ligament

FIG. 533.—THE LIVER VIEWED FROM BEHIND.

Comparison of the cut edges of peritoneum, as shown in this figure, with the cut edges of peritoneum in Fig. 509, p. 600, gives a very clear picture of the peritoneal reflexions from these surfaces of the liver.

posterior surface, in contact with the vena cava and with the diaphragm, continued on to the posterior portion of the upper surface, and (*b*) a part of the inferior surface in contact with the gall-bladder. Also, along certain definite lines the peritoneum passes from the liver to adjacent structures in the form of folds or reflexions which connect the liver with adjacent parts.

The largest of the folds is called the **falciform ligament.** It is a long, wide sheet, attached to the upper and anterior surfaces of the liver and to the lower surface of the diaphragm and the back of the linea alba—as far down as the umbilicus. Its line of attachment to the liver indicates the division of the liver into right and left lobes (see p. 630). Its lower border is free; it extends from the umbilicus to a notch in the lower border of the liver, and encloses a fibrous cord called the ligamentum teres. At the lower border of the liver the **ligamentum teres** enters a deep cleft in the inferior surface called the **fissure for the ligamentum teres** (see p. 631), along which it passes to end by fusing with the left branch of the portal vein. The ligamentum teres is the remains of the left umbilical vein of the fœtus and, during fœtal life, it conveyed purified, oxygenated, and food-laden blood from the placenta to the fœtus. Alongside it, in the adult, run some small venous channels which connect the left branch of the portal vein with the veins of the body wall in the region of the umbilicus.

The falciform ligament consists of two layers of peritoneum. At the back part of the upper surface of the liver the left layer turns to the left and forms the anterior layer of a triangular fold called the **left triangular ligament**, which passes from the upper surface of the left lobe to the diaphragm (Fig. 530). At the left end of the left triangular ligament that layer turns to the right as the posterior layer of the left triangular ligament, and at the upper end of the fissure for the ligamentum venosum (see Fig. 530) it becomes continuous with the upper end of the lesser omentum.

At the point where the left layer of the falciform ligament turns to the left, the right layer turns to the right in front of the inferior vena cava and along the posterior border of the upper surface, and then downwards along the posterior border of the right surface ; along the whole of that line it is reflected to the diaphragm, and the reflected part is called the *upper layer* of the **coronary ligament**. At or near the meeting of the right and lower surfaces, towards the back, the line of reflexion makes an angular bend from which a fold called the **right triangular ligament** passes to the diaphragm. From the right triangular ligament to the lower end of the groove for the vena cava, the peritoneum is reflected to the diaphragm ; that reflected portion is called the *lower layer* of the **coronary ligament** and it occasionally passes to the upper end of the right kidney instead of to the diaphragm. Continuing to the left, the line of reflexion passes in front of the inferior vena cava and behind a narrow bridge of liver, called the **caudate process**, which intervenes between the lower end of the groove for the inferior vena cava and the porta hepatis.

The part of the surface of the liver between the upper and lower layers of the coronary ligament, to the right of the inferior vena cava, is called the **bare area** of the liver, because it is devoid of peritoneum. It is closely attached to the diaphragm.

At the left border of the inferior vena cava the line of reflexion of the peritoneum ascends along the right border of the caudate lobe (Figs. 531, 533), and the reflected peritoneum, as it passes backwards to the diaphragm, forms the right boundary of the upper recess of the lesser sac ; the line of reflexion then turns to the left, above the upper end of that recess, and, at the upper end of the fissure for the ligamentum venosum, the layer reflected from the right lobe comes into relation with the layer reflected from the left lobe, which is continuous with the posterior lamella of the left triangular ligament. The layers from the two lobes dip into the fissure for the ligamentum venosum, and line its walls. They return from the fissure together and extend from it to the stomach as the upper, left part of the lesser omentum.

From the lower end of the fissure for the ligamentum venosum the lines of attachment of the two layers of the lesser omentum pass to the inferior surface of the liver where they turn to the right along the margins of the porta hepatis, the left layer passing in front of the porta and the right layer behind it ; and at the right end of the porta the two layers join each other in the anterior margin of the opening into the lesser sac.

Subdivision. — The liver is divided into two main lobes — a large right and a small left. The division is effected by the attachment of the falciform ligament on the upper and anterior surfaces (Figs. 530, 532), by the fissure for the ligamentum teres on the lower surface (Fig. 531), and by the fissure for the ligamentum venosum on the posterior surface (Fig. 533). But two subordinate lobes are cut off from the right lobe. They are the **quadrate** lobe on the lower surface to the left of the gall-bladder, and the **caudate** lobe on the posterior surface to the left of the inferior vena cava. The caudate lobe is connected by the caudate process with the remaining, large part of the right lobe.

Other fissures and grooves are : the fissure for the ligamentum teres, the fissure for the ligamentum venosum, the groove for the inferior vena cava, and the fossa for the gall-bladder. The first two are deep, narrow clefts ; the groove for the vena cava is a deep, wide furrow ; the fossa for the gall-bladder is usually a mere shallow depression. They all represent, in man, the much more definite fissures which, in many mammals, separate the liver into discrete or almost discrete segments.

The **fissure for the ligamentum teres** begins in a notch on the lower border of the anterior surface at the lower end of the attachment of the falciform ligament, and extends to the left end of the porta hepatis. It contains the ligamentum teres (p. 629). Occasionally it is bridged over by liver tissue.

The **fissure for the ligamentum venosum** is continuous with the fissure for the ligamentum teres at the left end of the porta hepatis; and it extends to the upper surface. The peritoneum which lines its sides is reflected from its floor as the upper, left part of the lesser omentum.

At the bottom of the fissure there is a fibrous cord, called the **ligamentum venosum,** which connects the left branch of the portal vein with the upper end of the abdominal part of the inferior vena cava. At the upper end of the fissure it turns to the right in front of the upper end of the caudate lobe, and fuses with the left wall of the inferior vena cava. The ligamentum venosum is the remains of a fœtal blood-channel, called the *ductus venosus,* which during fœtal life transmitted blood directly from the left umbilical vein to the inferior vena cava.

Left Lobe.—The **left lobe** fits into the left cupola of the diaphragm, to which its *upper surface* is attached by the left triangular ligament. Its *lower surface* presents, in front and to the left, a deep concavity—the **gastric impression**—for the fundus and body of the stomach, whilst behind and to the right it bulges as a prominence, called the **tuber omentale** because it rests against the front of the lesser omentum. The *left extremity* of the lobe is the apex of the liver.

Parts of the Right Lobe.—The **quadrate lobe** extends from the lower border in front to the porta hepatis behind, between the fissure for the ligamentum teres on the left and the fossa for the gall-bladder on the right. It is usually marked by impressions made by the pyloric end of the stomach and the first part of the duodenum.

The **fossa for the gall-bladder** extends from the lower border of the liver (at the level of the ninth right costal cartilage) to the right end of the porta hepatis. It is generally shallow, but sometimes it is so deep that the gall-bladder is almost entirely hidden in it. Its surface is devoid of peritoneum, and is directly attached to the upper surface of the gall-bladder by areolar tissue, through which small blood-vessels and lymph vessels pass—and occasionally also minute **hepato-cystic ducts** which connect the bile capillaries of the liver directly with the gall-bladder.

The **caudate lobe** is a relatively narrow, oblong lobe on the posterior surface of the right lobe. It forms the anterior boundary of the upper recess of the lesser sac, and is related to the crura of the diaphragm opposite the lower part of the thoracic aorta and the lower thoracic vertebræ. The fissure for the ligamentum venosum bounds it on the left, and the groove for the inferior vena cava on the right. Its lower end is connected with the rest of the right lobe by the caudate process, and is grooved antero-posteriorly by the cœliac artery. The part to the left of the groove is called the *papillary process*; and the part to the right is continuous with the caudate process.

The **caudate process** is a narrow band of liver substance on the lower surface of the right lobe. It lies between the porta hepatis and the fossa for the inferior vena cava, and forms the upper boundary of the opening into the lesser sac.

The **groove for the vena cava** is deep, rounded, and vertical—occasionally so deep that the vena cava is almost completely enveloped in it. Sometimes it is even bridged across posteriorly by liver substance (*pons hepatis*). In it the walls of the inferior vena cava are closely attached to the fibrous capsule of the liver, through which the hepatic veins emerge from the liver substance and join the vena cava on its anterior aspect—the larger, main veins at the upper end of the groove and the smaller, accessory veins at varying levels.

The **remainder of the right lobe** forms the whole of the right surface and parts of the other four surfaces of the liver. Its *lower surface* is covered with peritoneum and is marked by three impressions (Fig. 531, p. 627). The two to the

40 *b*

right are (*a*) the smaller, below and in front, for the right flexure of the colon, and (*b*) the larger, above and behind, caused by the right kidney. The third lies to the left of the renal impression and is caused by the commencement of the second part of the duodenum. Its *upper, anterior,* and *right surfaces* are covered with peritoneum, and lie in relation with the parietes (see Figs. 530, 532). The *posterior surface* is the **bare area** of the liver. Through the areolar tissue of this area lymph vessels from the liver pass to the diaphragm and so to the thorax, and also small veins which connect the portal circulaton in the liver with the systemic veins in the diaphragm.

Fixation of the Liver.—Adequate means of retaining the relatively heavy liver in its place is not provided by its connexions—which are the peritoneal folds, the attachment of its posterior surface to the diaphragm by areolar tissue, and its attachment to the vena cava by areolar tissue and the hepatic veins. The position is maintained partly by those connexions and partly by atmospheric pressure, but mainly by the **intra-abdominal pressure** caused by

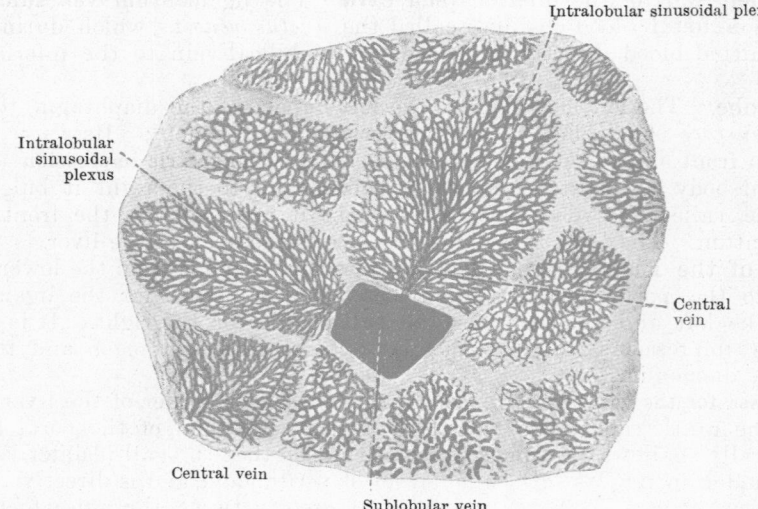

Intralobular sinusoidal plexus

Intralobular sinusoidal plexus

Central vein

Central vein

Sublobular vein

FIG. 534.—LIVER OF A PIG INJECTED FROM THE HEPATIC VEIN BY T. A. CARTER. (From a specimen presented to the Anatomical Department of Edinburgh University by Sir William Turner.)

the tonic contraction of the muscles of the abdominal walls, which press the more movable contents of the abdomen against the less movable and keep them all in comparatively fixed positions. Atmospheric pressure, however, prevents sudden displacement of the liver, for the abdomen is a closed cavity : before the liver could move from its close contact with the diaphragm some viscus would have to be available to occupy the vacated space and prevent a vacuum, and none of the abdominal contents is sufficiently movable for that purpose.

Variations.—Few organs vary more in size than the normal, healthy liver; but increase or decrease is often pathological. The **position** varies normally with the size. The liver also moves down and up with every breath ; and it descends slightly when the body is raised from the reclining posture to the erect. Occasionally, without any evident cause, the liver and diaphragm are higher or lower than usual. In apparently healthy bodies the upper surface of the right lobe may be at the level of the fourth rib ; or it may reach only the level of the sixth, and its lower border may be two or three inches below the costal margin—especially in women. Apart from pathological deformities, there may be congenital irregularities in **form** caused by additional fissures and lobes resembling those in the higher apes and commonly present in the fœtus (Thomson), or by division into several distinct lobes as in many other mammals. Grooving by the ribs and wrinkling on the surfaces opposed to the diaphragm are probably fixed by the hardening of the liver. In some cases a wide, tongue-like process (Riedel's lobe) projects downwards from the lower border on the right of the gall-bladder ; it is more common in women than in men ; it may be large enough to reach the iliac crest, and has been mistaken for a tumour. **Correlated variations in form and position** normally result from the varying pressure of surrounding parts. Distension of the stomach or of the left part of the transverse colon pushes the liver to the right and increases its vertical diameter. Distension of the intestines flattens it from below upwards and increases its transverse diameter. But variations may be due to malformations of the thoracic framework, either congenital or acquired. When tight lacing was common, such malformations were frequent in women. When the chief constriction was low, the liver was forced up against the diaphragm and filled the whole left cupola as well as the right. More often, the constriction caught the liver; its upper part was forced upwards and to the left, and its lower part downwards.

Structure of the Liver.—The liver is partially invested by an outer **serous coat**, which has been described with its peritoneal relations. Deep to that there is a thin **fibrous coat**—most evident where the serous coat is absent. In the neighbourhood of the porta hepatis it is more abundant, and there it surrounds the vessels entering the porta, and accompanies them through the portal canals in the liver substance. The fibrous coat is continuous with the fine areolar tissue which pervades the liver, surrounding its lobules and holding them together. The invest-ment of fibrous tissue as a whole is known as the *hepato-biliary capsule* [capsula fibrosa].

The **liver substance** proper is made up of an enormous number of small **lobules** $\frac{1}{25}$th to $\frac{1}{12}$th inch (1 to 2 mm.) in diameter, closely packed, and held together by a small amount of areolar tissue. In man the lobules are not completely separated from one another all round their circumference, but coalesce in places; the reverse is the case in certain animals such as the camel and the pig. Each lobule is composed of a large number of columns of liver cells, radiating from the centre to the periphery.

Between the columns—which interlace freely—there is a sinusoidal, capillary-like network through which blood passes from interlobular veins at the margins to a central vein.

The endothelial wall of the network is incomplete, so that the liver cells are in many places in contact with the blood. Some of the endothelial cells are modified into stellate cells which are a part of the reticulo-endothelial system, and are known as the "star cells" of Kupffer. The columns may be regarded as being composed of two layers of cells, between which is a minute channel, the intralobular bile duct, passing from the centre to the periphery of the lobule.

Vessels and Nerves.—Blood is con-veyed to the liver by the hepatic artery and the portal vein, which enter the liver at the porta hepatis, and break up into branches and finally into a sinusoidal net-work. The blood which has so entered is conveyed from the liver by the hepatic veins to the inferior vena cava.

The circulation within the liver is therefore arranged differently from that of other glands, and in order to understand properly the structure of the liver it is necessary to give some account of the re-lations which it presents to the blood-vessels which pass to and from it.

The **portal vein** and the **hepatic artery** pass to the liver between the two layers of the lesser omentum, accompanied by the bile duct. Each breaks up into two chief branches—a right and a left—and several smaller ones, which enter the liver sub-stance, surrounded by a prolongation of the fibrous tissue coat of the liver. Within the organ the three vessels run and divide together, so that every branch of the portal vein is accompanied by a corresponding (but much smaller) branch of the hepatic artery and of the hepatic duct; and the three, surrounded by a prolongation of the hepato-biliary capsule, and accom-panied by branches of the hepatic nerves and lymph vessels, run in special tunnels of the liver substance, which are known as **portal canals** (Fig. 535, B).

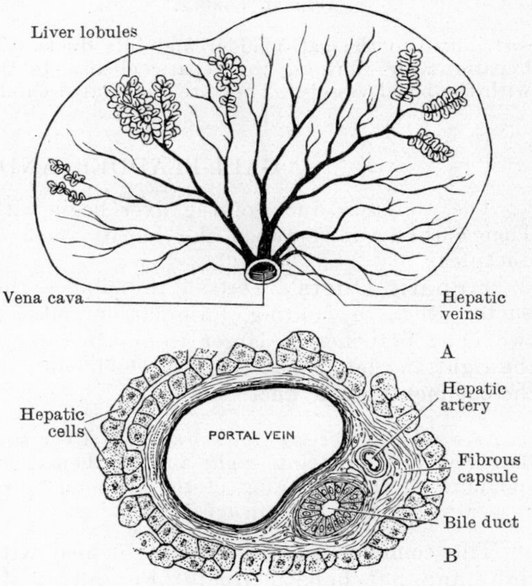

FIG. 535.—DIAGRAMS ILLUSTRATING THE STRUCTURE OF THE LIVER.

A, Arrangement of liver lobules around the sublobular tributaries of the hepatic vein; B, Section of a portal canal, showing its contained branches of the portal vein, hepatic artery, and bile duct, surrounded by a pro-longation of the hepato-biliary capsule.

The hepatic artery has but a small part to play in the hepatic circulation within the liver, and it supplies minute branches to the fibrous tissue of the portal canals and of the surface of the liver. The terminal branches of the artery end in the capillaries from the portal vein which go to the liver lobules.

The portal vein within the liver divides, like an artery, into numerous branches, which eventually form an elaborate meshwork of *interlobular veins* around the periphery of the liver lobules. From this meshwork the small capillary-like channels described above pass into the interior of each lobule between columns of liver cells, towards a channel in the centre of the lobule called the *central vein*. From the central veins the blood is carried into larger channels called *sublobular veins*, which pass to the hepatic veins.

The **hepatic veins** gradually unite with one another, and run towards the inferior vena cava. Their mode of termination is variable, but presents the following general arrangement: The left lobe is drained by a vessel which joins the superior part of the inferior vena cava. The right lobe is drained by one or two vessels which join the superior part of the inferior vena cava, and by a series of small vessels, 4 to 12 in number, which pass from the inferior portion of the right lobe to the inferior vena cava. The caudate lobe and the central portion of the liver are drained by vessels which pass to the inferior part of the hepatic portion of the inferior vena cava. The hepatic veins and their branches are not accompanied by branches of the bile ducts, and are surrounded by a very small amount of areolar tissue.

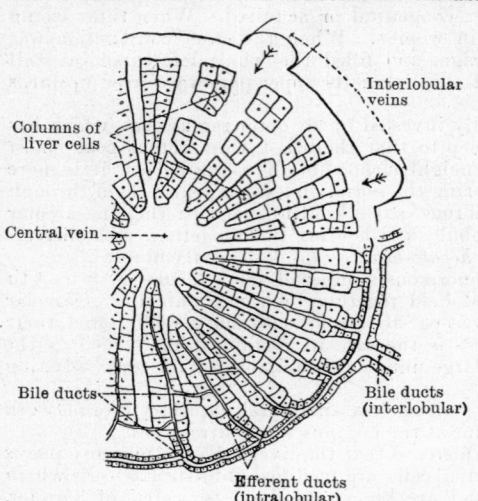

FIG. 536.—DIAGRAM TO ILLUSTRATE THE STRUCTURE OF A LIVER LOBULE.

The **lymph vessels** of the liver pass either directly to the surface, where they appear beneath the peritoneum, or accompany either (*a*) the portal or (*b*) the hepatic veins.

The **nerves** are chiefly of the non-medullated variety; they are derived from both vagi and from the cœliac plexus of the sympathetic. Branches of the anterior gastric nerve pass from the stomach between the layers of the lesser omentum to the liver and are distributed to the gall-bladder and bile ducts. Those from the cœliac plexus run along the hepatic artery—forming the hepatic plexus—to the porta hepatis, where they enter the liver with the blood-vessels. They are distributed chiefly to the walls of the vessels.

GALL-BLADDER AND BILE-PASSAGES

The excretory ducts of the liver begin within the hepatic cells as minute channels. Thence they run between the hepatic cells (Fig. 536), and are known as the **bile ductules**.

Hepatic Ducts.—Outside the lobules, the ductules join (Fig. 536) the **interlobular ducts**, which, by uniting, form larger and larger ducts, and finally end, as a rule, in two chief branches, a larger from the right and a smaller from the left lobe, called the **right** and **left hepatic ducts**, which unite immediately after leaving the liver to form the **common hepatic duct**.

As a rule, five or six ducts leave the liver substance at the bottom of the porta hepatis; they generally unite into right and left hepatic ducts; sometimes they all converge towards, and unite at the beginning of the common hepatic duct. The ducts from the caudate and quadrate lobes join the left hepatic duct.

The **common hepatic duct** is formed within the porta hepatis by the union of right and left hepatic ducts (Fig. 537). It passes downwards, and, just beyond the porta hepatis, is joined by the **cystic duct** to form the **bile duct**. In length the hepatic duct usually measures about 1 to $1\frac{1}{4}$ inch (25 to 31 mm.), and in breadth, when flattened out, nearly $\frac{1}{4}$ inch (6 mm.), or about as much as a goose quill. It lies, practically altogether, within the porta hepatis.

Gall-bladder and Cystic Duct.—The **gall-bladder** (vesica fellea), with the cystic duct, may be looked upon as a diverticulum of the bile duct, enlarged at its extremity to form a reservoir in which the bile is not merely stored but concentrated by the absorption of water from it by the mucous coat. It is pear-shaped, and lies obliquely on the inferior surface of the liver (Fig. 537). The wide end or **fundus** usually reaches the inferior border of the liver and comes in contact with the anterior abdominal wall behind the 9th costal cartilage opposite the lateral border of the rectus abdominis (Fig. 503). The **body** runs backwards, upwards, and to the left, lying in the fossa for the gall-bladder, and near the porta hepatis passes rather abruptly into the narrow neck. The **neck** is curved medially towards the porta hepatis, in the form of the italic letter *S*, and when distended it presents on its surface a spiral constriction which is continued into the beginning of the cystic duct, and is due to a series of crescentic folds placed more or less spirally round the interior of its cavity, forming the **spiral valve**. Having arrived near the porta hepatis, much reduced in size, it passes into the cystic duct.

As a rule the gall-bladder is covered with the peritoneum of the inferior surface of the liver, except on its antero-superior aspect, which is united to the walls of the fossa for the gall-bladder by areolar tissue. Sometimes, but rarely, the gall-bladder is suspended from the liver by a short peritoneal ligament. *Above*, the gall-bladder,

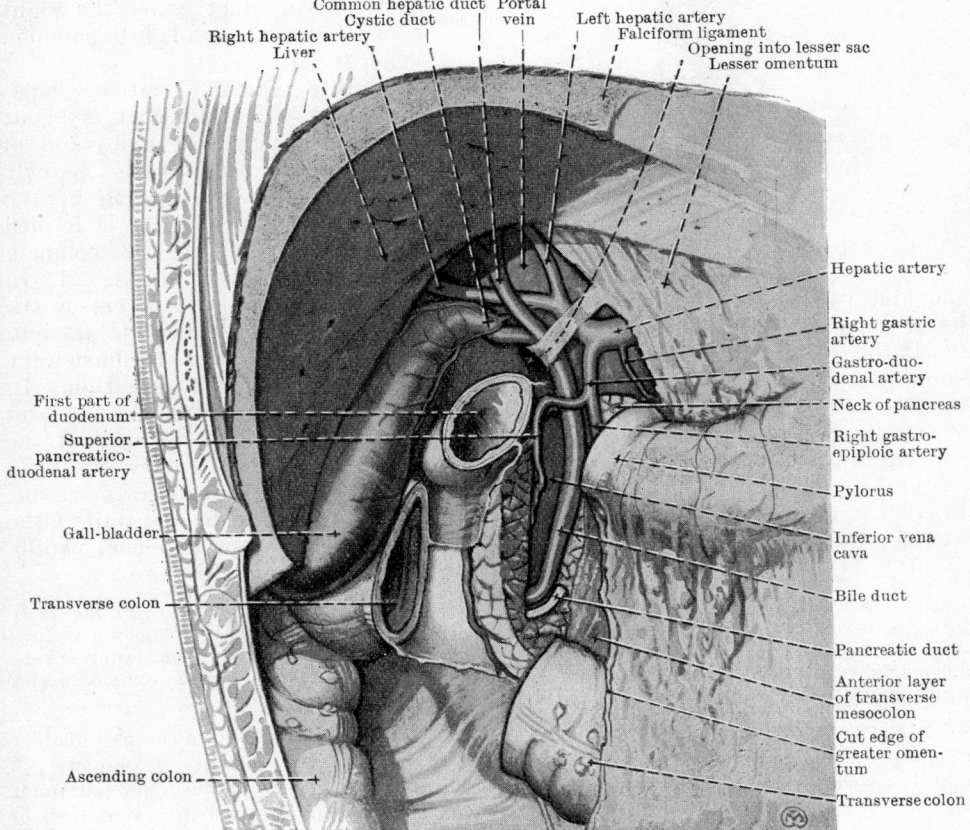

FIG. 537.—DISSECTION SHOWING THE BILE DUCTS AND THEIR RELATIONS.

lies against the liver; and *below*, it rests on the transverse colon in front, and behind, near its neck, on the duodenum.

The fundus of the gall-bladder may not reach the inferior border of the liver or the abdominal wall. It may lie to the right of the right sagittal plane—possibly as a result of distension of the stomach and colon—or it may lie to the left, near the median plane and far below the ribs. Its total absence, as well as the presence of two distinct gall-bladders, and several other irregularities in form, have been recorded.

Its *size* is usually about 3 inches (75 mm.) in length, and 1 to 1¼ inches (25 to 31 mm.) in diameter. Its capacity varies between 1 and 1½ fluid ounces.

Vessels and Nerves.—The **artery** is the **cystic**, which comes from the right branch of the hepatic artery; it divides into two branches which diverge to descend over the sides of the gall-bladder. The accompanying veins unite to form a single vein which ends in the right branch of the portal vein. The **lymph vessels** pass to glands that lie alongside the cystic duct and in the porta hepatis. The **nerves** come from the sympathetic plexus on the hepatic artery. Fibres from the right phrenic nerve are also probably distributed in the wall of the gall-bladder, and provide the afferent path for referred "shoulder pain" that is felt in disorders of the gall-bladder.

The **cystic duct**, about half the diameter of the common hepatic duct (3 mm.), but usually slightly longer ($1\frac{1}{4}$ to $1\frac{1}{2}$ inches: 31 to 37 mm.), begins at the neck of the gall-bladder, pursues an irregular course backwards and medially, and joins the

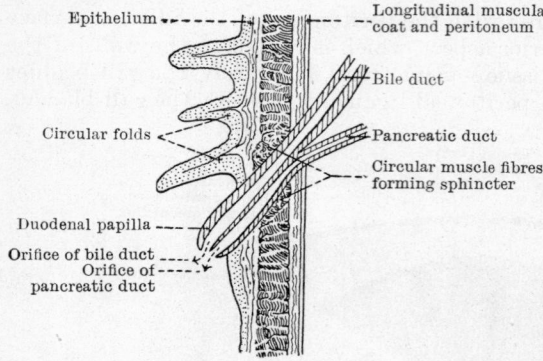

common hepatic duct at the mouth of the porta hepatis, to form the bile duct. The spiral constriction found in the neck of the gall-bladder is continued into the beginning of this duct. Sometimes the cystic duct joins the right hepatic duct instead of the common hepatic duct.

FIG. 538.—DIAGRAMMATIC SECTION OF WALL OF DUODENUM THROUGH PAPILLA.

Bile Duct (Ductus Choledochus).—The **bile duct** is about 3 inches long (75 mm.) and of variable width—usually $\frac{1}{4}$ inch. It begins at the mouth of the porta hepatis, where it is formed by the union of the common hepatic and cystic ducts. (1) In the first part of its course it passes downwards between the two layers of the lesser omentum, with the portal vein behind and the hepatic artery to its left. (2) It then descends behind and to the left side of the first part of the duodenum, and (3) it runs with a curve downwards and to the right to its termination. In that, the third part of its course, it is usually embedded in the tissue of the head of the pancreas. It may also in other specimens pass behind the head of the pancreas close to the inferior vena cava, or, again, in the angle between the head of the pancreas and the duodenum, more or less embedded in pancreatic tissue. Finally, it meets the pancreatic duct, and with it pierces the medial wall of the second part of the duodenum very obliquely, and opens on the duodenal papilla about $3\frac{1}{2}$ or 4 inches (8·7 to 10 cm.) beyond the pylorus (see p. 602).

As the bile and pancreatic ducts pierce the wall of the duodenum, they run obliquely through its coats for about $\frac{1}{2}$ or $\frac{3}{4}$ of an inch (12 to 18 mm.), and, as a rule, do not unite until they have almost reached the opening on the duodenal papilla (Fig. 538). That orifice is very much smaller than the lumen of either duct, and the short and relatively wide common cavity which precedes it is known as the **ampulla of the bile duct**.

Structure of Gall-bladder and Excretory Ducts.—The wall of the gall-bladder is composed of an outer coat of peritoneum—the *serous coat*—usually incomplete ; a middle *muscular coat* of unstriped muscle intermixed with fibrous tissue ; and an inner *mucous coat*, which is covered with columnar epithelium, and is raised into a number of small ridges which confer on it a honeycomb appearance. The mucous coat is always deeply stained with bile after death.

With the exception of the peritoneal coat, which is absent, the hepatic, cystic, and bile ducts agree with the gall-bladder in general structure. The mucous coat contains a large number of mucus-producing glands.

Variations of the Gall-bladder and its Duct and of the Ducts of the Liver.—The gall-bladder may be attached to the liver by a peritoneal ligament. It may be deeply embedded in the liver, and its fundus may fall short of the lower border of the liver. It may be sacculated by constriction in its walls. It may be divided longitudinally into two gall-bladders, each with its own duct opening separately into a hepatic duct. It may be directly connected with the smaller bile vessels by small channels, called **hepato-cystic ducts**, which pass from its upper wall into the liver. It may be absent, in which case one or other of the hepatic ducts usually is considerably dilated.

The hepatic ducts may be from two to five in number—accessory ducts coming usually from the right of the liver. The right and left hepatic ducts may be so long that they descend into the lesser omentum before they unite ; their increased length entails an elongated cystic duct and a shortened bile duct. The cystic and hepatic ducts may open into the duodenum separately ; and the orifice of the bile duct may be separate from the orifice of the pancreatic duct.

Radiographic Examination of the Gall-bladder.—Under normal conditions the gall-bladder and its contents do not throw a shadow on X-ray examination. By the use of artificial methods, however, especially by the injection of dyes which are excreted by the liver and concentrated with the bile in the gall-bladder, it is possible to demonstrate its position, from, and functional variations in size (Pl. XLVIII). Occasionally the wall of the gall-bladder becomes pathologically calcified and so appears in an ordinary radiograph (Pl. XLIII).

PANCREAS

The **pancreas** is a long, soft, lobulated reddish or yellowish-grey gland which lies transversely on the posterior abdominal wall, its right end in the concavity of the duodenum (Fig. 541), and its left end touching the spleen. It secretes a clear, watery, alkaline fluid—the *pancreatic juice*—which is conveyed to the duodenum by the **pancreatic duct**, and constitutes one of the chief agents in intestinal digestion, for it contains ferments which transform starch into dextrin and sugar, split fats into glycerine and fatty acids, and reduce alkaline albuminous substances to peptone.

In **shape** the pancreas, when hardened *in situ* (Fig. 539), may be compared to the letter J placed thus ⌐.

The gland is divisible into a **head** with an **uncinate process**, a **neck**, a **body**, and a **tail**. The **head** corresponds to the hook of the ⌐. The stem of the ⌐ represents the **body** of the gland, and the left extremity of the body forms the **tail**. The narrow part connecting the head and body is the **neck** (Symington). An extension from the head to the left behind the superior mesenteric vessels forms the **uncinate process**. When removed from the body without previous hardening, the pancreas loses its true form, and becomes drawn out into a slender, tongue-shaped mass, with a wider end turned towards the duodenum, and a narrow end corresponding to the tail.

Its total *length*, when fixed *in situ*, is about 5 or 6 inches (12·5 to 15 cm.); after removal, if not previously hardened, it is easily extended to a length of 8 inches (20 cm.).

Its *weight* is usually about 3 ounces (87 grammes).

Relations.—The general position and relations of the pancreas may be briefly stated as follows: The head (Fig. 539) lies in the concavity of the duodenum, with the inferior vena cava and abdominal aorta behind it; the body crosses to the left in front of the vertebral column, the left kidney, and suprarenal gland; and the tail touches the visceral surface of the spleen. The greater part of the organ lies behind the stomach.

In a description of the detailed relations, each part of the organ must be considered separately.

The **head of the pancreas**, flattened from before backwards, lies in the concavity of the duodenum. *Above*, in its right half, it is continuous with the neck; whilst to the left of the neck, a deep notch separates the upper and left part of the head from the neck, and contains the superior mesenteric vessels (Fig. 539). The margin of the head is moulded on the duodenum, which lies in a groove of the gland substance— the bile duct being interposed as far down as the middle of the second part of the duodenum. The posterior surface of the head is applied to the front of the inferior vena cava, the right renal vessels and the left renal vein, and the aorta. Its anterior surface is in contact above and on the right with the beginning of the transverse colon (Fig. 509), without the interposition of the peritoneum as a rule. Below that it is clothed with peritoneum, and is covered by the small intestine.

The superior mesenteric vessels, after passing forwards through the notch between the head and the neck, descend in front of the uncinate process. The superior pancreatico-duodenal artery runs downwards, and divides into branches at the upper border of the head (Fig. 539).

The **neck of the pancreas** (Fig. 539) is a thin portion of the gland which lies in front of the portal vein, and connects the head to the body. It is attached on the right to the upper portion of the head, and runs forwards, upwards, and to the left for about 1 inch (25 mm.), and passes into the body.

The neck is about ¾ inch (18 mm.) in width, and less than ½ inch (12·5 mm.) in thickness. *In front and to its right* lie the first part of the duodenum, the pylorus, and the lesser sac of the peritoneum ; *behind and to the left* it rests upon the beginning of the portal vein, which is formed under cover of its lower border by the union of the splenic and superior mesenteric veins. It is generally marked off from the head by two grooves of which the upper is occupied by the gastro-duodenal artery and its superior pancreatico-duodenal branch, and the lower by the superior mesenteric vessels.

As the transverse mesocolon is followed to the right it is found to end, as a rule, near

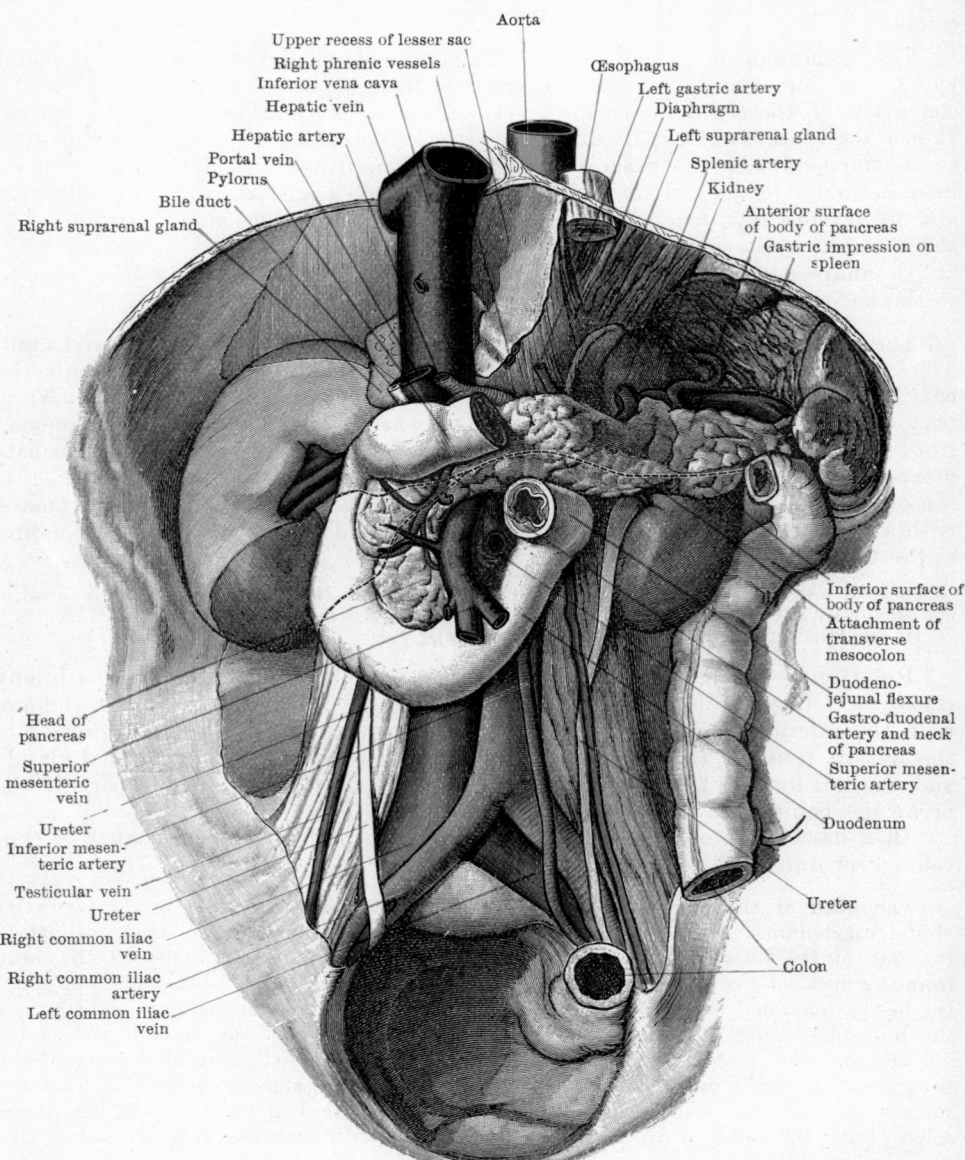

Fig. 539.—The Viscera and Vessels on the Posterior Abdominal Wall.

The stomach, liver, and most of the intestines have been removed. The peritoneum has been preserved on the right kidney and the recess behind the caudate lobe. When the liver was taken out, the inferior vena cava was left *in situ.* The stomach bed is well shown. (From a body hardened by chromic acid in·ections.)

the neck of the pancreas (Fig. 509). Beyond that, the posterior surface of the colon is connected by areolar tissue to the anterior surface of the head of the gland.

The **body of the pancreas** is of a prismatic form, and is largest where it lies in front of the left kidney (Fig. 539). From the neck it runs backwards and to the left across the front of the left kidney, beyond which its extremity or tail comes in contact with the spleen. When hardened *in situ* it presents three surfaces—anterior, inferior, and posterior—all of nearly equal width (namely, about 1¼ inches : 30 mm.).

The *anterior surface*, widest towards the left end, looks upwards and forwards (Fig. 539), and forms a considerable portion of the stomach-bed. It is completely covered with the peritoneum of the posterior wall of the lesser sac, which separates the pancreas from the stomach. Towards its right end where the body joins the neck it usually presents an elevation which, when the stomach is distended, projects against the back of the lesser omentum and is consequently known as the **tuber omentale**.

The *inferior surface* looks downwards and slightly forwards. It is completely covered with peritoneum, continuous with that which forms the posterior layer of the transverse mesocolon (Fig. 509). It lies in contact with the duodeno-jejunal flexure towards its right end, with the left flexure of the colon near its left end, and with

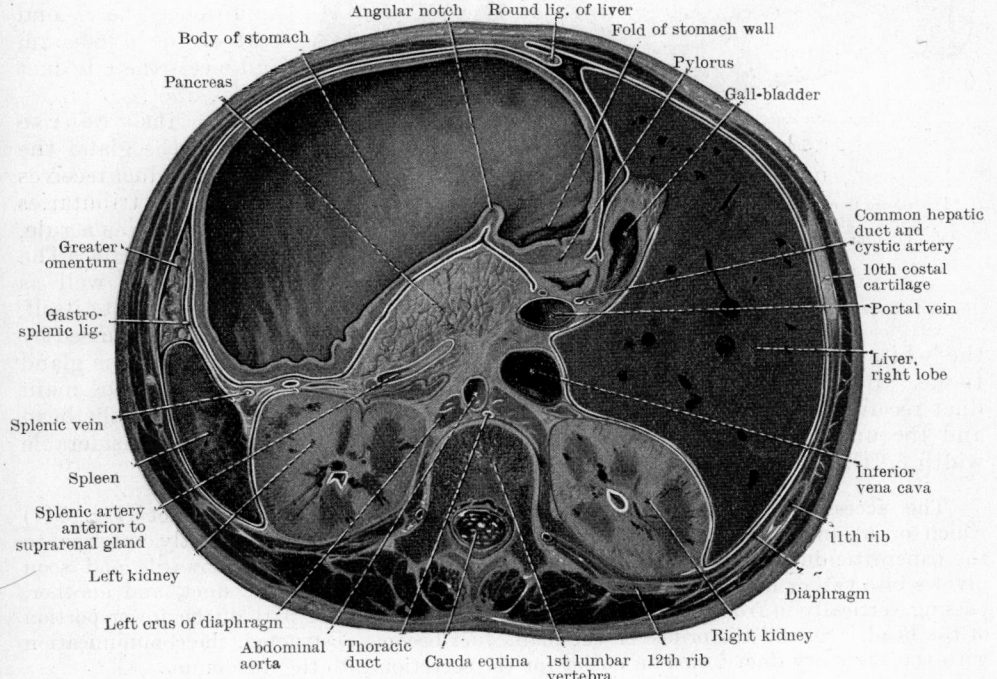

FIG. 540.—TRANSVERSE SECTION OF THE TRUNK AT THE LEVEL OF THE FIRST LUMBAR VERTEBRA.
Showing relations of stomach, pancreas, kidneys, etc. From a subject ten years old.

a mass of small intestine (jejunum, which is always found packed in beneath it) in the rest of its extent.

The *posterior surface* looks directly backwards, and is entirely destitute of peritoneum. It is connected by areolar tissue to organs lying upon the posterior abdominal wall. From right to left they are : the aorta with the origin of the superior mesenteric artery, the left renal vessels, the left suprarenal gland, and the left kidney. In addition, the splenic artery runs its tortuous course to the left along the superior border of the pancreas, whilst the splenic vein runs, behind the gland, at a lower level than the artery.

The three surfaces of the body of the pancreas are separated by three borders. The inferior is the most prominent, and gives attachment to the transverse mesocolon (Fig. 539). It is, as it were, squeezed forward, by the pressure of the stomach above and the small intestine below, into the interval between these two sets of viscera, thus following the line of least resistance (Cunningham). Towards the neck that border is no longer prominent, but becomes rounded off, so that there the anterior and inferior surfaces are confluent.

The cœliac artery projects over the upper border, and sends its hepatic branch to the right, resting upon it, whilst the splenic artery runs to the left along it (Fig. 509). The posterior border calls for no special description.

The **tail of the pancreas**, at the left end of the body, usually presents an abrupt, blunt ending, or it may be elongated and narrow. It is in near relation with the spleen to the left and with the left flexure of the colon below (Fig. 509).

Ducts of the Pancreas.—Almost invariably two ducts are found in the interior of the pancreas—the **pancreatic duct** and the **accessory pancreatic duct**.

The **pancreatic duct** begins at the tail by the union of small ducts that emerge from the lobules of that part of the organ. From there it pursues a rather sinuous or zigzag course (Fig. 541) in the axis of the gland; at first it runs nearly transversely to the right, until the neck is reached, and then bending downwards into the head, it approaches the second part of the duodenum and meets the bile duct (see p. 636).

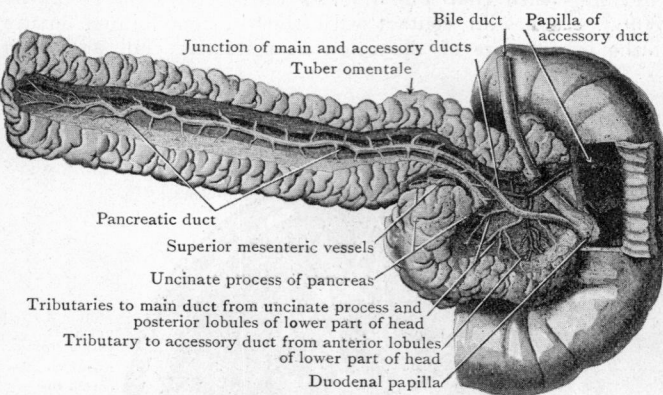

Bile duct Papilla of accessory duct
Junction of main and accessory ducts
Tuber omentale
Pancreatic duct
Superior mesenteric vessels
Uncinate process of pancreas
Tributaries to main duct from uncinate process and posterior lobules of lower part of head
Tributary to accessory duct from anterior lobules of lower part of head
Duodenal papilla

Fig. 541.—Dissection of the Pancreas from behind to show its Ducts.

In its course through the gland the pancreatic duct receives numerous tributaries which join it, as a rule, at a right angle. The tributaries, as well as the main duct itself, are easily recognised by the whiteness of their walls, which contrasts with the darker colour of the gland tissue. Beyond its point of junction with the accessory duct (see below), the main duct receives tributaries from the posterior part of the lower portion of the head and the uncinate process, and, towards its termination, it attains a considerable width ($\frac{1}{10}$th to $\frac{1}{6}$th of an inch : 2·5 to 4 mm.).

The **accessory pancreatic duct** is a small and variably developed duct (Fig. 541) which opens into the duodenum about $\frac{3}{4}$ of an inch above and slightly anterior to the pancreatic duct. From the duodenum it runs to the left and downwards, and soon divides into two or more branches, one of which joins the pancreatic duct, and another, passing vertically in front of the main duct, drains the anterior part of the lower portion of the head. Should the orifice of the main duct become obstructed, the communication with the accessory duct forms an outlet for the secretion into the duodenum.

Structure of the Pancreas.—The lobules of the pancreas resemble closely in structure the lobules of the salivary glands, and show a similar arrangement of secreting tubules and ducts. The tubules are lined with short cylindrical cells, with a deeply placed nucleus, and often showing granules in the free margin. In the centre of the base of the tubule, spindle-shaped epithelial cells are found, termed the *centro-acinar cells*.

In addition, however, each lobule contains irregular groups of cells known as **islets of Langerhans**. These cells are not connected with the ducts, and they produce the internal secretion known as *insulin*.

Variations.—The chief variations found are : (1) A separation of the part of the head known as the uncinate process, which then forms a *lesser pancreas*. (2) A growth of the pancreas around the duodenum, which it may practically encircle for a short part of its course. And (3) an opening of its duct into the duodenum independently of the bile duct. Accessory pancreatic tissue is also sometimes found in the wall of the stomach or of the jejunum, or even in the diverticulum ilei. Diverticula of the duodenum, already described (p. 603), ought perhaps to be mentioned in this connexion.

Vessels and Nerves.—The arteries of the pancreas are: (1) The *superior pancreatico-duodenal*, a branch of the gastro-duodenal artery ; its two terminal branches, anterior and posterior, run downwards, one in front of and the other behind the right margin of the head (Fig. 539), sending branches laterally to the duodenum, as well as numerous twigs into the substance of the pancreas. (2) The *inferior pancreatico-duodenal*, a branch of the upper part of the superior mesenteric artery, or from the root of one of the jejunal branches ; it runs upwards and to the right across the back of the head, and sends branches to it and to the duodenum, one of which runs between the head and the duodenum. The two pancreatico-duodenal arteries anastomose around the inferior border of the head. (3) *Pancreatic branches* of the *splenic artery* are several (3 to 5) fair-sized branches which come off from the splenic as it runs along the superior border of the gland; they enter the pancreas immediately, and traverse its substance from above downwards, some sending branches in both directions along the course of the pancreatic duct.

The **veins** are : (1) The *pancreatico-duodenal veins* (Fig. 539), of which some pass downwards and to the left, on the front of the head, and join the superior mesenteric ; while others cross the back of the head and open into the superior mesenteric or the portal vein ; (2) several small *pancreatic veins* which join the splenic.

The **lymph vessels** pass mainly to the supra-pancreatic glands.

The **nerves**, which are almost entirely non-medullated, are (1) sympathetic filaments which have passed through the hepatic and splenic plexuses, and (2) parasympathetic filaments from the vagi.

DEVELOPMENT OF DIGESTIVE SYSTEM

In the chapter on Embryology it has been pointed out that the alimentary canal is formed from three separate parts : (1) A middle large entodermal portion, and (2) two smaller ectodermal parts, one anterior, the stomodæum or oral pit, and one posterior, the proctodæum or anal pit. It has been shown further that the three portions are at first separated from one another by septa—the bucco-pharyngeal membrane and the anal membrane, respectively—but the septa disappear at an early date, and the three parts are thrown into continuity. There is thus formed a tube—the primitive alimentary canal—which extends through the body from the mouth aperture in front to the anal orifice behind.

The entodermal segment of the primitive alimentary canal is derived from the dorsal portion of the entodermal sac and is divided into three portions as follows :—That portion which is enclosed within the head fold and lies above the septum transversum is termed the fore-gut ; the portion within the tail fold is termed the hind-gut ; and the middle portion is termed the mid-gut. The mid-gut at first lies opposite the communication with the yolk sac, and the other portions cephalic to and caudal to this level. From the fore-gut are formed the posterior part of the mouth, the pharynx, œsophagus, stomach, and the greater part of the duodenum. From the mid-gut and hind-gut are formed the rest of the small intestine, and the whole of the large intestine, as far as the " white line " of the anal orifice.

The primitive intestinal tube not only forms the basis of the alimentary canal and its associated organs, but it is also the source from which many other organs, not ultimately connected with digestion, are formed. Thus, the respiratory tract below the level of the orifice of the larynx is formed as an outgrowth from the ventral wall of the primitive fore-gut, and remains permanently connected with it at that point, though in structure and function it becomes very different from the tube from which it is derived. Other structures also, namely, the thyroid gland, the parathyroid glands, and the thymus, are formed as diverticula of the primitive pharynx, but they soon lose their connexion with the wall of the tube. Furthermore, the allantois, a diverticulum from the hind-gut, and the ventral part of the primitive hind-gut are cut off to form the urinary bladder and a portion of the urethra.

Accounts of the development of the organs mentioned which are not connected with the alimentary canal in the adult will be found in the sections dealing with them.

Development of Mouth and Pharynx.—The mouth cavity of the adult is formed in part from the oral pit, and in part from the anterior end of the fore-gut or primitive pharynx. The line of division between the portions of the mouth derived from those two parts is difficult to trace, on account of the very extensive changes which occur after the bucco-pharyngeal membrane has disappeared, and are associated with the formation of the face and of the nose. The portion of the mouth cavity derived from the fore-gut is lined with entoderm, and that derived from the oral pit with ectoderm. The position of the original bucco-pharyngeal membrane may be represented by an imaginary plane extending from the anterior part of the body of the sphenoid to the lingual surface of the mandible at the junction of its alveolar part with the rest of its body.

The enamel of the teeth and the secreting epithelium of the parotid gland are ectodermal structures, while the epithelium of the tongue and of the submandibular and sublingual glands is entodermal in origin.

The **upper lip** is formed from the tissues covering the median nasal and maxillary processes (see development of face, p. 53). The **lower lip** similarly is formed from the tissues covering the mandibular arches. By an ingrowth of epithelium from the surface of the frontal and maxillary processes into the subjacent mesoderm and by subsequent desquamation of the superficial layers, a groove is formed between the lips and cheeks on the one hand and the alveolar ridges on the other. That groove when deepened forms the vestibule of the mouth, and is termed the *alveolo-labial sulcus*. The surface covered with mucous membrane becomes everted to form the red portion of the lips, and at birth is divided into an outer smooth portion and an inner portion, whose surface is villous. The distinction between these two parts disappears shortly after birth. Several explanations of the formation of the **philtrum** or groove on the front of the upper lip have been put forward ; most probably it is produced by the union of the margins of the two globular processes with each other, the floor of the groove being formed along their line of union, and the ridges bounding the groove at the sides corresponding to the medial portions of the globular processes.

The **parotid glands** are formed as outgrowths of the epithelium in the outer wall of the alveolo-labial sulcus. The outgrowth on each side has been found in embryos 8 mm. long. It

41

is at first a furrow. The posterior part of the furrow becomes closed off from the mouth cavity and forms a tube which grows backwards for some distance on the surface of the first pharyngeal arch. The terminal portion of the tube gives rise to a number of buds which divide repeatedly, and form the lobules of the gland. They are at first solid, and the alveoli do not become hollowed until about the twenty-second week. The epithelium of the terminal buds forms the secreting glandular epithelium, while that of the stalk forms the lining epithelium of the duct.

I. Shows the dental lamina D.L, the surface epithelium E and the enamel germ E.G.

II. Shows the further growth of the enamel germ and its invagination to form the enamel organ.

III. The enamel organ is more invaginated, and its inner layer of cells A becomes columnar. The dental lamina is thinner, but near its posterior or lingual edge there is an enlargement R.G which is the reserve germ for a permanent tooth. The superficial cells of the dental papilla P are becoming columnar.

IV. The inner columnar cells of the enamel organ (ameloblasts) A have formed a cap of enamel En, inside which the superficial cells of the papilla, the odontoblasts O, have formed a layer of dentine D.

V. Shows a still more advanced stage. The deposit of dentine is extending downwards, and enclosing the papilla to form the future pulp, in which a vessel V is seen.

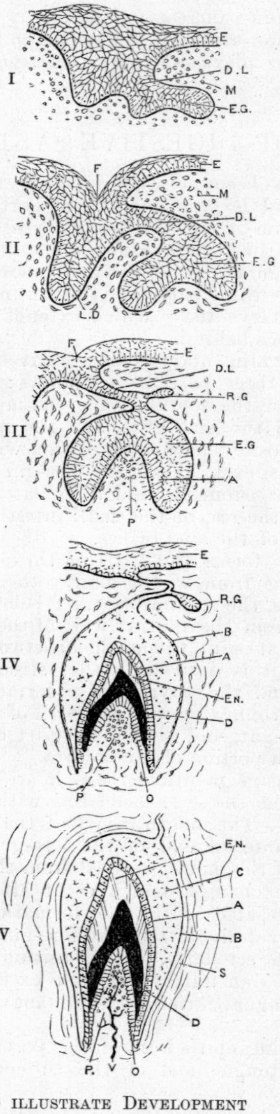

Fig. 542.—Diagrams to illustrate Development of a Tooth.

A, Ameloblasts; B, Outer layer of enamel organs; C, Stellate reticulum; D, Dentine; D.L, Dental lamina; E, Epithelium; E.G, Enamel germ or organ; En, Enamel; F, Primary dental lamina and furrow; L.D, Labio-gingival lamina; M, Mesoderm; O, Odontoblasts; P, Dental papilla; R.G, Reserve germ; V, Blood-vessel.

The **gums** are developed in two parts—labio-buccal and lingual (West). The labio-buccal part takes the larger share in the formation of the gums; its surface becomes villous, and it becomes divided into segments corresponding in number and size to the dental sacs of the deciduous teeth. The vessels of the developing gum furnish materials for the growth of the teeth, and even pierce the enamel reticulum.

DEVELOPMENT OF THE TEETH

Teeth, like the skin, are formed from two sources; the enamel is derived from ectoderm and the dentine with its associated tissues—tooth pulp and cement—from mesoderm. The stages of the formation and union of the two elements may be followed in the diagrams, Fig. 542.

The first stage is the formation, along the site of the future gum, of a thickened ridge of ectoderm which sinks to a deeper level by the active growth of the mesoderm on each side of it, and becomes slightly furrowed along its surface. The ridge is termed the **primary dental lamina**; and its deep border widens out and soon divides into two secondary ridges, separated from one another by a process of mesoderm. The outer ridge is known as the **labio-gingival lamina** as it marks the site of the formation of the groove between the lip and the gum; hollowed out by an extension of the primary furrow it is converted into the *labio-gingival groove*. The inner ridge, now termed the **dental lamina**, alone is shown in Figs. III, IV, and V, for it is the source of the formation of the enamel of the teeth. The dental lamina is at first a continuous band of equal width throughout, but in each jaw on each side its deep surface comes to show five enlargements, one corresponding to each deciduous tooth, and for a time these enlargements remain connected together by a narrow strip of ectoderm. Each of these enlargements or **enamel organs** is invaginated by a papilla of the mesoderm—the **dental papilla**—for which it forms a cap.

The connexion of the dental lamina with the surface ectoderm becomes drawn out into a thin stalk, and from the inner side of this stalk, superficial to each enamel organ of a deciduous tooth, a small bud arises which is the source of the enamel organ of the corresponding permanent tooth.

Each enamel organ is vesicular in shape: the cells in its interior form a loose *stellate reticulum* with fluid in its spaces; the row of long columnar cells (*ameloblasts*) in contact with the mesodermal papilla become the hexagonal enamel prisms, by the deposit on their free surface of successive droplets of calcareous enamel substance. This layer of cells caps not only the apex but also the upper part of the sides of the dental papilla. In the areas of this contact dentine is formed by the superficial cells of the papilla, which are known as the *odontoblasts*. The peripheral margins of the cells become calcified, around a central minute thread-like process from the cell body, forming eventually the hollow dentinal tubules. The dental papilla, underlying the enamel organ, assumes the shape of the crown of the future tooth ; in the case of the molars, for example, elevations are found in the position of the tubercles of the teeth. The cells in the interior of the papilla become the cells of the pulp of the tooth, vessels and nerves passing in among them from below.

Cement is formed, in the same manner as bone, around the deeper part of the papilla, up to and even beyond the level at which it is invested by the epithelial sheath formed by the prolongation of the enamel organ already mentioned, which is in part perforated by the cells forming the cement.

The tissues immediately surrounding the enamel organ and the dental papilla form a fibrous capsule termed the dental sac. The **dental sacs**, when fully developed, are large and distinct fibrous bags which lie in the tooth sockets of the maxilla and mandible, and are continuous above with the tissue of the gum. On the lingual side of the sacs of the deciduous teeth are found the germs of the permanent teeth, surrounded by their own sacs. The latter are at first very small, and are partly embedded in the posterior wall of the deciduous dental sacs, but subsequently they come to lie in distinct but incomplete bony cavities of their own. The bone surrounding the dental sacs, temporary and permanent, is always wanting over the summit of the sac, and the band of fibrous tissue by which the sac is connected with the overlying gum tissue, through the deficiency, is known as the **gubernaculum dentis.**

All the points mentioned are easily demonstrated on the mandible of a child at birth particularly when the tissues have been allowed to soften a little. If, in such a specimen, the gum and periosteum are reflected upwards from the labial and lingual surfaces of the mandible, and freed as far as the upper border of the jaw, the gum, with the tooth-sacs depending from it like small bags, can be pulled away out of the bony groove of the jaw ; and if the operation has been successfully performed, the tooth-sacs of the three front permanent teeth may be seen, in size from a small pin's-head to a hemp-seed, hanging down behind the upper part of the corresponding deciduous sacs.

The *roots* of a tooth are formed by downgrowths from the base of the dental papilla, each papilla lying in a groove in the surface of the developing jaw. The groove is divided into compartments for the individual teeth by the formation of intervening septa of bone.

Permanent Teeth.—The five anterior permanent teeth, replacing each a deciduous tooth, are developed from the bud-like process on the connecting stalk of epithelium already mentioned, and from a dental papilla which forms in relation to each of these buds, on the lingual side of its predecessor. The hinder three permanent teeth in each jaw are formed in the same way as the deciduous teeth from an extension backwards of the original dental lamina behind the last deciduous tooth.

Eruption of the Teeth, *i.e.,* the protrusion of the crown through the superficial investing tissues, is accompanied by an active absorption of these tissues and also by growth of the roots of the teeth. When the eruption of the deciduous teeth is about to take place, the anterior wall and roof of the socket are absorbed ; the tooth passes through the sac and appears above the gum, and the socket is re-formed closely around the tooth. The root, which is only partly formed at the time of the eruption, continues to elongate. When the permanent tooth is about to be erupted, it makes its way from its own bony cell through the posterior wall of the socket of its deciduous predecessor ; the root of the deciduous tooth undergoes absorption at the same time, but quite independently of pressure from the permanent tooth. The socket, now occupied by both teeth, is again much enlarged by absorption, particularly in front ; what remains of the temporary tooth is shed ; the permanent tooth passes onwards through the enlarged socket, and, making its way to the surface, appears above the gum. After some time, when the tooth has taken its final position, the socket is again re-formed, first around its neck, and later on, as the root is built up, around it also, and thus the tooth is permanently fixed. All these processes occur while the alveolar parts of the jaws are themselves growing in height.

MORPHOLOGY OF THE TEETH

In most vertebrates below mammals all the teeth are alike in form ; such a dentition is said to be **homodont.** In the majority of mammals, on the other hand, the teeth are arranged in groups of different size and form ; such a dentition is **heterodont.**

Again, mammals have, neglecting exceptional cases, but two functional sets of teeth ; they are consequently said to be **diphyodont.** Most vertebrates below mammals, on the other hand, have a continuous succession of teeth throughout life, and hence are said to be **polyphyodont.**

The teeth of fishes and reptiles, and even of some of the mammals, such as dolphins and porpoises, are conical pegs set in the jaw, and none of them have flattened crowns or crowns furnished with tubercles like those of human premolar and molar teeth.

An intermediate form of teeth is shown in some carnivorous mammals, in which at the base of a conical tooth a ring of enamel forming a cingulum is found. (See p. 539.)

The current view of the origin of the human teeth rests upon evidence that in each tooth three primary tubercles are represented. It is possible that this *tritubercular* origin may be accounted for by the fusion into one of three originally separate conical simple teeth.

The tubercles are found one on the lingual and two on the labial aspect. In the incisors and canine teeth the cingulum represents the lingual tubercle ; and the cutting margin of the incisors and the conical apex of the canines represent the two labial tubercles fused together In the premolars also the two labial tubercles are fused.

In the molar teeth, two labial tubercles and one lingual tubercle persist, but in these teeth additional secondary tubercles also are present. They are one or two in number, and are added to the original tubercles at the back, on the lingual side when four tubercles are present, and on both lingual and labial sides when there are five of them.

The complete or **typical mammalian dentition**, in its highest development, as in the horse, is represented by the following formula : I. $\frac{3}{3}$, C. $\frac{1}{1}$, PM. $\frac{4}{4}$, M. $\frac{3}{3}$ = 44. In the dentition of man, therefore, one incisor and two premolars are wanting. Different views are held as to which teeth have been suppressed—most probably they are the second incisors, and the first and second or first and last premolars.

In general it may be said that in the **dentition of the non-civilised races** the dental arches are squarer in front, the teeth larger and more regular, the canines stronger, the last molars better developed, and the tubercles on the molars more perfect than in the more civilised races. It may be mentioned that the teeth of a savage man, if seen in the mouth of a European, would be looked upon as an "exceedingly perfectly formed set of teeth" (Tomes).

For Flower's "dental index," which expresses the proportion in size of the crowns of the premolars and molars to the length of the cranio-facial axis in different races, see p. 316.

DEVELOPMENT OF PRIMITIVE PHARYNX AND PHARYNGEAL PORTION OF THE MOUTH

The anterior, blind terminal part of the fore-gut in the head region constitutes the primitive pharynx. Its roof is formed by the tissues covering the under aspect of the mid- and fore-brain, and its floor by the tissues overlying the heart and pericardium. Each side wall is a lamina of tissue extending from the floor to the roof, continuous, in front, with the bucco-pharyngeal membrane, which forms the oral wall of the pharynx and separates it from the oral pit. In the roof the tissues of the hinder part of the base of the skull are formed. In the side wall and in the floor extensive changes occur, connected with the appearance of structures known as the pharyngeal arches and pouches, and with the origin of numerous structures from them and the development of the tongue (see p. 59).

Tongue.—The **mucous membrane** of the tongue is formed from two sources, anterior and posterior, in the floor of the pharynx. The portion covering the anterior two-thirds of the tongue is formed from the tissue covering the tuberculum impar and the median parts of the second pair of arches. The portion covering the posterior third is formed from the tissues over the third pair of arches. The foramen cæcum and the sulcus terminalis mark the junction of the two parts, the foramen cæcum representing the position where the outgrowth took place which forms the thyroid gland. The epithelial covering is derived from the entodermal lining of the pharynx, while the muscle substance is derived from mesoderm which is continuous with the occipital myotomes and derives its nerve supply from the hypoglossal nerve.

The investing epithelium of the anterior two-thirds gives rise to the papillæ and the taste buds, while that covering the posterior portion remains smooth. The papillæ appear about the third month as elevations of the corium covered with epithelium. The vallate papillæ are formed by ingrowths of the epithelium, in rings, around a central core. The superficial layers of the epithelium desquamate and form the trench around the papilla.

Submandibular and Sublingual Glands.—These glands are formed in the alveolo-lingual groove, immediately behind the first arch, by outgrowths similar to those which form the parotid gland (p. 641). The submandibular outgrowths occur about the fifth week, and the sublingual, several in number, on the outer side of it at the ninth week.

Tonsil.—The palato-glossal arch arises in the position occupied earlier by the second pharyngeal arch, behind which, in the embryo, lies the lower portion of the second pharyngeal pouch. Part of that pouch enlarges, and forms a recess termed the *sinus tonsillaris*. From the lower and greater part of the sinus tonsillaris the tonsil is developed; the upper part of the sinus persists, however, as the intratonsillar cleft. The tonsil at first is a smooth depression of the mucous membrane. About the fourth month of intra-uterine life downgrowths of the epithelium take place, which are afterwards converted into the tonsillar pits. Subsequently lymph cells accumulate around the downgrowths and form the lymphoid tissue which constitutes the mass of the organ. The plica triangularis is formed from a tubercle which becomes flattened to form a fold on the anterior and medial aspect of the inferior part of the tonsil.

DEVELOPMENT OF ŒSOPHAGUS, STOMACH, AND INTESTINES

Development of the Tissues of the Œsophagus, Stomach, and Intestine.—The wall of those portions of the alimentary tube consists at first of an internal lining of epithelial entodermal cells, several layers thick, and of an external investment of mesenchyme. The intra-abdominal portion of the tube has also a partial external covering of the flattened cells which form the lining wall of the cœlom. The entodermal cells give rise to the epithelium of the adult œsophagus, stomach, and intestine (whether it is stratified and squamous as in the œsophagus or columnar as in the stomach and intestine), to the secreting cells of the glands of the canal, including the liver and pancreas, and to the lining epithelium of the ducts of those and other glands. The epithelium may be ciliated for a time in the œsophagus, and in the duodenum it may be so thickened as to obliterate the lumen of the tube for a time.

The epithelium shows early very active proliferation, so that ridges and furrows are formed; and the glands arise from downgrowth of the epithelium. In both large and small intestine, the longitudinal ridges become broken up into isolated, finger-like stalks to form villi, which are present for some time in the large as well as in the small intestine. Additional villi are formed later on by a rapid growth of the epithelium in the intervals between the original villi. The circular folds of the intestine are formed much later, but are well formed at birth.

The **muscular coats** are formed from the mesenchyme by a gradual extension of its cells and their modification into the multi-nucleated fibrils of non-striped muscle. The circular coat is the first to originate, and later the longitudinal coat. In the colon the latter coat is formed first at the rectal end and thence spreads headwards; from the first it is in the form of three separate longitudinal bands, while in the small intestine it is a continuous sheet.

Vessels and Nerves.—The nerves and probably also the vessels, both blood and lymph, grow into the wall of the intestine, the vessels being derived from the primitive vascular network connected with the yolk sac. The cœliac artery and the superior and inferior mesenteric arteries represent segmental vessels distributed to successive segments of the tube and to the organs derived from these segments.

Formation of Gastric and Intestinal Glands, etc.—The epithelial lining of the intestinal tube is composed, at first, of a single layer of cells, and the inner surface is smooth. In the second month the epithelium increases rapidly, and as a result its surface is thrown into folds and furrows, arranged irregularly. Mesenchymal tissue passes into the interior of the folds, and also blood capillaries. The folds appear first in the stomach, especially in the regions of the curvatures, and later in the duodenum and small intestine, and then in the large intestine, where they are formed first in the rectum and last in the vermiform appendix. In the stomach the folds are arranged so as to surround small isolated depressions which afterwards become the gastric pits. In the small intestine isolated elevations are found, in place of continuous folds, and at a later stage new elevations are formed between the primary ones. Those papillary elevations form the villi. In the large intestine the arrangement resembles that in the stomach. The glands of the stomach and intestine are formed by an active proliferation of the epithelium at the bottom of the furrows, and at first their cells are everywhere of a similar character, and become differentiated later. In the stomach the formation of the glands begins about the end of the third month. The intestinal glands of the large intestine appear as depressions between adjacent elevations, and there is not so much active proliferation of cells as in the formation of the glands in the small intestine. The glandular epithelium of the gastric glands begins to assume its differentiated form in different parts, i.e., cardiac and pyloric glands, towards the fifth month of development.

Organ Formation—Œsophagus.—The lengthening of the thoracic region of the trunk, which occurs with the growth and development of the heart and lungs, causes the œsophageal portion of the alimentary tube to become greatly lengthened. Vacuoles appear in the epithelial lining, and coalesce to form the lumen.

Stomach.—As early as the fourth week, the fore-gut exhibits a fusiform enlargement in the region of the developing heart which is the first evidence of the differentiation of the stomach : this enlargement first takes the form of an outgrowth on the dorsal border to form the fundus. Soon, however, as the diaphragm is being formed, the stomach passes into the abdomen, and its dorsal wall—the future greater curvature—begins to grow more rapidly than the ventral wall. As a result the whole organ becomes slightly curved, and its inferior end is carried forwards from the posterior abdominal wall, giving rise to the curvature of the duodenum. The excessive growth of its posterior wall and the development of the liver on the right side cause the stomach to turn over on to its right side, which now becomes posterior or dorsal. As it rotates the upper or cardiac portion moves to the left of the median plane, and the whole organ assumes an oblique direction across the abdomen. Already, at the fifth or sixth week, the adult form of the stomach is clearly indicated.

The rotation of the stomach around its long axis, which is accompanied by a rotation of the lower end of the œsophagus, explains the asymmetrical position of the two gastric nerves. In the adult the anterior gastric nerve is found on the front of the stomach, which was originally the left side of the organ; similarly, the posterior gastric nerve lies on the back, which was originally the right side. Nevertheless each nerve which issues from the lower end of the œsophageal plexus contains fibres from both the vagi, which enter the upper end of the plexus.

Intestines.—At first there is no separation into large and small intestines; the primitive canal is a simple, slender tube, with a convexity towards the umbilical orifice, through which the vitelline duct passes to the yolk sac. Later, the tube increases in length, and in embryos of 8 or 9 mm. an outgrowth of the canal appears which represents the future cæcum, and indicates the separation into large and small intestines. Growing longer, the intestine forms a large loop with the vitelline duct springing from its apex (Fig. 543), and the superior mesenteric artery running down between the layers of its mesentery. That loop passes outside the body of the embryo and lies for some time in a part of the cœlom in the umbilical cord; but as the abdominal cavity increases in size the loop retracts into the abdomen. The primary loop is known as the entero-colic loop, and from it are formed the intestine from the distal end of the duodenum to the left colic flexure. At the root of the loop, where the proximal and distal ends come to lie close to one another, lateral bendings of the intestine appear; the intestine headwards to the upper root bends over and forms a loop convex to the right—the gastro-duodenal loop, supplied by a branch of the cœliac artery, and giving origin to the duodenum. The caudal

41 a

portion of the intestine, supplied by the inferior mesenteric artery, forms a loop convex to the left on the posterior abdominal wall (Fig. 543). There now takes place a change which entirely modifies the position of the parts—that is a rotation of the entero-colic loop, with its mesentery, around the superior mesenteric artery as an axis (Fig. 543). The result of this rotation is that the original right side of the loop of gut and mesentery becomes the left side; and the beginning of the large intestine is carried across the duodenum (Fig. 543), thus explaining the passage of the transverse colon in front of the second part of the duodenum in the adult. At the same time the cæcum comes to lie near the middle of the abdomen below the liver—a position in which it is found during the third month. Subsequently, it passes farther to the right; and finally, descending, comes to occupy its adult position (Fig. 544).

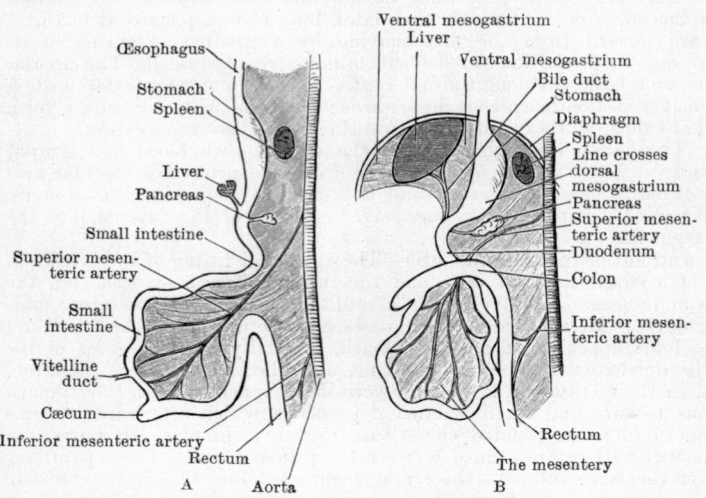

FIG. 543.—TWO DIAGRAMS TO ILLUSTRATE THE DEVELOPMENT OF THE INTESTINAL CANAL.

In both figures the parts are supposed to be viewed from the left side. The ventral mesogastrium is shown in Fig. B only, which shows also the rotation of the intestinal loop around the superior mesenteric artery.

The small intestine continues to grow in length, and, as a result, is thrown into coils, which become more and more complex as the length increases, until the adult condition is attained. The terminal portion of the large bowel retains its position on the left side, and passes down to the anus.

Cæcum and Vermiform Appendix.—The cæcum appears in the sixth week of development as a small outgrowth of the wall of the primitive gut (mid-gut) not yet differentiated into small and large intestines. The outgrowth is of the same size throughout, and is practically equal to the intestine in diameter. About the eleventh week it increases very considerably in length (its length being equal to about five times the diameter of the small intestine, and thus being relatively as long as in the adult); but even at that early date the basal portion, for about one-fifth of its length, is quite as wide as the intestine, whilst the remaining four-fifths of the outgrowth— the future vermiform appendix—is only about one-half or one-third the diameter of the gut. Thus, the distal portion of the outgrowth, which subsequently becomes the vermiform appendix, begins to lag behind even at this early period of its development.

The basal portion continues to expand with the gut; the distal part grows rapidly enough in length, but otherwise enlarges very slowly, so that, towards the end of fœtal life, the cæcum has attained a conical shape, the wider end joining the ascending colon, the narrow end tapering gradually and passing into the appendix. That form, known as the infantile type of cæcum, is retained for some time after birth, or even may (in 2 or 3 per cent. of cases) persist throughout life.

As early as the sixth or seventh month of intra-uterine life the wall of the terminal portion of the small intestine adheres to the medial side of the cæcum for some distance below the ileo-colic orifice. The connexion, which is made more intimate by the passage of two folds of peritoneum, one on the front, the other on the back, between the two parts, profoundly modifies the subsequent growth of the cæcum, and determines very largely its adult form. For, when the cæcum begins to expand, the medial aspect is prevented, by its connexion with the termination of the ileum, from enlarging as freely as the rest of the wall; in consequence of this the lateral part grows and expands much more rapidly, producing the lop-sided appearance already referred to, and soon comes to form the lowest part or fundus of the cæcum, and the greater part of its sac; whilst the original apex, with the vermiform appendix springing from it, anchored, as it were, to the end of the ileum, is thrust to one side, and is finally on the medial and posterior aspect of the cæcum, a little way below, and usually posterior to, the end of the ileum.

The position of the cæcum varies at different periods of intra-uterine life. About the eleventh or twelfth week it lies immediately beneath the liver, and to the left of the median plane; it then gradually travels to the right, crossing the second part of the duodenum, and is found lying on the right side, just beneath the liver, at the fourth month. From there it descends slowly to its adult position, which it usually approaches towards the end of fœtal life, but it may not actually reach it until some time after birth.

Rectum.—The rectum and anal canal are formed from the posterior portion of the hind-gut, and from the anal pit. The primitive closed cloacal portion of the hind-gut becomes divided by a septum into ventral and dorsal portions. The ventral portion, with the allantois growing from it, forms the urogenital sinus, the dorsal forms the rectum. The anal pit is separated from the rectum by the anal membrane, but that membrane disappears, and thus the rectum comes to open on the surface.

A spindle-shaped enlargement of the terminal portion of the rectum is early formed, and persists until birth, and a smaller temporary enlargement is formed proximal to it. The wall of the distal swelling is thrown into numerous longitudinal ridges and folds from which the anal columns are formed.

The rectum and anal canal at first form a single continuous straight tube which passes downwards in front of the comparatively straight pelvic surface of the sacrum to the anal orifice. That is the condition which the parts present at birth. After birth, the bony pelvis undergoes great enlargement. The sacrum and coccyx become curved, and the antero-posterior

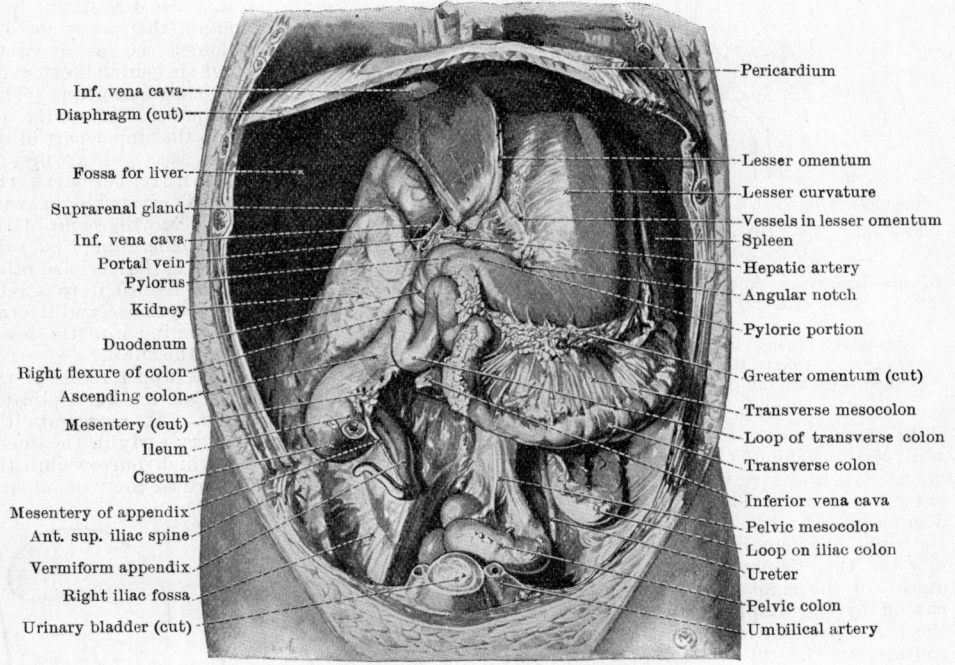

FIG. 544.—THE ABDOMINAL VISCERA IN THE NEW-BORN CHILD. The liver and the jejunum and ileum have been removed. The vertical stomach, the large suprarenal gland, the high position of the cæcum, and the whole arrangement of the large intestine are typical of the condition found at birth, and differ, as can be seen, largely from the adult condition.

diameter of the true pelvis increases very considerably. The urinary bladder and, in the female, the uterus—both organs at birth lying mainly in the abdomen—descend into the true pelvis. The anal orifice appears to be moved farther forwards in the perineum owing to the bending of the sacrum and coccyx, and the rectum is pushed back into the hollow of the sacrum, whose curvature it follows. Another curvature is formed by the junction of the curved rectum with the straight anal canal as it passes downwards and backwards through the tissues of the pelvic floor. The increase in the thickness of the pelvic floor gives to the anal canal the length which it attains in the adult.

DEVELOPMENT OF THE PERITONEUM

At first the primitive alimentary canal is suspended from the dorsal wall of the embryo along the median plane, by a simple **dorsal mesentery** which extends along the whole length of the tube, and is common to all its divisions—a condition found in the adult stage of many reptiles. In the upper part of the cavity, after the stomach and liver descend into the abdomen, there is also a **ventral mesogastrium** (Fig. 543) which connects the stomach and duodenum to the liver, and, passing on, connects the front of the liver to the anterior abdominal wall and septum transversum. The portion of the ventral mesogastrium between the stomach and liver becomes the lesser omentum; its anterior portion, between the liver and the abdominal wall, forms the falciform ligament (Fig. 543); and, in its inferior margin, the umbilical vein runs from the umbilicus to the liver.

The portion of the dorsal mesentery connected with the stomach is known as the **dorsal mesogastrium.** At first it is relatively short; but with the growth of the posterior border of the stomach, and the turning of that organ over on its right side, the dorsal mesogastrium becomes elongated, and is folded on itself, forming more or less of a pouch, directed downwards and

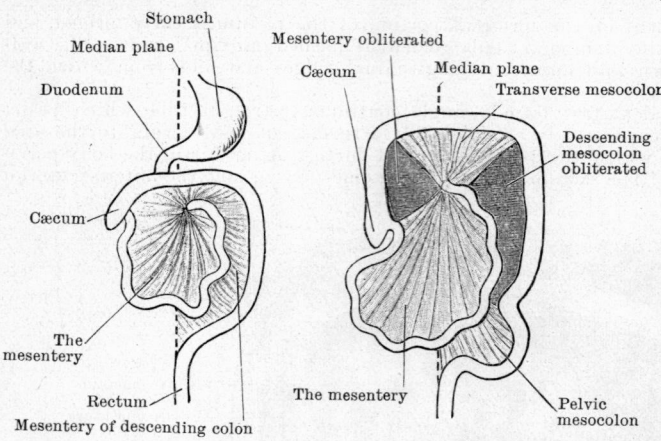

to the left. The wall of this pouch becomes in part the greater omentum, and the cavity enclosed by it forms the greater part of the lesser sac. In the rotation of the stomach and the accompanying passage of the lesser omentum from an antero-posterior to a more or less transverse direction, a portion of the cavity of the abdomen is, as it were, caught in behind the stomach and lesser omentum. That portion of the cavity becomes the upper part of the lesser sac, and at first it communicates with the general cavity by a wide opening to the right of the lesser omentum; but the growth of the liver and other factors reduce it to a relatively small size, and it forms the opening into the lesser sac in the adult.

FIG. 545.—TWO DIAGRAMS TO ILLUSTRATE THE DEVELOPMENT OF THE MESENTERIES.

In the first figure the rotation of the intestinal loop and the continuous primitive mesentery are shown. In the second figure (to the right), which shows a more advanced stage, the portions of the primitive mesentery (going to the ascending and descending colons) which disappear, through their adhesion to the posterior abdominal wall, are shaded dark; the portions which persist are lightly shaded.

right of two pocket-like recesses, a right and a left, which are formed very early in the dorsal wall of the cœlom. The two recesses are narrow and horizontal slits which burrow into the dorsal wall, and turn upwards by the side of the œsophagus. They are termed the "pneumato-enteric recesses." The left one disappears entirely. The apex of the right one remains occasionally as the "bursa infra-cardiaca" of the right lung, and is cut off by the diaphragm from the lower portion, which is the rudiment of the upper recess.

The upper recess of the lesser sac has a complicated origin. It represents the

The **greater omentum** is, as pointed out above, a bag-like growth of the lower part of the dorsal mesogastrium which passes downwards and to the left in front of the transverse colon. As shown in Fig. 546, A and B, it is first entirely unconnected with the transverse colon and mesocolon; but about the third or fourth month it becomes united to both, and the adult condition is established (Fig. 546, C). It would appear that the growth of the inferior part of the lesser sac, and of the greater omentum, is primarily due to a proliferation of the cells over a limited area of the dorsal mesogastrium, and a resulting folding of this layer downwards and to the left.

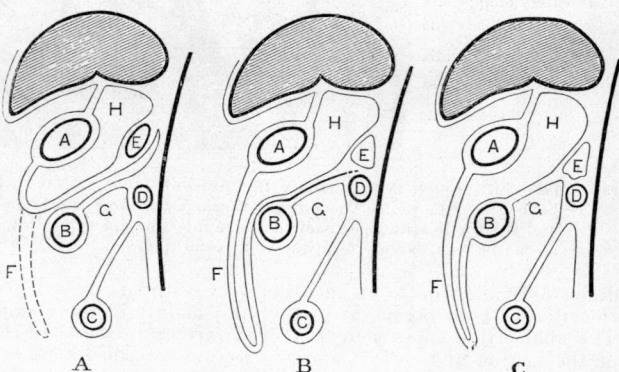

A   B   C

FIG. 546.—DIAGRAMS TO ILLUSTRATE THE DEVELOPMENT OF THE GREATER OMENTUM. (After Hertwig.)

A shows the beginning of the greater omentum and its independence of the transverse mesocolon; in B, the two come in contact; and in C, they have fused along the line of contact. (According to Lockwood, the two layers of the fold shown in A, instead of fusing, as shown in B, are drawn out—unfolded—producing the condition shown in C.) A, stomach; B, transverse colon; C, small intestine; D, duodenum; E, pancreas; F, greater omentum; G, placed in greater sac; H, in lesser sac.

In the upper part of the dorsal mesogastrium the **spleen** is developed, and the portion of that fold which intervenes between the stomach and spleen forms the gastrosplenic ligament, whilst the part behind the spleen becomes the lieno-renal ligament.

Of the primitive mesentery, the portion connected with the stomach—the mesogastrium—becomes modified in the manner just described. The next division—the mesoduodenum—

disappears completely, owing to the turning over of the duodenal loop on to its right side, and its subsequent adhesion to the posterior abdominal wall, accompanied by the absorption of the right side of its mesentery. The mesenteries of the small and large intestine are continuous at first (Fig. 543). When the rotation of the intestinal loop takes place around the superior mesenteric artery (see above), the beginning of the large intestine, with its mesentery, is carried to the right across the duodenum, and a fan-shaped portion of the general mesentery, lying within the concavity of the loop, is partially cut off; that, later on, forms the mesentery proper in the adult. At first it is continuous by its right border with the mesentery of the ascending colon (a part of the primitive mesentery) which itself is continued into the mesentery of the transverse, descending, and pelvic colons. Subsequently, as shown by the darkly shaded parts in Fig. 545, the backs of the mesenteries of the ascending and descending portions of the colon adhere to the posterior abdominal wall, and those mesenteries become lost; whilst the mesenteries of the transverse and pelvic portions of the colon remain free, and persist in the adult.

At the same time, the mesentery proper (which was at first attached only at its narrow neck, between the duodenum and transverse colon, and below that was continuous on the right with the ascending mesocolon) now acquires a new attachment to the posterior abdominal wall through the absorption of the ascending mesocolon (Fig. 546), and the adult condition is attained.

DEVELOPMENT OF LIVER AND PANCREAS

The glandular tissue of the liver and pancreas, and the epithelial linings of the ducts of those organs, including the gall-bladder and cystic duct, are formed from protrusions of the epithelial wall of the fore-gut, below the stomach. The areolar tissue framework of the glands is formed from the mesodermic tissue into which the protrusions grow.

The process of formation is as follows:—

1. **Liver.**—A longitudinal groove appears on the interior of the ventral wall of the fore-gut, close to its union with the mid-gut, at about the third week. The groove appears on the

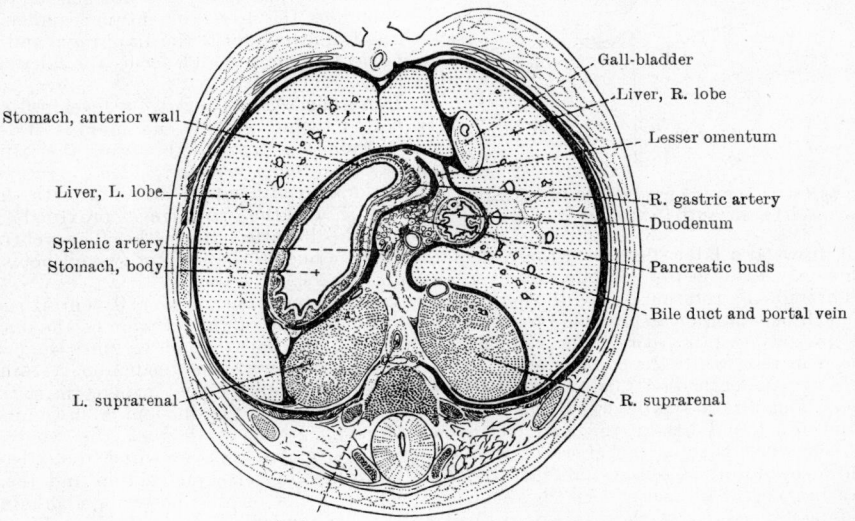

FIG. 547.—TRANSVERSE SECTION OF 26 MM. HUMAN EMBRYO, AT THE LEVEL OF THE UPPER PART OF THE UMBILICUS. (Embryo E 1, St. Andrews University Collection.)

The liver at this stage is of large size, and its left lobe extends into the left half of the abdominal cavity. The suprarenal glands are also relatively very large. The lesser omentum (ventral mesogastrium) is attached to the duodenum as well as to the lesser curvature of the stomach. Buds of developing pancreatic tissue are shown lying to the left side of the duodenum, while, dorsal to them, other buds surround the bile duct, on the left side of which lies the portal vein. The cavity of the lesser sac is shown in black, behind and to the right side of the stomach.

external surface of the gut as a projection which rapidly increases in size and grows forwards and upwards towards the lower part of the septum transversum. The septum transversum is a mass of mesodermic tissue which lies in front of the fore-gut, just caudal to the heart, and is attached to the anterior and side walls of the trunk. The umbilical and vitelline veins pass through it on their way to the sinus venosus.

The liver bud grows into the lower (caudal) portion of the septum transversum, and sends out strands of cells, termed trabeculæ, which come into contact with the vessels in the septum, and enclose them. By the growth of capillary vessels, from the vitelline and umbilical veins, and of the trabeculæ, a spongy network is produced, the framework of which is formed by branching and anastomosing trabeculæ, while the spaces of the network represent portions of the lumen of the vessels, and are filled with blood. This form of vascular network is known as a "sinusoidal tissue." The trabeculæ become hollowed out, and are reduced in size, so that eventually a minute channel is formed in the centre of each of them, surrounded by a single layer of cells. The lumen of the channel becomes the lumen of a bile capillary, and the cells surrounding it form the secreting cells of the liver lobule. The bile capillaries of adjacent trabeculæ meet and unite, and converging together constitute the bile ducts within the liver. Adjacent trabeculæ become arranged into the form of a lobule, each with a vascular channel in its interior which communicates with the vascular network in the surface of the lobule by capillary intervals between adjacent trabeculæ. The central vein becomes a tributary of a hepatic vein, and the capillary network becomes the terminal distribution of branches of the portal vein.

The proximal portion of the original hollow diverticulum becomes the bile duct, and the gall-bladder and cystic duct are formed by an evagination from it.

As the liver increases in size, it begins to project down from the inferior part of the septum transversum into the ventral mesentery, so that now, instead of being situated within the septum, it looks like an appendage of its inferior surface. In other words, the septum begins to differentiate into two parts—an inferior, the liver, and a superior, which constitutes the greater portion of the diaphragm, both of these having been at first one continuous mass. In the course of development the separation of the two becomes more marked, and finally is complete everywhere except at the coronary and triangular ligaments behind, and at the falciform ligament in front, where they are still connected. As the liver separates off from the future diaphragm, and descends into the abdomen, it lies between the layers of the **ventral mesentery**—a fold which connects the stomach and duodenum with the anterior abdominal wall. This fold is divided by the liver into two parts—a lower, stretching from the front (lesser curvature) of the stomach to the liver, which becomes the lesser omentum ; and an upper, stretching from the liver to the diaphragm and anterior wall of the abdomen, which forms the falciform ligament.

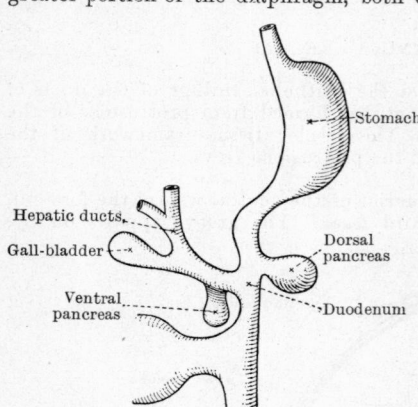

Fig. 548.—Diagram of the Origin of the Liver and Pancreas.

2. **Pancreas.**—The pancreas is developed at a very early period (being present in embryos of less than 5 mm.) from two outgrowths from the alimentary canal—a dorsal and a ventral.

The dorsal rudiment is an outgrowth from the dorsal wall of the intestine, proximal to the origin of the hepatic outgrowth. The ventral rudiment grows at a later stage from the root of the hepatic bud in the form of two offshoots, one on each side. That on the left side, however, soon disappears.

Through the rotation of the duodenum around its long axis, the dorsal and ventral rudiments approach one another and become fused, and their ducts open on the left side of the duodenum. The connecting stalk between the ventral rudiment and the hepatic bud becomes the main duct of the pancreas, while the connexion of the dorsal outgrowth with the duodenum remains as the accessory pancreatic duct. In embryos of the fifth week, a large dorsal pancreatic rudiment is present, and also a smaller ventral rudiment, which opens into the duodenum in common with the bile duct, and lies on the right of the portal vein. In the sixth week, the two rudiments meet and unite with one another, forming a long slender glandular mass which passes backwards within the dorsal mesentery (mesoduodenum), between the vertebral column and the greater curvature of the stomach. As the duodenum comes to lie on the posterior abdominal wall the dorsal extremity of the pancreas is displaced over to the left side, and the body of the gland and the head (included within the hollow of the curve formed by the duodenum) also come to lie on the posterior abdominal wall.

The dorsal (proximal) outgrowth, which passes in front of the portal vein, gives rise to the main mass of the gland, including the upper and anterior parts of the head, the body, and the tail, whilst the ventral outgrowth, lying dorsal to the vein, becomes the uncinate process and the posterior portion of the lower part of the head.

Each developmental portion of the pancreas has at first its own duct, but a connecting channel is formed between the ducts of the dorsal and ventral rudiments, so that the **pancreatic duct** is a composite structure. The **accessory duct** (see Fig. 541, p. 640) is the terminal part of the duct of the dorsal outgrowth.

The primary diverticula give off buds which are lined with cylindrical epithelium, and these in turn give off other buds, and the process goes on until the mass of the gland is formed.

The islets of Langerhans are formed at a very early stage from the entodermal lining cells of the branching diverticula which form the gland acini by separation of some of them from connexion with the system of ducts.

RESPIRATORY SYSTEM

Originally written by the late D. J. CUNNINGHAM, M.D., D.Sc., LL.D., F.R.S.,
Professor of Anatomy, University of Edinburgh

Revised and rewritten by T. WINGATE TODD

THE organs of respiration are the larynx and trachea, which constitute a median air-passage dividing distally into two bronchi, and the two lungs, to which the bronchi conduct the air. The portions of the thoracic cavity which contain the lungs are lined by a serous membrane, called the pleura, which gives a thin coating also to the lung.

The larynx opens into the inferior part of the pharynx, and the air which passes in and out from the air-passages traverses the pharynx, the nasal cavity, and also the oral cavity if the mouth be open. The connexion between the digestive and respiratory systems is explained by the fact that the respiratory apparatus is secondarily developed as an outgrowth from the ventral wall of the primitive fore-gut of the embryo.

LARYNX

The larynx is a mechanism specially adapted to protect the opening of the pulmonary airway, to close it against the entrance of solids, liquids, and even air on necessity, and to control the exhalation of air from the lungs, thus providing an organ of voice in Man. Above, it opens into the pharynx, whereas below its cavity becomes continuous with the lumen of the trachea or windpipe.

Position and Relations of the Larynx.—In the natural position of the neck the larynx is situated anterior to the bodies of the fourth, fifth, and sixth cervical vertebræ. Its highest point, represented by the tip of the epiglottis, extends to the superior border of the body of the third cervical vertebra, whilst its lowest limit (the inferior border of the cricoid cartilage) usually corresponds to the inferior border of the body of the sixth cervical vertebra. From the vertebral column the larynx is separated not only by the prevertebral muscles and the prevertebral fascia but also by the posterior wall of the pharynx—indeed the posterior surface of the larynx forms the inferior part of the anterior wall of the pharynx, and is covered by its mucous membrane.

The larynx lies below the hyoid bone and the tongue, and in the interval between the great vessels of the neck. It forms a more or less marked projection on the front of the neck, and, in the median plane, it is separated from the surface merely by skin and the two layers of fascia. Laterally it is overlapped by the sterno-mastoid muscle, and is clothed by the two strata of thin ribbon-like muscles which are attached to the thyroid cartilage and the hyoid bone. It is clasped, to some extent, by the upper parts of the lobes of the thyroid gland.

The position of the larynx is influenced by movements of the head and neck. Thus, it is elevated when the head moves backwards, and depressed when the chin is carried downwards towards the chest, but its relation to the vertebræ is scarcely changed. During deglutition the larynx moves upwards. The pharyngeal muscles attached to it, and more especially the palato-pharyngeus muscles, are responsible for bringing about those movements. In the production of vowel sounds the pharynx undergoes marked alterations in outline and the larynx accommodates itself to these in position and in the relation of thyroid to cricoid portions. In singing there are no changes of position other than those essential to vowel production. In untrained singers the pharyngeal and laryngeal movements are erratic and lacking in orderly control.

In the fœtus, shortly before birth, the larynx lies nearer the head. The epiglottic apex then corresponds in level to the arch of the atlas, and the lower border of the larynx to the lower border of the fourth cervical vertebra. From four years onwards, in both sexes, the larynx maintains a fairly constant position in the neck. The upper end of the epiglottis is opposite the body of the third cervical vertebra, the œsophageal orifice and arytenoid cartilages are opposite the disc between fourth and fifth cervical vertebræ. The cricoid lies opposite the sixth cervical vertebra. These levels can be definitely confirmed on X-ray examination and verified in the dissecting room. The elasticity of the trachea ensures practical uniformity of laryngeal relations in all positions of the head and neck.

General Construction of the Larynx.—The framework is composed of several cartilages which are connected by distinct joints and also by elastic membranes. Two elastic cords, which stretch from the anterior to the posterior wall of the larynx, form the groundwork of the vocal folds. Numerous muscles operate upon the cartilages of the larynx, bringing about changes in the relative positions of the vocal folds, and producing different degrees of tension of those folds. The cavity of the larynx is lined with mucous membrane, under which, in certain localities, are collected masses of mucous glands.

CARTILAGES OF THE LARYNX

There are three single cartilages and three pairs of cartilages in the laryngeal wall. They are named as follows :—

Single cartilages { Thyroid. Cricoid. Epiglottis. }   Paired cartilages { Arytenoid. Corniculate. Cuneiform. }

The **thyroid cartilage**, the largest of the laryngeal cartilages, is formed of two quadrilateral plates, called the **laminæ**, which are fused together in front in the median plane. The laminæ diverge posteriorly to enclose a wide angular space open behind. The *anterior borders* of the laminæ are fused only in their inferior parts. Above they diverge to produce a deep, narrow V-shaped median notch called the **thyroid notch** (incisura thyroidea). The angular prominence formed by the diverging laminæ is known as the **laryngeal prominence.**

The angle which is formed by the meeting of the two laminæ of the thyroid cartilage presents considerable individual variation and shows marked differences in the two sexes and at different periods of life. In the adult male the average angle is said to be 90°; in the adult female it is 120°. In the fœtus the larynx is relatively large compared with the trachea and is flattened antero-posteriorly. In the infant the laminæ still meet in the form of a gentle curve convex forwards.

The *posterior border* of each lamina of the thyroid cartilage is thick and rounded, and is prolonged beyond the superior and inferior borders in the form of two slender cylindrical processes, termed horns or cornua, of which the **superior** is the longer. It is directed upwards, with a slight dorso-medial inclination, and ends in a rounded extremity joined to the tip of the greater horn of the hyoid bone by the lateral thyro-hyoid ligament. The **inferior horn** is shorter and stouter. It curves downwards with a slight inclination towards the median plane. On the medial face of its extremity there is a circular, flat facet which articulates with a similar facet on the lateral surface of the cricoid cartilage.

The *superior border* of each lamina is, for the most part, slightly convex. In front it dips suddenly to become continuous with the margin of the thyroid notch, and behind, as it joins the superior horn, it exhibits a shallow notch or concavity. The *inferior border* is divided by a rudimentary **inferior tubercle** into a short concave posterior part and a longer anterior part, also concave, but to a less degree.

The *lateral surface* of each lamina is divided into two unequal areas by the **oblique line** which runs from a prominence (the **superior tubercle**) situated immediately below the superior border and a short distance anterior to the root of the superior horn forwards and downwards to end in the inferior tubercle. The area posterior to the oblique line is much smaller than that in front and is covered by the inferior constrictor muscle of the pharynx. The larger anterior area is, for the most part, covered by the thyro-hyoid muscle. To the oblique line are attached the sterno-thyroid, thyro-hyoid and inferior constrictor muscles.

The *medial surface* of the lamina is smooth and slightly concave.

The **cricoid cartilage** is shaped like a signet-ring. Its posterior part or lamina is a broad, thick plate, more or less quadrilateral in form. In front and laterally the circumference of the ring is completed by a curved band called the **arch**. The lumen of the ring is circular below but elliptical above. The upper border of the **lamina** presents a faintly marked median notch. On each side of the notch there is an

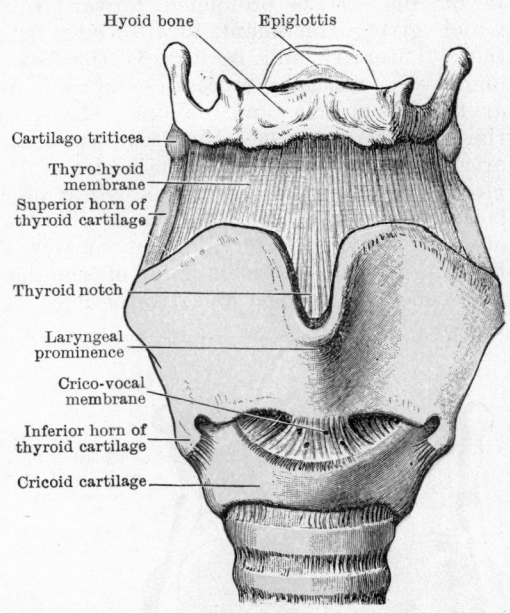

Hyoid bone · Epiglottis

Cartilago triticea

Thyro-hyoid membrane

Superior horn of thyroid cartilage

Thyroid notch

Laryngeal prominence

Crico-vocal membrane

Inferior horn of thyroid cartilage

Cricoid cartilage

FIG. 549.—ANTERIOR ASPECT OF THE CARTILAGES AND LIGAMENTS OF THE LARYNX.

obliquely placed oval facet which articulates with the base of the arytenoid cartilage. The posterior surface of the lamina is divided by an elevated median ridge into two depressed areas which give attachment to the posterior crico-arytenoid muscles. The **arch** of the cricoid is narrow in front, but laterally its upper border rises rapidly to join the margin of the lamina. The *inferior border* of the cricoid is nearly horizontal, although it frequently presents a median anterior projection and two lateral projections. It is connected to the first ring of the trachea by an elastic membrane — the crico-tracheal ligament. On the *lateral surface* of the cricoid cartilage, at the place where the arch joins the lamina, a vertical ridge runs downwards from the arytenoid articular facet. On this, a short distance from the inferior border of the cartilage, a prominent circular facet articulates with the inferior horn of the thyroid cartilage (Fig. 552, p. 656). The *inner surface* of the cricoid cartilage is smooth, and is covered with mucous membrane.

The narrow band-like arch of the cricoid cartilage lies below the inferior border of the thyroid cartilage. The lamina is received into the interval between the posterior portions

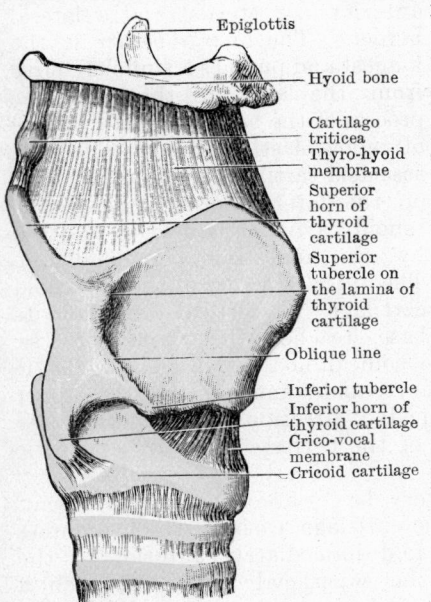

Epiglottis

Hyoid bone

Cartilago triticea
Thyro-hyoid membrane
Superior horn of thyroid cartilage
Superior tubercle on the lamina of thyroid cartilage

Oblique line

Inferior tubercle
Inferior horn of thyroid cartilage
Crico-vocal membrane
Cricoid cartilage

FIG. 550.—PROFILE VIEW OF THE CARTILAGES AND LIGAMENTS OF THE LARYNX.

of the laminæ of the thyroid cartilage.

The **arytenoid cartilages** rest, one on each side of the median plane, upon the upper border of the lamina of the cricoid cartilage, in the interval between the posterior portions of the laminæ of the thyroid cartilage. Each presents the form of a pyramid, the pointed **apex** of which curves backwards and medially. It supports the corniculate cartilage. The **base** is triangular in outline. It is prolonged forward into a small sharp-pointed **vocal process** which gives attachment to the vocal ligament or supporting band of the vocal fold. Laterally and backwards the base is prolonged into a stout prominent angle—the **muscular process**—to which are attached, in front, the lateral crico-arytenoid muscle and, behind, the posterior crico-arytenoid muscle. Near the muscular process the base bears an elongated concave **articular facet** for articulation with the superior border of the lamina of the cricoid cartilage. The *medial surface*, which is the smallest of the three, is triangular in outline and faces the corresponding surface of the opposite cartilage, from which it is separated by a narrow interval; it is narrow, vertical, and even, and is clothed with the lining mucous membrane of the larynx. The *posterior surface* is smooth and concave in the vertical direction. It lodges and gives attachment to the

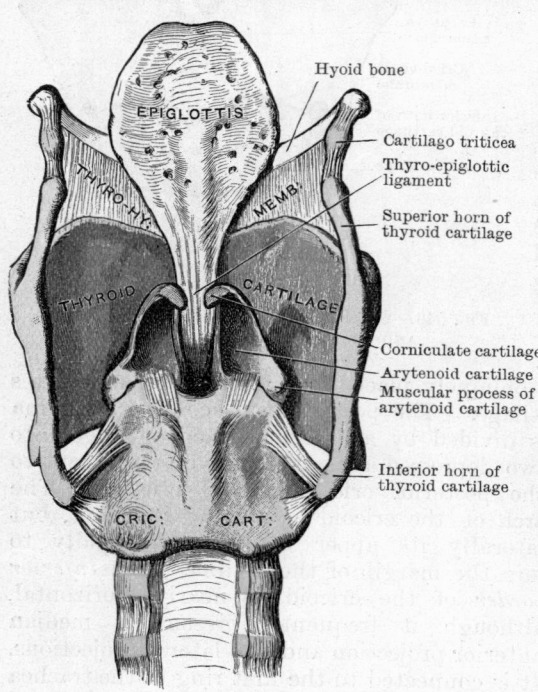

Hyoid bone

EPIGLOTTIS

Cartilago triticea

Thyro-epiglottic ligament

Superior horn of thyroid cartilage

THYRO-HY.

MEMB'.

THYROID　CARTILAGE

Corniculate cartilage

Arytenoid cartilage

Muscular process of arytenoid cartilage

Inferior horn of thyroid cartilage

CRIC:　CART:

FIG. 551.—POSTERIOR ASPECT OF THE CARTILAGES AND LIGAMENTS OF THE LARYNX.

transverse arytenoid muscle. The *antero-lateral surface* is the most extensive of the three (Fig. 552). Its middle part is marked by a deep depression in which a mass of mucous glands is lodged. Upon this surface of the arytenoid cartilage the vocalis and thyro-arytenoid muscles are inserted, whilst a small tubercle a short distance above the base gives attachment to the vestibular ligament— the feeble supporting ligament of the vestibular fold. The three surfaces of the arytenoid cartilages are separated from one another by an anterior, a posterior, and a lateral border. The *lateral border* is the longest and pursues a sinuous course from the apex to the muscular process of the base. A small nodule of yellow elastic cartilage, called the **sesamoid cartilage**, frequently found on the lateral border of the arytenoid cartilage, is held in position by the investing perichondrium. The *anterior border* of the arytenoid cartilage is vertical and, at its base, reaches the vocal process.

The **corniculate cartilages** are two minute conical nodules of yellow elastic cartilage which surmount the apices of the arytenoids, and prolong the upper curved ends of those cartilages in a postero-medial direction. Each corniculate cartilage is enclosed within the posterior part of the corresponding ary-epiglottic fold of mucous membrane.

The **cuneiform cartilages**, which may be very large, are not always present. They are two rod-shaped pieces of yellow elastic cartilage, each of which occupies a place in the corresponding ary-epiglottic fold immediately anterior to the arytenoid and corniculate cartilages. On the superficial surface of each a collection of mucous glands tends to make the cartilage stand out in relief under the mucous membrane.

Epiglottis.—The **epiglottis** is supported by a thin, leaf-like lamina of yellow fibro-cartilage, called the **epiglottic cartilage**, which is placed behind the root of the tongue and the body of the hyoid bone, and in front of the aperture of the larynx. When divested of the mucous membrane which clothes it behind and also covers its upper part in front, the epiglottic cartilage has the outline of a bicycle-saddle. It is indented by pits and shows numerous perforations. In the pits glands are lodged. Through the foramina, blood-vessels and nerves pass. The *broad end* of the epiglottic cartilage is directed upwards, and is free. Its *margins* are, to a large extent, enclosed within the ary-epiglottic folds. The *anterior surface,* free only in its upper part which is covered with mucous membrane, looks towards the pharyngeal part of the tongue. The *posterior surface,* covered throughout its whole extent by the lining mucous membrane of the laryngeal cavity, looks toward the vestibule or upper cavity of the larynx. The *inferior pointed extremity* or *stalk of the epiglottis* is attached by a strong fibrous band— the thyro-epiglottic ligament—low down on the posterior surface of the thyroid cartilage below the median notch.

Ossification of the Cartilages of the Larynx.—The thyroid and cricoid cartilages and the greater part of the arytenoid cartilages are composed of hyaline cartilage. The apical parts and the vocal processes of the arytenoid cartilages, the corniculate cartilages, the cuneiform cartilages, and the epiglottis are formed of yellow fibro-cartilage, and at no period of life do they exhibit any tendency towards ossific change. The thyroid, cricoid, and basal portions of the arytenoids, as life advances, may become more or less completely transformed into bone. This transformation bears no constant relation to age and is already present in some subjects in the third decade. The commonest sites of ossification are the posterior and lower margins of the thyroid and the lamina of the cricoid cartilages, and in old age the thyroid, cricoid, and the hyaline parts of the arytenoids may be completely ossified.

ARTICULATIONS, LIGAMENTS, AND MEMBRANES OF THE LARYNX

Crico-thyroid Joints.—These joints are formed by the apposition of the circular facets on the tips of the inferior horns of the thyroid cartilage with the elevated circular facets on the sides of the cricoid cartilage. Each joint has a ligamentous capsule lined by a synovial layer. Among the posterior fibres of the capsule is a strengthening band. The movement which takes place at the crico-thyroid joints is mainly rotatory, though some gliding is possible, especially in an antero-posterior direction. The thyroid cartilage rotates around a transverse axis which passes through the centres of the two joints.

Crico-arytenoid Joints.—Each of these joints has a ligamentous capsule lined by a synovial layer. The cricoid articular surface is convex, whereas that of the arytenoid is concave; both are elongated or elliptical in form, and they are applied to each other so that the long axis of the one intersects or crosses that of the other at an acute angle. In no position of the joint do the two surfaces accurately coincide—a portion of the cricoid facet is always left uncovered. The capsule of the joint is strengthened behind by a band which is inserted into the postero-medial part of the base of the arytenoid cartilage, and plays an important part in the mechanism of the joint : it effectually arrests excessive forward movement of the arytenoid cartilage.

The movements which take place at the crico-arytenoid joints are gliding and rotatory. During easy, quiet breathing the arytenoid rests upon the lateral part of the cricoid facet. It can glide upon the cricoid facet, and pass towards or from the median plane and its fellow of the opposite side. In the rotatory movement the arytenoid cartilage revolves around a vertical axis; by this movement the vocal process is swung laterally or medially so as to open or close the rima glottidis.

Between the arytenoid and corniculate cartilages there is a more or less rudimentary joint with a capsule, some fibres of which reach the cricoid cartilage. This joint frequently has no synovial lining.

Thyro-hyoid Membrane.—This is a broad, membranous, and slightly elastic sheet which occupies the interval between the hyoid bone and the thyroid cartilage. The central part is thickened to form the **median thyro-hyoid ligament**— composed largely of elastic fibres. This ligament is attached below to the margins of the thyroid notch. Above it is attached along the upper border of the posterior, hollowed-out surface of the hyoid bone, and a synovial *bursa* of variable extent lies between bone and ligament. On each side of the median ligament, the thyro-hyoid membrane is thin and loose. It is attached below, to the upper border of the thyroid cartilage, and above, to the medial aspect of the greater horn of the hyoid bone. It is pierced by the internal laryngeal nerve and by the superior laryngeal vessels. On each side the thickened cord-like lateral margin of the membrane, or **lateral thyro-hyoid ligament**, is composed chiefly of elastic fibres. It extends from the free end of the greater horn of the hyoid bone to the tip of the superior horn of the thyroid cartilage. In each lateral ligament the *cartilago triticea*, a small oval cartilaginous or bony nodule, usually develops (Figs. 549-551).

The median thyro-hyoid ligament lies in front of the epiglottis, from which it is separated by a fatty pad (Fig. 555, p. 658). The lateral part of the membrane is clothed on its deep aspect by pharyngeal mucosa (Fig. 554, p. 658).

Crico-vocal Membrane.—The crico-vocal membrane [conus elasticus] is attached beneath to the entire superior border of the ring of the cricoid cartilage from one arytenoid facet to the other. The median part, or **crico-thyroid ligament**, tense, strong, elastic, and of triangular shape, has its apex inserted into the lower border of the thyroid cartilage at the junction of the laminæ. From this attachment the lateral part of the crico-vocal membrane extends backwards to be inserted into the inferior border of the vocal process of the arytenoid cartilage. Between the anterior and posterior attachments the upper border of this part of the crico-vocal membrane is free and forms the thick **vocal ligament**—the supporting ligament of the vocal fold.

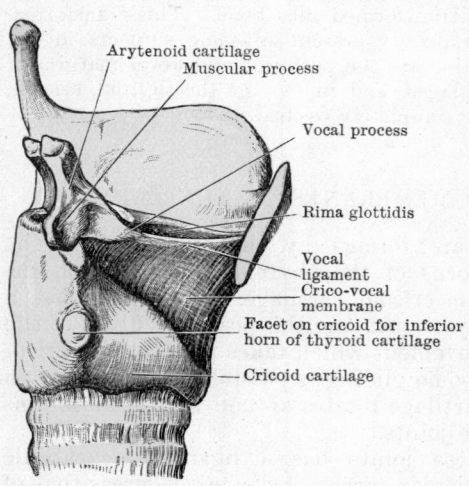

Arytenoid cartilage
Muscular process

Vocal process

Rima glottidis

Vocal ligament
Crico-vocal membrane
Facet on cricoid for inferior horn of thyroid cartilage

Cricoid cartilage

FIG. 552. — DISSECTION TO SHOW THE CRICO-VOCAL MEMBRANE. The right lamina of the thyroid cartilage has been removed.

The crico-thyroid ligament, pierced by minute vessels and crossed by the crico-thyroid branch of the superior thyroid artery, directly unites cricoid and thyroid cartilages. The lateral part of the membrane narrows the lumen of the larynx, is clothed on its deep face by the lining mucosa and is separated laterally from the thyroid lamina by the lateral crico-arytenoid muscle, which covers its superficial surface.

The **vocal ligament**, just defined as the superior border of the crico-vocal membrane, is attached in front, close to its fellow of the opposite side, to the middle of the angular depression between the two laminæ of the thyroid cartilage, and behind to the tip and superior border of the vocal process of the arytenoid cartilage. The vocal ligament is composed of yellow elastic fibres, and embedded in its anterior extremity there is, frequently, a minute nodule of elastic cartilage. Its medial border is sharp and free, and is clothed with mucous membrane which in that position is very thin and tightly bound to the ligament.

The **vestibular ligament** [lig. ventriculare] supports the vestibular fold. It is weak and indefinite, but slightly longer than the vocal ligament. In front it is attached to the angular depression between the two laminæ of the thyroid cartilage, above the vocal ligament and close to the attachment of the thyro-epiglottic ligament; it extends backwards to its insertion into a tubercle on the antero-lateral surface of the arytenoid cartilage, a short distance above the vocal process. It is composed of fibrous and elastic tissue continuous with the areolar tissue in the ary-epiglottic fold, and it is covered by loosely attached mucosa.

The **epiglottis** is bound by ligaments to the base of the tongue, to the wall of the pharynx, to the hyoid bone, and to the thyroid cartilage. The **glosso-**

epiglottic fold is a prominent median fold of mucous membrane which extends from the middle of the free part of the anterior surface of the epiglottis to the back of the tongue. The **pharyngo-epiglottic folds** are similar elevations of mucous membrane that pass from the lateral margins of the epiglottis to the lateral walls of the pharynx at the sides of the tongue. The two layers of mucous membrane which form each of these folds enclose a certain amount of elastic tissue. By these three folds the depression between the back of the tongue and the epiglottis is marked off into a pair of fossæ, termed the **epiglottic valleculæ**, which are invariably filled in swallowing soft, semi-solid masses of food. They are therefore the site in which foreign bodies like small fish bones should first be sought. From the lateral margins of the epiglottis there also pass to the arytenoids the **ary-epiglottic folds** which form the rim of the laryngeal inlet. Between the ary-epiglottic fold and the lamina of the thyroid cartilage is the lateral food gutter in which the opaque shadow of barium can be clearly seen on X-ray examination of swallowing (see Fig. 553).

The **hyo-epiglottic ligament** is a short, broad elastic band, partly broken up by adipose tissue, which connects the anterior surface of the epiglottic cartilage to the upper border of the hyoid bone (Fig. 555, p. 658). The **thyro-epiglottic ligament** is strong and thick (Fig. 551, p. 654); composed mainly of elastic tissue, it extends downwards from the stalk of the epiglottis to an attachment on the angular depression between the two laminæ of the thyroid cartilage below the median notch.

The triangular interval between the anterior surface of the epiglottis and the median thyro-hyoid ligament is imperfectly closed above by the hyo-epiglottic ligament and contains a pad of soft fat (Fig. 555, p. 658).

CAVITY OF THE LARYNX

The **cavity of the larynx** (cavum laryngis) is smaller than might be expected from an inspection of the exterior of the larynx. It is subdivided into three portions by two pairs of elevated folds of mucous membrane which extend antero-posteriorly and project medially from each lateral wall of the cavity. The upper pair of folds are the **vestibular folds** [plicæ ventriculares]; the lower, more definite pair are the **vocal folds** (Figs. 553, 554, 555). It is the latter which, controlling the exhalation of air, become of significance in voice production. By the construction of the larynx, changes in their relative position and in their tension are brought about by the action of muscles and the recoil of elastic ligaments.

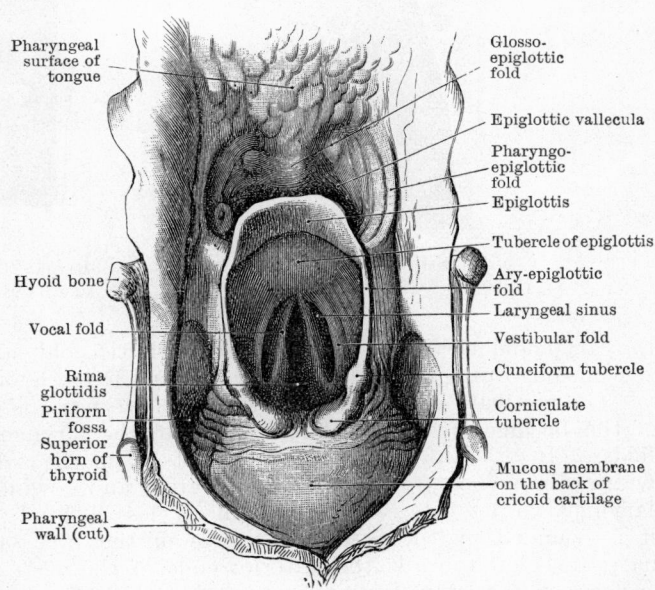

FIG. 553.—LARYNGEAL INLET, EXPOSED BY THE REMOVAL OF THE POSTERIOR WALL OF THE PHARYNX.

The **inlet of the larynx** (aditus laryngis) has a more or less triangular outline. Its anterior, basal part is formed by the free border of the epiglottis. The opening rapidly narrows towards its apex which is lower than the base and lies in the interval between the two arytenoid cartilages. Its sides are formed by the two sharp and prominent folds of mucous membrane already mentioned—the **ary-epiglottic folds**— which stretch

42

between the lateral margins of the epiglottis in front and the arytenoid cartilages behind. The two layers of mucous membrane which compose the ary-epiglottic folds enclose, between them, some areolar tissue, sphincteric muscular fibres belonging to the ary-epiglottic muscles, and, posteriorly, the cuneiform and corniculate cartilages, which produce rounded prominences of the fold called the *cuneiform* and *corniculate tubercles.* When the ary-epiglottic sphincter is in action, those tubercles assist the epiglottic tubercle to complete the closure of the laryngeal inlet.

On each side of the laryngeal opening there is a small pocket of the pharynx, termed the **piriform fossa,** which is part of the lateral food gutter leading from the oral pharynx behind the tongue round the laryngeal inlet to the entrance of the gullet. Foreign bodies may be caught in this pocket, which is bounded on the medial side by

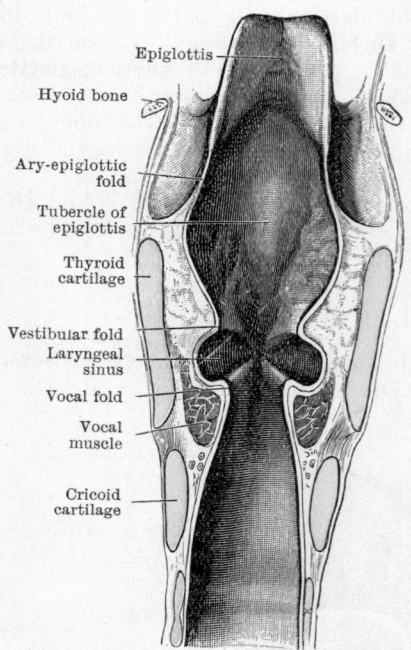

Epiglottis

Hyoid bone

Ary-epiglottic fold

Tubercle of epiglottis

Thyroid cartilage

Vestibular fold
Laryngeal sinus

Vocal fold

Vocal muscle

Cricoid cartilage

FIG. 554.—CORONAL SECTION THROUGH THE LARYNX TO SHOW ITS COMPARTMENTS.

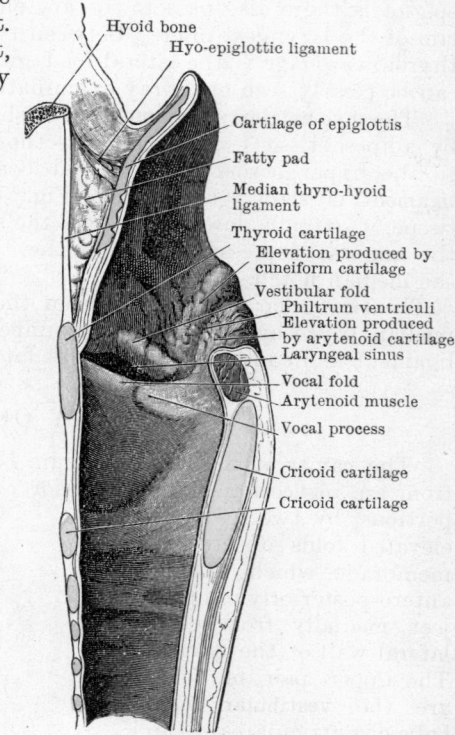

Hyoid bone
Hyo-epiglottic ligament

Cartilage of epiglottis

Fatty pad

Median thyro-hyoid ligament

Thyroid cartilage
Elevation produced by cuneiform cartilage
Vestibular fold
Philtrum ventriculi
Elevation produced by arytenoid cartilage
Laryngeal sinus

Vocal fold
Arytenoid muscle
Vocal process

Cricoid cartilage

Cricoid cartilage

FIG. 555.—SECTION THROUGH LARYNX IN THE MEDIAN PLANE TO SHOW THE SIDE WALL OF THE RIGHT HALF.

the arytenoid cartilage and the ary-epiglottic fold, and on the lateral side by the mucous lining of the thyroid lamina and thyro-hyoid membrane.

The **vestibule of the larynx** (vestibulum laryngis) is the **uppermost compartment** of the laryngeal cavity. It extends from the laryngeal inlet to the vestibular folds. In its inferior part it exhibits a marked lateral compression. Its width diminishes from above downwards, and, owing to the obliquity of the laryngeal inlet, its vertical height is less behind than in front. In front it is bounded by the posterior surface of the mucosa-covered epiglottis, which narrows below towards the anterior ends of the vestibular folds. The posterior surface of the epiglottis is convex above, owing to the manner in which its upper margin is curved forwards towards the tongue; below the convexity there is a slight concavity, and still lower a marked bulging over the superior part of the thyro-epiglottic ligament. That swelling—the **epiglottic tubercle**—forms a conspicuous object in a laryngoscopic examination of the larynx. Each *side wall* of the vestibule of the larynx is formed by the medial surface of the corresponding ary-epiglottic fold. For the most part it is smooth and slightly concave. Posteriorly it diminishes considerably in vertical depth where the cuneiform and corniculate eminences appear—the latter behind the former (Fig. 561, p. 665). The *posterior wall* of the laryngeal vestibule corresponds to the interval between the upper parts of the arytenoid cartilages. Its width, to a large extent, depends on the position of those cartilages; when they are placed near each other the mucous membrane which covers the posterior wall is thrown into longitudinal folds.

The **middle compartment of the larynx** is much the smallest of the three. Its side wall is bounded above by the vestibular folds and below by the vocal folds, and is depressed to enclose an elliptical concavity, called the *sinus of the larynx*, into whose upper and anterior part the *laryngeal saccule* opens (p. 660).

The **vestibular folds** [plicae ventriculares] or **false vocal cords** are two prominent folds of mucous membrane which extend antero-posteriorly, one on each side wall of the laryngeal cavity. In front they reach the angle between the two laminæ of the thyroid cartilage, but behind they do not extend so far as the posterior wall of the larynx; each ends at the lower end of the elongated swelling produced by the cuneiform cartilage. The vestibular fold is soft and rather flaccid, and presents a free border which is slightly arched—the concavity looking downwards. Deep to the mucosa of that fold are: (1) the feeble vestibular ligament; (2) numerous glands which are chiefly aggregated in its middle part; and (3) a few muscle fibres.

The interval between the vestibular folds is termed the **rima vestibuli** and is considerably wider than the interval between the two vocal folds. It follows, therefore, that when the cavity of the larynx is examined from above, with the laryngoscope, all four folds are distinctly visible.

The **vocal folds (true vocal cords)**, placed below the vestibular folds, extend from the angle between the laminæ of the thyroid cartilage in front, to the vocal

processes of the arytenoid cartilages behind. Each vocal fold is sharp and prominent, and the mucous membrane which covers it is very thin and firmly bound down to the subjacent ligament. In colour it is pale, almost pearly white, whilst behind it the point of the vocal process, which stands out clearly in relief, presents a yellowish tinge. In cross-section the vocal fold is prismatic in outline, and its free border looks upwards as well as medially.

The vocal folds, because they control the stream of air, are significant in voice production. The vestibular folds, being part of the protective mechanism by which the airway is closed against the entry of food or foreign bodies, take no part in voice production. Indeed, they can in great part be destroyed and no appreciable difference in the voice results.

Rima Glottidis.—This name is ap-

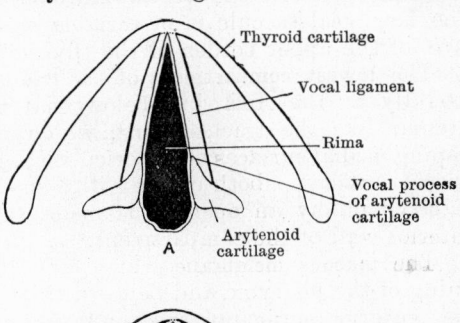

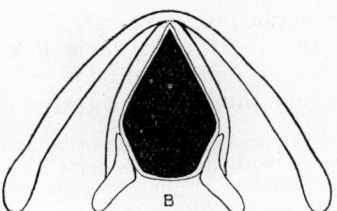

FIG. 556.—DIAGRAM OF RIMA GLOTTIDIS.
A. During ordinary easy breathing. B. Widely opened.

plied to the elongated fissure by means of which the middle compartment of the larynx communicates with the lower compartment. It is placed a little below the middle of the laryngeal cavity, of which it constitutes the narrowest part. Its anterior part is bounded by the vocal folds, its posterior part by the bases and vocal processes of the arytenoid cartilages. The narrow, anterior part between the vocal folds constitutes more than half of its length, and is called the **intermembranous part**. The broader, shorter portion between the arytenoid cartilages is termed the **intercartilaginous part**. By changes in the position of the arytenoid cartilages the form of the rima glottidis undergoes constant alterations. In ordinary easy breathing it is lanceolate in outline; it widens during inhalation and narrows during exhalation. When the rima is opened widely the broadest part of the fissure is at the extremities of the vocal processes of the arytenoids, and there each side of the rima glottidis presents a marked angle. During phonation the two vocal folds are approximated to each other so that the rima is reduced to a linear chink (Fig. 561).

The length of the rima glottidis differs very considerably in the two sexes, and upon this depends the different character of the voice in the male and female. According to Moura, the following are the average measurements in the quiescent condition of the rima :—

Male—Length of entire rima glottidis, 23 mm.　{ intermembranous, 15·5 mm.　{ intercartilaginous, 7·5 mm.

Female—Length of entire rima glottidis, 17 mm.　{ intermembranous, 11·5 mm.　{ intercartilaginous, 5·5 mm.

By stretching the vocal folds, however, the length of the rima glottidis in the male may be increased to 27·5 mm., and in the female to 20 mm.

The position of the rima glottidis may be indicated on the surface by marking a point on the median line of the neck 8·5 mm. below the thyroid notch in the male and 6·5 mm. in the female.

Each side-wall of the larynx, in the interval between the vestibular and the vocal folds, exhibits a marked pocket-like depression or recess called the **sinus of the larynx** [ventriculus laryngis]. The sinus passes upwards, lateral to the vestibular fold, and its mouth is slightly narrower than its cavity. In front, it reaches the angle between the laminæ of the thyroid cartilage; behind, it ends at the anterior border of the arytenoid cartilage.

Under cover of the anterior part of each vestibular fold a small slit-like aperture may be detected ; it leads into a small diverticulum of mucous membrane, termed the **saccule of the larynx** [appendix ventriculi laryngis], which passes upwards, between the vestibular fold and the lamina of the thyroid cartilage. The laryngeal saccule is of variable extent, but as a rule it ends blindly at the level of the upper border of the thyroid cartilage.

The **lowest compartment** of the cavity of the larynx is narrow and compressed laterally at the rima, but below that it gradually widens out until it becomes circular like the trachea, with which it is continuous. It is bounded by the sloping medial surfaces of the crico-vocal membrane and by the medial surface of the cricoid cartilage—both covered with smooth mucous membrane. In the operation of laryngotomy an opening is made through the crico-thyroid ligament in the anterior wall of the compartment.

The **mucous membrane** which lines the larynx is continuous above with the lining of the pharynx, and below with the mucous membrane of the trachea. Over the posterior surface of the epiglottis it is closely adherent, but elsewhere, above the level of the vocal folds, it is loosely attached by submucous tissue which extends into the ary-epiglottic folds. As it passes over the vocal folds the mucous membrane is very thin, and is tightly bound down.

In certain inflammatory conditions the lax submucous tissue in the upper part of the larynx becomes infiltrated with fluid, producing an œdema of the glottis which may even threaten suffocation from occlusion of the upper part of the cavity. The close adhesion of the mucous membrane to the vocal folds, however, prevents the œdema from extending below the level of the rima glottidis. Hence, as a last resort, an opening made into the respiratory passage below this level will always restore a free airway.

Above the level of the rima glottidis the laryngeal mucous membrane is extremely sensitive, and contact with a foreign body immediately induces an explosive cough. In the lower compartment of the larynx the mucous membrane, like that of the trachea, is lined with columnar ciliated epithelium. Over the vocal folds there is stratified squamous epithelium. In the sinus of the larynx and in the inferior part of the vestibule the columnar ciliated epithelium again appears. The upper part of the epiglottis and the upper parts of the side walls of the vestibule are covered with stratified squamous epithelium similar to that present in the mouth and pharynx.

The mucous membrane of the larynx has a plentiful supply of acinous glands, and in only one place, namely, over the surface of the vocal folds, are they completely absent. For the most part the glands are aggregated in groups.

MUSCLES OF THE LARYNX

Of the many muscles connected with the larynx, two groups may be recognised, extrinsic and intrinsic.

The **extrinsic muscles** are those which attach the larynx to other parts, and, strictly speaking, include all those attached to the hyoid bone, which is physiologically a part of the larynx.

The **intrinsic muscles** all lie within the compass of the larynx itself and perform the functions outlined below. They are composed of striated muscular fibres and are innervated by the accessory nerve through the laryngeal branches of the vagus. With the exception of the crico-thyroid muscle, they all lie under cover of the thyroid cartilage.

a. **Sphincters**

    i. Of *inlet*—

        Oblique arytenoids
        Ary-epiglottics
        Thyro-epiglottics

    ii. Of *vestibule*—

        Thyro-arytenoids

b. **Adjustors**

    i. Of *larynx*—

        Crico-thyroids

    ii. Of *rima glottidis*—

        Posterior crico-arytenoids
        Lateral crico-arytenoids
        Transverse arytenoids
        Vocal muscles

More or less inconstant muscular bundles partially separated from one or other of the foregoing by extension of attachment are sometimes dignified by special names and descriptions. There is no particular reason for including them in a practical account.

The muscles of the larynx ensure a free passage for the stream of air in respiration, control the speed of exhalation in speech and singing, shut off the air-stream in fixation of the chest, adjust the position of the larynx to that of the hyoid bone and tongue in movements of the throat, and provide an effective sphincter against the entrance of foreign material during swallowing. In closing the laryngeal entrance the arytenoid cartilages are closely approximated, glide forwards, and are inclined towards the curved epiglottis. Thus, the laryngeal inlet is converted into a T-shaped fissure. The median limb of the T is the interval between the closely approximated arytenoid cartilages and the cross limb is bounded in front by the epiglottis and behind by the cartilages in the ary-epiglottic folds. The apices of the arytenoid cartilages, with the corniculate cartilages, are pressed against the tubercle of the epiglottis, and the lateral margins of the epiglottis are pulled backwards so as to make the transverse limb of the fissure distinctly concave behind. The muscles which produce these movements are the sphincters already listed. The thyro-arytenoids with the assistance of the oblique arytenoid muscles form a true

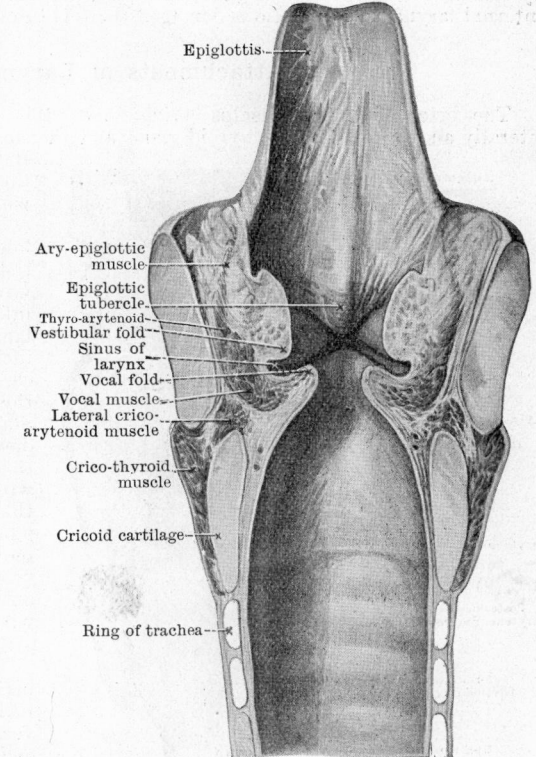

FIG. 557.—CORONAL SECTION OF THE LARYNX, SHOWING MUSCLES.

sphincter vestibuli. The oblique arytenoids, the ary-epiglottic and thyro-epiglottic muscles pull upon the epiglottis to produce tight application of its tubercle to the arytenoid cartilages and the corniculate cartilages.

Innervation of the Larynx.—The nerve-supply of the larynx is derived from the superior and recurrent laryngeal branches of the vagus nerve.

The **superior laryngeal nerve** is the "sensory" or receptor nerve from the mucous membrane of the larynx, and also gives off a branch which furnishes "motor" or effector fibres to the crico-thyroid muscle. All the other muscles of the larynx receive their "motor" or effector nerve fibres from the **recurrent laryngeal nerve**, which, as it winds around the arch of the aorta on the left side, is frequently involved in aneurysm of the aortic arch.

The recurrent laryngeal nerve may be damaged also in cancer of the gullet, thickening of the pleura, mediastinal tumors, extension of tumors from the neck and breast, wounds and operations in the neck, distension of the left atrium of the heart, progressive nervous diseases affecting the cervical spinal cord and medulla, and in toxic conditions like diphtheria, influenza, and lead poisoning. In recurrent laryngeal palsy the posterior crico-arytenoid is first affected and the corresponding vocal fold remains in the position of phonation. Later, when the palsy spreads to the other muscles supplied by the nerve, the vocal fold is fixed in the cadaveric position midway between adduction and abduction. The voice is hoarse but not lost since, during phonation, the healthy vocal fold crosses the median plane to meet its fellow. If both recurrent laryngeal nerves are damaged the vocal folds are fixed in the cadaveric position and phonation is impossible. There is no stridor except in deep inhalation.

Paralysis of the superior laryngeal nerve is very rare, but is stated to be caused by cold or overstrain of the voice as well as by lesions of the medulla oblongata. If the external laryngeal branch alone is damaged there is difficulty in producing high notes and the voice soon becomes tired. This is due to loss of flexion of the thyroid cartilage upon the cricoid normally produced by contraction of the crico-thyroid muscles whenever the root of the tongue is raised. If the internal laryngeal nerve also is damaged there is loss of laryngeal sensation.

Attachments of Laryngeal Muscles

The **crico-thyroid muscles** bridge over the crico-thyroid interval. Each is covered laterally and in part by the thyroid gland and the sterno-thyroid and the sterno-hyoid muscles. Between the two muscles of opposite sides there is an intermediate triangular area in which the crico-thyroid ligament is visible.

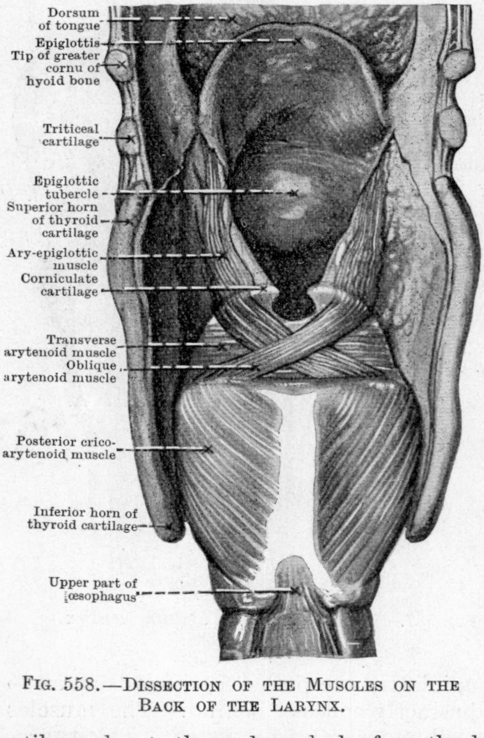
Dorsum of tongue
Epiglottis
Tip of greater cornu of hyoid bone
Triticeal cartilage
Epiglottic tubercle
Superior horn of thyroid cartilage
Ary-epiglottic muscle
Corniculate cartilage
Transverse arytenoid muscle
Oblique arytenoid muscle
Posterior crico-arytenoid muscle
Inferior horn of thyroid cartilage
Upper part of œsophagus

FIG. 558.—DISSECTION OF THE MUSCLES ON THE BACK OF THE LARYNX.

The crico-thyroid muscle **arises** from the lower border and lateral surface of the arch of the cricoid cartilage. Its fibres radiate backwards and upwards to be *inserted* into the inferior border and medial surface of the lamina of the thyroid cartilage, as far as and including the inferior horn. The muscle is closely associated and partly continuous with the inferior constrictor. The crico-thyroid muscles tilt the anterior part of the thyroid downwards upon the cricoid cartilage. While this action does, in certain combinations with other muscles, increase the tension of the vocal folds, its chief function is to render more flexible the form of the larynx in movements of the throat.

The **thyro-arytenoid muscle** is separable from the corresponding vocal muscle, with which it forms a common mass, only by artificial means.

It lies in the lateral wall of the larynx, between the lamina of the thyroid cartilage on its lateral side, and the sinus of the larynx, the vocal muscle, and the crico-vocal membrane on its medial side; its inferior border is in contact with the lateral crico-arytenoid muscle; its superior border extends farther upwards than the vocal fold, and is in contact with the inferior border of the thyro-epiglottic muscle.

It **arises** from the inferior half of the medial surface of the lamina of the thyroid cartilage, close to the angle, and also from the lateral part of the crico-vocal membrane. The muscular fibres pass backwards and upwards to be **inserted** into the lateral border and muscular process of the arytenoid cartilage; some of the fibres, however, turn round that cartilage and become continuous with the transverse arytenoid muscle.

The muscle, acting alone, would approximate the arytenoid cartilage to the thyroid and hence was formerly said to antagonise the crico-thyroid. But since it acts when the position of the arytenoid is stabilized by contraction of the crico-arytenoids and transverse arytenoid, the arytenoid cartilage obviously cannot move and the contraction of the thyro-arytenoid narrows the laryngeal vestibule and thrusts the vestibular folds into close contact. It is therefore the vestibular sphincter.

The **vocal muscle** of each side is a triangular, somewhat prismatic muscle which forms a common muscular mass with the thyro-arytenoid. It is closely applied to the lateral aspect of the vocal ligament, and receives its prismatic form from that adaptation.

The vocal muscle **arises** from the inferior part of the angular depression between the two laminæ of the thyroid cartilage, and also from the corresponding vocal fold, whence the fibres run backwards to be **inserted** into the lateral aspect of the vocal process and the depression on the antero-lateral surface of the arytenoid cartilage.

The muscle produces and adjusts tension throughout the vocal ligament and, with the assistance of the transverse arytenoid in approximating the vocal fold to its fellow of the opposite side, reduces the rima

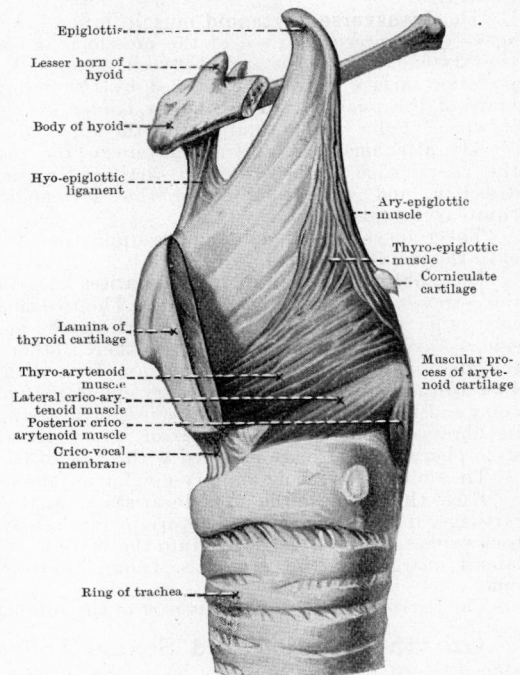

FIG. 559.—DISSECTION OF THE MUSCLES OF THE SIDE WALL OF THE LARYNX.

to a mere chink or even closes it altogether.

Each **posterior crico-arytenoid muscle** arises, by a broad origin, from the medial and inferior part of the depression on the posterior surface of the lamina of the cricoid cartilage at the side of the median ridge. The fibres converge upwards and laterally to be **inserted** into the muscular process of the corresponding arytenoid cartilage. The most superior fibres are short and nearly horizontal; they are inserted on the back of the muscular process. The intermediate fibres are the longest and are very oblique; they are inserted on the apex of the muscular process. The most inferior fibres are almost vertical in their direction and are inserted on the front of the muscular process in common with the lateral crico-arytenoid.

The posterior crico-arytenoid draws the muscular process of the arytenoid cartilage medially and backwards, swings the vocal process and the vocal fold laterally, and thereby opens the rima glottidis.

Each **lateral crico-arytenoid muscle** arises from the upper border and the lateral surface of the arch of the cricoid cartilage as far back as the facet which supports the arytenoid cartilage, and also from the lateral part of the crico-vocal membrane. The muscular fibres run backwards and upwards, and converge to be **inserted** into the anterior surface of the muscular process of the arytenoid cartilage. The muscle is not infrequently inseparable from the thyro-arytenoid muscle.

The lateral crico-arytenoid muscle draws the muscular process of the arytenoid cartilage

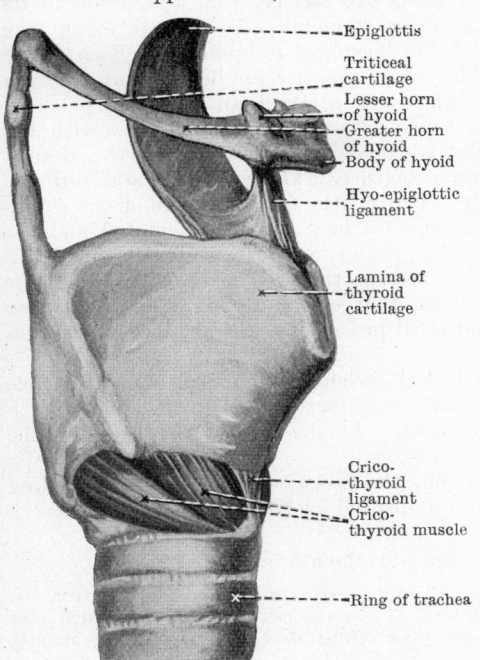

FIG. 560.—THE CRICO-THYROID MUSCLE OF THE RIGHT SIDE.

forwards and laterally, turning the vocal process of the same cartilage medially, and approxi-

42 c

mating it to its fellow of the opposite side, thus assisting in the closure of the rima glottidis.

The **transverse arytenoid muscle** bridges the interval between the two arytenoid cartilages. The anterior surface of the muscle is in contact with the posterior concave surfaces of the arytenoid cartilages and, between them, with the mucous membrane of the larynx. Its posterior surface is partly concealed by the oblique arytenoid covered by the mucous membrane of the pharynx. The inferior border extends to the lamina of the cricoid cartilage, and its upper border does not quite reach the apices of the arytenoid cartilages.

The **attachments** of the muscle are to the posterior surface of the muscular process and the lateral edge of the arytenoid cartilage on each side. All the fibres run in a transverse direction, and some turn round the arytenoid cartilage to become continuous with the thyro-arytenoid.

The transverse arytenoid muscle approximates the arytenoid cartilages, thereby tending to close the rima glottidis.

Each **oblique arytenoid muscle** arises from the posterior part of the muscular process of the corresponding arytenoid cartilage. The two muscles proceed upwards and medially, and cross each other in the median plane. Reaching the apex of the arytenoid cartilage of the opposite side, many of the fibres are **inserted** there; others are joined by a fresh slip that arises from the apex of the arytenoid cartilage and form with it the **ary-epiglottic muscle,** which extends forwards and upwards within the ary-epiglottic fold to terminate in the thyro-epiglottic ligament and the lateral margin of the epiglottic cartilage; as the muscle approaches the epiglottis its fibres are joined by the fibres of the thyro-epiglottic muscle and some fibres from the stylo-pharyngeus also are mingled with those of its upper border.

The oblique arytenoid and ary-epiglottic muscles form the sphincter of the laryngeal inlet.

Each **thyro-epiglottic muscle** arises from the medial surface of the lamina of the thyroid cartilage, immediately above the origin of the thyro-arytenoid. The fibres run upwards and backwards to be **inserted** partly into the margin of the ary-epiglottic fold and partly into the lateral margin of the epiglottis, being intermingled with the fibres of the ary-epiglottic muscle.

The thyro-epiglottic muscle is part of the sphincter of the inlet.

Growth-alteration and Sexual Differences in the Larynx.

A considerable amount of variation may be noticed in the size of the larynx in different individuals. It is quite independent of stature, and explains to a great extent the difference in the pitch of the voice in different persons. But quite apart from those individual variations, there is a sexual difference in the size of the larynx. The larynx of a man is not only absolutely but also relatively larger than the larynx of a woman in all its diameters, more particularly in the antero-posterior diameter. To a large extent the increase is produced by strong development of the laryngeal prominence in men. The greater antero-posterior diameter of the male larynx necessarily implies a greater length of the vocal folds and a lower or deeper tone of the voice in men than in women.

In a newly born child the larynx is relatively large and, in comparison with the calibre of the trachea, very large. The epiglottis varies much in size at birth : it may be large or quite diminutive, and is always soft in texture. The valleculæ and piriform fossæ are so small as to be almost rudimentary. During the first six years of the child's life great changes take place. The calibre of the trachea is much increased and the tracheal cartilages stiffened. The epiglottis also grows considerably and stiffens in texture. The larynx itself grows but at a slower rate, so that by the age of six years the calibre of the trachea is almost uniform in size with that of the larynx. As the larynx grows the vocal folds increase in length and the vocal processes of the arytenoid cartilages become relatively shorter.

From the age of six years, or four years in well-developed children, till adolescence there is little growth in tbe larynx, but in the male at puberty renewed vigor of growth results in the comparatively large size of the larynx. At the same time the valleculæ and piriform fossæ greatly increase in size in both sexes.

In a man who has been castrated when young, the larynx attains a size exceeding that of a woman only to a small degree, and the high pitch of the voice is retained.

Observation of laryngeal movements

When the cavity of the larynx is illuminated and examined by a laryngoscopic mirror, the parts which surround the inlet of the larynx, as well as the interior of the organ, come into view. Not only that, for when the vocal folds are widely separated it is possible to inspect the interior of the trachea as far as its bifurcation.

In such an examination the arched upper border of the epiglottis is a conspicuous object. Behind this the bulging on the anterior wall of the vestibule, formed by the tubercle of the epiglottis, may also be seen. The glosso-epiglottic fold, with an epiglottic vallecula on each side of it, also is seen in the interval between the epiglottis and the back of the tongue. The sharp ary-epiglottic folds are clearly visible, and in the posterior portion of each can be seen the two prominent tubercles which are formed by the enclosed cuneiform and corniculate cartilages. Posterior to those tubercles is the back wall of the pharynx, and to the lateral side of each the piriform fossa is visible. In the interior of the larynx the vestibular and vocal folds are easily recognised, and the interval between the two, *i e.* the entrance into the laryngeal sinus, appears as a dark line on the side wall of the larynx. The vestibular folds are red and fleshy-looking ; the vocal folds during phonation are tightly stretched and pearly white—the white colour being usually more apparent in the female than in the male. The outline and yellowish tinge of the vocal process at its attachment to the vocal fold, and the outline of the anterior part of the base of the arytenoid cartilage may be seen. The vocal folds during inhalation are seldom at rest. In quiet breathing the lanceolate outline of the rima (Fig. 556 A) is very characteristic, widening during inhalation and narrowing during exhalation. In forced or deep inhalation the rima opens widely, presenting a pentagonal outline (Fig. 556 B) and thus permitting the airway to be used to full capacity. It should be borne in mind that the picture afforded by the laryngoscope does not give a true idea of the level at which the different parts lie. The cavity is greatly shortened, and its depth appears diminished.

On the X-ray screen the respiratory airway is viewed from the side. In quiet breathing the laryngeal vestibule is fairly widely open though not dilated as in forced inhalation. The epiglottis and ary-epiglottic folds are conspicuous objects. The arytenoid cartilages with their surmounting corniculate cartilages are obvious and sometimes the cuneiform cartilages also are visible. In a good soft tissue radiograph the sinus itself, between vestibular and vocal folds, is clearly evident, and leading to this is the *philtrum* of the sinus, *i.e.* a groove between the arytenoid cartilage behind and the cuneiform in front.

In vocalization the vestibule is much constricted and becomes a narrow passage like a short organ pipe, though the form of its upper orifice—the laryngeal inlet—varies to conform to the

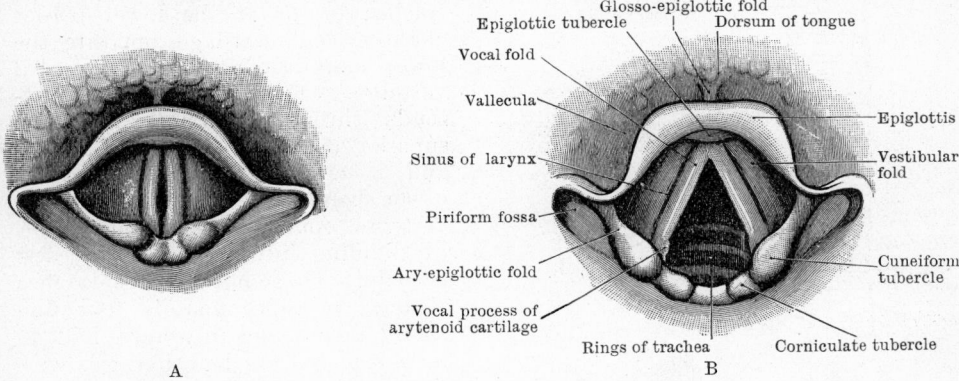

FIG. 561.—CAVITY OF THE LARYNX, as seen by means of the laryngoscope.

A. Rima glottidis closed.   B. Rima glottidis widely opened.

shape of the laryngeal and oral parts of the pharynx where the vowel sounds in speaking and singing are produced.

In speaking or singing the airway must be maintained unimpeded. It is in this connection that the epiglottic valleculæ become of service for they act as reservoirs for drooling saliva during inhibition of swallowing movements. When the saliva is mixed with a radio-opaque substance like barium sulphate, the overflowing vallecula is observed to lose some of its fluid into the lateral gutter or piriform fossa (Fig. 553), flow being directed thither by the slope of the epiglottis.

In mastication, a bolus of food in its semi-solid stage begins to slip past the shepherding veil of the soft palate and slides down the posterior third of the tongue towards or into the valleculæ. When the food has reached the epiglottis and valleculæ, swallowing can no longer be inhibited. The entire laryngeal vestibule can be seen to close, all air being eliminated as far down as the vocal folds. The orifice of the gullet is drawn upwards and sometimes the column of the palato-pharyngeus (and possibly stylo-pharyngeus) muscles can be clearly seen producing this raising of the throat, by which action the laryngeal inlet, protected by the epiglottis, is raised upwards to be partially overhung by the posterior third of the tongue. At this stage the soft palate rises to permit free passage of the bolus and to close off completely the naso-pharyngeal passage. The bolus then tips itself over the epiglottis. Some barium is observed to slip down the lateral food gutter and some passes right over the closed laryngeal inlet. If, however, there is an inadvertent relaxation of the sphincter of the inlet, barium at once forms a momentary dark shadow convex downwards in the upper vestibule but never descends past the vestibular folds. It is indeed immediately ejected by a convulsive cough.

The swallowing of fluid differs in no essential from the swallowing of solid food.

From these observations certain functions of the laryngeal muscles may be inferred.

For service in swallowing there is evidently a sphincter of the laryngeal inlet (ary-epiglottics, oblique arytenoids) which may in swallowing, be taken off its guard. Beneath this there is a second sphincter (thyro-arytenoids) which obliterates the cavity of the vestibule and acts as a second line of defence. It is rare indeed for any foreign body to pass both guards; if this happens bronchoscopic intervention is necessary. Also, in swallowing, the raising of the larynx under shelter of the tongue suggests activity of the thyro-epiglottic muscles.

In breathing the movements of the rima glottidis are evidently controlled by the posterior and lateral crico-arytenoids and the transverse arytenoid.

In vocalization the crico-arytenoids probably fix the arytenoid cartilages. These act as a base from which the vocal muscles (a part of the thyro-arytenoid) produce the proper tension in the vocal folds, and the crico-thyroids tilt the larynx to conform with the adaptation of pharyngeal form to produce the vowel sounds.

TRACHEA

The **trachea** or **windpipe** is kept patent by a series of **C**-shaped cartilaginous bars embedded in its wall. Behind, where the bars are deficient, the tracheal wall is flattened. In the young child the cartilaginous bars are soft and readily compressible, so that they are felt through the tissues with difficulty—a point which must be remembered in tracheotomy. The trachea begins at the lower border of the cricoid cartilage, opposite the lower margin of the sixth cervical vertebra. From that level it extends through the neck into the superior mediastinum of the thorax, and it ends, at the level of the upper border of the fifth thoracic vertebra, opposite the sternal angle, by dividing into the right and left bronchi. The length of the trachea in men is approximately four and a half inches, and in women half an inch less, but its length varies with the movements of the head and neck.

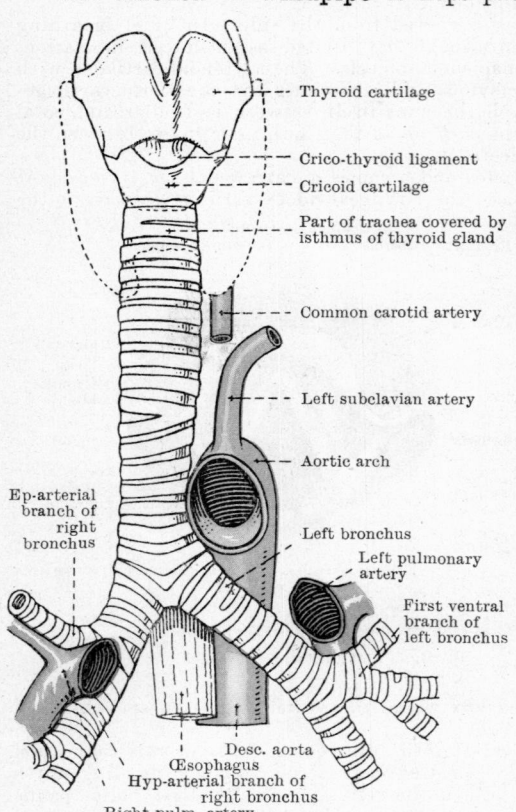

Thyroid cartilage

Crico-thyroid ligament
Cricoid cartilage

Part of trachea covered by isthmus of thyroid gland

Common carotid artery

Left subclavian artery

Aortic arch

Ep-arterial branch of right bronchus

Left bronchus
Left pulmonary artery

First ventral branch of left bronchus

Desc. aorta
Œsophagus
Hyp-arterial branch of right bronchus
Right pulm. artery

FIG. 562.—THE TRACHEA AND BRONCHI.
The dotted line gives the outline of the thyroid gland.

The lower end of the trachea is fixed in position, so that the roots of the lungs are stationary during movements of the head and neck. As the tracheal wall is highly elastic, increase and reduction in length readily occur.

About the middle of its length the trachea exhibits a slight expansion or dilatation, and from that the calibre diminishes towards both extremities. Close to the bifurcation it is again slightly expanded.

Those differences in the calibre of the tube are determined by the surroundings of the trachea. The cervical part is narrowed owing to its being clasped by the thyroid gland, to which in goitre it becomes bound by a rather dense fascia—an attachment which maintains its patency when the cartilaginous bars have become locally absorbed. After operation there is danger of suffocation through collapse of the weak-walled "scabbard" trachea. A short distance above its bifurcation there is an impression, sometimes strongly marked, on the left side of the trachea, due to the close contact of the aortic arch as it passes backwards against that part of the tube. Lejars gives the average antero-posterior diameter of the trachea in the living person as 11 mm., and the transverse diameter as 12·5 mm. In the dead subject the lumen of the tube is considerably greater.

The trachea adheres rigorously to the median plane except towards its termination, where it deviates very slightly to the right. As it passes downwards it recedes rapidly from the surface. That is due to its following the curvature of the vertebral column, from which it is separated by the œsophagus.

Relations of Trachea. —The **cervical part** of the trachea measures from 2 to $2\frac{1}{2}$ inches in length when the chin is held so that the face looks directly forwards but its length is considerably increased when the head is thrown backwards. The thyroid gland clasps this portion of the trachea, the anterior surface of the second, third, and fourth rings being covered by the isthmus and each side of the trachea as low as the fifth or sixth ring being covered by the corresponding lobe of the gland. On each side of the cervical part of the trachea lies the common carotid artery. The recurrent laryngeal nerve passes upwards in the groove between the trachea and the œsophagus. The trachea is separated from the bodies of the vertebræ by the œsophagus, which deviates somewhat to the left as it passes downwards.

Overlying the isthmus of the thyroid gland there are two thin muscular strata composed of the sterno-hyoid and sterno-thyroid muscles, as well as the deep and superficial fascia and skin. Between the approximated margins of those muscles in the median plane of the neck there is a narrow diamond-shaped space within which the trachea is covered merely by the fasciæ and skin. It is important to note that in the inferior part of the neck the deep cervical

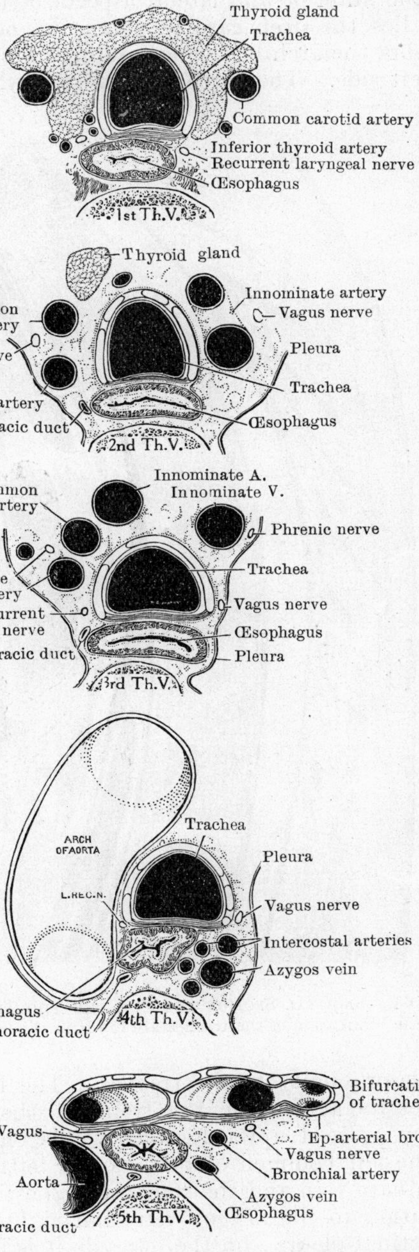

FIG. 563.—TRANSVERSE SECTIONS through the trachea and its immediate surroundings at the level of each of the upper five thoracic vertebræ.

fascia is composed of two layers—a strong stratum applied to the anterior surface of the sterno-hyoid and sterno-thyroid muscles, and a weaker superficial layer stretching across between the two sterno-mastoid muscles. Deep to those muscular and fascial layers the inferior thyroid veins pass downwards and the occasional thyroidea ima artery passes upwards on the anterior surface of the trachea. At the level of the superior border of the manubrium sterni the innominate artery crosses the trachea obliquely.

The **thoracic part** of the trachea is situated in the hinder part of the superior mediastinum, and is separated from the bodies of the vertebræ by the œsophagus. On the anterior and lateral aspects of the trachea immediately above its bifurcation lies the deep cardiac plexus of nerves. At the level of the fourth thoracic vertebra the arch of the aorta clings first to the front of the trachea and then to its left side. The three great vessels which spring from the arch also are placed

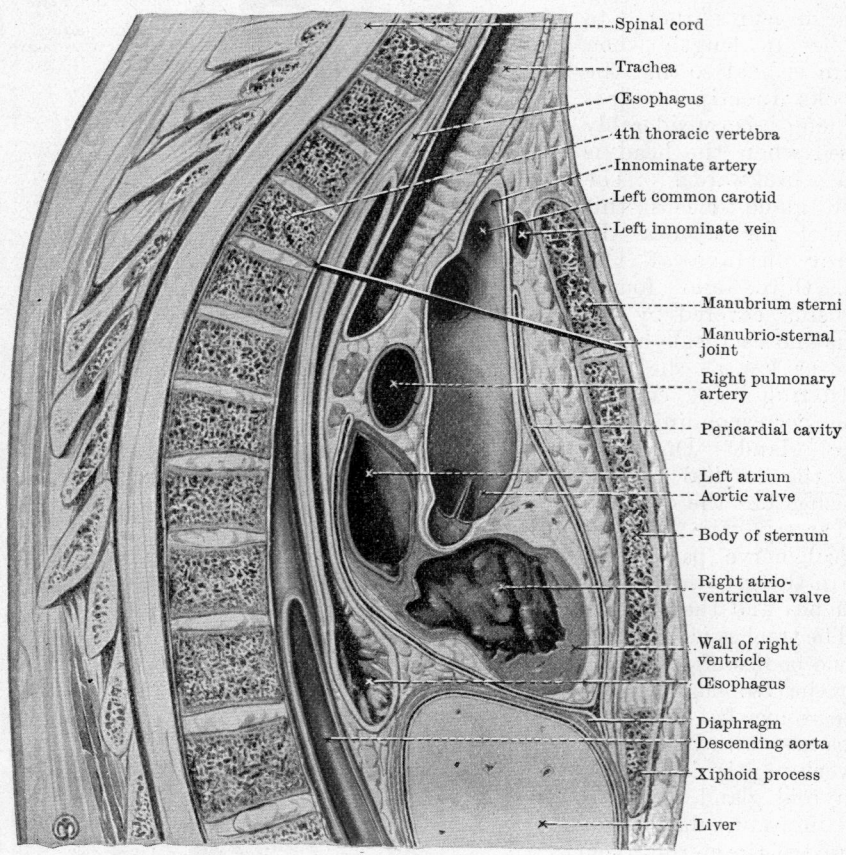

FIG. 564.—SAGITTAL SECTION THROUGH THE THORAX. The superior border of the manubrium sterni and the bifurcation of the trachea are lower in this section of an old man than in the average adult.

in close proximity to the trachea. The innominate and the left common carotid arteries lie at first on the front of the trachea, and then, gradually diverging as they proceed upwards, come to lie on its sides—the innominate to the right, and the left common carotid to the left. In front of those vessels are the left innominate vein and the remains of the thymus. On the right side the trachea is in relation to the azygos vein and right vagus nerve, and is clothed by the right mediastinal pleura; on the left side it is in relation with the left subclavian artery and the arch of the aorta, which separate it from the pleura.

Structure of the Wall of the Trachea.—The walls of the trachea and bronchi are composed of (1) a fibro-elastic membrane in which the tracheal cartilages are embedded; (2) internal to that, in the posterior wall of the tube, a layer of muscular tissue termed the trachealis muscle; (3) a submucous coat; and (4) the lining mucous coat.

The **fibro-elastic membrane** is strong and dense. It passes round the whole circumference of the tube, and is continuous, above, with the perichondrium which invests the cricoid cartilage. Embedded in its substance are the **tracheal cartilages**, which vary in number from 15 to 20, and are composed of hyaline cartilage. They are C-shaped, the posterior fourth of the circumference being deficient, and each cartilage ends behind in two rounded extremities. The outer surface of each tracheal cartilage is flat and even, and does not project much beyond the level of the membrane in which it is embedded; the inner surface, however, is convex in the vertical direction, and consequently it bulges slightly into the lumen of the tube. The intervals between the tracheal cartilages are slightly narrower than the cartilages themselves. Irregularities occur in the cartilages through partial fusion of some and bifurcation of others. The lowest tracheal cartilage inclines downwards in the median plane in front, and from this median peak a cartilaginous strip is carried backwards in the fork between the two bronchi, forming a ridge called the *carina*.

The **trachealis muscle** consists of involuntary muscular bundles placed in the posterior wall of the trachea internal to the fibro-elastic membrane. The bundles are arranged transversely and are attached to the inner surface of the tracheal cartilages either at or a small distance from their extremities. Divergent muscular bands extend from each

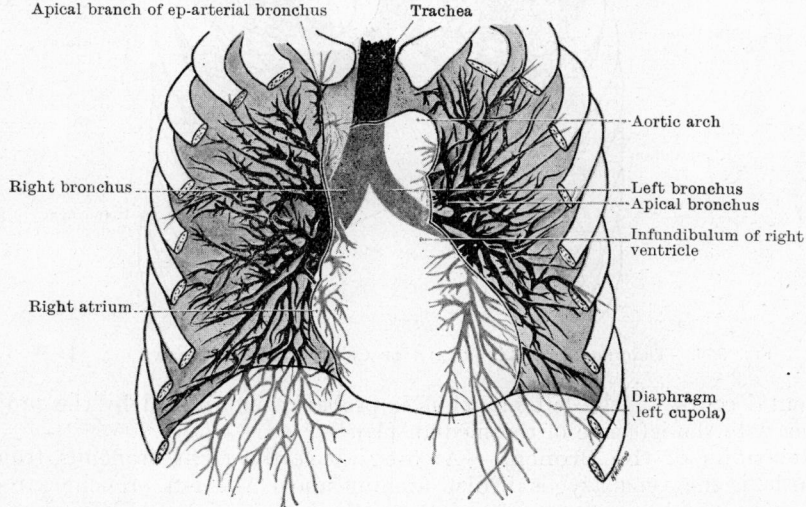

FIG. 565.—TRACING FROM RADIOGRAPH OF CHEST IN FULL INHALATION. (T. W. T.)

extremity of the carina to the lowest tracheal cartilages forming V-shaped depressions known as the anterior and posterior spur triangles.

The **mucous coat** is laid smoothly over the interior of the trachea upon a layer of submucous areolar tissue. Lymphoid tissue enters largely into the composition of the mucous coat and its inner surface is lined with pseudo-stratified columnar ciliated epithelial cells. The action of the cilia produces an upward movement of the mucus present on the surface of the mucosa.

Closely interwoven elastic fibres run lengthwise in the posterior wall of the trachea, more particularly in its inferior part, between the mucous membrane and the trachealis muscle. The rugæ of the mucosa, more obvious on the posterior wall, are produced by the trachealis muscle and not by the elastic fibres.

Mixed glands, containing both mucous and serous cells, lie in the submucous tissue and also on the exterior of the trachealis muscle as well as among its muscular bundles in the posterior part of the tube. Their ducts open by trumpet-shaped mouths on the surface of the mucous coat.

BRONCHI

The two chief **bronchi** proceed obliquely downwards and laterally from the termination of the trachea, each towards the hilum of the corresponding lung. Like the trachea, they are kept permanently patent by cartilages in their walls. The cartilages are deficient behind, so that each bronchus has a flattened posterior surface similar to that of the trachea. The two bronchi differ from each other in length, in width and in direction (Fig. 565).

The first collateral branch of the right bronchus or the ep-arterial bronchus arises nearer the trachea than the first branch of the left bronchus, but there is much variation in this. There are from six to eight cartilages in the right bronchus and from nine to twelve in the left. The right bronchus is wider than the left in the proportion of 100 to 78·4 and it has a more vertical course. It therefore lies more in the line of the trachea, and to this, as well as to its greater width, is due the greater tendency of foreign bodies to lodge in the right bronchus. The average angle formed by the right bronchus, with the median plane is 24·8°, whereas the average angle formed by the left bronchus is 45·6°. The more

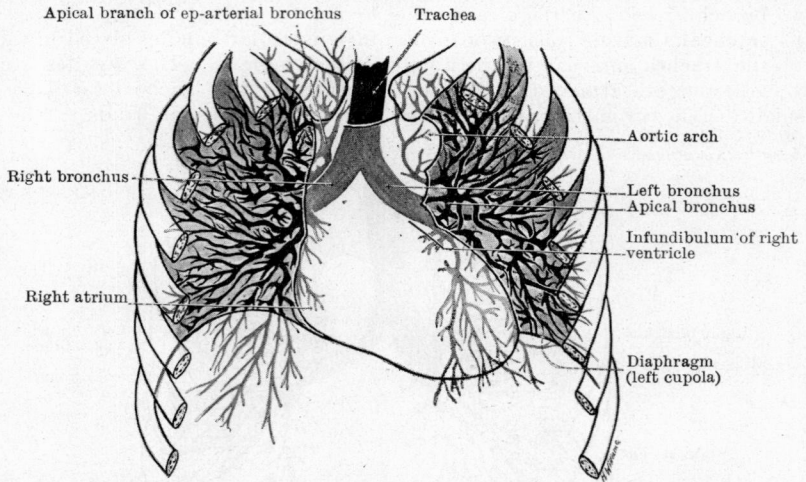

Apical branch of ep-arterial bronchus   Trachea

Aortic arch

Right bronchus

Left bronchus
Apical bronchus

Infundibulum of right ventricle

Right atrium

Diaphragm (left cupola)

FIG. 566.—TRACING FROM RADIOGRAPH OF CHEST IN FULL EXHALATION. (T. W. T.)

horizontal course of the left bronchus is probably determined by the projection of the heart to the left side of the median plane.

Relations of the Bronchi.—Arching above the right bronchus, from behind forwards, is the vena azygos, whilst arching above the left bronchus, from before backwards, is the arch of the aorta. A cluster of tracheo-bronchial lymph glands occupies the interval between the bronchi, and along each bronchus an irregular chain of similar glands is carried towards the hilum of the lung. On the posterior surface of each bronchus the vagus nerve breaks up into the posterior pulmonary plexus. In its course laterally and downwards the left bronchus crosses the anterior surfaces of the œsophagus and descending thoracic aorta. The left pulmonary artery crosses in front of the left bronchus above its first collateral branch and, turning round its lateral side, continues along its posterior surface (Fig. 577). All branches of the left bronchus therefore lie inferior to the corresponding branches of the left pulmonary artery and are in consequence termed **hyp-arterial**. The right pulmonary artery, on the contrary, crosses in front of the continuation of the right bronchus, below its first collateral branch. That branch is therefore termed the **ep-arterial bronchus**, whereas all the others are classified as hyp-arterial.

Structure of the Walls of the Bronchi.—The walls of the extra-pulmonary parts of the bronchi are identical in structure with the wall of the trachea.

Arteries which supply the bronchi and trachea arise from the upper aortic intercostal arteries.

THORACIC CAVITY

The **cavity of the thorax** is the space above the diaphragm enclosed by the ribs. It contains the two lungs each covered by its pleural coatings. It contains also a thick median mass of tissue—the mediastinum—interposed as a septum between the lungs.

Modification of Size.—The dimensions of the thoracic cavity depend on the phase of respiration in which they are measured. In inhalation the circumference is increased 2 to 4 inches in consequence of the raising of the anterior ends of the ribs, and the tilting upwards of their curved shafts. The former action increases the antero-posterior diameter of the thoracic cavity and the latter increases the transverse diameter. Vertical increase in the thoracic cavity is brought about by descent of the diaphragm in inhalation and, unlike the horizontal dimensions, is not measurable from the exterior. During exhalation elastic recoil of costal cartilages and external air pressure reduce the horizontal thoracic dimensions, and the rise of the diaphragm reduces the vertical extent. There are three sets of respiratory muscles :—(1) the intercostals, scalenes, and transversus thoracis, known as the muscles of the thoracic cone ; (2) the trapezius, levator scapulæ, pectorales, and serratus anterior, collectively styled the extraordinary muscles of respiration ; and (3) the diaphragm. The last mentioned is far more sensitive to nervous and emotional conditions and far less under the control of the will than the other two groups. The first group has rather greater power when the subject lies down and thus modifies the antagonistic action of his antero-lateral abdominal musculature. The extraordinary muscles, when they are called into action, assist those of the thoracic cone in expanding the upper lobe of the lung (upper and middle on right side). The diaphragm acts with almost equal power in both erect and horizontal postures and the right cupola moves with only slightly less freedom than the left. When the breath is held, it is the diaphragm which first breaks the voluntary control and returns to activity. The direction of diaphragmatic movement is forwards and downwards. This action expands more particularly the lower lobe. Deep inhalation in an unembarrassed subject results in a movement of the diaphragm of about three and a half times that of the excursion in quiet inhalation. In a nervous subject deep inhalation is almost always accompanied by an inability to hold the diaphragm steadily contracted : indeed diaphragmatic action may be negligible or erratic. These phenomena are readily seen on the X-ray screen.

MEDIASTINUM

The **mediastinum** is a thick mass of tissue that forms a septum between the lungs and extends from the vertebral column to the sternum. It contains :— the heart enveloped in its pericardium ; the thoracic aorta with the great vessels which spring from its arch ; the pulmonary trunk ; the great veins in the neighbourhood of the heart ; the thymus or its remains together with lymph glands and vessels ; the trachea, oesophagus and thoracic duct ; the vagi, left recurrent laryngeal, cardiac and phrenic nerves. Owing to the projection of the heart to the left side and to the position of the thoracic aorta on the left of the median plane the mediastinum encroaches on that side and the left lung is reduced in width. It is customary to subdivide the mass of tissue arbitrarily into four portions, termed the superior, the anterior, the middle, and the posterior mediastina.

The **superior mediastinum** is that part which lies above the pericardium. Its boundaries are as follows :—*Anteriorly*, the manubrium sterni, with the attached sterno-hyoid and sterno-thyroid muscles ; *posteriorly*, the bodies of the first four thoracic vertebræ ; *below*, an imaginary plane, approximately horizontal except in the aged (Fig. 564), which extends from the disc between fourth and fifth thoracic vertebræ to the manubrio-sternal joint ; *laterally*, the mediastinal pleura.

The superior mediastinum is crossed by indefinite fibrous tissue which binds the manubrium loosely to the pericardium over the roots of the great vessels. This fibrous tissue is termed the *superior sterno-pericardial ligament*. It is significant only in adherent pericardium (Pick's disease).

The structures in the superior mediastinum are : (1) the aortic arch and the three great arteries which spring from it ; (2) the innominate veins and part of the superior vena cava ; (3) the trachea, œsophagus, and thoracic duct ; (4) the phrenic, vagi, and cardiac nerves, and the left recurrent laryngeal nerve; (5) the thymus or its remains.

The **middle mediastinum** lodges the pericardium and its contents, and the phrenic nerves with their accompanying vessels.

The **anterior mediastinum** consists of fibro-areolar tissue between the pericardium behind and the body of the sternum in front. It is invaded by the pleural sacs which approach each other on the anterior aspect of the pericardium. In the anterior mediastinum there are a few lymph glands, some lymph vessels, and minute twigs from the internal mammary artery. Like the superior mediastinum it is crossed by indefinite fibrous tissue loosely binding the upper end of the xiphoid process to the pericardium. This fibrous tissue composes the *inferior sterno-pericardial ligament*—significant only in adherent pericardium.

The **posterior mediastinum** is situated behind the pericardium and the diaphragm. It is a prolongation of the hinder part of the superior mediastinum, and many of the structures in the one are continued into the other. *Anteriorly* it is bounded by the pericardium and the vertical part of the diaphragm. *Posteriorly* it is limited by the bodies of the last eight thoracic vertebræ. *Laterally* it is clothed by the mediastinal pleura. It contains the descending thoracic aorta, the posterior intercostal arteries, the azygos and hemiazygos veins, the thoracic duct, and the œsophagus with the two vagi.

When the living subject stands erect, leans forward or lies prone, his heart lies close behind the sternum and costal cartilages. The anterior mediastinum is therefore reduced and the posterior mediastinum increased in the antero-posterior dimension. When the subject reclines or is recumbent, his heart recedes from the anterior chest wall and, in consequence, the anterior mediastinum is increased while the posterior mediastinum is reduced in the antero-posterior dimension.

PLEURÆ

Each lateral portion of the thoracic cavity is clothed with a lining membrane—the **pleura**—which extends over costo-sternal, diaphragmatic, and mediastinal surfaces. The lung in embryonic life buds off from the alimentary tract and, as it grows, pushes before it a portion of the mediastinal pleura, which is thus invaginated into the potential pleural cavity and becomes the *visceral* or *pulmonary pleura* in contradistinction to the *parietal pleura*, which lines the bounding walls.

Each **pleural cavity** is bounded *inferiorly* by the corresponding cupola of the diaphragm; and as the right cupola rises to a higher level than the left, the right pleural cavity presents a smaller vertical depth than the left. *Anteriorly* the wall of each pleural chamber is formed by the costal cartilages and the sternum; *laterally*, by the shafts of the ribs and the intervening muscles (intercostal and subcostal) as far as the costal angles; *posteriorly* by the portions of the ribs, with the intervening muscles, which lie medial to the costal angles; and *medially* by the bodies of the vertebræ and the mediastinum, which completely shut off the one chamber from the other.

The pleura of each side therefore not only lines the corresponding pleural cavity, but, at the pulmonary root, is prolonged on to the lung so as to give it a complete investment. The inner surface of the pleura (*i.e.* that surface which is turned towards the interior of the pleural cavity) is coated with squamous endothelium and presents a smooth, glistening, and polished appearance; further, it is moistened by a small amount of serous fluid. In consequence of that, the surface of the lung covered by pulmonary pleura can glide on the wall of the cavity, lined as it is by parietal pleura, with the least possible degree of friction. In the pathological condition known as pleurisy the inner surface of the pleura becomes roughened by inflammatory exudation, and "friction sounds" are heard when the ear is applied to the chest.

The **pulmonary pleura** is comparatively thick in man. It is prolonged into the substance of the lung to form septa around the lobules. It lines the fissures of the lungs and thus completely separates the different lobes of the lungs from one another. The pulmonary pleura becomes continuous with the mediastinal pleura at the root of the lung, and also through the pulmonary ligament.

In structure the pulmonary pleura consists of four layers—the serous or mesothelial coat, the sub-mesothelial tissue, an elastic layer, and the deeper areolar tissue prolonged into the lung substance and containing nutrient blood-vessels, lymph vessels, and nerves.

Until three weeks after birth, there is no pigmentation in the pleura and the amount of lymphoid tissue underlying it is small. Thereafter both increase. The so-called stomata on the serous surface, by which the pleura was formerly supposed to communicate with pulmonary lymphatics, are really artifacts.

In some adult lungs, especially near the apex, small bubbles of air can be noted beneath the pleura, caused by rupture of alveoli. When this air is expressed the pleura appears wrinkled. These air blebs must be distinguished from the bullae of chronic bronchitis (p. 684).

The **parietal pleura** lines the wall of the cavity in which the lung lies and its several relationships are designated by appropriate nomenclature. Thus there are the *costal pleura*, the *diaphragmatic pleura*, the *mediastinal pleura*, and the *cervical pleura*.

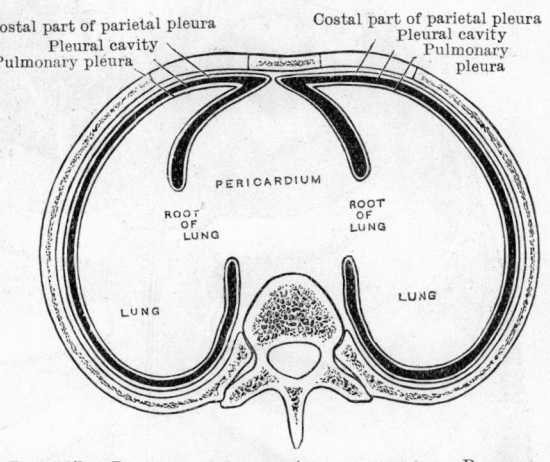

FIG. 567.—DIAGRAM SHOWING ARRANGEMENT OF PLEURAL SACS AS SEEN IN TRANSVERSE SECTION.

The **cervical pleura** [cupula pleuræ] rises into the root of the neck, through the inlet of the thorax, and forms a dome-shaped roof for the pleural cavity. Its highest point or summit reaches the level of the inferior border of the neck of the first rib; but owing to the great obliquity of the first costal arch, that point is placed from one to two inches above the anterior extremity of the first rib, and from a half to one and a half inches above the medial third of the clavicle. The cervical pleura is supported on the lateral side by the scalenus anterior and scalenus medius muscles, whilst the subclavian artery, arching laterally, lies in a groove on its medial and anterior aspects a short distance below its summit. At a lower level the innominate vein also lies upon its medial and anterior aspects.

The cervical pleura is strengthened by the supra-pleural membrane (Sibson's fascia)—an aponeurotic expansion attached to the internal margin of the first rib and derived from a small muscular slip that arises from the transverse process of the seventh cervical vertebra.

The **costal pleura** is the strongest and thickest part of the parietal pleura. It lines the internal surfaces of the costal arches and of the intervening muscles. In front it reaches the sternum, whilst behind it passes from the ribs over the sides of the bodies of the vertebræ. It is easily detached from the parts which it covers, except as it passes from the heads of the ribs on to the vertebral column. There it is rather tightly bound down.

The **diaphragmatic pleura** covers that portion of the thoracic surface of the diaphragm which lies lateral to the base of the pericardium, but it does not dip down to the bottom of the narrow interval between the thoracic wall and the diaphragm. In other words, a strip of the thoracic surface of the diaphragm adjoining its costal attachment is free.

The **mediastinal pleura** clothes the lateral face of the mediastinum and the structures contained in it. It is continuous with the pulmonary pleura around the root of the lung (Figs. 567, 574). It is continuous with the costal pleura anteriorly along the abrupt **line of sternal reflexion** and posteriorly along the bodies of

43

the thoracic vertebræ. Although posteriorly there is no sharp delimitation of mediastinal from costal pleura the indefinite junction of the two is called the **vertebral line of pleural reflexion** (Fig. 567). Inferiorly the mediastinal pleura is continuous with the diaphragmatic pleura at the base of the pericardium.

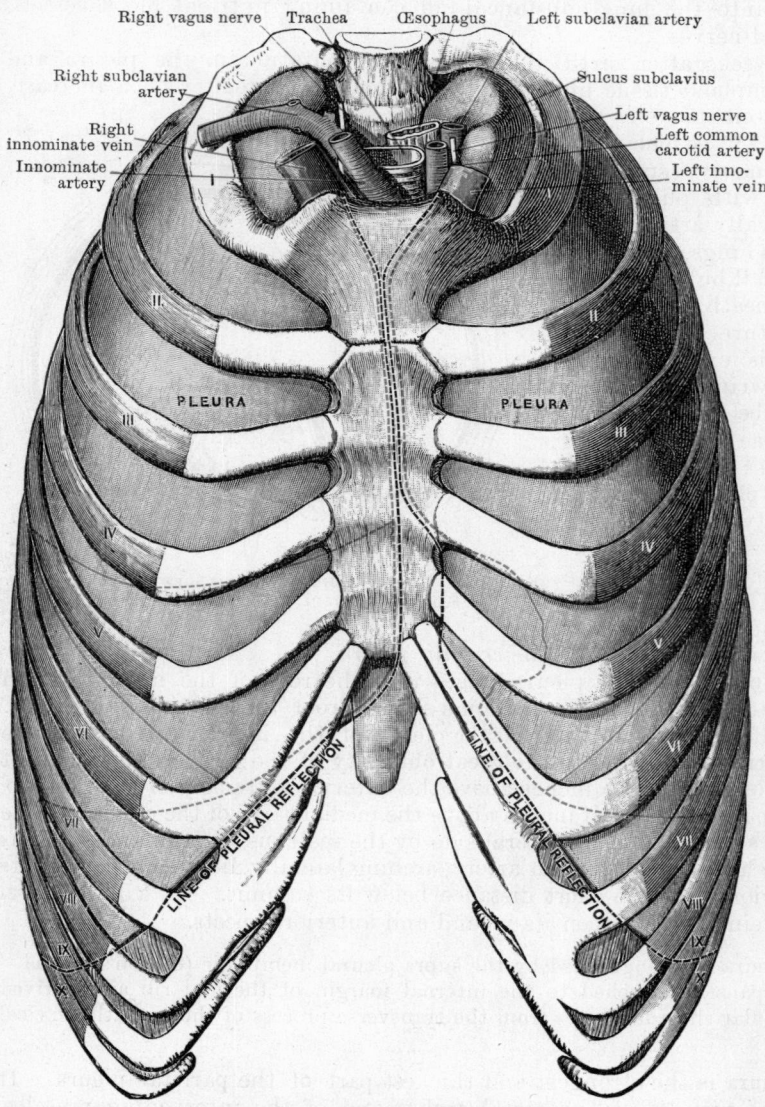

Above the root of the lung the mediastinal pleura passes directly from the sternum to the vertebral column. In that region the *left mediastinal pleura* is applied to the arch of the aorta and the phrenic and vagus nerves; to the left superior intercostal vein and the left common carotid and left subclavian arteries; to the œsophagus and the thoracic duct. The *right mediastinal pleura* is applied, above the root of the lung, to the upper part of the superior vena cava, to the lower part of the right innominate vein and the end of the left; to the innominate artery; to the vena azygos as it hooks forwards above the bronchus; to the vagus and phrenic nerves; and to the right side of the trachea.

FIG. 568.—DISSECTION OF A SUBJECT HARDENED BY FORMALIN INJECTION, to show the relations of the two pleural sacs, as viewed from the front. The anterior and diaphragmatic lines of pleural reflexion are exhibited by black dotted lines, whilst the outlines of the lungs and their fissures are indicated by the blue lines.

Below and in front of the root of the lung the mediastinal pleura clothes the pericardium (pericardial pleura), and is rather firmly attached to it. As the phrenic nerve passes downwards along the side of the pericardium it also is covered by the pleura. As already stated the mediastinal pleura forms an investment for the root of the lung and becomes continuous with the pulmonary pleura.

Below the root of the lung the two layers of pleura which invest it come into apposition with each other, and are prolonged downwards as a distinct fold termed the **pulmonary ligament**. This fold stretches between the pericardium and the inferior part of the mediastinal surface of the lung, and ends inferiorly in a free border. Lymph vessels from the pleura of the lower lobe pass between the layers of this fold to reach the posterior mediastinal lymph glands.

Behind the root of the lung and the pulmonary ligament the mediastinal pleura on the *right side* passes over the œsophagus to clothe, in part, the anterior aspect of the vertebral bodies, whilst on the *left side* it passes to the left side of the vertebral bodies over the thoracic aorta, and to a small extent over the lower end of the œso-phagus, in the region immediately adjoining the diaphragm and anterior to the thoracic aorta.

Lines of Pleural Reflexion.

—The pleural cavities are not symmetrical. The left is narrower than the right, and it thus happens that the lines of pleural reflexion do not accurately correspond on the two sides of the body. The vagueness of the vertebral line of reflexion has been mentioned (p. 674). The sternal and diaphragmatic reflexion-lines are subject to variations in different subjects.

In the vicinity of the manubrium sterni the two pleural sacs are separated from each other by an angular interval. The lines of reflexion at the inlet of the thorax pass behind the sterno-clavicular joints. From those points the lines, as they are traced downwards, converge behind the manubrium, until at last they meet at its inferior border. There the two sacs come into contact with each other, and the lines of reflexion coincide. Thence they proceed downwards, on the back of the body of the sternum, with a slight deviation to the left of the median plane, until a point immediately above the level of the sternal attachments of the fourth costal cartilages is reached, and there the two sacs part company. The line of reflexion of the *right pleura* is continued downwards in a straight line to the xiphoid process, where the sternal reflexion-line passes into the right diaphragmatic reflexion-line. Opposite the sternal attachment of the fourth costal cartilage the reflexion-line of the *left pleura* may deviate slightly, and is continued downwards behind the sternum, at a variable distance from the right pleura, to the sixth costal cartilage. There it turns laterally and downwards, and passes into the diaphragmatic reflexion-line of the left side. The degree of deviation shown in Fig. 568 is due to the method of preservation and must not be assumed to exist when a trocar is thrust alongside the sternum into the pericardium for the purpose of drawing off fluid ; for in so doing the pleura may be punctured unless it has been pushed aside by a distended pericardium.

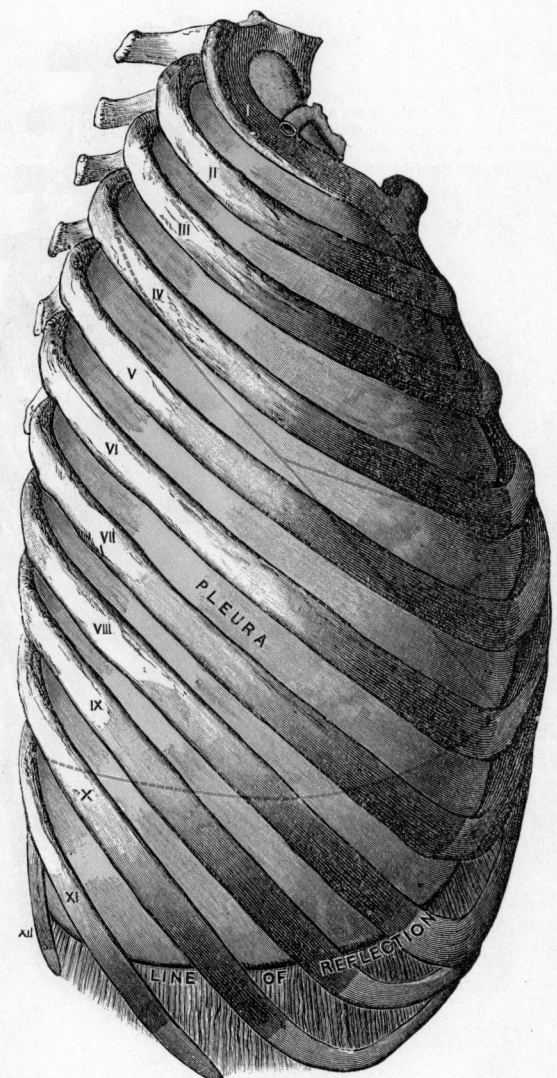

FIG. 569.—LATERAL VIEW OF THE RIGHT PLEURAL SAC IN A SUBJECT HARDENED BY FORMALIN INJECTION. The blue lines indicate the outline of the right lung, and also the position of its fissures.

Sternal line of pleural reflexion.—From the back of the sternum the right pleura is reflected, in the upper part of the chest, on to the remains of the thymus, the right innominate vein and the superior vena cava, and, at a lower level, directly on to the front of the pericardium. The left pleura is reflected from the back of the manubrium sterni on to the left common carotid artery and the aortic arch, and, at a lower level, directly on to the front of the pericardium.

Diaphragmatic line of reflexion.—From the back of the xiphisternal joint, the diaphragmatic line of reflexion crosses the seventh and sixth costal cartilages to reach the eighth costal arch near the junction between its cartilaginous and bony portions, close to its point of intersection with the mid-clavicular line. Beyond that point the line of diaphragmatic reflexion is carried downwards and laterally across the ninth and tenth ribs near their anterior extremities. As it crosses the tenth rib or, perhaps, as it proceeds across the tenth intercostal space, the line of pleural reflexion reaches its lowest point, which lies in the mid-axillary line (*i.e.* in a vertical line drawn on the side of the chest, midway between vertebral column and sternum). Thence, as it curves backwards towards the vertebral column, it passes slightly upwards. Thus, it cuts across the eleventh rib and reaches the twelfth rib. The relation which it presents to the twelfth rib varies with the length of that rib. When the last rib is not abnormally short the pleura clothes its medial half, and the line of reflexion falls below that portion of the rib so as to reach the vertebral column midway between the head of the last rib and the transverse process of the first lumbar vertebra (Fig. 571). There, therefore, the line of diaphragmatic reflexion falls below the inferior border of the thoracic wall; and this is a point of practical importance, because in operations on the kidney

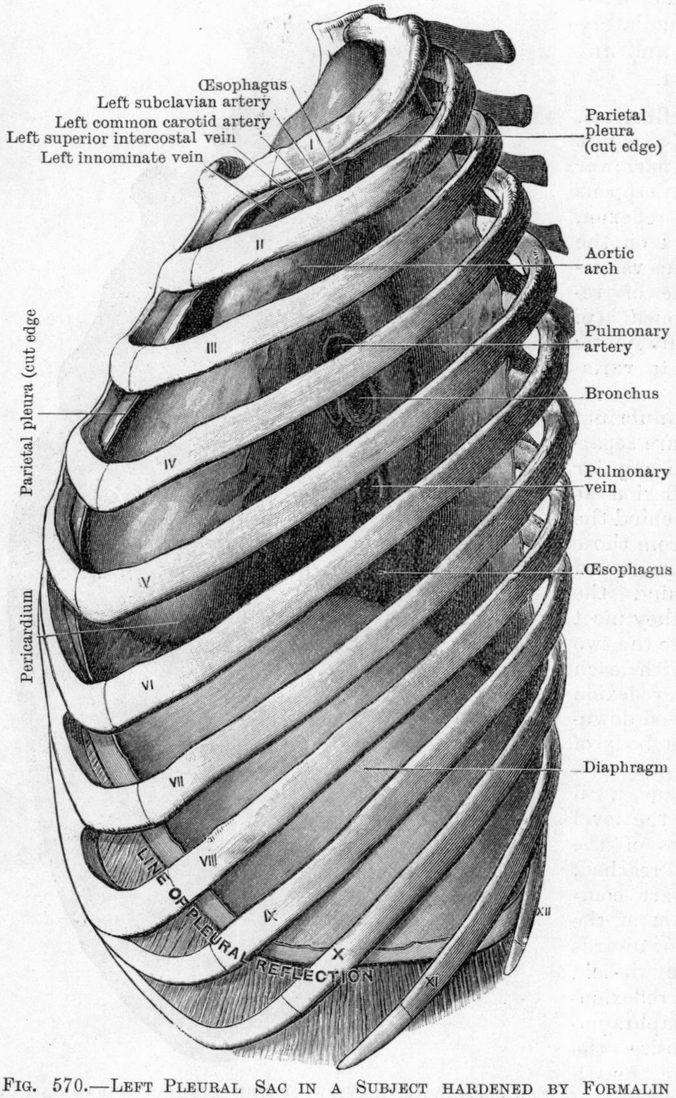

Fig. 570.—Left Pleural Sac in a Subject hardened by Formalin Injection, opened into by the removal of the costal part of the parietal pleura. The lung also has been removed so as to display the mediastinal pleura.

the incision cannot be carried above the level of the transverse process of the first lumbar vertebra and the lateral arcuate ligament [arcus lumbo-costalis] without the risk of wounding the pleura.

It is commonly stated that the left pleural sac reaches a lower level than the right; but that condition is by no means the rule: the right may reach a lower level than the left.

Along the line of the diaphragmatic reflexion, the **phrenico-pleural fascia** passes from the bare part of the diaphragm, and from the costal cartilages to the surface of the costal pleura, so as to hold it firmly in its place.

The parietal pleura, like other serous membranes, is composed of a stratum of fibrous tissue in which bundles of fibres cross each other in various directions, and are intermixed with a considerable quantity of elastic tissue. On the internal surface there is a continuous coating of thin endothelial cells placed edge to edge. The pleura so formed is attached to the parts which it lines and invests by a small amount of areolar tissue termed the **subserous layer.**

The pleura is plentifully supplied with blood, which is conveyed to it by minute twigs from the intercostal arteries and the internal mammary artery. Lymph vessels also are particularly abundant in the pleura and in the subserous layer.

LUNGS

When healthy and sound each **lung** (pulmo) lies free within the corresponding pleural cavity, and is attached only by its root and the pulmonary ligament. Adhesions between the pulmonary and parietal layers of pleura are due to pleurisy.

The right lung is larger than the left, in the proportion of about 11 to 10. It is also shorter and wider. The difference is due partly to the great bulk of the right lobe of the liver, which forces the right dome of the diaphragm to a higher level than the left dome, and partly to the heart and pericardium projecting more to

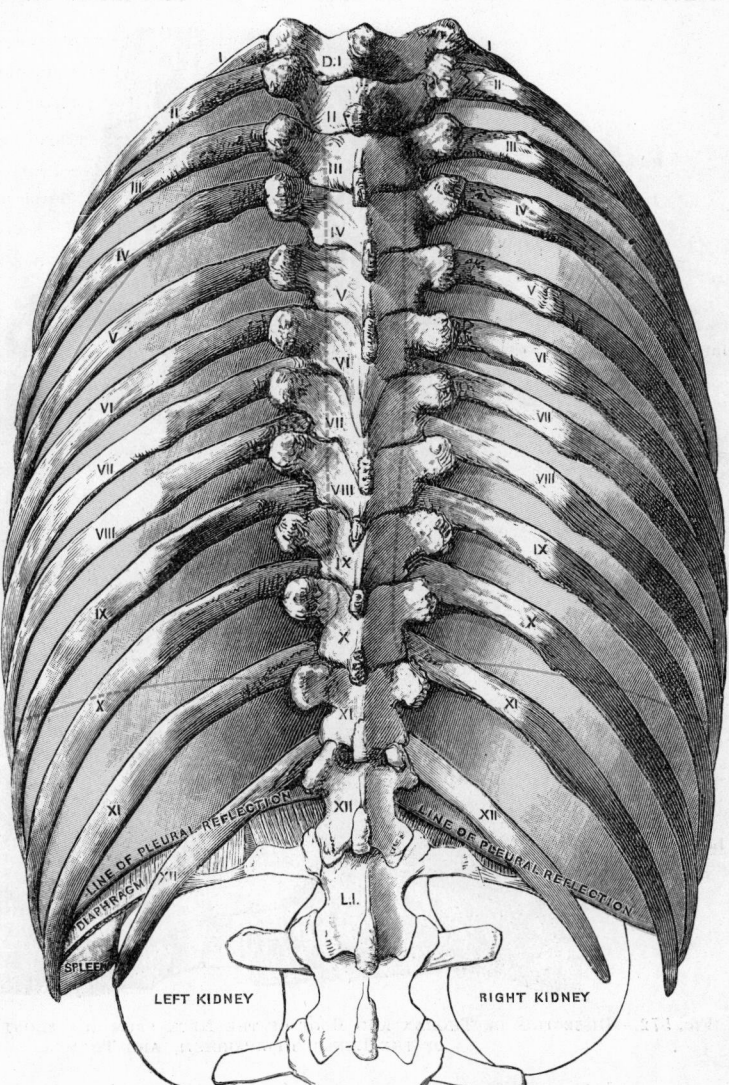

FIG. 571.—DISSECTION OF THE PLEURAL SACS FROM BEHIND.
The blue lines indicate the outlines and the fissures of the lungs.

the left than to the right, thus diminishing the width of the left lung.

The lung is light, soft, and spongy in texture; when pressed between the finger and thumb it crepitates, and when placed in water it floats. Pulmonary tissue is remarkable for its elasticity.

The surface of the adult lung presents a mottled appearance. The ground colour is a light slate-blue, but scattered over that there are numerous dark patches of various sizes, and also fine dark intersecting lines. The coloration of the lung differs considerably at different periods of life. In early childhood the lung is rosy-pink, and the darker colour and the mottling of the surface, which appear later, are due to the pulmonary substance, and particularly its interstitial areolar tissue, becoming more or less completely impregnated with atmospheric dust and minute particles of soot deposited there by the scavenging white cells (phagocytes) of the blood which gathered them from the finer air recesses of the lungs. Owing to the fact that the upper lobes of the lungs maintain a practically constant relationship to the enclosing ribs and intercostal spaces in inhalation

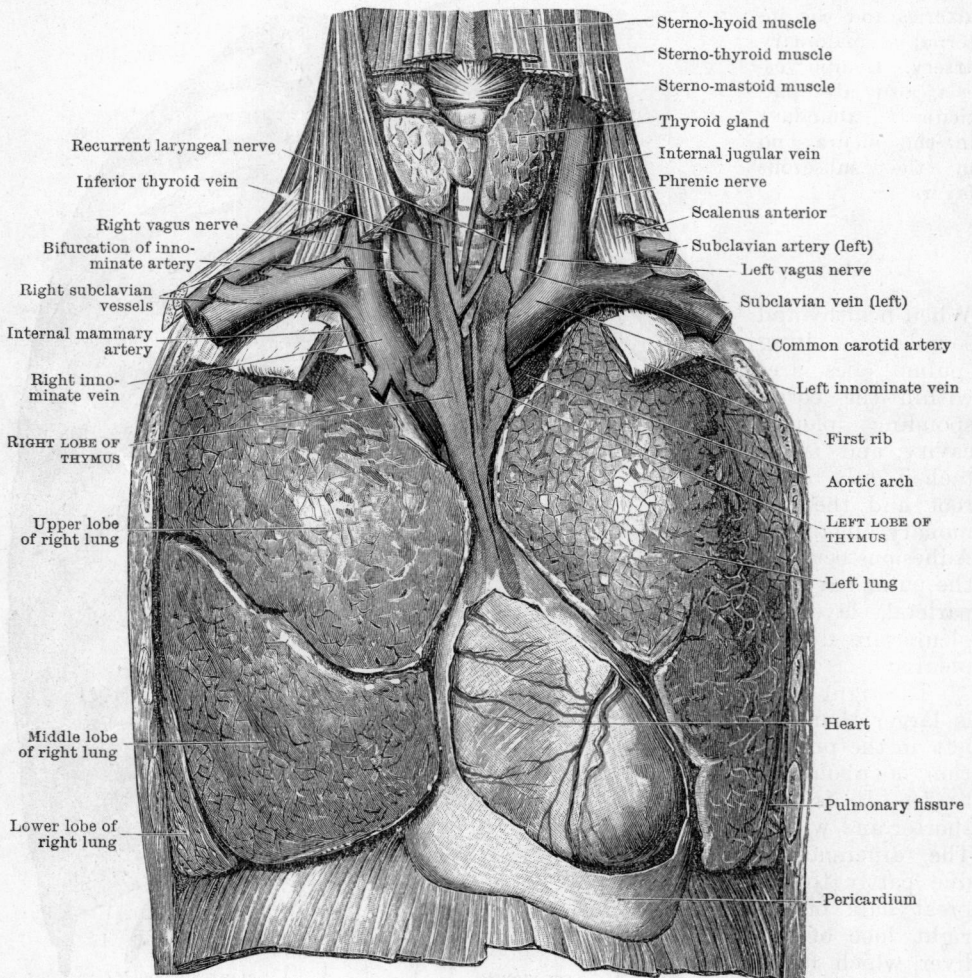

FIG. 572.—DISSECTION OF THORAX AND ROOT OF THE NECK FROM THE FRONT TO SHOW THE RELATIONS OF THE LUNGS, PERICARDIUM, AND THYMUS.

and exhalation alike, the pigmentation on the surface of these lobes tends to lie in bands beneath the intercostal spaces. In the lower lobes, which, owing to the action of the diaphragm, expand in a vertical direction across the obliquely lying ribs, this band-like pattern is distinct only on the upper part of the lobes, where vertical expansion is but feeble in extent.

At every breath foreign matter is inhaled, but only a small proportion of it reaches the lung tissue. The greater part of it becomes entangled in the mucus which coats the mucous membrane of the larger air passages, and is gradually got rid of along with the mucus through the activity of the cilia of the lining epithelium. By their constant upward sweep a current of mucus towards the pharynx is established. The fine dust and soot particles which reach the finer recesses of the lungs, and ultimately the interstitial tissue, are partly conveyed away by the lymph vessels to the bronchial glands, which in consequence become, in many cases, quite black. The colour of the lung, therefore, depends, to some extent upon the purity of the atmosphere which is inhaled, and it thus happens that in coal-miners the surface of the lung may be very nearly uniformly black.

The fœtal lung differs from that of a new-born child who has breathed, for it is firm to the touch, and sinks in water. With the first inhalation, air penetrates the lung— beginning with the antero- lateral parts. Then, success- ively, the diaphragmatic, the apical, and the posterior areas come into action until at the end of a fortnight the entire lung is fully functional. It is only when air and an increased supply of blood are introduced into the lung that it assumes its character- istic soft spongy and buoyant qualities.

Form of the Lungs.—The lungs are necessarily adapted

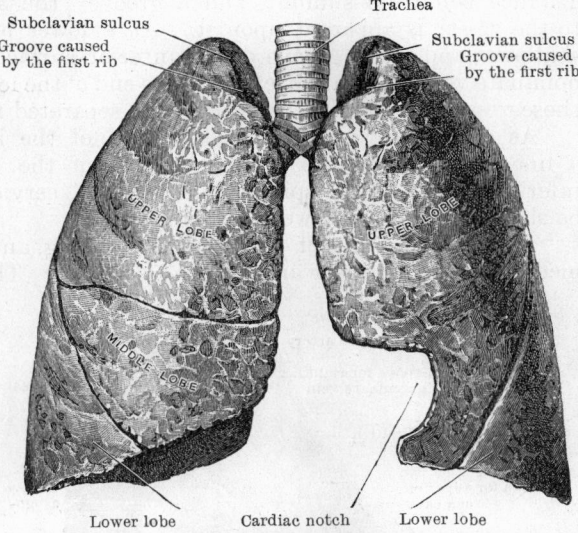

FIG. 573.—THE TRACHEA, BRONCHI, AND LUNGS OF A CHILD, HARDENED BY FORMALIN INJECTION.

to the walls of the pleural chambers in which they are placed and, when hardened by embalming fluid, bear on their surfaces the imprint of ribs, vertebræ and structures in the mediastinum. In this condition, then, each lung presents an apex, a base circumscribed by the inferior border, costal and medial surfaces sharply de- limited from each other in front by the anterior border and less clearly a little behind the hilum by an unobtrusive pos- terior border, which may be rendered more evident by appropriate illumination as in Figs. 574, 575. Curi- ously enough, this margin waited long to be given its name; and the bulky, rounded posterior part of the lung, lying in the deep hollow at the side of the vertebral column was wont to be named the "pos- terior border."

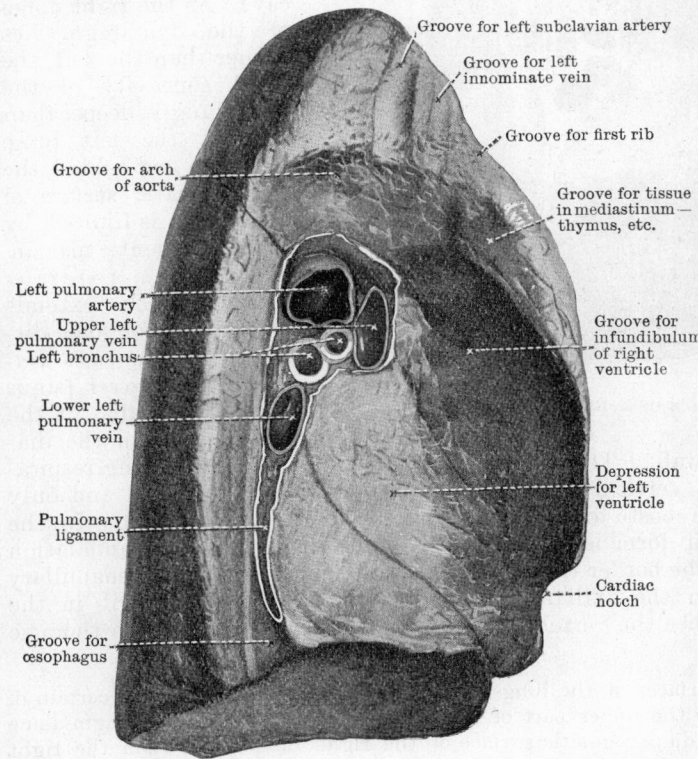

FIG. 574.—MEDIAL SURFACE OF A LEFT LUNG HARDENED *IN SITU*.

The **apex of the lung** is blunt and rounded, and rises through the thoracic inlet, bounded by the first costal arch, to the full height of the cervical pleura in the root of the neck.   The subclavian artery arches laterally on its anterior surface a short distance below its summit, and a groove—the *subclavian sulcus*—corresponding to the vessel is apparent upon it.   At a lower level on the apex of the lung a shallower and wider groove on its anterior surface marks the position of the innominate vein, and, on the left lung, the end of the left subclavian vein also. Although those vessels impress the lung they are separated from it by the cervical pleura.

As examined from behind, the apex of the lung usually extends as high as a line drawn from the highest portion of the acromion of the scapula to the inferior border of the spine of the seventh cervical vertebra. It may, however, be slightly higher or lower than this level.

The lateral limit of the apex of the lung, and consequently of the pleura, is medial to the superior angle of the scapula.   The line is then continued across the supra- and infraspinous fossæ obliquely to reach a point a little lateral to the line of the inferior angle of the scapula.

The **base of the lung** presents a semilunar outline, being curved around the base of the pericardium. It is adapted to the thoracic surface of the diaphragm, and is consequently deeply concave. As the right dome of the diaphragm lies higher than the left, the basal concavity of the right lung is deeper than that of the left lung. Laterally and behind, the **diaphragmatic surface** of each lung is limited by a thin salient margin, called the *inferior border*, which extends downwards for some distance into the *costo-diaphragmatic recess* [sinus phrenico-costalis] of the pleura between the diaphragm and the chest-wall. The thin inferior border of the lung during respiration moves freely in a vertical direction. It is practically horizontal and only approximately fills the costo-diaphragmatic recess in deep inhalation.   In the preserved cadaver, chest form is approximately mid-way between full inhalation and full exhalation. The border therefore crosses the sixth rib in the mamillary line; the eighth rib, in the axillary or mid-lateral line; the tenth rib in the scapular line, and reaches the vertebral column at the level of the tenth thoracic spine.

The diaphragmatic surfaces of the lungs establish important relations with certain of the viscera which occupy the upper part of the abdominal cavity, the diaphragm alone intervening. Thus, the diaphragmatic surface of the right lung rests upon the right lobe of the liver; whilst that of the left lung is in relation to the left lobe of the liver, the fundus of the stomach, the spleen, and, in some subjects, to the left colic flexure.

The **costal surface** is extensive and convex.   It is accurately adapted to that part of the wall of the pleural cavity which is formed by the sternum, the

Groove for right subclavian artery
Groove for right innominate vein
Groove for first rib
Groove for superior vena cava
Area for ascending aorta, thymus and fat
Depression for right atrium
Œsophageal area
Tracheal area
Groove for azygos vein
Groove for azygos vein
Groove for œsophagus
Groove for inferior vena cava
Pulmonary ligament

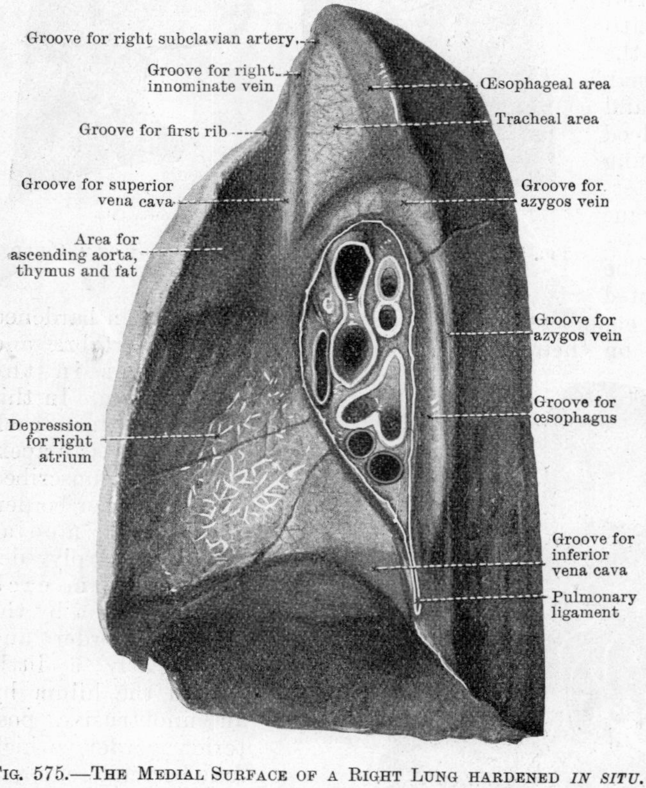

FIG. 575.—THE MEDIAL SURFACE OF A RIGHT LUNG HARDENED *IN SITU*.

costal arches and the intervening muscles, the imprints of which are left upon it in the preserved cadaver.

The **medial surface** is applied to the sides of the vertebral bodies and to the mediastinal septum, and the **mediastinal area** [facies mediastinalis] presents markings in accordance with the inequalities of the septum (Figs. 574 and 575). Thus, it is deeply hollowed out in adaptation to the pericardium, upon which it fits. This pericardial concavity comprises the greater part of the mediastinal area, and, owing to the greater projection of the heart to the left side, it is much deeper and more extensive in the left lung than in the right lung. Above and behind the pericardial hollow is the hilum of the lung. The **hilum** is a wedge-shaped depressed area within which the blood-vessels, nerves, and lymph vessels, together with the bronchus, enter and leave the organ. Amidst those structures there are also some bronchial glands. The hilum is surrounded by the reflexion of the pleura from the surface of the lung on to the pulmonary root. Behind the hilum and pericardial area there is on each lung a narrow strip of the mediastinal area of the lung which is in relation to the lateral wall of the posterior mediastinum. On the *right lung* that part of the surface is depressed, and corresponds to the œsophagus; on the *left lung* it presents a broad longitudinal groove which is produced by the pressure of the thoracic aorta on the pleura and lung, and also, close to the base in front of the aortic impression, a small flattened area which is related to the œsophagus immediately above the diaphragm.

The portion of the mediastinal area of the lung which lies above the hilum and pericardial hollow is applied to the lateral aspect of the superior mediastinum, and the markings are accordingly different on the two sides. On the *left lung* a broad deep groove, produced by the aortic arch, curves backwards above the hilum, and becomes continuous with the aortic groove on the hinder part of the mediastinal area. From the groove for the aortic arch a narrower, deeper, and much more sharply marked groove runs upwards to become continuous with the groove that arches laterally across the front of the apex. That is the **subclavian sulcus**, and it contains the left subclavian artery when the lung is in place. In front of the subclavian sulcus there is a small area related to the left common carotid artery and the phrenic and vagus nerves. In the *right lung* the hilum is also circumscribed above by a curved groove which is narrow and more distinctly curved than the aortic groove in the left lung. This lodges the vena azygos as it turns forwards to join the superior vena cava. From the anterior end of the azygos sulcus a wide shallow groove extends upward to the apex of the lung, a short distance below its summit. This is produced by the relation of the lung to the superior vena cava and the right innominate vein. Close to the summit there may be, on its medial aspect, a sulcus for the upper end of the innominate artery.

In addition to the hilum, it must now be evident that the mediastinal area of each lung presents three districts which correspond respectively with (1) the middle mediastinum (*i.e.*, the pericardial hollow), (2) the posterior mediastinum, and (3) the superior mediastinum; and that in each of those districts impressions corresponding to structures contained within the mediastinum may be noticed.

The **posterior border** of the lung divides the costal from the medial surface; as explained already (p. 679), it is a very ill-defined margin.

The **anterior border** of the lung is short, and exceedingly thin and sharp. It begins abruptly, an inch or more below the summit, opposite the sterno-clavicular joint, and extends to the base, where it becomes continuous with the sharp inferior border. The thin front part of the lung is carried forwards and medially, anterior to the pericardium, into the narrow *costo-mediastinal recess* [sinus] of the pleura behind the sternum and costal cartilages. The anterior border of the right lung completely fills this recess and in the upper part of the chest is separated from the corresponding border of the left lung only by the two layers of mediastinal pleura which are reflected from the sternum to the pericardium. The anterior border of the left lung, in its lower part, shows a deficiency of variable size, called the **cardiac notch**, which corresponds to the lower, left part of the heart, and where that notch exists the lung margin leaves a small portion of the pericardium uncovered, and fails to fill up the costo-mediastinal recess of the pleural cavity completely. During respiration the anterior margin of the left lung, at the cardiac notch, advances and retreats to a small extent in the pleural recess in front of the pericardium.

In childhood when the thymus is active and large the anterior borders of the lungs, in exhalation, are pressed apart by the thymus. But in inhalation, owing to expansion of the chest, the anterior borders of the lungs approximate each other and compress the thymus from the sides so that it sinks deeply into the intervening superior mediastinum. After the age of three years, however, the thymic shadow is no longer visible in radiographs of healthy children, for the involution of the organ has already begun.

Fissures and Lobes of the Lung.—The *left lung* is divided into two lobes by a long, deep, **oblique fissure** [incisura interlobaris], which penetrates its substance to within a short distance of the hilum. On the upper and lower sides of the hilum this fissure cuts right through the lung and appears on the medial surface. Viewed from the costal surface, it begins behind about two and a half inches below the apex, about the level of the vertebral end of the third rib, and is continued downwards and forwards in a somewhat spiral direction to the base of the lung, which is reached a short distance from its anterior end. The **upper lobe** lies above and anterior to the fissure. It is conical in form, with an oblique base, and the apex and the entire anterior border of the lung belong to it. The **lower lobe** lies below and behind the fissure. This is the more bulky of the two, and includes almost the entire base and the greater part of the thick, posterior part of the lung.

In the *right lung* there are two interlobar fissures which subdivide it into three lobes. One of them (the **oblique fissure**) is very similar in its position and relations to the fissure in the left lung. It is directed, however, rather more vertically, and ends a little farther from the lower end of the anterior border. It separates the lower lobe from the middle and upper lobes. The second interlobar or **horizontal fissure** begins in the main fissure at the posterior part of the lung, and proceeds forwards to end at the anterior border of the lung at the level of the fourth costal cartilage, separating the upper lobe from the middle lobe, which is triangular or wedge-shaped in outline.

Variations.—Variations in the pulmonary fissures are fairly common. Thus, it sometimes happens that the middle lobe of the right lung is imperfectly cut off from the superior lobe. Supernumerary partial fissures also are not infrequent, and in that way the left lung may be cut into three lobes, and the right lung into four lobes or even more. The occurrence of the cardiac lobe in the right lung is a variation of some interest, seeing that such a lobe is constant in certain mammals. It is a small accessory lobe, pyramidal in form, which makes its appearance on the lower part of the medial surface of the right lung. In certain subjects the azygos vein is enclosed within a fold of pleura, and is sunk so deeply in the pulmonary substance of the right lung that it marks off a small accessory lobe—the *lobe of the vena azygos*.

Weight.—The right adult lung, when filled with blood, weighs about 22 ounces, the left 20 ounces. In the nearly bloodless condition after electrocution the right lung weighs only about 8 ounces and the left 7 ounces.

Expansion of the Lung in Respiration.—Although the texture of the lung is uniform throughout, the occurrence of the great blood vessels and bronchi in the part around the hilum prevents that area from taking any active part in respiration. The middle zone of the lung surrounding the hilum area has but limited functional value. It is the outer zone near the visceral pleural surface which is most active in respiration. Probably only about 3 mm. depth of the superficial zone is active in quiet respiration and about 30 mm. depth in forced breathing. The parts most free to take part, in consequence of their anatomical relationships, are the costo-sternal and diaphragmatic areas. Apical, mediastinal and posterior regions are mechanically hampered in action. In expansion the upper lobe maintains almost unchanged its relation to the overlying costal arches and intercostal spaces. Consequently the pigmentation beneath the visceral pleura rather sharply defines the intercostal spaces. The lower lobe, following the diaphragm in its descent, modifies its relation to the overlying thoracic wall, and its sub-pleural pigmentation is therefore more diffuse. Owing to the mechanical method of enlarging the cavity of the thorax there is a slight rotatory movement of the bronchi in respiration which can be identified on cinematographic films.

ROOTS OF THE LUNGS

The term **root of the lung** (radix pulmonis) is applied to a number of structures which enter and leave the lung at the hilum on its medial surface. They are held together by an investment of pleura, and constitute a pedicle which attaches the lung to the medial wall of the pleural cavity. The phrenic nerve passes downwards a short distance anterior to the pulmonary root, whereas the vagus nerve breaks up into the posterior pulmonary plexus on its hinder aspect under the investing pleura. The delicate anterior pulmonary plexus is placed in front of the root of the lung under the pleura. From the inferior border of the root of the lung the pulmonary ligament extends towards the diaphragm. These relations are common to the pulmonary roots of both lungs, but there are others which are peculiar to each lung. On the *right* the superior vena cava lies anterior to the pulmonary root, and the vena azygos arches over its upper border. On the *left* the aorta arches above the root and the descending thoracic aorta passes behind it.

Constituent Parts of the Pulmonary Roots.—The large structures forming each pulmonary root are : (1) the two pulmonary veins ; (2) the pulmonary artery ; (3) the bronchus. There are also one or more small bronchial arteries and veins, the pulmonary nerves and the pulmonary lymph vessels, and some bronchial lymph glands.

The **bronchus** in the root of the lung lies behind the great pulmonary vessels. The **pulmonary artery** is differently situated on the two sides. On the right it gives off a branch corresponding to the ep-arterial bronchus but itself lies below that bronchus. On the left, where there is no ep-arterial bronchus, the pulmonary artery enters the hilum above the bronchus. On both sides the inferior of the two **pulmonary veins** lies at a lower level than the artery and the bronchus, whereas the superior lies in front of the artery and slightly below it (Figs. 574 and 575).

Distribution of the Bronchial Tubes within the Lungs.—The two lungs are not symmetrical ; the right lung is cleft into three lobes, the left lung into two. The bronchi exhibit a corresponding want of symmetry. The *right bronchus*, as it approaches the pulmonary hilum, gives off two branches for the upper and middle lobes of the right lung respectively, and then the main stem of the tube enters the lower lobe. The *left bronchus* sends off a large branch to the upper lobe of the left lung, and then sinks into the lower lobe. The first branch of the right bronchus, for the upper lobe, leaves the main stem about one inch from the trachea. The first branch of the left bronchus, on the other hand, takes origin about twice that distance from the trachea.

The relation of the pulmonary artery to the bronchial subdivisions is different on the two sides. On the right side it turns backwards, to reach the posterior surface of the bronchus, below the first (ep-arterial), and above the second bronchial branch. On the left side the pulmonary artery turns backwards above the level of the first bronchial branch. On the right side, therefore, the first bronchial branch originating above the pulmonary artery is termed the **ep-arterial bronchus** ; all the others lie below the artery, and are termed **hyp-arterial bronchi.** On the left side there is no ep-arterial bronchus.

The main stem of the bronchus, followed into the lower lobe of each lung, travels downwards and backwards in the pulmonary substance until it reaches the thin posterior part of the base of the lung which lies between the diaphragm and the thoracic wall, and there it ends. As it proceeds through the lower lobe it gives off a series of large **anterior** and a series of smaller **posterior branches.** As a rule these branches are four in number in each series, and the posterior and anterior branches do not arise opposite each other, but alternately, one from the back, and then another, after a slight interval, from the antero-lateral surface of the tube. The first hyp-arterial branch on each side (*i.e.* the branch to the middle lobe of the right lung and the branch to the upper lobe of the left) is generally regarded as the first member of the anterior group.

It was Aeby who first recognised the existence in each lung of a main or stem bronchus that gives off an anterior and posterior series of branches. He drew the distinction between ep-arterial and hyp-arterial bronchial rami. The distinction between the ep-arterial bronchus of the right side and the hyp-arterial bronchi of both sides is not of fundamental importance, and a branch which arises from the first hyp-arterial bronchus on the left side and turns upwards into the apex of the left lung is the direct equivalent of the ep-arterial bronchus of the right side. This is the **apical bronchus,** and represents the first dorsal branch of the left stem-bronchus. Huntington held that, except "for purposes of topography, we should abandon the distinction between eparterial and hyparterial bronchi." He regarded the ep-arterial bronchus as a secondary branch which has migrated in an upward direction on the main stem. According to Huntington, therefore, the topography of the lungs is the following :—

Right side				Left side
Superior	and	middle lobes	=	Superior lobe.
Inferior	and	cardiac lobes	=	Inferior lobe.

The cardiac lobe mentioned in this table (see p. 682) is rarely seen in the human lung, though the bronchus which corresponds to it is always present in the pulmonary substance as an accessory branch which proceeds from the main stem as it traverses the lower lobe of the right side. It receives the name of the **cardiac bronchus**.

STRUCTURE OF THE LUNG

The lung is constructed so that the blood which reaches it through the pulmonary artery is brought into the most intimate relation with the air which enters it through the trachea and bronchi. An interchange of materials between the blood and the air is thus made possible, and the object of respiration is attained. As a result of the interchange, the dark, impure blood which flows into the lung through the pulmonary artery becomes bright red and arterial before it returns to the heart through the pulmonary vein.

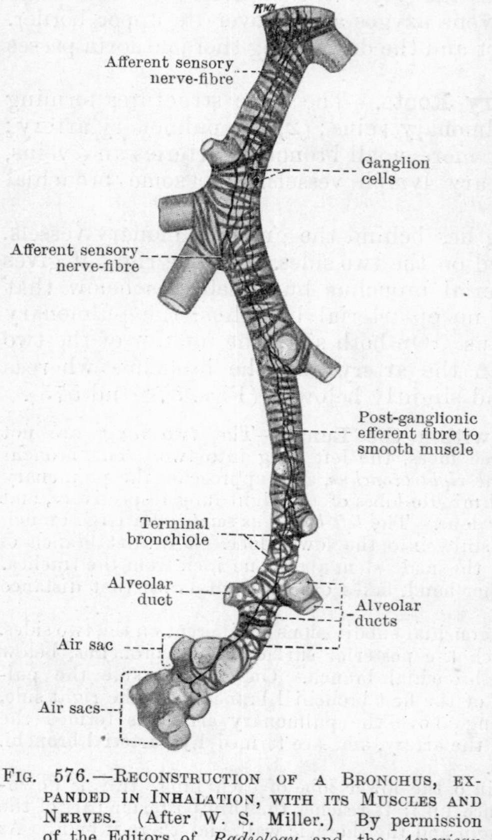

Lobules of the Lung.—A thin layer of subpleural fibro-areolar tissues lies subjacent to the continuous coating which the lung receives from the pulmonary pleura. From the deep surface of that subpleural layer fine septal processes penetrate into the substance of the lung, and those, with the areolar tissue which enters at the hilum upon the vessels and bronchi, constitute a supporting framework for the organ. The lung is lobular, and on the surface the small polygonal areas which represent the lobules are indicated by the pigment present in the areolar tissue septa which intervene between them. Although no pigment is present, the lobular character of the lung is particularly well marked in the fœtus, and with a little care the surface lobules in the fœtal lung can be separated from one another by gently tearing through the intervening areolar tissue. The lobules thus isolated are piriform or pyramidal in form. The broad bases of the lobules abut against the subpleural layer, whilst the deep narrow ends open into the terminal bronchioles. The lobules which lie more deeply in the substance of the organ are not so large, and are irregularly polygonal in form.

The Lung-Unit.—The anatomical unit of lung-structure comprises a terminal bronchiole with its air-spaces, blood-vessels, lymph vessels, and nerves.

The terminal bronchiole of the lung-unit is attained as follows : The larger branches of the bronchi, as they traverse the lung, give off numerous divisions, which, by repeated branching, ultimately form a system of tubes which pervade the entire organ. At first the bronchial divisions come off at very acute angles, but as the finer ramifications are reached that character becomes much less apparent. The finer ramifications of the bronchi are termed *bronchioles*, which by subdivision give rise to the *terminal bronchioles* [bronchioli respiratorii] of the lung-unit.

FIG. 576.—RECONSTRUCTION OF A BRONCHUS, EXPANDED IN INHALATION, WITH ITS MUSCLES AND NERVES. (After W. S. Miller.) By permission of the Editors of *Radiology* and the *American Review of Tuberculosis.* (T. W. T.)

Within the lung-unit the terminal bronchiole gives off a series of *alveolar ducts*, each of which leads to a group of air-spaces subdivided into smaller secondary air-sacs, the walls of which are pouched out to form the very numerous *alveoli* or *air-cells* of the lung-unit (Fig. 576). These alveoli are believed by some investigators to communicate with one another in order to equalise alveolar air-pressure in adjoining lung territories. In chronic bronchitis, alveoli, especially along the anterior border of the lungs, are apt to break down and communicate, forming bullæ, which are to be distinguished from sub-pleural blebs (see p. 673).

Structure of the Bronchi.—When the large bronchi enter the lung they become cylindrical and lose the flattening on the posterior aspect which is characteristic of the primary bronchi outside the lung. They possess the same coats as the trachea and primary bronchi, but as the tubes become smaller by repeated divisions, those coats become thinner and differently arranged.

In the **external fibro-cartilaginous coat** the cartilage is no longer present in the form of incomplete rings, but in irregular plates or flakes which are correspondingly smaller in size in the smaller tubes until, in bronchi of 1 mm. diameter, they disappear altogether. The **glands** for the most part cease to exist about the same point. The **muscular fibres**, which in the trachea and primary bronchi are confined to the posterior wall of the tube, form a lattice work in the non-cartilaginous bronchi and may be traced to the extremities of the alveolar ducts, where they form sphincters. Spasm of these sphincters accompanies asthmatic attacks. The **mucous lining** becomes greatly thinned in the smaller bronchioles. It contains a large number of longitudinally arranged elastic fibres, and is disposed in

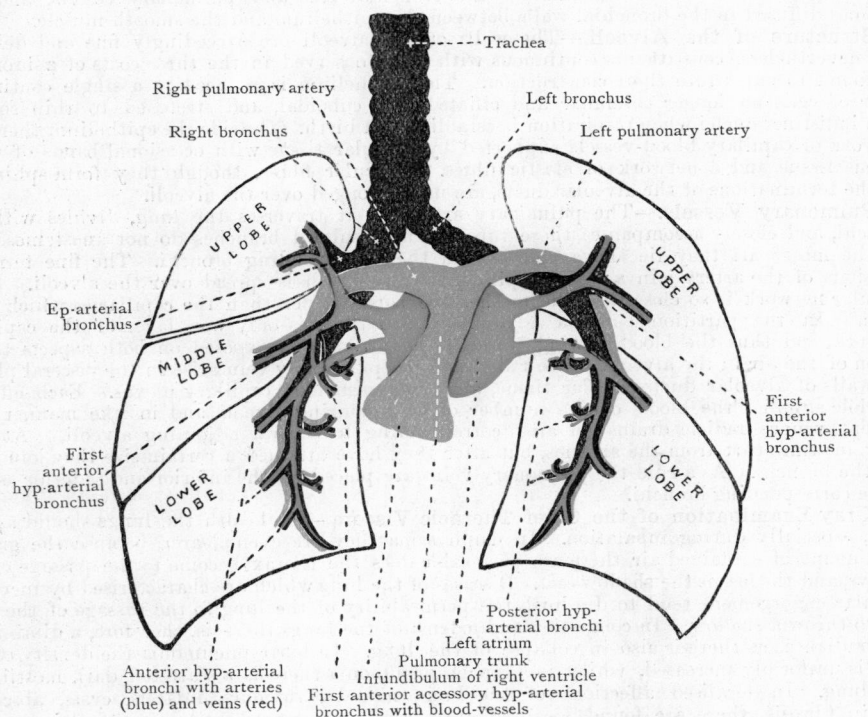

FIG. 577.—DIAGRAM OF THE LUNGS WITH THE BRONCHI AND BLOOD-VESSELS.

longitudinal folds, so that when the tube is cut across the lumen presents a stellate appearance. The mucous membrane is lined with ciliated columnar epithelium.

The **pulmonary nerves** are derived from the vagus nerve and from the autonomic nervous system. They enter the lung and follow the air-tubes through the organ. The small **bronchial arteries** supply the bronchi and the lung-tissue, the lymph glands of the hilum and the visceral pleura. They arise from the aorta or from an intercostal artery, and vary in number from one to three for each lung. In the root of the lung they lie on the posterior surface of the bronchus, and they follow the air-tubes through the organ. Their function is to supply oxygenated blood to lung tissue which is, for the moment, functionally inactive. Most of the blood conveyed to the lung by the bronchial arteries is returned by the pulmonary veins but special **bronchial veins**, from the hilum and main divisions of bronchi only, open into the vena azygos, the vena hemiazygos, or an intercostal vein. The respiratory bronchioles and air-spaces are supplied by the pulmonary, not by the bronchial arteries.

Wounds of the lung involving bronchial arteries are more fatal than those involving pulmonary arteries. They result in infarction, gangrene, and empyema.

The **lymph vessels** of the lungs are numerous, and are divided into two groups—superficial and deep.

The *superficial* lymph vessels form a network on the surface of the lung and eventually terminate by four or five vessels in the broncho-pulmonary lymph glands of the hilum. Free communication between the superficial and deep lymph vessels appears to occur only at the hilum of the lung.

The *deep* lymph vessels are designated bronchial when they accompany the bronchi, and vascular when they accompany the blood-vessels. Both systems communicate freely together, and at the level of the hilum terminate in the broncho-pulmonary lymph glands, situated either just outside the lung or within the lung-substance itself. Lymph glands are more numerous in the hilum of the right lung, and the upper lobe has more than the lower.

From the broncho-pulmonary glands the lymph-flow passes partly directly into the mediastinal lymph trunks, and partly to the tracheo-bronchial glands situated at the angle produced by the bifurcation of the trachea into the two bronchi. Of those glands there are, therefore, three groups, an inferior and right and left superior, and from them the lymph-flow is continued upwards through the paratracheal lymph glands on each side of the trachea into the deep cervical lymph glands, and thence into the thoracic duct or right lymphatic duct.

In addition to lymph glands and vessels there is lymphoid tissue scattered throughout the lung substance at the sites of division of bronchi and bronchioles, at the distal ends of alveolar ducts, and where venous radicles arise beneath the pleura. That lymphoid tissue is increased in old age, when it forms sheaths for the bronchial tree and pulmonary vessels, and also becomes diffused in the bronchial walls between the epithelium and the smooth muscle.

Structure of the Alveoli.—The walls of the alveoli are exceedingly fine and delicate, but, nevertheless, constituents continuous with those observed in the three coats of a bronchus are found to enter into their construction. The epithelium is reduced to a single continuous layer of cells no longer columnar and ciliated, but cuboidal, and stretched to thin squares with indistinct nuclei when respiration is established at birth. Outside the epithelium there is a network of capillary blood-vessels supported by reticular tissue with occasional bands of white fibrous tissue and a network of elastic fibres. Muscular fibres, though they form sphincters for the terminations of the alveolar ducts, are not prolonged over the alveoli.

Pulmonary Vessels.—The pulmonary artery, as it traverses the lung, divides with the bronchi, and closely accompanies those tubes. The resultant branches do not anastomose, and for the most part they lie above and behind the corresponding bronchi. The fine terminal divisions of the artery join a dense capillary plexus which is spread over the alveoli. That vascular network is so close that the meshes are barely wider than the capillaries which form them. In the partition between adjacent alveoli there is only one layer of the capillary network, and thus the blood flowing through those vessels is exposed on both aspects to the action of the air in the alveoli. The radicles of the pulmonary vein arise in the visceral pleura, the walls of alveolar ducts, areolar tissue, and the pulmonary capillary plexus. Each efferent arteriole supplies the blood over a number of neighbouring alveoli, and in like manner each afferent venous radicle drains an area corresponding to several adjoining alveoli. At first the veins run apart from the arteries, but after they have attained a certain size they join them and the bronchi. As a rule the pulmonary veins are placed on the inferior and anterior aspects of the corresponding bronchi.

X-ray Examination of the Chief Thoracic Viscera.—In health the lungs should appear clear, especially during inhalation. In emphysema they are even clearer, because the greater the amount of contained air the more permeable does the thorax become to the passage of the X-rays, and the less is the shadow cast. Diseases of the lung which are characterised by increased vascular engorgement tend to diminish the permeability of the lung to the passage of the rays, and to throw a shadow. In congestion and œdema of the lungs there is, therefore, a diminished transradiance, as there is also in collapse of the lung. In lobar pneumonia the density of the lung is uniformly increased, whilst in broncho-pneumonia there is a scattered dark mottling of the lung. In localised affections of the lung, namely, tumours, infarcts, cysts, abscesses, and in fibrosis, there are found localised areas casting a denser shadow. Small irregularly shaped densities are occasionally to be seen in the middle zone of the lung ; they are due to erratic pieces of cartilage. Ring-like densities sometimes are found also ; they are due to intrapulmonary bronchial cartilage rings—rarely found in Man. In old people the intrapulmonary cartilage may be replaced by bone. The circular disc-like opacities in the lung are blood-vessels seen in cross section. Areas of lung substance closely spattered by flecks of opacity betray an old and incompletely absorbed radio-opaque injection.

The dense branching shadows of the lung substance seen in radiographs or on the X-ray screen are the pulmonary arteries and their branches (Pl. L). They are solid shadows, obviously not tubes, and they become denser on deep inhalation owing to interference with blood circulation. In heart lesions the pulmonary arteries and their branches may be engorged. The intrapulmonary bronchi cannot ordinarily be seen on the X-ray screen if radio-opaque material has not been injected into them. Nor are they seen easily even on a stereoscopic radiograph of the lungs. On very clear stereoscopic radiographs, however, when the subject has remained perfectly motionless, the main intrapulmonary bronchi can readily be discerned lying medial to the dense shadows of the corresponding pulmonary arterial branches. The medial wall of the bronchus is seen as a fine dense outline : the lateral wall is totally obscured by the arterial shadow. Practice in examining the boundaries of trachea and extrapulmonary bronchi in contrast to their relatively translucent bore is necessary to establish confidence in descrying the intrapulmonary bronchi. Radio-opaque material injected down the trachea makes the intrapulmonary bronchi plainly visible and their relations to the arteries (Pls. L and LI) are then clearly seen. The drawbacks to this injection, however, are first, that it is not readily absorbed, and secondly, that only one lung may be attempted at one sitting and good results cannot be guaranteed. During inhalation, bronchi and their subdivisions in the lungs are lengthened, increased in breadth and less spread apart. In exhalation they become shorter, narrower, and are spread out in fan-shape. Figs. 565 and 566 give a general impression of the respiratory alternation in lung form. When a radio-opaque substance is injected through the air passages it does not penetrate to the alveoli, being prevented by the muscular sphincters at the terminations of the alveolar ducts. Cinematographic X-ray films by Drs. Hudson and Jarre show waves of rhythmic muscular contraction in the air passages during exhalation which gradually drive the opaque material back towards the trachea. They show also that in asthma, if the bronchial passages are not in spasm, the waves of muscular contraction occur in inhalation rather than in exhalation, and the disharmony is doubtless related to the physical distress of the patient. In chronic bronchitis with emphysema the alveolar duct sphincters break down and opaque material flows into the air sacs.

Bronchial lymph glands are rarely visible unless they are enlarged or tuberculous. They usually appear as separate, dark, mottled areas near the hilum.

The **pleura** is visible by the X-Rays only when diseased. In the presence of thickened pleura there may be an increased density which is not affected by position or by evacuation of fluid. Pleural effusion also gives an increased density of shadow with a blurring of the cardio-hepatic angle and the outline of the diaphragm.

Enlargement of the heart, pericardial effusion, mediastinal tumour, aneurysm of the aorta, and diaphragmatic hernia, all give rise to areas of increased density to X-rays, and by leading to compression of the lung may diminish its normal transradiance.

Foreign bodies in the bronchi, lungs, or pleural cavities are located by bronchoscopy or radiography.

DEVELOPMENT OF RESPIRATORY SYSTEM

The larynx, trachea, bronchi, and lungs all arise as an outgrowth from the ventral wall of the foregut about the fifteenth day of development, when the embryo is about 3·2 mm. in length. A median longitudinal groove makes its appearance in the ventral wall of the œsophageal portion of the primitive gut. The groove becomes deeper and is separated off from the foregut and converted into a distinct tube by a constriction which begins at the caudal end and proceeds headwards.

The cranial end of the respiratory tube forms the larynx, the intermediate portion forms the trachea, and the caudal end bifurcates into two tubes—the future bronchi are already indicated by slight bulgings before the two tubes divide—which grow tailwards, one on each side of the heart, into a mesodermic mass from which the areolar tissue of the future lungs is ultimately developed. The respiratory tube is lined with entoderm continuous with the entodermal lining of the foregut.

The Larynx.—The rudiment of the larynx appears as a U-shaped ridge, called the furcula, which intervenes between the ventral ends of the third pharyngeal arches and surrounds the pharyngeal end of the primitive respiratory tube. About the twenty-fifth day, and before the trachea separates off from the œsophagus, the arytenoid swellings, which lie caudal to the fourth pharyngeal pouches, and possibly represent rudimentary fifth pharyngeal arches (Kallius), are formed as secondary lateral elevations.

From the median elevation the epiglottis is developed ; the lateral—the arytenoid swellings—eventually form the ary-epiglottic folds. On the medial side of each of the latter, about the fourth month, a furrow marks the future site of the sinus of the larynx, the margin of which later becomes the vocal fold.

At the end of the fourth week the cartilaginous framework of the larynx is indicated by mesodermic condensations, though actual cartilage does not appear till the seventh week. Arytenoids, cricoid, and the cartilages of the trachea are all continuous at first.

The *epiglottic* and *cuneiform cartilages* are developed from the furcula, and are of the elastic variety.

The *thyroid cartilage* is laid down in the form of a pair of separate lateral mesodermic plates in each of which chondrification proceeds from two centres, anterior and posterior, which probably represent the cartilages of the fourth and fifth pharyngeal arches. The sheets of cartilage extend forwards to fuse in the median plane. Chondrification may be incomplete and thus a thyroid foramen is formed. The superior horn of the thyroid cartilage is at first continuous with the greater horn of the hyoid bone and part of the connecting bar remains as the cartilago triticea.

The pro-cartilaginous rudiments of the *cricoid* and *arytenoid cartilages*, though at first continuous with each other, become differentiated by the appearance of separate cartilaginous centres for the arytenoids, and an incomplete ring, for a time deficient behind, for the cricoid. The cricoid thus resembles developmentally a tracheal ring, with which it probably corresponds morphologically. Chondrification proceeds in the cricoid by two centres, one on each side. Those centres soon unite in front, but behind fusion does not take place until much later, and is finally completed by an extension of chondrification from the lateral into the posterior plate. The cricoid thus differs from the tracheal ring in having its chondrification completed behind. In early development the cricoid cartilage is disproportionately large (second month), the thyroid cartilage relatively small and the vocal ligaments short. Those proportions change as the larynx assumes the more distinct human pattern.

The *corniculate cartilages* are merely portions of the arytenoid cartilages separated off by segmentation.

The Trachea.—The trachea is developed from the intermediate portion of the respiratory tube.

The Lungs.—The lungs are developed from the two diverticula of the caudal end of the median longitudinal groove and the mesodermal tissue into which these grow. From the first the right pulmonary diverticulum or vesicle is slightly the larger of the two. Both diverticula elongate, and almost immediately undergo a subdivision—the right into three vesicles, and the left into two vesicles—thus early indicating the three lobes of the right lung and the two lobes of the left lung. As the primitive respiratory tube lies in the median plane in the posterior attachment of the septum transversum, the pulmonary diverticula grow laterally and backwards into the posterior parietal recesses—that is, into the future pleural cavities—carrying before them a covering of mesoderm. From that mesoderm are derived the blood-vessels and other tissues which build up the lung, whilst the entodermal cells which form the lining membrane of the primitive respiratory tube eventually develop into the epithelial lining of the air-passages, and are embedded within the surrounding mesoderm. The main entodermal subdivisions continue to branch and re-branch, pushing their way into the pulmonary mesoderm, until the complete bronchial tree is formed.

The primary pulmonary diverticula increase in size and complexity by subdivision of the enlarged terminal part of each diverticulum. From the first the various branches are bulbous or flask-shaped at their extremities. They bifurcate, and although at first the two main subdivisions appear, in each case, of equal importance, one grows out as the continuation of the main bronchial stem—the future hyp-arterial bronchus—whilst the other remains as a branch. The budding of the developing lung is at first monopodial, but later probably becomes dichotomous. When the ramification of the entodermal tubes into the lung-mesoderm is complete, the small terminal flask-shaped extremities of the various branches represent the alveoli clustering around the alveolar ducts into which each terminal bronchiole subdivides.

This repeated bifurcation results, as just stated, in the formation of a main bronchus which traverses the entire length of the lung, and into which numerous secondary bronchi open. The latter, from the manner in which they arrange themselves around the main stem of the pulmonary artery, are divided into posterior and anterior. Those alternate with each other, and usually number four in each series ; not infrequently the third posterior bronchus fails to develop. In the left lung the first posterior bronchus arises, not from the main tube as on the right side, but from the first anterior bronchus—an arrangement which probably results from the fusion on the left side of the upper and middle lobes of the left lung into one, namely, the so-called superior lobe of the adult left lung.

The secondary bronchi elongate, and give rise to the tertiary bronchi, and these in turn to lesser bronchi, and so on down to the terminal bronchioles, with their alveolar ducts and alveoli comprising the lung-unit. At first the lung-unit is devoid of air-cells, but bween the sixth month and full term the alveoli make their appearance on the alveolar ducts. By the close of the fourth month of intra-uterine life the columnar cells lining the trachea and bronchi have become ciliated.

Growth of the lung is not interrupted by birth, but since the terminal branches are now expanded by air there must be a new form of budding. At any stage of post-natal growth the terminal branches carry, in the alveoli projecting from them, the evidence that they were once alveolar ducts. These alveoli become obliterated by the advance of the muscular sheet which extends over the length of the alveolar duct.

The rudiments of the developing lungs grow backwards on each side of the œsophagus into the fissure-like portion of the cœlom which occupies the thoracic region. They push before them the endothelial lining of the cœlom, and thus come to acquire their covering of pulmonary pleura. By the development of the diaphragm and the pericardium the pleural portions of the cœlom become cut off from the peritoneal cavity and from each other

PLATE XLIX

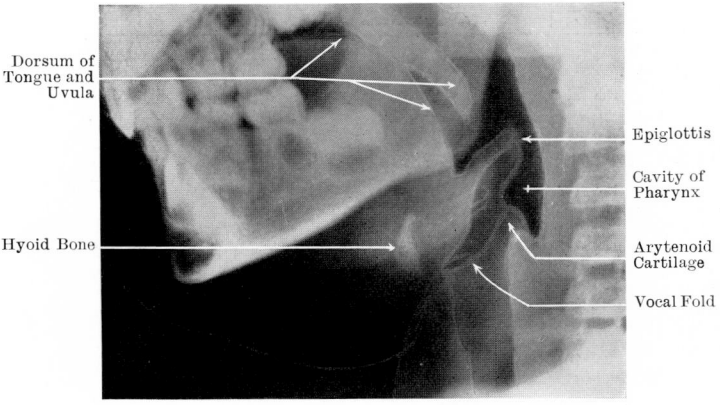

Dorsum of Tongue and Uvula

Hyoid Bone

Epiglottis

Cavity of Pharynx

Arytenoid Cartilage

Vocal Fold

A.   Girl, aged 4 years.

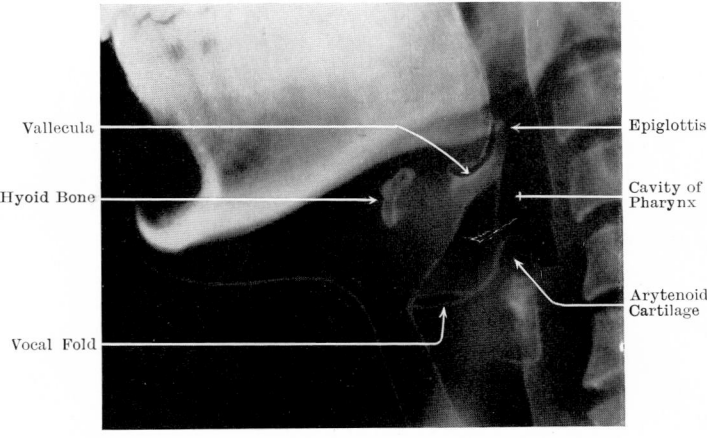

Vallecula

Hyoid Bone

Vocal Fold

Epiglottis

Cavity of Pharynx

Arytenoid Cartilage

B.   Woman, aged 35 years.

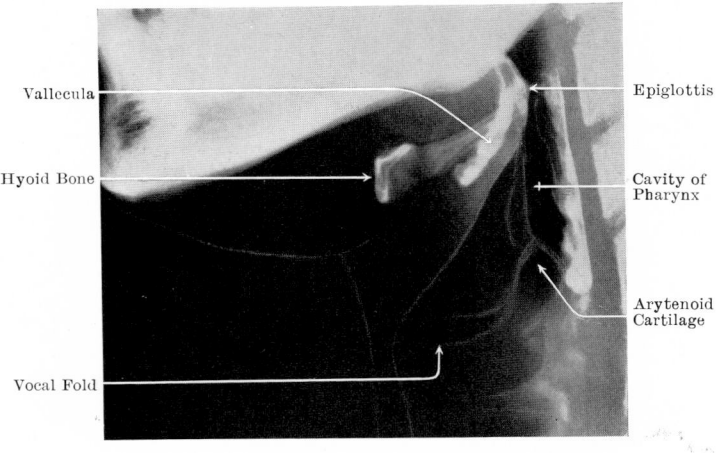

Vallecula

Hyoid Bone

Vocal Fold

Epiglottis

Cavity of Pharynx

Arytenoid Cartilage

C.   Man, aged 23 years.

PLATE XLIX.—RADIOGRAPHS OF PHARYNX AND LARYNX IN QUIET RESPIRATION.   (By courtesy of Dr. B. Holly Broadbent, Bolton Study, Western Reserve University, Cleveland, Ohio.)

In C barium outlines the Tongue, the Epiglottis, the Vallecula and the Posterior Wall of the Pharynx; a little barium clings to the dorsum of the Tongue in B; and in A the Tongue and the Uvula are outlined.

Note the fairly uniform diameter of larynx and trachea in the child contrasted with the greater antero-posterior depth of the former in the woman and the growth so great in the man that the pharyngeal space is triangular instead of cylindrical as in the woman and child.   The great growth of the thyro-hyoid membrane between childhood and adulthood is evident in the relative distance between the vocal folds and the hyoid bone.

PLATE L

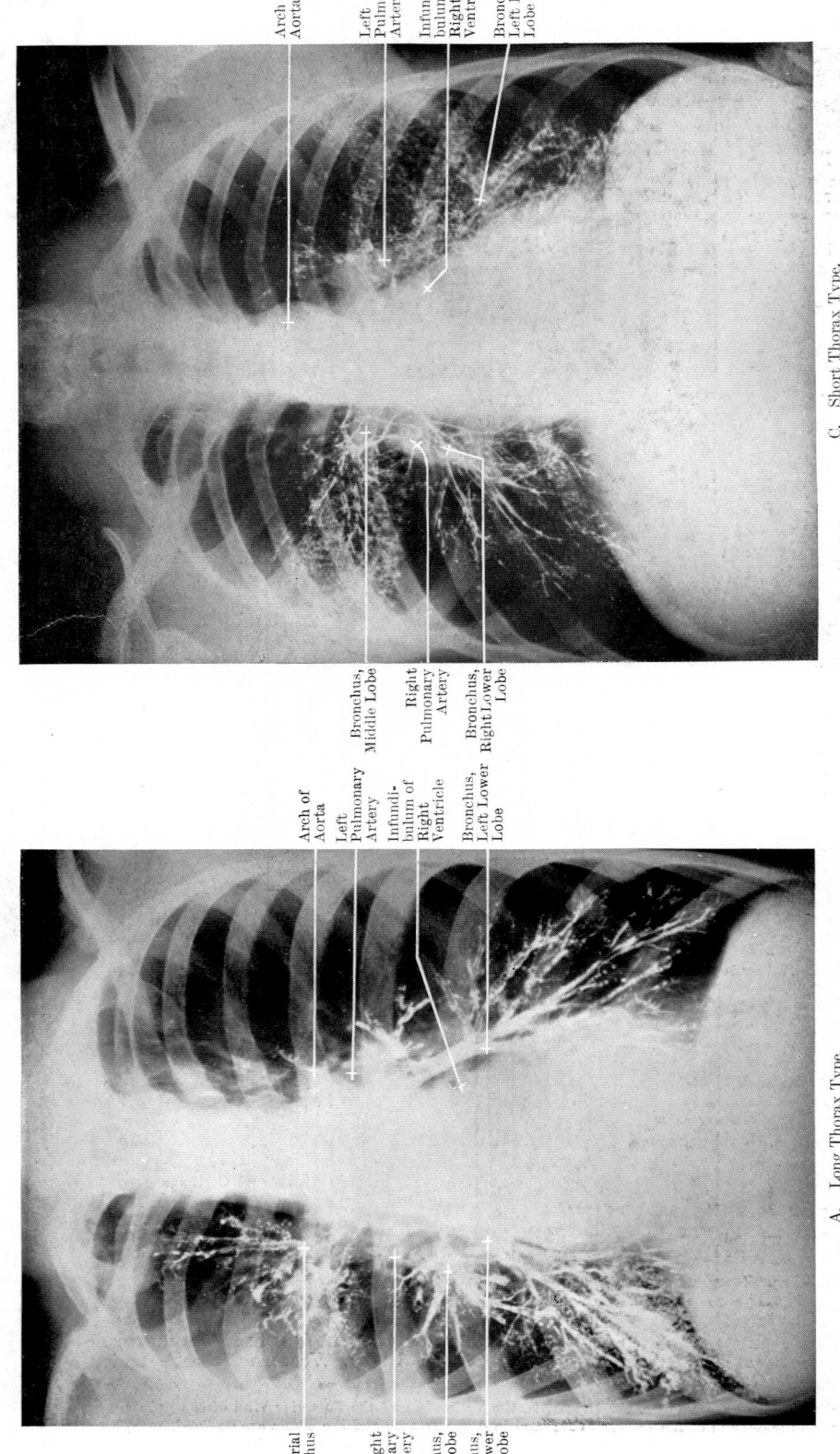

Arch of Aorta
Left Pulmonary Artery
Infundi-bulum of Right Ventricle
Bronchus, Left Lower Lobe

Bronchus, Middle Lobe
Right Pulmonary Artery
Bronchus, Left Lower Lobe
Bronchus, Right Lower Lobe

C. Short Thorax Type.

Arch of Aorta
Left Pulmonary Artery
Infundi-bulum of Right Ventricle
Bronchus, Left Lower Lobe

Ep-arterial Bronchus
Right Pulmonary Artery
Bronchus, Middle Lobe
Bronchus, Right Lower Lobe

A. Long Thorax Type.

PLATE L.—ANTERO-POSTERIOR RADIOGRAPHS OF LUNGS OF LONG AND SHORT THORAX TYPES OF INDIVIDUALS AFTER INTRA-BRONCHIAL LIPIODOL INJECTION. (By courtesy of Dr. Eugene Freedman, Lakeside Hospital, Cleveland, Ohio.) For oblique lateral radiographs of the same Individuals, see Plate LI.

The different forms of lung and heart outline in these two types of individual are clearly illustrated. In both sets of radiographs the hollow outline of the bronchi is made evident by the clinging of lipiodol to lateral and medial walls, particularly the latter. Injection can be traced to the bronchioles. The ep-arterial bronchus of the right side is well injected in A

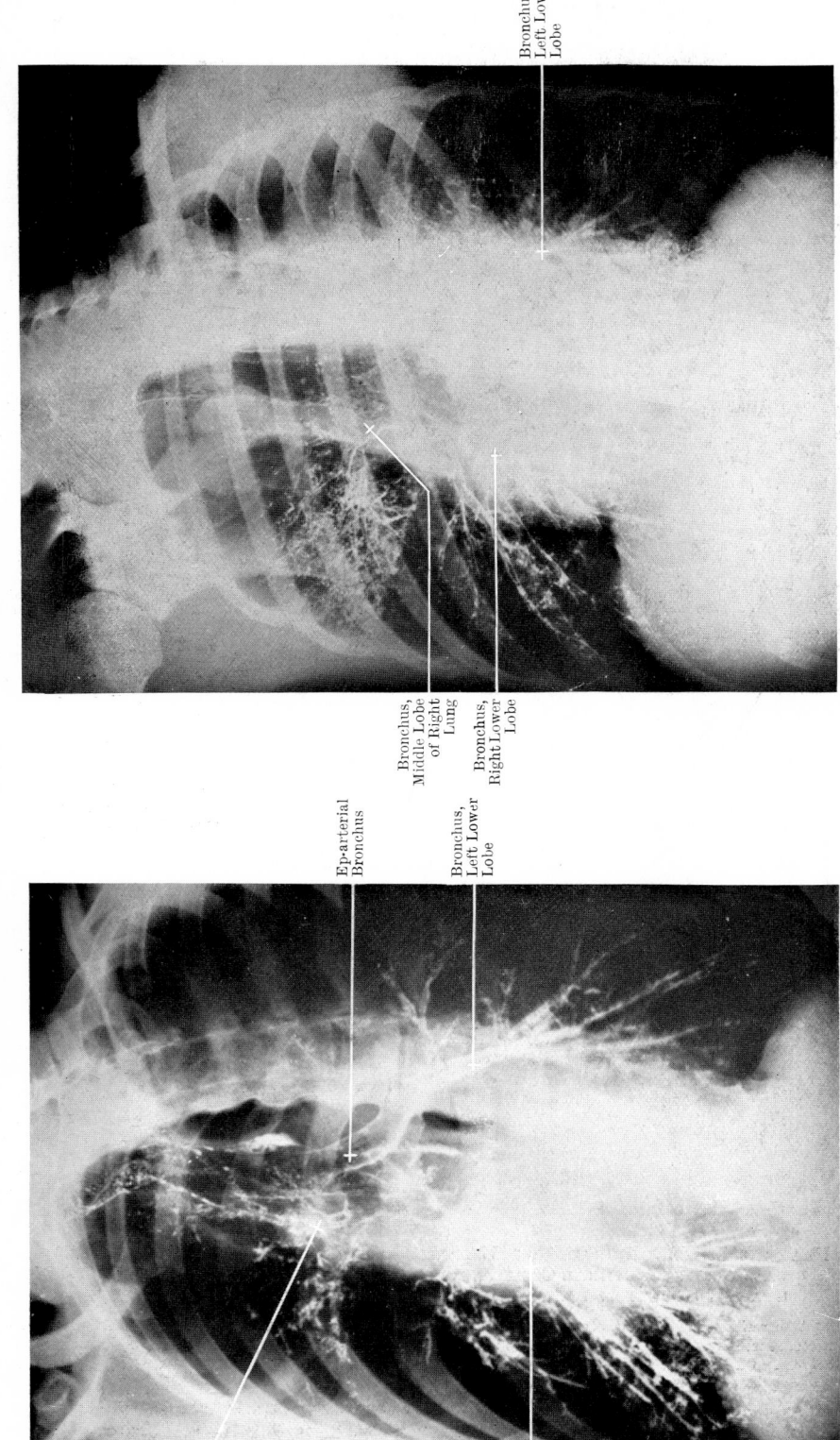

PLATE LI. Short Thorax Type.

Bronchus, Left Lower Lobe

Bronchus, Middle Lobe of Right Lung

Bronchus, Right Lower Lobe

Eparterial Bronchus

Bronchus, Left Lower Lobe

B. Long Thorax Type.

Bronchus, Middle Lobe of Right Lung

Bronchus, Right Lower Lobe

PLATE LI.—OBLIQUE LATERAL RADIOGRAPHS OF LUNGS OF LONG AND SHORT THORAX TYPES OF INDIVIDUALS AFTER INTRA-BRONCHIAL LIPIODOL INJECTION. (By courtesy of Dr. Eugene Freedman, Lakeside Hospital, Cleveland, Ohio.)

Fig. B is from the same individual as Fig. A in Plate L; and Fig. D is from the same individual as Fig. C.

PLATE LII

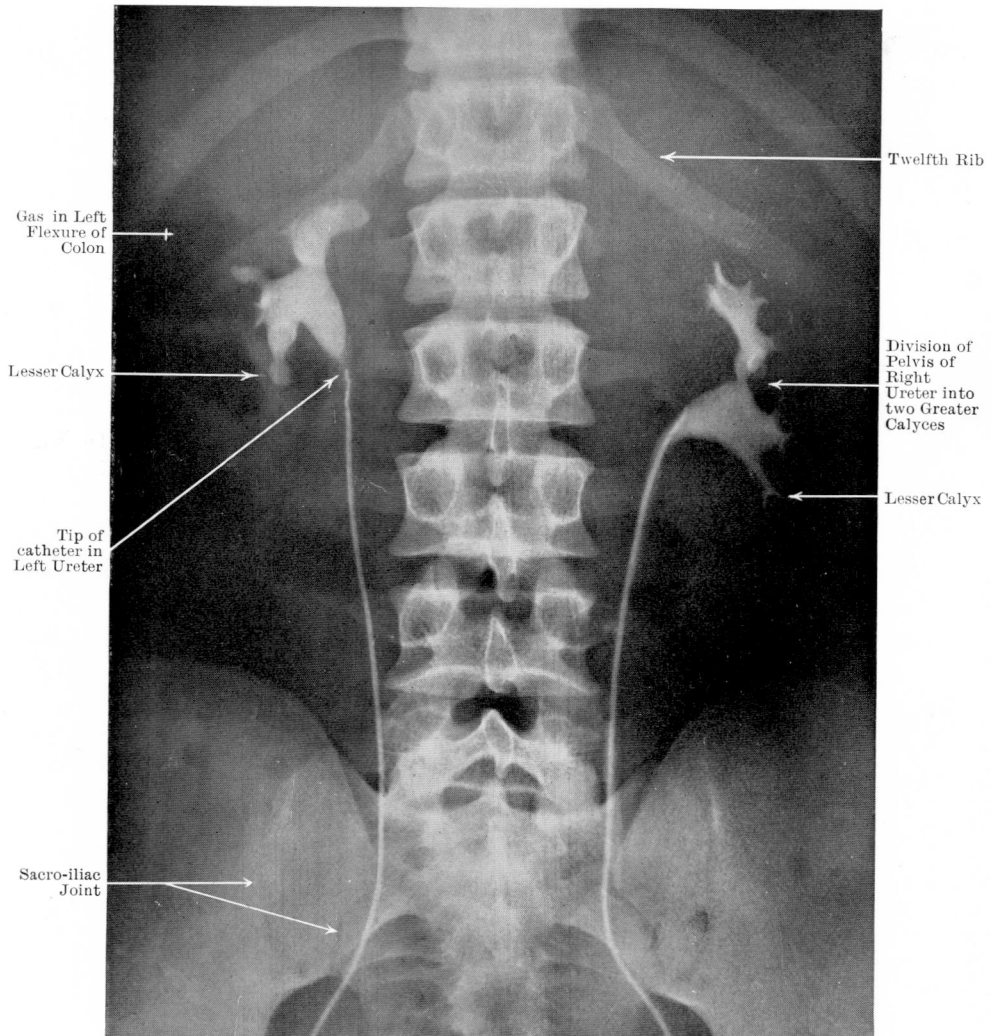

Twelfth Rib

Gas in Left
Flexure of
Colon

Lesser Calyx

Tip of
catheter in
Left Ureter

Division of
Pelvis of
Right
Ureter into
two Greater
Calyces

Lesser Calyx

Sacro-iliac
Joint

PLATE LII.—RADIOGRAPH OF URETERS FROM BEHIND, AFTER THE
PASSAGE OF URETERAL CATHETERS AND THE INJECTION OF A RADIO-
OPAQUE SOLUTION INTO THE PELVES AND CALYCES. (J. F.)

The resilience of the catheters has slightly displaced the lower abdominal portions of the
ureters medially. Note the higher position of the left kidney and the form of the pelves and
calyces. Cf. Fig. 585, p. 698, and Plate LIII.

URO-GENITAL SYSTEM

By the late A. Francis Dixon, M.B., Sc.D.,
Professor of Anatomy, Trinity College, University of Dublin

URINARY ORGANS

THE **kidneys**, or glands which secrete the urine, are a pair of almost symmetrically placed organs, situated in the posterior part of the abdominal cavity, one on each side of the lower movable portion of the vertebral column. The fluid, or urine, secreted by the kidneys is received into the upper, expanded portions of a pair of long tubes—the **ureters**—and by them it is conducted to the **urinary bladder**, which is placed within the true pelvis. From the bladder the urine is passed, during micturition, along a passage called the **urethra** to the exterior. In the male the urethra is a relatively long passage, and traverses the prostate and the whole length of the penis; in the female it is a short tube, and opens on the surface immediately in front of the vaginal orifice.

THE KIDNEYS

The **kidney** (ren), when removed soon after death, presents a bean-shaped contour. It is of a dark brown-red colour, and is surrounded by a thin fibrous capsule which gives to the whole organ a uniformly smooth surface. The kidney is not a solid body, but contains a cavity called the **renal sinus**, the opening into which, termed the **hilum**, is situated on the antero-medial part of the organ. Each kidney measures about $4\frac{1}{2}$ inches (11 cm.) in length, 2 inches (5 cm.) in width, and about $1\frac{1}{4}$ inches (3 cm.) in thickness, and is placed so that its long axis is nearly vertical. The weight of the adult kidney is about $4\frac{1}{2}$ ounces. In the freshly removed kidney the upper and lower ends are smoothly rounded, and the **upper end** is usually a little more bulky than the **lower end**. The **medial border**, on which the hilum is placed, is concave from above downwards. The **lateral border** is rounded and convex. These two borders separate the **anterior surface** from the **posterior surface** of the kidney.

The *fibrous capsule* which closely envelops the whole organ is continued over the lips of the hilum into the interior of the kidney, and lines the walls of the renal sinus. The upper, expanded portion of the ureter leaves the sinus, through the hilum, in company with the blood-vessels and nerves.

Position of the Kidneys.—The precise level of the kidney in the abdominal cavity is subject to considerable variation, and, further, it is usual to find a difference in the level of the right and left kidney in the same body. Most frequently the left kidney is on a higher level than the right, but in many cases the kidneys are found to occupy the same level, or, the more usual condition being reversed, the right kidney is a little higher than the left.

If a line is drawn round the body at the level of the lowest part of the thoracic wall seen from the front, the whole, or almost the whole, of the left kidney will be found to lie above the level of the subcostal plane so determined. The lower end of the right kidney, however, usually reaches a little below the subcostal plane. By far the greater part—usually two-thirds or more—of the kidney lies to the medial side of a line drawn vertically upwards from the mid-inguinal point.

44

The posterior surface of the kidney is closely applied against the muscles attached to the bodies of the last thoracic and upper three lumbar vertebræ, and is placed in front of the last rib and of the transverse processes of the upper three lumbar vertebræ. In some cases, more frequently on the left side of the body, the eleventh rib also lies behind the upper part of the kidney. The relationship of the kidney to the lower two ribs is, however, very inconstant, owing partly to the great variability in the size and inclination of these bones.

The lower end of the kidney is usually situated from $1\frac{1}{4}$ to 2 inches (3 cm. to 5 cm.) above the highest part of the iliac crest; the interval between the kidney and the ilium being usually greater on the left side of the body.

Occasionally the lower end of the kidney lies on the same level as the iliac crest or only a short distance above it; this condition is sometimes due to the crest rising to a higher level than usual, the kidney occupying its normal position in

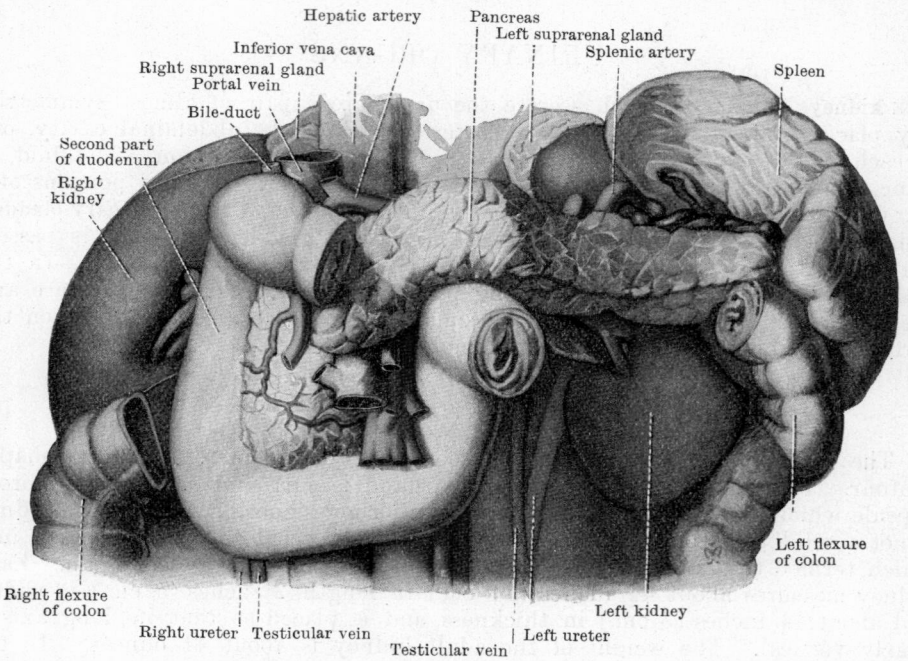

FIG. 578.—DISSECTION TO SHOW THE RELATIONSHIPS OF THE KIDNEYS. The greater part of the stomach has been removed by an incision made close to the pylorus. The transverse colon has been taken away, and the small intestine has been cut across close to the duodeno-jejunal flexure.
A model prepared by the late Professor Birmingham has been made use of in this drawing.

relation to the vertebral column. It is important to remember that during life the kidney moves upwards and downwards, following the respiratory movements of the part of the diaphragm against which it rests.

The long axis of each kidney is slightly oblique, its upper end being placed nearer to the median plane than the lower. The surface of the kidney which is applied against the muscles of the posterior wall of the abdomen looks, as a whole, backwards and medially, and that which bulges into the abdominal cavity looks forwards and laterally; the lateral border is therefore on a more posterior plane than the medial border. The kidney is rotated on its long axis to such a degree that the medial border and hilum are scarcely visible from behind, and only a limited view of the lateral border can be obtained from the front (Figs. 579 and 580).

The kidneys are placed behind the peritoneum, and bulge into the posterior part of the abdominal cavity. Each is surrounded by a considerable amount of loose tissue, often loaded with fat. The fatty tissue—**renal fat**—is present in greater quantity round the margins of the kidney, and to a less extent in front of and behind the organ. The renal vessels and nerves lie in the fat before they enter the kidney, and the adipose tissue is continued, along with the vessels, through the hilum into the renal sinus, where it fills up all the space unoccupied by the vessels and nerves.

Embedded in the soft fatty tissue around the kidney there is a layer of fibrous tissue to which the term **renal fascia** is applied. The renal fascia surrounds the kidney and a considerable amount of the neighbouring fat in the form of a loose sheath in which anterior and posterior walls may be distinguished. The sheath is open inferiorly and medially, but closed above and to the lateral side of the kidney by the apposition of its walls. Laterally, the anterior and posterior walls of the sheath come into contact and are connected with the fascia of the transversus muscle. Medially they remain separate, and the anterior wall is continued towards the median plane, in front of the renal vessels and the aorta, while the posterior wall fuses with the fascia that covers the psoas and quadratus lumborum muscles. Below the level of the kidney, the anterior and

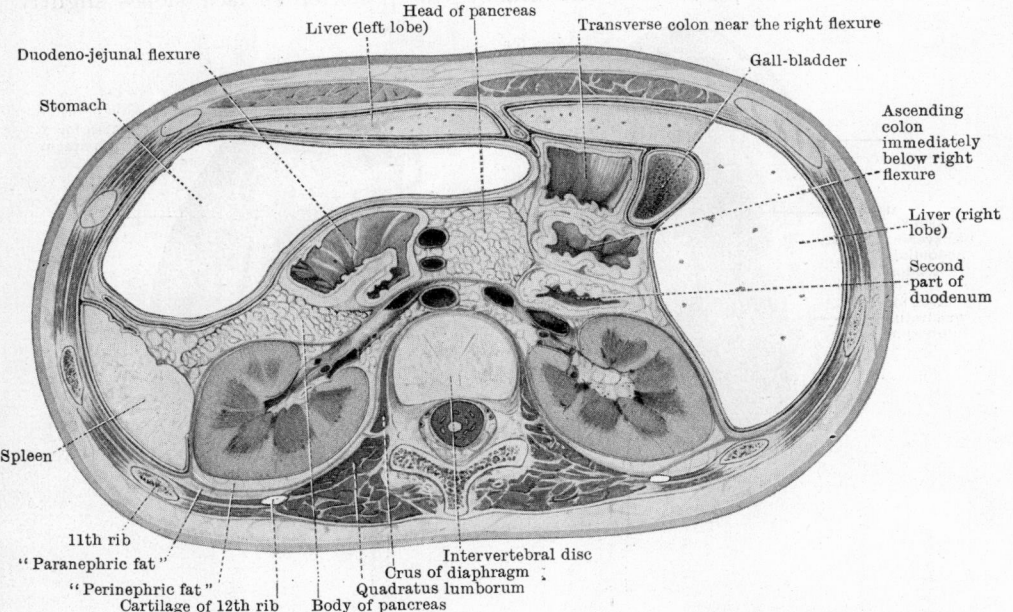

FIG. 579.—TRANSVERSE SECTION THROUGH THE BODY OF A CHILD. (A. F. D.) The position and relationships of the kidneys are well seen, and the arrangement of the renal fascia is indicated. The fascia is coloured green.

posterior layers of the renal fascia remain separate, and become lost as they are traced downwards towards the iliac fossa. Above the level of the kidney and the suprarenal gland the layers of the renal fascia unite and join the fascia of the diaphragm. The term "perinephric fat" is applied to the loose fatty tissue enclosed along with the kidney within the sheath of renal fascia, and "paranephric fat" is used to denote the tissue outside the renal fascia (Fig. 579). The fibrous capsule of the kidney is joined to the renal fascia by numerous fibrous tissue strands. These strands traverse the perinephric fat and undoubtedly assist in fixing the kidney in its place. The paranephric fat is present in greatest quantity behind the lower part of the kidney, and in this position the layer of fibrous tissue that separates the two masses of fat and forms the posterior layer of the renal fascia, is usually well marked (Fig. 579).

Fixation of the Kidney.—The kidney is not held in its place by any special folds of peritoneum or distinct ligaments; its fixation depends, to a large extent, on the pressure and counter-pressure exerted upon it by neighbouring structures, and on its connexions with the renal fascia.

Posterior Relations and Posterior Surface of Kidney (Figs. 579, 581.— The muscles on which the kidney rests are the psoas major, the quadratus lumborum, the diaphragm and the posterior aponeurosis of the transversus abdominis. The internal surfaces of the muscles do not lie on the same plane but slope towards one another, and thus the bed on which the kidney rests is not flat. When but little fat is present, the posterior surface of the kidney is moulded to fit the inequalities of the surface against which it is placed. When a kidney that has been hardened *in situ* is removed from the body, its posterior surface shows, near the medial border, a narrow area adapted to the psoas major muscle. The psoas area looks medially and backwards. More laterally may be seen the area for the quadratus lumborum muscle, and, more laterally still, the thick, lateral border of the kidney, which lies on the transversus abdominis and looks directly backwards. The part of the kidney related to the diaphragm is the upper part of the posterior surface; it rests on the crus and the origins of the diaphragm from the last rib and the arcuate ligaments [arcus lumbo-costales]—*see* Figs. 580 and 581.

Towards the upper end of the kidney the posterior surface slopes slightly

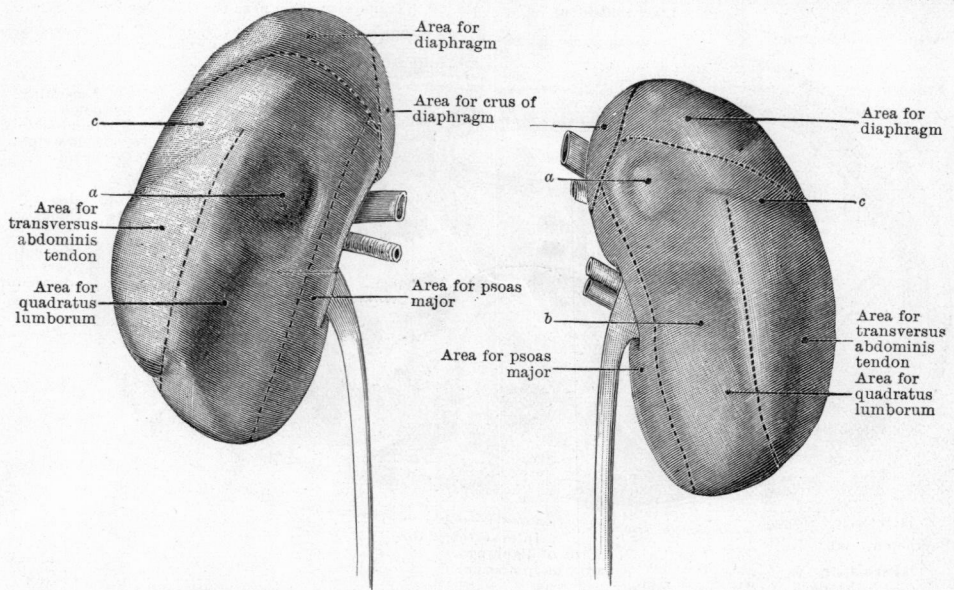

Fig. 580.—The Posterior Surfaces of the Kidneys. (A. F. D.) The dotted lines mark out the areas in contact with the various muscles of the posterior abdominal wall.

a and *b*. Depressions corresponding to the transverse processes of the first and second lumbar vertebræ. *c*. Depression corresponding to the twelfth rib.

forwards. Indeed, the upper part of the kidney is, as a whole, bent slightly forwards in conformity with the part of the diaphragm on which it rests, and thus a narrow interval is left in which the pleural cavity passes down behind the diaphragm and the upper part of the kidney. The relationship of the pleural cavity to the kidney is of great importance in connection with surgical operations performed through an incision in the lumbar region.

The subcostal nerve and the ilio-hypogastric and ilio-inguinal nerves pass downwards and laterally in close relationship to the back of the kidney.

The **lateral border** in its middle and lower part is a surface rather than a border, and looks for the most part directly backwards. It rests on the diaphragm and on the posterior aponeurosis of the transversus lateral to the quadratus lumborum muscle. It is narrowest above, and widest immediately below its middle point, corresponding to the greater thickness of the kidney at that level.

Anterior Relations and the Anterior Surface of the Kidney (Figs. 578, 582).—It is not possible to give more than a general account of the anterior relationships of the kidneys, for not only do those relations differ on the two sides of the body, but also many of the structures related to the anterior surface of each kidney undergo frequent changes in position during life.

Right Kidney.—A small area on the upper part of the anterior surface is in relation to the corresponding suprarenal gland The rest of the upper part is in contact with the liver, which is often hollowed out to form a fossa for the kidney.   The suprarenal gland is bound to the kidney by areolar tissue, while the part of the kidney in relation to the liver is, like the liver itself, covered with peritoneum, and thus the two organs, although closely applied, are really separated by a part of the general peritoneal cavity.   Immediately in front of the lower end of the right kidney two parts of the alimentary canal are usually found—namely

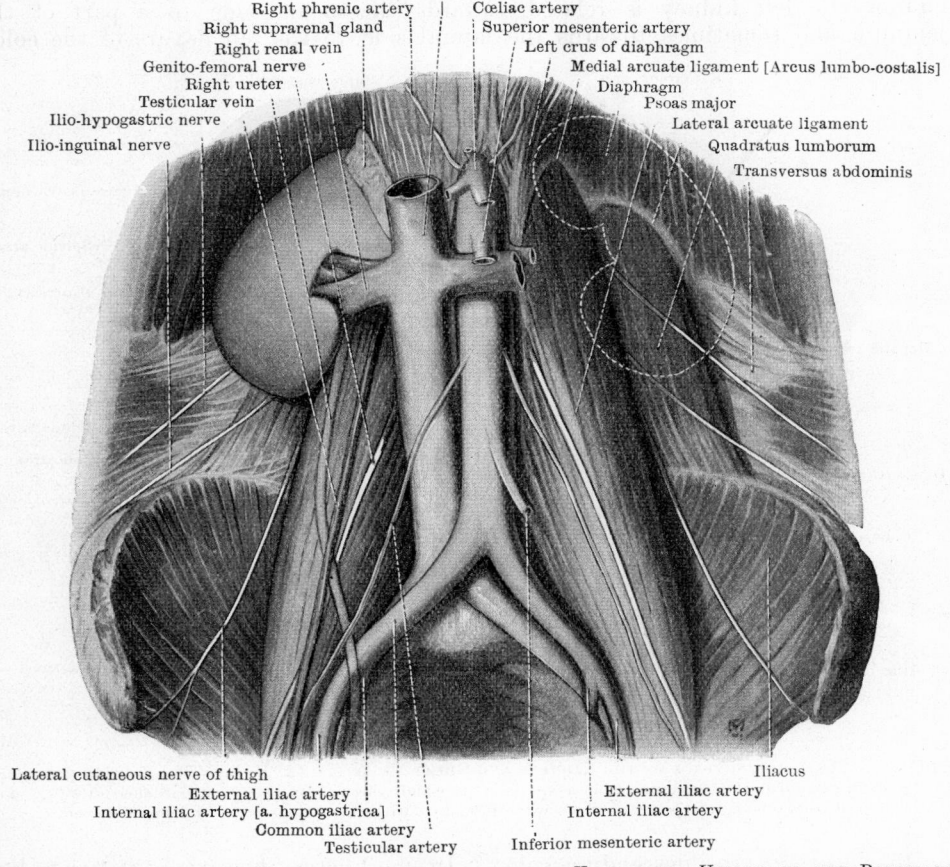

Inferior vena cava
Right phrenic artery | Cœliac artery
Right suprarenal gland | Superior mesenteric artery
Right renal vein | Left crus of diaphragm
Genito-femoral nerve | Medial arcuate ligament [Arcus lumbo-costalis]
Right ureter | Diaphragm
Testicular vein | Psoas major
Ilio-hypogastric nerve | Lateral arcuate ligament
Ilio-inguinal nerve | Quadratus lumborum
Transversus abdominis

Lateral cutaneous nerve of thigh | Iliacus
External iliac artery | External iliac artery
Internal iliac artery [a. hypogastrica] | Internal iliac artery
Common iliac artery
Testicular artery | Inferior mesenteric artery

FIG. 581.—DISSECTION TO SHOW THE RELATIONSHIPS OF THE KIDNEY AND URETER TO THE POSTERIOR ABDOMINAL WALL.   (A. F. D.)   The dotted outline indicates the position of the left kidney.

the second part of the duodenum and the right flexure of the colon or the beginning of the transverse colon.   The part of the kidney related to the duodenum is medial to the area which touches the colon, but the exact amount of the kidney in contact with each of those two parts of intestine varies much in different subjects.   Frequently the colon and the kidney are both covered with peritoneum where they are in contact, but the duodenum is bound down to the kidney by areolar tissue.   In addition to the structures mentioned, some portion of the jejunum and a branch of the right colic artery are often found in relation with a small part of the right kidney near its lower end between the colon and the duodenum (Fig. 578).   In some cases the peritoneum does not cover the whole of the surface in contact with the liver, and then the upper part of the hepatic area of the kidney is, like the front of the suprarenal gland, bound by areolar tissue to the bare area on the back of the liver.

Left Kidney.—The extreme upper and medial part of the front of the left kidney is united by areolar tissue to the lower part of the left suprarenal gland, and the area immediately below this is in relation with the stomach and the pancreas. The pancreas, like the suprarenal gland, is bound down to the kidney by areolar tissue, but the stomach is separated from it by a portion of the lesser sac of the peritoneum [bursa omentalis]. The area in relation with the stomach is a small, triangular district situated above the level at which the pancreas is related to the kidney. The upper and lateral part of the front of the kidney is related to the spleen, the two organs being separated by a portion of the general peritoneal cavity, except along the line where spleen and kidney are connected by the lieno-renal ligament. The anterior surface of the lower end of the left kidney is related, towards the medial side, to a part of the jejunum, and sometimes, towards the lateral side, to the left flexure of the colon

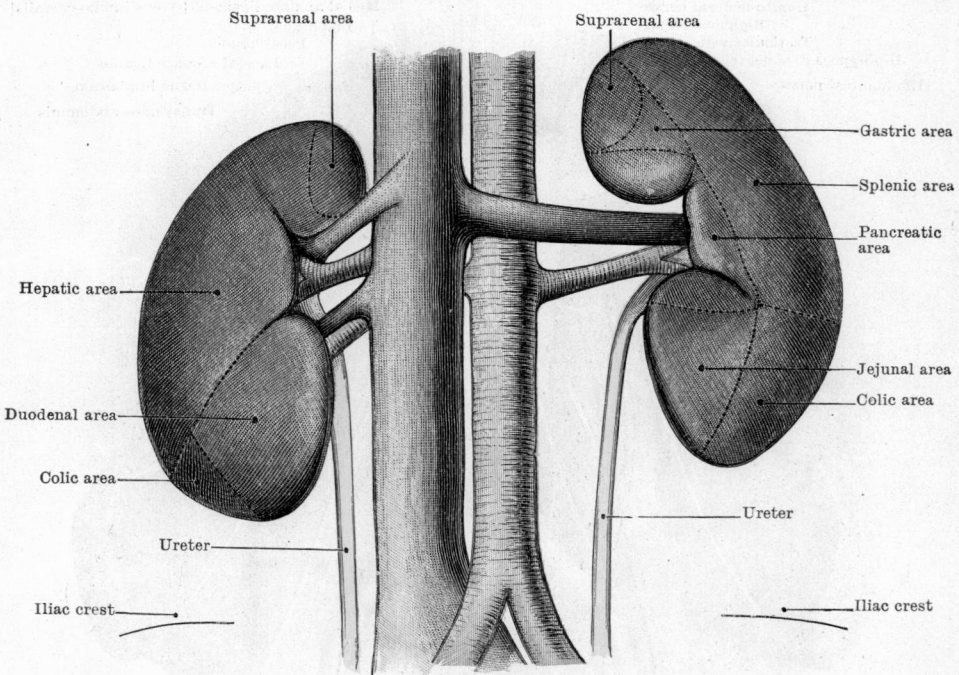

Suprarenal area — Suprarenal area — Gastric area — Splenic area — Pancreatic area — Hepatic area — Duodenal area — Colic area — Ureter — Iliac crest — Jejunal area — Colic area — Ureter — Iliac crest

FIG. 582.—ANTERIOR SURFACE OF THE KIDNEYS AND GREAT VESSELS. (A. F. D.) The drawing was made, before removal of the organs, from a specimen in which the viscera had been hardened *in situ*. The dotted lines mark out the areas which were in contact with the various other abdominal viscera.

or to a part of the descending colon. In most cases, however, the colon lies against the posterior abdominal wall lateral to the left kidney rather than on the front of it. The splenic vessels cross the left kidney about its middle, and the ascending branch of the superior left colic artery crosses it near its lower end.

Ends of the Kidney.—The kidney, fixed and hardened *in situ*, is usually more pointed at its lower end than at its upper end. The upper end is wider from side to side, and often slightly flattened from before backwards; it is bent slightly forwards and rests on the diaphragm, which separates it, as explained above, from the lower part of the pleural cavity.

Sinus of Kidney.—The sinus (Fig. 583), into which the hilum opens, is a narrow space, having its long axis corresponding to that of the kidney. The walls of the sinus are thick, being formed by the substance of the kidney, and they are lined with a part of the fibrous capsule which enters the sinus over the lips of the hilum. The floor of the sinus is not even, but presents a series of small projecting conical elevations, called **renal papillæ**, which vary from six to fifteen in number. Radiating from each papilla there is a number of slightly raised bars or ridges of kidney substance separated by depressed areas. The blood-vessels and nerves enter and leave the kidney by piercing the floors of the depressed areas. On the summit of each renal papilla there are many minute openings which are the terminal apertures of the secretory tubules of which the kidney is mainly composed; the urine escapes through these foramina into the subdivisions (calyces) of the ureter or kidney duct.

Kidney in Section.—Sections through the kidney (Figs. 973 and 978) show that it is composed to a large extent of a number of conical masses—known as **renal pyramids**. The pyramids con-

stitute, collectively, the **medulla** of the kidney, and are arranged with their bases directed towards the surface and their apices projecting into the lesser calyces of the pelvis of the ureter in the renal sinus, where they form the renal papillæ. The pyramids are more numerous than the papillæ, two or three usually ending in each papilla in the middle part of the kidney, and sometimes as many as six or more in each papilla near its ends. The bases of the pyramids are separated from the surface by a layer called the **cortex** of the kidney. The cortex not only covers over the bases of the pyramids, but also sends in prolongations, known as **renal columns**, between the pyramids, towards the sinus. The medulla exhibits in section a striated appearance, while the cortex is more granular and usually different in colour. The **basal part** of each pyramid appears in section to be composed of alternate dark and light streaks, while the **papillary part** is often of a lighter colour, and is very faintly striated.

In sections of the kidney the larger blood-vessels, after they have

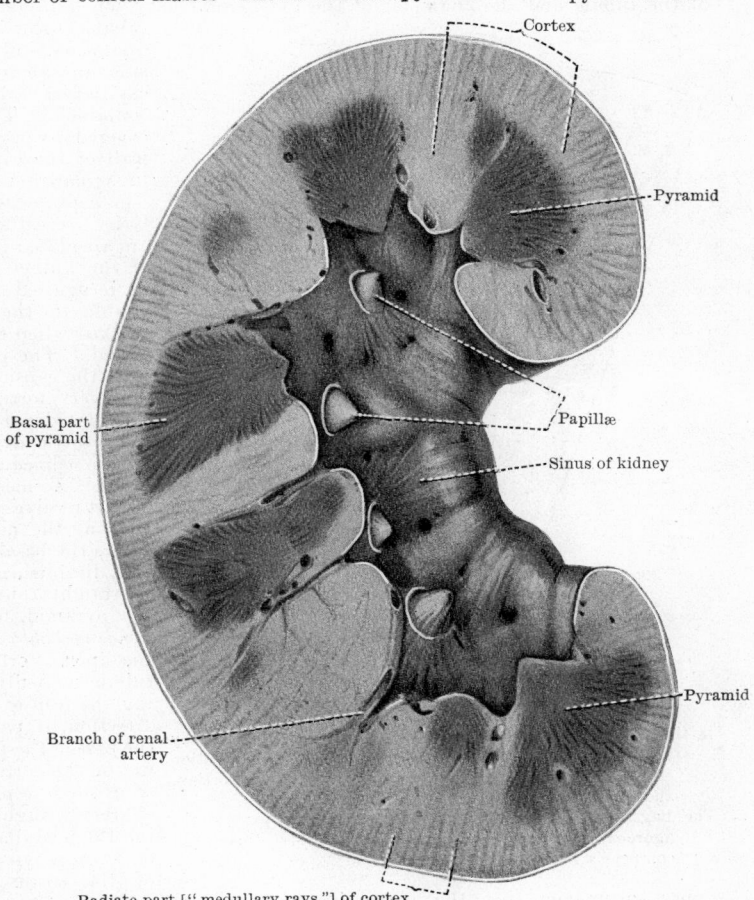

FIG. 583.—LONGITUDINAL SECTION THROUGH THE KIDNEY. (A. F. D.)
The vessels and fat have been removed to give a view of the wall of the kidney sinus. The points where the vessels enter the kidney substance are seen as holes in the sinus wall.

entered the kidney substance, are seen between the pyramids; and some of their main branches are visible passing across the bases of the pyramids.

In the fœtus and young child, and sometimes, though much less distinctly, in the adult, the surface of the kidney is marked by a number of grooves that divide it into polygonal areas. The areas represent the **lobes**, or reniculi, of which the kidney is originally composed, and each corresponds to one papilla with its pyramids and surrounding cortex.

An examination, with an ordinary pocket lens, of a section through the kidney shows that the lighter striæ of the bases of the pyramids are continued into the cortex. As they pass through the cortex towards the surface of the kidney the striæ become less distinct, and appear, when cut longitudinally, as separate ray-like prolongations carried outward from the bases of the pyramids. The parts of the cortex which seem in this way to be continuations of the medulla are called "medullary rays" of the cortex. The part of the cortex which intervenes between them is darker in colour and forms what is known as the **convoluted part** or "labyrinth." The appearance presented by the cortex of the kidney in section varies much according to

44 a

the plane in which the section has been taken. If the section is parallel to the axis of a pyramid, the medullary rays will appear as isolated streaks directed from the base of the pyramid towards the surface of the kidney, and separated from one another by narrow strips of the convoluted part of the labyrinth. On the other hand, in sections made at right angles to the axis of a pyramid, or cutting this axis obliquely, the convoluted portion of the cortex presents the appearance of a continuous net, the meshes of which are occupied by the rays, and the latter now exhibit circular or oval outlines. In a similar manner sections through the bases of the pyramids differ much in appearance according to the plane in which they are cut.

Kidney Tubules.—The glandular substance of the kidney is composed of a vast number of minute **renal tubules,** each of which has an exceedingly complicated course. The wall of each tubule consists throughout of a basement membrane and of an epithelial lining, but the lumen of the tubule and the character of the epithelium vary much in its different parts. Every tubule begins in a thin-walled spherical dilatation, known as a **glomerular capsule,** in which a complicated loop of capillary blood-vessels or **glomerulus** is contained. The tuft of capillaries is covered by a reflexion of the delicate wall of the capsule, and is, as it were, invaginated into the capsule (Fig. 584). The capsules with their enclosed capillaries are called **kidney corpuscles,** and are all placed in the convoluted portion of the kidney cortex, where they may be recognised as minute red points just visible to the unaided eye and best marked when the renal vessels are congested. The part of the tubule leading from the capsule—*first convoluted tubule* —is very tortuous, and lies within the convoluted part of the cortex. Passing from the convoluted part, the tubule enters a medullary ray, in which its course becomes less complicated, and here it receives the name of *spiral tubule.* Leaving the medullary ray, the tubule enters the basal portion of the pyramid, and, diminishing in diameter, it pursues a straight course towards the apex of the pyramid, forming the so-called *descending limb of Henle's loop.* Within the apical portion of the pyramid the tubule suddenly bends upon itself, forming the *loop of Henle,* and reversing its direction, it passes back again through the base of the pyramid into a medullary ray of the cortex as the *ascending limb of Henle's loop.* The ascending limb exhibits a slight spiral twisting. Leaving the medullary ray again, the tubule once more enters the convoluted part of the cortex, where its outline becomes

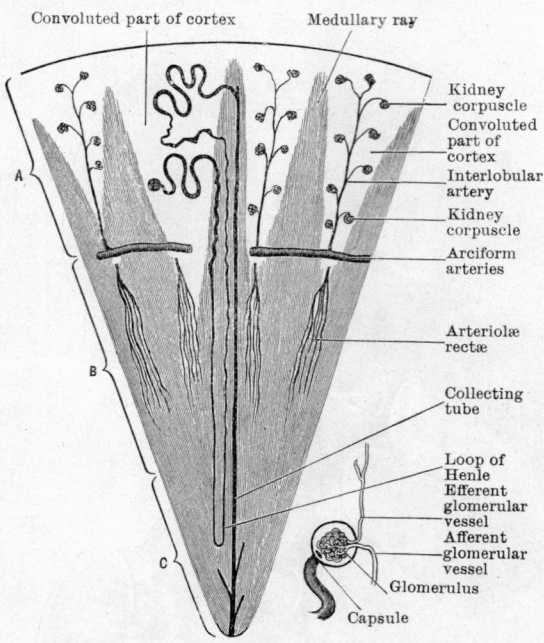

Convoluted part of cortex   Medullary ray

Kidney corpuscle
Convoluted part of cortex
Interlobular artery
Kidney corpuscle
Arciform arteries

Arteriolæ rectæ

Collecting tube

Loop of Henle
Efferent glomerular vessel
Afferent glomerular vessel
Glomerulus
Capsule

FIG. 584.—DIAGRAMMATIC REPRESENTATION OF THE STRUCTURES FORMING A KIDNEY LOBE.

In the middle part of the figure the course of one of the kidney tubules is indicated, and in the lateral parts the disposition of the larger arteries. A, Cortex; B, Basal portion, and C, Papillary portion of pyramid.
The diagram at the right-hand side of the lower part of the figure illustrates the connexions of the structures that compose a renal corpuscle.

comes so uneven that the name *irregular* or zigzag *tubule* is applied to it. While still within the convoluted part, its contour having acquired a more uniform appearance, the tubule receives the name of *second convoluted tubule*; the latter finally ends in a short *junctional tubule,* which passes back into a medullary ray and joins a *collecting tube.* Each collecting tube receives numerous renal tubules, and pursues a straight course through a medullary ray of the cortex and the pyramid. Finally, several collecting tubes, uniting together, form an *excretory tube,* which opens on the summit of a renal papilla into a calyx of the ureter by one of the minute foramina already described. In microscopic sections the various portions of the kidney tubule may be distinguished by the position which they occupy and by the character of the lining epithelium.

Supporting Tissue of the Kidney.—The tubules and the blood-vessels are all united together by a very small amount of areolar tissue which completely surrounds each tubule and blood-vessel and binds it to its neighbours. It has been found possible to obtain an accurate idea of the arrangement of this areolar tissue by submitting thin sections of the kidney to the action of certain digestive fluids. When that is done the tubules and blood-vessels are removed, and the areolar tissue stroma is left behind. The areolar tissue thus revealed is seen to form a continuous network, the spaces in which faithfully reproduce the outlines and the arrangement of the kidney tubules. The network of the stroma is continuous with the capsule of the kidney.

Vessels and Nerves of Kidney.—The **renal artery** arises directly from the aorta, and is very wide in proportion to the size of the organ. Its main branches, as they approach the kidney, lie between the tributaries of the renal vein in front and the ureter behind. Within the sinus of the kidney the branches of the renal artery become arranged in a dorsal and a ventral group, behind and in front of the subdivisions of the ureter. The ventral group of vessels supplies the anterior and lateral walls of the sinus; the distribution of the dorsal group is for the most part restricted to the portion of the kidney which lies behind the sinus and to its medial side. Entering the substance of the kidney, the larger arteries lie in the intervals between the pyramids, and are called **interlobar arteries**. These vessels, dividing, form a series of incomplete arterial arches—the **arciform arteries**—which pass across the bases of the pyramids. Although we speak of arterial arches, it must be understood that no anastomosis between the branches of the interlobar arteries actually takes place, but that each artery which enters the wall of the kidney sinus is an "end artery" with an isolated distribution. The arterial arches give off a number of vessels which pass through the convoluted part of the cortex towards the surface of the kidney; they are known as the **interlobular arteries**, and lie at very regular intervals. From them a number of short branches arise, termed **vasa afferentia**, each of which proceeds to the dilated extremity, or capsule, of a kidney tubule. There the vas afferens breaks up into a much convoluted capillary mass, called a *glomerulus*, which is contained within the invagination of the capsule. The little vessel—**vas efferens**—which issues from the glomerulus, instead of running directly into a larger vein, breaks up, after the manner of an artery, into capillaries which supply the tubules of the kidney cortex. Hence the blood which supplies the tubules of the cortical part of the kidney passes in the first instance through the glomeruli. The tubules of the bases of the pyramids also receive their blood-supply through vasa efferentia derived from the glomeruli which lie near. The little vessels that pass from the latter glomeruli break up into bundles of fine arterioles which give the bases of the pyramids their coarsely striated appearance. They are known as **arteriolæ rectæ**, and, like the interlobular arteries, are very conspicuous in injected preparations of the kidney (Fig. 584).

The fibrous capsule of the kidney receives minute branches from the interlobular arteries, some of which, piercing the capsule, communicate by capillaries with the vessels of the renal fat.

Veins corresponding to the interlobular arteries and arteriolæ rectæ collect the blood from the capillaries surrounding the tubules, and unite to form a series of complete arches across the bases of the pyramids. From the venous arcades, vessels arise which traverse the intervals between the pyramids and reach the sinus of the kidney, where they unite to form the dorsal and ventral tributaries of the renal vein. Some small veins in the superficial part of the cortex communicate through the fibrous capsule with minute veins in the renal fat. Issuing from the kidney sinus, the main tributaries unite to form the **renal vein**, which runs a direct course to end in the inferior vena cava.

The **lymph vessels** of the kidney end in the aortic lymph glands.

The **nerves** of the kidney accompany the branches of the artery, and are derived from the renal plexus. Their minute branches form regular net-like plexuses on the walls of the fine arteries and kidney tubules, and the presence of nerve terminations occurring among the epithelial cells lining the tubules has been demonstrated.

From clinical evidence it would appear that the afferent nerve fibres which supply the kidney are connected with the tenth, eleventh, and twelfth thoracic nerves.

Variations.—A marked difference in the size of the two kidneys is sometimes observed, a small kidney on one side of the body being usually compensated for by a large kidney on the opposite side. Cases of complete absence of one or other kidney are recorded. A few cases are on record in which an extra kidney was found on one or other side.

Traces of the superficial lobulation of the kidney, present in the fœtus and young child, are often retained in the adult.

Horse-shoe kidney is not an infrequent abnormality. In such cases the two kidneys are united at their lower ends, across the median plane below the inferior mesenteric artery, by a connecting piece of kidney substance. The amount of fusion between the two kidneys varies much; it is sometimes very complete, while in other cases it is but slight, the connexion being composed chiefly of fibrous tissue.

In very rare cases the kidney appears to be almost entirely surrounded by peritoneum and to be attached to the abdominal wall by a kind of mesentery which encloses the vessels and nerves passing to the hilum. The condition is believed to be congenital.

Not very infrequently one or both kidneys are found at a much lower level than usual, and occupying a position in the iliac fossa or the pelvic cavity. The condition, when congenital, is associated with an arrest in the normal change in position, relative to surrounding structures, which the kidney experiences during development. In such cases the kidney does not receive its blood-supply from usually placed renal arteries, but from vessels which arise from the lower end of the aorta, or from the iliac, or the middle sacral artery. Such congenital abnormally situated kidneys do not usually possess the typical outline of the normal organ, but vary much in shape, and the hilum is often malformed and misplaced.

In some mammalian animals, such as the bear, the kidneys are composed of a number of completely isolated lobes, each of which corresponds to one papilla, its pyramids and surrounding cortex; while in others, such as the horse, the fusion of the lobes is more complete even than in the human kidney, and a single mass represents the united papillæ.

URETERS

The **ureters** are the ducts that lead from the kidneys to the urinary bladder. Each ureter begins above in a thin-walled funnel-shaped expansion, called the **pelvis of the ureter**, which is placed partly within and partly outside the sinus of the kidney. Towards the lower end of the kidney the part of the pelvis which lies outside the sinus diminishes in calibre, and forms a tube-like duct which conveys the urine to the bladder.

Pelvis of Ureter.—Within the sinus of the kidney the pelvis lies among the larger renal vessels (Fig. 585). It is formed by the junction of two (or more

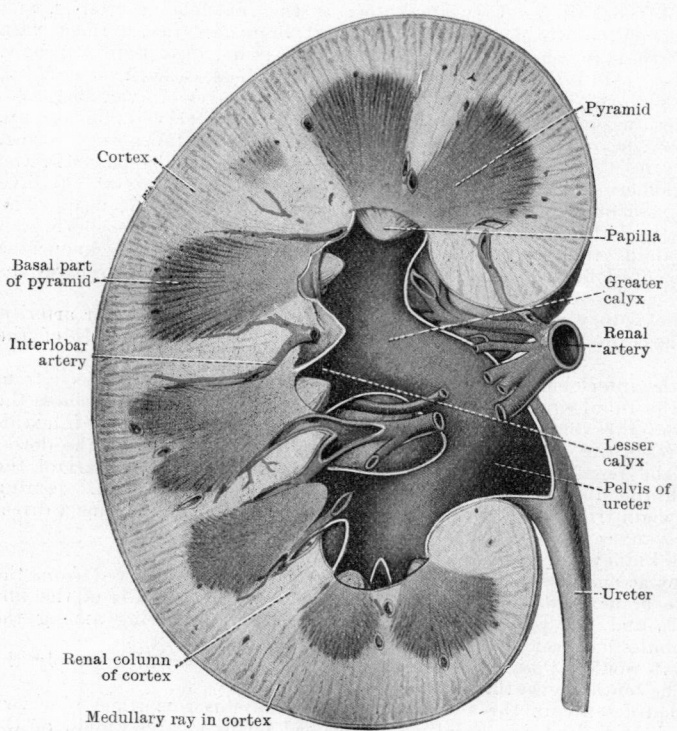

rarely three) thin-walled tubes — the **greater calyces** — each of which has a number of branches. The branches, called **lesser calyces**, are short, and increase in diameter as they approach the sinus wall, to which they are attached. Their wide, funnel-like ends enclose the renal papillæ and receive the urine. The lesser calyces are usually about eight in number, one calyx sometimes surrounding two or even three papillæ. The portion of the pelvis that lies outside the kidney has in front of it, in addition to the renal vessels, on the *right side*, the second part of the duodenum, and on the *left side*, a part of the pancreas and sometimes the duodeno-jejunal flexure (Fig. 578).

Fig. 585.—Longitudinal Section of Kidney, opening up the Sinus. (A. F. D.)

The pelvis of the ureter and some of its calyces have been laid open.

The ureter proper is a pale-coloured thick-walled duct with a small lumen. When *in situ* it has a total length of about ten inches, and lies throughout its whole course in the extra-peritoneal tissue behind the peritoneum, to which it is closely adherent. The upper part of the ureter lies in the abdominal cavity, and the lower part in the true pelvis (Figs. 578 and 586).

The **abdominal portion** of the ureter, about five inches in length, is directed downwards and slightly medially, and lies on the psoas major muscle (Fig. 578). Certain structures are related to the ureters in a similar manner on both sides of the body; for instance, the abdominal portion of each ureter is crossed very obliquely, in front, by the testicular or ovarian vessels, and behind each ureter the genito-femoral nerve passes downwards and laterally. Other structures are related to the duct of the right or left side alone. On the *right side*, the second part of the duodenum lies in front of the upper part of the ureter, and the line of attachment of the mesentery crosses it lower down, shortly before the ureter enters the true pelvis. The right colic and ileo-colic arteries also are anterior relations. On the *left side* the left colic vessels and the line of attachment of the pelvic mesocolon cross the ureter.

In X-Ray photographs, the shadow cast by the abdominal portion of the ureter, when it has been made opaque, is seen to fall on the tips of the transverse processes of the lower lumbar vertebræ. (Pls. LII and LIII).

Crossing the common iliac or the external iliac artery, the ureter enters the true pelvis. Usually the left ureter crosses the common iliac artery, and the right ureter the external iliac; but that arrangement is by no means constant.

The **pelvic portion** of the ureter is about five inches in length; it passes backwards and downwards on the side wall of the pelvis under cover of the peritoneum, describing a curve which is convex backwards and laterally (Fig. 586), the most convex point being close to the deepest part of the greater sciatic notch.

In its course within the pelvis the ureter lies below and in front of the internal iliac artery [a. hypogastrica], and crosses the medial side of the obturator nerve and vessels and of the umbilical artery. About the level of the ischial spine, the ureter is crossed from before backwards by the vas deferens, and from that point onwards it is not so intimately related to the peritoneum. It then bends slightly medially and forwards, to reach the lateral angle of the bladder, and comes into relationship with the upper end of the seminal vesicle, in front of which it lies (Fig. 591). The vas deferens having crossed the ureter also turns medially, and as it does so it lies on a plane posterior to the ureter. The lower end of the ureter is surrounded by a dense plexus of veins which brings the vesical plexus into communication with the internal iliac vein. The largest of the nerve cords which connect the hypogastric plexus with the pelvic plexus, also comes into relationship with the lower part of the pelvic portion of the ureter, in the region where the ureter is crossed by the vas deferens (Fig. 586).

As it descends the ureter forms the posterior boundary of a triangular peritoneal district known as the *obturator triangle*, the lower limit of which is formed by the vas deferens, and the upper and anterior boundary by the external iliac vessels and the pelvic brim (Fig. 586).

When the right and left ureters reach the bladder they are a little more than two inches apart. They pierce the bladder wall very obliquely, and are embedded within its muscular tissue for nearly three-quarters of an inch. Finally, they open into the bladder by a pair of minute slit-like apertures which are of a valvular nature, and prevent a backward passage of fluid from the bladder. It is probable, however, that an exaggerated idea of the valvular nature of the openings of the ureters into the bladder is obtained by an examination of the parts in the dead subject. When the bladder is empty the openings of the ureters are placed about one inch apart, but when the bladder is distended they may be two inches apart, or more. As the ureter pierces the bladder wall the muscular fibres of the bladder and ureter remain quite distinct, and so the ureter, remaining a thick-walled tubular structure, appears to pass through a gap in the muscular wall of the bladder. The mucous coat alone of the ureter becomes continuous with that of the bladder.

The lumen of the ureter proper is not uniform throughout; it is slightly constricted near its pelvis and where it crosses the iliac artery; and it is narrowest where it passes through the bladder wall.

In the female, the ureter, near its termination, passes below the root of the broad ligament of the uterus, and lies a little lateral to the cervix uteri above the lateral fornix of the vagina, and finally inclines medially to lie in front of the lateral margin of the vagina. Its lower part is accompanied by the uterine artery, which crosses above and in front of it not far from its termination. Higher up it lies in the peritoneal ridge which forms the posterior boundary of the fossa ovarica, which, in the female, is a posterior subdivision of the obturator triangle (Fig. 620).

Structure of Ureter.—The wall of the ureter proper, which is thick and of a whitish colour, is composed of mucous, muscular, and fibrous coats. The **mucous coat** is covered with an epithelium composed of many layers of cells, those nearest the lumen being of large size. When the canal is empty the mucous coat is thrown into numerous longitudinal folds, and so its lumen has a stellate outline in transverse section. The submucous tissue varies much in thickness in different parts of the ureter, and contains some elastic fibres. The **muscular coat** consists of unstriped muscle fibres collected into bundles which are separated by a considerable amount of fibro-areolar tissue, and are arranged, some longitudinally, some circularly. In the upper part of the ureter a relatively large amount of fibro-areolar tissue is present deep to and among the bundles of muscle fibres, which are arranged in three distinct strata—an inner longitudinal, middle circular, and an outer longitudinal. In the middle part of the tube the same layers may be recognised, but the circularly disposed bundles of fibres are more numerous than higher up. In the lower part of the ureter the fibro-areolar tissue is relatively scanty and the inner longitudinal fibres lie close to the mucous coat; in this region also the longitudinal folds of the mucous coat become fewer and less marked. A short distance above the bladder, a number of coarse bundles of longitudinally arranged muscle fibres are applied to the outer surface of the muscular coat. These form the so-called "sheath of the ureter," and are continuous with the superficial part of the muscular wall of the bladder. In the portion of the ureter which traverses the wall of the bladder nearly all the fibres of the muscular coat are disposed longitudinally. The muscle fibres lie immediately outside the epithelium, and end just where the mucous coats of the bladder and ureter become continuous. The outer, **adventitious coat** of fibrous tissue

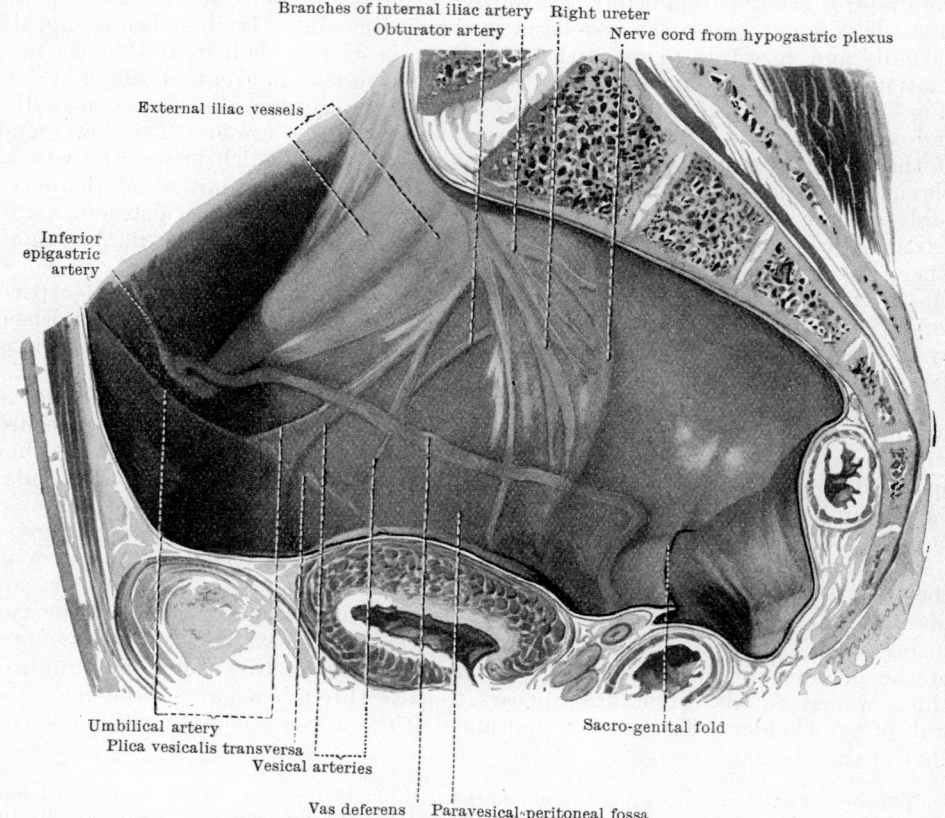

Branches of internal iliac artery   Right ureter
Obturator artery   Nerve cord from hypogastric plexus

External iliac vessels

Inferior
epigastric
artery

Umbilical artery
Plica vesicalis transversa
Vesical arteries

Sacro-genital fold

Vas deferens   Paravesical peritoneal fossa

Fig. 586.—Median Section of an Adult Male Pelvis. (A. F. D.)

A view of the side wall of the pelvic cavity.

varies in thickness at different levels, and in its lower part blends with the fibro-areolar tissue which lies among the muscle fibres forming the sheath of the ureter just mentioned.

The mucous membrane of the calyces and of the pelvis of the ureter has an epithelium like that of the ureter proper. Where each renal papilla projects into one of the calyces a deep circular recess is formed between the wall of the calyx and the sloping side of the papilla; at the bottom of this recess the epithelium of the calyx becomes continuous with that covering the papilla. At the apex of the papilla the epithelium joins that of the kidney tubules. The muscular fibres in the wall of the calyces and of the pelvis are collected into loosely arranged bundles separated by wide intervals occupied by fibrous tissue. As in the ureter proper, the outermost and innermost fibres are longitudinal, and the middle ones are circular. The circularly arranged fibres alone form a distinct layer.

Vessels and Nerves of the Ureter.—The abdominal part of the ureter receives its **blood supply** from the renal and the testicular or ovarian arteries; the pelvic portion is supplied by the vesical and middle rectal [hæmorrhoidal] vessels.

The **nerves** of the ureter are derived from the renal, testicular or ovarian, and hypogastric plexuses. The afferent fibres reach the spinal cord through the eleventh and twelfth thoracic and first lumbar nerves.

Variations.—The ureter is sometimes represented by two tubes in its upper portion. In rarer cases it is double throughout the greater part of its extent, or even in its whole length with two openings into the bladder. Asymmetry in such abnormalities is very common.

Variations in the form of the pelvis of the ureter are of frequent occurrence. Most usually the pelvis divides into two greater calyces, one of which passes towards the upper pole of the kidney, and the other towards the lower pole. In some cases the two calyces spring directly from the ureter without the intervention of a pelvis, or a marked subdivision may lead to the formation of two pelves.

URINARY BLADDER

The **urinary bladder** (vesica urinaria) is a hollow muscular organ situated in the lower and anterior part of the true pelvis, above and behind the pubic symphysis. It lies in front of the rectum, from which it is separated *in the male* by the seminal vesicles and the terminal portions of the vasa deferentia, and *in the female* by the vagina and uterus. The ureters open into the posterior part of the bladder about half an inch from the median plane. The urethra is the canal by which the urine reaches the surface from the bladder ; its vesical aperture lies in the median plane below the openings of the ureters.

The size and shape of the bladder, the thickness of its wall, and also to a great extent its relations, vary with the amount of distension or contraction of the organ. When empty, or only slightly distended, the bladder lies within the true pelvis ; as it becomes filled with urine it rises above the pubis and enters the abdominal cavity. The changes affect chiefly the upper part of the bladder, which becomes altered in shape and size, and acquires new connexions and relations ; the lower portion varies but slightly with the amount of distension of the organ (see Figs. 587 and 588). The upper part of the bladder is covered with peritoneum, which is reflected on to it from the anterior abdominal wall in front, from the sides of the pelvis laterally, and, *in the male*, across the seminal vesicles and terminal parts of the vasa deferentia from the rectum behind. *In the female* the peritoneum passes on to the bladder posteriorly from the vesical surface of the uterus. The peritoneum dips down posteriorly for a certain distance between the bladder and rectum in the male, forming the *recto-vesical pouch* ; in the female a slit-like peritoneal recess, called the *utero-vesical pouch*, intervenes between the uterus and the upper surface of the bladder (Fig. 593).

The lower part of the bladder lies below the peritoneum, and is for the most part directed towards the pelvic floor. Anteriorly in the median plane it is supported in both sexes by the pubic symphysis and the retro-pubic pad of fat. Farther back, *in the male*, it rests on the prostate and on the lower part of the rectum, from the latter of which it is separated by the seminal vesicles and the terminal portions of the vasa deferentia ; *in the female* it rests on the anterior wall of the vagina. On each side, the bladder is supported by the levator ani muscle and, farther from the median plane, by the obturator internus ; it is separated from the fascia that covers those muscles by loose areolar tissue.

The **internal urethral orifice** is in the part of the bladder wall which lies lowest in the pelvic cavity. The term **neck** is applied to this region—the bladder appearing as if it were suddenly constricted to form the urethra.

The portion of the bladder wall above and behind the urethral orifice is directed *in the male* towards the rectum and lies below and in front of the recto-vesical pouch ; it is called the **base** of the bladder, and is closely related to the seminal vesicles and the ampullæ of the vasa deferentia. The corresponding part of the bladder *in the female* rests against the anterior wall of the vagina.

The **apex** is the portion of the bladder which lies nearest to the upper border of the pubic symphysis when the organ is empty, and rises above the pubis into the abdominal cavity when the bladder is distended. Connected with the apex of the bladder there is a fibrous cord—the **median umbilical ligament** —which passes upwards, on the posterior surface of the anterior abdominal wall,

and reaches the umbilicus; it is the fibrous remnant of the *urachus*—the
passage which in the embryo connects the developing bladder with the allantois.

Position of Internal Urethral Orifice.—During the various changes in shape
and size which the bladder undergoes, the region of the internal urethral orifice
remains almost fixed in position. In the male the urethral orifice lies immediately
above the prostate, and behind and slightly below the level of the upper margin of
the pubic symphysis, from which it is distant about two to two and a half inches.

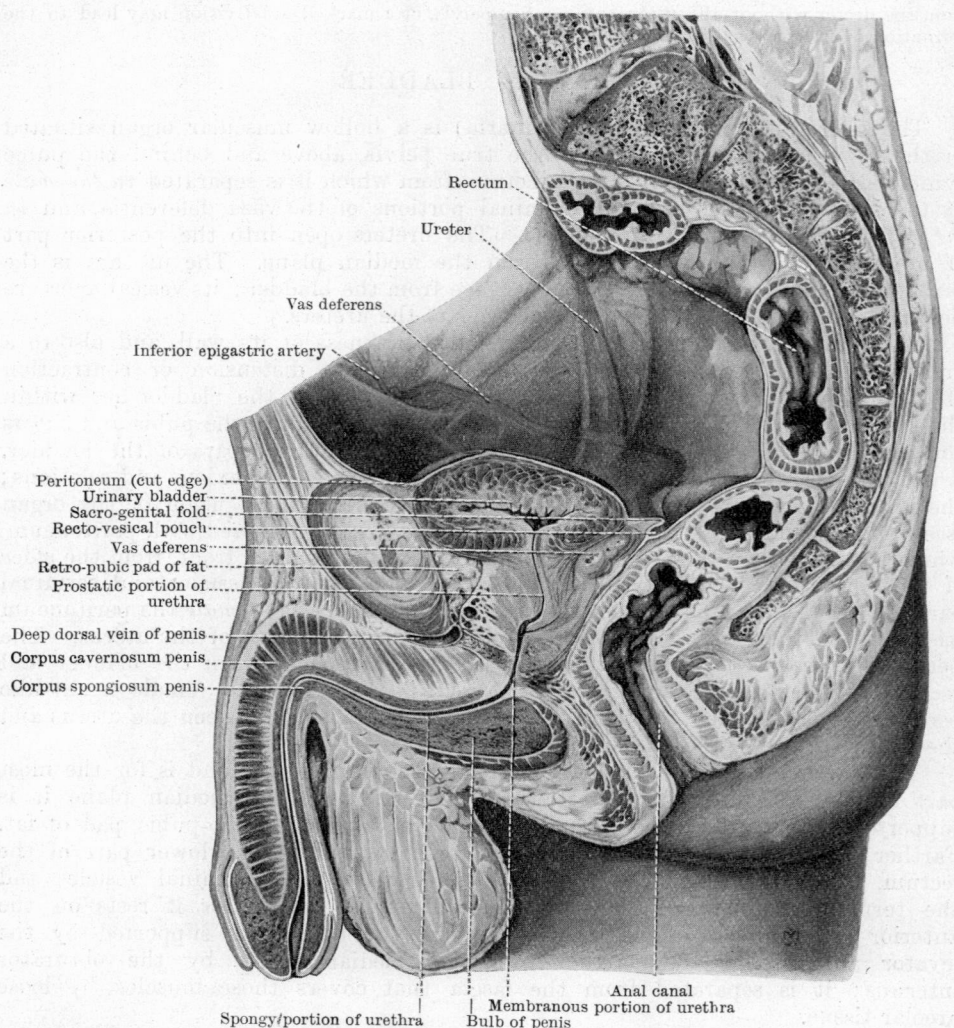

FIG. 587.—MEDIAN SECTION THROUGH THE PELVIS OF AN ADULT MALE SUBJECT. (A. F. D.)
The urinary bladder is empty and firmly contracted.

It can be reached by a finger introduced into the bladder through the abdominal
wall above the pubic symphysis. It is usually placed half an inch to one inch
above the level of a plane passing through the lower margin of the symphysis and
the lower end of the sacrum, but in some cases it is slightly lower. The comparatively small variations in the level of the internal urethral orifice which do
occur depend partly upon the quantity of fluid in the bladder, and partly upon
the amount of distension of the lower portion of the rectum. When the bladder
is very much distended the orifice lies at a slightly lower level than when the
organ is empty; on the other hand, distension of the lower part of the rectum
raises the level of the urethral orifice to some extent. In the female the internal

urethral orifice normally occupies a lower level than in the male (compare Figs. 587 and 593).

Inferior Aspect of the Bladder.—The lower part of the bladder is directed towards the pelvic floor, and, as we have seen, changes but slightly with the varying amount of distension of the viscus. When the organ has been hardened before its removal from the body, it is possible to map out on its inferior

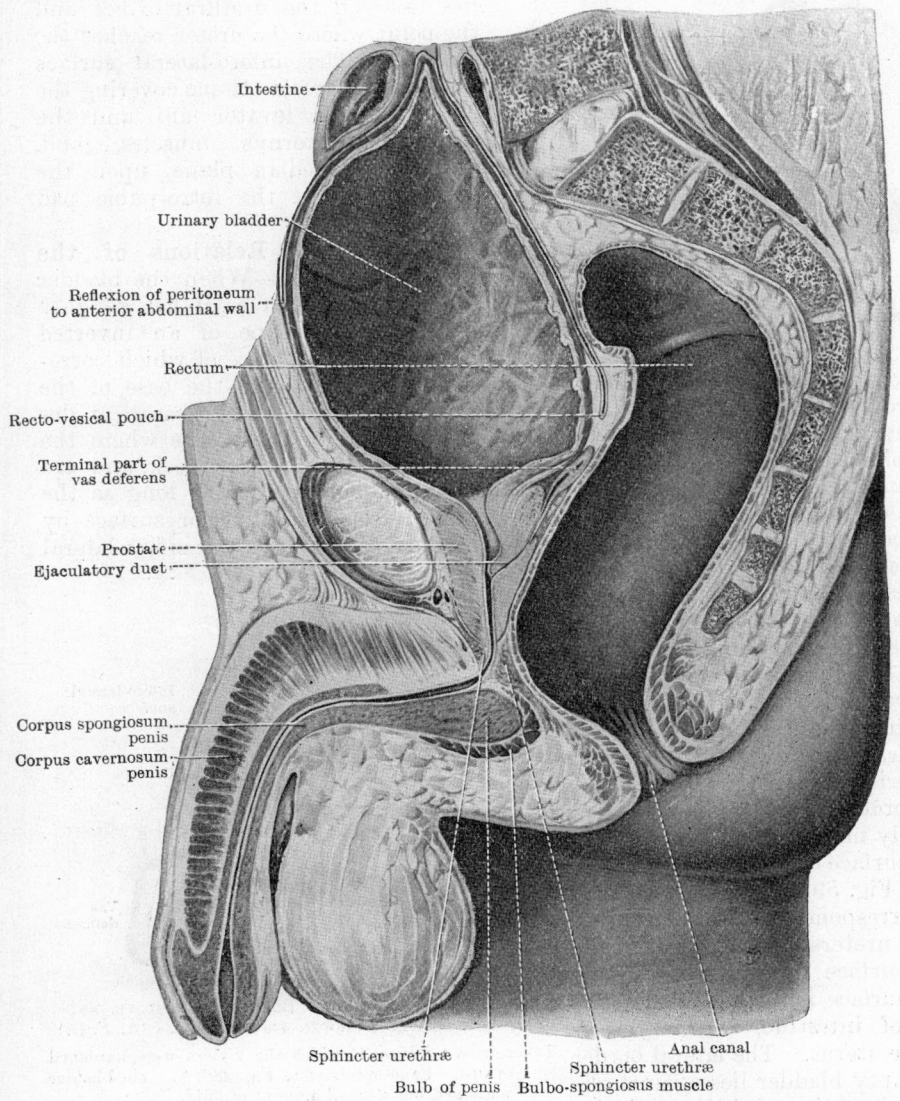

Intestine

Urinary bladder

Reflexion of peritoneum to anterior abdominal wall

Rectum

Recto-vesical pouch

Terminal part of vas deferens

Prostate
Ejaculatory duct

Corpus spongiosum penis
Corpus cavernosum penis

Sphincter urethræ

Bulb of penis

Anal canal

Sphincter urethræ
Bulbo-spongiosus muscle

FIG. 588.—MEDIAN SECTION OF THE PELVIS OF AN ADULT MALE SUBJECT. (A. F. D.)

The urinary bladder and rectum are both distended.

aspect three convex triangular areas which may be distinguished from one another by the directions in which they look. The three areas approach one another in the region of the urethral orifice, where, in the male, a portion of the inferior aspect of the bladder wall is structurally continuous with the upper part of the prostate. Behind the urethral orifice there is a triangular district directed backwards and downwards, and related, *in the male,* to the seminal vesicles and the ampullæ of the vasa deferentia, which, together with a layer of smooth muscle fibres and fibrous tissue, intervene in that position between the bladder and the rectum. This triangular area is the base of the bladder, and *in the female* it is directed against the anterior wall of the vagina. The rest of the inferior aspect of the bladder is formed by two **infero-lateral surfaces**, which meet in the median plane in front of the urethral orifice, and are directed for the most part downwards and laterally (see Figs. 589 to 591). Each of these

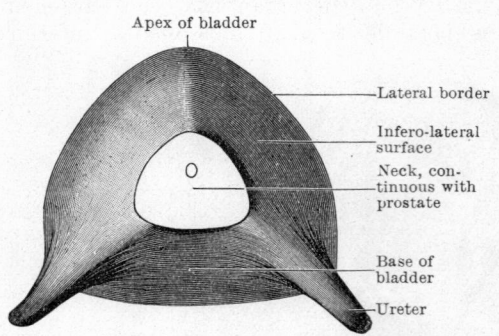

Apex of bladder

Lateral border

Infero-lateral surface

Neck, continuous with prostate

Base of bladder

Ureter

FIG. 589.—INFERIOR ASPECT OF THE EMPTY MALE URINARY BLADDER. From a subject in which the viscera had been hardened *in situ*. (A. F. D.)

areas extends backwards to join the base along a rounded border which lies between the urethral orifice and the point where the ureter reaches the bladder. The infero-lateral surface rests on the areolar tissue covering the fascia of the levator ani and the obturator internus muscles, and, nearer the median plane, upon the pubic bone and the retro-pubic pad of fat.

Shape and Relations of the Empty Bladder.—When the bladder is empty, or nearly so, it has, roughly speaking, the shape of an inverted tetrahedron, the apex of which corresponds to the point where the urethra leaves the organ, while the base of the tetrahedron is the superior surface of the bladder. The three basal angles of the tetrahedron correspond to the bladder apex and to the points where the ureters join the organ. The three surfaces meet inferiorly at the neck, and are marked off from one another by ill-defined, rounded borders, but as long as the organ is empty, or nearly so, they are separated from the superior surface by distinct borders. The three areas have been already described as the infero-lateral

surfaces and the base (Fig. 589), and their relations have been indicated. The **superior surface** of the empty bladder is convex when the organ is contracted and concave when relaxed. It is covered with peritoneum, and its outline, which is approximately triangular, is determined by lateral and posterior borders (Fig. 596). The **lateral borders** of the empty bladder are sharply marked, and separate the superior surface from the infero-lateral surfaces (Fig. 591, A). The **posterior border** corresponds to a line between the two ureters, and separates the superior surface from the base. The superior surface is related *in the male* to coils of intestine, *in the female* also to the uterus. The lateral border of the empty bladder lies against the lining fascia of the pelvis immediately

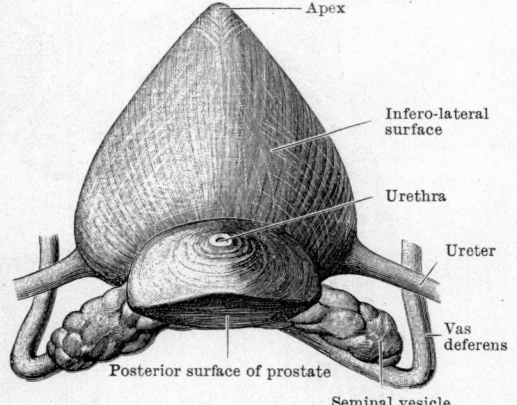

Apex

Infero-lateral surface

Urethra

Ureter

Vas deferens

Seminal vesicle

Posterior surface of prostate

FIG. 590.—THE URINARY BLADDER, PROSTATE, AND SEMINAL VESICLES, VIEWED FROM BELOW. (A. F. D.)

Taken from a subject in which the viscera were hardened *in situ*. Same specimen as Fig. 986, A. The bladder contained but a small amount of fluid.

above, or at the level of, the arcus tendineus of the levator ani. The vas deferens crosses the side wall of the pelvis parallel to it, but at a considerably higher level (Fig. 586).

The tetrahedral form of the empty, contracted bladder results from the relative fixity of the points where the median umbilical ligament, the ureters, and the urethra are attached to the organ. Those points are held apart as the organ contracts, and in this way determine the shape of the empty bladder.

In median section the cavity of the empty and relaxed bladder often presents the appearance of a Y-shaped chink, the stem of the Y being represented by the urethra as it leaves the organ, and the two limbs by the narrow intervals between the upper wall and the under parts of the bladder wall which lie in front of and behind the urethral orifice. The relaxed form of the empty bladder is found associated with a bladder wall of but little thickness, and with a concave

PLATE LIII

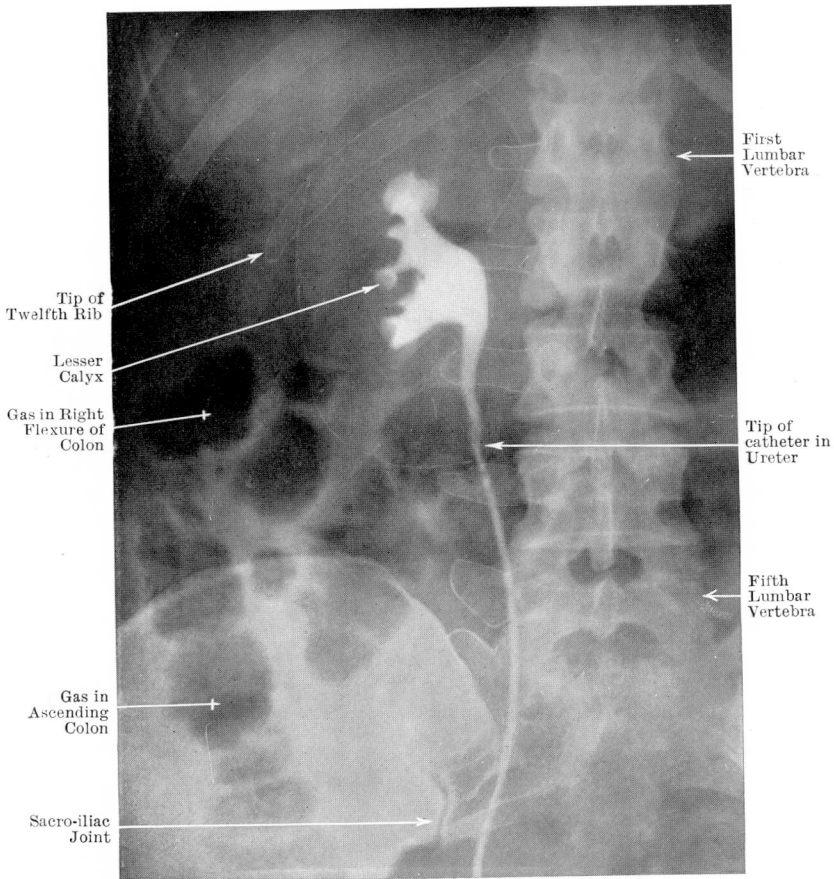

First
Lumbar
Vertebra

Tip of
Twelfth Rib

Lesser
Calyx

Gas in Right
Flexure of
Colon

Tip of
catheter in
Ureter

Fifth
Lumbar
Vertebra

Gas in
Ascending
Colon

Sacro-iliac
Joint

PLATE LIII.—RADIOGRAPH OF RIGHT URETER AFTER THE
PASSAGE OF A URETERAL CATHETER AND THE INJEC-
TION OF SODIUM IODIDE SOLUTION INTO THE PELVIS
AND CALYCES. (Dr. J. F. Brailsford.)

Note the division of the Pelvis of the Ureter into two Greater Calyces, and
the appearance of a Lesser Calyx. Cf. Fig. 585, p. 698 and Plate LII. The
resilience of the catheter has displaced the lower part of the abdominal
portion of the ureter medially. The outlines of the Kidney, the 11th and
12th Ribs, and the Transverse Processes of the Lumbar Vertebræ have been
slightly accentuated.

[Facing p. 704

PLATE LIV

Fifth Lumbar transverse process

Sacro-iliac Joint

Iliac crest

Pubic Arch and Symphysis

Anterior superior spine

Anterior inferior spine

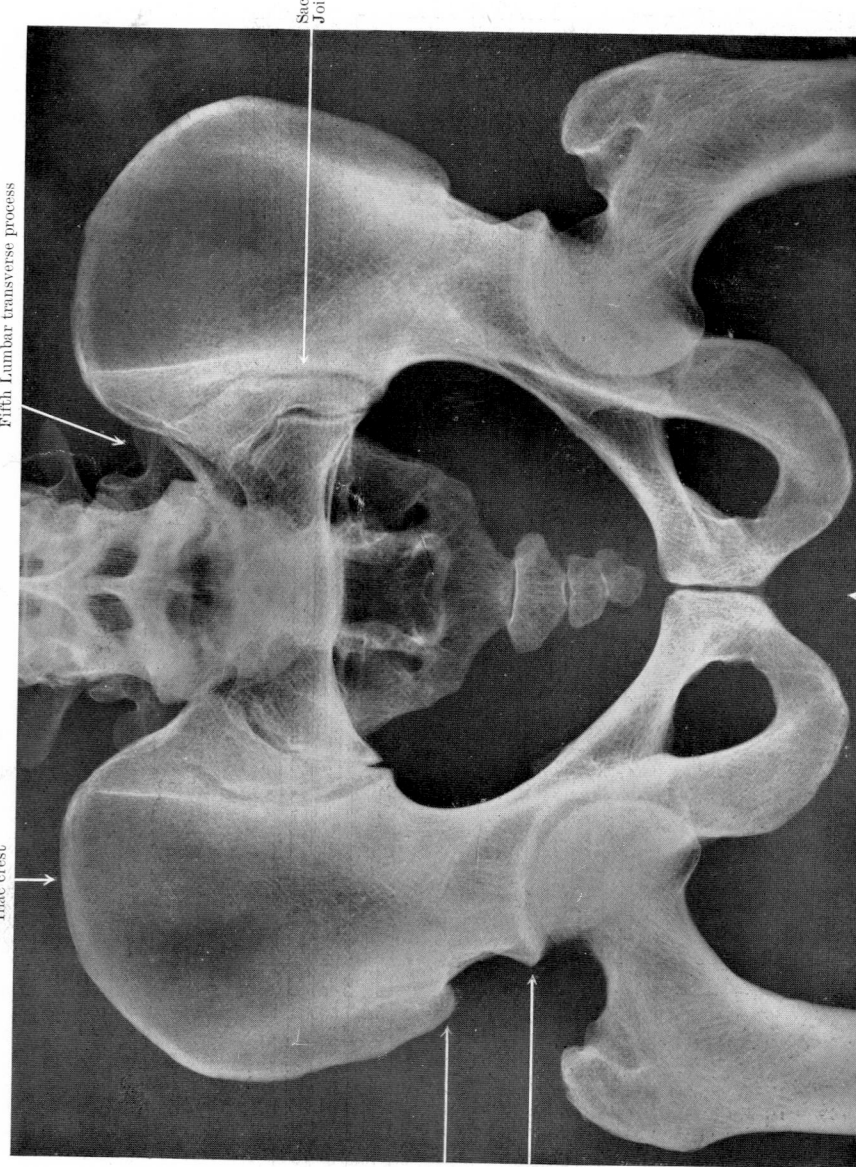

PLATE LIV.—RADIOGRAPH OF DRIED MALE PELVIS (MAN AGED 22).

Compare with Fig. 231, p. 267, and with radiograph of Female Pelvis, Plate XIII, noting the differences in proportion of the pelvis as a whole and in the form of the Pubic Arch and the Inlet of the True Pelvis.

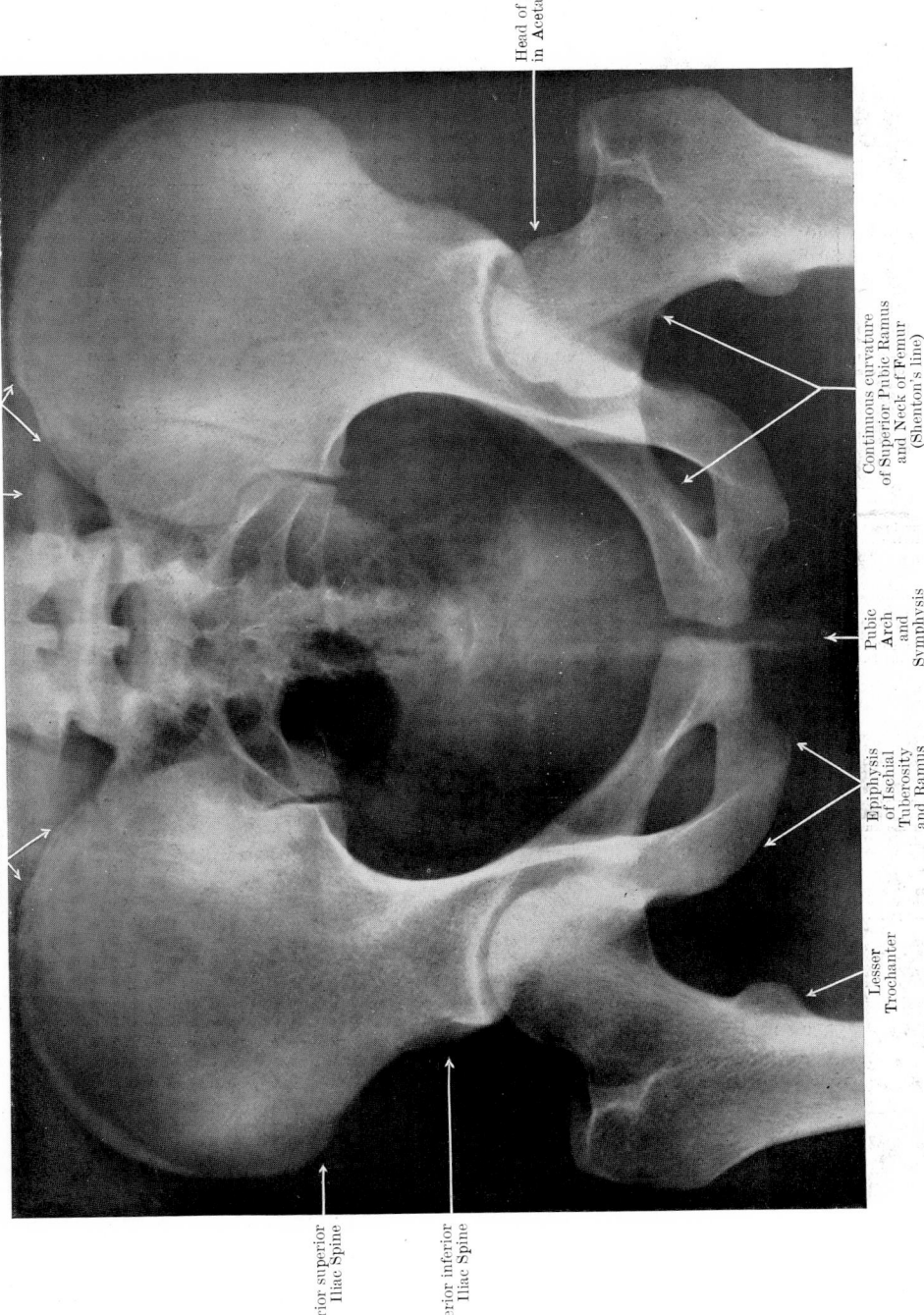

Epiphysis of
Iliac Crest

Fifth Lumbar
transverse process   Epiphysis of Iliac Crest

Head of Femur
in Acetabulum

Continuous curvature
of Superior Pubic Ramus
and Neck of Femur
(Shenton's line)

Epiphysis
of Ischial
Tuberosity
and Ramus

Pubic
Arch
and
Symphysis

Lesser
Trochanter

Anterior superior
Iliac Spine

Anterior inferior
Iliac Spine

PLATE LV.—RADIOGRAPH OF LIVING FEMALE PELVIS (GIRL AGED 17).
(Dr. J. Duncan White.)

Compare with Fig. 232, p. 268, and with Plate XII. For the Sexual Differences in the Pelvis see p. 269. Note
the presence of uniting epiphyses of the Iliac Crests and the Ischial Tuberosities (cf. Fig. 230, p. 266).

PLATE LVI

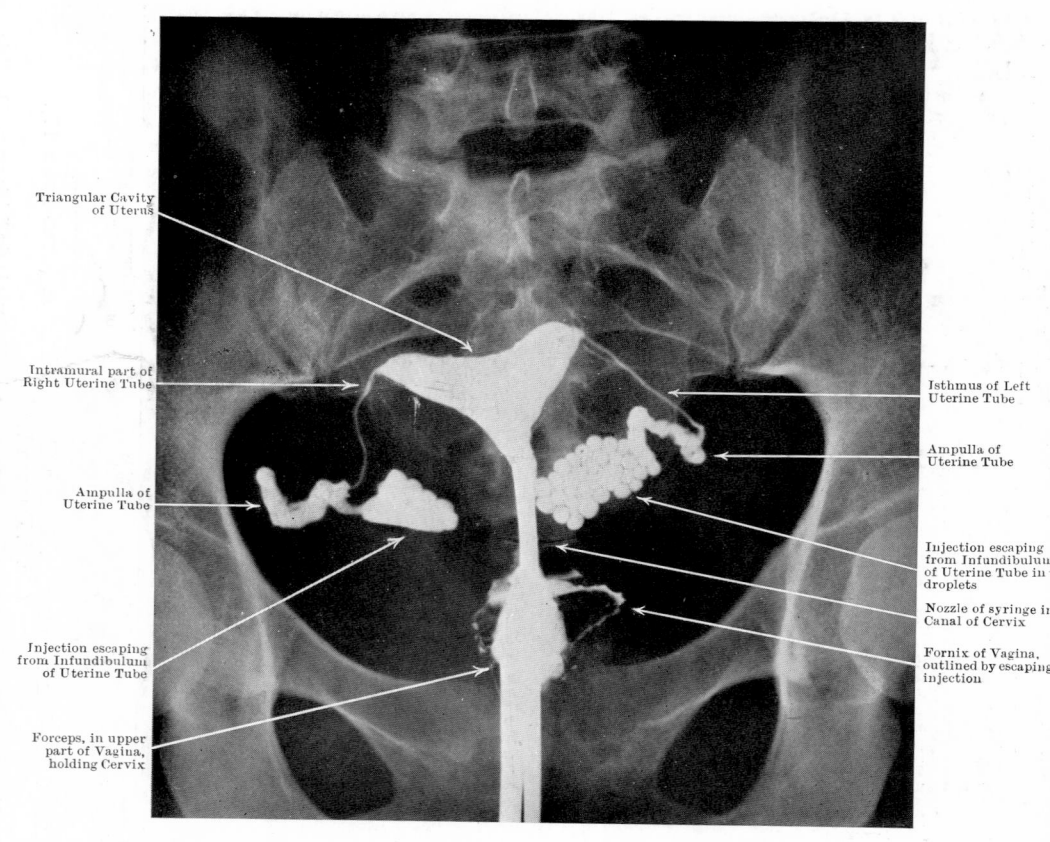

Triangular Cavity of Uterus

Intramural part of Right Uterine Tube

Ampulla of Uterine Tube

Injection escaping from Infundibulum of Uterine Tube

Forceps, in upper part of Vagina, holding Cervix

Isthmus of Left Uterine Tube

Ampulla of Uterine Tube

Injection escaping from Infundibulum of Uterine Tube in droplets

Nozzle of syringe in Canal of Cervix

Fornix of Vagina, outlined by escaping injection

PLATE LVI.—RADIOGRAPH SHOWING THE FORM OF THE CAVITIES OF THE UTERUS AND THE UTERINE TUBES AFTER INJECTION OF LIPIODOL. (Dr. J. B. King.)

Note the outlining of the Fornix of the Vagina and the escape of the injection into the peritoneal cavity in droplets.

upper surface. The condition is usually the result of an escape of fluid after death, when the bladder wall has lost the power of contracting. It does not represent a normal condition of the organ in the living. The normal empty bladder is strongly contracted, and its wall is thick and firm.

Distended Bladder.—As the bladder fills with fluid the superior wall is raised upwards from the base and infero-lateral walls. At the same time the borders separating the superior surface from the other surfaces become at first more rounded and then nearly obliterated (Fig. 591, B). The general shape becomes altered; the tetrahedral form of the empty organ is lost, and as it fills it assumes first a spherical and then an oval contour. The enlarging bladder gradually occupies more and more of the pelvic cavity, displacing upwards the portions of the colon and small intestine which may lie in the pelvis when the organ is empty. Until all the available pelvic space has been filled, the form of the distended bladder is spherical, or oval with the larger end directed downwards and backwards. When the pelvic wall prevents further expansion the outline of the oval changes, and the larger end is directed upwards and forwards into the abdominal cavity. The highest part of the distended bladder

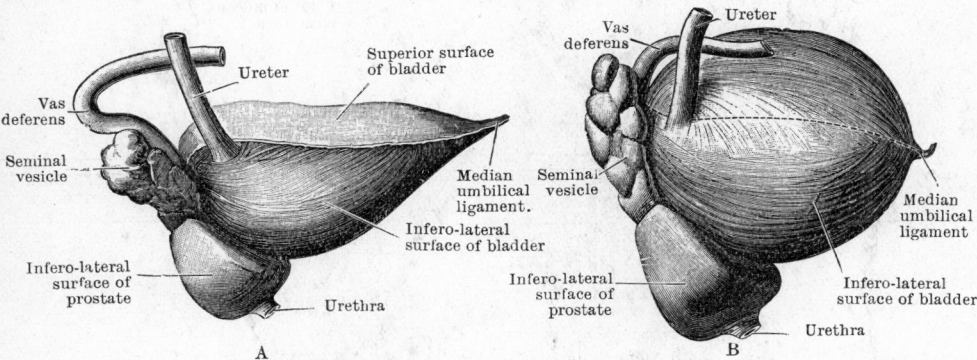

FIG. 591.—THE URINARY BLADDER, PROSTATE, AND SEMINAL VESICLE VIEWED FROM THE RIGHT SIDE. (A. F. D.)

Drawn from specimens in which the viscera were hardened *in situ.* In A the bladder contained but a very small quantity of fluid; in B the quantity was a little greater. In A the peritoneum is shown covering the superior surface of the bladder, and its cut edge is seen where it is reflected along the lateral border. In B the level of the peritoneal reflexion is indicated by a dotted line.

corresponds not to the attachment of the median umbilical ligament but to a point farther back. As the upper wall of the bladder is raised during distension it carries the peritoneum with it, and thus the reflexion of that membrane, from the anterior abdominal wall on to the apex of the bladder, comes to lie an inch and a half, or even more, above the upper margin of the pubic symphysis (Fig. 588). It is therefore possible to open into the distended bladder, through the anterior abdominal wall above the pubic symphysis, without at the same time opening into the peritoneal cavity. In a similar manner the line of reflexion of the peritoneum from the side wall of the pelvis on to the bladder is raised higher during distension, and may come to correspond, in part, to the level of the vas deferens, or to that of the umbilical artery. On the other hand, the level of the reflexion of the peritoneum from the rectum on to the bladder does not vary much with the distension or contraction of the organ (compare Figs. 587 and 588), and thus the fossa between the bladder and rectum becomes relatively very deep when the bladder is full. The bladder in normal distension may contain nearly one pint, but in most cases the organ is emptied when its contents reach from six to ten ounces. Under abnormal or pathological conditions the bladder capacity may be very much increased.

The lateral aspect of the distended bladder may be related to the umbilical artery as it passes forwards on the side wall of the pelvis. When the bladder is empty its lateral border lies about an inch and a quarter below that artery. The vas deferens, during a part of its course, is in contact with the lateral wall

45

of the distended bladder, but lies above and parallel to the lateral border when the organ is empty. The side wall of the distended bladder is closely related to the obturator vessels and nerve.

Interior of Bladder.—The mucous membrane which lines the bladder is loosely connected to the muscular coat, and when the bladder is contracted the mucous lining is thrown into a number of prominent wrinkles or folds (Fig. 592). At one place only is the mucous membrane firmly connected to the subjacent muscular coat, and the inner surface of that part of the bladder wall is smooth and free from wrinkles. This smooth area corresponds to a triangular surface above and behind the urethral orifice, called the **trigone of the bladder**, and to the part of the bladder wall which immediately surrounds the opening. The apex of the triangle lies at the beginning of the urethra, and the base is a line drawn between the openings of the ureters. Immediately

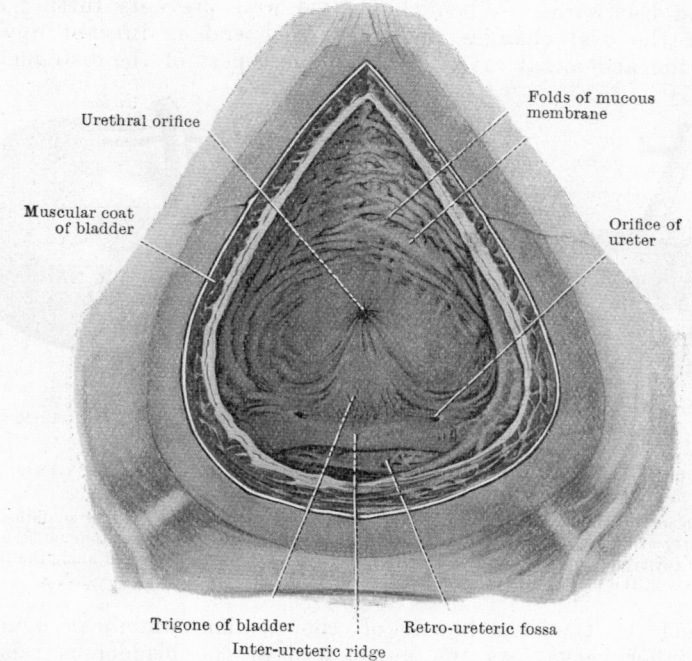

Urethral orifice

Muscular coat of bladder

Folds of mucous membrane

Orifice of ureter

Trigone of bladder   Retro-ureteric fossa
Inter-ureteric ridge

FIG. 592.—EMPTY AND CONTRACTED URINARY BLADDER, OPENED UP BY THE REMOVAL OF ITS UPPER WALL. (A. F. D.)
The peritoneum is seen spreading out from the lateral and posterior borders of the organ.
Compare with Fig. 596.

above and behind the urethral opening the bladder wall sometimes bulges slightly into the cavity owing to the presence of the median lobe of the prostate, which lies outside the mucous coat in that position. When well marked, as it often is in old people, the bulging is termed the **uvula of the bladder**. Stretching across between the openings of the ureters there is usually a smooth **inter-ureteric ridge**, due to the presence of a bundle of transversely disposed muscle fibres. It may be deficient near the median plane, and it is curved so as to be convex downwards and forwards. Lateral to the openings of the ureters there is a pair of ridges, called the **ureteric folds**, produced by the terminal parts of the ureters as they traverse the bladder wall and lie outside of the mucous coat of the bladder. In old people the region above and behind the trigone often bulges backwards and forms a shallow *retro-ureteric fossa*. A less distinct depression may sometimes be observed on each side of the trigone. Around the urethral orifice there is a number of minute radially disposed folds which, disappearing into the urethra, become continuous with the longitudinal folds of the mucous membrane of the upper part of that canal. The ureter pierces the bladder wall very obliquely, and so the minute ureteral orifice has an elliptical outline. The lateral boundary of each opening is formed by a thin, crescentic fold which, when the bladder is artificially distended in the dead subject, acts as a valve in preventing water or air from entering the ureter. In the empty bladder the urethral orifice and the openings of the two ureters lie at the angles of an approximately equilateral triangle, the sides of which are about an inch in length. When the bladder is distended the distance between the openings may be increased to two inches or more.

Bladder in the Female.—In the female the bladder is related posteriorly to the uterus and the upper part of the vagina. The vesical surface of the uterus in its

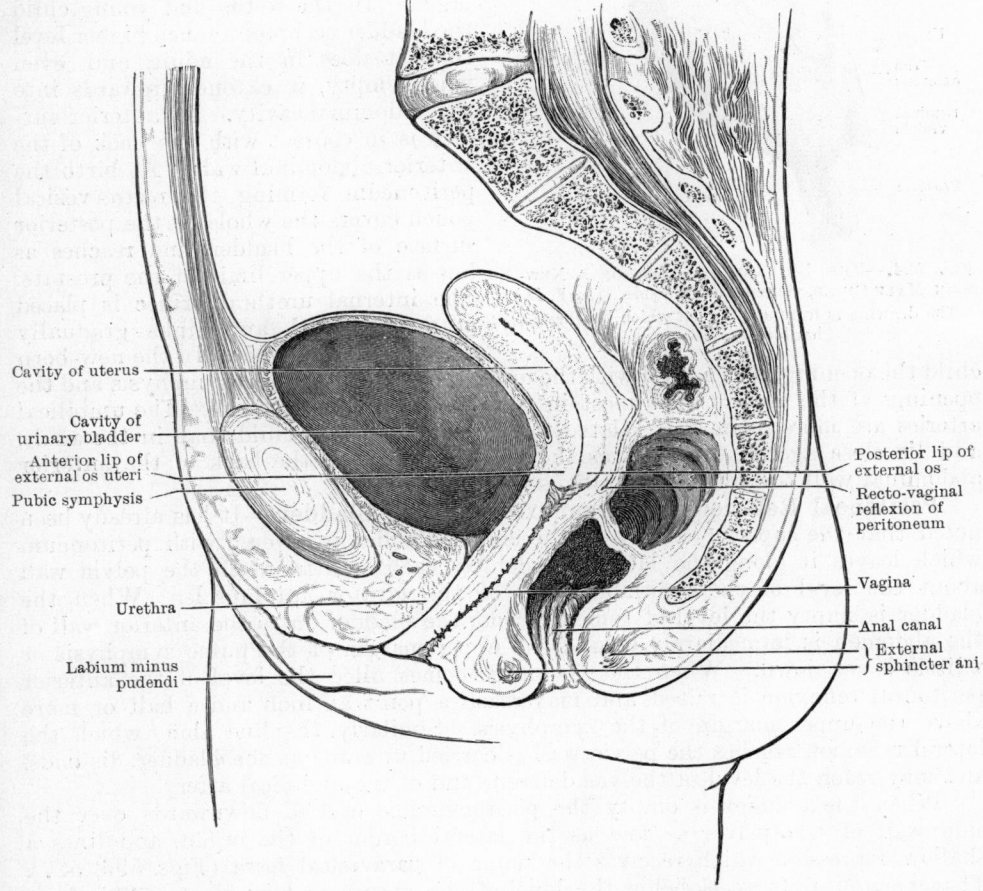

Cavity of uterus

Cavity of urinary bladder

Anterior lip of external os uteri

Pubic symphysis

Urethra

Labium minus pudendi

Posterior lip of external os

Recto-vaginal reflexion of peritoneum

Vagina

Anal canal

External sphincter ani

FIG. 593.—MEDIAN SECTION OF THE PELVIS IN AN ADULT FEMALE. (A. F. D.)
The cavity of the uterus is indicated diagrammatically.

upper part is separated from the upper surface of the bladder by the slit-like utero-vesical pouch of peritoneum, but the two organs are nevertheless normally in apposition. The lower part of the uterus and upper part of the vagina are not separated by peritoneum from the bladder, but are united to it by areolar tissue (Fig. 593). Thus, below the level of the utero-vesical pouch, the female bladder is related to the uterus and the vagina in much the same manner as the male bladder is related to the seminal vesicles and vasa deferentia. The apex of the bladder often lies on a lower level than in the male, so that the organ, even when distended, rises less freely into the abdomen. The bladder as a whole is placed deeper in the pelvis than in the male, and the internal urethral orifice lies immediately above, or immediately below, a line drawn from the lower margin of the

45 a

symphysis to the lower end of the sacrum (p. 702). The lower level of the
internal urethral orifice is probably correlated with the absence of a prostate in
the female. It is probable that as regards capacity no difference exists between
the bladder in the male and in the female.

Bladder in the New-born Child and in the Infant.—At birth the empty
bladder is spindle- or torpedo-shaped; its long axis extends from the apex to the
internal urethral orifice, and is directed downwards and backwards (Fig. 594).
The lateral and posterior borders seen in the adult organ cannot be recognised at

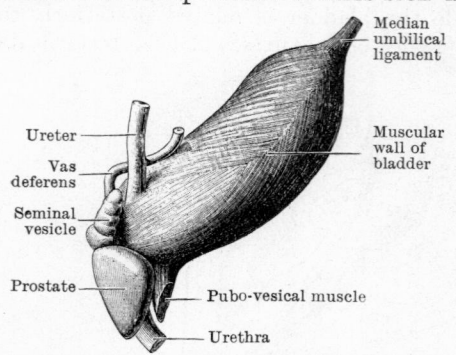

FIG. 594.—THE URINARY BLADDER OF A NEW-
BORN MALE CHILD, viewed from the side. (A. F. D.)
The drawing is from a specimen which had been
hardened *in situ.*

birth, nor is there any part of the
bladder wall directed backwards and
downwards, as is the base of the adult
organ. In the foetus and young child
the bladder occupies a much higher level
than it does in the adult, and, even
when empty, it extends upwards into
the abdominal cavity. Its anterior surface is in contact with the back of the
anterior abdominal wall. At birth the
peritoneum forming the recto - vesical
pouch covers the whole of the posterior
surface of the bladder, and reaches as
low as the upper limit of the prostate.
The internal urethral orifice is placed
at a high level, and sinks gradually
after birth (Fig. 595). In the new-born

child the opening is on a level with the upper margin of the pubic symphysis and the
openings of the ureters are almost in the plane of the pelvic brim. The umbilical
arteries are more intimately related to the bladder in the child than in the adult,
and lie close against its sides as they pass upwards on the back of the anterior
abdominal wall towards the umbilicus (Fig. 609).

Peritoneal Relations and Connexions of the Bladder.—It has already been
noted that the superior surface of the empty bladder is covered with peritoneum
which leaves it along the lateral border on each side to reach the pelvic wall
about the level of the tendinous arch of the levator ani muscle. When the
bladder is empty the level of reflexion from the bladder on to the anterior wall of
the abdomen is immediately behind the upper margin of the pubic symphysis or
a little lower down. When the bladder becomes filled the level of the anterior
peritoneal reflexion is raised, and may reach a point an inch and a half or more
above the upper margin of the symphysis. Similarly, the line along which the
lateral reflexion reaches the pelvic wall is carried upwards as the bladder distends,
and may reach the level of the vas deferens and of the umbilical artery.

When the bladder is empty the peritoneum is carried downwards over the
side wall of the pelvis as low as the lateral border of the organ, and lines a
shallow depression which receives the name of **paravesical fossa** (Figs. 596, 527).
That peritoneal fossa is below the level of the obturator triangle (p. 699), from
which it is separated by the vas deferens. As the bladder fills, the peritoneum
is raised off that part of the pelvic wall, and certain structures, such as the obturator
vessels and nerve and the vas deferens, come into direct relationship with the side
of the distended bladder.

Posteriorly, in the female, the peritoneum is reflected off the upper surface of
the bladder on to the vesical surface of the uterus at the junction of its body and
neck. In the male, it leaves the upper surface of the empty bladder at its
posterior border, and is carried backwards, forming a kind of horizontal, shelf-like
fold, for a distance of about half an inch, giving at the same time a partial covering
to the vasa deferentia and upper ends of the seminal vesicles. The peritoneum
then suddenly dips downwards to reach the bottom of the recto-vesical pouch,
where it is reflected on to the anterior surface of the rectum (Figs. 587, 588).
As a rule, no part of the base of the contracted and empty bladder receives
a covering from the peritoneum, since the seminal vesicles and terminal portions

of the vasa deferentia intervene as they lie in the anterior wall of the recto-vesical pouch. When the bladder is distended its posterior border is rounded out, and the peritoneum forming the horizontal shelf, just described, is taken up (compare Fig. 588).

It must be noted that the level of the peritoneal reflexion, forming the bottom of the recto-vesical pouch, varies little, as regards its relationship to the prostate, during distension and contraction of the bladder (Figs. 587 and 588).

The **sacro-genital fold** is a variable crescentic fold of peritoneum which bounds, on each side, the entrance to the recto-vesical pouch, and unites with the fold of the opposite side across the median plane, behind the posterior border of the bladder and the vasa deferentia (Figs. 587 and 596). These folds represent the recto-uterine folds found in the female (Fig. 597), and are to be regarded as connexions of the vasa deferentia rather than of the bladder.

The peritoneum covering the upper surface of the empty or partly distended bladder often exhibits a transversely disposed fold or wrinkle known as the **plica vesicalis transversa**. When well developed the fold can be traced across the paravesical fossa on to the side wall of the pelvis, and even beyond that—across the pelvic brim towards the deep inguinal ring (Fig. 596). Occasionally there is more than one fold.

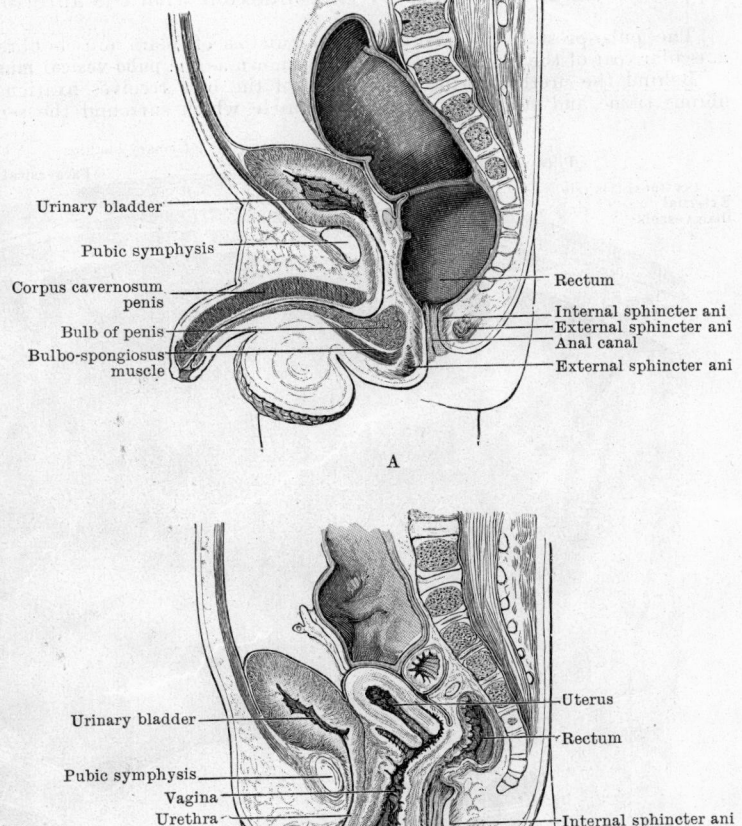

Urinary bladder
Pubic symphysis
Corpus cavernosum penis
Bulb of penis
Bulbo-spongiosus muscle

Rectum
Internal sphincter ani
External sphincter ani
Anal canal
External sphincter ani

A

Urinary bladder
Pubic symphysis
Vagina
Urethra
Urethral ridge
Labium minus

Uterus
Rectum

Internal sphincter ani
External sphincter ani
Anal canal
External sphincter ani

B

Fig. 595.—Median Section through the Pelvis of New-born Child. (A. F. D.)

A, Male, and B, Female.

Fixation of the Bladder.—When the median umbilical ligament and the peritoneal connexions are severed, the bladder is easily moved about, except in its lower part. The base and the neck have fairly firm connexions, but the other parts of the bladder wall are connected to the pubis and lining fascia of the pelvis only by loose areolar tissue, and thus free movement is permitted during expansion and contraction of the organ.

In both sexes, the neck is the most fixed part of the bladder. *In the male* the lower fixed part of the bladder is held in place chiefly by its firm connexion with the prostate, with which indeed it is structurally continuous. The prostate is surrounded by a dense fibrous sheath of fascia from which strong fascial connexions pass forwards to the back of the pubis and on each side to the lining fascia of the pelvis. Those fibrous connexions are known as the pubo-prostatic ligaments, and by fixing the prostate they maintain the lower part of the bladder in position. *In the female* similar connexions, called pubo-vesical ligaments, exist for the neck of the bladder and the upper part of the urethra, and the base is supported and held in place by its connexion with the anterior wall of the vagina.

The pubo-prostatic ligaments contain bundles of plain muscle fibres continuous with the muscular coat of the bladder, and they are known as the **pubo-vesical muscle**.

Behind the urethral orifice the region of the base receives fixation and support from the fibrous tissue and strands of unstriped muscle which surround the seminal vesicles and the

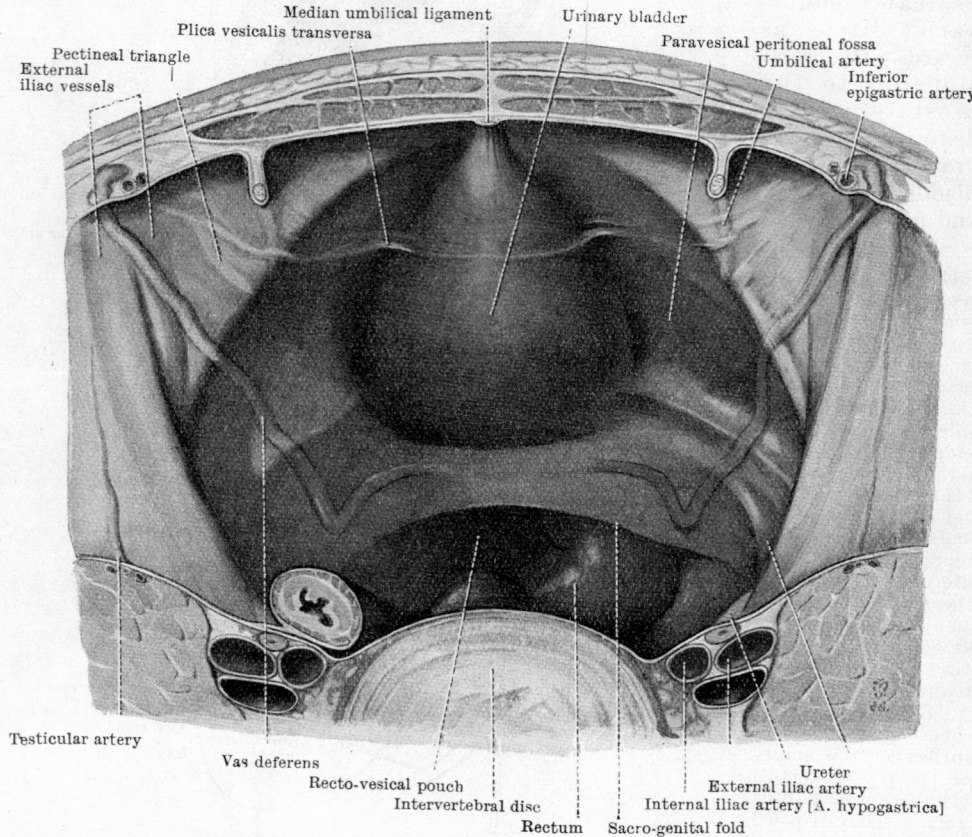

Median umbilical ligament   Urinary bladder
Plica vesicalis transversa

Pectineal triangle   Paravesical peritoneal fossa
External   Umbilical artery
iliac vessels   Inferior
                                                       epigastric artery

Testicular artery

Vas deferens   Ureter
Recto-vesical pouch   External iliac artery
Intervertebral disc   Internal iliac artery [A. hypogastrica]
Rectum   Sacro-genital fold

FIG. 596.—VIEW LOOKING INTO THE MALE PELVIS FROM ABOVE AND BEHIND. (A. F. D.)

From a specimen in which the bladder was firmly contracted and contained but a small amount of fluid. The peritoneal pouch in front of the rectum is bounded on each side by the crescentic sacro-genital folds, which meet together in the median plane some distance behind the posterior border of the bladder.

terminal portions of the ureters and vasa deferentia. On each side many of the fibrous and muscular strands forming this support are continued into the fascia that surrounds the branches of the internal iliac artery [a. hypogastrica].

Structure of the Bladder Wall.—The wall of the bladder from without inwards is composed of a serous, a muscular, a submucous, and a mucous coat. The **serous coat** is the peritoneum, and covers only the upper and posterior parts of the distended bladder (Fig. 588).

A considerable amount of loose fibro-areolar tissue surrounds the **muscular coat**, and penetrating it, divides it into numerous coarse bundles of muscle fibres. All the muscle fibres are of the unstriped variety, and the bundles which they form are arranged in three very imperfectly separated strata called external, middle, and internal. The **external stratum** is for the most part made up of fibres which are directed longitudinally, and it is best marked near the median plane on the upper and under aspects of the bladder. Farther from the median plane, on the sides of the bladder, the fibres composing the external stratum run more obliquely, and frequently cross one another. In the male many of the fibres of the external stratum pass into the prostate in front of and behind the urethral opening, and in the female the corresponding fibres join the dense tissue which in this sex forms the upper part of the wall of the urethra.

Other fibres of this stratum on each side of the middle line join the lower part of the pubic symphysis and constitute the **pubo-vesical muscle,** which follows the course of the pubo-prostatic ligaments. Lastly, some fibres of the external stratum blend posteriorly with the front of the rectum and receive the name of **recto-vesical muscle.** In both sexes many muscular fibres of the bladder are continued along the course of the ureter to form the sheath of the ureter already mentioned (p. 700). The **middle stratum** is composed of fibres which for the most part run circularly, and form the greater part of the thickness of the muscular coat. In the region of, and behind, the urethral orifice the bundles of fibres are finer and more densely arranged, and surround the opening in a plane which is directed obliquely downwards and forwards. This part of the middle stratum is often spoken of as the *sphincter vesicae.* Inferiorly the fibres of the sphincter vesicae are continuous with the muscular tissue of the prostate in the male, and with the muscular wall of the urethra in the female. In other parts of the bladder the bundles of the middle stratum are coarser and separated by intervals filled with fibro-areolar tissue. The **internal stratum** is composed of a thin layer of muscle fibres directed for the most part longitudinally.

The **submucous coat** is composed of areolar tissue which contains numerous fine elastic fibres.

The **mucous coat** is loosely attached by the submucous layer to the muscular coat, except in the region of the trigone. There the muscular fibres are firmly adherent to the mucous membrane. Over the trigone the mucous coat is always smooth and flat ; elsewhere it is thrown into folds when the bladder is empty. The mucous membrane of the bladder is continuous with that of the ureters and urethra. Its covering of epithelium varies much in appearance in different conditions of the organ, and is of the variety known as transitional epithelium. The appearance of the mucous coat is described on p. 706.

When as a result of urethral obstruction the muscular coat of the bladder becomes hypertrophied, strong strands of muscular tissue become raised up and project into the cavity of the bladder. The resulting net-like arrangement of ridges resembles the trabeculae carneae of the ventricles of the heart.

Vessels and Nerves of Bladder.—The **arteries** on each side are the *superior* and *inferior vesical arteries.* The largest **veins** are found above the prostate, and in the region where the ureter reaches the bladder. They form a dense plexus which pours its blood into tributaries of the internal iliac vein [v. hypogastrica], and communicates below with the prostatic venous plexus.

The **lymph vessels** from the bladder join the iliac groups of lymph glands.

The **nerve** supply of the bladder is derived on each side from the *vesical plexus,* the fibres of which come from two sources, namely, (1) from the *upper lumbar nerves* through the hypogastric plexus, and (2) from the *pelvic splanchnic nerves,* which spring from the *second* and *third* or the *third* and *fourth sacral nerves.* These splanchnic nerves join the vesical plexus directly.

URETHRA

The **urethra** is the channel which serves to convey the urine from the bladder to the exterior. In the *male* its proximal part, less than one inch in length, extends from the bladder to the points where the ducts of the reproductive glands join the canal ; a much longer distal portion serves as a common passage for the urine and for the generative products (see p. 729). The *female* urethra represents only the proximal part of the male canal. It is a short passage leading from the bladder to the external urethral orifice—an aperture placed within the pudendal cleft, immediately in front of the opening of the vagina.

Urethra Muliebris.—The **female urethra** is a canal of about an inch and a half in length which follows a slightly curved direction downwards and forwards, below and behind the lower border of the pubic symphysis. It is at first surrounded by a dense mass of smooth muscle fibres continuous with the bladder wall, and as it leaves the pelvis it is surrounded by the fibres of the sphincter urethrae muscle and pierces the perineal membrane. Except during the passage of fluid the canal is closed by the apposition of its anterior and posterior walls. The **external urethral orifice** is placed between the labia minora, immediately in front of the opening of the vagina, about one inch below and behind the clitoris (Fig. 627). The opening is slit-like, and is bounded by slightly marked lips. The posterior wall of the urethra, except in its upper part, is very intimately connected with the anterior wall of the vagina, and as it approaches the external urethral orifice the urethra is practically embedded in the anterior vaginal wall. The mucous lining of the canal is raised into a number of slightly marked longitudinal folds, one of which, more distinct than the others and placed on the posterior wall of the passage, receives the name of **urethral crest.**

Structure.—The thick **muscular wall** of the female urethra is connected by fibrous tissue to the back of the pubis and to the fascia over the lower part of the levator ani muscle. It is continuous above with that of the bladder, and is composed of layers of circularly disposed smooth muscle fibres, together with a few bundles which are longitudinally directed. Within the muscular coat the wall of the urethra is very vascular, and the canal itself is lined with a pale mucous membrane which is thrown into the longitudinal folds mentioned above. The epithelium of the canal, in its upper part, is of the transitional variety, like that of the bladder; in its lower part it becomes scaly. Numerous minute **urethral glands** and pit-like **urethral lacunæ** open into the urethra. One group of these glands on each side possesses a minute common duct, known as the **para-urethral duct**, which opens into the pudendal cleft by the side of the external urethral orifice. These glands represent the prostatic glands of the male. The vascular layer which lies between the muscular coat and the mucous membrane contains elastic fibres, and in appearance resembles erectile tissue. Striped muscle fibres are present on the outer surface of the muscular coat of the urethra. In the upper part of the canal those fibres form a complete ring-like sphincter, but in the middle and lower parts the striped

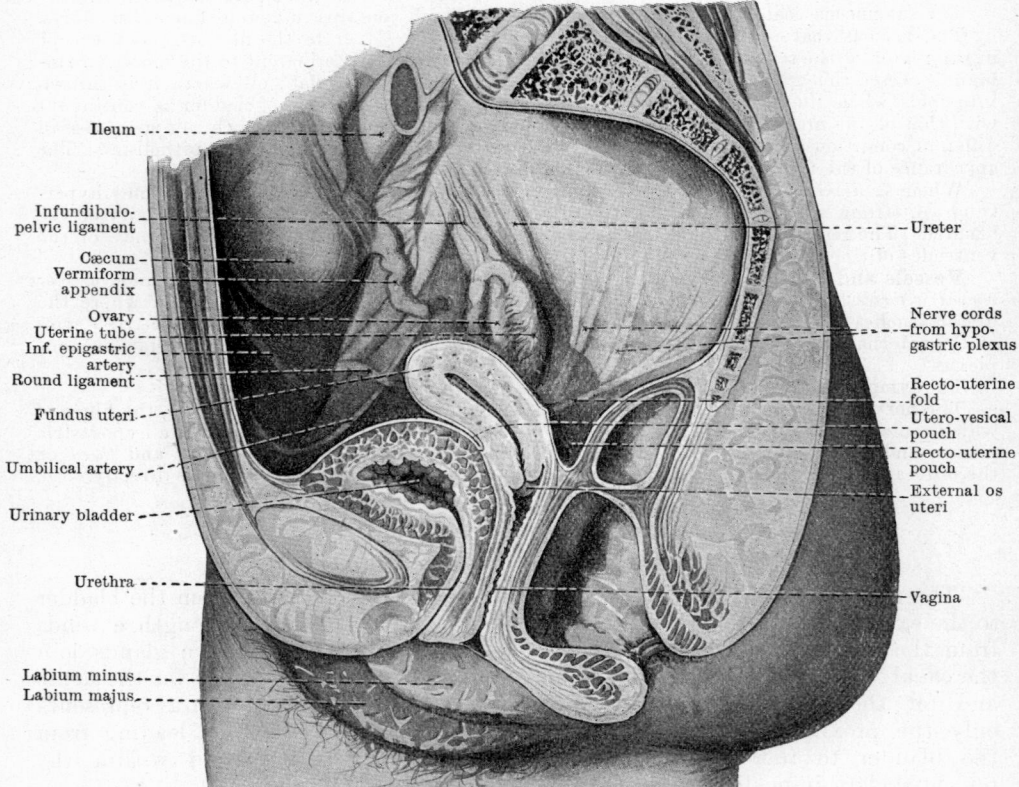

FIG. 597.—MEDIAN SECTION THROUGH THE FEMALE PELVIS. Drawn for the most part from a model of a dissection made by Professor Edward H. Taylor.

muscle fibres, though present in front, are absent on the posterior wall of the urethra, as at that level they pass backwards on the outer surface of the vagina, and enclose the latter passage together with the urethra in a single loop of muscle tissue. The lower fibres, therefore, form a uro-genital sphincter.

MALE GENITAL ORGANS

The male reproductive organs are (1) the testes together with their (2) coverings and (3) their ducts, (4) the prostate, (5) the bulbo-urethral glands, (6) the external genital organs, and (7) the male urethra.

The **testes** are the essential reproductive glands of the male, and are a pair of nearly symmetrical oval-shaped bodies situated in the scrotum. The duct of each testis is at first much twisted and contorted to form a structure known as the **epididymis**, which is applied against the back of the testis; the duct then emerges from the epididymis as the **vas deferens**, which passes upwards towards the lower part of the anterior abdominal wall and pierces it obliquely to enter the abdominal cavity. There, each vas deferens is covered with the peritoneum, and, crossing the pelvic brim almost at once, enters the true pelvis. The duct now runs on the side wall of the pelvis towards the base of the bladder, where it comes into relation with a branched tubular structure termed the **seminal vesicle**. Joined by the duct of the seminal vesicle, the vas deferens forms a short canal, called the **ejaculatory duct**, which terminates by opening into the prostatic part of the **urethra**. The **prostate**, and the **bulbo-urethral glands** are accessory organs connected with the male reproductive system.

The ducts of the bulbo-urethral glands and those of the prostate, like the ejaculatory ducts, open into the urethra, which thus serves not only as a passage for urine, but also for the generative products. The external genital organs are the **penis** and **scrotum**.

TESTES

The **testes** are a pair of oval, slightly flattened bodies of a whitish colour, measuring about an inch and a half in length, one inch from before backwards, and rather less in thickness. Each testis is placed within the cavity of the scrotum in such a manner that its long axis is directed upwards and slightly forwards and laterally. Usually the left gland is a little lower than the right. The testis (Fig. 600) has two slightly flattened surfaces: a *lateral surface*, which looks backwards as well as laterally, and a *medial surface*, which looks forwards as well as medially,

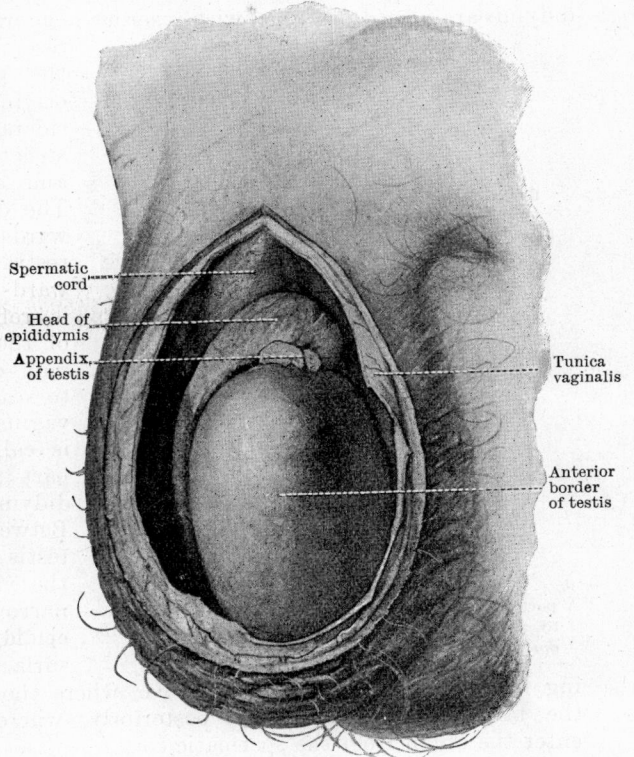

FIG. 598.—RIGHT TESTIS AND EPIDIDYMIS, EXPOSED BY THE REMOVAL OF THE ANTERIOR WALL OF THE SCROTUM. (A.F.D.)

and is usually the more flattened. The two surfaces are separated by rounded **anterior** and **posterior borders**. The anterior border is the more convex and is free. By the posterior border the testis is suspended within the scrotum. The **epididymis** and the lowest portion of the **spermatic cord** are attached to the posterior border of the testis.

Epididymis.—The epididymis is a crescentic structure that clasps the posterior border of the testis and to some extent overlaps the posterior part of its lateral surface (Fig. 598). The upper, swollen part is called the **head of the epididymis**, and overhangs the upper end of the testis, to which it is directly connected by numerous emerging ducts, by fibro-areolar tissue, and by the serous covering of the organ. The inferior and smaller end is termed the **tail of the epididymis**; it is attached, by loose areolar tissue and by the serous covering, to the lower part of the testis. The intervening part, or **body of the epididymis**, is applied against the posterior part of the lateral surface of the testis but is separated from it by an involution of the serous covering of the organ which forms an intervening pocket termed the **sinus of the epididymis**.

The main mass of the epididymis is composed of an irregularly twisted duct, called the **canal of the epididymis**, which forms the first part of the duct of the testis (Figs. 601, 602).

Minute sessile or pedunculated bodies are often found attached to the head of the epididymis or to the upper end of the testis. They are called appendices of the epididymis and testis, and have a developmental interest. The minute body which lies on the upper end of the testis represents the free end of the para-mesonephric duct [Müller's] of the embryo and the fimbriated end of the uterine tube of the female; it is usually sessile. Above the head of the epididymis and in front of the lower part of the spermatic cord, there may be present also a small vestigial body called the **paradidymis**; it is rarely seen in the adult, and is best marked in young children.

Tunica Vaginalis.—The walls of the cavity within which the testis and epididymis are placed are lined with a serous membrane—the **tunica vaginalis**—which

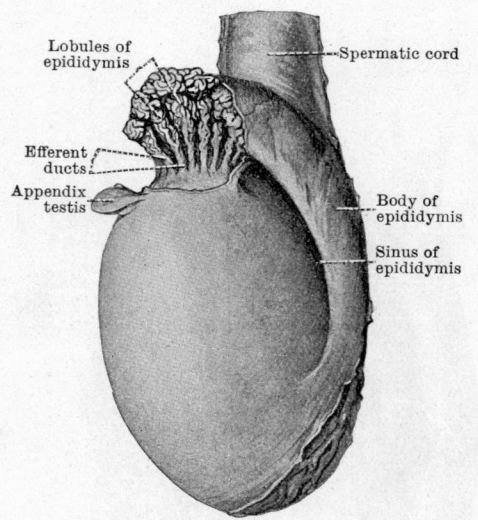

Lobules of epididymis

Spermatic cord

Efferent ducts

Appendix testis

Body of epididymis

Sinus of epididymis

FIG. 599.—LEFT TESTIS AND EPIDIDYMIS.

A part of the tunica vaginalis has been removed in order to show the efferent ducts and the lobules of the epididymis. (A. F. D.)

resembles in appearance and structure the peritoneum, from which it was originally derived. The cavity is considerably larger than the contained structures, and extends to both a higher and a lower level than the testis. The cavity tapers as it is traced upwards; and above the level of the testis the spermatic cord bulges forwards into it. The tunica vaginalis is reflected from the posterior wall of the scrotal chamber over the testis and epididymis, giving a covering to each. The part of the tunica vaginalis that lines the scrotal wall is called the **parietal layer**, and the part that clothes the testis and epididymis is termed the **visceral layer**. Between the lateral surface of the testis and the body of the epididymis the visceral layer dips in and lines a narrow interval called the **sinus of the epididymis**. In three positions the surface of the testis receives no covering from the tunica vaginalis—above, where the head is attached; below, where the tail is in contact; and posteriorly, where the blood-vessels and nerves enter the organ from the spermatic cord.

Structure of Testis.—Under cover of the tunica vaginalis the testis is invested by an external coat of dense white inelastic fibrous tissue called the **tunica albuginea**, from the deep surface of which a number of slender fibrous **septa** dip into the gland. These septa imperfectly divide the organ into a number of wedge-shaped parts called **lobes of the testis** (Fig. 600). All the septa end posteriorly in a mass of fibrous tissue called the **mediastinum testis**, which is directly continuous with the tunica albuginea, and projects forwards into the testis along its posterior border. It is traversed by an exceedingly complicated network of fine canals called the **rete testis**; the minute tubules that compose the substance proper of the testis open into the rete. The mediastinum is pierced also by the arteries, veins, and lymph vessels of the testis; they enter the posterior border of the organ, traverse the mediastinum, and spread out on the fibrous septa. In this way a delicate network of vessels is formed on the deep surface of the tunica albuginea and on the sides of the septa.

The mediastinum, the septa, and the tunica albuginea form a framework enclosing a number of imperfectly isolated spaces which are filled by a substance of a light brown colour called the **parenchyma testis**. The parenchyma is composed of enormous numbers of **convoluted seminiferous tubules**. The minute tubules look like fine threads to the unaided eye, and are but loosely held together by a small amount of areolar tissue. Usually two or four tubules are found in each lobule of the gland, and the total number in the testis has been estimated at more than 800. The convoluted tubules pass towards the mediastinum testis and unite at acute angles to form a smaller number of slender tubes which run a straight course and are called the **straight seminiferous tubules**; and they open into the rete testis (Fig. 601). The tubules are much more twisted and convoluted near the tunica vaginalis than in the region of the mediastinum.

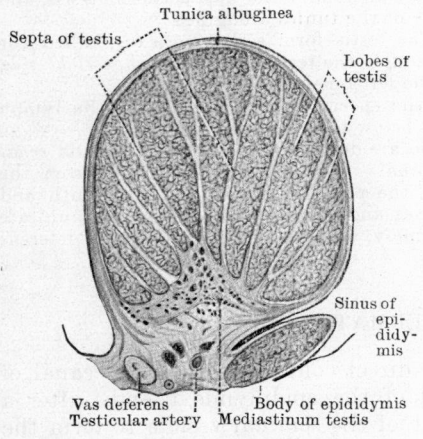

FIG. 600.—TRANSVERSE SECTION OF THE TESTIS AND EPIDIDYMIS. (A. F. D.)

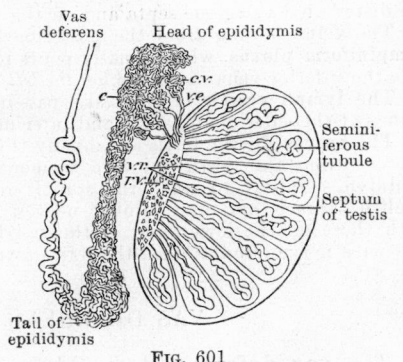

FIG. 601

DIAGRAM to illustrate the structure of the testis and epididymis.

c.	Canal of epididymis.	*v.e.*	Efferent ductules of testis.
c.v.	Lobules of epididymis.	*v.r.*	Straight seminiferous
r.v.	Rete testis.		tubules.

Microscopic sections show that the walls of the seminiferous tubules are composed of a basement membrane and of an epithelial lining formed of several layers of cells. Certain cells of the epithelium are, in the adult, constantly undergoing transformation into **spermatozoa**, and the appearance of the tubules in section varies much, according to age and to the greater or less activity of the epithelial cells.

Structure of Epididymis.— The secretion of the convoluted seminiferous tubules is carried through the straight tubules into the rete testis, and leaves the rete, to reach the canal of the epididymis, through from fifteen to twenty minute tubules called the **efferent ductules of the testis**. These efferent ductules pierce the tunica albuginea and enter the head of the epididymis. Each ductule is at first straight, but soon becomes much convoluted, and forms a little conical mass called a **lobule of the epididymis**. Within the head of the epididymis the little twisted canals open into the single, much-convoluted tube which constitutes the chief bulk of the epididymis, and is called the **canal of the epididymis**. This canal, which is about 20 feet in length, may be said to begin in the head of the epididymis, and to end,

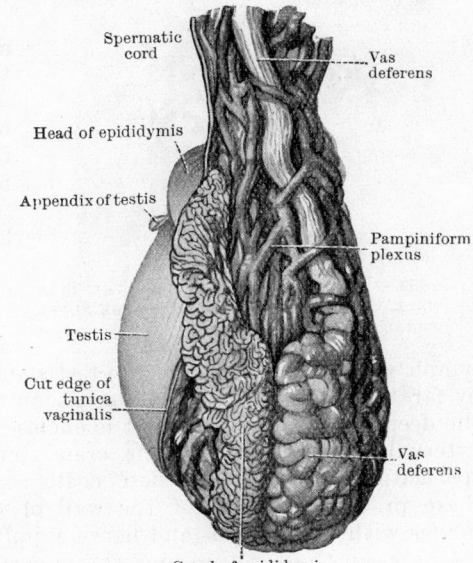

FIG. 602. — LEFT TESTIS AND EPIDIDYMIS VIEWED FROM BEHIND, showing the canal of epididymis and the first part of vas deferens. (A. F. D.)

after an extraordinarily tortuous course, at the tail by becoming the **vas deferens** (Figs. 601, 602).

In most cases one or more slender convoluted diverticula from the canal of the epididymis may be found near its lower end; they receive the name of **aberrant ductules**, and one of them which is very constantly present often measures a foot or more in length.

The canal of the epididymis and the efferent ductules of the testis are lined with a ciliated epithelium, the cilia of which maintain a constant current towards the vas deferens. The canal has a muscular coat composed of an inner stratum of circular fibres and an outer stratum of longitudinally directed fibres. The wall, at first thin, becomes much thicker as the canal approaches the vas deferens.

Vessels and Nerves of Testis.—The testis is supplied by the **testicular artery**, a branch of the aorta. It is a slender vessel which, after a long course, reaches the posterior border of the testis, where it breaks up into branches which enter the mediastinum testis, and are distributed along the septa and on the deep surface of the tunica albuginea.

The **veins** issuing from the posterior border of the testis form a dense plexus, called the **pampiniform plexus**, which finally pours its blood through the testicular vein, *on the right side*, into the inferior vena cava, and, *on the left side*, into the left renal vein.

The **lymph vessels** of the testis pass upwards in the spermatic cord, and end in the lymph glands at the sides of the aorta and inferior vena cava below the renal veins.

The **nerves** for the testis accompany the artery, and are derived through the *aortic* and *renal plexuses* from the tenth thoracic segment of the spinal cord. The afferent fibres from the epididymis appear to reach the spinal cord through the posterior roots of the eleventh and twelfth thoracic and first lumbar nerves. The arteries and nerves of the testis communicate with those on the lower part of the vas deferens, namely, with the artery of the vas deferens and with nerve bundles from the hypogastric plexus.

VAS DEFERENS AND SPERMATIC CORD

The **vas deferens** [ductus deferens] is the direct continuation of the canal of the epididymis. Beginning at the lower end of the epididymis, it ends, after a course of nearly 18 inches by joining the duct of the seminal vesicle to form the ejaculatory duct, which opens into the prostatic part of the urethra; in parts of its course it is slightly convoluted, and the actual distance traversed is not more than 12 inches. It first ascends to the superficial inguinal ring; it next runs laterally in the inguinal canal to the deep ring; and then, entering the abdomen, it bends medially and backwards to reach the true pelvis, where it ends behind the neck of the bladder.

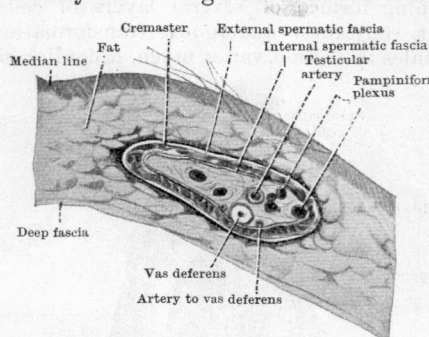

FIG. 603.—TRANSVERSE SECTION OF THE SPERMATIC CORD, IMMEDIATELY BELOW THE SUPERFICIAL INGUINAL RING. (A. F. D.)

At first it lies in the scrotum, where it ascends over the back of the testis along the medial side of the epididymis, and it is here that it is most convoluted (Fig. 602). At the upper end of the testis it falls in with the vessels and nerves of the testis and epididymis, and it is bound together with them by areolar tissue in a loose bundle called the spermatic cord.

The **spermatic cord** is therefore made up of (1) the vas deferens and its own artery, (2) the testicular artery and the pampiniform plexus of veins, and (3) the lymph vessels and nerves of the testis and epididymis—the plexus of veins being by far the bulkiest of these constituents. The cord extends from the testis to the deep inguinal ring, and it is enclosed in three tubular sheaths or **coats**—the external spermatic fascia, the cremasteric muscle and fascia, and the internal spermatic fascia. When these coats reach the scrotum they expand and take share in the formation of the wall of the scrotum; and the cremasteric coat carries with it its blood- and nerve-supply—*the artery and nerve to the cremaster.*

Between the scrotum and the superficial inguinal ring, the cord lies on the deep fascia of the muscles that spring from the pubis, and it is crossed by branches of the superficial inguinal vessels. In this part of the course the vas is in the posterior part of the cord, and is easily distinguished from the other constituents (even in the undissected body), by its hard, firm feel when the cord is gripped between finger and thumb. When the cord enters the inguinal canal it lies on the inferior crus of the superficial ring, immediately lateral to the pubic tubercle; and here it loses its external spermatic coat, which blends with the external oblique aponeurosis at the margins of the ring.

During its passage through the inguinal canal, the vas lies in the lower part of the cord on the grooved, upper surfaces of the inguinal ligament and its pectineal part [lig. lacunare]; the external oblique aponeurosis and the lower fleshy fibres of the internal oblique are in front; and the conjoint tendon [falx inguinalis] and the transversalis fascia are behind. Half way along the canal the cord loses its cremasteric coat, for that coat is derived from the lower border of the internal oblique muscle, which arches over the cord.

Less than half an inch above the mid-inguinal point, at the lateral side of the inferior epigastric artery, the cord reaches the deep inguinal ring. Here the cord loses its internal spermatic coat, which blends with the transversalis fascia at the margins of the ring. Here also, the cord ends, for at this point the vas deferens parts company with the vessels and nerves.

The vas deferens now curves medially across the external iliac artery behind

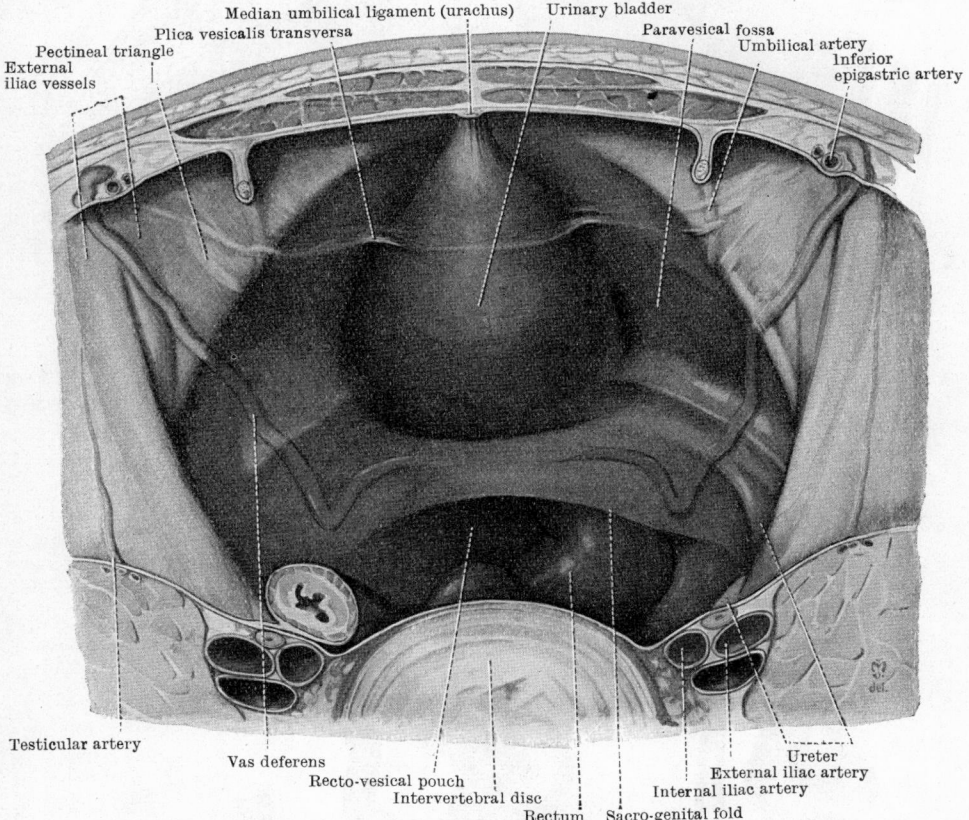

FIG. 604.—VIEW OF THE MALE PELVIS SEEN FROM ABOVE AND BEHIND. (A. F. D.)

the root of the inferior epigastric artery, and then, changing its direction, it runs for a short distance backwards, medially, and, upwards, outside the peritoneum, to a point one and a half or two inches from the pubic tubercle, where it crosses the pectineal line and enters the true pelvis. In that part of its course the vas usually lies at first in front of the external iliac vessels, and then in the floor of a little triangular fossa—the *pectineal triangle*—which lies between the external iliac vessels and the pelvic brim (Fig. 604). On the side wall of the pelvis the vas is continued backwards, and a little downwards and medially, in the direction of the ischial spine, and lies immediately external to the peritoneum, through which it can usually be seen. In the pelvic part of its course the vas crosses the medial side of (1) the umbilical artery, (2) the obturator nerve and vessels, (3) the vesical vessels, and (4) the ureter (Fig. 605).

Beyond the ureter the vas deferens takes a sudden bend and passes downwards and medially outside of the peritoneum of the pelvic floor. There the vas lies a short distance behind the terminal part of the ureter and immediately in front of the sacro-genital fold of peritoneum (Figs. 604, 605). Reaching the interval

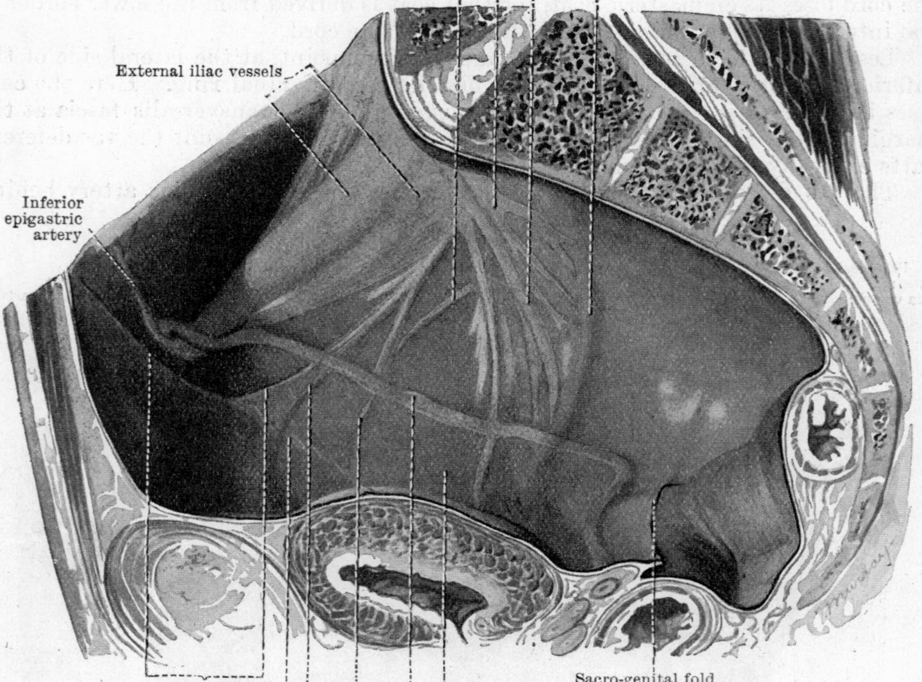

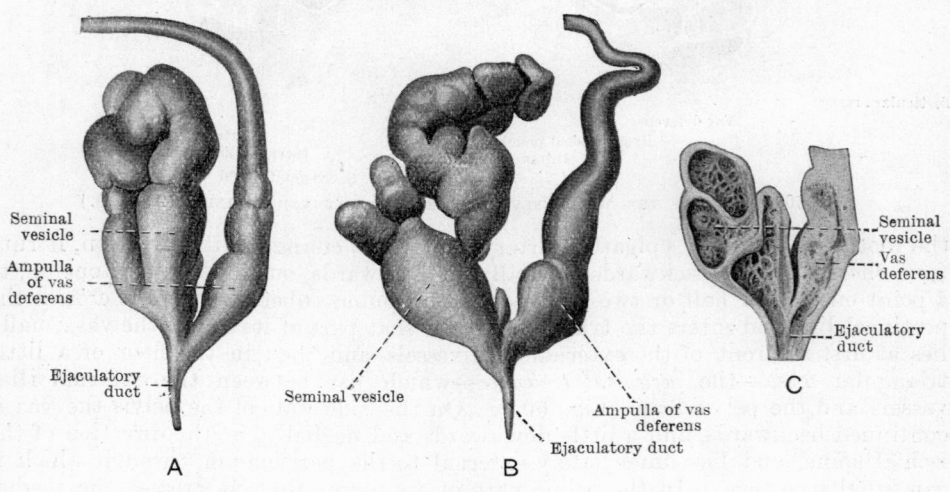

Branches of internal iliac artery Right ureter
Obturator artery   Nerve cord from hypogastric plexus
External iliac vessels
Inferior epigastric artery
Umbilical artery
Plica vesicalis transversa
Vesical arteries
Vas deferens   Paravesical peritoneal fossa
Sacro-genital fold

FIG. 605.—MEDIAN SECTION OF THE PELVIS IN AN ADULT MALE. (A. F. D.)
Showing the side wall of the pelvic cavity.

Seminal vesicle
Ampulla of vas deferens
Ejaculatory duct
A

Seminal vesicle
Ampulla of vas deferens
Ejaculatory duct
B

Seminal vesicle
Vas deferens
Ejaculatory duct
C

FIG. 606.

A and B. Drawings of seminal vesicle and ampulla of vas deferens taken from different subjects.
C. Seminal vesicle and ampulla of vas deferens cut to show the pitted structure of their walls.

between the base of the bladder in front and the rectum behind, the two vasa deferentia occupy the angle between the right and left seminal vesicles (Fig. 608).

As they approach each other each vas becomes slightly tortuous, sacculated, and dilated, and assumes a general resemblance in structure to a portion of the seminal vesicle. The dilated part of the vas is termed its **ampulla.** Immediately above the base of the prostate the vas deferens becomes once more a slender tube and is joined by the duct of the corresponding seminal vesicle to form the **ejaculatory duct.**

In some cases the vas deferens crosses the umbilical artery before it enters the cavity of the true pelvis ; it normally does so in the fœtus (Fig. 609).

Ejaculatory Duct.—This is the very slender tube formed by the union of the vas deferens with the duct of the corresponding seminal vesicle (Fig. 606). It is less than an inch in length, and lies very close to its fellow of the opposite side as it passes downwards and forwards through the prostate behind its median lobe. The ducts open by slit-like apertures into the first part of the urethra, one on each side of the mouth of the **prostatic utricule.** They are well seen in sections through the upper part of the prostate (Fig. 617, A).

The mucous membrane of the duct is thrown into numerous complicated folds, and in connexion with it there is a number of remarkable minute diverticula which are enclosed within the muscular coat of the duct.

SEMINAL VESICLES

The **seminal vesicles** are a pair of hollow sacculated structures placed on the base of the bladder in front of the rectum (Figs. 591, 608). Each vesicle is about two inches in length, and has its long axis directed downwards, medially, and slightly forwards. The upper end of the vesicle, which is partly covered with peritoneum, is large and rounded, and lies at a considerable distance from the median plane, behind the lower end of the ureter, and is separated from the rectum by the peritoneum of the recto-vesical pouch. Below the level of the peritoneal cavity the seminal vesicle and rectum are more intimately related.

The vesicle tapers towards its lower end, which is placed not far from the median plane immediately above the prostate. In this position the vesicle becomes constricted to form a short duct which joins the lateral side of the corresponding vas deferens at an acute angle. The common duct thus formed is the **ejaculatory duct.** The medial side of each vesicle is related to the vas deferens, and the lateral side, when the bladder is empty, lies close to the sloping pelvic floor. The seminal vesicles are more intimately

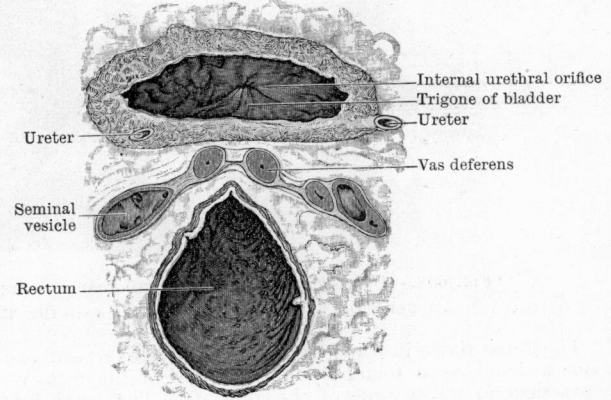

Internal urethral orifice
Trigone of bladder
Ureter

Ureter

Vas deferens

Seminal vesicle

Rectum

Fig. 607. — Horizontal Section through the Rectum and Urinary Bladder at the Level at which the Ureters pierce the Bladder Wall.
From a specimen in the Surgical Museum, Trinity College, Dublin.

related to the wall of the bladder than to that of the rectum. Their upper ends are separated from the rectum by a portion of the recto-vesical pouch, and lower down the partition of smooth muscle fibres and of fascia which intervenes between the seminal vesicles and the rectum is thicker than that which separates them from the bladder.

The seminal vesicle assumes a more vertical position when the bladder is distended, and a more horizontal direction when the bladder is empty. Its upper end is sometimes curved backwards against the side of the rectum. In some cases the seminal vesicles are much smaller than usual, and may be less than one inch in length. Frequently they are asymmetrical in size and shape.

Each seminal vesicle is in reality a tube bent in a tortuous manner on itself; if the dense tissue which envelops it is taken away, the length of the tube when untwisted may be found to be as much as five inches. The tube is closed above, and a variable number of short tortuous branches arise from it at different levels. The blind end of the tube usually lies at the upper end of the vesicle, but in some cases the tubular structure is so bent upon itself that the blind terminal part lies against the side of the issuing duct. Their mode of development shows that the seminal vesicles are diverticula of the vasa deferentia, from which they originally arise as small pouched outgrowths.

The seminal vesicles are not present in all mammals, and in those in which they do occur their relative size and form vary much. The carnivora and marsupials, for instance, have no seminal vesicles; in some other animals, e.g. hedgehog, they are relatively of enormous size.

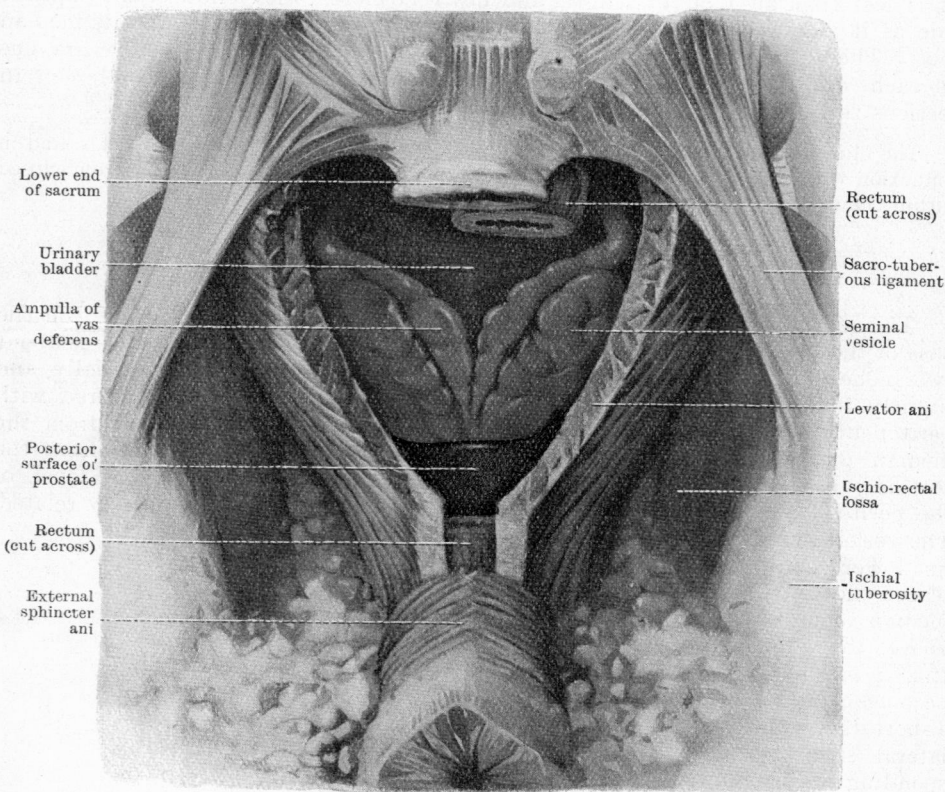

Fig. 608.—Dissection from behind to display the Seminal Vesicles, the Ampullæ of the Vasa Deferentia, and the Prostate. (A. F. D.)

The dense tissue in which the seminal vesicles are embedded contains much unstriped muscle tissue which sweeps round in the side wall of the recto-vesical pouch. Inferiorly this tissue is attached to the capsule of the prostate. The large veins coming from the prostatic and vesical plexuses are closely related to the seminal vesicles.

Structure of Vas Deferens and Seminal Vesicle.—Except at the ampulla, the vas deferens is a thick-walled tube with relatively a very small lumen. The hard cord-like sensation which it conveys to the touch is due to the thickness and denseness of its wall. The wall of the vas is composed of three layers — an outer **adventitious coat** of fibrous tissue, middle **muscular coat**, and an inner **mucous coat**. The thickness of the wall is due to the great development of its coat of unstriped muscle, which is arranged in three layers: an outer and an inner of longitudinal fibres, and a middle layer—by far the thickest—of circular fibres. The mucous membrane of the vas exhibits a number of slight longitudinal folds and is covered with a ciliated epithelium. The ampulla has a much thinner wall, and, as the surface of its mucous membrane has a number of ridges separating depressed areas, the lining of this part of the tube presents a honeycomb appearance. The wall of the seminal vesicle resembles that of the ampulla in being thin, and in having a mucous lining with uneven honeycomb-like ridges and depressions. In it the same coats are to be recognised as in the vas deferens, but the muscular layer is much thinner, and the strata composing it are less regularly arranged.

Vessels and Nerves of Vas Deferens and Seminal Vesicle.—The vas receives its main **artery** from the superior or the inferior vesical artery. This *artery to the vas* accompanies it as far as the testis, where it ends by anastomosing with branches of the testicular artery. The seminal vesicle is supplied by twigs from the *inferior vesical artery.* The **nerves** come from the hypogastric plexus. In lower animals the nerves for the seminal vesicles are derived from the nerve roots of the second, third, and fourth lumbar nerves.

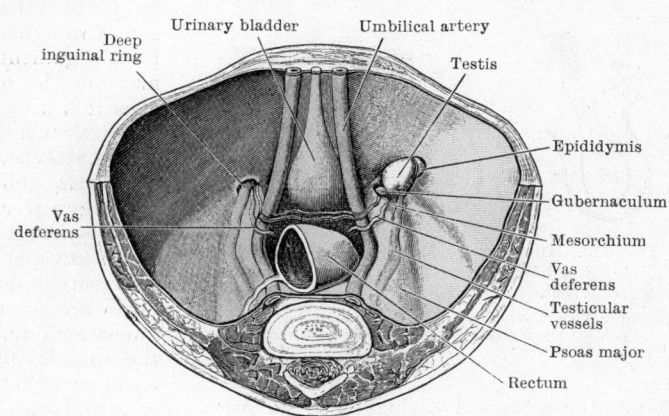

FIG. 609.—VIEW FROM ABOVE OF THE CAVITY OF PELVIS AND LOWER PART OF ABDOMEN IN A FŒTUS ABOUT THE SEVENTH MONTH. (A. F. D.).

On the left side, which represents a slightly more advanced condition than the right, the testis has entered the inguinal canal ; on the right side the testis is still within the abdominal cavity.

DESCENT OF THE TESTIS

The cause of the peculiar course pursued by the vas deferens in the adult and the manner in which it is related to the anterior abdominal wall, is made clear by a study of the arrangement of the parts in the fœtus. The testes until nearly the end of intra-uterine life are in the abdominal cavity. Lying at first on the posterior wall of the abdomen at the level of the upper lumbar vertebræ, and immediately below the level assumed at that time by the permanent kidney, the testis is held in place by a fold of peritoneum called the **mesorchium**. As growth goes on the testis comes to occupy a lower level in the abdominal cavity ; in the third month it lies in the iliac fossa, and in the seventh it is situated near the deep inguinal ring. Meanwhile a blind pouch or diverticulum of the peritoneal membrane, termed the **processus vaginalis**, has grown downwards and medially through the anterior abdominal wall towards the scrotum, deriving as it goes a covering from each of the layers of the abdominal wall through which it passes. The testis with its mesorchium enters the processus vaginalis and descends within it until the scrotum is reached. At a later stage the connexion between the part of the processus vaginalis that lies in the scrotum and the peritoneal lining of the abdomen becomes lost by the obliteration of the upper part of the pouch. The part of the processus vaginalis that persists in the scrotum becomes the parietal layer of the tunica vaginalis ; while the visceral layer is the primitive peritoneal covering of the testis and epididymis (Fig. 610).

Often a small fibrous band may be found in the adult passing through the inguinal canal and joining the peritoneum superiorly in the region of the deep inguinal ring. Sometimes the band is connected below with the tunica vaginalis, but more often it cannot be traced so far downwards. When present it represents the obliterated portion of the processus vaginalis, and is therefore known as the **vestige of the processus vaginalis.**

The processus vaginalis occasionally persists after birth as a channel freely open to the abdominal cavity above ; or the passage, becoming closed at intervals, may give rise to one or more cysts within the coats of the spermatic cord.

It sometimes happens that the descent of the testis is arrested, and then, either failing to enter the processus vaginalis the testis remains within the abdominal cavity, or entering the processus vaginalis it fails to reach the scrotum, and lies in the inguinal canal. The term "cryptorchism" is frequently applied to such cases.

In connection with the descent of the testis a remarkable cord-like structure—the **gubernaculum testis**—must be mentioned. The gubernaculum arises for the most part within a peritoneal fold which, at an early time in the development of the fœtus, may be seen stretching from the inguinal region to the mesonephric duct (future duct of the testis) and caudal end of the mesonephros or primitive kidney. This peritoneal fold is joined from above by a less marked fold which extends downwards from the caudal end of the testis, which, at that time, is situated in the abdomen close to the medial side of the mesonephros. Within the two folds smooth muscular and fibrous tissue arises and becomes a continuous band—the gubernaculum testis. The gubernaculum is there-fore to be regarded as originally composed of two portions separately developed in the two folds mentioned. It is interesting to note that in the female the representatives of those

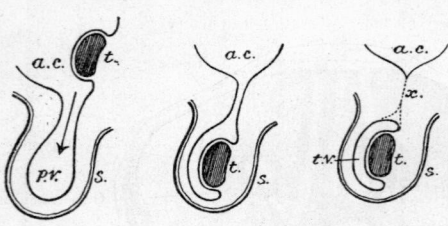

FIG. 610.—DIAGRAM to illustrate the descent of the testis and the manner in which the tunica vaginalis is derived.

a.c. Abdominal cavity.
p.v. Processus vaginalis.
t. Testis.
s. Scrotum.
t.v. Tunica vaginalis.
x. Vestige of processus vaginalis.

two parts of the gubernaculum remain sepa-rate throughout life, and constitute the round ligament of the uterus and the liga-ment of the ovary. The gubernaculum, when it is at its greatest development (about the sixth month), is rounded and cord-like, and is attached above to the lower end of the testis, while inferiorly it is fixed near the inguinal region. In the lower part of its course it is closely related to, and is partly covered by, the peritoneum of the processus vaginalis. Striped muscular fibres are present in the lower part of the gubernaculum, and have their origin from the muscles of the inguinal part of the anterior abdominal wall. As the testis enters the processus vaginalis the gubernaculum atrophies, but at birth a short part of the gubernaculum may still be found passing downwards towards the lower part of the scrotum and lying below the level of the tunica vaginalis. It is considered by some anatomists that the movement downwards of the testis may be partly due to a pull caused by the shrinking of the gubernaculum as it atrophies. In its descent the testis takes with it its duct and vessels and nerves, and they form the spermatic cord (p. 716).

In some mammals, such as the elephant, the testes remain permanently within the abdominal cavity; while in others, such as the rabbit and the hedgehog, the peritoneal pouches remain widely open throughout life, and the testes are periodically withdrawn into the abdomen.

SCROTUM

The **scrotum** varies much in appearance in different subjects, and even in the same person at different times. As the result of cold or of exercise, the wall of the scrotum becomes contracted and firm, and the skin covering it wrinkled; at other times the wall may be relaxed and flaccid, the scrotum then assuming the appearance of a pendulous bag. The left side of the scrotum reaches a lower level than the right, in correspondence with the lower level of the left testis. The skin of the scrotum is of a darker colour than the general skin of the body, and is covered sparsely with hair; it is marked in the median plane by a ridge called the **raphe scroti**, which is continued backwards towards the anus, and forwards on to the urethral surface of the penis. The difference in the appearance of the scrotum at different times is due to the amount of contraction or relaxation of a layer of muscular fibres, constituting the **dartos**, situated in the superficial fascia. When that muscular layer is contracted, the scrotum becomes smaller, and the skin is thrown into folds or wrinkles; when it is relaxed, the scrotum is flaccid and pendulous, and the skin becomes more smooth and even. The layer of fascia which contains the smooth muscle fibres can be shown to be continuous superiorly with the superficial fascia of the penis, and with the deep layer of the superficial fascia of the abdomen, and to be attached laterally to the sides of the pubic arch. The muscle fibres are arranged in a thick layer of interlacing bundles, and many of the deeper fibres are continued into the **septum of the scrotum**, which divides the scrotum into a pair of chambers, one for each testis. The wall of each chamber is formed by the corresponding tunica vaginalis, internal spermatic fascia, cremas-teric muscle and fascia, and external spermatic fascia; while the skin, the superficial fascia, and the dartos muscle form coverings which are common to the whole scrotum, and enclose both chambers. The layer of tissue immediately internal to the dartos is made up of exceedingly loose and easily stretched areolar tissue, and in it, as throughout in the superficial fascia of the scrotum, there is an entire absence of fat.

The scrotum in the fœtus contains no cavity, but, like the labia majora in the female, it is composed entirely of vascular and fatty areolar tissue.

Vessels and Nerves of Scrotum.—On each side the **arteries** are *scrotal branches* from the internal pudendal artery, which reach it from behind, and from the external pudendal arteries, which reach its upper and anterior part.

The **nerves** of the scrotum are derived on each side from the posterior scrotal branches of the pudendal nerve, from the perineal branch of the posterior cutaneous nerve of the thigh, and from the ilio-inguinal nerve. The branches from the pudendal and posterior cutaneous nerves reach the scrotum from behind, while the ilio-inguinal supplies its upper and anterior part. The nerve fibres for the dartos muscle are believed to arise in the hypogastric plexus.

PENIS

The **penis** is composed chiefly of erectile tissue, and is traversed by the urethra. The surface nearest the urethra is called the **urethral surface**; the opposite and more extensive aspect is the **dorsum penis**. The erectile tissue is

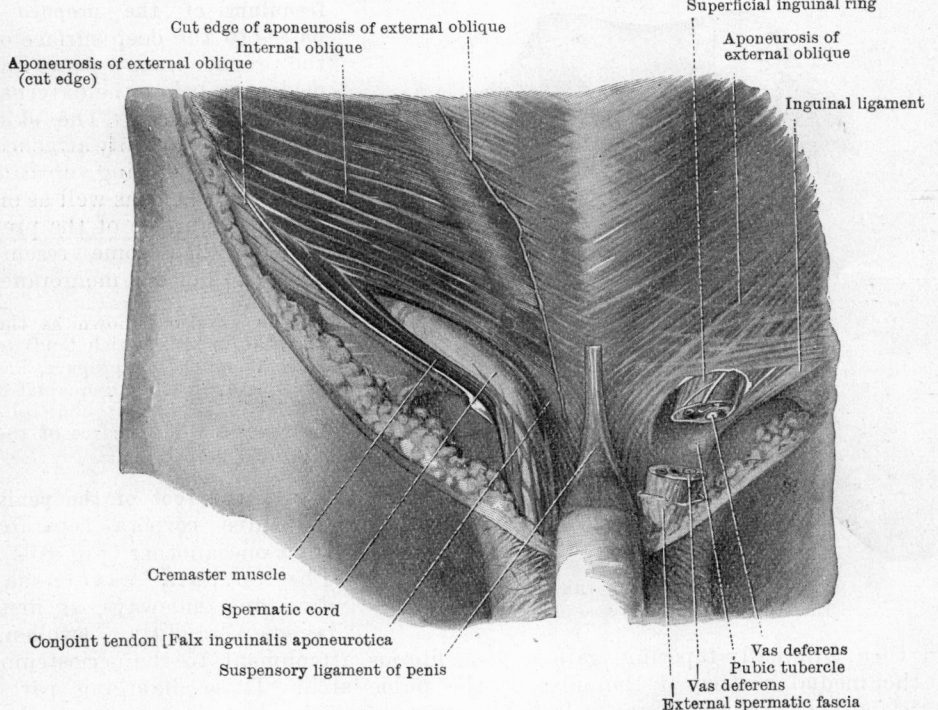

FIG. 611.—DISSECTION TO SHOW THE SPERMATIC CORD AS IT ISSUES FROM THE SUPERFICIAL INGUINAL RING. On the right side the external oblique muscle has been removed. (A. M. Paterson.)

for the most part disposed in three longitudinal columns, which in the body of the organ are closely united, while at the root of the penis they separate from one another, and become attached to the perineal membrane and the sides of the pubic arch. Two of the columns of erectile tissue are placed alongside the median plane; they form the dorsum and sides of the penis, and are called the **corpora cavernosa penis**. The third column is situated in the median plane near the urethral surface, and is called the **corpus spongiosum pénis**. The corpus spongiosum is the part of the penis traversed by the urethra, and it is considerably smaller than the corpora cavernosa, which form the chief bulk of the organ (Figs. 612, 613).

In the **body of the penis** each corpus cavernosum presents a rounded surface, except where it is flattened by contact with its fellow of the opposite side. They are separated on the dorsal surface by a shallow groove, and on the urethral aspect by a deeper and wider furrow in which the corpus spongiosum lies (Fig. 612). Towards the distal end of the penis the corpus spongiosum expands, and, spreading towards the dorsal surface forms a kind of conical cap—the **glans penis**—which covers over the blunt terminations of the corpora cavernosa.

46 a

The prominent margin of the glans, called the **corona glandis**, projects backwards and laterally beyond the ends of the corpora cavernosa. The glans is traversed by the terminal part of the urethra, which ends near the summit of the glans in a slit-like opening—the **external urethral orifice.** The united corpora cavernosa end in a blunt conical extremity, the apex of which is received into a hollow in the base of the glans. The skin of the body of the penis is thin, delicate, and freely movable, and, except near the pubis, is free from hairs; on the urethral aspect the skin is marked by a median raphe, continuous with the raphe of the scrotum. Traced towards the base of the glans, the skin forms a free fold—the **prepuce**—which overlaps the glans to a variable extent. From the deep surface of the prepuce the skin is reflected on to the terminal part of the penis, along a line a little proximal to the corona glandis, and is continued over the entire glans to the external urethral orifice. A small median fold—the **frenulum of the prepuce**—passes to the deep surface of the prepuce from a point immediately below the external urethral orifice. The skin of the glans is firmly attached to the underlying erectile tissue, and here, as well as on the deep surface of the prepuce, it has some resemblance to mucous membrane.

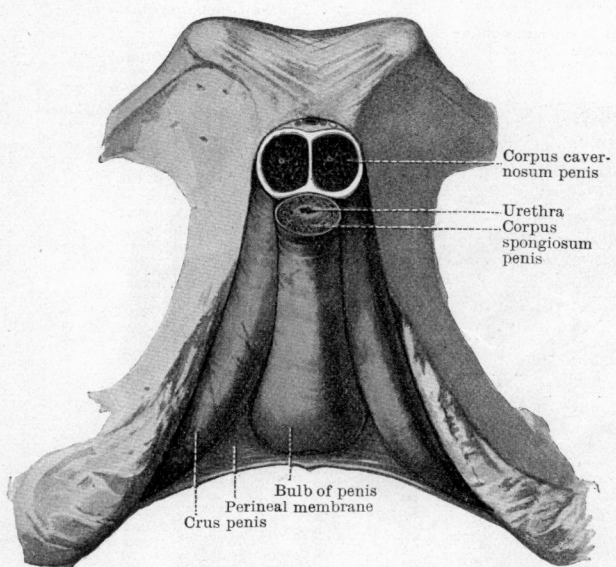

Corpus cavernosum penis

Urethra
Corpus spongiosum penis

Bulb of penis
Perineal membrane
Crus penis

FIG. 612.—THE ROOT OF THE PENIS.
The body of the penis is seen in section.

The secretion known as the **smegma præputii**, which tends to collect beneath the prepuce, has its source in the desquamated and broken-down epithelial cells derived from the surface of the glans and prepuce.

At the **root of the penis** its three corpora separate from one another (Fig. 612). The corpora cavernosa, diverging sideways, at first become slightly swollen, and then, gradually tapering, gain a firm, fibrous attachment to the periosteum on the medial surface of the sides of the pubic arch. These diverging parts of the corpora cavernosa are called the **crura penis**, and each is covered by the corresponding ischio-cavernosus muscle. The corpus spongiosum, lying between the crura, becomes enlarged, and forms a globular mass which receives the name of the **bulb of the penis.** The bulb varies much in size in different subjects, and is attached to the under surface of the perineal membrane. The posterior part and under surface of the bulb usually show a median notch—an indication that the bulb is originally composed of two symmetrical portions which during development have become fused in the median plane. A slightly marked median septum, situated within the tissue of the bulb, indicates, on a deeper plane, the line along which fusion took place. The urethra, piercing the perineal membrane, enters the bulb obliquely a short distance in front of its posterior end (Fig. 588). The superficial surface of the bulb is covered by the bulbo-spongiosus muscles.

A triangular band of strong fibrous tissue, called the **suspensory ligament of the penis,** is attached to the front of the pubic symphysis, and extends to the fascial sheath of the penis, with which it becomes continuous (Fig. 611).

Structure of the Penis.—Each corpus cavernosum penis is enclosed in a dense white fibrous coat which fuses with the corresponding coat of the opposite side to form the median **septum of the penis.** The septum is very incomplete, especially near the end of the penis, where it is interrupted by a number of nearly parallel slits (Figs. 613 and 614). Through these slits the erectile tissue of the two corpora cavernosa is continuous.

The fibrous coat contains some elastic fibres, and is divided into an outer layer of longitudinal fibres and an inner layer of circular fibres, some of which latter are continued into the septum. Numerous fibrous strands proceed from the deep surface of the fibrous coat, and, stretching across the interior of the corpus cavernosum, form a fine sponge-like framework whose interspaces communicate freely with one another, and are filled with blood. These spaces lead directly into the veins of the penis, and, like the veins, have a lining of flat endothelial cells. The size of the penis varies with the amount of blood in the erectile tissue. The structure of the corpus spongiosum resembles that of the corpora cavernosa, but the fibrous coat is much thinner and more elastic, and the trabeculæ are finer (Fig. 613).

The glans penis also is composed of erectile tissue which communicates by a rich venous plexus with the corpus spongiosum. No strongly marked fibrous coat is present, and the erectile tissue is bounded by the skin, which is exceedingly thin and firmly adherent. The urethra in this part of the penis is dilated and is compressed sideways into a slit-like passage called the fossa terminalis ; the fossa is surrounded by a mass of fibro-elastic tissue which forms a kind of double median septum within the glans. This septum is continued backwards to join the fibrous coat of the conical end of the corpora cavernosa, and ventrally it gives attachment to the frenulum of the prepuce. It imperfectly divides the erectile tissue of the glans into right and left portions, which, however, freely communicate dorsally. From the septum, trabeculæ pass out in all directions into the tissue of the glans.

A fascial sheath, containing numerous elastic tissue fibres, forms a loose common envelope for the corpora cavernosa and the corpus spongiosum. It is termed the *fascia penis*, and reaches

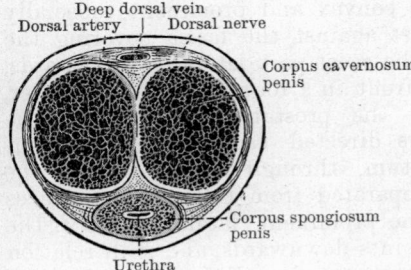

Deep dorsal vein
Dorsal artery | Dorsal nerve
Corpus cavernosum penis
Corpus spongiosum penis
Urethra

FIG. 613.—TRANSVERSE SECTION THROUGH THE BODY OF THE PENIS.

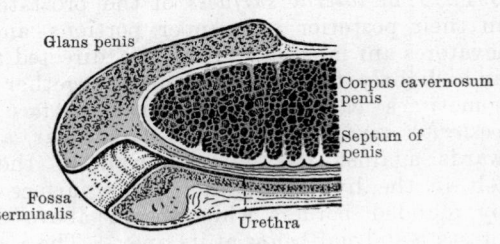

Glans penis
Corpus cavernosum penis
Septum of penis
Fossa terminalis
Urethra

FIG. 614.—A LONGITUDINAL SECTION OF THE TERMINAL PORTION OF THE PENIS.

as far as the base of the glans, where it becomes fixed to the floor of the groove limited by the corona of the glans. In its proximal part the sheath gives insertion to many of the fibres of the bulbo-spongiosus and ischio-cavernosus muscles.

Superficial to the fascia penis there is a layer of extremely lax areolar tissue, and more superficial still is a prolongation of the dartos tunic of the scrotum, covered by the delicate skin of the penis. Numerous sebaceous glands are present in the skin, especially on the urethral surface of the penis.

In some mammals, such as the walrus, dog, bear, and baboon, a bone called the **os penis** is developed in the septum which intervenes between the corpora cavernosa penis.

Vessels and Nerves of Penis.—The **arteries** are derived from the internal pudendal artery. The erectile tissue of the corpora cavernosa is supplied chiefly by the *deep arteries of the penis*, and that of the corpus spongiosum by the *artery to the bulb*. Branches of the *dorsal artery* of the penis piercing the fibrous coat of the corpora cavernosa furnish additional twigs to the erectile tissue. The glans receives its chief blood-supply from branches of the dorsal arteries. The small branches of the arteries run in the trabeculæ of the erectile tissue, and the capillaries, into which they lead, open directly into the cavernous venous spaces. As they lie in the finer trabeculæ the smaller branches often present a peculiar twisted appearance, and the name **helicine arteries** is therefore applied to them.

The **veins** with which the cavernous spaces communicate carry the blood, for the most part, either directly into the *prostatic plexus*, or into the *deep dorsal vein* and so to that plexus. The deep dorsal vein of the penis begins in tributaries from the glans and prepuce, and lies in the groove between the corpora cavernosa as it ascends to pass beneath the inferior pubic ligament to join the prostatic plexus. On each side of it lies a dorsal artery, and, still farther from the median plane, a dorsal nerve (Fig. 613).

The **lymph vessels** of the penis are arranged in a deep and superficial series, and end in the medial group of the *superficial inguinal lymph glands*.

The **nerve-supply** of the penis is derived from the pudendal nerve (2nd, 3rd, and 4th sacral nerves), and from the pelvic sympathetic plexuses. The branches of the pudendal are the *dorsal nerve of the penis*, and branches from the *perineal nerves*. They supply the cutaneous structures of the penis, while the filaments from the *pelvic plexuses*, which reach the penis through the prostatic nerve plexus, end in the erectile tissue.

PROSTATE

The **prostate** is a partly glandular, partly muscular organ of a dark brown-red colour which surrounds the beginning of the urethra in the male. It lies within the pelvis behind the pubic symphysis and is enclosed by a dense fascial sheath. Through the various connexions of this sheath the prostate is firmly fixed within the pelvic cavity. The ejaculatory ducts traverse the upper part of the prostate in their course to join the urethra. The size of the prostate varies considerably, but usually its greatest transverse diameter is an inch and a half, its antero-posterior diameter three-quarters of an inch, and its vertical diameter an inch and a quarter. Superficially the prostate is separated from the bladder by deep, wide lateral grooves and by a narrow posterior groove (Figs. 591, 615).

The prostate has an apex which is directed downwards, a base looking upwards, a posterior surface, and a pair of lateral surfaces. The *base* is directed upwards against the inferior aspect of the bladder in the neighbourhood of its urethral opening. The greater part of the base is structurally continuous with the bladder wall; only a narrow portion remains free on each side and forms the lower limit of the deep groove which marks the separation of the bladder and prostate (Fig. 591). The *lateral surfaces* of the prostate are convex and prominent, especially in their posterior and upper portions, and rest against the fascia covering the levatores ani muscles. They are directed for the most part laterally, downwards, and slightly forwards, and meet together in front in a rounded anterior border, sometimes called the "anterior surface" of the prostate (Fig. 617). The *posterior surface*, is flat and triangular, and is directed backwards and downwards against the anterior wall of the rectum, through which it may be felt in the living subject. This surface is separated from the lateral surfaces by rounded borders which begin above at the prominent lateral part of the prostate and end below at its apex. The apex points downwards, and is in relation to the fascial covering of the sphincter urethræ muscle. From the apex, the anterior border passes upwards in the median plane behind the pubic symphysis and retro-pubic pad of fat; and it is interrupted in its lowest part by the passage of the urethra.

When its fascial sheath is stripped off, the prostate has a more rounded outline, and the surfaces just described are not so clearly defined. The anterior border may now appear to be a surface rather than a border, and the antero-posterior diameter is considerably reduced.

The urethra enters the prostate at a point near the middle of its base, and leaves it at a point on its anterior border immediately above and in front of the apex, describing a curve which is concave forwards.

The ejaculatory ducts, entering a slit immediately in front of the posterior border of the base, run downwards and forwards, to open into the prostatic portion of the urethra at the margins of the mouth of the prostatic utricle.

The wedge-shaped portion of the prostate which separates these ducts from the urethra is called the *median lobe* (Fig. 617). It projects upwards against the bladder, and is continuous with the bladder wall immediately behind the urethral orifice. When hypertrophied, as it often is in old people, the median lobe of the prostate may cause a considerable elevation in the cavity of the bladder, which is of considerable surgical interest, and to which the term uvula of the bladder is applied. The remaining part of the prostate is described as being composed of a pair of large *lateral lobes*, which are, however, not marked off from one another superficially.

In front of the prostate, between it and the pubis, there is a close venous network called the prostatic plexus, with which the deep dorsal vein of the penis communicates. That plexus is continued backwards, round the sides of the prostate, and joins the large, thin-walled veins which are collected for the most part in the deep sulcus between the bladder wall and the prostate, and form the prostatico-vesical plexus. Most of the veins forming the plexus lie partly within and partly outside the fascial sheath of the prostate (Fig. 617).

Fascial Sheath of Prostate.—This sheath is a dense fibrous portion of the pelvic fascia, and closely invests the prostate. Inferiorly the sheath becomes continuous with the fascia on the sphincter urethræ muscle, and through it gains attachment to the sides of the pubic arch. In front a pair of thickened bands pass forwards from the anterior part of the sheath, close to the median plane, to reach the back of the lower part of the pubis, where they are attached

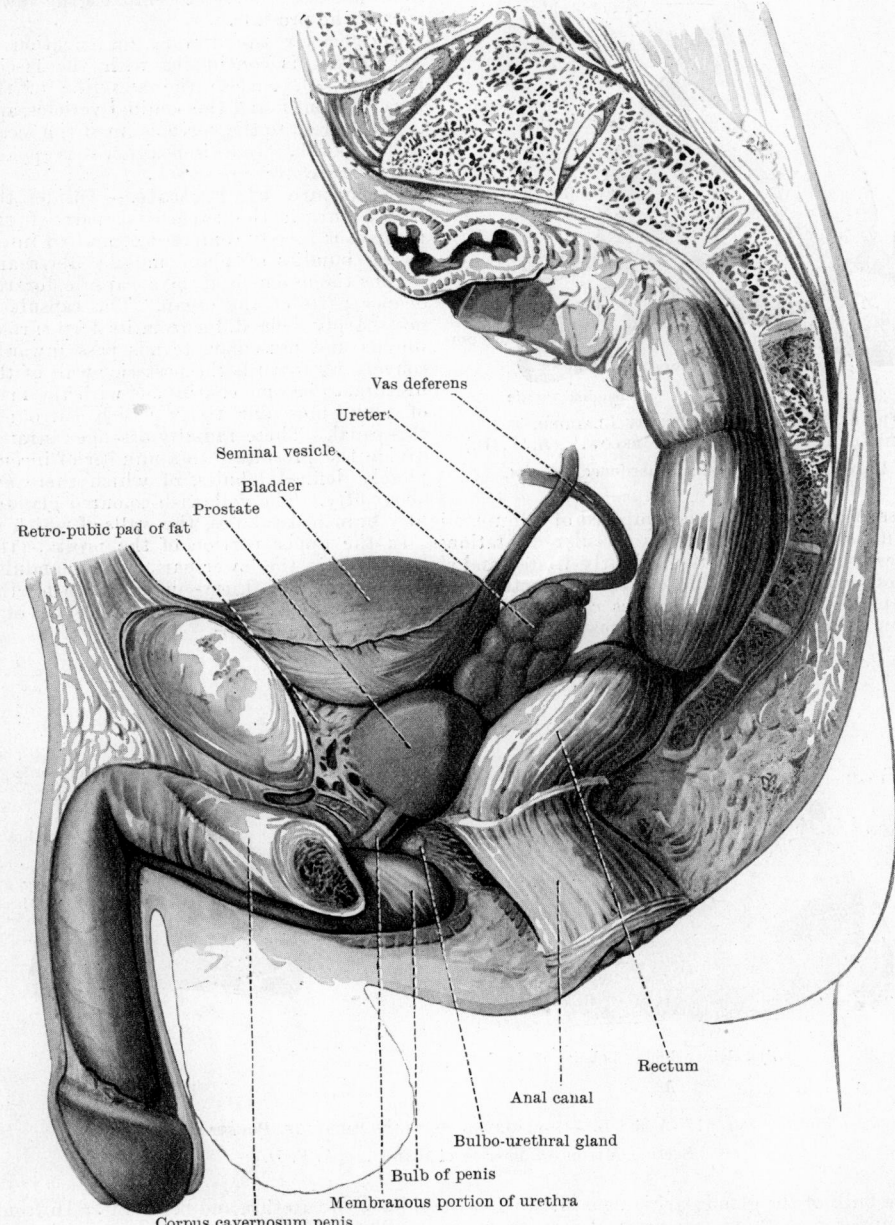

Vas deferens

Ureter

Seminal vesicle

Bladder

Prostate

Retro-pubic pad of fat

Rectum

Anal canal

Bulbo-urethral gland

Bulb of penis

Membranous portion of urethra

Corpus cavernosum penis

FIG. 615.—DISSECTION OF THE PENIS AND THE MALE PELVIC ORGANS FROM THE LEFT SIDE. (A. F. D.)
The deep dorsal vein of the penis and the prostatic venous plexus are coloured blue.

to the periosteum. They are the **medial pubo-prostatic ligaments**, and contain smooth muscle fibres as well as dense fibrous tissue. Some of the muscle fibres of the pubo-prostatic ligaments pass upwards and backwards to the bladder wall, and are spoken of as the **pubo-vesical muscles**. Laterally each medial ligament is continuous with the **lateral pubo-prostatic ligament**, which is the thin fascia that spreads from the side of the prostate over the anterior part of the levator ani. Between the two medial pubo-prostatic ligaments there is a shallow depression the floor of which is formed by a thin layer of fascia connecting the anterior

46 c

part of the sheath of the prostate with the back of the pubic symphysis. This layer and the two pairs of pubo-prostatic ligaments form the floor of the **retro-pubic space,** which separates the pubis from the bladder and the base of the prostate. Below the pubo-prostatic ligaments the medial (or anterior) edges of the levatores ani muscles pass medially and almost meet together in front of the apex of the prostate. When followed backwards the medial edges of

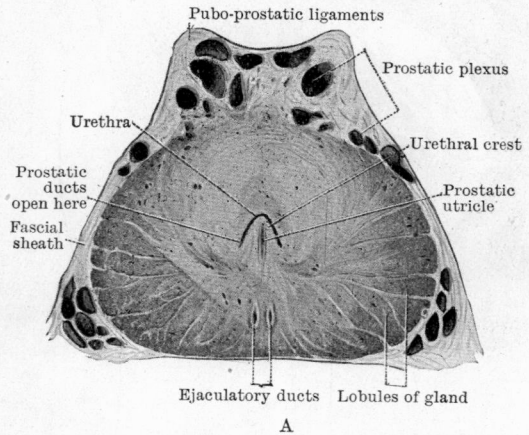

FIG. 616.—PROSTATE, URINARY BLADDER, AND SEMINAL VESICLES SEEN FROM BELOW. (A. F. D.)

Drawn from a specimen hardened *in situ.*

these muscles are seen to embrace the lower part of the prostate.

Posteriorly the upward prolongation of the sheath is continuous with the fascial layers which enclose the ampullæ of the vasa deferentia and the seminal vesicles, and it is adherent to the peritoneum of the recto-vesical pouch. In this position it is spoken of as the *recto-vesical septum.*

Structure of Prostate. — Inside the fascial sheath the superficial part of the prostate is largely composed of matted interlacing bundles of plain muscle fibres and fibrous tissue which form a capsule for the deeper parts of the organ. The **capsule** is not sharply defined, for from its deep surface fibrous and muscular strands pass inwards, converging towards the posterior wall of the urethra, to become continuous with the mass of plain muscular tissue which surrounds this canal. These radially arranged strands divide the prostate into a number of incompletely defined lobules, of which there are about fifty. The yellowish-coloured glandular tissue of the lobules is composed of minute, slightly branched tubules, the walls of which in certain places show numerous saccular dilatations. In the upper portion of the prostate the tubules are more convoluted, slightly dilated and shorter than in the lower part. The glandular tubules lead into the minute **prostatic ducts**—in number twenty or thirty—which open for the most part into a pair of grooves called the **prostatic sinuses,** which run along the sides of a median elevation—the **urethral crest**—in the posterior wall of the urethra.

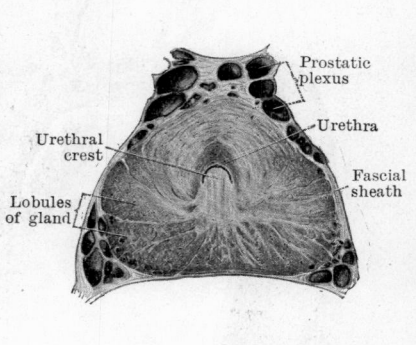

FIG. 617, A and B.—HORIZONTAL SECTIONS THROUGH PROSTATE.

Section A is at a higher level than B. (A. F. D.)

The bulk of the glandular tissue is situated at the sides of the urethra and behind it. In front of its upper part there is a mass of smooth muscular fibres which is continued upwards and backwards on its sides to form a part of the sphincter vesicæ. At a lower level striped muscular tissue, which is continuous with the deep part of the sphincter urethræ, occupies a position in front of the urethra.

The muscular tissue of the prostate is to be regarded as the thickened muscular layer of the wall of the urethra broken up and invaded by the prostatic glands, which arise and are developed from the lining layer of the canal during embryonic life.

In old age the prostate frequently undergoes a hypertrophy which may affect chiefly the glandular tissue, or the entire organ. Not infrequently calcareous concretions are found in it.

Vessels and Nerves of Prostate.—The **arteries** are branches of the rectal [hæmorrhoidal] and inferior vesical arteries, while the large **veins**—the prostatic plexus—communicate with the vesical plexus, and drain into the internal iliac veins [vv. hypogastricæ]. In old people the veins of the prostate usually become much enlarged. The **lymph vessels** are associated with those of the seminal vesicle and the neck of the bladder. The **nerves** of the prostate are derived from the pelvic sympathetic plexuses.

BULBO-URETHRAL GLANDS

The **bulbo-urethral glands** are a pair of small bodies placed behind the membranous part of the urethra and among the fibres of the sphincter urethræ. In old age they are often difficult to find without microscopical examination; in young adults they are each about the size of a pea and are of a yellowish-brown colour. Placed deep to the perineal membrane, the glands lie below the level of the apex of the prostate and above that of the bulb of the penis (Fig. 615). Each gland is made up of a number of closely applied lobules, and is of the compound racemose type. The ductules of the gland unite to form a single **duct** which enters the bulb of the penis, and, after a relatively long course (about an inch), ends by opening into the spongy portion of the urethra by a minute aperture. The secreting acini are lined with columnar epithelium.

The glands receive their arterial supply from the artery to the bulb.

URETHRA VIRILIS

The **male urethra** is a channel of about eight inches in length leading from the bladder to the external urethral orifice at the end of the glans penis. The canal not only serves for the passage of urine, it also affords an exit for the seminal products, which enter it by the ejaculatory ducts, and for the secretion of the prostatic and bulbo-urethral glands; in addition, numerous minute **urethral mucous glands** pour their secretion into the urethra.

As it passes from the internal urethral orifice to its external opening the urethra describes an ∽-shaped course, and it is customary to divide it into three sections. The first part is within the true pelvis, and has a nearly vertical course as it traverses the prostate. Turning more forwards, the urethra passes below the pubic arch and pierces the fibrous layers which form the pelvic wall in that region. Leaving the pelvis, the canal enters the bulb of the penis and throughout the rest of its course it lies in the erectile tissue of the corpus spongiosum and of the glans penis. The part of the urethra which is embedded in the prostate is called the **prostatic part**; the short part which pierces the pelvic wall is called the **membranous part**, and the part surrounded by the corpus spongiosum is the **spongy part** [pars cavernosa]. Of the three sections the spongy portion is much the longest, and the membranous is the shortest.

The **prostatic part** descends through the prostate from the base towards the apex, describing a slight curve which is concave forwards. It is about one inch in length, and is narrower above and below than in its middle portion, which is, indeed, the widest part of the whole urethral canal. Except while fluid is passing, the canal is contracted, and the mucous membrane of the anterior and posterior walls is in contact and thrown into a series of longitudinal folds. When distended, the middle, or widest part of the canal, may normally have a diameter of about one-third of an inch. The posterior wall, often termed the "floor," of the prostatic urethra presents a distinct median ridge called the **urethral crest** (Fig. 619). The crest projects forwards into the urethra to such an extent that the canal in transverse section presents a crescentic outline (Fig. 617). The groove on each side of the crest is known as the **prostatic sinus**, and into it the numerous ducts of the prostatic glands open by minute apertures. Some few ducts from the middle part open nearer the median plane, on the sides of the urethral crest. The highest point of the urethral crest is half-way down, and on it there is a small slit-like opening which leads backwards and upwards for a distance of about a quarter of an inch, as a blind pouch, in the substance of the prostate. That little cavity is known as the **prostatic utricle**, and represents the fused caudal ends of the para-mesonephric ducts [Müller's], from which the uterus and vagina are developed. On each side of the mouth of the utricle there is the much more minute opening of the ejaculatory duct. When traced upwards towards the bladder, the urethral crest diminishes in height and becomes indistinct, but it can often be traced as a slight median ridge as far as the uvula of the bladder. In the opposite direction the ridge becomes less marked, and can be followed into the membranous portion of the canal, where it divides into a pair of inconspicuous elevations which gradually fade out (Fig. 619).

The curvature and, to a less degree, the length of the prostatic urethra depend upon the amount of distension of the bladder and of the rectum (compare Figs. 587 and 588).

The **membranous portion** of the urethra leads downwards and forwards from the apex of the prostate to the bulb of the penis, and is the shortest and narrowest of the three subdivisions of the canal—its length being slightly less than half an inch. It begins at the layer of fascia which lies above the sphincter urethræ muscle, where it is continuous with the prostatic portion of the urethra. It ends, having pierced the perineal membrane, by becoming continuous with the spongy portion of the urethra. It lies about one inch behind and below the inferior pubic ligament and is surrounded by fibres of the sphincter urethræ muscle; and behind it, on each side of the median plane, lies a bulbo-urethral gland. The posterior part of the bulb of the penis projects backwards and overlaps the posterior wall of the membranous part of the urethra to a considerable extent (Fig. 615). The membranous portion of the urethra is the most firmly fixed and, excepting the external urethral orifice, least dilatable part of the urethra.

Beside the folds continued down from the urethral crest there are other longitudinal folds of mucous membrane seen when the canal is empty, and the lumen of the empty tube is therefore stellate in transverse section.

It is important to note that the lower part of the membranous portion of the urethra, where it is overlapped by the bulb, lies below the perineal membrane. It is considerably wider than the upper part, and is very thin-walled. It is the part of the canal which is most liable to rupture (Figs. 618 and 619).

The **spongy portion** of the urethra is about six inches in length and is much the longest of the three subdivisions. It begins at a point about half an inch in front of the posterior end of the bulb of the penis, and ends at the external urethral orifice. Its proximal, or perineal, portion has a fixed position and direction, while its distal part varies with the position of the penis. It traverses the corpus spongiosum, including the bulb and the glans, and is, therefore, entirely surrounded by erectile tissue in the whole of its length. Directed at first forwards through the bulb, it turns downwards and forwards at the point where it comes to lie in front of the lower part of the pubic symphysis (Fig. 618). The bend in the canal corresponds, roughly speaking, to the place of attachment of the suspensory ligament to the dorsum of the penis. When the penis is drawn upwards towards the front of the abdomen, the direction of the terminal half of the canal is, of course, changed, and at the same time the whole spongy urethra becomes more uniformly curved.

Immediately after the urethra has pierced the perineal membrane its under-surface comes into relation with the erectile tissue of the bulb, but the upper wall remains uncovered for a distance of about a quarter of an inch (Fig. 618). The wall of the urethra is there very thin, and the passage is more readily dilatable than in other parts. In this region the urethral wall may readily be torn through, if undue force is used, or if the handle of an instrument is depressed too soon, when an attempt is being made to pass it into the narrower, more fixed part of the canal. The urethra lies at first in the upper part of the erectile tissue, but as it passes forwards it sinks deeper, and comes to occupy the middle part of the corpus spongiosum. In the glans, on the other hand, the erectile tissue lies on the dorsal and lateral aspects of the urethra (Fig. 614). Like the other parts of the urethra, the spongy portion is closed except during the passage of fluid, the closure being effected by the apposition of its dorsal and ventral walls except in the glans penis, where the side walls of the canal are in contact. Thus the lumen of the first part of the canal, when empty, is represented in cross section by a transverse slit, and that of the terminal part by a vertical slit (Figs. 613 and 614). The spongy part of the urethra does not present a uniform calibre throughout; it is wider in the bulb and glans than in the corpus spongiosum. In the bulb the urethra expands downwards, forming a little bulging called the **intra-bulbar fossa**. The terminal dilated part is named the **fossa terminalis** [fossa navicularis] and opens on the surface by the slit-like **external urethral orifice**, which is the narrowest and least dilatable point of the whole urethral canal.

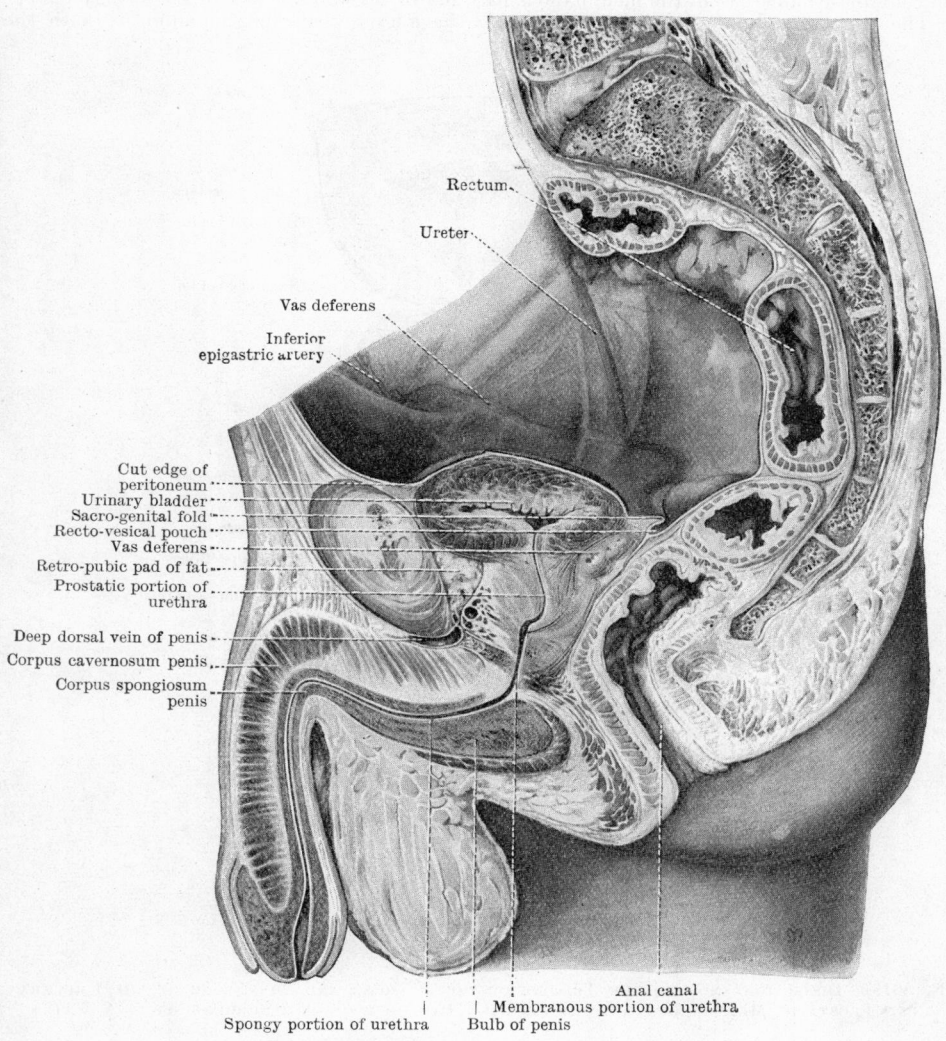

FIG. 618.—ADULT MALE PELVIS IN MEDIAN SECTION. (A. F. D.)

The urinary bladder is empty and firmly contracted. The urethra is opened up in its entire length.

The ducts of the bulbo-urethral glands open by very minute apertures in the inferior wall of the proximal part of the spongy portion of the urethra (Fig. 619). Before opening into the canal, they lie for some distance immediately outside its mucous membrane. A number of little pit-like recesses, called the **urethral lacunæ**, also open into the spongy part of the urethra, and their openings lead for the most part obliquely into the canal in the direction of its external orifice.

A valve-like fold of the mucous membrane is sometimes found in the upper wall of the urethra in the region of the fossa terminalis. Its free edge is directed towards the external orifice, and may engage the point of a fine instrument introduced into the urethra.

Structure.—The mucous membrane of the urethra contains numerous elastic fibres and varies in thickness in different parts of the canal. In many positions it shows distinct longitudinal folds and also minute depressions or pits—the urethral lacunæ already mentioned. The lining epithelium is composed of many layers of cells, and is continuous through the internal urethral orifice with the epithelium of the bladder, which at first it closely resembles. In the region of the fossa terminalis the lining cells, which throughout the spongy portion of the canal are of a columnar type, become flat and scaly.

Numerous minute glands—**urethral glands**—open into the urethra. They are most plentiful in the upper or anterior wall, but they occur in smaller numbers also in the floor and side walls. They are most numerous in the membranous part and in the anterior half of the spongy part.

The larger glands are deeply placed outside the mucous coat, and communicate with the

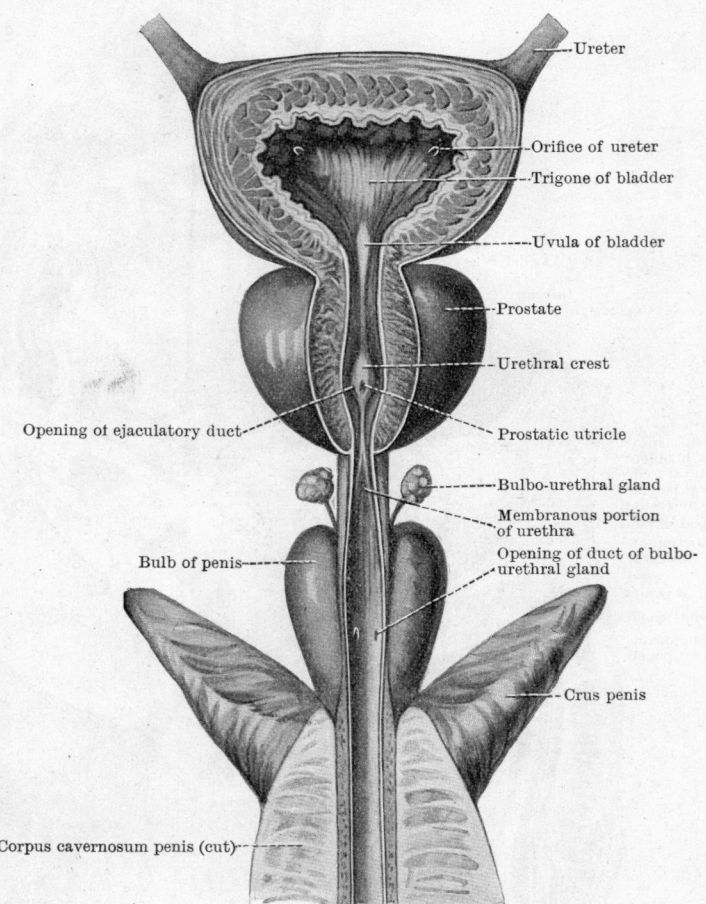

Fig. 619.—Dissection showing the Trigone of the Bladder and the Floor of the Urethra in its Prostatic, Membranous, and the Proximal Part of its Spongy Subdivisions.   (A. F. D.)

urethra by long, slender, obliquely placed branched ducts. The smaller glands lie in the mucous coat and form flask-like depressions with very short ducts. The ducts of some of the glands open into the lacunæ; but many lacunæ have no connexion with the urethral glands.

Frequently two or more elongated ducts belonging to some of the larger glands open into the urethra quite close to its termination. They are spoken of as *para-urethral ducts,* and may be traced backwards for some distance outside the mucous membrane of the roof of the urethra. Morphologically they do not correspond to the ducts in the female which have received the same name.

The muscular wall in the upper part of the urethra consists of plain muscle fibres directed for the most part longitudinally, but some circular fibres also are present. Throughout the greater part of the spongy urethra the muscular coat is either absent or exceedingly thin.

Around the beginning of the urethra there is an obliquely placed band of circularly arranged plain muscle fibres, which is continued downwards and forwards from below the anterior part of the trigone of the bladder. The lower and anterior fibres of this band lie in the anterior wall of the upper part of the prostatic urethra. The band is sometimes spoken of as the sphincter vesicæ internus. At a lower level, in front of the prostatic urethra, there is a band of striped muscular fibres which is continuous inferiorly with the inner circularly disposed part of the sphincter urethræ. Like the latter it is probably to be regarded as a part of a primitive voluntary uro-genital sphincter muscle, such as is represented also in the female subject.

FEMALE GENITAL ORGANS

The reproductive glands in the female are a pair of **ovaries** placed one on each side in the cavity of the pelvis. In connexion with each ovary there is an elongated tube—the **uterine tube** or **oviduct**—which leads to the uterus and opens into its cavity. There is no direct continuity between the ovary and the uterine tube, such as exists between the other glands of the body and their ducts, but the

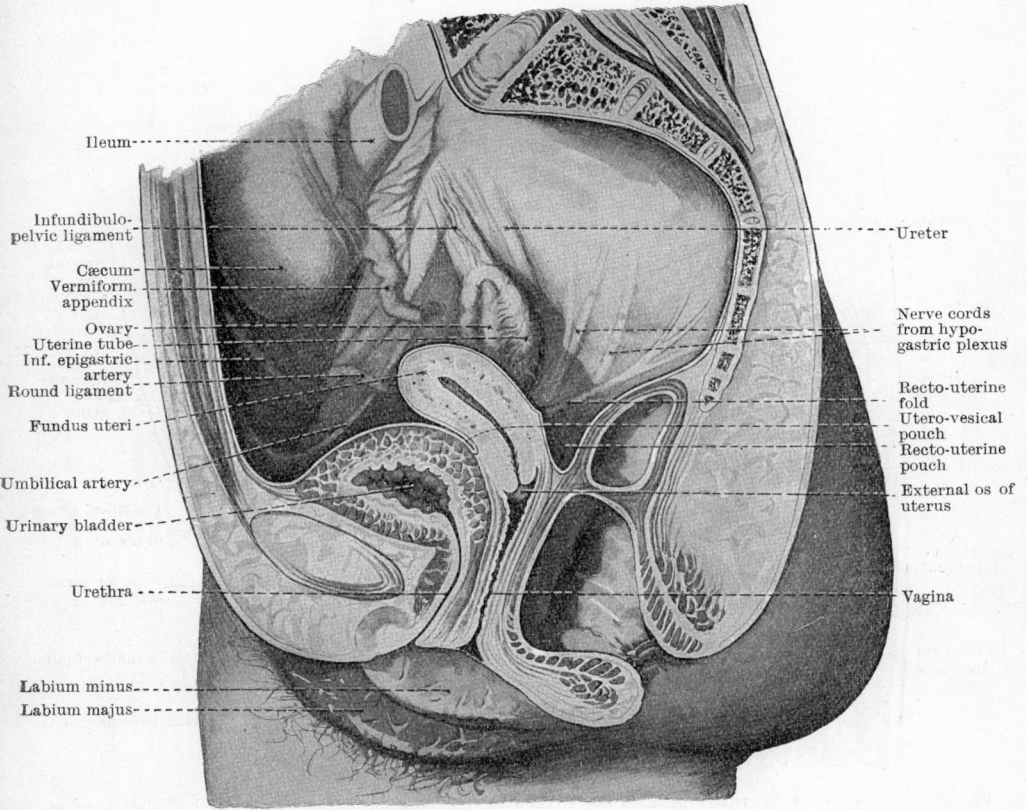

Fig. 620.—Median Section through the Female Pelvis.
Drawn for the most part from a model of a dissection made by Professor Edward H. Taylor.

ova, when shed from the ovary, pass into the pelvic opening of the tube, and are conducted by it to the uterine cavity. The **uterus** is a hollow muscular organ which occupies a nearly median position in the true pelvis. It is joined by the uterine tubes above, and communicates with the vagina below. The ovum, having passed through the tube, reaches the cavity of the uterus, and in it, if fertilisation has taken place, the ovum undergoes its development into the embryo and fœtus. The **vagina** is the passage which leads from the uterus to the exterior, and has its external opening behind that of the urethra, within the **pudendal cleft**. In connexion with the cleft there is a number of structures included under the term *external genital organs*, and which represent in the female the various parts of the penis and scrotum in the male. They are the **labia majora** and the **mons pubis**, the **labia minora**, the **clitoris**, and the **bulbs of the vestibule**. The **greater vestibular glands**, placed one on each side of the lower part of the vagina, are accessory organs of the female reproductive system.

OVARIES

The **ovaries** are a pair of solid bodies, flattened from side to side, each about the size and shape of a large almond. Their length is usually between an inch and an inch and a half, and the thickness from side to side about one third of an inch. In the adult the ovary is placed against the side wall of the pelvic cavity, and is connected by a peritoneal fold with the broad ligament of the uterus. The position occupied by the ovary within the pelvic cavity is fairly constant, although the broad ligaments do not hold the organ firmly fixed in any definite place.

The ovary has two ends—upper and lower. The upper end is the larger and more rounded; it is termed the **tubal end**, as it is most intimately connected with the uterine tube. The lower end is more pointed; it is called the **uterine**

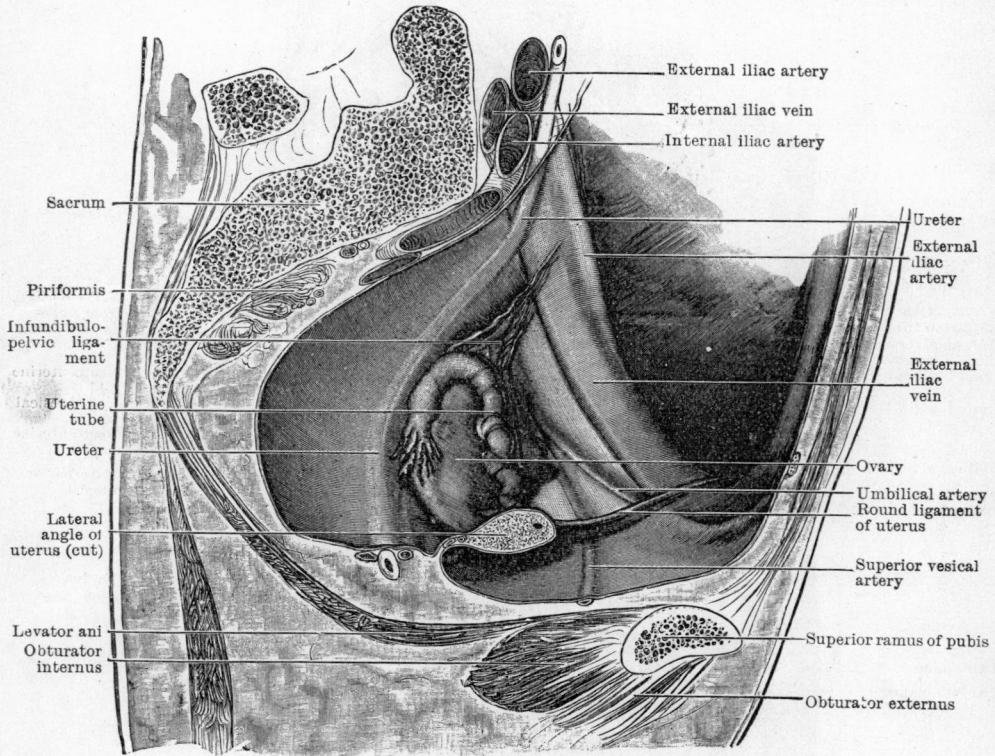

FIG. 621.—SIDE WALL OF THE FEMALE PELVIS, showing the position of the ovary and its relation to the uterine tube. The pelvis was cut parallel to the median plane, but at some distance from it. (A. F. D.)

end, since it is connected with the uterus by a fibrous cord termed the **ligament of the ovary**. The **surfaces** of the ovary are called **medial** and **lateral**, and the *borders* separating them the **mesovarian border** and the **free border**. The free border is convex, while the mesovarian border, which is straighter and narrower, is connected by two very short peritoneal layers, called the **mesovarium**, with the upper layer of the broad ligament of the uterus. The vessels and nerves enter the ovary at the mesovarian border, which is therefore termed its **hilum**.

Position and Relations of Ovary.—When the ovary is in its typical position its long axis is vertical. Its lateral surface lies against the wall of the true pelvis, and its medial surface looks into the pelvic cavity. The peritoneum of the pelvic wall, where the ovary lies against it, is depressed to form a shallow fossa between the ureter and the umbilical artery. Outside the peritoneum forming the floor of this fossa are the obturator nerve and vessels. The tubal end of the ovary lies below the level of the external iliac vessels, and its uterine end is placed immediately above the peritoneum of the pelvic floor. The mesovarian border is immediately behind the line of the umbilical artery, and the free border is immediately in front of the ureter (Fig. 621). The medial surface of the ovary is largely covered by the uterine tube, which, passing upwards on it near its mesovarian border, arches over the tubal end and then turns downwards in relation to the free border and posterior part of the medial surface.

The description given corresponds to the typical position of the organ in women who have not borne children. When the uterus is much inclined towards the right side of the body the left ovary has its long axis directed obliquely downwards and medially, the right gland remaining vertical.

Connexions of the Ovary.—When the ovary is in position a small peritoneal fold passes upwards from its tubal end and becomes lost in the peritoneum covering the external iliac vessels and the psoas major muscle (Fig. 621). It is called the **infundibulo-pelvic ligament** [lig. suspensorium ovarii], and is the lateral part of the anterior border of the broad ligament of the uterus, which there contains between its two layers the ovarian vessels and nerves as they pass down

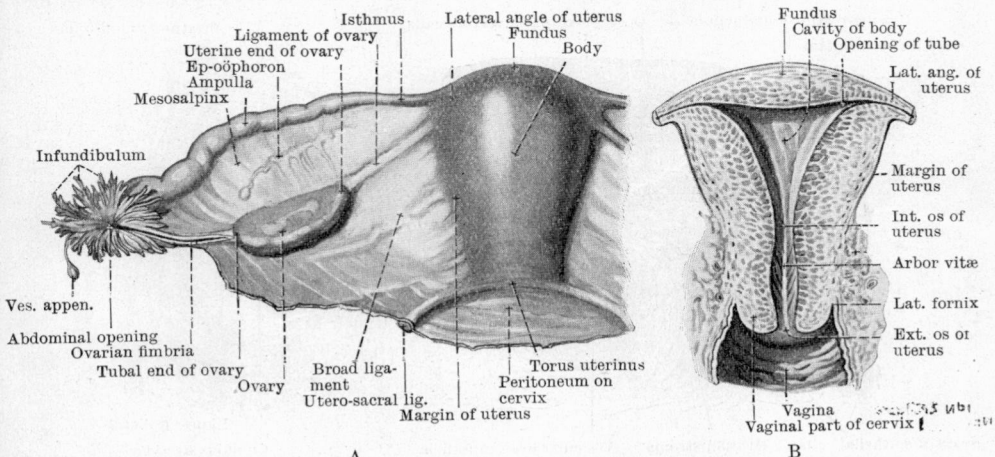

FIG. 622.—A. INTESTINAL SURFACE OF UTERUS AND BROAD LIGAMENT (the broad ligament has been spread out).

B. DIAGRAMMATIC REPRESENTATION OF UTERINE CAVITY.

The dense mass at the side of the cervix uteri represents the lateral cervical ligament. (A. F. D.)

into the pelvis to reach the hilum of the ovary. As the vessels and nerves enter the ovary they are enclosed between the two short layers of peritoneum derived from the upper layer of the broad ligament. In this way the ovary is connected with the broad ligament by a very short mesentery, or **mesovarium**, along the whole length of its mesovarian border. The uterine end of the ovary is connected with the lateral angle of the uterus by a rounded cord called the **ligament of the ovary**; this band is enclosed between the layers of the broad ligament, and is attached to the lateral angle of the uterus behind the point of entrance of the uterine tube. It is composed chiefly of plain muscle fibres continuous with those of the uterus. The tubal end of the ovary is directly connected with the **ovarian fimbria**—one of the largest of the fimbriæ of the uterine tube (Fig. 622).

Descent of the Ovary.—Like the testes, the ovaries at first lie in the abdominal cavity, and only later attain a position in the pelvis. At birth the ovary lies partly in the abdomen and partly in the pelvis; soon, however, it takes up a position entirely within the true pelvis. As in the male, a gubernaculum is present in the early stages of development. The ligament of the ovary represents the upper part of the gubernaculum, and the round ligament of the uterus the lower part. It is a rare abnormality for the ovary, instead of entering the pelvis, to take a course similar to that of the testis, and pass through the inguinal canal into the labium majus.

Structure of Ovary.—The ovary is for the most part composed of a fibro-areolar tissue, called the **stroma of the ovary**, richly supplied by blood-vessels and nerves. The stroma contains very numerous spindle-shaped cells, white fibres, and some elastic tissue. The surface of the ovary is covered with an epithelium composed of columnar or cubical cells, and continuous with the flat-celled epithelium of the peritoneum forming the mesovarium. The ovarian epithelium is a persistent portion of the germinal epithelium of the embryo which covers the genital ridges, and from which the oöcytes and other cells of the ovarian follicles are derived. The position in which it becomes continuous with the peritoneum can usually be distinguished as a fine white line near the hilum of the ovary. Shining through the epithelium of the fresh ovary (except in old age) are usually to be seen a variable number of small vesicles—the **vesicular ovarian follicles**—in which the egg-cells or oöcytes are contained. The number of follicles visible, and also the size which each follicle reaches before it ruptures and sheds its contents, are by no means constant. When a follicle ruptures and discharges the oöcyte its walls at first collapse, but later the cavity becomes filled with extravasated blood and cellular tissue of a yellowish colour. The resulting structure, called a **corpus luteum**, slowly degenerates unless impregnation has taken place, in which case it develops and becomes larger during pregnancy. As it atrophies the cells of the corpus luteum disappear, and the structure, losing its yellow colour, receives the name of **corpus albicans**. After a time the corpus albicans completely disappears. Owing to the periodic rupture of the ovarian follicles, the surface of the ovary, which is at first smooth and even, becomes in old age dimpled and puckered.

A section through the ovary, especially in the young child, presents in its superficial part a granular appearance which is due to the presence of large numbers of small follicles, or collections of epithelial cells, embedded in the fibro-areolar tissue near the surface of the ovary. The larger follicles lie deeper in the stroma, but when they become fully developed

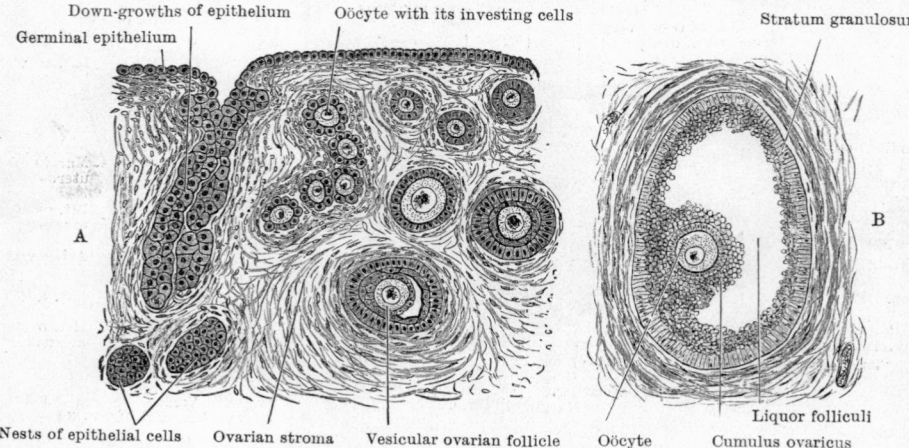

FIG. 623.—A. DIAGRAMMATIC REPRESENTATION OF THE MANNER IN WHICH THE VESICULAR FOLLICLES ARISE DURING THE DEVELOPMENT OF THE OVARY.

B. DIAGRAM ILLUSTRATING THE STRUCTURE OF A RIPE OR VESICULAR OVARIAN FOLLICLE.

they pass towards the surface, where the ripe follicles are often seen projecting slightly and ready to burst. In the deepest part of the ovary the blood-vessels are most numerous, and there also some plain muscle fibres are found.

The oöcytes and the other cells that compose the ovarian follicles are in part derived from the germinal epithelium which covers the developing ovary in the embryo. The epithelium, at first simple, grows down into the underlying tissue in the form of branching tube-like processes, or "egg tubes." This takes place during fœtal development, and the branching cellular processes so formed become broken up, within the stroma, into little nests or clumps of cells, each of which becomes a follicle. In the human embryo the earliest formed nests of epithelial cells arise *in situ* and only at a later stage become connected with the "egg tubes," derived from the ovarian epithelium. From the beginning some cells of the egg tubes are larger than the others; they become the future ova, while the cells round them become the investing cells of the follicle. The investing cells, at first flattened, form a single layer round each oöcyte. Later, becoming columnar, as the follicle increases in size and sinks more deeply in the stroma, those cells divide in such a manner that the oöcyte becomes surrounded by a double layer of cells. Fluid—**liquor folliculi**—accumulates between the two cellular layers, except at one place, where the inner cells surrounding the ovum remain attached to the outer layer or **stratum granulosum**. To the inner cellular mass enclosing the oöcyte the term **cumulus ovaricus** is applied (Fig. 623). The ripe follicle contains a relatively large amount of fluid, and the surrounding stroma becomes differentiated to form a capsule or **theca folliculi**. The capsule is composed of an *inner coat* which is vascular in character and an *outer coat* which is more fibrous in structure. In the young child there are numerous small follicles in the superficial parts of the ovary, but there is no definite evidence to show that any new ova are produced in the human ovary after birth. In some mammals—ferret (Robinson), mouse (Allen), rat (Arai)—new ova and new follicles are formed throughout the period of reproductive life.

The appearance and structure of the ripe ova are described on pp. 19-25.

Vessels and Nerves of Ovary.—The **ovarian arteries**, corresponding to the testicular arteries of the male, are a pair of long slender vessels which spring from the front of the aorta, below the level of origin of the renal vessels. Each gains the true pelvis in the infundibulo-pelvic ligament, and enters the ovary at its mesovarian border. Close to the ovary the ovarian artery anastomoses with branches of the **uterine artery**. The blood is returned by a series of communicating **veins**, similar to the *pampiniform plexus* in the male.

The **lymph vessels** of the ovary run with those from the upper part of the uterus to end in the lymph glands beside the aorta.

The **nerves** of the ovary are derived chiefly from a plexus which accompanies the ovarian artery, and is continuous above with the renal plexus. Other fibres are derived from the lower part of the aortic plexus, and join the plexus on the ovarian artery. The afferent impulses from the ovary reach the central nervous system through the posterior root fibres of the tenth thoracic nerve.

UTERINE TUBES

The **uterine tubes** are a pair of ducts which convey the oöcytes, discharged from the follicles of the ovaries, to the cavity of the uterus (Fig. 622 and Pl. LVI). Each tube is about four inches in length, and opens at one end into the pelvic cavity near the ovary, and at the other end by a smaller opening into the lateral part of the uterine cavity. The tube is enclosed in a fold of peritoneum called the **mesosalpinx**, which is a portion of the broad ligament of the uterus.

The **pelvic opening** of the tube is only about 2 mm. in diameter when its walls are relaxed, and much narrower when the muscular coat of the tube is contracted. It is placed at the bottom of a funnel-like expansion of the tube called the **infundibulum**, the margins of which are produced into a number of irregular processes, called **fimbriæ**, many of which are branched or fringed. The surface of the fimbriæ which looks into the cavity of the infundibulum is covered with a mucous membrane continuous with that lining the tube, while the outer surface is clothed with peritoneum. The mucous surfaces of the larger fimbriæ present ridges and grooves which are continued into the folds and furrows of the mucous coat of the tube. One of the fimbriæ, usually much larger than the rest, is connected either directly or indirectly with the tubal end of the ovary, and to it the name **ovarian fimbria** is applied. The part of the tube continuous with the infundibulum is called the **ampulla**. It is the widest and longest portion of the tube, is usually slightly tortuous and of varying diameter, being in some places slightly constricted and in others dilated. The ampulla ends in the narrower, thicker-walled, and much shorter **isthmus** of the tube, which joins the lateral angle of the uterus. The uterine part of the tube is embedded in the uterine wall, which it traverses to reach the cavity of the uterus (Fig. 622). The **uterine opening** is smaller than the pelvic opening, being about 1 mm. in diameter. The lumen of the canal gradually increases in width as it is traced from the uterus towards the ovary.

Course of the Uterine Tube.—From the lateral angle of the uterus, the uterine tube is directed at first horizontally towards the uterine end of the ovary, and then upwards in relation to the medial side of the mesovarian border, until it reaches the tubal end. Next arching backwards, it descends along the free border of the ovary and rests against its medial surface (Fig. 621). The looped portion of the tube often covers almost the entire medial surface of the ovary. The fimbriated end is applied against the free border and lower part of the medial surface of the ovary, and from it the ovarian fimbria passes upwards to gain attachment to the tubal end.

The fimbriated end of the uterine tube lies in the abdominal cavity until the ovary in its descent has entered the true pelvis.

Structure of the Uterine Tubes.—The wall of each tube is composed of a number of concentric layers. First a **serous coat** of peritoneum, under which there is a thin **subserous coat** of loose areolar tissue containing many vessels and nerves. Internal to the subserous coat there is the **muscular coat** composed of two strata of plain muscle fibres—a more superficial thin stratum of longitudinally arranged fibres, and a deeper, thicker layer, the fibres of which are circularly disposed. Inside the circular muscular coat is a *submucous layer*, and then the lining membrane or **mucous coat**. In the part of the tube near the uterus the muscular layer is thicker than towards the other end, and in the isthmus it forms the chief part of the wall. The mucous membrane, on the contrary, is thickest towards the fimbriated end, and there it forms the chief part of the tube wall. The stratum of circular muscle fibres is especially well developed near the uterus. The mucous membrane is thrown into numerous longitudinal folds, which in the ampulla are exceedingly complex, the larger folds bearing on their surface numerous smaller

47

ones. In transverse sections of that part of the tube, examined under the [microscope, the folds of the mucous membrane look like large branching processes projecting into the lumen of the tube and almost completely filling it. The mucous membrane is covered with a ciliated epithelium, the cilia of which tend to drive the fluid contents of the tube towards the uterus.

Vessels and Nerves of Uterine Tube.—The chief **artery** of the uterine tube is a tubal branch of the *uterine artery*, but it receives small branches of the *ovarian artery* also. The **veins** of the tube pour their blood partly into the *uterine* and partly into the *ovarian* veins. The **lymph vessels** run with those of the ovary and the upper part of the uterus to the lymph glands beside the aorta. The **nerves** are derived from the plexus that supplies the ovary, and also from the plexus in connexion with the uterus. The afferent fibres are believed to belong to the eleventh and twelfth thoracic and the first lumbar nerves.

EP-OÖPHORON AND PAR-OÖPHORON

The ep-oöphoron and the par-oöphoron are two vestigial structures found between the layers of the broad ligament.

The **ep-oöphoron** lies in the mesosalpinx between the uterine tube and the ovary. In the adult it consists of a number of small rudimentary blind tubules lined with an epithelium. One of the tubules—the **duct of the ep-oöphoron**—lies close to the uterine tube, and runs nearly parallel with it. It is joined by a number of **tubules** which enter it at right angles from the neighbourhood of the ovary. The duct is a persistent portion of the mesonephric [Wolffian] duct, and represents the canal of the epididymis; the tubules are derived from the mesonephros and represent the efferent ducts of the testis (and probably also the ductuli aberrantes of the canal of the epididymis).

One or more small pedunculated cystic structures, called **vesicular appendices,** are often seen near the infundibulum of the uterine tube. They are supposed to represent portions of the cephalic end of the mesonephric duct.

The **par-oöphoron** is a collection of very minute tubules that lie in the mesosalpinx nearer the uterus than the ep-oöphoron. They represent the paradidymis in the male, and are derived from the part of the mesonephros which lies nearer the caudal end of the embryo. Though sometimes visible in the child at birth, the par-oöphoron in the adult can be recognised only by microscopic examination.

UTERUS

The **uterus** or womb is a hollow, thick-walled, muscular organ placed in the true pelvis between the bladder in front and the rectum behind. The ova discharged from the ovary enter the uterus through the uterine tubes, and, if fertilisation has taken place, undergo their development within it. In form the uterus is more or less pear-shaped, the wide, free end of the organ projecting forwards and upwards, while the lower, more constricted part is connected with the vagina. The usual length of the adult uterus (when non-pregnant) is three inches, its greatest breadth is nearly two inches, and its maximum thickness is about one inch. The upper, larger portion of the uterus is slightly flattened from before backwards, and is separable into two parts called the fundus and the body. The lower, more cylindrical part is called the cervix (Fig. 622).

The **fundus uteri** is the free, convex end, or that part of the uterus which lies above the level of a line joining the points of entrance of the uterine tubes.

The **body of the uterus** diminishes slightly in width when traced from fundus to cervix. The two **margins** separate the **vesical surface** from the **intestinal surface** of the body. Both the surfaces are convex, but the intestinal is much the more rounded. The vesical surface rests against the upper surface of the bladder, from which it is separated by the utero-vesical pouch. The intestinal surface forms the chief part of the anterior wall of the deep recess situated between the uterus and rectum, and is usually in contact with some part of the small intestine or the pelvic colon. The broad ligament passes laterally from each margin of the organ.

The **cervix uteri** is cylindrical, and at its commencement it is sometimes marked off from the body by a slight constriction. Its length is about one inch, and its lower end, tapering slightly, enters the upper part of the vagina. The cervix is attached to the margin of the opening in the vaginal wall through which it passes, and a **supravaginal portion** of the cervix is thus marked off from a **vaginal portion**.

In the vaginal portion there is an opening—the **external os uteri**—through which the cavity of the uterus communicates with that of the vagina. In a uterus which has not been pregnant the os is a short transverse slit, but in women who have borne children the slit is longer and has an irregular outline. The *anterior lip* of the os is thicker, shorter, and more rounded than the *posterior lip*, which is at a slightly lower level. The cervix enters the vagina through the upper part of its anterior wall, and the external os is directed backwards and downwards against the upper part of the posterior vaginal wall (Fig. 620).

Cavity of Uterus.—In comparison with the size of the organ, the **cavity of the uterus** is small, owing to the great thickness of the uterine wall. In the body the cavity is merely a chink with a triangular outline between the upper and lower walls (Figs. 620, 622, and Pl. LVI). The base of the triangle corresponds to a line drawn between the openings of the uterine tubes, while the apex is directed towards the cervix. The sides of the triangle are convex inwards towards the cavity. The cavity of the body becomes continuous with that of the cervix by an opening called the **internal os uteri**, which is a little smaller and more circular than the external os. The cavity of the cervix, or **cervical canal**, extends from the internal os to the external os, where it opens into the vagina. It is a spindle-shaped passage, being narrower at its ends than in its middle part. Sections show also that its antero-posterior diameter is shorter than its transverse owing to an approximation of its anterior and posterior walls. In the body of the uterus the walls of the cavity are smooth and even, but in the cervical canal the mucous membrane forms a remarkable series of folds called the **arbor vitæ** [plicæ palmatæ]. They consist of an anterior and a posterior longitudinal fold or ridge from which a large number of secondary folds or rugæ branch off obliquely upwards and laterally (Fig. 622, B).

Position and Relations of Uterus.—The position occupied by the uterus varies with the conditions of the neighbouring organs. The cervical part is, however, much more firmly fixed in place than the body and fundus, which possess a considerable amount of mobility. Usually the level of the external os corresponds to that of a horizontal plane passing through the upper margin of the pubic symphysis, but its exact level is variable. The uterus rarely lies exactly in the median plane, but bends a little to one or other side—most frequently towards the right.

The vesical surface of the uterus rests against the bladder, and follows the rising or falling of the upper wall of the bladder as it becomes filled or emptied. When the bladder is empty the long axis of the uterus points forwards and upwards, and the organ is said to be in an *anteverted* position. Also, the long axis of the uterus is bent on itself where the body joins the cervix, and so the organ is said to be *anteflexed*. The anteflexion is due to the fact that the more rigid cervix is fixed, while the movable upper part of the uterus sinks—following the bladder wall. With the empty condition of the bladder the angle between the long axis of the uterus and that of the vagina is about a right angle. When the bladder becomes filled the anteversion and anteflexion of the uterus become less marked owing to the body and fundus being pushed backwards. Finally, if the rectum is empty and the bladder very much distended the uterus is pushed so much backwards that the long axis of the organ may nearly correspond to that of the vagina. The uterus is then said to be *retroverted*. Anteriorly, a part of the peritoneal cavity intervenes between the uterus and the bladder, but farther back the two organs are separated merely by a small quantity of areolar tissue.

The intestinal surface of the uterus looks into the recto-uterine pouch, and is usually, like the fundus, in relation to some loops of the small intestine or the pelvic colon. Laterally the uterus is related to the broad ligament. The terminal portion of the ureter passes downwards, medially, and a little forwards about three-quarters of an inch from the lateral side of the cervix.

On each side of the cervix uteri and upper part of the vagina there is an interval between the diverging layers of the broad ligament, in which numerous large vessels lie. The vessels are surrounded by bundles of smooth muscle fibres and by loose fatty tissue which is continued upwards for a considerable distance between the layers of the broad ligament. The loose tissue, which is of surgical importance, has received the name **parametrium**.

Connexions of Uterus and its Relations to Peritoneum.—In addition to the uterine tubes and the vagina, the uterus has other important connexions. Some of them are simply peritoneal folds passing from the uterus to neighbouring structures; others contain fibrous tissue or plain muscle fibres.

The peritoneum covering the fundus of the uterus is continued down over the vesical surface as far as the junction of the body and cervix, where it leaves the uterus to be reflected on to the bladder   The peritoneal recess between the bladder and the uterus is called the **utero-vesical pouch**.   Below the level of that pouch the

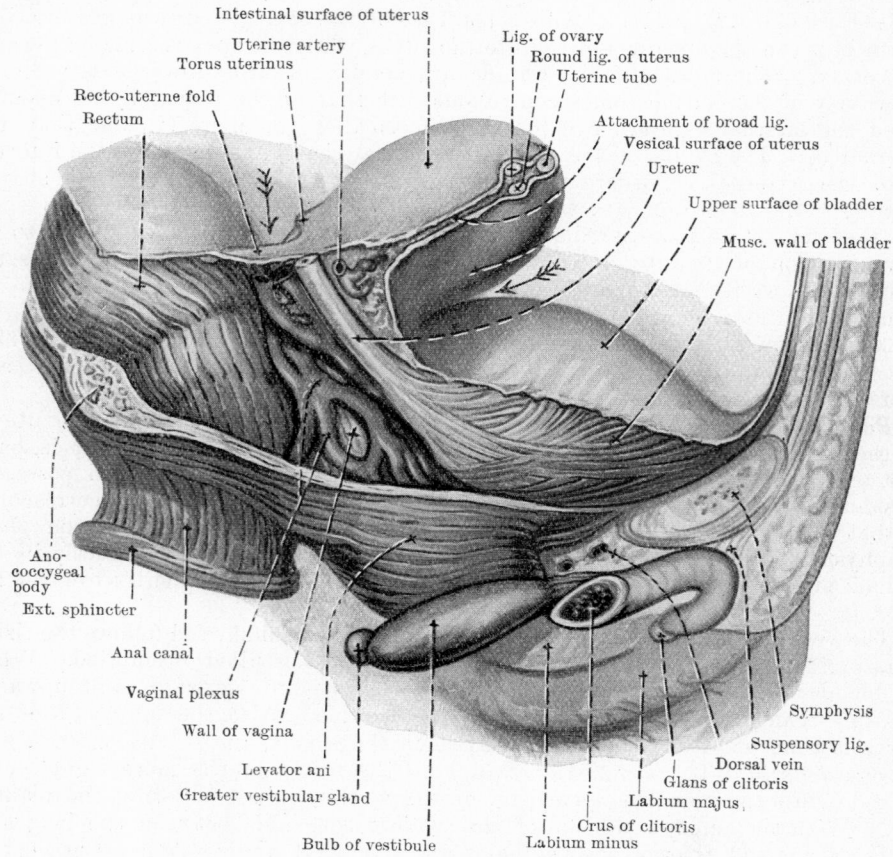

Fig. 624.—Model of a Dissection of the Female Pelvic Organs.   (A. F. D.)
The arrows point to the utero-vesical and recto-vaginal pouches.

anterior surface of the cervix is connected by areolar tissue with the wall of the bladder.   The peritoneum covers the whole of the intestinal surface of the uterus —except the small portion of the cervix which projects into the vagina—and is continued to such a depth that it invests a small portion of the posterior wall of the vagina before it is reflected on to the rectum (Fig. 624).   The deep pouch that separates the uterus and vagina from the rectum is called the **recto-uterine** or **recto-vaginal pouch** and its entrance is bounded on each side by a crescentic peritoneal fold which passes from the back of the cervix uteri to the dorsal wall of the pelvis, and ends near the side of the rectum.   These folds are known as the **recto-uterine folds**, and each contains between its layers a considerable amount of fibrous and plain muscular tissue.   A few of the muscular fibres, which are continuous with the uterine wall, pass backwards to reach the rectum and constitute the **recto-uterine muscle**; others are said to gain an attachment to the front of the sacrum, and form a *utero-sacral ligament*. In many cases the recto-uterine folds become continuous with each other across the back of the cervix uteri, and form, in that position, a transverse ridge termed the *torus uterinus* (Fig. 622).

The peritoneum of the vesical and intestinal surfaces, leaving the uterus along each margin to reach the side wall of the pelvis, forms the broad ligament of the uterus.

The **broad ligament of the uterus** is a wide peritoneal fold which passes from the margin of the uterus to the side wall of the pelvis, and contains between its layers several important structures (Fig. 622). The plane of the medial part of the ligament is determined by the position of the uterus. When the uterus is placed normally, one surface of the ligament looks downwards and slightly forwards, while the other looks upwards and backwards. Near its attachment to the pelvis the ligament is placed more vertically. The free edge of the ligament contains the uterine tube, and follows the course pursued by that structure. Thus, in the undisturbed condition of parts, it at first passes laterally towards the uterine end of the ovary, and then ascends to arch over the tubal end. Owing to the course pursued by the uterine tube round the ovary, the broad ligament forms a kind of curtain over the ovary, which lies in the little pocket—*bursa ovarica*—so formed (Figs. 620 and 621).

The various structures in connexion with the broad ligament are most easily demonstrated when the ligament is spread out as flat as possible (Fig. 622).

The ovary is connected with the upper layer of the broad ligament by two extremely short layers, called the **mesovarium**, which, passing to the hilum, enclose the ovarian vessels and nerves as they approach the ovary.

The part of the broad ligament which slings the uterine tube is called the **mesosalpinx**. In the normal position of the parts the mesosalpinx is folded round the ovary in the manner described above to form the bursa ovarica ; and it contains the ep-oöphoron and par-oöphoron (Fig. 622).

The part of the broad ligament below the level of the mesosalpinx is termed the **mesometrium**. It contains numerous blood-vessels and nerves, a considerable amount of fibro-areolar tissue, and unstriped muscle fibres, especially near its root, where it is attached to the pelvic floor. The ureter and the uterine vessels lie near its root. The fibrous and smooth muscle tissue which occupy the interval between the layers of the ligament, immediately below the uterine artery, form what is known as the *lateral cervical ligament* of the uterus. This ligament is continuous with the dense tissue which surrounds the branches of the internal iliac artery, and in sagittal section has a triangular outline near its attachment to the cervix uteri and to the lateral vault of the vagina (see Figs. 622, B and 624).

The highest part of the lateral portion of the broad ligament forms the **infundibulo-pelvic ligament** [lig. suspensorium ovarii], and contains between its layers the ovarian vessels and nerves as they enter and leave the true pelvis (Fig. 621).

The **ligament of the ovary** is a rounded fibrous cord, about one inch in length, which is attached laterally to the uterine end of the ovary, and medially to the lateral angle of the uterus immediately behind the entrance of the uterine tube. The ligament is largely composed of unstriped muscle fibres continuous with those of the uterus, and is enclosed in a slight ridge or fold of the upper layer of the broad ligament.

The **round ligament of the uterus** is a narrow, flat band attached to the uterus a little below the opening of the uterine tube. Near the uterus it contains numerous plain muscle fibres which are continuous with those of the uterine wall ; more laterally it is composed chiefly of fibrous tissue. Lying in the anterior part of the broad ligament, it reaches the wall of the true pelvis, and is then directed forwards and slightly upwards to cross the umbilical artery and the pelvic brim. After it has reached the pelvic wall its course is comparable to that of the vas deferens, and, like the vas, it leaves the abdomen to traverse the inguinal canal (Figs. 620 and 621). It finally ends in the subcutaneous tissue and skin of the labium majus. Its terminal part is composed of fibrous tissue only.

47 *a*

In some cases a minute diverticulum of the peritoneal cavity accompanies the round ligament through the abdominal wall. It is a vestige of the **processus vaginalis** of the peritoneum which is formed in the embryo in both sexes.

Supports of the Uterus.—During life the uterus is maintained in its normal anteverted and anteflexed position by the attachment of the cervix to the vaginal wall and by the pull of the smooth muscle fibres in the round ligaments, the utero-sacral ligaments (Fig. 622), and, in greater quantity, in the lateral cervical ligaments. The cervical ligaments fix not only the cervix uteri but also the upper end of the vagina. Inferiorly the uterus, like the other pelvic organs, is supported by the levatores ani muscles. The pressure and counter-pressure exerted by the bladder, colon, and rectum also influence the position of the uterus.

Structure of the Uterus.—The uterine wall is composed of three chief layers—the serous, the muscular, and the mucous coats.

The **serous coat,** or *perimetrium,* is the peritoneal covering. Over the fundus and body it is very firmly adherent to the deeper layers, and cannot be easily peeled off without tearing either it or the underlying muscular tissue. Near the lateral borders of the uterus the peritoneum is less firmly attached, and over the back of the cervix it may readily be stripped off without injury to the underlying structures.

The **muscular coat** is composed of unstriped fibres, and forms the chief part of the uterine wall. Inferiorly the muscular coat of the uterus becomes continuous with that of the vagina. The more superficial layer of the muscular coat sends prolongations into the recto-uterine folds, into the round and broad ligaments of the uterus, and into the ovarian ligaments. Other fibres join the walls of the uterine tubes. The main branches of the blood-vessels and nerves of the uterus lie among the muscle fibres. In the deeper layers of the muscular coat a considerable amount of fibrous tissue and some elastic fibres are to be found. The muscular coat of the cervix contains more fibrous and elastic tissue than that of the body, and hence its greater firmness and rigidity.

The deeper and thicker part of the muscular tissue of the uterus is considered by some anatomists to represent a lamina muscularis mucosæ, and is therefore described as part of the mucous coat. The deep and superficial portions of the muscular coat are, however, quite continuous, and there is no representative of a submucous vascular layer of tissue such as separates the muscular coat from the lamina muscularis mucosæ in the alimentary canal.

The **mucous coat** in the body of the uterus is smooth and soft and covered with columnar ciliated epithelium. Simple tubular glands, also lined with a ciliated epithelium, are present in the mucous membrane, and their deeper parts penetrate into the muscular coat. In the cervix the mucous coat is firmer and more fibrous than in the body, and its surface is not smooth but presents a number of peculiarly disposed ridges which have been mentioned already (p. 739). Like the mucous membrane of the body of the uterus, that of the cervix is covered with a ciliated epithelium which passes into squamous epithelium just inside the external os of the uterus. In addition to unbranched tubular glands, numerous slightly branched glands are found in the cervix uteri. Both kinds of glands are lined with ciliated epithelium. In many cases little clear retention cysts—ovules of Naboth—are to be seen in the cervical mucous membrane. They arise as a result of obstruction at the mouths of the glands.

Differences in the Uterus at Different Ages.—At birth the cervix uteri is relatively large, and its cavity is not distinctly marked off from that of the body by an internal os. At that time also the arbor vitæ extends throughout the whole length of the uterus. The organ grows slowly until just before puberty, when its growth is rapid for a time. As the body increases in size the mucous membrane becomes smooth and the arbor vitæ becomes restricted to the cervix. In women who have borne children the cavity remains permanently a little wider and larger than in cases where the uterus has never been pregnant. In old age the uterine wall becomes harder and has a paler colour than in the young subject.

Variations.—In rare cases the uterus may be divided by a septum into two distinct cavities, or its lateral angles may be produced into straight or curved processes, called "horns." The latter abnormality recalls the appearance of the bicornuate uterus of some animals. Both the above conditions arise from an arrest in the fusion of the two separate tubes— the paramesonephric [Müllerian] ducts—which normally unite in the embryo to form the uterus.

Periodic Changes in the Uterine Wall.—At each menstrual period a remarkable series of changes occurs which results in a periodic shedding of the superficial parts of the uterine mucous membrane. For a few days before menstruation begins, the mucous membrane gradually thickens and becomes more vascular, while at the same time its surface becomes uneven. Soon the superficial parts of the mucous membrane disintegrate and hæmorrhage takes place from the small superficial blood-vessels. In that way a hæmorrhagic discharge is caused, and the superficial parts of the uterine mucous membrane are shed at each period. When menstruation is over the mucous membrane is rapidly regenerated.

Pregnant Uterus.—The pregnant uterus increases rapidly in size and weight, so that from being three inches in length and a little over one ounce in weight, it becomes by the eighth month of pregnancy about seven or eight inches in length and sometimes as much as two pounds in weight. In shape the uterus is then oval or rounded, with a thick wall composed chiefly of muscle fibres arranged in distinct layers. The rounded fundus is very prominent. The round ligaments are stronger, and the layers of the medial parts of the broad ligaments become separated by the growth of the uterus between them. The blood-vessels, especially the arteries, are very large and tortuous.   The changes which occur in the mucous membrane of the pregnant uterus are described on p. 64 *et seq.*

Vessels and Nerves of Uterus.—The uterus receives its **arterial supply** mainly from the *uterine arteries*, which are branches of the internal iliac arteries, and also from the *ovarian* branches of the aorta. The vessels derived from these two sources communicate freely with one another. Each uterine artery, reaching the side of the uterus, divides into a large branch, which passes forwards to supply the body and fundus, and a much smaller branch, which passes downwards to supply the cervix. The vessels distributed to the body and fundus have an exceedingly tortuous course.   The branches of the uterine artery, having entered the muscular coat, break up within its deeper layers into smaller twigs, which supply the muscular

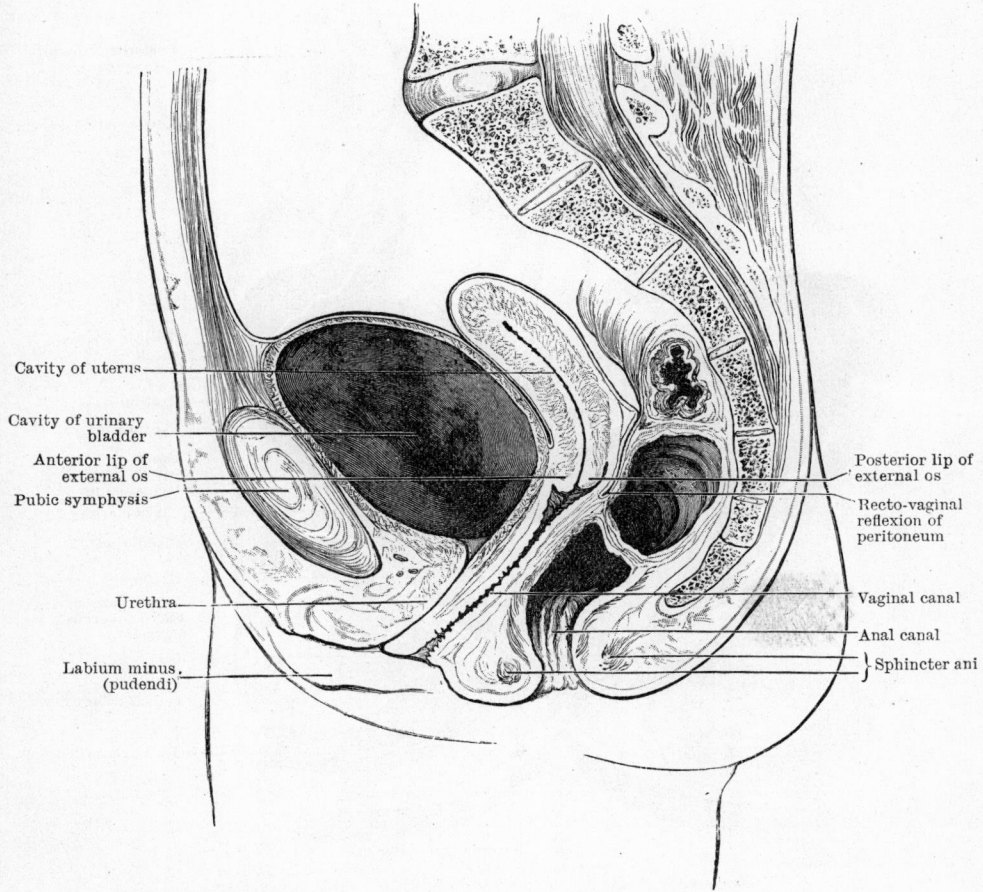

FIG. 625.—MEDIAN SECTION OF THE PELVIS IN AN ADULT FEMALE.   (A. F. D.)

The cavity of the uterus is indicated diagrammatically.

tissue and the mucous coat. The small uterine branch from the ovarian artery reaches the uterus in the region of the lateral angle. During pregnancy the arteries become enormously enlarged.

Numerous thin-walled **veins** form a plexus at the side of the cervix and pour their blood into the tributaries of the internal iliac vein [v. hypogastrica].

The **lymph vessels** from the fundus of the uterus join those from the ovary, and end in *aortic lymph glands.* One or two run along the round ligament to the *superficial inguinal lymph glands.* The lymph vessels from the cervix run to the sacral glands and all the iliac groups ; those from the body end chiefly in the external iliac glands.

The **nerves** of the uterus are derived chiefly from a plexus—*utero-vaginal*—placed in the neighbourhood of the cervix uteri. Superiorly this plexus is continuous with the hypogastric plexus, but it also receives fibres from the second, third, and fourth sacral nerves.

Clinical observations indicate that afferent impulses reach the central nervous system from the uterus through the posterior roots of the tenth, eleventh, and twelfth thoracic nerves, the first lumbar, and the second, third, and fourth sacral nerves.

VAGINA

The **vagina** is a passage about three inches in length, open at its lower end, and communicating above with the cavity of the uterus. The passage is directed downwards and forwards, describing a slight curve which is convex backwards. The axis of the vagina forms with that of the uterus an angle which is open forwards. This angle is usually a little greater than a right angle, but varies

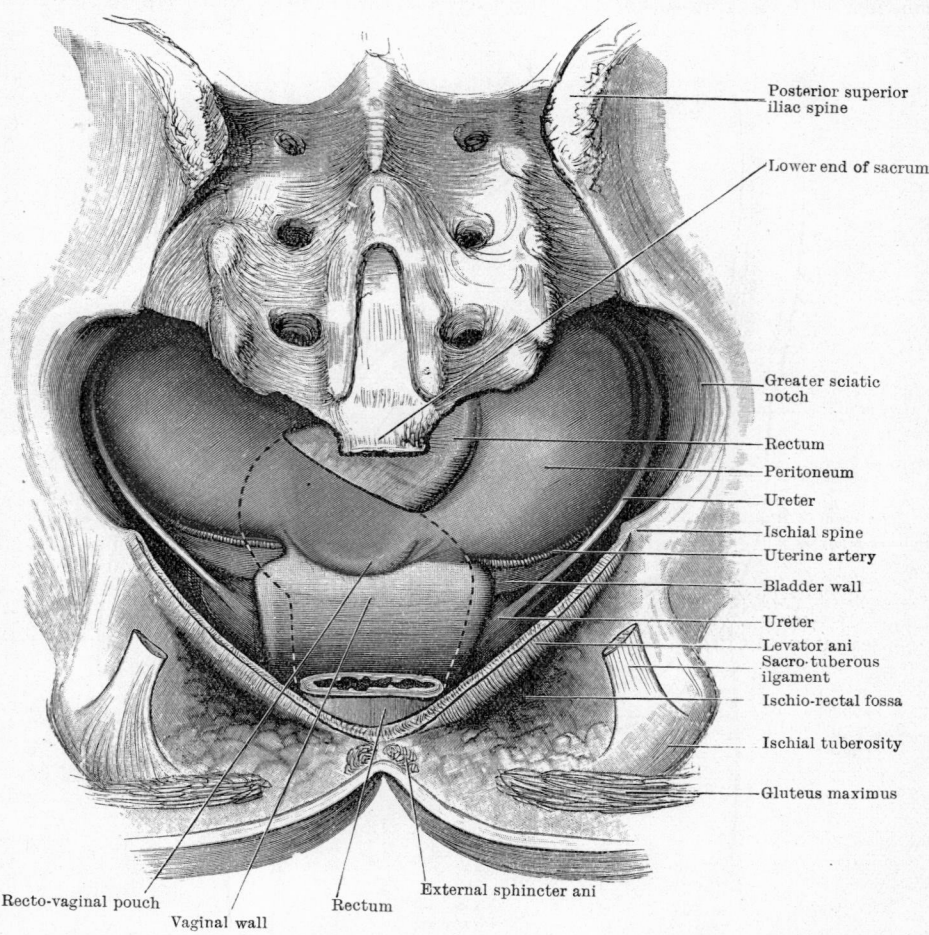

FIG. 626.—VAGINA, BASE OF BLADDER, AND RECTO-VAGINAL POUCH FROM BEHIND. (A. F. D.).

The coccyx and the sacro-tuberous and sacro-spinous ligaments have been removed. The levatores ani have been separated and drawn laterally. A considerable portion of the rectum has been removed, but its position is indicated by the dotted lines. The recto-vaginal pouch is probably not quite so deep as usual. The triangular interval between the ureter and uterine artery was filled by a mass of fibro-muscular tissue, forming the lateral cervical ligament of the uterus.

with the condition of the neighbouring viscera (p. 739). Its anterior and posterior walls are in contact except at its upper end, where the cervix is inserted; and that is its widest part also. In transverse section the lower part is usually an H-shaped cleft, the middle part a simple transverse slit, while the lumen of the upper portion is more open. The cervix uteri enters the vagina through the upper portion of its anterior wall (Fig. 625). As more of the posterior part of the cervix than of the anterior part projects into the vagina, a deeper recess is formed between the vaginal wall and the cervix behind than in front or laterally. The term **anterior fornix** is applied to the recess in front, **posterior fornix** to the deeper recess behind, and **lateral fornix** to the recess on each side. The *anterior* wall of the vagina is shorter than the *posterior*—the former being about three inches in length, the latter about three and a half inches. At its lower end the vagina opens into the pudendal cleft between the labia minora. The opening is partly closed in the virgin by a thin crescentic or annular fold, called the **hymen**, torn fragments of which persist round the opening, as the **carunculæ hymenales**, after the fold itself has been ruptured.

Relations of Vagina.—The anterior wall of the vagina in its upper part lies against the base of the bladder, but is separated from it by loose areolar tissue. Lower down, the anterior wall is intimately connected with the urethra in the median plane (Fig. 625). The posterior wall in its upper portion is covered for a distance of one-quarter to three-quarters of an inch with peritoneum, which there forms the anterior boundary of the deepest part of the recto-uterine pouch. The floor of the pouch practically corresponds to the level of the ischial spines. Lower down, the posterior wall lies close against the rectum, from which it is separated by a layer of areolar tissue. As the orifice of the vagina is approached the anal canal and the vagina become separated by a considerable interval, which is occupied by a mass of fibrous and fatty tissue called the *perineal body*. On each side the vagina is supported in its upper part by the lower fibres of the lateral cervical ligaments of the uterus and lower down by the levatores ani muscles. The terminal part of the ureter lies not far from the side wall of the upper part of the vagina, as it passes from above and behind downwards, medially and a little forwards to reach the bladder. Near its termination the vagina pierces the perineal membrane, and is related on each side to the greater vestibular gland, the bulb of the vestibule, and the bulbo-spongiosus muscle.

Structure of the Vagina.—The vaginal wall has a **muscular coat** composed of unstriped muscle fibres, most of which are longitudinally disposed. Towards the lower end, circularly disposed bundles of striped muscle fibres, some of which are continuous with those forming a part of the urethral wall, are found in the muscular coat. The **mucous coat** is thick and is corrugated by a number of transverse ridges or elevations known as **vaginal rugæ**; and it is covered with stratified squamous epithelium. In addition to the transverse rugæ, a slightly marked longitudinal ridge is to be seen on the anterior and on the posterior wall of the vagina. These receive the name **columns of rugæ**, and, like the transverse rugæ, are seen best in young subjects and in the lower part of the vagina. The urethra lies in close relationship to the anterior column in its lower part, and hence that portion of the column is called the **urethral ridge**. Between the muscular and mucous coats there is a thin layer of vascular tissue which resembles erectile tissue; and in the mucous coat there are small nodules of lymphoid tissue.

The vaginal wall is surrounded by a layer of loose vascular areolar tissue containing numerous large communicating veins.

Vessels and Nerves of Vagina.—The arteries are the *vaginal artery*, the vaginal branch of the *uterine artery*, the vaginal branches of the *middle rectal artery* [a. hæmorrhoidalis media], and branches of the internal pudendal. The veins form a plexus around the vaginal wall, and drain their blood into the tributaries of the *internal iliac*.

The **lymph-vessels** from the upper part of the vagina join the *external* and *internal iliac glands*, while those from the lower part end in the *superficial inguinal glands*.

The **nerves** of the vagina are derived from the *utero-vaginal plexus* and from the *vesical plexus*. Other fibres are derived directly from the *third* and *fourth sacral nerves*.

FEMALE EXTERNAL GENITAL ORGANS

The collective term **pudendum muliebre**, or **vulva**, is applied to the female external genital organs, *i.e.* to the mons pubis and the labia majora and the structures which lie between the labia.

Labia Majora.—The labia majora represent the scrotum in the male, and form the largest part of the female external genital organs. They are the boundaries of the **pudendal cleft**, into which the urethra and vagina open. Each labium is a prominent rounded fold of skin, narrow behind where it approaches the anus, but increasing in size as it passes forwards and upwards to end in a median elevation—the **mons pubis**. The mons pubis lies over the pubic symphysis, and, like the labia majora, it is composed chiefly of fatty and areolar tissue, and is covered with hair. The skin of the lateral, convex surface of each labium majus contains numerous sebaceous glands and resembles that of the scrotum in the male, but the medial, flatter surface is smooth, and has a more delicate integumentary covering.	In some cases the posterior, narrow ends of the labia majora are connected across the middle line, in front of the anus, by a slight transverse fold—the **posterior commissure.**

Usually the mons and the labia majora are the only visible parts of the external genital organs, since the labia are in contact with each other, and completely conceal the structures within the pudendal cleft.

The round ligament of the uterus ends in the skin and fibro-fatty tissue of the labium majus. The superficial layer of the subcutaneous tissue resembles that of the scrotum, but contains no muscular fibres.

The **nerve-supply** corresponds with that of the scrotum—the anterior part of each labium being supplied by the branches of the ilio-inguinal nerve, and the posterior part by branches from the pudendal and by the perineal branch from the posterior cutaneous nerve of the thigh. The **blood-vessels** are derived from the external pudendal branches of the femoral and from the labial branches of the internal pudendal vessels.

Labia Minora.

—The labia minora are a pair of much smaller and narrower longitudinal folds of skin usually completely hidden in the cleft between the labia majora. Their posterior parts diminish in size and end by gradually joining the medial surfaces of the labia majora. In the young subject a slightly raised transverse fold is usually seen connecting the pos-

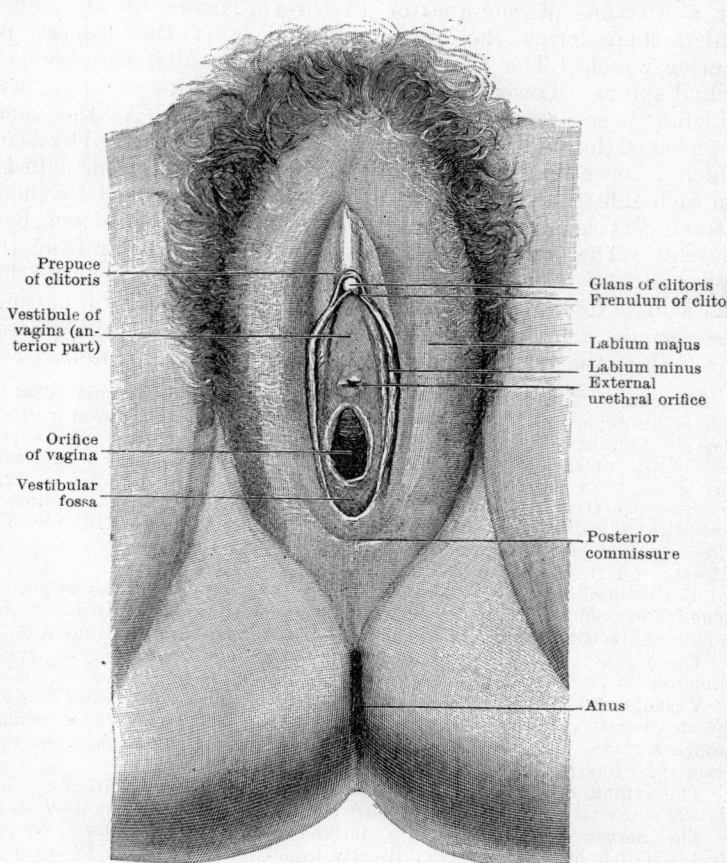

Prepuce of clitoris

Vestibule of vagina (anterior part)

Orifice of vagina

Vestibular fossa

Glans of clitoris
Frenulum of clitoris

Labium majus
Labium minus
External urethral orifice

Posterior commissure

Anus

FIG. 627.—FEMALE EXTERNAL GENITAL ORGANS. (A. F. D.)
The frenulum labiorum is seen stretching across behind the vestibular fossa.

terior ends of the labia minora ; to this fold the term **frenulum labiorum pudendi** is applied.	Traced forwards, each labium minus divides into two portions— a lateral and a medial. The lateral portions of the two labia unite over the glans clitoridis, and form for it a fold or covering called the **prepuce of the clitoris.**	The medial portions, uniting at an acute angle, join the glans and form the **frenulum of the clitoris.** The skin of the labia minora resembles that on the medial surface of the labia majora, being smooth, moist, and pink in colour. The medial surfaces of the labia minora are in contact with each other, and their lateral surfaces with the labia majora.

The openings of the urethra and vagina are in the median plane, between the labia minora, which must be separated to bring them into view.

Vestibule of Vagina.—The vestibule is the name applied to the space between the labia minora. In its floor are the openings of the urethra, the vagina, and the minute ducts of the greater vestibular glands.

The **vestibular fossa** [f. navicularis] is the part of the vestibule placed behind the vaginal opening and in front of the frenulum labiorum pudendi.

The **external urethral orifice** lies immediately in front of that of the vagina, and is about one inch behind the glans clitoridis. The opening has the appearance of a vertical slit, or of an inverted V-shaped cleft, the slightly prominent margins of which are in contact. Sometimes on each side of the urethral orifice there may be seen the minute opening of the para-urethral duct (see p. 712).

The **orifice of the vagina** varies in appearance with the condition of the **hymen**. When the hymen is intact the opening is small, and is seen only when that membrane is put on the stretch. When the hymen has been ruptured the opening is much larger, and round its margins are often seen small projections— **carunculæ hymenales**—which are to be looked upon as persistent fragments of the hymen.

The **hymen** is a thin membranous fold which partially closes the lower end of the vagina, and is perforated usually in front of its middle point. The position of the opening gives the fold, when stretched, a crescentic appearance. The opening in the hymen is sometimes cleanly cut, sometimes fringed. The membrane is not stretched tightly across the lower end of the vagina, but is so ample that it projects downwards into the pudendal cleft. The opening is thus a median slit whose margins are normally in contact. Developmentally the hymen appears to be a portion of the vagina.

On each side of the vaginal opening, and close against the medial side of the attached margin of the labium minus, is the minute opening of the duct of the **greater vestibular gland**. It is usually just large enough to be visible to the unaided eye.

Numerous minute mucous glands—the **lesser vestibular glands**—open into the vestibule between the urethral and vaginal orifices.

Clitoris.—The clitoris is the morphological equivalent of the penis, and has a body, a pair of crura, and a minute glans on the summit of the body. Unlike the penis, the clitoris is not traversed by the urethra.

The **body** is composed for the most part of erectile tissue resembling that of the penis. It is about an inch in length, and is bent upon itself, forming an angle open downwards. It tapers towards its distal end, which is covered by the glans. It is enclosed in a dense fibrous coat, and is divided by an incomplete **septum** into a pair of cylindrical **corpora cavernosa clitoridis**, which diverge from each other at the root of the clitoris to form the **crura clitoridis**. A fibrous *suspensory ligament* passes from the body of the clitoris to the pubic symphysis (Fig. 628).

The **glans clitoridis** is a small mass of erectile tissue fitted over the pointed end of the body, and, like the glans penis, it is covered with a very sensitive epithelium. The **prepuce**, or fold of skin which hoods over the glans, and the **frenulum clitoridis**, which is attached to it inferiorly, are continuous with the labia minora (Fig. 627).

The **crura clitoridis** diverge from the body posteriorly, and are attached to the sides of the pubic arch. Each is continuous with one of the corpora cavernosa, and has a firm fibrous sheath, which is covered by the corresponding ischiocavernosus. In structure the crura and body of the clitoris resemble the corpora cavernosa penis, while the glans more closely resembles the bulbs of the vestibule, with which it is connected by a slender band of erectile tissue (Fig. 628).

In the seal and some other animals a bone—the os clitoridis—which represents the os penis of the male, is developed in the septum of the clitoris.

The **arterial supply** of each crus is the deep branch from the internal pudendal. The glans is supplied by the dorsal arteries of the clitoris.

The **nerve-supply** of the clitoris is derived partly from the pelvic sympathetic plexuses and partly from the dorsal nerves of the clitoris, which are branches of the pudendal nerves.

Bulbs of the Vestibule.—These are a pair of masses of erectile tissue which correspond developmentally to the two halves of the bulb of the penis, but are almost completely separated from each other by the vagina and the urethra—being only slightly connected in front by a narrow median part called the **commissure.** Each bulb is thick posteriorly, and more pointed in front, where it joins the commissure. It rests against the lateral wall of the vagina and the lower surface of the perineal membrane. Superficially it is covered by the bulbo-spongiosus muscle. The commissure lies in front of the opening of the urethra, and is connected by a slender band of erectile tissue with the glans clitoridis. The bulb is for the most part composed of minute convoluted blood-vessels held together by a very small amount of areolar tissue; they frequently anastomose with one another, and with the vessels of the commissure and the glans clitoridis.

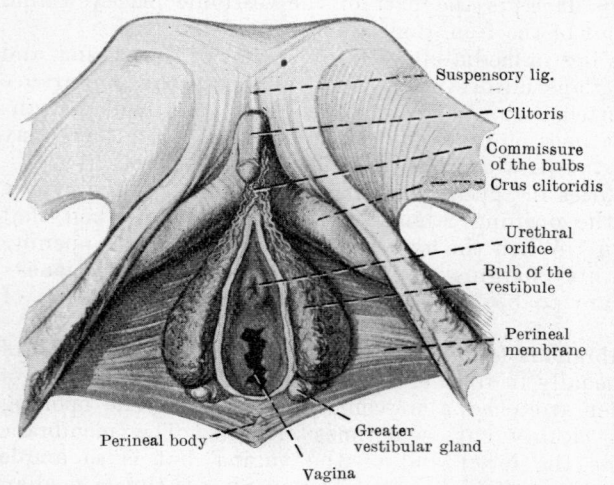

Fig. 628.—Dissection of Female Perineum to show the Clitoris, the Bulb of the Vestibule, and the Greater Vestibular Glands. (D. J. Cunningham.)

The **blood-supply** of the bulb is derived from a special branch of the internal pudendal.

GREATER VESTIBULAR GLANDS

The **greater vestibular glands** are placed one on each side of the lower part of the vagina. They are often overlapped by the posterior ends of the bulbs of the vestibule, and are covered by the bulbo-spongiosus muscles. Each is about the size and shape of a small bean, and has a long slender duct which opens into the vestibule in the angle between the labium minus and the vaginal opening (Figs. 624, 628).

DEVELOPMENT OF URO-GENITAL ORGANS

THE URO-GENITAL PASSAGES

General Account.—In tracing the developmental history of the uro-genital passages it is convenient to begin with an embryo of about $2\frac{1}{2}$ mm. in length. At that time a longitudinal duct on the lateral side of the mesodermal somites begins to develop on each side of the body. With the exception of the anterior portion of the cloaca and the proximal part of the allantois, that duct, which has received the name of *mesonephric duct* [ductus Wolffi] is the earliest formed structure from which, or in connexion with which, the parts of the adult uro-genital system arise.

The mesonephric duct serves as the canal for the primitive excretory organs—the pro-nephros and the mesonephros of the embryo. With the atrophy of these organs the duct suffers modification; yet both sexes in the adult possess structures which have their embryonic origin from it. In the male the **canal of the epididymis**, the **vas deferens**, and the **ejaculatory duct**, are directly developed from the mesonephric duct; in the female the **duct of the ep-oöphoron** and the **vesicular appendices** are vestigial structures having a like origin. The **ureter** and its **pelvis** arise in both sexes as an outgrowth from the mesonephric duct. In the male the **seminal vesicle** is developed as a diverticulum from it.

The primitive excretory organs—the **pronephros** and the **mesonephros**—develop in connexion with the anterior part of the mesonephric duct, and, during the early life of the embryo, are important structures. Even in the embryo, however, the pronephros soon becomes vestigial and it is replaced by the far more important mesonephros. With the development of the permanent kidney the mesonephros atrophies ; yet some of its tubules persist in the adult. The **efferent ductules** of the testis, the **ductuli aberrantes** and the **paradidymis** in the male, and the tubules of the **ep-oöphoron** and of the **par-oöphoron** in the female, are structures which owe their origin to the tubules of the mesonephros.

After the formation of the mesonephric ducts another pair of longitudinally disposed canals are developed, called the **para-mesonephric ducts** [ductus Muelleri]. They open at their cephalic ends into the body cavity, and at their caudal ends unite with each other in the median plane. From them are formed in the female the **uterine tubes**, the **uterus**, and the **vagina** ; and in the male the **appendices** of the testis and the **prostatic utricle**.

The mesonephric and the united para-mesonephric ducts open at their caudal ends into the ventral or uro-genital part of the **cloaca**, which in the course of development becomes transformed into the **urinary bladder** and the **uro-genital canal** of the embryo. The developing ureter at first arises as a diverticulum from the mesonephric duct at a short distance from the point where that duct joins the cloaca. Soon, however, the ureters acquire independent openings into the cloaca, and these openings become gradually shifted farther from each other and from those of the mesonephric ducts. The ureters come to open into the anterior portion of the cloaca, which lies nearer to the head of the embryo than the part with which the mesonephric ducts are connected. The cephalic portion of the anterior subdivision of the cloaca which receives the ureters becomes the urinary bladder and the upper part of the urethra. The caudal part, lying below the level of the entrance of the mesonephric ducts, is called the *uro-genital canal* and is represented in the adult male by the lower part of the prostatic urethra and by the whole of the membranous portion ; in the female by the lower part of the urethra and the part of the pudendal cleft which immediately surrounds the openings of the urethra and vagina (Figs. 636, 637). The united para-mesonephric ducts open into the caudal part of the cloaca or uro-genital canal between the mesonephric ducts of opposite sides. In the male the position of the opening, which is represented in the adult by the orifice of the prostatic utricle, remains almost unchanged. In the female, on the other hand, a shortening of the uro-genital canal causes the opening, which in that sex is represented by the vaginal orifice, to appear on the body surface in the pudendal cleft of the adult.

After the complete separation of the cloaca into anterior or uro-genital and posterior or rectal subdivisions, the rectum establishes a communication with the exterior in the floor of the shallow depression known as the ectodermal cloacal fossa. At a little later time the uro-genital canal also joins the cloacal fossa at a point in front of the opening of the rectum. The ectodermal cloacal fossa lies in front of the vestigial tail, and extends forwards as far as a tubercle known as the **cloacal tubercle**, which later gives rise to the **genital eminence** and a pair of elevations called the **labio-scrotal folds**. The genital eminence becomes converted into the clitoris or penis according to the sex. The labio-scrotal folds, extending backwards on each side, form the labia majora of the female, and, fusing posteriorly, give rise to the scrotum in the male. In the female the lower part of the uro-genital canal opens out to form a part of the floor of the pudendal cleft of the adult, and the shortening of the canal leads to the urethra and the vagina having independent openings into the cleft — the margins of the cleft becoming elongated to form the labia minora. In the male the slit-like opening of the uro-genital canal is prolonged forwards by an active growth at the base of the genital eminence, and, its margins uniting, it gives rise to the penile portion of the urethra.

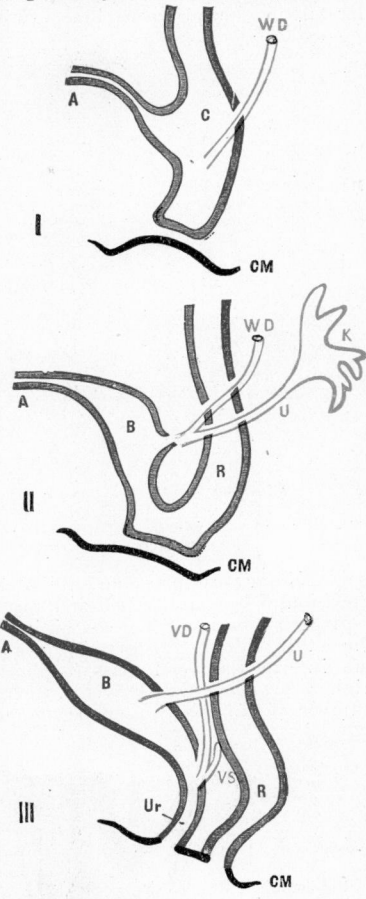

FIG. 629.—DIAGRAM TO ILLUSTRATE THE MANNER IN WHICH THE URETER, THE VAS DEFERENS, AND THE URINARY BLADDER ARISE IN THE EMBRYO.

The structures developed from the cloaca are indicated in blue, those from the mesonephric duct in red, and the ectoderm in black.

The manner in which the rectum and bladder become separated and acquire openings into the ectodermal cloacal fossa is shown in II and III. (A. H. Young and A. Robinson.)

A.	Allantois.	R. Rectum.
B.	Bladder.	Ur. Uro-genital canal.
C.	Cloaca.	U. Ureter.
CM.	Ectoderm of	VD. Vas deferens.
	cloacal fossa.	VS. Seminal vesicle.
K.	Pelvis of ureter.	WD. Mesonephric duct.

MESONEPHRIC DUCT AND EMBRYONIC EXCRETORY ORGANS

The mesonephric duct [ductus Wolffi] arises in the mesoderm of the intermediate cell mass, about the fifteenth day, as a solid cord of cells, and occupies a position immediately lateral to the protovertebral somites and medial to the body cavity. During the third

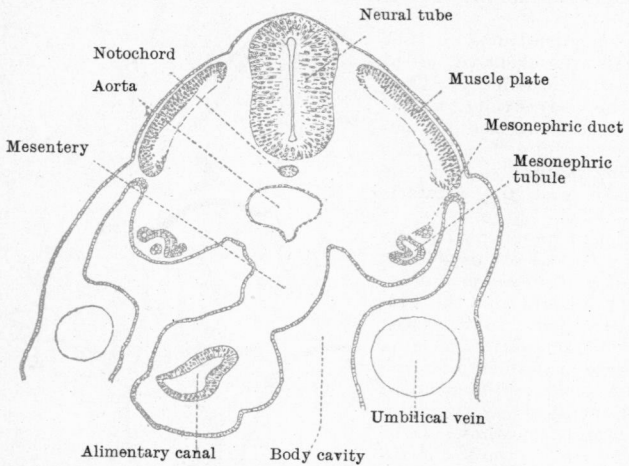

week this cellular cord acquires a lumen, and about the end of the same week the duct in its growth reaches the cloaca. As soon as the cloaca has become divided into dorsal and ventral parts, the mesonephric duct ends in the cephalic part of the ventral subdivision, which becomes the bladder and uro-genital canal (Fig. 632).

The **mesonephros** [corpus Wolffi] is developed in the mesoderm of the intermediate cell mass immediately adjoining the mesonephric duct, and consists of a number of minute transversely arranged tubules, each of which opens by one end into the mesonephric duct, while its other end is blind. The transverse tubules, like the canal into which they open, are at first

FIG. 630.—TRANSVERSE SECTION THROUGH THE TRUNK OF A HUMAN EMBRYO OF ABOUT 5 MM. LENGTH.

solid cellular structures, and only later acquire a lumen. Increasing rapidly in length and number, the tubules become twisted and tortuous, and the blind end of each dilates to form a capsule invaginated upon itself and containing a bunch of capillary blood-vessels similar to the glomeruli of the adult kidney. It would appear that primitively one tubule is developed in the portion of the intermediate cell mass (nephrotome) corresponding to each mesodermic somite, but, in higher vertebrates at all events, such a correspondence between the number of somites and the number of tubules cannot be demonstrated. In the posterior part of the mesonephros the

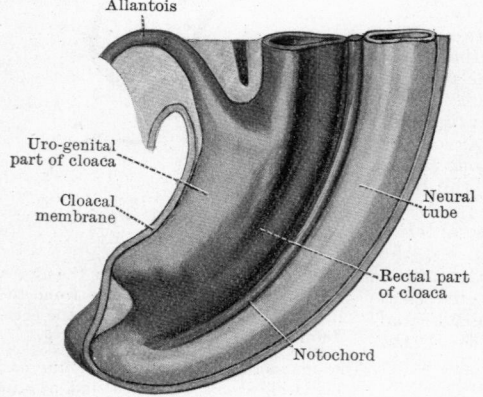

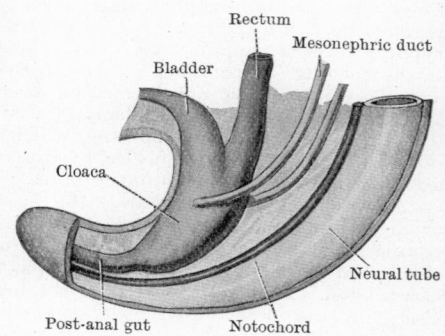

FIG. 631.—TAIL END OF 3 MM. HUMAN EMBRYO, BEFORE THE TIME AT WHICH THE MESONEPHRIC DUCTS REACH THE CLOACA. (Drawn from a model by Keibel.)

FIG. 632.—TAIL END OF 4·2 MM. HUMAN EMBRYO. The mesonephric ducts open into the anterior part of the cloaca. (Drawn from a model by Keibel.)

tubules are very numerous—more numerous than the segments in that region. The tubules of the mesonephros arise in all segments from the sixth cervical to the third lumbar. The tubules in the anterior part atrophy and disappear at a very early time, even while others are being formed towards the caudal end of the embryo. When at its greatest development (fifth to eighth week) the mesonephros is a relatively large glandular mass composed of tubules which resemble in a general way those of the adult kidney. At that time it bulges into the dorsal part of the body cavity, and extends from the region of the liver to the caudal end of the cavity. Along its lateral surface lies the mesonephric duct.

As the permanent kidney or metanephros is developed the mesonephros atrophies; a portion of it, however, is retained *in the male*, and forms the excretory apparatus of the testis. The mesonephric duct becomes the canal of the epididymis and the vas deferens of the adult (see p. 755). *In the female,* when the permanent kidney is formed, the mesonephros and its duct undergo atrophy to a greater extent than in the male, and they are represented in the

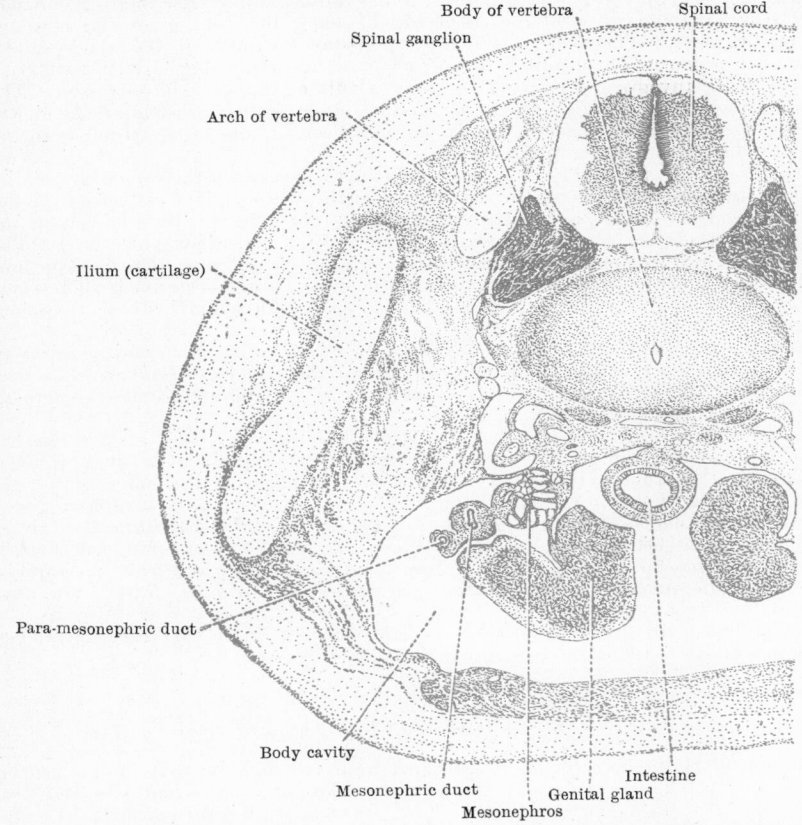

Fig. 633.—Transverse Section through the Lower Part of the Trunk of a Human Embryo of about 7 Weeks. (From a specimen prepared by the late Prof. J. Symington.)

adult only by the vestigial structures in the broad ligament of the uterus (see pp. 738 and 741).

In anamniate vertebrates—fishes and amphibia—the mesonephros persists as the excretory organ of the adult.

Pronephros.—From what is known regarding the development of lower animals it seems certain that the mesonephric duct originally served as the duct of the still earlier excretory organ—the **pronephros.** In man the pronephros arises earlier than the mesonephros, when the embryo possesses ten segments only, and its tubules, unlike those of the mesonephros, communicate not only with the duct but also with the body cavity. The pronephros is found in the anterior segments of the embryo only, and atrophies at a very early time in development.

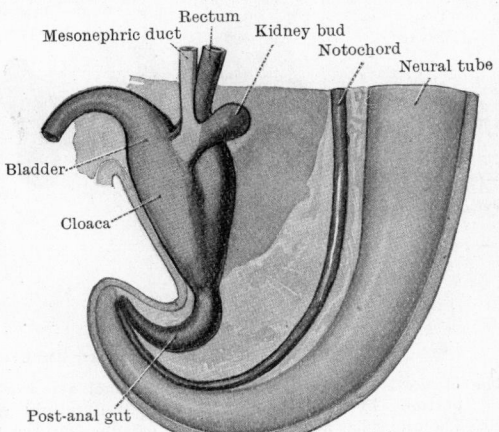

Fig. 634.—Tail End of 6·5mm. Human Embryo. The cloaca is dividing into rectal and uro-genital subdivisions. The ureter is arising as a bud from the mesonephric duct. (Drawn from a model by Keibel.)

Ureter and Permanent Kidney

The ureter arises as a tubular diverticulum from the mesonephric duct close to the point where the duct joins the cloaca (Figs. 634 and 635). The diverticulum appears during the fourth week, and grows headwards, dorsal to the body cavity. Even in its very early condition the portion of the outgrowth which lies nearest its origin from the mesonephric duct, and from which the adult ureter is developed, is more slender than the distal part which becomes branched, and grows out to form the pelvis and calyces of the ureter. From the calyces numerous collecting tubules grow out and acquire connexions with the glandular or uriniferous tubules of the kidney. The uriniferous tubules of the kidney arise independently of the ureter in a tailward prolongation of the tissue which, nearer the head, gives origin to the tubules of the mesonephros. The tissue in which the permanent kidney tubules arise is caudal to the third lumbar segment. The blind, distal end of each tubule soon dilates to form a capsule which, becoming invaginated on itself, encloses a tuft of capillary blood-vessels. The renal corpuscles arising in this manner are found in the human kidney as early as the eighth week. It must be specially noted that the origin of the collecting tubules and their branches is different from the origin of the secreting tubules.

As regards their origin in the embryo we have to distinguish between the collecting tubules and their branches, and the uriniferous secretory tubules of the kidney. The collecting tubules arise from the calyces of the ureter, and their branches grow out from the tubules; both the collecting tubules and their branches are derived therefore from the mesonephric duct. The secreting tubules are formed in mesoderm known as the *metanephric cell mass*, which is continuous at its headward end with the tissue from which the mesonephros is derived. The short junctional tubules of the adult lie in the region where those developmentally distinct portions of the kidney unite.

As the ureter increases in length, it separates from the mesonephric duct, and acquires an independent opening into the ventral part of the cloaca nearer the head of the embryo than that of the mesonephric duct. The part of the cloaca which receives the ureters becomes the urinary bladder.

The metanephric cell mass, in which the uriniferous tubules arise, lies at first on the medial side of the bud-like outgrowth which represents the ureter; at a later time it comes to lie dorsally. As the ureter grows towards the head end of the embryo the cell mass which gives rise to the uriniferous tubules follows it; hence the metanephric tissue ceases to lie to the caudal end of the mesonephros. As the ureter divides to form the calyces the metanephric cell mass becomes broken up into cap-like portions—one for each branch of the ureter, and later one for each of the collecting tubes which grow out from the calyces. The formation of uriniferous tubules within the cell masses is continued until a few days after birth.

The kidney is at first a distinctly lobulated body, and shows at birth, and sometimes even in the adult, distinct traces of its original subdivision into lobules.

URINARY BLADDER

The main portion of the urinary bladder is formed from the cephalic part of the ventral subdivision of the cloaca. This at an early time becomes flattened dorso-ventrally and produced laterally into two horn-like projections in the region where the mesonephric ducts open (Fig. 635). Its tailward part becomes constricted to form the uro-genital canal. Little by little the caudal ends of the mesonephric ducts open out and take part in the formation of the wall of the bladder and the upper portion of the prostatic part of the urethra. The openings of the ureters become shifted laterally, but the final position of the openings of the mesonephric ducts is close to the median plane in the prostatic part of the urethra. The urinary bladder has therefore a double origin: its main portion is derived from the entodermal cloaca; its smaller basal part arises from the opened-out caudal ends of the mesonephric ducts. The latter portion approximately corresponds to the trigone of the adult bladder, and must be regarded as having its source from the mesoderm. The extreme cephalic end of the ventral part of the cloaca tapers gradually, and beyond the umbilicus is continuous with the allantois. This part of the cloaca is the *urachus*; it

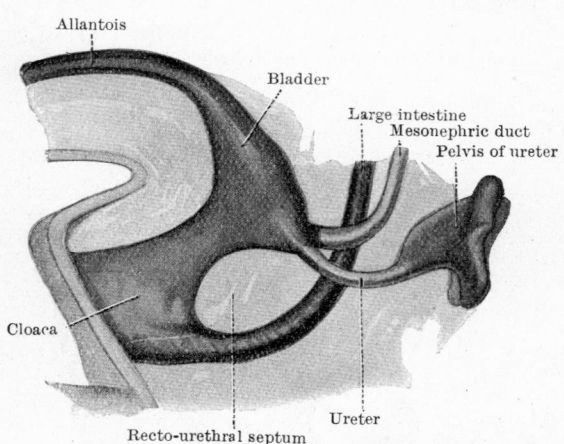

FIG. 635.—TAIL END OF 11·5 MM. HUMAN EMBRYO.

The cloaca is becoming separated into rectal and uro-genital portions by the formation of the recto-urethral septum. The ureter has acquired a separate opening into the ventral division of the cloaca. (Drawn from a model by Keibel.)

loses its lumen about the fifth week, and in the adult is represented by a fibrous cord—the median umbilical ligament.

The cavity of the urachus is sometimes not lost so early, and in rare cases it has been found persisting in the child or adult as a pervious channel extending from the apex of the bladder to the umbilicus. Here it may open on the surface of the body.

MALE URETHRA

The first part of the male urethra has an origin similar to that of the basal part of the bladder, and is derived from the ends of the mesonephric ducts. The remaining portion—beyond the openings of the vasa deferentia of the adult—is derived from the uro-genital canal or caudal subdivision of the ventral part of the cloaca. The uro-genital canal is early subdivided into a pelvic part which lies in the future true pelvis and a penile part which occupies the region where the corpus spongiosum is developed. The latter part of the uro-genital canal becomes filled with closely and irregularly packed cells which later, breaking down, re-establish the canal and give origin to a slit-like opening in the region in front of the anus. The canal for some time opens at a rhomboidal fossa situated in the groove at the base of the glans. In the glans penis a septum composed of densely packed cells is formed, and these cells, at a later stage, break down and form a groove the lips of which unite and enclose the terminal portion of the urethra. It is doubtful if any portion of the male urethra owes its origin to the ectoderm, but there is some evidence that the septum of the glans is ectodermal, in which case the part of the canal which traverses the glans must have a like origin.

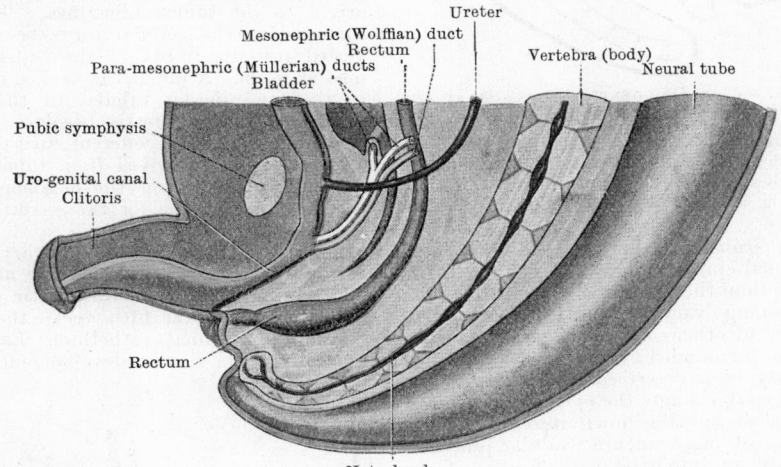

FIG. 636.—TAIL END OF 25 MM. FEMALE HUMAN EMBRYO.

The rectum has acquired an opening and the entoderm of the uro-genital canal is continued into the genital eminence (clitoris). (Drawn from a model by Keibel.)

FEMALE URETHRA

In the female the part of the urethra near the internal urethral orifice is developed from the caudal ends of the mesonephric ducts and has an origin similar to that of the basal portion of the bladder. The lower part of the passage is derived from the uro-genital canal. When the uro-genital canal opens on the surface it is continued forwards as a sulcus on the genital eminence, as in the male sex. The margins of the slit-like opening do not unite, but form the labia minora of the adult, and the sulcus which appears on the glans clitoridis is closed without forming a canal. At first the fused caudal ends of the para-mesonephric ducts open into the uro-genital canal, but later on a shortening and spreading out of the lower portion of the uro-genital canal, to form a part of the pudendal cleft of the adult, is responsible for bringing the opening of the fused para-mesonephric ducts (the vaginal orifice) to the surface. The female urethra corresponds to the part of the male passage which lies above the opening of the prostatic utricle.

SEXUAL GLANDS

In the development of the sexual glands, male and female, a differentiated thickened portion of the peritoneal epithelium is first recognised. This specialised epithelium, known as the **germinal epithelium,** is situated to the medial side of the mesonephros and of the mesonephric and para-mesonephric ducts. It covers a longitudinally disposed elevation called the **genital ridge.** The germinal epithelium is not strictly limited to the ridge, but extends a little beyond its limits. The genital ridge is soon found to have numerous epithelial cells embedded in its fibrous-tissue stroma, some of which appear to originate, in both sexes, by a proliferation from the deep surface of the germinal epithelium that covers the ridge. In both sexes, however, the earliest formed epithelial cells appear to arise in the genital ridge independently, and at first are not connected with the cells covering the genital gland. From these epithelial cells the male seminiferous tubules and female vesicular follicles with their contained ova are developed.

The tissue which gives rise to the genital ridge occurs in all the body segments from the sixth thoracic to the second sacral, but the cephalic end of the ridge atrophies before the germinal epithelium can be recognised in the more caudal segments, and only about one-fourth of the ridge gives origin to the permanent sexual gland.

In the male, as early as the thirty-third day, the epithelial cells embedded in the stroma of the developing testis have become arranged into a network of anastomosing cords within which certain larger cells are irregularly scattered. The larger cells have received the name of **primitive sperm cells,** and are relatively few in number. They undergo frequent division, and in the later stages are not to be distinguished from the other cells of the cords. The cellular cords undergo direct transformation into the **convoluted tubules,** the **straight tubules,** and the **rete testis.** At a very early stage the superficial part of the stroma of the developing testis becomes denser, and gives origin to the **tunica albuginea.** The tissue surrounding the cellular cords becomes converted into the septa of the testis and the mediastinum. A lumen can first be recognised in the seminiferous tubules in the seventh month. The rete testis becomes connected secondarily with the efferent ductules of the testis, which are derived from tubules of the mesonephros, and thus the mesonephric duct becomes the passage for the secretion of the testis.

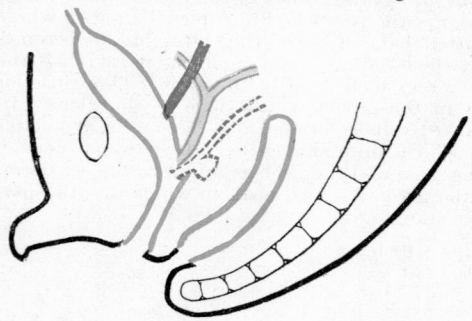

FIG. 637.—THE URO-GENITAL PASSAGES AT THE INDIFFERENT STAGE OF DEVELOPMENT.

Ureter : green solid outline. Mesonephric duct : green dotted outline. The origin of the seminal vesicle is indicated. Para-mesonephric ducts : orange. Rectum, bladder, and uro-genital canal : red.

In the female, large epithelial cells are found in the stroma of the developing ovary, beneath the germinal epithelium, as early as the thirty-third day. These **primitive ova** are much more numerous than the primitive sperm cells of the male, and form a very characteristic feature of the developing ovary. At first they are isolated, but later—about the fifth week—they become surrounded by other smaller cells having a like origin from the germinal epithelium. Each primitive ovum, surrounded by its cells, becomes a **primitive follicle,** the further development of which has already been described (pp. 20 and 736). During the later stages the epithelium has the appearance of growing down into the stroma in the form of long branching cellular processes which break up into little nests of cells to form the future follicles. The proliferation of cells from the surface epithelium goes on until birth, but, in the human ovary, it is doubtful if any new ova arise in the later months of intra-uterine life or after birth.

GENERATIVE DUCTS

As has been stated already, the male ducts arise from the mesonephric ducts and the female from the para-mesonephric ducts. The embryos of both sexes at first have well-developed mesonephric and para-mesonephric ducts, which are arranged in a very definite manner. The mesonephric ducts, communicating directly with the tubules of the mesonephros, lie at first parallel to each other, and at a considerable distance apart. As they pass towards the caudal end of the embryo they approach each other, and each becomes enclosed in a fold of peritoneum called the **plica urogenitalis.** More caudally the ducts become closely approximated to each other, and are embedded in a cord-like mass of fibro-areolar tissue to which the term **genital cord** is applied. They finally open into the ventral subdivision of the cloaca.

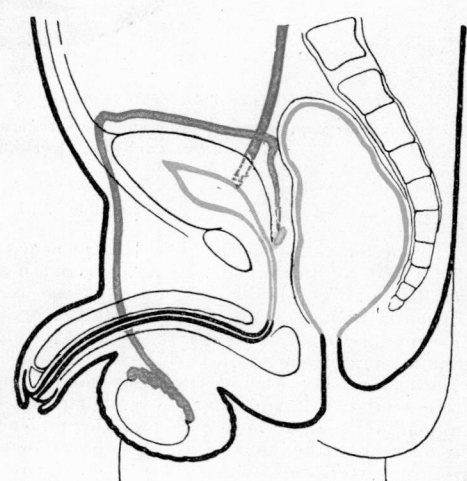

FIG. 638.—MALE URO-GENITAL PASSAGES.

Vas deferens : dotted green outline. Ureter : solid green outline. Prostatic utricle : orange. Bladder and pelvic part of urethra : red. Penile portion of urethra : black.

The para-mesonephric ducts open freely into the body cavity at their cephalic ends, and lie to the lateral side of the mesonephric ducts. As they are traced tailwards they are crossed by the mesonephric ducts and enter the genital cord ; in this cord they unite and form a median canal which opens into the ventral subdivision of the cloaca between the mesonephric ducts (Fig. 637). The manner in which the ureters become separated from the mesonephric ducts has been described already.

Ducts in the Male.—The seminiferous tubules of the testis become connected with the mesonephric duct through a fusion of certain tubules of the mesonephros with the **rete testis**. The connexion is definitely established in the third month. The number of tubules that take part varies considerably, but corresponds to the number of **efferent ductules** found in the adult. The connecting tubules, becoming more convoluted just as they join the mesonephric duct, form the **lobules of the epididymis**. The **canal of the epididymis** is directly formed from the cephalic part of the mesonephric duct, and the **vas deferens** from the more caudal portion. The **ductuli aberrantes** and the **paradidymis** are to be looked upon as persistent tubules of a more caudal portion of the mesonephros which have failed to become connected with the tubules of the testis.

The **seminal vesicles** are developed in the third month as evaginations from the mesonephric ducts near their caudal ends. Each at first is a longitudinal groove in the wall of the vas deferens, and then closes over and becomes cut off from the main tube except at the point where, later, the duct of the seminal vesicle joins the vas.

The para-mesonephric ducts atrophy in the male embryo, but the appendices of the testis are vestigial remains of their cephalic portions, while the **prostatic utricle** represents the caudal fused portions which, in the embryo, occupy the genital cord.

Ducts in the Female.—The para-meso-nephric ducts in the female retain their openings into the body cavity, and their cephalic portions become the uterine tubes. Their fused caudal parts, which at first join the uro-genital canal, give rise to the **uterus** and **vagina**. The manner in which the original position of the opening of the para-mesonephric ducts becomes shifted, by the formation of a new passage or by the shortening of the uro-genital canal, has been mentioned already (p. 753). The final position of the opening is in the pudendal cleft of the adult.

The mesonephric ducts and the mesonephros atrophy in the female, but traces of them are found in the ep-oöphoron and par-oöphoron of the adult. In the fœtus the mesonephric duct can be traced along the side of the uterus as far as the upper end of the vagina.

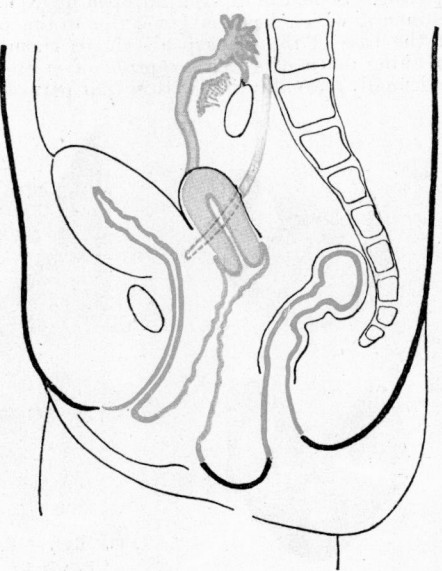

FIG. 639. —FEMALE URO-GENITAL PASSAGES.

Derivatives of the para-mesonephric duct: orange. Ureter: green solid outline. The ep-oöphoron is indicated in green near the opening of para-mesonephric duct and near the ovary.

ACCESSORY GLANDS

The glandular portion of the **prostate** arises as a series of solid outgrowths from the epithelium of the uro-genital canal during the third month. The outgrowths are simple at first, but become branched and finally acquire a lumen. They are arranged in three groups—an upper and a lower dorsal, and a ventral group. The glands of the ventral group soon become reduced in number and often completely disappear; those of the upper dorsal group form the chief part of the prostate. The prostatic glands arise in both sexes; but in the female, where they are known as *para-urethral glands*, they are few in number and not densely packed as in the male. The muscular tissue of the prostate is derived from the muscular wall of the urethra.

The **bulbo-urethral glands** arise in the third month as outgrowths from the epithelium of the uro-genital canal. The **greater vestibular glands** arise in the same manner.

EXTERNAL GENITAL ORGANS

The external genital organs are developed in the region of the ectodermal cloacal fossa, and the male and female are alike in the earlier stages. The fossa at first extends on the ventral aspect of the body almost from the tail to the umbilical cord. At its cephalic end there is a tubercle known as the **cloacal tubercle**, and at its caudal end there is a **coccygeal tubercle**. Immediately in front of the coccygeal tubercle the anus is formed, and between the anus and the cloacal tubercle the uro-genital canal opens on the surface by a median slit-like aperture—the **primitive uro-genital opening**.

The cloacal tubercle early becomes subdivided into—(1) an apical **genital eminence**, which occupies the median line and lies at the cephalic end of the slit-like uro-genital opening; and (2) a **basal portion**, which lies nearer the umbilicus and also curves round the sides of the genital eminence. At a later time the basal part is continued to form a pair of prominent folds at the sides of the ectodermal cloacal fossa. These folds are called the **labio-scrotal folds** and, *in the* *female*, give rise to the labia majora. The lateral margins of the primitive uro-genital opening give origin to the labia minora, and the genital eminence becomes the clitoris. On the clitoris at a very early date a relatively large glans is marked off by a surrounding sulcus. *In the male* the scrotal folds grow backwards, and, meeting behind the primitive uro-genital opening, fuse together. In that way the opening is pushed forwards. The genital eminence elongates rapidly owing to a growth at its basal part, and a sulcus which is formed on its cloacal aspect gradually becomes converted into a canal by the closure of the lips of the primitive uro-genital opening. Soon the uro-genital opening is found to lie nearer the apex than the base of the eminence, which has now given rise to the penis. For some time the opening in the male lies at the base of the glans penis and is rhomboidal in outline. At a later time, owing to the breaking down of a dense septum of epithelial cells which appears within the glans, a sulcus, and finally a canal, arises within that part of the penis; thus the terminal part of the urethra is

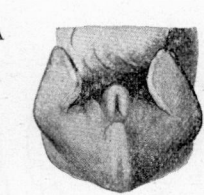
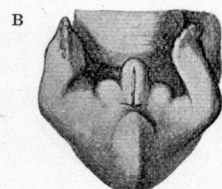

FIG. 640.—EXTERNAL GENITAL ORGANS OF HUMAN EMBRYOS. Indifferent stage. A. Embryo of 20 mm. B. Slightly larger.

The genital eminence and the labio-scrotal folds are well seen.

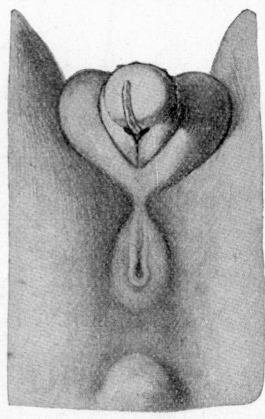

FIG. 641. — EXTERNAL GENITAL ORGANS OF MALE EMBRYO.

Formation of scrotum. The labio-scrotal folds, formerly best marked at the sides of the genital eminence, have grown backwards and united behind the primitive uro-genital opening, to form the raphe scroti. The genital folds embrace the base of the genital eminence or penis. The glans is very prominent.

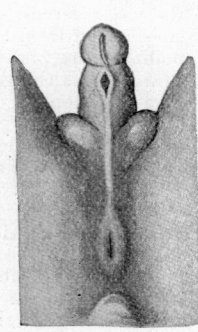

FIG. 642. — EXTERNAL GENITAL ORGANS OF MALE EMBRYO.

Behind the glans penis the urethra opens in a diamond-shaped fossa at the proximal end of which the median raphe ends. The prepuce is formed behind the constriction which marks off the glans, and grows forwards to cover it.

A little horn-like process of epithelium is present on the summit of the genital eminence.

formed. When the opening at the base of the glans is closed the continuous urethral passage is established. The main portion of the urethra is entodermal in origin, but there is some evidence that the part in the glans has its origin from the ectoderm.

MAMMARY GLANDS

The mammary glands are accessory organs connected with the female reproductive system. Each gland is situated on the front of the thorax in the superficial fascia of the hemispherical elevation known as the mamma or **breast**; it usually extends from the level of the second rib to that of the sixth rib, and lies on the pectoralis major and, to a less extent, on the obliquus externus abdominis and the serratus anterior. The **nipple** is situated near the summit of the breast, usually at the level of the fourth intercostal space; the lactiferous ducts open on it by minute apertures, and it is surrounded by a coloured, circular area of skin called the **areola**. The skin of the nipple is thrown into numerous wrinkles, and on the areola it exhibits many minute rounded projections due to the presence of underlying cutaneous glands. These **areolar glands** are considered to represent rudimentary portions of the mamma. The colour of the nipple and areola varies with the complexion, but in young subjects it is usually a rosy-pink, and changes to a deep brown during the second and third months of the first pregnancy. Also, during pregnancy, the areola increases in size and its glands become more marked. The nipple contains a considerable number of unstriped muscle fibres, and becomes firmer and more prominent as a result of mechanical stimulation.

The size and appearance of the breasts vary much, not only in the different races of mankind, but also in the same person under different conditions. In the young child they are small, and there is little difference between those of the male and female. Their growth is slow until the approach of puberty, and then the female mammary glands increase rapidly in size. At each pregnancy the breasts become large, and they attain their greatest development during lactation. The size of the breast depends partly on the amount of superficial fat and partly on the amount of glandular tissue present.

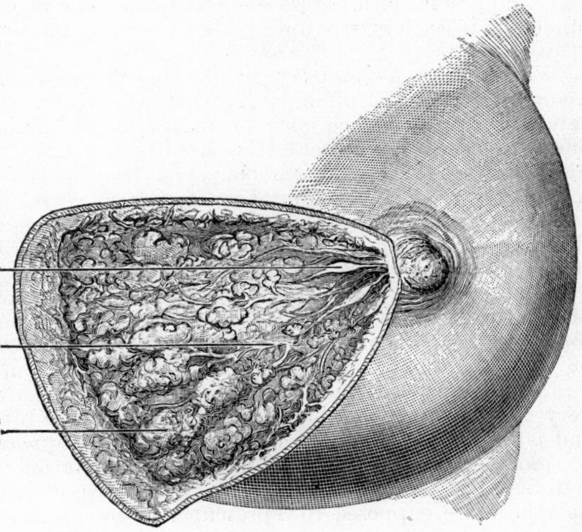

Structure of the Breast.— The mamma is composed of a mass of glandular tissue traversed and supported by strands of fibrous tissue, and covered with a thick layer of fat. The glandular tissue forms a flattened conical mass, the apex of which corresponds to the position of the nipple, while its base is loosely connected to the deep fascia covering the muscles on which the gland lies. In section it is readily distinguished from the surrounding fat by its firmer consistence and by its pinkish-white colour. It is composed of fifteen to twenty lobes subdivided into lobules, which make its superficial surface and edges very uneven — the inequalities of its surface being filled up by processes of the fatty tissue covering the gland. The fatty covering is incomplete in the region of the areola, and here the lactiferous ducts pass into the nipple. The **lobes** radiate from the nipple, each lobe being quite distinct from the others and possessing its own duct; the **lobules** are bound together and supported by a considerable amount of fibro-areolar tissue which forms the **stroma** of the gland.

The alveoli of the gland and the secretory epithelium lining them vary much under different conditions. At puberty the mammary gland is composed chiefly of fibro-areolar tissue stroma and the ducts; at that time the alveoli are small and few in number. During lactation, when the gland is fully functional, the alveoli are enlarged, distended with fluid, and much more numerous. The epithelial cells are cubical and filled with fat globules. When the gland is not secreting, the alveoli become small and reduced in number, while the cells of the lining epithelium, which are then small and glandular, do not contain fat globules.

FIG. 643.—DISSECTION OF THE BREAST. (A. F. D.)

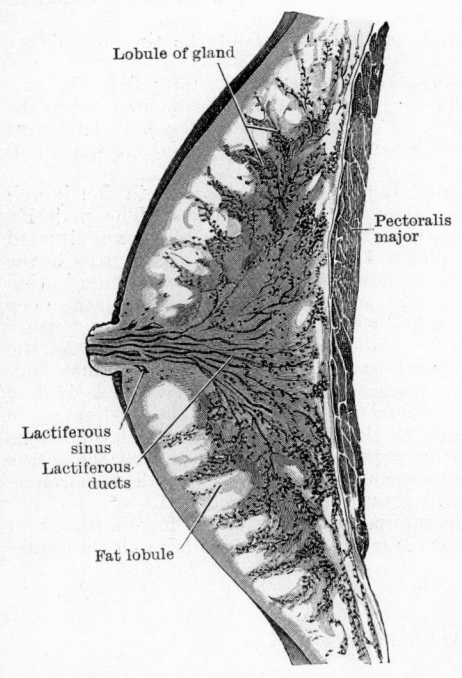

FIG. 644.—SECTION THROUGH A BREAST.
Prepared after immersion in nitric acid as recommended by Sir Harold Stiles. (D. J. Cunningham.)

The **lactiferous ducts**, passing towards the nipple, become enlarged to form small spindle-shaped dilatations called **lactiferous sinuses**; then, becoming once

48 b

more constricted, each duct passes, without communicating with its neighbours, to the summit of the nipple, where it opens.

In the male the various parts of the breast are represented in a rudimentary condition.

The presence of milk glands is characteristic of the class Mammalia, and the number of pairs of glands in each group of animals bears some relation to the number of young usually produced at each birth.

Variations.—Asymmetry in the development of the breasts is very common—the left mamma being very often larger than the right. Absence of one or both mammæ is a very rare abnormality which may or may not be associated with absence of the nipples. When one nipple only is present it is usually the left. The presence of supernumerary glands or nipples is not very uncommon. The term **polymasty** has been applied to cases in which more than the normal number of mammæ are present, and **polythely** to those in which additional glands, in a rudimentary condition, are represented by accessory nipples. Usually the accessory glands, or nipples, are present on the front of the thorax, and in most instances they occur below and a little to the medial side of the normal site. When the abnormal glands are found above the normal site they generally lie farther from the median plane. Much more rarely accessory glands have been found on the abdomen, in the axilla, or in some other situation, including even the back of the trunk. As many as three extra pairs of mammæ have been found in the same person, and cases in which the probable representatives of mammary glands were even more numerous have been recorded. Asymmetry is very common in those abnormal structures. It is interesting to note that examples of polymasty and polythely occur in the male rather more frequently than in the female. In some women the accessory breasts have yielded milk during lactation ; in most cases the abnormal organs are very rudimentary—being represented only by a minute nipple or a pigmented areola. Polymasty and polythely are supposed to represent a reversion to an ancestral condition in which more than two mammary glands were normally present, and in which probably many young were produced at each birth. In this connexion it is interesting to observe that usually the accessory glands occur in positions normally occupied by mammary glands in lower animals. In the course of the development of the breasts in man, specialised areas of the epidermis, similar to those which give origin to the mammæ, have been observed both above and below the region in which the adult mammæ are developed. These areas appear to be present normally, but usually they disappear at an early stage in the history of the embryo. In some other mammals rudimentary mammary glands may occur, as, for instance, in lemurs and in cows.

A slight functional activity of the mammary glands of the male about the time of puberty is stated to be a not very uncommon occurrence.

Vessels and Nerves of the Breast.—The mamma receives its **arterial** supply from the perforating branches of the *internal mammary artery* and from the external mammary branches of the *lateral thoracic*. Additional supply is derived from some of the intercostal vessels. The **veins** from the gland pour their blood into the *axillary* and *internal mammary veins*. Some small superficial veins from the breast join tributaries of the external jugular.

The **lymph vessels** of the breast are very numerous, and for the most part join the lymph glands of the axilla. They take origin from an extensive *perilobular plexus*. The majority follow the lactiferous ducts and thus converge towards the nipple, and they join a plexus situated beneath the areola (*subareolar plexus*). From this plexus the main efferent vessels pass to the *anterior (pectoral) axillary glands*, but it is important to remember that free communication exists between all the subgroups of axillary glands. In addition, vessels pass from the deep surface of the lateral part of the breast directly to the lower axillary glands, and a few run either through or behind the pectoral muscles to the *apical axillary glands*. A few vessels from the medial part of the breast, following the course pursued by the perforating arteries, may join the lymph glands situated along the course of the internal mammary artery. It is also to be remembered that a few, probably irregular, communications exist across the median plane with the lymph vessels of the opposite breast ; and, further, that under diseased conditions communications may exist with lymph vessels in the upper part of the sheath of the rectus abdominis, and so with the *retro-sternal* and internal mammary glands. The surgical importance of the facts regarding the lymphatic drainage of the breast cannot be exaggerated.

The **nerve-supply** of the gland is derived from the **intercostal nerves** of the fourth, fifth, and sixth intercostal spaces. Along the course of these nerves sympathetic filaments reach the breast from the thoracic part of the sympathetic trunk.

DEVELOPMENT OF THE MAMMARY GLANDS

The mammary glands are developed as ingrowths of the ectoderm into the underlying mesodermic tissue. In the human embryo a thickened raised area of the ectoderm can be recognised in the region of the future gland at the end of the fourth week. The thickened ectoderm becomes depressed in the underlying mesoderm, and thus the mammary area soon becomes flat, and finally sunk below the level of the surrounding epidermis. The mesoderm, where it is in contact with the ingrowth of the ectoderm, is compressed, and its elements become arranged in concentric layers which, at a later stage, give rise to the fibrous tissue stroma of the gland. The ingrowing mass of ectoderm cells soon becomes flask-shaped, and grows out into the surrounding mesoderm as a number of solid processes which represent the future ducts of the gland. These processes, by dividing and branching, give rise to the future lobes and lobules, and, much later, to the alveoli. The mammary area becomes gradually raised again in its central part to form the nipple. A lumen is formed in the different parts of the branching system of cellular processes only at birth, and with its establishment is associated the secretion of a fluid resembling milk, which often takes place at that time. The lactiferous sinuses appear as thickenings on the developing ducts before birth.

In those animals which possess a number of mammary glands—such as the cat and pig— the thickening of the ectoderm, which is the first indication of the development of those glands, takes the form of a pair of ridges that extend from the level of the forelimb towards the inguinal region. The ridges converge caudally, and at their terminations lie not far from the median line. By the absorption of the intervening portions the ridges become divided up into a number of isolated areas in connexion with which the future glands arise. Similar linear thickenings of the ectoderm have been recognised in the human embryo also, and the usual positions assumed by the accessory glands when present lead us to suspect that in all probability the ancestors of man possessed numerous mammary glands arranged, as in lower animals, in lines converging towards the inguinal region.

DUCTLESS GLANDS

Originally written by the late D. J. CUNNINGHAM, M.D., F.R.S.,
Professor of Anatomy, University of Edinburgh

Revised and rewritten by A. B. APPLETON

THE term "ductless" is applied to certain glands whose products reach the circulation without passing through any special channels or ducts. They differ widely in structure, function, and development, exhibiting a diversity similar to that of glands in general.

Glands.—From the functional point of view a gland may belong to one (or more than one) of the following categories :

(1) **excretory** (*e.g.* kidney);
(2) **secretory,** A. *exocrine* (*e.g.* salivary and intestinal glands);
               B. *endocrine* (*e.g.* thyroid, testis, hypophysis cerebri);
(3) **reproductive** (testis and ovary);
(4) **vascular** (*e.g.* spleen, lymph glands, thymus, tonsil).

Glands may be classified also with reference to their developmental history. Thus, they are referable to one or other of the primary germ-layers of the embryo—ectoderm, mesoderm, or entoderm. Later stages in development also provide a basis for classification. For instance, certain glands are described as "**pharyngeal derivatives**" with reference to their mode of development, namely, thyroid, parathyroids, thymus, and tonsils. In a similar manner the hypophysis cerebri and the pineal body have been associated in a "cerebro-glandular" group.

The reproductive and vascular glands are sometimes grouped together as "**cytogenic**" with reference to their cell-producing functions.

The same gland may belong to more than one category. The pancreas, for example, has both exocrine and endocrine functions, and the testis and ovary belong to both reproductive and endocrine categories. The thymus, which belongs to the vascular group, may yet prove to have also an endocrine function.

Of the *ductless glands* some have endocrine functions and others belong to the vascular group. But in different ways both of these varieties of ductless glands are intimately related to the vascular system.

Endocrine Glands.—These organs produce chemical substances, commonly known as hormones [ὁρμᾶν (horman) = to excite], which control and modify the functional activity of the cells of other tissues in specific ways. They are the basis of a great chemical system co-ordinating the activities of the various tissues.

The effects produced by these substances may be either excitatory or inhibitory, and the general term "autacoid" is thus sometimes employed to describe the products of endocrine glands.

Histologically the endocrine glands exhibit various grades of specialisation (Cowdry). These grades probably illustrate the steps by which the structural and functional differentiation of endocrine organs took place in the course of evolution. The production of a hormone has, indeed, fundamental resemblance to an activity displayed by all living cells, for these all give off substances into the circulation which affect the activities of other cells. Hormones are distinguished by their specific nature, which in some instances is recognised only by the effects they produce.

The first stage in the differentiation of a tissue as an endocrine organ is illustrated by certain tissues (*e.g.* gastric and duodenal mucosa) which, though primarily adapted by their structure to some other function, also produce a hormone as a secondary function without any evident cytological differentiation of the cells concerned. The placenta and plain muscle tissue may be mentioned as other examples of this stage.

A second stage in differentiation is illustrated in organs such as the pancreas, in which there is a recognisable specialisation of structure as well as of function. In this organ some of the cells remain epithelial in structure and act as an exocrine secretory organ, whilst other cells are budded off from the epithelium in the course of development to form 'islets of Langerhans,' which act as a purely endocrine organ. The testis and the ovary (ovarian follicles and corpus luteum) also are examples.

It is unsettled whether the specific testis hormone is produced by the interstitial cells or by the tubular genital epithelium. If the latter view proves to be correct, the testis as an endocrine gland would fall to be graded in the first stage.

A further stage of differentiation is seen in the thyroid and parathyroid glands; for in the development of these glands there comes about a complete separation from the pharyngeal epithelium of masses of cells destined for specialisation with an endocrine function. Chromaffin tissue and the thymus may perhaps be included here.

Lastly, two masses of cells, each of specialised structure and function, may come into such intimate relation in the course of development as to constitute a single organ from the topographical point of view. Examples are furnished by the buccal and neural parts of the hypophysis cerebri, and by the cortex and medulla of the suprarenal gland. It has been suggested that such close approximation may perhaps play an important rôle in the co-ordination of the respective functions.

In this chapter the more specialised endocrine glands alone are described, namely, those belonging to the third and fourth grades. Certain other organs of doubtful hormone-producing function are included, namely, the carotid body, the glomus coccygeum, and the pineal body.

Vascular Glands.—These are organs which develop in intimate relation to the vascular and reticulo-endothelial systems (p. 786). They serve as reservoirs and germinating centres for the cellular constituents of these systems. Certain of these glands exhibit a special structure which fits them to act also as filtering organs—the lymph glands for lymph, the hæmolymph glands and spleen for blood; but in certain others, such as the lymphatic nodules in the walls of the alimentary canal, there is no such provision.

The tonsil, lymph glands, and lymphatic nodules are dealt with elsewhere in this book: the thymus and spleen are included in this chapter as a matter of convenience. Yet it should be remembered that the thymus may prove to have an endocrine function.

The organs described in this chapter are taken in the following order:

(1) The *suprarenal glands,* which are compound organs including chromaffin and cortical tissue.

(2) The *chromaffin system,* of ectodermal origin, including the medulla of the suprarenal gland and various " paraganglionic " masses of chromaffin tissue.

(3) The *cortical system,* of mesodermal origin, represented by the cortex of the suprarenal gland and by the occasional " accessory cortical bodies."

(4) The *pharyngeal pouch organs,* of entodermal origin, including the thyroid and parathyroid glands, and the ultimo-branchial bodies. Developmentally the thymus also belongs to this group, but is described with the spleen in the vascular category of the ductless glands.

(5) The *cerebro-glandular organs* of ectodermal origin, consisting of the hypophysis cerebri and the pineal body.

(6) A *vascular gland* group, containing the spleen and the thymus.

SUPRARENAL GLANDS

The **suprarenal glands** (Figs. 645-652) are normally two in number, situated one on each side of the vertebral column in intimate relation with the superomedial aspects of the kidneys.

Each gland consists of a relatively thick layer of cortex enclosing a medulla of chromaffin tissue (p. 767). It is extremely vascular: the amount of blood passing through it, relative to its size, surpasses that in any other organ in the body, with the possible exception of the thyroid gland. Arterial blood enters the gland from a plexus on the surface of the cortex and passes through the cortical tissue to the medulla, whence it is drained by the venous system (Fig. 651).

The cortex and medulla are of different developmental origin; they are in effect two distinct endocrine organs—though it is possible that the function of the medulla is influenced by its intimate vascular relationship with the cortex. The cortex secretes a hormone (*cortin* or *inter-renalin*) which is believed to act as a general cell-stimulant: it stores vitamin C and lipoids, and perhaps plays a part in nitrogenous metabolism. The medulla secretes a hormone (*adrenaline*) which reinforces the action of the sympathetic nervous system and facilitates carbohydrate metabolism. This is perhaps the only hormone which has so far been actually recognised in its cells of origin and whose discharge into the blood stream can be followed microscopically (Fig. 650).

The cortex is essential to life; the medulla is not essential. Nor does the medulla display the functional changes of size which are seen in the cortex under various circumstances (*e.g.* during menstruation, after extirpation of the contralateral gland, in certain disturbances of metabolism, and under the influence of one of the hormones of the hypophysis cerebri).

In colour the cortex is bright yellow except close to the medulla, where the colour is darker on account of the amount of blood in it. The medulla is seen in a section of the fresh healthy gland as a dark streak within the yellow cortex.

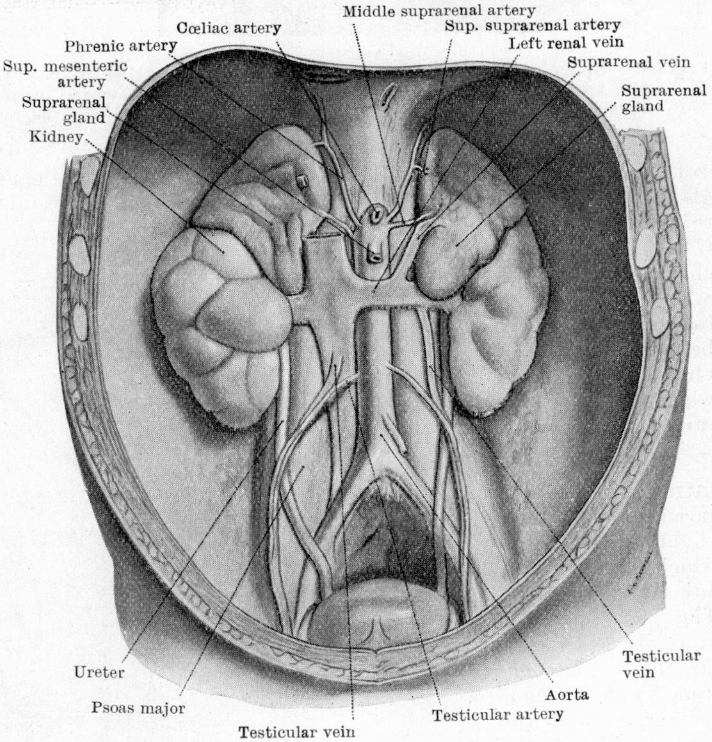

The post-mortem size of the gland varies within wide limits, mainly on

FIG. 645.—POSTERIOR ABDOMINAL WALL OF A FULL-TERM FOETUS, illustrating the relatively large size of the suprarenal glands and the lobulation of the kidneys.

account of the great modifications produced by certain pathological conditions. Average dimensions are as follows: height, 3-5 cms.; breadth, 2·5-3 cms.; thickness, slightly under 1 cm.; and the weight is about 7-12 gms. The medulla forms only about one-tenth part of the whole gland. The glands are relatively much larger in the fœtus than in the adult. Even at birth they are still relatively large (Fig. 645); they are indeed little smaller than in the adult.

Rarely only one gland is present; occasionally one is quite small, the other unusually

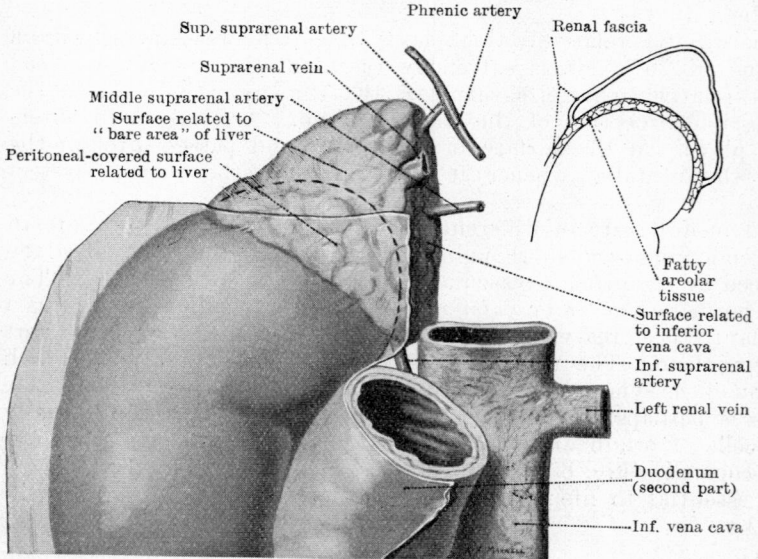

large; as a rule they are unequal in size, the left being more frequently the larger. Sometimes the two glands are fused (cf. horse-shoe kidney). Frequently there are accessory glands. These develop in the neighbourhood of the main gland, and usually remain there, but may become attached, early in embryonic life, to originally adjacent organs which subsequently change their position. As a result, they may be found not only beside the main gland but also in the broad ligament

FIG. 646.—RIGHT SUPRARENAL GLAND WITH ITS RELATION TO PERITONEUM AND SOME ADJACENT STRUCTURES. The small diagram is a schematic vertical section illustrating the relation of the gland to the kidney and the renal fascia.

of the uterus, on the spermatic cord, or even attached to the epididymis. Like the main glands, true accessory suprarenals are compounded of cortex and medulla, and require

to be distinguished from the purely chromaffin bodies and accessory cortical bodies which may be found in any of the positions in which accessory suprarenal glands occur.

Form and Relations.—The suprarenal glands differ slightly in their form, which is moulded by adjacent structures. The right gland is more or less triangular, the left is semilunar and extends farther down the medial side of the kidney than the right one. Each presents a posterior and an anterior surface : the right one has also

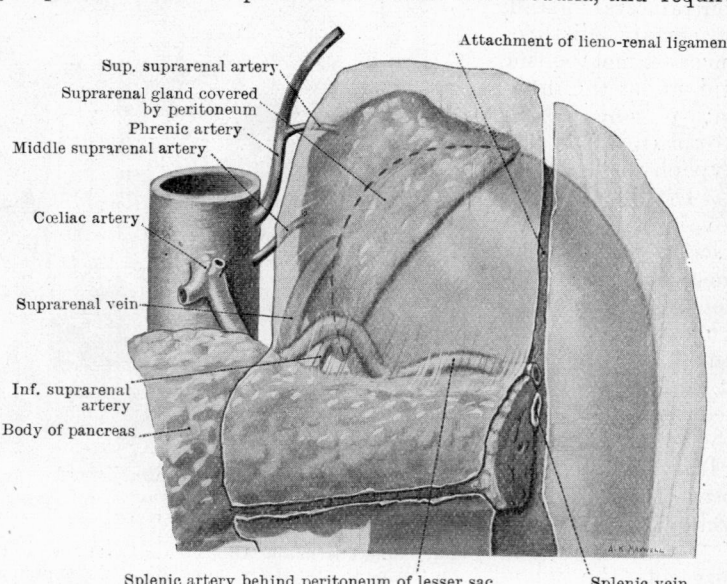

FIG. 647.—LEFT SUPRARENAL GLAND WITH ITS RELATION TO PERITONEUM AND SOME ADJACENT STRUCTURES.

an antero-medial surface. The posterior surface comprises a lower portion which is moulded to the medial part of the upper pole of the kidney, and an upper portion which lies against the diaphragm. The anterior relations differ on the two sides. The left gland is situated behind the lesser sac of peritoneum, which separates it from the stomach ; the infero-medial extremity is, however, separated from the lesser sac by the body of the pancreas and the splenic artery. The right gland is related by its antero-medial surface to the inferior vena cava. Its anterior surface is related to the liver, being in immediate contact with it in its upper part but separated from it in its lower part by peritoneum. The cœliac plexus and ganglia are situated between the two glands.

The suprarenal gland is separated from the kidney by a small amount of fatty areolar tissue, and is enclosed along with the kidney in the renal fascia.

A cleft is found in each gland where the suprarenal vein leaves it. The cleft or *hilum* is situated in the right gland on the antero-medial surface, in the left one near the lower end of the medial margin.

The level of the gland varies in relation to the adjacent structures. Thus, the infero-medial part of the right gland is sometimes overlapped by the duodenum, and the area covered with peritoneum is correspondingly restricted. On the left side the pancreas and splenic artery sometimes lie at a lower level than the gland. In the infant the spleen makes contact with the upper part of the left suprarenal; sometimes it still does so in the adult. Respiratory movements bring about modifications in the relations, for the suprarenal is displaced along with the kidney by movements of the diaphragm.

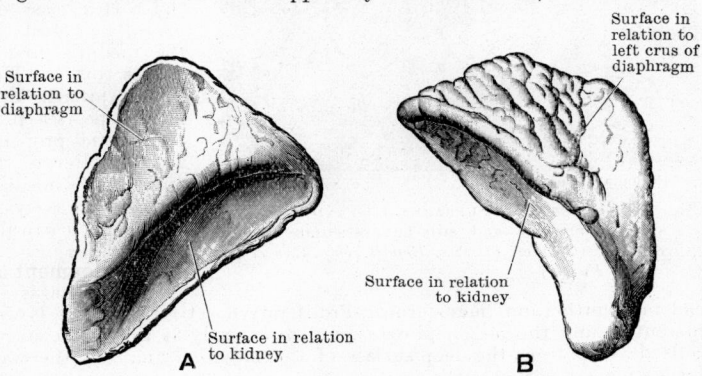

FIG. 648.—SUPRARENAL GLANDS ISOLATED AND VIEWED FROM BEHIND.

A. Right.   B. Left.

Vessels and Nerves.—The abundance of the blood-supply of the suprarenal glands should be emphasised again. Each gland receives three **arteries**—one direct from the aorta, one above from the phrenic artery, and one below from the renal artery (Figs. 646, 647). Each gland is drained by the large **vein** which emerges through the hilum, the right one to join the inferior vena cava, the left to join the left renal vein behind the body of the pancreas. The arrangement of the blood-vessels within the gland is described with its structure. Numerous **lymph vessels** pass from the suprarenal glands to the aortic lymph glands.

The medulla of the gland is more richly supplied with **nerves** than any other organ, but the innervation is relatively poor in the cortex. The nerves comprise two groups of filaments—the one derived from the *greater splanchnic nerve* and *upper lumbar sympathetic ganglia* through the cœliac plexus and ganglion, the other from the *vagus* and *phrenic* nerves. These filaments form a plexus of medullated and non-medullated nerves in the fibrous capsule, and from this plexus they pass into the gland. Many of these nerves are vaso-motor ; others end in synaptic relation with the secretory cells of the medulla, and it has been shown that stimulation of the nerve filaments entering the gland results in an increased outflow of adrenaline into the blood.

Structure.—The suprarenal gland consists of a highly vascular central mass of chromaffin tissue—the *medulla*—enclosed within a thick parenchymatous layer of cortical substance—the *cortex*—which in turn is enveloped in a capsule of fibrous tissue.

The **cortex** of the human suprarenal is so folded or convoluted as to increase its surface of contact with the medulla. From the deep aspect of the capsule, fibrous tissue trabeculæ pass inwards to support the glandular parenchyma. In the superficial part of the cortex the trabeculæ interlace freely so as to enclose a series of small rounded clusters of cortical cells, thus forming the *zona glomerulosa* (Fig. 651, 1) ; in the deeper intermediate region of the cortex elongated cell columns, usually formed of two or three rows of cortical cells, lie at right angles to the surface, forming a *zona fasciculata* (Fig. 651, 2) ; in the deepest part of the cortex the cell columns are more irregularly arranged and form a reticulum—*zona reticulata* (Fig. 651, 3). Degeneration of cells occurs in the zona reticulata and new formation in the outer part of the zona fasciculata.

The cortical parenchyma consists of large polyhedral cells arranged in the interstices of the fibrous trabeculæ. The cells contain more or less granular lipoid material, fat, and pigment which gives a yellow colour to the cortex as a whole. The cortex is richer in cholesterol than any other tissue in the body. The glomerular zone is larger and richer in fat in females than in males, and swells with each menstruation and pregnancy.

The **medulla** (Fig. 651, 4) is formed of a spongework of cell columns separated by anastomosing venous sinusoids. The cells are large and granular and exhibit the characteristic chromaffin reaction. In a fresh gland the medulla is of a dark red colour owing to the presence of blood in its sinusoidal spaces.

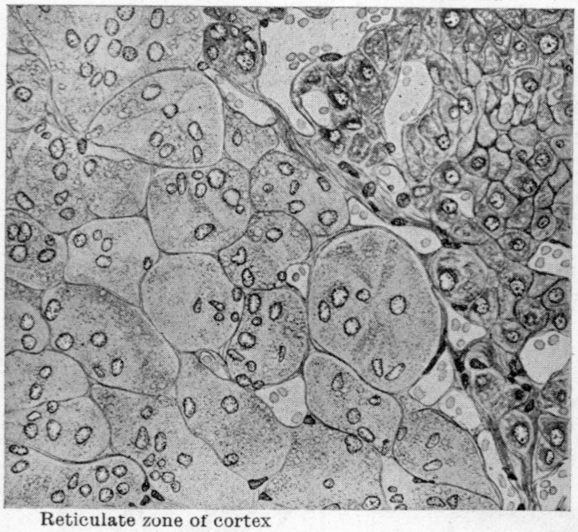

Reticulate zone of cortex

Fig. 649.—Section of Suprarenal Gland of Rabbit, showing medulla and adjacent reticulate zone of cortex. (Cramer, 6th Sci. Report, Imp. Cancer Research Fund.)

From the main blood-vessels, smaller vessels enter at numerous points in the fibrous capsule and run in the trabeculæ, forming a close network around and between the cell masses and columns of the zona glomerulosa and zona fasciculata. In the zona reticulata the blood-vessels open up to form a venous plexus which is continuous with the sinusoidal plexus in the medulla, and thus with the central efferent vein of the medulla which emerges at the hilum of the organ as the suprarenal vein. Few of the arterioles that enter the cortex pass directly through into the medulla. Most of the blood which reaches the medulla first passes through capillaries in the cortex. The endothelial cells lining these capillaries are of the "specific endothelial" type (see p. 786) showing pronounced phagocytic properties. These vessels thus act as a filter to the blood reaching the medulla. The medulla is, moreover, the first tissue in the body to receive *cortin* or vitamin C from the cortical tissue.

Development of the Suprarenal Glands.

—The cortical system is a derivative of the cœlomic epithelium (mesoderm). Proliferative activity in this layer between the root of the mesentery and the mesonephros is evident as early as the 6 mm. stage, when numerous buds of cells develop from the deep surface of the mesothelium. By the stage of 8-10 mm. those cells form a mass of cortical cells separate from the mesothelium. In Man the greater part of that tissue is ultimately included in the suprarenal cortex, but small masses may separate off, sooner or later, to form either independent cortical bodies or portions of accessory suprarenals (see p. 764). At the 12 mm. stage the main cortical mass is seen to lie in a tailward prolongation of the dorsal portion of the pleuroperitoneal membrane called the suprarenal ridge.

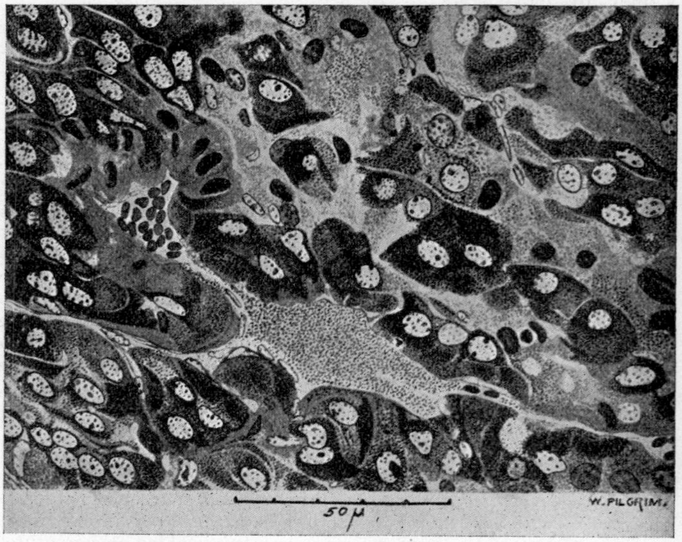

Meanwhile the sympatho-chromaffin primordium of the medulla has appeared, as early as the 5 mm. stage. The cells of that tissue early make contact with the cortex-primordium and later invade it. According to Lucas Keene and Hewer, invasion of the cortical mass by sympathochromaffin tissue begins

Fig. 650.—Medulla of Mouse's Suprarenal Gland, showing discharge of adrenaline in asphyxia. Granules of adrenaline blackened by osmic acid are seen in the medullary cells (in different phases of activity) and in the venous spaces. (Cramer, *Fever, Heat, etc.*)

about the 12 mm. stage, is most active towards the middle of the intra-uterine period, and ceases about full term. Not until the 19 cm. stage does the immigrant chromaffin tissue reach the neighbourhood of the central vein and form a true medulla (Zuckerkandl). Cortical envelopment of the medulla is probably due as much to progressive cortical overgrowth as to chromaffin invasion.

The relatively bulky *foetal cortex* degenerates progressively during the last ten weeks of intra-uterine life. At birth two parts of the cortex are distinguished, a still bulky fœtal cortex and a thin overlying true cortex. The characteristic cortical tissue of the fœtus disappears in the course of the first year and the volume of the entire cortex thus diminishes rapidly for a time.

The final specialisation of the cortex is not complete until much later. The definitive zona reticulata does not begin to appear until the fourth post-natal month, although the inner zone of the fœtal cortex is sometimes so named. The zona fasciculata is differentiated as such within

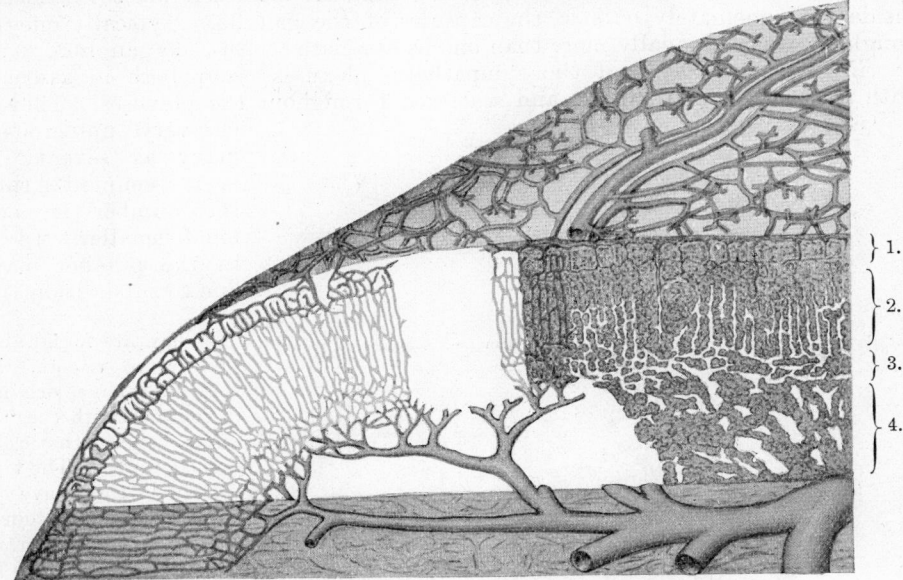

FIG. 651.—RECONSTRUCTION OF SUPRARENAL GLAND OF A DOG. (Marshall Flint.)
The upper part of the figure shows the arrangement of blood-vessels on the surface of the gland, the lower part their arrangement within its substance.
1. = Zona glomerulosa. 2. = Zona fasciculata. 3. = Zona reticulata. 4. = Medulla.

three weeks after birth, but the zona glomerulosa not until the second or third years. Until then it appears to be represented by a layer of incompletely specialised cells immediately underneath the fibrous capsule. In the pre-puberty period there is accelerated growth of the cortex ; and in middle age its involution begins.

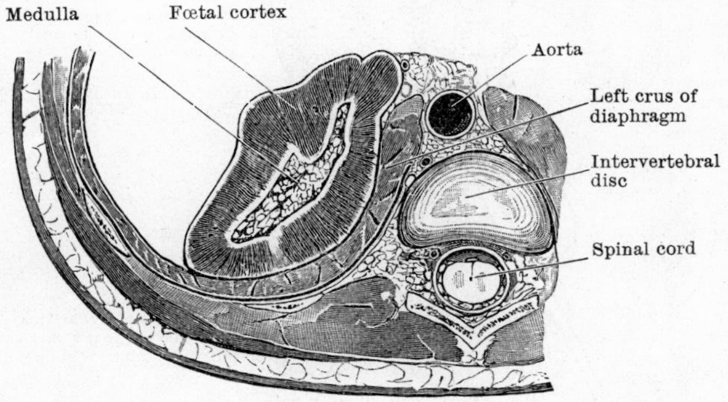

CHROMAFFIN SYSTEM

This system comprises a large number of masses of tissue similar in development, structure, and micro-chemical reactions to the medulla of the suprarenal gland.

FIG. 652.—TRANSVERSE SECTION THROUGH THE SUPRARENAL GLAND OF A NEW-BORN CHILD IN SITU.

The tissue is called chromaffin, or chromaphil, on account of its affinity for chromium salts, which give a brownish reaction with it. The general distribution of the masses of tissue forming the system is shown in Fig. 653. They all originate in intimate association with the rudiments of the sympathetic nervous system. Indeed, the characteristic chromaffin cells and the neurones of the sympathetic ganglia are derivatives from a common mother cell.

The chromaffin system includes paraganglia associated with the ganglia of the sympathetic trunk and with the collateral ganglia of the abdominal region, but none, so far as is known, associated with the terminal sympathetic ganglia. It includes also the medullary portions of the suprarenal glands, and possibly the carotid bodies and the glomus coccygeum. While the similarity of all chromaffin tissue points to a common function, it is by no means certain that the paraganglia secrete a hormone like the adrenaline of the suprarenal medulla.

(i.) The **paraganglia** associated with the ganglia of the sympathetic trunk are rounded masses of chromaffin tissue, 1-3 mm. in diameter, placed inside, half inside, or immediately outside the capsules of the ganglia. Typically one paraganglion, but occasionally more than one, is associated with each ganglion.

(ii.) The **paraganglia** of the sympathetic plexuses occur both in association with the prevertebral ganglia and scattered throughout the plexuses. They may be very numerous—as many as seventy have been counted, though the number is usually much smaller. Increase in the number may be due to subdivision.

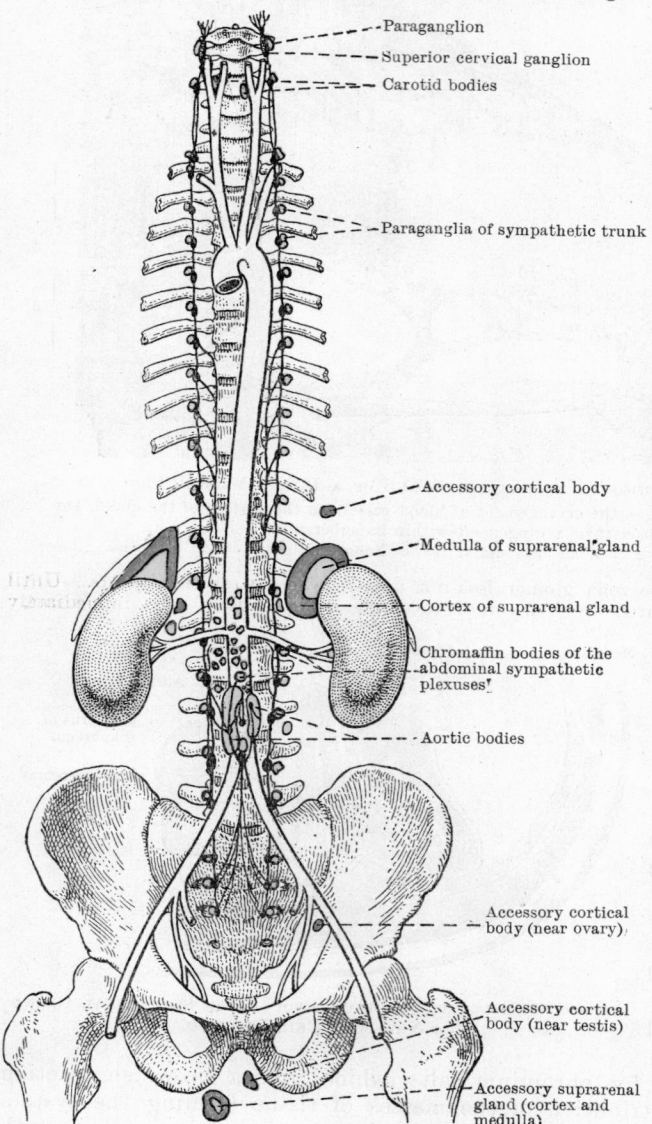

They are found also in relation to viscera, where they may have originated in common with the "peripheral" sympathetic ganglionic groups. The viscera to which they have been found related include the kidney and ureter, the suprarenal gland, the prostate, the par-oöphoron and ovary, and the epididymis. The most prominent paraganglia of the sympathetic plexuses are the two **aortic bodies** (aortic paraganglia) which lie anterior to the aorta in the region of the origin of the inferior mesenteric artery (Fig. 653). In the new-born child they are paired elongated structures, usually about a centimetre in length. Up to the age of 12-18 months they show increase in growth and in secretory activity. After the middle of the second year they—with many other paraganglia—undergo retrogressive changes. By the period of puberty they have practically ceased to be visible to the naked eye, though vestiges may be recognised, at least under the microscope, to a much later period of life. Even at the height of their development the aortic bodies are subject to

Labels in figure: Paraganglion; Superior cervical ganglion; Carotid bodies; Paraganglia of sympathetic trunk; Accessory cortical body; Medulla of suprarenal gland; Cortex of suprarenal gland; Chromaffin bodies of the abdominal sympathetic plexuses; Aortic bodies; Accessory cortical body (near ovary); Accessory cortical body (near testis); Accessory suprarenal gland (cortex and medulla)

FIG. 653.—DIAGRAM OF THE CHROMAFFIN AND CORTICAL SYSTEMS. Modified from Swale Vincent. Chromaffin tissue = yellow ; cortical tissue = blue.

considerable variation in size, form, and arrangement. They are commonly more or less asymmetrical and are often connected by a commissure. That appears to be a typical embryonic feature and is characteristic of the growth period, becoming progressively rarer during the period of decline. After the fourth year the commissure is no longer met with (Iwanoff). In the vicinity of the aortic bodies there are numerous smaller masses of like character and of varying size and shape. Fig. 654 illustrates the relations of the aortic bodies to the structures in their vicinity. The darker stippled areas along the periphery of the bodies represent developing sympathetic ganglia of the abdominal plexus.

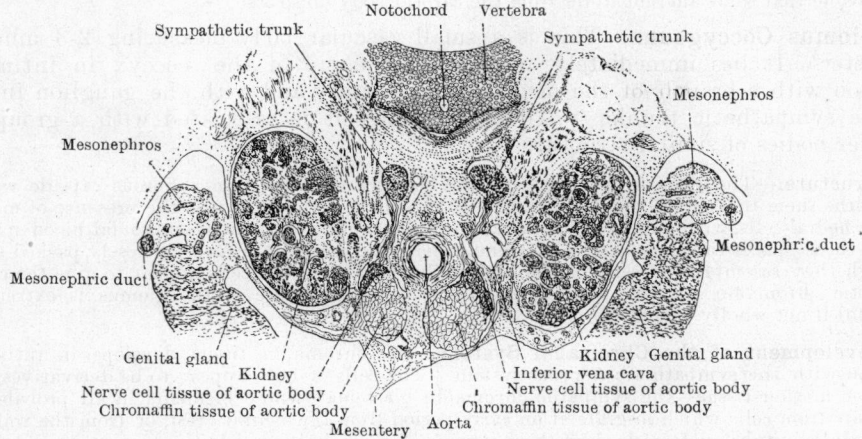

FIG. 654.—TRANSVERSE SECTION OF PART OF THE ABDOMINAL REGION OF A 25 MM. HUMAN EMBRYO. Seen from below, showing aortic bodies.

Carotid Body.—The carotid body [glomus caroticum] is situated in close but slightly variable relation to the bifurcation of the common carotid artery (Fig. 655), adjacent to the carotid sinus (p. 1165). Frequently the gland lies deep to the bifurcation; sometimes it is wedged in between the roots of the internal and external carotids; sometimes it is placed between them at a slightly higher level.

It is a small neuro-vascular structure of a shape that varies with its position. When free from pressure from its surroundings, it is oval; when situated between the internal and external carotids, it is wedge-shaped. On the average its height is about 7 mm., its breadth 1·5-5 mm. It sometimes comprises two or more separate nodules. Its colour is yellowish-grey to brownish-red.

Structure.—The carotid body consists of cellular groups or nodules surrounded by, and interspersed with, fibro-areolar tissue. The nodules are permeated by small arteries which are provided with abundant sensory nerve-endings. Some large chromaffin-like cells are present, and for this reason the carotid body has commonly been regarded as a part of the chromaffin system. Its structure and abundant sensory nerves passing into the sino-carotid nerve-plexus point, on the other hand, to a close relationship with the reflex depressor functions of the carotid sinus.

Nerve Supply.—Numerous afferent nerves pass from the carotid sinus and carotid body to a *sino-carotid nerve plexus.*

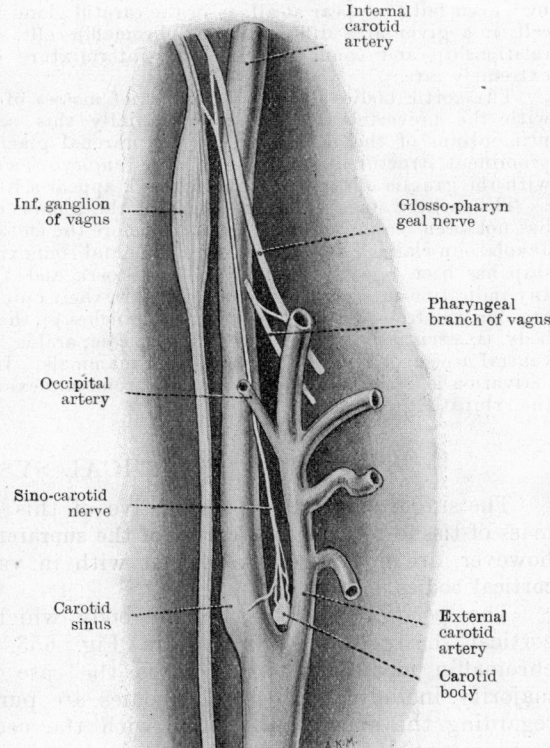

FIG. 655.—THE CAROTID BODY AND THE SINO-CAROTID NERVE WITH ITS PRINCIPAL CONNEXIONS.

From this plexus an *intercarotid* or *sino-carotid* nerve (Fig. 655) passes upwards with the pharyngeal branch of the glosso-pharyngeal nerve and divides into two branches, one of which joins the inferior ganglion of the vagus, the other the glosso-pharyngeal nerve. Other nerve filaments from the plexus pursue an independent but similar course, and join the glosso-

49

pharyngeal and vagus nerves and the cervical sympathetic trunk. The afferent fibres pass mainly to the glosso-pharyngeal nerve ; but some of those from the *carotid sinus* join the vagus, and it is probable that some afferent fibres from the carotid body do so also.

Glomus Coccygeum.—This is a small vascular body measuring 2-3 mm. in diameter. It lies immediately anterior to the tip of the coccyx in intimate relation with a branch of the median sacral artery and with the ganglion impar of the sympathetic trunks (p. 1066). Usually it is associated with a group of smaller bodies of similar structure.

Structure.—The glomus and the satellite bodies are enclosed in a fibrous capsule which ensheaths them individually. The characteristic feature of the glomus is the presence of masses of polyhedral cells, with large nuclei, surrounding the lumina of tortuous sinusoidal blood spaces. From those spaces capillary channels extend among the investing masses of closely packed cells. Though they resemble the cells of the carotid body, none of the cells appear to give the characteristic chromaffin reaction ; hence, the paraganglionic nature of the glomus is extremely doubtful if not wholly excluded.

Development of the Chromaffin System.—All chromaffin tissue develops in intimate relation with the sympathetic nervous system. The cells of both appear to be derivatives of a common mother-tissue—the sympatho-chromaffin blastema—whose elements in all probability originate from cells which migrate at an early period from the neural crest, or from the wall of the medullary tube, or from both of those sources.

In the 16 mm. embryo, sympatho-chromaffin tissue is met with in situations which more or less correspond to the distribution of the sympathetic nervous system. Differentiation of chromaffin cells from sympathetic neuroblasts begins about the 18 mm. stage (eighth week), but is not completed till late in the period of gestation, if then. The process is characterised by increase in the size of the chromaffin cells and a diminution of the intensity of their reaction to ordinary stains. Later the specific chromic-staining reaction develops, but its period is uncertain and it may even fail to appear at all, as in the carotid gland in some animals. It is stated that if any cells in a given area differentiate as chromaffin cells, all do ; so that, in spite of their intimate relationship and common origin, an intermixture of chromaffin and sympathetic cells is extremely rare.

The aortic bodies develop as the chief masses of a paired discontinuous series associated with the prevertebral plexuses. Cranially this series is originally continuous with the primordium of the medulla of the suprarenal gland on each side. The aortic bodies are prominent structures in the two-months embryo (*vide* Fig. 654). The paraganglia associated with the ganglia of the sympathetic trunk appear a little later.

The earliest stages of development of the glomus coccygeum are still obscure. Its presence has not been recognised with certainty before the end of the fourth month of intra-uterine life. Jakobssohn claimed to show its developmental connexion with the sympathetic. This relationship has been rejected as unproved by Stoerk and V. Schumacher, who searched in vain for any indication of a chromaffin reaction. In their opinion the characteristic cells of the glomus are derived from cells of the walls of branches of the median sacral artery, and the coccygeal body is essentially glomerular in type, comparable with caudal glomeruli present on the ventral aspect of the tail of some other mammals. In support of the view of its sympathetic derivation is its indubitably intimate nervous connexion with the terminal ganglion impar of the sympathetic trunks.

CORTICAL SYSTEM

The single constant representative of this system in higher vertebrates is the mass of tissue forming the **cortex of the suprarenal gland**. Masses of similar tissue, however, are not infrequently met with in various situations, forming **accessory cortical bodies**.

The positions in the human body which may be occupied by accessory cortical masses are indicated in Fig. 653. They may be associated with chromaffin medullary tissue, as is the case in the suprarenal itself, but the majority, including the smaller bodies, are purely cortical. The justification for regarding the suprarenal cortex, with the occasional accessory cortical masses, as representing a distinct system, is based upon both phylogenetic and ontogenetic considerations. These warrant the conception of an originally more extensive distribution of cortical tissue, distinct from the chromaffin system. In the higher vertebrates the cortical system would appear to have undergone concentration, thus coming to be represented mainly by the cortex of the suprarenal gland.

THYROID GLAND

COMPARATIVE ANATOMY OF THE CHROMAFFIN AND CORTICAL SYSTEMS

A knowledge of the main facts of the comparative anatomy of these systems throws light on their arrangement and function in man. Chromaffin tissue similar to that of mammals is found throughout the vertebrates, but its location is different in various groups. In the Cyclostomata it is arranged in thin strips on the walls of the larger arteries. Cortical tissue, rich in lipoids, also is recognised; it is arranged in small lobulated masses (the "inter-renal corpuscles") in the walls of the posterior cardinal veins and renal arteries. In the Elasmobranchii chromaffin bodies are arranged segmentally (the so-called "suprarenals") in close relation to the ganglia of the sympathetic trunk. The cortical tissue in these fish is represented by a pair of yellow "inter-renals" in the region of the kidney.

It is only in the Tetrapoda that cortical tissue and chromaffin tissue come into intimate topographical relation. Thus, in the Amphibia there is a composite organ—the "adrenal"—which is applied to each kidney. The greater part of each mass is made up, as in Man and other mammals, of columns of cortical cells, but at the borders of the gland collections of chromaffin cells occur. Among the higher Tetrapoda the detailed relation of the cortical and chromaffin tissues varies. In the Sauropsida the chromaffin tissue almost completely surrounds the cortical or "inter-renal" tissue, whereas in Mammalia the cortical tissue encloses the chromaffin tissue.

The very long phylogenetic history of both chromaffin and inter-renal tissues points to the fundamental part played by endocrine systems similar to that of the human suprarenal gland in the co-ordinating hormone apparatus of vertebrates generally. It seems possible that the paraganglia and the accessory cortical bodies of man have endocrine functions similar to, if not identical with, the medulla and cortex respectively of the suprarenals, but definite confirmation of this is not yet available. Nor is it yet known what differences of function are brought about by the difference of topographical relationship between the "inter-renal" and chromaffin tissue in Amphibia, Sauropsida and Mammalia respectively. Differences of detail in the Mammalia include a tendency to folding or convolution of the suprarenal cortex in Man and various other primates, and variations in the number of accessory cortical bodies. In some mammals (e.g. the rabbit) they are numerous; in others (e.g. the dog) they are rare—facts which have a bearing on the interpretation of the results of extirpation experiments.

THYROID GLAND

The **thyroid gland** is situated in the lower part of the front of the neck, and is enclosed in a fascial compartment formed by the sheath of pretracheal fascia which fixes it firmly to the trachea and larynx. The thyroid is an endocrine gland which produces a hormone of the greatest importance for the proper growth and function of most of the tissues in the body. This hormone is known as *thyroxine*. Characteristic of this organ is the storage of its secretion within small closed cavities—the vesicles of the thyroid. It is an organ of very ancient history, yet one that exhibits remarkably little evolutionary change, for its histology and endocrine action are similar throughout the whole series of vertebrates. The gland is yellowish red, soft, and extremely vascular; in this last respect it surpasses all other organs in the body excepting possibly the suprarenal glands. It varies in size with age, sex, and general nutrition, being relatively large in youth, in women, and in the well-nourished. In women it increases temporarily with menstruation and pregnancy. Its average dimensions are: height 5 cm., breadth 6 cm., thickness of each lobe 1-2 cm., weight 25-30 gm.; but these measurements are of little value because of the range of variation. Even the normal gland is stated to attain a weight of 60 gm. occasionally.

Usually the thyroid gland consists of a pair of conical **lobes** united across the median plane by a narrow band of gland tissue called the **isthmus**. But to many thyroid glands this description is inapplicable. In men and thin elderly women the gland is not uncommonly horse-shoe shaped; in young well-nourished women and during pregnancy its general contour is more rounded, deeply notched above to accommodate the larynx and deeply grooved behind for the trachea and œsophagus. Rarely, the gland is in two separate parts. Not infrequently, it is asymmetrical. In about 40 per cent. of specimens, a process of gland tissue called the **pyramidal lobe** extends upwards from the upper border of the isthmus, in front of the cricoid and thyroid cartilages, towards the hyoid bone. That process is seldom median, lying more often on the left than on the right; in rare cases, it is double; less rarely, it is double below and single above; sometimes it is represented by a strip of fibrous tissue or a narrow muscle (m. levator glandulæ thyreoideæ). The muscle may, however, be present independently of the pyramidal lobe.

Small oval accessory thyroid glands are common in the region of the hyoid bone, and are occasionally met with in relation to the right and left lobes. They may occur in the superior mediastinum of the thorax also.

Relations.—The gland itself has an external layer of fibrous tissue—the fibrous capsule—which is loosely connected by areolar tissue to the fascial sheath; the gland with its capsule is thus readily taken out of its sheath of pretracheal fascia. It is under cover of the sterno-thyroid, sterno-hyoid, and omo-hyoid muscles and, more laterally, it is overlapped by the sterno-mastoid (Fig. 352). The isthmus is, however, comparatively superficial between the margins of the sterno-thyroid muscles a short distance above the suprasternal notch. The isthmus usually lies on the front of the 2nd, 3rd, and 4th rings of the trachea; but occasionally it lies as high as the cricoid cartilage or as low as the 4th, 5th, and 6th rings of the trachea. The lobes extend below to the level of the 6th ring of the trachea, or even lower, and above as far as the middle of the thyroid cartilage. Superficially they are covered by the muscles mentioned, along with twigs of the ansa hypoglossi, and the anterior jugular vein. The upper part of each lobe is moulded medially to the thyroid and cricoid cartilages together with the crico-thyroid and inferior constrictor muscles; the external laryngeal nerve passes across the surface of the latter muscle. The lower part is moulded to the sides of the trachea and oesophagus and thus comes into close relation with the recurrent laryngeal nerve.

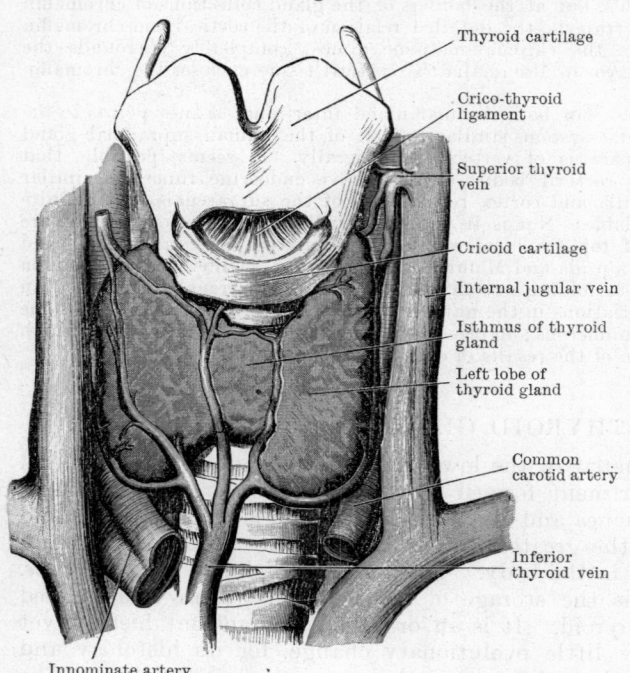

The posterior surface of each lobe is variable in width. It is in relation to the longus cervicis muscle and the sympathetic trunk, and more laterally to the carotid sheath, which becomes displaced in a postero-lateral direction by simple enlargements of the gland. The inferior end of the left lobe approaches or even makes contact with the thoracic duct. Closely applied to the posterior surface, within the fibrous capsule, are the two pairs of parathyroid glands; they may even be embedded within the substance of the thyroid.

Labels in figure:
Thyroid cartilage
Crico-thyroid ligament
Superior thyroid vein
Cricoid cartilage
Internal jugular vein
Isthmus of thyroid gland
Left lobe of thyroid gland
Common carotid artery
Inferior thyroid vein
Innominate artery

FIG. 656.—DISSECTION OF THE THYROID GLAND AND OF THE PARTS IN IMMEDIATE RELATION TO IT.

Vessels and Nerves.—The extraordinarily rich **arterial supply** is effected through the *superior* and *inferior thyroid arteries*. Occasionally (10 per cent. of cases) a fifth artery—the *thyroidea ima*, normally present in the embryo—persists in the adult. It is usually a branch of the innominate. The pyramidal lobe, if well developed, receives a special branch from one of the superior thyroid arteries, usually the left. The arteries are remarkable for their large size and for the frequency and freedom of their anastomoses. An anastomosing trunk courses up over the back of each lobe within the fascial sheath, and unites the inferior and superior thyroid arteries; it is of interest in connection with the recognition of the parathyroid glands (q.v.). Typically, three pairs of **veins** drain the gland. The upper two pairs, the *superior* and *middle thyroid veins*, join the internal jugular veins; the lower pair, the *inferior thyroid veins*, join the innominate veins. The veins take origin from the venous plexus on the surface of the gland or, in the case of the inferior, from a downward extension of the plexus in front of the trachea. When the gland is very large, accessory veins are present, sometimes in considerable numbers. Most of them pass to the internal jugular veins. A free, transverse, venous anastomosis is effected along the borders of the isthmus through superior and inferior communicating veins.

The **lymph vessels** pass directly from the subcapsular plexus to the *deep cervical lymph glands*; a few descend in front of the trachea to the *pretracheal lymph glands*, through which they are connected with *innominate glands* behind the manubrium sterni.

The **nerves** are non-medullated pre-ganglionic fibres which come from the *superior* and *middle cervical sympathetic ganglia*. They reach the gland by way of the cardiac and the superior and recurrent laryngeal nerves, and along the superior and inferior thyroid arteries. The nerves are partly vasomotor in character ; others, however, end in close relation with the epithelial cells of the vesicles of the gland—though as yet they have not been shown to be secretory in function.

Structure.—The gland consists of a mass of minute rounded vesicles, of various sizes and commonly about 300 μ in diameter (Figs. 657, 664). Each vesicle consists of a layer of epithelial cells enclosing a mass of colloid. They are embedded in a fibrous tissue framework or stroma which is continuous externally with the capsule. Numerous lymph vessels, arteries, veins and nerves course in the stroma. The lymph vessels appear to be mainly concerned in the drainage of the intervesicular tissue (Figs. 657, 658) ; the larger trunks pass to a dense plexus on the surface of the gland.

Development.—The thyroid gland is developed from a median ventral diverticulum of the floor of the pharynx, and from two lateral primordia which are identified with the "ultimo-branchial bodies" (*vide infra*). The long-disputed question of the participation of these structures in the development of the thyroid gland seems now to be settled in favour of this view.

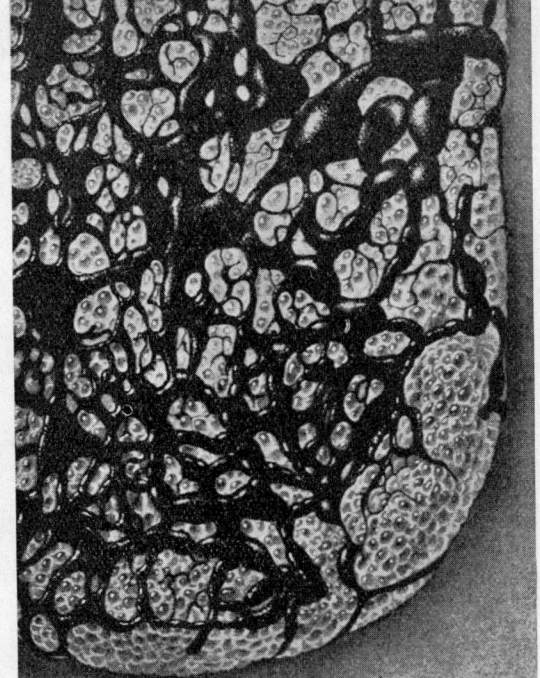

FIG. 657.—SURFACE VIEW OF DOG'S THYROID GLAND (slightly magnified) showing individual vesicles and the injected extraglandular plexus of lymph vessels. (Rienhoff, *Archives of Surgery*.)

According to Weller the median diverticulum forms the isthmus and a small part only of each lobe. It appears in embryos less than 2 mm. in length (possessing about six mesodermal somites) as a small out-pocketing of the pharyngeal floor. The tuberculum impar (p. 59) at first surrounds the opening of the diverticulum but later is entirely anterior to it. The diverticulum by rapid downgrowth soon forms a plate-like structure ventral to the trachea, connected by a narrow tube called the *thyro-glossal duct* with the pharyngeal floor.

This duct disappears normally in embryos of six weeks, but a vestige of its original opening into the pharynx persists in the adult as the foramen cæcum of the tongue (p. 545). The "ultimo-branchial bodies," which form the greater part of the lobes of the thyroid gland, are developed a little later than the median thyroid primordium — appearing as ventral diverticula of the 4th pharyngeal pouches (Fig. 659). In the sixth week the 4th pharyngeal pouch, with this ventral diverticulum, is still connected by a narrow tubular stalk with the pharynx ; but by the seventh week the connexion is interrupted and the ultimo-branchial body is then closely applied to the lateral wing of the median thyroid primordium.

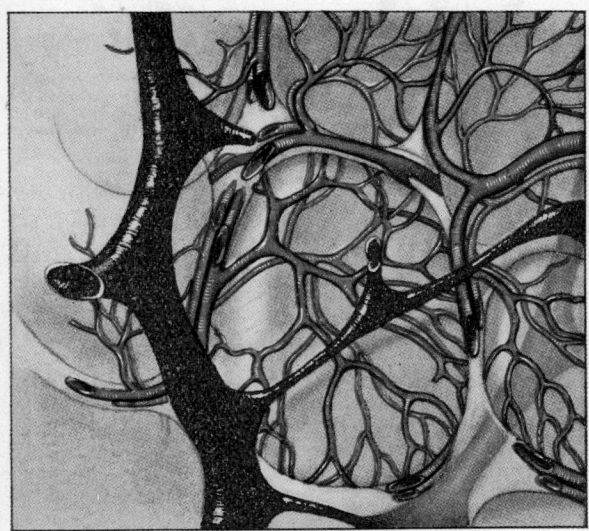

FIG. 658.—INJECTED SPECIMEN OF DOG'S THYROID GLAND. Enlarged drawing demonstrating the relative size of the lymph and blood capillary plexuses and their relation to the individual vesicles. Note that the lymphatic plexus (black) lies external and in less intimate contact with the individual vesicles than the blood capillary plexus, which is specific for each vesicle. (Rienhoff, *Archives of Surgery*.)

plied to the lateral wing of the median thyroid primordium. At the same time it has become sharply differentiated from the parathyroid IV gland (p. 775) developed from the 4th pharyngeal pouch (Fig. 659).

Histological differentiation of the gland proceeds by the arrangement of the embryonic epithelial cells in two sheets, with disappearance of the original lumen of the diverticular primordium ; this stage is fol-

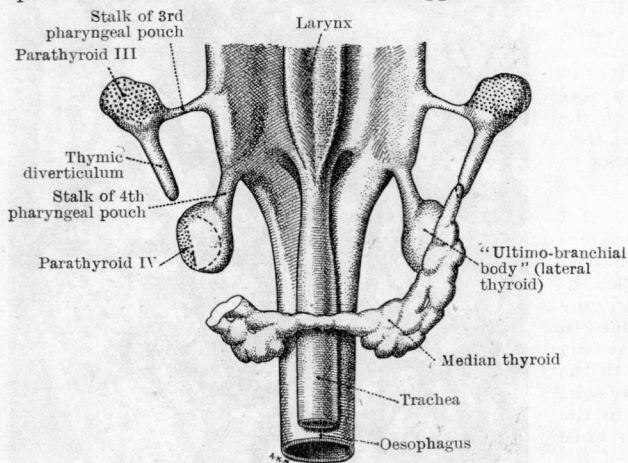

lowed by the formation of definite follicles which later become vesicular. The median primordium passes through the earlier stages of histological differentiation before the lateral primordia, and at the time of its fusion with them it is histologically distinct from them. Additional " secondary " follicles are added throughout fœtal life but the process slows down before birth and probably ceases about puberty. Postnatal growth of the gland consists mainly in an increase in size of the vesicles.

The developmental history of the gland affords a ready explanation of its variations in the adult. Thus, the development of a pyramidal lobe and its variations, partial and complete duplication, are due to the development of gland tissue from that part of the thyro-glossal duct which has a double lumen and the more or

FIG. 659.—DIAGRAMMATIC VENTRAL VIEW OF WALL OF PRIMITIVE PHARYNX, showing the " pharyngeal derivatives " in an embryo of the sixth week.

less complete fusion or separation of the masses thus formed. *Accessory thyroid glands* near the hyoid bone are the result of development of gland tissue from isolated remnants of the duct. Their occurrence behind the sternum above the arch of the aorta is probably due to a downward displacement of thyroid tissue along with that vessel, with which the median thyroid diverticulum is in close relation at an early stage.

The occurrence in the adult of a duct leading from the foramen cæcum to, or towards, the hyoid bone (*lingual duct*) is due to a persistence of the upper part of the thyro-glossal duct. Similarly, *thyro-glossal cysts* are due to the persistence of short segments of the duct.

Comparative Anatomy.—A thyroid gland similar in structure and probably also in function to that of Man and other mammals is found throughout the vertebrates. In Cyclostomata it is isolated from the pharyngeal epithelium only in the adult ; in the larval stage the specific thyroid tissue is situated at the sides of a diverticulum which has an opening on the

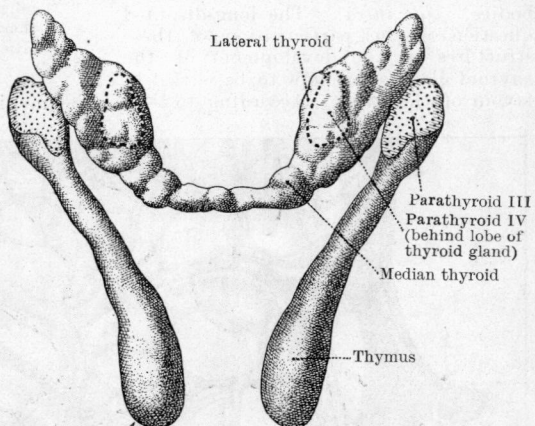

FIG. 660.—THE THYMUS, THYROID AND PARATHYROID GLANDS IN AN EMBRYO OF THE SEVENTH WEEK.

floor of the pharynx. This diverticulum is elsewhere lined with ciliated epithelium and it appears to be representative of the same organ as the endostyle of *Amphioxus*. The thyroid gland consists of two separate structures, right and left, in certain fish, amphibia, birds, and mammals. When this arrangement occurs in a mammal (as usually in the dog) it is probably the result of atrophy of the isthmus. It is uncertain whether any part of the thyroid is developed from a median pharyngeal diverticulum in submammalian vertebrates as it is in Man. Structures which appear to correspond to the human ultimo-branchial bodies are seen in vertebrates generally, forming in many of them small isolated **supra-pericardial bodies** close to the pericardium.

ULTIMO-BRANCHIAL BODIES

The 4th pharyngeal pouch of each side has, in embryos of 8-12 mm. in length, a ventral diverticulum known as the ultimo-branchial body (Figs. 72 and 659). This diverticulum is perhaps a part of the 4th pouch, but owes its customary name to the view which has been commonly held that it is a vestige of a fifth pharyngeal pouch. The opinion formerly held that the ultimo-branchial bodies give rise to a part of the lobes of the thyroid gland has been discredited for many years; it has been thought that they degenerate and disappear. Recent investigation tends, however, to confirm the original view that thyroid tissue is developed from these bodies (Weller).

PARATHYROID GLANDS

The **parathyroid glands** are two pairs of small glands closely applied to the back of the thyroid gland within its fibrous capsule (Fig. 661). They are distinguished as the superior and inferior parathyroid glands; but in reference to their developmental origin (q.v.), the upper pair is sometimes known also as the parathyroids IV and the lower pair as the parathyroids III.

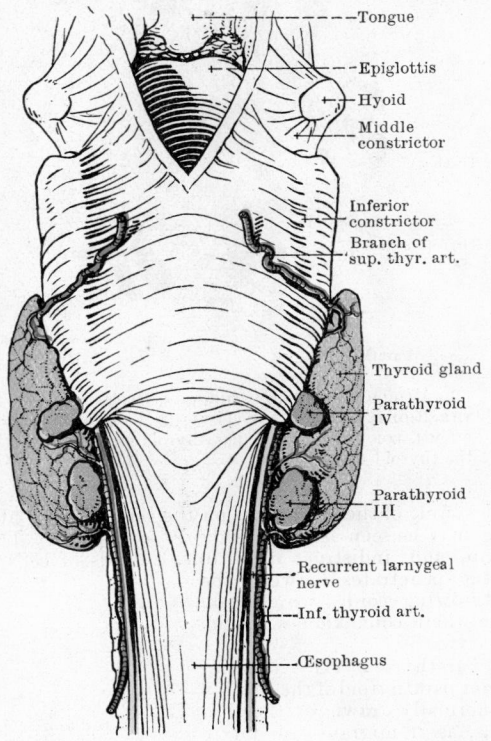

The parathyroid glands produce a hormone which plays a part in maintaining the relation between the blood and skeletal calcium. Possibly they produce another hormone. Extirpation of all four of the glands in a mammal causes death within a few days, but such is the margin of safety that removal of two of them produces no obvious effect.

The parathyroid glands are yellowish-brown, ovoid or lentiform structures, varying in size between extremes of 1 to 20 mm. in their long (generally vertical) diameter. Most commonly they are from 5 to 7 mm. in length, 3 to 4 mm. in width, and 1 to 2 mm. in thickness. Their individual weights vary within wide limits. The total amount of parathyroid gland tissue has been stated to show a mean variation from 0·8 to 1·2 gm.

FIG. 661.—DISSECTION SHOWING THYROID AND PARATHYROIDS OF ADULT FROM BEHIND.

The normal number of parathyroids may be diminished, though not very commonly in early life, to three, two, or even one. In some such cases, however, it is not easy to be certain that a minute ectopic gland may not have escaped notice. On the other hand the number may be increased, probably as a result of division of the original primordia. Thus five to eight—even in an extreme case as many as twelve—have been recorded : the distinguishing numerals are then applied to the gland-groups attributed to the respective pouches.

The **superior parathyroid gland** is usually embedded in the capsule of the thyroid gland at the back of the corresponding lobe, about its middle. The **inferior parathyroid gland** is similarly embedded on the back of the lower end of the lobe. As a rule the anastomosing arterial channel which connects the inferior and superior thyroid arteries passes near both parathyroids and furnishes the best guide to them, but the range of exceptional positions which the glands may occupy is wide. Thus, the superior parathyroid may be found (1) behind the pharynx or œsophagus, (2) in the fibrous tissue at the side of the larynx, above the level of the thyroid gland, (3) behind any part of the corresponding lobe of the thyroid gland or even embedded in the thyroid substance ("internal parathyroid"); whereas the inferior parathyroid may be found (1) near the bifurcation of the common carotid artery, (2) behind any part of the corresponding lobe of the thyroid gland, (3) on the sides of the trachea, or (4) in the thorax close to the thymus. This wide range of variation in position is explicable by the close association of the inferior parathyroid with the main thymus element in development (see next page).

49 a

Vessels and Nerves.—The **artery** to each parathyroid may spring from any branch of the *inferior* or *superior thyroid arteries*, but most commonly is a branch of the large anastomosing vessel between them. The **lymph vessels** drain with those of the thyroid gland. The **nerve supply** is abundant and comes from the plexus surrounding the thyroid gland (*v. supra*).

Structure.—The parathyroids are built up of interconnected trabeculæ of epithelial cells with strands of vascular fibro-areolar tissue between them. Sometimes the cellular arrangement is of a more compact character, or again, some of the cells may be arranged in follicle-like clumps enclosing a colloid material (devoid of iodine). The "principal" cells, which contribute the majority, are large and clear ; but after the age of eight or nine, some of the cells contain acidophil granules and are believed to be degenerating principal cells.

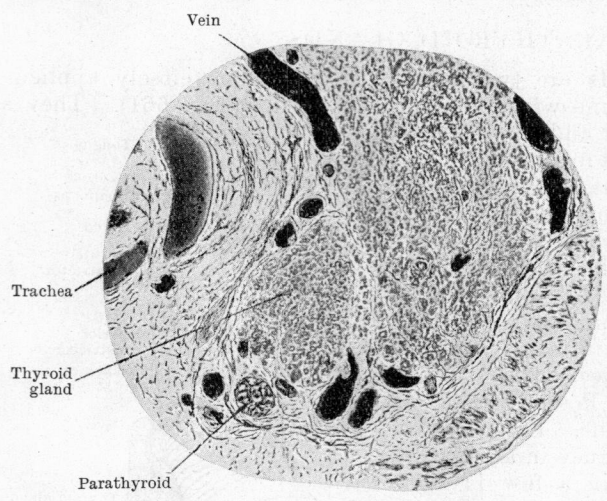

Blood and lymph vessels and nerves course in the interstitial stroma. The parathyroids produce their hormone after transplantation ; the nerves are apparently vasomotor and not secretory.

FIG. 662.—OBLIQUE SECTION THROUGH PART OF THE TRACHEA AND THE RIGHT LOBE OF THE THYROID GLAND OF A HUMAN FŒTUS 60 MM. LONG, showing a parathyroid embedded in the capsule of the thyroid gland.

Development.—The parathyroid glands develop from the dorsal diverticula of the third and fourth pharyngeal pouches (Fig. 659). The first indication of their development is a proliferation and thickening of the epithelium on the cephalic and lateral aspects of the diverticula. This thickening may be seen as early as the 10 mm. stage. The cells forming it are vacuolated, difficult to stain, and indistinct in outline. Cords of cells grow out from the thickening, and fibrous tissue penetrates between the outgrowing cords, which soon lose their connexion with the pharynx.

Parathyroid III — the inferior parathyroid of the adult— is normally drawn by the thymus, as it migrates, caudal to parathyroid IV. As a rule it halts at the level of the lower end of the lobe of the thyroid gland, but may continue its descent into the thorax. On the other hand it may not descend at all. In the latter case it remains near the bifurcation of the common carotid artery, where it is liable to be confused with the carotid body.

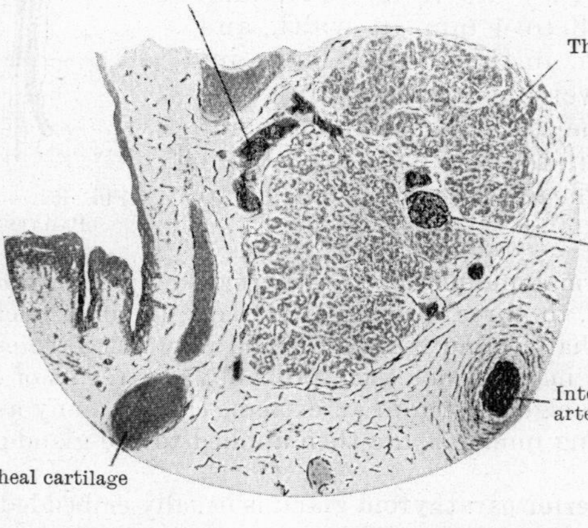

Comparative Anatomy.— Parathyroid glands occur throughout the Tetrapoda. In some reptiles they are stated to develop from the second pharyngeal pouch as well as from the third and fourth. In certain mammals, *e.g.* the mole, only those which are formed from the third pouches are developed.

FIG. 663.—OBLIQUE SECTION THROUGH PART OF THE TRACHEA AND THE LEFT LOBE OF THE THYROID GLAND OF A HUMAN FŒTUS 60 MM. LONG, showing a parathyroid embedded in the thyroid gland.

HYPOPHYSIS CEREBRI

The **hypophysis cerebri** is a small gland of duplex origin. It forms a median basal appendage of the hypothalamus, behind and below the optic chiasma (Figs. 665, 666). It is lodged in the hypophyseal fossa, between the cavernous sinuses and above the hinder part of the sphenoidal air-sinuses. It was formerly known as the *pituitary body* from an old notion that it secreted the nasal mucus.

Relations.—It occupies the hypophyseal fossa (Pl. LX) between the dorsum sellæ behind, and the tuber-culum sellæ in front. This cavity is lined with dura mater and roofed over by the diaphragma sellæ. The hypophysis is covered with a layer of tissue continuous with the pia mater, and is enclosed by the arachnoid mater in an extension of the subarachnoid space, except behind where arteries and veins join the gland. Through a small aperture in the dia-phragma sellæ, the infundi-bulum connects the main portion of the hypophysis with the tuber cinereum of the floor of the third ventricle. The cavernous sinus is lateral to the hypophysis, and the inter-cavernous sinuses pass be-low, behind, and in front of it. The internal carotid artery, in the cavernous

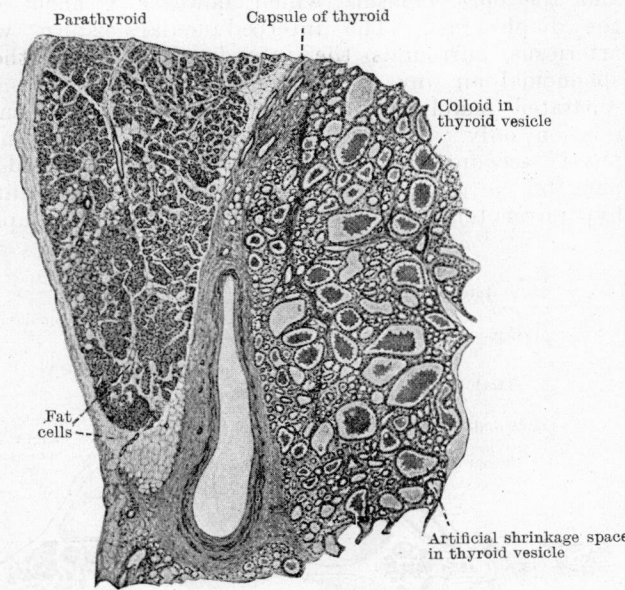

FIG. 664.—SECTION THROUGH THYROID AND PARATHYROID GLANDS (Maximow and Bloom, *Text Book of Histology*, after Braus).

sinus, is a fairly close lateral relation to the hypophysis, and more distantly, to

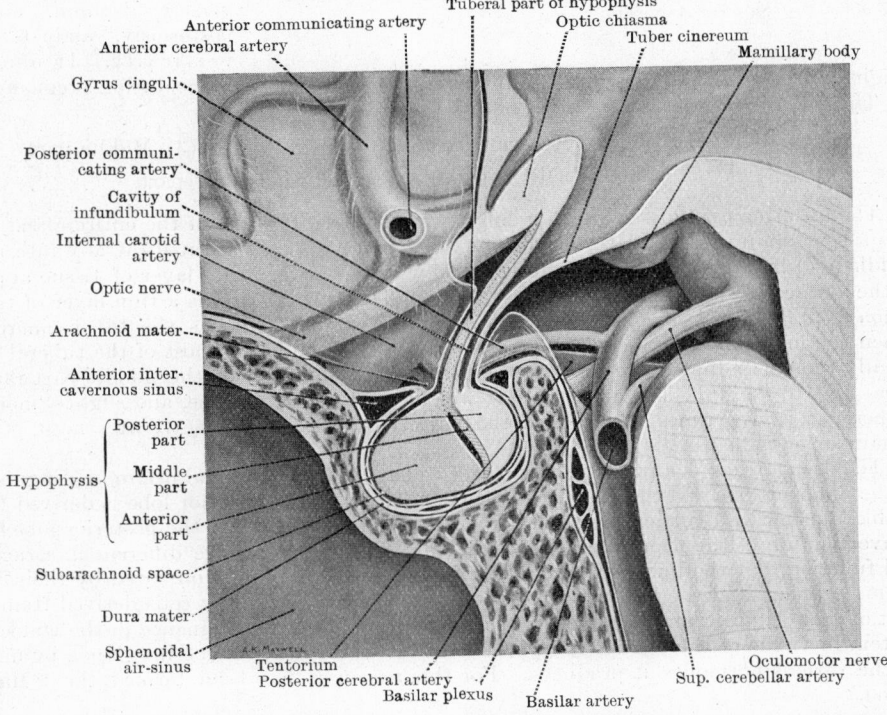

FIG. 665.—DIAGRAMMATIC MEDIAN SECTION OF HYPOPHYSIS *IN SITU*, showing the parts of the organ and its relations to adjacent structures.

the lateral side, are situated the oculomotor, trochlear, and abducent nerves and the ophthalmic division of the trigeminal nerve. The anterior part of the diaphragma sellæ intervenes between the anterior part of the hypophysis and the optic chiasma, which, however, is about one third of an inch above the diaphragma. The interpeduncular cistern, with the contained circulus arteriosus, surrounds the infundibulum above the diaphragma sellæ. The sphenoidal air-sinus is situated below and in front of the hypophyseal fossa, separated merely by a thin wall of bone; if small, it is an antero-inferior relation only. The close proximity of important structures to the hypophysis accounts for various symptoms associated with pathological enlargement of the gland (as in acromegaly). Enlargement of the anterior part of the hypophysis tends to thrust the forepart of the diaphragma sellæ upwards and to cause bitemporal hemianopsia through pressure on the more anterior fibres in the optic chiasma. An enlarged hypophysis sometimes also gives rise to symptoms which are due to encroachment upon the roof of the sphenoidal air-sinus or to pressure upon the cavernous sinus and the oculomotor and abducent nerves.

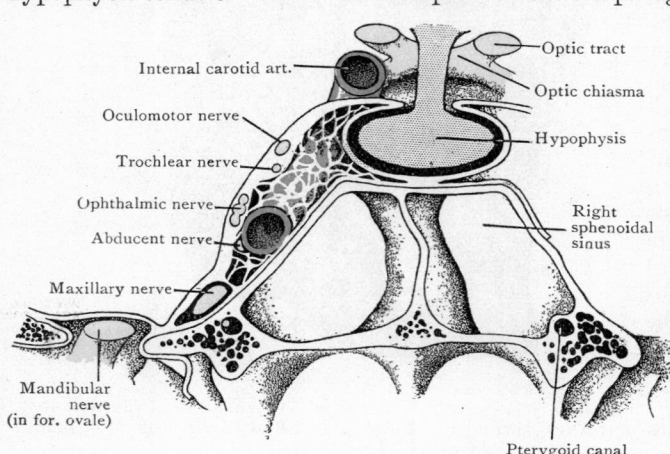

FIG. 666.—DIAGRAMMATIC CORONAL SECTION THROUGH CAVERNOUS SINUS showing the relations of the Hypophysis (Beesly and Johnston's *Manual of Surgical Anatomy*).

The hypophysis is a rounded structure with the following average dimensions: 14 mm. transversely, 9 mm. anteroposteriorly, and 6 mm. vertically. It usually weighs a little over half a gramme. It undergoes some enlargement during pregnancy.

The following parts are distinguished (Figs. 665, 669):

ANTERIOR LOBE: (1) Anterior part; (2) Tuberal part; (3) Middle part.

POSTERIOR LOBE: (4) Posterior or "nervous" part.

The **anterior part** of the anterior lobe forms the greater part of the entire gland, and comprises its anterior and lateral portions (Fig. 670). It is separated (at any rate until middle age) by a cleft from the **middle part**, which is a very thin layer of tissue applied to the surface of the **posterior lobe** (Fig. 665). The **tuberal part** is a thin layer of tissue which encircles the front of the infundibulum, and extends as far as the tuber cinereum. When the infundibulum is cut across in the removal of the brain, most of the tuberal part usually remains adherent to the tuber cinereum. The weight of the middle part ranges from $\frac{1}{2000}$ to $\frac{1}{50}$ gm. The anterior part weighs over half a gramme, and slightly more in women; it is five times as large as the posterior part, which contributes most of the remainder of the entire organ.

The hypophysis comprises two parts of different developmental origin, distinguished as the anterior lobe and the posterior lobe respectively. The anterior lobe is derived from Rathke's pouch, a diverticulum of the oral (stomodæal) pit (p. 52), the posterior lobe from a diverticulum of the floor of the diencephalon. The two parts are different in structure and function, but the line of demarcation between them becomes obscured by their very intimate union, and the infiltration of the part of neural origin by cells derived from the part of oral origin. The hypophysis occupies a position of pre-eminence in the endocrine system in virtue of the control it exerts over most of the other endocrine glands by means of the various hormones it produces. For this reason it has been termed the "Master Gland."

Vessels and Nerves.—The anterior and tuberal parts of the gland have an abundant **arterial supply**; that of the middle and posterior parts is relatively poor. A branch of the *internal carotid* artery enters the gland on each side at the junction of anterior and posterior lobes, and is distributed to both lobes. Other small arteries arise from the circulus arteriosus and reach the gland by passing down the surface of the infundibular stalk. Blood leaves the gland by means of **veins** which pass into the *cavernous* and *intercavernous sinuses*. There is a series of fine channels in the walls of the infundibular stalk in which small particles of colloid are sometimes seen. According to Popa and Fielding these constitute a "portal" blood system which conveys blood from the vessels of the hypophysis to a system of capillaries in the hypothalamus. **Lymph vessels** have not been demonstrated in the gland.

The **nerves** of the anterior part are a rich supply of unmyelinated fibres from the carotid plexus. While many of these are vasomotor in function, there are some nerve-fibres which have terminals in intimate relation with the epithelial cells and may be secretory in function. That the nervous connexions are not essential to all its endocrine functions is shown by the fact that grafts of the gland produce active secretions. Some nerve-fibres pass between the middle part and the posterior lobe. The posterior lobe is joined to the supra-optic nucleus (Cajal) by a large tract of fibres which runs along the infundibulum. Whether these fibres are afferent or efferent in respect of the hypophysis is not settled. Functionally there is some connexion between the hypophysis and the hypothalamus.

Structure and Function.—The *anterior part* of the **anterior lobe** is composed in the adult mainly of columns of epithelial cells supported by areolar tissue. In the central part of each half there is a vascular pocket of areolar tissue containing vessels of considerable size. Capillaries pass from these vessels into intimate relation with the epithelial cells, and

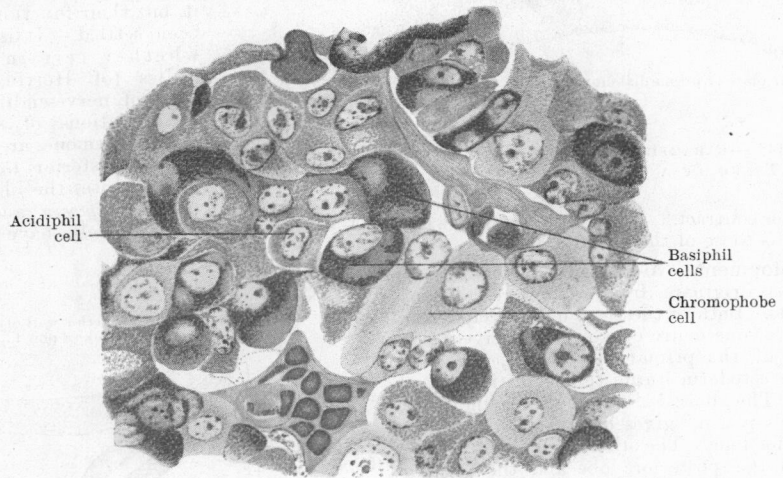

FIG. 667.—SECTION OF ANTERIOR PART OF PIG'S HYPOPHYSIS, stained with safranin-acid violet to show the three principal kinds of cell. (S. Maurer and D. Lewis, *Journ. Exper. Med.*)

eventually reach a vascular plexus on the periphery of the anterior part. The tubular arrangement of the epithelial cells seen in fœtal life disappears before birth. Vesicles of colloid material are to be seen at all ages from the fourth month of intra-uterine life; colloid also appears in the intraglandular cleft.

Three principal kinds of cells are recognised :—*Chromophobe, Acidiphil, Basiphil*. The first-named form about half the total number (Fig. 667); most of the remainder are acidiphils, basiphils forming only about one-tenth of the total.

The anterior part is known to produce numerous distinct hormones, several of which influence the activity of other endocrine glands. Since there are only three principal types of cell it is evident that one or more of them must produce more than one hormone. The growth hormone appears to be derived from the acidiphil cells, and the hormone which influences the sex glands from the basiphil. The precise source of the others is not known. The unequal distribution of basiphils and acidiphils in the anterior part (the former mainly peripherally and near the cleft) assists the comparative study of experimental injuries. Tumours consisting of the different types of cell produce different effects—basiphil ones causing obesity and various other changes, known collectively as Cushing's syndrome, acidiphil ones causing acromegaly. Various conditions have been recognized which appear to depend on hyposecretion, viz. the syndromes of Fröhlich and Simmonds and Lorain's type of infantilism. The condition of diabetes insipidus is thought to be due to a lesion of the posterior lobe or of the hypothalamus or of both.

Absence of the acidiphils is found to be related in mice to defect in respect of a certain gene; the effect on the sex glands is then found to be present but not the growth-stimulating effect.

The *middle part* is almost avascular. It appears to be the least specialised portion of the hypophysis; it grows less, shows an accumulation of colloid, and occasionally has ciliated cells. No acidiphil cells are differentiated; chromophobes and basiphils are present. In the fœtus gland tubules are present and open into the cleft, which is a vestige of the lumen of the buccal diverticulum (Rathke's pouch). These gland tubules subsequently extend into the posterior lobe; and basiphil cells also migrate from the middle part into the posterior lobe (Lewis and Lee).

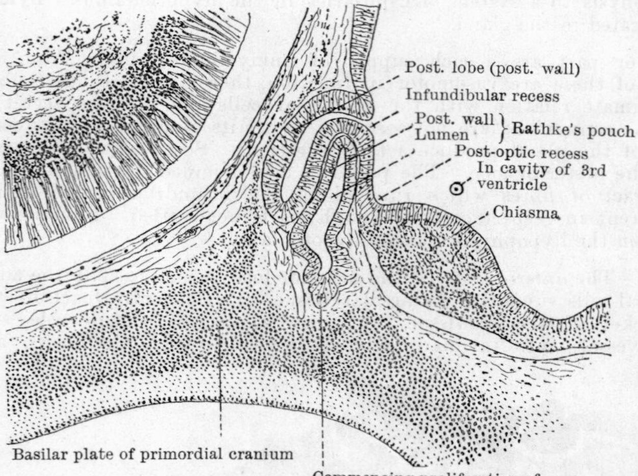

The *tuberal part* consists mainly of small basiphil cells with small accumulations of colloid.

The **posterior lobe** or "nervous part" consists of a mass of neuroglia, and of small cells that resemble neuroglia cells. The invasion of this part by gland tubules and basiphil cells from the middle part of the anterior lobe has been mentioned above. Thousands of nerve-fibres enter it, but their function has not been settled. It is doubtful whether certain hyaline bodies (of Herring) are a kind of nerve-ending or are accumulations of secretions. Potent hormones are produced in the posterior lobe; *vaso-pressin* raises the blood pressure and *oxytocin* cause uterine muscle to contract. It is not known whether the immigrant basiphil cells have the same function as those of the anterior lobe.

FIG. 668.—PARAMEDIAN SAGITTAL SECTION OF THE HYPOPHYSEAL REGION OF A HUMAN EMBRYO (20 MM. CR LENGTH).

[Figure 668 labels: Post. lobe (post. wall); Infundibular recess; Post. wall / Lumen } Rathke's pouch; Post-optic recess; In cavity of 3rd ventricle; Chiasma; Basilar plate of primordial cranium; Commencing proliferation of glandular buds from anterior lobe]

Development.—As already mentioned, the hypophysis originates from two entirely distinct rudiments. Both of these are hollow ectodermal diverticula, one neuro-ectodermal, derived from the floor of the primary fore-brain, the other from the ectoderm lining the primitive mouth cavity. The buccal diverticulum, known as "Rathke's pouch," gives origin to the whole of the anterior lobe. The other diverticulum gives origin to the posterior lobe and the infundibulum.

The first indication of the appearance of the hypophysis is met with in embryos of 2-3 mm. in the shape of an angular depression at the bottom of the oral pit (p. 52) immediately in front of the dorsal attachment of the bucco-pharyngeal membrane. It deepens progressively, and in the 7 mm. embryo it has become a deep and wide saccular diverticulum, compressed antero-posteriorly, and opening by an aperture of equal width into the primitive mouth cavity. The earliest indication of the appearance of the posterior lobe is a slight funnel-like depression in the floor of the fore-brain vesicle (Fig. 76, p. 61) in the 4-5 mm. embryo. At the 10-12 mm. stage the recess has become deeper and more sharply marked, and its anterior wall is already in close apposition with the fundus of the saccular anterior lobe. After the 12 mm. stage the portion of the buccal diverticulum nearest its mouth rapidly narrows and elongates to form a slender tubular stalk. By the stage of the 20 mm. embryo this stalk has become interrupted, separating the embryonic anterior lobe from its original connexion with the mouth epithelium. Remnants of the obliterated stalk persist, not only at that stage but up to much later periods of intra-uterine life, and may sometimes be

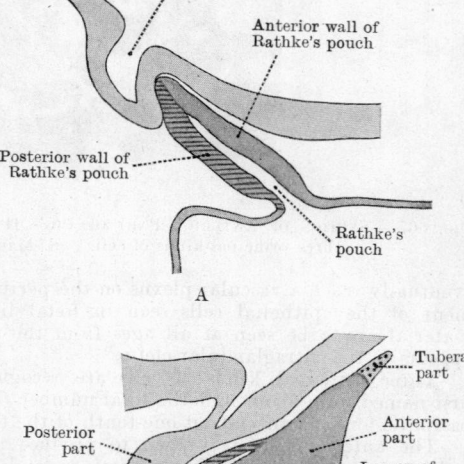

FIG. 669.—DIAGRAMMATIC MEDIAN SECTIONS OF HYPOPHYSIS IN EARLY STAGES OF DEVELOPMENT, showing (A) approximation of the infundibular recess to Rathke's pouch, and (B) the origin of the various parts of the organ. The posterior wall of Rathke's pouch develops into the middle part of the hypophysis, its anterior wall into the anterior and tuberal parts.

[Figure 669 labels: Infundibular recess; Anterior wall of Rathke's pouch; Posterior wall of Rathke's pouch; Rathke's pouch; A; Tuberal part; Anterior part; Posterior part; Lumen of Rathke's pouch; Middle part; B] detected in the postnatal period. In some cases the basilar plate remains incomplete immediately around the stem of the hypophysis, so that a cranio-pharyngeal canal may be found later in the osseous cranial base and sometimes even containing vestiges of epithelial stalk tissue.

At the end of the second month the anterior lobe is a broad compressed sac, deeply notched for the reception of the posterior lobe. On each side of that notch the fundus of the sac is prolonged backwards in the form of paired hollow cornual extensions of the anterior lobe at the sides of the neck of the posterior lobe (they are already conspicuous in that situation in transverse sections as early as the 14 mm. stage). At the two-months period the original anterior surface of the sac has become secondarily cupped, its concavity now looking towards the brain floor in front of the infundibular region. The concavity is partially subdivided by a prominence in the middle into two fossæ which are occupied by tissue continuous with the surrounding mesoderm. These fossæ are presently invaded by the proliferating glandular cell-cords of the anterior wall of the sac during the process of formation of the anterior part of the organ. The bilateral pockets of areolar tissue, representing these mesodermal accumulations, were noted on p. 779 in the course of the description of the anterior part of the adult gland.

The recurved proximal margin of the anterior lobe extends forwards and upwards towards the brain and eventually reaches the tuberal region of the floor of the diencephalon, where it spreads out to a greater or lesser extent, as the tuberal part.

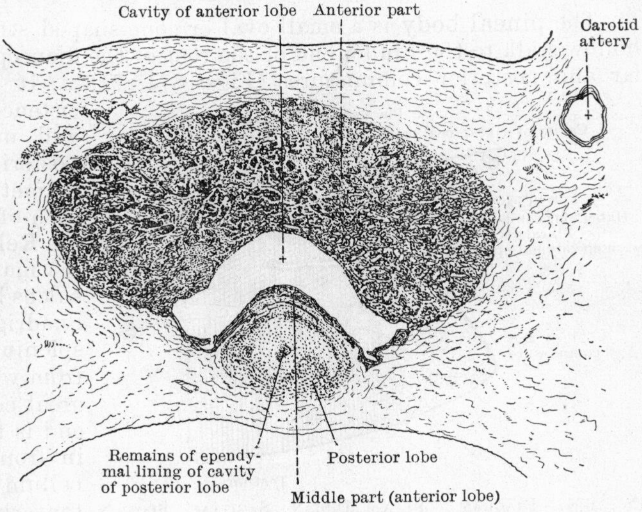

Up to about the 20 mm. stage the wall of the anterior lobe preserves its simple epithelial character. Already, however, it has begun to show indications of a process of proliferative budding (Fig. 668) and in this manner the cell-cords become intermingled with highly vascular mesenchyme which will form the sinusoidal stroma of the fully developed anterior part. In a fœtus of the third month (Fig. 670) the epithelial posterior wall of the anterior lobe is closely applied to the anterior surface of the posterior lobe and shows very little, if any, proliferative increase in thickness. It is this epithelial lamina which forms the middle part of the anterior lobe. In front of it the lumen of the anterior lobe of the hypophysis is still quite roomy. Later

FIG. 670.—HORIZONTAL SECTION OF THE HYPOPHYSEAL REGION OF A HUMAN FŒTUS (71 MM. CR LENGTH).

on it undergoes reduction and at least partial obliteration, the "intraglandular cleft" or clefts representing it becoming occupied by globules and irregular masses of colloid. The lumen shown in Fig. 670 does not, however, represent the whole of the earlier cavity of the anterior lobe, for portions of the sac become involved in the proliferative activity producing the solid tissue of the anterior part.

During the course of development from the 20 mm. stage onwards the cavity of the posterior lobe in the human hypophysis tends to become obliterated, and finally the lobe becomes solid, as does the infundibular stalk also. The lumen persists in the root of the stalk as the infundibular recess of the third ventricle.

In the later stages of antenatal growth there is a progressive invasion of the posterior lobe by glands and by basiphil cells belonging to the middle part of the anterior lobe, i.e. to the posterior wall of the original buccal diverticulum. These glands undergo atrophy in the adult. Replacement of worn-out cells is apparently not a feature of the adult hypophysis, for cell-division and degeneration of cells are seldom seen. The intraglandular cleft, commonly filled with colloid in the child, becomes obliterated in many adults, though in others it persists as a space still filled with colloid.

Comparative Anatomy.—The hypophysis cerebri is an organ possessed of a very ancient history. Its essential features are similar throughout the vertebrates, even those most primitive of all surviving vertebrates—the Agnatha. An anterior lobe and a posterior lobe, developed in a manner similar to that described for Man, and with similar cellular constituents, are found in all of them. It has been settled experimentally that the hypophysis is an endocrine organ in the lower Tetrapoda, e.g. Amphibia, producing hormones like some of those described in Man. The anterior lobe appears to have been originally an exocrine gland. Its essential cells are always developed from the epithelial wall of Rathke's pouch. In the Agnatha, as indeed in the modern fish *Polypterus* and probably also in various fossil ones, it remains in communication with the exterior throughout life, but the presence of masses of acidiphil and basiphil cells along the dorsal wall of the blunt end of the hypophyseal sac points to its already possessing typical endocrine functions.

This exocrine gland of the pre-vertebrates is perhaps represented by the ciliated organ of Müller in *Amphioxus*. To this organ endocrine functions were added in the evolution of the vertebrates, and an intimate relationship was established with the *neural hypophysis* or infundibulum, with the formation of the compound hypophysis characteristic of the vertebrates.

The actual orientation acquired by various parts of the hypophysis differs considerably in the various vertebrates. Thus, the anterior lobe of Reptilia acquires a position caudal and ventral to the middle part and the posterior lobe. Amphibia exhibit a similar orientation of parts. In various Mammalia the hypophysis retains features which are lost in the course of human development. Thus, in the cat the cavity of the posterior lobe remains patent and is lined with ependyma, communicating with the third ventricle through a tubular infundibulum. Mammals differ greatly in the size and form of the middle part of the anterior lobe. It may, as in Man, merely form a thin sheet of tissue behind the intraglandular cleft. On the other hand it may enclose the posterior lobe almost completely, as in the cat. Or it may be extremely thick, as in the ox.

PINEAL BODY

The **pineal body** is a small oval or cone-shaped structure, attached by a short hollow stalk to the hinder end of the roof of the diencephalon, between the habenular and posterior commissures (Figs. 671, 718). It is moderately firm in consistence, reddish-brown in colour, and measures 5-10 mm. anteroposteriorly, 3-7 mm. in its other diameters. It weighs about one-fifth of a gramme.

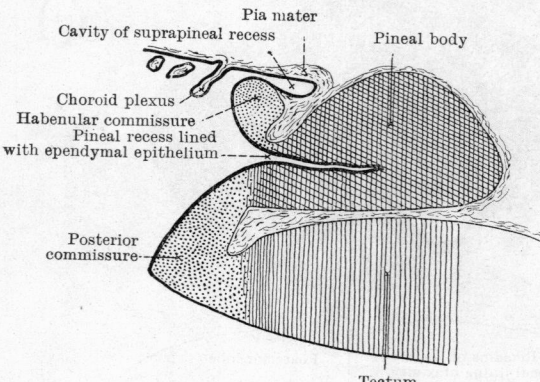

Fig. 671.—Diagram of a Median Sagittal Section through the Pineal Body and its Immediate Attachments.

Relations.—It is covered with pia mater, and lies in the shallow sulcus between the superior corpora quadrigemina. It is below the splenium of the corpus callosum, from which it is separated by the great cerebral vein. Its posterior end is free, and is a short distance in front of the vermis of the cerebellum and the free edge of the tentorium.

The cavity of the stalk is the pineal recess of the third ventricle. On the dorsal lip of this recess is the habenular commissure. Immediately above the habenular commissure and the stalk of the pineal body is another smaller recess of the third ventricle called the suprapineal recess.

Structure.—The pineal body consists mainly of a mass of distinctive cells (the pineal parenchyma) interspersed with neuroglia cells. This tissue becomes subdivided into lobules by the ingrowth of fibrous tissue septa from the pia mater, a process which takes place mostly during childhood. Vascularised fibrous tissue invades the organ during early intra-uterine life. The characteristic parenchyma cells have long processes which end in bulbous extremities some of which are on the surfaces of the lobules, next to the intervening fibrous septa, and others within the lobule on the fibrous tissues which enclose the blood-vessels.

The body of each cell is rounded and has a large round nucleus and granular cytoplasm. They offer a marked contrast with nerve cells—which are wanting in the pineal body except close to the habenular commissure. The granules of the cytoplasm have been claimed as being secretory in character but they show no variation in number at different ages, nor does the pineal body display any differences in appearance under different physiological conditions. There is no evidence of histological change at puberty. Evidence in support of a suggested endocrine function is lacking. The non-medullated nerves which are found in the organ appear to be distributed to the blood-vessels. Calcareous deposits usually make their appearance in the organ from adolescence onwards, and the pineal body thus becomes visible in radiographs (Pl. LX).

Development.—The pineal body develops as a pouch-like evagination of the hinder part of the roof of the diencephalon, separated from the mid-brain by the posterior commissure only. Its epithelial wall becomes thickened, with restriction of the lumen to the neighbourhood of the stalk of attachment. Later, this epithelial mass is invaded by cellular sprouts from the ependymal lining of the cavity; these form the characteristic pineal parenchyma. Blood-vessels also invade the organ. The development of the septa takes place actively in early postnatal life.

Comparative Anatomy.—A pineal structure is present throughout the vertebrates. In certain groups (*e.g.* Agnatha and certain Reptilia) it takes the form of a "pineal eye" or parietal organ. This organ may have a gland-like structure at its base similar to the mammalian pineal body. The pineal body of man is similar to that of other mammals. The reptilian forerunners of mammals also appear from a study of their skulls to have possessed a well-developed parietal organ.

The suprapineal recess is the vestige of a similar structure ("parapineal eye") which is situated in front of the parietal organ in certain vertebrates. There are grounds for believing that the parapineal and parietal organs were originally the left and right members respectively of a pair of organs, visual in function, in the pre-vertebrates. This view finds support in the nerve-connexions of the two organs. Further, certain fossil remains of the dermal roofing bones of primitive vertebrates show a pair of depressions which are believed to represent the position of these organs.

SPLEEN

The **spleen** (**lien**) (Fig. 672) is a soft contractile organ of purplish colour. It is freely movable, situated far back in the upper part of the abdominal cavity on the left side, behind the stomach and in close relation with the diaphragm.

The spleen is the headquarters of the reticulo-endothelial cells or macrophages —that great system of scavengers that cleanse the blood. It acts as a great blood-filter in which a slowly moving stream of blood is brought into an intimate relation of unique character with tissue cells and fluids, for the endothelial barrier between blood and tissue

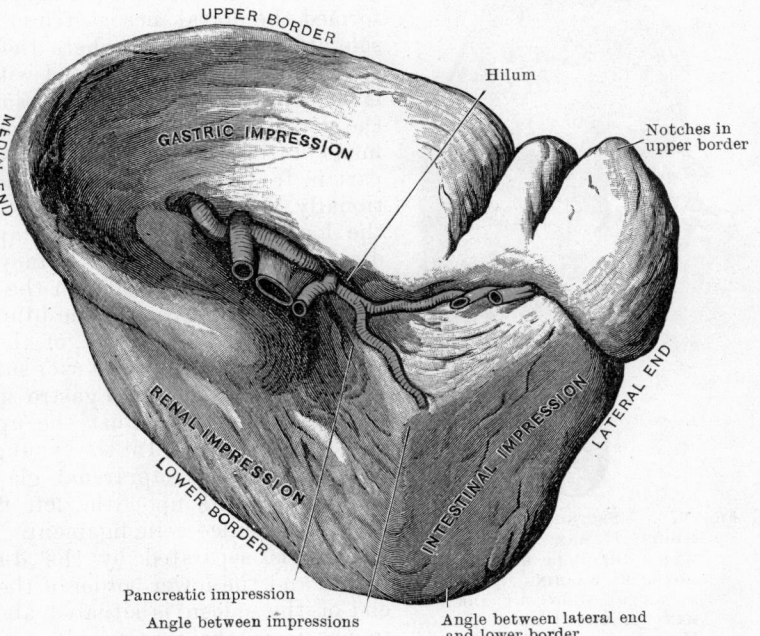

FIG. 672.—THE SPLEEN—VISCERAL ASPECT, TETRAHEDRAL FORM.

fluid is here incomplete. Lymphoid tissue is present, but differs from that of the lymph glands and nodules inasmuch as it is interposed in the arterial system and is not drained by lymph vessels. The spleen serves also as a blood-reservoir on account of the large amount of blood it accommodates when expanded and the very material contribution it is capable of making to the amount of blood in the general circulation when it contracts. If removed from the living subject after ligation of its vessels it is found to be about three or four times as heavy as the spleen of the cadaver. The average weight after sudden death in the healthy subject (as after accidents) is about 150 grammes (52 adults from 29 to 50 years of age—Hellman).

Form and Relations.—The form and position of the spleen are influenced largely by changes in adjacent structures. The stomach and colon show great variations of size, with corresponding effects upon its form; and the descent of the diaphragm during inspiration results in a downward displacement of the spleen. Notches are developed on the upper border, sometimes also on the lower border when the spleen is shrunken to a small size as in the cadaver: fissures indeed may extend across the diaphragmatic surface from the one border to the other. Two principal **surfaces** are recognised—the diaphragmatic and the visceral. The *diaphragmatic surface* is moulded to the under surface of the diaphragm. It is separated by upper and lower **borders** from the visceral surface. The *visceral surface* exhibits renal and gastric impressions separated by a more or less distinct but blunt border. The spleen has *medial* and *lateral* **ends**: the lateral end shows a flattening of varying extent—the colic impression—for the left flexure of the colon (Fig. 672). When the stomach is distended and the colon relaxed the spleen is similar in form to a segment of an orange, while distension of the colon causes it to assume an irregular tetrahedral form owing to the flattening of the lateral end. A *hilum* is recognised, at the junction of the gastric, renal, and colic impressions. It is here that branches of the splenic artery enter the gland, and tributaries of the splenic vein leave it. At the hilum the spleen is moored by its peritoneum and its vessels to the fold of peritoneum which originally formed the dorsal mesogastrium; this constitutes its sole attachment. Elsewhere than at the hilum the spleen is completely invested with peritoneum which is firmly adherent to its capsule. The portion of the dorsal mesogastrium which is behind this attachment of the spleen is the lieno-renal ligament; the part in front is the gastro-splenic ligament. Exceptionally, the lieno-renal ligament is opened up so that the lower part of the renal impression comes into direct contact with the kidney. The tail of the pancreas makes contact with the spleen immediately below the lateral part of the hilum.

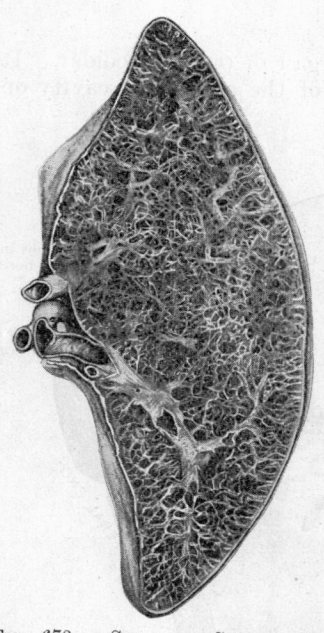

FIG. 673. — SECTIONAL SURFACE OF ADULT HUMAN SPLEEN, FROM WHICH THE PULP HAD BEEN REMOVED BY WASHING WITH WATER SO AS TO SHOW THE ARRANGEMENT OF THE TRABECULAR AND MAIN VASCULAR STRUCTURES.

The *gastric impression* of the spleen lies against the upper part of the posterior surface of the *stomach*, separated from it by the gastro-splenic ligament; the *renal impression* against the upper lateral part of the left kidney. In the young child the spleen touches the left suprarenal gland also. The *colic impression* rests upon the left flexure of the colon and the phrenico-colic ligament. The diaphragmatic surface is separated by the diaphragm from the pleura and the lower border of the lung. The medial end of the spleen is situated about one and a half inches from the median plane, at the level of the tenth thoracic spine in the cadaver and somewhat lower in full inspiration. The lateral end is just above the costal margin immediately behind the mid-axillary line. The long axis of the spleen is opposite the tenth rib (separated from it by diaphragm and pleura) when the body is in a supine posture, but in the erect attitude the long axis of the spleen tends to be more vertical, especially in women.

The size of the spleen is subject to great changes in life. Observation on the "exteriorised" spleen of the dog has shown that it exhibits reflex contraction in response to various stimuli. After a meal the spleen slowly increases in size for some hours, then gradually shrinks. Exercise diminishes the size. The living spleen exhibits slow rhythmic contractions, and it has been stated that these take place even when the nerve supply is interrupted, as in the excised and perfused spleen.

Small rounded accessory spleens are often present, attached like the spleen to the dorsal mesogastrium, usually on the gastro-splenic ligament.

Vessels and Nerves.—The spleen receives its blood from the **splenic artery**, which reaches it through the lieno-renal ligament. At the hilum the artery breaks up into six or more branches which enter independently. The **splenic vein** is formed within the lieno-renal ligament by the union of several tributaries which emerge from the hilum. By the splenic vein the blood is carried to the portal vein. The **lymph vessels** also leave the spleen at the hilum. They are small and come only from the capsule and trabeculæ, not from the gland substance, which is devoid of lymph vessels. They drain into the *splenic lymph glands* placed near the hilum and into the *left supra-pancreatic* glands.

The **nerves** are almost entirely non-medullated and come through the cœliac plexus from the *greater splanchnic nerve,* and possibly from the lesser splanchnic nerve. Some of these nerves are vasomotor in function; others supply the unstriped muscle of the organ. It is probable that *afferent* nerves pass from the spleen into the greater splanchnic nerve. The contractions of the spleen are in some circumstances brought about through the nervous system, but they take place also without its intervention, *e.g.* the slow, rhythmic contractions. The strong contraction which takes place on stimulation of the greater splanchnic nerve is due in part to the action of the adrenaline liberated from the suprarenal glands.

Structure.—There is an elastic contractile framework of trabeculæ which radiate from the hilum to the surfaces, where they become continuous with the fibrous capsule (tunica albuginea). The trabeculæ contain unstriped muscle-fibres, and the larger arteries and veins pass along them from the hilum. The peritoneal covering (serous coat) covers almost the whole organ and is firmly bound to the underlying tunica albuginea. The essential substance of the spleen is a spongy network of tissue, comprising reticular and other cellular elements, together with small vessels. The ultimate subdivisions of the trabecular framework outline small areas of splenic pulp (lobules of Mall) (Fig. 674) which are most evident on and near the surface of the organ. These are about 1 mm. in diameter, irregular in shape and at best very imperfectly circumscribed. Each splenic lobule comprises a central lymphoid core—the *lymphatic nodule* [Malpighii]—a surrounding marginal zone containing capillaries, and a peripheral zone of venous sinuses. The

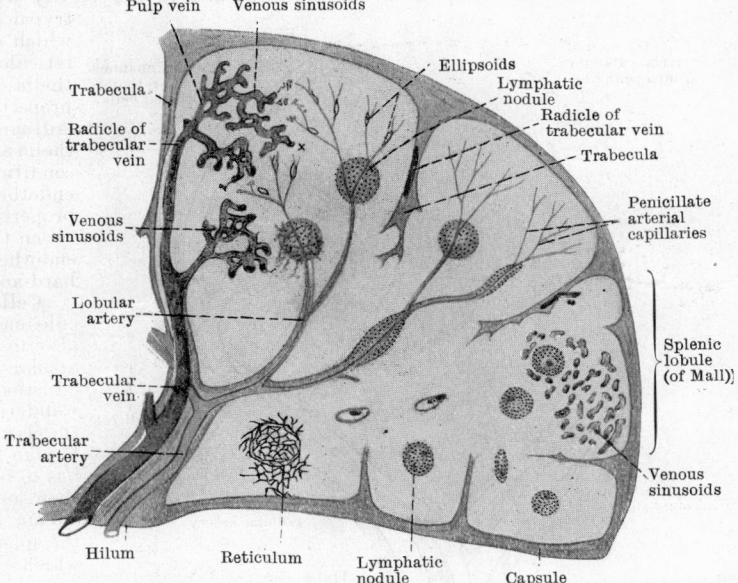

FIG. 674.—SCHEMATIC REPRESENTATION OF SPLENIC STRUCTURE, MUCH SIMPLIFIED BY THE SUPPRESSION OF RAMIFICATIONS OF THE TRABECULÆ AND VASCULAR TREE. (After Stöhr. By permission of Gustav Fischer.)

NOTE.—Both the pulp reticulum and the system of venous sinusoids supported by it must be understood as pervading the entire extent of the area figured except the trabeculæ and the splenic nodules; and, further, that the meshes of the reticulum itself are occupied by a varying content of red blood corpuscles, together with various types of splenic cells.

lymphatic nodules vary in size, from about 0·2 to 0·7 mm., and undergo individual alterations of size. Some atrophy takes place in middle age as in the lymphatic nodules elsewhere in the body.

Fine arterioles leave the smaller arteries of the trabecular framework and enter the lobules. Each here constitutes an end-artery without effective anastomoses with the vessels of other lobules. The lobular artery conveys blood into the lymphatic nodule, where a network of anastomosing vessels is formed. Capillaries emerge from the nodule and pass into the marginal zone of the lobule. Some, perhaps all, of these capillaries then divide into a penicillus of fine vessels (Fig. 675) each of which displays a local thickening of its wall called the "ellipsoid." From the ellipsoids the blood finds its way into the venous sinuses and so to the veins of the trabecular framework. The precise character of the vascular arrangements between the ellipsoids and the venous sinuses is, however, not fully known. It is probable that the blood passes, partly at least, through channels devoid of definite endothelial walls, and between the reticular cells. There is evidence that blood from the lobular arteries can also find its way to the venous sinuses without first passing through the lymphatic nodules and penicilli. Thus, Indian ink finds its way direct into the larger arteries when injected into the veins, if the spleen is well distended; the arterial networks of the lymphatic nodules are found to be free of ink. There thus appears to be a short circuit between arteries and veins alternative to the passage through the lymphatic nodules, which is opened up more freely when the spleen is expanded. The passage of blood through the vessels in the lymphatic nodules is controlled, not only by the vasomotor nerves, but is furthered by the mechanical effect of the contractions of the trabecular musculature.

No special cells are found in the spleen which are not found elsewhere. The distinctive feature of the spleen is the large number of reticulo-endothelial cells (macrophages) and their relations to the vascular system.

Reticulo-endothelial cells are found in the blood; they form the wall of blood-vessels in certain parts of the body; and they are found in the loose areolar tissues. They show great differences of form in various places, and at different times; one morphological type will at times change into another type. They act as the scavengers of the body. They are engaged in the destruction of blood cells, in bile-pigment production, in the metabolism of iron, fats, and proteins, in the elaboration of anti-bodies, and in the clearing of the body of bacteria, protozoa, and non-living bodies. In the *blood* they are represented by the lymphocytes and by the monocytes, which are perhaps derived from the lymphocytes. In the walls of blood-vessels, as *specific endothelia* or reticular cells, they lie in wait for foreign bodies where the blood-stream is slowed, as in the spleen, the lymph glands and liver sinuses (where they are known as the "stellate" cells of von Kupffer). Such endothelial cells are distinguished from ordinary endothelial cells in their phagocytic properties, and in the avidity with which they take up trypan-blue dye—a property in which they are like other reticulo-endothelial cells. Endothelial cells intermediate in properties between those of ordinary and "specific" endothelia also occur. Under certain conditions, indeed, ordinary endothelia acquire phagocytic properties. The distinction between the ordinary and specific endothelia is therefore not a hard-and-fast one.

Cells belonging to the reticulo-endothelial system are also to be found in the loose areolar tissues in the form of "histiocytes" or "resting wandering cells." These are the last to be mobilised when foreign matter in the circulation has to be dealt with; they may then migrate into the blood-stream. A special feature of the spleen is the direct contact which is effected in that organ between the blood and these extravascular reticulo-endothelial cells.

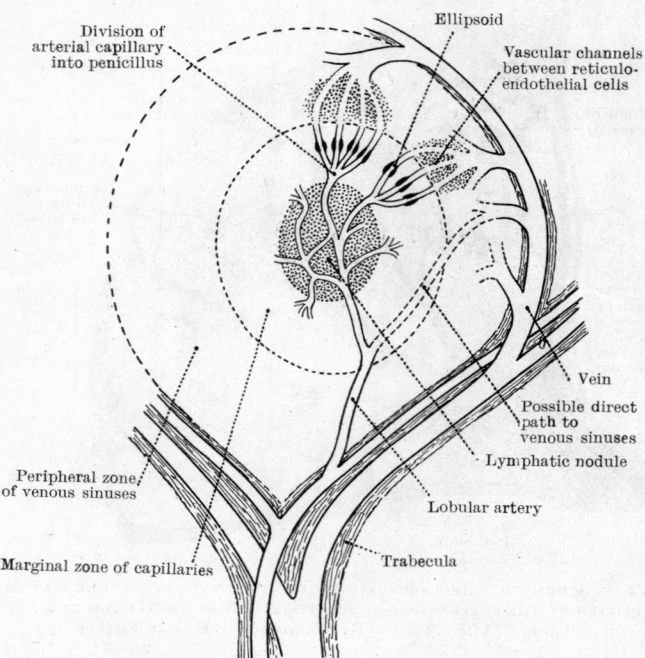

Fig. 675.—Diagram of the Structure of a Splenic Lobule. (After Cowdry, *Text Book of Histology.*)

Development.—The spleen is developed in the dorsal mesogastrium. The first indication is a thickening of this mesogastrium in embryos of about five weeks. In embryos of 10–12 mm. in length, there is a temporary thickening of the cœlomic epithelium over the swelling with several layers of cells, but the deeper layers are soon transformed into mesenchyme. The mesenchymal rudiment at first shows no subdivision into lobules; a capillary network is present which forms the basis of the final vascular pattern. With the formation of the trabecular fibrous tissues along the course of the main vessels the future lobules become mapped out. Continued differentiation of the terminations of the arterial capillaries in the lobules leads eventually to the establishment of the characteristic capillary systems of the adult organ opening into wide venous capillaries. This arterio-venous capillary bed forms the rudiment of the adult splenic pulp. In it giant cells and erythroblasts make their appearance, and blood formation is active from about the fourth month of intra-uterine life. The lymphatic nodules and the ellipsoids arise as clumps of lymphocytic tissue in the adventitia of the arterial capillaries, in the middle and later periods of intra-uterine development.

Comparative Anatomy.—The spleen is found throughout the gnathostome vertebrates, but is wanting in the Agnatha (*e.g.* the lamprey). Its structure is similar in fish, amphibia, reptiles, birds, and mammals, and it is in all instances developed in the dorsal mesentery of the gut. Its situation, however, relative to the alimentary canal, varies considerably; in some amphibia and reptiles, the spleen is opposite the intestines, in others opposite the stomach. Certain fish normally possess several spleen-like structures.

THYMUS

The **thymus** is situated in the superior mediastinum between the sternum and the great vessels; and it usually extends down for a short distance into the anterior mediastinum in front of the pericardium. In the new-born child, in which it is relatively much larger than in the adolescent or adult, it commonly extends laterally between the thoracic wall and the anterior borders of the pleuræ and lungs (Fig. 676).

It is essentially an organ of the growth-period of life, and it undergoes a gradual diminution in size after puberty. From birth to puberty it grows relatively slowly. There is great individual variation in its size at any given age. Thus, at birth it ranges in weight from 2 to 17 gms. with an average of about 13 gms. At puberty the average weight is about 37 gms., though it may be so small as to be hardly recognizable. In the young adult the average weight is reduced to about 25 grs. even at the age of 30, but the organ is occasionally still quite large.

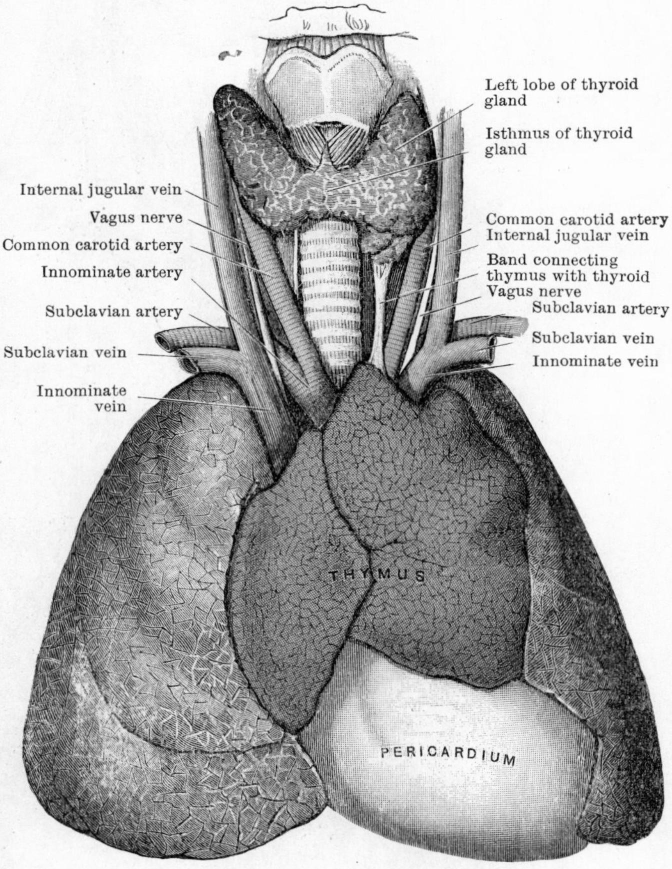

During the period of its fuller development the thymus appears as a pinkish mass (yellower in later life), consisting of a pair of laterally compressed, more or less pyramidal, asymmetrical lobes. The lobes are connected with each other, not by any bridge of glandular tissue but by areolar tissue.

The surface of the organ, in the young, more actively glandular condition, is finely lobulated.

FIG. 676.—THYMUS AND THYROID GLAND IN A FULL-TIME FŒTUS HARDENED BY FORMALIN INJECTION.

The thymus is soft in consistence, and the details of its shape are determined by its size and by the structures upon which it is moulded, namely, the pericardium and the great vessels of the superior mediastinum and the root of the neck. Its shape varies with its size and the age of the individual. In infants with short thoraces it is broad and squat; in adults with long thoraces it is drawn out into two irregular but more or less flattened bands (Fig. 677).

It is in relation posteriorly from below upwards with the pericardium, ascending aorta, left innominate vein and the trachea with inferior thyroid veins. Anteriorly it is related to the sternum and the lower ends of the sterno-thyroid muscles. In the young child the lateral margin is insinuated between the pleura and the upper costal cartilages, intercostal spaces and internal mammary artery.

Variations of the form as well as in the size of the thymus sometimes occur, attributable to a partial persistence of the slender stalks by which at first the developing thymus remains attached to the third pharyngeal pouches. Thus, the thymus may exhibit slender prolongations into the neck on each side, antero-lateral to the trachea. These processes may be connected to the lower parathyroid glands by strands of fibrous tissue (Fig. 679); or again, the whole of the cervical processes may be represented by fibrous strands (atrophic cervical thymus). An isolated portion of thymus tissue may persist in close relation with the lower parathyroid (accessory cervical thymus III).

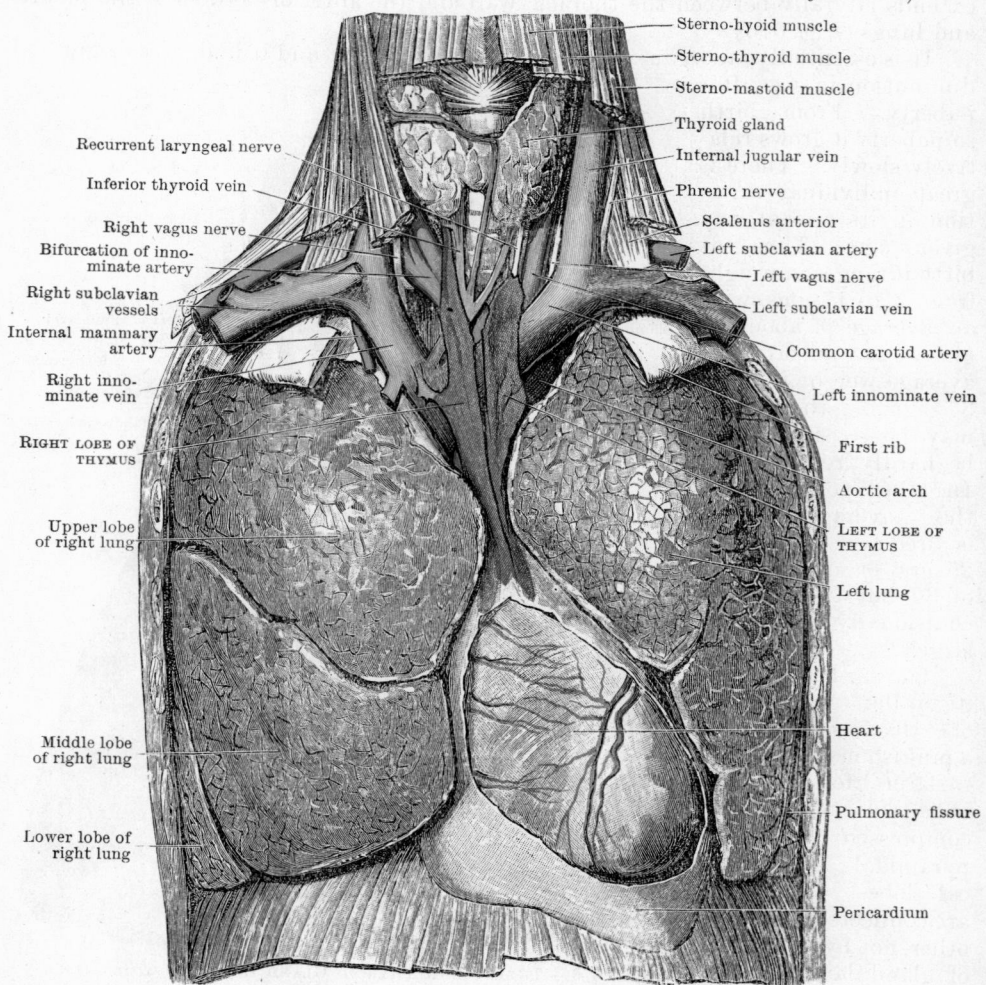

FIG. 677.—DISSECTION TO SHOW THE THYMUS IN AN ADULT FEMALE.

Vessels and Nerves.—The **arterial** supply of the thymus is effected through inconstant branches, chiefly of the *internal mammary arteries* and their branches. Its **veins** are irregular and mostly join the internal mammary and left innominate veins. Its **lymph vessels** are abundant. Although they are not related to the organ in the same manner as in a lymph gland, they have been found filled with lymphoid corpuscles derived from the gland. They enter the *innominate* [anterior mediastinal] *lymph glands*.

Its **nerves** are minute and are derived from the vagus and the sympathetic. The branches of the *vagus* descend directly to the thymus from about the level of the thyroid cartilage; the *sympathetic* fibres run with the blood-vessels. The fibrous capsule of the thymus receives small irregular branches from the phrenic nerves, but they do not supply the gland tissue in any way.

Structure.—The thymus is invested by a fibrous capsule which sends septa into its substance between its constituent lobules. The two "lobes," though really independent paired glands, are also bound together more or less intimately by their capsular investments. If the young gland is dissected so as to liberate its *lobules* from the fibro-areolar tissue between them, it will be found to consist of an elongated series of lobules each connected with a central parenchymatous cord along which they are arranged in irregular necklace fashion. The cord, mainly of medullary substance, represents the original thymic diverticulum of which the lobular masses are secondary derivatives.

The *lobules of the thymus* (whose outlines are visible in Fig. 676) are very irregular in shape and variable in size, between 4 and 11 mm. They are further partially subdivided into follicles (secondary lobules) which average a little over a millimetre in diameter, and are imperfectly separated from one another by delicate septal ingrowths from the inter-follicular areolar tissue. The follicle may be taken as the unit of thymic structure (Fig. 678). Each shows a cortical layer characterised by its rich content of closely packed lymphoid cells, the typical thymic cells, embedded in a delicate reticulum. The cortex of the follicle incompletely surrounds the medulla, which is continuous with that of adjacent follicles,

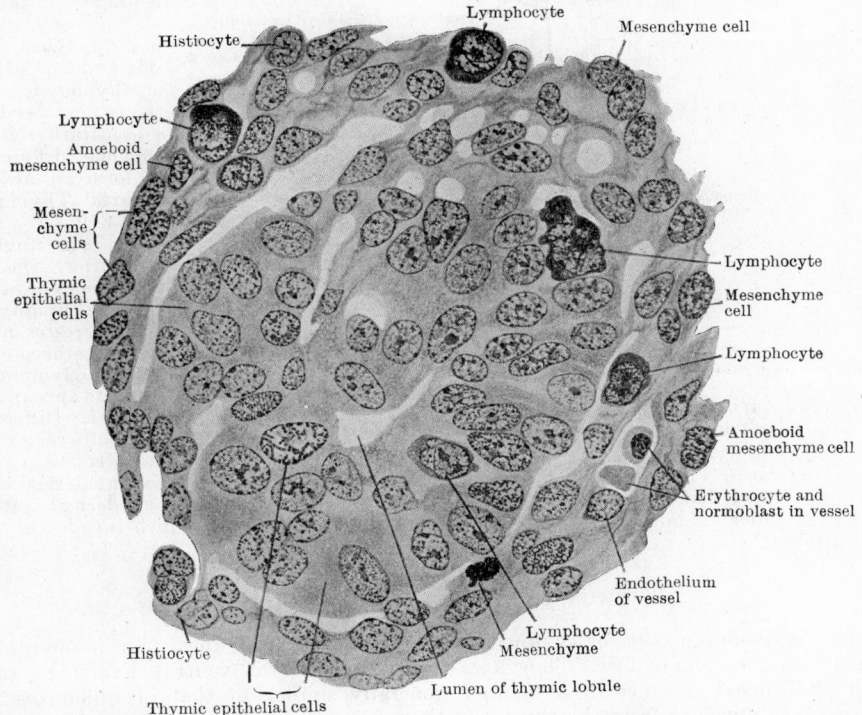

FIG. 678.—SECTION OF EMBRYONIC THYMUS OF RABBIT. (Maximow and Bloom, *Text Book of Histology*). A hollow lobule is surrounded by mesenchyme in which some histiocytes of the reticulo-endothelial system are seen. Lymphocytes are present both around and among the thymic epithelial cells.

and, through the lobular stem, with the central parenchymatous cord of the gland. In its intimate structure the medulla differs from the cortex in being much poorer in lymphocytes, in the greater coarseness of its reticulum, and in the presence in it of a variable number of the so-called corpuscles of Hassall, which are concentrically arranged nests of epithelioid cells varying in size from about 25 to 75 μ in diameter. The central cells often show granular degeneration. They vary in number not only in different individuals but also at different periods of life. They appear to have a common origin with the reticulum of the gland.

In a general way the structure of the thymus follicle resembles that of a lymph gland, but there are neither lymph sinuses nor germinal centres and the syncytial supporting reticulum differs from that of other lymphoid tissue in being of entodermal and not of mesodermal origin. No doubt the vascular tissue elements and some associated areolar tissue are derived from invading mesenchyme during the course of development.

The thymus appears, then, to have some special relation with the cellular constituents of the vascular system. It has been claimed that it has an endocrine function with an influence on the growth of the gonads, but this cannot be regarded as established.

Development.—As has been stated, there are in reality two organs. The paired thymus glands, or "lobes," right and left, arise from the ventral diverticula of the third pharyngeal pouches. (In the pig a component derived from the ectodermal "cervical vesicle" has been described as entering into the constitution of the embryonic thymus, *Badertscher*.) The first indication of the developing gland—a cylindrical elongation of the diverticulum—is present in the 5 mm. embryo; the wall of the cylinder, more particularly its dorsal part, soon thickens. Coincidently the neck of the pharyngeal pouch becomes constricted to form the pharyngo-branchial duct III (Fig. 659). That soon disappears, when the thymus rudiment loses all connexion with the pharynx. At this time the upper part of the rudiment still has a lumen ; the lower part is solid. Soon the lumen vanishes ; the solid part thickens and the developing thymus migrates tailwards to reach the pericardium at the 15 mm. stage. As a result of the migration the upper part becomes drawn out and normally disappears. It is in that process that parathyroid III is involved ; it is attached to the upper part of the migrating thymus—the part which disappears (Fig. 660).

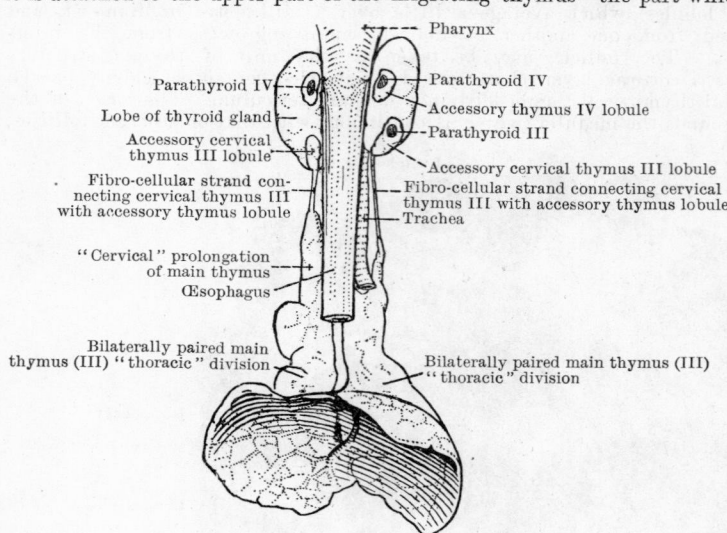

The relative time of the disappearance determines the permanent level of parathyroid III, for until it happens that gland is dragged in the wake of the thymus (see p. 776). Some times a small detached mass of thymus formative tissue may persist beside parathyroid III, and may differentiate to form an Accessory Cervical Thymus III (Fig. 679).

During migration and after, the cells continue to proliferate and the thymus rudiment increases in mass. In the embryo of two months lymphocytes begin to appear in the thymus. Differentiation of cortex and medulla is visible

Fig. 679.—Illustrating the Condition reported by Groschuff in which Accessory Thymus Lobules were present.

shortly afterwards. The syncytial reticulum and concentric corpuscles are of entodermal origin. It has been stated that the lymphocytes arise *in situ* by metamorphosis of entodermal epithelial cells. It is probable, however, that the lymphocytes are immigrants which invade the organ from outside it.

Thymus IV Vestiges (*vide* Fig. 679).

Small accessory masses of thymus tissue are in very rare instances found in close relation to parathyroids IV. They are developed from the ventral diverticula of the fourth pharyngeal pouches in a manner generally similar to that in which the main thymus gland develops from the third. Although extremely rare in Man, such accessory thymic derivatives from the fourth pharyngeal pouch are not uncommonly met with in other mammals. They must not be confused with the accessory thymic lobules referred to in the preceding paragraph, which are to be regarded as detached portions of the cervical part of the main thymus. The accessory thymus IV may, as in some animals (*e.g.* the cat), be enclosed, along with an "internal" parathyroid IV, in the substance of the thyroid gland, thus forming a so-called "internal thymus."

NEUROLOGY

CENTRAL NERVOUS SYSTEM

Originally written by the late D. J. Cunningham, M.D., F.R.S.,
Professor of Anatomy, University of Edinburgh

Revised and rewritten by Sir Grafton Elliot Smith

ELEMENTS OF THE CENTRAL NERVOUS SYSTEM

Every type of nervous system with which we are acquainted, from the simplest and most primitive, such as that of Hydra, to the complex and highly elaborated mechanism found in man, is composed essentially of three categories of elements. These are (1) **sensory cells,** so situated and so specialised in structure as to be capable of being affected by changes in the animal's environment, and of transmitting the effects of such stimulation, directly or indirectly, to (2) **efferent nerve-cells,** which influence the muscles and other active tissues, so that the stimulation may find expression in some appropriate action; and (3) **intercalated nerve-cells,** which regulate such responsive behaviour by bringing it

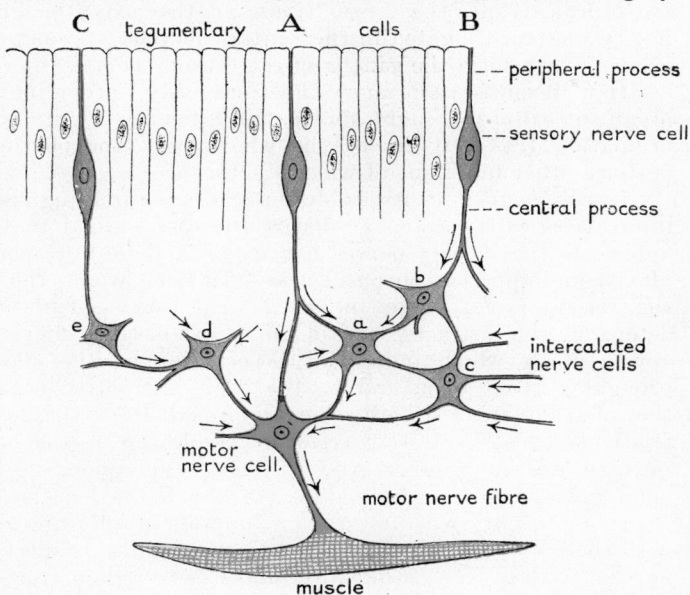

Fig. 680.—A Diagram representing the Essential Features in the Arrangement of the most primitive Type of Nervous System. (G. E. S.)

under the influence of other sensory impressions and of the state and activities of the body as a whole.

The study of a simple scheme representing the relationship that obtains among the three classes of elements in the primitive animal, Hydra (Fig. 680), will make these fundamental facts plain. Changes in the animal's environment affect the extremities of the **peripheral processes** of the sensory cells (*A*, *B*, and *C*), which in Hydra are situated amongst the ordinary tegumentary cells: the effect is transmitted by the **central processes** of such cells (*A*, for example), either directly to the efferent cell, represented in the diagram by a **motor nerve-cell,** or more usually to an intercalated nerve-cell (*a*, *b*, or *e*). Into that (*a*) impulses

791

50 *b*

stream from other intercalated cells (*b* and *c*), bringing the impulse from the sensory cell *A* under the influence of those coming from *B* and from more distant parts of the body through the intermediation of the intercalated cell *c*. The cells *a*, *c*, and *d* are connected with the motor nerve-cell. Thus, there is provided a mechanism whereby the conditions affecting other regions of the body, *B* and *C*, may influence the nature of the response which the stimulation of *A* evokes— either increasing or diminishing its effect or perhaps altering its character.

In this way the intercalated nerve-cells form a great co-ordinating mechanism, linking together all parts of the body in such a way that the activity of any part of the organism may be influenced by the rest, and thus be enabled to act in the interest of the whole.

Hence, the nervous system becomes the chief means whereby the various parts of the body are brought into functional relationship one with the other, and co-ordinated into one harmonious whole.

Throughout the whole course of its subsequent evolution the nervous system is formed of the same three kinds of elements ; and the essential feature in its elaboration and increasing complexity is the multiplication of the intercalated cells, and their concentration, together with the motor nerve-cells, to form a definite organ which we call the **central nervous system.**

During the process of development of the more complex forms of nervous system, most of the sensory cells migrate from their primitive positions in the skin (Fig. 680) ; and, as the free extremity of the peripheral process retains its primitive relationship to the skin, such migration of the cell bodies necessitates a great elongation of their peripheral processes. Although the sensory cells thus move inwards into the deeper tissues of the body, the great majority of them do not become incorporated in the central nervous system, but become collected into groups which form the **ganglia** of the sensory nerves.

In addition to its primary functions of (*a*) providing the means whereby the organism can be brought under the influence of its surroundings, and (*b*) co-ordinating the activities of the whole body, the nervous system comes also to perform other functions of wider significance.

In the course of its evolution the co-ordinating mechanism formed by the intercalated cells becomes so disposed in each animal that an appropriate stimulus applied to the sensory nerves can evoke a definite response—often of great complexity and apparent purposiveness. In other words, the nervous system becomes the repository of those inherited dispositions of its constituent parts which determine the instincts : and in the course of time it eventually provides also the apparatus by which individual experience and the effects of education can be brought to bear upon and modify such instinctive behaviour. In other words, the instrument of intelligence is formed from the nervous system ; and the relatively great bulk and extreme complexity of that instrument—the brain— in man are in a sense the physical expression of human intellectual pre-eminence.

In conformity with its primary function of affording a means of communication with the outside world, a great part or, according to most writers, the whole of the nervous system in the human embryo, as in other animals, is developed from the ectoderm, as has already been explained in the chapter dealing with General Embryology. In the most primitive Metazoa the sensory cells remain in the ectoderm (Fig. 680), but other cells become converted into motor nerve-cells and intercalated nerve-cells which are found in the underlying tissues (Fig. 681). In the human embryo there is an analogous process of development, but with the important difference that the various nervous elements do not wander into the mesoderm individually. A definite patch of ectoderm is set apart to produce the greater part of the nervous tissues for the whole body ; and all except the margins of that area sinks into the body *en masse.*

In one area all the motor nerve-cells develop (Fig. 681, *d*), in another (*c*) only intercalated nerve-cells, in yet another (*b*) the sensory cells originate ; and the rest forms the epidermis of the skin (*a*). With our knowledge of the fact that the sensory cells were originally distributed throughout the skin (Fig. 680), the idea naturally suggests itself that in man also the units of the sensory ganglia might be formed *in situ* in the ectoderm, and that the collection of sensory cells in the ganglia might possibly be brought about by the migration of such sensory cells inwards, while their peripheral processes elongate to permit such migration of the cell bodies without disturbing their original endings in the skin.   But there is

no evidence to show, or even to suggest, that such a process takes place in the human embryo.   The facts at our disposal seem to indicate that the sensory cells are derived from sharply circumscribed patches of ectoderm, and that the peripheral processes of those cells are distributed to the outlying area of ectoderm beyond them from which the epidermis is eventually formed (Fig. 681).

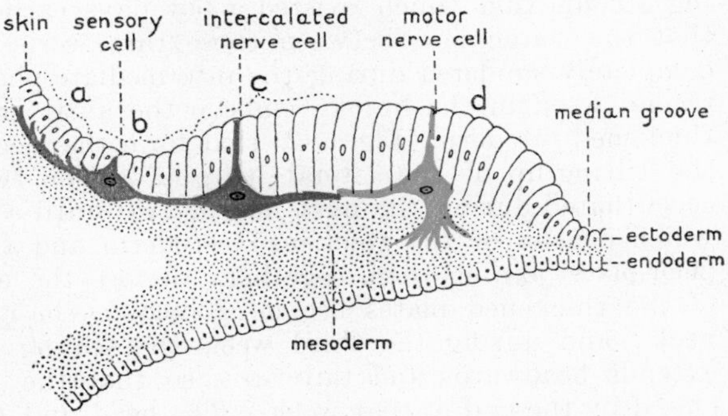

At the beginning of the second week the nervous system of the human embryo is represented by two thickened plates of ectoderm lying parallel the one to the other alongside the median axis of the embryo (Fig. 682), which is occupied by a shallow furrow.

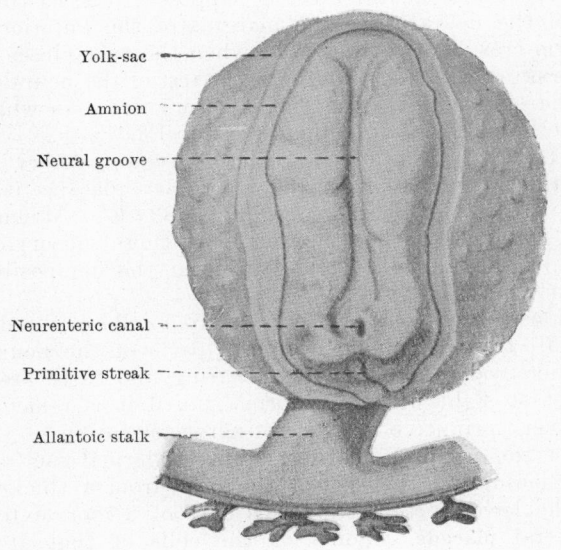

FIG. 681.—DIAGRAM REPRESENTING (IN BLACK) THE LEFT HALF OF A TRANSVERSE SECTION OF A 2-MM. HUMAN EMBRYO. Superimposed upon it there is shown (in colours) the hypothetical primitive arrangement of the nervous elements derived from each part of the ectoderm.   (G. E. S.)

In a diagram (Fig. 681) representing a transverse section through one-half of such an embryo (the uncoloured part), colours corresponding to those employed in Fig. 680 have been placed to indicate the nature of the elements that are known to

FIG. 682.—THE DORSAL SURFACE OF A VERY EARLY HUMAN EMBRYO.   (After von Spee.)

develop in relation with each area of the ectoderm at a later period in the history of the embryo: *b* represents an area which later will form the **neural crest**, from which the sensory cells will be developed.   The peripheral processes of those cells will pass into the skin (*a*) and their central processes into the area *cd*, which will become part of the neural tube.   In the area *c*, intercalated cells will develop to receive the incoming sensory nerves; and in connexion with the area d the motor nerve-cells (as well as other intercalated cells) will be formed.

While we are studying Fig. 681 it is important to emphasise the fact that in accordance with the commonly accepted ideas it is taught that the area b becomes completely severed from a and c, and shortly afterwards fibres are budded off from the cells in the area b to form the sensory nerves linking a to c, thus re-establishing a connexion which existed a few days earlier. This suggests the possibility that the connexions between those three series of elements may not have been completely sundered during the intermediate phase of development. Early in the second week in the human embryo the axial groove separating the two bands of thickened ectoderm (Fig. 682) that form the medullary plate becomes deepened by the tilting-up of the lateral margins of the two bands. That process becomes accentuated during the next day or two until a deep cleft is formed, the walls of which consist of the thickened ectoderm and the floor of the thinner ectoderm (floor-plate) joining them together. Before the end of the week the dorsal edges of the thickened plates become joined in the region which will develop into the neck; and during the third week the sealing of the lips of the neural groove extends headwards and tailwards, so that the neural tube becomes completely closed by the end of that week. The head and tail ends of the tube are the last parts to close, the latter being, as a· rule, a little later than the former. When the tube is in the stage of being patent only at its two ends, the openings are known as the **anterior** and **posterior neuropores.**

In the process of closing, the extreme dorsal edge of the medullary plate becomes excluded, in the greater part of its extent, from participation in the constitution either of the neural tube or of the skin, and forms a column of cells lying between the two. This is the **neural crest** (Fig. 683, A, B, and C; x and y represent the places where the apparent sundering occurs).

It is commonly supposed that the neural crests do not extend the whole length of the neural tube. Nevertheless, peculiar ectodermal areas, which ultimately give origin to sensory nerves, are found at the junction of the medullary plate with the skin in those regions where the neural crest is supposed to be lacking. At the extreme anterior end of the neural tube the margins of the anterior neuropore become thickened to form crest-like patches; but when the tube closes these areas do not separate from the skin (at x, Fig. 683, D), as the rest of the neural crest does. They remain part of the skin and become the olfactory areas, in which sensory cells, precisely like those found in Hydra (Fig. 680), develop.

A little farther on the caudal side of the olfactory region a very large crest-like mass of ectoderm fails to separate from the medullary plate as it closes, and becomes a constituent part of the neural tube (Fig. 683, E). When the optic diverticulum grows out it carries out to the periphery those sensory cells mixed with intercalated cells of the medullary tube to form the composite sensitive membrane of the eye known as the retina.

In several other regions sensory nerves originate from cells of ectodermal, and possibly even entodermal, areas which do not form parts of the neural crest, as that term is usually understood. The nerves of hearing and taste are developed in a way that seems at first sight utterly abnormal, until it is remembered that they afford examples of very primitive methods of nerve-formation.

The essential part of the organ of hearing is an ectodermal sac (otic vesicle) that develops as a diverticulum on the side of the head from a thickened patch of ectoderm which in the lower vertebrates forms part of a more extensive area known as the **dorso-lateral placode.** Some of the cells of that area seem to become transformed into nerve-cells which migrate into the space between the otic vesicle and the neural tube (Fig. 684) and form the auditory ganglion.

At the upper margins of the branchial clefts a series of thickenings develop, which are known as the **epibranchial placodes.** Comparison with the process of development in fish embryos, which was elucidated by Landacre, suggests that the nerve-cells which give origin to the nerves of taste arise from those placodes. Fibres of such origin are found in the facial, glosso-pharyngeal and (in some animals) vagus nerves (Fig. 684).

When first formed, the neural tube is compressed from side to side and presents an elliptical outline in transverse section (Fig. 683). The two side walls are very thick, whilst the narrow dorsal and ventral walls are thin, and are termed the **roof-plate** and **floor-plate** respectively (Fig. 685). The cavity of the tube in trans-

verse section appears as a narrow slit. The wall of the neural tube consists at first of low columnar epithelium arranged in a fairly regular series, but with a certain number of large, spherical, so-called **germinal cells** scattered between the columns. But this regular disposition as a single layer of cells does not last long. For even by the second week the rapid proliferation of the cells has led to a marked increase in the thickness of the side wall and a scattering of the more numerous nuclei, apparently irregularly, throughout its substance (Fig. 685). The latter consists of a network of protoplasm in which definite outlines of cells cannot be detected. As growth proceeds the innermost part of this nucleated protoplasmic syncytium becomes condensed to form a delicate membrane, termed the **internal limiting membrane**, which lines the lumen of the tube, whilst its outermost part presents a similar relation to an **external limiting membrane**, which invests the outer surface of the tube. Toward

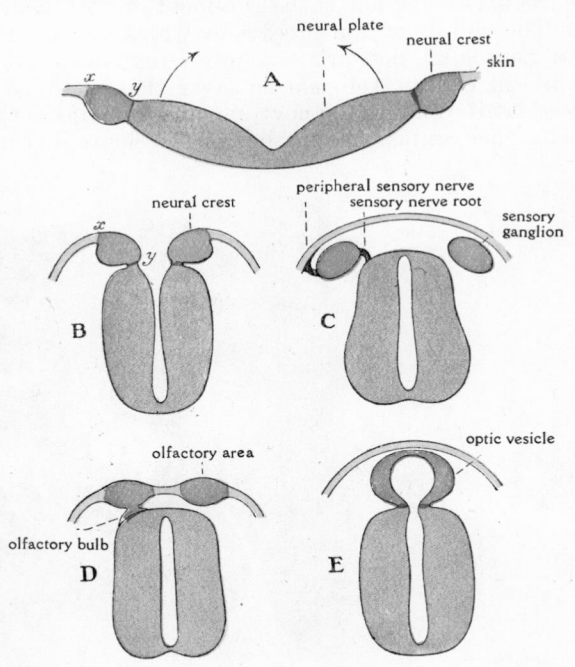

FIG. 683.—DIAGRAMS OF TRANSVERSE SECTIONS REPRESENTING THREE STAGES (A, B, AND C) IN THE DEVELOPMENT OF A SENSORY GANGLION FROM THE NEURAL CREST; AND TWO DIAGRAMS (D AND E) SUGGESTING A POSSIBLE HOMOLOGY OF THE OLFACTORY (D) AND VISUAL (E) EPITHELIUM WITH THE NEURAL CREST. The optic vesicle is a mixture of sensory and intercalated nerve-cells: hence it is not correct to represent it as a purely sensory element. The hypothetical arrangement labelled "optic vesicle" is the optic placode, the sensory elements of which mingle with the neuroblasts of the neural tube and a mixture of the two elements grows out to form the true optic vesicle. (G. E. S.)

the end of the first month the side walls of the tube show signs of a differentiation into three layers. Next to the central canal there is an epithelial-like arrangement of the innermost cells of the syncytium that forms the **ependyma**. Then there is an intermediate layer crowded with nuclei and known therefore as the nuclear or **mantle layer**. On the surface there is a layer singularly free from nuclei, which is called the non-nuclear or **marginal layer**. The germinal cells are placed in the ependymal layer between its radially arranged cells as they pass in towards the internal limiting membrane; and the protoplasm of the germinal cells forms part of the syncytium.

At one time it was imagined that the germinal cells were embryonic nerve-cells—the parent-cells of the real **neuroblasts**—and that the whole of the rest of the syncytium represented the supporting tissues, which in the adult form the **neuroglia**. But it is now known that from the proliferation of the germinal cells, in which mitotic figures can usually be seen, some cells are formed which become ependymal epithelium, and others which migrate peripherally into the mantle layer. There, while forming part of the mantle syncytium, they undergo further proliferation and some of the resulting cells develop into **spongioblasts**, which constitute the supporting framework or embryonic neuroglia; others become rudimentary nerve-cells or **neuroblasts**; and others again are known as **indifferent cells**. The latter are destined to undergo further subdivision and become the parents of more spongioblasts and neuroblasts.

From this it is clear that the greater part—all except the germinal cells—of the syncytium, which is known as the **myelospongium**, is not merely supporting neuroglial tissue, but is the rudiment of both neuroglia and true nervous tissues.

The details of the process by which the neuroblasts become dissociated from the neuroglial network are quite unknown. It is commonly supposed that a spherical cell in the mantle layer that is to be transformed into a neuroblast frees itself from the syncytium, and remains for a time independent and wholly unattached amidst the meshes of the neuroglial network. It is supposed further

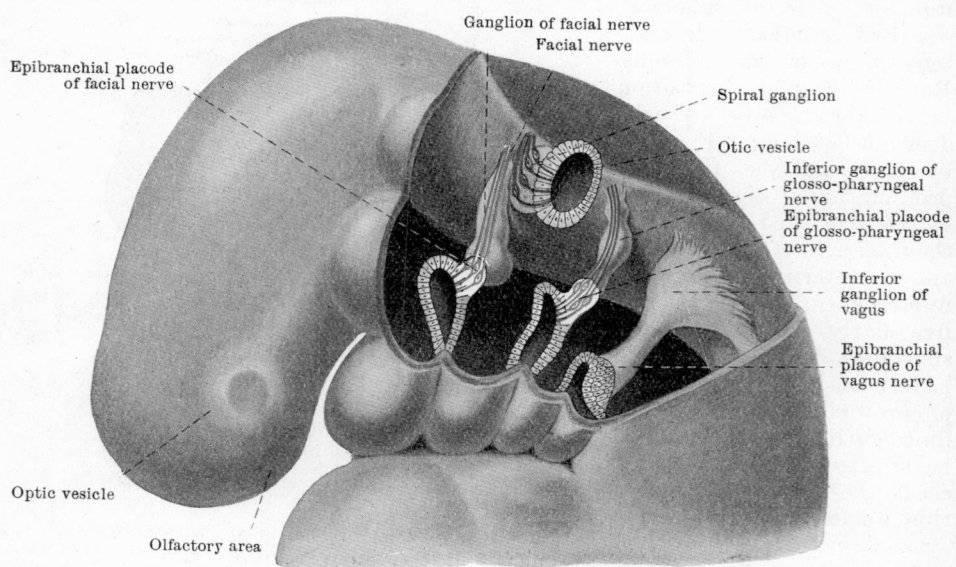

FIG. 684.—RECONSTRUCTION OF THE GANGLIA OF THE FACIAL, COCHLEAR, GLOSSO-PHARYNGEAL, AND VAGUS NERVES OF A HUMAN EMBRYO 5 MILLIMETRES LONG. (G. E. S.)

The epithelium of three pharyngeal grooves and the otic vesicle is represented diagrammatically; and the supposed mode of origin of the gustatory nerve-cells (and their fibres) from the epibranchial placodes is indicated in blue, and of the auditory nerve-cells from the otic vesicle in purple.

that its true nature as a neuroblast becomes revealed when it takes on a pear shape, and a protoplasmic process—the stalk of the pear—pushes its way into some other part of the nervous system, or out of it into the mesoderm to reach some muscular or glandular tissue, and becomes the axon of the nerve-cell.

Such an interpretation of the appearances exhibited in the walls of the neural tube at the end of the first month is adduced in support of a view concerning the constitution of the nervous system known as the **neurone theory**. "Neurone" is the term applied to a nerve-cell and all its processes; and the neurone doctrine assumes that there is no continuity whatever between the substance of one neurone and that of another, such as occurs in Hydra (Fig. 680), and that the functional connexions between them are brought about merely by the contact of the processes of one element with the processes, or the cell-body itself, of another element. In accordance with this conception the facts of embryology were supposed by His to demonstrate that when the axon grows out from a previously spherical and unattached cell it is able to push into the surrounding tissues, and, as it were guided by some instinct, eventually to find its way to that particular area of skin, muscle, gland, or other part of the body where nature intends it to go.

This is the current teaching in regard to the neurone theory; and it is supposed to have been conclusively demonstrated by the facts revealed not only by embryology and the study of the minute structure of the nervous system but also by the phenomena of degeneration and regeneration. Harrison has shown that the outgrowth of processes can be witnessed in the living nerve-cells of the frog. There are certain facts, however, which have always led some anatomists to refuse to believe in the validity of the neurone doctrine as a true expression of the real constitution of the nervous system.   It has been clearly demonstrated by Graham Kerr that at a very early stage of development the neural syncytium of the spinal cord (of the mud-fish Lepidosiren) is in free and uninterrupted continuity with the protoplasm of the muscle-plate which lies in contact with the neural tube; and no stage is known in which these connexions do not exist.   When, in the course of the subsequent growth of the embryo, the muscle-plate becomes removed farther and farther away from the central nervous system the protoplasmic strand, which links them the one to the other, gradually becomes stretched and elongated.   As

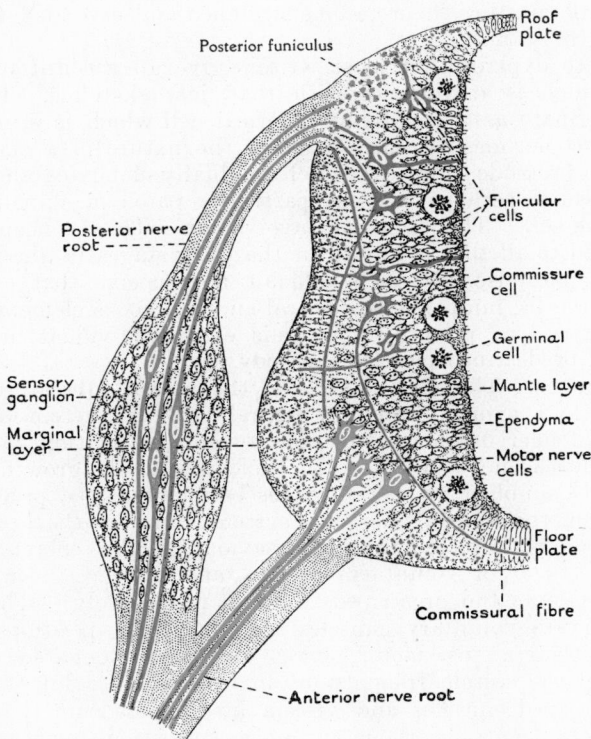

FIG. 685.—DIAGRAM OF TRANSVERSE SECTION OF EARLY NEURAL TUBE.   (G. E. S.)

the neuroblast matures its chemical constitution becomes modified; it becomes specialised in structure to fit it for the peculiar functions it has to perform.   These changes manifest themselves first in the body of the neurone itself and thence spread along its processes.   With the knowledge that protoplasmic bridges exist long before the time His supposed the axon of his neuroblast to push its way outward, it seems not unreasonable to suppose that it is the chemical modification of these existing bridges which has been revealed in stained specimens, as it spreads from the cell-body outwards into its processes.

   It is now a well-recognised fact that soon after the neural tube becomes closed the outlines of its constituent cells become blurred and then disappear, and a continuous protoplasmic network or syncytium is formed.   No one has ever been able to detect the process of detachment of embryonic nerve-cells (neuroblasts) from this syncytium; and it is at least a possibility that the free anastomosis of the protoplasmic processes of many of the cells is not destroyed in the way demanded by the neurone doctrine.   The known facts might be interpreted, at least as reasonably, by supposing that when nerve currents begin to traverse the syncytium (Fig. 685) structural modifications occur around the nuclei of the cells affected, and gradually spread along their processes, so as to give the appearance (in sections stained by special methods) of processes growing out from each neurone.

Impulses brought from the skin by the sensory nerves, the nutrition of which is controlled by the cells in the sensory ganglion (Fig. 685), are carried into the wall of the neural tube, where they are received by processes of intercalated cells, which in turn transmit their effects directly or indirectly to (a) motor nerve-cells (or other kind of efferent nerve-cells) which stimulate a muscle, a viscus, or other active tissue to perform some work, or (b) to intercalated cells, the axons of which proceed to some other part of the nervous system, perhaps above or below the place where the sensory nerve enters (Fig. 685, *funicular cells*). As the walls of the neural tube increase in size the various neurones gradually become drawn apart, and the protoplasmic links uniting them become stretched and extended to form processes of varying length.

It is right to explain that most writers give an account of the process of development which is at variance with that just sketched. The neuroblast is supposed to originate as a free-lying spherical cell which is stimulated by some unknown force, sometimes assumed to be of the nature of a chemical attraction (chemotaxis), to protrude a process which gradually elongates and pushes its way through the tissues, perhaps to some particular patch of skin, muscle, gland, or some other nerve-cell. The difficulty involved in such a conception is not only that it is opposed to all that is known of the early stages in the evolution of the nervous system, but also that it is difficult to conceive that every one of the millions of nerve-cells, muscle-cells, visceral and cutaneous elements can each have some specific attractive power which leads every individual nerve fibril to its appropriate and predestined place in the body.

Efferent Nerves.—The efferent cells of the neural tube are distinguished by the fact that their axons leave the central nervous system and traverse the mesoderm for a longer or shorter distance to end in relation to some muscle or nerve-cell outside the nervous axis. In the course of the growth of the body the various structures supplied by efferent fibres become removed progressively farther and farther from the central nervous system; and in that process (Fig. 686) a distinction can be detected in the behaviour of the efferent fibres (a) proceeding to the striped or voluntary muscles, and those (d) conveying impulses destined for viscera and unstriped muscle, respectively. The efferent cells (a) which innervate voluntary muscles take up their positions in the central nervous system, their axons (motor nerves) becoming elongated in proportion to the migration of the muscle from its original situation. But the cells (c) which innervate non-striped muscles and viscera are disposed in a different manner. They lie outside the central nervous system as constituent elements of one of the autonomic ganglia. Impulses from the central nervous system are transmitted to such ganglia by means of fibres arising from cells (d) within the central organ; and it is customary to distinguish the latter elements as **splanchnic efferent cells.** It is, however, a matter of fundamental importance to recognise clearly that the real splanchnic efferent cells—the homologues of the **somatic efferent cells**—are found in the autonomic ganglia, and that the elements to which this term is usually applied are in reality intercalated cells.

Nerve Components.—From the statements in the preceding paragraphs it must be evident that there are several varieties of afferent and efferent nerves respectively entering and leaving the central nervous system. The cells of origin of the efferent nerves collect in the ventral part of the side wall of the neural tube; and for this reason that part of the wall becomes swollen at an early stage of development (Figs. 686 and 687). It is called the **basal lamina.** Most of the cells that emit afferent fibres are situated in the sensory ganglia outside the central nervous system, and their growth can therefore have no direct influence upon the form of the neural tube; but their central processes become inserted into the dorsal part of the side wall of the tube, which is called the **alar lamina**; and groups of intercalated cells collect around the entering fibres to form **receptive** or **terminal nuclei.** The growth of the terminal nuclei leads to an expansion of the alar lamina which is analogous to that seen in the basal lamina but is much less extensive. The unequal swelling of the dorsal and ventral parts of each side wall of the neural tube leads to the development of a longitudinal groove—**sulcus limitans**—as a demarcation between the alar and basal laminæ.

The nuclei of origin of the efferent fibres, which are found in the basal laminæ, may be divided into two main groups (and, in some regions of the nervous axis, three). There is first the group of large multipolar nerve-cells which emit fibres to innervate the ordinary striped voluntary muscles. This is commonly called the **somatic efferent nucleus.** Then there is a group of small multipolar cells, the axons of which pass out into autonomic ganglia, and indirectly control the involuntary unstriped muscles and other active parts of viscera. Those cells form the **splanchnic efferent nucleus.**

In the upper cervical and lower cranial region a portion of the somatic efferent nucleus is set apart to innervate the striped muscles developed in the pharyngeal arches. That is the **lateral somatic efferent nucleus.** Many recent writers are of the opinion that that nucleus is **splanchnic**; but its component nerve-cells are typically somatic and its fibres directly innervate striped voluntary muscles developed from the same material (myotomes) from which the other striped muscles are formed (Agar and Graham Kerr). It is therefore unjustifiable to refuse it the designation "somatic."

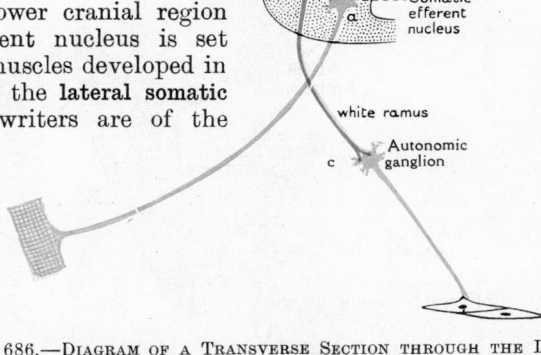

Fig. 686.—Diagram of a Transverse Section through the Left Half of the Neural Tube representing the Arrangement of the Autonomic Nerves, to suggest the Possible Homology of a Sympathetic Ganglion Cell and a Central Motor Cell and of a White Ramus with the Axons of Intercalated Cells. (G. E. S.)

The alar lamina also can be subdivided into a series of functional areas (Fig. 687).

At the dorsal edge there is the **somatic afferent terminal nucleus**, which receives impulses coming from the skin. In one region a part of that nucleus is specialised for the reception of impulses from the internal ear (**acoustico-lateral terminal nucleus**). Then there is a group of cells collected around the incoming visceral sensory nerves—the **splanchnic afferent terminal nucleus.** A part of that is specialised to receive taste impressions—the **gustatory nucleus**—but this has not yet been clearly demarcated from the rest of the nucleus.

This analysis of the various functional elements that may enter into the constitution of the various cranial and spinal nerves is made use of in elaborating the **theory of nerve components**, which will help us to understand many features of the structure of the nervous system that otherwise would be unintelligible.

Nerve-cells.—We have already noticed that there is a broad distinction between the nerve-cells found in the ganglia of sensory nerves and those found in the rest of the nervous system. They differ not only in their mode of origin and in their subsequent development, but also in the connexions of their nerve-fibre processes.

Nerve-cells of the Brain and Spinal Cord.—The cells in the cerebro-spinal axis are variable both in size and form. Some are relatively large, as, for example, certain of the pyramidal cells of the cerebral cortex and the motor cells in the spinal cord, which almost come within the range of unaided vision; others are exceedingly minute, and require a high power of the microscope to bring them into view. The cell consists of a protoplasmic nucleated body, with which two kinds of processes are connected—the **axon** or emitting process and the **dendrites**, or receiving processes (Fig. 692).

The **axon** presents a uniform diameter and a smooth and even outline. It gives off in its course fine collateral branches, but does not suffer thereby any marked diminution in its girth. The most important point to note in connexion with the axon, however, is the fact that it becomes continuous with the axis-cylinder of a nerve-fibre. The axon then is simply a nerve-fibre, and in certain circumstances it assumes one or two investing sheaths, of which more will be said later. The axon may run its entire course within the substance of the brain or spinal cord, either for a short or a long distance (intercalated cells), or it may emerge from the brain or spinal cord in one of the cranial or spinal nerves as the

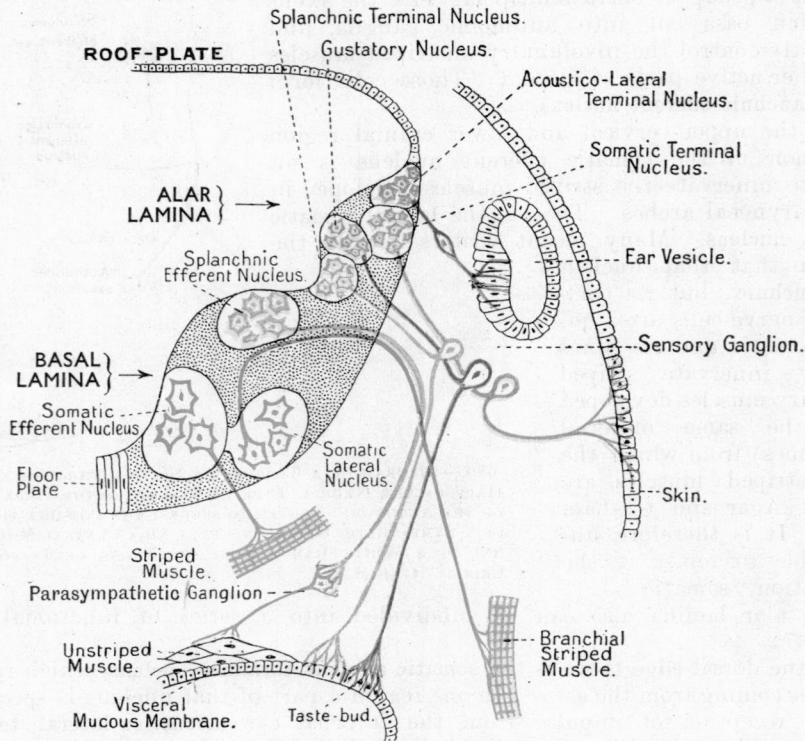

Fig. 687.—Diagram of a Transverse Section through the Right Half of the Fœtal Rhomben-cephalon and Epithelial Areas associated with it to illustrate the Different Categories of Nerve Components and their Central Nuclei. (G. E. S.)

essential part of an efferent nerve-fibre, and run a variable distance before it finally reaches the peripheral structure in relation to which it ends (efferent nerve-cells). The axon and its collaterals appear to terminate either in small button-like knobs, or more frequently in terminal arborisations, the extremities of which seem to be furnished with exceedingly small terminal varicosities. When the axon or its collaterals end within the brain or spinal cord, some of the terminal arborisations interlace with the dendrites of nerve-cells, and others are twined around the bodies of other cells. In the latter case the interlacement may be so close and complete that it almost presents the appearance of an enclosing basket-work. When the axon emerges from the cerebro-spinal axis its terminal arborisa-tion ends in relation to a muscle-fibre or some other tissue in the manner described below.

Nerve-fibres.—Nerve-fibres, arranged in bundles of greater or less bulk, form the nerves which pervade every part of the body. They also constitute the greater part of the brain and spinal cord. Nerve-fibres are the conduct-ing elements of the nervous system; they serve to bring the nerve-cells into relation both with one another and with the various tissues of the body.

There are different varieties of nerve-fibres, but in all of them the leading and essential constituent is a delicate thread-like axon. The most obvious difference between individual fibres depends upon the nature of the covering of the axon. When it is coated on the outside by a more or less thick sheath of a fatty substance termed **myelin,** it is said to be a myelin-ated or medullated fibre. When the coating of myelin is absent the fibre is termed a non-myelin-ated or a non-medul-lated fibre. A second sheath — thin, deli-cate, and membran-ous, and placed externally—also may be present in both cases. It is termed the **neurolemma** (or **primitive sheath**). From a structural point of view, there-fore, four different forms of nerve-fibre may be recognised :—

Non-medullated—
 1. Naked axons.
 2. Axons with neuro-
     lemma.
Medullated—
 3. Neurolemma ab-
     sent.
 4. Neurolemma pre-
     sent.

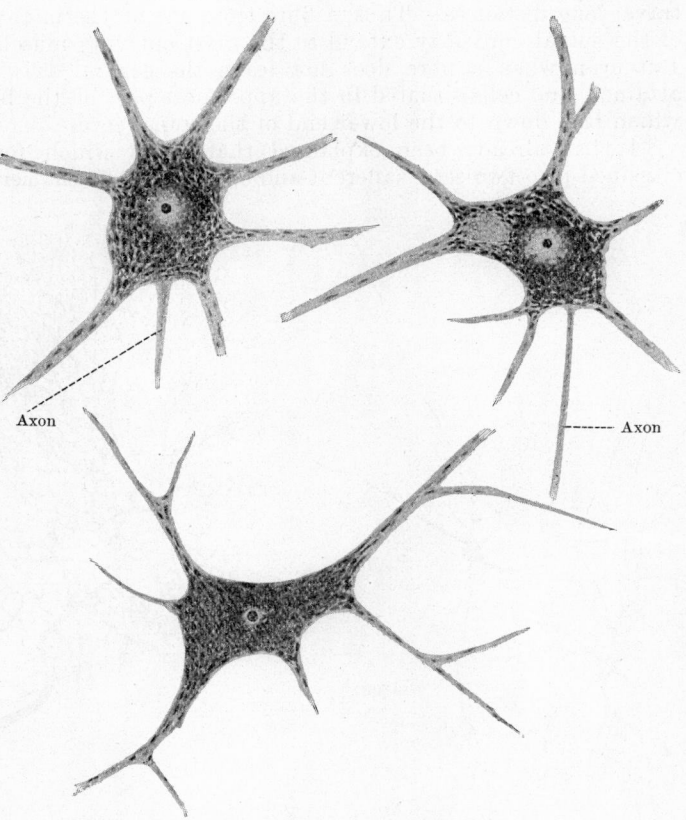

Axon

Axon

FIG. 688.—THREE NERVE-CELLS FROM THE ANTERIOR GREY COLUMN OF THE HUMAN SPINAL CORD.

Every nerve-fibre near its origin and as it approaches its ter-mination is unprovided with sheaths of any kind, and is simply represented by a non-medullated, naked axon. The fibres of the olfactory nerves afford us an example of non-medullated fibres furnished with a neurolemma.

Medullated fibres are present in greater quantity in the cerebro-spinal system than non-medullated fibres. Thus all the nerves attached to the brain and spinal cord, with the exception of the olfactory and optic, are formed of medullated fibres provided with a neurolemma; whilst the entire mass of the white substance of the brain and spinal cord, and also the optic nerves, are formed of medullated fibres devoid of a neurolemma.

It is important to note that the distinction between the medullated and non-medullated fibres is not one which exists throughout all stages of development. As will be presently pointed out, every fibre is the prolongation of a cell, and in the first instance it is not provided with a medullary sheath. Indeed, it is not until about the fifth month of intra-uterine life that those fibres which are to form the white substance of the cerebro-spinal axis begin to acquire their coating of myelin. Further, that coating appears in the fibres of different fasciculi or tracts at different periods, and a knowledge of the fact has enabled anatomists to follow out the connexions of the tracts of fibres which compose the white matter of the brain and spinal cord.

Every nerve-fibre is directly continuous by one extremity with a nerve-cell, whilst its opposite extremity breaks up into a number of ramifications, all of which end in relation to another nerve-cell, or in relation to certain tissues of the body, as, for example, muscle-fibres or the epithelial cells of the epidermis. The length of nerve-fibres, therefore, varies very greatly. Some fibres are short and merely bring two neighbouring nerve-cells into relation with each other; others travel long distances. Thus, a fibre from one of the motor cells of the lower part of the spinal cord may extend to the most outlying muscle in the sole of the foot. But even when a fibre does not leave the central axis, a great length may be attained, and cells situated in the uppermost part of the brain give origin to fibres which pass down to the lower end of the spinal cord.

It has already been explained that fibres which form the nerves may be classified into two sets—afferent and efferent. **Afferent nerve-fibres** conduct impres-

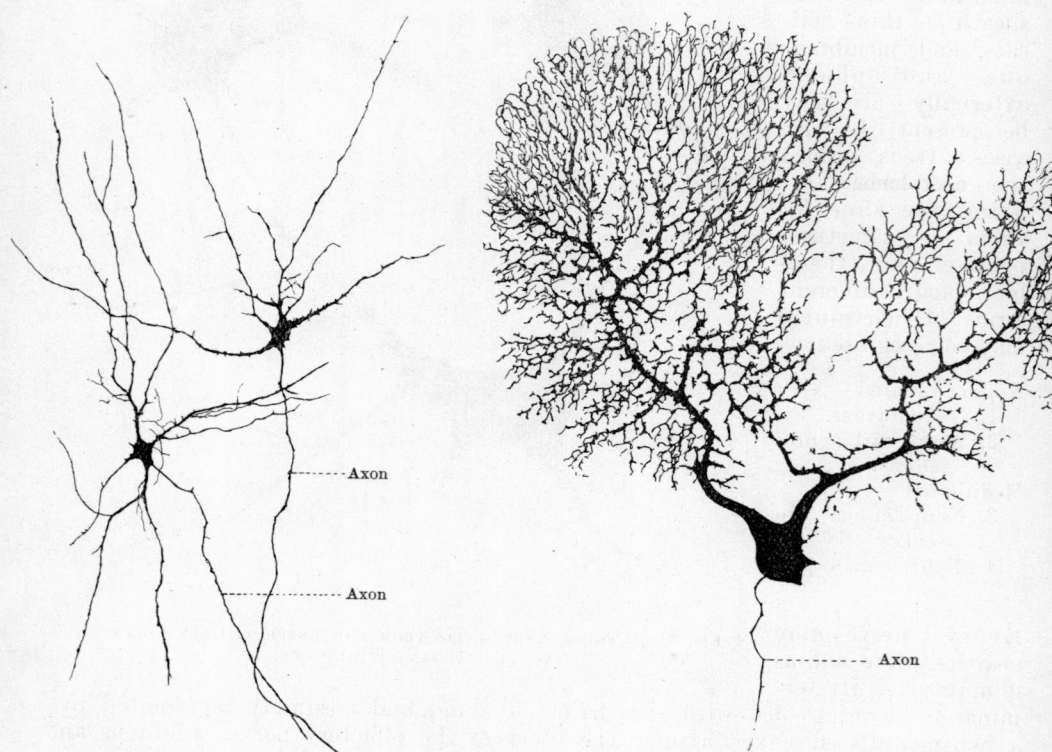

FIG. 689.—TWO MULTIPOLAR NERVE-CELLS. (From a specimen prepared by the Golgi method.)

FIG. 690.—NERVE-CELL FROM CEREBELLUM (CELL OF PURKINJE) SHOWING THE BRANCHING OF THE DENDRITES. (From a photograph by Professor Symington.)

sions from the peripheral organs into the central nervous system; and as a change of consciousness, or, in other words, a sensation, is a frequent result, they are often called *sensory fibres*. **Efferent nerve-fibres** carry impulses out from the brain and spinal cord to peripheral organs. The majority of them go to muscles and are termed *motor fibres*; others, however, go to glands and are called *secretory*; whilst some are *inhibitory* and serve to carry impulses which restrain or check movement or secretion.

The **dendrites** or receiving processes of the nerve-cell are thicker than the axon, and present a rough-edged irregular contour. They divide into numerous branches, and gradually become more and more attenuated until finally they appear to end in free extremities. The branching of the dendrites sometimes attains a marvellous degree of complexity (Fig. 690), but it is commonly supposed that there is no anastomosis between the dendrites of neighbouring cells, or between the dendrites of the same cell.

It is commonly believed that the neuroblast passes through stages analogous to those shown in the diagram (Fig. 692); that just as a seed gives off a root which strikes downward and leaflets which grow upward, so the neuroblast sprouts out an axon (*a*) and subsequently develops a bunch of dendrites (*b*). In the case of the axon reasons have already been given for not accepting this view as the whole explanation; and in the case of the dendrites, although the appearance of microscopic sections seems to favour the view expressed in the diagram, the fact that the neuroblasts are united into a continuous network or syncytium at an early stage of development (see p. 797) raises the possibility that the dendrites may be formed by the gradually drawing out of the existing bridges as the linked cell-bodies move apart.

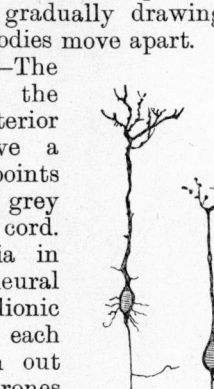

Ganglia of Sensory Nerves.—The cells found in the ganglia of the cranial nerves and on the posterior roots of the spinal nerves have a different origin, and present many points of contrast with neurones in the grey matter of the brain and spinal cord. As already indicated, the ganglia in question are derived from the neural crest. The cells in those ganglionic masses are oval in form, and each extremity or pole becomes drawn out into a process, so that the neurones become bipolar. The processes are distinguished as central and peripheral according to the direction which they take. The central processes penetrate the wall of the neural tube. In the region of the spinal cord they form almost the whole of the fibres which enter into the composition of the posterior roots of the spinal nerves. In the substance of the cerebro-spinal axis they give off numerous collaterals, and after a course of varying extent they end, after the manner of an axon, in terminal arborisations which enter into relationships with certain

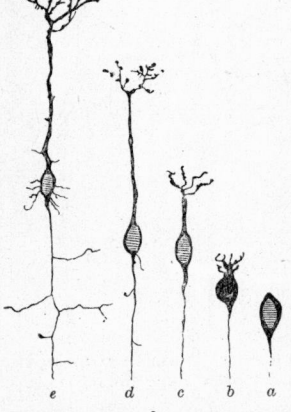

FIG. 692.—Ramón y Cajal's Interpretation of the Developmental Stages exhibited by a Pyramidal Cell of the Brain.

a, Neuroblast with rudimentary axon, but no dendrites ; *b* and *c*, the dendrites beginning to sprout out ; *d* and *e*, further development of the dendrites and appearance of collateral branches on the axon.

FIG. 691.
NERVE-FIBRE
FROM A FROG.
(After v. Kölliker.)

nerve-cells in the cerebro-spinal axis. The peripheral processes proceed along the path of the particular nerve with which they are associated, and they finally reach the skin or other sensory surface. Thus, to take one example: the majority of the fibres which go to the skin break up into fine terminal filaments which end freely between the epithelial cells of the epidermis. The two processes of a ganglion cell, therefore, form the afferent fibres, and constitute the path along which the influence of peripheral impressions is conducted towards the brain and spinal cord. The body of the cell is, as it were, interposed in the path of such impulses.

But the original bipolar character of those cells, with very few exceptions (ganglia in connexion with the auditory nerve and the bipolar nerve-cells in the olfactory mucous membrane), gradually undergoes a change which ultimately leads to their transformation into unipolar cells. That is brought about by the tendency which the cell-body has to grow to one side, viz., the side towards the surface of the ganglion (v. Lenhossek). The unilateral growth leads to a gradual approximation of the attached ends of the processes, and finally to a condition in which they appear to arise from the extremity of a short common stalk in a T-shaped manner (Fig. 693). It is interesting to note that in fishes the original bipolar condition of the spinal ganglion cells is retained without change throughout life.

Both the central and peripheral processes of those ganglionic cells become the axons of nerve-fibres, which, acquiring a medullary sheath, belong therefore to the medullated variety. From this it might very naturally be thought that the ganglionic neurone, with its two axons and no typical dendrites, is a nervous unit very different from a neurone in the grey matter of the cerebro-spinal axis. It is believed by some, however (van Gehuchten and Cajal), that the peripheral process, in spite of its enclosure within a medullary sheath, and though presenting all the characters of a true axon, is in reality a dendrite. If that is the case, the morphological difference between a dendrite and an axon disappears, and van Gehuchten's functional distinction alone remains characteristic, viz., that the axon is *cellulifugal* and conducts impulses away from the cell, whilst the dendrites are *cellulipetal* and conduct impulses towards the cell.

It is, however, more in accordance with the facts to regard the sensory neurones as genetically quite distinct from the rest of the nervous system (see p. 794).

Neuroglia.—The neuroglia is the supporting tissue of the cerebro-spinal axis. It may be considered to include two different forms of tissue viz. the lining ependymal cells and the neuroglia proper. We place these under the one heading, seeing that they have a common developmental origin.

The **ependymal cells** are the columnar epithelial cells which line the central canal of the spinal cord and the ventricles of the brain. In the embryonic condition a process from the deep extremity of each cell traverses the entire thickness of the neural wall and reaches the surface. It is not known whether or not that is the case in the adult.

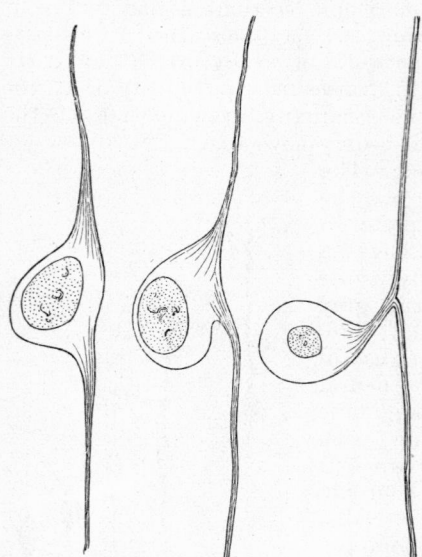

FIG. 693.—THREE STAGES IN THE DEVELOPMENT OF A CELL IN A SPINAL GANGLION.

The **neuroglia proper** is present in both the white and the grey matter of the cerebro-spinal axis. It constitutes an all-pervading basis substance in which the various nerve elements are embedded in such a way that they are all bound together into a consistent mass and are yet all severally isolated from one another. Neuroglia is composed of cells and fine filaments. The filaments are present in enormous numbers, and by their interlacements they constitute what appears to be a fine feltwork. At the points where the filaments intercross may be seen the flattened *glial cells*. Whilst the neuroglia is for the most part intimately intermixed with the nerve elements, there are, in both brain and spinal cord, certain localities where it is spread out in more or less pure layers. Thus, upon the surface of the brain and of the cord there is such a layer; likewise beneath the epithelial lining of the central canal and of the cavities of the brain there is a thin stratum of neuroglia.

The ependyma and the neuroglia proper are products of the ectoderm, being derived from the neuro-epithelium of the early neural tube; but some of the glial cells (mesoglia) are derived from mesodermal elements that accompany blood-vessels.

Summary.—1. The cerebro-spinal nervous system is composed of two parts, (*a*) a **central part**, consisting of the brain and spinal cord, with the efferent nerve-fibres which pass out from them; (*b*) the **ganglionic part**, with the afferent nerve-fibres.

2. Each of those parts has a different origin, and is composed of neurones which possess characteristic features.

3. The ganglionic neurones are derived from the primitive cells of the neural crest, and have each one process which divides into two. Of those, the central division enters the cerebro-spinal axis, whilst the peripheral division becomes connected with a peripheral part. The central fibres from the ganglionic cells in the region of the spinal cord form the posterior roots of the spinal nerves.

The cells of origin of the posterior roots are outside the cord, and carry impulses into its substance.

4. The cerebro-spinal neurones are derived from the neuroblasts in the wall of the early neural tube. Some of them furnish efferent nerve-fibres, which issue from the spinal cord in separate bundles termed the anterior roots of the spinal nerves. In the cranial nerves, however, with the exception of the trigeminal and facial nerves, the efferent fibres are not thus separated from the afferent fibres at their attachment to the brain.

5. The brain and spinal cord, when studied by the naked eye, are seen to be composed of white matter and grey matter. The white matter forms very nearly two-thirds of the entire cerebro-spinal axis. It is composed of medullated nerve-fibres embedded in neuroglial tissue. The grey matter is composed of nerve-cells with their dendrites and axons. Some of the axons are in the form of naked axis cylinders, whilst others have a coating of myelin. Intimately intermixed with those parts is the neuroglia, which isolates them more or less completely from one another.

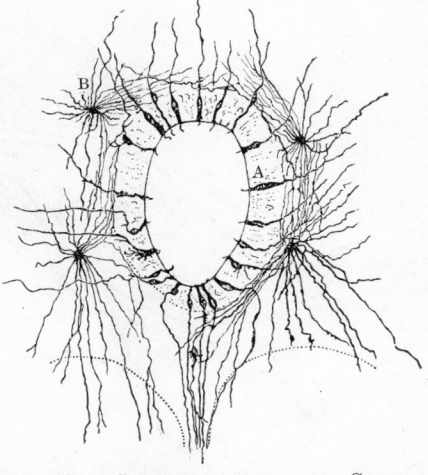

FIG. 694.—SECTION THROUGH THE CENTRAL CANAL OF THE SPINAL CORD OF A HUMAN EMBRYO, SHOWING EPENDYMAL AND NEUROGLIAL CELLS. (After v. Lenhossek.)

A, Ependymal cell.   B, Neuroglial cell.

[Note that the dorsal (posterior) aspect is *below*.]

NATURE OF THE BRAIN

In the foregoing account it has been explained that the nervous system is composed of a series of afferent nerves bringing information from every part of the body into the central nervous system, from which efferent nerves pass out to the muscular and other active parts of the body, providing the means for translating such information into appropriate action. But it has been seen that the essential parts of the central nervous system are the intercalated cells, which provide the means whereby the information brought in by any sensory nerve may be placed at the service of the whole body, and the response which it excites may be controlled and regulated by the condition of the rest of the body. The system of intercalated cells links together into one co-ordinated mechanism the whole nervous system, and, through it, every part of the body itself.

In some very primitive and remote ancestor of man (and in fact of the vast majority of animals) one end of the nervous system became enhanced in importance to form a brain, which assumed a dominant influence over the rest. This was brought about in the first place by the fact that in an elongated prone animal moving forwards the front end would naturally come first into relationship with any change in environment; and that earlier acquisition of information concerning the outside world would necessarily give the head end of the nervous system exceptional opportunities for influencing the rest of the nervous system. This predominance is further accentuated by the development in the head region of the organs of special sense, which provide mechanisms specially adapted to be influenced by light, sound, and such delicate chemical forms of stimulation as excite in ourselves sensations of smell and taste. As the information conveyed by the special senses, such as the scent of food or the visual impression of some enemy, must be able immediately to influence the movements of the whole body, it follows that a specially abundant system of intercalated elements link the central ends of the nerves of the special senses with the rest of the central nervous system. Moreover the predominant influence of the head end of the central nervous system implies that it must be provided with a specially large series of nerve-fibres, not only for the purpose of bringing influence to bear upon the rest of the nervous system, but also of being itself brought into intimate relationship with the nervous system as a whole, seeing that sensory impulses are constantly pouring into every part of it.

Thus the head end of the central nervous system becomes the brain, which is characterised by a series of large irregular swellings, due to (a) the development around the insertion of each special sensory nerve of a mass, or group of masses, of intercalated cells which will enable the effects of the visual, auditory, olfactory, gustatory, or other sensations to influence the whole nervous system,

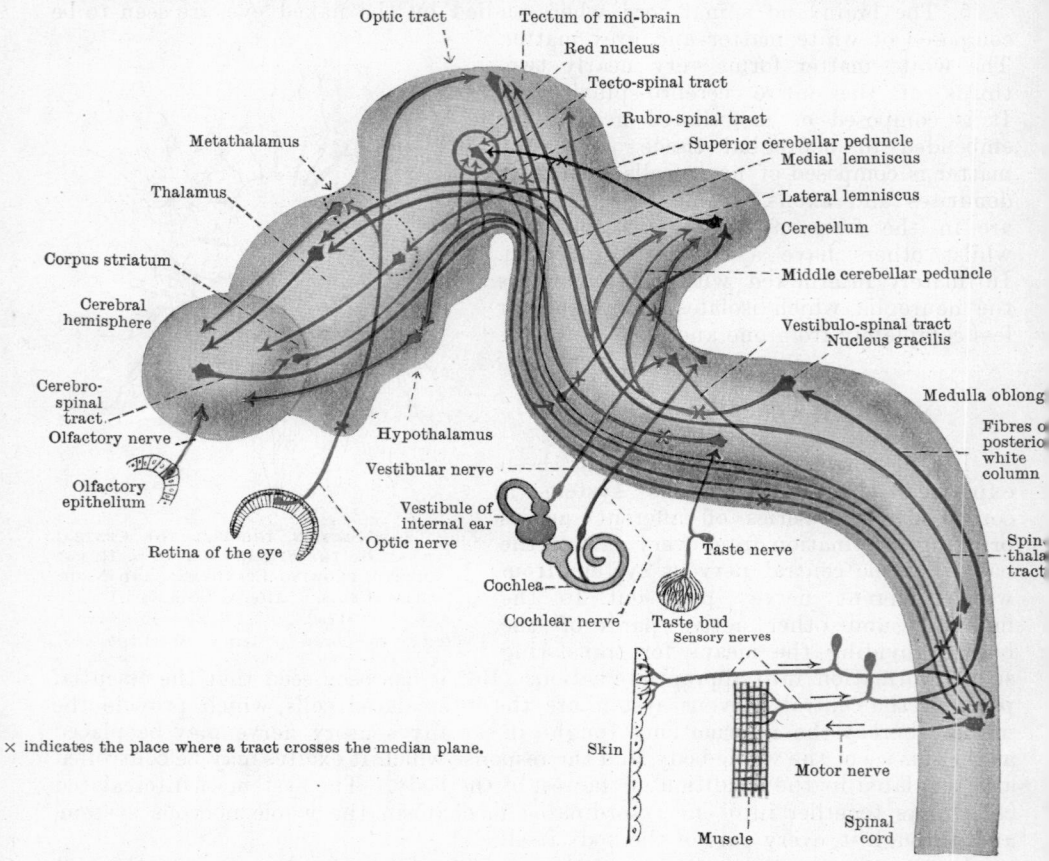

Optic tract   Tectum of mid-brain
Red nucleus
Tecto-spinal tract
Rubro-spinal tract
Superior cerebellar peduncle
Medial lemniscus
Metathalamus
Lateral lemniscus
Thalamus
Cerebellum
Corpus striatum
Middle cerebellar peduncle
Cerebral hemisphere
Vestibulo-spinal tract
Nucleus gracilis
Cerebro-spinal tract
Medulla oblong
Olfactory nerve
Fibres o posterio white column
Hypothalamus
Olfactory epithelium
Vestibular nerve
Vestibule of internal ear
Optic nerve
Retina of the eye
Taste nerve
Spin thala tract
Cochlea
Cochlear nerve   Taste bud
Sensory nerves
× indicates the place where a tract crosses the median plane.
Skin
Motor nerve
Spinal cord
Muscle

Fig. 695.—Diagram representing the Connexions of some important Sensory and Motor Tracts in the Brain to which references are made in pages 825 to 829. Motor paths in red; sensory in other colours. (G. E. S.)

and (b) the evolution of complicated systems of intercalated cells which receive, and in a sense blend, impressions coming from all parts of the nervous system, and emit fibres which pass, directly or indirectly, to the various groups of motor nerve-cells to control their activities and, through them, the behaviour of the animal.

In the development of the human embryo the distinction between the head end and the rest of the central nervous system is indicated even before the medullary plate is completely folded up to form the neural tube. The widened part represents the rudiment of the brain; and the rest of the tube will become converted into the spinal cord.

If the attempt is made to analyse the meaning of the early broadening of the brain rudiment it will be found to be due in great measure to the fact that there is added to the margins of the medullary plate (see Fig. 683, E, p. 795) the material from which the sensitive part of the eye and the optic nerve will be developed; but soon after the neural tube is closed irregular swellings will make their appearance around the attachments of the nerves of smell, vision, hearing, and taste (Fig. 695), and also of the vagus nerve, which is widely distributed to the viscera of the neck, thorax, and abdomen.

But there are other factors besides the irregularities of growth of its walls which add complexity to the form of the brain in the embryo. In the course of their growth both parts (brain and spinal cord) of the neural tube undergo great extensions in length, breadth, and thickness; but in the case of the cord it is the increase in length that is most distinctive, whereas in the brain the irregular expansion in breadth and thickness is more striking. Nevertheless, the brain elongates more rapidly than that part of its mesodermal capsule which ultimately becomes the brain-case; and hence it becomes bent to permit of its being packed in the limited length of the cranial cavity. But if it is admitted that these mechanical considerations are in a measure responsible for the three bends which develop in the embryonic brain, their situation and the forms they assume are determined by the irregularities of growth inherent in the brain itself.

Even at a time, during the second week, when the anterior (head) end of the neural tube is still open (anterior neuropore), a right-angled bend has already developed in the rudiment of the brain (**cerebral vesicle**). Slightly less than half of the length of the vesicle has projected beyond the headward end of the notochord and become flexed ventrally round it (Fig. 696).

That bend is known as the **cephalic flexure**. The region of the brain vesicle in which it develops will later on become the **mid-brain** or **mesencephalon**; and even at the early stage of development now under consideration (Fig. 696) there is a slight narrowing of the tube (**isthmus**) that marks the boundary between the mid-brain and the **hind-brain** or **rhomben-cephalon**. Immediately beyond the end of the notochord there is an even fainter trace of a constriction that indicates the line of demarcation between the mid-brain and the **fore-brain** or **prosencephalon**.

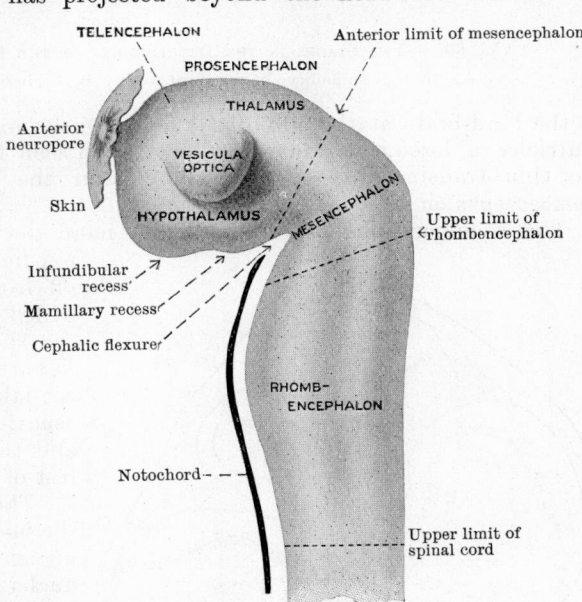

FIG. 696.—LEFT SIDE OF AN EARLY HUMAN EMBRYO.
(After His's model, reversed.)

Shortly after the appearance of the cephalic flexure a similar bending occurs in the region where the brain becomes continuous with the spinal cord (Fig. 697, A). It is called the **cervical flexure**.

But at that stage, or even earlier (Fig. 696), there has been developing a third bend which produces effects differing from those just mentioned. At the end of the second week a slight bulging can be detected on the ventral side of the hind-brain (Fig. 697): during the next four weeks it steadily becomes accentuated and forms the **pontine flexure**. The convexity of the bend is directed ventrally, differing in that respect from both of the other flexures. The difference in direction has a profound influence upon the form which the hind-brain assumes. If a plastic tube is bent a strain is thrown upon the wall in the concavity of the flexure. If that wall is strong and resisting, like the floor-plate of the neural tube (in the cases of the cephalic and cervical flexures) the bending does not affect the outline of the tube (in section) very materially. But when the strain is thrown upon the thin roof-plate during the development of the pontine flexure it is not strong enough to resist; it becomes stretched and allows the side walls of the neural tube to splay laterally in precisely the same manner as occurs when a rubber tube is bent towards a side which has been split (or weakened) longitudinally (Fig. 697). This mechanical factor determines the form assumed

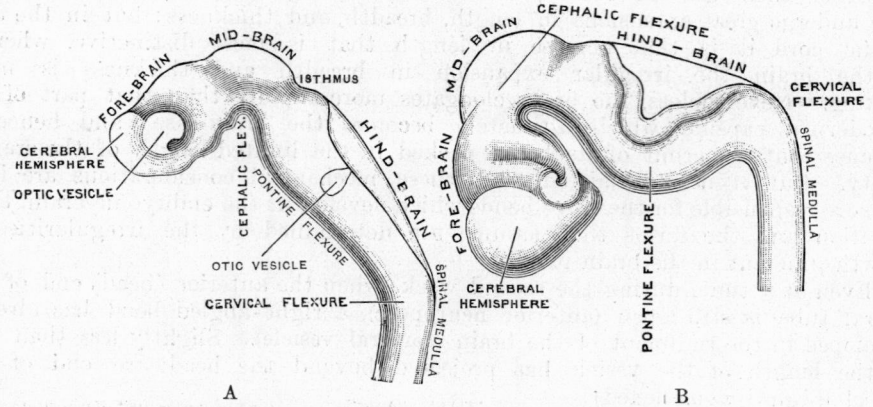

FIG. 697.—TWO STAGES IN THE DEVELOPMENT OF THE HUMAN BRAIN. (After His.)

A, Brain of an embryo of the third week. B, Brain of an embryo of five weeks.

by the hind-brain at the end of the first month; and gives its cavity—the fourth ventricle—a lozenge or rhomboid form when seen from its dorsal aspect through the thin translucent roof. For this reason the hind-brain is known as the **rhombencephalon.**

The rhombencephalon forms at first more than half of the brain and as it expands it appears to become marked off from the rest by a constriction called the **isthmus rhombencephali.**

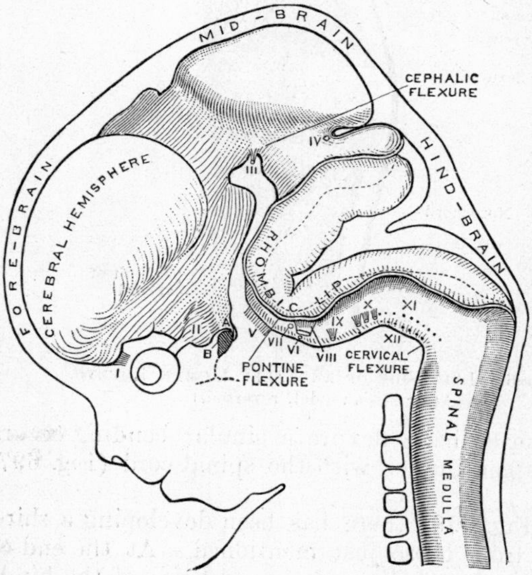

The development of the pontine flexure subdivides the rhombencephalon into two parts—the **myelencephalon,** joined to the spinal cord, and the **metencephalon,** joined to the rest of the brain.

The myelencephalon is known as the **medulla oblongata,** and important nuclei develop in it. They are the nuclei of the nerves which regulate the activities of the heart, lungs, and a considerable part of the alimentary canal, and also the receptive nuclei of the nerves of taste.

The insertion of the auditory nerve in the neighbourhood of the outsplayed lateral angle of the rhombencephalon leads to the profound transformation of the metencephalon. The auditory nerve conveys into the hind-brain impulses which are stimulated by movements of fluid in the closed sac developed from the otic vesicle (Fig. 687,

FIG. 698.—PROFILE VIEW OF THE BRAIN OF A HUMAN EMBRYO OF TEN WEEKS. (His.)

The various cranial nerves are indicated by numerals.

A, Cerebral diverticulum of hypophysis cerebri.
B, Oral diverticulum of hypophysis cerebri.

p. 800). The truly auditory function of the apparatus is called into activity when the movements of the fluid are caused by waves of sound transmitted to it from the outside world. But it is obvious that motion may also be set up in the fluid by changes in position of the body itself; in other words, movements in the fluid of the otic vesicle may stimulate nerves to convey to the brain information concerning the position' and movements of the body itself. There are separate fibre bundles in the auditory nerve to serve each of these func-

tions, and they are referred to as the cochlear and vestibular divisions of the nerve. A great mass of nerve-cells develops around the insertion of that part of the auditory nerve which is called vestibular to make use of the information for the regulation of the movements of the body in balancing or equilibration. To enable the terminal vestibular nucleus the better to perform its function of equilibration, depending as it does upon the co-operation and adjustment of the movements of vast numbers of widely separated muscles, nerve tracts coming from muscles and skin areas of all parts of the body make their way into the vestibular nucleus; and it expands and forms a great excrescence known as the **cerebellum**. And as the cerebellum has to adjust the activities of all the muscles of the body it necessarily becomes the great organ of muscular co-ordination, and as such it is made use of by those parts of the brain which have to initiate and control complex actions such as

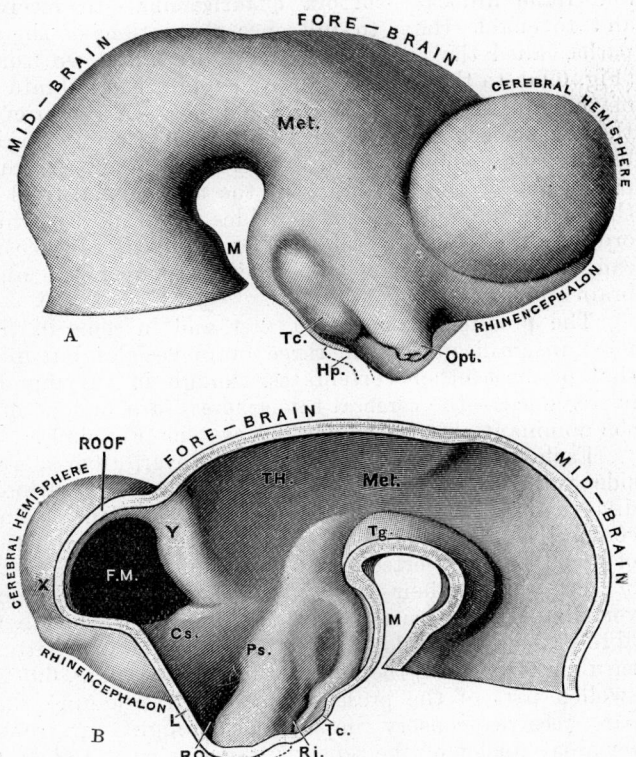

FIG. 699.—THE BRAIN OF A HUMAN EMBRYO IN THE FIFTH WEEK. (From His.)

A, Brain as seen in profile. B, Median section through the same brain. M, Mamillary eminence; Tc, Tuber cinereum; Hp, Hypophysis (hypophyseal diverticulum from oral cavity); Opt, Optic stalk; TH, Thalamus; Tg, Tegmental part of mesencephalon; Ps, Hypothalamus; Cs, Corpus striatum; FM, Interventricular foramen; L, Lamina terminalis; RO, Optic recess; Ri, Infundibular recess.

skilled movements. It will be shown in the subsequent account how the cerebellum becomes linked to the mid-brain to co-ordinate the movements of the body which are excited by this part of the brain; and later how it becomes associated with the fore-brain, when the latter becomes responsible for the acquisition and control of the most highly skilled actions. For the latter purpose a great pathway of nerve-fibres is laid down to connect the fore-brain with the cerebellum: the terminal stage of that connexion is situated on the ventral (anterior) aspect of the metencephalon in the form of a great mass of transverse fibres. At one time these strands of nerve-fibres were looked upon as a bridge between the two hemispheres of the cerebellum: hence the name **pons** was applied to them. This term is now applied not only to the fibres themselves, but also to the upward prolongation of the medulla oblongata, to the surface of which they are related.

The subdivision of the rest of the brain into **mesencephalon** and **prosencephalon** develops later and is less fundamental than the primary demarcation of the rhombencephalon.

The visual apparatus is connected with both the mid-brain and the forebrain, but at first more intimately with the mid-brain, to which also nerve pathways are established to convey sensory impressions of touch and hearing from the spinal cord and medulla oblongata. From the alar laminæ of the mesencephalon the **tectum** or dorsal part of the mid-brain is formed, and in it there are developed four little hillocks—**corpora quadrigemina**—to receive those varied impressions and to enable them to influence the actions of the whole body. Special nerve paths, called the **tecto-spinal tracts**, are laid down from the corpora quadrigemina (Fig. 695) to the spinal cord to enable the mid-brain to control the motor nuclei of the muscles of the trunk and limbs. A group of intercalated cells known as the **red nucleus** develops in each half of the mid-brain for the purpose of establishing connexions between the cerebellum and the mid-brain. When an impulse passes out of the mid-brain by the tecto-spinal tract to excite some movement of the body, the red nucleus provides the link by which the cerebellum can co-ordinate the actions of the muscles involved. By means of a **rubro-spinal tract** it can bring its influence to bear directly upon the nuclei of motor nerves in the brain and spinal cord (Fig. 695).

The prosencephalon is at first, and in some of the lower fishes remains, the most insignificant of the three brain vesicles, but in the human brain (as also in that of most other vertebrates, though in varying degrees) a pair of enormous excrescences—the **cerebral hemispheres**—are budded off from it; and they become the dominant part of the nervous system (Fig. 699).

Each hemisphere is formed, however, from a relatively small part of the side wall of the prosencephalon, the rest of which goes to form the optic diverticula, the thalamus, and the hypothalamus, among other structures. The cerebral hemisphere is at first pre-eminently olfactory in function, the nerves of smell being inserted directly into it. But impressions of the associated sense of taste make their way into the cerebral hemisphere in the most primitive vertebrates: the gustatory nerves are inserted into the medulla oblongata, but fibre-paths are laid down to establish connexions with the hypothalamus, which in turn emits fibres to the cerebral hemisphere (Fig. 695). The thalamus is a greatly swollen part of the prosencephalic wall adjoining the mesencephalon. Its main part receives sensory impressions brought up from the spinal cord and the terminal nuclei of the sensory cranial nerves and transmits them to the cerebral hemisphere. Its caudal portion becomes specialised as a special receptive nucleus for visual and auditory impressions for transmission to the cerebral hemisphere. It is called the **metathalamus** or **geniculate bodies**. Thus the cerebral hemisphere, from being essentially a receptive organ for smell impressions, ultimately becomes the terminus of all the sensory paths, and the structure that is concerned with the consciousness of all kinds of sensations. It also controls the voluntary movements of one-half of the body and emits a great strand of fibres—the **cerebral peduncle**—to establish relations with the cerebellum and all the motor nuclei on the other side of the brain and spinal cord (Fig. 695, p. 806).

SPINAL CORD

The **spinal cord** is the part of the central nervous system which occupies the upper two-thirds of the vertebral canal. It is an elongated cylindrical structure, slightly flattened in front and behind, and extends from the foramen magnum to the lower border of the body of the first lumbar vertebra or to the upper border of the second. Its average length is 45 cm. in men and 43 cm. in women.

The level of the lower end of the cord varies from the middle of the last thoracic vertebra to the upper border of the third lumbar and is said to be slightly lower in women than in men. It varies also in the fœtus and infant at different periods of development. Up to the third month of intra-uterine life the spinal cord occupies the entire length of the vertebral canal. But from that time onwards, the vertebral column lengthens at a more rapid rate than the cord. The spinal cord, therefore, has the appearance of shrinking in an upward direction within its canal, and at birth the lower end usually is opposite the body of the third lumbar vertebra. The attitude of the body affects to a small degree the position of the lower end of the cord. When the trunk is bent well forwards, the terminal part of the cord rises slightly.

At the margin of the foramen magnum the spinal cord becomes continuous with the medulla oblongata, whilst below it tapers rapidly to a point and forms a conical extremity termed the **conus medullaris**. From the end of the conus medullaris a slender glistening thread is prolonged downwards within the vertebral canal, and finally anchors the cord to the back of the coccyx. The prolongation receives the name of the **filum terminale**.

The diameter of the cord is very much smaller than that of the vertebral canal. The wide interval left between it and the walls of its canal is clearly a provision for allowing free movement of the vertebral column without producing any jarring contact between the cord and the surrounding bones.

Three protective membranes are wrapped around the cord. From within outwards they are termed (1) the pia mater, (2) the arachnoid mater, and (3) the dura mater. The **pia mater** is a vascular fibrous membrane which forms the immediate investment. It is closely applied to the cord, and from its deep surface numerous fine septa penetrate into the substance of the cord. The **arachnoid mater** is an exceedingly delicate, transparent membrane which is loosely wrapped around the cord so as to leave a considerable interval, between itself and the pia mater, termed the subarachnoid space, in which there is always a varying amount of cerebro-spinal fluid. Outside the arachnoid mater the **dura mater** forms a wide, dense, fibrous, sheath which extends downwards for a considerable distance beyond the cord.

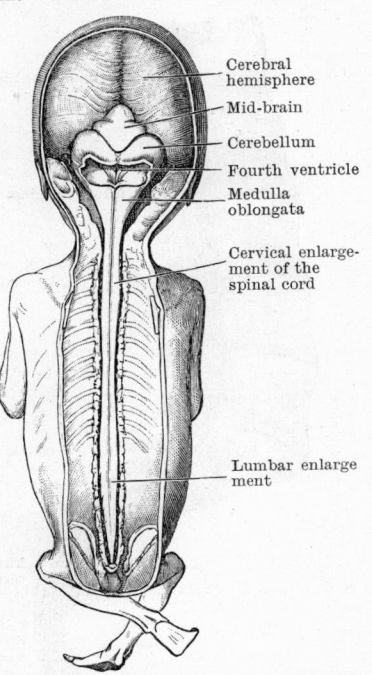

Cerebral hemisphere

Mid-brain

Cerebellum

Fourth ventricle

Medulla oblongata

Cervical enlargement of the spinal cord

Lumbar enlargement

FIG. 700.—HUMAN FŒTUS IN THE THIRD MONTH OF DEVELOPMENT, WITH THE BRAIN AND SPINAL CORD EXPOSED FROM BEHIND.

The cord is suspended within its sheath of dura mater by a pair of wing-like ligaments, termed the **ligamenta denticulata**, which extend from the sides of the spinal cord and each of them is attached by a series of pointed or tooth-like processes to the inner surface of the dura mater. Between the wall of the vertebral canal and the dura mater there is a narrow interval, called the extra-dural space, which is filled up by soft areolo-fatty tissue and numerous thin-walled veins arranged in a plexiform manner.

Thirty-one pairs of spinal nerves arise from the sides of the spinal cord. They are classified into eight cervical, twelve thoracic, five lumbar, five sacral, and one coccygeal; and according to the attachments of those groups of nerves the cord is divided into cervical, thoracic, lumbar, and sacral *regions*. It must be understood that these regions are determined by the nerve attachments and not by any direct relationship between the parts of the spinal cord and the sections of the vertebral column which bear the same names.

Each spinal nerve is attached to the cord by an anterior and a posterior root, and as the roots are traced to their central attachments they are seen to break up into a number of separate bundles which spread out (in some cases very widely), as they approach the side of the cord (Fig. 702). Each pair of nerves is therefore attached to a portion of cord of some length, and such a portion receives the name of a *segment* of the spinal cord. There is, however, no means of marking off one segment from another except by the nerve attachments.

In the cervical and lumbar regions the nerve-roots are crowded together, so that little or no interval is left between the roots of neighbouring nerves. In the thoracic region, however, distinct intervals may be observed, and the root bundles are more loosely arranged. From this it will be evident that the segments are not of equal length. In the cervical region they measure about 12 mm. in length, in the thoracic region from 20 to 24 mm., and in the lumbar region about 10 mm.

Owing to the great difference between the lengths of spinal cord and vertebral column, the farther we pass down the greater is the distance between the attachment of the nerve-roots and the intervertebral foramina through which the corresponding nerves leave the vertebral canal. As the nerve-

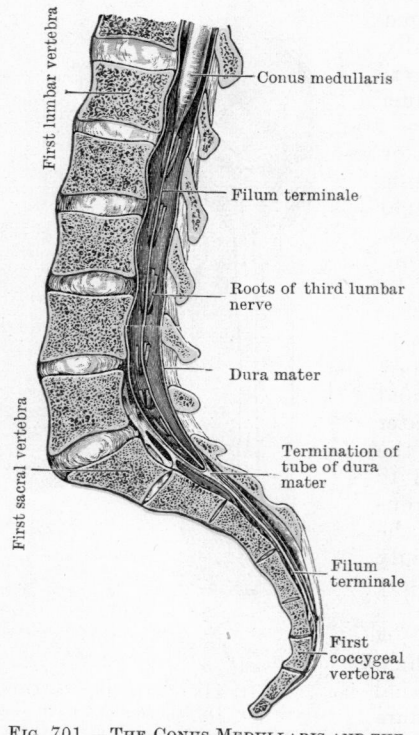

FIG. 701.—THE CONUS MEDULLARIS AND THE FILUM TERMINALE.

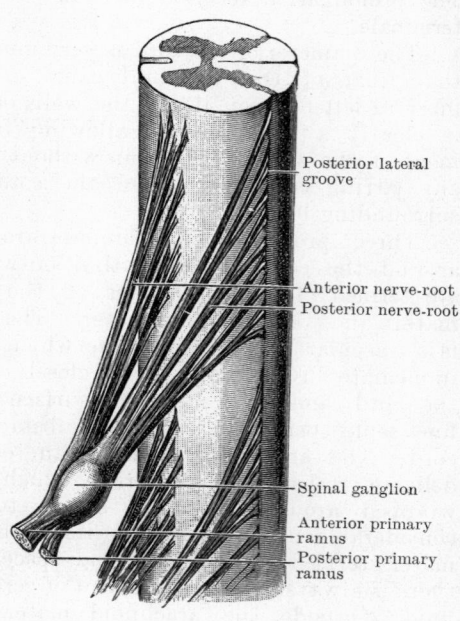

FIG. 702.—THE ROOTS OF THE SEVENTH THORACIC NERVE (semi-diagrammatic).

roots do not unite to form a spinal nerve trunk till they reach the intervertebral foramen, it thus happens that the nerve-roots which spring from the lumbar and sacral regions attain a very great length and descend vertically in the lower part of the vertebral canal in a bunch or leash, in the midst of which lie the conus medullaris and the filum terminale. That great bundle of nerve-roots receives the appropriate name of the **cauda equina**.

Enlargements of Spinal Cord. —Throughout the greater part of the thoracic region, the cord presents a uniform girth and a very nearly circular outline. In the cervical and lumbar regions, however, it shows marked swellings. The **cervical enlargement** is the more evident of the two. It begins very gradually at the upper end of the cord, attains its greatest breadth (12 to 14 mm.) opposite the fifth or sixth cervical vertebra, and finally subsides opposite the second thoracic vertebra. That portion of the cord gives attachment to the great nerves which supply the

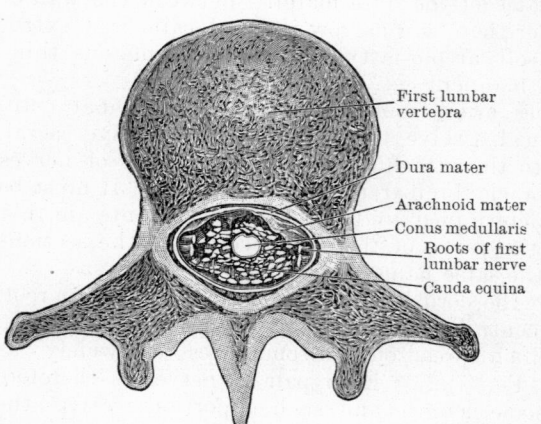

FIG. 703.—SECTION THROUGH CONUS MEDULLARIS AND CAUDA EQUINA AS THEY LIE IN THE VERTEBRAL CANAL.

upper limbs. The **lumbar enlargement** begins at the level of the tenth thoracic vertebra, and acquires its maximum transverse diameter (11 to 13 mm.) opposite the last thoracic vertebra. Below, it rapidly tapers away into the conus medullaris. To the lumbar enlargement are attached the great nerves of the lower limbs.

The enlargements of the cord are associated with the outgrowth of the limbs. In the earlier developmental stages they are not present, and they take form only as the limbs become developed. In different animals their size corresponds with the size of the limbs. Thus, in the long-armed orang and gibbon the cervical swelling is very pronounced.

Development of Spinal Cord.—The early stages of the process by which the originally simple epithelial neural tube becomes converted into the central

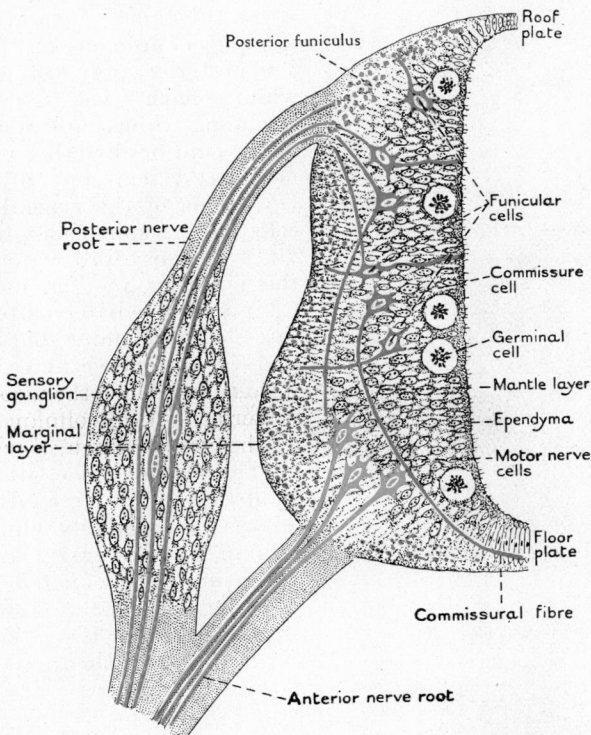

FIG. 704.—DIAGRAM OF TRANSVERSE SECTION OF THE LEFT HALF OF EARLY NEURAL TUBE. (G. E. S.)

nervous system have already been considered. It remains to be explained how the features specially distinctive of the spinal cord are produced.

In the early stages (Fig. 704), the neuroblasts are scattered in the intermediate one of the three bands of which the thick side wall of the neural tube is composed—the mantle layer. The motor nerve-cells soon congregate in large numbers in the ventral part of the basal lamina (Fig. 705), so that the mantle layer expands there into a broad excrescence, which is the rudiment of the **anterior grey column**. The anterior grey column contains the efferent or motor nerve-cells, the axons of which emerge as the **anterior root** of a spinal nerve. At that stage the rest of the mantle layer consists of a thin stratum of neuroblasts (Fig. 705)—mainly intercalated cells—which receive the sensory impressions that enter the cord through the **posterior root** and transmit impulses into axons passing (a) to the motor nuclei, (b) to the other side of the cord through the floor-plate (Fig. 704), or (c) into the superficial stratum (peripheral layer) of the cord, where they bend upwards or downwards as constituent elements of the **white columns**.

As development proceeds (Fig. 704) the **grey substance** formed of these inter-calated cells becomes much more abundant and forms a broad blunt boss (Figs. 705, B and C) which is the rudiment of the **posterior grey column.**

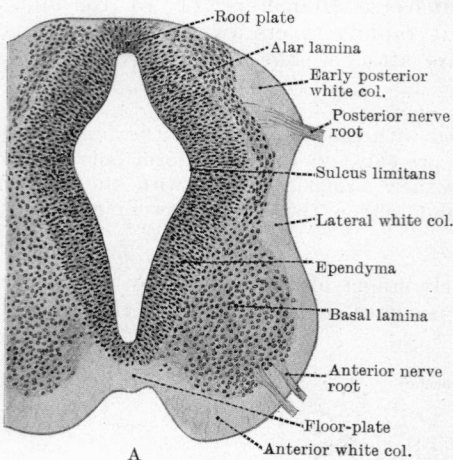

The surfaces of the grey columns become coated with a layer of white substance, composed at first mainly of the axons of cells in the root ganglia and intercalated cells in the cord; and as the white columns increase in thickness they help to mould the form of the grey columns. That is displayed best in the case of the posterior grey column. The major portion of the white substance which accumulates behind (and afterwards lies on the medial side of) the posterior grey column—the **posterior white column**—does not consist of fibres springing from intercalated cells, either of the cord or any other part of the central nervous system, but of the direct con-tinuations of the central processes of the cells in the spinal ganglia (Figs. 704 and 705). A large proportion of the fibres of the posterior root do not enter the grey columns immediately after their insertion into the alar lamina, but bifurcate to form two vertical nerve-fibres, one passing up-wards, and the other downwards, in the posterior white column before they end in the grey column, some distance above or below the place where they gained admission to the cord. As the cord grows, the originally blunt posterior grey column becomes drawn backwards into an increasingly attenuated edge and the posterior white column, which was placed originally upon its lateral surface (Fig. 705, A), and then upon its posterior surface (Fig. 705, B), gradually assumes a wedge-shaped form (Figs. 705, C, and 707), on the medial side of the grey matter.

Development of Anterior Median Fissure, Posterior Median Septum, and Central Canal.—As the anterior columns of grey matter and white matter increase in size, the anterior surface of the cord, on each side of the median plane, bulges for-wards, and the **anterior median fissure** (Fig. 705, A, B, and C) is produced as the natural result.

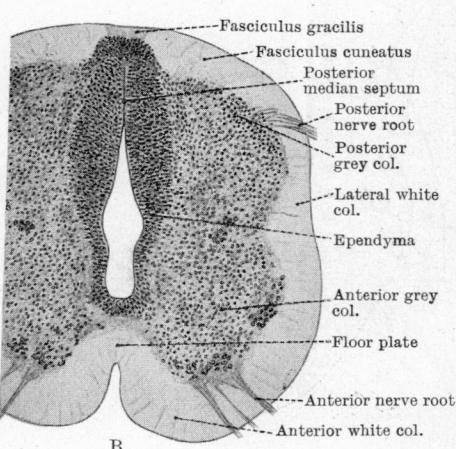

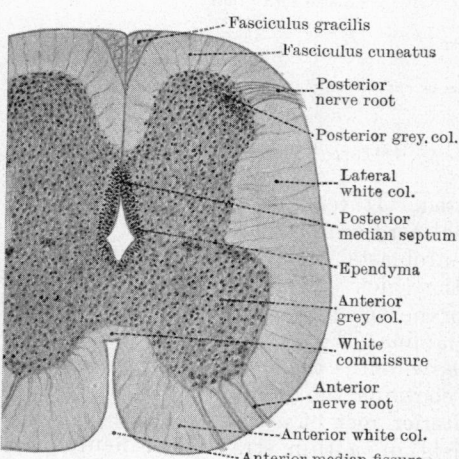

FIG. 705.—THREE STAGES IN THE DEVELOPMENT OF SPINAL CORD. (After His.)

There has been considerable discussion as to the mode of formation of the **pos-terior median septum**; but there is now no doubt as to the essential facts. Early in the third month the walls of the posterior three-fourths (of the sagittal extent) of

the **central canal** become approximated (Fig. 705), and later they fuse to obliterate that part of the canal. But the part of the septum thus formed is only an insignificant portion of the whole. For most of the septum is produced by the gradual elongation of the epithelial cells that line the remnant of the central canal as the fibre-masses of the posterior white columns expand and separate the posterior surface of the cord farther and farther from the canal (see Fig. 694).

Furrows of Spinal Cord.—When cross-sections of the adult cord are made it is seen to be a bilateral structure partially subdivided into a right and a left half by the anterior median fissure in front and the posterior median septum behind. The anterior median fissure penetrates for rather less than a third of the antero-posterior diameter of the cord. The pia mater dips into it and forms a fold within it. The posterior median septum in the cervical and thoracic regions penetrates into the cord until it reaches a point slightly beyond its centre. It is extremely thin, and consists of ependymal and neuroglial elements, and is intimately connected with the adjacent sides of the two halves of the cord. The pia mater passes over the posterior median septum and sends no prolongation into it. In the lumbar region the septum becomes shallower, whilst the anterior median fissure deepens, and ultimately in the lower part of the cord the fissure and septum are very nearly equal in depth.

The two halves of the cord may show slight differences in the arrangement of parts; but to all intents and purposes they are symmetrical. They are joined together by a fairly broad commissure which intervenes between the median fissure and the septum.

An inspection of the surface of each half of the cord brings into view a longitudinal groove or furrow, at some little distance from the posterior medial septum, along its whole length. Through the bottom of this groove the bundles of the posterior nerve-roots enter the spinal cord in accurate linear order. There is no corresponding furrow on the anterior part of each half of the cord in connexion with the emergence of the bundles of the anterior nerve-roots. They emerge irregularly over a broad strip of the anterior surface of the cord which corresponds in its width to that of the subjacent anterior grey column.

The grey columns and the nerve-roots divide the white matter into three white columns—anterior, lateral and posterior—the most lateral of the bundles of the anterior roots being taken as the line of demarcation between the anterior and lateral columns.

In the cervical region a distinct longitudinal groove marks on the surface the position of a septum of pia mater which dips into the cord and sub-divides the posterior white column into a lateral part termed the **fasciculus cuneatus** and a medial portion named the **fasciculus gracilis**.

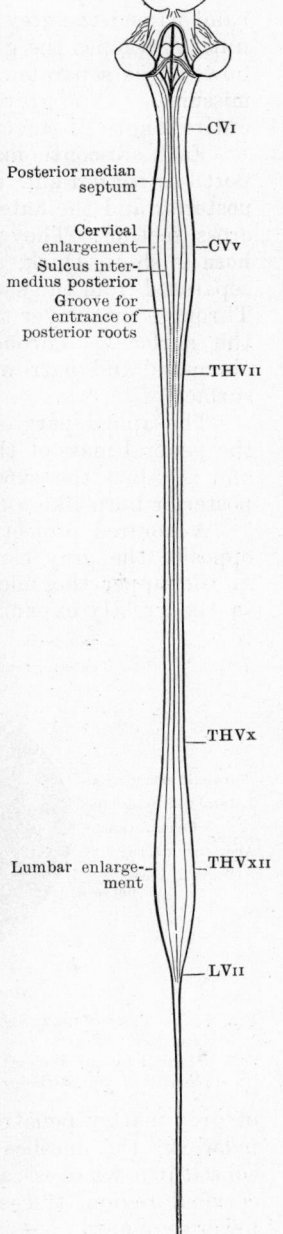

FIG. 706.—DIAGRAM OF THE SPINAL CORD AS SEEN FROM BEHIND.

CVI shows the level of the 1st cervical vertebra; CVv of the 5th cervical vertebra; THVII of the 2nd thoracic vertebra; THVx of the 10th thoracic vertebra; THVxII of the 12th thoracic vertebra; LVII of the 2nd lumbar vertebra.

INTERNAL STRUCTURE OF SPINAL CORD

The spinal cord is composed of a central core of grey matter thickly coated with white matter. At only one spot does the grey matter come close to the surface, viz. at the entrance of the posterior nerve roots.

Grey Matter of Spinal Cord.—The grey matter of the cord has the form of a fluted column, but it is customary to describe it as it appears in transverse sections. It then presents the appearance of the capital letter H. In each half of the cord there is a crescentic mass the concavity of which is directed laterally. The crescents of opposite sides are connected across the median plane by a transverse band named the **grey commissure**. The posterior median septum extends forwards until it reaches the grey commissure. The bottom of the anterior median fissure, however, is separated from it by a strip of white matter termed the **white commissure**. In the grey commissure may be seen the **central canal**, which tunnels the entire length of the cord and is just visible to the naked eye as a minute speck.

Each crescentic mass of grey matter presents certain well-defined parts. The portions behind and in front of the grey commissure are termed respectively the **posterior** and the **anterior horns** and are the corresponding grey columns as seen in cross section. They stand out in marked contrast to each other. The **anterior horn** is short, thick, and very blunt at its extremity. Further, its extremity is separated from the surface of the cord by a moderately thick layer of white matter. Through that layer the bundles of the anterior nerve-roots pass on their way to the surface. Throughout the greater part of the cord the **posterior horn** is elongated and narrow, and is drawn out to a fine point which almost reaches the surface.

The apical part of the posterior horn differs considerably in appearance from the general mass of the grey matter. It has a lighter and more translucent look, and is called the **substantia gelatinosa**; it is V-shaped in outline and fits on the posterior horn like a cap.

A pointed projection juts out from the lateral side of the grey matter nearly opposite the grey commissure. That is the **lateral horn** and it is best marked in the upper thoracic region (Fig. 708, B). Traced upwards it becomes absorbed in the greatly expanded anterior grey column of the cervical enlargement, but it reappears again in the uppermost part of the cord, and is particularly noticeable in the second and third cervical segments; followed in a downward direction it blends with the anterior column in the lumbar enlargement and contributes to the thickening of that column.

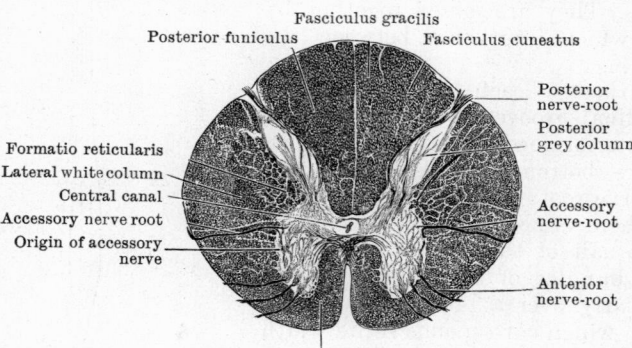

Fasciculus gracilis
Posterior funiculus
Fasciculus cuneatus
Posterior nerve-root
Posterior grey column
Formatio reticularis
Lateral white column
Central canal
Accessory nerve root
Origin of accessory nerve
Accessory nerve-root
Anterior nerve-root
Anterior white column

FIG. 707.—TRANSVERSE SECTION THROUGH THE UPPER PART OF THE CERVICAL REGION OF THE SPINAL CORD. (From a specimen prepared by the Weigert-Pal method, by which the white matter is made dark whilst the grey matter is bleached.)

The grey matter is for the most part fairly sharply mapped off from the surrounding white matter; but in the cervical region, on the lateral side of the crescentic mass, fine bands of grey matter penetrate the white matter, and, joining with one another, form a network, the meshes of which enclose small islands of white matter. That constitutes what is called the **formatio reticularis**. Although best marked in the cervical region, traces of the same reticular formation may be detected in the lower segments.

Characters presented by Grey Matter in Different Regions of Spinal Cord.—The grey matter is not present in equal quantity nor does it exhibit the same form in all regions of the cord. Indeed, each segment presents its own special characters in both respects, but it will be sufficient if the broad distinctions which are evident in the different regions are pointed out.

It may be regarded as a general law that wherever there is an increase in the size of the nerves attached to a particular part of the cord, a corresponding increase in the amount of grey matter will be observed. The regions where the grey matter bulks most largely are therefore the lumbar and cervical enlargements, for the great nerve-roots which go to form the nerves of the large limb-plexuses enter and pass out from those portions of the cord. In the thoracic region there is a reduction in the quantity of grey matter in correspondence with the smaller size of the thoracic nerves.

In the *thoracic region* (Fig. 708, B) both horns of grey matter are narrow, but the posterior horn is the more attenuated. In that region the lateral horn also is characteristic, and the substantia gelatinosa in transverse section is pointed and spear-shaped.

In the **upper three segments** of the *cervical region* the anterior horns are not large and they resemble the corresponding horns in the thoracic region. A lateral horn also is present. But in those segments (and more especially in the first and second) there is a marked attenuation of the neck of the posterior horn and the grey commissure is very broad.

In the **cervical enlargement** the contrast between the two horns is most striking; the anterior horn is of great size and presents a very broad surface towards the front of the cord, whilst the posterior horn remains narrow. The great increase in the bulk of the anterior horn is due to a marked addition of grey matter on its lateral side, and seeing that that additional matter is traversed by a greater number of fibres, it stands out, in well prepared specimens, more or less distinctly from the part of the horn that lies to the medial side and represents the entire anterior horn in the thoracic and upper cervical segments. This lateral addition contains the nuclei of origin of the motor nerves of the upper limb. The characteristic thickening of the anterior horn is evident, therefore, in those segments of the spinal cord which supply fibres to the brachial plexus, viz., the lower five cervical segments and the first thoracic segment.

In the **lumbar enlargement** the anterior **horns** again broaden out, and for the same reason as in the cervical enlargement. The nuclear masses from which the motor fibres of the lower limbs take origin are added to the lateral part of the columns and give them a very characteristic appearance. In that region, however, the posterior horns also are broad and are capped by substantia gelatinosa which has a semilunar outline. There is consequently no difficulty in distinguishing, from an inspection of the grey matter alone, between transverse sections of the spinal cord taken from the cervical and lumbar enlargements.

In the lower part of the **conus medullaris** the grey matter in each half is an oval mass joined to its fellow of the opposite side by a thick grey commissure. There, almost the entire bulk of the cord consists of grey matter, the white matter being reduced to a thin coating on the outside.

White Matter of Spinal Cord.—In transverse sections of the cord, the three columns into which the white matter is subdivided become very apparent. The **posterior white column** is wedge-shaped, and lies between the posterior median septum and the posterior grey column. The **lateral white column** occupies the concavity of the grey crescent. Behind, it is bounded by the posterior grey column, whilst in front it extends as far as the most lateral fasciculi of the anterior nerve-roots. The **anterior white column** includes the white matter between the anterior median fissure and the anterior grey column, and also the white matter in front of the anterior grey column. The latter portion is traversed by the emerging fibres of the anterior nerve-roots.

In cross-sections the partition of pia mater which divides the posterior white column into the **fasciculus gracilis** and the **fasciculus cuneatus** is very strongly marked in the cervical region, but as it is traced downwards it becomes shorter and fainter, and finally disappears altogether at the level of the eighth thoracic nerve.

The white matter is not present in equal quantity throughout the entire length of the spinal cord. It increases steadily from below upwards, and this increase is most noticeable in the lateral and posterior columns. In the lower part of the conus medullaris the amount of grey matter is actually greater than that of the white matter; but in the lumbar region the proportion of grey to white matter is approximately 1 : 2, and in the thoracic and cervical regions 1 : 5.

Central Canal.—The central canal is a very minute tunnel situated in the grey commissure, and is barely visible to the naked eye in transverse section. It traverses the entire length of the spinal cord; above, it passes into the

52

medulla oblongata, where it opens into the fourth ventricle of the brain; below, it is continued for a variable distance into the filum terminale, and there it ends blindly. Only in the lumbar region does the central canal occupy the centre of the cord. In the thoracic and cervical regions, it lies much nearer the front than the back of the cord; but, as it is traced down into the conus medullaris, it inclines backwards. The width of the canal also varies in different parts

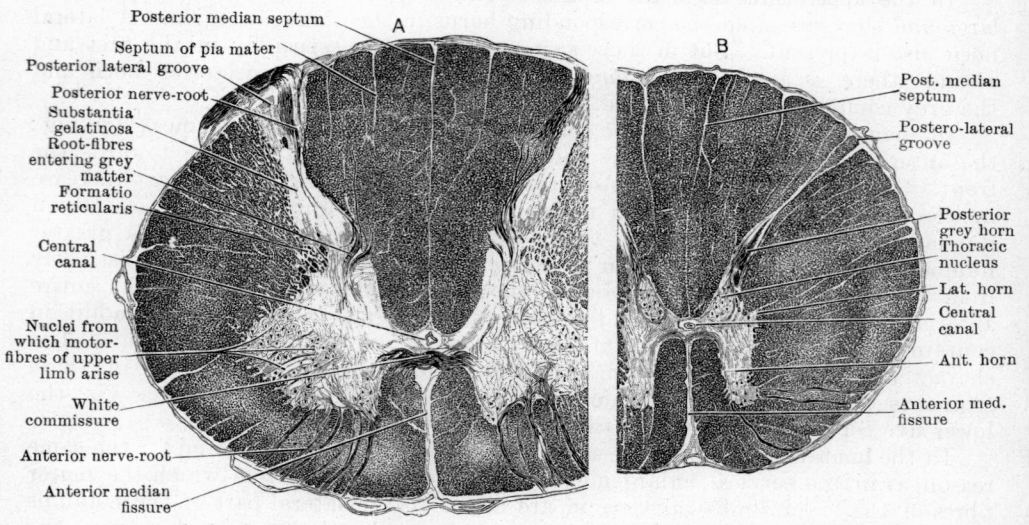

A.—At the level of the fifth cervical nerve.
(From a specimen prepared by Dr. A. Bruce.)

B.—Through the mid-thoracic region.

C.—At the level of the fourth lumbar nerve.

D.—At the level of the third sacral nerve. (From a specimen prepared by Dr. A. Bruce.)

FIG. 708.—SECTIONS THROUGH EACH OF THE FOUR REGIONS OF SPINAL CORD. From specimens prepared by the Weigert-Pal method (the white matter is dark; the grey matter is bleached).

of the cord. It is narrowest in the thoracic region; and in the lower part of the conus medullaris it expands into a fusiform dilatation very nearly 1 mm. in diameter.

The central canal is lined with a layer of ciliated columnar cells whose outer ends taper into slender processes which penetrate into the substance of the cord; their cilia are very early lost, and it is not uncommon to find the canal blocked up by epithelial debris.

Filum Terminale.—The delicate thread to which this name is applied is continuous with the pia mater at the end of the conus medullaris. It is easily distinguished, by its silvery and glistening appearance, from the nerve-roots (**cauda equina**) amidst which it lies. It is about six inches long, and down to the level of the second sacral vertebra it is enclosed with the nerve-roots within the arachnoid and dura mater; and as it pierces them at that point it derives a sheath from the dura mater. It then proceeds downwards in the sacral canal, and finally gains attachment to the periosteum on the back of the coccyx (Fig. 701, p. 812). It encloses the lowest part of the central canal surrounded by a variable amount of grey matter. Clinging to the outer surface of the grey matter there are some bundles of nerve-fibres associated with some nerve-cells identical with those in the spinal ganglia. Those nerve fibres represent vestigial caudal nerves (Rauber).

SUMMARY OF CHIEF CHARACTERS OF DIFFERENT REGIONS OF SPINAL CORD

Cervical Region.	Thoracic Region.	Lumbar Region.	Sacral Region.
In transverse section, **outline of cord** transversely oval; in the middle of cervical enlargement the transverse diameter being nearly one-third longer than the anteroposterior.	In transverse section, **outline of cord** more nearly circular; but still the transverse diameter is greater than the anteroposterior.	In transverse section, **outline of cord** more nearly circular than in thoracic region.	In transverse section, **outline of cord** nearly circular, but still slightly compressed from before backwards.
Posterior median septum very deep, extending beyond the centre of the cord; **anterior median fissure** shallow.	**Posterior median septum** very deep, extending beyond the centre of the cord: **anterior median fissure** shallow.	**Posterior median septum** not nearly so deep as in regions above: **anterior median fissure,** on the other hand, much deeper.	**Posterior median septum** and **anterior median fissure** of equal depth.
Grey matter greatly increased in quantity in the cervical enlargement: anterior horn thick and massive; posterior horn slender in comparison. Lateral horn evident only above the level of the fourth cervical nerve. Formatio reticularis strongly marked.	**Grey matter** greatly reduced in quantity. Both horns slender. Lateral horn well marked. Formatio reticularis scarcely apparent.	**Grey matter** greatly increased in the lumbar enlargement. Both horns very thick and massive. Lateral horn absorbed in anterior horn. Formatio reticularis absent.	Both horns of **grey matter** very thick and massive. Lateral horn apparent. No formatio reticularis.
White matter in great quantity, and especially massed in the lateral and posterior white columns.	**White matter** less in quantity than in cervical region, but bulking largely in comparison with the quantity of grey matter.	**White matter** small in quantity compared with higher regions, and very small in amount in relation to increased quantity of grey matter.	**White matter** very small in quantity in comparison with the grey matter.
Central canal considerably nearer the front than the back of the cord.	**Central canal** considerably nearer the front than the back of the cord.	**Central canal** in the centre of the spinal cord.	**Central canal** in the centre of the spinal cord.

COMPONENT PARTS OF GREY MATTER OF SPINAL CORD

Neuroglia enters largely into the constitution of the grey matter of the cord. The **nervous elements** are (1) nerve-cells and (2) nerve-fibres—both medullated and non-medullated. The nerve-cells lie in small spaces in the neuroglia, whilst the nerve-fibres traverse fine passages in the same substance.

In two situations the grey matter presents peculiar features, viz., the apex of the posterior grey column and the tissue surrounding the central canal. In both situations the grey matter stains more deeply with carmine and is more translucent ; in other respects the central grey matter and the substantia gelatinosa are very different. The **central grey matter** forms a thick ring around the central canal. It is composed almost entirely of neuroglia, and is traversed by the fine processes from the outer ends of the ependymal cells which line the canal. In transverse sections, the **substantia gelatinosa**, in the cervical and thoracic regions, is V-shaped in outline, and embraces the tip of the posterior grey horn ; in the lumbar region this cap has a semilunar outline. In the substantia gelatinosa the neuroglia is present in small quantity, and small nerve-cells are developed within it in considerable numbers.

Nerve-Cells.—The nerve-cells are scattered plentifully throughout the grey matter, but perhaps not in such great numbers as might be expected when we note the enormous number of nerve-fibres with which they stand in relation. They are all multipolar, and send off several branching dendrites, and one axon, which becomes the axis-cylinder of a nerve-fibre. In size they vary considerably, and as a rule (to which, however, there are many exceptions) the bulk of a nerve-cell has a more or less definite relation to the length of the axon which proceeds from it.

When the nerve-cells are studied in a series of transverse sections of the spinal cord, it will be noticed that a large proportion of them are grouped in clusters in certain districts of the grey matter ; and as those groups are seen in very much the same position in successive sections, it is clear that the cells are arranged in longitudinal columns of greater or less length. Thus we recognise—(1) a ventral column of cells in the anterior grey column ; (2) an intermedio-lateral column in the lateral grey column, where that exists ; and (3) a posterior vesicular column of cells (thoracic nucleus), forming a most conspicuous group in the medial part of the neck of the posterior grey column in the thoracic region.

Other cells, besides those forming these columns, are scattered irregularly throughout the posterior grey column and the part of the grey crescent which lies between the two columns.

Ventral Cell-Column and the Origin of Fibres of Anterior Nerve-roots.— The ventral cell-group occupies the anterior grey column, and in it are found the largest and most conspicuous cells in the spinal cord. It extends from one end of the cord to the other. These ventral nerve-cells have numerous widespreading dendritic processes, and it is to be noticed that certain of the dendrites do not confine their ramifications to the grey matter. Thus, some of the cells along the medial border of the anterior grey column send dendrites across the median plane in the commissure to end in the anterior grey column of the opposite side ; whilst others, lying along the lateral margin of the anterior grey column, send dendrites in amongst the nerve-fibres of the adjoining white matter.

The axons of a large proportion of the ventral cells converge together ; and, becoming medullated, they form bundles which pass out from the grey matter, and through the white matter in front of the anterior grey column, to emerge finally as the fibres of the anterior nerve-roots. Those cells, then, are the sources from which the nerve-fibres of the anterior nerve-roots proceed, and in consequence they are frequently spoken of as the "motor cells" of the spinal cord. Whilst that is the arrangement of the axons of the great majority of the motor cells, it should be noted that a few cross the median plane in the white commissure and emerge among the fibres of origin of the opposite anterior nerve-root.

The ventral cells are not scattered uniformly throughout the anterior grey column. They are aggregated more closely together in certain parts of the column, and thus form sub-columns more or less perfectly marked off from each other.

Thus, one sub-column of ventral cells occupies the medial part of the anterior grey column throughout almost its whole length. In only two segments of the cord is it absent, viz. the fifth lumbar and the first sacral; at that level alone is its continuity broken (Bruce). It is termed the *antero-median column* or group of ventral cells. Behind that cell-column there is another classed with it to which the name of *postero-median column* is given, but that column of cells is not continuous throughout the entire length of the spinal cord. It is present in the thoracic region, where the motor nuclei

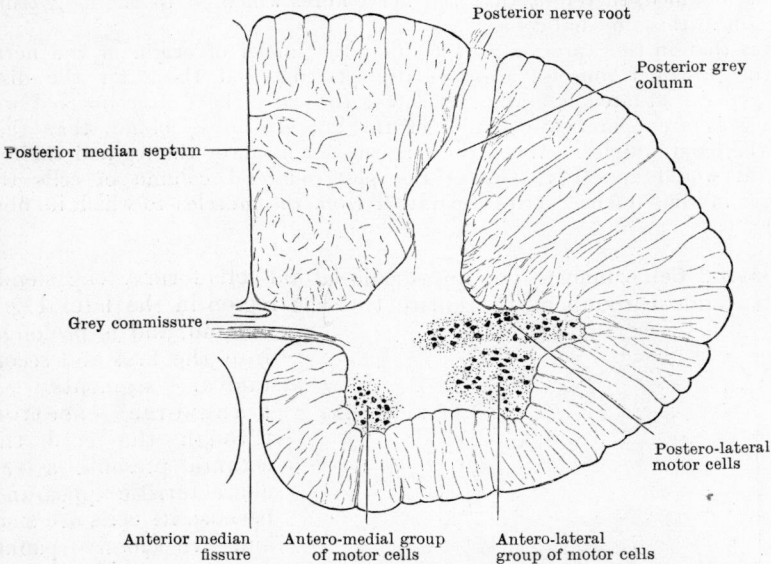

FIG. 709.—SECTION THROUGH THE FIFTH CERVICAL SEGMENT OF THE SPINAL CORD.
(This and the following three figures are to a large extent founded on Plates in Dr. Bruce's *Atlas*.)

for the muscles of the limbs are absent; and it is seen also in two or three of the segments of the cervical region and in the first lumbar segment (Bruce); elsewhere it is not represented.

In the cervical and lumbar enlargements, where the marked lateral out-growth is added to the lateral side of the anterior grey column, certain groups of large multipolar cells are visible. They are the nuclei of origin of the motor-fibres of the limbs, and consequently they are not represented in the upper three cervical segments, nor in any of the thoracic segments (with the exception of the first) nor in the lowest two sacral segments.

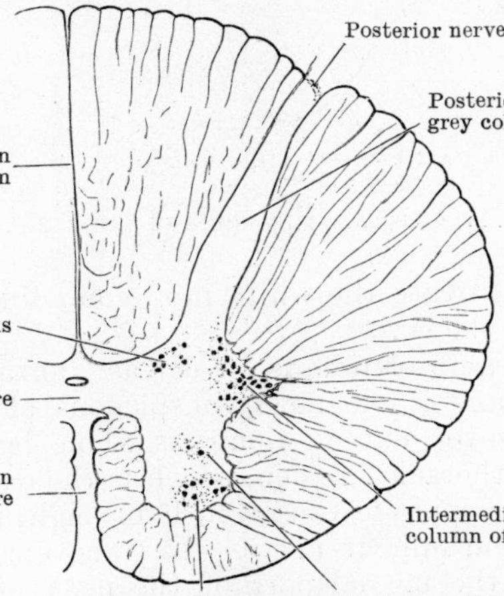

Those *lateral cells* are arranged in several columns, which extend for varying distances in the superadded lateral parts of the anterior grey column. The two main columns are an *antero-lateral* and a *postero-lateral column*; in certain segments there is also a *retro-postero-lateral column*, and in a number of segments in the lumbar and sacral regions a *central column* of cells (Bruce).

There cannot be a doubt that the grouping of the motor

FIG. 710.—SECTION THROUGH THE EIGHTH THORACIC SEGMENT.

cells in the anterior grey column stands in relation to the muscle groups to which their axons are distributed; but from what has been said it will be apparent that sharply defined cell-clusters associated with particular muscles do not exist. Still, much can be learned regarding the localisation of the motor nuclei in the anterior grey column from the study of the changes which occur in the cell-columns after atrophy of isolated muscles or groups of muscles, and after complete or partial amputation of limbs. It has been pointed out that the long muscles of the trunk (as, for example, the different parts of the sacro-spinalis muscle) receive nerve-fibres from all the segments of the cord. Now, it has been noted that there is only one cell-column—the antero-medial column —which pursues an almost uninterrupted course throughout the entire length of the cord. It may be assumed, therefore, that the nerve-fibres which go to the long trunk-muscles take origin in those medial cells.

Edinger states that in the anterior grey column the nuclei of origin of the nerves which supply the proximal muscles are medially placed; that those for the distal muscles are in general situated laterally. If this is the case, the cells connected with the shoulder-muscles are nearer the middle of the anterior grey column than those connected with the hand-muscles. When the forearm and hand, or the leg and the foot, are amputated, it would appear that it is the postero-lateral column of cells that undergoes changes in consequence of its separation from the muscles to which its fibres are distributed.[1]

Intermedio-lateral Cell-column.—The intermedio-lateral cells form a long slender column which extends throughout the entire thoracic region in the lateral grey column, and is prolonged into the first and second lumbar segments. In transverse sections through the cord, that column presents a very characteristic appearance, because its cells are small and are closely packed together. Although these cells, as a continuous column, are restricted to the region indicated, it should be noted that the same group reappears in certain of the cervical segments and also in the third and fourth sacral segments. From those cells very fine fibres arise and leave the spinal cord, intermingled with the motor fibres of the anterior nerve-roots; they pass into the sympathetic ganglia, of which

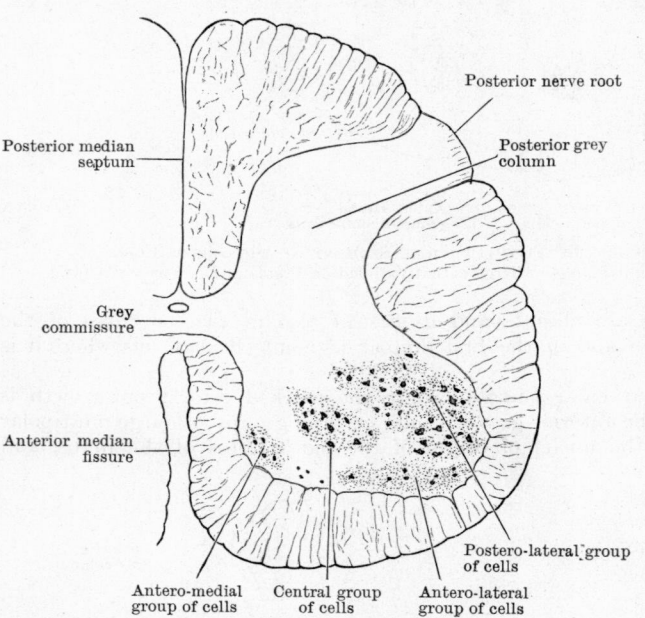

Posterior nerve root

Posterior grey column

Posterior median septum

Grey commissure

Anterior median fissure

Postero-lateral group of cells

Antero-medial group of cells   Central group of cells   Antero-lateral group of cells

FIG. 711.—SECTION THROUGH THE THIRD LUMBAR SEGMENT.

they constitute the white rami communicantes. They are the splanchnic efferent fibres of the cord.

Thoracic Nucleus [Nucleus dorsalis].—This occupies the posterior grey column and is the most conspicuous of all the cell-groups in the cord. It does not, however, extend along its whole length; indeed it is almost entirely confined to the " thoracic " region, which is the reason for the designation " thoracic nucleus." It begins opposite the seventh or eighth cervical nerve, and ends at the level of the second lumbar nerve. In transverse section it presents an oval outline, and is seen in the medial part of the neck of the posterior grey column, immediately behind the grey commissure (Fig. 710, p. 821). On the lateral side it is circumscribed by numerous curved fibres from the entering posterior nerve-root, and in the lower thoracic region (opposite the eleventh and twelfth thoracic nerves) it becomes so marked that it forms a bulging on the medial side of the posterior grey column.

---

[1] Those who seek further information regarding the grouping of the ventral cells of the cord may with advantage study Dr. Alexander Bruce's *Atlas of the Spinal Cord*.

The cells of the thoracic nucleus are large, and have several dendrites. The axons enter the lateral white column to form a strand of fibres described later as a spino-cerebellar tract.

Nerve-fibres in the Grey Matter of Spinal Cord.—Nerve-fibres both medullated and non-medullated pervade every part of the grey matter. They are of three kinds, viz., (1) collaterals, (2) terminations of nerve-fibres, (3) axons of the cells. Many of the nerve-fibres which compose the white columns give off numerous fine collateral branches which pass into the grey matter from all sides and finally end in relation with the nerve-cells. The majority of the nerve-fibres themselves, which thus give off collaterals, finally enter the grey matter, and end similarly. The axons of the majority of the cells leave the grey matter and enter either a peripheral nerve or a tract in the white matter.

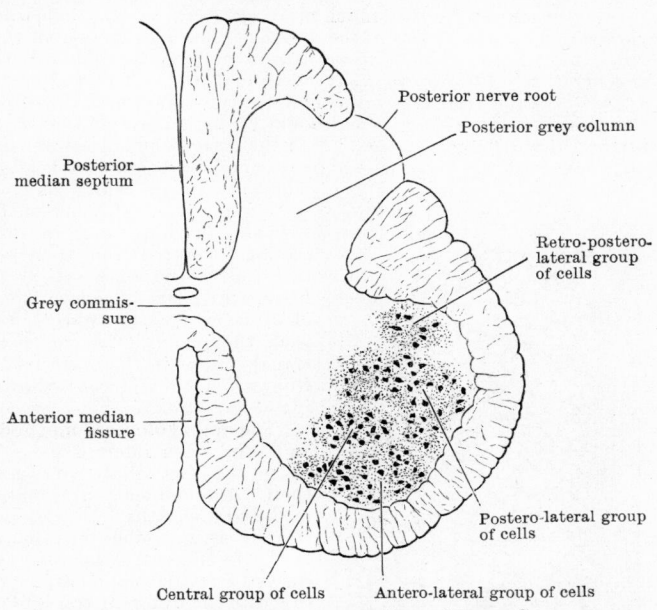

FIG. 712.—SECTION THROUGH THE FIRST SACRAL SEGMENT.

The nerve-fibres thus derived are interwoven together in the grey matter in a dense inextricable interlacement.

COMPONENT PARTS OF WHITE MATTER OF SPINAL CORD

The white matter is composed of nerve-fibres embedded in neuroglia. The fibres, for the most part, pursue a longitudinal course; and, from the deep surface of the pia mater, fibrous septa are carried in along vertical planes between the fibres so as to form an irregular and very imperfect fibrous framework of support. The neuroglia is disposed in a layer of varying thickness subjacent to the pia mater, and is carried into the cord so as to give a coating to both sides of the various pial septa. The neuroglia is disposed also around the various nerve-fibres, so that each of them may be said to lie in a tunnel of that substance. The nerve-fibres are mostly medullated, but are not provided with neurolemmal sheaths. It is the medullary substance of the nerve-fibres which gives to the white matter its opaque, milky-white appearance. When a thin transverse section is stained in carmine and examined under the microscope the white matter presents the appearance of a series of closely applied circles, each with a dot in the centre (Fig. 713). The dot is the cut axon, and the dark ring which forms the circumference of the circle is the wall of the neuroglial canal occupied by the fibre. The medullary substance is very faintly seen. It presents a filmy or cloudy appearance between the axon and the neuroglial ring.

Arrangement of the Nerve-fibres of the White Matter in Tracts.—When the white matter of a healthy adult spinal cord is examined, the fibres are seen to vary considerably in size; and although there are special places where large fibres—or it may be small fibres—are present in greater numbers than elsewhere, yet, as a rule, both large and small fibres are mixed together. From normal preparations no conclusive evidence can be obtained of the fact that the longitudinally arranged fibres are grouped together in more or less definite tracts the fibres of which run a definite course and present definite connexions. Yet this is known to be the case, and the existence of the separate tracts has been proved both by embryological investigation and by the examination of the effects of injuries produced experimentally or accidentally on the nervous system in living animals.

· By the **experimental method** it has been shown that when a nerve-fibre is severed the part which is detached from the nerve-cell degenerates, whilst the part which remains connected with the nerve-cell undergoes little or no change. This is called the law of "Wallerian" degeneration. Thus, if in a living animal one-half of the spinal cord is cut across, and after a few weeks the animal is killed and the cord examined, it will be seen that there are degenerated tracts of fibres in the white matter, both above and below the plane of division; but, still further, it will be manifest also that the tracts which are degenerated above the plane of division are not the same as those which are degenerated below that level. The interpretation is obvious.

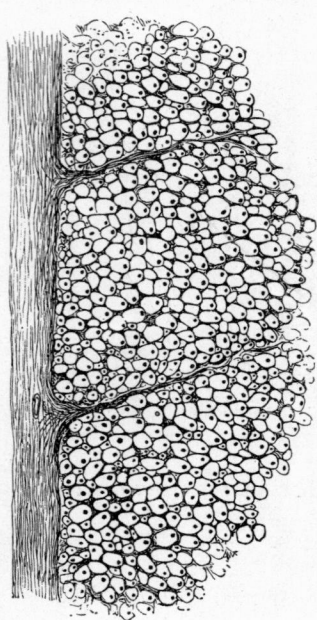

The nerve-tracts which have degenerated above the plane of section are the offshoots of nerve-cells which lie in lower segments of the cord or in spinal ganglia below the plane of section. Severed from their nerve-cells, they undergo what is called *ascending degeneration*. The nerve-tracts, on the other hand, which have degenerated in the portion below the plane of division are the axons of cells which lie at a higher level than the plane of section, either in higher segments of the spinal cord or in the brain itself. Cut off from the nerve-cells from which they proceed, they provide an example of *descending degeneration*.

The **embryological method** was first employed by Flechsig, and it is often referred to as Flechsig's method. It is based upon the fact that nerve-fibres in the earliest stages of their development are naked axons, unprovided with medullary sheaths. Further, the nerve-fibres of different strands assume the medullary sheaths at different periods. If the fœtal central nervous system is examined at different stages of its development, it is a comparatively easy matter to locate the different tracts of fibres by evidence of this kind. Speaking broadly, the tracts which myelinate first are those which bring the central nervous system into relation with the peripheral parts (skin, muscles, etc.); then, those fibres which bind the various segments of the central nervous system together; next, those which connect the spinal cord with the cerebellum; and, lastly, the tracts which connect the cerebral hemispheres with the spinal cord. The nervous apparatus for the performance of automatic movements is fully provided, therefore, before it is put under the control and direction of the higher centres. It by no means follows that in all the higher animals corresponding strands myelinate at relatively corresponding periods. Take a young animal which from the time of its birth is able to move about and perform voluntary movements of various kinds in a more or less perfect manner, and compare it with the helpless new-born infant, which is capable of automatic movements only. In the lower animal, the motor tracts which descend from the cerebrum into the spinal cord, and are the paths along which the mandates of the will travel, myelinate at an early period; in the infant, the corresponding fibres do not obtain their medullary sheaths until after birth. The study of the dates at which the various strands of nerve-fibres myelinate therefore not only gives the anatomist a means of locating their position in the white matter of the central nervous system, but also affords the physiologist most important information regarding their functions and the periods at which these functions are called into play.

It is a matter of interest to note that influences which either accelerate or retard the periods at which nerve-fibres are brought into functional activity have also an effect in determining the dates at which the fibres assume their sheaths of myelin. Thus, when a child is prematurely born the whole process of myelinisation is, as it were, hurried up; and further, when in new-born animals light is freely admitted to one eye and carefully excluded from the other, the fibres of the optic nerve of the former myelinate more rapidly than those of the other.

Study of the minute structure (**anatomical method**) of the central nervous system, especially of material that has been stained by the methods of Golgi and Ramón y Cajal or by the use of methylene blue, completes the results attained by the other methods, by demonstrating the precise mode of origin and termination of the various tracts.

Posterior White Column and the Posterior Roots of Spinal Nerves.—In the cervical and upper thoracic regions of the spinal cord the posterior white column is divided by a septum of pia mater into the **fasciculus cuneatus**, which lies laterally and next to the posterior grey column, and the **fasciculus gracilis**, which lies medially and next to the posterior median septum. The

nerve-fibres of the fasciculus cuneatus are for the most part larger than those of the fasciculus gracilis; and both tracts have a most intimate relation to the posterior nerve-roots; indeed, they are both composed almost entirely of fibres which enter the cord by those roots, and then pursue a longitudinal course.

The nerve-fibres of the posterior nerve-roots enter opposite the apex of the posterior horn and divide within the fasciculus cuneatus into ascending and descending branches which diverge abruptly as they pass upwards and downwards.

The **descending fibres** are, as a rule, short, and soon end in the grey matter. They form a bundle, called the **semilunar tract**, which lies between the fasciculus gracilis and fasciculus cuneatus, and undergoes descending degeneration when the cord is divided (Fig. 714).

The **ascending fibres** vary greatly in length, and at differing distances from the point where the parent fibres enter the cord they end in the grey matter. A small contribution, however, of ascending fibres, from each posterior nerve-root, extends upwards to end in the medulla oblongata (Figs. 695 and 716).

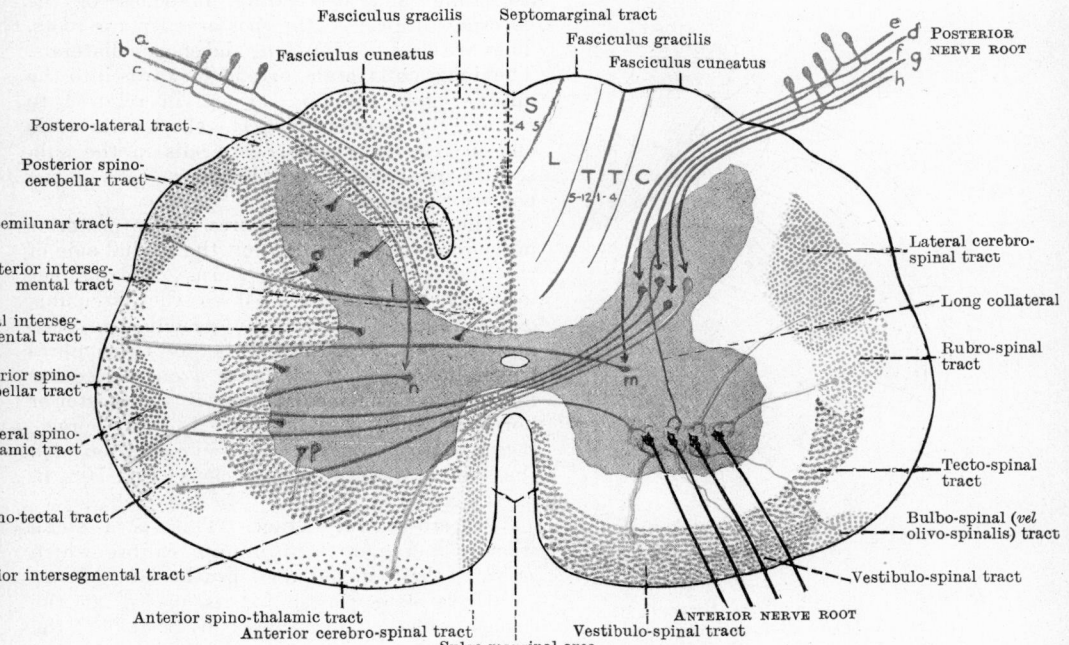

FIG. 714.—DIAGRAM TO ILLUSTRATE THE POSITION OF THE VARIOUS TRACTS IN THE SPINAL CORD (in transverse section). (G. E. S.)

As each posterior nerve-root enters, its fibres range themselves in the lateral part of the posterior white column close up against the posterior grey column. The nerve-fibres of the nerve-root next above take the same position, and consequently those which entered from the nerve immediately below are displaced medially, and come to lie in the posterior white column nearer to the median plane. That process goes on as each nerve-root enters, and the result is that the fibres of the lower nerves are gradually pushed nearer and nearer to the posterior median septum in a successive series of lamellar bundles. The greater number of the fibres which are thus carried upwards from the posterior nerve-roots sooner or later leave the posterior white column and enter the grey matter, to end there in relation to some of its cells; but every posterior nerve-root sends a few fibres up the whole length of that portion of the spinal cord which lies above, and thus the posterior white column gradually increases in bulk as it is traced upwards, and in all except the lowest part of the cord, the posterior white column is separable into a fasciculus gracilis and a fasciculus cuneatus. The fasciculus gracilis is composed of the long ascending fibres of the posterior nerve-roots which have entered the lower segments. To put the matter differently: the fibres of the sacral roots are displaced medially by the entering lumbar fibres, these are in their turn pushed medially by the entering thoracic fibres, and, lastly, the fibres of the cervical roots displace the thoracic fibres.

The difference between the fasciculi simply is this, that the fasciculus gracilis is composed of the fibres of posterior nerve-roots which have entered the cord at a lower level than those that form the fasciculus cuneatus. The fibres of the fasciculus gracilis, taking them as a whole, run therefore a very much longer course.

Our knowledge of the constitution of the posterior white columns is derived largely from the study of the course of degeneration in monkeys, after the cord has been cut across—either partially or completely. But we have also a direct knowledge of the lamination of the posterior columns of the human spinal cord (Fig. 714) acquired from the examination of cases in which the cord or its nerve-roots had been injured during life We have some information of the lamination of ascending fibres also in the anterior and lateral white columns of the human cord. That information is given diagrammatically in Fig. 715. It will be noted that of the fibres which cross before they ascend in this column, those from the lower segments are superficial, and the latest arrivals from the opposite side (i.e. those from the upper segments) travel deep in the white matter.

Numerous collateral fibrils stream into the posterior grey column both from the ascending and descending branches of the entering fibres of the posterior nerve-roots. They are classified into long and short collaterals. The **long collaterals** extend forwards into the anterior grey column and end in relation to the anterior nerve-cells. The **short collaterals** end in relation to the nerve-cells in the substantia gelatinosa and other nerve-cells of the posterior grey column.

The majority of the fibres of the posterior nerve-root enter the cord on the medial side of the apex of the posterior horn. The manner in which they are related to the fasciculus cuneatus and the fasciculus gracilis has been noticed ; but a certain number of those fibres which lie most laterally take a curved course forwards on the medial side of the posterior horn and then pass into it. In the thoracic region those curved fibres end in connexion with the cells of the thoracic nucleus (Fig. 708, B, p. 818, and Fig. 695).

Postero-lateral Tract.—This is a small tract of nerve-fibres of minute calibre which assume their medullary sheaths at a comparatively late period. It is placed at the surface of the cord close in front of the entering posterior nerve roots. It is formed by some of the lateral fibres of the posterior nerve-roots which do not enter the fasciculus cuneatus, but pass upwards close to the substantia gelatinosa, in which most of them ultimately end.

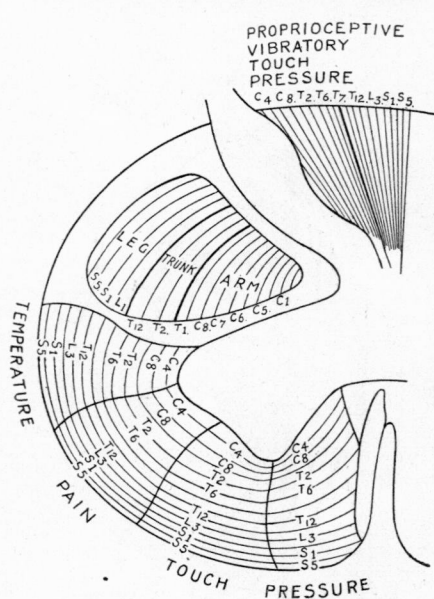

FIG. 715.—DIAGRAM (after O. Föerster) to show : (i) The peripheral position in the antero-lateral white column of ascending fibres from the lowest segments of the cord and the position progressively nearer the grey matter of those from higher segments ; (ii) The medial position in the posterior white column of fibre ascending from the lowest segments and the progressively lateral position of those from higher segments ; (iii) Lamination of fibres within the lateral cerebro-spinal tract.

It is evident that the fibres which enter the cord through each posterior nerve-root have three main modes of distribution : (1) the majority take part in the formation of the fasciculus cuneatus, and pass upwards or downwards to end in the grey matter at some other level in the central nervous system ; (2) some fibres, and many collaterals of fibres in the fasciculus cuneatus, lie close to the posterior grey column and describe a series of graceful curves as they pass forwards, prior to turning laterally into all regions of the grey matter to end at the same level as they enter the cord ; (3) a third series form the postero-lateral tract and end in connexion with the cells of the substantia gelatinosa and other cells in the posterior and anterior grey columns (Fig. 695).

The fibres derived from the posterior nerve-roots which ascend in the posterior white columns to the medulla oblongata of the brain constitute a direct sensory tract ; other fibres are described which give rise to crossed sensory tracts termed **the spino-thalamic tracts.** The latter fibres arise as the axons of certain of the cells in the posterior grey column near which fibres from the posterior nerve-roots have ended, and, crossing to the opposite side of the cord through the white commissure, they ascend through the cord to the brain, where they ultimately reach the thalamus. As the spino-thalamic fibres ascend in the cord they are gathered into two loose strands, called the **anterior** and **lateral spino-thalamic tracts**, which pass upwards in the corresponding white columns.

Association Fibres in the Posterior White Column.—The whole of the fibres of the posterior white column are not derived from the posterior nerve-roots. A few fibres have a different origin. They are derived from certain of the cells of the grey matter, and, entering the posterior white column, they divide into branches which

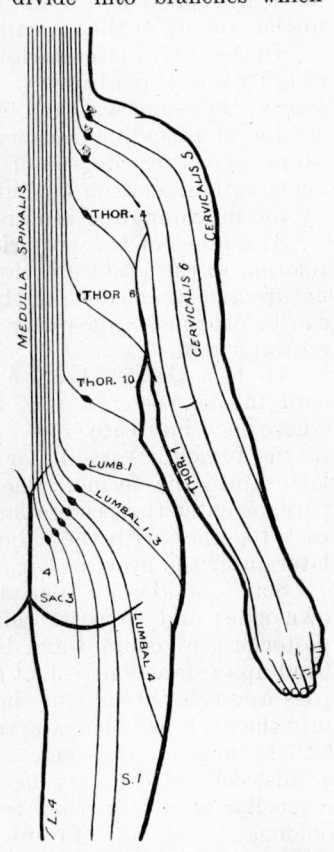

FIG. 716.—DIAGRAM TO SHOW THE MANNER IN WHICH THE FIBRES OF THE POSTERIOR NERVE-ROOTS ENTER AND ASCEND IN THE POSTERIOR WHITE COLUMN.

pass upwards and downwards in the column for a varying distance before they finally turn in to end in the grey matter at higher and lower levels. Those fibres, therefore, are links of connexion between different segments of the cord, and they constitute the **posterior intersegmental tract** [fasciculus proprius]. Our information regarding those fibres is at present defective; but it is believed that the deepest part of the column, *i.e.* the part next the grey commissure, and the **septomarginal tract**, placed in apposition with the posterior median septum and in the adjoining part of the surface, belong mainly to this category.

Lateral and Anterior White Columns.—It is convenient to consider the anterior along with the lateral column and to call the whole mass of white substance left after elimination of the posterior white column the **antero-lateral white column.** In contact with the surface of the grey columns there is a broad band of white matter the parts of which are known respectively as **anterior** and **lateral intersegmental tracts** [fasciculi proprii]. They are composed wholly of fibres which spring from nerve-cells in the grey columns, and, after passing for varying distances upwards or downwards, end in the grey matter of the cord. They constitute an intrinsic system of fibres linking together different levels of the spinal cord. They become medullated before any other fibres, except the root-fibres and their continuations in the posterior white column. When cut across some of the fibres degenerate above the injury and others below it.

The best-known long or extrinsic systems of fibres in the antero-lateral white column are the **cerebro-spinal** and **spino-cerebellar tracts**.

There are, however, many other tracts at least as important as these, but there is as yet no close agreement as to their precise limits or connexions. One reason for this is that some of the elements of one tract may become intermingled with those of another; moreover, the position and relations of certain of them vary considerably at different levels of the cord. In Fig. 714 an attempt has been made to indicate the present state of our knowledge of these great strands of white fibres. The diagram is not intended to represent any definite level of the cord, though certain features are shown which occur only in the cervical region ; and in respect of other features, the arrangement found in lower regions of the cord has been introduced to make the diagram more serviceable.

Much of the apparent complexity of this chart will disappear if the reader recalls some general statements (p. 805) made with regard to the outstanding features of the brain. It was then explained that when afferent nerves, coming from the skin and muscles, enter the cord, they not only establish relations with the motor nuclei and other spinal structures in the neighbourhood of their insertion, but also give rise, directly or indirectly (see Fig. 695), to many tracts which pass upwards to reach the medulla oblongata, the pons and cerebellum, the midbrain, the thalamus, and the cerebral hemisphere. In the neighbourhood of each level where those ascending sensory tracts end, such as for example the region of the vestibular nucleus and cerebellum, the tectum of the mid-brain, the corpus striatum, and the cerebral hemisphere, great descending tracts originate and pass downwards in the spinal cord (Fig. 695—the red lines). Thus, we have cerebrospinal, rubro-spinal, tecto-spinal, vestibulo-spinal, and bulbo-spinal tracts passing down the spinal cord; and each system eventually ends around the series of motor nuclei—many of them in the spinal cord.

In the antero-lateral white column the various fasciculi will be found to be grouped roughly into three bands:—Next to the grey columns there are the intersegmental tracts; then comes a band of descending (motor) fasciculi; and then, on the surface, a series of ascending (sensory) fasciculi. That arrangement, however, is not maintained with any degree of exactitude in the anterior column, where the sharp demarcation between ascending and descending fasciculi is in great part destroyed by the intermingling of fibres passing in opposite directions.

The fibres of the posterior nerve-root have already been studied so far as their relation to the posterior white column is concerned. No clear conception of the nature and significance of the ascending fasciculi in the antero-lateral white column can be obtained unless they also are studied in relationship with the fibres of the posterior root.

It has already been explained that of the fibres which enter the spinal cord in the posterior root the great majority enter the posterior white column, where they bifurcate (Fig. 714, a); one branch of each fibre passes upwards either in the funiculus gracilis or in the funiculus cuneatus, or it may pass from the latter into the former; the other descends in the semilunar tract. Other fibres perhaps enter the postero-lateral tract. But all the other fibres of the posterior root, together with the majority of the fibres of the fasciculus cuneatus, sooner or later enter the grey matter (Fig. 714, b to h) of the cord.

Some of them (b) pass directly to end in the thoracic nucleus of their own side; and from its cells fresh fibres arise which pass laterally through the posterior grey column and lateral white column to reach the surface, where they bend upwards as constituent fibres of the posterior spino-cerebellar tract. These fibres pass upwards throughout the whole length of the cord (above their place of origin), into the medulla oblongata, thence into the cerebellum through its inferior peduncle. Other fibres on the same side (c), and perhaps also on the other side (d), end amidst cells of the grey matter the axons of which pass into the anterior spino-cerebellar tract. In that tract they ascend throughout the spinal cord, medulla oblongata, and pons, to enter the cerebellum by the superior peduncle. The two spino-cerebellar tracts convey to the cerebellum information from the muscles and overlying skin which assists it to co-ordinate the muscles for carrying on precisely adjusted movements.

Other fibres of the posterior nerve-root (Fig. 714, e, f, g, and h) terminate in relationship with cells in the grey columns of their own side of the cord; and the axons of these cells cross the median plane in the white commissure to pass into (e) the anterior spino-cerebellar tract, (f) the lateral spino-thalamic tract, (g) the spino-tectal tract, and (h) the anterior spino-thalamic tract.

The investigations of the late Dr. Page May led him to attach a definite physiological significance to this grouping of the ascending paths. The **lateral spino-thalamic tract** is supposed to convey to the thalamus (for transmission to the part of the cerebral cortex concerned with the conscious appreciation of sensations) all impulses of *pain, heat,* and *cold* coming from the skin of the opposite side of the body. The **anterior spino-thalamic tract** conveys impulses of *touch* and *pressure* from the opposite side.

The **spino-cerebellar tracts** [anterior and posterior] convey to the cerebellum respectively the bilateral, homolateral and unconscious afferent impulses that underlie muscular co-ordination and reflex tone.

Among the descending tracts that establish connexions between various parts of the brain (see Fig. 695) and the motor nerve-cells in the anterior grey column may be mentioned the **cerebro-spinal**, the **rubro-spinal** (from the red nucleus), the **tecto-spinal** (from the corpora quadrigemina), the **vestibulo-spinal** (from the terminal nucleus of the vestibular nerve), and the **bulbo-spinal tracts**. The last-mentioned forms a peculiar triangular area at the surface immediately to the lateral side of the anterior nerve-roots (Fig. 714), but there is great uncertainty as to its mode of origin: it is often called the **fasciculus olivo-spinalis**, from the fact that its discoverer, Helweg, believed it to originate from the olivary nucleus in the bulb or medulla oblongata. It may be regarded as an outlying part of the vestibular (or cerebellar) tract to the motor nuclei of the spinal cord.

The **lateral cerebro-spinal tract** is a large well-defined descending tract which lies immediately in front of the posterior grey column, and subjacent to the posterior spino-cerebellar tract, which shuts it out from the surface. Below the point where the posterior spino-cerebellar tract begins the cerebrospinal tract becomes super-ficial, and in this position it can be traced as low as the fourth sacral nerve. The cerebro-spinal tract is composed of an admixture of large and small fibres. They arise from the large pyramidal cells of the motor area of the cerebral cortex, and pass downwards through various subdivisions of the brain to gain the spinal cord. As they enter the cord they cross the median plane from one side to the other, and it thus happens that the cerebro-spinal tract in the right lateral white column has its origin in the left cerebral hemisphere, and *vice versa*. As the tract descends in the cord it gradually diminishes in size; because, as it traverses each spinal segment, numerous fibres leave it to enter the anterior grey column and end in connexion with the motor cells from which the fibres of the anterior nerve-roots arise. The entire strand is ultimately exhausted in that way. Numerous collateral fibrils spring from the cerebro-spinal fibres; they enter the grey matter and end in a similar manner. Thus, a single cerebro-spinal fibre may be connected with several spinal segments before it finally ends. The lateral cerebro-spinal tract must be regarded as a great motor strand which brings the spinal motor apparatus under the control of the will.

Sharpey Schafer believed that many of the fibres of the cerebro-spinal tract end in connexion with the cells of the thoracic nucleus.

In many marsupials, rodents, and ungulates the lateral cerebro-spinal tract lies in the posterior white column of the spinal cord.

The **lateral intersegmental tract** represents the remainder of the lateral white column. Its fibres are largely derived from the cells situated in all parts of the grey matter, and also from the nerve-cells of the opposite side of the cord. After a course of very varying length these fibres turn medially and re-enter the grey matter. Such fibres may thus be regarded as **inter-segmental association fibres** that bind two or more segments of the cord together. It may be mentioned that the association fibres which link adjacent segments are close to the grey matter, whilst those which connect the more distant segments are farther away.

One well-defined tract situated in the white column, not yet described, is called the **anterior cerebro-spinal tract**. It is usually of small size, and lies near the anterior median fissure. As a rule it cannot be traced lower than the middle of the thoracic region. It is a descending tract and must be associated with the lateral cerebro-spinal tract of the opposite side, seeing that both of those strands arise from the motor area of the same cerebral hemisphere. From this it must be clear that the anterior cerebro-spinal tract does not cross the median plane as it enters the cord, but descends on the side that corresponds to the cerebral hemisphere in which it arises. Nevertheless, its fibres do not end in the same side of the cord; at every step along the path of the strand they make use of the white commissure, and cross to the opposite side to terminate in relation to motor cells in the same manner as the lateral cerebro-spinal fibres.

From the crossing of the cerebro-spinal tract, it follows that the destruction of their fibres as they descend in one side of the brain must result in paralysis of the muscles supplied by the efferent nerves of the opposite side of the spinal cord.

In cases of old brain lesion it is sometimes possible to detect some degenerated fibres in the lateral cerebro-spinal tract of the sound side, and from that it is supposed that the tract contains a few uncrossed fibres. If this is the case, each side of the spinal cord stands in connexion with the motor area of both cerebral hemispheres.

It is well to note that the fibres of the cerebro-spinal tracts are not medullated until the time of birth. They are the latest of all the tracts of the spinal cord to myelinate.

White Commissure.—The white commissure is composed of medullated nerve-fibres that pass from one side of the spinal cord to the other and enter the anterior grey column and the anterior white column. It is to be regarded more as a decussation than as a commissure, and its width, which varies slightly in different regions, fluctuates in correspondence with the diameter of the spinal cord.

Amongst the fibres which cross in the white commissure may be mentioned: (1) The fibres of the anterior cerebro-spinal tract; (2) collaterals from both the anterior and lateral white columns; (3) axons of many of the cells of the grey matter; (4) the dendrites of some of the medial anterior cells.

Grey Commissure.—Although this is composed of grey matter with a large admixture of neuroglia, numerous nerve-fibres pass transversely through it to establish relations between the cells of the two sides of the spinal cord.

THE ENCEPHALON OR BRAIN

The **brain** is the enlarged and greatly modified upper part of the cerebro-spinal nervous axis. It is surrounded by the same membranes that envelop the cord (viz., the dura mater, the arachnoid mater, and the pia mater), and it almost completely fills the cavity of the cranium. So closely, indeed, is the skull capsule moulded on the brain that the impress of the brain is almost everywhere evident upon the inner surface of the cranial wall. The relations of cranium to brain are therefore totally different from those presented by the vertebral canal to the cord, which, as we have noted, occupies only a part of the cavity of its bony case.

Weight of the Brain.—The average weight of a man's brain may be said to be about 1360 grammes. A woman's brain weighs rather less, but this is to be expected from the smaller bulk of the body. Probably the relative weight of the brain in the two sexes is very much the same. The variations met with in brain-weight are very great, but it is doubtful if normal intellectual functions could be carried on in a brain which weighs less than 960 grammes. The brains of microcephalic idiots are sometimes very small.

General Appearance of the Brain.—When viewed from above the brain presents an ovoid figure, the broad end of which is directed backwards. Its greatest transverse diameter is usually at or near the part opposite the two parietal eminences of the cranium. The only parts visible when the brain is inspected from above are the two **cerebral hemispheres.** They present an extensive convex surface which is closely related to the inner surface of the cranial vault, and are separated from each other by a deep median cleft, termed the **longitudinal fissure**, which extends from the front to the back of the brain.

The lower surface of the brain is usually termed the **base of the brain**. It is an uneven surface, more or less accurately adapted to the inequalities on the floor of the cranial cavity. Upon this surface of the brain all its main subdivisions may be recognised. Thus, posteriorly, is seen the short cylindrical portion, called the **medulla oblongata**, through which, at the foramen magnum, the brain becomes continuous with the spinal cord. The medulla oblongata lies on the ventral aspect of the cerebellum, and occupies the vallecula or hollow which intervenes between the two cerebellar hemispheres. The **cerebellum** is a mass of considerable size placed below the posterior portions of the two cerebral hemispheres. It is easily recognised on account of the closely set, curved, and parallel fissures which traverse its surface and give it a foliated appearance. Above the medulla oblongata, and in close connexion with it, is a prominent white elevation called the **pons**.

Immediately in front of the pons there is a deep hollow or recess. It is bounded behind by the pons, on each side by the temporal lobe of the cerebral hemisphere, and in front by the orbital portions of the frontal lobes of the cerebral hemispheres. Passing laterally from each side of the anterior part of the recess is the deep cleft, called the **lateral sulcus** of the cerebrum, which intervenes between the projecting extremity of the temporal lobe and the frontal lobe of the cerebrum, whilst, in

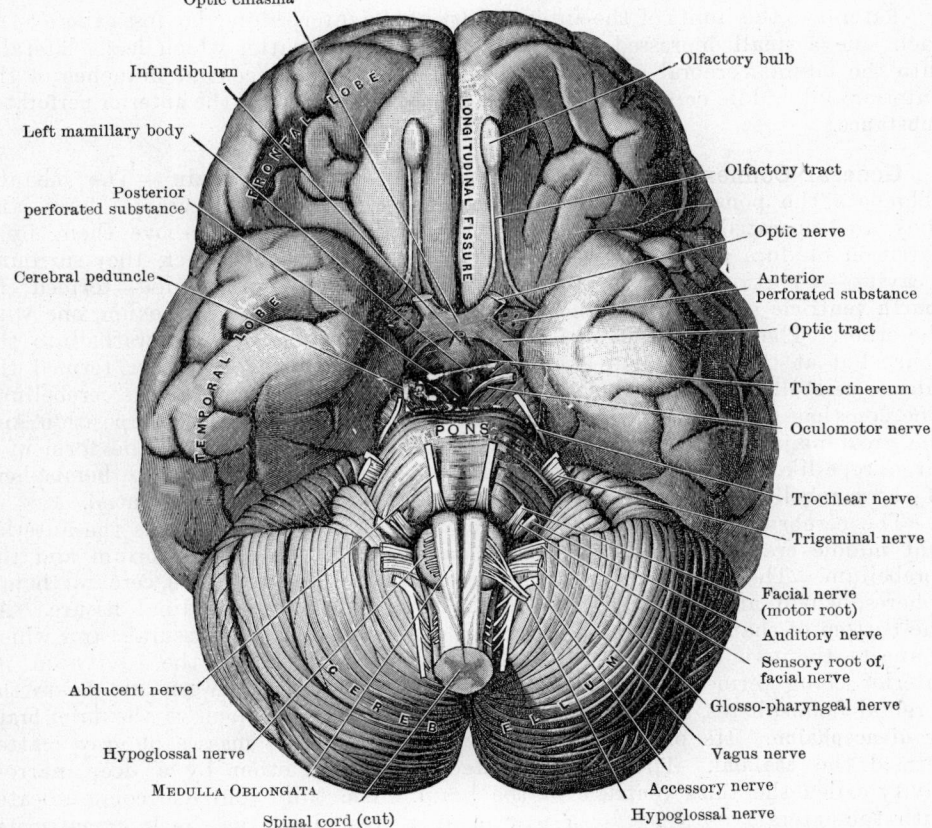

Optic chiasma

Infundibulum

Left mamillary body

Posterior
perforated substance

Cerebral peduncle

Olfactory bulb

Olfactory tract

Optic nerve

Anterior
perforated substance

Optic tract

Tuber cinereum

Oculomotor nerve

Trochlear nerve

Trigeminal nerve

Facial nerve
(motor root)

Auditory nerve

Sensory root of
facial nerve

Glosso-pharyngeal nerve

Vagus nerve

Accessory nerve

Hypoglossal nerve

Abducent nerve

Hypoglossal nerve

MEDULLA OBLONGATA

Spinal cord (cut)

FIG. 717.—THE BASE OF THE BRAIN WITH THE CRANIAL NERVES ATTACHED.

the median plane in front, the longitudinal fissure, which separates the frontal portions of the cerebral hemispheres, opens into the recess.

Within the limits of the deep hollow on the base of the brain, two large rope-like strands—the **cerebral peduncles**—may be seen issuing from the inferior surface of the cerebral hemispheres. As they pass downwards those peduncles are inclined obliquely towards the median plane, so that when they plunge into the pons they are in close apposition the one to the other (Fig. 717). Turning round the lateral side of each peduncle, where it emerges from the cerebrum, is a flattened band termed the **optic tract**. At the anterior part of the hollow, the optic tracts are joined together by a short connecting piece termed the **optic chiasma**. The **optic nerves** join the antero-lateral angles of the chiasma.

The peduncles, the optic tracts, and the optic chiasma enclose a deep lozenge-shaped interval which is termed the **interpeduncular fossa**. Within the limits of that area the following parts may be seen as we pass from behind forwards: (1) the posterior perforated substance; (2) the mamillary bodies; (3) the tuber cinereum and the stalk of the hypophysis cerebri.

At its posterior angle, immediately in front of the pons, the interpeduncular fossa is very deep and is roofed by a layer of grey matter in which there are numerous small apertures. That is the **posterior perforated substance**, and through the apertures the central branches of the posterior cerebral artery enter the brain.

The **mamillary bodies** are two small white pea-like eminences placed side by side in front of the posterior perforated substance.

The **tuber cinereum** is a slightly-raised field of grey matter which occupies the interval between the anterior portions of the optic tracts in front of the mamillary bodies. Springing from the anterior part of the tuber cinereum, immediately behind the optic chiasma, is the **infundibulum**, or the stalk which connects the hypophysis cerebri with the base of the brain (Figs. 717-719).

Lateral to the limits of the anterior part of the interpeduncular fossa there is, on each side, a small depressed triangular field of grey matter which leads laterally into the lateral cerebral sulcus. It is perforated by the central branches of the anterior and middle cerebral arteries and receives the name of the **anterior perforated substance**.

General Connexions of the Several Parts of the Brain.—The medulla oblongata, the pons, and the cerebellum occupy the posterior cranial fossa, and they are separated from the cerebral hemispheres, which lie above them, by a partition of dura mater termed the tentorium cerebelli. Further, they surround a cavity—a portion of the primitive cavity of the early neural tube—termed the **fourth ventricle** of the brain, and they all stand in intimate connexion, one with the other. The medulla oblongata is for the most part carried upwards into the pons; but at the same time two large bundles from its dorsal part, termed the **inferior cerebellar peduncles** [corpora restiformia], are prolonged into the cerebellum. The pons has large numbers of transverse fibres entering into its composition, and the great majority of them are gathered together on each side in the form of a large rope-like strand. The strand plunges into the corresponding hemisphere of the cerebellum, and constitutes its **middle peduncle** [brachium pontis].

The cerebrum, which forms the great mass of the brain, occupies the anterior and middle cranial fossæ, and extends backwards above the tentorium and the cerebellum. The greater part of the cerebrum is formed by the cerebral hemispheres, which are separated from each other by the longitudinal fissure. At the bottom of that fissure is the **corpus callosum**—a broad commissural band which connects the two hemispheres. Each hemisphere is hollow, the cavity in its interior being termed the **lateral ventricle** of the brain. Between and below the cerebral hemispheres, and almost completely concealed by them, is the **inter-brain** or **diencephalon**. Its principal parts are a pair of large masses of grey matter termed the **thalami**. They are separated from each other by a deep, narrow cavity called the **third ventricle** of the brain. The third ventricle communicates with the lateral ventricles by a pair of apertures known as the **interventricular foramina**.

The cerebrum is connected with the parts in the posterior cranial fossa (pons, cerebellum, and medulla oblongata) by a short, thick stalk called the **mid-brain**. The mid-brain is built up of—(1) a pair of **cerebral peduncles** passing between the cerebrum and the pons; (2) the **tectum** or **corpora quadrigemina**, forming its dorsal part; and (3) a pair of **superior cerebellar peduncles**, proceeding from the cerebellum to the cerebrum. It is tunnelled by a narrow passage—the **aqueduct**—which extends between the third and fourth ventricles.

In a view of the intact brain the greater part of the mid-brain and diencephalon is hidden by the cerebral hemispheres; but a precise idea will be obtained of the inter-relationships of the various parts of the brain, if we study the relationship of those structures to the series of cavities in the interior of the brain as they are displayed in a median section (Fig. 718).

The central canal of the spinal cord is seen to extend into the medulla oblongata for a short distance; then it expands into the cavity of the fourth ventricle, the floor (anterior wall) of which is formed partly by the medulla oblongata and partly by the pons. Behind the fourth ventricle lies the cerebellum, but it forms only a small part of the roof (posterior wall). The roof consists mainly of the **superior medullary velum** [velum medullare anterius] above and the thin ependymal lamina below.

The fourth ventricle is continued upwards into the **aqueduct**, which tunnels the mid-brain between the tectum behind and the thick mass called the tegmentum in front.

The aqueduct opens superiorly into the third **ventricle**, the major portion of each side wall of which is formed by the **thalamus**. Near the antero-superior corner of each side wall of the third ventricle the **interventricular foramen** leads into the cavity of the corresponding cerebral hemisphere, which is known as the **lateral ventricle**.

MEDULLA OBLONGATA

The **medulla oblongata** is the continuation upwards of the spinal cord. It is a little more than one inch (25 mm.) in length, and it may be regarded as

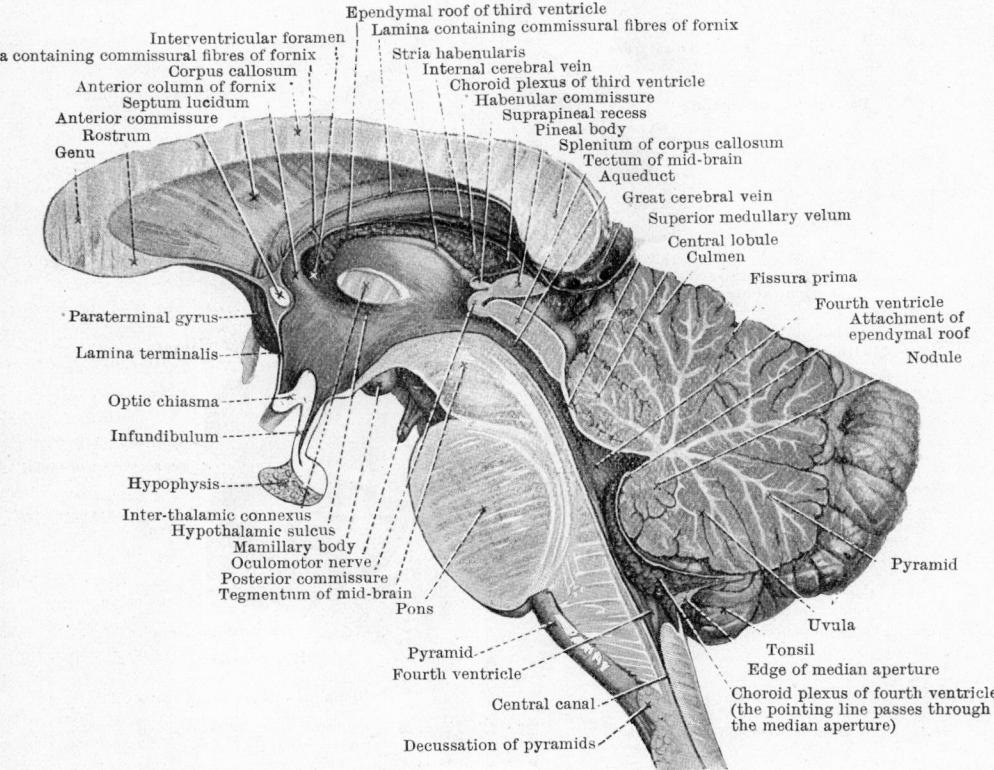

FIG. 718.—THE PARTS OF THE BRAIN CUT THROUGH IN A MEDIAN SECTION. (G. E. S.)
The side walls of the ventricular cavities also are shown.

beginning about the level of the foramen magnum. From there it proceeds upwards in a very nearly vertical direction, and ends at the lower border of the pons. At first its girth is similar to that of the spinal cord, but it rapidly expands as it approaches the pons, and consequently it presents a more or less conical form. Its anterior surface lies behind the grooved surface of the basilar portion of the occipital bone, and its posterior surface is related to the vallecula of the cerebellum. The medulla oblongata is a bilateral structure, and its bilateral character is indicated by the **anterior and posterior median fissures**.

The **anterior median fissure**, as it passes from the spinal cord on to the medulla oblongata, is interrupted at the level of the foramen magnum by several strands of fibres which cross the median plane from one side to the other. This intercrossing is termed the *decussation of the pyramids*. Above the decussation it is continued upwards to the lower border of the pons, but is often made very shallow by numerous external arcuate fibres which emerge between its lips and then curve laterally to reach the posterior part of the medulla oblongata. At the lower margin of the pons the fissure expands slightly and ends in a blind pit named the **foramen cæcum.**

The **posterior median fissure** is present only on the lower half of the medulla oblongata. As it ascends it rapidly becomes shallower. Half-way up, where the central canal opens into the fourth ventricle, the lips of the posterior median fissure are thrust apart and constitute the boundaries of a triangular field which is seen when the ependymal roof of the lower part of the fourth ventricle is removed. That triangular field is the lower part of the floor of the fourth ventricle. The lower half of the medulla oblongata, containing as it does the continuation of the

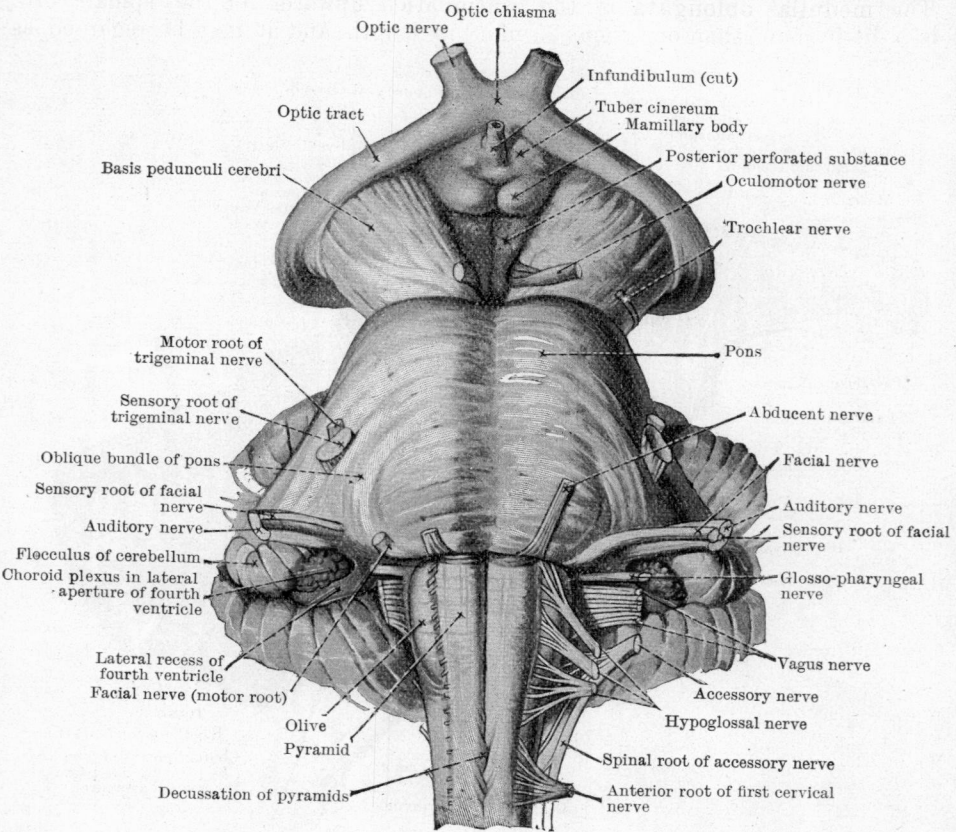

Optic chiasma
Optic nerve
Infundibulum (cut)
Optic tract
Tuber cinereum
Mamillary body
Basis pedunculi cerebri
Posterior perforated substance
Oculomotor nerve
Trochlear nerve
Motor root of trigeminal nerve
Pons
Sensory root of trigeminal nerve
Abducent nerve
Oblique bundle of pons
Facial nerve
Sensory root of facial nerve
Auditory nerve
Auditory nerve
Sensory root of facial nerve
Flocculus of cerebellum
Choroid plexus in lateral aperture of fourth ventricle
Glosso-pharyngeal nerve
Lateral recess of fourth ventricle
Facial nerve (motor root)
Vagus nerve
Accessory nerve
Hypoglossal nerve
Olive
Pyramid
Spinal root of accessory nerve
Decussation of pyramids
Anterior root of first cervical nerve

FIG. 719.—FRONT VIEW OF THE MEDULLA OBLONGATA, PONS, AND MID-BRAIN. (G. E. S.)

central canal of the spinal cord, is frequently termed the closed part of the medulla oblongata; the upper half, above the opening of the canal, which contains the lower part of the fourth ventricle, is called the open part of the medulla oblongata.

The examination of the floor of the fourth ventricle will be deferred for the present, and the appearance presented by the surface of the medulla oblongata may now engage our attention. In the spinal cord the corresponding surface area is divided into three districts by the motor and sensory roots of the spinal nerves. Of those the sensory enter along the bottom of a narrow groove, whilst the motor are spread over a relatively broad surface area and have no groove in connexion with their emergence. In the medulla oblongata corresponding rows of rootlets enter and emerge from the surface of each side. The rootlets of the hypoglossal nerve carry up the line of the anterior nerve-roots of the spinal cord. In one respect, however, they differ: they emerge in linear order and along the bottom of a distinct furrow termed the antero-lateral sulcus. The rootlets which carry up the line of the posterior nerve-roots are those of the accessory, the vagus, and the glosso-pharyngeal nerves. They are attached along the bottom of a furrow named the postero-lateral sulcus. The root-bundles of those nerves differ, however, in so far that they are not all composed of afferent fibres. Certain of them are purely efferent (roots of accessory), whilst others contain a considerable number of efferent as well as afferent fibres, and are therefore to be regarded as mixed roots.

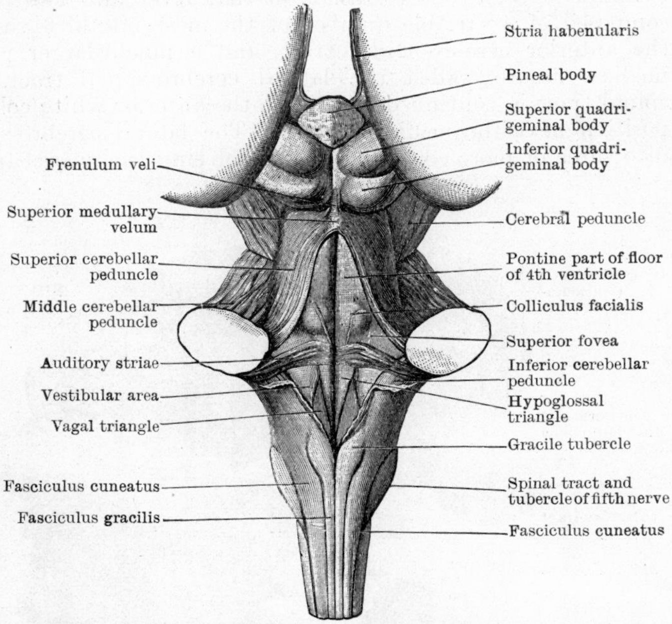

The sulci and the two rows of nerve roots divide the surface of each half of the medulla oblongata into three districts, viz., an anterior, a lateral, and a posterior, similar to the surface areas of the three white columns of the spinal cord.

FIG. 720.—POSTERIOR VIEW OF THE MEDULLA, PONS, AND MID-BRAIN OF A FULL-TIME HUMAN FŒTUS.

Indeed, at first sight, they appear to be direct continuations upwards of those three columns; that, however, is not the case, because the fibres of the columns undergo a rearrangement as they proceed upwards into the medulla oblongata.

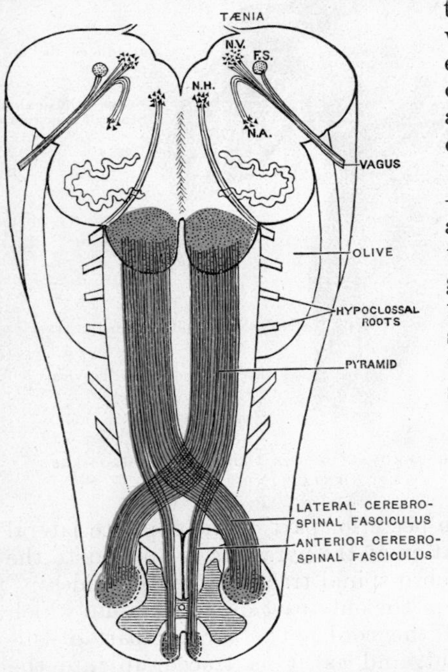

Anterior Area of Medulla Oblongata—Pyramid.—The district between the anterior median fissure and the groove through which the rootlets of the hypoglossal nerve issue from the medulla oblongata receives the name of the **pyramid.** An inspection of the surface is sufficient to show that the pyramid is composed of a compact strand of longitudinally directed nerve-fibres. It represents, in fact, the portion of the great cerebro-spinal tract which carries fibres from the cerebral hemisphere to all the motor nuclei on the other side of the medulla oblongata and spinal cord. Slightly constricted at the place where it emerges from the pons (Fig. 719), it swells immediately to form a prominent rounded column which passes vertically downwards, separated from the pyramid of the other side by the anterior median fissure. Towards the lower part of the medulla oblongata it gradually tapers.

Although the pyramid at first sight appears to be continuous with the anterior

FIG. 721.—DIAGRAM OF THE DECUSSATION OF THE PYRAMIDS (modified from van Gehuchten).

NH, Hypoglossal nucleus ; NV, Vago-glosso-pharyngeal nucleus; FS, Tractus solitarius ; NA, Nucleus ambiguus.

white column of the cord, only a very small proportion of the fibres contained in that column are derived from the pyramid. This at once becomes manifest when the lips of the lower part of the anterior median fissure are thrust apart. The pyramid is then seen to divide at that level into two parts, viz. a small portion composed of a variable number of the most lateral fibres of the pyramid, termed the anterior cerebro-spinal tract, and a much larger portion, situated next the median fissure, called the lateral cerebro-spinal tract. The anterior cerebro-spinal tract is continued down into the anterior white column, where it takes up a position next the median fissure. The lateral cerebro-spinal tract is broken up into three or more coarse bundles which sink backwards and at the same time cross

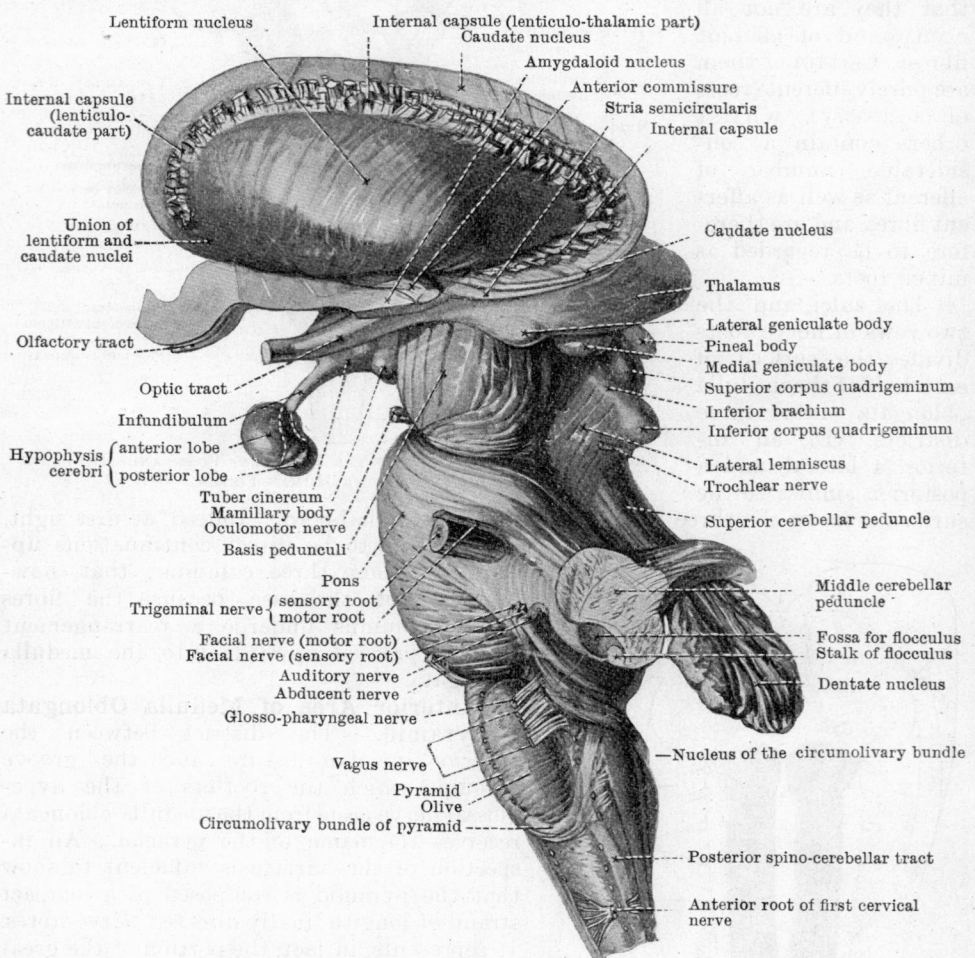

Fig. 722.—Left Lateral Aspect of a Brain after removal of the Cerebral Hemisphere (except Corpus Striatum) and the Cerebellum (except Dentate Nucleus). (G. E. S.)

the median plane to take up a position in the posterior part of the opposite lateral white column of the cord. The term **decussation of the pyramids** is applied to the intercrossing of the bundles of the lateral cerebro-spinal tracts of opposite sides.

The anterior cerebro-spinal tract is therefore the only part of the pyramid which has a place in the anterior white column of the cord. The largest part of this column is the anterior intersegmental tract, and as it is traced up into the medulla oblongata, it is thrust aside by the decussating bundles of the lateral cerebro-spinal tract and thus comes to occupy a deep position in the substance of the medulla oblongata, behind and to the lateral side of the pyramid.

Lateral Area of Medulla Oblongata.—This is the district between the hypoglossal roots in front and the root-bundles of the accessory, vagus, and glosso-pharyngeal nerves behind. It presents a very different appearance in its upper and lower parts. In its lower portion it simply appears to be a continuation upwards of the lateral area of the cord; in its upper part a striking oval prominence bulges out on the surface, and receives the name of the olive.

The lower part of this district, however, is very far from being an exact counterpart of the lateral white column of the cord. The lateral cerebro-spinal tract is no longer present, seeing that, in the medulla oblongata, it forms the greater part of the pyramid of the opposite side. Another strand of fibres, viz. the posterior spino-cerebellar tract, prolonged upwards in the lateral white column, gradually leaves this portion of the medulla oblongata. This tract lies on the surface, and is frequently visible to the naked eye as a white band (Fig. 722) which inclines obliquely backwards into the posterior district of the medulla oblongata to join the inferior cerebellar peduncle. The remainder of the fibres of the lateral white column are continued upwards in the lateral area of the medulla oblongata.

The **olive** is a smooth oval prominence on the upper part of the lateral area of the medulla oblongata. Its long axis is vertical and is about half an inch long. It is the bulging produced by the subjacent **olivary nucleus**—a crumpled thin-walled sac of grey matter which is separated from the surface by a thin layer of white matter.

Posterior Area of Medulla Oblongata.—In its lower half, this district is bounded behind by the posterior median fissure, and in its upper half by the lateral margin of the medullary part of the floor of the fourth ventricle. In front it is separated from the lateral area by the row of rootlets belonging to the accessory, vagus, and glosso-pharyngeal nerves. The upper and lower parts appear to be continuous but in reality are almost quite distinct the one from the other—as in the lateral area.

The lower part of the posterior area corresponds more or less closely with the posterior white column of the cord. In the cervical region the posterior white column is divided by a septum of pia mater into the **fasciculus gracilis** medially and the **fasciculus cuneatus** laterally. They are prolonged upwards into the medulla oblongata, and in the lower part of the posterior area they stand out distinctly, and are separated one from the other by a distinct groove. When they reach the level of the lower part of the fourth ventricle, they end in slight prominences called respectively the **gracile tubercle** and the **cuneate tubercle**. The right and left gracile tubercles are thrust apart by the opening up of the medulla oblongata to form the floor of the fourth ventricle, and the central canal connects with the fourth ventricle in the angle between the two.

The elongated prominences formed by the two strands and their enlarged extremities are due to two elongated nuclei which lie subjacent to the strands, and represent the termini of the uppermost extensions of the spinal posterior root-fibres. They are termed respectively the **nucleus gracilis** and **nucleus cuneatus**.

But a third longitudinal elevation is apparent on the lower part of the posterior area of the medulla. That is placed on the lateral side of the fasciculus cuneatus—between it and the posterior row of nerve-roots—and it has no counterpart in the posterior white column of the cord. It is called the **tubercle of the trigeminal nerve**. It is produced by a mass of substantia gelatinosa coming close to the surface and forming a bulging in that situation. Extremely narrow below, it widens as it is traced upwards, and finally ends in an expanded extremity. A thin layer of white matter, composed of longitudinally arranged fibres, is spread over this district, and separates the substantia gelatinosa from the surface. Those fibres constitute the **spinal tract** of the **trigeminal nerve**, which here assumes a superficial position as it descends in the medulla oblongata. In the upper half of the medulla the spinal tract lies immediately in front of the inferior cerebellar peduncle—so closely applied that, on surface view, the tract seems to form part of the peduncle. In that part of its course, the tract is shut off from the surface by the posterior spino-cerebellar tract, the anterior external arcuate fibres, and the circumolivary bundle as they incline backwards towards the peduncle, and, further, the root-fibres of the glosso-pharyngeal and vagus nerves emerge through it.

Inferior Cerebellar Peduncle [Corpus Restiforme].—The inferior cerebellar peduncle forms almost the whole of the upper part of the posterior area of the medulla oblongata. It lies between the floor of the fourth ventricle and the roots of the vagus and glosso-pharyngeal nerves. It is a thick, round bundle which inclines upwards and laterally, and then takes a sudden bend backwards to enter the cerebellum. It is the link that connects the cerebellum with the medulla oblongata and spinal cord. A study of the surface of the medulla oblongata yields some important information regarding the constitution of the inferior cerebellar peduncle. Thus, the posterior spino-cerebellar tract (Fig. 722), from the lateral column of the cord, can be traced into it; and large numbers of fibres which take a curved course on the surface of the medulla oblongata may likewise be followed into it; these are the external arcuate fibres. Numerous other fibres enter this peduncle on its deep aspect, but they will be studied at a later stage.

External Arcuate Fibres (Fig. 722).—These fibres are in two groups—posterior and anterior.

The **posterior external arcuate fibres** are a small group that arise in the nucleus gracilis and nucleus cuneatus, and pass upwards to enter the inferior cerebellar peduncle at once.

The **anterior external arcuate fibres** are more numerous, and are seen best in the neighbourhood of the olive, over the surface of which they may be observed coursing in the form of a number of fine curved bundles or as a continuous sheet of fibres. They vary greatly in number and in distinctness, and they are some-times so numerous that they cover the olive almost entirely. They arise in the nucleus gracilis and nucleus cuneatus, arch forwards, cross the median plane, and appear on the front of the medulla oblongata. An attentive examination will show that the majority of them come to the surface in the median fissure between the pyramids, and also, not infrequently, in the groove between the pyramid and olive, or through the substance of the pyramid itself; the anterior median fissure in its upper part is often almost completely blocked up by those emerging fibres. Reaching the surface in this manner, they curve laterally and backwards, enter the inferior cerebellar peduncle and form a considerable part of its outer portion.

There is frequently present, especially on the left side, a bundle of fibres that is often mistaken for a group of arcuate fibres. It is the **circumolivary bundle of the pyramid** (Fig. 722). It is a bundle of varying size which emerges from the pyramid, bends backwards, curving round the lower border of the olive, and then passes obliquely upward and backwards to end in a fusiform ridge of grey matter—the **nucleus of the circumolivary bundle**—which crosses the inferior peduncle very obliquely (Fig. 722, the ridge immediately behind the roots of the vagus nerve). This bundle and the nucleus in which it terminates are of great morphological interest, and will be referred to again in the succeeding pages (see Fig. 736, p. 855).

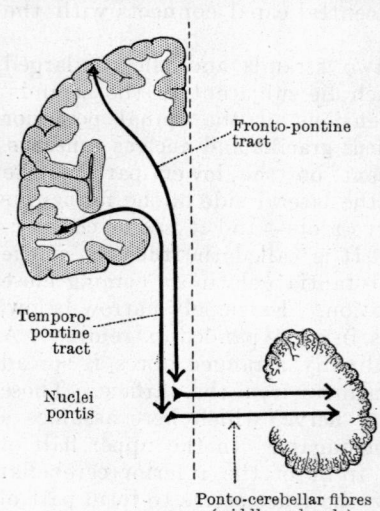

Fronto-pontine tract

Temporo-pontine tract

Nuclei pontis

Ponto-cerebellar fibres (middle peduncle)

FIG. 723.—DIAGRAM OF CORTICO-CEREBELLAR CONNEXION. (G. E. S.)

PONS

The **pons** is the marked white prominence seen on the base of the brain between the medulla oblongata and the cerebral peduncles in front of the cerebellum. It is convex from side to side and from above downwards, and transverse streaks on its surface show that, superficially at least, it is composed of bundles of nerve-fibres, most of which course transversely. On each side those transverse fibres form a large compact strand which sinks in a backward and lateral direction into the hemisphere of the cerebellum. That strand is termed the **middle cerebellar peduncle** [brachium pontis]. It forms the second stage in the connexion between the cerebral cortex of the other side and the cerebellum of the same side in Fig. 723.

The *anterior surface* of the pons is in relation to the dorsum sellæ and the upper part of the clivus of the skull. It presents a median groove (**basilar sulcus**) which gradually widens as it is traced upwards; it lodges the basilar artery. The median depression is produced by the prominence caused on each side by the passage of the cerebro-spinal bundles downwards through the pons. The **trigeminal nerve**, with its large, entering sensory root and its small, emerging motor root, is attached to the side of the pons, nearer its upper than its lower border (Fig. 722). The term *pons* is restricted to that portion which lies between the two trigeminal nerves, and the designation *middle cerebellar peduncle* is applied to the part which extends beyond the nerve into the hemisphere of the cerebellum. The **abducent nerve**, the **facial nerve**, and the **auditory nerve** are attached to the brain at the lower border of the pons—the abducent nerve opposite the lateral border of the pyramid and the facial and auditory farther from the median plane. The auditory nerve is in contact with the flocculus of the cerebellum; the motor root of the facial is on its medial side, and the sensory root [nervus intermedius], which is very much thinner, is more or less hidden between them (Figs. 719, 722). A large bundle of fibres on the front of the pons departs from the transverse course pursued by most of the pontine fibres, and, starting at the medial side of the trigeminal nerve, passes almost vertically downwards between the motor and sensory roots of the facial nerve (Fig. 719, p. 834) and reaches the side of the medulla oblongata, where it passes into the nucleus of the circumolivary bundle (Fig. 722). That bundle is known as the **oblique bundle of the pons**.

Immediately below the insertion of the auditory nerve at the lower margin of the pons a little calyx-like appendage of the ependymal roof of the fourth ventricle (**lateral recess**) projects laterally, partly behind the glosso-pharyngeal nerve. Through an elliptical aperture in this ependymal process (**lateral aperture of the fourth ventricle**) a little cauliflower-like mass of choroid plexus is extruded between the auditory and the glosso-pharyngeal nerves (Fig. 719, p. 834).

The *posterior surface* of the pons looks towards the cerebellum, and presents a triangular area covered with grey matter which forms the upper part of the floor of the fourth ventricle. That area is directly continuous inferiorly with the medullary part of the floor of the ventricle, and is bounded on each side by a band of white matter termed the **superior cerebellar peduncle** (Fig. 724).

Superior Cerebellar Peduncles [Brachia Conjunctiva].—The superior peduncles are hidden from view by the upper part of the cerebellum. They emerge from the hemispheres of the cerebellum, and, as they proceed upwards on the back of the pons, they converge towards each other until, at the lower margin of the inferior corpora quadrigemina, the medial margins of the two peduncles become almost contiguous (Fig. 724, p. 840). At first they form the lateral boundaries of the upper part of the fourth ventricle; but, as they ascend and approach closer to each other, they gradually come to overhang that cavity, and thus enter into the formation of its roof. They disappear from the surface by dipping under cover of the quadrigeminal bodies and entering the substance of the mid-brain.

Superior Medullary Velum.—Filling up the triangular interval between the medial margins of the two superior peduncles there is a thin layer of white matter which completes the roof of the upper part of the fourth ventricle; it receives the name of the **superior medullary velum** [velum medullare anterius]. When traced downwards, the velum is seen to be carried, with the brachia conjunctiva, into the white matter of the cerebellum. Spread out on its posterior surface there is a small, thin tongue-shaped prolongation of the cortex of the cerebellum termed the **lingula**; and the fourth pair of cranial nerves (**trochlear**) issues from its substance close to the inferior quadrigeminal bodies.

FOURTH VENTRICLE

The **fourth ventricle of the brain** is rhomboidal in outline. Below, it tapers to a point and becomes continuous with the central canal of the lower half of the medulla oblongata; above, it narrows in a similar manner and is continued into the **aqueduct** of the mid-brain. The posterior wall is termed the **roof** and is concealed by the cerebellum. The anterior wall is called the **floor** and is formed by the dorsal surface of the pons and the corresponding surface of the medulla oblongata. On each side a long, curved, and narrow prolongation of the ventricular cavity is carried laterally from its widest part and curves round the upper part of the corresponding inferior cerebellar peduncle. It is termed the **lateral recess**. The roof of the cavity is very thin and is intimately connected with the cerebellum. It is better, therefore, to defer its description until that part of the brain has been studied.

Floor of the Fourth Ventricle.—The widest part of the floor is opposite the inferior cerebellar peduncles as they turn dorsally to enter the cerebellum (Fig. 724). Above this level the floor is formed by the pons, and below it by the ventral

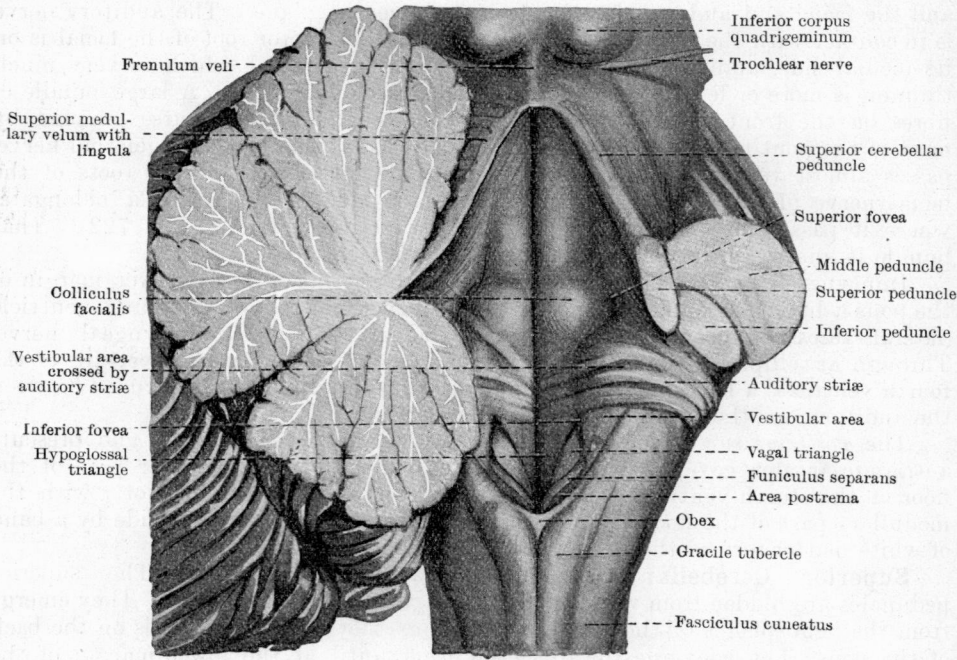

FIG. 724.—FLOOR OF THE FOURTH VENTRICLE. The right half of the cerebellum has been removed. The left half is drawn over to the left so as to expose the floor of the ventricle fully. (D. J. C.)

part of the upper half of the medulla oblongata. Under the ependyma of the floor there is a thick layer of grey matter continuous below with that which surrounds the central canal and above with that around the aqueduct. The floor is circumscribed by definite lateral boundaries. From below upwards these are: (1) the gracile tubercle, (2) the cuneate tubercle, (3) the inferior peduncle and (4) the superior peduncle of the cerebellum.

The floor of the fourth ventricle is divided into two symmetrical portions by a median groove. Crossing each half of the floor, at its widest part, there are several more or less conspicuous bundles of fibres termed the **auditory striæ**. They begin on the side and the back of the inferior peduncle, where they spring from the cochlear nuclei, pass transversely medially, and disappear from view in the median furrow. The auditory striæ vary in different specimens, both in direction and prominence. It is not uncommon to find that no trace of them is visible on the surface.

On the medullary part of the floor a small, triangular depression, immediately below the auditory striæ, catches the eye. It is termed the **inferior fovea**. The apex points upwards towards the striæ, and the basal angles are prolonged downwards as diverging grooves (Fig. 724). The medial groove runs towards the opening of the central canal; the lateral groove runs towards the lateral boundary of the floor. In that manner the lower half of the floor is mapped out into three triangular areas. The medial subdivision is slightly elevated and is termed the **hypoglossal triangle**, because subjacent to the medial part of this area is the nucleus of the hypoglossal nerve. The intermediate area, between the two diverging grooves, is the **vagal triangle**—so called because the dorsal nucleus of the vagus and glosso-pharyngeal nerves is subjacent to it. Near the lateral angle is the **vestibular area**. The base of this area is directed upwards and runs directly into an eminence over which the auditory striæ pass. Subjacent to that district of the floor of the ventricle lies the chief nucleus of the vestibular division of the auditory nerve.

A close inspection will show that the base of the vagal triangle is separated from the medial margin of the gracile tubercle by a narrow lanceolate strip to which Retzius gave the name of **area postrema**. Beneath that area, which is very vascular, lies the **nucleus postremus** (J. T. Wilson), and marking it off from the base of the vagal triangle there is a translucent cord-like ridge called the **funiculus separans**.

When the floor of the ventricle is examined under water with a magnifying glass, the hypoglossal triangle is seen to consist of a narrow medial strip which corresponds to the hypo-glossal nucleus, and a wider lateral part which has been shown to be the surface representation of another nucleus termed the **nucleus intercalatus**.

On the upper half of the floor also there is a slight depression which is termed the **superior fovea**. The longitudinal prominence between the superior fovea and the median fissure is called the **eminentia medialis**; it swells out inferiorly to form a rounded hillock called the **colliculus facialis**, and, below that, it is continuous with the floor of the hypoglossal triangle. As already stated, the **vestibular area** extends upwards into the pontine part of the ventricular floor and forms an elevated region in the most lateral part of its widest portion, below and to the lateral side of the superior fovea. Proceeding upwards from the superior fovea to the opening of the aqueduct there is a shallow depression termed the **locus cœruleus**, because it usually presents a faint slate-blue colour. When the ependyma is scraped away from the surface of the locus cœruleus, the colour is seen to be due to the **substantia ferruginea**—a name applied to a linear group of strongly pigmented cells. In transverse sections through the upper part of the pons, the substantia ferruginea appears on the cut surface as a small black spot.

INTERNAL STRUCTURE OF MEDULLA OBLONGATA

The structure of the medulla oblongata and also of the pons differs in a marked degree from that of the spinal cord: indeed, in its upper part, it presents very little in common with the cord. Some of the largest fasciculi which come up from the spinal cord (such as the posterior white columns) end in the lower part of the medulla oblongata; others leave the medulla oblongata and pass into the cerebellum; and most of the bundles of fibres which pass upwards or downwards, from or to the spinal cord, come to occupy very different positions in the medulla oblongata and pons.

The grey matter instead of being moulded into one compact column becomes broken up into a series of discrete nuclei. Thus, there are developed from the basal lamina of the rhombencephalon not one compact mass like the spinal anterior grey column, but three distinct broken columns of efferent nuclei (Figs. 721 and 728):—(1) a **medial somatic column**, which in turn is broken up into two parts, a medullary nucleus (*hypoglossal*) which supplies the motor fibres to the tongue muscles, and a pontine nucleus (*abducent*) which supplies the lateral rectus muscle of the eye; (2) a **lateral somatic column**, broken up into separate nuclei, viz., *accessory, ambiguus, facial,* and *trigeminal,* supplying the sterno-mastoid and trapezius muscles and the striated muscles of the larynx, pharynx, and face and those concerned with mastication; and (3) a **splanchnic column** of nuclei, giving efferent fibres which pass out in the vagus, glosso-pharyngeal, and facial nerves, to be widely distributed to unstriped muscle, glands, and other tissues in the head, neck, thorax, and abdomen.

Further, the terminal nuclei of the sensory nerves which are developed in the alar lamina of the rhombencephalon do not unite to form a definite posterior grey column, as happens in the spinal cord, but form discrete masses; and as those act as receptive organs for a much greater variety of sensory nerves than are represented in the spinal nerves there is a much greater number of nuclei than would be formed if the various components of the posterior grey column in the spinal cord were dissociated. Thus, there are terminal nuclei in the medulla oblongata not only for the ordinary cutaneous nerves, but also for nerves coming from the mucous membranes of the alimentary and respiratory organs, as well as from other visceral structures; and there are also special nerves of taste (glosso-pharyngeal and the sensory root of the facial), of hearing (cochlear part of the auditory), and of equilibration (vestibular part of the auditory). But that does not exhaust the peculiar features of the terminal sensory nuclei of the rhomben-cephalon. In the description of the spinal cord attention was called to the fact that certain of the fibres of the posterior nerve-root did not end in the grey matter of the cord but passed upwards to the medulla oblongata. Special terminal nuclei are developed from the alar lamina to receive these fibres. They are the nucleus gracilis and nucleus cuneatus.

In addition, part of the terminal vestibular nucleus receives accessions of fibres from these (gracile and cuneate) nuclei as well as from other sensory terminal nuclei in the spinal cord and develops into that great mass of tissue—the cerebellum—to which vast numbers of other fibres come and go, adding considerably to the complexity of the region of the pons and medulla oblongata. Moreover, there is developed from the alar lamina a whole series of other masses of grey matter—the **olivary nucleus, arcuate nuclei, nucleus of the circumolivary bundle,** and **nuclei pontis**—as links in the complex chains that bind all parts of the central nervous system to the great co-ordinating mechanism of the cerebellum.

Thus it comes about that, instead of having, as in the spinal cord, a definite column of grey matter ensheathed in a thick mass of white substance, the rhomb-encephalon is composed of many scattered masses of grey matter; and its white substance is represented partly by great longitudinal strands, and also by many great systems of fibres that pass transversely through its substance or on its surface, e.g., the superficial fibres of the pons and many of the arcuate fibres.

From what has already been said concerning the external form of the medulla oblongata and pons it will be apparent that the distortion of the neural tube which occurred as the result of the pontine flexure has also been largely responsible for the distinctive features of that region of the brain.

As the pontine flexure develops, a strain is thrown upon the thin roof-plate, which yields and becomes stretched so as to permit the thick lateral walls of the neural tube to fall laterally (Figs. 725 and 726). One result of this process is the great lateral expansion of the cavity of the hind-brain, which assumes the charac-teristic rhomboid form. If the thin and greatly attenuated ependymal roof is torn away from the rhombencephalon of an embryo of the third month the fourth ventricle will present the appearance (viewed from behind) shown in Fig. 726. The ventricle is seen to be prolonged laterally, on each side, to form a little recess on the lateral side of the rhombencephalon. This is called the **lateral recess.**

The ependymal roof becomes invaginated towards the cavity of the fourth ventricle, on each side of the median plane, in the whole length of the roof, i.e. from the cerebellar attachment, almost as far as the middle of the medulla oblongata (Fig. 718). The upper end of that invaginated fold, on each side, becomes prolonged laterally as far as the extremity of the lateral recess (Fig. 719). Pia mater and blood-vessels extend into the folds, and form the **choroid plexuses** of the fourth ventricle. At the extremities of the two plexuses, which are situated at the three corners of the roof of the ventricle, oval or elliptical perforations develop in the ependymal roof and the overlying pia at about the fifth month of intra-uterine life. They are known as the **median aperture** (which opens between the gracile tubercles on the posterior surface) and the **lateral apertures** (which open on the anterior faces of the lateral recesses (Fig. 719), behind the insertion of the glosso-pharyngeal nerve on each side). Through each of the lateral openings the swollen, cauliflower-like extremity of the choroid plexus becomes extruded from the ventricle. The lower ends of the two plexuses, lying side by side, present an analogous relationship to the median aperture, but they are exceedingly attenuated, and the ependymal lamella from which they spring becomes dragged backwards into contact with the cerebellum (Fig. 718), so that, when seen from below, the median aperture is a great funnel-shaped tube leading into the fourth ventricle, and the choroid plexuses look like two delicate vascular fringes on the cerebellum.

Those three apertures are the only means provided for the escape of the fluid contained in the ventricles of the central nervous system. The fluid is poured into the subarachnoid space.

As a result of the pontine flexure the side walls of the neural tube in the neighbourhood of the bend fall away the one from the other and eventually come to be placed in the same transverse plane, one with the other and also with the floor-plate. At the time this process is in operation (see Fig. 725) the alar and basal laminæ are particularly well defined, and the limiting sulci are accentuated by the bending of the side wall; but that sharp distinction is soon lost as the result of the great expansion of the basal lamina (Fig. 727). That is due not only to growth of its intrinsic elements but even more to its invasion by large numbers of neuroblasts which migrate from the alar into the basal lamina. Later still, the development of the great sensory and motor tracts contributes largely to the increase of the dimensions of the basal lamina.

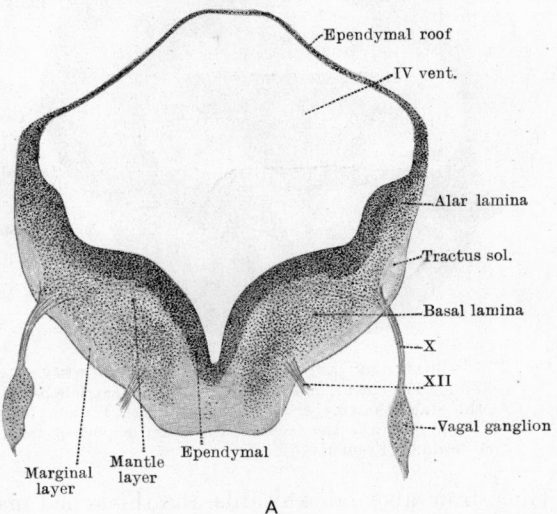

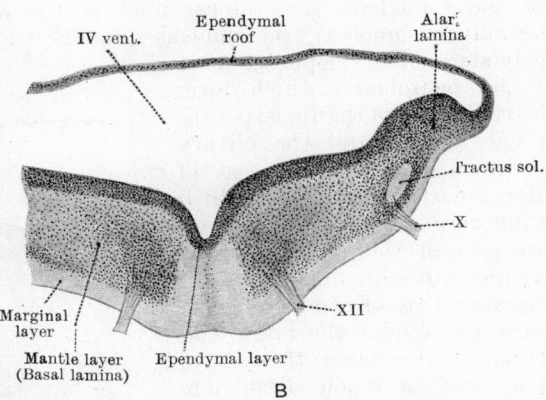

FIG. 725.—TRANSVERSE SECTIONS ACROSS THE MEDULLA OBLONGATA IN TWO HUMAN EMBRYOS, REPRESENTING DIFFERENT STAGES IN THE EXPANSION OF THE ROOF AND THE FALLING LATERALLY OF THE SIDE WALLS. (From His, slightly modified.)

As the two basal laminæ (one on each side of the median plane) increase in thickness the epithelial cells in the intervening floor-plate become stretched and lengthened (Fig. 725), so that a definite septum or **raphe** is formed between the two halves of the rhombencephalon.

The fate of the extreme posterior edge of the alar lamina is very interesting. The auditory nerve is inserted into it in the region of the lateral recess, and from it masses of neuroblasts develop to form receptive nuclei for the two parts of the nerve, which are the cochlear and vestibular nerves, and the nuclei are the **cochlear nucleus** and **vestibular nucleus**. Sensory fasciculi, bringing impulses from muscles, skin and related structures in all parts of the body, make their way into the upper part of the vestibular nucleus, and it grows and forms a large thickening of the posterior edge above the lateral recess. Eventually, as it extends medially (Fig. 726), it reaches and invades the roof-plate and fuses with the corresponding rudiment of the other side. Thus a semilunar band—the primitive cerebellum — is formed as an arch across the back of the metencephalon. The part of the dorsal edge which lies below the vestibular nucleus becomes bent over ventrally to form what is known as the **rhombic lip** (Fig. 727). It is destined to be transformed into a series of masses of grey matter the chief function of which is to emit fibres to carry impulses into the cerebellum. But most of these fibres pass not so much to the part of the cerebellum derived from their own side as to that of the opposite side.

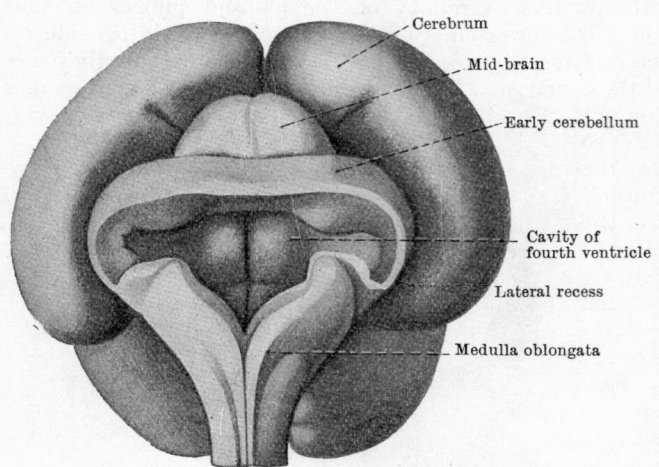

Cerebrum

Mid-brain

Early cerebellum

Cavity of
fourth ventricle

Lateral recess

Medulla oblongata

FIG. 726.—BRAIN OF AN EMBRYO OF ELEVEN WEEKS, viewed from behind. The ependymal roof of the fourth ventricle has been removed. At this stage the cerebellum is in the form of a simple band or plate which arches over the back of the anterior part of the cavity of the hind-brain. (From His.)

Thus, from above downwards, the thickened margin of the floor of the ventricle on each side develops into the following structures: cerebellum, the rest of the vestibular nucleus, the cochlear nucleus, the nuclei pontis (and arcuate nuclei), the olivary nucleus, the nucleus gracilis and the nucleus cuneatus. At an early stage of development most of the neuroblasts which form the rudiments of the nuclei pontis, arcuate nuclei, and the olivary nucleus begin a process of migration the course of which is determined by the source and direction of the afferent tracts passing into each nucleus. Such migrations are of common occurrence throughout the brain, and attempts to explain them have given rise to much discussion. The factor that appears to lead certain nerve-cells away from the place where they originally developed has been called *neurobiotaxis* by Ariëns-Kappers. But the solution of the problems of those apparent migrations is quite a simple one. Take the

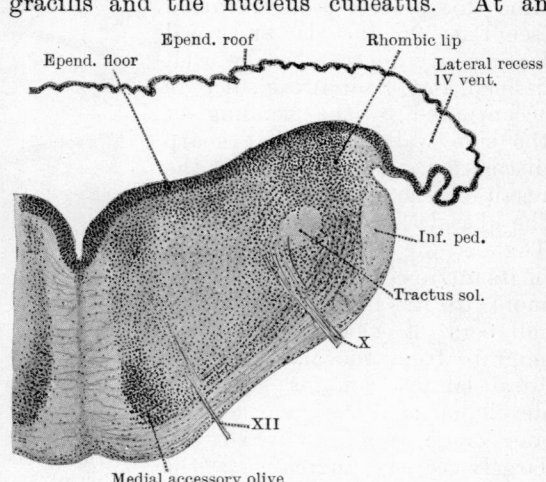

Epend. roof

Rhombic lip

Epend. floor

Lateral recess
IV vent.

Inf. ped.

Tractus sol.

X

XII

Medial accessory olive

FIG. 727.—TRANSVERSE SECTION OF THE MEDULLA OBLONGATA AT A LATER STAGE THAN THOSE SHOWN IN FIG. 725. (After His.)

case of a nerve-cell (*A*), at an early stage of development, which collects afferent impulses through its dendrites from the cell *B*, and emits an efferent impulse through its axon to the cell *C*: as the whole nervous system is very small at the stage under consideration, the three cells will necessarily be close together—a fact which may be represented by the positions of the letters thus:—

$$B—A—C.$$

In the course of subsequent growth it must inevitably happen that the points *B* and C will become removed farther and farther apart. If we suppose that the cell B remains constant, the cell A will be faced with two alternatives if it is to continue to link together the elements B and C: either its dendrites or its axon must elongate. Now the axon is specially modified in structure for conducting impulses for long distances, and the dendrites are not so specialised. Therefore it invariably happens that it is the axon that becomes lengthened. In other words the cell-body A, considered in its relations to C, appears to migrate towards the direction B from which its chief supply of afferent impulses comes. This may be represented thus :—

$$B—A\text{————————————————}C.$$

In the specific case we are considering the vestibular nucleus and the cerebellum receive their chief supply of afferent fibres from the incoming vestibular nerve: hence there is no reason for migration. Similarly the nucleus gracilis and nucleus cuneatus receive the fibres which come up through the posterior white column, and they remain where they are. But the nuclei pontis, the olivary nucleus, and the arcuate nuclei are " fed " with impulses that pass downwards (and some perhaps upwards) in the basal lamina, close to the median plane, and they "migrate" towards the direction from which their afferent paths are approaching—the nuclei pontis towards the cerebral peduncles bringing cerebro-pontine fibres from the cerebral cortex, and the olivary nucleus to the neighbourhood of certain descending tegmental tracts and ascending spinal sensory tracts that seem to supply the attractive force which leads them to forsake the rhombic lip of the alar lamina and migrate into the basal lamina.

The majority of the cells destined to form the nuclei pontis wander obliquely upwards and forwards between the facial and auditory nerves to reach the basal lamina of the metencephalon. But strewn along the pathway from the edge of the ventricular floor to the front of the pons are scattered nerve-cells which have, so to speak, fallen by the way, and remain to indicate in the adult brain the path taken by the majority of their sister cells. That remnant forms the nucleus of the circumolivary bundle: the pontine fibres that spring from its cells and are making their way upwards to fall in line (Fig. 736, p. 855) with the other transverse fibres of the pons form the oblique bundle of the pons (Fig. 719, p. 834), and the cerebro-pontine fibres that pass below the pons in order to reach this outlying part of the nuclei pontis constitute the circumolivary bundle (Fig. 722, p. 836).

But not all of the elements of the nuclei pontis that migrate pass into the metencephalon; a certain number of them invariably pass into the myelencephalon. They collect on the anterior surface of the pyramids to form small irregular patches of grey matter which have received the name arcuate nuclei. Their afferent fibres (probably cerebro-pontine) come from the pyramids; and their efferent fibres (which proceed to the cerebellum) form some of the anterior external arcuate fibres (Fig. 732).

Olivary Nuclei.—The most conspicuous of the isolated clumps of grey matter in the medulla are the olivary nucleus and the two accessory olivary nuclei. The **olivary nucleus** is the grey substance which produces the swelling known as the olive, and is a very striking object in transverse sections through that region. It is seen as a thick wavy line of grey matter folded on itself to enclose a space filled with white matter. It is in reality a crumpled lamina arranged in a purse-like manner, with an open mouth or **hilum** directed towards the median plane. The hilum does not reach the ends, and in transverse sections through either end of the nucleus the grey lamina is seen in the form of a completely closed capsule. Into and out of the mouth of the olivary nucleus streams a dense crowd of fibres.

The **accessory olivary nuclei** are two band-like laminæ of grey matter which are placed the one behind the main nucleus and the other medial to it. In transverse section each of those nuclei is rod-like (Fig. 728).

The **medial accessory olivary nucleus** extends lower down than the main nucleus, and its lower part is much larger than its upper. It begins immediately above the decussation of the pyramids, where it is seen on the lateral side of the cerebro-spinal tract and the medial lemniscus (Fig. 730). Higher up, it lies across the mouth of the main nucleus and on the lateral side of the medial lemniscus. The **dorsal accessory olivary nucleus** is close behind the main nucleus. The two accessory nuclei fuse together at their upper ends.

The nerve-cells of the olivary nucleus are small and round, and emit a large series of short, radiating, complexly branched dendrites, so that the cell-body seems to lie in the centre of a spherical mass formed by its own dendrites and an almost equally complex mass of intertwined end branches of the axons which carry impulses into those cells. A large descending tract which arises in the globus pallidus of the corpus striatum and in the red nucleus descends in the mesencephalon and rhombencephalon to end amidst the cells of the lateral part of the olivary nucleus. It is the **pallidorubro-olivary tract**, Fig. 733).

The axons emitted by the cells of the olivary nucleus cross the median plane to the opposite inferior peduncle and pass into the cerebellum. These fibres are

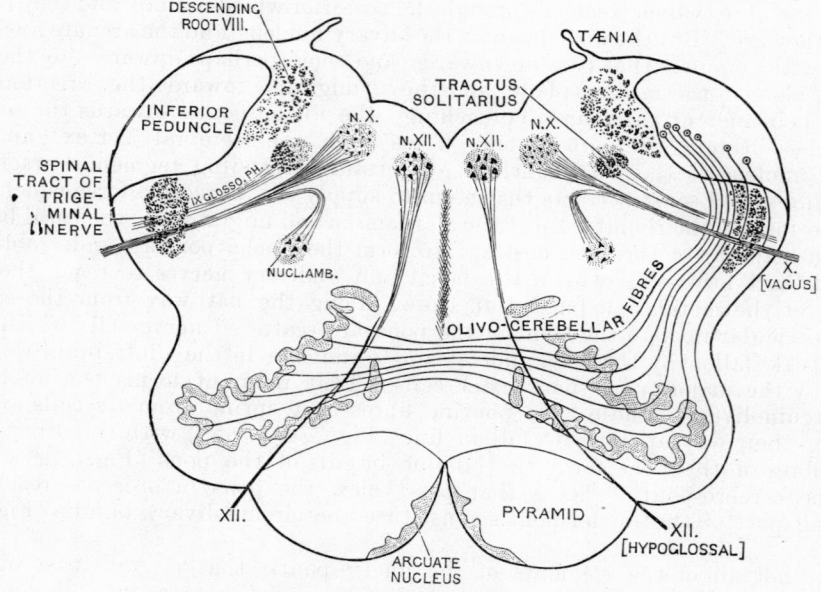

FIG. 728.—DIAGRAM OF THE OLIVO-CEREBELLAR TRACT.

N.X., Vago-glossopharyngeal nucleus.   N.XII., Hypoglossal nucleus.

seen only in the upper part of the medulla oblongata. They form the deep part of the inferior cerebellar peduncle and constitute its chief bulk. Streaming out from the hilum of the olivary nucleus, they cross the median plane, and in the opposite side of the medulla oblongata they pass through and around the olivary nucleus of that side. Ultimately, they are gathered together behind the olivary nucleus to take up a position in the deep part of the inferior peduncle. In passing back, they traverse the spinal tract of the trigeminal nerve and break it up into several separate bundles. The olivo-cerebellar fibres thus connect the olivary nucleus of one side with the opposite side of the cerebellum, and each part of it is connected with a definite part of the cerebellum.

It is only within recent times that any exact information has been obtained concerning the connexions and the morphological significance of the olivary nuclei. The connexion of the cerebral cortex with the cerebellum by means of cortico-pontine and ponto-cerebellar fibres (Fig. 723) is found only in mammals. In all other vertebrates the olivary nucleus is the link between the higher motor centres (the globus pallidus of the corpus striatum, the red nucleus, and the tectum of the mid-brain) and the cerebellum. Fibres from these three motor controlling centres descend (in the brain of birds, reptiles, amphibians, and fishes) to terminate in a structure homologous with the medial accessory olivary nucleus in the human brain, which is connected with the vermis of the cerebellum. In the mammalian brain, when motor functions are assumed by the cerebral cortex, the cortex becomes connected (Fig. 723) with the opposite cerebellar hemisphere by means of a new system of fibres— the middle peduncle. The assumption of motor control by the cerebral cortex, however, does not minimise the importance of the olive. On the contrary, a new olivary structure develops on the lateral side of the archaic olive, and in monkeys and men that lateral nucleus attains a large size and complexity so as to become much the largest element in the olivary complex. The newly developed lateral olive receives fibres (pallidorubro-olivary tract) from the globus pallidus and from the red nucleus, and each part of the rapidly expanding olivary lamina becomes connected with a definite part of the hemisphere of the cerebellum (Fig. 750, p. 863). As the cerebellum develops the olivary nucleus increases in size. The function of the cerebellum is now believed to be concerned with the control of muscular tone. Hence, as more highly skilled movements are made possible by the development of the cerebral cortex, the connexions of the globus pallidus and the red nucleus with the parts of the cerebellum which regulate the tone that is essential for the development of skill keep pace with the cerebral connexion of the corresponding cerebellar areas (see Gordon Holmes and Grainger Stewart, *Brain*, May 1908).

Decussation of the Pyramids and the Changes produced thereby.—As a series of successive transverse sections through the lower part of the medulla oblongata and the upper part of the spinal cord are examined, under the microscope, the most striking change which meets the eye is the decussation of the lateral cerebro-spinal tracts. From their position alongside the anterior median fissure of the medulla oblongata most of the fibres of the pyramid cross the median plane and, after passing through the anterior grey column, bend downwards in the lateral white column of the opposite side of the cord. Strands from the right lateral cerebro-spinal tract alternate with corresponding strands from the left side, and the interval between the bottom of the anterior median fissure and the grey matter surrounding the central canal becomes filled up with a great mass of inter-crossing bundles of fibres.

As a rule the medial three fourths of the pyramid are composed of fibres which, lower down in the opposite lateral white column of the spinal cord, form the lateral cerebro-spinal tract, and the lateral fourth of the pyramid proceeds downwards in the anterior white column of the same side as the anterior cerebro-spinal tract. A considerable amount of variation, however, occurs in the proportion of fibres allotted to the two tracts. Sometimes the lateral cerebro-spinal tract is much larger than usual, and the anterior tract correspondingly smaller; and occasionally the entire pyramid enters into the decussation. Further, it is not uncommon to meet with variations of an opposite kind which lead to an increase of the anterior cerebro-spinal tract at the expense of the lateral cerebro-spinal tract. Sometimes the decussation is asymmetrical, and the corresponding cerebro-spinal tracts are then unequal in size. One factor that often comes into play and causes asymmetry is the prolongation downwards into the pyramid on one side (usually the left) of some of the cerebro-pontine fibres. In such cases these fibres soon leave the pyramid and form the **circumolivary bundle**.

The variations indicated above receive an additional interest when viewed in the light of comparative anatomy. It would appear that only in man and the anthropoid apes is the decussation of the pyramids incomplete. According to Sherrington, the anterior cerebro-spinal tract in the anthropoid apes stands in connexion with the centre for the upper limb in the cerebral cortex. In man it must have other connexions as well, seeing that it is carried down for a considerable distance beyond the level of the spinal segments which give motor fibres to the upper limb.

As we have noted, the decussating pyramidal bundles pass through the anterior grey column, and cut it into two portions (Fig. 729). The basal part remains in position on the front and lateral side of the central canal, and forms part of the thick layer of grey matter which surrounds it. The detached head of the anterior column is set free; and from the large multipolar cells which lie in its midst some of the fibres of the anterior root of the first cervical nerve, and also some of the fibres of the accessory nerve, take origin.

In the medulla oblongata another effect of the decussation of the pyramids is seen in the submergence from the surface of the anterior intersegmental tract. While the decussation is going on, the intersegmental tract is thrust aside, and in the medulla oblongata it takes up its position as a flattened band on the lateral side of the pyramid (Fig. 729). Above the decussation, this strand lies close to the median plane behind the pyramid, where it is separated from its fellow of the opposite side by the median raphe alone (Fig. 730). In the upper part of the medulla oblongata it approaches still nearer to the dorsal surface and appears to form the greater part of a strand termed the medial longitudinal bundle (Figs. 732 and 733). The detached head of the anterior grey column of the cord, as it is traced upwards, clings closely to its original relationship with the anterior intersegmental tract. It is applied to the lateral side of that strand,

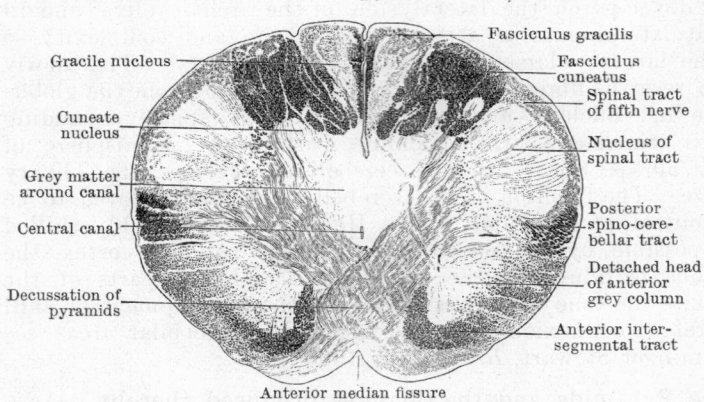

Fig. 729.—Transverse Section through the Lower End of the Medulla Oblongata of a full-time Fœtus.

Treated by the Weigert-Pal method. The grey matter is bleached white, and the tracts of medullated fibres are black.

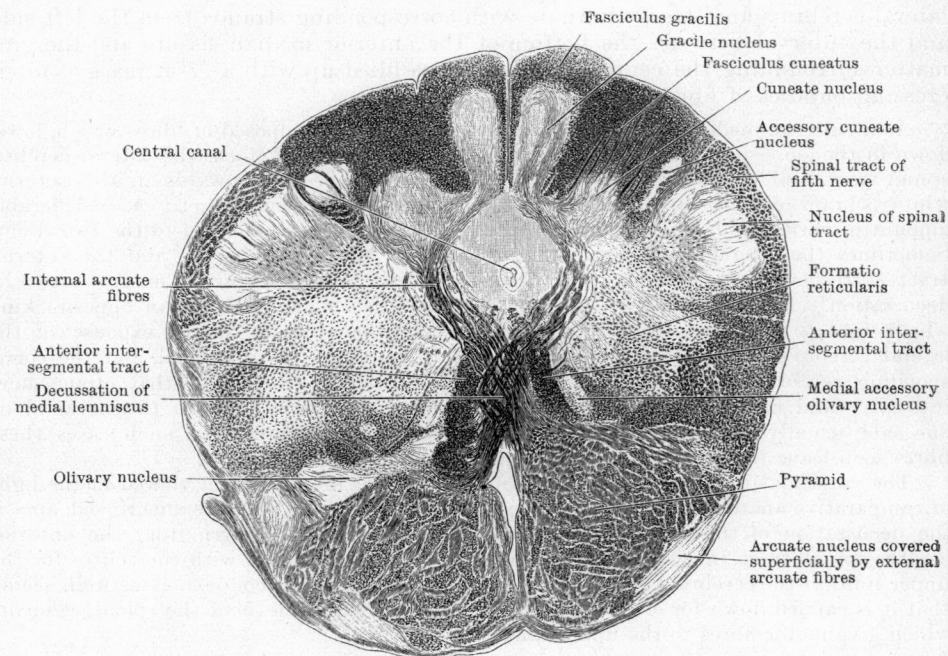

Fig. 730.—Section through an Adult Medulla Oblongata immediately above the Decussation of the Pyramids (Weigert-Pal specimen).

and, gradually becoming smaller, finally disappears at the level of the lower part of the olivary nucleus.

Cuneate and Gracile Fasciculi, with their Nuclei.—As the fasciculus gracilis and the fasciculus cuneatus of the the spinal cord are traced up into the medulla oblongata they seem to increase in bulk, and in transverse sections appear as wedge-shaped strands quite distinct from each other. They increase in width and lose considerably in depth, and consequently the transverse diameter of the area which they occupy becomes greater. As a result of that, and also owing to the removal of the lateral cerebro-spinal tract from the lateral white column of the cord immediately in front, the posterior grey column is gradually rotated forwards and comes to lie transversely and in the same straight line with its fellow of the opposite side (Figs. 729 and 730). The substantia gelatinosa, simultaneously, becomes increased in quantity and presents a horseshoe-shaped outline in transverse section. It clasps within its concavity the slightly reduced head of the posterior grey column, and forms with it a conspicuous circular mass of grey matter which lies close to the surface, producing a slight bulging called the **tubercle of the trigeminal nerve** (see p. 837). The basal portion of the posterior grey column remains posterior and lateral to the central canal, and forms a portion of the central grey mass of the closed part of the medulla oblongata ; but

very soon the neck of the column, which at that level is greatly reduced owing to the absence of entering posterior nerve-roots, is invaded by bundles of fibres which traverse it in different directions and convert it into a *formatio reticularis*. By that means the rounded head of the posterior grey column is cut off from the central grey matter, and from that point up-

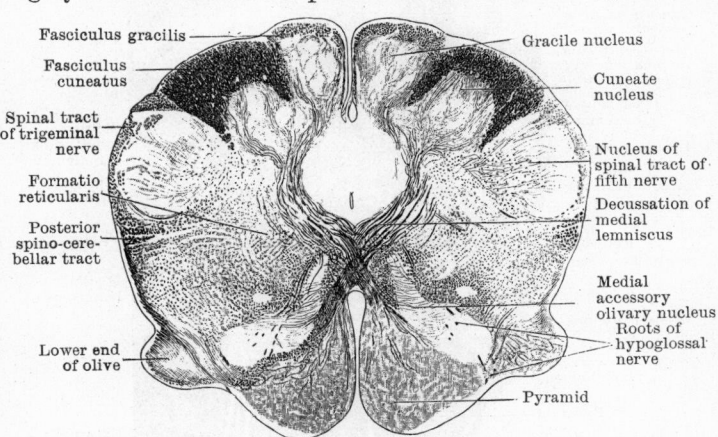

FIG. 731.—TRANSVERSE SECTION THROUGH A FŒTAL MEDULLA OBLONGATA IMMEDIATELY ABOVE THE DECUSSATION OF THE PYRAMIDS.
Treated by Weigert-Pal method.

wards it remains as an isolated grey column intimately associated with the spinal tract of the trigeminal nerve. It has, in fact, become the **nucleus of the spinal tract of the trigeminal nerve.**

The **gracile** and **cuneate nuclei** are seen in their most typical form in sections at the level of the decussation of the pyramids (Figs. 730 and 731).

The **gracile nucleus** appears as a relatively slender mass of grey matter in the interior of the fasciculus gracilis.

The **cuneate nucleus** is a direct offshoot from that part of the base of the posterior grey column which is preserved as a portion of the central grey mass. In transverse section it is seen to invade the deep part of the fasciculus cuneatus, and it gradually grows backwards into its substance. It differs in appearance from the gracile nucleus, because throughout its whole length the grey nucleus and the fibres of the strand are separated from each other by a sharp line of demarcation. A little higher up, a second and much smaller mass of grey matter termed the **accessory cuneate nucleus** appears in the fasciculus cuneatus, superficial to the main nucleus (Fig. 730).

As a series of sections is studied from below upwards, it will be noticed that the number of fibres in the gracile and cuneate fasciculi rapidly decreases, until, at the level of the gracile and cuneate tubercles, those eminences are composed almost entirely of the grey nuclei, covered by a thin layer of the few remaining fibres of the two fasciculi.

When the central canal of the medulla oblongata opens up into the fourth ventricle the gracile and cuneate nuclei are pushed laterally, and the gracile nucleus soon comes to an end ; but the cuneate nucleus extends upwards for a short distance farther, and terminates only when the inferior cerebellar peduncle [restiform body] begins to take definite shape.

Sensory Decussation [Decussatio Lemniscorum].—Immediately above the level of the decussation of the pyramids another decussation of fibres takes place in the substance of the medulla oblongata in the median plane behind the pyramids. That is the **decussation of the lemniscus medialis**, or the **sensory decussation**, so called in contradistinction to the term " motor decussation," which is sometimes applied to the decussation of the pyramids. The fibres which take part in this decussation are called **internal arcuate fibres**, and they are derived from the cells of the gracile and cuneate nuclei. From the deep aspects of those nuclei fibres

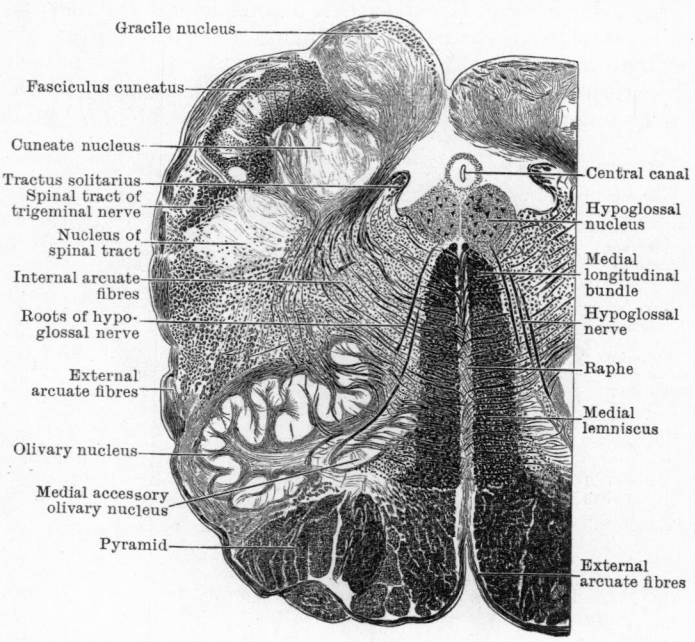

stream forwards and medially towards the median raphe, forming a series of concentric curves in the substance of the medulla oblongata. They cross the median plane and decussate with the corresponding fibres of the opposite side behind the pyramids. Having gained the opposite side some of them pass forwards to appear on the front of the medulla as anterior external arcuate fibres (p. 838), but most of them immediately turn upwards and form a conspicuous strand

Gracile nucleus

Fasciculus cuneatus

Cuneate nucleus

Tractus solitarius
Spinal tract of trigeminal nerve

Nucleus of spinal tract

Internal arcuate fibres

Roots of hypoglossal nerve

External arcuate fibres

Olivary nucleus

Medial accessory olivary nucleus

Pyramid

Central canal

Hypoglossal nucleus

Medial longitudinal bundle

Hypoglossal nerve

Raphe

Medial lemniscus

External arcuate fibres

FIG. 732.—TRANSVERSE SECTION THROUGH THE MEDULLA OBLONGATA AT THE LEVEL OF THE OLIVE.

of longitudinal fibres which ascends close to the median plane and is separated from its fellow of the opposite side by the median raphe alone. This strand is termed the **medial lemniscus**.

As we proceed up the medulla oblongata, the first internal arcuate fibres seen are coarse bundles which curve forwards in a narrow group round the central grey matter (Figs. 730 and 731). Soon, finer bundles are seen describing wider curves on the lateral side of the coarser group, until a very large part of each half of the medulla is seen to be traversed by these arcuate fasciculi (Fig. 732). The internal arcuate fibres decussate in the median plane with their fellows of the opposite side. They then change their direction and turn upwards, and the lemniscus, as already stated, takes form and gradually increases in volume as it ascends. That great and important tract is thus laid down between the pyramid and the medial longitudinal bundle, and, as a result, this bundle is pushed still farther backwards; therefore, when the lemniscus is fully established, the longitudinal bundle comes to lie immediately beneath the grey matter of the floor of the fourth ventricle (Fig. 733). But the lemniscus is not in direct contact with the longitudinal bundle, for a strand of fibres—the **tecto-spinal tract**—separates them, as well as fibres from sensory nuclei of the cranial nerves which are crossing the raphe to join the medial lemniscus (Fig. 733).

It is important to realise at this stage the full significance of the decussation of the lemniscus and to have a clear conception of the connexions of the fibres which take part in it. The posterior white column, which ends in the cuneate and gracile nuclei, is derived from the posterior roots of the spinal nerves. The lemniscus fibres therefore carry on the continuity of part of the posterior white column—the gracile and cuneate nuclei, which are thrown across its path in the lower part of the medulla oblongata, constituting merely a nodal interruption. At that point the lemniscus is transferred to the opposite side of the medulla oblongata. But it will be remembered that a large proportion of the fibres of the entering posterior nerve-roots of the spinal nerves end in connexion with the cells of the posterior grey column of the cord. It must not be supposed that the path represented by the latter fibres comes to a termination thereby; for, from the posterior column cells, other fibres arise which cross, in the white commissure, to the opposite side and proceed up the spinal cord to the lateral part of the medulla oblongata. Those fibres constitute the **spino-thalamic tracts** already referred to. *The practical bearing of this is that, owing to the crossing of the*

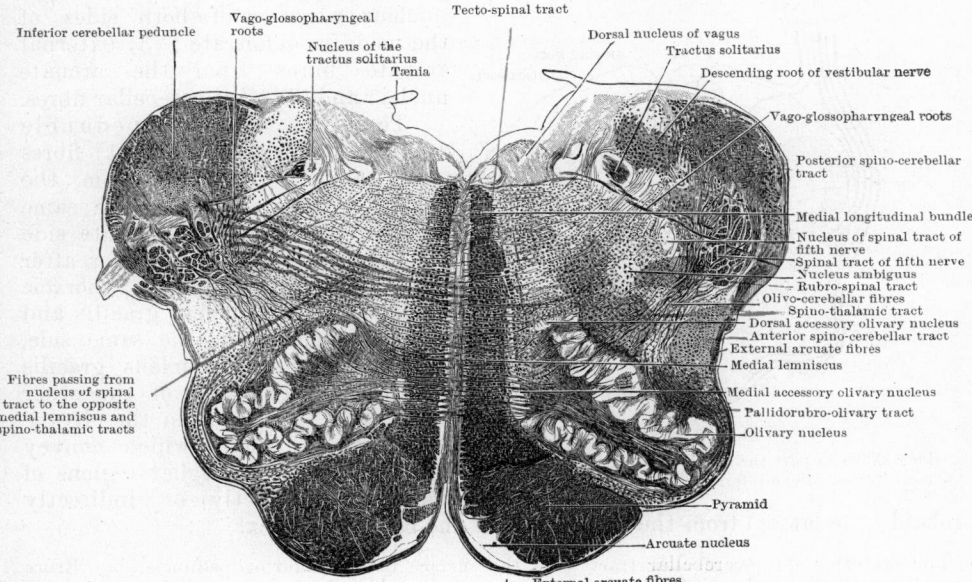

FIG. 733.—TRANSVERSE SECTION AT THE LEVEL OF THE MIDDLE OF THE OLIVE.

The floor of the fourth ventricle is seen, and it will be noticed that the inferior cerebellar peduncles have now taken definite shape. Some of the descending tracts in red ; ascending tracts in blue.

medial lemniscus and lower down of the spinothalamic fibres, unilateral lesions of the medulla oblongata are apt to produce complete hemi-anæsthesia ; whilst unilateral lesions of the spinal cord produce only partial hemi-anæsthesia.

The pyramid forms a massive tract in front of and quite distinct from the medial lemniscus. The medial lemniscus, the tecto-spinal tract, and the medial longitudinal bundle are, in the first instance, not marked off from each other. They appear as a broad flattened band applied to the raphe with its posterior edge in contact with the grey matter on the floor of the fourth ventricle, and the anterior edge with the pyramid, but in the upper part of the medulla the lemniscus and medial longitudinal bundle begin to draw asunder, and to grow denser, making the intervening tecto-spinal tract more distinct (Fig. 733).

The **medial longitudinal bundle** occupies a position corresponding to that occupied in the spinal cord by the anterior intersegmental tract, with which it appears to be continuous. As they are followed upwards these fibres are thrust back by the two decussations: the lower decussation pushing them behind the pyramids, and the upper decussation displacing them still farther backwards to a position behind the medial lemniscus. The bundle consists of a heterogeneous collection of fibres, ascending and descending, which link together the nuclei at different levels in the brain-stem. Its most important element consists of fibres from the vestibular nucleus proceeding to motor nuclei, in particular those of the third, fourth, sixth and eleventh cranial nerves of both sides.

Inferior Cerebellar Peduncle [Corpus Restiforme].—The gracile and cuneate nuclei gradually give place to the **inferior peduncle** in the upper part of the medulla oblongata. Fibres from various quarters converge to form that great strand. It first takes shape as a thin superficial layer of longitudinal fibres which are gathered together immediately lateral to the cuneate nucleus; but after that nucleus has come to an end, and as the upper part of the medulla oblongata is reached, the inferior peduncle is seen to have grown into a massive strand which presents a kidney-shaped or an oval outline on transverse section (Fig. 733); and it ultimately enters the white central core of the cerebellum. The principal fibres which build up this peduncle are the following: (1) the posterior spino-cerebellar tract, (2) external arcuate fibres from the nucleus gracilis and nucleus cuneatus of both sides of the medulla oblongata; (3) external arcuate fibres from the arcuate nuclei; and (4) olivo-cerebellar fibres.

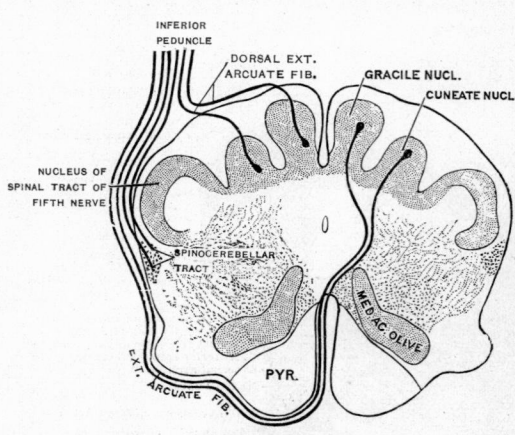

INFERIOR PEDUNCLE
DORSAL EXT. ARCUATE FIB.
GRACILE NUCL.
CUNEATE NUCL.
NUCLEUS OF SPINAL TRACT OF FIFTH NERVE
SPINOCEREBELLAR TRACT
MED. AC. OLIVE
EXT. ARCUATE FIB.
PYR.

FIG. 734.—DIAGRAM,
which shows in part the fibres which enter into the constitution of the inferior cerebellar peduncle.

Thus, the inferior peduncle conveys to the cerebellum (1) fibres that conduct impulses from the posterior spinal roots of the same side and also from the opposite side of the spinal cord, the former after being interrupted in the thoracic nucleus and the nucleus gracilis and nucleus cuneatus of the same side, the latter in the nucleus gracilis and nucleus cuneatus of the other side; and (2) fibres from the olivary and arcuate nuclei which convey impulses from the higher regions of the brain, directly or indirectly (probably the latter) from the motor area of the cerebral cortex.

The posterior spino-cerebellar tract joins the surface of the inferior peduncle, but Bruce showed that its fibres ultimately lie in the centre of the peduncle, forming as it were its core, and that, in the cerebellum, they can be traced to the superior vermis.

Formatio Reticularis.—Behind the olive and the pyramid is the **formatio reticularis.** In the medulla oblongata it occupies a position which, to a large extent, corresponds with that of the lateral white column in the spinal cord. In transverse section it appears as an extensive area divided into a lateral and a medial field by the roots of the hypoglossal nerve as they traverse the substance of the medulla oblongata to reach the surface. In the lateral portion, which lies behind the olive, a considerable quantity of grey matter, continuous with that in the spinal cord, is present in the reticular formation; it is therefore called the **formatio reticularis grisea.** In the medial part, which lies behind the pyramid, the grey matter is extremely scanty, and the reticular matter here is termed the **formatio reticularis alba.**

The nerve-fibres which traverse the formatio reticularis run both in a transverse and in a longitudinal direction. The **transverse fibres** are the internal arcuate and olivo-cerebellar fibres. The **longitudinal fibres** are derived from different sources in the two fields. In the formatio grisea they represent to a large extent the fibres of the lateral white column of the cord, after the removal of the posterior spino-cerebellar and the lateral cerebro-spinal tracts. They consist, therefore, of the fibres of the rubro-spinal, pallidorubro-olivary, spino-thalamic, and anterior spino-cerebellar tracts of the spinal cord. In the formatio alba the longitudinal fibres are the medial lemniscus, the tecto-spinal tract, and the medial longitudinal bundle, all of which have been described already.

Central Canal and the Grey Matter which surrounds it.—The central canal, as it proceeds upwards through the lower half of the medulla, is gradually forced backwards, owing to the accumulation of fibres in front of it. (Moreover, the posterior, cleft-like part of the cavity of the fœtal neural tube which becomes obliterated in the spinal cord by the fusion of its walls, remains patent in the medulla oblongata. Hence the central canal in the closed part of the medulla oblongata extends backwards to the roof-plate.) First the decussation of the pyramids and then the sensory decussation tend to push it backwards; and the formation of the longitudinal strands in which those intercrossings result (viz. the pyramid and the medial lemniscus), together with the continuation upwards of the anterior intersegmental tract, leads to a great increase in the amount of tissue which separates it from the anterior surface of the medulla oblongata. The canal is surrounded by a thick layer of grey matter which is continuous with the basal portions of the anterior and posterior grey columns of the cord. That central grey matter is sharply defined on each side by the internal arcuate fibres as they curve forwards and medially around it. Finally, the central canal opens, in the upper part of the medulla oblongata, into the cavity of the fourth ventricle. The central mass of grey matter which surrounds the canal is now spread out in a thick layer on the floor of the fourth ventricle, and in such a manner that the portion which corresponds to the basal part of the anterior grey column is close to the median plane, whilst the part which represents the base of the posterior grey column occupies a more lateral position. It is important to note this because the nucleus of origin of the hypoglossal nerve is placed in the medial part of the floor, whilst the nuclei of termination of the afferent fibres of the vagus, glosso-pharyngeal, and auditory nerves lie in the lateral part of the floor.

Three Areas of Flechsig.—In transverse sections through the upper part of the medulla oblongata, the root-fibres of the hypoglossal and vagus nerves are seen traversing its substance. The nucleus of origin of the hypoglossal is placed in the grey matter of the floor of the fourth ventricle close to the median plane; the nucleus of the vagus is situated immediately to the lateral side of the hypoglossal nucleus. From those nuclei the root-bundles of the two nerves, passing forwards, diverge from each other and subdivide the substance of the medulla, as seen in transverse section, into the three areas of Flechsig, viz. an anterior, a lateral, and a posterior.

The **anterior area**, which is bounded medially by the median raphe and laterally by the hypoglossal roots, contains: (*a*) the pyramid; (*b*) the medial lemniscus; (*c*) the tecto-spinal tract; (*d*) the medial longitudinal bundle; (*e*) the medial accessory olivary nucleus; (*f*) the arcuate nucleus.

The **lateral area** lies between the root fibres of the hypoglossal and those of the vagus. It contains: (*a*) the olivary nucleus; (*b*) the dorsal accessory olivary nucleus; (*c*) the nucleus ambiguus; (*d*) the splanchnic efferent nucleus of the vagus and glosso-pharyngeal nerves; (*e*) the formatio reticularis grisea.

The **posterior area** is situated behind the vagus roots, and within its limits are seen: (1) the inferior cerebellar peduncle; (2) the upper part of the cuneate nucleus; (3) to the medial side of that a crowd of transversely cut bundles of fibres, loosely arranged and forming the descending root of the vestibular nerve; (4) close to them, but placed more deeply, a round, compact, and very conspicuous bundle of transversely cut fibres, viz. the tractus solitarius; (5) a large bundle—the spinal tract of the trigeminal nerve—close to the lateral side of its nucleus, which is composed of substantia gelatinosa.

INTERNAL STRUCTURE OF PONS

When transverse sections are made through the pons, it is seen to be composed of a basilar part and a dorsal part. The dorsal part is the upward prolongation of the medulla oblongata, exclusive of the pyramids, which are drawn forward into the basilar part.

Basilar Part of Pons.—This constitutes the chief bulk of the pons. It is composed of: (1) **transverse fibres** arranged in coarse bundles; (2) **longitudinal fibres**, gathered together in massive bundles; and (3) a large amount of grey matter, termed the **nuclei pontis**, which fills up the interstices between the inter-secting bundles of fibres.

The **longitudinal bundles**, to a large extent, consist of the same fibres which, lower down, are gathered together in the two pyramids of the medulla oblongata. When the pyramids are traced upwards into the pons they are first a pair of compact bundles, and then are broken up by the transverse fibres of the pons into smaller bundles which are spread out over a wider area. At the upper border of the pons they again come together and form a pair of solid strands, each of which is continuous with the middle part of the corresponding basis pedunculi. Added to these bundles of the pyramid, there are twice as many other fibres that enter the pons from the basis pedunculi to terminate in the nuclei pontis.

The **transverse fibres** are placed in front of the pyramidal bundles at the lower border of the pons. Farther up they increase in number, and many are seen

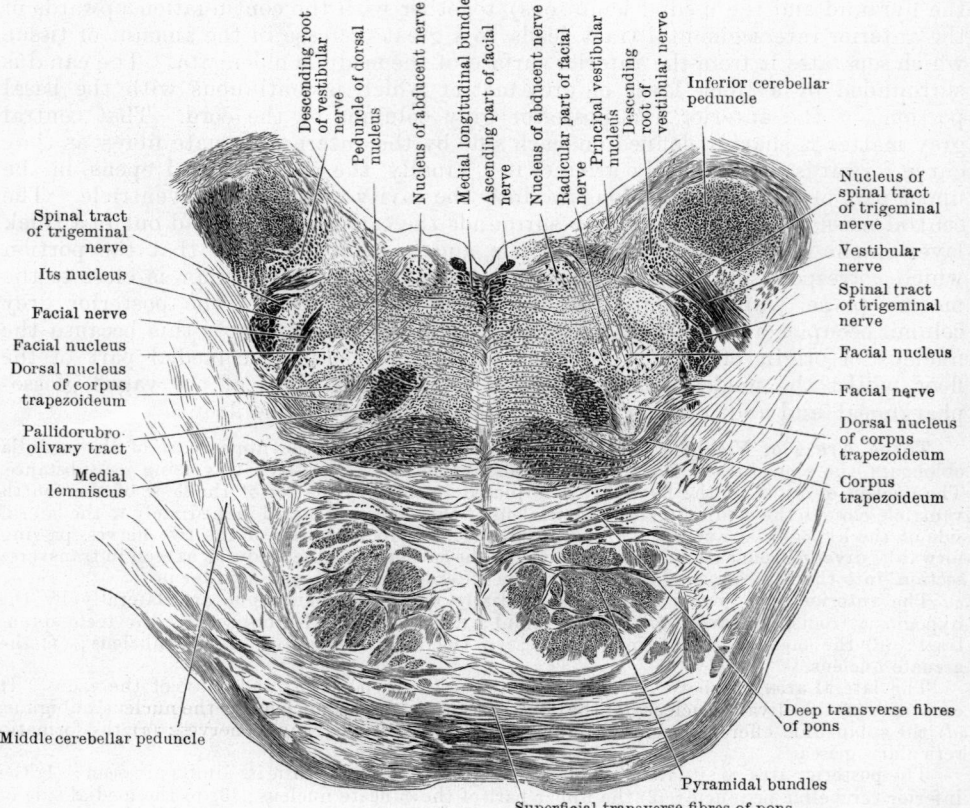

FIG. 735.—SECTION THROUGH THE LOWEST PART OF THE PONS.

breaking through the pyramids and also passing behind them. Laterally, these transverse fibres are collected together into one compact mass which enters the white core of the cerebellum as the **middle cerebellar peduncle.** At the median plane the transverse fibres of the two sides form a coarse decussation.

There is some analogy between the pyramidal portions of the medulla oblongata and the basilar part of the pons. In the medulla oblongata fine external arcuate fibres, on their way to the surface, pass through the pyramids; other external arcuate fibres sweep over the surface of the pyramids. These resemble the transverse fibres of the pons, and, like them, reach the cerebellum—although by a different route, viz. the inferior peduncle. The nuclei pontis are represented also in the pyramidal part of the medulla oblongata by the arcuate nuclei, which are covered over by the external arcuate fibres, and even tend to penetrate into the pyramids. These arcuate nuclei, as already pointed out, are continuous with the nuclei pontis.

Connexions of the Longitudinal and Transverse Fibres.—When a transverse section through the upper part of the pons is compared with one close to its lower border, it becomes at once apparent that the numerous scattered bundles of longitudinal fibres which enter the basilar part of the pons from above, if brought together into one tract, would form a strand very much larger than the two pyramids. The reason is this: The majority of the fibres of the basis pedunculi—those forming its lateral and medial parts—

are **cortico-pontine fibres**; they arise in the cerebral cortex and end in the nuclei pontis. The pyramidal fibres, which occupy the intermediate part of the basis pedunculi, also suffer loss when they descend into the pons because some of them end in the pons by synapsing with the cells of the motor nuclei of the trigeminal, abducent, and facial nerves; but that accounts for only a very small part of the difference between the bulk of the basis and that of the pyramid.

The transverse fibres take origin as axons of the cells of the nuclei pontis. Crossing the median plane, they enter the middle peduncle of the opposite side, and thus reach the cerebellar cortex, where they end in ramifications around certain of the cortical cells. Some authorities believe that there are also fibres passing in the opposite direction, *i.e.* from the cerebellum to the nuclei pontis; but there is some doubt concerning the existence of any such fibres. The middle peduncle thus may contain both efferent and afferent cerebellar fibres; but no fibres pass continuously through the pons from one middle peduncle into the other.

Certain of the transverse fibres of the pons turn backwards and enter the dorsal part of the pons, but the precise connexions of those are doubtful.

Corpus Trapezoideum.—This name is applied to a group of transverse fibres which traverse the lower part of the pons (Fig. 735). They are quite distinct from those which have been just described as entering the middle peduncle, and they lie in the boundary between the dorsal and basilar parts of the pons, but encroaching considerably into the ground of the former. They arise from the cells of the terminal nuclei of the cochlear nerve, and constitute a tract which establishes certain central connexions for that nerve. They will be more fully described when we treat of the cerebral connexions of the auditory nerve.

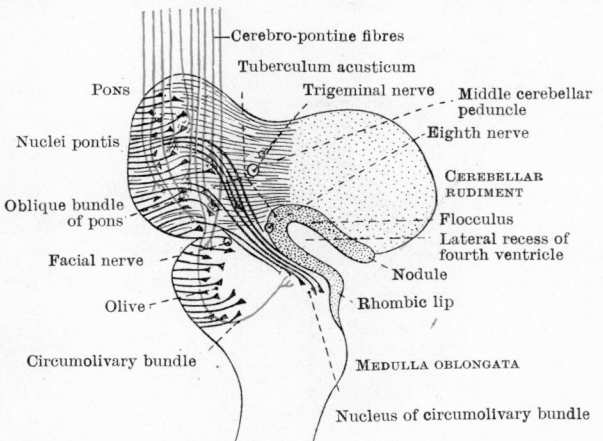

FIG. 736.—DIAGRAM OF THE LEFT LATERAL ASPECT OF THE FŒTAL RHOMBENCEPHALON REPRESENTING SOME OF THE CELL GROUPS AND FIBRE TRACTS.

Dorsal Part of the Pons.—On the dorsal surface of the pons there is spread a thick layer of grey matter, covered with ependyma, which forms the floor of the upper or pontine part of the fourth ventricle. Beneath that the median raphe of the medulla oblongata is continued up into the pons, so as to divide its dorsal part into symmetrical halves.

In the *lowest part of the pons* the inferior cerebellar peduncle is placed on the lateral side of the dorsal part (Fig. 735). In transverse sections through the pons it appears as a large, massive oval strand of fibres which inclines backwards into the cerebellum, and thus leaves the pons. Between the inferior peduncle and the median raphe the dorsal part of the pons is composed of formatio reticularis, continuous with the same material in the medulla oblongata. Thus, transverse fibres, curving in towards the raphe, and also longitudinal fibres, are seen breaking through a mass of grey matter which occupies the interstices of the intersecting fibres. To the naked eye the formatio reticularis appears uniformly grey, but its constituent parts are revealed by low powers of the microscope in properly stained and prepared specimens. Embedded in the formatio reticularis are various clumps of compact grey matter and certain definite strands of fibres. Those we shall describe as we pass from the inferior peduncle towards the median raphe.

(1) **Spinal Tract of Trigeminal Nerve and its Nucleus.**—Close to the medial side of the inferior peduncle, but separated from it by the vestibular nerve as it proceeds backwards through the pons, is seen a large crescentic group of coarse

bundles of fibres. That is the spinal tract of the trigeminal nerve; and applied to its medial, concave side there is a small mass of grey matter which is the direct continuation upwards of the substantia gelatinosa.

(2) The **nucleus of the motor root of the facial nerve** comes next. It is a conspicuous, obliquely placed, ovoid clump of grey matter that lies close to the corpus trapezoideum. The root-fibres of the facial nerve stream backwards and medially from it towards the floor of the fourth ventricle. Passing forwards between that nucleus and the trigeminal sensory nucleus a solid nerve-bundle may

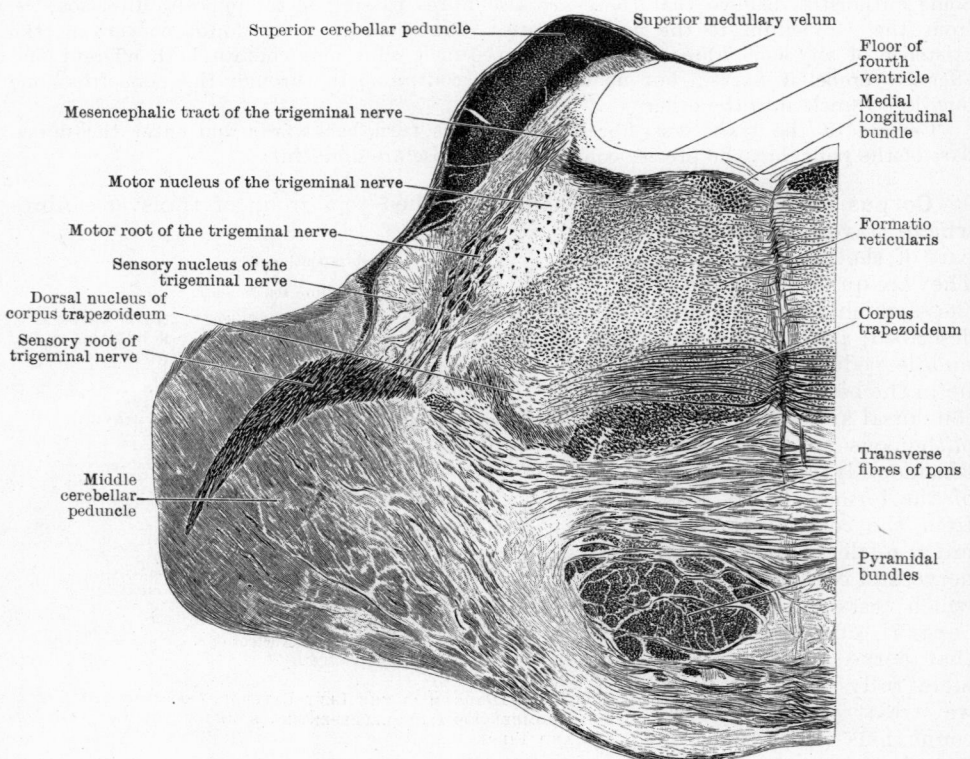

FIG. 737.—TRANSVERSE SECTION THROUGH PONS AT THE LEVEL OF THE TRIGEMINAL NUCLEI.

be observed. This is the facial nerve, traversing the pons towards its place of emergence from the brain.

(3) Immediately medial to the facial nucleus, but partly sunk in the corpus trapezoideum, is the **dorsal nucleus of the corpus trapezoideum** [nucleus olivaris superior], and some of the fibres of the corpus may be observed penetrating into its substance. In man, it is a very small mass of grey matter. In sections through the part of the pons where it attains its greatest size, it appears in the form of two, or it may be three, small isolated masses. It is intimately connected with the auditory fibres, and establishes manifold connexions between them and the nuclei of other nerves. A dense group of longitudinal fibres lies behind and medial to it; they constitute the **pallidorubro-olivary tract**, to which we have already referred in discussing the olivary nucleus (Fig. 735).

(4) The **medial longitudinal bundle** and the **medial lemniscus** come next. As they proceed upwards through the pons, they occupy the same relative position as in the medulla oblongata. They are placed close to the median raphe and are separated from each other by the **tecto-spinal tract**. The **medial longitudinal bundle** lies immediately under cover of the grey matter of the floor of the fourth ventricle. The **medial lemniscus** is placed close to the corpus trapezoideum, many of whose fibres traverse it as they pass towards the median plane.

(5) The **nucleus of the abducent nerve** also forms a conspicuous object in sections through the lower part of the pons. It is a round mass of grey matter situated close to the lateral side of the medial longitudinal bundle, and immediately under cover of the grey matter of the floor of the fourth ventricle. From its medial side numerous root-bundles of the abducent nerve pass out and proceed forwards between the medial lemniscus and the dorsal nucleus of the corpus trapezoideum. They occupy in the pons, therefore, a position similar to that occupied by the hypoglossal root-fibres in the medulla oblongata.

Up to the present only the lowest part of the dorsal portion of the pons has been described. As we proceed upwards and gain a point *above the level of the corpus trapezoidum*, the floor of the ventricle becomes narrower, the medial lemniscus becomes markedly increased in size by the addition of the fibres of the spino-thalamic tracts, but many of the structures that have attracted attention lower down gradually disappear, while other objects make their appearance in the formatio reticularis.

The **superior cerebellar peduncle** is the group of fibres proceeding from the nuclei

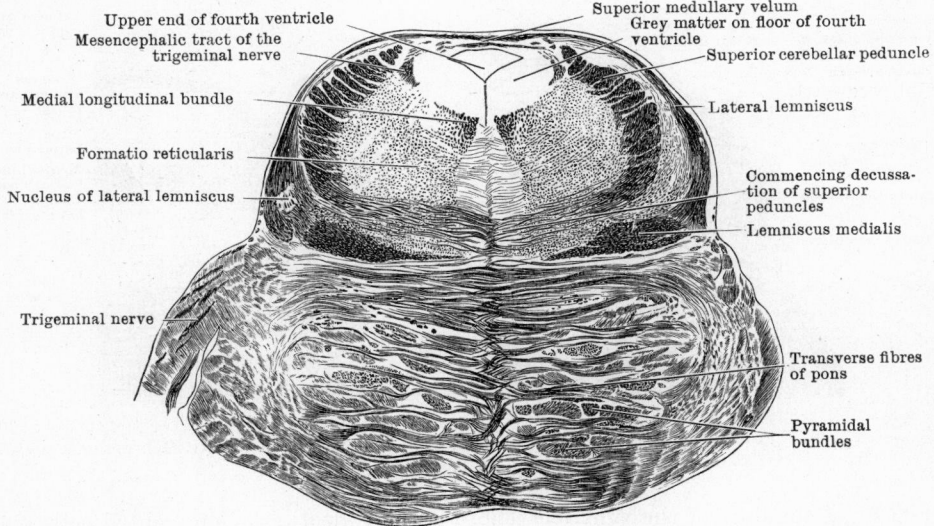

Upper end of fourth ventricle
Mesencephalic tract of the trigeminal nerve
Superior medullary velum
Grey matter on floor of fourth ventricle
Superior cerebellar peduncle
Medial longitudinal bundle
Lateral lemniscus
Formatio reticularis
Nucleus of lateral lemniscus
Commencing decussation of superior peduncles
Lemniscus medialis
Trigeminal nerve
Transverse fibres of pons
Pyramidal bundles

FIG. 738.—SECTION THROUGH PONS, ABOVE THE LEVEL OF THE TRIGEMINAL NUCLEI.

of the cerebellum to the red nucleus in the opposite side of the brain-stem. It is a very conspicuous object in sections through the middle and upper parts of the pons. In transverse section it has a semilunar outline, and as it emerges from the cerebellum it lies immediately on the lateral side of the fourth ventricle, towards which its concave aspect is turned (Fig. 738). Its dorsal border is joined with the opposite peduncle by the thin lamina of white matter termed the *superior medullary velum*, whilst its ventral border is sunk to a small extent in the dorsal part of the pons. As it is traced upwards it sinks deeper and deeper into the pons until it becomes completely submerged, with the exception of the dorsal border. It now lies on the lateral side of the reticular formation of the pons, and that position it maintains until the mid brain is reached (Fig. 738).

About *half-way up the pons* the nuclei of the trigeminal nerve mark a very important stage in its dorsal portion. These nuclei are two in number on each side, viz. a large oval terminal nucleus for certain of the sensory fibres of the nerve and a nucleus of origin, equally conspicuous, for certain of the motor fibres (Fig. 737). The **sensory nucleus** lies close to the lateral surface of the dorsal portion of the pons. The **motor nucleus** is placed on the medial side of the sensory nucleus, but rather nearer the dorsal surface of the pons. At this level the spinal tract of the trigeminal nerve begins by the bending downwards of the fibres of the sensory portion. The sensory and motor roots of the fifth nerve traverse the basilar part of the pons on their way to and from the nuclei.

Above the level of the nuclei of the trigeminal nerve a new tract of fibres comes into view. It is the **mesencephalic tract** of the trigeminal nerves, as it descends towards the rest of the nerve. It is a small bundle of nerve-fibres, semilunar in cross section, which lies close to the medial side of the superior peduncle and on the lateral and deep aspect of the grey matter on the floor of the fourth ventricle (Figs. 737 and 739). It consists of *proprioceptive* fibres from the muscles of mastication—*i.e.* afferent fibres which convey to the central nervous system, impulses set up in muscle-spindles, end-organs of tendons and the nerve-endings in relation to joints. It probably contains fibres from the extrinsic muscles of the eyeball also.

On a slightly deeper plane than the mesencephalic tract of the fifth nerve, between it and the medial longitudinal bundle, and in close relation to the grey

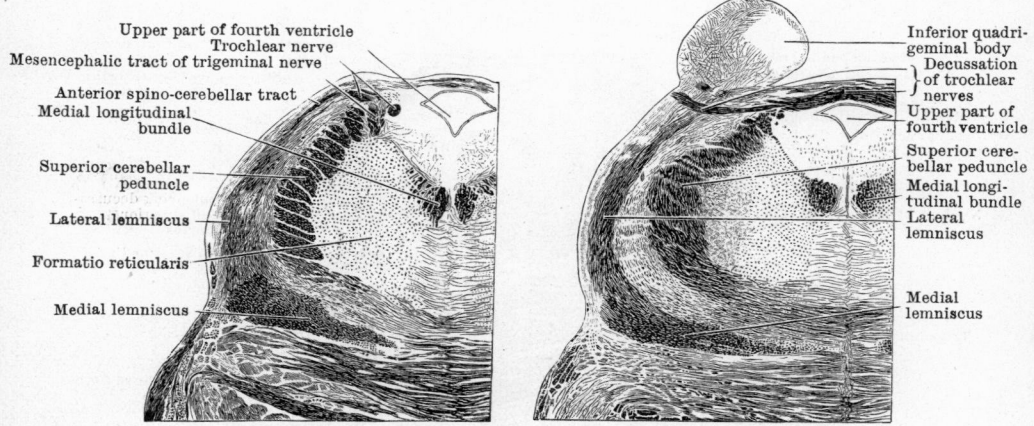

FIG. 739.—Sections through Dorsal Part of Pons close to the Mid-brain.
A is at a slightly lower level than B.

matter of the floor of the ventricle, there is the collection of pigmented cells which constitutes the **substantia ferruginea**.

The **medial longitudinal bundle**, as it is traced upwards, maintains the same position throughout, and as it ascends it becomes more clearly mapped out as a definite and distinct tract. It lies close to the median raphe, and immediately subjacent to the grey matter of the floor of the fourth ventricle.

The **medial lemniscus**, as it ascends, undergoes striking changes in shape. In the lower portion of the pons its fibres, which in the medulla oblongata are spread out along the side of the median raphe, are collected together in the form of a loose bundle which occupies a wide field immediately behind the basilar portion of the pons. As it proceeds up, the fibres spread out laterally until a compact ribbon-like layer is formed which ascends between the dorsal and ventral parts of the pons (Figs. 738 and 739).

Above the level of the trigeminal nuclei another flattened layer of fibres comes into view to the lateral side of the medial lemniscus. To it the name of **lateral lemniscus** is given. Its fibres spread laterally and backwards, and finally take up a position on the lateral surface of the superior cerebellar peduncle. In the angle between the medial and lateral lemnisci a little knot of compact grey matter, termed the **nucleus of the lateral lemniscus**, comes into view (Fig. 739). It gives origin to many of the fibres of the lateral lemniscus, and it appears to be in more or less direct continuity with the dorsal nucleus of the trapezoid body.

CEREBELLUM

The **cerebellum** forms the largest subdivision of the hind-brain. It lies behind the pons and medulla oblongata, and occupies the greater part of the

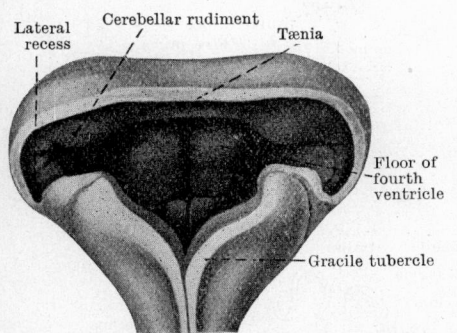

FIG. 740.—DORSAL ASPECT OF THE RHOMB-ENCEPHALON IN A HUMAN EMBRYO.

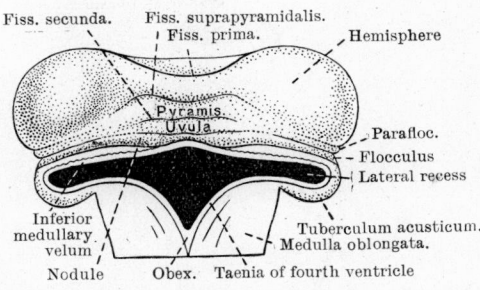

FIG. 741.—THE DORSAL ASPECT OF A FŒTAL (FOURTH MONTH) CEREBELLUM, MEDULLA OBLONGATA AND FOURTH VENTRICLE.

posterior cranial fossa. Above it lies the tentorium cerebelli, which separates it from the posterior part of the cerebral hemispheres. Laterally the cerebellum is related to the temporal bone; behind and below, it occupies a deep fossa of the occipital bone. In the dura mater of the posterior fossa there are various venous sinuses which are related to the cerebellum (Fig. 832, p. 948).

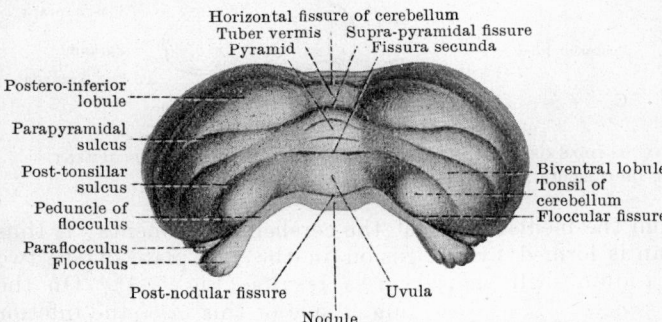

FIG. 742.—INFERIOR SURFACE OF THE CEREBELLUM OF A HUMAN FŒTUS WHICH HAS REACHED THE END OF THE FIFTH MONTH OF DEVELOPMENT.

The whole organ is divisible for descriptive purposes into a pair of **hemispheres** united by a smaller median part called the **vermis** (Fig. 747). When viewed from above, the vermis projects as a low ridge but is not clearly separable from the hemispheres. Inferiorly (Fig. 748) the vermis lies in a deep gutter—**the vallecula**—between

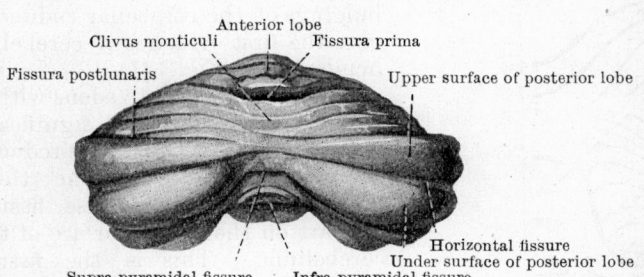

FIG. 743.—CEREBELLUM OF A HUMAN FŒTUS WHICH HAS REACHED THE END OF THE FIFTH MONTH OF DEVELOPMENT. Viewed from above and behind.

the hemispheres and is more clearly demarcated from them. Anteriorly the cerebellum, as it faces the pons and medulla, is related to the fourth ventricle of the brain (Fig. 749).

DEVELOPMENT AND SUBDIVISION OF CEREBELLUM

It has been shown that the cerebellum is formed from two distinct rudiments, each derived from the posterior edge of the alar lamina close to the insertion of the eighth nerve. During the second month of intra-uterine life there is a rapid proliferation of the cells of the mantle layer of the cerebellar rudiments which thus becomes considerably thickened (Fig. 740).

The accentuation of the pontine flexure brings the cerebellar rudiments into the transverse direction. The roof plate that unites them becomes thickened by

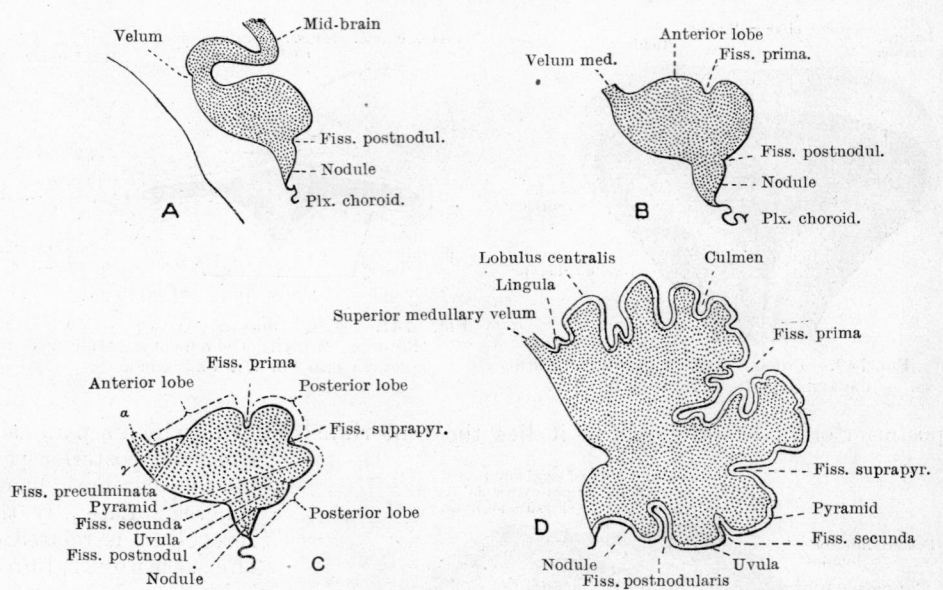

FIG. 744.—MEDIAN SAGITTAL SECTIONS OF FŒTAL CEREBELLA IN FOUR STAGES OF DEVELOPMENT.
A and B, third month ; C, fourth month ; D, fifth month.

immigrant neuroblasts from the medial parts of the cerebellar rudiments ; it thus comes about that one organ is formed by the fusion in the roof-plate of the two original rudiments, and a dumb-bell shaped mass results (Fig. 741). On the under side of this mass the inferior medullary velum and the choroid plexus of the fourth ventricle develop. In the third month, lateral bulgings of the cerebellar rudiment give the first evidence of cerebellar hemispheres (Fig. 741).

Of the many subdivisions within the cerebellum the most significant from all aspects is that produced towards the close of the third month when a transverse fissure appears on the upper surface of the cerebellum. This is the **fissura prima**. It cuts off a lozenge-shaped area in the front part of the cerebellum named the **anterior lobe**. The remaining and greater part of the organ behind the fissura prima is known as the **posterior lobe**.

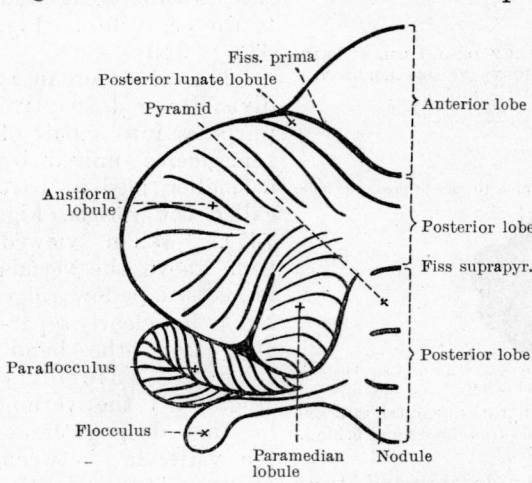

FIG. 745.—DIAGRAM OF LOBULATION OF LEFT HALF OF MAMMALIAN CEREBELLUM.

Secondary fissures appear in each of these lobes and many resulting insignificant subdivisions of the cerebellum have in the past received names which served to complicate rather than clarify the study of this organ.

It has been noted that the early cerebellum is a dumb-bell shaped mass, and to some extent this form persists, for the fully developed organ will be observed to consist of a pair of swollen lateral portions—the hemispheres—joined by the narrow, median part called the vermis. But such a distinction is of little value for other than descriptive purposes; each part—vermis and hemisphere—contributes to the formation of the main anterior and posterior lobes of the whole organ.

The **anterior lobe** consists ultimately of a median part belonging to the vermis —comprising the *lingula, central lobule,* and the *culmen* (Fig. 744, D)— together with right and left hemisphere components each consisting of two lesser parts known as the *ala* and the *anterior lunate lobule.* Medially, the ala is continuous with the central lobule of the vermis and the anterior lunate lobule with the culmen. Bounding the whole anterior lobe behind is the deep V-shaped cleft called the *fissura prima.*

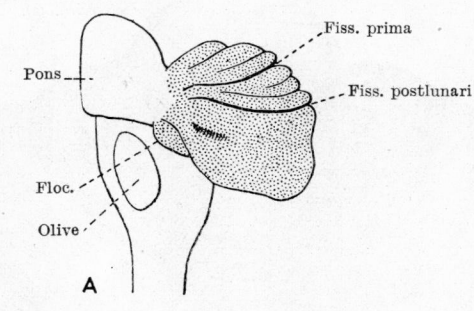

The **posterior lobe** is much larger than the anterior; it forms the postero-superior part of the cerebellum and the whole of its inferior surface. Like the anterior lobe, it consists of a median part belonging to the vermis and lateral parts belonging to the hemispheres. The median part consists of numerous small lobules, named in order from the fissura prima,

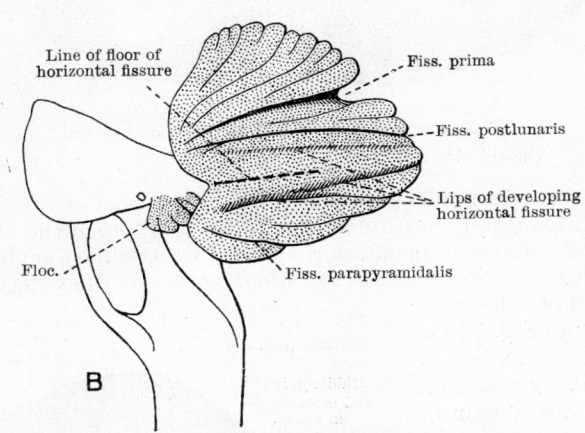

Fig. 746.—The Left Lateral Aspect of the Fœtal Rhombencephalon at the Fourth (A) and Fifth (B) Months.

The cerebellum is stippled.

lobulus clivi, lobulus folii, lobulus tuberis, the *pyramid,* the *uvula* and the *nodule* (Figs. 744 and 748). It will be noted that the four last-mentioned elements are on the inferior surface of the cerebellum and together form what is sometimes called the *inferior vermis.* The hemispheral components of the posterior lobe are massive and considerably subdivided. On the superior surface, a curved fissure (post-lunate fissure) (Fig. 746) separates the *posterior lunate lobule* in front from the *ansiform lobule* behind. The ansiform lobule extends round on to the inferior face where it is separated by the retro-tonsillar fissure from the tonsil. The *tonsil* is a curiously circumscribed mass that lies in the antero-medial part of the inferior face of the cerebellum. A deep fissure—the *horizontal fissure*—divides the right and left ansiform lobes into upper and lower parts. There is another small lobe—the *flocculus*—on the inferior face of the cerebellum and belonging to the posterior lobe. This structure is placed below the eighth nerve at the point where it enters the brain and has the lateral recess of the fourth ventricle in front of it. It is finely lobulated and connected to the cerebellum in front of the tonsil by a peduncle (Fig. 748). The peduncle contains afferent and efferent fibres that link the flocculus with other parts of the cerebellum and with the vestibular nuclei. Closely attached to the flocculus there is a very small vestigial structure—the *paraflocculus*—(Fig. 748). This never attains a large size in Man, but in most mammals its dimensions are considerable. In marine mammals its development is exuberant; and it is thought to be concerned with the regulation of tone in those muscles which control the tendency to roll in the lateral direction—that is, around the long axis of the body.

Roof of the Fourth Ventricle.—The most anterior and posterior parts of the cerebellum are approximated to form as it were a hilum, occupied in the middle

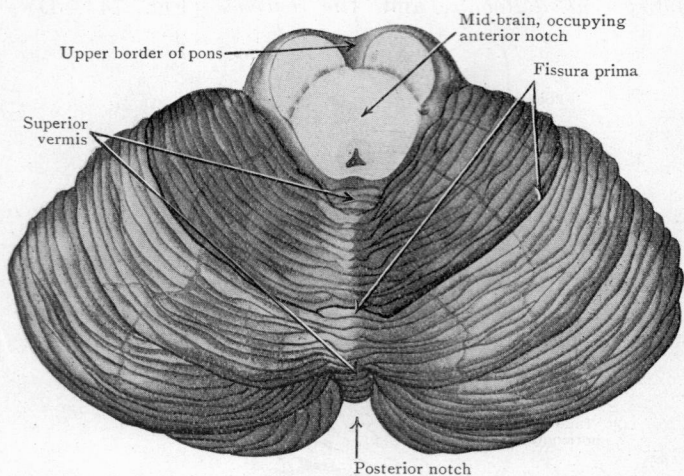

FIG. 747.—SUPERIOR SURFACE OF THE CEREBELLUM.
The anterior lobe is coloured blue, the posterior yellow.

by the tent-like fourth ventricle and on each side by the cerebellar peduncles (Figs. 744, D, and 749). This hilum is part of the **horizontal fissure**. The cerebellar substance forms only a small part of the roof of the fourth ventricle. Both above and below there are thin sheet-like structures, known as the superior and inferior medullary vela, which form part of the ventricular roof.

The **superior medullary velum** stretches between the superior cerebellar peduncles and roofs in the upper part of the fourth ventricle. It consists of white matter continuous with the white core of the vermis of the cerebellum, and is covered with ependyma on its ventricular surface. Dorsally, it is closely related superiorly to the trochlear nerves as they decussate, and inferiorly to the lingula of the cerebellum (Fig. 749).

The **inferior medullary vela** (Fig. 748) are a pair of exceedingly thin laminæ that lie at the sides of the nodule, hidden by the tonsils. They meet in a median ridge, and serve to connect the nodule with the flocculi of the two sides. They form, however, only a small part of the lower section of the tent-like roof of the fourth ven-tricle. The rest is composed of epen-

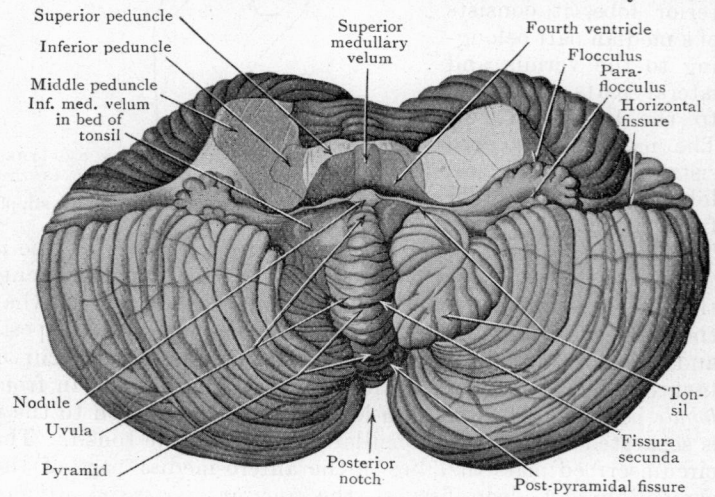

FIG. 748.—INFERIOR SURFACE OF THE CEREBELLUM.
The right tonsil has been removed so as to display more fully the inferior medullary velum. The anterior lobe is coloured blue, the posterior yellow.

dyma, covered with the vascular pia mater that enters into the formation of the choroid plexus of the fourth ventricle. At the lower end of the fourth ventricle the ependymal roof is deficient, and so is the pial layer. This aperture of com-munication between the ventricular system of the brain and the subarachnoid space is called the **median aperture of the fourth ventricle**. There are two other such aper-tures in this roof—one on each side in the ventrally drawn part at the extremity of the lateral recess. These are called the **lateral apertures of the fourth ventricle**.

The ependymal roof of the fourth ventricle becomes thickened at its attach-ment to the main mass of the medulla oblongata, and where the thickened strips of the two sides (*tæniæ*) come together at the low-est part of the roof they form a small semilunar lamina which stretches across between the inferior parts of the two gracile tubercles, and over-hangs the opening of the central canal. This is called the **obex** (Fig. 724, p. 840). A downwardly directed protru-sion of the ependy-mal roof is often found behind the obex.

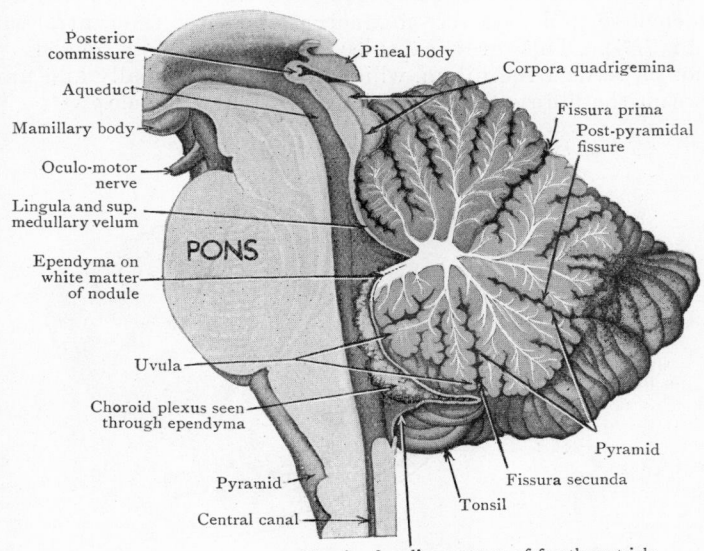

Fig. 749.—Median Section through Brain Stem and Cerebellum, show-ing the Arbor Vitæ of the Vermis and the Fourth Ventricle.

The anterior lobe of the cerebellum is coloured blue, the posterior yellow.

STRUCTURE AND CONNEXIONS OF CEREBELLUM

Arrangement of Grey and White Matter of Cerebellum. — The white matter of the cerebellum forms a solid compact mass in the interior, and over it is spread a continuous and uniform layer of grey matter. In each hemisphere the white central core is more bulky than in the vermis, in which the central white matter is reduced to a relatively thin bridge thrown across between the two hemispheres. When sagittal sections are made through the cerebellum, the grey matter on the surface stands out clearly from the white matter in the interior. Further, from all parts of the surface of the central core stout stems of white matter are seen projecting into the lobules of the cerebellum. From the sides of those white stems secondary branches proceed at various angles, and from those again tertiary branches are given off. Over the various lamellæ of white matter thus formed the grey cortex is spread, and the fissures on the surface show a corresponding arrangement, dividing up the organ into lobes, lobules, and folia. When the cerebellum is divided at right angles to the general direction of its fissures and folia, a highly arborescent appearance is presented by the cut surface. To this the term **arbor vitæ** is applied (Fig. 749).

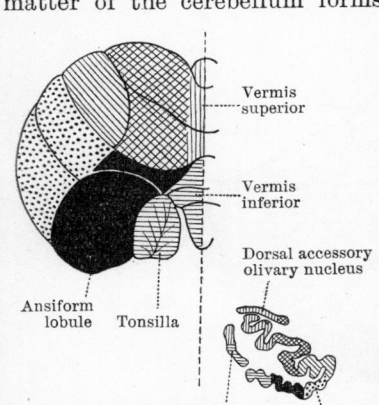

Fig. 750.—Diagram to indicate the Parts respectively of the Right Olivary Nucleus in the Medulla Oblongata and of the Left Half of the Cerebellum, which are linked together by Olivo-Cere-bellar Fibres. (After Gordon Holmes and Grainger Stewart.) (By permission of the Authors and of the Editor of *Brain*.)

Dentate Nucleus and other Nuclei in the White Matter of Cerebellum. —Embedded in the midst of the white matter which forms the central core of each hemisphere there is an isolated nucleus which presents a strong resemblance to the olivary nucleus of the medulla oblongata. It is called the **dentate nucleus,** and it consists of a corrugated lamina of grey matter folded on itself so as to enclose, in a flask-like manner, a portion of the central white matter (Figs. 751 and 753). This grey capsule is not completely closed. It presents an open mouth, termed the hilum, which is directed medially and upwards, and out of this stream the fibres of the superior cerebellar peduncle.

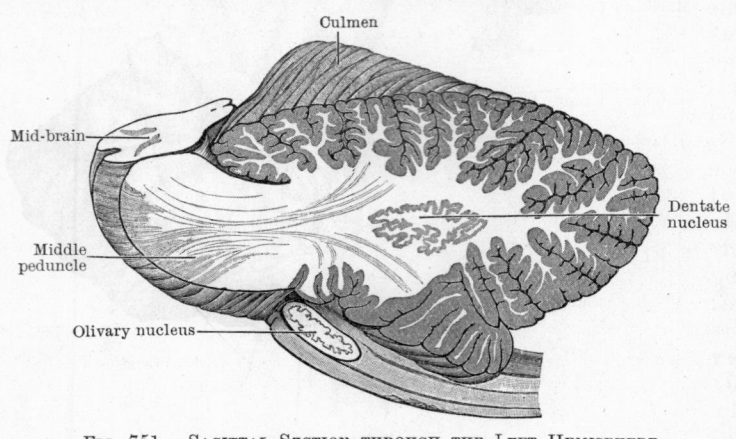

FIG. 751.—SAGITTAL SECTION THROUGH THE LEFT HEMISPHERE OF THE CEREBELLUM.

Showing the arbor vitæ and the dentate nucleus.

Three small additional masses of grey matter are present on each side of the median plane in the central white matter of the cerebellum. They are termed the nucleus emboliformis, the nucleus globosus, and the nucleus fastigii. The **nucleus emboliformis** is a small lamina of grey matter which lies just medial to the hilum of the dentate nucleus. The **nucleus globosus** lies medial to the nucleus emboliformis and on a slightly deeper horizontal plane. The **nucleus fastigii** or **roof nucleus** is placed in the white substance of the vermis close to the median plane and its fellow of the opposite side. It is, therefore, situated on the medial aspect of the nucleus globosus.

Cerebellar Peduncles.—These are three in number on each side, viz. the middle, the inferior, and the superior (Figs. 724, 753). The fibres of which

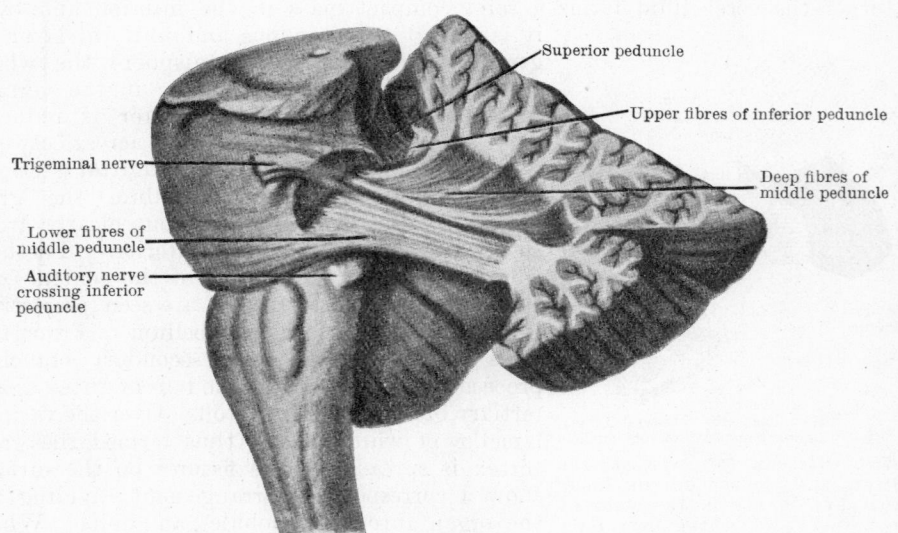

FIG. 752.—DISSECTION OF THE CEREBELLAR PEDUNCLES FROM THE SIDE TO SHOW THEIR RELATION TO EACH OTHER.

they are composed all enter or emerge from the white medullary centre of the cerebellum.

The **middle peduncle** [brachium pontis] is much the largest of the three and has already been described on pp. 854 and 855. It enters the cerebellar hemisphere on the lateral side of the other two peduncles. The lips of the anterior part of the horizontal fissure are separated widely to give it admission (Fig. 748). Within the cerebellar hemisphere its fibres are distributed in two great bundles. Of those, one, composed of the superficial fibres of the pons, radiates out in the lower part of the hemisphere; whilst the other, consisting of the deep transverse fibres of the pons, spreads out in the upper part of the hemisphere (Fig. 752).

The **inferior peduncle** [restiform body] ascends for a short distance on the dorsal surface of the pons and then turns sharply backwards to enter the cerebellum between the other two peduncles.

The **superior peduncle** [brachium conjunctivum], as it issues from the cerebellum, lies close to the medial side of the middle peduncle (Figs. 752, 753). Its further course upwards on the dorsum of the pons towards the inferior quadrigeminal body has been previously described (pp. 839 and 857).

Connexions established by the Peduncular Fibres.—The fibres of the **middle peduncle** represent the second stage of the connexion between the cerebral hemisphere

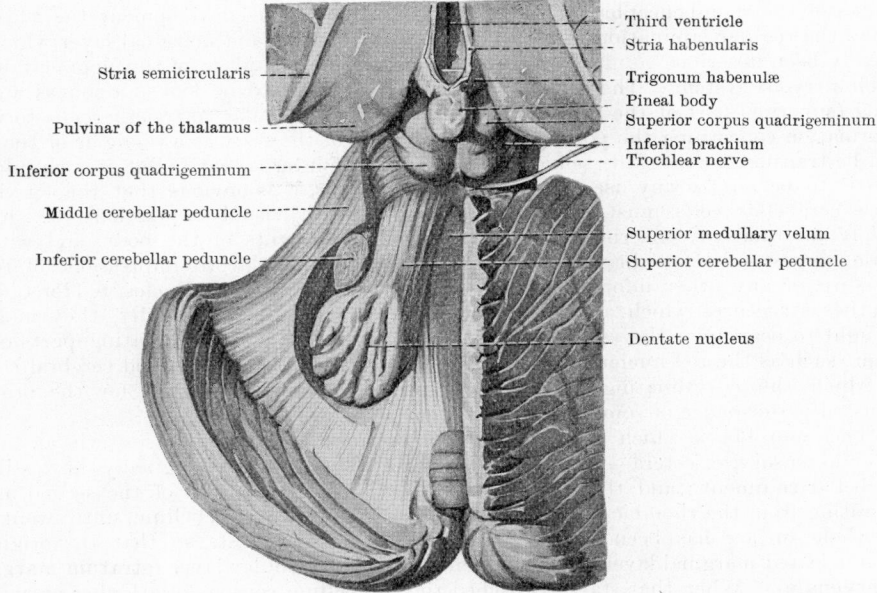

Stria semicircularis

Pulvinar of the thalamus

Inferior corpus quadrigeminum

Middle cerebellar peduncle

Inferior cerebellar peduncle

Third ventricle
Stria habenularis
Trigonum habenulæ
Pineal body
Superior corpus quadrigeminum
Inferior brachium
Trochlear nerve

Superior medullary velum
Superior cerebellar peduncle

Dentate nucleus

Fig. 753.—Dissection from above to show the Dentate Nucleus, the Cerebellar Peduncles and the Lateral Lemniscus.

of one side and the opposite cerebellar hemisphere. The connexions which they establish in the pons are described on p. 855.

The **inferior peduncle** also is composed of afferent fibres (see p. 852); only the more important connexions which they establish in the cerebellum can be touched on here. The principal afferent strand is the *posterior spino-cerebellar tract*. The fibres of this strand end in the cortex of the *superior vermis* on both sides of the median plane, but chiefly on the opposite side. The *olivo-cerebellar tract* is also afferent. It appears that its fibres end in connexion with cells in the cortex of both the vermis and hemisphere (Fig. 750), and also with cells in the dentate nucleus. The numerous *external arcuate fibres* which enter the peduncle establish connexions with cells in the cortex of the hemisphere and of the vermis.

The **superior peduncle** is an efferent tract: its fibres spring from the cells of the dentate nucleus and other nuclei of the cerebellum, and pass to the red nucleus and thalamus of the opposite side. According to Ramón y Cajal collateral branches springing from those fibres descend to the motor nuclei in the medulla oblongata and spinal cord.

There is, however, a bundle of fibres passing *downwards* alongside the superior peduncle from the tegmentum of the mid-brain and possibly from the thalamus: those fibres cross in the mid-brain and pass inferiorly to the cerebellum, in contact with the lateral margin of (or intermingled with) the fibres of the peduncle. They probably convey to the cerebellum fibres from the visual centres of the opposite side.

The **anterior spino-cerebellar tract** also enters the cerebellum alongside the emerging superior peduncle. It has been noticed in connexion with the lateral white column of the spinal cord (p. 828). The fibres which compose it are carried upwards through the formatio reticularis grisea of the medulla oblongata and the dorsal portion of the pons. In this part of its course the fibres are scattered and do not form a compact strand. Reaching the upper end of the pons the tract turns backwards across the superior peduncle, enters the superior medullary velum, and proceeds downwards in it into the cerebellum.

HISTOGENESIS AND MINUTE STRUCTURE OF CEREBELLUM

The developmental history of the cerebellum presents certain peculiar features which seem quite enigmatic unless considered from the point of view of the evolution of the connexions and functions of the organ. The cerebellum is derived from part of the alar lamina of the rhombencephalon, and at an early stage of its development the rudiment shows the regular lamination into ependyma, mantle layer, and marginal layer which has already been described as distinctive of the corresponding place of development in the whole nervous system. The cells of the mantle layer are to be looked upon as an out-lying (superior) part of the receptive nucleus of the vestibular nerve, the cells to which information concerning the position and movements of the body as a whole or of the head will be transmitted from the semicircular ducts of the internal ear. But, if such information is to be put to any use in influencing behaviour, it is obvious that the activity of those cerebellar cells must, firstly, be correlated with visual impressions, which also supply information concerning the position and movements of the body, and with all those nerves which are bringing into the brain and spinal cord impressions of touch, pressure, or any other information concerning the state of the muscles, tendons, joints, or other structures which are concerned in movements ; and, secondly, they must be brought to bear upon the various motor nuclei and other motor regulating parts of the brain (such as the red nucleus, tectum of the mid-brain, basal nuclei, and cerebral cortex) to which the co-ordinating influence of the cerebellum is essential for the properly adjusted performance of complex actions.

The neuroblasts which receive all those extrinsic sensory impulses—visual, tactile, musculo-sensory, et cetera—assemble at the threshold of what was originally the vestibular cerebellar rudiment ; and they can be seen during the latter part of the second month migrating from the rhombic lip into the marginal layer of the cerebellum, until eventually its whole surface has been invaded by those alien neuroblasts, so that the originally non-nucleated marginal layer becomes a densely packed granular layer (**stratum marginale embryonale**). When that stage is reached the cerebellum consists of an inner ependymal layer, a mantle layer crowded with locally developed neuroblasts, a clear layer (the inner part of the original marginal layer), and the superficial layer of neuroblasts which have invaded the outer part of the marginal layer. As development proceeds in the mantle layer the axons of its neuroblasts are directed mainly towards the ventricular surface—the reverse of what happens in the spinal cord ; and as the fibre-masses increase in quantity the main part of the mantle layer becomes pushed farther and farther away from the ependyma by the accumulation of their own (and other) axons. Some of the neuroblasts, however, do not become pushed out into the line of the embryonic cerebellar cortex, but remain behind amidst the fibre-mass and receive the axons that come from the cortical cells. Those neuroblasts left amidst the fibres gradually assume the form of the dentate, fastigial, globose, and emboliform nuclei, which lie in the white substance of the hemisphere and vermis of the cerebellum ; and their axons pass out (as the superior cerebellar peduncles) to the thalamus, mid-brain, pons, and medulla. In the meantime many of the neuroblasts of the mantle layer have been converted into the large pear-shaped **Purkinje cells.**

While those events were occurring in the true mantle layer a peculiar process took place in the superficial layer of immigrant cells. One by one they began to leave their places on the surface and dipped into the mantle layer ; many of them passed between the Purkinje cells to a deeper plane, where they ceased their wanderings and formed a densely packed layer of granule cells (Fig. 754), the axons of which indicate the course of the migration.

MINUTE STRUCTURE OF A CEREBELLAR FOLIUM

A cerebellar folium is composed of a central core of white matter covered with a layer of grey matter. The grey cortex is arranged into two very evident layers, viz. a superficial **molecular layer** and a subjacent rust-coloured **granular layer.** Between those

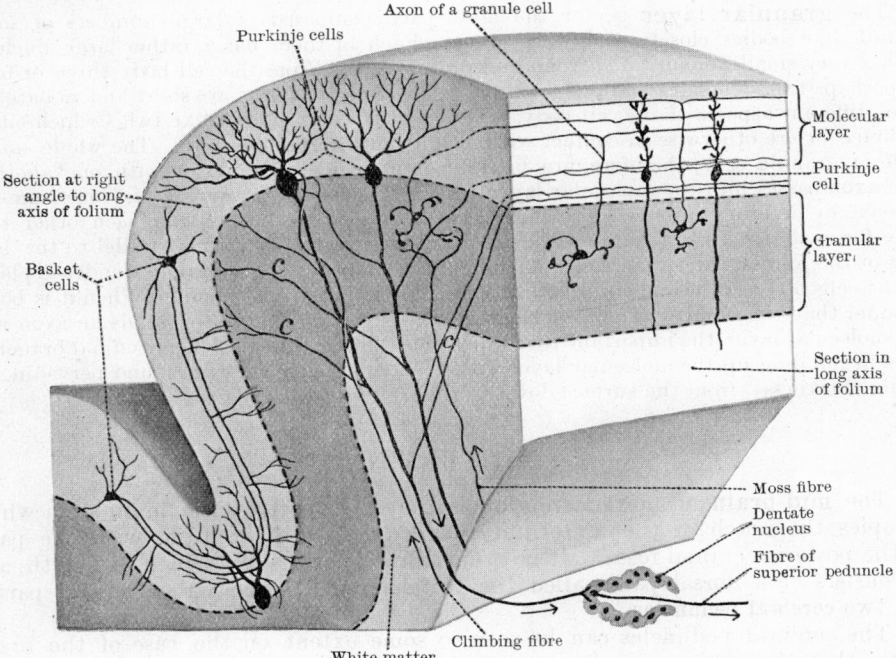

FIG. 754.—DIAGRAM TO SHOW THE MINUTE STRUCTURE OF A CEREBELLAR FOLIUM. The surface to the right shows a section in the long axis of a folium and that to the left is a section at right angles to the long axis of a folium. *C* = recurrent collaterals from the axons of Purkinje cells.

strata a single layer of large cells, termed the **cells of Purkinje,** is disposed in the form of a very nearly continuous sheet. The cells of Purkinje constitute the most characteristic constituents of the cerebellar cortex.

The **cells of Purkinje** are most numerous on the summit of a folium. At the bottom of a fissure they become fewer in number, and, therefore, looser in their arrangement. Each consists of a large flask-shaped cell body, the narrow end of which projects into the molecular layer, whilst the thicker, deeper end rests on the granular layer. From the deep end arises a **single axon**, which passes into the granular layer and presents the peculiarity of almost immediately assuming its medullary sheath. From that axon a few collateral branches soon arise, which, taking a recurrent course, enter the molecular layer, to end in connexion with certain of the adjoining cells of Purkinje. They would seem to have the function of binding together adjacent cells, and thus enabling them to carry on their operations in harmony with one another.

The **dendrites** spring from the narrow end of the cell in the form of either one or perhaps two stout stalks. They ascend into the molecular layer, branching and rebranching until an arborescent arrangement of extraordinary richness and extent results. The dendritic branches extend throughout the entire thickness of the molecular layer, and the branching takes place in one plane only, viz. in a plane which is transverse to the long axis of the folium. Consequently, it is only when transverse sections through a folium are made that the full dendritic effect is obtained (Fig. 754); in sections made parallel to the long axis of the folium the cells are seen in profile, and are observed to occupy quite a narrow area. The branching of the dendrites of a cell of Purkinje may, therefore, be compared to that which takes place in the case of a fruit-tree trained against a wall.

In the **molecular layer** the cells are not very numerous, and of these the most characteristic are the **basket-cells** which lie in the deeper part of the layer. In addition to numerous dendrites the basket-cell gives off an axon which runs transversely, as regards the long axis of the folium, between the planes of adjacent dendritic arborisations of the cells of Purkinje. At first very fine, those axons gradually become coarse and thick, and at intervals they give off collaterals which run towards the bodies of the cells of Purkinje. Reaching those, they break up into an enormous number of fine terminal branches which enclose the cells of Purkinje, as well as the short non-medullated portions of their axons, in a close basket-work of fine filaments.

The **granular layer** is, for the most part, composed of large numbers of small granule-like bodies closely packed together. Each of them has a rather large nucleus, with a very small amount of surrounding protoplasm. From the cell body three or four, or perhaps five, dendrites and one axon proceed. The **dendrites** are short and radiate out from different aspects of the cell body. They end in tufts of claw-like twigs which either embrace or are otherwise in contact with neighbouring granule cells. The whole multitude of granule cells, therefore, are brought into intimate connexion with one another. The **axon** passes into the molecular layer, in which it ends, at a varying distance from the surface, by dividing into two branches. Those diverge so sharply from each other that they form almost a right angle with the parent stem, and they run parallel to the long axis of the folium, threading their way among the branches of the various dendritic planes of the cells of Purkinje and entering into contact association with them. When it is borne in mind that the number of granule cells is very great, and that each sends an axon into the molecular layer, the important part which those fibres, with their longitudinal branches, take in building up the molecular layer will be understood. They are found pervading its entire thickness—from the surface down to the bodies of the cells of Purkinje.

MID-BRAIN

The **mid-brain** or **mesencephalon** is the short part of the brain-stem which occupies the notch of the tentorium and connects the cerebrum with the parts in the posterior cranial fossa. It is about three-quarters of an inch in length, and it consists of a dorsal part called the **tectum**, and a much larger ventral part— the two **cerebral peduncles.**

The cerebral peduncles can be seen to some extent on the base of the brain, where they bound the posterior part of the interpeduncular fossa (see p. 831).

The mid-brain is tunnelled lengthwise by a narrow passage, called the **aqueduct**, which connects the third ventricle with the fourth ventricle (Fig. 718, p. 833). That channel is much nearer the back of the mid-brain than the front.

Tectum [Lamina quadrigemina].—This name is applied to the dorsal part of the mid-brain. Its free surface is heaped up into two pairs of rounded eminences called the **corpora quadrigemina** [colliculi] (Figs. 720 and 755). The **superior pair** are larger and broader than the **inferior pair**, but they are not so well defined nor are they so prominent. A longitudinal and a transverse groove separate the corpora from one another. The longitudinal groove occupies the median plane and extends upwards to the posterior commissure of the brain. The upper part of the groove widens out into a shallow depression in which the **pineal body** rests. From the lower end of the same groove a short but well-defined ridge—the **frenulum veli**—passes to the superior medullary velum, which lies immediately below the inferior corpora quadrigemina The transverse groove curves round below each of the superior pair of corpora and separates them from the inferior pair. It is also continued in an upward and ventral direction on the side of the mid-brain.

The quadrigeminal bodies are not marked off laterally from the sides of the mid-brain, for each has in connexion with it, on that aspect, a prominent strand which is prolonged upwards and forwards towards the thalamic region. Those strands are called the **brachia quadrigemina**, and they are separated from each other by a continuation of the transverse groove that separates the two pairs of corpora.

The **medial geniculate body** is closely associated with the brachia, although it does not form part of the mid-brain, but belongs to the thalamus. It is a small, sharply defined oval eminence which lies on the lateral side of the upper part of the mid-brain under shelter of the pulvinar.

The **inferior brachium**, proceeding upwards from the inferior corpus, advances towards the medial geniculate body and disappears from view under cover of it.

The **superior brachium** is carried upwards and forwards between the overhanging thalamus and the medial geniculate body. A superficial examination of the mid-brain is sufficient to show that while a large part of that strand enters the lateral geniculate body (Fig. 756, p. 870) a considerable portion is a continuation of the lateral root of the optic tract. The lateral geniculate body is an ill-defined prominence at the posterior end of the optic tract; it belongs to the thalamus, and, as its name implies, it lies lateral to the medial geniculate body.

Cerebral Peduncles.—The cerebral peduncles (Figs. 756 and 766) appear on the base of the brain as three large rope-like strands which emerge from the cerebral hemispheres and disappear below by plunging into the basilar portion of the pons. At the place where each peduncle emerges from the corresponding side of the cerebrum it is encircled by the optic tract.

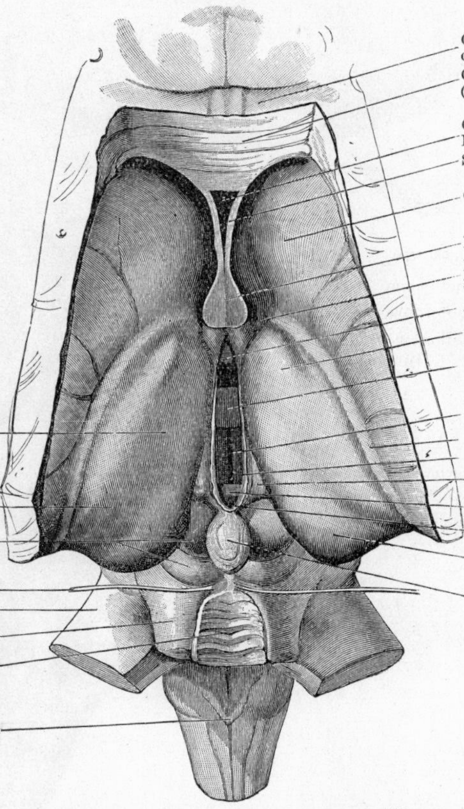

Each cerebral peduncle is composed of three parts, viz. a dorsal tegmental part (**tegmentum**), which is prolonged upwards into the region below the thalamus (hypothalamus), and a ventral portion (**basis pedunculi**), which, when traced upwards into the cerebrum,

FIG. 755.—THE CORPORA QUADRIGEMINA AND THE NEIGHBOURING PARTS.

is seen to take up a position on the lateral side of the thalamus and to be continuous with the internal capsule of the brain; and an intervening part—the **substantia nigra**. When the base of the brain is examined it is the basis pedunculi which is seen, and it is observed to be white in colour and streaked in the longitudinal direction. In the tegmentum the longitudinally arranged fibres are, in large part, *corticipetal*, or, in other words, fibres which are ascending towards the cortex of the cerebrum; the basis pedunculi, on the other hand, is composed entirely of longitudinal strands of fibres which are *corticifugal*, or fibres which descend from the cerebral hemisphere.

On the surface of the mid-brain the separation between the tegmental and basal portions of the cerebral peduncle is clearly indicated by a medial and a lateral groove. The **medial sulcus** is the more distinct of the two. It looks into the interpeduncular fossa, and from it emerge the roots of the oculomotor nerve.

The **lateral sulcus** extends from the thalamus to the groove between the superior and middle cerebellar peduncles, and the medial geniculate body is lodged at its upper end.

A close inspection of the lateral surface of the tegmental part of the cerebral

55 b

peduncle, below the level of the brachia, will reveal some faintly marked bundles of fibres curving obliquely upwards and backwards to reach the inferior corpus quadrigeminum (Fig. 756). They are fibres of the **lateral lemniscus**, coming

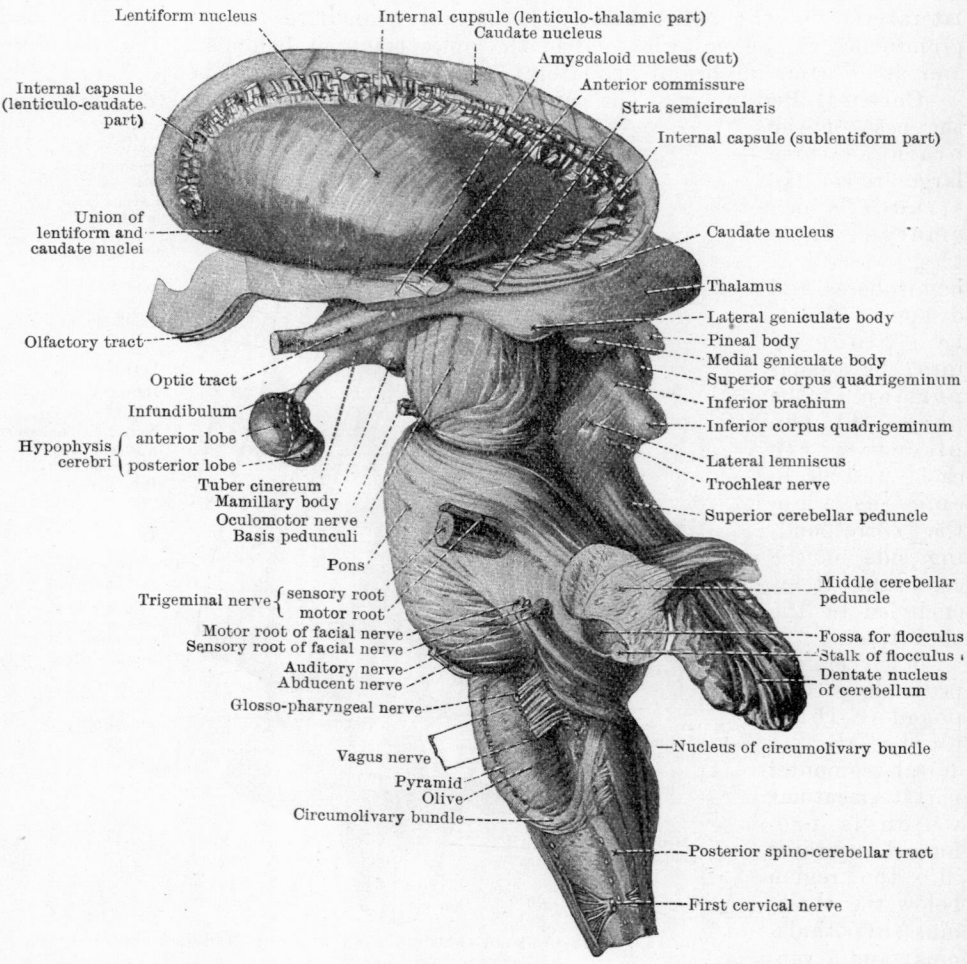

Lentiform nucleus

Internal cupsule (lenticulo-thalamic part)
Caudate nucleus

Amygdaloid nucleus (cut)

Internal capsule (lenticulo-caudate part)

Anterior commissure
Stria semicircularis

Internal capsule (sublentiform part)

Union of lentiform and caudate nuclei

Caudate nucleus

Thalamus

Lateral geniculate body
Pineal body
Medial geniculate body
Superior corpus quadrigeminum
Inferior brachium
Inferior corpus quadrigeminum

Olfactory tract

Optic tract

Infundibulum

Hypophysis cerebri { anterior lobe / posterior lobe

Lateral lemniscus
Trochlear nerve

Superior cerebellar peduncle

Tuber cinereum
Mamillary body
Oculomotor nerve
Basis pedunculi

Pons

Trigeminal nerve { sensory root / motor root

Middle cerebellar peduncle

Motor root of facial nerve
Sensory root of facial nerve
Auditory nerve
Abducent nerve

Glosso-pharyngeal nerve

Fossa for flocculus
Stalk of flocculus
Dentate nucleus of cerebellum

Vagus nerve

Nucleus of circumolivary bundle

Pyramid
Olive
Circumolivary bundle

Posterior spino-cerebellar tract

First cervical nerve

Fig. 756.—Left Lateral Aspect of a Brain after the Cerebral Hemisphere (except Corpus Striatum) and the Cerebellum (except Dentate Nucleus) have been removed. (G. E. S.)

to the surface at the lateral sulcus and sweeping over the subjacent superior cerebellar peduncle to gain the inferior corpus quadrigeminum, inferior brachium, and medial geniculate body.

Internal Structure of Mid-Brain

When transverse sections are made through the mid-brain the aqueduct is seen to be surrounded by a thick layer of grey matter—the **central grey matter of the aqueduct**. Behind that, there is the **tectum** with its *corpora quadrigemina*; in front and laterally there are the **cerebral peduncles**, each subdivided into *tegmentum*, *substantia nigra* and *basis pedunculi*. (Fig. 757).

Central Grey Matter and **Aqueduct of Mid-brain.**—The aqueduct is not quite three-quarters of an inch in length, has a variable outline, and is much nearer the dorsal surface than the ventral surface of the mid-brain. It is lined with ciliated epithelium, and outside that is the thick layer of central grey matter, which is continuous below with the grey matter of the floor of the fourth ventricle, and above with grey matter on the floor and sides of the third ventricle. Scattered more or less irregularly throughout the central grey matter are numerous nerve-cells of varying forms and sizes, whilst in addition to those there are three definite clusters of cells which constitute the nuclei of origin of the trochlear and oculomotor nerves, and the terminal nucleus of the mesencephalic tract of the trigeminal nerve. The position and relations of those nuclei will be given later.

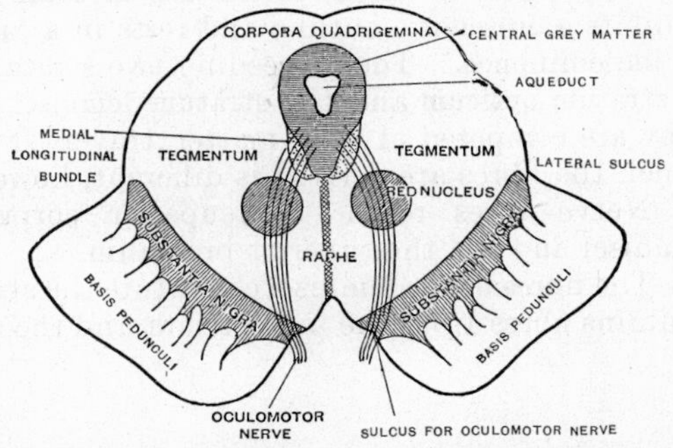

Inferior Quadrigeminal Bodies. —Each inferior corpus quadrigeminum is composed largely of a mass of grey matter which is oval in transverse section, (Fig. 758). This central nucleus is, to a large extent, encapsulated by white matter.

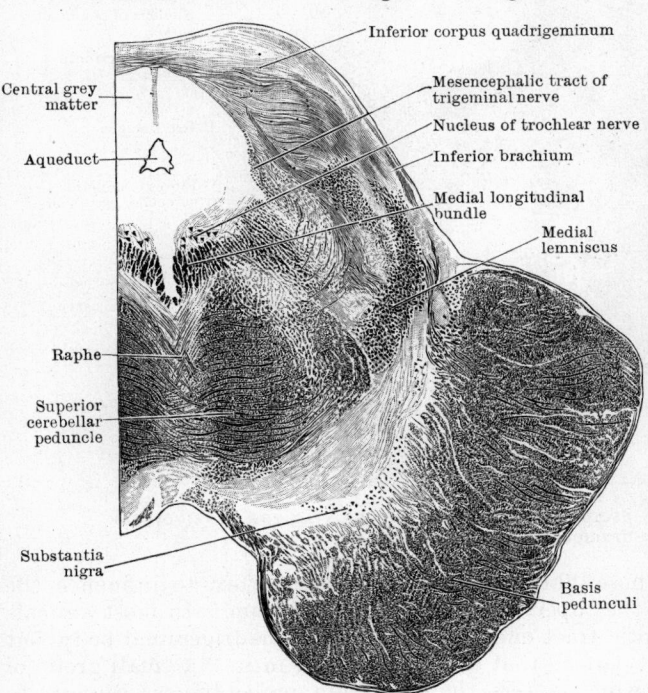

Fig. 757.—DIAGRAMMATIC VIEW OF A TRANSVERSE SECTION THROUGH THE UPPER PART OF THE MID-BRAIN.

Numerous cells of various sizes are scattered throughout it, and the whole mass is pervaded by an intricate interlacement of fine fibres derived, to a large extent, from the lateral lemniscus.

In transverse sections through that region, the lateral lemniscus is seen to abut against the lateral margin of the central nucleus of the inferior quadrigeminal body. Many of the fibres of this tract enter it at once and become dispersed amongst its cells; others sweep over its dorsal surface, so as to give it a superficial covering; whilst a third group is carried medially in front of it in the form of a thin layer that marks it off from grey matter of the aqueduct (Fig. 761). In that manner, therefore, the inferior quadrigeminal body becomes partially circumscribed by the fibres of the lateral lemniscus. Some of the lateral lemniscus fibres, which proceed over the surface of the nucleus, reach the median plane and form a loose decussation with the corresponding fibres of the opposite side.

FIG. 758.—TRANSVERSE SECTION THROUGH THE MID-BRAIN AT THE LEVEL OF THE INFERIOR CORPUS QUADRIGEMINUM.

The intimate connexion thus exhibited between the fibres of the lateral lemniscus and the nucleus of the inferior corpus quadrigeminum is very significant. The lateral lemniscus, to a large extent, comes from the nuclei of termination of the cochlear nerve of the opposite side. We must associate, therefore, the inferior corpus quadrigeminum, and also the medial geniculate body, which likewise receives fibres from the lateral lemniscus, with the organ of hearing.

This view regarding the inferior quadrigeminal body is supported both by experimental and by morphological evidence. Speaking broadly, it may be stated that the inferior corpora quadrigenima become prominent only in mammals, and then they are invariably correlated with a spirally wound and well-developed cochlea.

Superior Quadrigeminal Bodies.—The superior quadrigeminal body has a more complicated structure (Fig. 759). Superficially, it is coated with a very thin layer of white matter which is termed the **stratum zonale.** Underneath that there is a grey nucleus, called the **stratum griseum,** which, in transverse section, exhibits a crescentic outline and rests in a cap-like manner upon the subjacent part of the eminence. The succeeding two strata, which respectively receive the names of **stratum opticum** and the **stratum lemnisci,** present this feature in common, that they are composed of grey matter traversed by numerous fibres. The source from which the fibres are derived is different, however, in each case.

Nerve-fibres reach the superior corpus quadrigeminum through (1) the lemnisci and (2) the superior brachium.

The fibres of the lemnisci constitute the **stratum lemnisci.** The superior brachium contains fibres from the area striata and the area parastriata of the occipital region

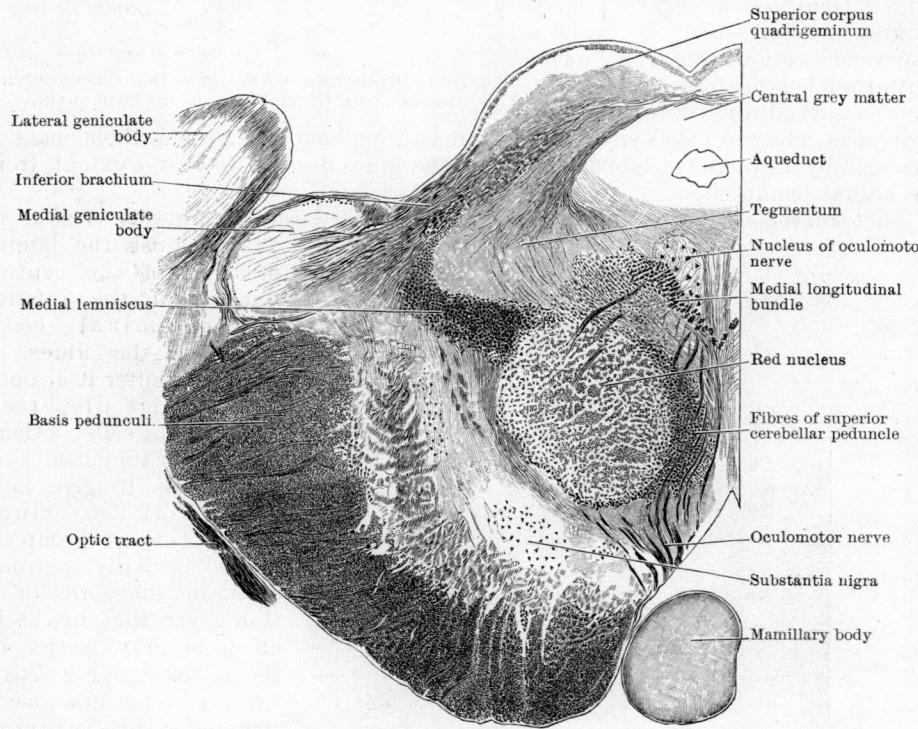

Fig. 759.—Transverse Section through the Mid-brain at the Level of the Superior Corpus Quadrigeminum.

of the cerebral cortex. Those fibres enable the visual cortex to influence the oculomotor nuclei through the superior corpus quadrigeminum. In most animals many of the fibres of the optic tract end in the superior quadrigeminal body, but in the human brain it is not certain that any of them end in it. A small group of fibres from the optic tract which enters the mid-brain probably goes directly to the oculomotor (Edinger-Westphal) nucleus.

Tegmentum.—The tegmentum of the cerebral peduncle may be regarded as the continuation upwards of the dorsal portion of the pons. It consists, therefore, of fine bundles of longitudinal fibres intersected by arching fibres which take a transverse and curved course. The interstices between these bundles are occupied by grey matter containing irregularly scattered nerve-cells. Posteriorly the tegmentum is continuous, at the side of the central grey matter, with the bases of the corpora quadrigemina, whilst anteriorly it is separated from the basis pedunculi by the substantia nigra. The tegmenta of opposite sides are, to some extent, marked off from each other in the median plane by a prolongation upwards of the median raphe of the pons, although, in their lower part, that is much obscured by the decussation of the superior cerebellar peduncles. The two longitudinal strands, termed the **medial longitudinal bundle** and the **medial lemniscus**, are prolonged upwards throughout the entire length of the mid-brain; and they present the same relations to the tegmentum as in the lower parts of the brain—the longitudinal bundle being placed behind the lemniscus.

The tegmentum is divisible into two parts: viz. (1) a lower part subjacent to the inferior corpus quadrigeminum, and largely occupied by the decussation of the superior cerebellar peduncles (Fig. 760); and (2) an upper part subjacent to the superior corpus quadrigeminum, and traversed by the emerging bundles of the oculomotor nerve. The upper part contains a large and striking nuclear mass, termed the **red nucleus** (Fig. 759). The lower part of the central grey matter contains the nucleus of the trochlear nerve; the upper part contains the nucleus of the oculomotor nerve.

Superior Cerebellar Peduncles [Brachia Conjunctiva]. —As the superior cerebellar peduncles leave the pons and sink into the tegmentum they undergo a complete decussation subjacent to the inferior corpora quadrigemina and the central grey matter (Figs. 758, 759, and 760); the decussation is completed at the level of the upper borders of the inferior corpora quadrigemina. Having crossed to the opposite side, each peduncle proceeds upwards into the upper part of the tegmentum, where it encounters the red nucleus and a large number of its fibres plunge into it, and come to an end in connexion with the nuclear cells.

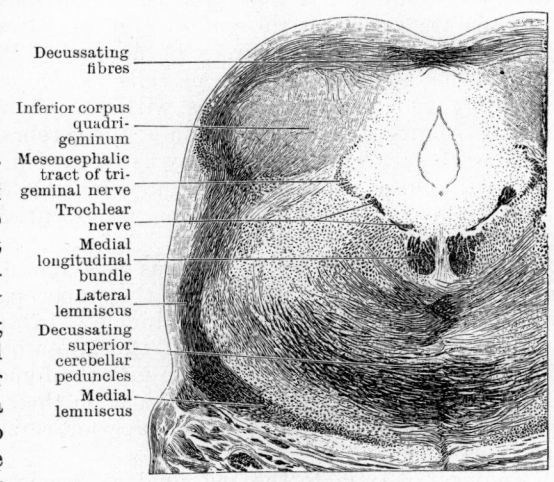

Decussating fibres

Inferior corpus quadrigeminum

Mesencephalic tract of trigeminal nerve

Trochlear nerve

Medial longitudinal bundle

Lateral lemniscus

Decussating superior cerebellar peduncles

Medial lemniscus

FIG. 760.—SECTION THROUGH THE INFERIOR CORPUS QUADRIGEMINUM AND THE TEGMENTUM BELOW THE LEVEL OF THE NUCLEUS OF THE TROCHLEAR NERVE. (The decussation of the superior cerebellar peduncles and the course of the trochlear nerve in the central grey matter are seen.)

Many of the fibres, however, are carried around the nucleus, forming a capsule for it (Fig. 759), and are prolonged into the thalamus to end in connexion with the ventral thalamic cells. The superior peduncle is, therefore, a great efferent tract which issues from the dentate nucleus of the cerebellum, crosses the median plane in the lower part of the mid-brain, and ends in the red nucleus and the ventral part of the thalamus.

Substantia Nigra.—When seen in transverse section, the **substantia nigra** presents a semilunar outline. It consists of a mass of grey matter in the midst of which there are large numbers of deeply pigmented nerve-cells. This remarkable pigment—a melanin—differs from that which often develops in nerve-cells undergoing senile changes. It is not found in the homologues of the substantia nigra of most mammals, and in the human subject it is not present at birth, but develops only in the second or third year. In the adult the large cells of the substantia nigra and those of the globus pallidus contain more iron than any other nuclear territories of the nervous system. The substantia nigra is disposed in the form of a thick layer interposed between the tegmental and basal portions of the cerebral peduncle. It begins below at the upper border of the pons and extends upwards into the hypothalamus. The margins of this layer of dark-coloured substance come to the surface at the medial and the lateral sulci of the mid-brain, and its medial part is traversed by the emerging rootlets of the oculomotor nerve. It is not equally thick throughout. Towards the lateral sulcus it becomes thin, whilst it thickens considerably near the medial side of the cerebral peduncle. The surface turned towards the tegmentum is concave and uniform; the opposite surface is convex and made irregular by the presence of numerous slender prolongations of the substance into the basis pedunculi.

During recent years the investigation of the damage to the brain in such affections as encephalitis lethargica ("sleepy sickness") has directed particular attention to the substantia nigra and revealed its association with such symptoms as diminution of muscular tone and involuntary rhythmic movements.

The substantia nigra receives impulses from all the afferent pathways of the mid-brain, *i.e.* from the lateral and medial lemnisci, from the superior corpus quadrigeminum and the tractus peduncularis transversus (optic), and from the fasciculus retroflexus and the mamillary body (olfactory). Its efferent fibres pass to the red nucleus, the corpora quadrigemina, and the formatio reticularis. This part of the substantia nigra and its connexions are present in all mammals, and the cells are known as the *palaeo-nigrum*. But in Man and the higher mammals distinguished by high degrees of manual skill there is added to the front of the nucleus a new collection of cells (*neo-nigrum*) which is connected, both by ascending and descending fibres, with the globus pallidus of the corpus striatum and the fronto-parietal operculum of the cerebral cortex.

The whole nigral system may be regarded as the system for organising the afferent impulses concerned in regulating voluntary skilled movements. It is the counterpart on the afferent side of the essentially motor red-nucleus, with which it is intimately connected.

Red Nucleus.—The red nucleus is a rounded nuclear mass, of a reddish tint in the fresh brain, which lies in the upper part of the tegmentum, and in the path of the superior cerebellar peduncle. In transverse section it has a circular outline. It begins at the level of the lower border of the superior corpus quadrigeminum and it extends upwards into the hypothalamus. The emerging bundles of the oculomotor nerve pass through it on their way to the surface. The relation which the fibres of the opposite superior cerebellar peduncle present to it has been described.

In most mammals the red nucleus consists of a small group of large cells (*palaeo-rubrum*) emitting fibres, called the **rubro-spinal tract**, which, after crossing to the other side, descend in the tegmentum to reach the lateral white column of the spinal cord (Fig. 714, p. 825). In Man the large-celled nucleus and the rubro-spinal tract become reduced to small proportions, and some of the fibres of the tract remain uncrossed. In the higher mammals, and especially in the human brain, a very large nucleus (*neo-rubrum*), composed of small cells, develops in front of the old rubrum and forms the major part of the red nucleus. It becomes closely linked by fibre-connexions with the neo-nigrum (as also is the palæo-rubrum with the palæo-nigrum). Ascending tracts proceed from the neo-rubrum to the ventro-lateral nuclei of the thalamus, and to the fronto-parietal regions of the cerebral cortex.

Descending fibres (fronto-rubral and pallido-rubral tracts) proceed from the frontal area of the cerebral cortex and globus pallidus to the neo-rubrum. Other fibres arising in the corpus striatum and red nucleus (pallidorubro-olivary tracts and pallidorubro-reticular tracts) proceed to the olivary nucleus and the formatio reticularis of the mid-brain, pons, and medulla oblongata.

Those complex connexions (Fig. 808) are involved in the regulation of muscular tone, and are concerned in the performance of skilled movements.

Medial Longitudinal Bundle.—This is a very conspicuous tract of longitudinal fibres which extends throughout the whole length of the medulla oblongata, pons, and mid-brain, in the formatio reticularis or dorsal part of each. Below, at the level of the decussation of the pyramids, it becomes continuous with the anterior intersegmental tract of the spinal cord (p. 827), whilst, by its opposite end, it establishes intricate connexions in the region immediately above the mid-brain. Throughout its whole length it lies close to the median plane and its fellow of the opposite side. In the mid-brain it is applied to the front of the central grey matter, whilst in the pons and medulla oblongata it is situated immediately subjacent to the grey matter of the floor of the fourth ventricle. One of its most salient features is the intimate association which it presents with the three motor nuclei from which the nerves for the supply of the muscles of the eyeball take origin, viz. the oculomotor nucleus, the trochlear nucleus, and the abducent nucleus. The first two of those are closely applied to its medial and dorsal aspect, whilst the abducent nucleus is placed on its lateral side. Into each of those nuclei it sends many collaterals, and probably also some of its constituent fibres, and they end around the nuclear cells. It would appear, therefore, that one of the most important functions of the strand is to bind together those nuclei, and thus enable them to act in harmony one with the other. *The most important element in the medial longitudinal bundle, however, consists of fibres that come from the vestibular nucleus, and proceed to the oculomotor group of nuclei of both sides as well as to both nuclei of the accessory nerve in the medulla oblongata and spinal cord.* By means of those connexions movements of the fluid in the semicircular canals can reflexly move the eyes and the head.

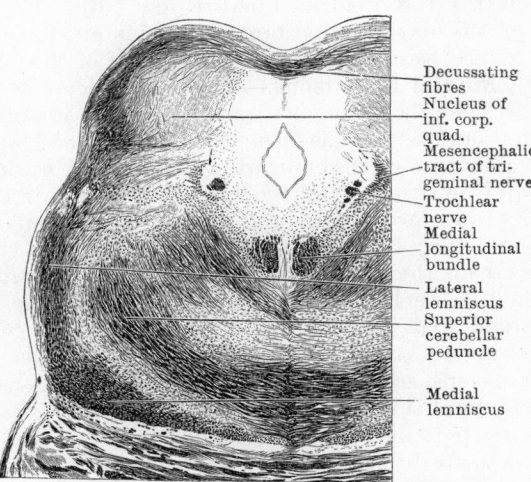

FIG. 761.—SECTION THROUGH INFERIOR CORPUS QUAD-RIGEMINUM AND TEGMENTUM OF MID-BRAIN AT A SLIGHTLY LOWER LEVEL THAN FIG. 760.

Labels for Fig. 761: Decussating fibres / Nucleus of inf. corp. quad. / Mesencephalic tract of trigeminal nerve / Trochlear nerve / Medial longitudinal bundle / Lateral lemniscus / Superior cerebellar peduncle / Medial lemniscus

It is evident that it is a brain tract of high importance from the fact that it is present in all vertebrates, and, further, that its fibres assume their medullary sheaths at an extremely early period. In fishes, amphibians and reptiles, it is one of the largest bundles of the brain-stem. In Man, its fibres medullate between the sixth and seventh months of intra-uterine life, and at the same time as the fibres of the anterior intersegmental tract of the spinal cord, with which it stands in connexion.

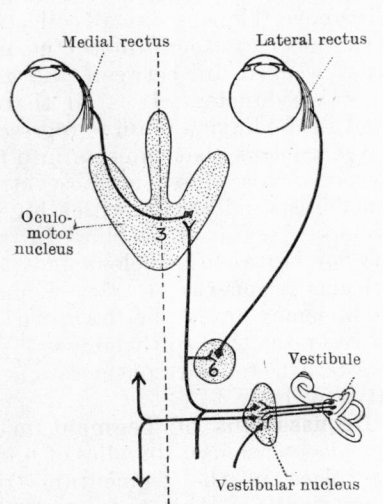

FIG. 762.—PLAN OF SOME OF THE VESTI-BULAR ELEMENTS IN THE MEDIAL LONGITUDINAL BUNDLE. (G. E. S.)

Labels for Fig. 762: Medial rectus / Lateral rectus / Oculo-motor nucleus / Vestibule / Vestibular nucleus

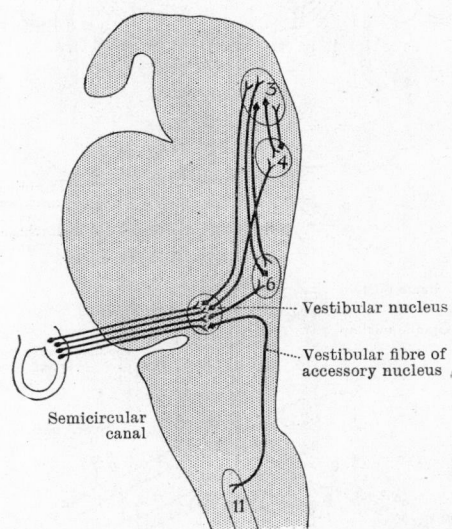

FIG. 763.—PROFILE PLAN OF IMPORTANT ELEMENTS IN THE MEDIAL LONGITUDINAL BUNDLE. (G. E. S.)

Labels for Fig. 763: Vestibular nucleus / Vestibular fibre of accessory nucleus / Semicircular canal

Lateral Lemniscus.—The lateral lemniscus is a definite tract of longitudinal fibres which lies in the upper part of the dorsal division of the pons, and extends upwards through it and through the tegmentum of the mid-brain near their lateral surface. It is formed by the fibres of the corpus trapezoideum and auditory striæ in the lower part of the pons turning abruptly upwards and taking a course towards the quadrigeminal region. But the details of the arrangement and connexions of this important fasciculus must be left for fuller consideration when we are discussing the central connexions of the auditory nerve.

Medial Lemniscus.—The medial lemniscus has already been followed through the medulla oblongata and pons, and its position in each of those portions of the brain-stem has been defined (pp. 850 and 858). In the lower part of the tegmentum of the mid-brain it is carried up in the form of a more or less flattened band in front of the decussating superior cerebellar peduncles. To its lateral side, and forming an angle with it (as seen in transverse section), is the lateral lemniscus (Figs. 738 and 739), and at that level there is no clear demarcation between these two tracts. In the upper part of the mid-brain the appearance of the red nucleus in the tegmentum causes the medial lemniscus to take up a more lateral and dorsal position, so that it now comes to lie subjacent to the medial geniculate body (Fig. 761). At that level it exhibits a crescentic outline in transverse section, and the lateral lemniscus has to a large extent disappeared from its lateral side.

A part of the medial lemniscus takes origin in the lower part of the medulla oblongata from the gracile and cuneate nuclei of the opposite side (p. 850). Seeing that the posterior white column of the spinal cord ends in those nuclei, the medial lemniscus may be considered to continue that column upwards into the brain. Other fibres arise from the terminal nuclei of the various sensory cranial nerves of the opposite side. The rest of the tract consists of the upper part of the spino-thalamic tracts from the spinal cord. In the mid-brain a considerable contribution of fibres is given by the medial lemniscus to the substantia nigra and the superior corpus quadrigeminum, and then the remainder of the tract proceeds into the ventral part of the lateral nucleus of the thalamus. There its fibres end amidst the thalamic cells (Fig. 776).

Interpeduncular Nucleus and Fasciculus Retroflexus.—Immediately above the pons a small collection of nerve-cells is found in the median plane, wedged in between the two cerebral peduncles. It is all that is found in the human brain to represent a large nucleus that projects into the interpeduncular fossa in most other animals, especially those with a highly developed sense of smell. In the interpeduncular nucleus ends the **fasciculus retroflexus**—a tract of fibres which comes from the habenular nucleus of the epithalamus. We shall return to the consideration of that tract later.

Decussations of Tegmentum.—Three decussations of bundles of fibres take place in the tegmentum—the decussations of the superior cerebellar peduncles, of the tecto-spinal tracts, and of the rubro-spinal tracts. The **decussation of the superior cerebellar peduncles** has been described already (p. 873). If the region ventral to the medial longitudinal bundles is examined in the upper part of the mid-brain, two groups of

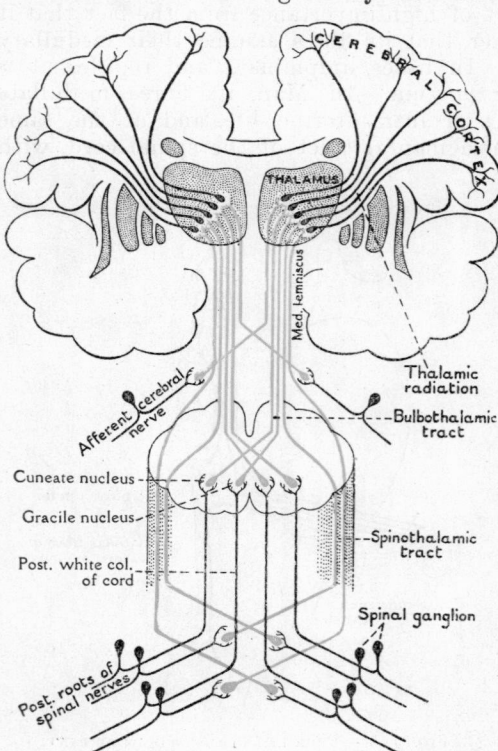

FIG. 764.—DIAGRAM OF THE CONNEXIONS OF THE MEDIAL LEMNISCUS AND ALSO OF CERTAIN OF THE THALAMO-CORTICAL FIBRES.

decussating fibres will be observed in the interval between the red nuclei—one dorsal to the other. The dorsal one is the **decussation of the tecto-spinal tracts**; the other is the **decussation of the rubro-spinal tracts**; both of these pairs of tracts cross the median plane immediately after their origin, decussating with their fellows, and descend in the opposite half of the brain-stem to the spinal cord—the tecto-spinal from the superior and inferior corpora quadrigemina, the rubro-spinal from the red nucleus.

Basis Pedunculi.—The basis pedunculi is slightly crescentic in outline in transverse section, and stands quite apart from its fellow. It is composed of a compact mass of longitudinally directed fibres, all of which arise in the cortex of the cerebrum and pursue an unbroken corticifugal course into and through the basis pedunculi. Those fibres may be classified into two distinct sets, viz. cerebro-pontine and pyramidal.

The **cerebro-pontine fibres** possess this leading character: in their course downwards they are all arrested in the basilar part of the pons, and end amidst the cells of the nuclei pontis. Those tracts hold a very definite position in the basis pedunculi. Thus, it has been satisfactorily established that in the basis pedunculi the fibres from the temporal area of the cortex form the lateral fifth, whilst those from the frontal area occupy the medial fifth.

The **pyramidal fibres** constitute the great motor tract from the cerebral cortex. They occupy the middle three-fifths of the basis. This tract differs from the cerebro-pontine strands in being carried downwards through the basilar part of the pons and on the front of the medulla oblongata into the spinal cord, which it enters in the form of the *anterior* and *lateral cerebro-spinal tracts*. On its way through the mid-brain, pons, and medulla oblongata it sends fibres across the median plane to the various motor nuclei on the opposite side of those sections of the brain-stem; these may be termed *cortico-nuclear fibres*.

DEVELOPMENT OF MID-BRAIN

Even in the early embryo the mesencephalon is the smallest section of the brain-tube, although the disproportion in size between it and the other primitive subdivisions of the brain is not nearly so marked as in the adult. Owing to the cephalic flexure, the mid-brain for a time occupies the summit of the head. Later it becomes completely covered over by the expanding cerebral hemispheres.

The corpora quadrigemina are derived from the alar laminæ of the side walls of the brain-tube, whilst the basal laminæ thicken and ultimately form the tegmenta. The original cavity of the mid-brain is retained as the aqueduct.

For a considerable time the cavity of the mid-brain remains relatively large, and the lower part of its dorsal wall is carried downwards in the form of a diverticulum or recess which overlaps the cerebellar plate. About that time, also, the dorsal wall shows a median fold or ridge. Both of those conditions are transitory. As the corpora quadrigemina take shape, the median ridge disappears and is replaced by the median longitudinal groove which separates the quadrigeminal bodies. Only its lower part is retained, and that is represented by the frenulum veli of the adult brain. The diverticulum of the cavity gradually becomes reduced, and finally disappears as the aqueduct assumes form.

The precise mode of origin of the red nucleus is not known.

Later in this account reasons will be given for the belief that the representatives of the neural crests in the region of the mid-brain become absorbed and assimilated in the walls of the neural tube as it closes in.

DEEP CONNEXIONS OF THE CRANIAL NERVES ATTACHED TO THE MEDULLA OBLONGATA, PONS, AND MID-BRAIN

There are twelve pairs of cranial nerves, of which the lower eight are attached to the medulla oblongata and pons. From above downwards these eight are named the trigeminal (fifth), the abducent (sixth), the facial (seventh), the auditory (eighth), the glosso-pharyngeal (ninth), the vagus (tenth), the accessory (eleventh), and the hypoglossal (twelfth). Two others—the trochlear (fourth) and oculomotor (third)—spring from the mid-brain. The hypoglossal, the accessory, the greater part of the facial, the abducent, the motor root of the trigeminal, the trochlear, and the oculomotor are efferent nerves; the auditory and the sensory root of the trigeminal are purely afferent nerves; the vagus and the glosso-pharyngeal are composed of both efferent and afferent fibres; and the sensory root of the facial nerve [n. intermedius] contains not only afferent fibres but also the efferent, para-sympathetic preganglionic fibres which later pass into the chorda tympani. In all those cases (with the exception of the mesencephalic tract of the trigeminal) afferent fibres arise from ganglionic cells placed outside the brain and penetrate the brainstem, to end in connexion with the cells of certain **nuclei of termination**. Efferent fibres, on the other hand, take origin within the brain as the axons of cells which are grouped together in certain places in the form of **nuclei of origin**.

Nuclei of Origin, or Motor Nuclei.—In the spinal cord the nuclei of origin are represented by elongated columns of cells which run more or less continuously through successive spinal segments in the anterior grey column, and from them the series of efferent anterior nerve-roots take origin. In the medulla oblongata,

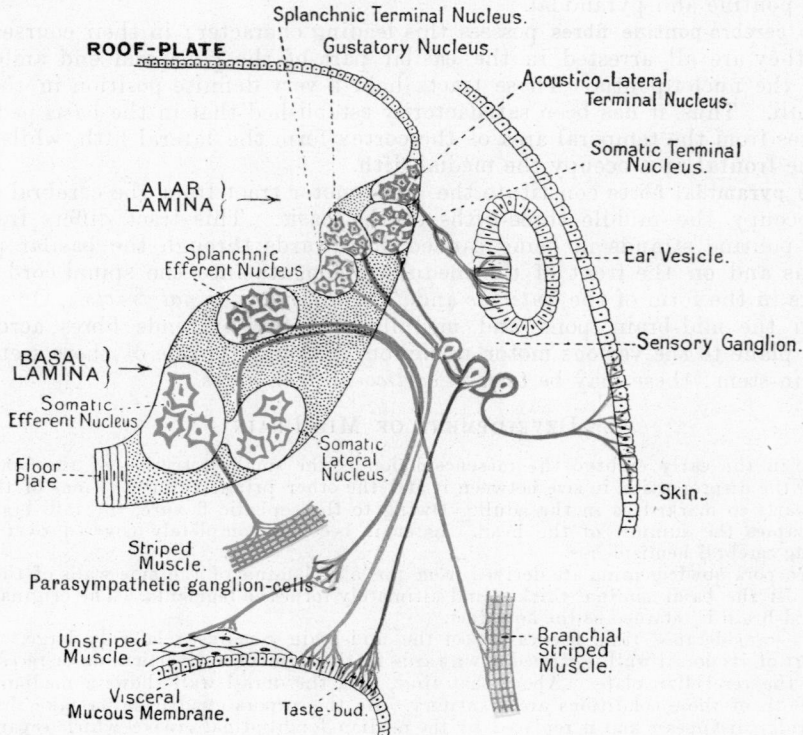

FIG. 765.—DIAGRAM REPRESENTING THE DIFFERENT KINDS OF COMPONENTS FOUND IN THE CRANIAL NERVES AND OF THEIR NUCLEI OF ORIGIN OR TERMINATION. (G. E. S.)

pons, and mid-brain the nuclei of origin, or, in other words, the motor nuclei of the individual nerves, become, for the most part, discontinuous, and are represented by certain isolated clumps of compact grey matter in which are placed the clusters of cells from which the fibres of the efferent nerves arise. The nucleus ambiguus, however, which consists of a column of cells from which root-fibres of the upper part of the accessory, of the vagus, and also of the glosso-pharyngeal are derived, is an exception to this rule. At the decussation of the pyramids, the anterior grey column of the spinal cord is broken up by the intercrossing bundles into a detached head and a basal part which remains in relation with the ventro-lateral aspect of the central canal. Certain of the efferent nuclei of the medulla oblongata, pons, and mid-brain lie in the line of the basal portion of the anterior grey column close to the median plane. They are termed **medial somatic nuclei**, and are met with at different levels in the brain-stem. This group comprises the hypoglossal nucleus, the abducent nucleus, and, in the mid-brain, the trochlear nucleus and part of the oculomotor nucleus. Other motor nuclei of origin are present in the form of isolated clumps or columns of grey matter which lie at different levels in the medulla oblongata and pons in a more lateral and deeper situation. They are the nucleus ambiguus of the accessory, vagus, and glosso-pharyngeal, the motor nucleus of the facial nerve, and the nucleus of the motor root of the trigeminal nerve. From their position in the formatio reticularis of the medulla oblongata and pons they constitute a group to which the name of **lateral somatic nuclei** is applied.

In addition to those two columns of motor nuclei there is a third efferent column of **splanchnic nuclei** represented by the dorsal nucleus of the vagus and glosso-pharyngeal nerves, and similar nuclei emitting sympathetic fibres into the

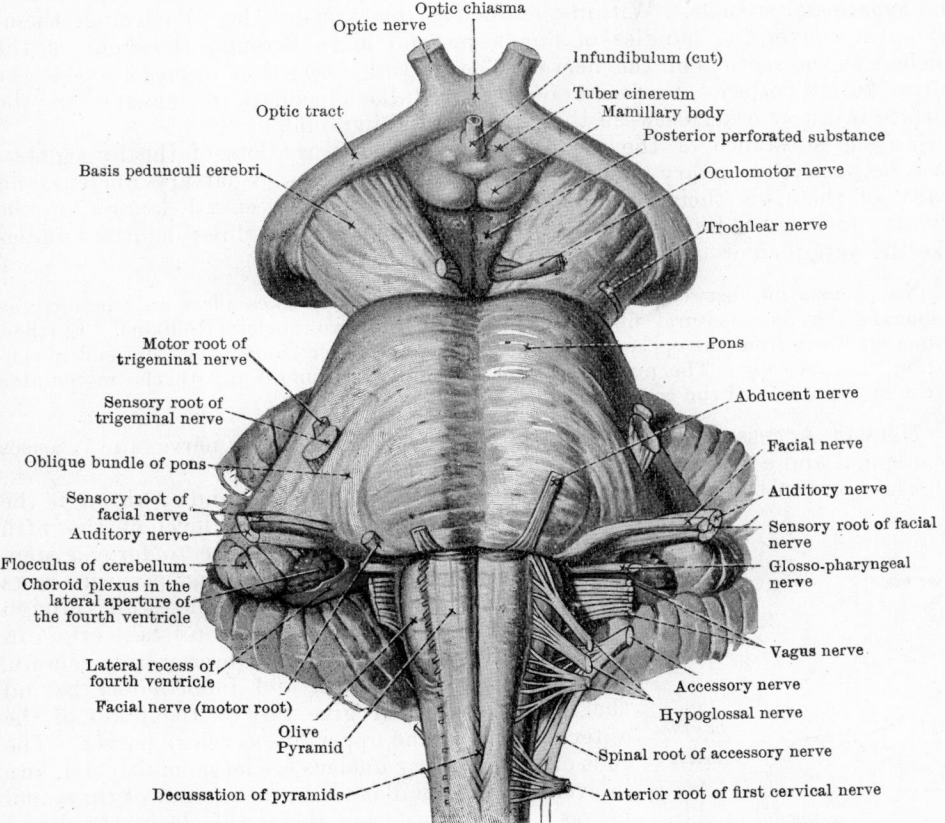

Optic chiasma
Optic nerve
Optic tract
Infundibulum (cut)
Tuber cinereum
Mamillary body
Posterior perforated substance
Basis pedunculi cerebri
Oculomotor nerve
Trochlear nerve
Motor root of trigeminal nerve
Pons
Abducent nerve
Sensory root of trigeminal nerve
Facial nerve
Oblique bundle of pons
Auditory nerve
Sensory root of facial nerve
Sensory root of facial nerve
Auditory nerve
Glosso-pharyngeal nerve
Flocculus of cerebellum
Choroid plexus in the lateral aperture of the fourth ventricle
Vagus nerve
Lateral recess of fourth ventricle
Accessory nerve
Facial nerve (motor root)
Hypoglossal nerve
Olive
Pyramid
Spinal root of accessory nerve
Decussation of pyramids
Anterior root of first cervical nerve

FIG. 766.—ANTERIOR SURFACE OF BRAIN-STEM, showing the nerve roots.   (G. E. S.)

facial and oculomotor nerves. It is possible some splanchnic efferent fibres may pass into the trigeminal nerve.

The different nuclei of origin of the efferent fibres which belong to the various cranial nerves, both medial and lateral, are connected with the motor area of the cerebral cortex by cortico-nuclear fibres of the pyramidal tract of the other side which enter the nuclei and end in association with their cells.

Terminal Nuclei.—The general scheme of arrangement of the **terminal nuclei** has already been explained (Fig. 765); its details will be further elucidated as the various nerves are considered seriatim.

The axons of many of the cells of the nuclei of termination enter the formatio reticularis as arcuate fibres, and, crossing the median plane, are carried upwards in the formatio reticularis of the opposite side to establish direct connexions with the thalamus and, indirectly through it, with the cerebral cortex. Others pass to the motor nuclei, to the cerebellum or other groups of nerve-cells, to form connexions necessary for the performance of reflex actions.

Hypoglossal Nerve.—The nucleus of origin of the hypoglossal nerve—the motor nerve of the tongue—lies in the substance of the medulla oblongata. It is composed of several groups of large multipolar cells which closely resemble the cells in the anterior grey column of the spinal cord, and is pervaded by an intricate network of fine fibrils. In form it is a slender rod about 18 mm in length. It extends from a point immediately above the decussation of the pyramids up to the level of the auditory striæ. The lower part is in front of the central canal of the medulla close to the median plane in that part of the central grey matter which is continuous with the basal part of the anterior grey column of the spinal cord. The upper part is in the grey matter on the floor of the fourth ventricle, subjacent to the medial part of the surface area named the **hypoglossal triangle.** Within the nucleus the axons of the cells arrange themselves in converging bundles of fine fibres and leave through the front of the nucleus as the rootlets of the nerve. The nerve bundles thus formed traverse the entire antero-posterior thickness of the medulla oblongata to emerge on the surface in linear order between the olive and the pyramid.

In the substance of the medulla oblongata the rootlets of the hypoglossal pass between the olivary nucleus and the medial accessory olivary nucleus, and many of them on their way to the surface pierce the ventral lamina of the olivary nucleus. After they emerge they collect to form three definite bundles like the anterior nerve-roots of three spinal nerves (Fig. 766).

No decussation between the nerves of opposite sides takes place in the medulla oblongata, but commissural fibres pass between the two nuclei (Kölliker). Further, numerous fibres from the opposite cerebro-spinal tract enter the nucleus and end in connexion with its cells. The nucleus is thus brought into connexion with the motor area of the opposite side of the cerebral cortex.

Nervus Accessorius.—The **accessory nerve** also is a motor nerve, and it arises by a spinal and a cranial root.

The fibres of the **spinal root** emerge as a vertical row of bundles through the side of the spinal cord from the level of the fifth cervical nerve upwards; they unite to form a stem that ascends between the anterior and posterior roots of the cervical nerves and enters the skull through the foramen magnum. The root-fibres take origin in a column of cells situated in the anterior grey column, close to its lateral margin and immediately behind the nerve-cells which give rise to the fibres of the anterior roots of the upper five cervical nerves. The cells of the accessory nucleus are large, multipolar, and in every respect similar to the motor cells of the spinal nerves. The axons from these cells leave the dorsal surface of the nucleus in converging groups to form the root-bundles of the nerve. These, in the first place, proceed straight backwards in the anterior grey column. Reaching the bay between the two columns of grey matter, they turn sharply laterally into the white matter and traverse the lateral white column to gain their points of exit from the cord. At the decussation of the pyramids additional rootlets proceed from the detached head of the anterior grey column.

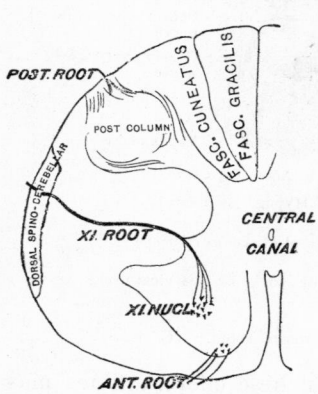

FIG. 767.—DIAGRAM OF THE SPINAL ORIGIN OF THE ACCESSORY NERVE. (After Bruce.)

The fibres of the **cranial root** arise in the medulla oblongata. As they proceed laterally from their nucleus they cross in front of the spinal tract of the trigeminal nerve; that distinguishes them from the fibres of the vagus, for the vagal fibres pass through the tract or behind it. The nucleus of origin of the cranial rootlets is the **nucleus ambiguus,** which, at a higher level, gives motor fibres to the vagus and glosso-pharyngeal nerves.

The part of the accessory nerve which takes origin in the spinal cord supplies the sterno-mastoid and trapezius muscles. The cranial portion joins the vagus, and through the recurrent laryngeal nerves it supplies all the intrinsic muscles of the larynx except the crico-thyroid (see p. 983). The portion of the nucleus ambiguus from which it arises has thus been termed the laryngeal nucleus (Edinger), but it is not certain whether it is vagal or accessory.

Collaterals and fibres of the opposite lateral cerebrospinal tract end in connexion with the cells of origin of the accessory nerve, and thus bring its nucleus into connexion with the motor area of the cerebral cortex. Fibres also from the posterior roots of the spinal nerves (afferent or sensory fibres) end in the nucleus.

Vagus and Glossopharyngeal Nerves.

The vagus and glossopharyngeal nerves have similar connexions with the brain, and they may therefore be studied together. The greater part of both nerves is composed of afferent fibres

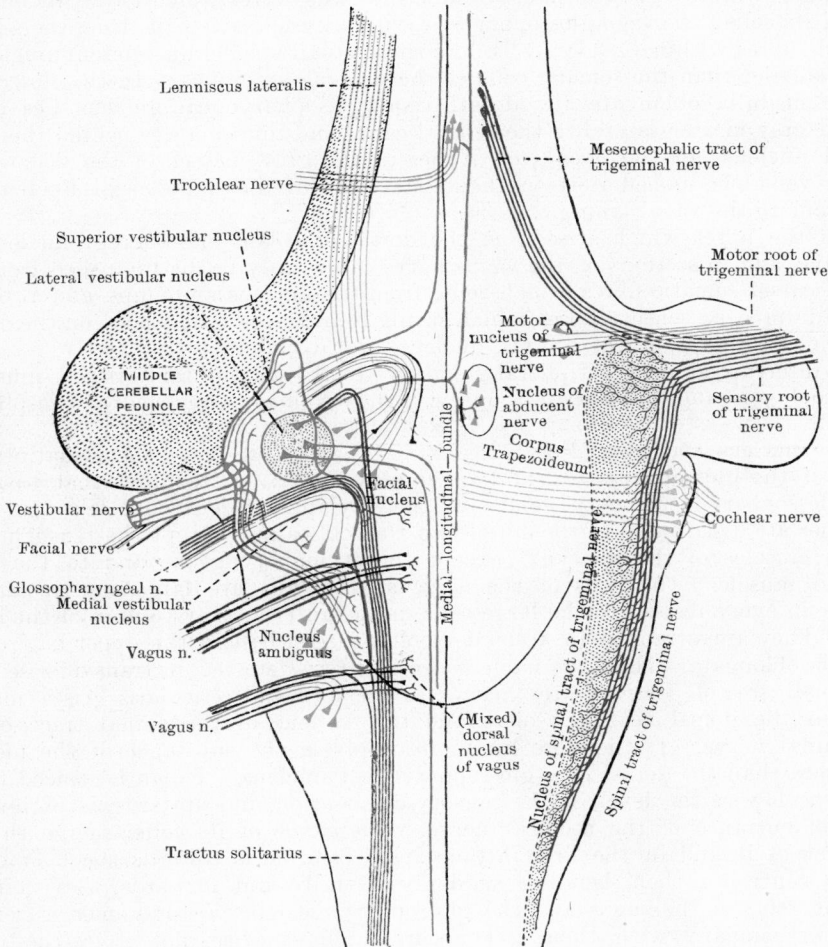

FIG. 768.—DIAGRAM showing the brain connexions of the vagus, glossopharyngeal, auditory, facial, abducent, and trigeminal nerves.

which arise outside the brain-stem from ganglionic cells placed in relation to the nerve-trunks. Both nerves possess efferent fibres also, which spring from two special nuclei of origin situated within the medulla oblongata and termed respectively the **dorsal** or **splanchnic nucleus** and the **nucleus ambiguus**, which is the **somatic nucleus**. The afferent ganglionic fibres of the vagus and glossopharyngeal enter the brain by a series of roots which penetrate the medulla oblongata along the ventral side of the inferior cerebellar peduncle. Within the medulla oblongata they separate into two sets, viz., a series of bundles (composed chiefly of vagus fibres, *i.e.*, afferent splanchnic), which end in the **dorsal nucleus of termination** of the vagus and glossopharyngeal nerves, and another series of bundles (composed chiefly of glossopharyngeal fibres, *i.e.*, taste fibres), which join a conspicuous longitudinal tract of fibres called the **tractus solitarius.**

The **dorsal nucleus** (Figs. 728, p. 846, and 733, p. 851) of the vagus and glosso-pharyngeal nerves is mixed; it contains motor cells which give origin to efferent fibres, and cells around which afferent fibres of the vagus, and possibly also of the glossopharyngeal nerve, break up into terminal arborisations. It is almost as long as the nucleus of the hypoglossal nerve, with which it is closely related. Above, it reaches as high as the auditory striæ, whilst, below, its inferior end falls slightly short of that of the hypoglossal nucleus. In specimens stained by the Weigert-Pal method the two nuclei offer a marked contrast. The hypoglossal nucleus has a dark hue, owing to the enormous numbers of fine fibres which twine in and out amidst its cells; the vago-glossopharyngeal dorsal nucleus is pale, from the scarcity of such fibres within it. Its cells, like those of all splanchnic efferent nuclei, are much smaller than the somatic cells of the nucleus ambiguus. In the closed part of the medulla oblongata the dorsal vago-glossopharyngeal nucleus lies in the central grey matter lateral to the central canal and immediately behind the hypo-glossal nucleus; in the open part it lies in the grey matter of the floor of the fourth ventricle, immediately to the lateral side of the hypoglossal nucleus and subjacent to the vagal triangle.

All the fibres which arise from the dorsal or splanchnic efferent nucleus are very fine, and in sections of the vagus nerve can readily be distinguished from the much coarser somatic fibres, which come from the nucleus ambiguus, and also from the medium-sized sensory fibres, which spring from the ganglia placed on the nerves. The fine fibres from the dorsal nucleus are distributed (indirectly, *i.e.* after being interrupted in a peripheral ganglion) to the involuntary striped muscle of the œsophagus, and the unstriped muscle of the œsophagus, stomach, and respiratory system.

The **nucleus ambiguus** (Figs. 728, 733, 768) gives origin to the somatic motor fibres of the glossopharyngeal and vagus nerves. All of its fibres that pass into the glossopharyngeal nerve end in the stylopharyngeus muscle; the vagal branches are distributed to the muscles of the soft palate (except the tensor palati), to the muscles of the pharynx (except the stylopharyngeus), and to the crico-thyroid muscle. The cells of the nucleus ambiguus are large, multipolar, and similar in every respect to the large cells in the anterior grey column of the spinal cord. They are arranged in a slender column seen best in the upper half of the medulla oblongata. There the nucleus can easily be detected, in transverse sections, as a small area of compact grey matter in the formatio reticularis grisea, midway between the dorsal accessory olive and the nucleus of the spinal tract of the trigeminal nerve. It therefore lies more deeply in the substance of the medulla oblongata than the dorsal vago-glossopharyngeal nucleus. It can be traced down-wards as low as the level of the sensory decussation, and upwards as high as the place of entrance of the cochlear nerve. The axons of its cells emerge through the back of it, and in the first instance pass backwards towards the floor of the fourth ventricle; then, bending suddenly laterally and forwards, they join the afferent roots of the vagus and the glossopharyngeal nerves, and emerge from the brain in company with them. The cardiac fibres arise, not from the dorsal splanchnic efferent nucleus, but from a group of slightly larger cells alongside the nucleus ambiguus (Kosaka).

Sensory Nuclei of Glossopharyngeal and Vagus (Splanchnic and Gustatory Components).—The cells in the portion of the dorsal nucleus which acts as a *nucleus of termination* are spindle-shaped in form and similar to those found in the posterior grey column in the spinal cord. The greater number of the afferent fibres of the vagus nerve, and a small proportion of the afferent fibres of the glosso-pharyngeal nerve, end around these cells in fine terminal arborisations. A small part of the upper portion of the nucleus may be said to belong to the glosso-pharyngeal nerve and the remainder to the vagus nerve.

The **tractus solitarius** (Figs. 727, p. 844; 728, p. 846; and 733, p. 851) is a round bundle of longitudinal fibres which forms a very conspicuous object in trans-verse sections through the medulla oblongata. It begins at the upper end of the medulla oblongata, and can be traced downwards through its whole length. Its precise point of termination is not known; some authorities believe that it extends into the spinal cord—according to Kölliker, to the level of the fourth cervical nerve—but most modern writers limit it to the medulla oblongata. The relations of the tractus solitarius are not the same in all parts of its course. It lies immediately to the lateral side of the dorsal vago-glossopharyngeal nucleus—rather in front of it in the upper part of the the medulla, and behind it in the lower part. Throughout its entire length it is intimately associated with a column of gelatinous grey substance, called the **nucleus of the tractus solitarius**, which is its nucleus of termination. Most of the fibres of the tractus solitarius are derived from the glossopharyngeal nerve; only a few of the afferent fibres of the vagus enter it, but fibres of the sensory root of the facial [nervus intermedius] also enter it. As the fibres of the three nerves join the fasciculus they immediately turn downwards, and at different levels come to an end in the associated nucleus.

As the afferent rootlets of the vagus and the glossopharyngeal nerves traverse the substance of the medulla oblongata in a backward and medial direction to reach the tractus solitarius and the dorsal nucleus of termination, they pass through the spinal tract of the trigeminal nerve and the nucleus of that tract. As the afferent root of the vagus passes through the spinal tract and its nucleus (which is somatic sensory in nature), it gives off to that nucleus its own somatic sensory branches, the peripheral ends of which constitute the auricular branch, distributed to the skin on the back of the auricle. The other afferent fibres in the glossopharyngeal and vagus nerves include taste fibres, sensory fibres from the pharynx, larynx, and other parts of the respiratory and alimentary systems, and other splanchnic afferent fibres. Although there is no sharp demarcation between the terminal nuclei of those various components, it is probable that the taste fibres proceed to the nucleus of the tractus solitarius, the splanch-nic afferent fibres to the dorsal nucleus, and the somatic afferent fibres to the nucleus of the spinal trigeminal tract.

Auditory Nerve.—As this is a nerve of special sense it will be left for consideration after the rest of this series.

Facial Nerve (Figs. 768 and 769).—The facial nerve is a mixed nerve with two separate roots—sensory and motor.

The **motor root** is so much the larger that the term **facial nerve** is often applied to it alone. It emerges through the lower border of the pons a little medial to the auditory nerve. The **sensory root** [nervus intermedius] is a very slender cord that lies between the auditory nerve and the motor root —but nearer the former than the latter (Fig. 766)—and it sinks into the upper end of the medulla oblongata. The two roots run alongside the auditory nerve be-tween the pons and the internal auditory meatus.

The fibres of the sensory root

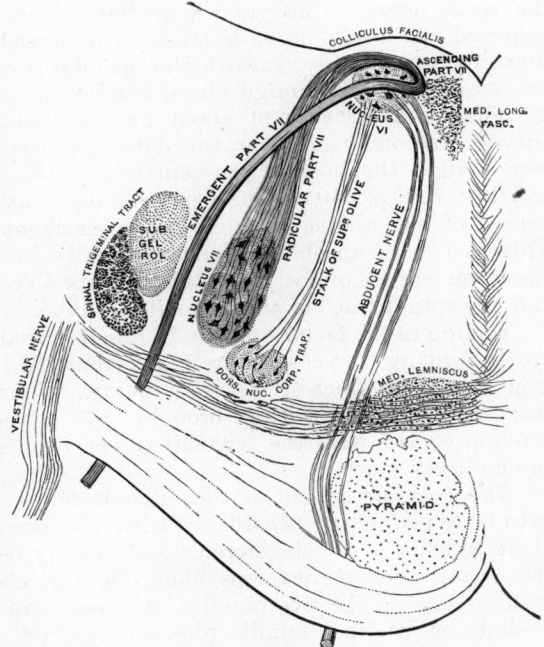

FIG. 769.—DIAGRAM OF THE INTRAPONTINE COURSE OF THE FACIAL NERVE.

Sub. gel. rol. refers to the nucleus of the spinal trigeminal tract.

arise in the temporal bone from the cells of the ganglion of the facial nerve. Those, like the cells of a spinal ganglion, are unipolar—the single process in each case dividing into a peripheral and a central branch. The group of peri-pheral fibres represent parts of the greater superficial petrosal nerve and chorda tympani nerve. The central fibres form the sensory root; they penetrate the brain, and, passing either through or behind the spinal tract of the trigeminal nerve, they finally reach the upper part of the column of grey matter in connexion with the tractus solitarius, and in that they end. The sensory root has therefore the same terminal connexions as the glossopharyngeal nerve.

The motor nucleus of the facial nerve contains elements serially homologous with both the somatic (nucleus ambiguus) and splanchnic (nucleus dorsalis) efferent nuclei of the glossopharyngeal and vagus. It is composed partly of the larger cells characteristic of the former and the smaller cells distinctive of the latter. The axons of the somatic cells innervate the striated muscles of the face, whereas the splanchnic efferent fibres pass to the sphenopalatine, otic and submandibular ganglia (as their white rami communicantes), and are concerned with the regulation of the secretory activity of the large salivary glands and other glands around the mouth; these secretory fibres of the seventh nerve leave the brain with its sensory root [nervus intermedius], which, as has been explained already, is not composed wholly of afferent fibres.

The facial nucleus is situated close to the place where the nerve emerges from the brain, but the nerve does not at once pass to the point of exit. It pursues a long and devious path within the pons before it finally reaches the surface. This intrapontine part of the nerve may be divided into three parts, viz.: (1) a radicular part, (2) an ascending portion, and (3) an emergent part.

The **radicular part of the facial nerve** (Fig. 769) is composed of a large number of fine, loosely arranged bundles of fibres which issue from the lateral and dorsal aspect of the nucleus and proceed backwards and slightly medially through the pons. Reaching the floor of the fourth ventricle they curve medially, and the bundles which lie highest up sweep over the lower part of the nucleus of the sixth nerve. Close to the median plane they turn sharply upwards and are collected into a solid nerve-bundle. This **ascending part** (Figs. 768 and 769) proceeds upwards immediately beneath the ependyma of the ventricular floor on the dorsal surface of the medial longitudinal bundle, and along the medial side of the abducent nucleus for a distance of about five millimetres; it then bends laterally, and curves a second time over the dorsal surface of the abducent nucleus, and that bend bulges the floor of the ventricle, producing the **colliculus facialis** (Fig. 769 and Fig. 724, p. 840). The nerve having thus made a curved loop over the dorsal aspect of the abducent nucleus, its **emergent part** now begins (Figs. 768, 769). This part takes an oblique course laterally and downwards to its place of exit at the lower border of the pons; and, on its way, it passes between its own nucleus and the spinal tract of the trigeminal nerve.

Ending in the facial nucleus, in fine terminal arborisations around its cells, there are: (1) many cortico-nuclear fibres from the opposite pyramidal tract; (2) fibres from the spinal tract of the fifth nerve; (3) fibres from the corpus trapezoideum, etc. The nucleus is thus brought into connexion with the motor area of the cerebral cortex, with the trigeminal nerve or sensory nerve of the face, and with the auditory nerve.

The peculiar course of the efferent fibres of the facial nerve within the pons is to be explained in accordance with the general principle regulating migrations of nerve-cells, to which reference has already been made (p. 844). In the embryo the facial nucleus develops alongside the abducent nucleus. The latter, controlling one of the eye-muscles, receives most of its afferent impulses from the medial longitudinal bundle (descending from the optic centres in the superior corpus quadrigeminum), and therefore it remains alongside the medial longitudinal bundle and perhaps moves slightly upwards, i.e., towards the mid-brain. The facial nucleus, however, receives most of its stimuli from the nucleus of the spinal tract of the trigeminal nerve, and therefore, as the walls of the metencephalon thicken during their growth, that nucleus retains its proximity to the trigeminal nucleus (Fig. 769), and so migrates along a course which remains mapped out by its emerging fibres. Streeter, working with human embryos, and Ariëns-Kappers, on comparative and therefore broader lines, have elucidated the meaning of the peculiar intrapontine course of the facial nerve.

Abducent Nerve (Figs. 735 and 769). — The abducent nerve is a small motor nerve which emerges from the brain at the lower border of the pons above the lateral side of the pyramid of the medulla oblongata. It is the nerve of supply to the lateral rectus muscle of the eyeball. Its **nucleus** of origin is a small spherical mass of grey matter, containing large multipolar cells, which lies in the lower part of the pons, close to the median plane and immediately subjacent to the grey matter of the floor of the fourth ventricle. Its position can be easily indicated on the ventricular floor, seeing that it is placed subjacent to the facial colliculus and immediately above the level of the auditory striæ. Its peculiar and intimate relation to the intrapontine portion of the facial nerve has already been indicated.

The axons of the multipolar cells of the nucleus emerge from the medial side of the nucleus in several bundles which proceed through the whole dorso-ventral

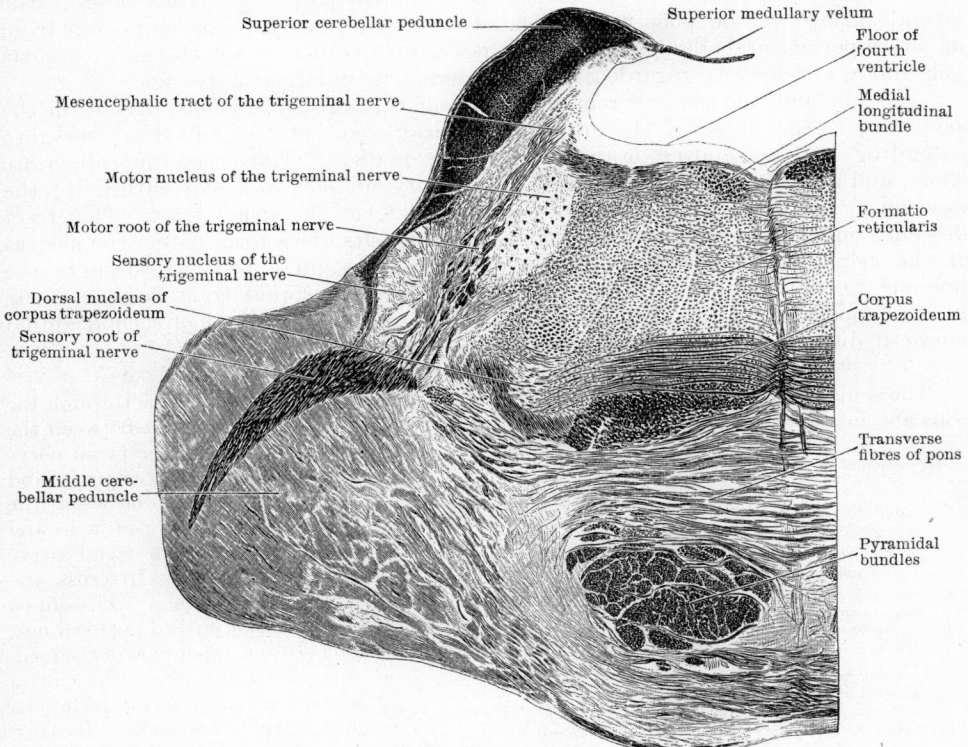

Superior cerebellar peduncle

Superior medullary velum

Floor of fourth ventricle

Mesencephalic tract of the trigeminal nerve

Medial longitudinal bundle

Motor nucleus of the trigeminal nerve

Formatio reticularis

Motor root of the trigeminal nerve

Sensory nucleus of the trigeminal nerve

Dorsal nucleus of corpus trapezoideum

Corpus trapezoideum

Sensory root of trigeminal nerve

Middle cerebellar peduncle

Transverse fibres of pons

Pyramidal bundles

FIG. 770.—SECTION THROUGH THE PONS AT THE LEVEL OF THE NUCLEI OF THE TRIGEMINAL NERVE.

thickness of the pons towards the place of exit. As they pass forwards they incline downwards and slightly laterally. In the dorsal part of the pons they proceed forwards on the medial side of the dorsal nucleus of the corpus trapezoideum, whilst in the basilar part of the pons they keep for the most part to the lateral side of the pyramidal bundles, although several of the nerve rootlets pierce these on their way to the surface.

It would appear probable that certain of the axons of the cells of the abducent nucleus enter the medial longitudinal fasciculus and proceed upwards in it to end in the oculomotor nucleus of the opposite side. Fibres and collaterals from the basis pedunculi of the opposite side enter the nucleus, and, ending around the cells, bring the nucleus into connexion with the motor area of the cerebral cortex. A slender bundle of fibres connects it with the dorsal trapezoid nucleus, and is called the *peduncle* of that nucleus (named "stalk of sup^r. olive" in Fig. 769).

Trigeminal Nerve.—The **fifth cranial nerve** strikes its roots deeply into the brain and establishes a connexion with it which extends from the upper part of the mid-brain to the level of the second cervical nerve. No other cranial nerve presents so extensive a connexion (Fig. 768, p. 881). It has two roots—a large afferent or sensory root and a small efferent or motor root; both roots appear close together on the surface of the pons, rather nearer its upper than its lower border, and in the same line as the facial, and glossopharyngeal and vagus nerves (Fig. 766, p. 879).

The **sensory root** is composed of fibres which arise outside the brain from the cells of the trigeminal ganglion [g. semilunare]. They end within the brain in a tadpole-shaped nucleus, the swollen body of which is situated in the pons and is termed the main sensory nucleus of the trigeminal nerve: the tail is a long column of grey matter which is directly continuous below with the substantia gelatinosa of the spinal cord.

The **main sensory nucleus** (Fig. 770) is an oval mass of grey matter placed half-way up the pons in the lateral part of its dorsal portion. It lies close to the lateral surface of the pons and immediately subjacent to the submerged margin of the superior cerebellar peduncle. It is directly continuous with the substantia gelatinosa, and may be regarded as being merely its enlarged upper end.

The fibres of the sensory root, on reaching the sensory nucleus, divide (in the same way as the fibres of the entering posterior roots of the spinal nerves) into ascending and descending branches (Fig. 768, p. 881). The ascending fibres are short, and almost immediately enter the sensory nucleus and end within it; the descending fibres turn sharply downwards and form the **spinal tract**. That tract descends on the lateral side of the nucleus in which its fibres terminate—the **nucleus of the spinal tract of the fifth nerve**. Fibres constantly leave it to enter the nucleus, so that the lower it gets the smaller does the spinal tract become, until, in the upper part of the spinal cord, about the level of the first or second spinal nerve, it disappears altogether.

The spinal tract of the trigeminal nerve is a conspicuous object in sections through the pons and medulla oblongata. In the pons it traverses the dorsal part—first between the emergent part of the facial nerve and the vestibular nerve, and then, lower down, between the inferior cerebellar peduncle and the nucleus of the facial nerve (Fig. 735, p. 854). In cross sections it presents a well-defined semilunar or curved piriform outline. In the upper part of the medulla oblongata it lies on the ventral surface of the inferior peduncle, and is, therefore, nearer the surface than in the pons (Fig. 733, p. 851); here it is traversed and broken up into bundles by the olivo-cerebellar fibres and the roots of the glossopharyngeal and vagus nerves. Finally, it comes to the surface and its fibres are spread over the area on the side of the medulla oblongata known as the **tubercle of the fifth nerve**. (Fig. 732, p. 850).

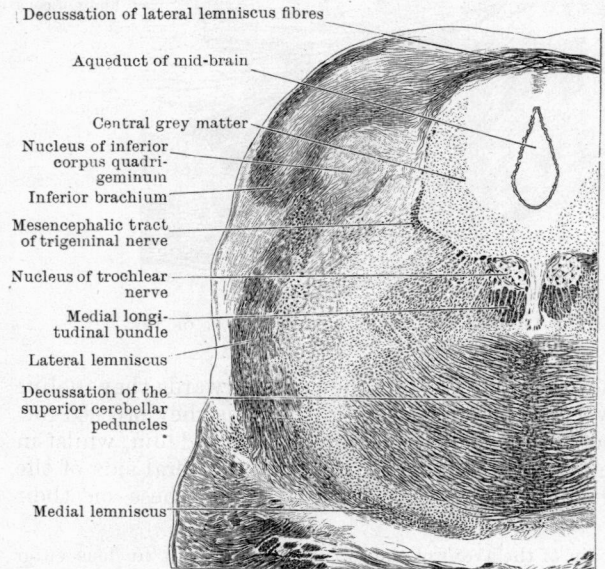

Decussation of lateral lemniscus fibres

Aqueduct of mid-brain

Central grey matter

Nucleus of inferior corpus quadrigeminum

Inferior brachium

Mesencephalic tract of trigeminal nerve

Nucleus of trochlear nerve

Medial longitudinal bundle

Lateral lemniscus

Decussation of the superior cerebellar peduncles

Medial lemniscus

FIG. 771.—SECTION THROUGH THE INFERIOR CORPUS QUADRIGEMINUM AND THE TEGMENTUM OF THE MID-BRAIN AT THE LEVEL OF THE MIDDLE PART OF THE TROCHLEAR NUCLEUS.

The **motor root of the trigeminal nerve** is distributed chiefly to the muscles of mastication, and derives its fibres from the motor nucleus.

The **motor nucleus** (Fig. 770) lies in the lateral part of the dorsal division of the pons, close to the medial side of the main sensory nucleus, but slightly nearer the floor of the fourth ventricle. It is serially homologous with the motor nuclei of the lateral somatic group, namely, the facial nucleus and the nucleus ambiguus. It does not become displaced so far forwards as these nuclei, because its chief source of sensory impulses—the terminal nucleus of the trigeminal afferent fibres—is placed alongside it, and there is no need for any definite migration (Fig. 769).

The **mesencephalic tract of the fifth nerve** takes origin from a column of loosely arranged pear-shaped unipolar cells placed in the extreme lateral part of the grey matter around the aqueduct. As that tract is traced downwards it gradually increases in size by the accession of new fibres, and it is crescentic in transverse section (Figs. 737, p. 856; 738, p. 857; and 739, p. 858). In the lower part of the mid-brain it lies on the medial side of the superior cerebellar peduncle; and the trochlear nerve, on its way to the surface, runs downwards in its concavity and on its medial side. In the upper part of the pons it continues its course downwards on the lateral and deep aspect of the grey matter in the floor of the fourth ventricle. Finally, reaching the level of the nuclei of the trigeminal nerve, the fibres of the mesencephalic tract turn forwards and pass into the *motor* root, in association with which they proceed to the muscles of mastication, of which they represent the proprioceptive fibres. There is some evidence that the mesencephalic tract contains, besides the proprioceptive afferents from the masticatory muscles, similar fibres from the extrinsic muscles of the eyeball. The evidence to hand points to the fact that these latter fibres enter the brain stem not by the fifth, but by the trunks of the third, fourth, and sixth cranial nerves. (Sherrington, Woollard, Stibbe, Tarkhan.)

The reason why its afferent nature was not suspected until recent times is no doubt the fact that its fibres arise not in some **ganglion** outside the central nervous system, like other afferent nerves, but from cells inside the mid-brain. The neural crest in the mesencephalic region must have been drawn into the neural tube during development and given rise to that sensory nucleus of origin (*not* a terminal nucleus) within the central nervous system.

Trochlear Nerve.—The **fourth cranial nerve** supplies the superior oblique muscle of the eyeball. It emerges through the back of the brain-stem, at the upper part of the superior medullary velum, immediately below the lower border of the inferior corpus quadrigeminum (Fig. 753, p. 865). Its **nucleus** is a small oval mass of cells, placed in the ventral part of the central grey matter, at the level of the upper part of the inferior corpus quadrigeminum. The close association of this nucleus with the medial longitudinal bundle has already been referred to. It is sunk deeply in a bay which is hollowed out on the dorsal and medial aspect of that tract. The nerve has a course of some length within the mid-brain. The axons of the cells leave the lateral aspect of the nucleus, and curve backwards

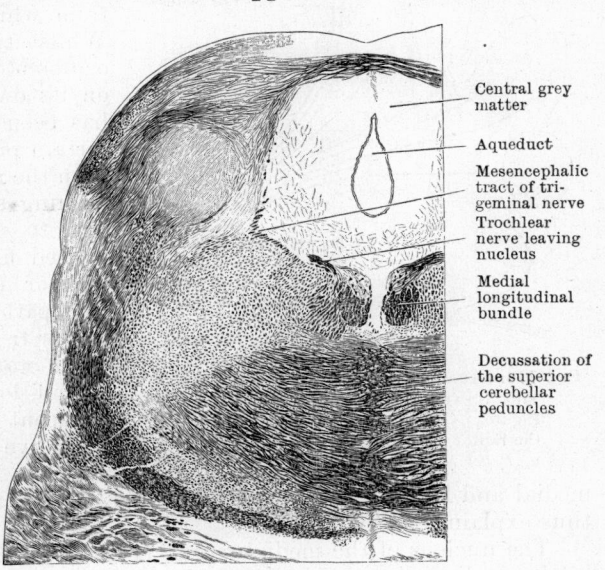

Central grey matter

Aqueduct

Mesencephalic tract of trigeminal nerve

Trochlear nerve leaving nucleus

Medial longitudinal bundle

Decussation of the superior cerebellar peduncles

FIG. 772.—SECTION THROUGH THE INFERIOR CORPUS QUADRIGEMINUM AND THE TEGMENTUM OF THE MID-BRAIN AT THE LEVEL OF THE LOWER PART OF THE TROCHLEAR NUCLEUS.

and laterally in the central grey matter until they reach the medial surface of the mesencephalic tract of the trigeminal nerve. There they are gathered together into one or two round bundles, which, bending sharply, turn downwards at a right angle and descend on the medial side of the trigeminal tract. When the region below the inferior corpus quadrigeminum is reached, the nerve makes another sharp bend. This time it turns medially, enters the upper end of the superior medullary velum, in which it decussates with its fellow of the opposite side. Having thus crossed the median plane, the trochlear nerve emerges at the medial border of the superior cerebellar peduncle. The course of the trochlear nerve in the central grey matter may be traced by examination in the order given of Fig. 771, Fig. 772, Fig. 739, p. 858, and Fig. 753, p. 865.

Oculomotor Nerve.—The **third cranial nerve** supplies the levator palpebræ superioris, all the extrinsic muscles of the eyeball (with the exception of the superior oblique and the lateral rectus) and also two muscles within the eyeball, viz., the sphincter pupillae and the ciliary muscle. The **nucleus** of origin is in the ventral part of the central grey matter subjacent to the superior corpus quadrigeminum (Fig. 759, p. 872). In length it measures from 5 to 6 mm. Its relation to the medial longitudinal fasciculus (Fig. 759) is even more intimate than that of the trochlear nucleus. It is closely applied to the dorsal and medial aspect of this strand; many of its cells occupy a position in the intervals between the nerve-bundles of the tract, and some are seen even in front of it. The axons of the cells leave the nucleus in numerous bundles which describe a series of curves as they proceed forwards through the medial longitudinal fasciculus, the tegmentum, red nucleus, and medial margin of the substantia nigra, to emerge finally from the brain-stem along the bottom of the medial sulcus of the mid-brain.

The cells are not uniformly distributed throughout the oculomotor nucleus. They are grouped into several more or less distinct clumps, some of which possess cells which differ in size and appearance from the others. These cell-clusters are very generally believed to possess a definite relation to the several branches of the nerve and the muscles which they supply. Perlia recognises no less than seven such cell-clusters in each nucleus, with a small median nucleus from which fibres for both nerves spring. Whilst the majority of the fibres in an oculomotor nerve arise from the cell-groups on its own side of the median plane, it has been satisfactorily established that a certain proportion of its fibres are derived from the nucleus of the opposite side, thus forming a crossed connexion and giving rise to a median decussation. Those crossed fibres proceed to the medial and inferior recti and the inferior oblique. The part of the nucleus of the medial rectus from which crossed fibres are derived stands in connexion, through the medial longitudinal fasciculus, with the abducent nucleus, from which proceeds the nerve of supply for the lateral rectus muscle. The harmonious action of the medial and lateral recti in producing the conjugate movements of the eyeballs is thus explained.

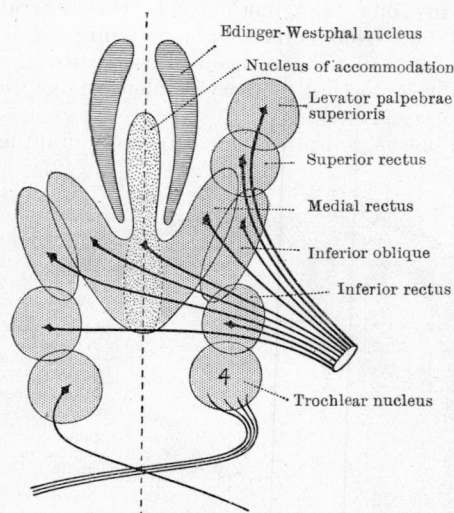

Edinger-Westphal nucleus
Nucleus of accommodation
Levator palpebrae superioris
Superior rectus
Medial rectus
Inferior oblique
Inferior rectus
4
Trochlear nucleus

Fig. 773.—Diagram of the Oculomotor and Trochlear Nuclei (modified from Brouwer's Figure). (By permission of the Author and of the Editor of the *Zeitschr. f. d. gesamte Neur. u. Psych.*)

The nucleus of the medial rectus is larger than the rest and becomes blended in the median plane with the nucleus of the other side to form a special nucleus of convergence which pushes forward as a great tongue-shaped process (Fig. 773).

The oculomotor nucleus is connected—(1) with the occipital part of the cerebral cortex by fibres which reach it through the optic radiation; (2) with the vestibular, trochlear, and abducent nuclei (and probably with other nuclei) by fibres which come to it through the medial longitudinal fasciculus; (3) possibly with the facial nerve by fibres which pass out from it into the medial longitudinal fasciculus (p. 851); (4) with the fibres which enter it from the optic tract.

It is important to recognise that although the main part of the oculomotor nucleus belongs to the medial somatic group, which also includes the trochlear, abducent, and hypoglossal nuclei, it includes also a representative (the Edinger-Westphal group of small cells) of the column of splanchnic efferent nuclei (parasympathetic) in series with those of the facial, glossopharyngeal, and vagus nerves. Its axons pass out with the other fibres of the oculomotor nerve and enter the ciliary ganglion, where they end in relationship with the cells that innervate the ciliary muscle and the sphincter pupillae. The third, fourth, and sixth cranial nerves, which supply motor fibres to the extrinsic muscle of the eye contain also proprioceptive afferent fibres (p. 887).

Auditory Nerve.—The **eighth cranial nerve** is a thick composite bundle that enters the brain at the lower border of the pons. Its fibres spring from bipolar ganglionic cells in the immediate neighbourhood of the internal ear (see section dealing with the Organs of Sense). One group of them forms the **spiral ganglion**, the peripheral branches of which are distributed to the spiral organ in the cochlea: another group constitutes the **vestibular ganglion**, which distributes fibres to the ampullæ of the semicircular ducts, the utricle, and the saccule. Although the central processes of the cells in the two ganglia accompany one another

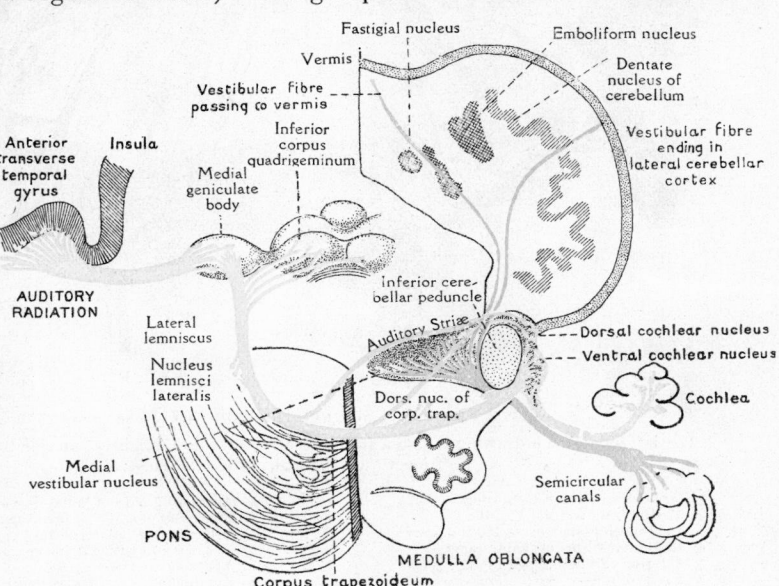

FIG. 774.—CENTRAL CONNEXIONS OF COCHLEAR AND VESTIBULAR NERVES.
Vestibular fibres green.   Cochlear fibres yellow.

and are known collectively as the auditory nerve, they really remain distinct throughout, in their mode of termination in the brain as well as in their peripheral distribution. Reaching the brain the auditory nerve divides into two parts, viz., the cochlear nerve and the vestibular nerve, which have totally different connexions, corresponding to their distinct functions. At the pons, the two nerves separate to embrace the inferior cerebellar peduncle—the vestibular nerve entering the pons on the medial side of the peduncle, whilst the cochlear nerve sweeps round its lateral surface; and special nuclei of termination require to be studied in connexion with each of them.

The **cochlear nerve** is composed of finer fibres than the vestibular nerve, and they acquire their medullary sheaths at a later period. It is the true nerve of hearing, and its fibres end in two nuclei which are intimately related to the inferior cerebellar peduncle. One of them, called the **dorsal cochlear nucleus**, is a piriform mass placed on the back of the inferior peduncle—between it and the flocculus. The other, termed the **ventral cochlear nucleus**, is placed on the front of this peduncle in the interval between the cochlear and vestibular nerves, after they have separated from each other. The fibres of the cochlear nerve enter those two nuclei and end around the cells in arborisations which are finer, closer, and more intricate than those met with in any other nerve-ending in the brain.

The **vestibular nerve** enters the brain at a slightly higher level than the cochlear nerve. It proceeds backwards through the pons between the inferior cerebellar peduncle, which lies on its lateral side, and the spinal tract of the trigeminal nerve, which is placed on its medial side. Its fibres end in a series of terminal nuclei—medial, lateral, superior and inferior—and in the cerebellar cortex.

The **medial nucleus** (Figs. 735, p. 854; and 774) is the principal one. It is a large diffuse nuclear mass which lies in the floor of the fourth ventricle subjacent to the vestibular area (Fig. 724, p. 840). It is situated, therefore, in both the

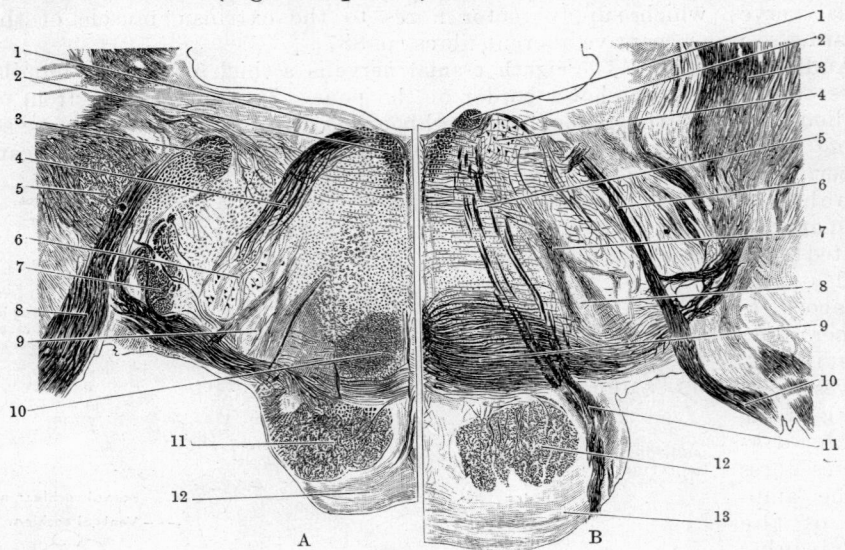

FIG. 775.—SECTION THROUGH THE PONS.

The left side of the drawing is taken from a section at a level slightly inferior to the section from which the right side is taken.

A	B
1. Ascending part of facial nerve.	1. Ascending part of facial nerve.
2. Medial longitudinal bundle.	2. Emergent portion of facial nerve.
3. Descending tract of vestibular nerve.	3. Inferior cerebellar peduncle.
4. Radicular fibres of facial nerve.	4. Nucleus of abducent nerve.
5. Inferior cerebellar peduncle.	5. Abducent nerve.
6. Facial nucleus.	6. Emergent part of facial nerve.
7. Spinal tract of trigeminal nerve.	7. Peduncle of dorsal nucleus of corpus trapezoideum.
8. Vestibular nerve.	8. Dorsal nucleus of corpus trapezoideum.
9. Dorsal nucleus of corpus trapezoideum.	9. Corpus trapezoideum.
10. Medial lemniscus.	10. Facial nerve.
11. Pyramidal tract.	11. Abducent nerve.
12. Transverse fibres of pons.	12. Pyramidal tract.
	13. Transverse fibres of pons.

pons and the medulla oblongata to the lateral side of the foveæ. In transverse section it is prismatic in outline, and its surface is crossed by the auditory striæ.

When the vestibular nerve enters the brain on the medial side of the inferior peduncle, its fibres bifurcate to form ascending and descending branches. The latter pass vertically downwards in separate bundles and form the **descending tract of the vestibular nerve** (Figs. 735, p. 854; 733, p. 851; and 768, p. 881). This proceeds through the lower part of the pons into the medulla oblongata, in which it may be traced as far as the level of the sensory decussation. The **inferior nucleus** is associated with the descending tract; it is a column of grey matter containing sparsely strewn nerve-cells around which the fibres end in fine arborisations.

Some of the ascending fibres end in the **lateral nucleus**. That nucleus is composed of a number of large and conspicuous multipolar nerve-cells scattered amidst the bundles of the vestibular nerve. As it is traced upwards into the pons the nucleus gradually inclines backwards, and finally it occupies a place in the side wall of the fourth ventricle. It attains its greatest size at the level of the emerging part of the facial nerve, and that upper part is termed the **superior nucleus**. Other ascending fibres pass without interruption into the cerebellum to terminate in the cortex of the vermis and hemisphere. In their course many of those fibres pass through the nucleus fastigii, and many writers describe them as terminating in this nucleus; but according to Ramon y Cajal they merely traverse it on their way to the cerebellar cortex.

From the lateral nucleus a strand of fibres passes medially to reach the medial longitudinal bundle, of which it forms one of the most important constituents. Some of these fibres pass upwards to the nuclei of the oculomotor, trochlear, and abducent nerves to influence the movements of the eyes automatically, so that the visual field remains constant when the head moves (and stimulates the vestibular nerve); others downwards, probably to the nucleus of the accessory nerve, which is concerned in regulating the movements of the head.   Other fibres

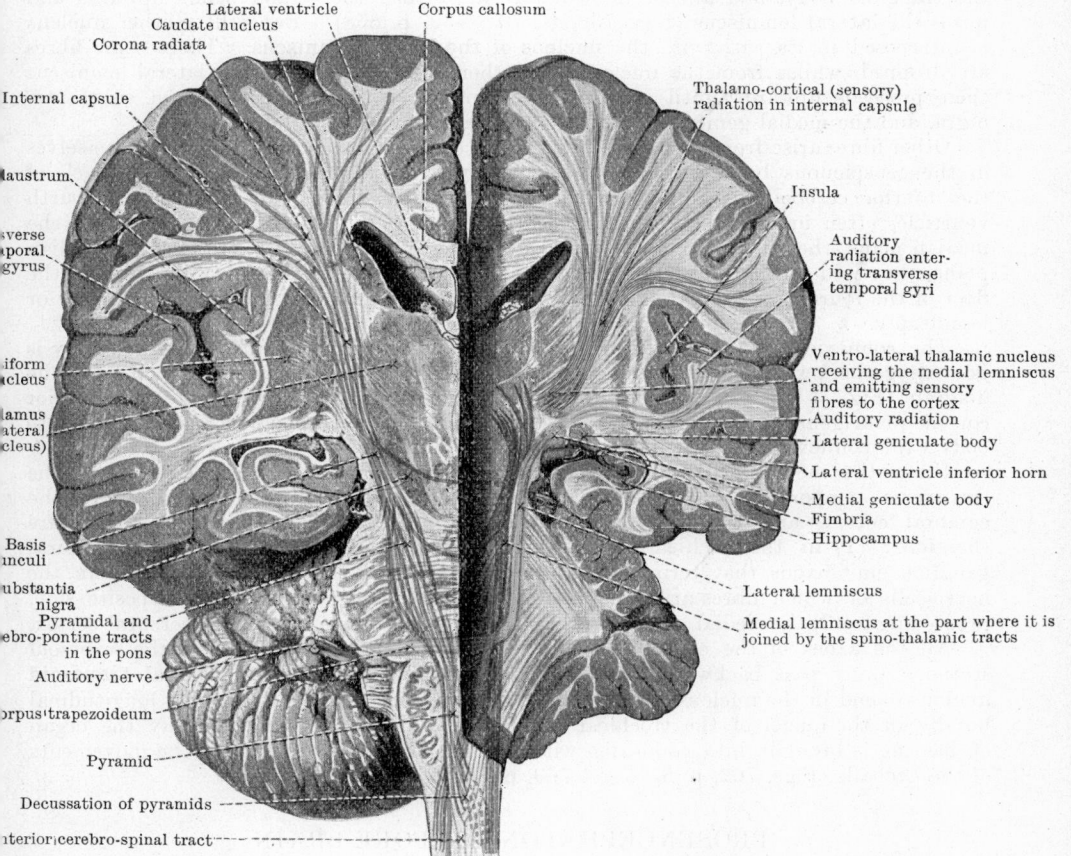

Fig. 776.—Coronal Section of Brain to show the Whole of the Central Auditory Path.
The left hemisphere (right side of the figure) is cut on a plane posterior to that of the right.
Motor fibres red.   Sensory fibres blue.   Auditory fibres yellow.

arise from the lateral nucleus and pass directly to the spinal cord without passing through the medial longitudinal bundle; they form the **vestibulo-spinal tract**, which passes downwards in the anterior white column and distributes fibres to the various motor nuclei in the anterior grey column of the spinal cord (Fig. 714, p. 825).

The **superior nucleus** also emits a group of fibres which pass directly to the mid-brain, chiefly to the oculomotor and trochlear nuclei.

Central Connexions of the Cochlear Nerve.—The cochlear nuclei are brought into connexion with the inferior corpus quadrigeminum and the medial geniculate body of the opposite side by the fibres of the corpus trapezoideum and the lateral lemniscus.

The fibres of the cochlear nerve end in the cochlear nuclei.   From the cells of those nuclei two tracts arise, viz., a **ventral tract**, composed of the fibres of the corpus trapezoideum, and a **dorsal tract**, which is represented by the auditory striæ.

The **corpus trapezoideum** (Figs. 735 and 770) is formed of the axons of the cells of the ventral cochlear nucleus, as well as the axons of certain of the cells of the dorsal nucleus. In the midst of the corpus trapezoideum are lodged large cells which are known as the *ventral nucleus of the corpus trapezoideum*, and these give off axons which join the strand with which they are associated. Many of the fibres of the corpus trapezoideum end in a small mass of grey matter called the **dorsal nucleus of the corpus trapezoideum** [n. olivaris superior], which is placed immediately behind the trapezoid body. The trapezial fibres cross the median plane and decussate with the corresponding fibres of the opposite side. Reaching the opposite dorsal trapezoid nucleus, more fibres leave the trapezoid body, and almost immediately after that the strand bends upwards and forms the **lateral lemniscus** (Figs. 738, p. 857 ; 739, p. 858). But still another nucleus is interposed in its path, viz., the **nucleus of the lateral lemniscus**. There some fibres are dropped, whilst from the nuclear cells others are acquired, and the lateral lemniscus then proceeds upwards until it reaches the inferior corpus quadrigeminum, substantia nigra, and the medial geniculate body, in which its fibres end.

Other fibres arise from the cells of the dorsal cochlear nucleus, and arrange themselves in the conspicuous bundles, called the **auditory striæ**, which sweep round the back of the inferior cerebellar peduncle and proceed medially across the floor of the fourth ventricle, often immediately beneath the ependyma (Fig. 724, p. 840). Reaching the median plane, they dip forwards into the substance of the pons, and, crossing the median plane, they join the lateral lemniscus. The auditory striæ are not always visible in the floor of the fourth ventricle (Fig. 724), for more often than not they are buried more or less deeply.

The connexion between the cochlear nuclei and the inferior quadrigeminal body is not altogether with that of the opposite side, as the foregoing description and the diagram (Fig. 774) might lead one to infer. A few fibres pass directly to the inferior corpus quadrigeminum of the same side, but none to the corresponding medial geniculate body : the connexion with the latter is entirely *crossed*.

From the medial geniculate body there proceeds a tract to the cortex of the transverse temporal gyri. The whole nervous apparatus is thus linked on to the cerebral cortex, and the successive neurones which build up the entire chain are therefore : (1) in the cochlea of the internal ear, the bipolar cells of the spiral ganglion emit axons that terminate in the brain ; in (2) the cochlear nuclei, from the nerve-cells of which fibres arise and cross to the lateral lemniscus of the opposite side, proceeding to (3) the medial geniculate body, from which fibres pass to the cerebral cortex.

All the axons of the cells of the dorsal trapezoid nucleus do not join the trapezoid strand. Many pass backwards in a group called the **pedicle of the dorsal trapezoid nucleus** to end in the nucleus of the abducent nerve, and, through the medial longitudinal bundle, in the nuclei of the trochlear and oculomotor nerves. In that way the organ of hearing is brought into connexion with the nuclei which preside over the movements of the eyeballs (Figs. 762, p. 875, and 769, p. 883).

PROSENCEPHALON OR FORE-BRAIN

The fore-brain vesicle in the embryo is subdivided, more or less arbitrarily, into two parts—an anterior termed the **telencephalon**, and a posterior called the **diencephalon**, which forms the greater part of the walls of the third ventricle. The extreme anterior part of the third ventricle belongs to the telencephalon; it includes the anterior wall of the neural tube, which is known as the **lamina terminalis** (Fig. 782).

DEVELOPMENT OF PARTS DERIVED FROM THE FORE-BRAIN

The alar part of each side wall of the telencephalon grows out to form a diverticulum which ultimately constitutes the cerebral hemisphere, and thus, from a very early period, the primitive position of that part of the side wall is indicated by the interventricular foramen—a wide aperture of communication between the cavity of the cerebral hemisphere and the third ventricle (Fig. 777).

The alar part of the side wall of the diencephalon is utilised for the development of the thalamus, the epithalamus, and the metathalamus. Of those the thalamus is derived from the anterior and by far the greatest part of the alar wall. It arises as a large oval swelling which gradually approaches its fellow of the opposite side, and thus diminishes the width of the third ventricle. Finally, the two bodies sometimes come into contact in the median plane and cohere over an area corresponding to the interthalamic connexus [massa intermedia]. This may occur about the end of the second month.

From that section of the side wall to which the name of metathalamus is given the two geniculate bodies arise. Each of them shows, in the first place, as a depression on the inside of the wall of the diencephalon, and a slight elevation on the outside. As the thalamus grows backwards, it encroaches greatly upon the territory occupied by the geniculate bodies. It thus comes about that in the adult brain the medial geniculate body seems to hold a position on the lateral aspect of the mid-brain, whilst the lateral geniculate body, viewed from the surface, appears to be a part of the thalamus.

From the epithalamic region of the wall of the diencephalon are developed the pineal body, its peduncle, and the habenular region. Those parts are relatively much more evident in the embryonic than in the adult brain. The pineal body appears to be developed as a diverticulum of the posterior part of the roof of the diencephalon, but in reality it is a derivative of the alar lamina. Viewed from the dorsal aspect of the brain-tube, that diverticulum shows, in the first

instance, as a rounded elevation, from each side of which a broad ridge runs forwards. The ridge becomes the stria habenularis, [stria medullaris thalami] whilst in the region of its junction with the pineal elevation the trigonum habenulæ takes shape. The pineal diverticulum ultimately becomes solid, but a small portion of the original cavity is retained as the pineal recess of the third ventricle.

The part of the diencephalon and telencephalon which represents the basal lamina (*i.e.* the part below the level of the hypothalamic sulcus) retains its primitive form, and undergoes only slight change. Consequently, when that region in the adult brain is compared with the corresponding region in the embryonic brain, the resemblance between the two is very striking.

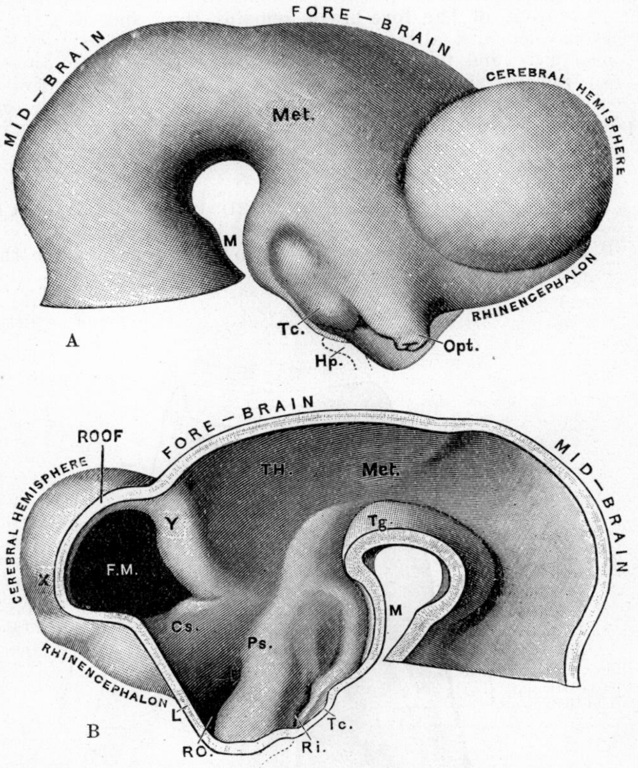

In the fore-brain, therefore, it is the alar lamina which plays the predominant part in the formation of the cerebrum. The value, also, of the basal part of the wall of that portion of the neural tube is still further reduced by the fact that it no longer contains the nuclei of origin of efferent nerves. The highest of those nuclei (the oculomotor) is placed in the mesencephalon. The connexions of the olfactory nerves with the fore-brain are described on page 908, *et seq.*, and those of the optic nerves on page 903. An additional cranial nerve attached to the fore-brain and known as the

FIG. 777.—TWO DRAWINGS OF THE EMBRYONIC BRAIN. (After His.)

A, Reconstruction of the fore-brain and mid-brain of His's embryo KO; profile view. B, Same brain as A, divided along the median plane. M, Mamillary eminence; Tc, Tuber cinereum; Hp, Hypophysis (hypophyseal diverticulum from buccal cavity); Opt, Optic stalk; TH, Thalamus; Tg, Tegmental part of mid-brain; Ps, Pars hypothalamica; Cs, Corpus striatum; FM, Interventricular foramen; L, Lamina terminalis; RO, Optic recess; Ri, Infundibular recess.

nervus terminalis has been described in all classes of vertebrates from fishes to man. Peripherally it is distributed in the nasal mucosa, and its fibres pass towards the brain in close association with the olfactory nerves and tracts; and they have been followed as a distinct bundle in man to the vicinity of the olfactory pyramid. In amphibia the fibres of the nervus terminalis have been followed into the hypothalamus. The functions and central connexions of this nerve are not yet understood.

The region of the fore-brain which lies below the hypothalamic sulcus is termed the hypothalamus. From its diencephalic part [pars mamillaris hypothalami] are derived the mamillary body and a portion of the tuber cinereum. The anterior or telencephalic part of the hypothalamus [pars optica hypothalami] gives rise to the following: the tuber cinereum with the infundibulum and the cerebral part of the hypophysis, the optic chiasma and recess, and the lamina terminalis. The mamillary body forms, in the first instance, a relatively large ventral bulging of the floor of the brain-tube. As development goes on that bulging becomes relatively small, and about the fourth month the single projection becomes divided into a pair of tubercles. The infundibulum and the posterior or cerebral lobe of the hypophysis are developed as a hollow downgrowth of the floor of the telencephalon (Fig. 777). A portion of the original cavity is retained in the upper part of the infundibulum, and constitutes the infundibular recess in the floor of the third ventricle.

The optic nerve is formed chiefly by the growth of fibres backwards from the retina in the wall of the original optic stalk, whilst the chiasma takes form by the passage of fibres across the median plane in front of the infundibulum and behind the optic recess. To a large extent those fibres are derived from the optic nerve. The optic recess of the third ventricle marks the spot where the optic vesicle was originally attached to the inferior and lateral part of the fore-brain, and in the adult it therefore represents a portion of the primitive cavity of the tubular stalk of the optic vesicle. In the course of development the optic nerve fibres, which appear in the stalk of the optic vesicle to form the optic nerve, seek an attachment much farther back, and through the optic tract they are even carried as far as the mid-brain.

The **roof of the fore-brain** remains thin, and does not proceed to the development of nervous elements, although its posterior part becomes invaded by nervous tissue to form the pineal body and the posterior commissure. In front of those structures the roof of the fore-brain remains ependymal and constitutes the roof of the third ventricle. Along the mid-line it becomes invaginated into the third ventricle to form the choroid plexus (Fig. 782, p. 900). The posterior commissure appears as a transverse thickening at the bottom of the groove which lies in the roof of the early brain-tube behind the pineal diverticulum.

PARTS DERIVED FROM THE DIENCEPHALON

Under this heading we have to consider: (1) the **thalamus**; (2) the **epithalamus**, which comprises the pineal body and the habenular region; (3) the **metathalamus** or the geniculate bodies; and (4) the **hypothalamus**.

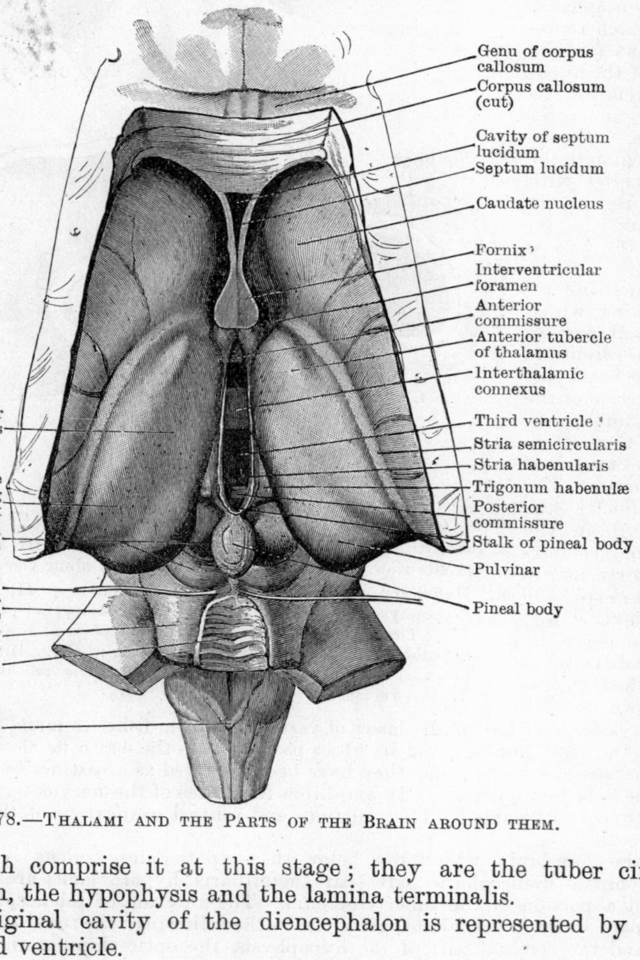

The hypothalamus consists of two portions. One is derived !from the diencephalon [pars mamillaris] and comprises the mamillary body and the portion of the central grey matter which forms the floor of the third ventricle in its immediate vicinity. The other belongs to the telencephalon [pars optica], but it is convenient to study the parts which comprise it at this stage; they are the tuber cinereum, the infundibulum, the hypophysis and the lamina terminalis.

FIG. 778.—THALAMI AND THE PARTS OF THE BRAIN AROUND THEM.

Labels:
- Genu of corpus callosum
- Corpus callosum (cut)
- Cavity of septum lucidum
- Septum lucidum
- Caudate nucleus
- Fornix
- Interventricular foramen
- Anterior commissure
- Anterior tubercle of thalamus
- Interthalamic connexus
- Third ventricle
- Stria semicircularis
- Stria habenularis
- Trigonum habenulæ
- Posterior commissure
- Stalk of pineal body
- Pulvinar
- Pineal body
- Non-ventricular part of thalamus
- Groove corresponding to fornix
- Quadrigeminal bodies
- Trochlear nerve
- Middle cerebellar peduncle
- Superior cerebellar peduncle
- Lingula
- Medulla oblongata

The original cavity of the diencephalon is represented by the greater part of the third ventricle.

Thalamus.—The thalamus is the principal object in this section of the brain (Fig. 778). It is a large ovoid mass of grey matter which lies obliquely across the path of the cerebral peduncle. The anterior end of the thalamus lies close to the median plane, and is separated from the corresponding part of the opposite side by a very narrow interval. The posterior ends of the thalami are larger, and are farther apart, being separated by a fairly wide interval in which the corpora quadrigemina are seen.

The two thalami, in their anterior two-thirds, lie close together, one on each side of the deep median cleft called the third ventricle of the brain. The inferior and lateral surfaces are in apposition with, and indeed, directly connected with, adjacent parts of the brain, and on that account it is customary to study them by means of sections through the brain. The superior and medial surfaces face towards ventricular cavities and are mainly free.

The *lateral surface* of the thalamus is applied to a thick layer of white matter, interposed between it and the lentiform nucleus, called the **internal capsule** and composed mainly of fibres passing to and from the cerebral cortex ; a large proportion of these fibres descend to form the basis pedunculi. From the entire extent of the lateral surface of the thalamus large numbers of fibres stream out and enter the internal capsule, to reach the cerebral cortex. They constitute what is termed the **thalamic radiation**. As the fibres leave the thalamus over the whole of the lateral surface of the ganglionic mass they form a very distinct reticulated zone or stratum which is termed the **external medullary lamina**.

The *inferior surface* of the thalamus rests on the hypothalamus. From the latter region many fibres enter the thalamus on its inferior surface, whilst other fibres leave that surface of the thalamus to take part in the thalamic radiation.

The *superior surface* of the thalamus is free. Laterally it is bounded by a groove which traverses the floor of the lateral ventricle of the brain and intervenes between the thalamus and the caudate nucleus. In that groove is placed a slender band of longitudinal fibres termed the **stria semicircularis**, and in its forepart the thalamo-striate vein [stria and vena terminalis]. Medially, the superior surface is separated from the medial surface in its anterior half by a sharp ledge of the ependyma of the third ventricle raised up by a subjacent longitudinal strand of fibres called the **stria habenularis**. When those two structures, viz., the ependymal ridge and the subjacent stria, are traced backwards, they are seen to turn medially and become continuous with the stalk of the pineal body. Behind the portion of the stria which turns medially towards the pineal body a small depressed triangular area—the **trigonum habenulæ**—situated in front of the superior corpus quadrigeminum, forms a very definite medial boundary for the posterior part of the superior surface of the thalamus.

The superior surface of the thalamus is slightly bulging or convex, and is of a whitish colour, owing to the presence of a thin superficial covering of nerve-fibres termed the **stratum zonale**. It is divided into two areas by a faint oblique groove which corresponds to the edge of the fornix. The two areas which are thus mapped out are very differently related to the ventricles of the brain, and also to the parts which lie above the thalamus. The *lateral area*, which includes the anterior end of the thalamus, forms a part of the floor of the lateral ventricle ; it is covered with ependyma, and is overlapped by the choroid plexus of this ventricle. Along the line of the groove the ependymal lining of the lateral ventricle is reflected over the choroid plexus. The *medial area*, which includes the posterior end of the thalamus, intervenes between the lateral and third ventricles of the brain, and takes no part in the formation of the walls of either. It is covered by a fold of pia mater, termed the tela chorioidea of the third ventricle, above which is the fornix, and those two structures intervene between the thalamus and the corpus callosum (Fig. 782, p. 900, and Fig. 807, p. 922).

The *anterior end* of the thalamus bulges up into the lateral ventricle, forming what is called the **anterior tubercle of the thalamus**, and it is separated from the anterior column of the fornix by the interventricular foramen. The ependymal roof of the passage between the two interventricular foramina is, on each side, continuous with an ependymal strip that extends along the medial wall of the hemisphere behind the foramen. These ependymal strips in the walls of the hemispheres and in the roof of the third ventricle between them are invaginated by the vascular pia to form a continuous sulcus in the ependymal area of the brain wall called the **choroid fissure**. The vascular pia mater covered by the ependymal brain wall is called the **choroid plexus** (Figs. 782, 789, and 790).

The *posterior end* of the thalamus is very prominent and forms a cushion-like projection which overhangs the brachia of the corpora quadrigemina. That prominence is called the **pulvinar**. On the lateral part of the lower surface of the pulvinar there is a small bulging called the **lateral geniculate body** ; most of the fibres of the optic tract end in it.

The *medial surfaces* of the two thalami are placed close together, and are covered not only by the lining ependyma of the third ventricle, but also by a moderately thick layer of grey matter, continuous below with the central grey substance which surrounds the aqueduct in the mid-brain. A band of grey matter, termed the **interthalamic connexus** [massa intermedia], crosses the third ventricle and joins the two thalami together.

Intimate Structure and Connexions of the Thalamus.—The uppermost layer of the thalamus is the **stratum zonale**—a thin coating of white fibres derived to some extent from the optic tract, and probably also from the optic radiation. The medial surface has a thick coating of central grey matter ; whilst intervening between the internal capsule and the lateral surface is the **external medullary lamina**. The lower surface merges into the hypothalamus.

The grey matter of the thalamus is marked off into three very apparent parts —termed the anterior, the medial, and the ventro-lateral thalamic nuclei —by a thin vertical sheet of white matter, continuous with the stratum zonale, termed the **internal medullary lamina**. The **ventro-lateral nucleus** is by far the largest of the three. It stretches backwards beyond the medial nucleus, and includes the whole of the pulvinar (Fig. 780) ; it is pervaded by fibres that arise in it and pass through it towards the internal capsule, forming by far the greatest part of the thalamic radiation. The **medial nucleus** reaches only as far back as the habenular region ; it is much less extensively pervaded by fibres than the ventro-lateral nucleus is. The **anterior nucleus** is the smallest of the three thalamic nuclei. It forms the anterior tubercle, and is prolonged in a wedge-shaped manner, for a short distance, downwards and backwards between the anterior parts of the other two nuclei. The internal medullary lamina splits into two parts and partially encloses the anterior nucleus. In connexion with its large cells a very conspicuous bundle of fibres, called the **mamillo-thalamic tract**, comes to an end.

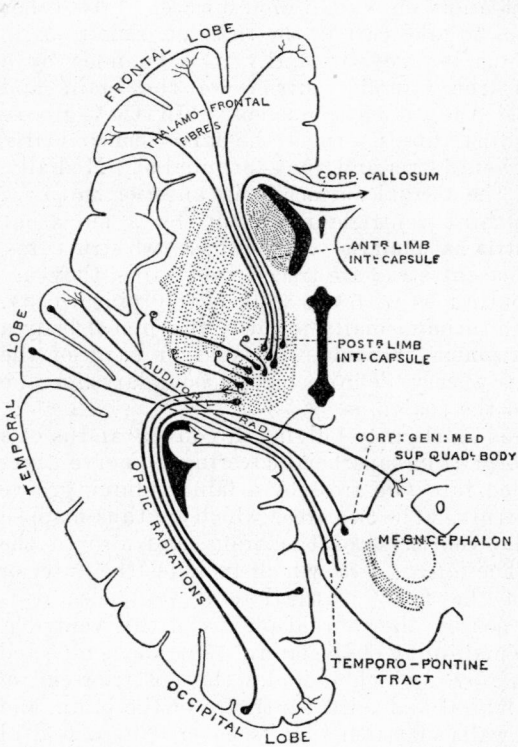

Fig. 779. — Diagram of the Connexions of the Thalamus with the Cerebral Cortex, and of the Latter with the Mid-brain.

The optic radiations are not connected with the thalamus, as shown in this diagram, but with the lateral geniculate body.)

The **connexions of the thalamus** become comprehensible if it is remembered that the grey matter is a ganglionic mass interposed between the sensory tracts and the cerebral cortex. The ascending tracts, which enter it from below, end in the lower part of the ventro-lateral nucleus of the thalamus in connexion with its cells. In addition to them, enormous numbers of fibres, arising within the thalamus as the axons of its cells, stream out from its lateral surface into the internal capsule. Those **thalamo-cortical fibres** pass to every part of the cortex. But fibres from the cortex—**cortico-thalamic fibres**—also stream into the thalamus in large numbers, and end in fine arborisations around its cells. Those fibres enable the cerebral cortex to control the activities of the thalamus. The discriminative powers of the cortex are able to restrain the affective activities of the thalamus.

Fibres emerge from the anterior part of the lateral surface of the thalamus and pass through the anterior limb of the internal capsule to reach the cortex of the frontal lobe. Other fibres end in the caudate and lentiform nuclei, between which they proceed. The fibres issuing from the lateral surface farther back pass through the internal capsule (and to some extent, also, through the lentiform nucleus and the external capsule) to gain the cortex of the posterior part of the frontal lobe and of the parietal lobe.

Numerous fibres that arise in both medial and ventro-lateral nuclei stream out from the under surface of the anterior part of the thalamus, in front of the hypothalamic tegmental region and the mamillary body, and sweep downwards and laterally to reach the region below the lentiform nucleus. One very distinct band which lies above the other fibres (**ansa lenticularis**) goes from the lentiform nucleus to the thalamus, whilst the other (**ansa peduncularis**) proceeds in a lateral direction from the thalamus below the lentiform nucleus and gains the cortex of the temporal lobe and of the insula.

Intimate Structure of the Lateral Geniculate Body.—The lateral geniculate body is composed of a series of alternate grey and white curved laminæ. The alternation gives it a very characteristic appearance in section. The white laminæ are composed of fibres which enter the body from the optic tract.

The connexions of the geniculate bodies will be studied with the optic tract.

Hypothalamic Region.— The tegmentum of the cerebral peduncle is prolonged upwards and assumes a position below the posterior part of the thalamus. The **red nucleus** is a conspicuous object in sections through the lower part of this region

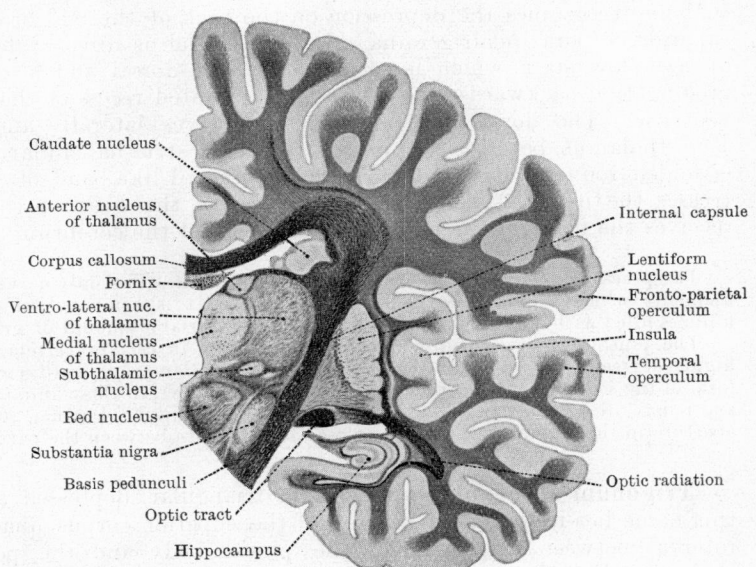

Caudate nucleus

Anterior nucleus of thalamus

Corpus callosum
Fornix
Ventro-lateral nuc. of thalamus
Medial nucleus of thalamus
Subthalamic nucleus

Red nucleus

Substantia nigra

Basis pedunculi

Optic tract

Hippocampus

Internal capsule

Lentiform nucleus
Fronto-parietal operculum
Insula
Temporal operculum

Optic radiation

FIG. 780.—FRONTAL SECTION THROUGH THE CEREBRUM.

(Fig. 780). It presents the same appearance as in the mid-brain, and, gradually diminishing, it disappears before the level of the mamillary body is reached. Carried up around it are the same longitudinal tracts of fibres which have been studied in relation to it in the mid-brain. Certain of those fibres, placed in immediate relation to the red nucleus, form a *capsule* for it. This capsule is partly derived from those fibres of the superior cerebellar peduncle which pass directly up into the thalamus and also partly from fibres which issue from the nucleus itself. The **medial lemniscus** also, which in the upper part of the mid-brain is observed to take up a position behind and lateral to the red nucleus, maintains a similar position in the hypothalamic region. When the red nucleus comes to an end these various fibres are continued onwards and form, in the position previously occupied by the nucleus, a very evident and dense mass of fibres. The fibres of the medial lemniscus, of the superior cerebellar peduncle, and of

57

the red nucleus are prolonged upwards into the ventral part of the thalamus, where they end in connexion with the cells of the ventro-lateral nucleus.

The **substantia nigra** also is carried into the hypothalamic region, where it maintains its original position on the back of the basis pedunculi. As it is traced upwards, it is seen to diminish gradually in amount. It shrinks from the medial to the lateral side, and finally disappears when the posterior part of the mamillary body is reached.

In coronal sections through the hypothalamic region, the most conspicuous object which comes into view is the **subthalamic nucleus** (Fig. 780). It is a small brownish mass of grey matter, shaped like a biconvex lens, which makes its appearance behind the basis pedunculi immediately to the lateral side of the substantia nigra, and, enlarging rapidly in a medial direction, it takes the place of the diminishing substantia nigra. The subthalamic nucleus is made all the more evident by the fact that it is sharply defined by a thin capsule of white fibres. On its medial side these fibres proceed medially and form a very evident decussation across the median plane in the floor of the third ventricle, immediately above the posterior ends of the mamillary bodies. It receives fibres from the globus pallidus of the corpus striatum and emits fibres to the substantia nigra and the tegmentum. (Dr. Purdon Martin associates injury of the subthalamic nucleus with the condition known clinically as chorea.)

Pineal Body.—This is a small, dark, reddish body, about the size of a cherry-stone and shaped like a fir-cone. Placed between the posterior ends of the two thalami, it occupies the depression on the back of the mid-brain between the two superior corpora quadrigemina. Its base, which is directed forwards, is attached by a hollow stalk which is separated into a dorsal and a ventral part by the prolongation backwards into it of a small pointed recess of the cavity of the third ventricle. The dorsal part of the stalk curves laterally and forwards, and, on each thalamus, becomes continuous with the stria habenularis; the ventral part is folded round a narrow but conspicuous cord-like band of white matter which crosses the median plane immediately below the base of the pineal body and receives the name of the **posterior commissure** of the cerebrum (Fig. 782, p. 900).

The pineal body is not composed of nervous elements. The only nerves in it are sympathetic filaments which enter it with its blood-vessels. It is composed of spherical and tubular follicles filled with epithelial cells and containing a variable amount of gritty, calcareous matter.

The pineal body is a rudimentary structure, but in certain vertebrates it attains a much higher degree of development than in man. In the lamprey, lizard, etc., it is present in the form of the so-called pineal eye. In structure it resembles, in these animals, an invertebrate eye, and it has a long stalk in which nerve-fibres are developed. Further, it is carried through an aperture in the cranial wall, and lies close to the surface between the parietal bones.

Trigonum Habenulæ.—The small, triangular, depressed area which receives this name lies immediately in front of the superior corpus quadrigeminum in the interval between the stalk of the pineal body and the posterior end of the thalamus (Fig. 778, p. 894). It marks the position of a small mass of nerve-cells which constitute the **habenular nucleus.** The axons of those cells emerge through the lower surface of the ganglion and form a bundle, called the **fasciculus retroflexus**, which takes a curved course downwards and forwards in the tegmentum of the mid-brain, close to the medial side of the red nucleus, and ends in the **interpeduncular nucleus** (p. 876).

The habenular nucleus is intimately connected also with the striæ habenulares and the dorsal part of the stalk of the pineal body.

As previously stated, the **stria habenularis**—a very evident band of white matter—lies on the thalamus at the junction of its medial and superior surfaces, subjacent to an ependymal ridge. When traced backwards, many of the fibres of the stria are observed to end amongst the cells of the habenular nucleus, whilst others are continued past the nucleus to enter the stalk of the pineal body, and, through it, to reach the habenular nucleus of the opposite side, in connexion with the cells of which they terminate. The stria habenularis, therefore, ends partly in the habenular nucleus of its own side and partly in the corresponding nucleus of the opposite side. The decussation of fibres across the median plane forms the dorsal part of the pineal stalk, and is termed the **habenular commissure.**

When the stria habenularis is traced in the opposite direction, it is noticed to split into dorsal and ventral parts near the anterior column of the fornix. The *dorsal part* arises from cells in the hippocampus : those fibres pass into the fornix and when they reach its anterior column they turn abruptly backwards to enter the stria habenularis. The *ventral part* springs from a collection of cells in the grey matter on the base of the brain close to the optic chiasma. The striæ habenulares are believed to form a part of the olfactory apparatus.

Posterior Commissure.—This slender band of white matter crosses the median plane under cover of the stalk of the pineal body and overlies the entrance of the aqueduct into the third ventricle. Its fibres are believed to arise in a special nucleus placed in the central grey matter immediately above the oculomotor nucleus. They decussate with one another across the median plane and thus the commissure is formed. The other connexions of this little band are not satisfactorily established.

Posterior Perforated Substance.—This has already been described on p. 831. Some delicate bands of white matter, termed the **tænia pontis,** may frequently be seen emerging from the grey matter of this region ; they then curve round the cerebral peduncle in close relation to the upper border of the pons, with which they enter the cerebellum to end in the dentate nucleus (Horsley).

Mamillary Bodies.—These are a pair of round white bodies, each about the size of a pea, which lie side by side in the interpeduncular fossa on the base of the brain, immediately in front of the posterior perforated substance.

Each mamillary body is coated on the outside by white matter derived from the anterior column of the fornix, and contains, in its interior, a composite grey nucleus with numerous nerve-cells. Several important strands of fibres are connected with the mamillary body : (1) The anterior **column of the fornix** curves downwards in the side wall of the third ventricle to reach the mamillary body in which its fibres end amidst the cells. (2) A bundle of fibres—the **mamillo-thalamic tract**—takes origin in the midst of each mamillary body and extends

upwards into the thalamus to end in fine arborisations around the large cells in its anterior nucleus. (3) Another bundle of fibres—the **mamillo - tegmental tract** — takes form within the mamillary body and extends downwards in the grey matter of the floor of the third ventricle, to reach the tegmentum of the mid-brain. Those tracts, together with the striæ habenulares and the fasciculi retroflexi, are amongst the most ancient fibre-systems in the brain. They represent the paths by which olfactory impulses may reach the brain-stem, and perhaps the spinal cord also, and so influence the muscles of the body.

Tuber Cinereum and Infundi-bulum.—The tuber cinereum is a small, slightly prominent field of grey matter which occupies the anterior part of the interpeduncular fossa between the mamillary bodies behind and the optic chiasma.

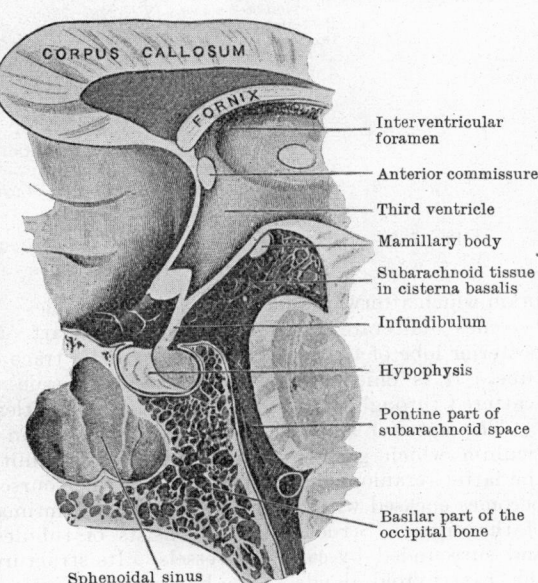

FIG. 781.—MEDIAN SECTION THROUGH THE HYPOPHYSEAL REGION.

From its anterior part the **infundibulum,** or stalk of the hypophysis, projects downwards and forwards to connect the hypophysis with the base of the brain. In its upper part the infundibulum is hollow

—a small, funnel-shaped diverticulum of the cavity of the third ventricle being prolonged downwards into it.

Hypophysis.—This is a small oval structure, flattened from above downwards, and with its long axis directed transversely, which occupies the hypophyseal fossa in the floor of the cranium. It has two lobes—a large anterior lobe and a smaller posterior lobe—which are closely applied the one to the other. The infundibulum is attached to the posterior lobe.

The infundibulum and posterior lobe of the hypophysis are developed in the form of a hollow diverticulum which grows downwards from the floor of that part of the embryonic

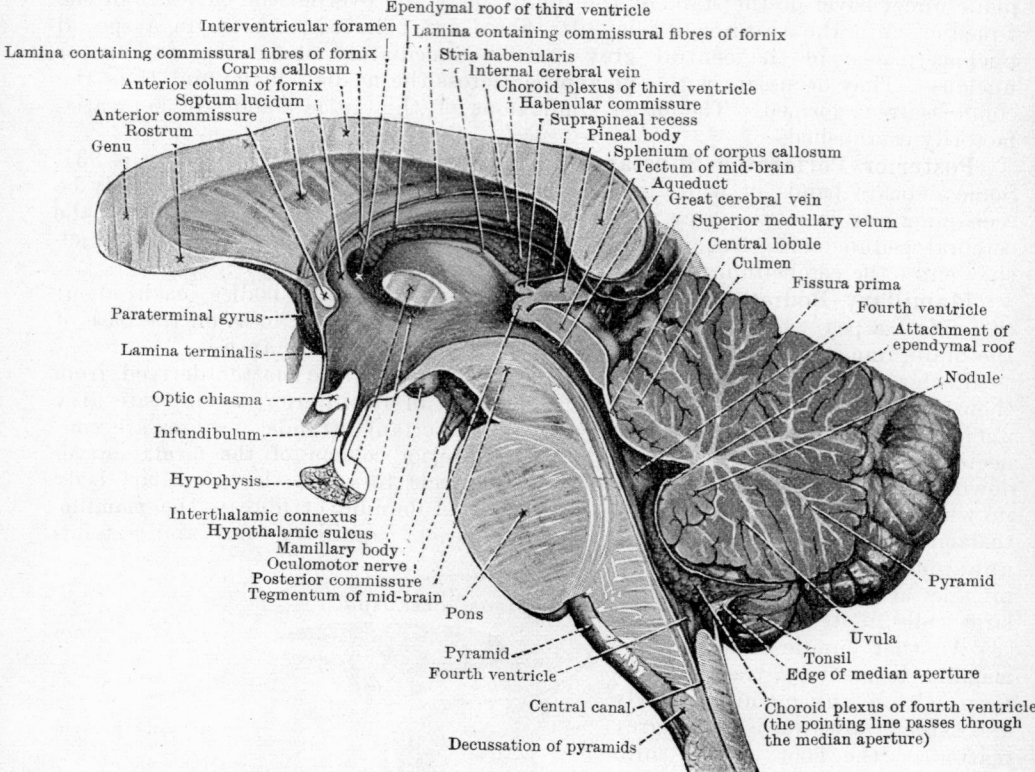

FIG. 782.—THE PARTS OF THE BRAIN CUT THROUGH IN A MEDIAN SECTION. (G. E. S.)
The side walls of the ventricular cavities also are shown.

brain which afterwards forms the third ventricle. The original cavity of that diverticulum becomes obliterated, except in the upper part of the infundibulum. In structure, the posterior lobe of the hypophysis shows little trace of its origin from the wall of the brain-tube. It is chiefly composed of areolar tissue and blood-vessels, with branched cells scattered throughout it (see the chapter on Ductless Glands).

The anterior lobe has quite a different origin—being derived from a tubular diverticulum which grows upwards from the primitive oral cavity. Its connexion with the latter (craniopharyngeal canal) is in the course of time cut off, and the diverticulum becomes encased within the cranial cavity in intimate association with the cerebral portion of the organ. Structurally, it consists of tubules or alveoli lined with epithelial cells and surrounded by capillary vessels. Its structure is in some respects not unlike that of the parathyroid glands. The hypophysis is intimately connected with the hypothalamus by (1) vessels which carry blood from the sinusoids in the oral portion of the gland through the nervous stalk to the hypothalamus (Popa and Fielding) and (2) by nerve fibres that issue from the hypothalamus and pass into the nervous portion of the hypophysis. In the disease known as acromegaly, the hypophysis is usually greatly enlarged. The proximity of the hypophysis to the optic chiasma accounts for the frequent affection of the visual paths by tumours of the gland.

Lamina Terminalis (Fig. 782).—This is a thin, delicate lamina which stretches from the optic chiasma in an upward direction to become connected with the rostrum of the corpus callosum.

Anterior Commissure of the Cerebrum.—In the anterior part of the cleft between the two thalami, and immediately in front of the anterior columns of the fornix, a round bundle of fibres crosses the median plane in the lamina terminalis. This is the anterior commissure.

Third Ventricle.—The third ventricle is the narrow cleft between the two thalami. Its depth rapidly increases from behind forwards, and it extends from the pineal body behind to the lamina terminalis in front. Its *floor* is formed by the tuber cinereum and the mamillary bodies, the posterior perforated substance, and the tegmenta, as they separate from each other (Figs. 781 and 782). It is interesting to note that the central grey matter which surrounds the aqueduct is directly continuous with the grey matter of the posterior perforated substance and

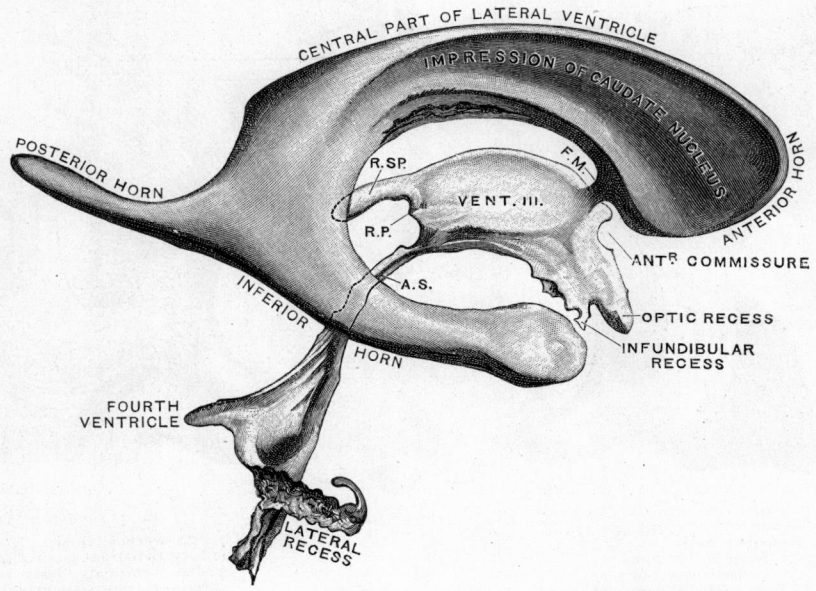

FIG. 783.—PROFILE VIEW OF A CAST OF THE VENTRICLES OF THE BRAIN. (From Retzius.)

R.SP. Suprapineal recess.   A.S. Aqueduct.
R.P. Pineal recess.   F.M. Interventricular foramen.

tuber cinereum, and in that way it comes to the surface in the base of the brain. The optic chiasma crosses the floor in front and marks the place where the floor becomes continuous with the anterior wall. The *anterior wall* is formed by the lamina terminalis, which extends upwards from the optic chiasma. The anterior commissure bulges into the ventricle from the anterior wall, but, of course, it is excluded from the cavity by the ventricular ependyma. It may be taken as indicating the place where the roof joins the anterior wall. The *roof* is merely the part of the ependymal lining that stretches across the median plane from one stria habenularis to the other. Applied to the upper surface of the ependymal roof is the fold of pia mater termed the tela chorioidea, and the roof is invaginated into the cavity along its whole length by two delicate choroid plexuses which hang down from the under surface of the fold. When the tela is removed the ependymal roof is torn away with it, leaving only the lines of attachment in the shape of the ridges covering the striæ habenulares (Fig. 778).

Each *side wall* of the third ventricle is formed for the greater part of its extent by the medial surface of the thalamus. A little in front of the middle of the ventricle the cavity is often crossed by the interthalamic connexus [massa intermedia], which links the thalami one with the other; in front of that the

57 *a*

anterior column of the fornix is seen curving downwards and backwards in the side wall. At first the bulging which it forms is distinctly prominent, but it gradually subsides as the strand, on its way to end in the mamillary body, becomes more and more sunk in the grey matter on the side of the ventricle.

The third ventricle communicates with both of the lateral ventricles, and also with the fourth ventricle. The aqueduct of the mid-brain brings it into communication with the fourth ventricle. The opening of this aqueduct is at the

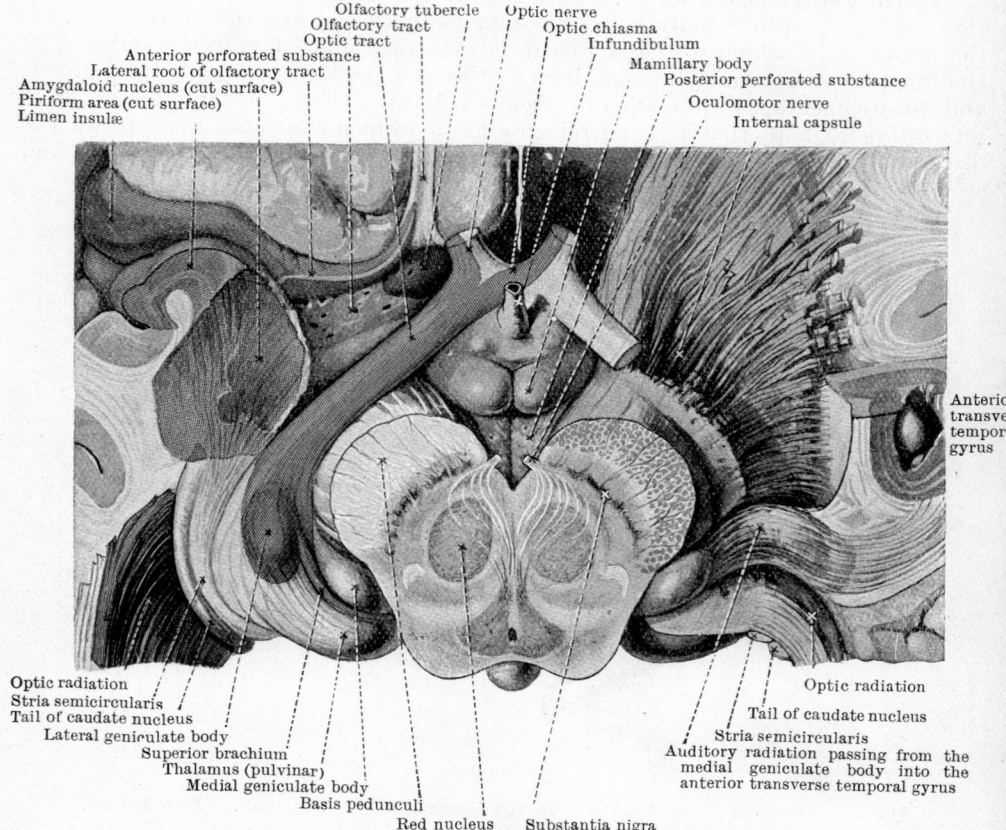

FIG. 784.—THE VENTRAL ASPECT OF PART OF THE PROSENCEPHALON, SHOWING THE RIGHT OPTIC TRACT. The mesencephalon has been cut across. Olfactory area, dull yellow; optic fibres, blue; motor fibres, red; auditory fibres, bright yellow. (G. E. S.).

posterior part of the floor, immediately below the posterior commissure. The **interventricular foramina**, which bring it into communication with the lateral ventricles, are at the upper and anterior parts of the side walls; each leads laterally and slightly upwards between the anterior column of the fornix and the anterior end of the thalamus. They are very variable in width but usually are just large enough to admit a crow-quill; and through them the ependymal lining of the three ventricles becomes continuous. From the foramen a distinct groove on the side wall of the ventricle leads backwards towards the mouth of the aqueduct. It is termed the **hypothalamic sulcus,** and is of interest inasmuch as it was considered by His to represent in the adult brain the furrow (sulcus limitans) which divides the side wall of the embryonic brain-tube into an alar and a basal lamina.

The outline of the third ventricle, when viewed from the side in a median section through the brain (Fig. 782), or as it is exhibited in a plaster cast of the ventricular system of the brain (Fig. 783), is seen to be very irregular and to have several recesses. Thus, in the anterior part of the floor there is a funnel-shaped recess that leads down through the tuber cinereum into the infundibulum. Immediately in front of this *infundibular recess*, the *optic recess* passes forwards above the optic chiasma. Posteriorly there are two recesses. One, the *pineal recess*, passes backwards for a short distance into the stalk of the pineal body. The second, the *suprapineal recess*, is carried backwards for a greater distance; it is a diverticulum of the ependymal roof, and is therefore difficult to demonstrate.

CEREBRAL CONNEXIONS OF THE OPTIC TRACT

At the optic chiasma the optic nerves are joined together and a partial decussation of fibres takes place. The fibres which arise in the medial half of each retina cross the median plane and join the optic tract of the opposite side. Each optic tract proceeds backwards round the side of the cerebral peduncle, and in the neighbourhood of the geniculate bodies appears to divide into two roots, viz., a lateral and a medial (Fig. 784), but only the former is really part of the tract.

Optic Tract. — The optic tract is composed of fibres which come—(1) from the lateral half of the retina of its own side; and (2) from the medial half of the retina of the opposite side. But in addition to the afferent

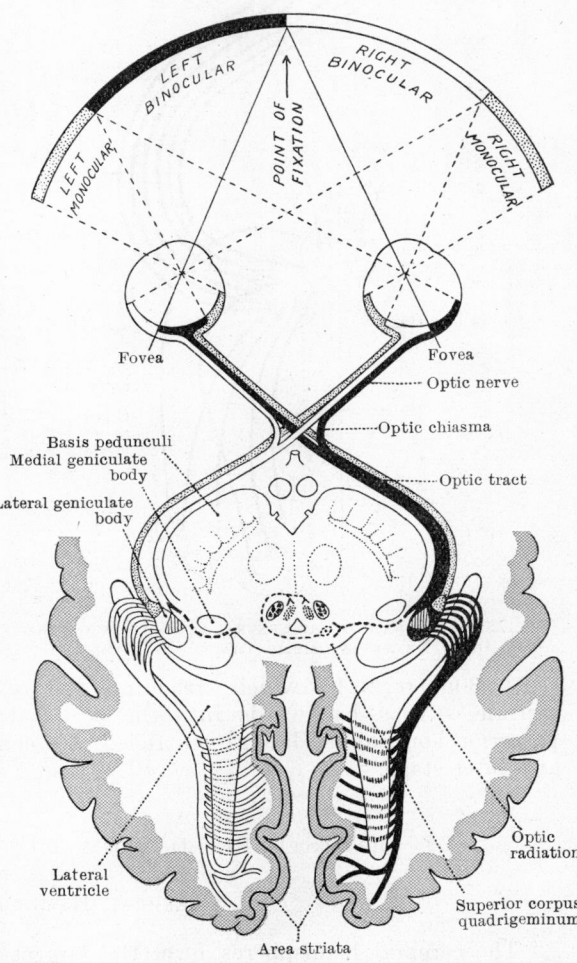

FIG. 786.—COMPOSITE DIAGRAM TO SHOW THE PROJECTION OF THE VISUAL FIELD UPON THE RETINÆ AND THE RELATIONSHIP OF THE RETINÆ TO THE LATERAL GENICULATE BODIES OF THE THALAMUS AND AREA STRIATA OF THE CEREBRAL HEMISPHERES. The fibres from the maculæ, some crossed and some uncrossed, are not shown separately in the optic nerves and optic tracts, but their place of delivery in the lateral geniculate body—the intermediate part of its caudal $\frac{2}{3}$—is shown by hatching. The remainder of the caudal $\frac{2}{3}$ receives the fibre from non-macular regions of the binocular retinal field. The monocular retinal field is shown projecting into the cranial $\frac{1}{3}$ of the lateral geniculate body. No attempt has been made in this figure to localise the delivery within the area striata of fibre from these different regions of the lateral geniculate body. After Ivy Mackenzie (*Journ. Path. and Bact.*) and Winton and Bayliss (*Text-Book of Human Physiology*).

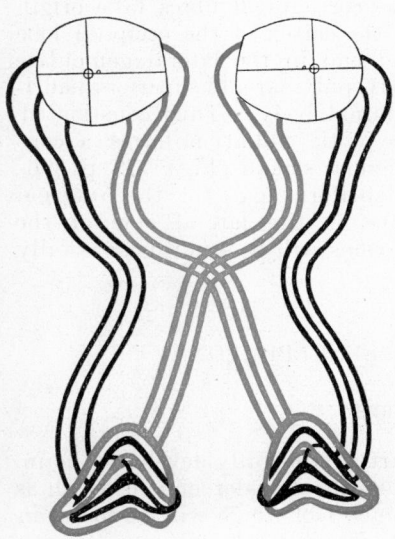

FIG. 785.—DIAGRAM TO SHOW THE RELATIONSHIP OF THE CROSSED AND UNCROSSED FIBRES FROM THE RETINÆ TO THE CELL LAMINÆ OF THE LATERAL GENICULATE BODIES. The macular fibres, some of which are crossed and some uncrossed, are not shown separately. They are delivered to the cells lying between the medial and lateral edges of the body in its caudal $\frac{2}{3}$, cf. Fig. 786. From Ivy Mackenzie (*Journ. Path. and Bact.*), after Le Gros Clark.

fibres there are a few efferent fibres in the optic tract—fibres which take origin in the brain and end in the retina. They are distinguished from the afferent fibres by their exceeding fineness.

Most of the fibres of the optic tract end in the lateral geniculate body, but a few fibres proceed, by way of the superior brachium, to the mid-brain and end in terminal arborisations in the small-celled part of the oculomotor nucleus. (Edinger-Westphal nucleus).

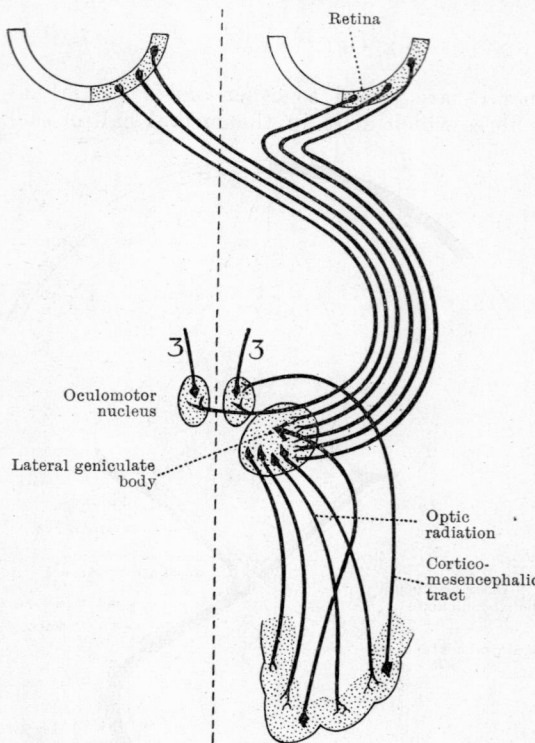

FIG. 787.—DIAGRAM OF THE CENTRAL CONNEXIONS OF THE OPTIC NERVE AND OPTIC TRACT. (G. E. S.)

Cortical Connexions of the Optic Path.—The lateral geniculate body and the mid-brain are the lower visual centres or terminal nuclei of the optic tract. The higher visual centre is in the cortex of the occipital lobe, and the connexions between that and the lower centres are established by the **optic radiation**. This radiation is a wide, thin sheet that lies in the white matter of the posterior part of the cerebral hemisphere, and is composed of both corticipetal and corticifugal fibres. The former arise as the axons of the cells in the lateral geniculate body around which the retinal fibres end, and they terminate in the area striata, which is part of the occipital cortex. The corticifugal fibres take origin in the cortex of the occipital lobe and end in the lateral geniculate body, pulvinar and superior quadrigeminal body. Thus constituted, the optic radiation forms a conspicuous strand (Figs. 779, p. 896; 787; 805, p. 921), which, reaching the retrolentiform part of the internal capsule, sweeps backwards into the occipital lobe on the lateral side of the posterior horn of the lateral ventricle. Its connexions will be studied more fully at a later stage.

PARTS DERIVED FROM THE TELENCEPHALON

CEREBRAL HEMISPHERES

The cerebral hemispheres form the largest part of the fully developed brain. When viewed from above they form an ovoid mass, the broader end of which is directed backwards, and the longest transverse diameter of which will be found in the vicinity of the parts which lie subjacent to the parietal eminences of the cranium. The massive rounded character of the anterior or frontal end of each cerebral hemisphere is a leading human characteristic; but the posterior or occipital end is narrow and pointed, and is directed slightly downwards. The two cerebral hemispheres are separated from each other by a deep median cleft termed the longitudinal fissure.

The cerebral hemisphere is formed from a small area of the extreme anterior end of the alar lamina, in the angle between the foremost part of the roof and the upper end of the lamina terminalis (Fig. 788, L), which becomes continuous with the roof (at the point marked X).

The rapid expansion of that area leads to the development of a lateral bulging containing a diverticulum of the third ventricle known as the lateral ventricle. That at first communicates with the third ventricle by means of a wide opening (F.M.)—the interventricular foramen—corresponding in size to the extent of the area of the side wall that was bulged outwards to form the hemisphere vesicle. The thin, ependymal roof of the telencephalon takes no share in the formation of the two cerebral hemispheres, but serves with the lamina terminalis (L) as a bond of union between them;

it forms, also, the upper boundary of the interventricular foramen. At a later stage in development two folds become invaginated from the ependymal roof in the whole extent of the prosencephalon—both its telencephalic and diencephalic parts. In the greater part of their length those folds project into the third ventricle, and form its **choroid plexuses** (Fig. 782); but the anterior parts of the two choroidal folds, namely, those parts formed from the roof of the interventricular foramina (F.M.), become greatly enlarged and project each into the corresponding lateral ventricle. The furrow corresponding to this invagination of the roof is called the **choroid fissure** (p. 896). When the hemisphere vesicle first begins to expand, the thinner part of the hemisphere wall, which is called the **pallium**, is freely continuous around the vertical caudal margin of the interventricular foramen (Fig. 788, Y) with the thalamus (TH).

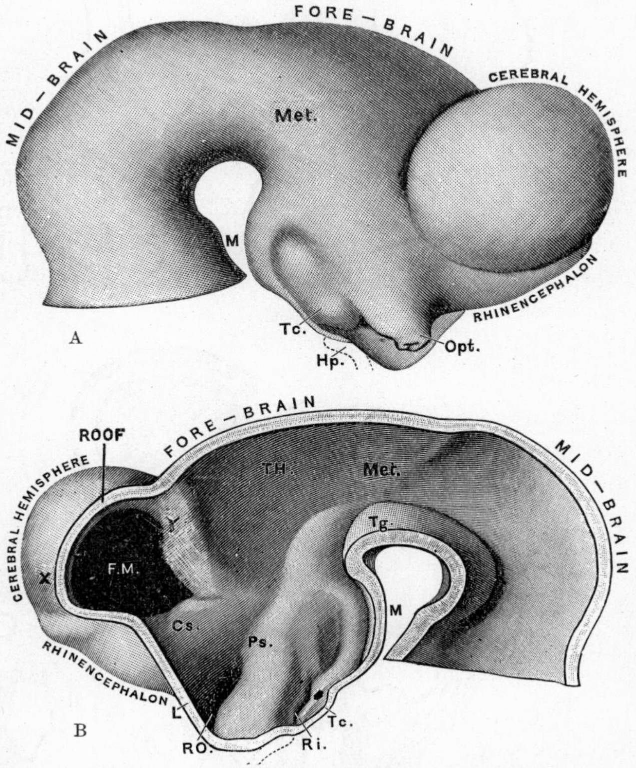

But as development

Fig. 788.—Two Drawings of the Embryonic Brain.   (After His.)

A, Reconstruction of the fore-brain and mid-brain of His's embryo KO; profile view. B, Same brain as A, divided along the median plane and viewed upon its inner aspect.

M, Mamillary eminence; Tc, Tuber cinereum; Hp, Hypophysis (hypophyseal diverticulum from buccal cavity); Opt, Optic stalk; TH, Thalamus; Tg, Tegmentum of mid-brain; Ps, Pars hypothalamica; Cs, Corpus striatum; FM, Interventricular foramen; L, Lamina terminalis; RO, Optic recess; Ri, Infundibular recess; Met, Metathalamon.

proceeds the wall of the prosencephalon becomes attenuated along the line of the choroid fissure, and eventually the pia mater of the choroid tela of the third ventricle extends laterally into the fissure to produce the **choroid plexus** of the lateral ventricle. It is obvious, therefore, that the choroid plexus of the lateral ventricle will become continuous with that of the third ventricle at the upper margin of the interventricular foramen, and that the choroid plexuses of the third and lateral ventricles all have a common origin from the same tela. Below and lateral to the choroid fissure the hemisphere wall remains in close contact with the thalamus. In this way the thalamus comes, in part, to face directly into the lateral ventricle, and the corpus striatum, developing in the floor of the cerebral hemisphere, acquires its close relationship with the thalamus (Fig. 790).

At a very early stage in the development of the embryo, long before there is any sign of the hemisphere vesicles, the ectoderm on each side of the anterior neuropore (see p. 794) becomes thickened to form the **area olfactoria** (see Fig. 683, D, p. 795). Certain of the epithelial cells in this area become converted into bipolar sensory cells which become specially adapted to be affected by certain

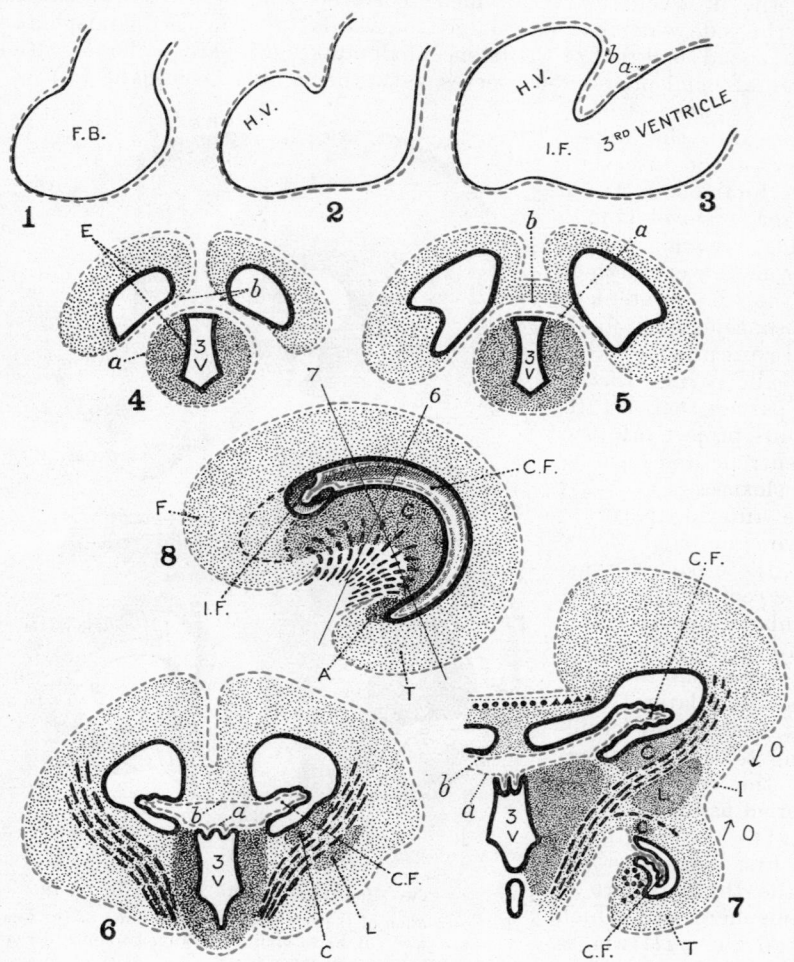

Fig. 789.—Diagrams to show the formation of the Tela Chorioidea and its Relation to the Choroid Fissure and Choroid Plexuses of the Lateral and Third Ventricles.

Adapted from figures in Frazer's *Manual of Embryology*.

In Fig. 1 the vascular mesoderm forming the primitive pia mater is shown as a broken red line surrounding the front end of the neural tube (F.B.). In Fig. 2 a developing cerebral hemisphere vesicle (H.V.) is seen carrying out over it a covering of pia mater continuous with that surrounding the original forebrain vesicle. Fig. 3 shows that the backward growth of the hemisphere leads to the formation of a double layer of pia mater interposed between it and the roof of the 3rd ventricle. This double layer of vascular pia mater is the tela chorioidea. "The layer 'b' is derived from the original 'a,' so that any veins in 'b' run to the roof of the interventricular foramen (I.F.) to enter one of the veins of 'a' and so drain. The tela chorioidea then extends to the interventricular foramen because the upper layer was reflected at this point." (Frazer, p. 193.) But the layer 'b' is carried out on each hemisphere vesicle Fig. 4, and the two vesicles become connected by commissures Fig. 5, and are also stalked to the mid-line vesicle containing the 3rd ventricle so that the condition shown in Fig. 6 results. The plane of Fig. 6 is shown on Fig. 8 by a line labelled 6. The ependyma (E) lining the lateral ventricles and the 3rd ventricle is shown by a heavy black line, so that the strip of the medial wall of each hemisphere which consists only of ependyma and likewise the roof of the 3rd ventricle can be easily seen in Figs. 4, 5, 6, 7, 8. The inthrust of the ependymal region of the hemisphere wall is called the choroid fissure (C.F.) (see also description in text, pp. 896, 905). In Fig. 7 the choroid fissure is cut twice. A glance at Fig. 8, upon which the plane of Fig. 7 is indicated by a line labelled 7, will show the reason for this.

C = caudate nucleus.　　O = opercula of insula.　　L = lentiform nucleus.　　F = frontal pole.
A = amygdaloid nucleus.　　T = temporal pole.　　I = insula.

kinds of air-borne chemical stimuli that awaken a consciousness of smell. Those cells always remain *in situ* in the olfactory epithelium. just as the most primitive sensory cells do in Hydra (Fig. 680, p. 791). But other nerve-cells seem to be derived from the area olfactoria which do not remain in the parent epithelium, but become attached to the adjoining part of the neural tube. Those cells form the receptive organ for the impressions brought into the brain by the processes of the sensory cells in the olfactory epithelium; and the area of the neural tube to which it becomes attached is destined to become part of the cerebral hemisphere. At the end of the first month that portion of the hemisphere becomes

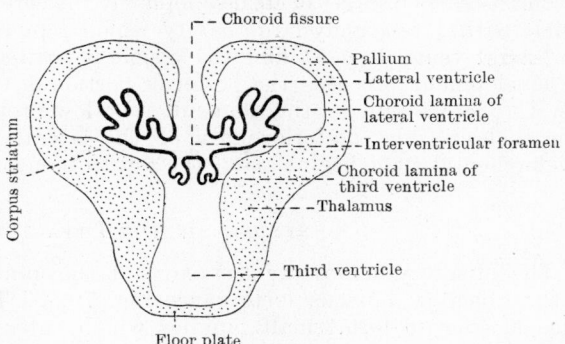

FIG. 790.—DIAGRAM OF A TRANSVERSE SECTION THROUGH A FŒTAL BRAIN TO SHOW THE INVAGINATION OF THE ROOF THROUGH EACH INTERVENTRICULAR FORAMEN.

drawn out as a hollow protrusion, the distal end of which is coated with a layer of grey matter and is known as the **olfactory bulb**; the rest forms a peduncle. In the course of its subsequent development in the human brain (though not in those of most mammals) the cavity in the bulb and peduncle becomes completely obliterated.   The peduncle becomes so greatly elongated and attenuated that, to the unaided eye, it appears to be formed wholly of white nerve-fibres passing to and fro between the olfactory bulb and the hemisphere; hence it is called the **olfactory tract** (Figs. 784 and 793).

The cerebral hemisphere first appears in the form of a slight bulging on each

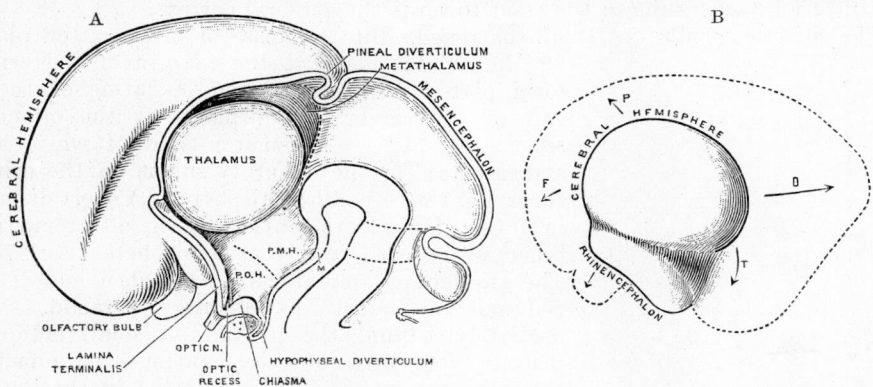

FIG. 791.—TWO DRAWINGS BY HIS, ILLUSTRATING THE DEVELOPMENT OF THE HUMAN BRAIN.

A, Median section through a fœtal human brain in the third month of development.
B, Schema showing the directions in which the cerebral hemisphere expands during its growth.

P.M.H. Diencephalic part of hypothalamus.	M. Mamillary region.	O. Occipital lobe.
P.O.H. Telencephalic part of hypothalamus.	F. Frontal lobe.	T. Temporal lobe.
	P. Parietal lobe.	

side of the fore-brain, but it soon assumes large dimensions.   At first it grows forwards and upwards (Fig. 791), and a distinct cleft, the floor of which is the roof-plate and lamina terminalis, appears between the two hemispheres: it is known as the **longitudinal fissure**.   The separation of the two cerebral vesicles by the longitudinal fissure begins at the end of the first month, and the fissure becomes occupied by the mesodermic tissue which later on forms the **falx cerebri**. The cerebral hemisphere, in its further growth, is carried progressively backwards over the other parts of the developing brain.   At the end of the third month it has covered the thalamus.   A month later it reaches the corpora quadrigemina, and by the seventh month it has covered not only those, but also the entire upper surface of the cerebellum. From the latter it is separated by a mesodermal sheet which forms the basis of the **tentorium cerebelli**.

In the earlier stages of its development the cerebral hemisphere is a thin-walled vesicle with a relatively large cavity which represents the primitive condition of the **lateral ventricle**. At first the vesicle is bean-shaped and the cavity is curved. As development proceeds the posterior portion of the hemisphere grows backwards over the cerebellum in the shape of a hollow protrusion, and a distinct occipital lobe enclosing the posterior horn of the lateral ventricle is the result. That developmental stage begins about the fourth month.

Connexions of the Olfactory Nerves

The olfactory nerves are the axons of the spindle-shaped bipolar cells situated in the olfactory mucous membrane (Fig. 792). These axons collect in the sub-mucous layer to form small bundles which enter the cranial cavity through the foramina in the cribriform plate of the ethmoid bone. They at once enter the lower surface of the olfactory bulb, and each fibre breaks up into a tuft of terminal filaments. Towards those tufts dendrites proceed from large **mitral cells** placed in a deeper plane within the bulb, and each dendrite also breaks up into numerous terminal branches intertwined with those of the olfactory nerves. In that way are formed a large number of globular bodies, each consisting of the arborescent terminations of a mitral dendrite and of certain olfactory nerve-fibres. The globular bodies are called the **olfactory glomeruli**. Each mitral cell gives off several dendrites and one axon. Only one dendrite enters into the formation of a glomerulus, but several nerve-fibres may be connected with it. It thus happens that a mitral cell, through its dendrite, may stand in connexion with several olfactory nerve-fibres. The axon of the mitral cell passes upwards to the white matter of the bulb, enters that, and, bending backwards, runs in the tract towards the cerebral cortex.

The **olfactory bulb** is a small, flattened, elliptical mass of grey matter placed on the orbital plate at the margin of the cribriform plate. Its posterior end is attached to the rest of the cerebral hemisphere by the olfactory tract (Fig. 717)—a prismatic band of white substance placed in the olfactory sulcus on the orbital surface of the cerebral hemisphere. A short distance in front of the optic chiasma each olfactory tract becomes inserted into the hemisphere (Fig. 784). The swollen pyramidal-shaped attached end of the peduncle is called the **olfactory pyramid**. Immediately behind the pyramid a small obliquely placed ovoid area of grey matter—the **olfactory tubercle**—can sometimes be detected in the human brain; but in the brains of most mammals with a greater development of the organs of smell that swollen area is much more prominent and constant. In most human brains, however, it is difficult to distinguish it from a much more extensive area, situated behind it and to its lateral side, and named the **anterior perforated substance** (Fig. 784). Along the anterior margin of that perforated substance there can sometimes be detected a small, rounded, rope-like strand of grey matter, the medial end of which passes into the olfactory pyramid. That is the anterior part of the **area piriformis**—the stalk of the pear-shaped lobe—and on its surface is placed a very well-defined narrow band of nerve-fibres—the *lateral root of the olfactory tract*—which is composed of axons of mitral cells proceeding to the piriform

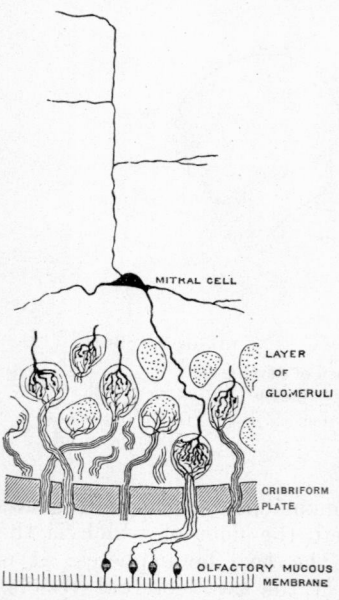

MITRAL CELL

LAYER
OF
GLOMERULI

CRIBRIFORM
PLATE

OLFACTORY MUCOUS
MEMBRANE

Fig. 792.—Diagram of the Minute Structure of the Olfactory Bulb.

area. Even when the anterior part of the piriform area is not distinguishable, the lateral root is always a prominent feature.

The piriform area extends laterally in the deep valley between the orbital and temporal regions of the hemisphere; becoming slightly broader, and reaching what is known as the **insula** (of which it forms the **limen insulæ**), it becomes sharply bent upon itself (Figs. 784 and 793, C). It then passes medially and backwards, and emerges from the valley as a broad area on the under surface of the temporal region (Fig. 793, C). This greatly expanded caudal extremity of the pear is the **area piriformis** in the strict sense of the term.

If the brain of almost any other mammal is examined (take the rabbit's as an example), the area piriformis will be found to constitute relatively an enormously larger proportion of the cerebral hemisphere than it does in the human brain;

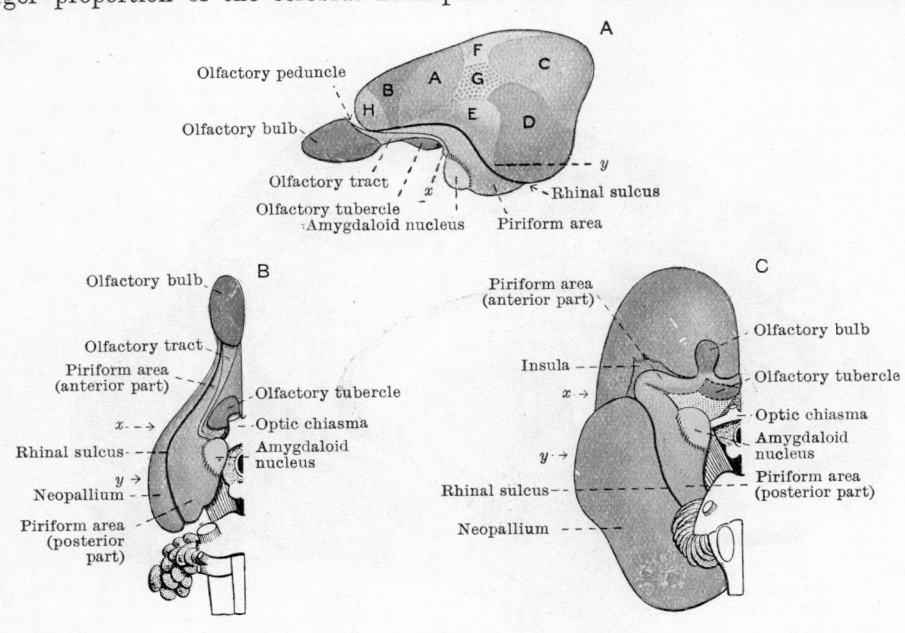

FIG. 793.

A, lateral aspect of left cerebral hemisphere of a rabbit (A-H, areas of neopallium). B, inferior aspect of right half of a rabbit's brain. C, corresponding view of a human fœtal brain at the fifth month.

Olfactory areas, green; neopallium, blue.

and it is separated from the part of the hemisphere (**neopallium**) that lies above it by a longitudinal furrow called the **rhinal sulcus**. The enormous expansion of the neopallium in the human brain accentuates the flexure of the piriform area at the point x (Fig. 793), and at the point y the exuberant growth of neopallium relegates the swollen, posterior part of the piriform area on to the medial surface (Fig. 794), where the posterior part of the rhinal sulcus persists to separate it from the neopallium.

The surface of the piriform area often presents numerous small wart-like excrescences; and it is whitened by a thin layer of fibres prolonged backwards from the lateral root of the olfactory tract. By those fibres olfactory impulses are poured directly from the mitral cells of the bulb into the piriform area. If we call the olfactory nerves the **primary olfactory neurones**, the fibres which pass from the bulb to the piriform area would then be **secondary olfactory neurones**.

Hippocampal Formation.—From all parts of the area piriformis, as well as the olfactory pyramid and tubercle, fibres arise (**tertiary olfactory neurones**), and proceed on to the medial side of the hemisphere, where they terminate in the edge of the pallium, alongside the choroid fissure. In the human brain the vast majority of those tertiary neurones proceed from the posterior end of the piriform area, but a certain number arise in the neighbourhood of the anterior perforated substance and proceed at once on to the medial surface of the hemisphere. The large number of small nerve-cells that collect in the medial edge of the pallium become specially modified in structure to form a receptive organ for impressions of smell known as the **dentate gyrus**; and the axons of those cells pass into the part of the pallium which immediately surrounds the peripheral edge of the dentate gyrus and is known as the **hippocampus** (Fig. 796). In the hippocampus impressions of smell are brought into relation with those of other senses (probably taste); and from the hippocampal cells fibres are emitted to form a system known as the **fornix**, which establishes connexions with the hippocampus of the other hemisphere and with the hypothalamus, thalamus, and more distant parts of the brain.

The rudiment of the hippocampal formation (coloured orange in Fig. 794) that

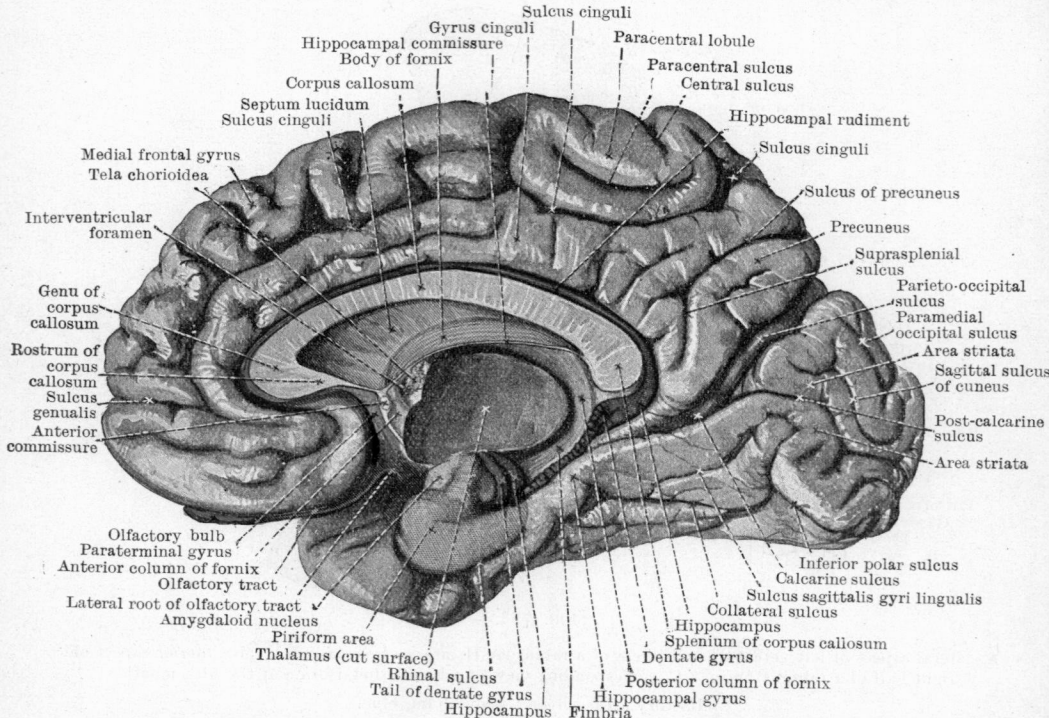

FIG. 794.—MEDIAL ASPECT OF THE RIGHT CEREBRAL HEMISPHERE, WITH THE OLFACTORY PARTS COLOURED.

develops on the medial surface begins in front, alongside the place where the stalk of the olfactory peduncle (which becomes the olfactory pyramid) is inserted; it passes upwards to the upper end of the lamina terminalis, from the rest of which it is separated by a triangular mass of grey matter called the **paraterminal gyrus** (shown in blue in Fig. 794); and then it proceeds upward to the rostrum of the corpus callosum and passes forward around the genu to reach the upper surface of the corpus callosum. Extending backwards, it passes round the splenium to join the fully developed part of the hippocampal formation. The anterior part of the great hippocampal fringe of the pallium does not attain its full development in the human brain and remains as a more or less vestigial aborted structure; but the posterior part undergoes a peculiar transformation. The tertiary olfactory neurones, coming mainly from the posterior part of the area piriformis (green in the figure), enter the margin of the hippocampal formation, and the small cells which receive those incoming fibres multiply rapidly during the third month, and arrange themselves in a densely packed row of granules which represent the distinctive feature of the dentate gyrus (Fig. 796). At first that cell-column is continuous at its peripheral margin with a much more loosely packed column of larger and less numerous cells which represent the **hippocampus**; and these in turn give place to the more diffusely arranged and laminated cells of the typical **cortex cerebri**, which we call the **neopallium**.   As development proceeds both the dentate and hippocampal columns of cells rapidly increase in length, and both appear to push their way towards the ventricle (Fig. 796, B) into the substance of the wall, which becomes correspondingly thickened.   The ventricular swelling thus formed is the hippocampus.   The swelling is not produced by any invagination of the surface, such as has been described under the name of the **hippocampal fissure**; *there is no hippocampal fissure in the human brain*; what is usually described under this name is an artificial cleft made by pushing the handle of a scalpel into the hippocampal formation at the edge of the exposed part of the dentate gyrus (Fig. 796, B and C, at *x*) and separating the morphological surface of the hippocampus from that of the buried part of the dentate gyrus.   Cleavage readily occurs along that line because there are numerous nerve-fibres, hippocampal and dentate respectively, upon each side of it.

As development proceeds a break occurs in the cell-column at the junction of its hippocampal and dentate parts, and the two columns (Fig. 796, C) become partially interlocked.

FORNIX

The **fornix** is the efferent tract from the hippocampus (*a*) to the hippocampus in the other hemisphere, and (*b*) to the brain-stem.

The axons of the hippocampal cells collect on the ventricular surface to form a white layer

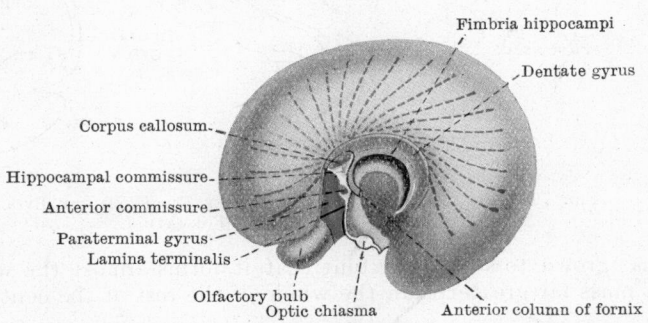

Corpus callosum
Hippocampal commissure
Anterior commissure
Paraterminal gyrus
Lamina terminalis
Olfactory bulb
Optic chiasma
Fimbria hippocampi
Dentate gyrus
Anterior column of fornix

FIG. 795.—MEDIAL ASPECT OF THE RIGHT CEREBRAL HEMISPHERE OF A HUMAN FŒTUS OF THE FOURTH MONTH.

The broken red lines indicate the paths taken by callosal fibres in the neopallium to reach the upper end of the lamina terminalis.

called the *alveus* (Fig. 796), the fibres of which converge towards the margin of the dentate gyrus, where they bend into the longitudinal direction (*i.e.* parallel to the edge of the pallium and the choroid fissure) to form a prominent white marginal fringe called the **fimbria** (Fig. 796).   The fibres of the fimbria pass upwards and forwards (Fig. 795), and ultimately reach the upper end of the lamina terminalis, which provides a bridge to conduct a certain number of them across the median plane into the fornix or fimbria of the other hemisphere, so as to link together in functional association the two hippocampi.   The crossing fibres are known as the **hippocampal commissure**.

Most of the fibres that go up in the fimbria from the hippocampus do not pass into the hippocampal commissure, but bend downwards in the anterior lip of the interventricular foramen to enter the thalamic region.   They are collected into a vertical rounded column which is called the **anterior column of the fornix**; when it reaches the hypothalamus it bends backward to end in the mamillary body.   A further relay of neurones then runs back from the mamillary body in the tegmentum to establish connexions with lower parts of the brain.

The olfactory bulb and tract, the area piriformis, olfactory tubercle, paraterminal gyrus, and the hippocampal formation together form a part of the hemisphere which is concerned mainly with the function of smell.   Hence they may be grouped together as the **rhinencephalon**; but this term has been used in so many different ways that it is of doubtful utility.

In the lowest vertebrates the whole hemisphere is practically rhinencephalon. Nevertheless, fibres coming from other parts of the nervous system and conveying impressions from other sense organs than those of smell make their way into the cerebral hemisphere and influence the state of its activities.   In other words, the hemisphere is primarily an olfactory receptive nucleus, but is also the place where impressions of smell are brought under the modifying influences of other sensory impressions before they make their effects manifest in behaviour.

But it is only in the most highly organised types of brain, more especially those of mammals and birds, that the non-olfactory senses acquire a representation in the hemisphere which is relatively independent of the influence of the sense of smell or, at any rate, not wholly subservient to it. In the mammalian brain a definite area of pallium is set apart to receive impressions of the tactile, visual, auditory, and other senses. That area is the **neopallium**. In the human brain it

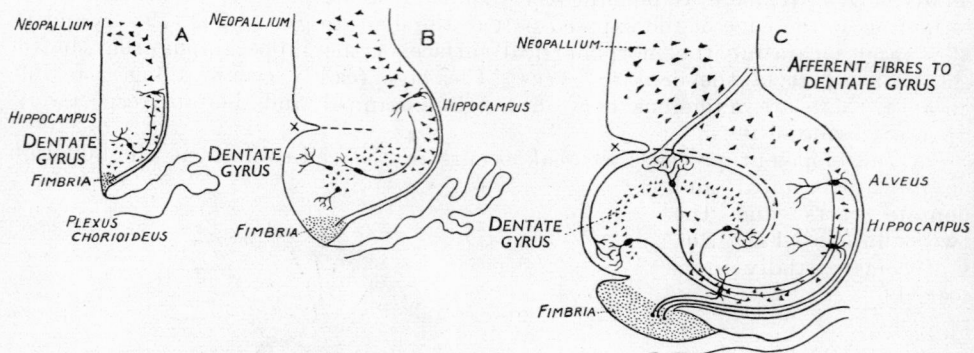

FIG. 796.—DIAGRAMS REPRESENTING THREE STAGES IN THE EVOLUTION OF THE HIPPOCAMPAL FORMATION.

has grown to such an extent that it forms almost the whole of the hemispheres— a mass far greater than the whole of the rest of the central nervous system.

CEREBRAL COMMISSURES AND THE SEPTUM LUCIDUM

We have seen that certain fibres from the hippocampi cross from one hemisphere to the other, using the upper part of the lamina terminalis as a bridge across the median plane. But at an even earlier stage of development other fibres can be detected at a slightly lower level in the lamina terminalis forming a bundle, of oval outline in sagittal section, called the **anterior commissure**. Its fibres come from the olfactory bulb, area piriformis, olfactory tubercle, and a small temporal area of neopallium. If the composition of the hippocampal commissure is analysed in a foetus of the third month, it will be found that there are intermingled with the truly hippocampal fibres some which come from the neopallium. During the fourth month the bulk of the neopallial element in this dorsal commissure outgrows the hippocampal element. These hippocampal fibres become crowded into the postero-inferior corner of the commissure and the neopallial fibres come to form a flattened transverse bridge—the **corpus callosum**—above them. Those fibres are enclosed in a neuroglial matrix derived from the lamina terminalis and the adjoining paraterminal gyri. Some nerve-cells also may make their way into the matrix. As it elongates, the corpus callosum pushes its way forwards in the upper part of the paraterminal gyrus of each hemisphere, and as development proceeds a small area of that gyrus becomes almost completely circumscribed by the corpus callosum and hippocampal commissure. As these commissural bands increase in size the small circumscribed patch of paraterminal gyrus becomes greatly stretched and expanded to form a thin translucent leaf. The two leaves thus formed in the medial walls of the two hemispheres are known as the **septum lucidum**; and the narrow cleft that separates them the one from the other in the median plane is called the *cavity of the septum lucidum.*

There is still some uncertainty concerning the precise manner in which these changes are brought about, and especially as to the precise mode of closure of the cavity of the septum. As the cerebral hemisphere expands, some parts of it grow forwards, others upwards, and others backwards.   Such growth in each part will naturally tend to exert traction on its commissural fibres that pass through the corpus callosum.   Hence, the anterior part of that great commissure becomes drawn forwards, its posterior part backwards, and the greater intermediate part upwards, so that it comes to assume the form shown in Fig. 797, C. As the posterior part of the corpus callosum pushes its way backwards, it exerts traction on the fibres of the hippocampal commissure and their matrix, which becomes enormously stretched so as to form a thin lamella (the floor of the cavity of the septum) stretching from a point just above the anterior commissure to the under surface of the swollen posterior end of the corpus callosum, which is called the **splenium** (Fig. 794).   The hippocampal commissural fibres are scattered throughout that lamella.   The backward growth of the splenium also thrusts back the upper end of the hippocampal formation so that it becomes removed far from the lamina terminalis.   The fibres of the fimbria, which are prolonged forwards under the corpus callosum and septum lucidum to bridge this great gap, form the **posterior column of the fornix** on each side.   As a rule in the human adult brain the right and

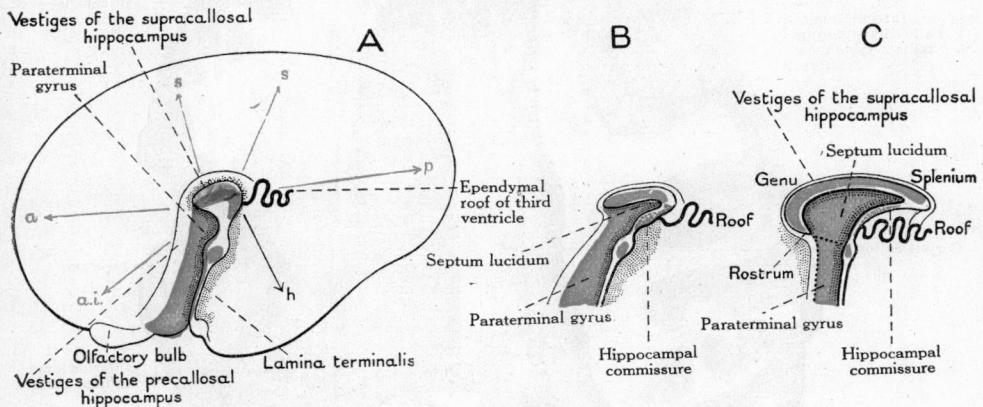

FIG. 797.—THREE STAGES IN THE DEVELOPMENT OF THE CORPUS CALLOSUM.

left posterior columns of the fornix become crowded together at the median plane so as to obscure the connecting lamella which serves as a matrix for the hippocampal commissure (Fig. 797, C); but the true arrangement can be seen in the brains of fœtuses of the sixth, seventh, and eighth months, and is at once revealed in the adult if the corpus callosum is raised up by an accumulation of fluid in the lateral ventricles (hydrocephalus), so as to put a strain on the septum lucidum.   The mass formed by the posterior columns and their commissure is **the body of the fornix.**

The dentate gyrus appears as a notched band behind and below the fimbria; its upper end passes on to the under surface of the splenium of the corpus callosum, where it tapers and ends (**splenial gyrus**); but as it dwindles the upper end of the hippocampus emerges on the surface below and behind it and passes into a thin film of grey matter—**indusium griseum**—which is prolonged on to the upper surface of the corpus callosum.   It proceeds forwards, becoming as a rule still more attenuated, and after surrounding the anterior end (**genu**) of the corpus callosum it passes downwards towards the olfactory pyramid along the line that separates the paraterminal gyrus from the neopallium.   The indusium represents the atrophied remains of the anterior part of the hippocampal arc of the fœtal brain (Fig. 795), from which the dentate gyrus has entirely disappeared.   It is accompanied by longitudinal fibres homologous to the fornix system—in other words, the fornix fibres of the atrophied supracallosal hippocampus; they form the **striæ longitudinales** of the corpus callosum (Fig. 794; Fig. 802, p. 919; Fig. 797, p. 914).

The inferior (or anterior) end of the dentate gyrus dips into a deep furrow around which the area piriformis is bent in a hook-like manner (**uncus**); in that it becomes considerably reduced in diameter and then emerges (at right angles to its previous direction) to form the **tail of the dentate gyrus**. Behind that the lower end of the hippocampus comes to the surface, but is turned inside out—*hippocampus inversus*. Immediately in front of the upper ending of the tail of the dentate gyrus a little knob of solid grey matter appears upon the surface, surrounded by the area piriformis. It is the **amygdaloid nucleus** (Fig. 794).

Corpus Callosum.—The corpus callosum is the great neopallial commissure. It is placed nearer the anterior than the posterior end of the brain; it unites the medial surfaces of the hemispheres throughout very nearly a half of their

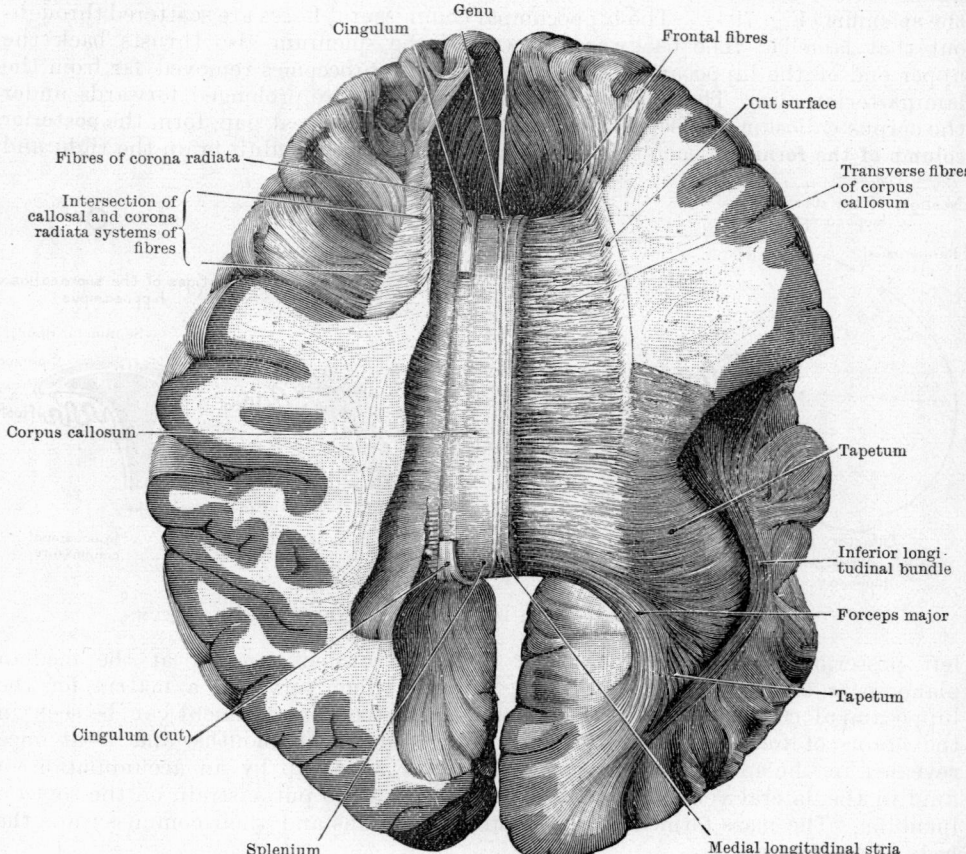

Fig. 798.—CORPUS CALLOSUM, exposed from above and the right half dissected.

antero-posterior length, and is highly arched from before backwards, when viewed from the side (Fig. 782).

The *superior surface* of the corpus callosum forms the bottom of the longitudinal fissure, and on each side of this it is separated from the gyrus cinguli by a slit called the *callosal sulcus*. The surface is covered with the **indusium griseum**, which is continuous at the bottom of the callosal sulcus with the cortex of the hemisphere. Two pairs of delicate longitudinal bands or striae are embedded in the indusium. The **medial longitudinal stria** is the more strongly marked, and is separated from its fellow of the opposite side by a faint median furrow. The **lateral longitudinal stria** is under cover of the gyrus cinguli. The indusium, with the striae, represents the aborted remains of the hippocampus (see p. 913). So thin is the indusium that the transverse direction pursued by the callosal fibres can be easily perceived through it.

The *two ends* of the corpus callosum are much thicker than the main part or **trunk**. The *posterior end*, which is full and rounded, lies over the mid-brain and extends backwards as far as the highest point of the cerebellum. It is called the **splenium,** and its lower part is bent forwards under the upper part, to the inferior surface of which it is closely applied. The *anterior end* is folded downwards and backwards on itself. It is termed the **genu.** The recurved inferior part of the genu rapidly thins as it passes backwards, and receives the name of the **rostrum.** The fine terminal edge of the rostrum becomes connected by means of a band of neuroglial tissue with the lamina terminalis on the front of the anterior commissure (Fig. 782 and dotted line in Fig. 797 C).

The *inferior surface* of the corpus callosum, on each side of the median plane, is coated with ependyma (Fig. 802, p. 919), and forms the roof of the anterior horn and the central part of the lateral ventricle. In the median plane, however, it is attached to subjacent parts, viz., to the septum lucidum in front and directly or indirectly (Fig. 782) to the body of the fornix behind (Fig. 802, p. 919).

The transverse fibres of the corpus callosum, as they enter the white centre of the cerebral hemisphere, separate from one another so as to reach most parts of the cerebral cortex. These diverging fibres intersect those which form the *corona radiata,* that is, the fibres which extend between the internal capsule and the cerebral cortex (Figs. 806 and 807, p. 922). The more anterior of the fibres which compose the genu of the corpus callosum sweep forwards in a series of curves into the anterior region of each hemisphere, and the name **forceps minor** is given to the figure formed by these curving bundles. A large part of the splenium, forming a solid bundle termed the **forceps major,** bends suddenly and abruptly backwards into the occipital lobe (Fig. 798). Fibres from the trunk and upper part of the splenium, curving round the lateral ventricle, form a very definite stratum called the **tapetum.** It is a thin layer in the white centre of the hemisphere which constitutes the immediate roof and lateral wall of the posterior horn and the lateral wall of the inferior horn of the lateral ventricle. In coronal sections through the occipital and posterior temporal regions the tapetum stands out very distinctly (Fig. 798, p. 914; see also Figs. 803, p. 919, and 805, p. 921).

Septum Lucidum (Fig. 782).—This is a thin vertical partition which intervenes between the two lateral ventricles. It is triangular in shape, and posteriorly it is prolonged backwards for a variable distance between the trunk of the corpus callosum and the fornix, to both of which it is attached. In front it occupies the gap behind the genu of the corpus callosum, whilst below, in the narrow interval between the posterior edge of the rostrum of the corpus callosum and the fornix, it is continuous, in early stages, with the paraterminal gyrus; but the subsequent development of the band of neuroglial tissue (p. 913) extending from the rostrum to the lamina terminalis breaks this continuity. The septum lucidum is composed of a pair of thin laminæ lying close together, but separated (Fig. 800; Fig. 802, p. 919) by a cavity which varies greatly in size in different brains.

LATERAL VENTRICLE

The cavity in the interior of the cerebral hemisphere is called the **lateral ventricle.** It is lined throughout with ependyma, and is filled with cerebro-spinal fluid; it is of varying size, being reduced to a mere chink in places, *e.g.* the posterior horn; and it communicates with the third ventricle of the brain by means of the **interventricular foramen** (Figs. 782, 801 and Pl. LX.).

The highly-irregular shape of the lateral ventricle can be best understood by the study of a cast of its interior (Figs. 783, p. 901, and 799, p. 916). It is divisible into a central part and three horns,—anterior, posterior, and inferior. The **anterior horn** is the part of the cavity in front of the interventricular foramen. The **central part** extends from the interventricular foramen to the splenium of the corpus callosum. At that level it is continuous with the posterior and inferior horns, which diverge from each other. The **posterior horn** curves backwards and medially into the occipital lobe. It is very variable in its length and capacity, for adhesions may occur between its walls. The **inferior horn** proceeds

58 *a*

with a bold sweep round the posterior end of the thalamus, tunnels downwards and forwards in the temporal lobe, and then turns medially to end in the region of the uncus (Fig 804).

The early fœtal lateral ventricle is very capacious and presents an arched form. Its parts correspond to the anterior horn, the central part and the inferior horn, and there is little or no demarcation between them. The posterior horn is a later production which grows backwards from the primitive cavity.

The **anterior horn** extends in a forward and lateral direction in the frontal lobe. When seen in coronal section (Fig. 800) it presents a triangular outline. It is bounded *in front* by the genu of the corpus callosum; the *roof* is the trunk of the corpus callosum and the floor is the rostrum. The *medial wall*, which is vertical, is the septum pellucidum; the sloping *lateral wall* presents a marked elevation or bulging, viz., the smooth, rounded head of the caudate nucleus.

The **central part** of the cavity also is *roofed* by the trunk of the corpus callosum.

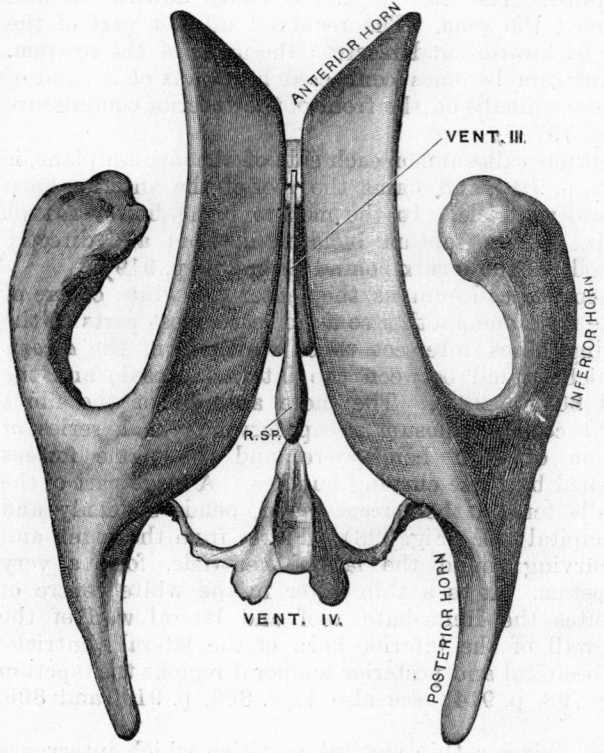

FIG. 799.—DRAWING TAKEN FROM A CAST OF THE VENTRICULAR SYSTEM OF THE BRAIN, as seen from above. (After Retzius.)

Vent. III. Third ventricle.　　Vent. IV. Fourth ventricle.
R.SP. Suprapineal recess.

On the *medial side* it is bounded by the posterior part of the septum lucidum. On the *lateral side* it is closed by the meeting of the floor and the roof of the cavity. On the *floor* a number of important objects may be recognised. From the lateral to the medial side they are met in the following order: (1) the body of the caudate nucleus; (2) a groove which extends obliquely from before backwards and laterally between the caudate nucleus and the thalamus, and in which are placed the thalamo-striate vein and a white band called the stria semicircularis [vena and stria terminalis]; (3) a portion of the upper surface of the thalamus; (4) the choroid plexus; (5) the sharp edge of the body of the fornix (Fig. 801).

The **caudate nucleus** narrows rapidly as it proceeds backwards on the lateral part of the floor of the lateral ventricle. The thalamo-striate vein is covered over with ependyma; it joins the internal cerebral vein close to the interventricular foramen. The connexions of the **stria semicircularis** will be dealt with later. The portion of the upper surface of the **thalamus** which appears in the floor of the ventricle is in great part hidden under the choroid plexus. The ependymal strip of the hemisphere wall, as it extends between the sharp edge of the fornix and the upper surface of the thalamus, is invaginated at the choroid fissure into the central part of the lateral ventricle by the richly vascularised edge of the pial fold called the tela chorioidea. This vascular fringe with its ependymal covering is called the **choroid plexus**. In front it is continuous, in the interventricular foramen, with the corresponding choroid plexus of the third ventricle (Fig. 782 and Fig. 807), whilst behind, it is carried into the inferior horn of the ventricle. Although the choroid plexus has all the appearance of lying free within the ventricle, it must be borne in mind that it is invested by the ependyma which represents a portion of the hemisphere wall and excludes it from the cavity.

The **posterior horn** is an elongated diverticulum carried backwards into the occipital lobe from the posterior end of the ventricle. It tapers to a point and describes a gentle curve, the convexity of which is directed laterally. Its *roof* and *lateral wall* are formed by the tapetum of the corpus callosum. In coronal sections through the occipital lobe the tapetum is seen as a thin but distinct white layer, immediately lateral to the ependyma and to the medial side of a much larger sheet of fibres, viz., the optic radiation.

On the *medial wall* two elongated curved elevations may be observed. The upper of them is termed the **bulb of the posterior horn,** and is produced by the forceps major. Below the bulb is the elevation known as the **calcar avis.** It varies greatly in size in different brains, and is caused by an infolding of the ventricular wall in correspondence with the calcarine sulcus on the exterior of the hemisphere.

It may come into contact with and adhere to the lateral wall of the horn in a part or even the whole of its extent.

The **inferior horn** is the continuation of the cavity into the temporal lobe. At first directed backwards and laterally, the inferior horn suddenly sinks downwards behind the thalamus into the temporal region, in the centre of which it takes a curved course forwards and medially as far as the uncus.

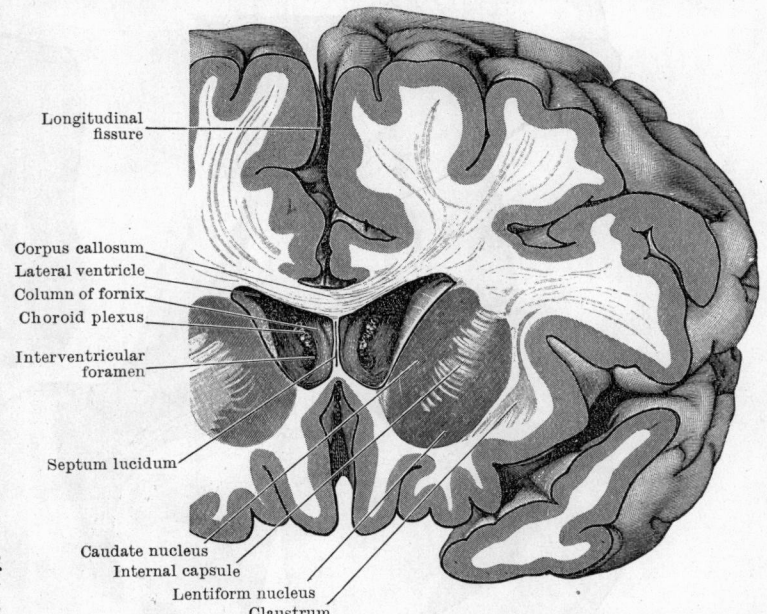

Longitudinal fissure

Corpus callosum
Lateral ventricle
Column of fornix
Choroid plexus
Interventricular foramen

Septum lucidum

Caudate nucleus
Internal capsule
Lentiform nucleus
Claustrum

FIG. 800.—CORONAL SECTION THROUGH THE CEREBRAL HEMISPHERES so as to cut through the anterior horns of the lateral ventricles, through which the central part of the ventricles, the anterior columns of the fornix, and the interventricular foramina can be seen.

In the angle between the diverging posterior and descending horns, and therefore between the calcar avis and the hippocampus as they diverge, the cavity presents an expansion of triangular shape, the floor of which is raised and is known as the **collateral trigone.**

The *lateral wall* of the inferior horn is formed by the tapetum of the corpus callosum. At the end of the horn the roof presents a bulging produced by a collection of grey matter termed the **amygdaloid nucleus.** The **stria semicircularis** and the attenuated **tail of the caudate nucleus** are both prolonged into the inferior horn and are carried forwards, in its roof, to the amygdaloid nucleus. The ependymal *medial wall* of the descending horn is inthrust to form the temporal continuation of the choroid fissure, in which the choroid plexus is carried downwards and forwards.

On *the floor* of the inferior horn the following structures are seen: (1) hippocampus; (2) the choroid plexus; (3) the fimbria; and (4) the collateral eminence.

The **hippocampus** is for the most part covered by the choroid plexus. If that is detached the course of the choroid fissure is seen between the fimbria and the roof of the horn. This fissure appears at a very early date in the development of the cerebral hemisphere, and takes an arcuate course round the posterior end of the thalamus.   In the region of the central part of the ventricle it extends as far forwards as the interventricular foramen and is formed by the involution of the ependymal part of the wall of the ventricle over the choroid pléxus.

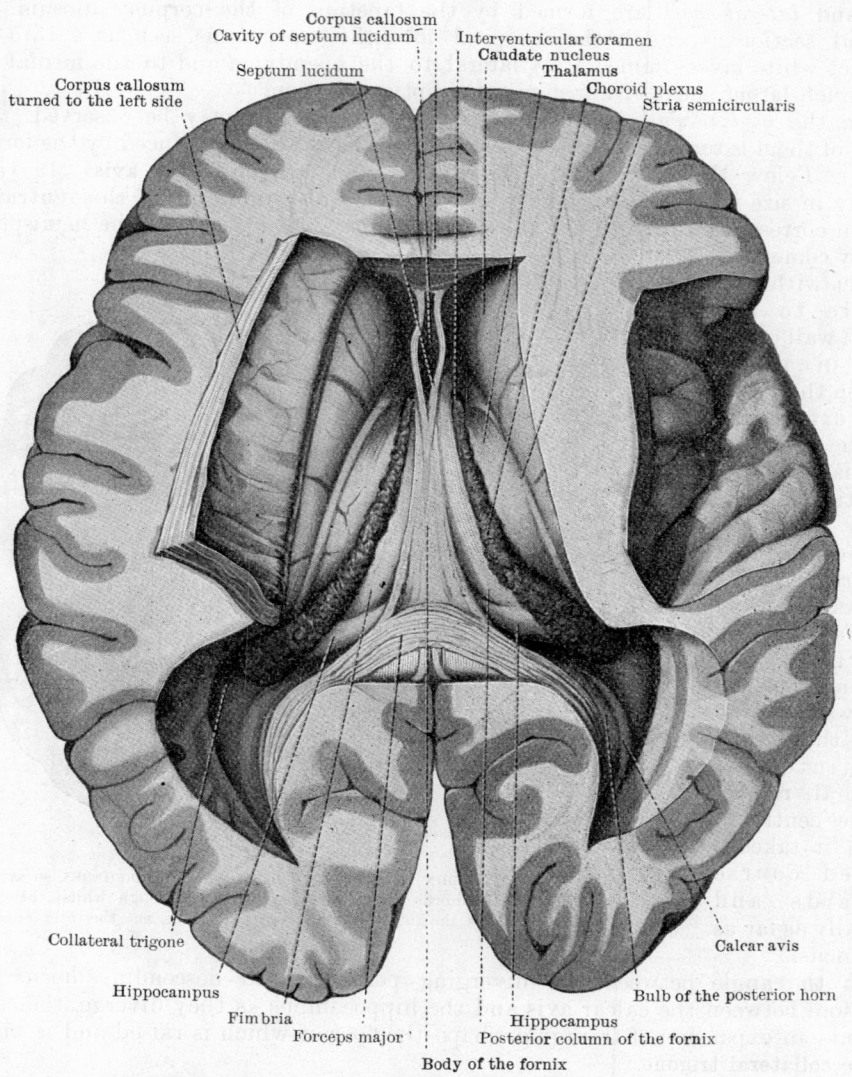

Corpus callosum
Cavity of septum lucidum
Septum lucidum
Corpus callosum turned to the left side
Interventricular foramen
Caudate nucleus
Thalamus
Choroid plexus
Stria semicircularis

Collateral trigone
Hippocampus
Fimbria
Forceps major
Body of the fornix
Hippocampus
Posterior column of the fornix
Calcar avis
Bulb of the posterior horn

FIG. 801.—DISSECTION to show the fornix and lateral ventricles.

In the region of the inferior horn, when the choroid plexus, with the involuted ependymal layer which covers it, is withdrawn, the choroid fissure is converted into an artificial gap which leads directly into the horn.

The **choroid plexus** is a convoluted system of blood-vessels in connexion with a fold of pia mater which is carried into the central part and the inferior horn of the ventricle.   It lies on the surface of the hippocampus and is continuous, behind the posterior part of the thalamus, with the choroid plexus in the central part of the ventricle.   But the choroid plexus does not lie free in the ventricular cavity.   It is clothed in the most intimate manner by an ependymal layer which represents the medial wall of the inferior horn and central part of the ventricle involuted into the cavity over the plexus.   The ventricle, therefore, opens on the surface through the choroid fissure only when that thin epithelial layer is torn away by the withdrawal of the choroid plexus. From the above, it will be understood that the choroid fissure, throughout its whole length (viz., from the interventricular foramen to the end of the inferior horn), is formed by the invagination of a portion of the wall of the hemisphere which remains ependymal.

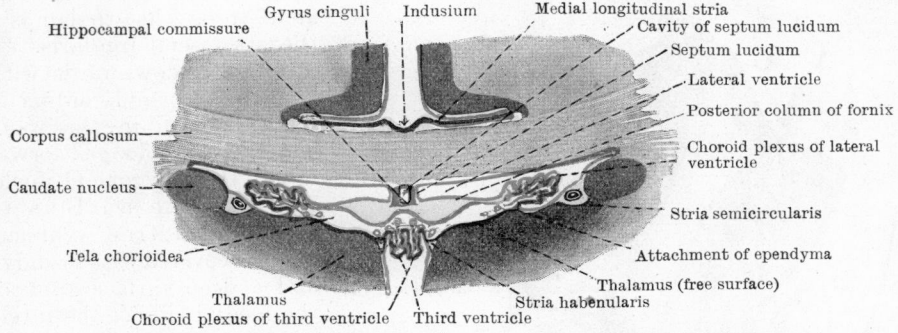

FIG. 802.—DIAGRAM OF TRANSVERSE SECTION ACROSS THE CENTRAL PARTS OF THE LATERAL VENTRICLES.

In the central part of the ventricle that layer is attached, on the one hand, to the margin of the fornix, and on the other to the upper surface of the thalamus; in the inferior horn it is attached to the edge of the fimbria, whilst, above, it joins the roof of the horn along the line of the stria semicircularis.

The **collateral eminence** shows very great differences in its degree of develop-

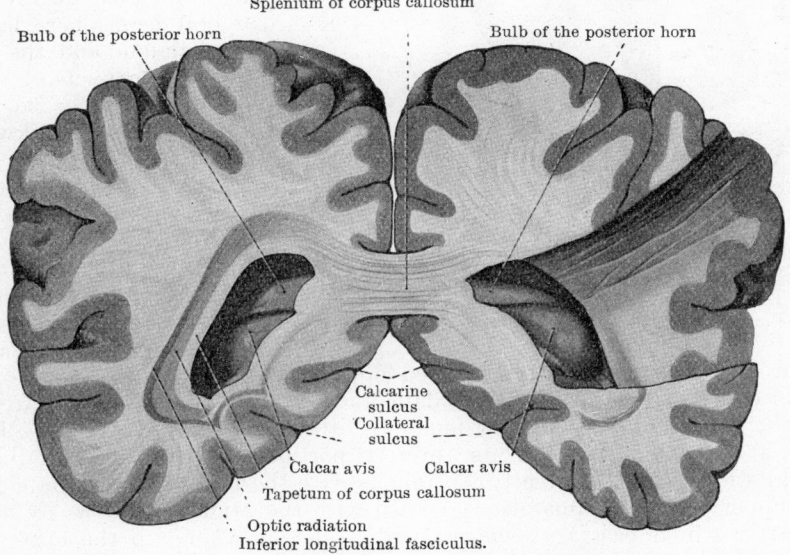

FIG. 803.—CORONAL SECTION THROUGH THE POSTERIOR HORNS OF THE LATERAL VENTRICLES, VIEWED FROM THE FRONT.

ment, which depends upon the depth of the corresponding part of the collateral sulcus in the tentorial surface of the temporal lobe.

BASAL NUCLEI

Under this heading are included certain masses of grey matter more or less completely embedded in the white substance of the hemisphere. They are the caudate and lentiform nuclei (which together form the corpus striatum) the amygdaloid nucleus, and the claustrum.

The **caudate nucleus** bulges into the lateral ventricle. It is a long curved mass of grey matter divisible into a head, a body and a tail. The head is the smooth bulging seen in the lateral wall of the anterior horn of the ventricle; and its lower part is continuous with the anterior perforated substance. The body—much narrower—extends backwards in the floor of the central part of the ventricle, where it is separated from the thalamus by the stria semicircularis. The tail curves downwards with a bold sweep and enters the inferior horn, in the roof of which it is prolonged forwards to join the amygdaloid nucleus. The caudate nucleus thus presents a free ventricular surface, covered with ependyma, and a deep surface applied to the medial side of the internal capsule and the base of the corona radiata; and, owing to its arched form, it is cut in two places in many of the sections of the hemispheres—both horizontal and coronal.

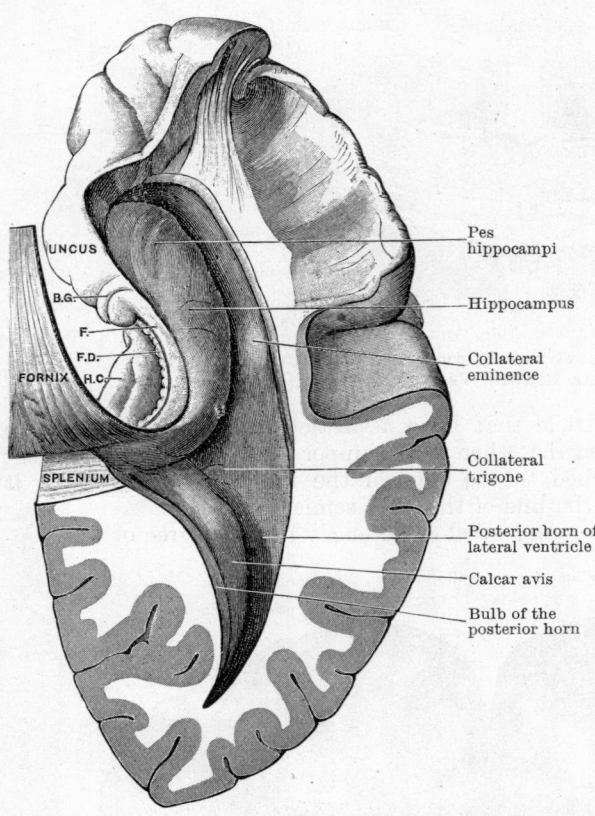

FIG. 804.—DISSECTION from above to show the posterior and inferior horns of the lateral ventricle.

B.G. Tail of dentate gyrus.   F.D. Dentate gyrus.
F.   Fimbria hippocampi.   H.C. Hippocampal gyrus.

The **lentiform nucleus** is for the most part embedded in the white substance of the cerebral hemisphere lateral to the thalamus and the head of the caudate nucleus. It does not extend either so far forwards or so far backwards as the caudate nucleus; indeed, in extent, it corresponds very closely with the insula. When seen in horizontal section, it presents a shape similar to that of a biconvex lens. Its medial surface bulges more than the lateral surface, and its point of highest convexity is placed opposite the stria semicircularis and the interval between the head of the caudate nucleus and the thalamus. In coronal section the appearance differs very much in different planes of section. Fig. 806 represents a section through its anterior portion. Here it is semilunar in outline; its lower part is directly continuous with the head of the caudate nucleus, and its upper part is intimately connected with the caudate nucleus by bands of grey matter which pass between the two nuclei, breaking up the anterior part of the internal capsule. It is due to the ribbed or barred appearance presented by such a section as this that the term **corpus striatum** is applied to the two nuclei. In the region of the anterior perforated substance both nuclei reach the surface and become continuous with the cortex.

When a section is made in a plane farther back (*e.g.*, immediately behind the anterior commissure, as in Fig. 807) the lentiform nucleus has an altogether different shape, and is seen to be completely cut off from the body of the caudate nucleus by the base of the corona radiata (the knife having passed between two uniting bars of grey matter). It is now wedge-shaped. Its *base* is turned towards the insula and is in direct relation to a thin lamina of white matter termed the external capsule. Its *medial surface* is oblique and is applied to the internal capsule, whilst its *inferior surface* is horizontal and is related to the amygdaloid nucleus and the white matter above the roof of the inferior horn of the ventricle. But, further, two white laminæ are now evident; they traverse its substance in a vertical direction and divide it into three masses; the lateral and larger mass is termed the **putamen**, and the medial two portions together constitute the **globus pallidus**.

The **putamen** is much the largest part of the lentiform nucleus. In colour it resembles the caudate nucleus, with which it is closely associated both in

structure and in mode of development; and it is the only part of the lentiform nucleus which is connected by bands of grey matter with the caudate nucleus. In antero-posterior length as well as in vertical depth, the putamen is larger than the globus pallidus; consequently, in both coronal and horizontal sections through the cerebrum it is encountered before the plane of the globus pallidus is reached.

The external capsule is loosely connected with the lateral surface of the putamen, and it can be readily stripped off. This accounts for the tendency, exhibited in hæmorrhages in this locality, for the effused blood to spread out in the interval between these structures.

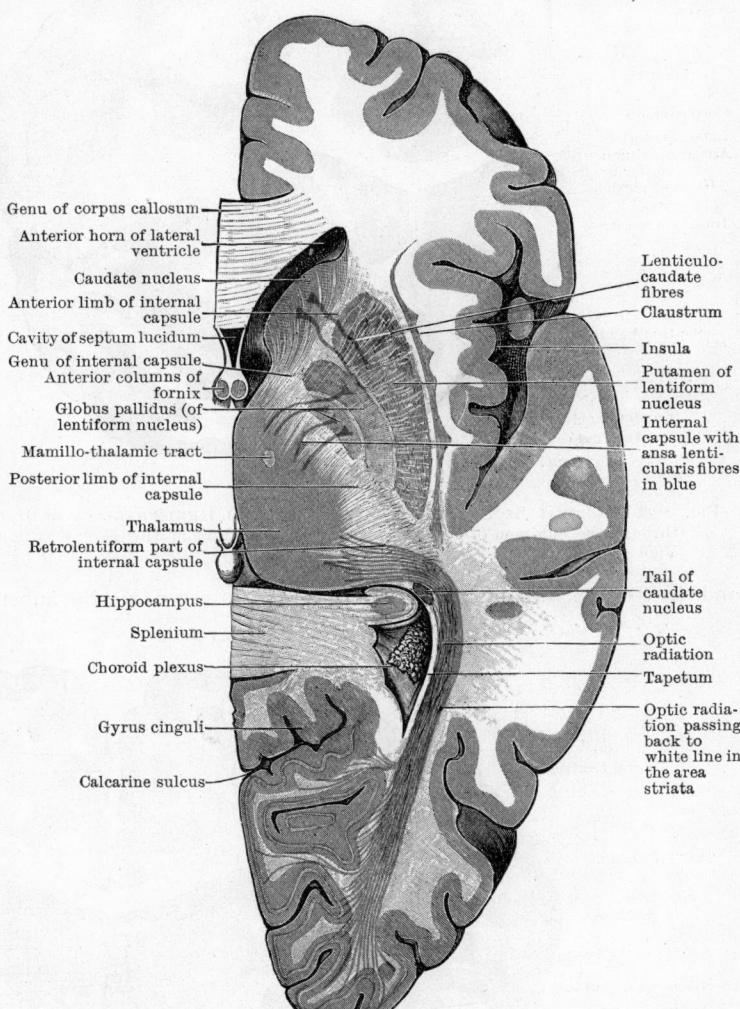

FIG. 805.—HORIZONTAL SECTION THROUGH THE RIGHT CEREBRAL HEMISPHERE AT THE LEVEL OF THE WIDEST PART OF THE LENTIFORM NUCLEUS.

The **globus pallidus** is composed of the two smaller and medial masses of the lentiform nucleus. They present a faint yellowish tint, and are paler and more abundantly traversed by fibres than the putamen. The part next the putamen is much larger than the other and extends forwards to a point a little in front of the plane of the anterior commissure.

Connexions of the Corpus Striatum, Thalamus, and other Masses of Associated Grey Matter.

—Recent research in clinical medicine and pathological anatomy has directed attention to the importance of the corpus striatum, red nucleus, substantia nigra, and subthalamic nucleus and of the so-called extrapyramidal systems of fibres connected with those bodies for the regulation of muscular activity. Hence the anatomy of those structures cannot be ignored. In a student's text-book, however, it would be out of place to attempt a detailed description of a neural machinery of amazing complexity. Hence the attempt is made graphically to present the present state of our knowledge by means of three diagrams (Figs. 808-810).

The fibres of the medial lemniscus that carry impulses from the skin, muscles, tendons, and joints, proceed to the substantia nigra (as well as the thalamus and tectum of the midbrain). In addition to the fibres shown in the diagrams (Figs. 808 and 809), afferent fibres proceed to the substantia nigra from the lateral lemniscus

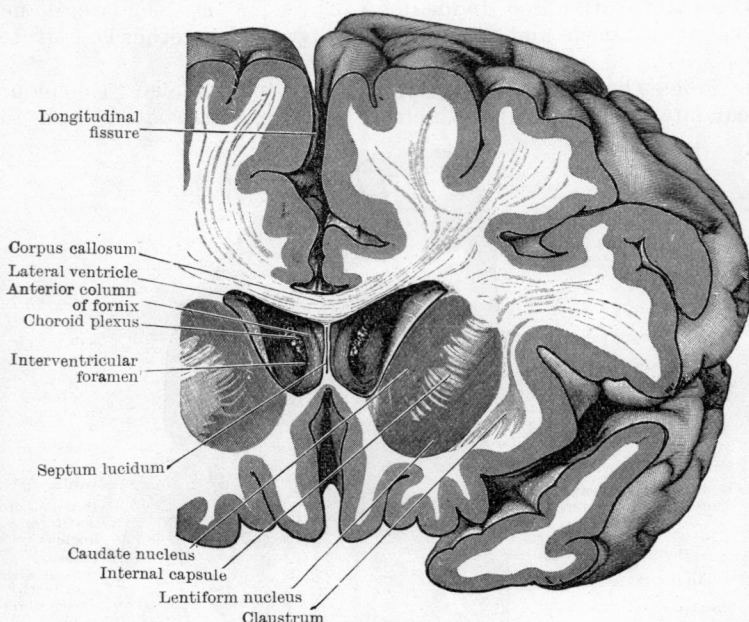

FIG. 806.—CORONAL SECTION THROUGH THE CEREBRAL HEMISPHERES so as to cut through the putamen of the lentiform nucleus in front of the globus pallidus. Viewed from in front.

and the tectum. Winkler is probably correct in regarding the substantia nigra as the in-

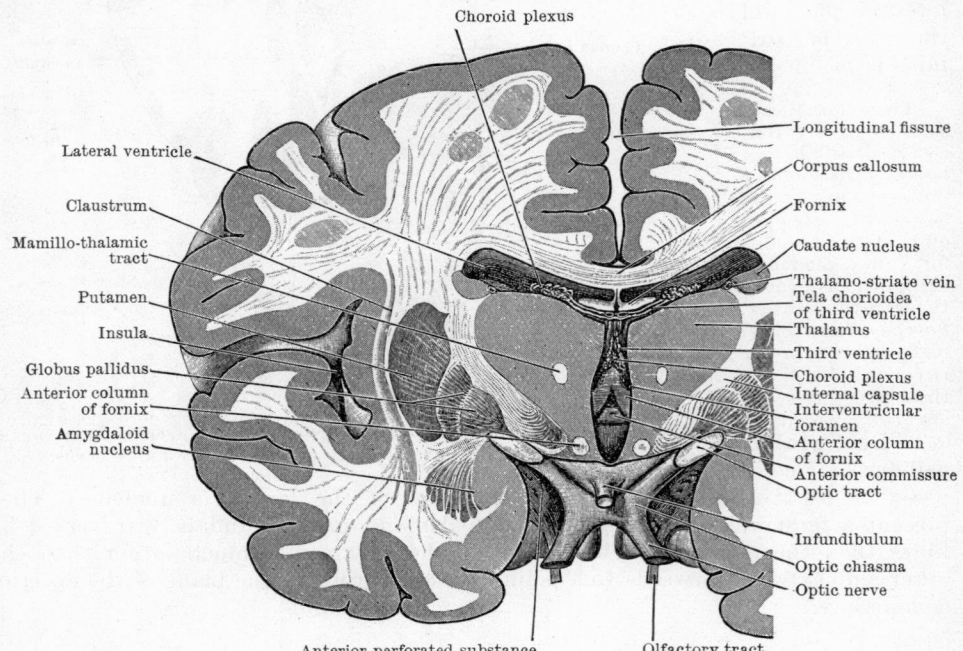

FIG. 807.—CORONAL SECTION THROUGH THE CEREBRUM so as to cut through the three divisions of the lentiform nucleus ; the posterior surface of the section is shown here.

strument for organising the afferent impulses that are concerned with muscular activity, and transmitting to the red nucleus (Fig. 808) the impulses essential for its functions.

In the higher mammals, and especially in man, there is added to the archaic substantia nigra (the palæo-nigrum, Fig. 808, PN) a new formation (neo-nigrum, NN) for the purpose

of establishing connexions with the newly evolved part of the red nucleus, as well as with the cerebral cortex (Nigro-cortical tract, Fig. 808) in the inferior frontal region. The neo-rubrum (NR) also establishes connexions (rubro-cortical tracts) with the frontal cortex, from which also descending tracts (cortico-rubral) pass to the red nucleus. The globus pallidus of the corpus striatum (Fig. 808, pallidum) is linked by efferent fibres with the red nucleus, as well as with the subthalamic nucleus (Figs. 808 and 809) and the olive (pallido-olivary tract, Fig. 808). The red nucleus also is linked to the olive by the rubro-olivary tract (Fig. 808). The red nucleus receives from the cerebellum a large bundle of fibres—the superior cerebellar peduncle. Impulses from the cerebellar cortex are transmitted to the dentate nucleus and the roof nuclei, and they emit the superior cerebellar peduncle, which emerges from the cerebellum, and crosses the median plane to enter the red nucleus (Fig. 759).

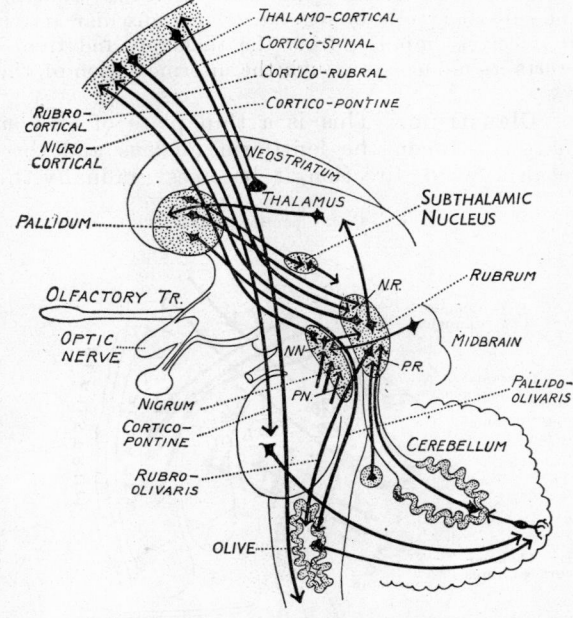

FIG. 808.—DIAGRAM OF THE CONNEXIONS OF THE BASAL NUCLEI WITH THE CEREBRAL CORTEX AND THE CEREBELLUM—VIEWED IN PROFILE FROM THE LEFT SIDE. (G. E. S.)

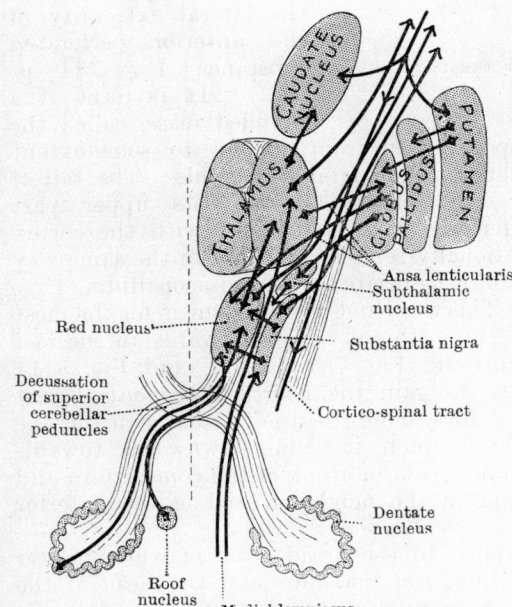

FIG. 809.—DIAGRAM OF A CORONAL SECTION TO ILLUSTRATE THE FIBRE CONNEXIONS OF THE BASAL NUCLEI AND CEREBELLAR NUCLEI. (G. E. S.)

The fibres from the group of roof nuclei in the vermis of the cerebellum proceed to the palæo-rubrum (the archaic large-celled part of the red nucleus). The fibres from the dentate nucleus proceed to the neo-rubrum. The subthalamic nucleus receives impulses from the pallidum, and its efferent tracts pass into the tegmentum immediately below it (Figs. 808 and 809).

The transverse bundle of fibres which crosses the route of the internal capsule just as it is emerging to become the basis pedunculi is known as the **ansa lenticularis**. It includes efferent fibres from the globus pallidus to the subthalamic nucleus and the red nucleus, as well as afferent fibres from the thalamus to the globus pallidus (Fig. 809).

The ventral part of the lateral nucleus of the thalamus receives the fibres of the medial lemniscus, as well as fibres from the red nucleus (Fig. 809). It emits fibres which pass to the globus pallidus and caudate nucleus as well as to the cerebral cortex (Fig. 809). The caudate nucleus and putamen of the lentiform nucleus represent an addition (Fig. 808, neo-striatum) to the old striatum (globus pallidus—evolved in reptiles when large thalamic tracts stimulated the sudden expansion of the cerebral cortex) which pushed its way into the lateral ventricle and so added a new (cortical) element to the striatum. It was the earliest device for the control of muscular action by the cerebral cortex : but when, in mammals, the neopallium assumed control of skilled movements the new striatum—caudate nucleus and putamen—assumed the subsidiary rôle of regulating the muscular activities initiated by the cerebral cortex. It receives impulses from the thalamus and from the cerebral cortex (Fig. 809) and exerts its influence through the intermediation of the globus pallidus.

Claustrum.—This is a thin plate of grey substance embedded in the white matter between the lentiform nucleus and the cortex of the insula. Followed in an upward direction, it becomes gradually thinner and ultimately disappears. As it is traced downwards, however, it thickens considerably, and at the base of the brain it comes to the surface at the anterior perforated substance. Its extent corresponds very closely with the area occupied by the insula, and its lateral surface shows ridges and depressions corresponding to the insular gyri and sulci.

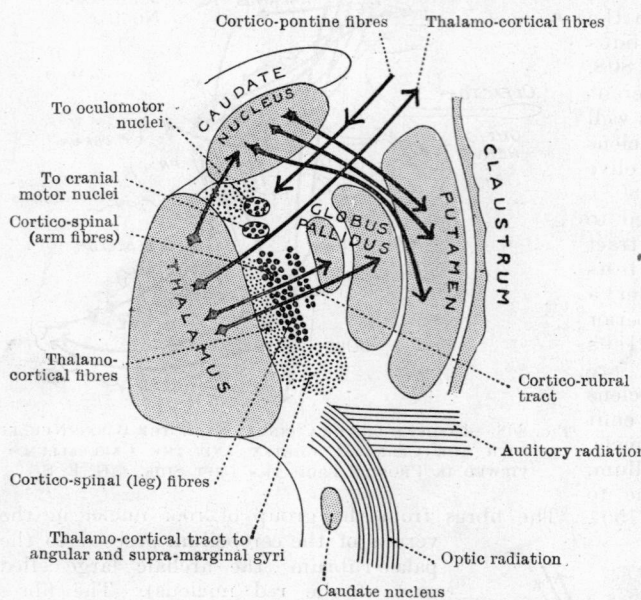

Cortico-pontine fibres　　Thalamo-cortical fibres

To oculomotor nuclei

CAUDATE NUCLEUS

To cranial motor nuclei

Cortico-spinal (arm fibres)

GLOBUS PALLIDUS

THALAMUS

PUTAMEN

CLAUSTRUM

Thalamo-cortical fibres

Cortico-rubral tract

Auditory radiation

Cortico-spinal (leg) fibres

Thalamo-cortical tract to angular and supra-marginal gyri

Optic radiation

Caudate nucleus

FIG. 810.—DIAGRAMMATIC REPRESENTATION OF THE INTERNAL CAPSULE (AS SEEN IN HORIZONTAL SECTION). (G. E. S.)

Amygdaloid Nucleus. —In the anterior part of the temporal region, above the piriform area, a fusiform mass of grey matter appears on the surface (Fig. 794, p. 910), at the lateral extremity of the anterior perforated substance (Fig. 784, p. 902). It is part of a rounded mass, called the amygdaloid nucleus, which occupies a position in front of and to some extent above the anterior end of the inferior horn of the lateral ventricle. The tail of the caudate nucleus joins its lower part (Fig. 811), and its upper part is carried up into the putamen. Inferiorly it is continuous with the cortex of the piriform area, to which it is functionally related, probably in the same way that the major part of the corpus striatum is associated with the neopallium.

Stria Semicircularis [S. Terminalis].—This is a band of fibres which, for the most part, arises in the amygdaloid nucleus. From this it runs backwards in the roof of the inferior horn of the lateral ventricle (Fig. 784, p. 902, and Fig. 811), and then arches upwards and forwards, to gain the floor of the central part of the ventricle. In both situations it lies close to the medial side of the caudate nucleus : at the interventricular foramen, it bends downwards towards the anterior commissure. Some of its fibres pass in front of the commissure and others behind it, and ultimately they end in the neighbourhood of the anterior perforated substance (Kölliker).

Internal Capsule.—This term is applied to the broad band of white matter which separates the lentiform nucleus from the thalamus and the head of the caudate nucleus. It presents different appearances according to the plane in which the brain is cut. A coronal section which passes through the cerebral peduncles shows that, in great part, the internal capsule is directly continuous with the basis pedunculi (Fig. 776, p. 891). Viewed from the lateral aspect after removal of all else of the cerebral hemisphere except the corpus striatum (Fig. 811), the cut ends of the fasciculi of the internal capsule form three-fourths of an ellipse, the other fourth of which is occupied by the bridge of union between the lentiform and caudate nuclei, the anterior perforated substance, the amygdaloid nucleus and the anterior commissure. It may be divided into an **anterior (lenticulo - caudate) part**, a **posterior (lenticulo - thalamic) part**, a **retrolentiform part** (not labelled in the figure), and a **postero-inferior (sublentiform) part**. The last three parts are usually grouped together as the posterior limb. In horizontal section the internal capsule is observed to be bent upon itself opposite the stria semicircularis at the interval between the thalamus and the head of the caudate nucleus. That bend, which points medially, is called the **genu**.

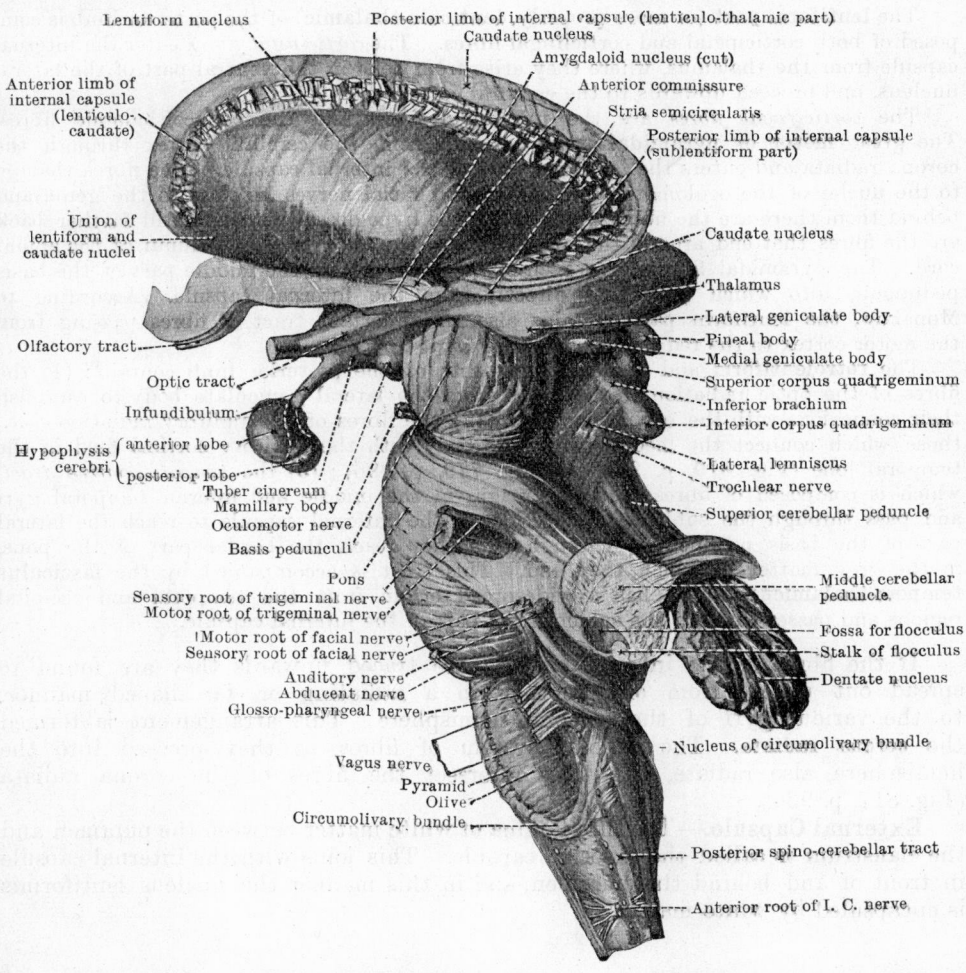

FIG. 811.—DISSECTION EXPOSING THE LENTIFORM NUCLEUS OF THE LEFT HEMISPHERE. (G. E. S.)

About one-third of the internal capsule lies in front of the genu, and is termed the anterior limb; the remaining two-thirds, which lie behind the genu, constitute the posterior limb (Fig. 805).

The **anterior limb of the internal capsule** intervenes between the lentiform nucleus and the head of the caudate nucleus. In its inferior and anterior part it is much broken up by the connecting bands of grey matter which pass between the anterior part of the putamen and the caudate nucleus.

The anterior limb of the internal capsule is composed largely of *corticipetal fibres* that arise in the median and anterior part of the ventro-lateral nucleus of the thalamus, and go through the anterior limb to reach the cortex of the frontal lobe. It contains *corticifugal fibres* also. These are the frontal members of the cerebro-pontine fibres. The

fronto-pontine fibres arise in the cortex of the frontal region, traverse the anterior limb of the internal capsule, form the medial fifth of the basis pedunculi, and finally end in the nuclei pontis.

The **posterior limb of the internal capsule** is placed between the thalamus and the lentiform nucleus, and it extends backwards for a short distance beyond the posterior end of the putamen on the lateral side of the posterior part of the thalamus. The posterior limb may therefore be described in three parts—lentiform, retrolentiform, and sublentiform.

The **lentiform part** (or more properly, **lenticulo-thalamic**) of the posterior limb is composed of both corticipetal and corticifugal fibres. The *corticipetal fibres* enter the internal capsule from the thalamus, where they arise from cells in the ventral part of the lateral nucleus, and proceed upwards to the cerebral cortex.

The *corticifugal fibres* are the pyramidal fibres and the cortico-thalamic fibres. The great **motor** or **pyramidal tract** descends from the cerebral cortex through the corona radiata and enters the lentiform part of the internal capsule. The fibres that go to the nuclei of the oculomotor, trigeminal, and facial nerves lie close to the genu, and behind them there are the fibres which go to the hypoglossal nucleus; still farther back are the fibres that end around the motor cells of the anterior grey column of the spinal cord. The pyramidal fibres have been observed occupying the middle part of the basis pedunculi, into which they pass directly from the internal capsule. According to Monakow, the lentiform part contains also an important tract of fibres passing from the motor cortex to the red nucleus (*cortico-rubral tract*).

The **retrolentiform** and **sublentiform parts** of the posterior limb contain: (1) the fibres of the optic radiation as they pass from the lateral geniculate body to establish their connexions with the occipital cortex; (2) the fibres of the auditory radiation—*i.e.*, those which connect the medial geniculate body with the auditory cortical field in the temporal lobe (Fig. 810, p. 924, and Fig. 779, p. 896); (3) the *temporo-pontine tract*, which is composed of fibres that take origin in the middle and inferior temporal gyri and pass through the sublentiform section of the internal capsule to reach the lateral part of the basis pedunculi. Through this they reach the basilar part of the pons, in the grey matter of which they end. This tract is accompanied by the **fasciculus temporo-thalamicus**, which has a widespread origin from the temporal and occipital regions and passes through the sublentiform part of the internal capsule.

If the fibres of the internal capsule are traced upwards they are found to spread out widely from one another in a radiating or fan-shaped manner, to the various gyri of the cerebral hemisphere. This arrangement is termed the **corona radiata.** The callosal system of fibres, as they proceed into the hemisphere, also radiate, and they intersect the fibres of the corona radiata (Fig. 817, p. 934).

External Capsule.—The thin lamina of white matter between the putamen and the claustrum is called the external capsule. This joins with the internal capsule in front of and behind the putamen, and in this manner the nucleus lentiformis is encapsuled by white matter.

INTIMATE STRUCTURE OF THE CEREBRAL HEMISPHERE

The cerebral hemisphere is composed of an external coating of grey matter, termed the **cortex**, spread over an internal mass of white matter. The cortex is of peculiar interest, seeing that there is good reason for believing that in it the higher functions of the brain, or those which may be classed under the general designation of the intellectual functions, take place. It is within the same layer of grey matter that the influence of those external impressions which gain access to the cerebrospinal axis through the senses finally take shape as consciousness; and in it are placed also the centres which carry on the psycho-motor functions. The white centre is composed of nerve-fibres which constitute the paths along which the influence of impressions is carried to and from the cortex, and from one part of the cortex to another.

CEREBRAL CORTEX

The cortex is spread over the entire surface of the cerebral hemisphere, but it does not form a layer of equal thickness. At the summit of a gyrus it is usually thicker than at the bottom of a furrow. The maximum thickness of cortex (about 4 mm.) is attained in the upper part of the motor area, whilst the minimum

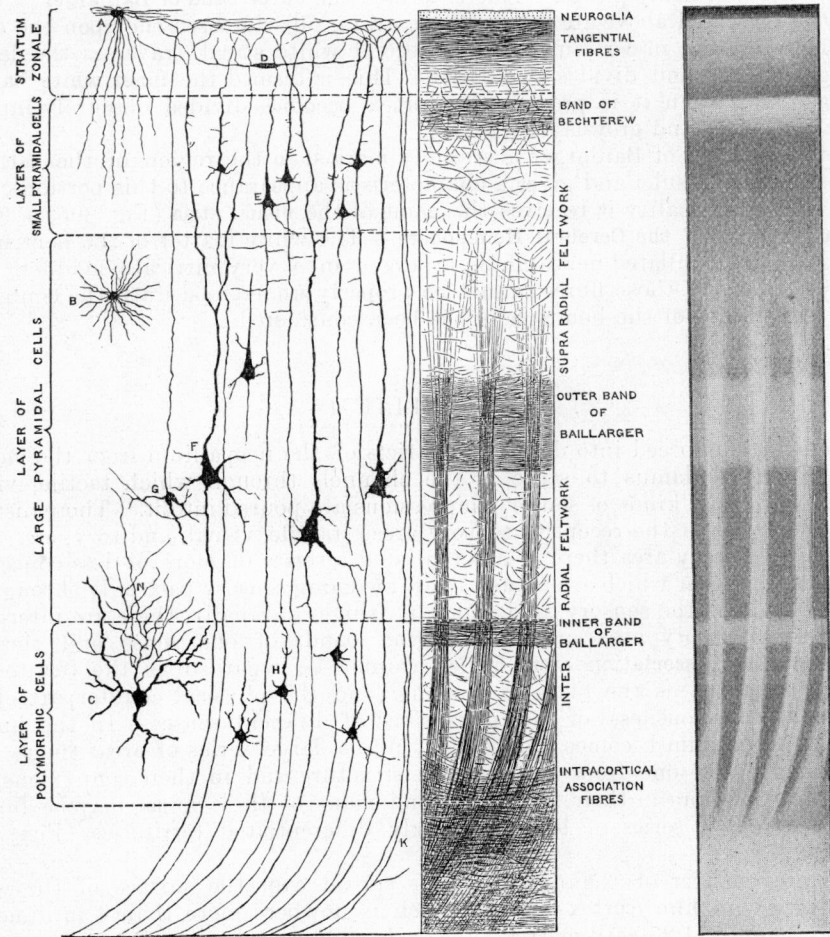

FIG. 812.—DIAGRAM TO ILLUSTRATE THE MINUTE STRUCTURE OF THE CEREBRAL CORTEX
AND EXPLAIN HOW IT INFLUENCES THE MACROSCOPIC APPEARANCE.

A. } Neuroglia cells.
B. }
C. Cell with short axon (N) which breaks up in a free arborisation.
D. Spindle-shaped cell in stratum zonale.

E. Small pyramidal cell.
F. Large pyramidal cell.
G. Cell of Martinotti.
H. Polymorphic cell.
K. Corticipetal fibres.

(about 1·25 mm.) occurs at the occipital pole. The amount of cortex differs considerably in different subjects and appreciably diminishes in old age.

In structure also, marked differences may be noted in the cortex of different regions, and much has been recently done in the direction of pointing out the connexion of these structural peculiarities with the functional characteristics of particular areas and applying them to the determination of the significance of the furrows that subdivide the cerebral cortex into a series of ridges or gyri. This structural difference is quite apparent to the naked eye when sections are made through the cortex in a fresh brain, and sharp transitions in structure occur at the place where one area joins another. It is only to those general structural features which more or less characterise the entire cortical layer that we shall be able to refer.

When sections are made through the fresh brain, and the cut surface is closely inspected, it will usually be apparent that the cortex is distinctly stratified. On the outside there is a thin, whitish layer, and beneath this the grey matter presents two strata of very nearly equal thickness, viz., a middle, grey-coloured stratum and an inner, yellowish-red stratum. Between the two latter layers a narrow white band is visible in many places. This is termed the **outer band of Baillarger**. When the layers indicated above are present, four strata, superimposed one upon the other, are recognised; but in certain regions a second white streak traverses the deep or inner grey layer and divides it further. This is termed the **inner white band of Baillarger**, and, when it is present, the cortex becomes divided obscurely into six alternating white and grey layers.

The outer band of Baillarger is strongly marked in the region of the calcarine and post-calcarine sulci and gives a characteristic appearance to this portion of the cortex. In this locality it receives the name of the **visual stria** (Fig. 805, p. 921).

White Centre of the Cerebral Hemisphere.—The white matter of the hemisphere is composed of medullated nerve-fibres, arranged in a very intricate manner. But the arrangement of those fibres cannot be properly understood until the configuration of the surface of the hemisphere has been considered.

NEOPALLIUM

Fibre-tracts proceed into different districts of the neopallium from the various nuclei of the thalamus to serve as the channels through which tactile, visual, auditory, and other kinds of sensory impressions are poured into it. Those districts may be regarded as the receptive sensory areas (tactile, visual, auditory, etc.); but around each sensory area there is differentiated a series of more or less concentric bands of neopallium which are related to an incoming sensory path only through the intermediation of the sensory area which it fringes. Finally, there are interposed between the sensory area and its fringing bands of one sense and those of another, certain **association areas** which cannot be regarded as the territory of any one sense, but as the place of meeting (and the physical counterpart of the blending in consciousness) of the impressions of different senses. In the human brain the neopallium becomes mapped out into a large series of areas (more than forty) which differ one from the other in structure and in their connexions, and presumably therefore in their functions; and many of these areas may be further subdivided into a series of less obtrusively differentiated territories (Figs. 819, 823 and 827).

The grey matter of the neopallium is spread over the surface of the white matter as a thin film (**cortex cerebri**) which is nowhere more than 4 millimetres, and may be only 1·25 millimetres thick. In different regions it presents every gradation of thickness between these two extremes. As the cortex increases in volume it does so not by any addition to its depth, but solely by an expansion of its area. Thus, it happens that in all larger mammalian brains, as the cerebral hemisphere expands and there is an increasing disproportion between the bulk of the hemisphere and the area of its surface, the cortex must become folded to accommodate itself to the limited area of surface upon which it has to be packed. But this process of folding does not take place in any haphazard or purely mechanical way. The situations of the furrows or **sulci** which make their appearance are determined, generally, by the arrangement and the relative rates of expansion of the various areas into which the neopallium becomes differentiated.

The great majority of the furrows belong to a group which we may call (1) **terminal sulci**, i.e., they make their appearance along the boundary lines between areas of different structure; the rhinal and central sulci are examples of this group. Another group, which may be called (2) **axial sulci**, develop by the folding of areas of uniform structure, i.e., along the axis of certain territories; the post-calcarine sulcus and the lateral occipital sulcus belong to this group. There is a

third group of (3) **operculated sulci**, where the edge of one area becomes pushed
over an adjoining territory, so that a trough is formed (Fig. 813, C), which is neither
a limiting nor an axial sulcus; the sulcus lunatus is an example. And finally
(4) there is a group in which some more definitely mechanical factor comes
into play to complicate the operation of these other factors, or even to determine
the development of a furrow; the parieto-occipital sulcus and the lateral sulcus are
examples of the fourth group.

Longitudinal Fissure.—The longitudinal fissure is not a sulcus of the cortex
but is the great cleft between the two cerebral hemispheres. In front and behind
it separates the cerebral hemispheres completely. In its middle part, however,
the fissure is interrupted and floored by the corpus callosum—a white commissural
band which passes between the hemispheres and connects them together. The
longitudinal fissure is occupied by a median fold of dura mater, termed the falx
cerebri, which partially subdivides the part of the cranial cavity allotted to the
cerebrum into a right and left chamber.

External Configuration of each Cerebral Hemisphere.—Each cerebral hemisphere has three surfaces—supero-lateral, medial, and inferior. The *supero-lateral
surface* is convex and is adapted accurately to the internal surface of the cranial
vault. The *medial surface* is flat and perpendicular, and bounds the longitudinal

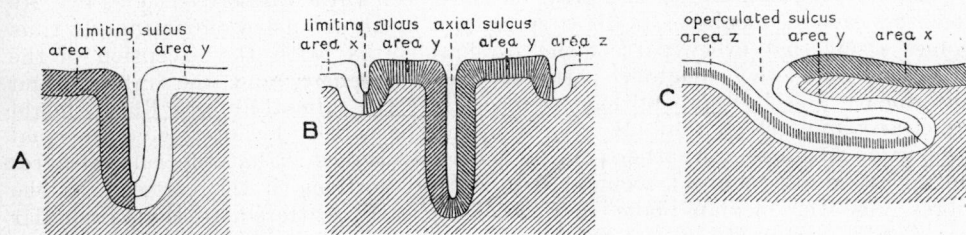

FIG. 813.—DIAGRAMS TO EXPLAIN THREE TYPES OF CEREBRAL FURROWS.

fissure; in great part it is separated from the corresponding surface of the opposite
hemisphere by the falx cerebri. The *inferior surface* is irregular and is adapted
to the floors of the anterior and middle cranial fossæ and, behind them, to the
upper surface of the tentorium cerebelli. Traversing that surface in a transverse
direction, nearer the anterior end of the hemisphere than the posterior end, is
the stem of the lateral sulcus. That deep cleft divides the inferior surface into an
anterior or *orbital area*, which rests on the orbital part of the frontal bone and is
consequently concave from side to side, and a more extensive posterior or *tentorial
area*, which lies on the floor of the lateral part of the middle cranial fossa and on
the tentorium cerebelli. That surface is arched from before backwards, and looks
medially as well as downwards. In its posterior two-thirds it is separated from
the cerebellum by the tentorium cerebelli.

The borders between the surfaces are the supero-medial, the superciliary, the
infero-lateral, the medial occipital, and medial orbital. The *supero-medial border*,
convex from before backwards, intervenes between the supero-lateral surface and
the medial surface of the hemisphere. The *superciliary border* is highly arched and
separates the orbital surface from the supero-lateral surface. The *infero-lateral
border* marks off the tentorial surface from the supero-lateral surface. The *medial
occipital border* can be seen only when the brain has been hardened *in situ*. It
extends from the occipital pole towards the splenium of the corpus callosum, and
intervenes between the medial and tentorial surfaces. It lies along the straight
blood sinus, and occupies the angle between the falx cerebri and the tentorium
cerebelli. The *medial orbital border* separates the orbital surface from the medial
surface.

The anterior end of the cerebral hemisphere is called the **frontal pole**, whilst the
posterior end is termed the **occipital pole**. On the inferior surface of the hemisphere the prominent point of cerebral substance which extends forwards below
the lateral sulcus receives the name of the **temporal pole**. In a well-hardened

brain a broad groove is usually present on the medial and inferior aspect of the occipital pole of the right hemisphere; it corresponds to the commencement of the right transverse venous sinus; the left transverse sinus may make a less distinct groove on the occipital pole of the left hemisphere. On the tentorial surface, a short distance behind the temporal pole, a well-marked depression, called the **petrous impression**, is always visible; it corresponds to the elevation on the anterior surface of the petrous portion of the temporal bone over the superior semicircular canal.

White Matter of the Cerebral Hemispheres

According to the connexions which they establish the nerve fibres in the white matter of the hemispheres may be classified into three groups, viz. (1) commissural fibres; (2) association fibres; and (3) itinerant (projection) fibres.

Commissural Fibres.—These are fibres which link together portions of the cortex of opposite cerebral hemispheres. They are arranged in three groups forming three definite structures, viz. the corpus callosum, the anterior commissure, and the hippocampal commissure.

The **corpus callosum** has in a great measure been already described (p. 914). As it enters each hemisphere, its fibres spread out in an extensive radiation. It thus comes about that every part of the cerebral cortex, with the exception of the olfactory bulb, the olfactory parts of the hemisphere, and the inferior and anterior part of the temporal lobe, is reached by the callosal fibres. But it should be clearly understood that all the regions of the cortex do not receive an equal proportion of fibres. Another point of some importance is that the callosal fibres do not, as a rule, connect together symmetrical portions of the cortex. As the fibres cross the median plane they become greatly scattered, so that dissimilar parts of the cortex of opposite hemispheres come to be associated with one another.

The **anterior commissure** is a structure supplemental to the corpus callosum, although originally it was the principal cerebral commissure long before the corpus callosum was evolved. It connects together the two olfactory bulbs, and also portions of the opposite temporal lobes. It has a cord-like appearance and in median section appears as a small oval bundle in the lamina terminalis (Fig. 794, p. 910). The median free portion is placed immediately in front of the anterior columns of the fornix as they curve downwards, and also in intimate relation to the anterior end of the third ventricle. Posteriorly the small portion of the anterior commissure which appears in the ventricle between the two columns of the fornix is clothed with ependyma; anteriorly the commissure lies within the lamina terminalis as it stretches from the optic chiasma upwards towards the inferior (anterior) end of the hippocampal commissure.

The lateral part of the anterior commissure penetrates the cerebral hemisphere, and, gaining the inferior part of the anterior end of the internal capsule, divides into two portions, viz. a small olfactory part and a much larger temporal part.

The **olfactory portion** of the anterior commissure is an exceedingly small fasciculus. It passes downwards and forwards, and finally enters the olfactory tract. It is composed (1) of true commissural fibres which bind one olfactory bulb to the other, and (2) of other fibres which connect the olfactory bulb of one side with the piriform area of the other side.

The **temporal portion** is formed of almost the whole of the fibres of the commissure. It is carried laterally under the lentiform nucleus, until it gains the interval between the globus pallidus and the putamen. At that point it changes its direction and sweeps backwards. In coronal sections through the brain, behind this bend, the temporal portion of the anterior commissure appears as an oval bundle of fibres cut transversely and placed in close contact with the inferior surface of the lentiform nucleus. Finally it turns sharply downwards on the lateral aspect of the amygdaloid nucleus, and its fibres are lost in the white centre of the temporal lobe. When the lateral part of the anterior commissure is displayed by dissection, it is seen to be twisted like a rope.

The **hippocampal commissure** is composed of fibres that connect the two hippocampi.   It is described on p. 910.

Association Fibres.—The association fibres bind together different portions of the cortex of the same hemisphere.   They are grouped into long and short association bundles.

The greater number of the **short association fibres** pass between adjacent gyri.   They curve round the bottoms of the sulci in U-shaped loops.   Some of them occupy the deepest part of the cortex itself, and are termed *intracortical association fibres* (Figs. 813 and 814); others lie immediately subjacent to the grey matter and receive the name of *subcortical fibres*.   Many groups of short association fibres, instead of linking together contiguous gyri, pass between gyri more or less remote.   It is only after birth, when intellectual effort and education have stimulated different portions of the cortex to act in harmony and in conjunction with each other, that these association fibres assume their sheaths of myelin and become functional.

The **long association bundles** lie more deeply and can be traced by dissection for considerable distances in the white matter.   They contain fibres that unite districts of the cortex far removed from each other, but experiments on cats and

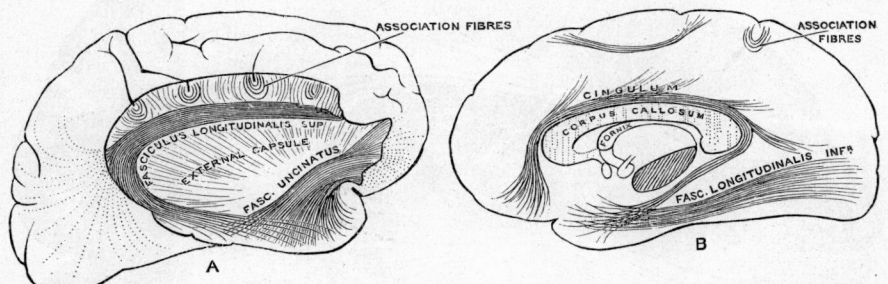

FIG. 814.—DIAGRAMS OF THE LEADING ASSOCIATION BUNDLES OF THE CEREBRAL HEMISPHERE.
(Founded on the drawings of Dejerine.)

A, Lateral aspect of hemisphere.   B, Medial aspect of hemisphere.

monkeys (Poljak), as well as ordinary dissection, suggest that they are largely made up of groups of fibres that run in them for relatively short distances.   The better known of these long fasciculi are the following: (1) the uncinate; (2) the cingulum; (3) the superior longitudinal; (4) the inferior longitudinal; and (5) the fronto-occipital.

The **fasciculus uncinatus** is composed of fibres which arch over the stem of the lateral sulcus and connect the frontal pole and the orbital gyri with the anterior portion of the temporal lobe; its middle and most definite part is easily found if the grey matter of the limen insulae is scraped away.

The **cingulum** is a very well-marked and distinct band which is closely associated with the medial edge of the neopallium.   Beginning in front, in the region of the anterior perforated substance, it arches round the genu of the corpus callosum and is carried backwards on its upper surface under cover of the gyrus cinguli, and it stands in intimate relation to the white centre of this gyrus (Fig. 798, p. 914). At the posterior end of the corpus callosum the cingulum turns round the splenium and is carried forwards, in relation to the hippocampal gyrus, to the uncus and the temporal pole.

The **superior longitudinal bundle** is an arcuate bundle placed on the lateral side of the base of the corona radiata ; it connects the frontal, occipital, and temporal regions of the hemisphere.   It lies in the root of the fronto-parietal operculum and sweeps backwards over the insular region to the posterior end of the lateral sulcus.   There it bends downwards round the posterior end of the putamen and proceeds forwards in the temporal lobe to reach its anterior extremity.   As it turns downwards to reach the temporal lobe numerous fibres radiate from it into the occipital lobe.

The **inferior longitudinal bundle** is a very conspicuous one which extends along the whole length of the occipital and temporal regions (Fig. 814 B). In the occipital lobe the inferior longitudinal bundle is immediately lateral to the optic radiation, which takes a similar direction and from which it is distinguished by the greater coarseness of its fibres (Figs. 803, p. 919; 815). It is not present in the macaque monkey (Ferrier and Turner), but is well developed in the orang and the chimpanzee.

The **fronto-occipital bundle** is very slender. It runs in a sagittal direction between the frontal and occipital lobes, lying immediately below the trunk of the corpus callosum between the caudate nucleus and the base of the corona radiata; posteriorly, it fans out and its fibres are lost in the tapetum. It has been pointed out (Forel, Onufrowicz, and others) that in brains where the corpus callosum has failed to develop the tapetum remains

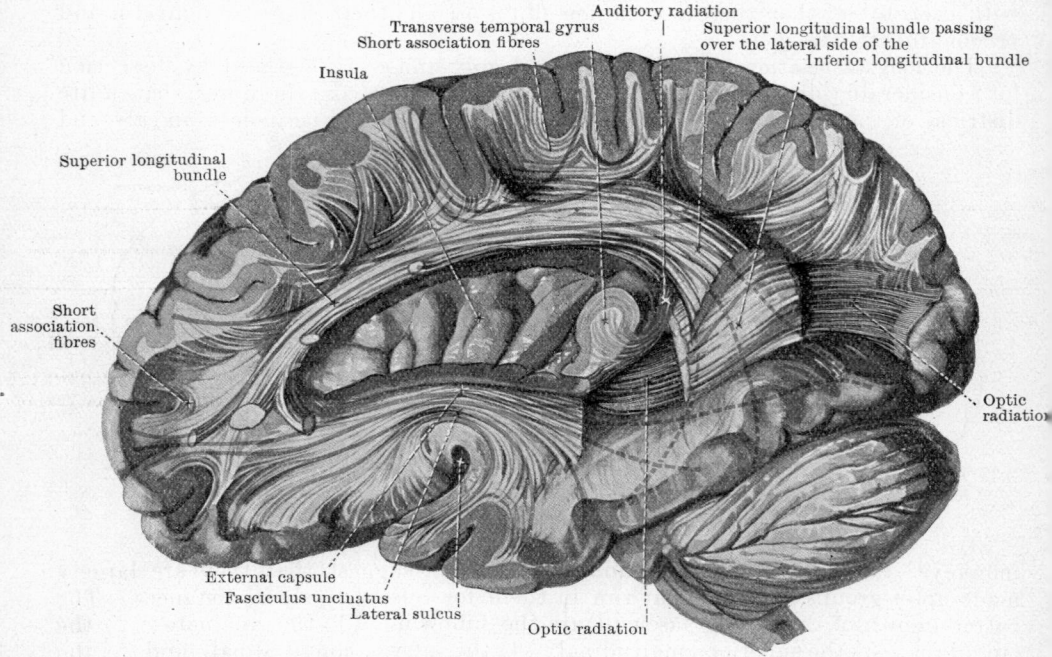

FIG. 815.—DISSECTION TO DISPLAY SOME OF THE PRINCIPAL ASSOCIATION BUNDLES.

apparently unaffected, and Dejerine endeavoured to prove that the fibres of the tapetum really belong to the fronto-occipital bundle.

Itinerant Fibres (Projection Fibres).—We have already seen that every part of the cerebral cortex is linked to other cortical areas, not only in its own neighbourhood (short association fibres) (Fig. 815), but also in the most distant parts of the hemisphere (long association fibres), as well as to the cortex of the other hemisphere (commissural fibres). In addition there are two large series of fibres: (i) an ascending group which conveys to the cerebral cortex impulses coming from the thalamus and metathalamus, the corpora quadrigemina and the red nucleus, and the various other sensory nuclei scattered throughout the brain stem and spinal cord; and (ii) a descending group connecting the cerebral hemisphere with the corpus striatum, various parts of the diencephalon, mesencephalon and cerebellum, as well as with all the motor nuclei scattered throughout the central nervous system. These two groups of tracts, respectively passing to and from the cerebral cortex, are known collectively as its **itinerant fibres**.

While examining the general arrangement of the itinerant fibres of the cerebral hemisphere it is convenient to refer incidentally to certain other fibre-tracts which do not fall strictly within this group.

The Sensory Tracts.—A certain proportion of the fibres that enter the spinal cord by its posterior root, mediating impulses from muscles, tendons, and joints, pass upwards without interruption in the posterior white columns throughout the whole length of the spinal cord until they reach the medulla oblongata, where they end in the nucleus gracilis and nucleus cuneatus.   From those nuclei, arcuate fibres arise, and, after crossing the median plane, proceed upwards in the **medial lemniscus** of the other side to end in the ventral part of the lateral nucleus of the thalamus, from which a third group of fibres arises and proceeds upwards through the internal capsule to the cerebral cortex, where the impulses conveyed by it excite a consciousness of position and movement.   But the sensory fibres that transmit impulses subserving touch, pain and temperature end in the spinal cord near their place of entry into it, and from the cells related to the endings of those fibres new tracts (**spino-thalamic**) arise, cross the median plane to reach the anterior and lateral white columns of the opposite side, in which they proceed upwards throughout the whole length of the spinal cord and brain-stem to the thalamus, where they end in relationship with cells of the ventral part of the lateral nucleus.   The fibres arising from that nucleus proceed to the postcentral gyrus, and convey impulses to it which may excite a consciousness of touch, pressure, pain, heat, or cold.

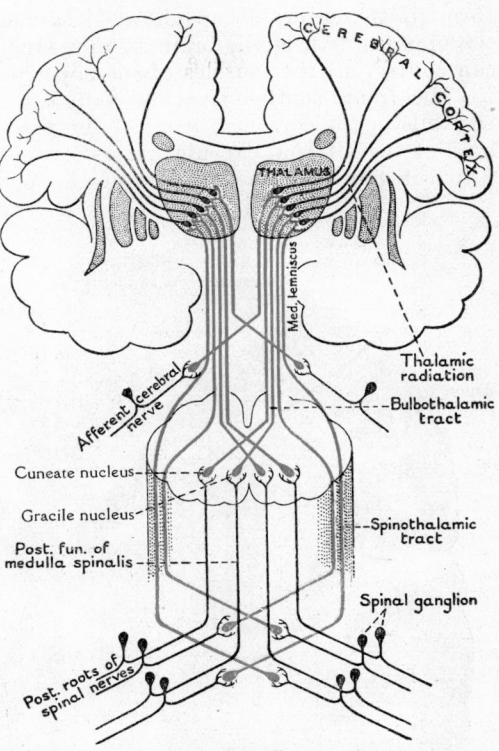

FIG. 816.—DIAGRAM OF THE SENSORY TRACTS FROM THE SPINAL CORD TO THE CEREBRAL CORTEX.

Some of these spino-thalamic fibres enter the medial lemniscus in the medulla oblongata, but others remain separate from it until they reach the level of the pons, where they become added to its lateral margin (Fig. 816).

Other groups of fibres, serially homologous to both medial lemniscus and the spino-thalamic tracts, come from the nuclei of the various sensory cranial nerves—trigeminal, facial, glosso-pharyngeal, and vagus—and become added to the great strands that are proceeding upwards to the thalamus (Fig. 816).

Of the other great ascending tracts in the spinal cord, such as the two pairs of spino-cerebellar tracts, nothing further need be said; nor is it necessary to do more than remind the reader that from the dentate nucleus of the cerebellum a great tract (superior cerebellar peduncle) ascends to the opposite red nucleus and thalamus, and through them establishes an indirect connexion with the cerebral cortex in the precentral and frontal regions.

The other sensory pathways to the cerebrum—auditory, vestibular, visual, gustatory, and olfactory—are described elsewhere.

The Corticifugal Strands.—The **pyramidal tract**—the great motor tract—is composed of fibres which arise from the giant pyramidal cells of Betz in the district immediately in front of the central sulcus (p. 944).   The fibres descend through the corona radiata into the posterior limb of the internal capsule.   From this point the further course of the pyramidal fibres has been traced, viz. through the basis pedunculi and pons, and the pyramid of the medulla oblongata. At the level of the foramen magnum the pyramid decussates in the manner already described, and enters the spinal cord as the lateral cerebro-spinal and anterior cerebro-spinal tracts.   The fibres that compose these tracts end in connexion with the motor column of cells from which the fibres of the anterior roots of the spinal nerves arise.

Similar fibres arise from the lower part of the precentral area and proceed through the internal capsule and cerebral peduncle to all the motor nuclei of the opposite half of the brain stem. Hence the cerebral cortex of one hemisphere can control all the muscles of the opposite half of the body.

The **fronto-pontine tract** is composed of fibres which arise as the axons of the cells in the cortex in front of the precentral sulci. It descends in the anterior limb of the internal capsule, enters the medial part of the basis pedunculi, through which it gains the basilar part of the pons. In the pons its fibres end amongst

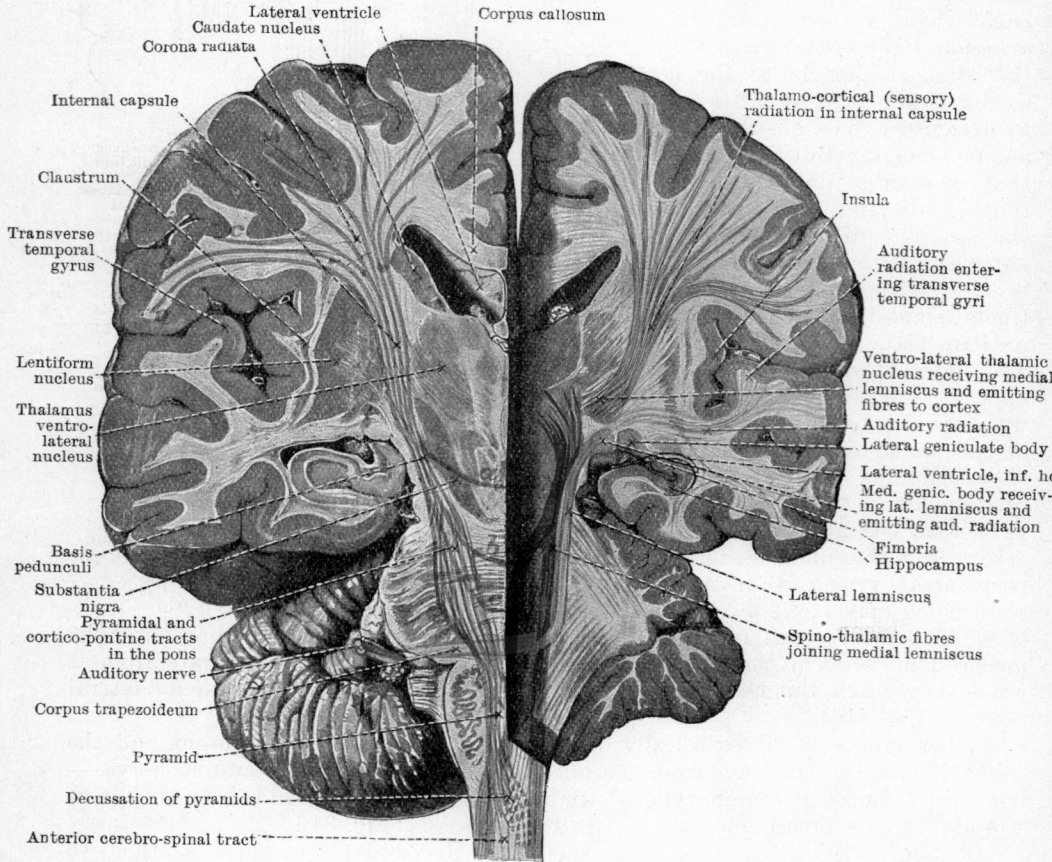

Fig. 817.—Coronal Section of Brain, passing in the Line of the Pyramidal Tract (*marked in red*) in the Right Hemisphere (left side of Fig.), and on a more posterior plane in the left hemisphere, where the sensory paths (tactile in blue, and auditory in yellow) have been represented. (G. E. S.)

the cells of the nuclei pontis, from which axons arise and establish relations with the cortex of the opposite cerebellar hemisphere.

The **temporo-pontine tract** consists of fibres which spring from the cells of that part of the cortex which covers the middle portions of the lower two temporal gyri. It passes medially under the lentiform nucleus, enters the sublentiform part of the posterior limb of the internal capsule, and thus gains the lateral part of the basis pedunculi. From there it descends into the basilar part of the pons, in which it ends in the nuclei pontis.

Cortico-striate and other Descending Fibres.—From the fibres of the internal capsule numerous collateral branches are given off to the caudate nucleus and lentiform nucleus, and from these basal nuclei fibres arise which enter the cerebral peduncle as constituent elements of the great pyramidal tract.

Some of the fibres from the corpus striatum (especially the lentiform nucleus) as well as others from the frontal cortex, pass into the red nucleus (Fig. 809), which also receives afferent tracts from the tectum of the mid-brain and from the cerebellum: it emits an important efferent tract (**rubro-spinal**) which crosses

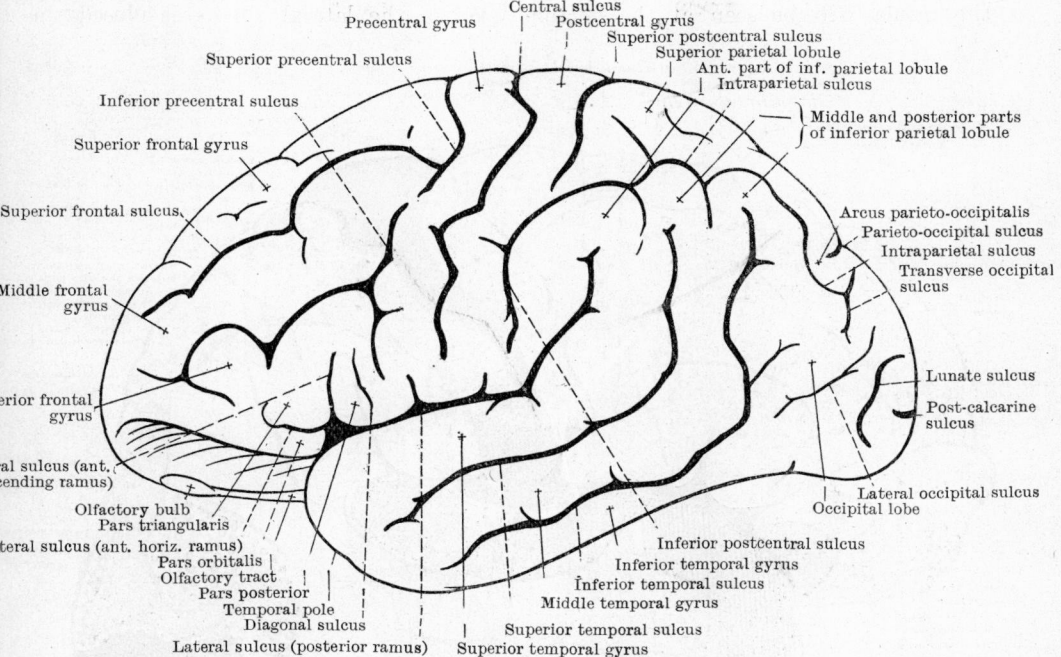

FIG. 818.—DIAGRAM OF THE SULCI AND GYRI ON THE SUPERO-LATERAL SURFACE OF THE HEMISPHERE. The middle frontal sulcus, which sometimes lies between the superior and inferior frontal sulci, is not shown.

the median plane and descends in the brain stem and spinal cord to the various motor nuclei (see Fig. 695).

SULCI AND GYRI OF THE CEREBRAL HEMISPHERES

Lateral Sulcus of Cerebrum.—This is the most conspicuous furrow on the surface of the cerebral hemisphere. In reality it is formed not as a furrow on the surface of the hemisphere but as a great fossa, the margins of which develop into large lip-like folds that bulge over the fossa and meet to form the superficial pattern of the lateral sulcus. It has a main stem and three rami. The **stem** is on the inferior surface of the hemisphere. It begins at the vallecula cerebri and passes laterally, forming a deep cleft between the temporal pole and the orbital surface of the frontal region. Appearing on the lateral surface of the hemisphere, the sulcus divides into three radiating rami. These are: (1) the posterior ramus, (2) the anterior horizontal ramus, (3) the anterior ascending ramus—the last of which is inconstant.

The **posterior ramus** is the longest and most constant of the three branches. It extends backwards, with a slight inclination upwards, on the lateral surface of the hemisphere for a distance of about three inches. It separates the frontal and parietal regions, which lie above it, from the temporal region, which lies below it; and it finally ends in the region subjacent to the parietal eminence of the cranial wall by turning upwards into the parietal region.

The **anterior horizontal ramus** extends forwards in the frontal region for a distance of about three-quarters of an inch, immediately above and parallel to the posterior part of the superciliary margin of the hemisphere.

The **anterior ascending ramus** proceeds upwards and slightly forwards, into the lower part of the lateral surface of the frontal region for a variable distance (an inch or less). In many cases the two anterior limbs spring from a short common stem, and not infrequently there is only a single anterior limb.

Circular Sulcus.—If the lips of the posterior ramus are pulled widely asunder, the **insula** will be seen at the bottom. When the lateral sulcus is closed the

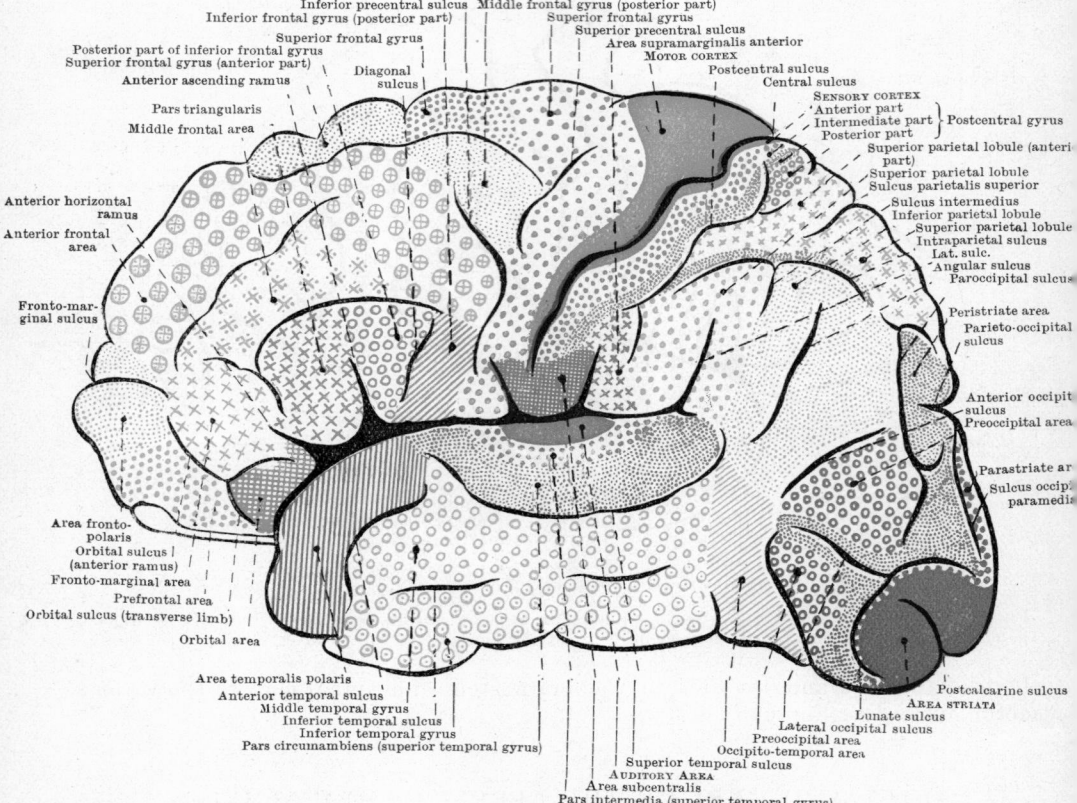

FIG. 819.—DIAGRAM OF LATERAL ASPECT OF LEFT CEREBRAL HEMISPHERE. (G. E. S.)

Showing the various different structural areas. The *superior middle* and *inferior frontal sulci* are not labelled.

insula is completely hidden from view by overlapping portions of the cerebral hemisphere, and, when brought into view in the manner indicated, it is observed to present a triangular outline and to be surrounded by a limiting groove named the **circular sulcus**.

The insula consists of three areas of different structure. At the antero-inferior corner (where the circular sulcus is deficient) the knee-like bend of the area piriformis (see Figs. 794 and 820) appears at the **limen insulæ**. The rest is subdivided by an oblique furrow into a posterior part divided into two *long gyri* and an anterior part divided into several *short gyri*.

Opercula Insulæ.—The overlapping portions of the cerebral substance which cover over the insula are termed the insular opercula, and they form, by the apposition of their margins, the boundaries of the three rami of the lateral sulcus.

The **temporal operculum** extends upwards over the insula from the temporal region, and its upper margin forms the lower lip of the posterior ramus.

The **fronto-parietal operculum** is carried downwards from the frontal and parietal regions over the insula, and its lower margin, meeting the temporal operculum, forms the upper lip of the posterior ramus.

The small triangular piece between the ascending and horizontal anterior rami is called the **frontal operculum**. It covers over a small part of the anterior portion of the insula, and is sometimes termed the **pars triangularis**.

The **orbital operculum** is, for the most part, on the inferior surface of the hemisphere. It lies below and to the medial side of the horizontal anterior ramus of the lateral sulcus, and proceeds backwards from the orbital surface of the frontal lobe over the anterior part of the insula.

Development of Lateral Sulcus and of Insular District of Cerebral Hemisphere.— It is only during the latter half of intra-uterine life that the opercula take shape and grow over the insula to shut it out from the surface. In its early condition the insula presents the form of a depressed area on the side of the cerebral hemisphere, surrounded by a distinct boundary wall (Fig. 820, A). After a time the depressed area assumes a triangular outline, and then the bounding wall is observed to be composed of three distinct parts, viz. a superior or fronto-parietal, an inferior or temporal, and an anterior or orbital part (Fig. 820, B). The angle formed by the meeting of the superior and anterior portions of the boundary may become flattened, and a short oblique part of the limiting wall develop into a small triangular frontal operculum (Fig. 820, F.). Each of these portions of the bounding wall of the depression becomes a line of growth from which an operculum takes origin, and by the approximation of these opercula the insula becomes closed in and the rami of the lateral sulcus are formed (Fig. 820, C).

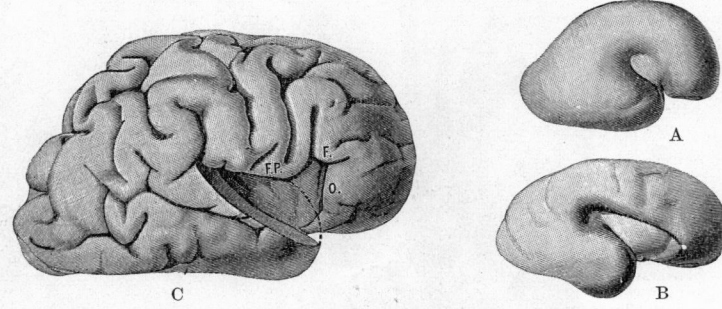

FIG. 820.—RIGHT HEMISPHERES OF HUMAN FŒTUSES SHOWING THREE STAGES IN THE DEVELOPMENT OF THE INSULA AND THE INSULAR OPERCULA.

A, Right cerebral hemisphere from a fœtus in the latter part of the fourth month of development; B, Right cerebral hemisphere in the fifth month; C, Right cerebral hemisphere in the latter part of the eighth month. In C the temporal operculum has been removed, and a large part of the insula is thus exposed. The outline of the temporal operculum is indicated by a dotted line. F.P., Fronto-parietal operculum. F., Frontal operculum. O., Orbital operculum.

The lateral sulcus is an example of the fourth category of furrows enumerated above. It is largely the result of the operation of the mechanical factors incidental to the bending downwards of the pallium in front of and behind the place where the hemisphere-wall is supported and held in position by the corpus striatum. The cortical area roughly corresponding to the surface of the corpus striatum is the insula; the temporal region extends downwards behind it, and the frontal region to a less extent in front of it (Fig. 820, A). Then towards the end of the fifth month of intra-uterine life the exuberant growth of the free fronto-parietal pallium above the insula (Fig. 820, B) and the temporal pallium below and behind it leads to the development of lip-like folds of neopallium—the opercula—which gradually approach one another (Fig. 820, C) and eventually cover up the insula. Other factors come into play in determining the form and topographical relations of the lateral sulcus. For example, the posterior part of the sulcus is the morphological boundary between the auditory and tactile territories of the neopallium.

AUDITORY AREA AND FIBRE-TRACTS

At the fifth month of intra-uterine life (Fig. 820, B), as well as in every later stage, even up to the adult condition (Fig. 821), an area on the upper surface of the temporal operculum can be seen to slope medially towards the circular sulcus, behind the insula. That area constitutes the receptive centre for auditory impressions—the **transverse temporal gyrus**—although the extent of the acoustico-sensory area does not coincide exactly with that of the transverse temporal gyrus.

The area formed by the upper surface of the temporal operculum immediately behind the transverse gyrus is also called by the same name, so that there are anterior and posterior transverse temporal gyri (Fig. 821; the posterior transverse temporal gyrus is not labelled in the figure).

In studying the brain-stem we have seen that a tract of fibres originating in the cochlear nuclei (in the medulla oblongata) crosses the median plane (corpus trapezoideum) and bends upwards in the lateral lemniscus of the other side (Fig. 774) to end in the medial geniculate body. From the medial geniculate

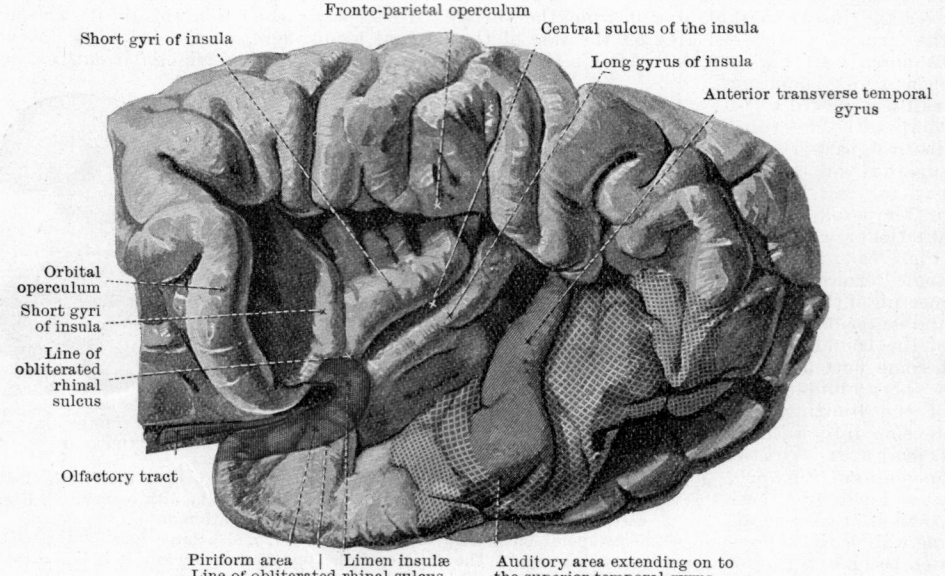

Fig. 821.—Part of a Left Cerebral Hemisphere with the Opercula of the Insula widely separated to expose the Insula and the Superior Surface of the Temporal Operculum.

The *auditory area* is coloured a uniform blue, the *pars intermedia* with large blue spots, and the *pars circumambiens* with fine blue dots.

body a new tract arises (composed of tertiary auditory neurones), and passes laterally (Figs. 774 and 817) to end in the transverse temporal gyri.

The area into which that auditory radiation is inserted occupies not only the region of the anterior transverse temporal gyrus (Fig. 821) hidden within the lateral sulcus, but also extends over its lower lip on to the exposed surface of the superior temporal gyrus (Fig. 819). Surrounding the area there are two concentric bands which are also concerned with auditory functions, but are related to the auditory radiation only through the intermediation of the **auditory area** of the transverse gyrus (Figs. 819 and 821).

These areas may be distinguished as the **pars intermedia** and **pars circumambiens**, respectively, of the **gyrus temporalis superior** (*cf.* arrangement of areas in visual cortex). During the sixth month of intra-uterine life a furrow makes its appearance along the line of the lower boundary of the superior temporal area (Fig. 828). It is called the **superior temporal sulcus.**

At a much later stage of development another furrow (**anterior temporal sulcus**) makes its appearance farther forwards in the temporal region, as the posterior boundary of the **area temporalis polaris**; it often becomes confluent with the real superior temporal sulcus, and is usually described as part of it. But it is genetically quite distinct from it (Fig. 819).

If the auditory area is cut across in a perfectly fresh brain it will be found to be composed of a thin layer (1·75 mm.) of grey matter in which two very dense and fairly broad bands of white matter are visible (Fig. 784). These bands are composed largely of fibres of the auditory radiation which have entered the cortex to terminate in it. The superior temporal area is composed of thicker cortex with two bands which are not so densely white as those of the auditory area. The cortex of the temporal polar area is moderately thick and clear, with a single, narrow, sharply defined white line in it.

The remainder of the true temporal region is the extensive district below the superior temporal sulcus. The cortex is thicker in it than in the superior temporal area—ranging from 3 mm. immediately below the superior temporal sulcus to 2·5 mm. at the lower border of the hemisphere; and it is divided into bands of different texture—the **middle temporal gyrus,** the

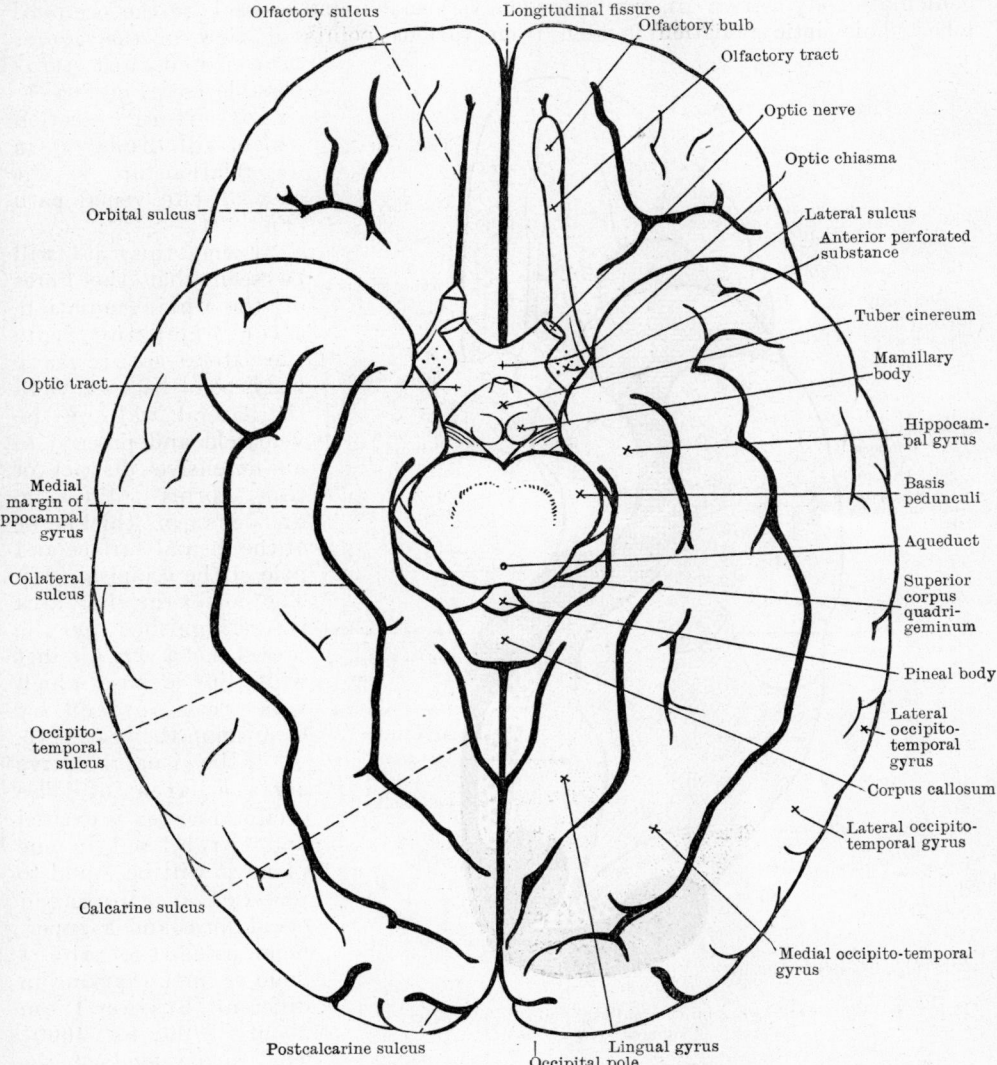

FIG. 822.—DIAGRAM OF THE GYRI AND SULCI OF THE INFERIOR SURFACE OF THE HEMISPHERES.

inferior temporal gyrus and, on the tentorial surface of the lobe, the **lateral** and **medial occipito-temporal** and the **hippocampal gyri.** On the lateral side of the temporal region a series of irregular furrows are situated along the line of demarcation between the **middle and inferior temporal gyri**; they are considered to represent the **inferior temporal sulcus** [S. temporalis medius], but they are subject to much irregularity, especially in highly developed brains.

The great extent of the middle and inferior temporal gyri constitutes one of the outstanding features distinctive of the human brain. Flechsig has shown that the fibres passing to and from these two gyri are the last to become medullated—later even than the important parietal and frontal areas.

VISUAL AREAS AND FIBRE-TRACTS

We have already seen (Fig. 784) that each optic tract ends in the lateral geniculate body and sends a few fibres to the mid-brain. From the lateral geniculate body a tract arises which conveys visual impulses back to the occipital lobe. This **optic radiation** is seen from various points of view in the figures mentioned, but it is possible (see Fig. 805) to expose it in a section which will display it in its relationship to the rest of the visual path (Fig. 824).

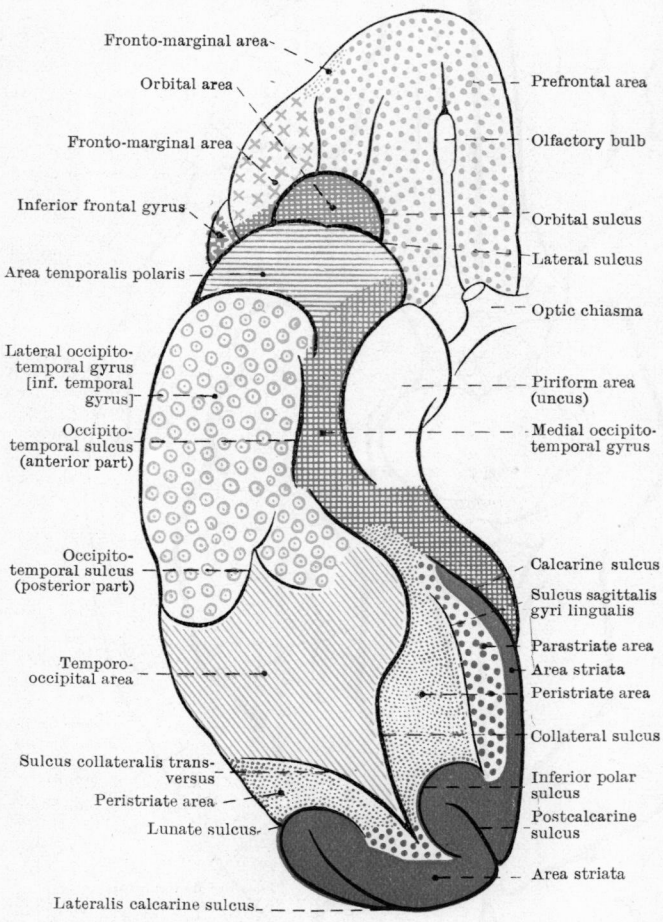

From this it will be seen that the fibres of the optic radiation, after emerging from the lateral geniculate body, bend backwards in the lateral wall of the ventricle and proceed to an extensive district of thin cortex (1·5 mm. or less in thickness), of the medial surface and pole of the occipital area. The cortex in that area is distinguished by the presence of a very distinct white line or stria, which was first noticed by Gennari in the year 1776.

If the visual receptive **striate area** of the occipital cortex is excised and spread out in one plane it will be found to present an elongated ovoid form and a superficial extent of about 3000 sq. mm. (varying in different brains from about 2700 to 4000). The narrow end of the

Fig. 823.—Cortical Areas on the tentorial and orbital surfaces of the cerebral hemispheres. (G. E. S.)

oval is a short distance behind and below the splenium of the corpus callosum; and from that point the area extends horizontally backwards to the occipital pole, or even beyond it on to the lateral aspect of the hemisphere. In the course of development the area striata becomes folded during the sixth month, and the furrow thus formed becomes the **calcarine** and **postcalcarine sulci**. The name "calcarine" was applied to the furrow by Huxley because its deep, anterior part indents the whole thickness of the medial wall of the hemisphere, and the swelling so produced in the posterior horn of the lateral ventricle resembles a cock's spur and was hence called the **calcar avis** (see Fig. 804, p. 920).

The calcarine sulcus is much deeper, more constant in form and position, more precocious in development, and phylogenetically much older than the postcalcarine. If the area striata is prolonged on to the lateral surface, it also may become folded in the line of its axis, and so give rise to a **sulcus calcarinus lateralis**.

There is a fundamental distinction between the calcarine sulcus and the postcalcarine in their relations to the area striata. For the visual stria is found only in the inferior wall of the calcarine sulcus, which is therefore a sulcus limitans; whereas the stria extends throughout both walls of the postcalcarine sulcus, and in most cases beyond its lips on to the surface of the **cuneus** and the **lingual gyrus** (Figs. 825 and 827), *i.e.* the exposed cortical areas above and below the postcalcarine sulcus.

Along the upper and lower boundary lines of the area shallow limiting sulci usually develop (Fig. 827), and those furrows often pass backwards into little arched furrows (sulci polares) of the operculated variety called into existence by the unfolding of the area striata as it passes round the edge of the hemisphere.

At the point of transition from the calcarine sulcus into the shallower postcalcarine sulcus (Fig. 825) a submerged ridge (anterior cuneolingual gyrus) is usually found; and other similar ridges, which may be exposed on the surface or may be submerged, are often found interrupting the postcalcarine and lateral calcarine sulci (Fig. 825).

The postcalcarine and lateral calcarine sulci are subject to a very wide range of variation in form, but they are always axial foldings of the area striata.

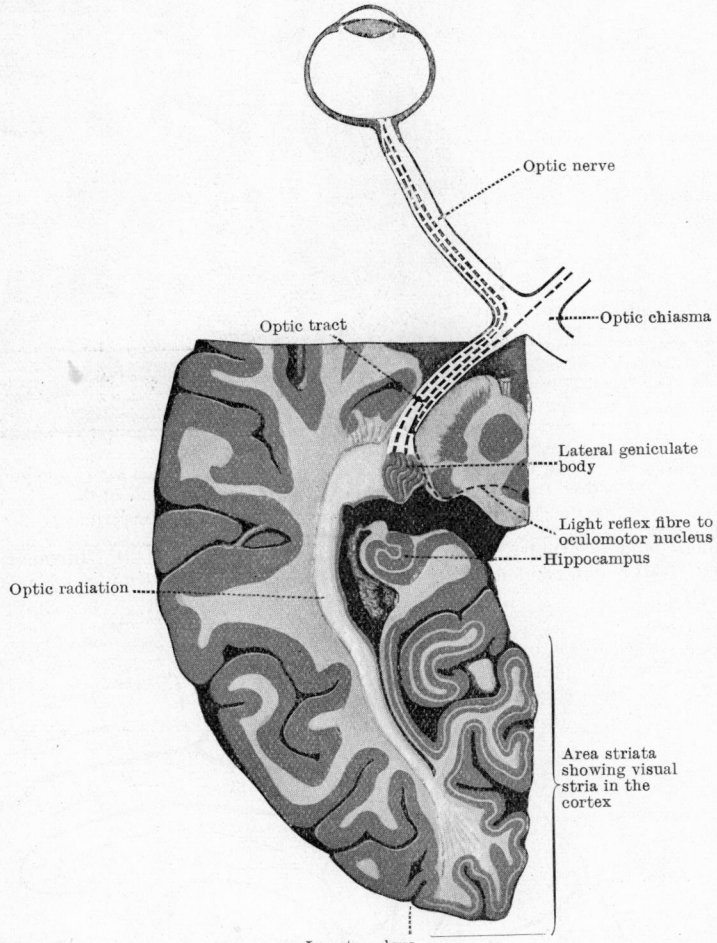

FIG. 824.—A HORIZONTAL SECTION TO DISPLAY THE COURSE OF THE OPTIC TRACT AND OPTIC RADIATION IN THE LEFT HALF OF THE BRAIN. (G. E. S.)

When the area striata crosses on to the lateral surface of the hemisphere a small semilunar furrow may develop a short distance in front of its anterior edge. This is the **sulcus lunatus**. The larger the lateral extension the closer does the edge of the area striata approximate to the caudal lip of the sulcus, which under such circumstances assumes a definitely operculated form. Such cases occur most often in the left hemisphere and in the brains of primitive people; and they represent a perfect realisation of a furrow once supposed not to occur in the human brain but to be distinctive of the ape.

The area striata is surrounded by two peripheral concentric bands—an inner, which may be called **area parastriata**, and an outer, the **area peristriata**. Sulci develop along the boundary lines of each of those areas; and those which indicate the upper and lower limits of the peripheral band (*i.e.* peristriate area) make their appearance relatively early in development and become very deep furrows.

The lower of them is on the tentorial surface and is known as the **collateral sulcus**; the upper limiting furrow of the visual territory (its peristriate part) is on the superior surface of the hemi-

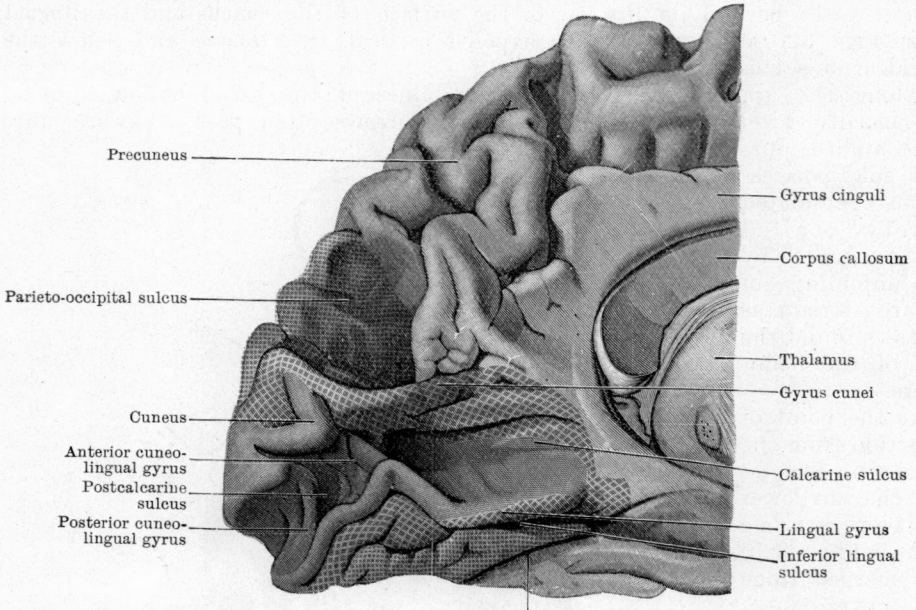

Fig. 825.—The Parieto-occipital and the Calcarine Sulci fully opened up, so as to show the deep transitional gyri marking off the several elements of the ❭-shaped system.
Area striata, uniform blue ; *area parastriata*, large blue spots ; *area peristriata*, fine blue dots.

sphere and is usually regarded as the **occipital ramus** of the **intraparietal sulcus**. But it is genetically independent of that furrow and may be distinguished as the **paroccipital sulcus**.

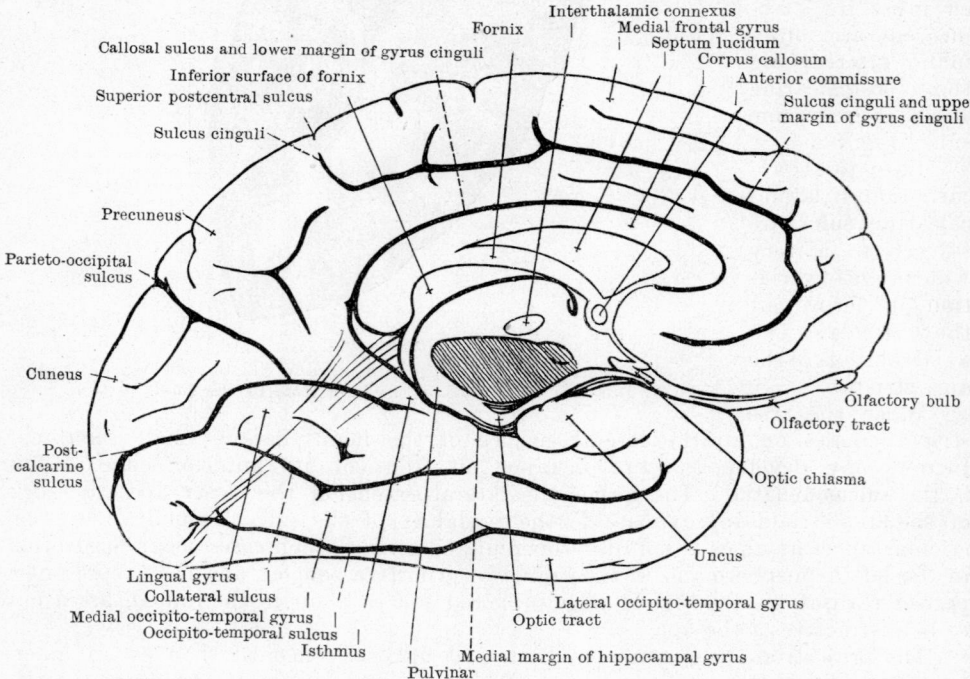

Fig. 826.—Diagram of Sulci and Gyri of Medial and Tentorial Surfaces of Hemisphere.

Near the supero-medial margin of the hemisphere there is a furrow which indicates the line of demarcation between the para- and the peristriate areas—the **sulcus occipitalis paramedialis**.

It may be situated on either the medial or the superior surface of the hemisphere. In some cases it belongs to the category of limiting sulci, in others to the group of operculated sulci.

Passing horizontally forwards on the lateral surface of the hemisphere there is a constant furrow formed by the axial folding of part of the peristriate area, approximately in line with the axial folding of the striate area (sulcus calcarinus lateralis); it is the **lateral occipital sulcus**. When there is a fully developed sulcus lunatus the lateral occipital sulcus joins it near its midpoint (Fig. 819, p. 936).

The **parieto-occipital sulcus** (Fig. 826) is a deep furrow on the medial surface of the hemisphere which passes vertically downwards from the supero-medial border

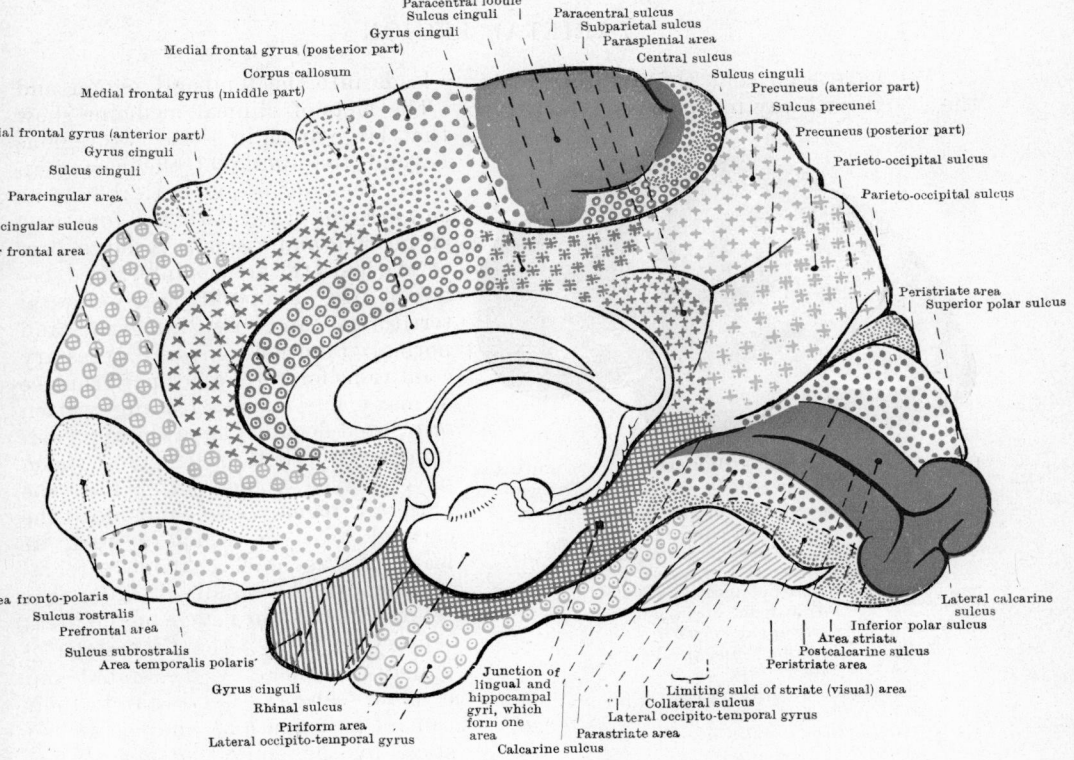

FIG. 827.—CORTICAL AREAS ON THE MEDIAL ASPECT OF THE CEREBRAL HEMISPHERE. (G. E. S.)

and appears to join the calcarine sulcus near its union with the postcalcarine, forming on the surface a <-shaped pattern, the stem of which is calcarine, the limbs postcalcarine and parieto-occipital, and the wedge-shaped area between the limbs the **cuneus** (Fig. 826).

If, however, the lips of the three furrows are divaricated (Fig. 825), the parieto-occipital depression will be found to be separated from the calcarine by a prominent submerged cortical ridge (gyrus cunei), and the parieto-occipital will be found to be something more than a mere sulcus. It is, in fact, a great fossa in which are submerged the anterior parts of the parastriate and peristriate areas, and the posterior part of the parietal area known as the **precuneus**, as well as the sulci which separate those territories one from the other. It is a great trough formed by the splenium of the corpus callosum as in the course of its development it thrusts itself backwards and crumples up the cortex. When the corpus callosum fails to develop no parieto-occipital sulcus makes its appearance.

Collateral Sulcus.—This is a strongly marked furrow on the tentorial surface. It begins near the occipital pole and extends forwards towards the rhinal sulcus, with which it sometimes becomes confluent. In its posterior part it is parallel to the calcarine and postcalcarine sulci, from which it is separated by the **lingual gyrus**. From the posterior extremity a sulcus proceeds forwards and then laterally across the inferior surface of the occipital region, forming a V-shaped pattern with the collateral sulcus (Fig. 823). As it is serially homologous with the latter, being, like it, an inferior boundary of the area peristriata, it may be called the **sulcus collateralis transversus.** The lingual gyrus is sometimes subdivided by a furrow (*sulcus sagittalis gyri lingualis*) midway between the collateral sulcus and the inferior margin of the area striata. It is the line of demarcation between the parastriate and peristriate areas, and, when deep, is often mistaken for the collateral sulcus.

PARIETAL REGION

We have seen that the auditory pathway leads into the temporal region and the visual pathway into the occipital region. The facts of clinical medicine show

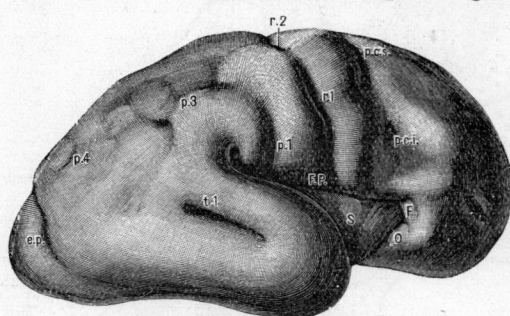

FIG. 828.—LEFT CEREBRAL HEMISPHERE, from a fœtus in the early part of the seventh month of development.

p.c.s.	Superior precentral sulcus.
p.c.i.	Inferior precentral sulcus.
r¹.	Inferior part of central sulcus.
r².	Superior part of central sulcus.
p¹.	Inferior postcentral sulcus.
p³.	Intraparietal sulcus proper.
p⁴.	Paroccipital sulcus.
t¹.	Superior temporal sulcus.
S.	Lateral fossa.
F.P.	Fronto-parietal wall.
F.	Frontal wall.
O.	Orbital wall.

that large areas in these two regions beyond the limits of the cortex in which the auditory and optic radiations end are concerned with the functions of hearing and vision. A large part of the parietal area is interposed between the temporal and occipital territories, and its integrity and normal functioning are necessary conditions for the proper performance of many acts, such as reading written or printed documents, in the appreciation of which both hearing and vision have played some part. But the parietal region also includes the cortical area in which a part, at least, of the chief thalamo-cerebral tract ends—the bundle of fibres that represents the third stage of the great sensory pathway—the first stage of which is formed by the spinal and cerebral sensory nerves and their central prolongations, and the second stage by the spino-thalamic, bulbo-thalamic and ponto-thalamic tracts, which pass upwards in the medial lemniscus and end in the ventral part of the lateral nucleus of the thalamus. The sensory area in question forms part of the **postcentral gyrus,** which intervenes between two oblique furrows,—the **central** and **postcentral sulci**—which extend across the whole breadth of the hemisphere above the lateral sulcus (Fig. 819).

Central Sulcus.—During the sixth and seventh months of intra-uterine life the expanding postcentral area becomes raised up into a prominent ridge, and a similar ridge is formed immediately in front of it (Fig. 828) from the area which emits the great motor tract. As these ridges become raised up a depression is left between them: this is the *central sulcus.* At first it is in two parts (an upper and a lower Fig. 828, r² and r¹); but as a rule they become confluent later.

The central sulcus in the adult takes an oblique course across the superolateral surface of the hemisphere, and, intervening between the frontal and parietal regions, it forms the immediate posterior boundary of the motor area of the cortex. Its upper end cuts the supero-medial border of the hemisphere a short distance behind the mid-point between the frontal and occipital poles, and is then continued backwards for a short distance on the medial surface, whilst its lower end terminates above the middle of the posterior ramus of the lateral sulcus. In its general direction, the sulcus is oblique, and it is very far from being straight. It takes a sinuous course across the hemisphere. That is largely due to the varying breadth of the motor areas representing the lower limb, trunk, upper limb, and head, which are placed immediately in front of it.

When the central sulcus is widely opened up, so that its bottom and its opposed sides may be fully inspected, it will be seen that the two bounding gyri are dovetailed into each other by a number of interlocking gyri which do not appear on the surface (Fig. 829). Further, two of these, placed on opposite sides of the sulcus, are frequently joined across the bottom of the sulcus in the form of a sunken bridge termed a *deep transitional gyrus*. The continuity of the sulcus is thus, to some extent, interrupted. This condition is made interesting when considered in connection with the development of the sulcus. The deep interlocking gyri indicate a great exuberance of cortical growth in this situation in the early stages of the development of the sulcus; and the presence of the deep transitional gyrus is explained by the fact that the sulcus generally develops in two pieces which run into each other to form the continuous sulcus of the adult, viz., a part corresponding to the lower two-thirds, and a part which represents the upper third and appears at a slightly later date. In very rare cases the two parts of the sulcus fail to unite, and the deep transitional gyrus remains on the surface. Heschl, who examined 2174 cerebral hemispheres, found this anomaly only six times; Eberstaller met with it twice in 200 brains.

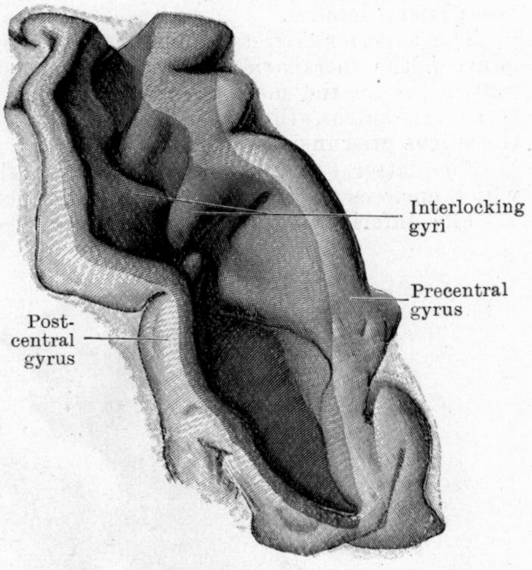

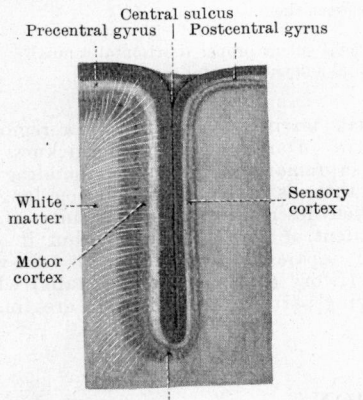

FIG. 829.—RIGHT CENTRAL SULCUS FULLY OPENED UP, so as to exhibit the interlocking gyri and deep transitional gyrus within it.

Motor cortex coloured red, *sensory cortex* blue.

If a section is made at right angles to the central sulcus in a fresh brain (Fig. 830), it will be seen that its anterior and posterior walls present a marked contrast the one to the other, and that the transition from the one type of cortex to the other takes place at or near the bottom of the sulcus. The cortex of the anterior wall is thick (3·5 to 4 mm.) and is pervaded by white matter arranged in the form of three or four pale bands with blurred edges and multitudes of fine pencils of fibres passing to and fro between it and the white centre of the hemisphere. The cortex of the posterior wall is thin (1·5 mm.), and contains two narrow and sharply defined white lines.

The sensory area forms little more than the posterior wall of the central sulcus, and barely emerges on the surface to form the posterior lip of the sulcus (Fig. 829). Here it becomes continuous with a slightly thicker cortex with doubled lines which are less dense than those of the sensory cortex; that area forms the crest of the postcentral gyrus, and then gives place to another slightly modified type of cortex which forms the anterior wall of the postcentral sulcus. Thus the sensory cortex has two fringing bands analogous to those already noticed alongside the visual and auditory areas.

FIG. 830.—SECTION ACROSS THE SUPERIOR PART OF THE CENTRAL SULCUS IN A FRESH BRAIN.

The motor and sensory areas cross on to the medial surface of the hemisphere, into a region known as the **paracentral lobule**.

That portion of the parietal region which intervenes between the postcentral gyrus and the occipital region is usually subdivided into two distinct parts—the **superior** and **inferior parietal lobules**—by a horizontal furrow, called the **intraparietal sulcus**. The term "sulcus intraparietalis" used to be applied in a purely arbitrary manner to a complex of four genetically distinct and independent furrows which may unite to form any possible combination (Fig. 831, p^1, p^2, p^3, and p^4).

The individual names of these furrows are the **inferior postcentral sulcus** (p^1), the **superior postcentral sulcus** (p^2), the **intraparietal sulcus** (p^3), and its occipital ramus (p^4), which ends in the **transverse occipital sulcus**.

These four sulci develop quite independently of one another, the post-central sulci as the posterior boundary of the sensory territory, the occipital ramus as the supero-lateral boundary of the visual territory, and the more variable intraparietal sulcus, as a demarcation between the two parietal lobules.

The superior parietal lobule is composed of moderately thick cortex (2·5 to 3 mm.) placed between the intraparietal sulcus and the superior border of the hemisphere, where it becomes continuous on the medial surface with the precuneus. Each of those parts is subdivided by a transverse sulcus, the superior lobule by the **sulcus parietalis superior** and the precuneus by the **sulcus præcunei** (Fig. 827).

The latter sulcus usually joins a small inverted U-shaped furrow **(suprasplenial sulcus)** which encloses a cortical territory of distinctive structure—the **area parasplenalis** [præcunei].

The **inferior parietal lobule**, which from its position is the natural meeting-place for

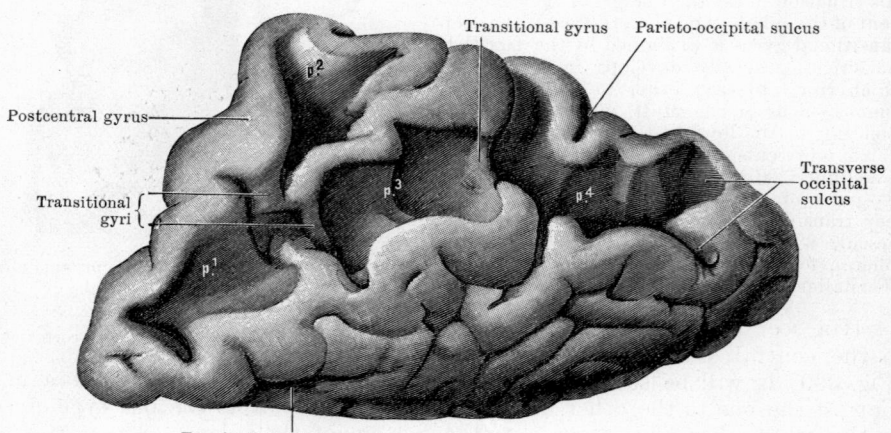

FIG. 831.—THE FOUR SULCI OF THE INTRAPARIETAL COMPLEX OPENED UP, so as to show the deep transitional gyri intervening between them.

p^1. Inferior postcentral sulcus.   p^3. Intraparietal sulcus proper (horizontal ramus).
p^2. Superior postcentral sulcus.   p^4. Paroccipital sulcus (occipital ramus).

impressions coming from the visual, auditory, and tactile territories, is naturally a region of great functional significance. It is composed of a series of areas differing in thickness and texture. The anterior region forms a convolution [supramarginal gyrus] surrounding the upturned extremity of the lateral fissure ; behind it there is a second convolution [angular gyrus] which surrounds a vertical **angular sulcus**, often described as the extremity of the superior temporal sulcus ; in reality it is quite independent of the latter furrow, but it often becomes confluent with it. Behind this gyrus and separated from it by a transverse furrow **(anterior occipital sulcus)** there is a cortical territory **(area parieto-occipitalis)** which may perhaps be looked upon as a specialised and outlying part of the peristriate area of the visual cortex.

FRONTAL REGION

The frontal region is the biggest of the main cortical areas—the so-called "lobes." On the supero-lateral surface, it is bounded behind by the central sulcus and below, in part, by the lateral sulcus. It has a supero-lateral surface, a medial surface, and an inferior or orbital surface. The *supero-lateral surface* is broken up by a large number of variable furrows.

The **precentral sulcus** is more or less parallel with the central sulcus, and is usually divided into upper and lower parts.

The **precentral gyrus** is the long gyrus between the central and precentral sulci. Inferiorly it is continuous with the post-central gyrus below the lower end of the central sulcus.

The **superior frontal sulcus** extends forwards in a more or less horizontal direction from the upper part of the precentral sulcus and maps off the **superior frontal gyrus** between itself and the supero-medial border.

The **inferior frontal sulcus** begins at or near the lower part of the precentral sulcus ; it proceeds forwards towards the superciliary margin of the hemisphere and ends a short distance from that in a terminal bifurcation (Fig. 818). The **middle frontal gyrus** is the name given to the broad convolution which lies between the superior and inferior frontal sulci. The **inferior frontal gyrus** is the region in front of the lower part of the precentral sulcus and below the inferior frontal sulcus. It includes three cortical areas (Fig. 819) differing in structure the one from the other. The **diagonal sulcus** separates the middle one of the three from the posterior.

On the *medial surface* of the frontal region there are two gyri separated by the **sulcus cinguli** (Fig. 826). The larger, peripheral area is named the **medial frontal gyrus**, and the smaller inner part encircling the corpus callosum is the **gyrus cinguli**. The posterior part of the sulcus cinguli is genetically distinct from the anterior part and it circumscribes a broader area—the **paracentral lobule**—which is continuous with the precentral and postcentral gyri of the supero-lateral surface.

On the *orbital surface of the frontal region* there are two sulci, viz., the olfactory and the orbital. The **olfactory sulcus** is a straight furrow which runs parallel to the medial orbital border of the hemisphere. It is occupied by the olfactory tract and bulb, and it cuts off a narrow strip alongside the medial border named the **gyrus rectus**. The **orbital sulcus** is a composite furrow which assumes many different forms. It is essentially a U-shaped furrow, the convexity of which is directed forwards (Fig. 823), and one or two variable branches passing forwards from it.

The conventional manner of subdividing the cortex in front of the central sulcus into gyri, which has just been sketched, is apt to convey a misleading idea of the distribution of the anatomical areas of differentiated cortex.

The precentral gyrus together with the major portion of the paracentral lobule and the posterior part of the superior, middle and inferior frontal gyri form a natural subdivision of the cortex which is concerned with voluntary movement. It is composed of a series of areas of different structure. The posterior of these areas, often called the *motor cortex proper* (area 4 of Brodmann, pyramidal area), is coloured solid red in Fig. 827. It contains the giant pyramids of Betz, the axons of which (pyramidal fibres) have been followed to the motor nuclei of the 5th, 7th, 10th (nucleus ambiguus), 11th (nucleus ambiguus), and 12th cranial nerves, and to the cells of the anterior grey column of the spinal cord.

The posterior end of the middle frontal gyrus emits axons from its largest pyramids which pass to the motor nuclei of the 3rd, 4th, and 6th cranial nerves.

The area immediately in front of the motor cortex proper is called by many writers the pre-motor cortex (area 6 of Brodmann). All the areas in the wide region defined above have been found to be electrically excitable, and so also have certain cortical areas behind the central sulcus. But the thresholds for the various areas differ and so does the nature of the muscular response obtained. Although intensive research is proceeding on the subject of the cortical control of striped musculature, the functional significance attaching to histological differentiation within the excitable area cannot yet be defined, nor are we able to state with precision the anatomical connexions of any of these areas except the Betz cell-area.

MENINGES OF THE BRAIN AND SPINAL CORD

The brain and spinal cord are enclosed in three membranes or meninges named, from without inwards, dura mater, arachnoid mater, and pia mater. The capillary interval between the dura and the arachnoid mater receives the name of subdural space ; the much more roomy interval between the arachnoid and pia mater is called the subarachnoid space ; and the interval that separates the spinal dura mater from the walls of the vertebral canal is called the extra-dural space.

DURA MATER

The dura mater is a dense and strong fibrous membrane divisible into two parts—the spinal dura mater and the dura mater of the brain—which are continuous with each other at the foramen magnum.

Dura Mater of the Brain.—This part of the dura mater is adherent to the inner surface of the cranial wall, and performs a double office. It serves as an internal periosteum for the bones which it lines, and it constitutes an envelope for the brain. Its inner surface is smooth and glistening, and is covered with a layer of endothelial cells. The outer surface, when separated from the cranial wall, is rough—that being due to numerous fine fibrous processes and blood-vessels which pass between it and the bones. Its degree of adhesion to the cranial wall differs

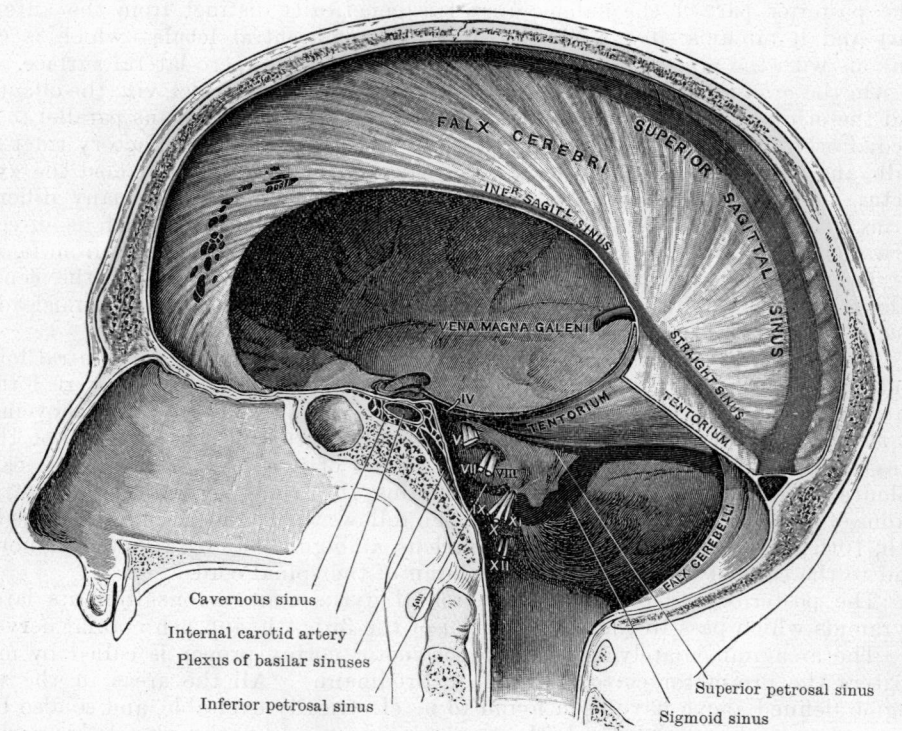

Cavernous sinus
Internal carotid artery
Plexus of basilar sinuses
Inferior petrosal sinus
Superior petrosal sinus
Sigmoid sinus

FIG. 832.—SAGITTAL SECTION THROUGH THE SKULL, A LITTLE TO THE LEFT OF THE MEDIAN PLANE, to show the arrangement of the dura mater.

The cranial nerves are indicated by numerals.

considerably in different regions. To the vault of the cranium, except along the lines of the sutures, the connexion is by no means strong, and in the intervals between the fibrous processes which pass into the bone there are minute lymph spaces (extra-dural spaces) where the outer surface of the membrane is covered with endothelial cells. So long as the sutures are open the dura mater is connected with the periosteum on the exterior of the skull by the sutural ligaments. Around the foramen magnum, and on the floor of the cranial cavity, the dura mater is very firmly adherent to the bone. That is more particularly marked in the case of the projecting parts of the cranial floor, as, for example, the petrous portions of the temporal bones, the clinoid processes, and so on. The firm adhesion in those regions is still further strengthened because the nerves, as they leave the cranium through the various foramina, are followed by sheaths of the fibrous dura mater. Outside the cranium the prolongations of the membrane blend with the fibrous sheaths of the nerves, and also become connected with the periosteum on the exterior of the skull. In the child, during the growth of the cranial bones, and also in old age, the dura mater is more adherent to the cranial wall than during the intervening portion of life.

The dura mater of the brain has two layers intimately connected with each other, but yet capable of being demonstrated in most regions; and along certain lines they separate to enclose channels lined with endothelium. Those channels are the **venous blood-sinuses**, and they receive the blood from veins which come from various parts of the brain. They are described in the section dealing with the Vascular System.

Strong fibrous septa are given off along certain lines from the deep surface of the dura mater. They project into the cranial cavity, and subdivide it partially into compartments which all freely communicate with one another, and each of which contains a definite subdivision of the brain. These septa are: (1) the falx cerebri; (2) the tentorium cerebelli; (3) the falx cerebelli; and (4) the diaphragma sellæ.

The **falx cerebri** is a sickle-shaped partition which descends in the great longitudinal fissure between the two hemispheres of the cerebrum. Its anterior end is narrow, and is attached to the crista galli of the ethmoid; it increases in its vertical measurement as it is traced backwards; its upper border is highly convex and is attached to the cranial vault along the median line from the crista galli to the internal occipital protuberance; the anterior and longer part of its lower border is concave and free, and comes into close relation with the splenium of the corpus callosum at its posterior end; the posterior part of this border is united to the tentorium cerebelli. The anterior part of the falx is often cribriform, and may even resemble lacework. Along its borders it splits to enclose blood sinuses—the superior sagittal sinus in the upper border, the inferior sagittal in the free part of the lower border, and the straight sinus along the attachment to the tentorium.

The **tentorium cerebelli** is a large crescentic partition which forms a membranous tent-like roof for the posterior cranial fossa, and thus intervenes between the posterior portions of the cerebral hemispheres and the cerebellum. It is accurately applied to the upper surface of the cerebellum. Thus, its highest point is in front and in the median plane, and thence it slopes downwards towards its attached border. It is kept at a high degree of tension, and that depends on the integrity of the falx cerebri, which is attached to its upper surface in the median plane.

The *posterior border* of the tentorium is convex, and is attached to the horizontal ridge which marks the inner surface of the occipital bone. Beyond the occipital bone, on each side, it is fixed to the postero-inferior angle of the parietal bone, and then forwards and medially along the upper border of the petrous portion of the temporal bone. From the internal occipital protuberance to the postero-inferior angle of the parietal bone the border encloses the *transverse sinus*, whilst along the upper border of the petrous bone it encloses the *superior petrosal sinus*. The *anterior border* of the tentorium is sharp, free, and concave, and forms with the dorsum sellæ an oval opening shaped posteriorly like a pointed arch. The opening is called the **tentorial notch**, and within it lies the mid-brain. Beyond the apex of the petrous part of the temporal bone the two margins of the tentorium cross each other; the free margin is continued forwards to be attached to the anterior clinoid process, whilst the attached border proceeds medially to be fixed to the posterior clinoid process.

The **falx cerebelli** is a small, sickle-shaped ridge of dura mater which projects forwards from the internal occipital crest, and occupies the posterior notch of the cerebellum.

The **diaphragma sellæ** is a small circular fold of dura mater which forms a roof for the hypophyseal fossa. A small opening is left in its centre for the transmission of the infundibulum.

Spinal Dura Mater.—In the vertebral canal the dura mater forms a tube which encloses the spinal cord, and extends from the foramen magnum above to the level of the second piece of the sacrum below. It is very loosely related to the spinal cord and the cauda equina; in other words, it is very capacious in comparison with the volume of its contents. Moreover, its calibre is not uniform. In the cervical and lumbar regions it is considerably wider than in the thoracic region, whilst in the sacral canal it rapidly contracts, and finally ends blindly. At the upper end of the vertebral canal the spinal dura mater is firmly fixed to the second and third cervical vertebræ, and around the margin of the foramen magnum. In the sacral canal the filum terminale, which pierces it and drags off a sheath from it, extends downwards to blend with the periosteum on the back of the coccyx; the inferior end of the tube is thus securely anchored and held in its place.

Within the cranial cavity the dura mater is closely adherent to the bones, and forms for them an internal periosteum. As it is followed into the vertebral canal its two constituent layers separate. The inner layer is carried downwards as the long cylindrical tube which encloses the spinal cord. The outer layer, which is much thinner, becomes continuous round the margin of the foramen magnum with the periosteum on the exterior of the cranium. The spinal dura mater, therefore, corresponds to the inner layer of the cranial dura mater, and to it alone. It is separated from the walls of the vertebral canal by an interval—the **extra-dural space**—which is occupied by soft fat and a plexus of thin-walled veins. In connexion with the spinal dura mater there are no blood-sinuses such as are present in the cranial cavity, but it should be noted that the veins in the extra-dural space, placed as they are between the periosteum of the vertebral canal and the tube of dura mater, occupy the same morphological plane as the cranial blood-sinuses. Another feature which serves to distinguish the spinal dura mater from the cranial dura mater is that it gives off no partitions or septa from its deep surface.

The spinal dura mater does not lie quite free within the vertebral canal. Its attachments, however, are of such a character that they in no way interfere with the free movement of the vertebral column. On each side the spinal nerve-roots, as they pierce the dura mater, carry with them into the intervertebral foramina tubular sheaths of the membrane, whilst in front loose fibrous prolongations—more numerous above and below than in the thoracic region—connect the tube of dura mater to the posterior longitudinal ligament of the vertebral column. No connexion of any kind exists between the dura mater and the posterior wall of the vertebral canal.

When the interior of the tube of spinal dura mater is inspected, the series of apertures of exit for the roots of the spinal nerves is seen. They are ranged in pairs opposite each intervertebral foramen.

Viewed from the inside of the tube of dura mater, each of the two roots of a spinal nerve is seen to carry with it a special and distinct sheath. When examined on the outside, however, the appearance is such that one might be led to conclude that both roots are enveloped in one sheath of dura mater. That is due to the fact that the two sheaths are firmly held together by areolar tissue. The two tubular sheaths remain distinct as far as the spinal ganglion, and then blend with each other.

Subdural Space.—The dura mater and the arachnoid mater are closely applied to each other, and the capillary interval between them is termed the **subdural space**. It contains a film of fluid—just sufficient to moisten the opposed surfaces of the two membranes.

The subdural space in no way communicates with the subarachnoid space. The fluid which it contains is led into the venous blood-sinuses around the arachnoid granulations, and thus gains exit. The subdural space is carried outwards for a very short distance on the various cranial and spinal nerves, and it has a free communication with the lymph-paths present in those nerves. In the case of the optic nerve the sheath of dura mater is carried along its whole length, and with it the subdural space is prolonged to the back of the eyeball.

ARACHNOID MATER

The **arachnoid mater** is a very thin membrane, remarkable for its delicacy and transparency, which envelops both the brain and the spinal cord between the dura mater and the pia mater. The **arachnoid mater of the brain** is carried into

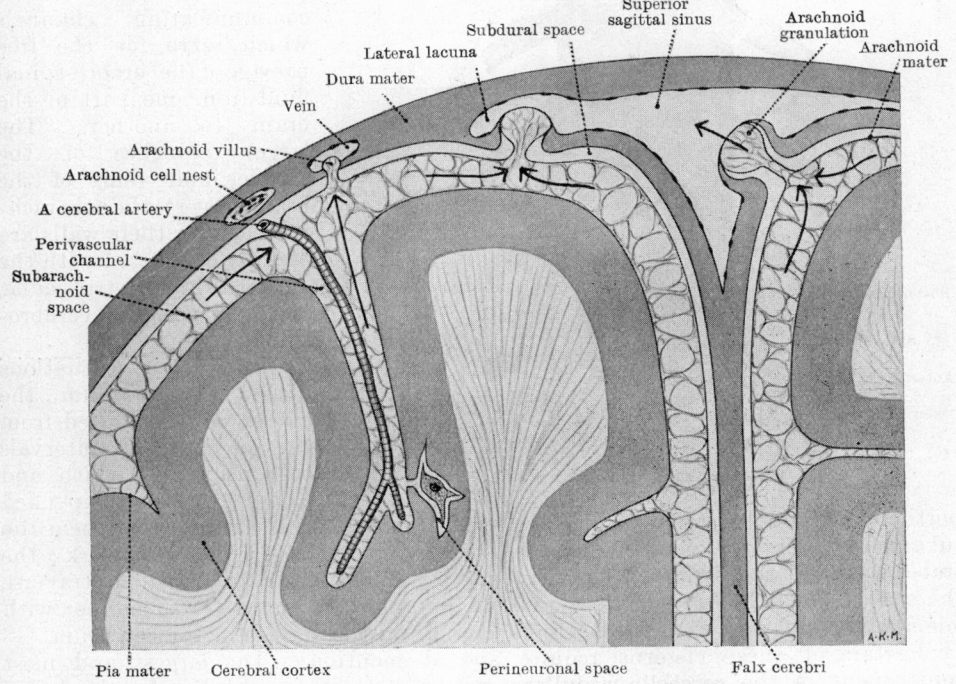

FIG. 833.—DIAGRAM TO SHOW THE RELATIONS OF THE MENINGES TO THE BRAIN and how the subarachnoid space and its ramifications are related, by way of the arachnoid villi and arachnoid granulations, to the venous channels of the dura mater.

the longitudinal fissure by the falx cerebri and into the stem of the lateral sulcus by the lesser wing of the sphenoid; but otherwise it does not dip into the sulci. In that respect it differs from the pia mater. It bridges over the inequalities on the surface of the brain. Consequently, on the basal aspect it is spread out in the form of a very distinct sheet over the medulla oblongata, the pons, and the hollow above the pons, and in certain of those regions it is separated from the brain-surface by wide intervals.

The **spinal arachnoid mater**, which is directly continuous with that of the brain, forms a loose, wide investment for the spinal cord. The spinal arachnoid sac is most capacious towards its lower part, where it envelops the lower end of the spinal cord and the cauda equina.

As the cranial and spinal nerves pass outwards they receive an investment from the arachnoid which runs for a short distance upon them.

Subarachnoid Space.—The interval between the arachnoid and the pia mater receives the name of the **subarachnoid space**. It contains the cerebro-spinal fluid, and communicates freely, through apertures in the roof of the fourth ventricle, with the cavities in the interior of the brain.

Within the cranium the subarachnoid space is broken up by a meshwork of fine filaments and trabeculæ which connects the arachnoid and pia mater in the most intimate manner, and forms a delicate sponge-like interlacement between them. Where the arachnoid mater passes over the summit of a gyrus, and is consequently closely applied to the subjacent pia mater, the meshwork is so dense and the trabeculæ so short that it is hardly possible to discriminate between the two membranes.

To all intents and purposes they form in those localities one lamina. In the intervals between gyri, however, there are distinct angular spaces where the sub-arachnoid trabecular tissue can be studied to great advantage. Those intervals on the surface of the cerebrum constitute numerous communicating channels which serve for the free passage of the cerebro-spinal fluid from one part of the brain to another. The larger branches of the arteries and veins of the brain traverse the subarachnoid space; their walls are directly connected with the subarachnoid trabeculæ, and are bathed by cerebrospinal fluid.

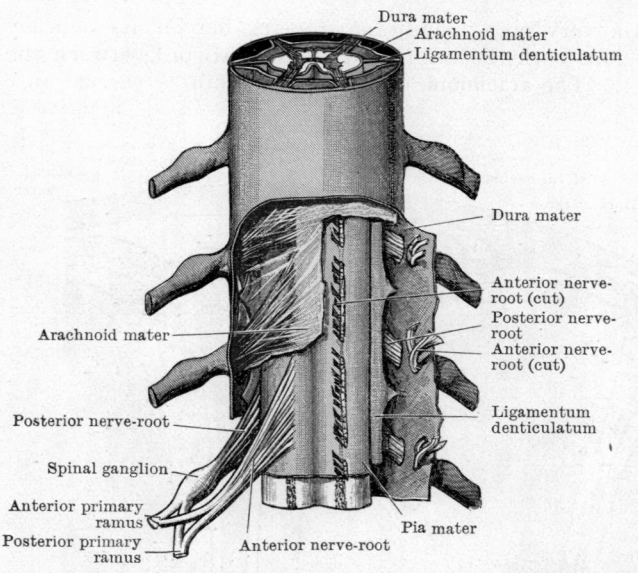

FIG. 834.—MEMBRANES OF THE SPINAL CORD, AND THE MODE OF ORIGIN OF THE SPINAL NERVES.

In certain situations within the cranium the arachnoid is separated from the pia mater by intervals of considerable width and extent. Those expanded portions of the subarachnoid space are termed **subarachnoid cisterns**. In them the subarachnoid tissue is much reduced. There is no longer a close meshwork; the trabeculæ take the form of long filamentous intersecting threads which traverse the spaces. All the subarachnoid cisterns communicate in the freest manner with one another and also with the narrow channels on the surface of the cerebrum.

Certain of these cisterns require special mention. The largest and most conspicuous is the **cerebello-medullary cistern**. It is formed by the arachnoid

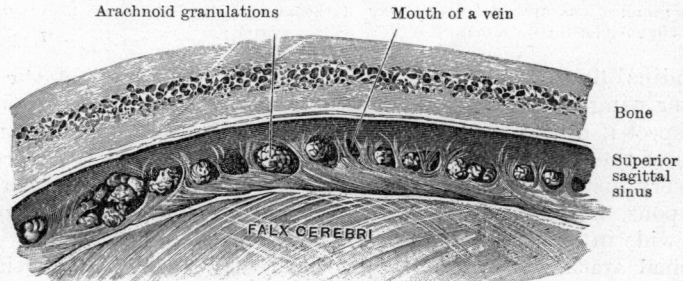

FIG. 835.—MEDIAN SECTION THROUGH THE CRANIAL VAULT IN THE FRONTAL REGION, *ENLARGED.*
Displays a portion of the superior sagittal sinus and the arachnoid granulations protruding into it.

membrane bridging over the wide interval between the posterior part of the cerebellum and the medulla oblongata. It is continuous through the foramen magnum with the posterior part of the subarachnoid space of the spinal cord.

The **pontine cistern** is the continuation upwards on the floor of the cranium of the anterior part of the subarachnoid space of the spinal cord. In the region of the medulla oblongata it is continuous behind with the cerebello-medullary cistern; therefore that subdivision of the brain, like the spinal cord, is surrounded by a wide subarachnoid space.

Above the pons the arachnoid mater bridges across between the temporal lobes, and covers in the deep hollow in this region of the brain. That space is called the **interpeduncular cistern**, and within it are placed the large arteries which take part in the formation of the arterial circle. Leading out from the inter-

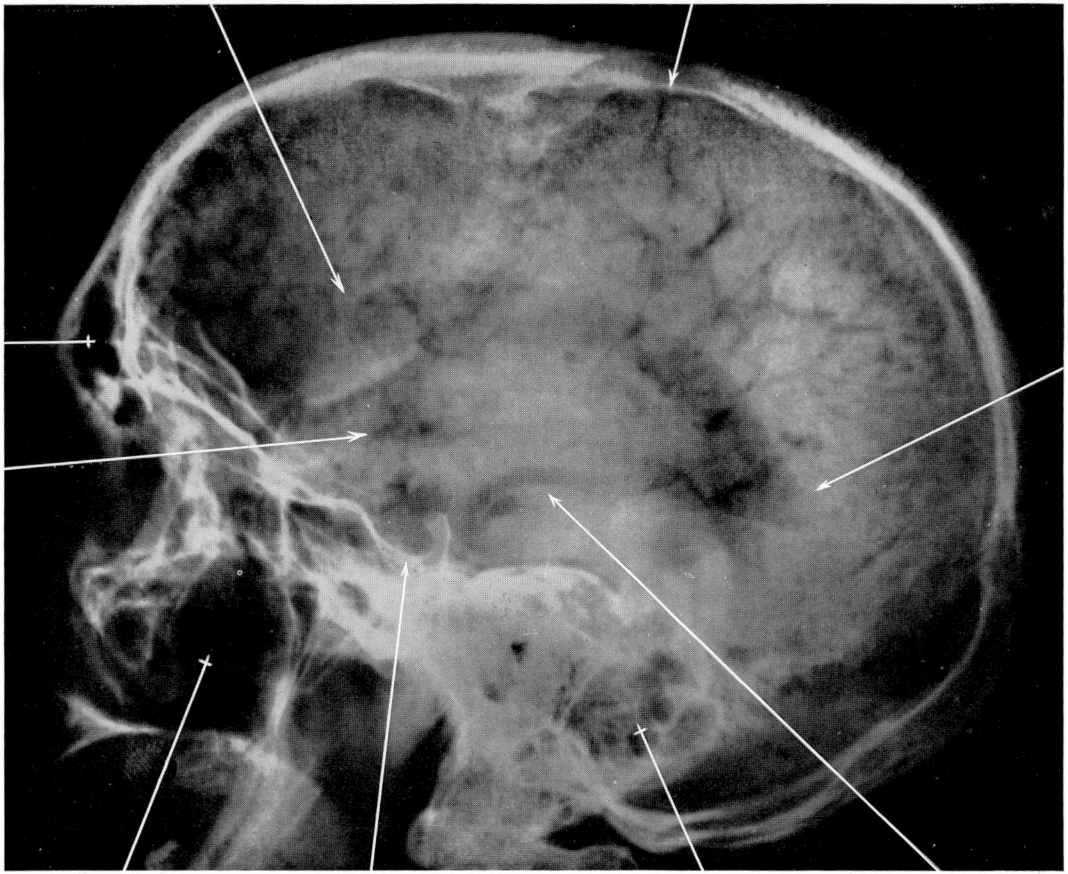

Upper end of Central Sulcus

Posterior horn of Lateral Ventricle

Inferior horn of Lateral Ventricle

Anterior horn of Lateral Ventricle

Mastoid Air Cells

Hypophyseal fossa

Maxillary Sinus

Frontal Sinus

Stem of Lateral Sulcus

PLATE LVII.—LATERAL RADIOGRAPH OF LIVING HEAD OF MAN AGED 24, AFTER INJECTION OF OXYGEN INTO THE SPINAL SUBARACHNOID SPACE BY LUMBAR PUNCTURE (Encephalograph : Mr. Norman M. Dott).

The Sulci of the Cerebral Hemisphere appear in the radigraph on account of the relative translucency to the X-Rays of the oxygen-filled subarachnoid spaces. The oxygen has entered the Ventricular System also, and the form, size and position of a Lateral Ventricle are well shown. Compare with Plate LX in which the Lateral Ventricles, directly injected, are more obvious but considerably enlarged.

[Facing p. 952

PLATE LVIII

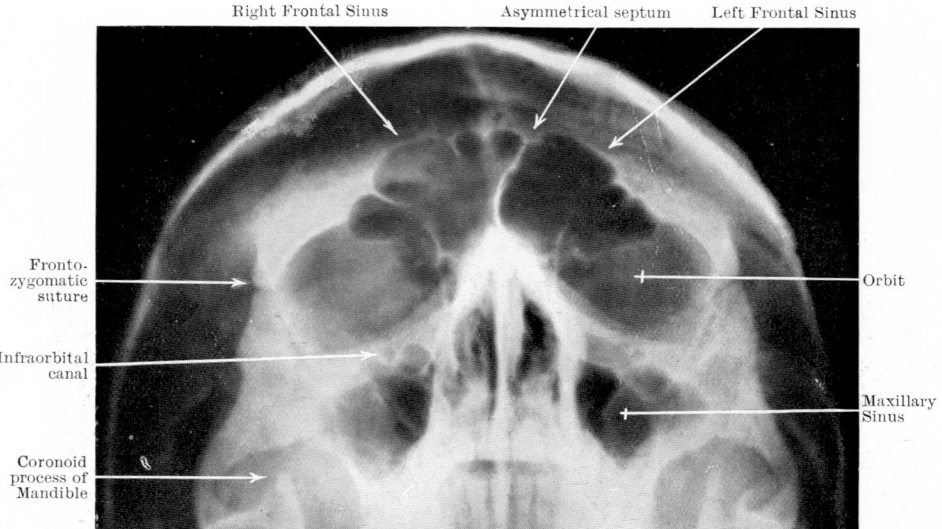

Right Frontal Sinus   Asymmetrical septum   Left Frontal Sinus

Fronto-
zygomatic
suture

Infraorbital
canal

Coronoid
process of
Mandible

Orbit

Maxillary
Sinus

FIG. 1.—RADIOGRAPH OF THE FRONTAL SINUSES OF MAN AGED 34. (Dr. J. F. Brailsford.)

Note the asymmetrical position of the septum, and the extension of the sinuses into the roofs of the orbits. Compare with Plate VIII, and for lateral views of the Frontal Sinuses see Fig. 2 and Plates V, LVII, LIX and LX.

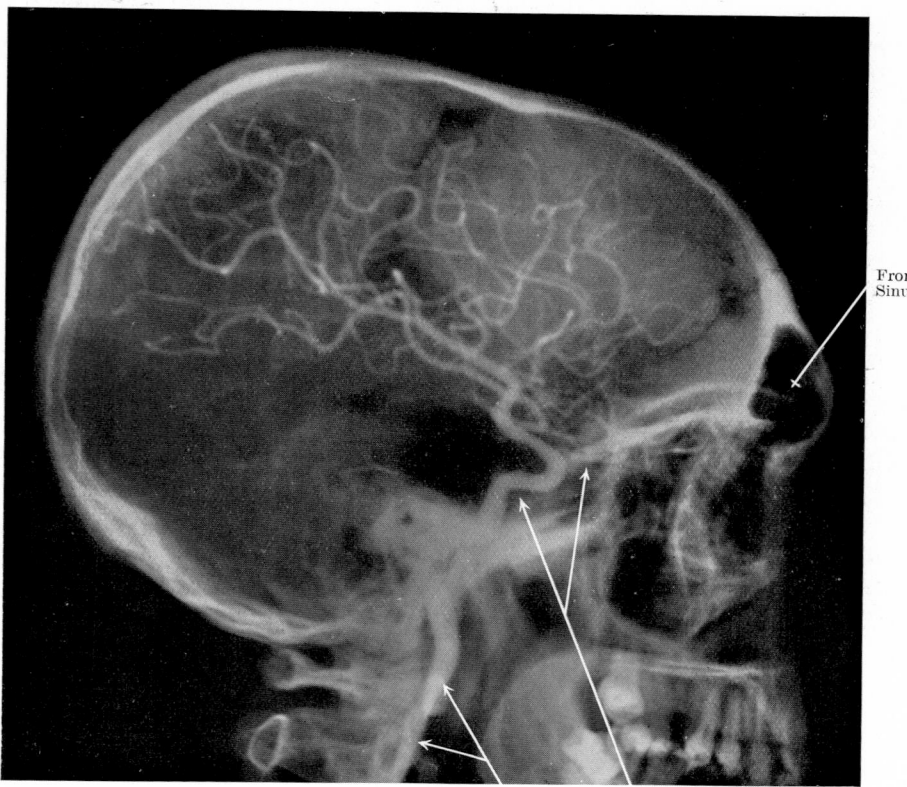

Frontal
Sinuses

Internal Carotid Artery   Internal Carotid Artery in Cavernous Sinus
in Neck   and Ophthalmic Artery

FIG. 2.—LATERAL RADIOGRAPH OF LIVING HEAD OF MAN AGED 24, AFTER INJECTION OF THORIUM DIOXIDE (THOROTRAST) INTO THE RIGHT INTERNAL CAROTID ARTERY (Cerebral Arteriograph : Mr. Norman M. Dott).

The Internal Carotid Artery is seen in the upper part of the Neck, in the Carotid Canal, and in the Cavernous Sinus. Note its division into Anterior and Middle Cerebral Arteries and the appearance of their branches. The Ophthalmic Artery is also seen leaving the internal carotid and ramifying in the orbit.

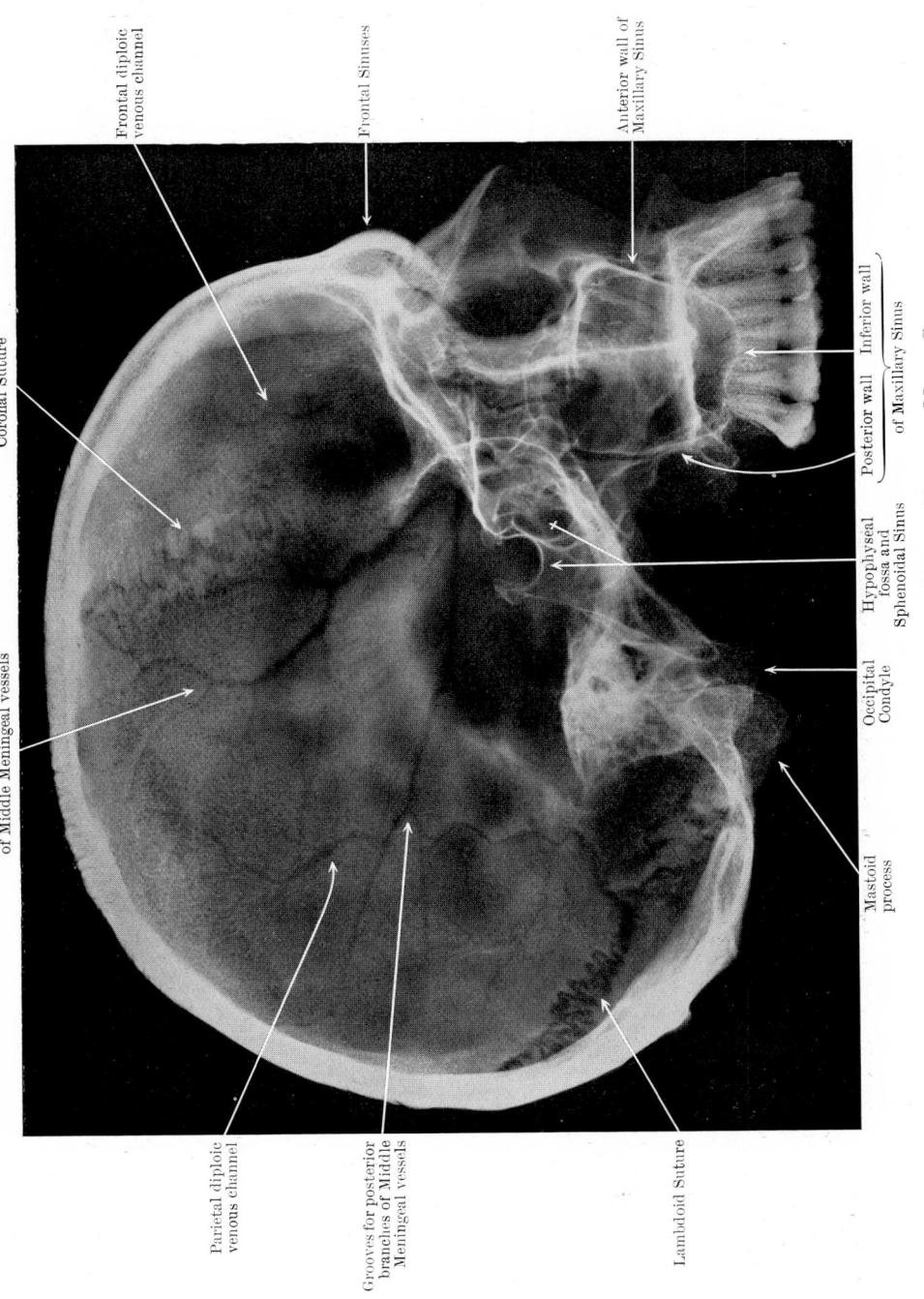

Frontal diploic venous channel

Frontal Sinuses

Anterior wall of Maxillary Sinus

Coronal Suture

Grooves for anterior branches of Middle Meningeal vessels

Inferior wall

Posterior wall } of Maxillary Sinus

Hypophyseal fossa and Sphenoidal Sinus

Occipital Condyle

Mastoid process

Parietal diploic venous channel

Grooves for posterior branches of Middle Meningeal vessels

Lambdoid Suture

PLATE LIX.—LATERAL RADIOGRAPH OF RIGHT HALF OF MALE SKULL.

Compare with Fig. 138, p. 147; Fig. 147, p. 179; with Plate V (radiograph of the same skull complete), and with radiographs of the living head (Plates LVII, LVIII (Fig. 2), and LX).

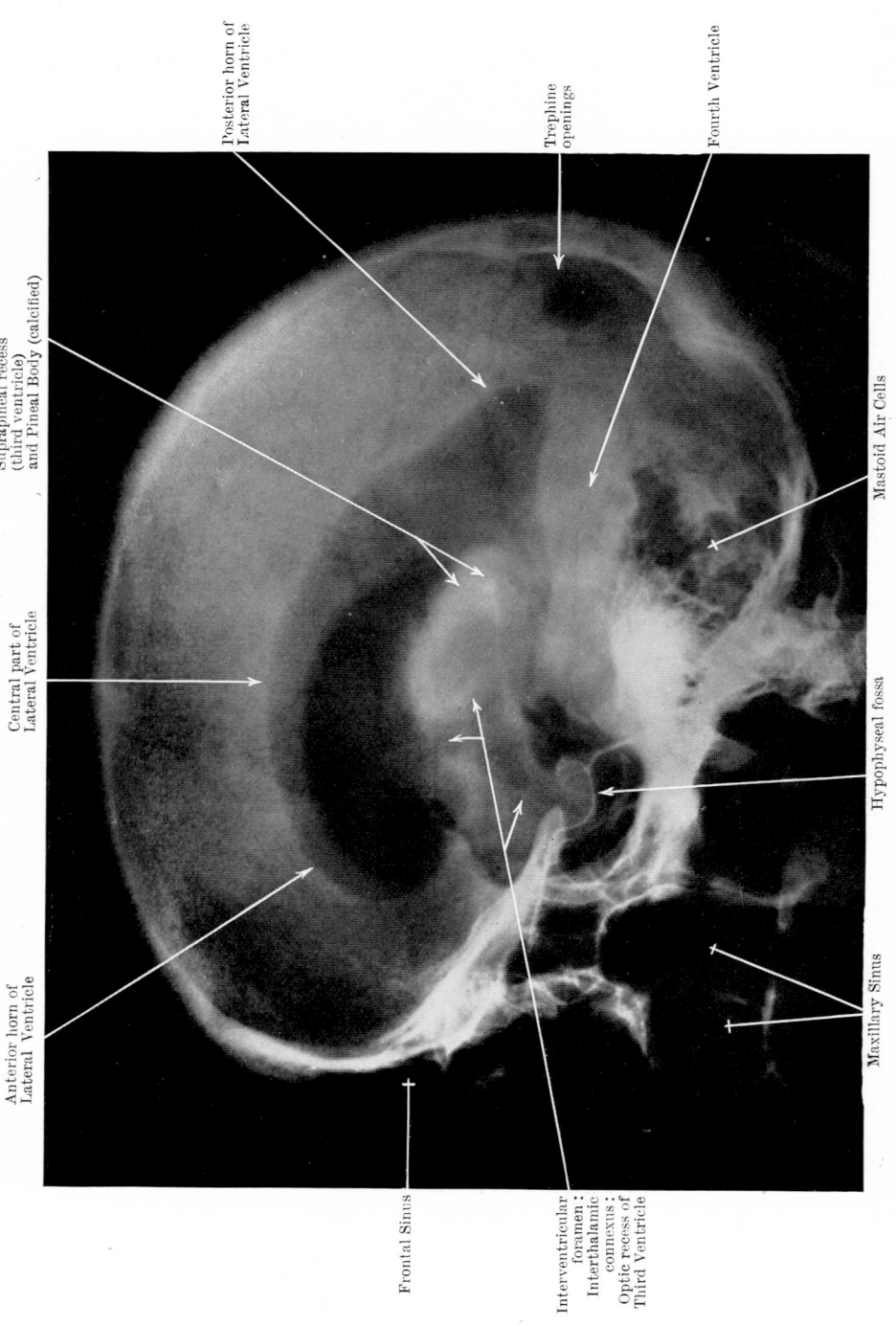

PLATE LX

Posterior horn of
Lateral Ventricle

Trephine
openings

Fourth Ventricle

Suprapineal recess
(third ventricle)
and Pineal Body (calcified)

Central part of
Lateral Ventricle

Mastoid Air Cells

Anterior horn of
Lateral Ventricle

Hypophyseal fossa

Maxillary Sinus

Frontal Sinus

Interventricular
foramen:
Interthalamic
connexus:
Optic recess of
Third Ventricle

PLATE LX.—LATERAL RADIOGRAPH OF LIVING HEAD OF WOMAN AGED 47, AFTER DIRECT INJECTION OF OXYGEN INTO THE
LATERAL VENTRICLES (Ventriculograph: Mr. Norman M. Dott).

The oxygen-filled Ventricular System appears in the radiograph, like the air-filled sinuses, on account of its relative translucency to the X-Rays. The central darker
area is due to the overlap of the two Lateral Ventricles; in this patient they were pathologically distended, but the general form is well shown; compare with Plate
LXI for corrected impression of the normal shape of the ventricles.

[Facing p. 953

peduncular cistern there are certain wide subarachnoid channels. A pair of these are the **cisterns of the lateral sulci.** Each accommodates the middle cerebral artery. Anteriorly the interpeduncular cistern passes into a space in front of the optic chiasma, and from there it is continued into the longitudinal fissure above the corpus callosum. In that subarachnoid passage the anterior cerebral arteries are lodged.

The spinal part of the subarachnoid space is a very wide interval partially subdivided into compartments by three incomplete septa. One of these is a median partition which connects the pia mater covering the back of the spinal cord with the arachnoid. In the upper part of the cervical region this partition is imperfect, and is represented merely by some strands passing between the two membranes; in the lower part of the cervical region and in the thoracic region it becomes more complete. The other two septa are formed by the **ligamenta denticulata** which spread laterally one from each side of the spinal cord. They will be described with the pia mater.

Arachnoid Villi and Granulations.—When the surface of the dura mater is inspected after the removal of the calvaria, a number of small fleshy-looking excrescences, purplish-red in colour, are seen ranged in clusters on each side of the superior sagittal sinus, and when the sinus is opened they are observed protruding into its interior. They are the arachnoid granulations, and they are found also, in smaller numbers and distinctly smaller size, in connexion with other blood-sinuses, such as the transverse sinus, the straight sinus, and the cavernous sinus. At first sight they appear to belong to the dura mater, but in reality each granulation is a bulbous protrusion of the arachnoid mater. It is attached to the arachnoid by a narrow pedicle, and into its interior there is prolonged through the pedicle a continuation of the subarachnoid space filled with cerebro-spinal fluid. The distal end of the protrusion passes between the interstices of the dura mater into contact with the endothelial lining of the sinus, with which the extremity of the diverticulum becomes fused. In this situation the subdural space is obliterated and the single membrane resulting from the fusion alone separates the blood from the cerebro-spinal fluid.

On each side of the superior sagittal sinus there is a number of irregular spaces in the dura mater which communicate with the sinus either by a small aperture or a narrow channel. These spaces are called the **lacunæ laterales**, and it is into these cavities that most of the arachnoid granulations insinuate themselves, a few only being invaginated directly into the sinus. The granulations enlarge with age and the cranial wall overlying them becomes absorbed so that small pits are hollowed out on its internal surface for their reception, though of course the granulations do not come directly into contact with the bone but are separated from it by the periosteal layer of the dura, the lumen of the lacuna or sinus, and except where the arachnoid is fused with endothelium, by the dura of the sinus floor and the subdural space.

Besides these macroscopic protrusions of the arachnoid mater there are innumerable microscopic processes of this membrane, called **arachnoid villi**, which have the same relation to the venous sinuses. These arachnoid villi and arachnoid granulations form the most important pathway for the return of the cerebro-spinal fluid to the venous blood. This takes place by filtration through the membrane formed by the fusion of the arachnoid mater with the vascular endothelium. In infants no arachnoid granulations can be seen, but as age advances some of the villi, especially those in relation to the posterior part of the superior sagittal sinus, become enlarged to form arachnoid granulations.

PRODUCTION AND CIRCULATION OF THE CEREBRO-SPINAL FLUID

The main bulk of the cerebro-spinal fluid is formed within the lateral ventricles of the brain through the agency of the choroid plexuses. It is a clear, colourless fluid of low specific gravity and alkaline reaction which in health is almost free of protein and cells (2 or 3 lymphocytes per c. mm.) but contains the same crystalloids as the blood. From the lateral ventricles this fluid passes by way of the interventricular foramina into the third ventricle. Here more fluid is added from the choroid plexus of the roof. Then the fluid passes through the aqueduct into the fourth ventricle where further additions are made from the choroid plexuses in its roof. From the fourth ventricle the fluid escapes by the median and lateral apertures into the subarachnoid space, and is received into the adjacent cisterns which lie below the tentorium. Some of the fluid passes downwards into the spinal subarachnoid space, but the major part rises through the tentorial notch and finds its way slowly over the surface of the hemispheres to be absorbed mainly through the arachnoid villi and granulations into the venous system. Some cerebrospinal fluid is carried away by the perineural lymphatics. The subarachnoid space is carried outwards for a short distance on the nerves in their arachnoid sheaths, and it is in the region where the arachnoid sheath comes to an end that the cerebrospinal fluid gains access to the lymphatic channels of the nerves. This connexion is more free in the olfactory, the optic, and the auditory nerves than in other nerves.

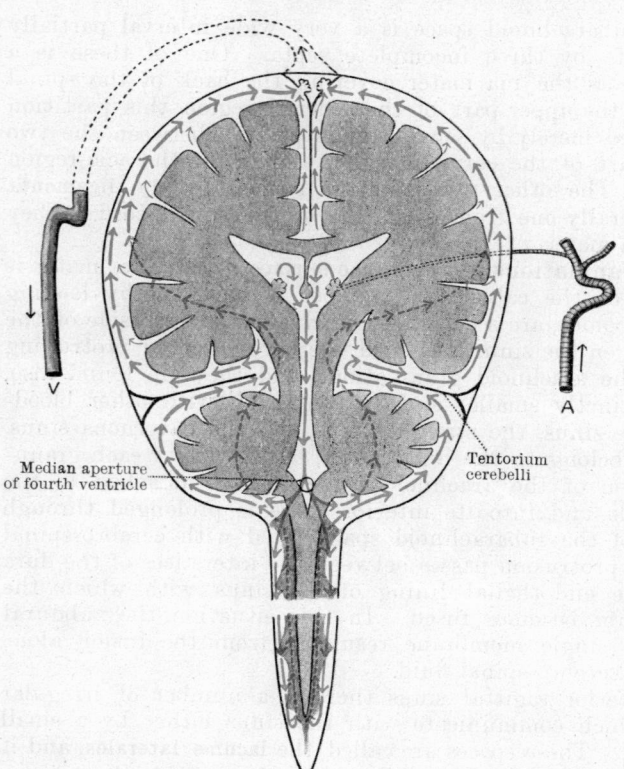

Fig. 836.—Diagram to show the main points relating to the Production, Course, and Absorption of the Cerebro-spinal Fluid. After Dott (*Edin. Med. Journ.*).

Median aperture of fourth ventricle

Tentorium cerebelli

Each blood-vessel as it enters or leaves the brain is surrounded by a tubular prolongation of the subarachnoid space by means of which cerebro-spinal fluid follows all the vascular ramifications. The finest perivascular channels communicate with the perineuronal spaces and so lead the fluid into contact with the neurones themselves (Fig. 833). The normal flow of the cerebro-spinal fluid in these perivascular channels is from within outwards into the main subarachnoid space so that certain products of metabolism may be eliminated by these currents. It is into these channels also, in certain pathological conditions, that the brain capillaries discharge great numbers of leucocytes (in some diseases polymorphs, in others lymphocytes) which are passed out to the main subarachnoid space, thus altering the cellular content of the cerebro-spinal fluid.

PIA MATER

The pia mater is the immediate investment of the brain and spinal cord, and is a delicate and very vascular membrane. The nerves that leave both the brain and spinal cord receive closely applied sheaths from the pia mater, which blend with the fibrous tissue sheaths of the nerves.

Pia Mater of the Brain.—The pia mater which covers the brain is finer and more delicate than that which clothes the spinal cord. It follows closely all the inequalities on the surface of the brain, and in the case of the cerebral hemisphere it dips into each sulcus in the form of a fold which lines it completely. On the cerebellum the relation is not so intimate; it is only into the larger fissures that it penetrates in the form of folds.

The larger blood-vessels of the brain lie in the subarachnoid space. The finer twigs ramify in the pia mater before they proceed into the substance of the brain. As they enter they carry with them sheaths derived from the pia and arachnoid mater. When a portion of the membrane is raised from the surface of the brain, numerous fine processes are withdrawn from the cerebral surface. They are the blood-vessels with their sheaths, and they give the deep surface of the pia mater a rough and flocculent appearance.

As the pia mater is carried over the lower part of the roof of the fourth ventricle it receives the name of the **tela chorioidea of the fourth ventricle**, and it is in connexion with that portion of the pia mater that the choroid plexuses of that cavity are developed. The **tela chorioidea of the third ventricle** is a fold of pia mater which is invaginated (as it were) into the brain, so that it comes to lie over the third ventricle and to project, in the shape of choroid plexuses, into the lateral ventricles. The invaginated fold requires special notice.

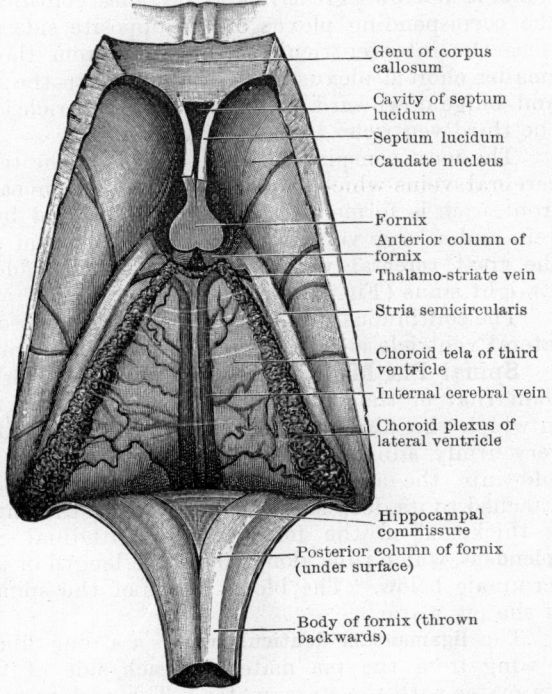

FIG. 837.—DISSECTION TO SHOW THE CHOROID TELA OF THE THIRD VENTRICLE, AND THE PARTS NEAR IT.

The **tela chorioidea of the third ventricle** is a double layer of pia mater which intervenes between the body of the fornix, which lies above it, and the ependymal roof of the third ventricle and the two thalami, which lie below it. Between its two layers there are blood-vessels and some subarachnoid tissue. In shape it is triangular, and the narrow, anterior end or apex lies between the interventricular

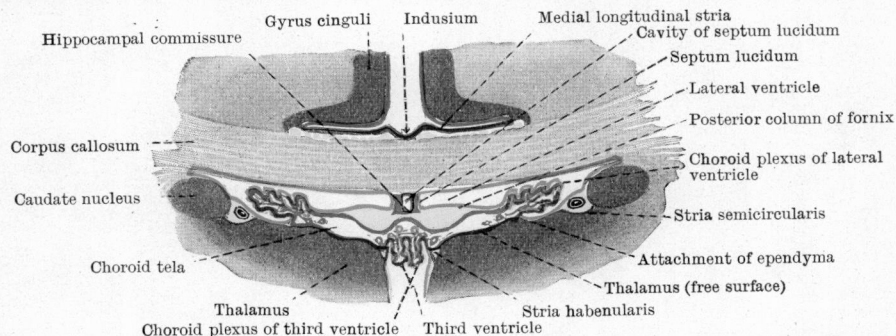

FIG. 838.—DIAGRAM OF A CORONAL SECTION ACROSS THE CHOROID TELA OF THE THIRD VENTRICLE.

foramina. The base lies under the splenium of the corpus callosum, and here the two layers of the tela separate and become continuous with the pia mater on the surface of the brain by passing out through a cleft called the **transverse fissure**.

Along each margin the tela chorioidea of the third ventricle is bordered by the choroid plexus of the central part of the lateral ventricle, which projects into the ventricular cavity from under cover of the margin of the fornix. It should be borne in mind that the ependymal lining of the ventricle gives a complete covering to the choroid plexus. Posteriorly the choroid plexus is continuous with the similar structure in the inferior horn of the ventricle, whilst in front it narrows greatly, and becomes continuous across the median plane with the corresponding plexus of the opposite side, behind the ependymal layer which lines the interventricular foramen. From the median junction a pair of much smaller choroid plexuses run backwards on the under surface of the tela chorioidea, and bulge downwards into the third ventricle. They are the choroid plexuses of the third ventricle.

The most conspicuous blood-vessels in the tela chorioidea are a pair of internal cerebral veins which run backwards, one on each side of the median plane. In front, each is formed at the apex of the fold by the union of the thalamo-striate vein and a large vein issuing from the choroid plexus ; behind, they unite to form the **great cerebral vein**, and that pours its blood into the anterior end of the straight sinus (Fig. 832, p. 948).

The continuous cleft through which the choroid plexuses are introduced into the lateral ventricle is called the choroid fissure, and is described on pp. 896, 905, 917.

Spinal Pia Mater.—The pia mater of the spinal cord is thicker and denser than that of the brain. That is largely due to the addition of an outer layer in which the fibres run chiefly in the longitudinal direction. The pia mater is very firmly adherent to the surface of the spinal cord, and in front it sends a fold into the anterior median fissure. The posterior median septum is firmly attached to its deep surface. In front of the anterior median fissure the pia mater is thickened in the form of a longitudinal glistening band, termed the **linea splendens**, which runs along the whole length of the cord, and blends with the filum terminale below. The blood-vessels of the spinal cord lie between the two layers of the pia mater.

The **ligamentum denticulatum** is a strong fibrous band which stretches out like a wing from the pia mater on each side of the spinal cord, and connects the pia mater with the dura mater. The pial or medial attachment of the ligament extends in a continuous line between the anterior and posterior nerve-roots, from the level of the foramen magnum to the level of the first lumbar vertebra. Its lateral margin is serrated or denticulated, and for the most part free. From twenty to twenty-two denticulations may be recognised. They occur in the intervals between the spinal nerves, and, pushing the arachnoid before them, they are attached by their pointed ends to the inner surface of the dura mater, and by means of them the spinal cord is suspended in the middle of the dural tube.

PERIPHERAL NERVOUS SYSTEM

Originally written by the late A. M. PATERSON, M.D., F.R.C.S.,
Professor of Anatomy, University of Liverpool

Revised and rewritten by JOHN S. B. STOPFORD

THE Peripheral Nervous System, as distinct from the Central Nervous System comprised by the brain and spinal cord, is broadly divisible into three series of fibres. (I.) The **cranial nerves**, which are attached to the brain and pass through openings in the base of the skull, to be distributed for the most part to the head region. (II.) The **spinal nerves**, which are attached to the spinal cord, pass through the intervertebral foramina, and innervate the trunk and limbs, that is, the somatic area of the body. These two sets of fibres are sometimes grouped together as the cerebro-spinal system of nerves. (III.) The **autonomic nervous system**, which is subdivided into (*a*) the sympathetic system and (*b*) the parasympathetic system. Each of these parts has a wide distribution and is composed of ganglia and nerve fibres which in many localities form complicated plexuses. The sympathetic system is connected with spinal nerves in the thoracic and upper lumbar regions, whilst the parasympathetic system is associated with certain cranial and sacral spinal nerves. No one of the three groups can be considered wholly apart from the others, since, although presenting certain differences in structure, arrangement, and distribution, they are not independent or separate systems; the subdivision is, however, the most convenient one for descriptive purposes.

CRANIAL NERVES

The cranial nerves are twelve pairs of symmetrically arranged nerves which are attached to the brain, leave the skull through foramina at its base, and are generally distributed to the various structures of the head and neck. The site where the nerve fibres composing it (rootlets) enter or leave the brain surface is usually termed the **superficial origin** of the nerve, and the more deeply placed group of cells from which the fibres arise or around which they terminate is called the **nucleus of origin** or of **reception** respectively, and forms the **deep origin** of the nerve. It is also customary to trace the course of a nerve from its superficial origin to the periphery irrespective of the actual direction of the impulses carried by it. In this chapter the cranial nerves are described from their superficial origins onwards; their deep origins and connexions are dealt with in the section which treats of the Brain (pp. 877-892), and certain general points are also touched upon in the chapter introductory to the Nervous System (p. 792).

Classification of the Cranial Nerves.—Recent studies of the central connexions and peripheral distribution of the cranial nerves would point to those designated as the fifth, seventh, and eighth under the customary terminology, being each really divisible, both anatomically and physiologically, into two components, which are given separate names. None of the cranial nerves corresponds closely to a typical spinal nerve with motor and sensory roots. The fifth nerve, sometimes so compared, might well be considered as composed of an afferent nerve, the trigeminal, allied to a separate efferent nerve, the *masticator* (nervus masticatorius or motor root of the fifth) which accompanies for part of its course the mandibular division only of the former. Similarly, the usually designated seventh nerve can be resolved into two components, the facial proper and the *glosso-palatine* (nervus intermedius or the sensory root of the seventh), the latter including the ganglion of the facial nerve and the chorda tympani. The separation of the eighth nerve into two entirely different functional elements—the cochlear and vestibular divisions—though both are afferent, is more obvious. Such a reclassification would give fifteen pairs of nerves instead of the customary twelve.

THE CRANIAL NERVES

Number.	Name.	Function.		
		Efferent.	Afferent.	Parasympathetic.
I.	Olfactory	...	Smell.	...
II.	Optic	...	Sight.	...
III.	Oculomotor	Sup., med., and inf. rectus, and inf. oblique of eyeball.	...	Ciliary & sphincter pupillæ muscles of eyeball.
IV.	Trochlear	Sup. oblique of eyeball.	...	...
V.	Trigeminal	Muscles of mastication. Tensor tympani and tensor palati. Ant. digastric and mylo-hyoid.	Face, tongue (ant. ⅔), palate, gums, and teeth.	...
VI.	Abducent	Lat. rectus of eyeball.	...	...
VII.	Facial	Muscles of face and scalp. Platysma, post. digastric, stylo-hyoid and stapedius.	Taste (ant. ⅔ tongue).	Submandibular and sublingual salivary glands and lacrimal gland.
VIII.	Auditory	...	Hearing and equilibrium.	...
IX.	Glosso-pharyngeal	Stylo-pharyngeus.	Sens. pharynx and post. ⅓ of tongue. Taste (post. ⅓ of tongue).	Parotid salivary gland.
X.	Vagus	Muscles of palate and pharynx, striated muscles of œsophagus, and crico-thyroid.	Small part of ext. ear.	Heart, lungs, œsophagus, stomach, prox. intestine, liver, pancreas, spleen, and kidneys.
XI.	Accessory	(a) **Accessory to vagus.**—Muscles of larynx (except crico-thyroid). (b) **Spinal part.**—Trapezius and sterno-mastoid.	...	...
XII.	Hypoglossal	Muscles of tongue.	...	...

OLFACTORY NERVE

In the older accounts, the **first** or **olfactory nerve** is described as consisting of several parts : (1) a series of fine **nerves** which arise from (2) the **olfactory bulb**. That again is connected by (3) the **olfactory tract** with the brain, to which it is attached by (4) two **roots** (Fig. 839).

The anatomy of the olfactory bulb, the olfactory tract and its roots is described on pp. 908 to 912; and the histology of the cells on p. 908.

The **olfactory nerve** consists of about twenty separate filaments which arise in the olfactory mucous membrane and terminate in the olfactory bulb. The fibres are non-medullated. After their origins from the olfactory cells of the olfactory region on the upper third of the nasal septum and nearly the whole of the opposed superior nasal concha (Figs. 846, 847), the nerve fibres form fine plexuses from which the terminal filaments pass through the cribriform plates of the ethmoid on their way to the olfactory bulb. The filaments are held together in bundles by extensions of the pia, arachnoid, and dura mater, and the subarachnoid space is continued for some distance along the nerves.

Two other pairs of nerves have been found related to the olfactory system in lower vertebrates and in mammals with a well-developed sense of smell. Both are closely related to the olfactory nerve itself throughout its course. They are

(1) the *vomero-nasal nerve*, which supplies the vomero-nasal organ, and in

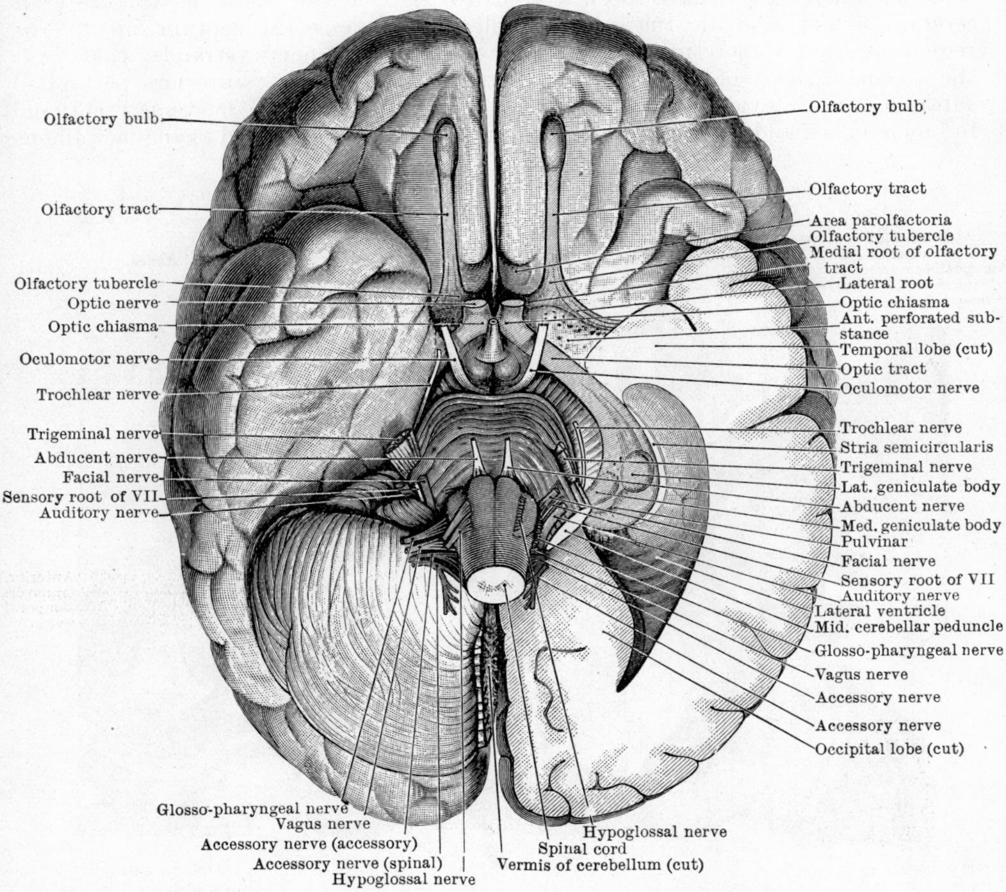

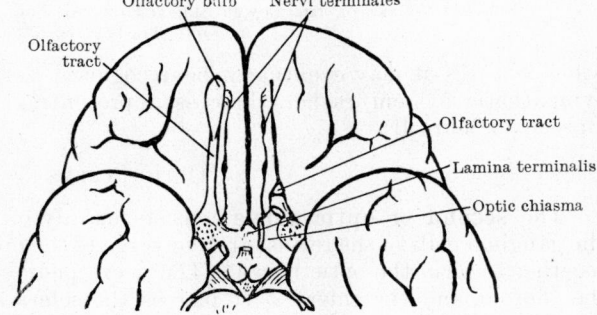

Olfactory bulb
Olfactory tract
Olfactory tubercle
Optic nerve
Optic chiasma
Oculomotor nerve
Trochlear nerve
Trigeminal nerve
Abducent nerve
Facial nerve
Sensory root of VII
Auditory nerve

Olfactory bulb
Olfactory tract
Area parolfactoria
Olfactory tubercle
Medial root of olfactory tract
Lateral root
Optic chiasma
Ant. perforated substance
Temporal lobe (cut)
Optic tract
Oculomotor nerve
Trochlear nerve
Stria semicircularis
Trigeminal nerve
Lat. geniculate body
Abducent nerve
Med. geniculate body
Pulvinar
Facial nerve
Sensory root of VII
Auditory nerve
Lateral ventricle
Mid. cerebellar peduncle
Glosso-pharyngeal nerve
Vagus nerve
Accessory nerve
Accessory nerve
Occipital lobe (cut)

Glosso-pharyngeal nerve
Vagus nerve
Accessory nerve (accessory)
Accessory nerve (spinal)
Hypoglossal nerve
Hypoglossal nerve
Spinal cord
Vermis of cerebellum (cut)

FIG. 839.—VIEW OF THE INFERIOR SURFACE OF THE BRAIN,
with the lower portion of the temporal and occipital lobes, and the cerebellum on the left side removed, to show the origins of the cranial nerves.

the domestic animals joins the olfactory nerve itself to terminate in an accessory olfactory bulb; in Man the vomero-nasal organ is rudimentary after birth, and the nerve is absent; (2) the terminal nerve.

The **terminal nerve** (*nervus terminalis*) has been found present in all groups of vertebrates, in the human embryo, and recently in the human adult. It is a very fine plexiform nerve consisting of non-medullated fibres with small groups of ganglion cells, and may be discovered in the cranial cavity as two or three strands in the pia mater covering the gyrus rectus along the

Olfactory bulb   Nervi terminales
Olfactory tract
Olfactory tract
Lamina terminalis
Optic chiasma

FIG. 840.—DIAGRAM OF PART OF THE LOWER SURFACE OF AN ADULT HUMAN BRAIN to show the position of the central parts of the Nervi Terminales and their relations to the Olfactory Tracts and Gyri Recti. (After Brookover.) (S. E. W.)

The olfactory bulb and part of the tract have been removed on the left side, and the right optic nerve and the greater part of the optic chiasma have been cut away to expose the lamina terminalis.

medial side of the olfactory tract. Peripherally (anteriorly) its fibres join the olfactory nerve filaments and have a similar distribution to the nasal mucosa; in some mammals they have been traced to end in the walls of the anterior cerebral artery and in the vascular plexus of the nasal septum up to the region of the vomero-nasal organ. Centrally, the nerve strands pass over the medial root of the olfactory tract towards the anterior perforated substance. The evidence points to the conclusion that the nerve is functional in mammals, and, from the appearance of its fibres and ganglia, among

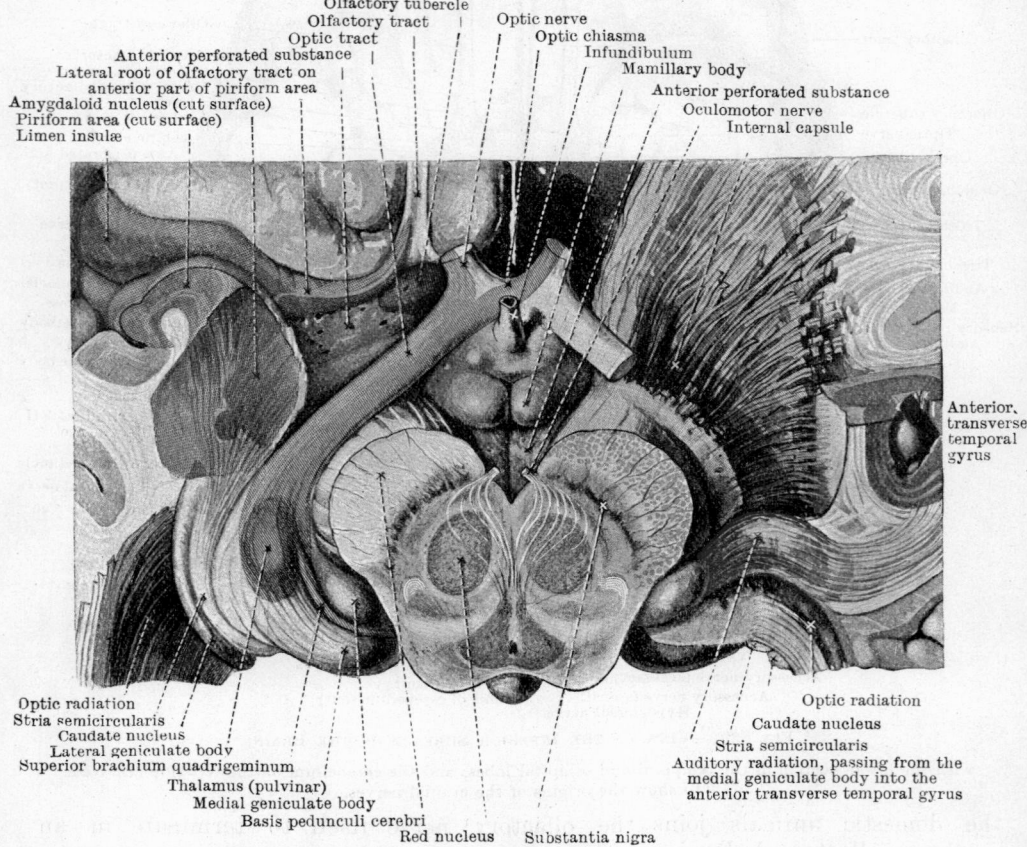

FIG. 841.—PART OF THE LOWER SURFACE OF THE FORE-BRAIN, showing the Olfactory and Optic Tracts. (G. E. S.)

other features, it may eventually be recognised as related in part at least to the sympathetic system rather than as representing a separate nerve (Johnstone, Brookover, Larsell).

OPTIC NERVE

The **second** or **optic nerve** consists mainly of nerve fibres which spring from the ganglion cells of the retina, and converge to the optic disc, where they are grouped together to form the optic nerve. The nerve pierces the outer layers of the retina, the choroid, and the sclera. It pierces the sclera 3 mm. (one-eighth of an inch), to the medial side of the posterior pole of the eyeball, the nerve fibres being divided into bundles by the lamina cribrosa, and enters the orbital fat, surrounded by the ciliary vessels and nerves. It then runs backwards and slightly medially towards the optic foramen, being crossed by the ophthalmic artery and naso-ciliary nerve, and is pierced on its inferior surface by the central artery and vein of the retina. It is surrounded by sheaths from all three membranes of the brain, that formed by the dura being especially robust, and by prolongations of the subdural and subarachnoid spaces which lie between them. To enter the optic foramen, it passes through the common tendinous ring from which the four rectus muscles of the eyeball arise. In the foramen it is separated from the sphenoidal air sinus by only a thin plate of bone, the ophthalmic artery accompanies it on its lower and lateral sides, and the arteria retinæ centralis may enter it in this part of its course. It then enters the middle fossa of the skull and ends in the optic chiasma, which lies at the base of the brain, anterior to the interpeduncular area and between the right and left valleculæ of the cerebrum. The chiasma is in close relation on each side to the internal carotid artery, but lies a little distance superior to the hypophysis cerebri.

From each of the two postero-lateral angles of the optic chiasma an optic tract sweeps round to the posterior part of the thalamus and to the mid-brain, between the cerebral peduncle and the hippocampal gyrus of the corresponding side, and each tract terminates in connexion with the lateral geniculate body. Formerly it was thought that fibres of the optic tract terminated in all three lower visual centres (the lateral geniculate body, pulvinar of thalamus and superior quadrigeminal body), but recent researches have shown that in Man none go to the superior quadrigeminal body and probably none to the pulvinar, a change having been brought about in the arrangement of the fibres in consequence of the development of the macula of the retina and the increased functional importance of the visual cortex, which is connected with all three lower visual centres (see p. 903).

When the optic nerve reaches the optic chiasma the fibres from the lateral half of each retina pass to the optic tract of the same side and the fibres from the medial half to the optic tract of the opposite side. Therefore, each optic nerve is connected with both sides of the brain. But each optic tract, in addition to some fibres of both optic nerves, contains also fibres passing from the medial geniculate body of one side to the inferior quadrigeminal body of the opposite side ; those fibres constitute a commissure between those two lower centres for hearing (Gudden's).

OCULOMOTOR NERVE

The **third** or **oculomotor nerve** supplies the levator palpebræ superioris, and all the extrinsic ocular muscles, save the lateral rectus and superior oblique. It arises

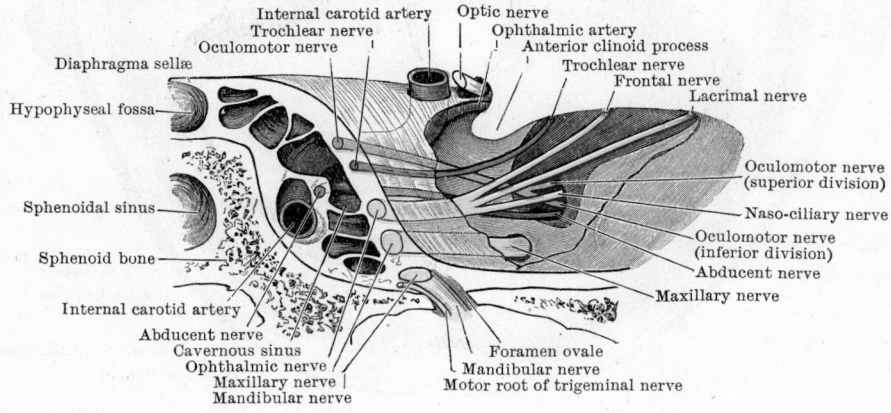

FIG. 842.—RELATIONS OF STRUCTURES IN THE CAVERNOUS SINUS AND SUPERIOR ORBITAL FISSURE.

from the brain, near the posterior perforated substance, by several rootlets which emerge from the medial sulcus of the cerebral peduncle, just in front of the pons (Fig. 839). (For deep origin, see p. 888). Passing forwards, between and close to the posterior cerebral and superior cerebellar arteries, then along the lateral aspect of the posterior communicating artery through the cisterna interpeduncularis, the nerve pierces the dura mater antero-lateral to the posterior clinoid process, in a small triangular space between the free and attached borders of the tentorium cerebelli. Embedded in the dura mater, the nerve courses through the lateral wall of the cavernous sinus, above the trochlear nerve, and enters the orbit through the superior orbital fissure, and then lies within the common tendinous ring from which the four rectus muscles arise. At the point of entry into the orbit the nerve divides into upper and lower branches, separated by the naso-ciliary nerve.

Branches.—The **superior branch** of the nerve supplies two muscles of the orbit —the superior rectus and the levator palpebræ superioris.

The **inferior branch** passes forwards, and, after giving branches to the medial and inferior recti, ends in the inferior oblique muscle. From the branch which

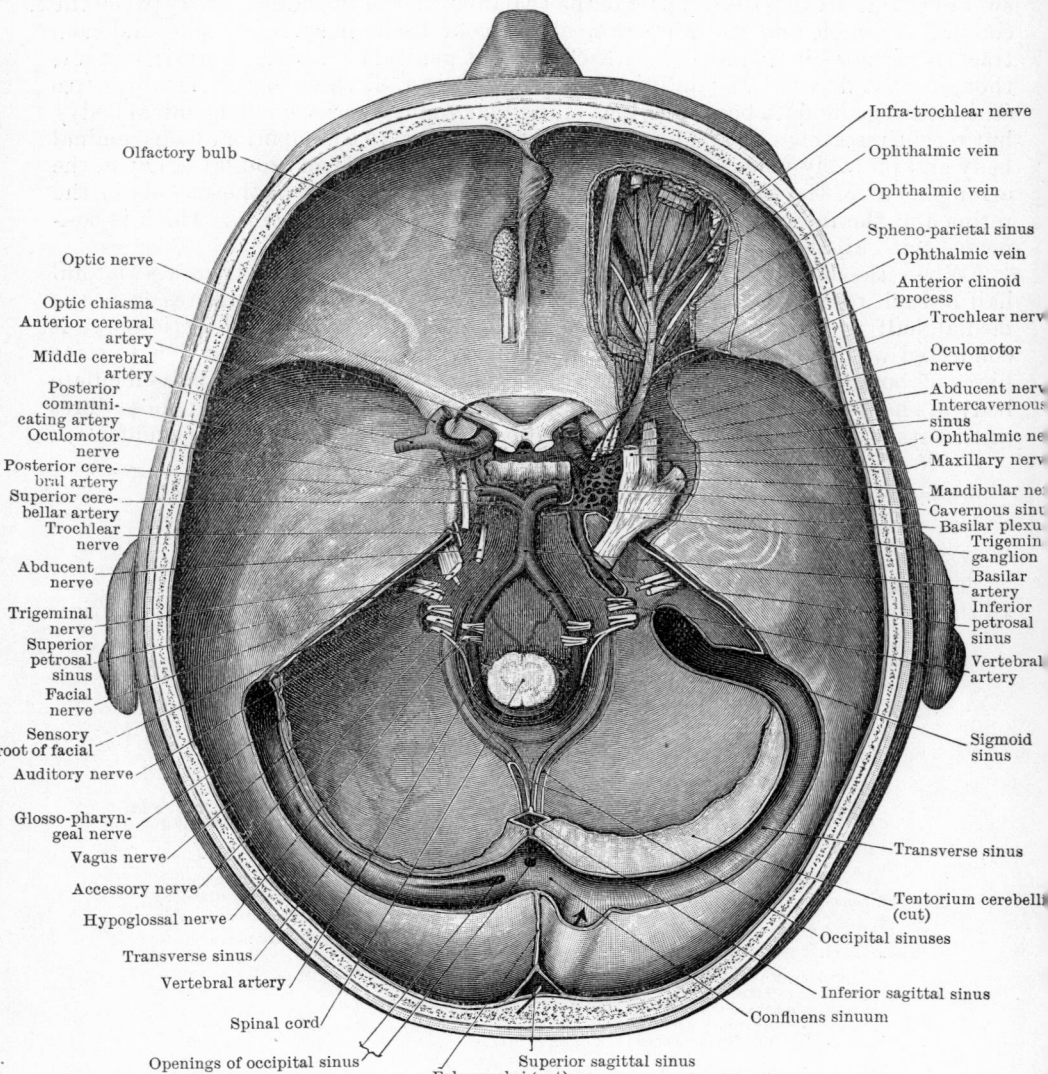

FIG. 843.—THE BASE OF THE SKULL, to show the dura mater, sinuses, arteries, and nerves.

supplies the inferior oblique a filament (the parasympathetic root) extends to the ciliary ganglion and is concerned with the innervation of the ciliary and sphincter pupillæ muscles of the eyeball.

Communications.—In the cavernous sinus the oculomotor nerve receives filaments from (1) the sympathetic plexus on the internal carotid artery; and (2) A slender communication from the ophthalmic division of the trigeminal nerve.

TROCHLEAR NERVE

The **fourth** or **trochlear nerve** supplies only the superior oblique muscle of the eyeball. It arises at the side of the *frenulum veli* from the upper end of the superior medullary velum, just below the inferior quadrigeminal bodies (Fig. 755, p. 869). (For deep origin see p. 887.) It is extremely slender, and of considerable length. Passing round the lateral side of the cerebral peduncle, the nerve appears at the base of the brain behind the optic tract, in the interval between the cerebral peduncle and the temporal lobe of the brain, and between the superior cerebellar and posterior cerebral arteries. Continued forwards, it pierces the free border of the tentorium cerebelli, postero-lateral to the oculomotor nerve, and proceeds forwards, in the lateral wall of the cavernous sinus, to the superior orbital fissure, lying between the oculomotor nerve and the ophthalmic division of the trigeminal nerve. It enters the orbit above the muscles of the eyeball, turns medially between the levator palpebræ superioris and the periosteum of the orbital roof, and terminates in the orbital surface of the superior oblique muscle.

Communications.—In the cavernous sinus the nerve receives (1) a communicating branch from the sympathetic plexus on the internal carotid artery, and (2) a slender filament from the ophthalmic division of the trigeminal nerve.

TRIGEMINAL NERVE

The **fifth** or **trigeminal nerve**, the largest of the cranial nerves, is the nerve of common sensation to the superficial and deep parts of the face, and is motor to the muscles of mastication (see summary of distribution on p. 957).

It arises from the lateral part of the inferior surface of the pons by two roots— a large **sensory root** and a small **motor root** (Fig. 756, p. 870). (For deep origin see p. 885.) The two roots proceed forwards in the posterior fossa of the skull, and pierce the dura mater beneath the attachment of the tentorium cerebelli to the upper border of the petrous part of the temporal bone, and enter a cavity in the dura mater (*cavum trigeminale*) on the anterior surface of the petrous bone. The sensory (afferent) root gradually conceals the motor (efferent) root in its course forwards, and expands beneath the dura mater into a large flattened ganglion—the **trigeminal ganglion** [g. semilunare]. That ganglion occupies an impression on the petrous portion of the temporal bone. The internal carotid artery and the posterior part of the cavernous sinus are on its medial side. From the ganglion three large trunks arise—the **ophthalmic** or first, the **maxillary** or second, and the **mandibular** or third **divisions** of the nerve. The motor root of the nerve passes forward beneath the ganglion, and is incorporated wholly with the mandibular division of the nerve; on developmental and functional grounds the motor root is sometimes described as a separate nerve— the *nervus masticatorius*.

OPHTHALMIC NERVE

The **ophthalmic nerve** passes forwards to the orbit through the middle fossa of the skull, in the dura mater. It lies in the lateral wall of the cavernous sinus, at a lower level than the trochlear nerve, and reaches the orbit through the superior orbital fissure (Fig. 842).

In the wall of the cavernous sinus the ophthalmic nerve gives off (1) a small recurrent branch to the dura mater (*n. to tentorium*), (2) small communicating sensory twigs to the trunks of the oculomotor, trochlear, and abducent nerves, and it receives branches from the sympathetic plexus on the internal carotid artery.

In the superior orbital fissure the nerve divides into three main branches— lacrimal, frontal, and naso-ciliary (Fig. 842).

The **lacrimal nerve** enters the orbit through the lateral angle of the superior orbital fissure, above the orbital muscles. It passes forwards, between the periosteum and the orbital contents, to the anterior part of the orbit, and ends by supplying branches (a) to the lacrimal gland, (b) to the conjunctiva, and (c) to the skin of the lateral part of the upper eyelid.

The lacrimal nerve *communicates* in the orbit with the zygomatic branch of the maxillary nerve (whereby some secretory fibres are probably conveyed to the lacrimal gland), and on the face, by its terminal branches, with the temporal branches of the facial nerve.

The **frontal nerve** enters the orbital cavity through the superior orbital fissure, courses forwards above the ocular muscles, and divides at a variable point into two branches—a larger supra-orbital and a smaller supra-trochlear nerve.

The **supra-orbital nerve** passes directly forwards, and leaves the orbit, through the supra-orbital groove or foramen, to reach the forehead. It gives off secondary branches which are distributed to: (1) the forehead and scalp, reaching backwards as far as the vertex; (2) the upper eyelid; and (3) the frontal sinus. On the forehead the supra-orbital nerve communicates with the temporal branches of the facial nerve.

The **supra-trochlear nerve** courses obliquely forwards and medially, above the tendon of the superior oblique muscle, to reach the medial part of the supra-orbital margin, where it leaves the cavity of the orbit; it is distributed to the skin and fascia of the medial part of the forehead and the medial part of the upper eyelid.

It communicates with the infra-trochlear branch of the naso-ciliary nerve, either before or after leaving the orbit.

The **naso-ciliary nerve** enters the orbit through the superior orbital fissure, and between the two divisions of the oculomotor nerve (Fig. 849, p. 968). It crosses the orbital cavity obliquely to reach the anterior ethmoidal foramen, lying in its course

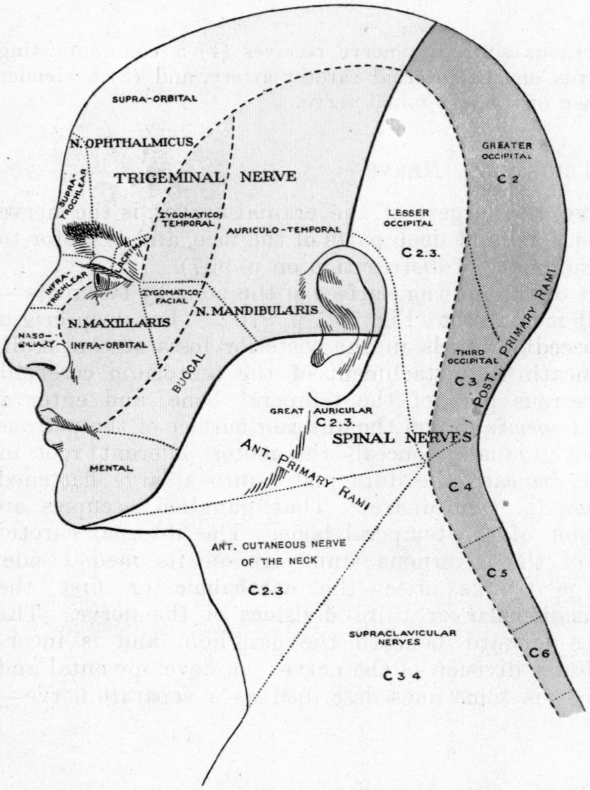

FIG. 844.—DISTRIBUTION OF SENSORY NERVES TO THE HEAD AND NECK.

below the superior rectus and superior oblique muscles and above the optic nerve and medial rectus muscle. The nerve is transmitted, under the name of *anterior ethmoidal*, through the anterior ethmoidal foramen into the cranial cavity, where it lies embedded in dura mater on the cribriform plate of the ethmoid bone. It enters the nasal cavity through the nasal slit, and terminates by dividing into medial and lateral **internal nasal branches**. The medial division supplies the mucous membrane over the upper and anterior part of the nasal septum. The lateral branch, after supplying collateral offsets to the lateral wall of the nasal cavity, finally appears on the face, as the **external nasal branch**, between the nasal bone and the upper nasal cartilage, and supplies branches to the skin and fascia of the lower part of the dorsum and the tip of the nose. The anterior ethmoidal nerve supplies, then, the cartilaginous part of the nose, both internally and externally.

The **branches** of the naso-ciliary nerve may be divided into three sets, arising (*a*) in the orbit, (*b*) in the nose, and (*c*) on the face.

In the orbit the branches are given off in three situations—lateral to, above, and medial to the optic nerve. (*a*) As the nerve lies on the lateral side of the optic nerve, it gives off the **ramus communicans** to the ciliary ganglion. (*b*) As it crosses above the optic nerve, **two long ciliary nerves** arise and pass forwards alongside the optic nerve to the eyeball. They convey sympathetic fibres to the dilator pupillæ muscle and afferent fibres to the iris and ciliary muscle. (*c*) On the medial side of the optic nerve the **infratrochlear nerve** arises as a slender branch which courses forwards below the pulley of the superior oblique muscle to the front of the orbit. It ends on the face by supplying the skin of the root of the nose and the eyelids, and communicates either in the orbit or on the face with the supra-trochlear nerve. On the face it also communicates with zygomatic branches of the facial nerve. A minute *posterior ethmoidal branch* may arise from the nerve near the back of the orbit, and enter the foramen of the same name to be distributed to the sphenoidal sinus and posterior ethmoidal sinuses.

In the nose the **medial internal nasal branches** supply the mucous membrane of the anterior part of the nasal septum; and **lateral internal nasal branches** supply the anterior part of the lateral wall of the nasal cavity.

On the face the terminal filaments of the **external nasal branch** are distributed to the skin and fascia of the lower half and tip of the nose. The terminal branch communicates with the zygomatic branches of the facial nerve.

Ciliary Ganglion.—This ganglion, though associated with the naso-ciliary branch of the ophthalmic nerve and with the inferior division of the oculomotor nerve, is regarded more properly as belonging to the parasympathetic system (see p. 974) and only parasympathetic fibres are relayed in the ganglion. It is a small reddish ganglion, about the size of a pin's head, placed near the back of the orbit, between the lateral rectus muscle and the optic nerve, and in front of the ophthalmic artery. Its so-called *roots* are three in number: (1) the **ramus communicans** [radix longa] derived from the naso-ciliary branch of the ophthalmic nerve; (2) **parasympathetic** [radix brevis], derived from the inferior division of the oculomotor nerve; and (3) **sympathetic**, slender filaments from the plexus on the internal carotid artery, which may exist as an independent root

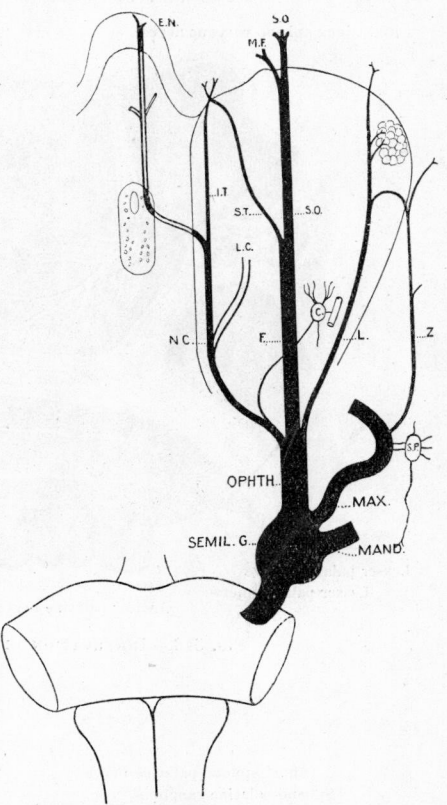

FIG. 845.—SCHEME TO SHOW THE DISTRIBUTION OF THE OPHTHALMIC NERVE. (S. E. W.)

F., frontal nerve, giving off the supra-trochlear branch (S.T.) and afterwards being known as the supra-orbital (S.O.), which may divide before leaving the orbit into a medial frontal branch (M.F.) and a lateral frontal or supra-orbital proper.

N.C., the naso-ciliary nerve; it is shown to give off the ramus communicans to the ciliary ganglion (C.), the two long ciliary nerves (L.C.) to the eyeball, and, just before leaving the orbit through the anterior ethmoidal canal, the infra-trochlear nerve (I.T.); the rest of its course up to its termination on the nose as the external nasal nerve (E.N.) illustrates the description given in the text.

L., the lacrimal nerve, the communication of which with the zygomatico-temporal branch of the zygomatic nerve (Z.) is represented.

S.P., the spheno-palatine ganglion.

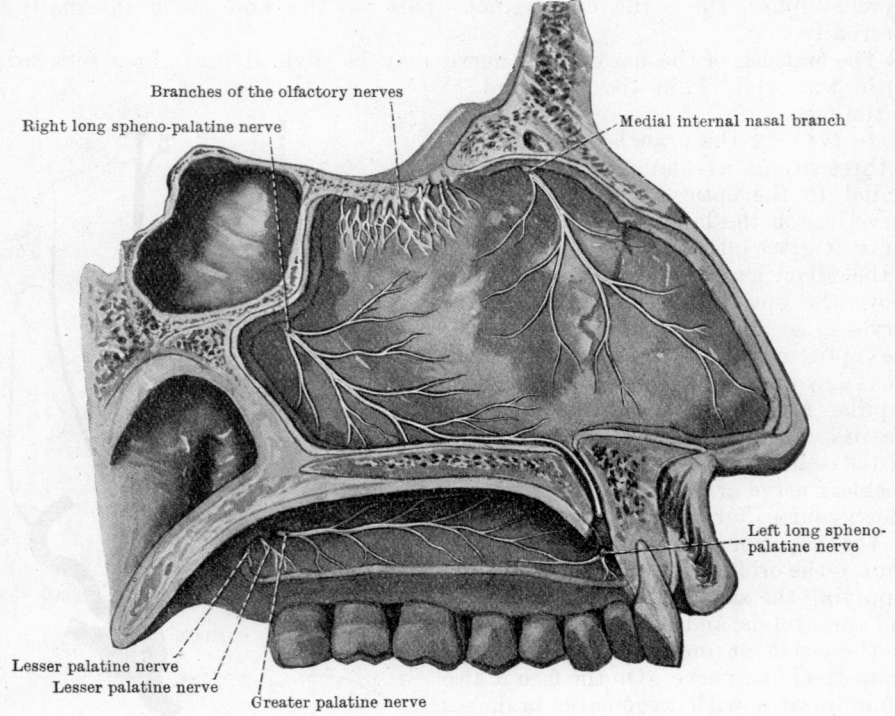

FIG. 846.—INNERVATION OF NASAL SEPTUM AND PALATE.

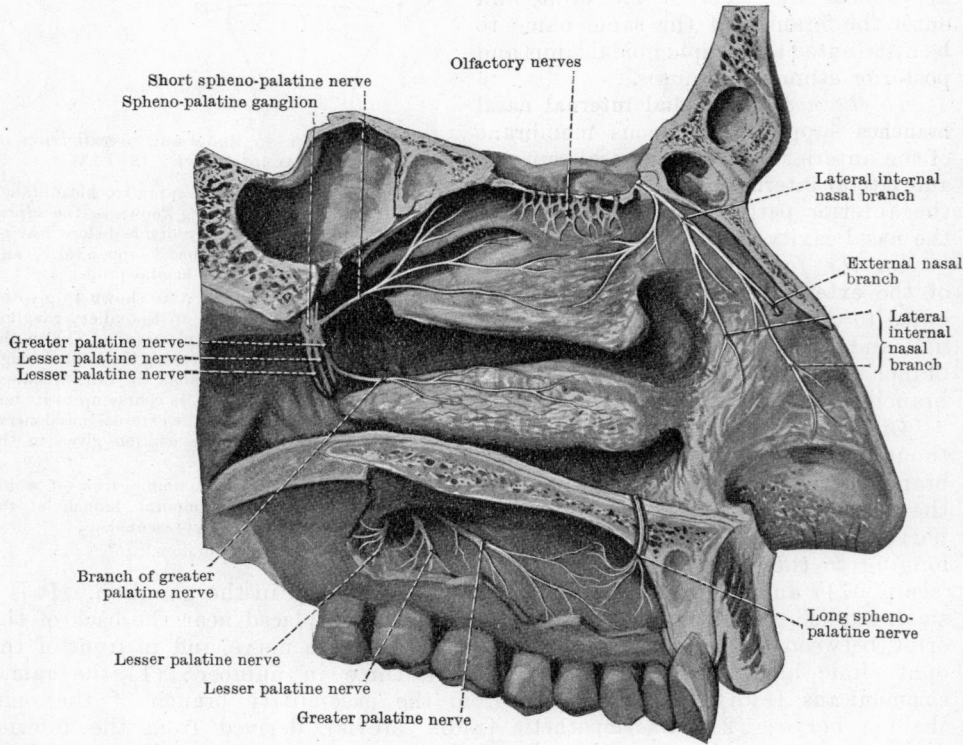

FIG. 847.—INNERVATION OF LATERAL WALL OF NASAL CAVITY AND PALATE.

or may be incorporated with the root from the naso-ciliary nerve. The branches from the ciliary ganglion are twelve to fifteen **short ciliary nerves**, which pass to the eyeball in two groups above and below the optic nerve. They convey parasympathetic fibres (from the third nerve) to the sphincter pupillæ fibres of the iris and the ciliary muscle, sympathetic fibres to the blood-vessels, and they carry afferent fibres from all parts of the eyeball.

MAXILLARY NERVE

The **maxillary nerve** courses forwards from the trigeminal ganglion through the middle fossa of the skull, in the dura mater, and in relation to the lower part

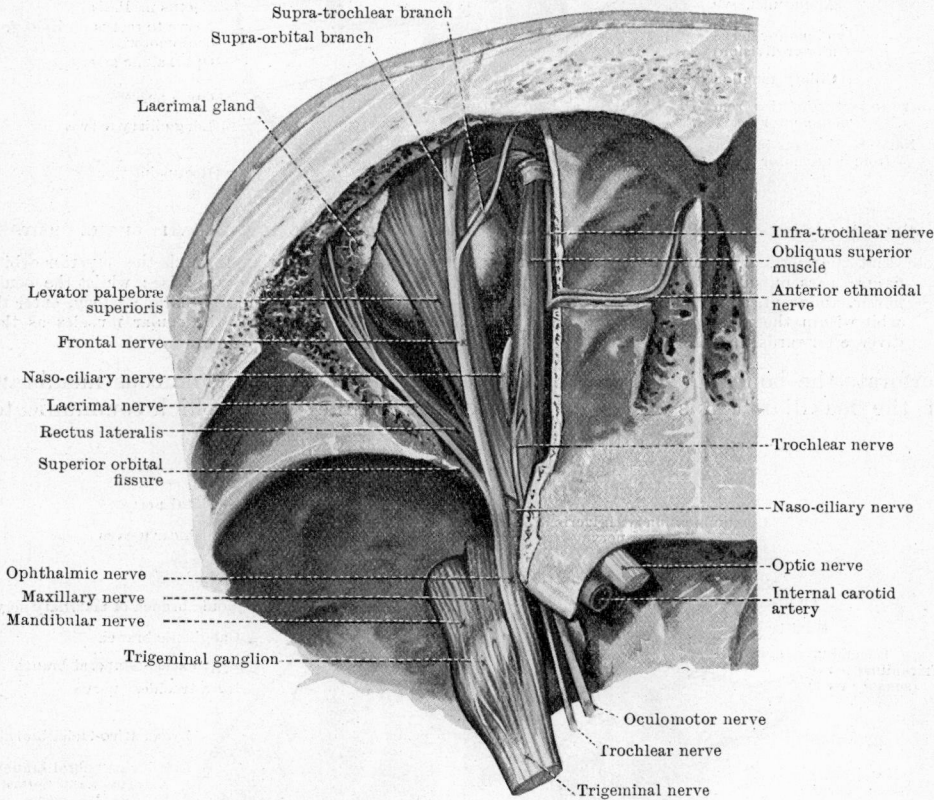

Supra-trochlear branch
Supra-orbital branch
Lacrimal gland
Infra-trochlear nerve
Obliquus superior muscle
Levator palpebræ superioris
Anterior ethmoidal nerve
Frontal nerve
Naso-ciliary nerve
Lacrimal nerve
Rectus lateralis
Superior orbital fissure
Trochlear nerve
Naso-ciliary nerve
Ophthalmic nerve
Maxillary nerve
Mandibular nerve
Optic nerve
Internal carotid artery
Trigeminal ganglion
Oculomotor nerve
Trochlear nerve
Trigeminal nerve

FIG. 848.—THE NERVES OF THE ORBIT FROM ABOVE.

of the cavernous sinus (Fig. 842, p. 961). It passes through the foramen rotundum, traverses the pterygo-palatine fossa, and enters the orbit as the infra-orbital nerve through the inferior orbital fissure. In the orbit it occupies successively the infra-orbital groove and canal, and it finally appears on the face through the infra-orbital foramen (Fig. 851).

The branches and communications of this nerve occur (*a*) in the cavity of the cranium, (*b*) in the pterygo-palatine fossa, (*c*) in the infra-orbital canal, and (*d*) on the face.

(*a*) *In the cavity of the cranium* the nerve gives off a minute **meningeal branch** to the dura mater of the middle fossa of the skull.

(*b*) *In the pterygo-palatine fossa* the nerve gives off—(1) two short thick **ganglionic branches** [nn. sphenopalatini] to the spheno-palatine ganglion. Most of their fibres, however, do not traverse the ganglion but pass over it to enter its branches. (2) **Posterior superior dental** [alveolar] **nerves**, usually two, descend through the pterygo-maxillary fissure to the posterior surface of the maxilla, and proceed forwards in the alveolar arch, in company with the posterior superior dental artery.　They supply the gum and the upper molar teeth by branches which

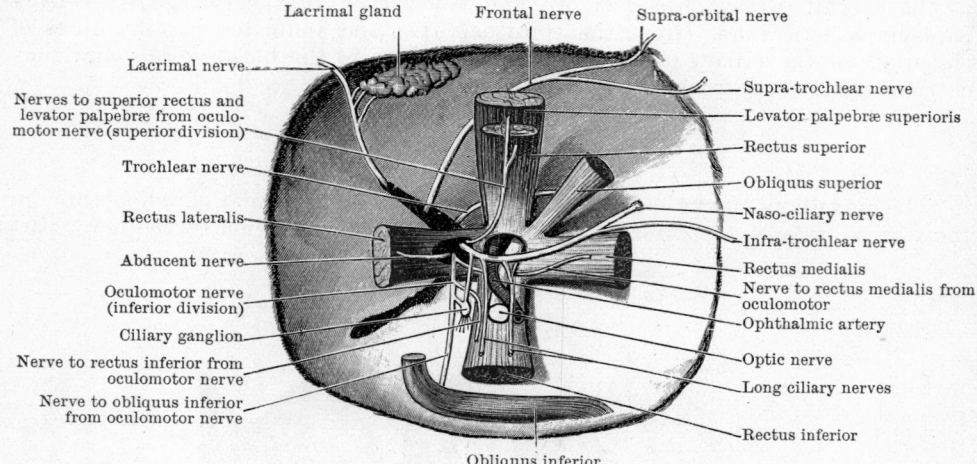

FIG. 849.—SCHEMATIC REPRESENTATION OF THE NERVES WHICH TRAVERSE THE CAVITY OF THE ORBIT.

Note that the lacrimal, frontal, and trochlear nerves, after entering the orbit through the superior orbital fissure, pass outside the common tendinous ring from which the recti muscles arise; whilst the oculomotor, abducent, and naso-ciliary nerves, together with the optic nerve and ophthalmic artery, enter the orbit within the ring, and therefore lie at first within the cone formed by the ocular muscles as they diverge forwards from it.

perforate the bone to reach the tooth-sockets; they supply the mucous membrane of the maxillary sinus also.　The nerves form a fine plexus which communicates

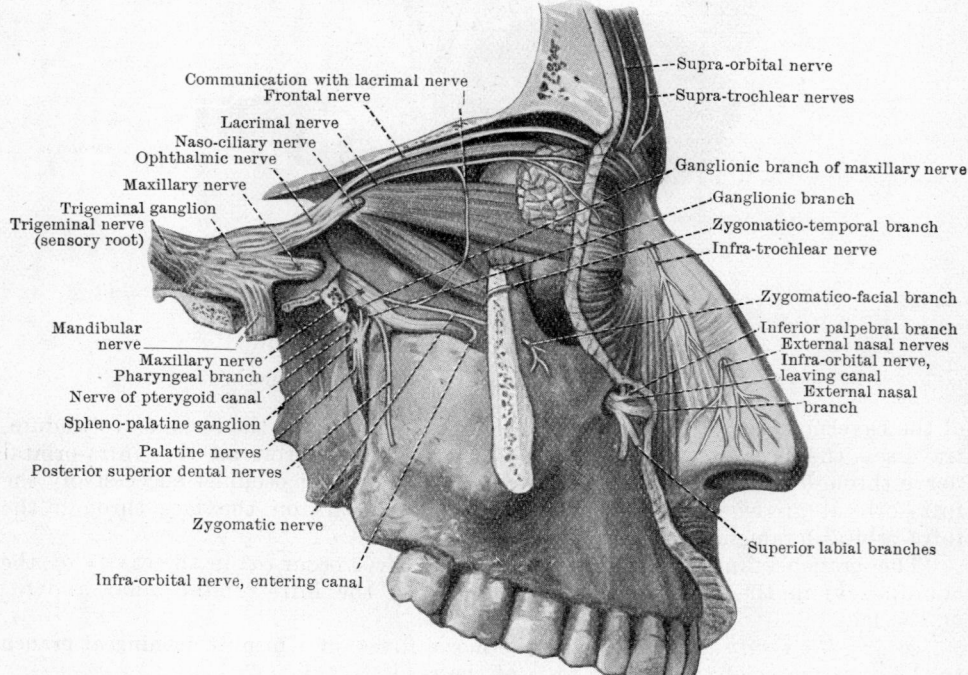

FIG. 850.—THE COURSE OF THE OPHTHALMIC AND MAXILLARY NERVES.

with the middle superior dental nerve before finally reaching the teeth.　(3) A small orbital branch—the *zygomatic nerve*—enters the orbital cavity through the inferior orbital fissure, and, proceeding along the lateral wall, divides into two branches—(1) a *zygomatico-facial branch*, which appears on the face, after traversing the zygomatic bone through the zygomatic foramen, and supplies the skin and fascia over that bone ; it communicates with the zygomatic branches of the facial nerve. (2) A *zygomatico-temporal branch* perforates the temporal surface of the zygomatic bone, or passes through the spheno-zygomatic suture, and is distributed, after piercing the temporal fascia, to the skin and fascia over the anterior part of the temple. In the orbit it communicates with the lacrimal nerve, and on the face with the temporal branches of the facial nerve. The filament communicating with the lacrimal nerve probably contains some of the parasympathetic fibres from the spheno-palatine ganglion which are innervating

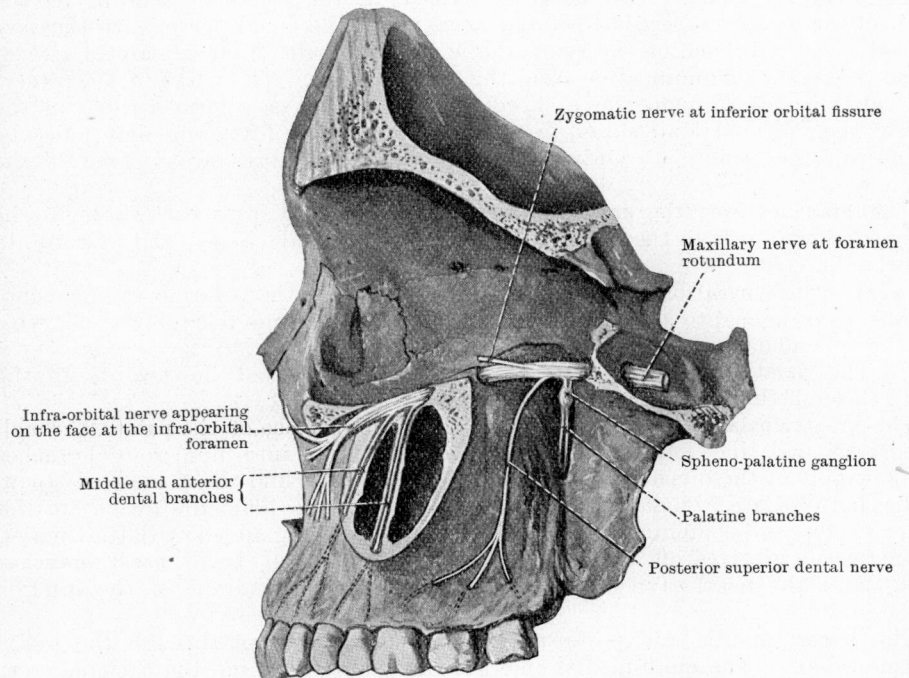

Zygomatic nerve at inferior orbital fissure

Maxillary nerve at foramen rotundum

Infra-orbital nerve appearing on the face at the infra-orbital foramen

Middle and anterior dental branches

Spheno-palatine ganglion

Palatine branches

Posterior superior dental nerve

FIG. 851.—COURSE AND BRANCHES OF THE MAXILLARY NERVE.

the lacrimal gland. The zygomatico-temporal branch may be very minute, and not pass farther than the temporal fascia, between the two layers of which it may form a communication with the facial nerve.

The **infra-orbital nerve** is the terminal branch of the maxillary nerve, which enters the orbit through the inferior orbital fissure and traverses the infra-orbital canal to reach the face.

(c) *In the infra-orbital canal* the infra-orbital nerve supplies one and sometimes two branches to the teeth—the **middle** and **anterior superior dental nerves.** The former may be only a secondary branch of one of the latter nerves, or it may arise independently from the infra-orbital nerve. However formed, the nerves descend, in bony canals, to the alveolar arch. The bony canals may form internal bony ridges in the wall of the maxillary sinus, to the lining membrane of which branches are given. In the alveolar arch the nerves form minute plexuses containing gangliform enlargements, and they supply the teeth (joining posteriorly with the branches of the posterior superior dental nerves). The anterior superior dental nerve supplies the incisor and canine teeth, and also gives off a *nasal branch* which enters the nasal cavity through a minute foramen to supply the forepart of the inferior concha and nasal floor; the middle superior dental nerve supplies the premolar teeth.

In the face, after emerging from the infra-orbital foramen, the infra-orbital nerve divides into a number of radiating branches arranged in three sets—

(*a*) **palpebral** for the skin and conjunctiva of the lower eyelid; (*b*) **nasal**, for the skin and fascia of the side of the nose; and (*c*) **labial**, for the cheek and upper lip. These branches form communications with the zygomatic branches of the facial nerve, and form with them the *infra-orbital plexus* (Fig. 856, p. 976.)

Sphenopalatine Ganglion.—This ganglion belongs to the parasympathetic system (see note on p. 974). It lies deeply in the upper part of the pterygo-palatine fossa, close to the spheno-palatine foramen, and is a small reddish-gray ganglion, suspended from the maxillary nerve by the two **ganglionic branches** which constitute its afferent roots. The **parasympathetic** and **sympathetic roots** of the spheno-palatine ganglion are derived from the **nerve of the pterygoid canal**. This nerve is formed in the foramen lacerum by the union of the *greater superficial petrosal nerve*, from the facial nerve, with the *deep petrosal nerve*, a branch of the sympathetic plexus on the internal carotid artery; it also receives a communication from the otic ganglion. The nerve of the pterygoid canal passes through the pterygoid canal (which may form a ridge in the floor of the sphenoidal air sinus) to the pterygo-palatine fossa, where it joins the spheno-palatine ganglion. Only the parasympathetic fibres are relayed in the ganglion.

The **branches from the ganglion** are numerous. They pass backwards to the pharynx, downwards to the palate, medially to the nasal cavity, and upwards to the orbit.

(*a*) The **pharyngeal** branch passes backwards through the palatino-vaginal canal [canalis pharyngeus] to supply the mucous membrane of the roof of the pharynx and the sphenoidal sinus.

(*b*) The **palatine nerves**, three in number, are directed downwards to the palate through the palatine canals.

The **greater palatine nerve** emerges on the under surface of the palate, through the greater palatine foramen, and at once separates into numerous branches for the supply of the mucous membrane of the soft palate and the muco-periosteum of the hard palate, which they groove. Its anterior filaments reach to the incisor sockets and communicate with branches of the long spheno-palatine nerve. The main nerve gives off, as it lies in the palatine canal, small **nasal branches** which enter the nasal cavity and supply the mucous membrane of the inferior concha.

The **lesser** [middle and posteror] **palatine nerves** descend through the lesser palatine canals. The more medial emerges immediately behind the palatine crest and supplies branches to the soft palate. The more lateral is distributed to the soft palate and the tonsil.

(*c*) The branches directed medially from the spheno-palatine ganglion enter the nasal cavity through the spheno-palatine foramen. They are the long and short spheno-palatine nerves. (1) The **long spheno-palatine nerve** [n. nasopalatinus], after passing through the spheno-palatine foramen, crosses the roof of the nasal cavity, and extends obliquely downwards and forwards along the nasal septum, grooving the vomer in its course between the mucous membrane and periosteum, to reach the incisive fossa near the front of the hard palate. The nerves pass through the median incisive foramina, the left nerve in front of the right. In the incisive fossa the two nerves communicate together. They then turn backwards and supply the mucous membrane of the hard palate. They communicate posteriorly with terminal filaments of the greater palatine nerves. In its course through the nasal cavity each long spheno-palatine nerve furnishes collateral branches to the mucous membrane of the roof and septum of the nose (Fig. 846, p. 966). (2) The **short spheno-palatine nerves** are small branches [rami nasales post. sup.] distributed to the mucous membrane of the superior and middle conchæ, and to the postero-superior part of the nasal septum.

(*d*) The **orbital branches**, one or more minute branches, pass upwards to the lacrimal gland (providing some secretory fibres) and they supply the periosteum of the orbit.

MANDIBULAR NERVE

The **mandibular nerve** is formed by the union of two roots; a large **afferent root** from the semilunar ganglion, and the small **efferent root** of the trigeminal nerve, which is wholly incorporated with the mandibular trunk. The two roots pass together, in the dura mater of the middle fossa of the base of the skull, to the foramen ovale, through which they emerge into the infratemporal fossa. As they leave the skull they combine to form a single, short trunk which

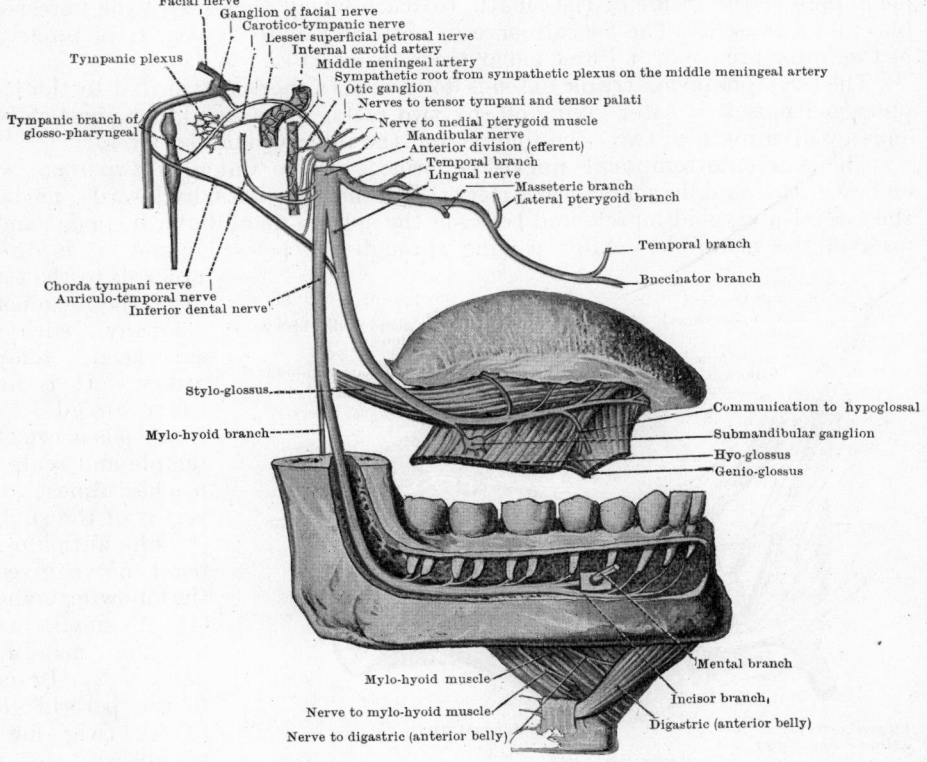

FIG. 852.—SCHEME OF THE DISTRIBUTION AND CONNEXIONS OF THE MANDIBULAR NERVE.

separates into anterior and posterior divisions immediately below the foramen ovale.

At its emergence from the skull the nerve is deeply placed in the infratemporal fossa, and is concealed by the ramus of the mandible, and by the masseter and lateral pterygoid muscles; behind it lies the middle meningeal artery.

The branches of the nerve may be divided into two series—(1) those derived from the undivided nerve, and (2) those derived from its terminal divisions.

The branches of the undivided nerve are two in number; they arise from its medial aspect. (a) A small **nervus spinosus** arises just outside the skull. It accompanies the middle meningeal artery through the foramen spinosum, and supplies the dura mater and the mastoid cells. (b) A small branch for the supply of the **medial pterygoid muscle**; that branch forms a connexion with the otic ganglion and conveys fibres to the tensor tympani and tensor palati muscles.

The terminal divisions of the nerve are a small anterior and a large posterior trunk.

The small **anterior trunk** passes downwards and forwards medial to the lateral pterygoid muscle, and separates into the following branches: (1) A branch for the lateral pterygoid muscle which supplies it on its deep surface; (2) a branch to the masseter muscle which passes over the upper border of the lateral pterygoid and through the mandibular notch and gives a filament to the mandibular joint; (3) and (4) two deep temporal branches, an anterior (which often accompanies the buccal branch) and a posterior (with sometimes a third, the middle) to the temporal muscle, which also ascend above the lateral pterygoid muscle; and (5) the buccal nerve, which passes obliquely forwards between the two heads of the lateral pterygoid to reach the buccinator muscle. *The buccal nerve is afferent,* and its fibres are, in part, distributed to the skin and fascia of the cheek (communicating with buccal branches of the facial nerve which supply the muscle itself); they are also, in part, distributed to the mucous membrane of the inside of the mouth, to reach which they pierce the fibres of the buccinator muscle. The buccal nerve in addition usually assists in the innervation of the lower premolar and first molar teeth (Stewart and Wilson).

The large **posterior trunk** extends downwards a short way medial to the lateral pterygoid muscle. After giving off, by two roots, the auriculo-temporal nerve, it ends by dividing into two—the lingual and the inferior dental nerves.

The **auriculo-temporal nerve** is formed by the union of two roots which embrace the middle meningeal artery. The nerve passes backwards, medial to the lateral pterygoid muscle and between the spheno-mandibular ligament and the neck of the mandible. After passing through the parotid gland, it is directed upwards to the temple over the zygoma, in company with the superficial temporal artery. It is finally distributed as a cutaneous nerve of the temple and scalp, and reaches almost to the vertex of the skull.

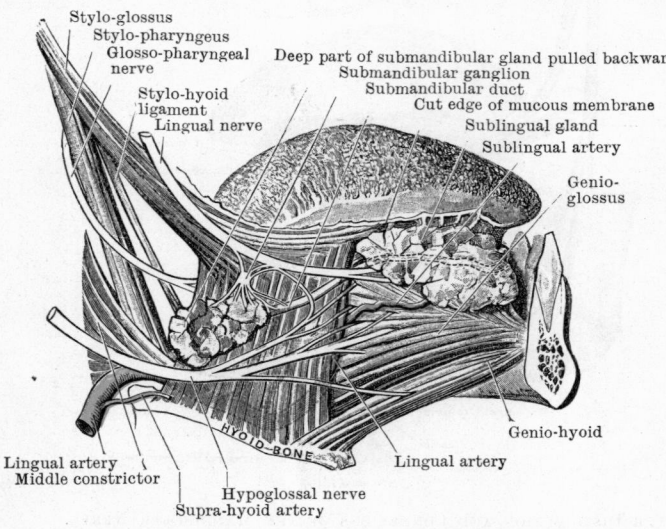

FIG. 853.—LINGUAL AND HYPOGLOSSAL NERVES IN THE SUBMANDIBULAR REGION.

The auriculo-temporal nerve gives off the following branches: (1) A small branch to the mandibular joint. (2) Branches to the parotid gland. (3) A twig for the supply of the skin of the external auditory meatus and tympanic membrane. (4) Auricular branches to the upper half of the auricle on its lateral aspect. (5) Terminal temporal branches to the skin and fascia of the temple and scalp.

It has the following **communications** with other nerves: (1) Important communications are effected by the roots of the nerve, which are separately joined by small branches from the otic ganglion; those convey secretory fibres from the glosso-pharyngeal nerve (parasympathetic) and the sympathetic system to the parotid gland. (2) The parotid and temporal branches of the nerve are connected with branches of the facial nerve in the substance of the parotid gland.

The **lingual nerve** is the smaller of the two terminal branches of the posterior division of the mandibular trunk. It proceeds downwards in front of the inferior dental nerve, medial to the lateral pterygoid muscle, to its inferior border. After passing between the medial pterygoid muscle and the ramus of the mandible close to the last molar tooth, it crosses beneath the mucous membrane of the floor of the mouth in the interval between the mylo-hyoid and hyo-glossus muscles, first lateral to, then beneath the duct of the submandibular gland. It sweeps forwards and medially to the side of the tongue, to the mucous membrane over the anterior two-thirds of which it is distributed.

Three nerves communicate with the lingual nerve in its course to the tongue : (1) The **chorda tympani branch** of the facial nerve joins it at an acute angle medial to the lateral pterygoid muscle, and is incorporated with it in its distribution to the tongue. The chorda tympani contains parasympathetic fibres and also gustatory fibres from the anterior two-thirds of the tongue. (2) At a lower level it usually communicates with the inferior dental nerve. (3) The **hypoglossal nerve** forms larger or smaller loops of communication with the lingual nerve as they course forwards over the hyo-glossus muscle.

Besides supplying the aforesaid branches to the mucous membrane over the sides and dorsum of the tongue in its anterior two-thirds, the lingual nerve supplies the mucous membrane of the side wall and floor of the mouth and the sublingual gland. It also assists, along with the chorda tympani nerve, in forming the afferent and parasympathetic roots of the submandibular ganglion.

Submandibular Ganglion (see note on p. 974).—This ganglion is a small reddish structure placed on the hyo-glossus muscle, between the lingual nerve and the duct of the submandibular gland. It is suspended from the lingual nerve by two **communicating branches**, consisting for the most part of fibres of the lingual and chorda tympani nerves which at that point separate from the lingual nerve and pass to the ganglion. The **roots** of the submandibular ganglion are—(1) an afferent root, from the lingual nerve ; (2) a parasympathetic root, from the chorda tympani ; and (3) a sympathetic root, from the sympathetic plexus on the facial artery. Only parasympathetic fibres are relayed in the ganglion.

The **glandular branches from the ganglion** are distributed to the submandibular gland and duct and, by fibres which become reunited with the trunk of the lingual nerve, to the sublingual gland.

The **inferior dental [alveolar] nerve** is larger than the lingual nerve. It passes from beneath the inferior border of the lateral pterygoid muscle to reach the interval between the ramus of the mandible and the spheno-mandibular ligament. It enters the mandibular canal through the mandibular foramen in company with the inferior dental artery, traverses the substance of the ramus and body of the mandible, distributing branches to the teeth in its course, and it terminates by dividing into a mental and an incisor branch.

Branches.—(1) The **mylo-hyoid nerve** is a small branch that arises just before the inferior dental nerve passes through the mandibular foramen. It pierces the spheno-mandibular ligament and grooves the ramus as it descends into the sub-mandibular triangle, where it lies on the superficial surface of the mylo-hyoid muscle, deep to the submandibular gland. It is distributed to the mylo-hyoid muscle and the anterior belly of the digastric muscle. (2) The **dental branches** arise from the nerve whilst in the mandibular canal, and form a fine *inferior dental plexus*, from which filaments supply the molar and premolar teeth and adjacent gums. Clinical observations have shown that usually the lingual and the buccal nerves also assist in the innervation of the premolar and first molar teeth (Stewart and Wilson). (3) The **mental nerve** is a trunk of considerable size which arises from the inferior dental in the mandibular canal. It emerges from the mandible through the mental foramen, and is distributed by many branches to the chin and lower lip. It communicates, under cover of the facial muscles, with the mandibular branch of the facial nerve (Fig. 856, p. 976). (4) The **incisor branch** is the terminal part of the inferior dental nerve remaining after the origin of the mental branch. It supplies the canine tooth and the incisor teeth, and a few fibres cross the middle line and take part in the innervation of the medial incisor of the opposite side.

Otic Ganglion.—This minute ganglion is situated medial to the mandibular nerve just below the foramen ovale, at the posterior border of the medial pterygoid muscle. Like the other parasympathetic ganglia described above, the otic ganglion possesses three roots : (1) An *efferent root*, derived from the nerve to the medial pterygoid muscle ; (2) a *parasympathetic root*, formed by the *lesser superficial petrosal nerve* from the tympanic plexus (through which communications are effected with the tympanic branch of the glosso-pharyngeal nerve and a branch from the ganglion of the facial nerve) ; (3) a *sympathetic root*, from the plexus on the middle meningeal artery (Fig. 852).   The parasympathetic fibres are the only ones to be relayed in the ganglion.

Five **branches** arise from the ganglion—three communicating and two motor branches.   The three **communicating nerves** are fine branches which join the nerve of the pterygoid canal, the roots of the auriculo-temporal nerve (supplying parasympathetic fibres to the parotid gland), and the chorda tympani nerve. The two **motor nerves** supply the tensor tympani and tensor palati muscles.

Summary.—The trigeminal is the largest and most complex of the cranial nerves.   (1) It is the chief afferent nerve for the face, the anterior half of the scalp, the orbit and eyeball, the nose and nasal cavity and paranasal sinuses, the lips, teeth, mouth, and anterior two-thirds of the tongue.   (2) Its efferent fibres supply the muscles of mastication, the mylo-hyoid and anterior belly of the digastric, and the tensor tympani and tensor palati muscles (the fibres passing through the otic ganglion).   (3) It supplies the mandibular joint, and the dura mater. (4) Through the ganglia placed on the three divisions of the nerve, not only are important organs, areas, and muscles innervated, but communications are also effected with the autonomic system.

In its distribution to the skin of the face the branches of the fifth nerve present two striking peculiarities : (1) While the branches to the skin reach the surface at many points and in diverse ways, the three main divisions are severally, by their branches, responsible for the supply of three clearly demarcated cutaneous areas (Fig. 844, p. 964).   Moreover, since in embryonic life the general distribution of the nerve is outlined by the outgrowth from the trigeminal ganglion of the three main divisions, ophthalmic, maxillary, and mandibular, into the fronto-nasal, maxillary, and mandibular processes respectively, each nerve trunk supplies, broadly speaking, the deeper structures of the face lying opposite its own area of cutaneous distribution.   (2) By numerous communications with the facial nerve, afferent fibres are given to the muscles of expression supplied by the facial nerve.

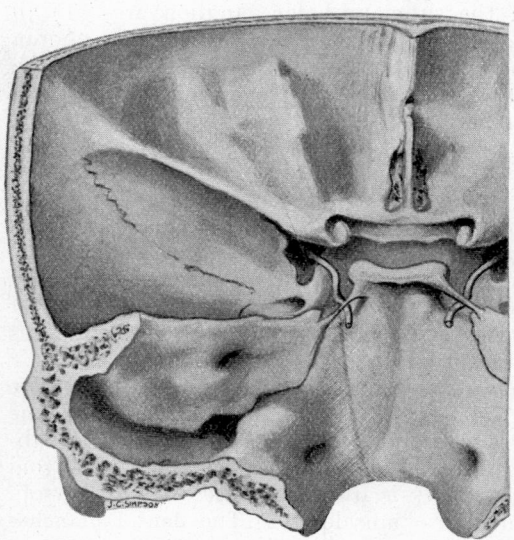

FIG.   854.—THE PETRO-SPHENOIDAL LIGAMENT.   The interior of the base of the skull viewed from behind to illustrate a dissection of the abducent nerve passing beneath the ligament before entering the cavernous sinus.   The ligament, which is formed by the deeper or osteogenetic layer of the dura mater, presents differences in its extent and attachments, as is illustrated on the two sides.   (S. E. W.)

Though the **ganglia associated with the fifth nerve**, namely, the ciliary, spheno-palatine, otic, and submandibular, are conveniently described in their relations to its branches, it should be realised that functionally that nerve has less to do with them than any of the other cranial nerves with which they are connected, for the ganglia properly belong to the parasympathetic system.   In structure they largely consist of the stellate or multipolar neurones characteristic of the autonomic system elsewhere; and developmentally they are formed by cell bodies which have migrated from the trigeminal ganglion along the branches of the trigeminal nerve—an origin paralleled by that of the ganglia of the trunks in the lower part of the system.   Moreover, the fibres they receive from other nerves (the ciliary ganglion from the oculomotor, the submandibular and spheno-palatine ganglia from the facial, and the otic ganglion from the glosso-pharyngeal and facial) may be likened to the splanchnic efferent fibres received by the ganglia of the sympathetic trunk through the white rami communicantes of the spinal nerves.   Their development is described together with that of the autonomic system on p. 1072.

Each of the ganglia contains three varieties of fibres : (1) afferent, visceral, and somatic ; (2) parasympathetic, visceral, efferent and afferent, derived from one of the cranial nerves ; and (3) sympathetic, which are derived from the superior cervical ganglion.   Many of the so-called roots and branches are mixed, though they are generally named according to the predominating kind of fibres they contain.   Lastly, it is to be noted that only the parasympathetic paths have a cell station in the ganglia ; all the other fibres pass uninterruptedly through them.

ABDUCENT NERVE

The **sixth** or **abducent nerve** supplies only the lateral rectus muscle of the eyeball.   It issues from the brain at the inferior border of the pons, just above the pyramid of the medulla oblongata (for the deep origin, see p. 885).   It is directed forwards and usually lies behind the anterior inferior cerebellar artery but may be in front of it. It pierces the dura mater in the posterior fossa of the skull alongside the dorsum sellæ, passing beneath the petro-sphenoidal ligament (Fig. 854), and enters the cavernous sinus (Fig. 842, p. 961). In the sinus it is placed close to the lateral side of the internal carotid artery. After traversing the sinus it passes through the superior orbital fissure below the oculomotor and naso-ciliary nerves and enters the orbit (Fig. 849, p. 968). In the cavity of the orbit it supplies the lateral rectus muscle on its deep (ocular) surface.

Communications.—In the cavernous sinus the sixth nerve receives two communicating filaments : (1) From the carotid plexus of the sympathetic, and (2) from the ophthalmic division of the trigeminal nerve.

FACIAL NERVE

The **seventh** or **facial nerve** is a mixed nerve. It consists of two parts :— The larger part is the **motor root**; it supplies all the superficial muscles of the scalp, face, and neck, and some of the deep ones. The smaller part is called

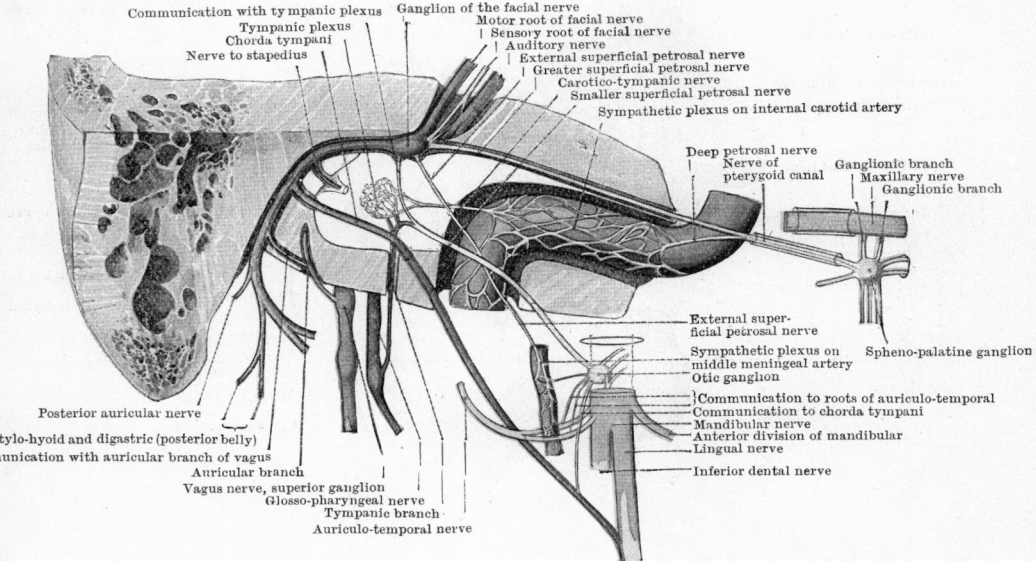

Fig. 855.—THE CONNEXIONS OF THE FACIAL NERVE IN THE TEMPORAL BONE.

the **sensory root** [N. intermedius], but it contains not only afferent taste fibres for the anterior two-thirds of the tongue but also efferent parasympathetic fibres connected with the spheno-palatine, otic, and submandibular ganglia for the supply of the lacrimal and salivary glands. The ganglion of the facial nerve (see p. 976) is the cell station for the afferent fibres. The **motor root** emerges from the brain at the inferior border of the pons, medial to the auditory nerve (for the deep origin, see p. 883). Between it and the auditory nerve is the much smaller **sensory root** (Fig. 717, p. 831). The facial nerve enters the internal auditory meatus, passes through the facial canal in the petrous portion of the temporal bone, emerges at the base of the skull by the stylo-mastoid foramen, and passes forwards through the parotid gland to supply the muscles of the face. *In the internal auditory meatus* the nerve is placed above the auditory nerve, the sensory root intervening, and all three are surrounded by sheaths of the dura, arachnoid, and pia. *In the facial canal* the nerve first passes forwards and laterally to the hiatus in the canal for the greater superficial petrosal nerve, then abruptly backwards in the upper part of the medial wall of the tympanum, and finally downwards behind the tympanum,

In the parotid gland it crosses the external carotid artery and the posterior facial vein superficially. *On the face* its branches radiate from the anterior border of the parotid gland and enter the deep surfaces of the facial muscles.

Branches and Communications.—(i.) *In the internal auditory meatus* the sensory root lies between the motor root and the auditory nerve and sends communicating

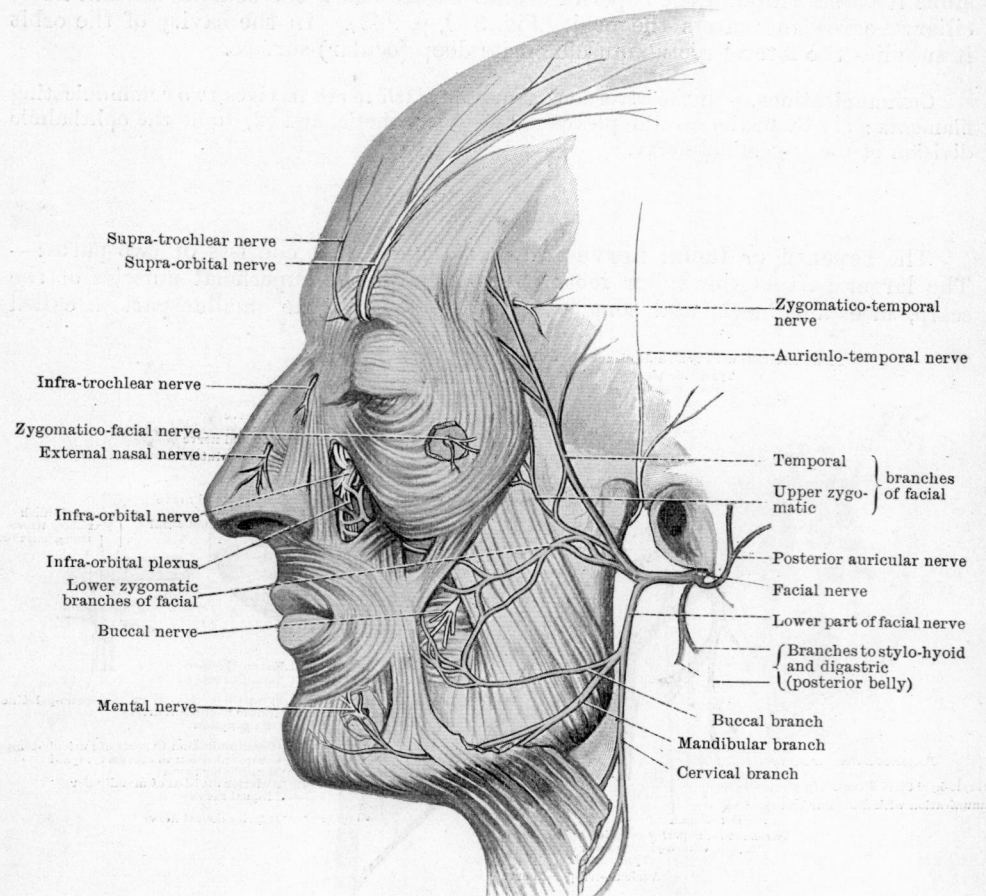

Supra-trochlear nerve
Supra-orbital nerve

Zygomatico-temporal nerve
Auriculo-temporal nerve

Infra-trochlear nerve
Zygomatico-facial nerve
External nasal nerve

Temporal
Upper zygo-matic ⎱ branches of facial

Infra-orbital nerve

Infra-orbital plexus
Lower zygomatic branches of facial
Buccal nerve

Posterior auricular nerve
Facial nerve
Lower part of facial nerve
Branches to stylo-hyoid and digastric (posterior belly)

Mental nerve

Buccal branch
Mandibular branch
Cervical branch

FIG. 856.—DISTRIBUTION OF THE TRIGEMINAL AND FACIAL NERVES ON THE FACE.

branches to both of them. The branch to the auditory nerve probably separates from it again to join the ganglion of the facial nerve (Fig. 857).

(ii.) *In the facial canal* the **ganglion of the facial nerve** is formed at the point where the nerve bends backwards at the genu. It is an oval swelling on the nerve, and is joined by a branch from the upper (vestibular) trunk of the auditory nerve, by which it probably receives fibres of the sensory root. From the ganglion three small nerves arise: (1) The **greater superficial petrosal nerve** passes forwards through the hiatus in the canal for the facial nerve to the middle fossa of the skull. It contains parasympathetic fibres which, after interruption in the spheno-palatine ganglion, are distributed through the orbital and the zygomatic branches of the maxillary nerve to the lacrimal gland, and afferent fibres which supply the mucous membrane of the soft palate through the lesser palatine nerves. The afferent fibres are probably gustatory in function. It receives a twig from the tympanic plexus. In the upper part of the foramen lacerum it is joined by the **deep petrosal nerve** from the sympathetic plexus on the internal carotid artery to form the **nerve of the pterygoid canal**, which, after traversing the pterygoid canal, passes to the spheno-palatine ganglion. (2) A minute filament which pierces the temporal bone and joins the tympanic branch of the glosso-pharyngeal in the substance of the bone. By their union the **lesser superficial petrosal nerve** is formed, which pierces the temporal bone and ends in the otic ganglion. (3) The **external superficial petrosal nerve** is a minute inconstant branch which joins the sympathetic plexus on the middle meningeal artery.

From the facial nerve in the descending part of its canal behind the tympanum, three branches arise: (1) The small **nerve to the stapedius** passes forwards to that muscle. (2) The **chorda tympani** (containing taste and para-sympathetic fibres) enters the tympanic cavity through a *posterior canaliculus*, passes across the membrana tympani and the handle of the malleus, and leaves the cavity through the *medial end of the squamo-tympanic fissure* by an *anterior canaliculus* to reach the infra-temporal fossa; medial to the lateral pterygoid muscle, after receiving a fine communication from the otic ganglion, it becomes incorporated with the lingual branch of the mandibular nerve, and in its further course is inseparable from that nerve; it supplies the parasympathetic root to the submandibular ganglion, and is finally distributed to the side and dorsum of the tongue in its anterior two-thirds; it largely consists of afferent

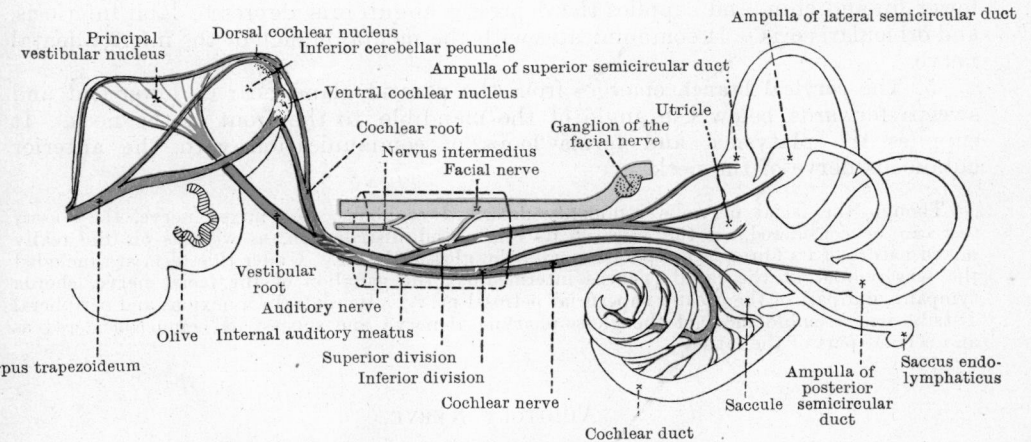

FIG. 857.—SCHEME OF THE ORIGIN AND DISTRIBUTION OF THE AUDITORY NERVE.

(taste) fibres derived from the ganglion of the facial nerve, but also contains some secretory parasympathetic fibres which enter the submandibular ganglion and thence supply the submandibular and sublingual glands. (3) Before the facial nerve leaves its canal a fine **communicating branch** arises from it to join the auricular branch of the vagus nerve.

(iii.) *In the neck* the facial nerve gives off three muscular branches: (1) and (2) small branches, frequently arising together, supply the **stylo-hyoid** and the posterior belly of the **digastric**; the latter nerve sometimes communicates with the glosso-pharyngeal. (3) The **posterior auricular nerve** bends backwards and upwards over the anterior border of the mastoid process along with the posterior auricular artery. It divides into two branches—an *auricular branch* for the posterior auricular muscle and the intrinsic muscles of the auricle, and an *occipital branch* for the occipital belly of the epicranius muscle. The posterior auricular nerve, in its course, communicates with the great auricular, lesser occipital, and with the auricular branch of the vagus nerve.

(iv.) *In the parotid gland* the facial nerve spreads out in an irregular series of branches which communicate in the substance of the gland with branches of the great auricular and auriculo-temporal nerves.

1. The **temporal branches** are of large size, and, sweeping out of the parotid gland over the zygomatic arch, are distributed to the orbicularis oculi, frontal belly of occipito-frontalis, auriculares anterior and superior. The temporal branches

62

communicate in their course with the auriculo-temporal, zygomatico-temporal, lacrimal, and supra-orbital branches of the trigeminal nerve.

2. The **zygomatic branches** are in two sets. The **upper** are small, and sometimes are inseparable from the temporal or lower zygomatic branches. Extending forwards across the zygomatic bone, they supply the orbicularis oculi and zygomatic muscles, and communicate with the zygomatico-facial branch of the maxillary nerve.

The **lower** are of considerable size. Passing forwards over the masseter muscle, in company with the parotid duct, they supply the orbicularis oculi, the zygomaticus major, buccinator, and the muscles of the nose and upper lip. The **infra-orbital plexus** is formed by the union of these nerves with the infra-orbital branch of the maxillary nerve below the lower eyelid. Smaller communications occur with the infra-trochlear and external nasal branch of the naso-ciliary nerves on the side of the nose.

3. The **buccal branch** (or branches) extends forwards to the angle of the mouth to supply the muscles converging on the mouth, including the buccinator. It communicates with the buccal branch of the mandibular nerve in front of the masseter muscle.

4. The **mandibular branch** passes along the mandible to the interval between the lower lip and chin, and supplies the depressor anguli oris, depressor labii inferioris, and orbicularis oris. It communicates with the mental branch of the inferior dental nerve.

5. The **cervical branch** emerges from the parotid gland near its lower end, and sweeps forwards, below the angle of the mandible, to the front of the neck. It supplies the platysma, and forms loops of communication with the anterior cutaneous nerve of the neck.

Though the facial nerve is commonly described as above, as a mixed nerve, the sensory root can be considered, on the basis of its origin and distribution, as well as on the really mixed nature of its fibres, as a separate nerve, the **glossopalatine**. Under this term are included the sensory root of the facial [nervus intermedius], the ganglion of the facial nerve, chorda tympani, and part of the greater superficial petrosal nerve. Its central connexions and peripheral distribution resemble those of the glosso-pharyngeal nerve, and suggest its being considered as an aberrant part of the latter.

AUDITORY NERVE

The **eighth** or **auditory nerve** consists of two functionally entirely different parts—the *vestibular nerve* concerned with equilibration, and the *cochlear nerve,* the true nerve of hearing; they differ also in their peripheral endings and central connexions.

The combined trunk arises from the brain by two roots, medial and lateral. The **medial, vestibular root** emerges between the olive and the inferior cerebellar peduncle. The **lateral, cochlear root**, continuous through the cochlear nuclei with the auditory striæ of the fourth ventricle, winds round the lateral side of the inferior cerebellar peduncle (for the deep connexions, see p. 889). The two roots unite with each other to form the trunk of the auditory nerve, which is attached to the brain on the lateral side of the roots of the facial nerve, at the lower border of the pons (Fig. 717, p. 831).

The nerve passes laterally through the internal auditory meatus, lying below the roots of the facial nerve (Fig. 855, p. 975). In the meatus the trunk separates into two divisions, an upper consisting of vestibular fibres only, and a lower which consists mainly of cochlear fibres but contains also some vestibular fibres. The divisions subdivide, and their branches pierce the fundus of the internal auditory meatus to supply the several parts of the labyrinth.

The **superior division** usually receives fibres in the meatus from the sensory root of the facial nerve, and gives off a communicating branch to the ganglion of the facial nerve. It then separates into three terminal branches which pierce the lamina cribrosa. (1).—The **utricular nerve** supplies the macula of the **utricle**. (2) and (3).—The **superior** and **lateral ampullary nerves** supply the ampullæ of the **superior** and **lateral semicircular ducts.**

The **inferior division** gives off (1) a **saccular nerve** to the macula of the saccule which pierces the inferior vestibular area, (2) an **inferior ampullary nerve** to the ampulla of the **posterior semicircular duct** which pierces the foramen singulare, and (3) is continued as the **cochlear nerve**, which is distributed through the modiolus and osseous spiral lamina to the spiral organ in the cochlea.

Both the vestibular and cochlear nerves contain among their fibres collections of bipolar nerve cells, forming in each nerve a distinct ganglion —the **vestibular ganglion** on the vestibular trunk at the bottom of the internal auditory meatus, and the **spiral ganglion** on the cochlear trunk within the modiolus. The cells of these ganglia give origin to the fibres of the vestibular and cochlear parts of the nerve respectively.

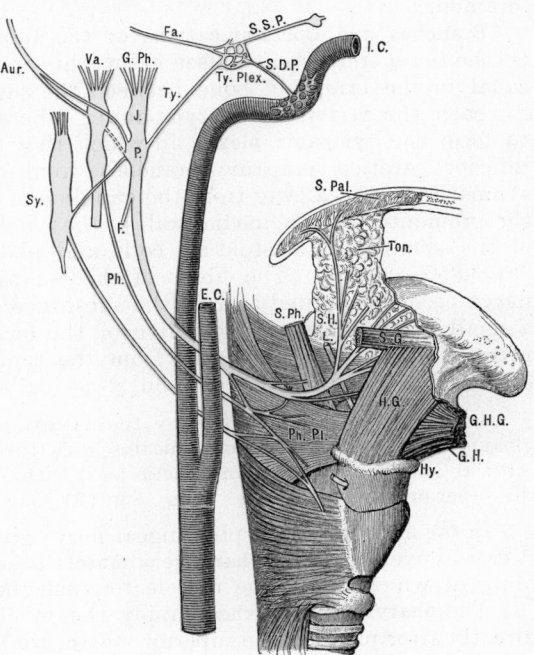

FIG. 858.—SCHEME OF THE DISTRIBUTION OF THE GLOSSO-PHARYNGEAL NERVE.

G.Ph., Glosso-pharyngeal nerve; J., Superior, and P., Inferior ganglia; Ty., Tympanic nerve; Ty.Plex., Tympanic plexus; Fa., Root from ganglion of facial nerve; S.S.P., Lesser superficial petrosal nerve to the otic ganglion; S.D.P., Carotico-tympanic nerve; I.C., Internal carotid artery; Va., Vagus nerve; Aur., Auricular branch of vagus; Sy., Superior cervical sympathetic ganglion; F., Communicating branch to facial nerve; Ph., Pharyngeal branch of vagus; E.C., External carotid artery; Ph.Pl., Pharyngeal plexus; S.Ph., Stylo-pharyngeus muscle; S.H.L., Stylo-hyoid ligament; H.G., Hyo-glossus; S.G., Stylo-glossus; S. Pal., Soft palate; G.H.G., Genio-glossus; G.H., Genio-hyoid; Hy., Hyoid bone.

GLOSSO-PHARYNGEAL NERVE

The **ninth** or **glosso-pharyngeal nerve** is a mixed nerve, consisting of a smaller efferent element which supplies the stylo-pharyngeus, a larger efferent part which supplies the pharynx and tongue, and parasympathetic fibres which pass to the otic ganglion. It arises from the brain by five or six fine rootlets which are attached to the side of the medulla oblongata, close to the facial nerve above, and in series with the rootlets of the vagus nerve below (Fig. 717, p. 831; for the deep connexions, see p. 882). The rootlets combine to form a nerve which passes through the jugular foramen, along with the vagus and accessory nerves, but enveloped in a separate sheath of dura mater (Fig. 843, p. 962). In the neck the nerve first descends medial to the styloid process and between the internal carotid artery and the internal jugular vein; then it curves forwards to the side of the pharynx, above the level of the hyoid bone. As it runs forwards it curves round the posterior border of the stylo-pharyngeus muscle and passes superficial to that muscle and usually deep to the stylo-hyoid ligament, and between the external and internal carotid arteries, to the posterior border of the hyo-glossus muscle, then onwards deep to the hyo-glossus. The terminal branches are distributed to the region of the oro-pharyngeal isthmus [isthmus faucium], the tonsil, and the pharyngeal part of the dorsum of the tongue (Fig. 858).

The **branches** of the nerve may be classified in three series according to their origin—(i.) in the jugular foramen; (ii.) in the neck; (iii.) in relation to the tongue.

In the jugular foramen there are two enlargements on the trunk of the nerve—the superior and inferior ganglia—which give origin to the afferent fibres. The **superior ganglion** is small, and does not implicate the whole width of the nerve; it may be fused with the inferior ganglion, or even be absent altogether. No branches arise from it.

The **inferior ganglion of the glossopharyngeal nerve** is distinct and constant. It is placed on the nerve at the lower part of its course through the jugular foramen.

Branches and Communications of the Inferior Ganglion.—The **tympanic branch** is the most important offset from this ganglion. It passes through a small canal in the bridge of bone between the jugular foramen and the carotid canal to reach the cavity of the tympanum, where it breaks up into branches to help to form the **tympanic plexus**, in which they are associated with the superior and inferior carotico-tympanic branches from the internal carotid plexus of the sympathetic, and a twig from the ganglion of the facial nerve. The plexus lies on the promontory of the medial wall of the middle ear, and supplies the mucous lining of the tympanum, mastoid air cells, and pharyngo-tympanic tube [tuba auditiva] (Fig. 855, p. 975). The fibres of the tympanic branch of the glosso-pharyngeal nerve become reunited and, in the substance of the temporal bone, they join with a small branch from the ganglion of the facial nerve to form the **lesser superficial petrosal nerve**, which emerges from the temporal bone and pierces the base of the skull to join the otic ganglion.

Besides its communications by the tympanic branch, the inferior ganglion of the glosso-pharyngeal nerve communicates with three other nerves—(1) with the superior cervical ganglion of the sympathetic ; (2) with the auricular branch and sometimes with the superior ganglion of the vagus ; and (3) sometimes with the facial nerve.

In the neck the glosso-pharyngeal nerve gives off the following branches : (1) As it crosses over the **stylo-pharyngeus muscle** it supplies the nerve to that muscle, some fibres of which pierce the muscle to reach the mucous membrane of the pharynx. (2) The **pharyngeal branches** supply the mucous membrane of the pharynx either directly after piercing the superior constrictor muscle, or indirectly after joining with the pharyngeal offsets from the vagus and the superior cervical ganglion of the sympathetic to form the **pharyngeal plexus** (Fig. 858). (3) The *ramus caroticus* consists of filaments which innervate the carotid sinus and body (Fig. 655, p. 769).

The **terminal branches** of the nerve supply the mucous membrane of the tongue and adjacent parts. A **tonsillar branch** forms a plexus to supply the mucous membrane covering the tonsil, the adjacent part of the soft palate, and the palatine arches. The **lingual branches** contain taste fibres, as well as ordinary sensory fibres, for the posterior third of the tongue.

VAGUS NERVE

The **tenth** or **vagus nerve** is a mixed nerve. It contains a large number of parasympathetic fibres (afferent as well as efferent), and is the most widely distributed of the cranial nerves, for it passes through the neck and thorax into the abdomen. It supplies afferent fibres chiefly to the pharynx, œsophagus, stomach, larynx, trachea, and lungs ; efferent fibres to the unstriped musculature of the same series of organs, as well as to most of the voluntary muscles of the soft palate, pharynx, and larynx ; and special fibres to the heart and abdominal viscera. Each nerve is connected with the seventh, ninth, eleventh, and twelfth cranial nerves, with the first and second cervical spinal nerves, and with the sympathetic system. The cranial (accessory) portion of the eleventh cranial nerve contributes efferent fibres to the vagus for the innervation of the voluntary muscles of the larynx except the crico-thyroid.

It arises from the brain by numerous rootlets attached to the side of the medulla oblongata, in series with the glosso-pharyngeal nerve above and the accessory nerve below it (for the deep connexions, see p. 882). The rootlets unite to form a single trunk which emerges into the neck through the jugular foramen.

In the jugular foramen the nerve occupies the same sheath of dura mater as the accessory nerve, it is placed behind the glosso-pharyngeal nerve, and a small ganglion—the **superior ganglion**—is developed on it.

In the neck the vagus nerve pursues a vertical course in front of the vertebral column. It occupies the carotid sheath, lying between and behind the internal and

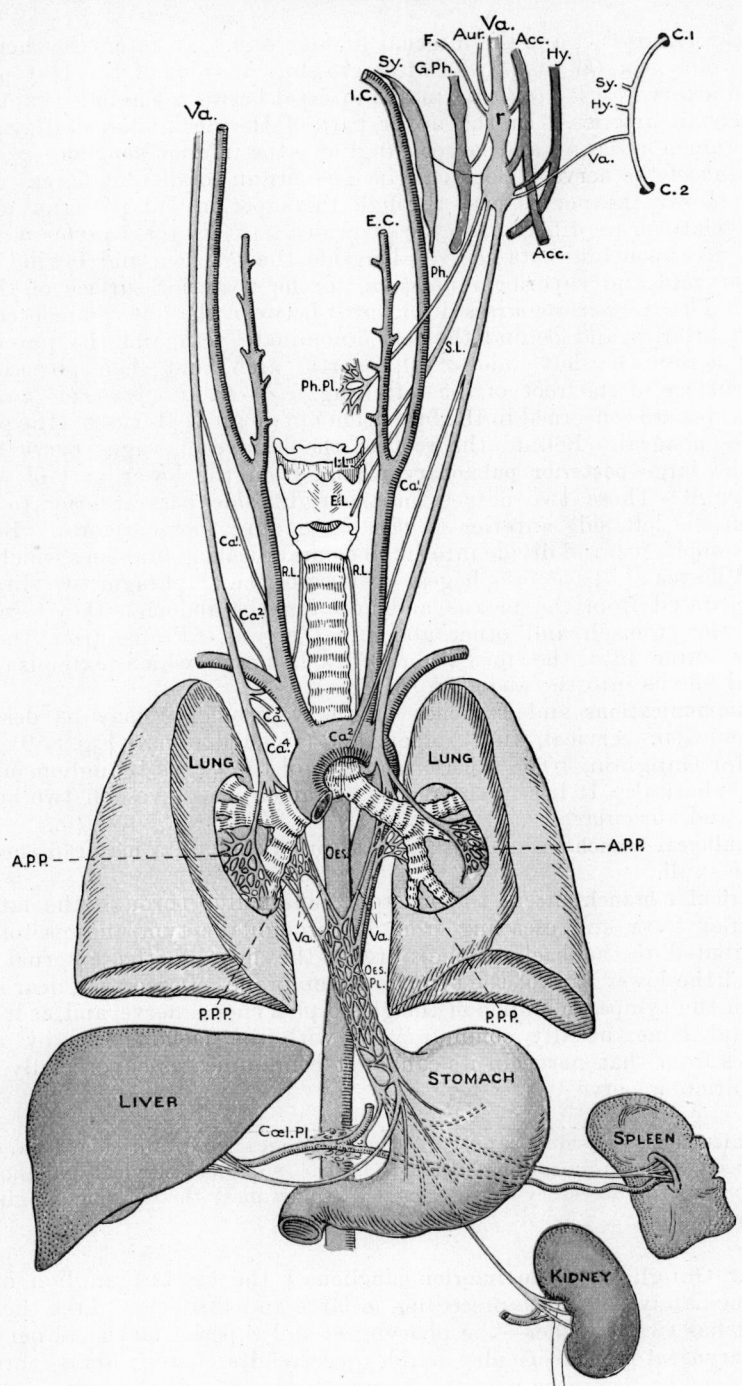

FIG. 859.—SCHEME OF THE DISTRIBUTION OF THE VAGUS NERVE.

Va., Right and left vagi ; r, Superior ganglion and connexions with Sy., Sympathetic, superior cervical ganglion ; G.Ph., Glosso-pharyngeal ; Acc., Accessory nerve ; F, Meningeal branch ; Aur., Auricular branch ; Va., Connexion with inferior ganglion of vagus ; Sy., Nerve to stylo-hyoid ; Hy., Nerve to hyo-glossus ; C1, C2, Loop between the first two cervical nerves ; Sy., Sympathetic, superior cervical ganglion ; Acc., Accessory nerve ; Ph., Pharyngeal branch ; Ph.Pl., Pharyngeal plexus ; S.L., Superior laryngeal nerve ; I.L., Internal laryngeal branch ; E.L., External laryngeal branch ; I.C., Internal, and E.C., External carotid arteries ; Ca1, Upper cervical cardiac branch ; Ca2, Lower cervical cardiac branch ; R.L., Recurrent laryngeal nerve ; Ca3, Cardiac branches from recurrent laryngeal nerves ; Ca4, Thoracic cardiac branch (right vagus) ; A.P.P., Anterior, and P.P.P., Posterior pulmonary plexuses ; Oes.Pl., Œsophageal plexus ; Coel.Pl., Cœliac plexus.

common carotid arteries and the internal jugular vein.   It enters the thorax behind the large veins : *on the right side,* after crossing in front of the first part of the subclavian artery ; *on the left side,* in the interval between the left common carotid and subclavian arteries.   In the upper part of the neck, immediately below the jugular foramen, a second and larger ganglion—the **inferior ganglion**—is developed on the trunk of the nerve.   Both ganglia give origin to afferent fibres.

In the thorax the nerves pass through the superior and posterior mediastina, and their relations are different on the two sides.   (*a*) *In the superior mediastinum* the *right nerve* continues its course alongside the trachea, and behind the right innominate vein and superior vena cava, to the posterior surface of the root of the lung.   The *left nerve* courses downwards between the left common carotid and subclavian arteries, and behind the left innominate vein and the phrenic nerve. It passes across the left side of the aortic arch, and then proceeds to the posterior surface of the root of the left lung.   (*b*) *In the posterior mediastinum* the vagi nerves are concerned in the formation of two great plexuses—the pulmonary and the œsophageal.   Behind the root of the lung each vagus nerve breaks up to form the large **posterior pulmonary plexus**, from the lower part of which two nerves emerge.   Those two nerves on the right side pass anterior to the vena azygos ; on the left side anterior to the descending thoracic aorta.   Both series reach the œsophagus, and divide into small communicating branches which form the **œsophageal plexus**.   At the œsophageal opening of the diaphragm two single nerves become separated from the plexus, and entering the abdomen they terminate by supplying the stomach and other abdominal organs.   Fibres from the vagi of both sides enter into the formation of each nerve which extends from the œsophageal plexus into the abdomen (M'Crea).

The **communications** and **branches** of the vagus nerve may be described as (i.) ganglionic, (ii.) cervical, (iii.) thoracic, and (iv.) abdominal (Fig. 859).

Superior Ganglion.—The **superior ganglion** of the vagus [ganglion jugulare] is small and spherical.   It lies in the jugular foramen, and gives off two branches— meningeal and auricular.

The **meningeal branch** passes backwards to supply the dura mater of the posterior fossa of the skull.

The **auricular branch** enters the mastoid canaliculus through the lateral wall of the jugular fossa, and, escaping from it through the tympano-mastoid fissure, it is distributed to the back of the auricle, the floor of the external auditory meatus, and the lower part of the tympanic membrane.   It receives, near its origin, a twig from the tympanic branch of the glosso-pharyngeal nerve, and, as it traverses the temporal bone, usually communicates with the facial nerve by a branch which arises from that nerve in its canal; it communicates superficially with the posterior auricular nerve.

Communications.—Besides supplying the meningeal and auricular branches, this ganglion receives communications from : (1) the superior cervical ganglion of the sympathetic ; (2) the accessory nerve ; and (3) (sometimes) the inferior ganglion of the glosso-pharyngeal nerve.

Inferior Ganglion.—The **inferior ganglion** of the vagus [ganglion nodosum], placed immediately below the preceding, is large and fusiform.   Like the superior ganglion, it has two branches—the pharyngeal and superior laryngeal nerves.

The **pharyngeal branch** (usually double) receives its efferent fibres (through the ganglion) from the accessory nerve.   It passes obliquely downwards and medially to the pharynx between the internal and external carotid arteries, and combines with the pharyngeal branches from the glosso-pharyngeal and superior cervical ganglion of the sympathetic to form the **pharyngeal plexus**, which lies on the wall of the pharynx at the level of the middle constrictor (Fig. 858, p. 979).   From this plexus the muscles of the pharynx and soft palate (except the stylo-pharyngeus and tensor palati) are supplied.   The **lingual branch** is a minute nerve which separates itself from the plexus and joins the hypoglossal nerve in the anterior triangle of the neck.

The **superior laryngeal nerve** passes obliquely downwards and medially, medial to the external and internal carotid arteries, towards the thyroid cartilage. It is joined by twigs from the sympathetic and the pharyngeal plexus, and is said to give a filament to the internal carotid artery. It ends by dividing in its course into two unequal parts—a larger internal and a smaller external laryngeal branch.

The **internal laryngeal nerve** passes medially into the larynx. It pierces the thyro-hyoid membrane, in company with the corresponding branch of the superior laryngeal artery under cover of the thyro-hyoid muscle, and divides into three branches. These supply the mucous membrane of the larynx, reaching upwards to the epiglottis and the posterior part of the dorsum of the tongue. The lowest branch forms communications on the medial side of the lamina of the thyroid cartilage with the branches of the recurrent laryngeal nerve.

The **external laryngeal nerve** passes downwards deep to the infra-hyoid muscles and upon the inferior constrictor muscle of the pharynx. It supplies branches to that muscle, and ends in the **crico-thyroid** muscle.

Communications.—Besides supplying the pharyngeal and laryngeal nerves, the ganglion has the following communications with other nerves : (1) with the superior cervical ganglion of the sympathetic ; (2) with the hypoglossal ; (3) with the loop between the first and second cervical nerves ; and (4) with the accessory nerve, which applies itself to the ganglion, and thereby supplies to the vagus nerve the efferent fibres for the muscles of the larynx, except the crico-thyroid.

In 1888 (*Proc. Roy. Soc.* vol. xliv.) Charles E. Beevor and Victor Horsley, on the basis of a series of experiments on monkeys, came to the conclusion : (1) That the glosso-pharyngeal nerve supplies the stylo-pharyngeus and the middle constrictor. (2) That the vagus supplies no muscles in the head and neck. (3) That the accessory nerve supplies the levator palati and the muscles of the pharynx and larynx.

Branches of the Vagus in the Neck. — In the neck the vagus nerve supplies cardiac branches and (on the right side) the recurrent laryngeal nerve (Fig. 859).

The **cervical cardiac branches** are **upper** and **lower**. *On the right side* both cardiac branches pass downwards into the thorax behind the subclavian artery, and along the side of the trachea to the deep cardiac plexus. *On the left side* the two nerves separate on reaching the thorax. The *upper nerve* passes deeply alongside the trachea to join the deep cardiac plexus. The *lower nerve* accompanies the vagus nerve across the aortic arch, along with the cardiac branch of the superior cervical ganglion of the sympathetic, to end in the superficial cardiac plexus.

The **right recurrent laryngeal nerve** arises at the root of the neck as the vagus crosses in front of the first part of the subclavian artery. It hooks round the artery, and passes obliquely upwards and medially behind the subclavian and the common carotid, and either in front of or behind the inferior thyroid artery ; it then ascends in the groove between the œsophagus and trachea, along the medial side of the corresponding lobe of the thyroid gland. It finally disappears under cover of the inferior border of the inferior constrictor muscle to end in **laryngeal branches** which supply all the intrinsic muscles of the larynx except the crico-thyroid.

In its course it gives off the following branches :—

(1) **Cardiac branches** arise as the nerve winds round the subclavian artery, and descend alongside the trachea to end in the deep cardiac plexus.

(2) **Communicating branches** to the inferior cervical ganglion of the sympathetic arise from the nerve behind the subclavian artery.

(3) **Muscular branches** supply the trachea, œsophagus, and the inferior constrictor of the pharynx.

(4) **Terminal branches** supply the muscles of the larynx (except the crico-thyroid) and communicate medial to the lamina of the thyroid cartilage with branches of the internal laryngeal nerve.

Branches of the Vagus in the Thorax.—In the thorax the vagi form the great pulmonary and œsophageal plexuses. The right nerve, in addition,

62 *b*

furnishes cardiac branches; and the left nerve gives off the recurrent laryngeal nerve.

The **left recurrent laryngeal nerve** differs from the nerve of the right side mainly in its point of origin and in the early part of its course. It springs from the vagus as it crosses the aortic arch, and, after hooking below the arch, behind the *ligamentum arteriosum*, it passes upwards in the superior mediastinum to the neck, where its course and relations are similar to those of the nerve of the right side. The branches of the nerve are the same as those of the right nerve. The **cardiac branches** are larger; they arise below the aortic arch, and pass to the deep cardiac plexus.

The **thoracic cardiac** branches on the right side are derived from the trunk of the vagus as it lies beside the trachea; on the left side they arise from its recurrent branch. All join the deep cardiac plexus.

Branches of the Vagus in the Abdomen.—From the lower end of the œsophageal plexus two nerves (each containing fibres from both vagi) pass on the walls of the gullet through the diaphragm into the abdomen. Since these nerves contain fibres from both vagi they should not be called right and left vagi, but may be named **anterior** and **posterior gastric nerves**. The **posterior gastric nerve** is distributed to the posterior surface of the stomach and sends communicating offsets to the cœliac, splenic, and renal plexuses of the autonomic system. The **anterior gastric nerve** applies itself to the anterior surface and small curvature of the stomach, to which it is distributed. It sends communicating offsets between the layers of the lesser omentum to the hepatic plexus, and from those offsets fine filaments pass in the omentum to the pylorus and first part of the duodenum.

The two gastric nerves innervate the muscular walls of the viscera, blood-vessels, and glands.

Certain **asymmetrical features** of the two vagus nerves are explained by a reference to the process of development. The course of the recurrent laryngeal nerves is explained by the absence of neck in the early embryo, and by the primitive aortic arches between which they passed having occupied a higher position before the heart descended into the thorax, when it dragged these branches of the nerves down with it. The corresponding arches (the fourth pair), beneath which they originally passed, develop into the subclavian artery on the right side, the aorta on the left (see Fig. 1064, p. 1283).

THORACIC PLEXUSES

Of the plexuses formed by the vagus nerves in the thorax—cardiac, pulmonary, and œsophageal—the **cardiac plexuses** are described under the autonomic system, on p. 1066. The fibres of the vagus which take part in the formation of thoracic and abdominal plexuses belong to the parasympathetic system.

Pulmonary Plexuses.—As already stated, the vagus nerve on each side, on reaching the back of the root of the lung, breaks up into numerous plexiform branches for the formation of the posterior pulmonary plexus. From each nerve a few fibres pass to the front of the root of the lung, above its upper border, to form the much smaller anterior pulmonary plexus. These plexuses communicate freely with each other, fibres connect the plexuses of the two sides, they are intimately connected with the cardiac plexuses, and they receive branches from the sympathetic. Reference is made to the pulmonary plexuses in the section dealing with the autonomic system (see p. 1067).

The **anterior pulmonary plexus** on each side is joined by a few fibres from the corresponding part of the deep cardiac plexus, and on the left side from the superficial cardiac plexus as well. It surrounds and supplies the constituents of the root of the lung anteriorly.

The **posterior pulmonary plexus**, placed behind the root of the lung, is formed by the greater part of the vagus nerve, reinforced by fine branches from the second, third, and fourth thoracic ganglia of the sympathetic.

Numerous branches extend from the anterior and posterior pulmonary plexuses into the substance of the lung. The entering fibres, arranged in a plexiform manner, form three groups. One accompanies the bronchi, another the vessels, and a third is distributed to the pulmonary pleura.

Œsophageal Plexus.—The œsophagus in the thorax is supplied by the vagus nerve both in the superior and posterior mediastina. *In the superior mediastinum* it receives branches from the vagus nerve on the right side, and from the recurrent laryngeal nerve on the left side.

In the posterior mediastinum the gullet is surrounded by the large œsophageal plexus, formed from the trunks of the vagi nerves emerging from the posterior pulmonary plexuses. That part of the œsophagus also receives fibres from the greater splanchnic nerve and the splanchnic ganglion. From the œsophageal plexus branches supply the muscular wall and mucous membrane of the œsophagus.

A few filaments also pass from the plexus to the posterior surface of the pericardium.

ACCESSORY NERVE

The **eleventh** or **accessory nerve** consists of two essentially separate parts, different both in origin and in distribution. One, the **bulbar portion, is accessory to the vagus nerve,** and arises by the *cranial root* in series with the rootlets of that nerve, from the side of the medulla oblongata; its fibres are contributed to the recurrent branches of the vagus for the supply of the laryngeal muscles with the exception of the crico-thyroid. The other, the **spinal portion,** arises by the *spinal root* from the side of the spinal cord, between the anterior and posterior roots of the spinal nerves, its origin extending from the level of the cranial root as low as the origin of the fifth or sixth cervical nerve (for the deep origin, see p. 880). This portion of the nerve supplies the sterno-mastoid and trapezius muscles. Successively joining together, the rootlets form a trunk which ascends in the subdural space of the vertebral canal, posterior to the ligamentum denticulatum, to the foramen magnum. Approaching the jugular foramen, the spinal and cranial roots unite into a single trunk, which leaves the cranial cavity through the jugular foramen in the same compartment of dura mater as the vagus nerve (Fig. 843, p. 962).

In the jugular foramen the **accessory branch to the vagus** [ramus internus] (after furnishing a small branch to the superior ganglion of the vagus) applies itself to the inferior ganglion. At this point some fibres join the ganglion and the rest become incorporated in the trunk of the vagus beyond the ganglion. Its fibres are distributed to the recurrent laryngeal branches of the vagus. See also p. 983.

The **spinal portion** of the nerve extends into the neck, where at first it lies along with

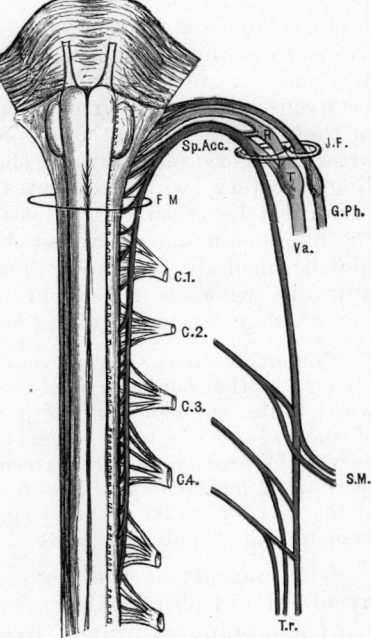

FIG. 860.—SCHEME OF THE ORIGIN, CONNEXIONS, AND DISTRIBUTION OF THE ACCESSORY NERVE.

Sp. Acc., Accessory nerve ; C.1-4, First four cervical nerves (posterior roots) ; Va , Vagus nerve ; R, Superior ganglion ; T, Inferior ganglion ; G.Ph., Glosso-pharyngeal nerve ; S.M., Nerves to sterno-mastoid ; Tr., Nerves to trapezius ; F.M., Foramen magnum ; J.F., Jugular foramen.

other nerves in the interval between the internal carotid artery and the internal jugular vein. It then passes obliquely downwards and laterally superficial (sometimes deep) to the vein, under cover of the posterior belly of the digastric; still descending, it pierces the deep part of the sterno-mastoid muscle or lies close to its deep surface, and it supplies the muscle. It appears at the posterior border of the sterno-mastoid, at or below the junction of the upper and middle thirds, and about the level of the upper border of the thyroid cartilage. After crossing obliquely downwards through the posterior triangle the nerve descends under cover of the trapezius muscle, which it supplies. That portion of the nerve *communicates* in three situations with nerves from the cervical plexus— (1) in or under cover of the sterno-mastoid, with the branch for the muscle derived from the second cervical nerve; (2) in the posterior triangle, with branches from the third and fourth cervical nerves; (3) deep to the trapezius, with the branches for the muscle derived from the third and fourth cervical nerves.

HYPOGLOSSAL NERVE

The **twelfth** or **hypoglossal nerve** is a purely efferent nerve, supplying all the muscles of the tongue, both intrinsic and extrinsic, except the palato-glossus. It arises by numerous rootlets from the front of the medulla oblongata between the pyramid and the olive (Fig. 839, p. 958; for the deep origin, see p. 880). The rootlets arrange themselves in two bundles which separately pierce the dura mater, and unite in the anterior condylar canal, or after emerging from the skull. In the upper part of the neck it is closely associated with the glosso-pharyngeal, vagus, and accessory nerves, and lies, with them, medial to and between the internal carotid artery and the internal jugular vein, and deep to the posterior belly of the digastric and the stylo-hyoid muscle. As it descends it becomes more superficial and is closely attached to the lateral surface of the inferior ganglion of the vagus. Midway between the posterior belly of the digastric and the greater horn of the hyoid bone it turns forwards, through the angle between the occipital artery and its sterno-mastoid branch, and passes to the floor of the mouth. In its course forwards it lies superficial to the internal carotid artery, the occipital artery, the external carotid artery, and to the loop of the lingual artery (which separates it from the middle constrictor muscle). Farther forward it lies between the posterior belly of the digastric muscle laterally and the hyo-glossus medially and then between the mylo-hyoid laterally and the hyo-glossus medially, where it breaks up into terminal branches which continue onwards between the mylo-hyoid and genio-glossus muscles. The terminal branches communicate with filaments of the lingual nerves.

Communications.—In its course the hypoglossal nerve has the following communications with other nerves: Near the base of the skull it is connected by small branches with (1) the superior cervical ganglion of the sympathetic; (2) the inferior ganglion of the vagus; (3) by a larger branch, with the loop between the first two cervical nerves; (4) as it crosses the external carotid artery it receives a communication from the pharyngeal plexus (*lingual branch of the vagus*); and (5) medial to the mylo-hyoid muscle, at the anterior border of the hyo-glossus, it forms loops of communication with the lingual branch of the mandibular nerve.

The **branches** of the nerve are: (1) Meningeal; (2) Descending; (3) Thyro-hyoid; and (4) Terminal.

The **meningeal branch** passes from the nerve near its origin to supply the dura mater of the posterior fossa of the skull. It probably derives its fibres from the communication with the first and second cervical nerves.

The **descending branch of the hypoglossal nerve** is the chief branch given off in the neck. It arises from the hypoglossal nerve as it crosses the internal carotid artery, and descends in the anterior triangle superficial to the carotid sheath. It is joined about the middle of the neck by the **nervus descendens cervicalis** (from the second and third cervical nerves). By their union the **ansa hypoglossi (hypoglossal loop)** is formed, from which branches are distributed to the majority of the infra-hyoid muscles—both bellies of the omo-hyoid, the sterno-hyoid, and the sterno-thyroid. The descending branch of the hypoglossal nerve derives its fibres from the communication to the hypoglossal nerve from the loop between the first and second cervical nerves; the ansa hypoglossi therefore is made up of fibres of the first three cervical nerves.

The **nerve to the thyro-hyoid muscle** is a small branch which arises from the hypoglossal nerve before it passes medial to the mylo-hyoid muscle. It descends behind the greater horn of the hyoid bone to reach the muscle. When traced backwards this nerve is found associated with the loop between the first and second cervical nerves.

The **terminal [lingual] branches** of the hypoglossal nerve are distributed to

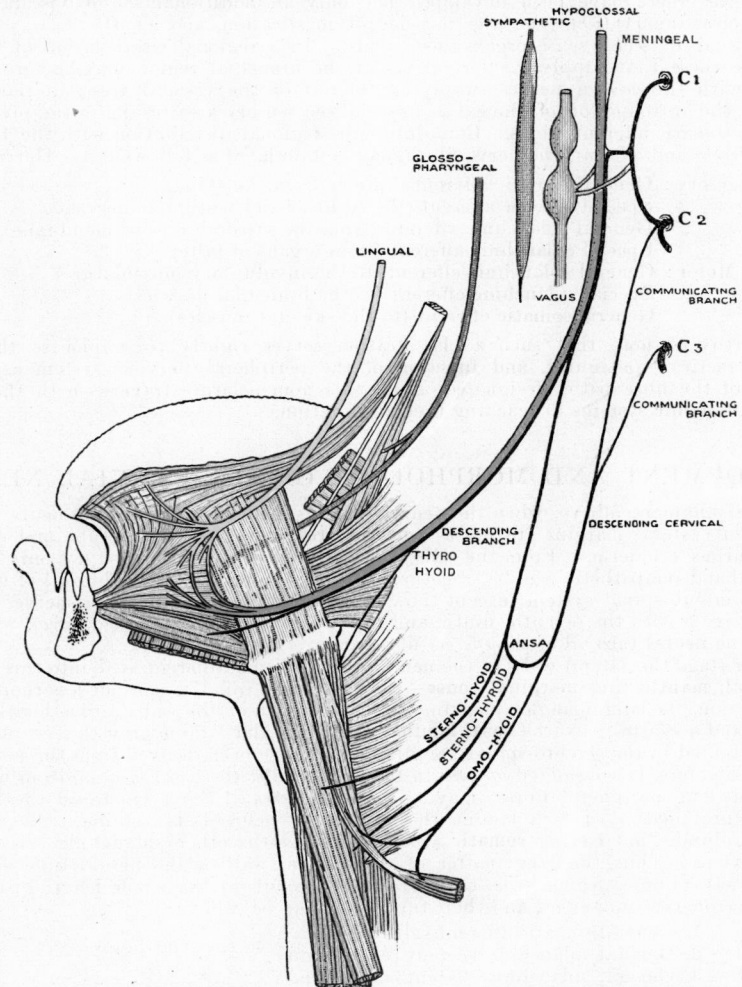

FIG. 861.—THE MUSCLES OF THE HYOID BONE AND STYLOID PROCESS, AND THE EXTRINSIC MUSCLES OF THE TONGUE, WITH THEIR NERVES.

the hyo-glossus, genio-hyoid, and genio-glossus, and to all the intrinsic muscles of the tongue. The nerve to the genio-hyoid is said to be derived from the loop between the first and second cervical nerves.

COMPONENT FIBRES OF THE CRANIAL NERVES

The third, fourth, sixth, eleventh, and twelfth pairs are composed of large and small myelinated fibres; non-myelinated fibres have been found in the fifth, sixth, ninth, eleventh, and twelfth, of which those in the sixth, eleventh, and twelfth are probably all derived from the sympathetic system (Koch). As regards the function of the fibres, although the cranial nerves are usually broadly classified as efferent and afferent, as well as mixed nerves, it is now recognised that few of them consist exclusively of one or the other order of fibres. The optic nerve itself is described as containing efferent fibres which may control the movements of the retinal elements in response to light. The third, fourth, and sixth nerves are not purely efferent in function, as was formerly considered, but contain also some afferent (somatic afferent, *proprioceptive*) fibres, as well as fibres from the sympathetic system, and the same may prove true for the eleventh and twelfth nerves. Indeed the cranial nerves vary greatly in their functional composition, and, moreover, no nerve, save the olfactory and auditory, is made up of one functional order of fibres.

The animal body is naturally divided into two different areas or regions—the **somatic** area, forming the body wall and limbs, and the **splanchnic** or visceral area, comprising the chief viscera contained within the body cavity. In the head and neck an additional factor has to be considered owing to the presence of the series of pharyngeal or branchial arches, for in connexion with that series there have been developed not only an additional set of visceral muscles, requiring motor innervation (*e.g.*, the muscles of mastication, and of the face, palate, and pharynx), but also visceral sense organs (taste buds). In a regional classification of the nerves on these lines those that supply the derivatives of the branchial region may be termed *special* in contrast with the *general* nerves supplying the rest of the visceral area; similarly in the somatic area the introduction of the ear as a specialised sensory area results in the presence of a special set of somatic afferent fibres. Combining the regional distribution with the function of the fibres, *efferent* and *afferent*, the nerve fibres may be tabulated as follows (after Herrick):—

Sensory : General somatic afferent (sensory from the skin).
Special somatic afferent (the cochlear and vestibular nerves).
General splanchnic afferent (from the visceral mucous membrane).
Special splanchnic afferent (from organs of taste).
Motor : General splanchnic efferent (to the involuntary musculature).
Special splanchnic efferent (to the branchial muscles).
General somatic efferent (to the skeletal muscles).

It is worthy of note that such a classification serves rightly to emphasise the central connexion, practical continuity, and function of the peripheral nervous system as a whole, since many of the fibre paths designated under this nomenclature traverse both the cerebro-spinal and autonomic systems in reaching their destinations.

DEVELOPMENT AND MORPHOLOGY OF THE CRANIAL NERVES

In the early human embryo, when the neural plate is folded in to form the neural tube, the cells forming its lateral margins are left as a **neural crest**, lying above the tube and connecting it with the surface ectoderm. From the cells of the crest there are developed not only all of the cerebro-spinal and sympathetic ganglia, together with the chromaffin bodies, but all of the *afferent* fibres of the cerebro-spinal system (except those of the first and second cranial nerves and a few fibres in connexion with the seventh, ninth, and tenth nerves to be mentioned later), whilst from the walls of the **neural tube** all of the *efferent* fibres arise.

At a later stage the lateral walls of the neural tube become differentiated into three layers—the **ependymal, mantle,** and **marginal** zones—and the neural canal is more or less rhomboidal in transverse section, its lateral angles marking the subdivision of the walls into a dorsal part (the **alar lamina**) and a ventral part (the **basal lamina**). Into the alar lamina grow the central processes of the cells situated in the cerebro-spinal ganglia, which have been derived from the neural crest, and it may, therefore, be considered *afferent* in function, whilst the basal lamina, from whose cells there grow out long peripheral fibres, may be termed *efferent*. Furthermore, in the middle or mantle zone (grey matter) of each lamina the developing neuroblasts become arranged in two longitudinal columns, one having **somatic** (body wall) and the other **splanchnic** (visceral) peripheral connexions. Thus, the grey matter of each lateral wall of the neural tube shows four longitudinal cell-columns, which, from their presence throughout the whole length of the neural tube, their peripheral connexions, and their functions, may be called :—

1. General somatic afferent cell-column } in the Alar lamina,
2. General splanchnic afferent cell-column }
3. General splanchnic efferent cell-column } in the Basal lamina,
4. General somatic efferent cell-column }

corresponding to Gaskell's four primary functional divisions of the activities of the organism.

In the hind- and mid-brain regions, however, other cell columns are added, consequent upon the presence of (1) the great **special sense organs** (nose, eye, ear) which demand specialised somatic afferent connexions, and (2) the **branchial system** and its derivatives, which, as a specialised part of the visceral area, demand special splanchnic connexions, both afferent and efferent. In the developing brain-stem, therefore, three additional cell columns are to be found :—

1. Special somatic afferent cell column } in the Alar lamina,
2. Special splanchnic afferent cell column }
3. Special splanchnic efferent cell column in the Basal lamina.

As is pointed out above in the discussion of their components, few of the cranial nerves are composed exclusively of fibres of one functional order; in most, however, there is such a preponderance of one type that we are justified in grouping them into three series :—

Somatic Afferent.	Somatic Efferent.	Splanchnic Afferent and Efferent.
I. Olfactory.	III. Oculomotor.	V. Trigeminal.
II. Optic.	IV. Trochlear.	VII. Facial.
VIII. Auditory.	VI. Abducent.	IX. Glosso-pharyngeal.
	XII. Hypoglossal.	X. Vagus.
		XI. Accessory.

Though this grouping is purely *functional*, it is, as we might expect, reflected anatomically in development, for the somatic afferent group of nerves (I., II., and VIII.) is connected with the alar lamina, corresponding in this respect to the posterior roots of the spinal nerves, whilst the somatic efferent group (III., IV., VI., and XII.) arises from the medial part of the basal lamina in line with the anterior roots of the spinal nerves. The splanchnic group (V., VII., IX., X., and XI.), which is composed of afferent and efferent nerves specialised in connexion with the branchial system, forms an intermediate series lying between the other two. It must be said, however, that though there is some degree of correspondence between cranial and spinal nerves, any attempt to show a strict homology leads to insuperable difficulties.

SOMATIC AFFERENT GROUP

Of the three cranial nerves composing this group, the eighth only is developed from the neural crest, and is to that extent comparable to the posterior root of a spinal nerve. It is quite

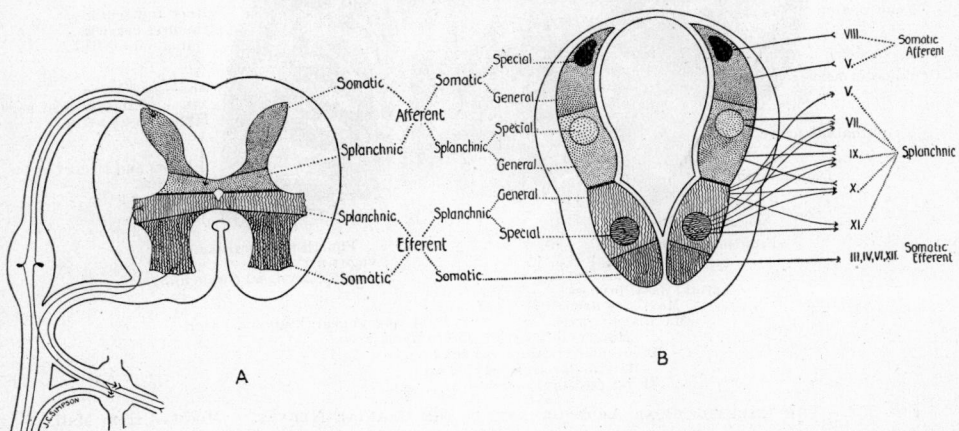

FIG. 862.—SCHEME SHOWING A COMPARISON OF THE ORIGINS AND COMPOSITION OF THE NERVE ROOTS FROM THE SPINAL CORD AND HIND-BRAIN. (S. E. W.)

A. Spinal cord ; B. Hind-brain.

probable, however, that some of its fibres come from cells developed from the ectoderm of the auditory vesicle, and, moreover, its distribution is limited to a specialised sensory area of the ectoderm. The first and second nerves are developed in connexion with outgrowths of the brain ; and it is obvious that neither of them is strictly comparable to any of the other nerves, cranial or spinal.

I. Olfactory Nerve.—At the end of the fourth week an olfactory plate becomes differentiated in the ectoderm lying under the fore-brain on each side. By the growth of the medial and lateral nasal processes around it, the plate comes to form the roof of the olfactory pit. The sensory cells of the plate now take on the character of true nerve cells, and send in basal fibres which arborise around the cells of the olfactory bulb. At first the olfactory plates are directly in contact with the bulb, which is developed from the fore-brain, but later, by the development of the cribriform plate and meninges, they become pushed apart, and the fibres connecting them are lengthened to form the true olfactory nerves. Those nerves are peculiar in that, though afferent, they have no ganglia ; the cells giving rise to their fibres remain in the surface epithelium, and the fibres themselves are unmyelinated.

II. Optic Nerve.—The optic nerve is developed in the stalk of the optic vesicle—an outgrowth from the fore-brain, and, morphologically, is a part of the central nervous system. When the optic cup is formed (see under Development of the Eye) its inner or retinal layer becomes differentiated into the rods and cones (the true neuro-epithelial cells, corresponding to the olfactory cells) and nerve cells, the processes of which grow back along the optic stalk to form the optic nerve, chiasma, and tract. Those nerve cells are true intermediate cells, corresponding to those of the grey matter of the central nervous system, and their fibres are largely supported by neuroglia.

VIII. Auditory Nerve.—The internal ear first arises as an ectodermal plate lying dorsal to the first pharyngeal groove. That plate invaginates to form a flask-like auditory vesicle (otocyst) from the lining cells of which patches of neuro-epithelium are later differentiated. The vestibular and cochlear ganglia develop between the vesicle and the hind-brain in close association with the ganglion of the seventh nerve. Although the origin of the common mass is usually said to be from the neural crest, it is probable that some at least of the cells going to form the auditory ganglia are derived from the neuro-epithelium of the auditory vesicle. The ganglia grow in direct proportion to the vestibular and cochlear outgrowth of this vesicle, and their central and peripheral fibres form the vestibular and cochlear nerves.

SOMATIC EFFERENT GROUP

The hypoglossal nerve and the three nerves to the eye muscles all arise from the somatic efferent cell column in the basal lamina of the neural tube, and on that account, as well as by reason of the fact that they innervate somatic muscles, are usually considered as being in series with the anterior roots of the spinal nerves.

Though the primitive vertebrate head undoubtedly was segmental, little reliable evidence

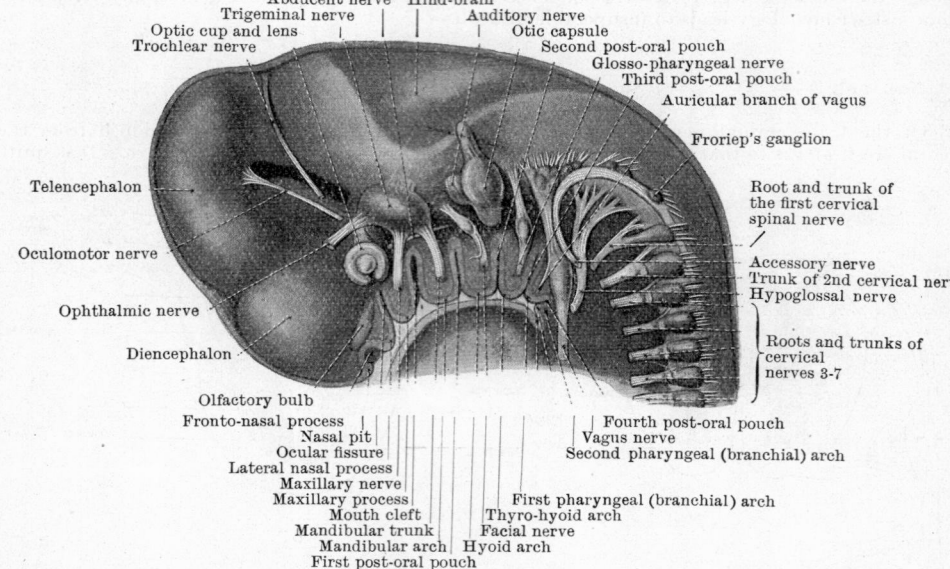

FIG. 863.—THE EMBRYOLOGICAL ARRANGEMENT OF THE CRANIAL NERVES. (Modified from Mall.)

remains upon which to base a reconstruction of its segmentation, and various investigators have placed the number of the primitive cephalic segments between eight and nineteen. No distinct myotomes are visible in the head of the human embryo, but a study of the lower vertebrates leads to the conclusion that the pre-muscle mass from which the extrinsic ocular muscles are developed represents the first three cephalic myotomes. The first myotome forms the superior, inferior, and medial recti and the inferior oblique, supplied by the oculomotor nerve ; the second myotome forms the superior oblique, supplied by the trochlear nerve ; and the third forms the lateral rectus, supplied by the abducent (see Fig. 447, p. 526).

Similar studies tend to show that the intrinsic muscles of the tongue are derived from the last three cephalic myotomes. Between those two sets of persisting myotomes (ocular and lingual) there is a gap which probably represents three or more myotomes which have disappeared.

III. Oculomotor Nerve.—This nerve arises from neuroblasts in the basal lamina of the mid-brain. The fibres emerge in small bundles from the anterior surface of the lamina and converge to form the trunk of the nerve, which runs to the premuscle mass from which the extrinsic muscles of the eye (with the exception of the superior oblique and lateral rectus) are formed.

IV. Trochlear Nerve.—The neuroblasts from which this nerve arises lie just caudal to and in line with the nucleus of the third nerve. Instead of leaving the basal lamina by its anterior surface, however, the fibres grow backwards, curve round the neural canal (aqueduct), and, crossing above it, emerge on the opposite side at the junction of the mid-brain and hind-brain.

VI. Abducent Nerve.—The nucleus of origin lies in the basal lamina of the hind-brain under the floor of the fourth ventricle. The fibres emerge at a point caudal to the future pons and run to the rudiment of the lateral rectus muscle.

XII. Hypoglossal Nerve.—The twelfth is a compound nerve representing the fused efferent nerves of three, or possibly more, precervical neural segments. Its fibres take origin from neuroblasts in the somatic efferent cell column and emerge from the walls of the basal lamina in several groups ; they then converge anteriorly to form the trunk of the nerve and grow forwards to end in the muscle rudiment of the tongue.

SPLANCHNIC (AFFERENT AND EFFERENT) GROUP

The nerves of this group are essentially related to the **pharyngeal arches** (see p. 54). In the embryo each of those arches contains a muscle plate which differs from the myotomes in that it is developed from splanchnic mesoderm. Associated with each arch is a nerve which contains both afferent and efferent fibres, and runs along the upper or cephalic border of the arch ; that nerve sends a small branch (*pretrematic*) round the dorsal end of the pharyngeal pouch to run along the lower, or caudal, border of the arch in front of the one from which it arises.   The nerve of the first or mandibular arch is the mandibular division of the trigeminal nerve ; the nerve of the second arch is the facial, and that of the third is the glosso-pharyngeal ; the nerves of the remaining arches are fused to form the vagus and accessory nerves.

The nerve of each arch has a ganglion developed on its root, and supplies (1) efferent (special splanchnic efferent) fibres to the muscle plate, and (2) afferent (general splanchnic afferent) fibres to the pharyngeal mucosa covering the inner surface of the arch and the pharyngeal pouch in front of it.

Furthermore, in connexion with the branchial system there are in the human embryo vestiges of a series of sense organs which have been lost by the higher vertebrates.   They are small areas of modified ectoderm which are found at the dorsal end of each external pharyngeal groove or branchial cleft and are known as epibranchial **placodes**.   During the fifth week of embryonic development the placodes are in contact with the ganglia of the facial, glosso-pharyngeal, and vagus nerves—and contribute cells to the formation of these ganglia.

Whilst the nerves of the splanchnic group typically do not possess somatic afferent fibres, the trigeminal, in conformity with the large part taken by the first arch in the formation of the face, receives a preponderance of that type of fibre.   In reality, however, the trigeminal is a double nerve, and the present tendency is to regard its (branchial) part as a separate nerve (the masticator) ; and the remainder as a somatic afferent nerve.   The vagus nerve also contains a limited number of somatic afferent fibres which supply the skin around the persistent dorsal part of the first pharyngeal groove—that is, the external auditory meatus.

V. Trigeminal Nerve.—The trigeminal ganglion [g. semilunare] arises very early from the neural crest at the extreme cranial end of the hind-brain.   Central processes from its cells form the large afferent root of the nerve, and, reaching the hind-brain at the level of the pontine flexure, divide to run up and down in the alar plate, where the descending fibres form the spinal tract of the fifth nerve.   The peripheral fibres separate into three large divisions which grow out into the three processes that take part in the formation of the face (the fronto-nasal, maxillary, and mandibular processes) and form the three divisions of the fully developed nerve.

The efferent fibres arise from the special splanchnic efferent column of the basal lamina, where the cell bodies form a dorsal nucleus lying opposite the point at which the afferent fibres enter the brain.   The efferent fibres emerge as a distinct trunk in the embryo, and, coursing along the medial side of the trigeminal ganglion, run to the muscle plate of the first arch, which later forms the muscles of mastication.

VII. Facial Nerve.—The facial is composed mainly of efferent fibres which arise from a nucleus in the special splanchnic efferent column of the basal lamina.   Growing out from that nucleus they emerge from the hind-brain just medial to the auditory ganglion and run to the muscle plate of the second or hyoid arch from which the platysma group of muscles is later developed.   At first the fibres run directly from their nucleus of origin to the lateral surface of the hind-brain, passing above (rostral to) the nucleus of the abducent nerve.   Later, however, the facial nucleus shifts downwards (caudally) and ventro-laterally towards the afferent nuclei of the solitary tract and the spinal tract of the trigeminal nerve, following the general law of neurobiotaxis that the chief dendrite and body of a neurone tend to move towards the source of the majority of their afferent impulses.

The afferent fibres are developed from the ganglion of the facial nerve, which is derived from the neural crest and lies in close association with the ganglia of the auditory nerve.   It is probable that certain cells are also contributed to this ganglion by the epibranchial placode of the first pharyngeal groove.   The central fibres enter the alar lamina and form, together with fibres from the glosso-pharyngeal nerve, the solitary tract.   The peripheral fibres run in front of the pharyngeal groove and form the chorda tympani and greater superficial petrosal nerves, which represent the pretrematic branch of the facial nerve.

IX. Glosso-pharyngeal Nerve.—The efferent fibres arise from the nucleus ambiguus, which is a common nucleus of origin for the efferent fibres of the glosso-pharyngeal, vagus, and accessory nerves and lies in the special splanchnic efferent column in line with the efferent nuclei of the fifth and seventh nerves.   Emerging from the hind-brain they grow out ventrally to meet the muscle plate of the third arch, and eventually supply the pharyngeal muscles derived from that element.

The afferent fibres, which form the larger part of the nerve, are derived from two ganglia— the superior ganglion, developed from the neural crest, and the inferior ganglion, formed in part from the neural crest, and in part from an epibranchial placode with which it is in contact. Centrally the fibres enter the alar lamina and join fibres from the facial and vagus to form the solitary tract.   Most of the peripheral fibres from the ganglia run ventrally to enter the third arch, passing, as a lingual branch, to that part of the tongue which is later developed from it. Some of the peripheral fibres, however, form a pretrematic branch in front of the second pharyngeal pouch, and, as the tympanic nerve, supply the structures derived from the dorsal extremity of the first and second pouches (tympanum, etc., see p. 57).

X. Vagus.—The vagus is a composite nerve representing, with the accessory, the union of the nerves of all the pharyngeal arches behind the third.   Its afferent fibres, therefore, grow out from several root ganglia developed from the neural crest.   The superior ganglion is the most cephalic of those ;   the others are vestigial and are called accessory ganglia.   The ganglion inferior, like the inferior ganglion of the glosso-pharyngeal, is developed in contact with an epibranchial placode, and in all probability receives cells from that source as well as from the neural crest. The central fibres grow towards the alar lamina, and, entering it, turn downward to form, in conjunction with fibres from the facial and glosso-pharyngeal nerves, the solitary tract. The peripheral fibres grow downward to form the bulk of the vagus nerve.

The efferent fibres arise from two nuclei in the basal lamina—the nucleus ambiguus in the special splanchnic efferent column, and a dorsal efferent nucleus which lies in the general somatic efferent column. The fibres from these two sources emerge laterally in two separate bundles and join the afferent fibres to form the trunk of the nerve. Those from the nucleus ambiguus grow out to the muscle plates of the fourth and succeeding arches, from which the laryngeal and part of the pharyngeal muscles are developed. The fibres from the dorsal nucleus run to the parasympathetic plexuses of the vagus.

XI. Accessory Nerve.—This nerve is closely associated with the vagus ; both embryologically and morphologically it may be regarded as the caudal part of the vagus complex which has become specialised because of a new rôle assumed by the branchial muscles which it supplies, these muscles (sterno-mastoid and trapezius) having been pressed into service as limb-girdle muscles.

The efferent fibres, of which alone it is composed, arise from two sources. The larger number grow out from cell groups which are developed in the lateral grey column of the upper four or more cervical segments of the spinal cord (special splanchnic efferent column) in series with the nucleus ambiguus of the tenth. Emerging from the cord laterally, these fibres run upwards along the line of the neural crest as the spinal accessory trunk to join the vagus. Leaving this nerve after a short course, however, they run to their destination. A few fibres of the accessory nerve arise from cells in the dorsal motor nucleus of the vagus and after pursuing a short course with the accessory proper, rejoin the vagus and are distributed to its plexuses.

SPINAL NERVES

The spinal nerves are characterised by being attached to the spinal cord and by passing from the vertebral canal through the intervertebral foramina. There are usually thirty-one pairs, which are grouped as cervical, thoracic, lumbar, sacral, and coccygeal, in relation to the vertebræ between which they emerge. There are eight cervical nerves, the first passing out of the vertebral canal between the occipital bone and the atlas, and the last appearing between the seventh cervical and first thoracic vertebræ ; the other cervical nerves are numbered in correspondence with the vertebræ *above* which they emerge from the canal. There are twelve thoracic, five lumbar, five sacral nerves, and one coccygeal nerve, all appearing *below* the corresponding vertebræ.

The thirty-first nerve is occasionally absent ; and there are sometimes one or two additional pairs of minute filaments below the thirty-first, which, however, do not emerge from the vertebral canal. They are the rudimentary caudal nerves.

The size of the spinal nerves varies. The largest are those which take part in the formation of the great nerve trunks of the limbs (lower cervical and first thoracic, and lower lumbar and upper sacral nerves) ; and of those the nerves destined for the lower limbs are the larger. The coccygeal nerve is the smallest of the spinal nerves ; the thoracic nerves (except the first) are more slender than the limb nerves ; and the cervical nerves diminish in size from below upwards.

Origin of the Spinal Nerves.—Each nerve is attached to the spinal cord by two roots, one of which is ganglionic and the other not ; they are called respectively **posterior** (dorsal or afferent) and **anterior** (ventral or efferent).

The **posterior root** is larger than the anterior root ; it contains a larger number of radicular fibres, and the individual fibres are of larger size than in the anterior root. It has a vertical linear attachment to the postero-lateral sulcus of the spinal cord. The fibres of contiguous posterior roots are in close relation, and, in some instances, overlap. The radicles of the posterior root pass away from the spinal cord ; they form two bundles, both of which become connected with the proximal end of a **spinal ganglion.** From the distal end of the ganglion the posterior root proceeds to its junction with the anterior root in the intervertebral foramen.

The **spinal ganglia** are found on the posterior roots of all the spinal nerves. (In the case of the first cervical nerve, the spinal ganglion may be rudimentary or absent ; and the posterior root itself may be wanting, or derived from the accessory nerve.) They occupy the intervertebral foramina, except in the case of the sacral and coccygeal nerves, the ganglia of which lie *within* the vertebral canal; and the first and second cervical nerves, the ganglia of which lie upon the vertebral arches of the atlas and axis respectively. With the exception of the coccygeal ganglia they are outside the cavity of the dura mater, but are invested by the membrane. The ganglia are of ovoid form, bifurcated in some cases at their proximal ends. They consist of unipolar nerve-cells, whose axons, after a very

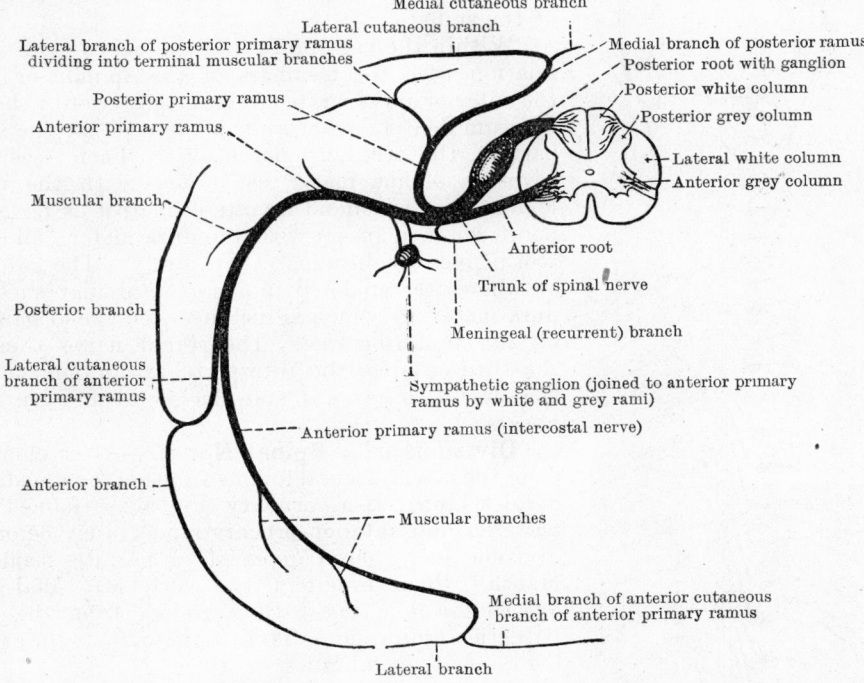

FIG. 864.—DIAGRAM OF THE ORIGIN AND DISTRIBUTION OF A TYPICAL SPINAL NERVE.

Note that the medial branch of the posterior primary ramus is represented as distributed to skin and fascia, whilst the lateral branch terminates at a deeper level in muscle. Both branches, however, supply muscles; and in the lower half of the body it is the lateral branch that supplies skin and fascia.

short course, divide into central (root) fibres and peripheral (trunk) fibres. The central fibres form the portion of the root which enters the spinal cord; the peripheral fibres are continued in a lateral direction from the ganglion into the spinal nerve.

Aberrant Spinal Ganglia.—Between the spinal ganglion and the spinal cord small collections of cells are occasionally found on the posterior roots, either as scattered cells or distinct ganglia. They are most frequently met with on the posterior roots of the lumbar and sacral nerves.

The anterior root is smaller than the posterior root. It arises from the anterior surface of the spinal cord (*anterior root zone*) by means of scattered bundles of nerve-fibres, which occupy a greater horizontal area and are more irregular in their arrangement than the fibres of the posterior root. It possesses no ganglion in its course. The rootlets sometimes overlap, and are not infrequently connected with neighbouring radicular fibres above and below.

The posterior and anterior roots proceed laterally in the vertebral canal from their attachment to the spinal cord towards the intervertebral foramina, where they unite to form the spinal nerve. The direction of the roots of the first two nerves is upwards and laterally; the roots of the remaining nerves course obliquely downwards and laterally, the obliquity gradually increasing until, in the case of the lower lumbar, the sacral and coccygeal nerve-roots, their course is vertically downwards in the vertebral canal. This increasing obliquity of the roots is due to the fact that the spinal cord extends down only as far as the lower border of the first lumbar vertebra, and results in the length of the roots being steadily augmented from cervical to sacral region (Fig. 865). The collection of nerve-roots which occupies the lower part of the canal, below the first lumbar vertebra, and comprises all the nerve-roots below those of the first lumbar nerve, is designated the **cauda equina**. They arise from the lumbar enlargement and the conus medullaris, and surround the filum terminale of the spinal cord.

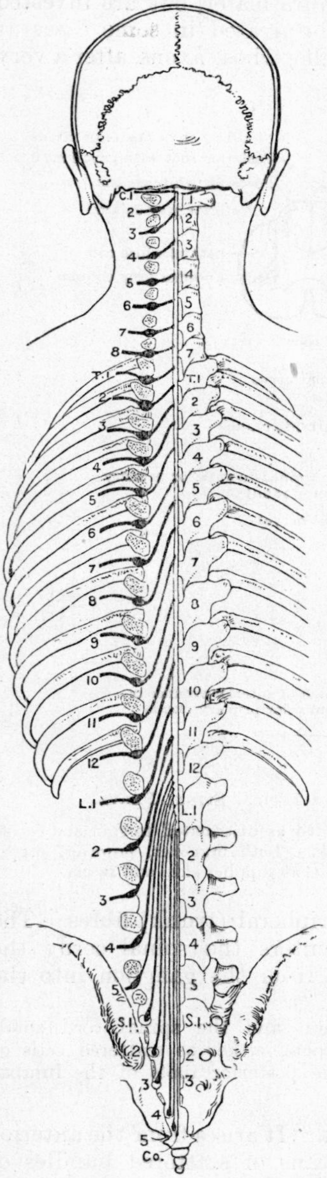

Within the vertebral canal the nerve-roots are in relation with the **meninges** of the spinal cord, and the anterior are separated from the posterior by the ligamentum denticulatum, and, in the neck, by the spinal part of the accessory nerve also. Each receives a covering of pia mater, continuous with the neurilemma; the arachnoid invests each root as far as the point where it meets with the dura mater; and each root pierces the dura mater separately. The two roots are thereafter enclosed in a single tubular sheath of dura mater, in which is included the spinal ganglion of the posterior root. The spinal nerve thus ensheathed occupies the intervertebral foramen (except the first two cervical and the sacral and coccygeal nerves).

Divisions of a Spinal Nerve.—After emerging from the intervertebral foramen the nerve immediately divides into two primary divisions, named the **posterior** and **anterior primary rami**. Just before its division each nerve gives off a minute **meningeal branch**, which re-enters the vertebral canal after effecting a junction with a branch from the sympathetic trunk, and is distributed to the spinal cord and its membranes.

The **posterior** and **anterior primary rami** of the spinal nerves are mainly somatic in their distribution, and are responsible for the innervation of the skeletal muscles and of the skin and fascia covering the trunk and limbs.

The primary rami of the nerves contain fibres from both posterior and anterior roots. Indeed, each root can be seen, on removal of its sheath, to divide into two portions, of which one portion enters into the formation of the posterior primary ramus, the other into the formation of the anterior primary ramus. The posterior primary rami, with the exception of the first two, are smaller than the anterior primary rami. They are responsible for the innervation of the skin, fascia, and axial muscles of the back.

FIG. 865.—DIAGRAMMATIC REPRESENTATION OF THE ORIGIN OF THE SPINAL NERVES, showing the position of their roots and ganglia in relation to the vertebral column. The nerves are shown as thick black lines on the left side.

They do not supply the muscles of the limbs, although in their cutaneous distribution they are prolonged on to the back of the head, the shoulder, and the gluteal region. They form two small plexuses—the **posterior cervical** and the **posterior sacral plexuses**. The anterior primary rami are, with the exception of the first two cervical nerves, much larger than the posterior primary rami. They supply the sides and anterior parts of the body, the limbs, and the perineum. For the most part they have a complicated arrangement. The thoracic or intercostal nerves alone have a simple mode of distribution; the other nerves give rise to the plexuses—cervical, brachial, lumbar, sacral, and coccygeal.

White Rami Communicantes.—From the anterior primary rami of certain nerves (first or second thoracic to second lumbar inclusive) a series of fine nerves arises which serves to connect the spinal with the sympathetic system.   Those **white rami communicantes**, through the medium of the gangliated trunk of the sympathetic, have a wide distribution to blood-vessels, viscera, certain glands, and other structures.

A second stream of nerves called **pelvic splanchnic nerves** (parasympathetic), associated with the second and third or third and fourth sacral nerves, connects these spinal nerves with the pelvic plexuses of the autonomic system (p. 1071).

Distribution of the Spinal Nerves.—Although the distribution, like the origin of the spinal nerves, presents primarily and essentially a segmental arrangement, that is masked, and in some instances obliterated, by developmental changes in the parts supplied. In no region can an isolated nerve be traced to a complete segment.   The nearest approach to a complete girdle of innervation is found in the thoracic region, in such a nerve as the sixth thoracic nerve.   Yet even such a nerve is not distributed to any part entirely alone.   In its cutaneous distribution it supplies a distinctly segmental area of skin, from the median plane posteriorly to the median plane anteriorly ; yet at the same time the adjacent nerves overstep, so to speak, the boundaries of the area and assist in its cutaneous nerve supply.   Its muscular distribution, also, is segmental ; the anterior primary ramus supplies the intercostal

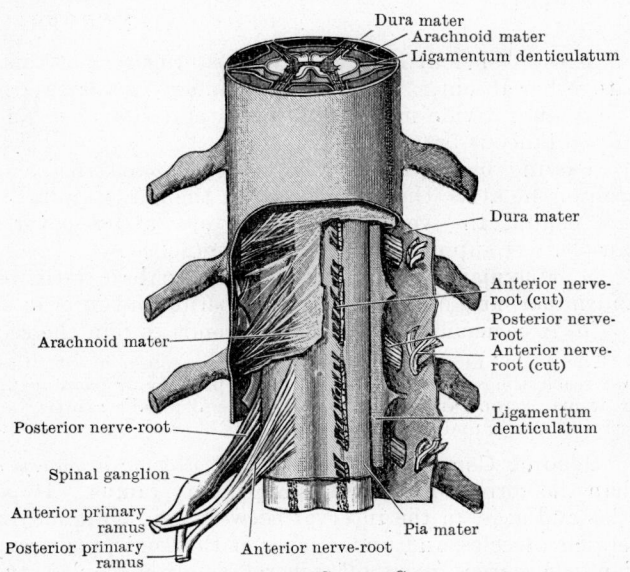

FIG. 866.—MEMBRANES OF THE SPINAL CORD, AND THE MODE OF ORIGIN OF THE SPINAL NERVES.

muscles of the space in which it lies ; but in that it forms communications with adjacent nerves.   The posterior primary ramus supplies axial muscles of the back, not, however, in an obviously segmental manner, on account of the fusion of the segmental myotomes in the formation of complex longitudinal muscles, which are together supplied by the series of muscular branches derived from the posterior primary rami of contiguous nerves.   In other regions still greater changes of structure are accompanied by deviations from a segmental type of distribution, causing the foundation of the nerve-plexuses by which the trunk and limbs are innervated.

When describing the distribution of nerves it is important to bear in mind that the descriptions "muscular" and "cutaneous" applied to branches may be misleading. Muscular branches contain afferent as well as efferent fibres, and so-called cutaneous branches are invariably distributed to the neighbouring subcutaneous fascia as well as skin.   In certain regions, for example the digits, they supply filaments to joints also.

POSTERIOR PRIMARY RAMI OF THE SPINAL NERVES

The **posterior primary rami** of the spinal nerves innervate skin, fascia, and muscles : the skin of the trunk posteriorly, the back of the head, the shoulder and the gluteal region ; and the longitudinal muscles of the back, but not the muscles of the limbs.

Each posterior ramus divides as a rule into two parts, a **medial** and a **lateral** branch (Fig. 864, p. 993).   In the upper half of the body the medial branches generally supply the cutaneous fibres, while the lateral trunks are purely muscular nerves.   In the lower part of the body the opposite is the case : the lateral branches provide the cutaneous nerves and the medial branches are distributed entirely to muscles.   The cutaneous nerves have a different course in the two cases. In the upper half of the back they course backwards deep to and among the muscles to within a short distance of the spines of the vertebræ, close to which they become superficial. They then extend laterally in the superficial fascia. In the lower half of the back the cutaneous nerves are directed downwards and laterally among the muscles, and become superficial at a greater distance from the median plane. In both regions the nerves pursue a sinuous course to the surface, and the lower series emerge and become superficial a considerable distance below the level of their origin. There are considerable individual differences in the origin, course, and distribution of the several nerves.

CERVICAL NERVES

First Cervical Nerve.—The posterior root of this nerve may be small or even altogether absent. Its *posterior primary ramus* is larger than the anterior ramus; it does not divide into medial or lateral branches, and it does not directly supply any cutaneous branch.

Passing backwards, in the space between the occipital bone and the posterior arch of the atlas, the nerve occupies the sub-occipital triangle, and is placed below and behind the vertebral artery, and under cover of the semispinalis capitis muscle. It supplies the following branches:—

(*a*) **Muscular branches** to the semispinalis capitis, rectus capitis posterior major and minor, and obliquus capitis superior and inferior.

(*b*) A **communicating branch** descends to join the second cervical nerve.

The communicating branch may arise in common with the nerve to the obliquus inferior, and reach the second cervical nerve by piercing or passing superficial or deep to that muscle; or it may accompany the nerve to the semispinalis capitis and communicate with the greater occipital nerve, under or over that muscle.

Second Cervical Nerve.—The *posterior primary ramus* of this nerve is larger than the corresponding anterior primary ramus. It passes backwards between the atlas and axis, in the interval between the obliquus inferior and the semispinalis cervicis muscles, and under cover of the semispinalis capitis muscle. In that situation the nerve gives off several small muscular and communicating branches. The main trunk, after piercing the semispinalis capitis and trapezius muscles, accompanies the occipital artery to the scalp as the **greater occipital nerve**. This is the chief cutaneous nerve for the posterior part of the scalp. It enters the superficial fascia at the level of the superior nuchal line of the occipital bone and about an inch from the external occipital protuberance. Ramifying over the surface, it supplies the skin and subcutaneous tissues of the scalp as far as the vertex. It *communicates* on the scalp with the following nerves: great auricular, lesser occipital, posterior auricular, and third occipital.

The **muscular branches** of the second cervical nerve are destined for the semispinalis capitis, obliquus inferior, semispinalis cervicis, and multifidus.

Associated with the posterior primary ramus is the **posterior cervical plexus**. Descending over the posterior arch of the atlas is a branch from the first cervical nerve which forms a loop or network with a branch of the second nerve. From that loop twigs are supplied to the surrounding muscles. A similar loop is formed by a communication between the posterior primary rami of the second and third nerves, from which muscles are also supplied. Occasionally an additional loop is formed between the posterior primary rami of the third and fourth nerves.

Third Cervical Nerve.—This *posterior primary ramus* is much smaller than that of the second nerve. Near its origin it forms a loop of communication with the second, and it may give off a similar communicating branch to the fourth nerve. The main trunk divides into medial, cutaneous, and lateral, muscular, branches. The lateral muscular branch enters contiguous muscles; the medial cutaneous branch passes backwards and medially, and becomes superficial as the **third occipital nerve**, close to the median plane of the neck. It supplies fine branches to the skin and fascia of the neck and scalp, and communicates with the greater occipital nerve.

The **posterior primary rami** of the **fourth, fifth, and sixth cervical nerves** are still smaller. Deep to the semispinalis capitis each divides into lateral, muscular, and medial, cutaneous, branches. The muscular branches supply neighbouring muscles; the cutaneous branches are small nerves which, passing backwards, become

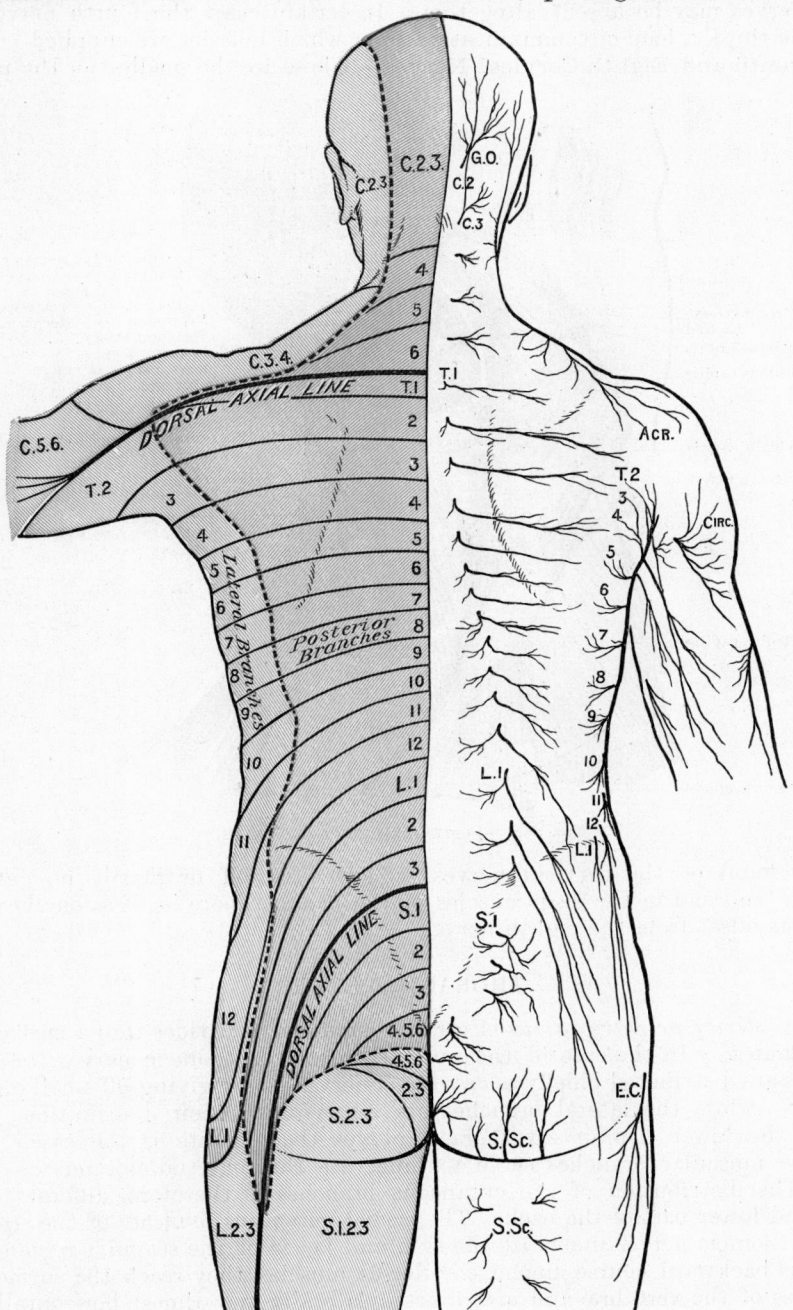

Fig. 867.—The Distribution of Cutaneous Nerves on the Back of the Trunk.

On one side the distribution of the several named nerves is represented.

G.O. (C.2), Greater occipital; C.3, Third occipital; T.1 *et seq.*, Posterior primary rami of thoracic nerves; L.1 *et seq.*, Posterior primary rami of first three lumbar nerves; S.1 *et seq.*, Posterior primary rami of sacral nerves; Acr., Supra-clavicular branches from cervical plexus; T.2-12, Lateral branches of thoracic nerves; Circ. Cutaneous branches of circumflex nerve; L.1, Lateral cutaneous branch of ilio-hypogastric nerve; E.C., Lateral cutaneous nerve of thigh; S.Sc., Posterior cutaneous nerve of thigh.

On the other side a schematic representation is given of the areas supplied by the above nerves, the numerals indicating the spinal origin of the branches of distribution to each area.

superficial close to the median plane. They supply the skin of the back of the neck. The sixth is the smallest, and the cutaneous branches of the fifth and sixth nerves may be absent altogether. In certain cases the fourth nerve forms, with the third, a loop of communication from which muscles are supplied.

Seventh and Eighth Cervical Nerves.—These are the smallest of the posterior

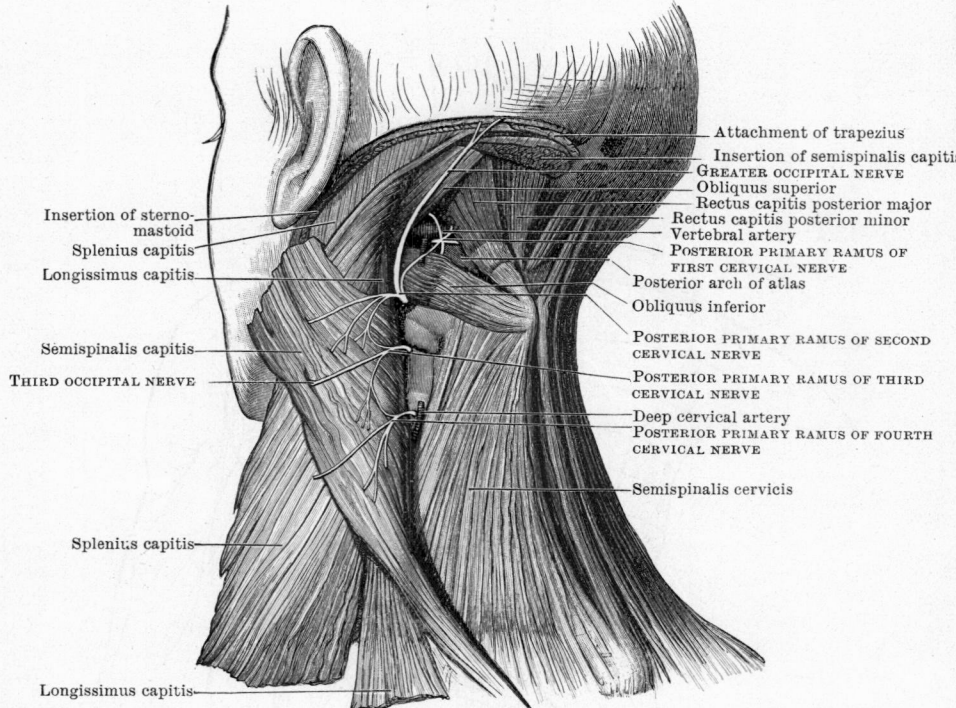

Insertion of sterno-mastoid
Splenius capitis
Longissimus capitis

Semispinalis capitis
THIRD OCCIPITAL NERVE

Splenius capitis

Longissimus capitis

Attachment of trapezius
Insertion of semispinalis capitis
GREATER OCCIPITAL NERVE
Obliquus superior
Rectus capitis posterior major
Rectus capitis posterior minor
Vertebral artery
POSTERIOR PRIMARY RAMUS OF FIRST CERVICAL NERVE
Posterior arch of atlas
Obliquus inferior
POSTERIOR PRIMARY RAMUS OF SECOND CERVICAL NERVE
POSTERIOR PRIMARY RAMUS OF THIRD CERVICAL NERVE
Deep cervical artery
POSTERIOR PRIMARY RAMUS OF FOURTH CERVICAL NERVE
Semispinalis cervicis

FIG. 868.—POSTERIOR CERVICAL PLEXUS.

primary rami of the cervical nerves. They give off ordinarily no cutaneous branches, and end in the deep muscles of the back. There is occasionally a small cutaneous offset from the eighth nerve.

THORACIC NERVES

The *posterior primary ramus* of each thoracic nerve divides into a **medial** and a **lateral branch.** In the case of the upper six or seven thoracic nerves the medial branches are distributed chiefly as *cutaneous* nerves—only giving off small muscular branches—while the lateral branches are *muscular* in their distribution; in the case of the lower five or six thoracic nerves the opposite is the case. In all cases the muscular branches serve to innervate the longitudinal muscles of the back. The distribution of the cutaneous branches is therefore different in the upper and lower part of the back. The **medial cutaneous branches** of the *upper six* or *seven* thoracic nerves innervate the skin and fascia of the scapular region; after a sinuous backward course among the dorsal muscles, they reach the surface near the spines of the vertebræ and are directed laterally and almost horizontally over the trapezius muscle. The first is small; the second is very large and reaches to the acromion. The rest diminish in size, from above downwards, and become more and more oblique in direction. The **lateral cutaneous branches** of the *lower five* or *six* thoracic nerves are directed from their origin obliquely downwards and laterally among the parts of the sacro-spinalis muscle. Becoming cutaneous by piercing the latissimus dorsi at some distance from the median plane, they supply the skin and fascia of the back in the lower part of the chest and loin, the lowest nerves (eleventh and twelfth) passing over the iliac crest into the gluteal region.

The lower nerves often subdivide into two branches before or after they emerge from the latissimus dorsi muscle. Owing to the obliquity of their course, each of those cutaneous branches supplies an area of skin which lies at a lower level than does the posterior primary ramus from which the branch arises.

LUMBAR NERVES

The *posterior primary rami* of the **first three lumbar nerves** subdivide into medial and lateral branches in the same way as the lower thoracic nerves. The medial branches are muscular and innervate the deep muscles of the back. The lateral branches are chiefly cutaneous. They are directed obliquely downwards and laterally among the fibres of the sacro-spinalis and become superficial by piercing the lumbar fascia, just above the iliac crest and a short distance in front of the posterior superior iliac spine. They are then directed downwards in the superficial fascia of the gluteal region, and supply a lengthy strip of skin, extending from the median plane above the iliac crest to a point distal to and behind the greater trochanter of the femur. There may be only two cutaneous branches, derived from the first two lumbar nerves.

The *posterior primary rami* of the **fourth and fifth lumbar nerves** (like those of the last two cervical nerves) usually supply only muscular branches to the longitudinal muscles of the back. The fifth nerve in many cases sends a branch to form a loop of connexion with the posterior primary ramus of the first sacral nerve, contributing to the posterior sacral plexus.

SACRAL AND COCCYGEAL NERVES

The *posterior primary rami* of the sacral nerves issue from the posterior sacral foramina. As in the case of the thoracic and lumbar nerves, the upper sacral nerves differ from the lower in their distribution.

The *posterior primary rami* of the **first three sacral nerves** supply medial muscular branches for the multifidus and lateral cutaneous branches which pierce the fibres of the sacro-tuberous ligament and the gluteus maximus muscle, and supply the skin and fascia over the back of the sacrum and contiguous part of the gluteal region, giving rise to the posterior sacral plexus.

The **posterior sacral plexus** consists, like the posterior cervical plexus, of loops or plexiform communications over the back of the sacrum between the posterior primary rami of the first three sacral nerves, to which are frequently joined branches of the last lumbar nerve and the fourth and even the fifth sacral nerve. From those loops branches proceed to supply the multifidus muscle; others pierce the sacro-tuberous ligament and form secondary loops deep to the gluteus maximus muscle. From the secondary loops two or more cutaneous branches arise, which, after traversing the muscle, supply the skin and fascia over the sacrum and medial part of the gluteal region.

The *posterior primary rami* of the **fourth and fifth sacral nerves** do not divide into medial and lateral branches. They unite together to form a loop which is joined by the minute *posterior primary ramus* of the **coccygeal nerve.** The union of the three constitutes a nerve which, after perforating the sacro-tuberous ligament, is distributed to the skin and fascia in the neighbourhood of the coccyx. It supplies no muscles. This nerve is the representative of the **superior caudal trunk** of tailed animals.

Morphology of the Posterior Primary Rami

1. **Muscular Distribution.**—In their muscular distribution they are strictly limited to the longitudinal muscles of the back : namely, those associated with the axial skeleton alone.

2. **Cutaneous Distribution.**—Their cutaneous distribution presents two points of interest.

A. In the first place, while the skin of the back is supplied in a fairly regular segmental manner by the several nerves, certain of them fail to reach the surface at all. The absence of a cutaneous branch from the first cervical nerve may be due either to the absence of a perfect posterior root, or to its communication with the second nerve. The other nerves which do not usually supply the skin are the last two, three, or four cervical, and the fourth and fifth lumbar nerves. Those nerves are placed in the centre of regions in which the upper and lower limbs are developed. They are minute nerves, while the corresponding anterior primary rami are among the largest of the spinal nerves. Thus opposite the centre of each limb posteriorly there is a hiatus in the segmental distribution of the posterior primary rami of the spinal nerves to the skin of the shoulder and gluteal region, attributable to the formation of the limbs and the extension into them of the greater part of the nerves of the region. The gap, in the case of the upper limb, begins at the level of the vertebra prominens; in the case of the lower limb it commences at the level of the posterior superior iliac spine. It can be continued on to each limb as a hypothetical area (the **dorsal axial line**) which indicates the area of contact (and overlapping) of cutaneous nerves not in strictly numerical sequence. Thus, in the region of the shoulder, the sixth (or fifth) cervical nerve innervates an area of skin adjoining that supplied by the eighth cervical or first thoracic nerve; in the gluteal region the third lumbar nerve supplies an area contiguous with that supplied by the fifth lumbar or first sacral nerve.

B. The cutaneous branches of the posterior primary rami of the spinal nerves differ from the muscular branches in respect of their penetration into regions beyond those supplied by their motor roots. The cutaneous branches, in regions where outgrowths or extensions from the trunk have occurred, follow those extensions; and, in consequence, supply skin covering parts which do not belong to segments represented by the nerves in question. Thus the second and third cervical nerves (greater and third occipital) are drawn upwards so as to supply the posterior part of the *scalp*; the upper thoracic nerves are drawn laterally over the *scapular region*; the upper lumbar and sacral nerves supply the skin of the *gluteal region*; and the lower lumbar and coccygeal nerves form a rudimentary *caudal nerve*.

3. **Plexuses.**—The plexuses formed by the posterior primary rami of the upper cervical and upper sacral nerves are the simplest met with in the human body. The posterior cervical plexus is one from which muscular branches are supplied; the posterior sacral plexus is mainly concerned with cutaneous offsets.

ANTERIOR PRIMARY RAMI OF THE SPINAL NERVES

The **anterior primary rami** of the spinal nerves are, with the exception of the first two cervical nerves, much larger than the corresponding posterior primary rami. Composed of elements of both posterior and anterior roots, each nerve separates from the posterior primary ramus on emerging from the intervertebral foramen, and, proceeding laterally, is distributed to structures on the lateral and anterior aspects of the body—including the limbs.

Each nerve is joined near its origin by a **grey ramus communicans** from the corresponding sympathetic trunk; and in the case of the thoracic and certain lumbar nerves the anterior primary ramus gives off a delicate bundle of fibres which forms the **white ramus communicans** to the sympathetic trunk. From two of the sacral nerves white rami (belonging to the parasympathetic) pass to the pelvic plexuses of the autonomic nervous system; those rami form the *pelvic splanchnic nerve* on each side as they extend towards the plexuses. That part of a spinal nerve which is distributed to the body wall and limbs may be termed **somatic**; the small white ramus communicans, innervating structures in the splanchnic area, may be termed the **visceral** or **splanchnic** part of a spinal nerve.

The anterior primary rami of the spinal nerves are distributed in a regular segmental manner only in certain cases. Except in the case of the thoracic nerves, the anterior primary rami combine to form **plexuses**—cervical, brachial, and lumbar, sacral and coccygeal—and their arrangement and distribution is exceedingly complex.

An **intercostal nerve,** such as the fifth or sixth, may be regarded as a type to illustrate the mode of distribution of the anterior primary rami of the spinal nerves (Fig. 864, p. 993). It occupies an intercostal space; near its origin it possesses *grey* and *white rami communicantes*; it courses through the interval between the intercostal muscles; it supplies branches to those muscles and gives off, when it reaches the side of the chest, a *lateral cutaneous branch*, which, after supplying small muscular branches, pierces the external intercostal muscle and is distributed to an area of skin and fascia over the lateral part of the trunk contiguous dorsally with a similar area innervated by the cutaneous branches of the posterior primary ramus of the same nerve. The lateral branch generally subdivides into a smaller *posterior* and a larger *anterior branch* as it pierces the muscles clothing the wall of the chest. The main trunk of the nerve, having given off its lateral branch, then pursues its course obliquely forwards to the side of the sternum, where, after piercing the pectoral muscles, it terminates superficially as the *anterior cutaneous branch*. That supplies an area of skin and fascia con-

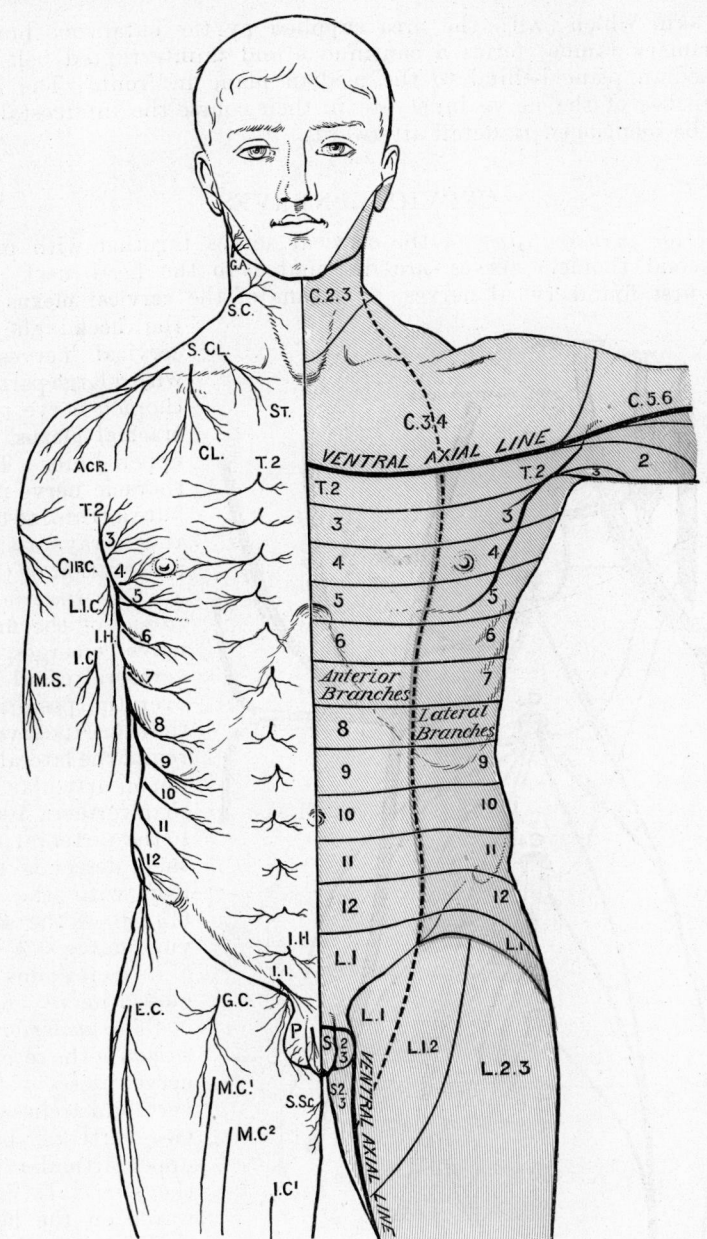

FIG. 869.—DISTRIBUTION OF CUTANEOUS NERVES ON THE FRONT OF THE TRUNK.

On one side the distribution of the several named nerves is represented.

G.A., Great auricular nerve ; S.C., anterior cutaneous nerve of the neck ; S.CL., Supra-clavicular nerves :—
ACR., Lateral ; CL., Intermediate ; ST., Medial. T.2-12, Lateral and anterior branches of thoracic
nerves ; I.H. (below) Ilio-hypogastric nerve ; I.I., Ilio-inguinal nerve ; CIRC., Cutaneous branch of
circumflex nerve ; L.I.C., Medial cutaneous nerve of the arm ; I.H. (above) Intercosto-brachial ; I.C.,
Medial cutaneous nerve of the forearm ; M.S., Cutaneous branch of radial nerve ; E.C., Lateral cutaneous
nerve of thigh ; G.C., Femoral branch of genito-femoral nerve ; M.C.[1],[2], Branches of intermediate
cutaneous nerve of thigh ; I.C.[1], Branch of medial cutaneous nerve of thigh ; P., Branches of pudendal
nerve ; S.SC., Branches of posterior cutaneous nerve of the thigh.

On the other side a schematic representation is given of the areas supplied by the above nerves, the numerals
indicating the spinal origin of the branches of distribution to each area.

tinuous with that supplied by the anterior part of the lateral branch of the same
nerve. Such a nerve thus supplies, by means of its lateral and anterior branches,

an area of skin which (with the area supplied by the cutaneous branch of its posterior primary ramus) forms a continuous and uninterrupted belt, extending from the median plane behind to the median plane in front. The lateral and anterior branches of the nerve innervate in their course the intercostal and other muscles, to be mentioned in detail afterwards.

CERVICAL NERVES

The *anterior primary rami* of the cervical nerves, together with parts of the first and second thoracic nerves, are distributed to the head, neck, and upper limb. The first four cervical nerves, by means of the **cervical plexus**, innervate the neck; the last four cervical nerves, together with a large part of the first thoracic nerve, through the **brachial plexus**, supply the upper limb. The second thoracic nerve may contribute a trunk to this plexus, and always assists in the innervation of the arm.

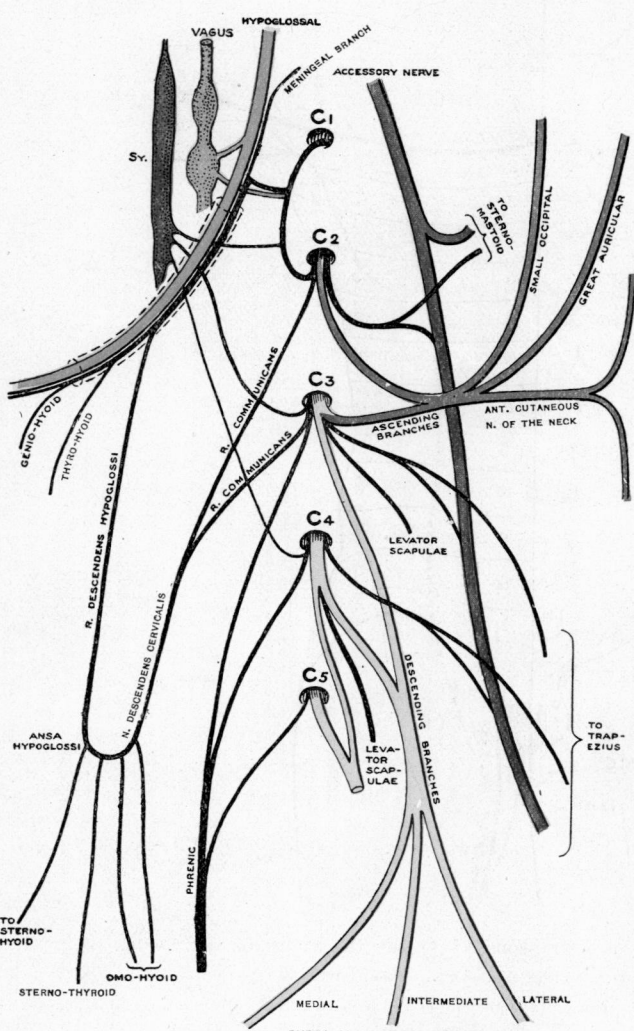

Fig. 870.—The Left Cervical Plexus.

The *anterior primary ramus* of the **first cervical nerve** emerges from the vertebral canal by passing over the posterior arch of the atlas; it curves forwards round the lateral side of the upper articular process of that vertebra, lying medial to the vertebral artery, and then descends to form a loop with the ascending branch of the second cervical nerve. A large part of its fibres joins the hypoglossal nerve (*vide infra*).

The *anterior primary ramus* of the **second cervical nerve** passes between the vertebral arches of the first two vertebræ, behind the upper articular process of the axis. It curves forwards on the lateral side of the vertebral artery and divides into an ascending portion, which unites with the first cervical nerve and also contributes fibres to the hypoglossal nerve, and a descending part, which joins the third cervical nerve and takes part in the cervical plexus.

CERVICAL PLEXUS

The *anterior primary rami* of the first four cervical nerves are concerned in forming the **cervical plexus**. Each nerve emerges from the vertebral canal posterior to the vertebral artery. Each is joined on its emergence from the intervertebral foramen at the side of the vertebral column by a **grey ramus communicans** from the superior cervical ganglion of the sympathetic trunk. In the neck the cervical nerves are concealed at their origins by the sterno-mastoid muscle; in front lies the longus capitis muscle, and behind are the scalenus medius, and (behind the first nerve) the rectus capitis lateralis. The cervical plexus is constituted by the combination of the four nerves in an irregular series of loops under cover of the sterno-mastoid muscle, and overlapped, in part, by the internal jugular vein.

From the loops of the plexus the branches of distribution arise, as (*a*) **cutaneous branches** to the head, neck, and shoulder; (*b*) **muscular branches** to muscles of the neck and to the diaphragm; and (*c*) **communicating branches** to the vagus, accessory, hypoglossal, and sympathetic nerves.

For convenience of description, the nerves derived from the plexus may be classified as follows :—

I. Superficial (Cutaneous) Branches—

A. Ascending Branches (C. 2, 3).

Lesser occipital,
Great auricular,
Anterior cutaneous of the neck.

B. Descending (supraclavicular) Branches (C. 3, 4).

Medial supraclavicular,
Intermediate supraclavicular,
Lateral supraclavicular.

II. Deep (Muscular and Communicating) Branches—

A. Lateral Branches.

1. Muscular branches to
   Sterno-mastoid (C. 2),
   Trapezius (C. 3, 4),
   Levator scapulæ (C. 3, 4),
   Scaleni (medius and posterior) (C. 3, 4).
2. Communicating branches to
   Accessory nerve (C. 2, 3, 4).

B. Medial Branches.

1. Muscular to
   Prevertebral muscles (C. 1, 2, 3, 4),
   Infrahyoid muscles (C. 1, 2, 3)
   (ansa hypoglossi),
   Diaphragm (C. 3, **4**, 5) (phrenic nerve).
2. Communicating branches to
   Vagus nerve (C. 1, 2),
   Hypoglossal nerve (C. 1, 2),
   Ansa hypoglossi (C. 2, 3),
   Sympathetic (C. 1, 2, 3, 4).

The second, third, and fourth cervical nerves are the chief nerves engaged in forming the plexus. The first cervical nerve only enters into the formation of a small part—the medial portion of the deep part of the plexus.

Superficial Cutaneous Branches.—Those nerves, six in number, are entirely cutaneous. They radiate from the plexus, and appear in the posterior triangle of the neck a little above the mid-point of the posterior border of the sterno-mastoid muscle. They are divisible into three series—(1) the **ascending** : lesser occipital, great auricular; (2) **transverse** : the anterior cutaneous nerve of the neck; (3) **descending** (supraclavicular): lateral intermediate and medial.

Ascending Branches.—The **lesser occipital nerve** is variable in size and is sometimes double. Its origin is from the second and third cervical nerves (more rarely from the second only). It extends backwards under cover of the sterno-mastoid, and then upwards along its posterior border. Piercing the deep fascia near the apex of the posterior triangle, it divides into branches for the supply of the skin and fascia of the upper part of the neck, the cranial surface of the auricle and part of the scalp adjoining. The nerve communicates on the scalp with the greater occipital and great auricular nerves, and with the posterior auricular branch of the facial nerve.

The **great auricular nerve** is the largest of the cutaneous branches. It arises from the second and third cervical nerves (or, more rarely, from the third alone). Winding round the posterior border of the sterno-mastoid muscle, it proceeds upwards and forwards towards the front of the auricle. In its course it crosses the sterno-mastoid muscle obliquely and is covered by the platysma muscle. Before arriving at the auricle it subdivides into three groups of branches. The posterior ascend over the mastoid process and supply the skin and fascia of the scalp immediately behind the auricle, communicating with the lesser occipital and posterior auricular nerves. The middle ones ascend to the auricle and supply its lower part on both surfaces; their communications are similar to those of the posterior branches. The anterior pass over the angle of the mandible and through the substance of the parotid gland to supply the skin and fascia of the face over the inferior part of the masseter muscle and the parotid gland. They communicate with branches of the facial nerve in the parotid gland.

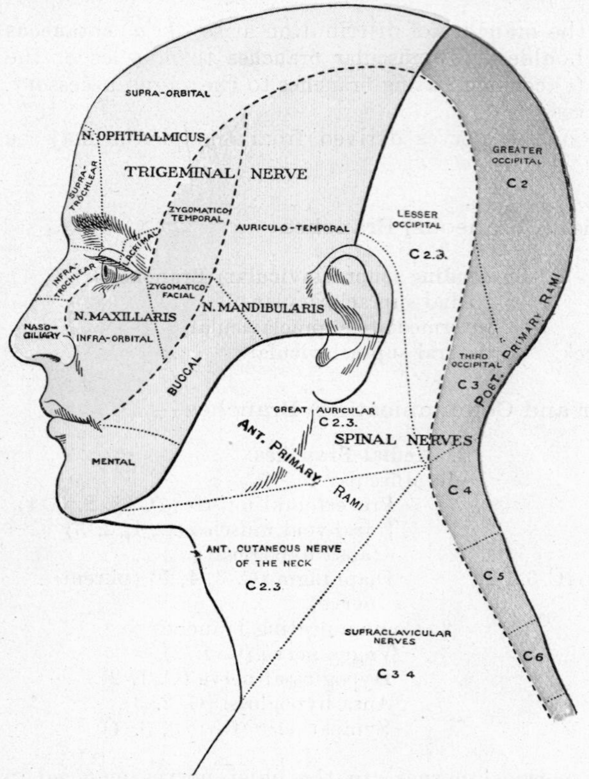

FIG. 871.—DISTRIBUTION OF CUTANEOUS NERVES TO THE HEAD AND NECK.

Transverse Branch.— The **anterior cutaneous nerve of the neck** [N. cutaneus colli] arises from the second and third cervical nerves. It winds round the posterior border of the sterno-mastoid muscle, and crosses the muscle to reach the anterior triangle, under cover of the platysma muscle and the external jugular vein. It divides near the anterior edge of the sterno-mastoid muscle into superior and inferior branches which are distributed through the platysma to the skin and fascia covering the anterior triangle of the neck. The upper branches communicate freely, under cover of the platysma, with the cervical branch of the facial nerve.

Descending (Supra-clavicular) Branches. — By the union of two roots derived from the third and fourth cervical nerves a considerable trunk is formed which emerges from under cover of the sterno-mastoid muscle and extends obliquely downwards through the inferior part of the posterior triangle of the neck. It subdivides into radiating branches—**medial, intermediate,** and **lateral**—which pierce the deep fascia of the neck above the clavicle, and are distributed to the skin and fascia of the inferior part of the side of the neck, to the front of the chest, and the shoulder. The **medial branches** are the smallest. They pass over the medial part of the clavicle, and supply the skin and fascia of the neck and chest as far down as the angle of the sternum. The **intermediate branches** pass over the intermediate third of the clavicle, deep to the platysma, and can be traced as low as the third rib. The **lateral branches** pass over or through the insertion of the trapezius muscle and over the lateral third of the clavicle to the shoulder, where they supply the skin and fascia as far down as the distal third of the deltoid muscle. Occasionally one of these branches pierces the clavicle.

Deep Branches.—The deep branches of the cervical plexus are separated into a **lateral** and a **medial set**. Deep to the sterno-mastoid muscle, the lateral branches are directed laterally towards the posterior triangle; the medial branches pass medially towards the anterior triangle.

The **lateral branches** consist of muscular and communicating nerves, which for the most part lie in the posterior triangle.

The **muscular branches** are the following: (1) To the *sterno-mastoid*, from the second cervical nerve; it enters the muscle on its deep surface and communicates with the accessory nerve. (2) To the *trapezius*, from the third and fourth cervical nerves; these branches cross the posterior triangle and end in the trapezius, after communicating with the accessory nerve, both in the posterior triangle, and under cover of the muscle. (3) To the *levator scapulae*, from the third and fourth

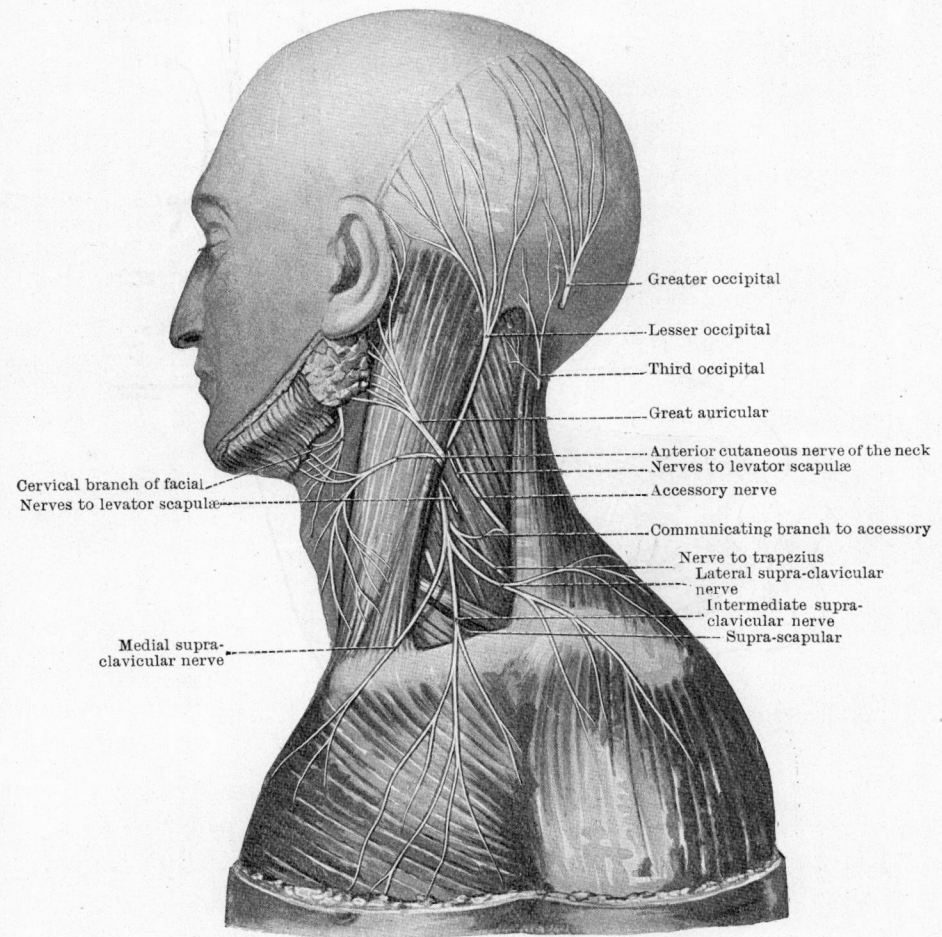

Cervical branch of facial
Nerves to levator scapulæ

Greater occipital

Lesser occipital

Third occipital

Great auricular

Anterior cutaneous nerve of the neck
Nerves to levator scapulæ
Accessory nerve

Communicating branch to accessory

Nerve to trapezius
Lateral supra-clavicular nerve
Intermediate supra-clavicular nerve
Supra-scapular

Medial supra-clavicular nerve

FIG. 872.—THE NERVES OF THE SIDE OF THE NECK.

cervical nerves; two independent branches enter the lateral surface of the muscle in the posterior triangle. (4) To the *scaleni* (medius and posterior), from the third and fourth cervical nerves.

The **communicating branches** are three in number. They join the accessory nerve in three situations: (*a*) A branch from the second cervical nerve to the sterno-mastoid joins the accessory nerve *under cover of that muscle*. (*b*) Branches to the trapezius from the third and fourth nerves are connected with the accessory nerve *in the posterior triangle*. (*c*) Branches from the same nerves join the nerve *under cover of the trapezius muscle*.

The **medial branches** of the plexus also comprise muscular and communicating branches. The anterior ramus of the first cervical nerve assists in the formation of this series of nerves, forming a slender loop with part of the second nerve in front of the transverse process of the atlas.

Communicating Branches.—(*a*) *With the sympathetic.*—A grey ramus communicans passes to each of the first four cervical nerves, near its origin, from the superior cervical ganglion or from the trunk below the ganglion. (*b*) *With the vagus nerve.*—The inferior ganglion of the vagus nerve may be connected by a slender nerve with the loop between the first two cervical nerves. That communication is not constant. (*c*) *With the hypoglossal.*—An important communication occurs between the hypoglossal nerve and the loop between the first and second

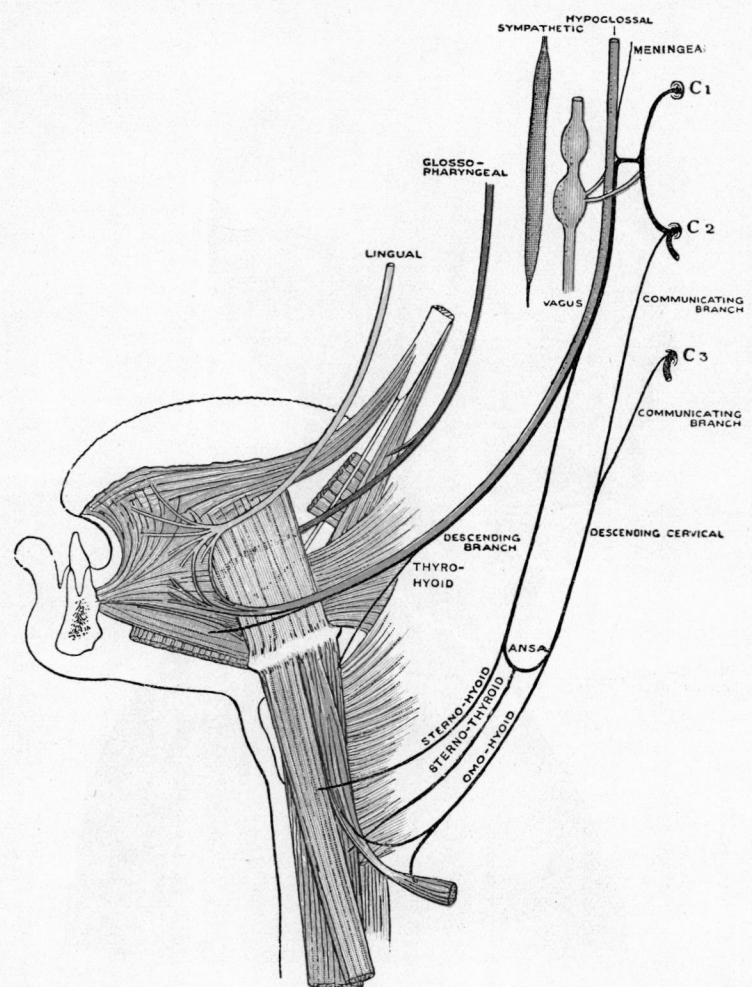

FIG. 873.—THE MUSCLES OF THE HYOID BONE AND STYLOID PROCESS, AND THE EXTRINSIC MUSCLES OF THE TONGUE, WITH THEIR NERVES.

cervical nerves (Fig. 873). A trunk from the loop joins the hypoglossal just beyond its exit from the skull. One fine branch from this trunk passes upwards along the hypoglossal nerve to the cranium (*meningeal branch*). The main part of the trunk accompanies the hypoglossal and separates from it to form successively three nerves—the **descending branch** of the hypoglossal (ramus descendens), and the **branches to the thyro-hyoid** and **genio-hyoid muscles**. The portion of the nerve which remains accompanies the hypoglossal to the muscles of the tongue. It is probable that no part of the hypoglossal nerve itself is concerned in the formation of those three branches. The descending branch of the hypoglossal descends in front of the internal and common carotid arteries, and is joined in the anterior triangle of the neck by the **nervus descendens cervicalis** to form the **ansa hypoglossi**, from which the infra-hyoid muscles, except the thyro-hyoid, are innervated. (The "descending branch of the hypoglossal," in some cases, arises from the vagus nerve.)

Muscular Branches.—The muscles supplied by the medial branches of the plexus are the prevertebral muscles, the genio-hyoid and the infrahyoid muscles, and the diaphragm.

(*a*) **Prevertebral Muscles.**—(1) From the loop between the first and second cervical nerves a small branch arises for the supply of the rectus capitis lateralis, longus capitis, and the rectus capitis anterior. (2) From the second, third, and fourth nerves small branches supply the intertransverse, longus cervicis, and longus capitis muscles. (3) From the third and fourth nerve a branch arises for the supply of the scaleni (medius and posterior).

(*b*) **Genio-hyoid and Infrahyoid Muscles.**—The **nervus descendens cervicalis** is formed in front of the internal jugular vein by the union of two slender trunks from the second and third cervical nerves. It forms a loop of communication in front of the carotid sheath with the descending branch of the hypoglossal nerve (derived ultimately from the first two cervical nerves). The loop of communication is called the **ansa hypoglossi.** It is often plexiform; and from it branches are given to the sterno-hyoid and sterno-thyroid muscles and both bellies of the omo-hyoid muscle. The nerve to the sterno-hyoid muscle is often continued behind the sternum, to join, in the thorax, with the phrenic nerve or the cardiac plexus.

The thyro-hyoid and genio-hyoid muscles are supplied by branches of the hypoglossal nerve which are also traceable back to the communication between the hypoglossal and the first two cervical nerves.

The anterior muscles in immediate relation to the median plane of the neck, between the chin and the sternum, are thus continuously supplied by the first three cervical nerves. The hypoglossal is the source of supply to the muscles of the tongue, and it is improbable that it contributes any fibres to the above-named muscles.

(*c*) **Diaphragm.**—The phrenic nerve supplies the diaphragm.

PHRENIC NERVE

The **phrenic nerve** is derived mainly from the **fourth cervical nerve**, reinforced by roots from the third (either directly or through the nerve to the sterno-hyoid) and fifth (either directly or through the nerve to the subclavius muscle). It runs downwards in the neck upon the scalenus anterior muscle; at the root of the neck it passes between the subclavian artery and vein, enters the thorax and traverses the mediastinum to reach the diaphragm, lying in the middle mediastinum between the pericardium and pleura and anterior to the root of the lung. In its course it presents certain differences on the two sides. In the neck, on the left side, it crosses the first part of the subclavian artery; on the right side it crosses the second part. In the superior mediastinum, on the left side, it lies between the left subclavian and carotid arteries, and crosses lateral to the vagus nerve and the aortic arch. On the right side it accompanies the innominate vein and superior vena cava, and is entirely separate from the vagus nerve. The left nerve is longer than the right, owing to the position of the heart and the left half of the diaphragm. The right nerve sends fibres along the inferior vena cava through the hiatus venæ cavæ. Reaching the diaphragm the nerve separates into numerous branches for the supply of the muscle; some enter its thoracic surface (subpleural branches), but most of the fibres supply it after piercing the muscle (subperitoneal branches). It is apparent, from clinical observations, that the nerve contains some afferent fibres as well as motor.

The **branches of the phrenic nerve** are: (1) Muscular (to the diaphragm); (2) pleural; (3) pericardial; (4) abdominal.

The branches to the pleura and pericardium arise as the phrenic nerve traverses the mediastinum. The abdominal branches arise after communication of the phrenic nerve with the phrenic plexus of the sympathetic on the abdominal surface of the diaphragm.

Of interest to the surgeon, particularly with reference to the operation of avulsion of the phrenic, is the occasional presence of an *accessory phrenic nerve.*

It arises from the fifth or fifth and sixth cervical nerves and, after descending for a variable distance, joins the main nerve in the lower part of the neck or in the thorax.

Communications of the Phrenic Nerve.—(1) The phrenic nerve may communicate with the nerve to the subclavius muscle. (2) It may communicate with the *ansa hypoglossi*, or a branch from it (the nerve to the sterno-hyoid). (3) It frequently communicates with the cervical part of the sympathetic. (4) It communicates with the cœliac plexus by a junction on the abdominal surface of the diaphragm with the *phrenic plexus* on the phrenic artery, in which a small *phrenic ganglion* is found on the right side. From the junction branches are given off to the inferior vena cava, suprarenal gland, and hepatic plexus.

Morphology of the Cervical Plexus

The characteristic feature of the cervical plexus is the combination of parts of adjacent nerves into compound nerve-trunks by the formation of series of loops. The result of the formation of those loops is that parts (particularly cutaneous areas) are supplied by branches of more than one spinal nerve.

A. **Cutaneous Distribution.**—By the combinations of the nerves into loops the discrimination of the elements in the upper cervical nerves, corresponding to the lateral and anterior branches of a typical intercostal nerve, is made a matter of some difficulty. The second, third, and fourth nerves, through the cervical plexus, supply an area of skin extending laterally from the side of the head to the shoulder; anteriorly from the face to the level of the third rib. The higher nerves supply the upper region (second and third); the lower nerves supply the lower region (third and fourth). It is not possible to compare the individual nerves strictly with the lateral and anterior branches of an intercostal nerve. A line drawn from the auricle to the middle of the clavicle separates, however, a lateral from an anterior cutaneous area; and certain of the cutaneous nerves fall naturally into one of these two categories. The nerves homologous with the anterior continuations of the anterior branches of intercostal nerves are the anterior cutaneous nerve of the neck and the medial branches of the supraclavicular series; those homologous with lateral branches are the lesser occipital and lateral supraclavicular branches. The great auricular and intermediate supraclavicular branches are mixed nerves, comprising elements belonging to both sets.

B. **Muscular Distribution.**—The nerves from the cervical plexus that supply muscles are simpler in their arrangement. They are not generally in the form of loops, and they are easily separated into lateral and medial series. The lateral nerves comprise the branches to the rectus capitis lateralis, sterno-mastoid, trapezius, levator scapulæ. The nerves in the medial series are those to the longus capitis, rectus capitis anterior, the hyoid muscles, and the diaphragm.

It is noteworthy that the last-named muscles—genio-hyoid, thyro-hyoid, sterno-hyoid, omo-hyoid, sterno-thyroid, and diaphragm—are continuously supplied by branches from the first five cervical nerves: the higher muscles by the higher nerves; the lower muscles by the lower nerves.

BRACHIAL PLEXUS

The **brachial plexus** is formed by the anterior primary rami of the fifth, sixth, seventh and eighth cervical nerves, along with the greater part of that of the first thoracic nerve. More often than not a slender branch of the fourth cervical nerve is also engaged; and the second thoracic nerve always contributes to the innervation of the arm through the intercosto-brachial nerve. Frequently it contributes also directly to the plexus by an intrathoracic communication with the first thoracic nerve.

Position of the Plexus.—The nerves forming the brachial plexus appear in the posterior triangle of the neck between the scalenus anterior and scalenus medius muscles in series with the nerves that form the cervical plexus. In the triangle the plexus is covered by the skin, platysma, supraclavicular nerves, and the deep fascia, and is crossed by the nerve to the subclavius muscle, external jugular vein, inferior belly of the omo-hyoid muscle, and the transverse cervical artery, which vessel sometimes passes between its branches. At the root of the neck the plexus passes behind the clavicle, subclavius muscle, and suprascapular vessels, and it lies above and behind the third part of the subclavian artery. In the axilla its branches surround the upper part of the axillary artery.

Composition of the Brachial Plexus.—Whilst liable to some variation in the sequence of separation and junction of its individual parts, in a typical plexus four stages may always be identified :—

(1) The undivided anterior primary rami of the nerves.
(2) The formation of three trunks.
(3) The separation of each trunk into an anterior and a posterior division.
(4) The union of the divisions to form three cords from which the principal nerves of distribution originate.

(1) The undivided **nerves** or **roots of the plexus** have only a very short independent course at the side of the neck whilst passing between the scalene muscles.

(2) Immediately after entering the posterior triangle, there are formed three **trunks** in order from above downwards : the *upper trunk* is formed by the union

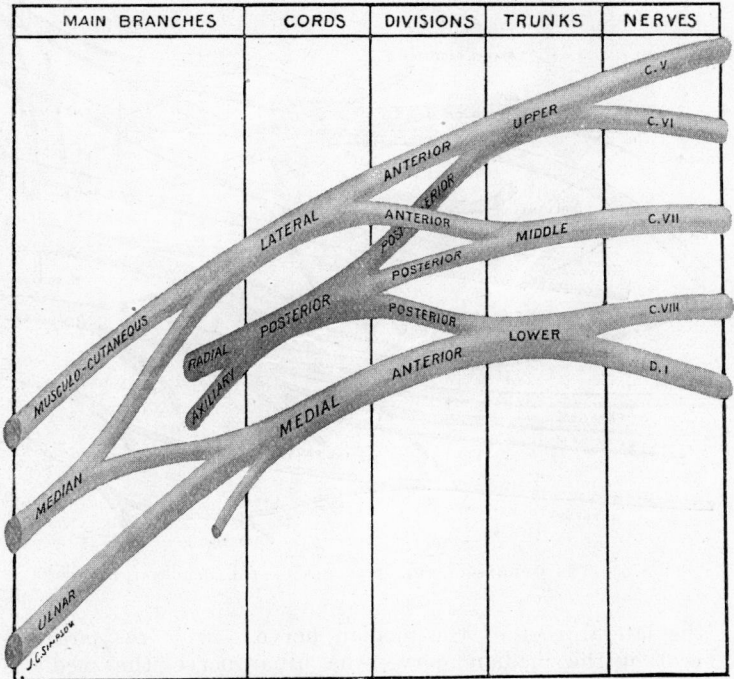

MAIN BRANCHES	CORDS	DIVISIONS	TRUNKS	NERVES

Fig. 874.—Scheme to show the Stages of Formation of the Brachial Plexus. (S. E. W.)

of the fifth and sixth nerves ; the *middle trunk* is always formed by the seventh nerve alone ; and the *lower trunk*, by the union of the eighth cervical and first thoracic nerves. The lower trunk often grooves the upper surface of the first rib behind the groove for the subclavian artery.

(3) Each trunk divides into anterior and posterior **divisions**, which represent corresponding separation of the nerves ; sometimes the nerves themselves divide before or during the formation of the trunks, making identification of those two stages difficult. The anterior and posterior divisions of the fifth, sixth, and seventh nerves are nearly equal in size ; the posterior division of the eighth cervical nerve is much smaller ; and that of the first thoracic nerve is minute and may not be present at all. The division is of morphological significance, since it indicates the separation of the nerve-fibres destined for the supply of the originally ventral parts of the limb from those which supply the dorsal parts.

(4) The **cords** of the plexus are formed by combinations of the anterior and posterior divisions. They are three in number, and lie in relation to the axillary artery. The *lateral cord* is formed by union of the anterior divisions of the upper and middle trunks, or of the fifth, sixth, and seventh

nerves, and lies on the lateral side of the axillary artery. The *medial cord* is formed by the anterior division of the lower trunk, containing the corresponding division of the eighth nerve with the part of the first thoracic nerve; it lies on the medial side of the axillary artery. The *posterior cord* is made up of the posterior divisions of all three trunks, that is, of the fifth, sixth, seventh, and eighth cervical and first thoracic nerves; it lies behind the axillary artery. The first thoracic nerve may not contribute to the posterior cord, and the branch, when present, is very small.

The **nerves of distribution** for the shoulder and arm are derived from the cords, and receive in that way various contributions from the constituent spinal nerves. *From the lateral cord* arise the lateral pectoral and musculo-cutaneous

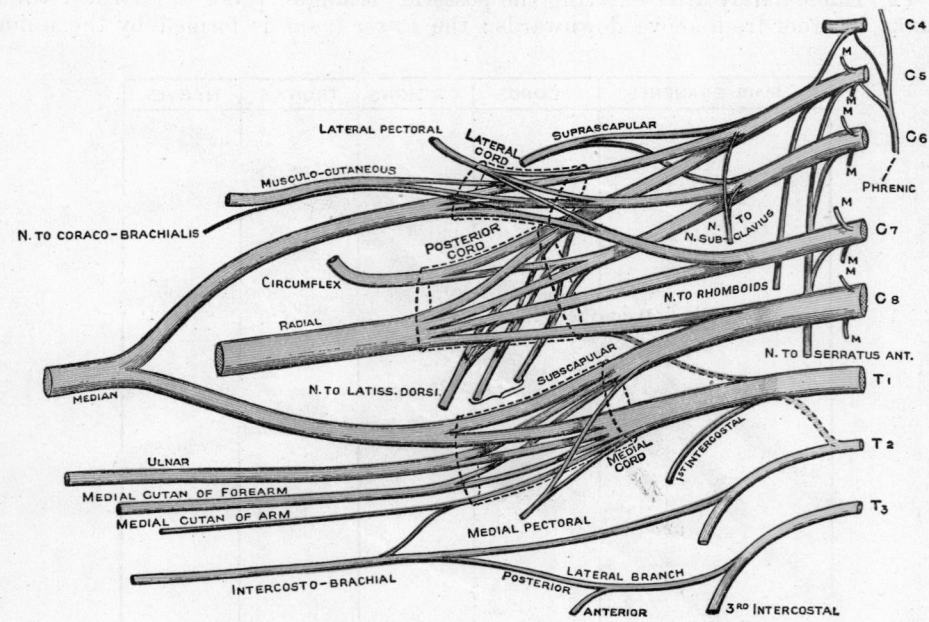

FIG. 875.—THE ORIGINS OF THE BRANCHES OF THE BRACHIAL PLEXUS.

nerves, and the lateral root of the median nerve. *From the medial cord* arise the medial root of the median nerve, the ulnar nerve, the medial cutaneous nerve of the arm, the medial cutaneous nerve of the forearm, and the medial pectoral nerve. *From the posterior cord* arise the circumflex nerve, the two subscapular nerves, the nerve to the latissimus dorsi, and the radial nerve.

It is to be remembered that, although derived from a cord formed by a certain set of spinal nerves, any given nerve does not necessarily contain fibres from all the constituent nerves; *e.g.* both the musculo-cutaneous and the circumflex nerves, from the lateral and posterior cords respectively, are ultimately derived only from the fifth and sixth cervical nerves. In other words, the cords are merely collections of nerves of distribution bound together in a common sheath in their passage through the axilla. It may be pointed out also that it is impossible in nearly all cases to dissect out and trace the fibres of a given spinal nerve through the plexus to their ultimate distribution, owing to the complex manner in which the nerve bundles interlace with one another.

Communications with the Sympathetic.—The lower four cervical nerves communicate with the cervical portion of the sympathetic by means of **grey rami communicantes.** Commonly two branches arise from the middle cervical ganglion; they join the anterior primary rami of the fifth and sixth nerves. Two or more from the inferior cervical ganglion join the seventh and eighth nerves. They reach the nerves either by piercing the prevertebral muscles or by passing round the border of the scalenus anterior muscle.

Variations are found (1) in the number of nerves taking part in the formation of the plexus; and (2) in the pattern formed by the union and division of its constituent parts. (1) As regards the former, Kerr, on an examination of 175 plexuses, forms three groups : (*a*) a part of the fourth nerve joins the plexus in nearly two-thirds of cases ; (*b*) no contribution is received from the fourth nerve, but all the fifth joins the plexus in one-third of cases ; (*c*) a part only of the fifth enters the plexus in about 7 per cent. of cases. At the lower end of the plexus there is an intra-thoracic communication between the second and first thoracic nerves in one-third or more of cases. These figures indicate a higher or lower position of the plexus relative to the vertebral column, though it is evidently subject to very slight variation. The presence of a cervical rib may coincide with little or no change in the relation of the nerves. (2) Variations in the pattern of the plexuses are due to (*a*) the stage of either trunk, divisional or even cord formation being absent in one or other part of the plexus, prior to a succeeding stage ; in all such cases, however, there is no alteration in the typical nerve source of the ultimate terminal branches ; (*b*) in very few cases the lateral or the medial cord may receive fibres from nerves below the seventh or above the eighth, respectively—that is, a new element is introduced into their composition.

Branches of the Brachial Plexus

It is customary to separate artificially the nerves of distribution of the brachial plexus into two sets : (1) supra-clavicular and (2) infra-clavicular, a topographical division which is to some extent affected by the alteration in position of the bone in raising or lowering the shoulder.

The point of junction of the three posterior divisions of the trunks to form the posterior cord has been found fairly constantly situated 6·75 cm., or 2¾ inches, horizontally lateralwards, from the lateral border of the common carotid artery at the root of the neck, the arm being fully abducted ; a vertical line passing through this point separates the trunks from the cords (Linell).

Clinically it is important to realise the position of origin of the nerves relative to the different stages of formation of the plexus. (*a*) The nerves to the prevertebral muscles, the communication with the phrenic, the nerves to the rhomboids and serratus anterior arise from the *anterior primary rami* of the nerves involved in the plexus. (*b*) The supra-scapular and the nerve to the subclavius arise at the level of formation of the *trunks*. (*c*) The pectoral and subscapular nerves, the nerve to the latissimus dorsi, and the medial cutaneous nerves of the arm and forearm arise from the *cords*, prior to their ultimate subdivision into the nerves of distribution for the upper limb. (*d*) All the rest are terminal branches.

Supra-clavicular Branches.—The nerves derived from the plexus above the level of the clavicle are, like the main trunks, divisible into two series : **anterior branches**, arising from the front of the plexus ; **posterior branches**, arising from the back of the plexus (Fig. 875).

(*a*) *Arising from the primary rami.*

Anterior Branches	Posterior Branches
1. Nerves to scalenus anterior and longus cervicis.	1. Nerves to scalenus medius and scalenus posterior.
2. Communicating nerve to join the phrenic nerve.	2. Nerve to the rhomboids.
	3. Nerve to serratus anterior.

(*b*) *Arising from the trunks.*

3. Nerve to the subclavius muscle.	4. Supra-scapular nerve.

The **muscular twigs** to the anterior scalene and longus cervicis muscles arise from the lower four cervical nerves, as they emerge from the intervertebral foramina.

The **communicating branch to the phrenic nerve** arises usually from the fifth cervical nerve at the lateral border of the anterior scalene muscle. It is sometimes absent, and occasionally an additional root is present from the sixth cervical nerve. In some instances the nerve is replaced by a branch which springs from the nerve to the subclavius, and passes medially behind the sterno-mastoid muscle to join the phrenic at the inlet of the thorax.

The **nerve to the subclavius** is a slender nerve which arises from the front of the upper trunk of the plexus, and usually receives fibres from the fourth, fifth, and sixth cervical nerves. It descends in the posterior triangle of the neck anterior to the third part of the subclavian artery. It often communicates with the phrenic nerve.

The **branches to the scalenus medius and scalenus posterior** are small, and arise from the lower four cervical nerves as they emerge from the intervertebral foramina.

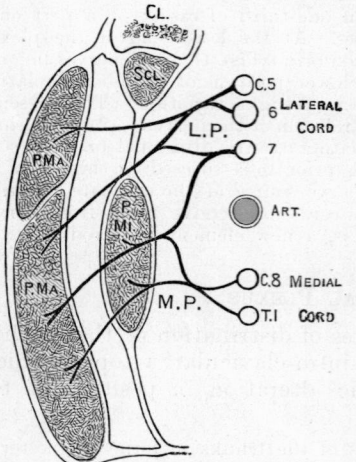

FIG. 876.—DIAGRAM OF THE ORIGIN AND DISTRIBUTION OF THE NERVES TO THE PECTORAL MUSCLES.

L.P., Lateral pectoral nerve; M.P., Medial pectoral nerve; C. 5, 6, 7, C. 8, T. 1, Nerves of the brachial plexus; ART., Axillary artery; CL., Clavicle; SCL., Subclavius muscle; P.MI., Pectoralis minor, joined to subclavius by clavipectoral fascia; P.MA., Pectoralis major.

The **nerve to the rhomboids** [N. dorsalis scapulæ] arises from the back of the fifth cervical nerve as it emerges from the intervertebral foramen. It appears in the posterior triangle of the neck, after piercing the scalenus medius muscle, and it passes downwards, under cover of the levator scapulæ and rhomboid muscles, and along the medial border of the scapula, to be distributed to the levator scapulæ, rhomboideus minor, and rhomboideus major muscles. It occasionally pierces the levator scapulæ.

The **nerve to the serratus anterior** [N. thoracalis longus] arises by three roots, of which the middle one is usually the largest, from the back of the fifth, sixth, and seventh nerves as they emerge from the intervertebral foramina. The upper two roots pierce the scalenus medius and unite into one stem which is joined by the contribution from the seventh cervical nerve which passes in front of that muscle. The nerve descends in the neck behind the cords of the brachial plexus and enters the axilla between the superior edge of the serratus anterior muscle and the axillary artery. It continues downwards on the axillary surface of the serratus, to the slips of which it is distributed.

There is a more or less definite relation between the roots of the nerve and the parts of the serratus muscle. The upper part of the muscle is innervated by the fifth nerve alone; the middle part by the fifth and sixth, or the sixth alone; the lower part by the sixth and seventh, or the seventh nerve alone.

The **supra-scapular nerve** arises from the back of the upper trunk of the plexus, receiving fibres from the fourth, fifth, and sixth cervical nerves. It occupies a position above the cords of the brachial plexus, and courses downwards and laterally parallel to them towards the superior border of the scapula, where it passes through the supra-scapular notch to the dorsum of the scapula. After supplying the supraspinatus muscle it passes through the spino-glenoid notch in company with the supra-scapular artery and terminates in the infraspinatus muscle. It also supplies articular branches to the shoulder joint.

Infra-clavicular Branches.—The so-called infra-clavicular branches of the brachial plexus all arise from the *cords* of the plexus and are distributed to the chest, shoulder, upper arm, and forearm. According to their origin they are divisible into two sets—an **anterior set,** derived from the lateral and medial cords, and a **posterior set,** derived from the posterior cord. In their distribution the same arrangement is maintained. The anterior nerves of distribution, springing from the lateral and medial cords, supply the chest and the front of the limb; the posterior nerves, springing from the posterior cord, supply the shoulder and the back of the limb.

(c) and (d) *Arising from the cords.*

Anterior Branches

From the Lateral Cord	From the Medial Cord
Lateral pectoral.	Medial pectoral.
Median (lateral root).	Median (medial root).
Musculo-cutaneous.	Ulnar.
	Medial cutaneous nerve of arm.
	Medial cutaneous nerve of forearm.

Posterior Branches

Circumflex nerve.
Radial nerve.
Two subscapular nerves.
Nerve to latissimus dorsi.

PECTORAL NERVES

The **pectoral nerves** [Nn. thoracales anteriores] are two in number, lateral and medial. The **lateral pectoral nerve** arises from the anterior divisions of the fifth, sixth, and seventh cervical nerves just before they form the lateral cord of the plexus. The **medial pectoral nerve** arises from the medial cord of the plexus immediately after its formation, receiving fibres from the eighth cervical and first thoracic nerves. Both course downwards and forwards, one on each side of the axillary artery, and a loop of communication is formed between them in front of the artery. They are distributed to the pectoralis major and minor muscles (Fig. 876).

The nerves are distributed to the pectoral muscles in the following way. Two sets of branches from the lateral pectoral nerve pierce the clavi-pectoral fascia. The superior branches supply the *clavicular part* of the pectoralis major; the inferior branches are distributed to the superior fibres of the *sterno-costal portion* of the muscle. The superior branches come from the fifth and sixth cervical nerves; the inferior branches, from the fifth, sixth, and seventh nerves. The *pectoralis minor* is pierced by two sets of nerves—the superior set is derived from the loop of communication between the two pectoral nerves over the axillary artery; the inferior set is derived from the medial pectoral nerve alone. The two sets supply the *pectoralis minor* muscle, and, after piercing it, supply the *sterno-costal part* of the pectoralis major. The inferior set, in many cases, sends its branches to the pectoralis major round the infero-lateral border of the pectoralis minor, and they may supply the *axillary arches*, if present. The two branches of the superior set are derived from the seventh and eighth cervical and first thoracic nerves; those of the inferior set from the eighth cervical and first thoracic nerves. The pectoral muscles are thus both supplied by the two pectoral nerves. The clavicular fibres of the pectoralis major are innervated by the fifth and sixth nerves; the sterno-costal fibres, from above downwards, by the fifth, sixth, seventh, and eighth cervical, and first thoracic nerves; and the pectoralis minor is supplied by the seventh and eighth cervical and first thoracic nerves.

MUSCULO-CUTANEOUS NERVE

The **musculo-cutaneous nerve** takes origin from the lateral cord of the plexus, from the fifth and sixth cervical nerves, and also from the fourth in over half the number of cases (Fig. 875). The **nerve to the coraco-brachialis muscle**, arising from the seventh or sixth and seventh nerves, is usually incorporated with it. After it separates from the lateral root of the median nerve, the musculo-cutaneous nerve lies at first between the coraco-brachialis muscle and the axillary artery. It then passes between the two parts of the coraco-brachialis, and runs between the biceps and brachialis muscles, to the bend of the elbow. It pierces the deep fascia over the front of the elbow, between the biceps and brachio-radialis, and terminates as the *lateral cutaneous nerve of the forearm*. Whilst behind the biceps it may send a communicating branch to the median nerve.

The branches of the nerve are muscular and cutaneous. The **muscular branches** are supplied to the two heads of the biceps and the brachialis, as the nerve lies between the muscles, and to the coraco-brachialis. The nerve to the coraco-brachialis (usually incorporated with the trunk of the musculo-cutaneous nerve) has an independent origin from the seventh or sixth and seventh nerves (possibly the fifth also). The **lateral cutaneous nerve of the forearm** divides into anterior and posterior branches. The **anterior branch** descends along the front of the lateral aspect of the forearm to the wrist, and supplies an area of skin and fascia extending medially to the middle line of the front of the forearm, and distally to the ball of the thumb. It usually communicates, proximal to the wrist, with

64 *b*

the radial nerve, and supplies branches to the radial artery. The **posterior branch** passes backwards and downwards over the extensor muscles and supplies over a variable extent the skin and fascia on the lateral aspect of the forearm posteriorly.

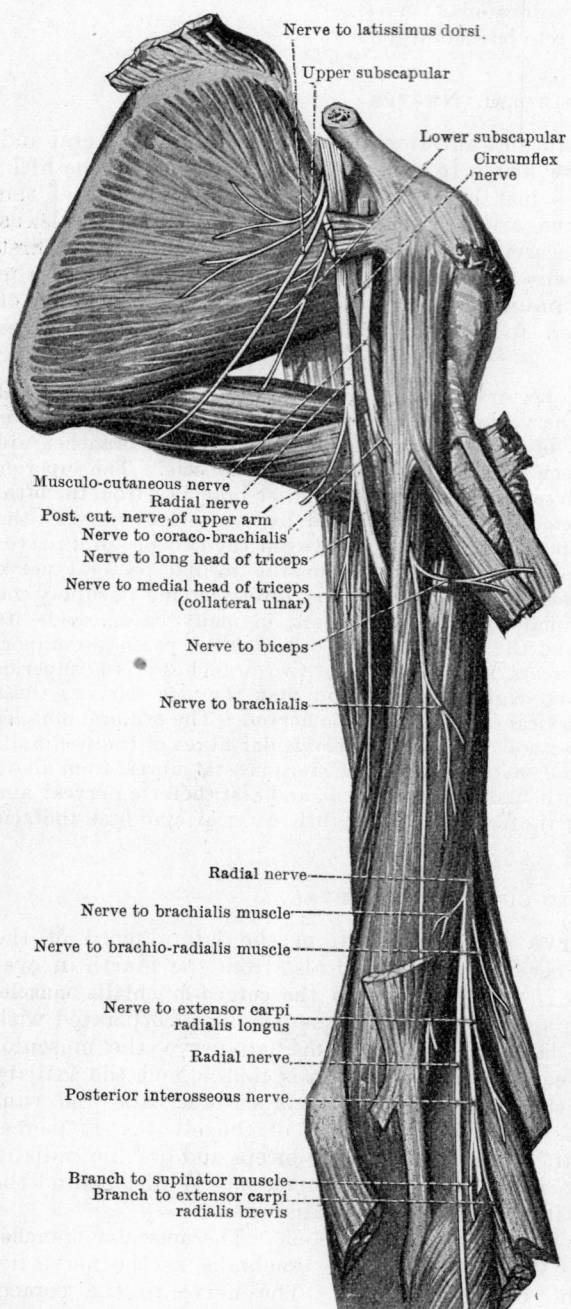

It communicates with the cutaneous branches of the radial nerve, and it sometimes extends on to the dorsum of the hand, supplying the skin and fascia over the first meta-carpal bone.

In addition to the above branches, the musculo-cutaneous nerve supplies in many cases the following small twigs in the arm : (1) a medullary branch to the humerus ; (2) a periosteal branch to the distal end of the humerus on its anterior surface ; and (3) a branch to the brachial artery.

MEDIAN NERVE

The **median nerve** arises by two roots—one from the lateral cord of the brachial plexus, the other from the medial cord. The lateral root, from the (fifth), sixth, and seventh nerves, descends along the lateral side of the axillary artery ; the medial root, from the eighth cervical and first thoracic nerves, crosses in front of the terminal part of the axillary artery or the beginning of the brachial artery, to join the lateral root in the proximal part of the upper arm. The trunk therefore receives fibres from all the main nerves that form the plexus. It descends along the lateral side of the brachial artery to the level of the insertion of the coraco-brachialis, where it crosses the artery (usually in front). Thereafter it lies on the medial side of the artery and in the hollow of the elbow it is behind the bicipital apo-neurosis [lacertus fibrosus] and the median cubital vein. It passes into the forearm between the two heads of the pronator teres muscle, separated,

Labels on figure:
Nerve to latissimus dorsi
Upper subscapular
Lower subscapular
Circumflex nerve
Musculo-cutaneous nerve
Radial nerve
Post. cut. nerve of upper arm
Nerve to coraco-brachialis
Nerve to long head of triceps
Nerve to medial head of triceps (collateral ulnar)
Nerve to biceps
Nerve to brachialis
Radial nerve
Nerve to brachialis muscle
Nerve to brachio-radialis muscle
Nerve to extensor carpi radialis longus
Radial nerve
Posterior interosseous nerve
Branch to supinator muscle
Branch to extensor carpi radialis brevis

FIG. 877.—THE DEEPER NERVES OF UPPER ARM.

from the ulnar artery by the ulnar origin of that muscle, and extends downwards, along the middle of the forearm between the superficial and deep muscles, to the wrist. As it approaches the wrist it becomes more superficial and enters the palm of the hand by passing deep to the flexor retinaculum in front of the tendons of the flexor digitorum sublimis. In the hand, it spreads out at the distal border of the flexor retinaculum [lig. carpi transversum], under cover of the palmar aponeurosis and superficial palmar arch, and separates into its six terminal branches. In the forearm a small artery accompanies it—the median branch of the anterior interosseous artery.

Branches.—The median nerve usually gives off no branches in the upper arm.

Branches in the Forearm.—(1) **Articular Branches.**—Minute articular filaments arise from the muscular branches and are distributed to the front of the elbow joint.

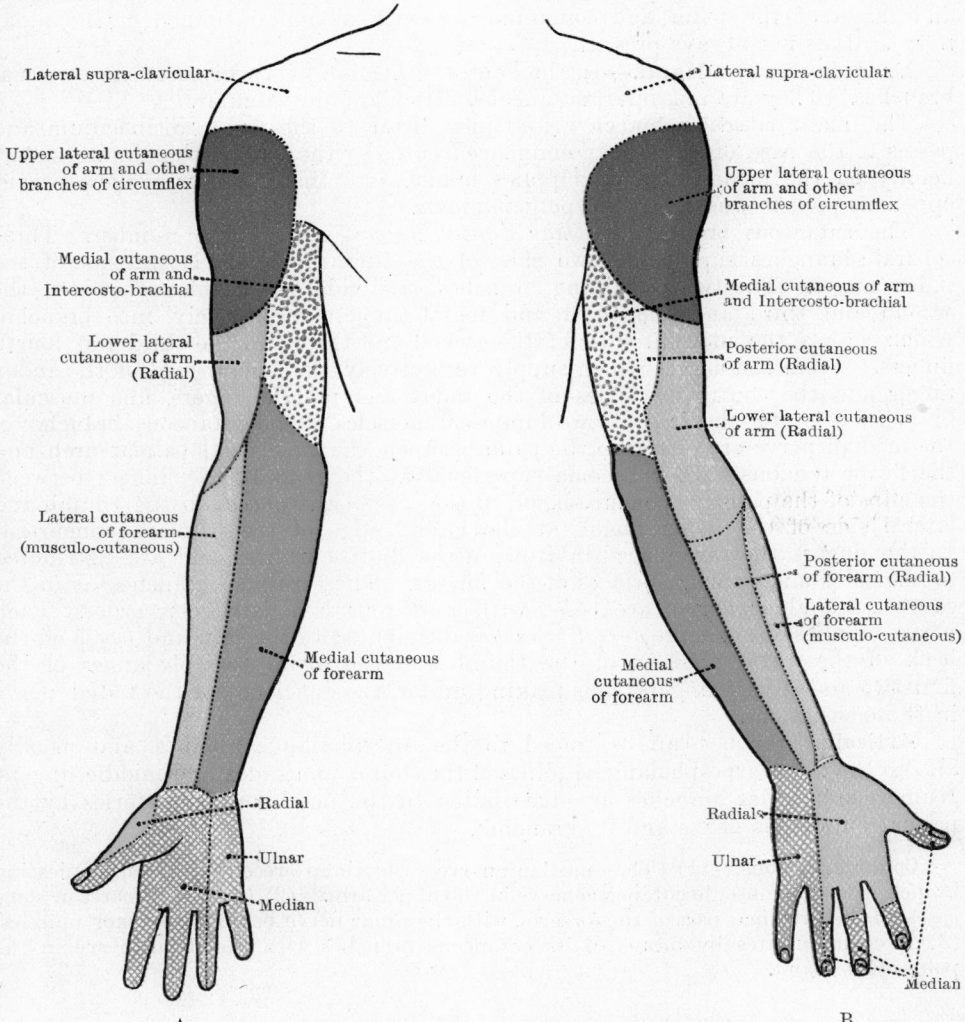

Lateral supra-clavicular

Upper lateral cutaneous of arm and other branches of circumflex

Medial cutaneous of arm and Intercosto-brachial

Lower lateral cutaneous of arm (Radial)

Lateral cutaneous of forearm (musculo-cutaneous)

Medial cutaneous of forearm

Radial

Ulnar

Median

Lateral supra-clavicular

Upper lateral cutaneous of arm and other branches of circumflex

Medial cutaneous of arm and Intercosto-brachial

Posterior cutaneous of arm (Radial)

Lower lateral cutaneous of arm (Radial)

Posterior cutaneous of forearm (Radial)

Lateral cutaneous of forearm (musculo-cutaneous)

Medial cutaneous of forearm

Radial

Ulnar

Median

A   B

FIG. 878.—DISTRIBUTION OF CUTANEOUS NERVES : A, ON THE FRONT ; B, ON THE BACK OF THE UPPER LIMB.

(2) **Muscular Branches.**—In the hollow of the elbow a bundle of nerves arises to be distributed to the following muscles : pronator teres, flexor carpi radialis, palmaris longus, flexor digitorum sublimis. Nerves are also generally traceable from that bundle to the upper fibres of the flexor pollicis longus and flexor digitorum profundus. A separate branch to the index belly of the sublimis often leaves the nerve in the lower half of the forearm. The nerve to the pronator teres, which is the first given off, often arises independently in the hollow of the elbow but seldom proximal to the joint.

(3) The **anterior interosseous nerve** arises from the posterior surface of the median nerve in the cubital fossa. It extends downwards on the front of the interosseous membrane along with the anterior interosseous artery, passes behind

the pronator quadratus muscle, and terminates by supplying articular filaments to the radio-carpal joint. In its course the nerve supplies muscular branches to the flexor pollicis longus, the lateral half of the flexor digitorum profundus, and the pronator quadratus, minute medullary branches to the radius and ulna and twigs to the periosteum and interosseous membrane.

(4) **Palmar Cutaneous Branch.**—In the distal third of the forearm a small cutaneous branch arises which pierces the deep fascia and crosses the flexor retinaculum to reach the palm of the hand. It supplies a small piece of the skin and fascia of the palm and communicates with a similar branch of the ulnar nerve. It is not always present.

Branches in the Hand.—In the hand the median nerve gives off its terminal branches. They are muscular, cutaneous, articular, and vascular.

The main **muscular branch** arises just distal to the flexor retinaculum and passes to the base of the thenar eminence ; entering the ball of the thumb superficially on the medial side, it supplies branches to the abductor pollicis brevis, opponens pollicis, and the flexor pollicis brevis.

The **cutaneous branches** (*palmar digital nerves*) are five in number. Three separate branches supply the two sides of the thumb and the lateral side of the index finger. The two remaining branches subdivide, at the clefts between the second and third and the third and fourth fingers respectively, into branches which supply the adjacent sides of the second and third and the third and fourth fingers. From the nerves which supply respectively the lateral side of the index finger and the contiguous sides of the index and middle fingers, fine muscular branches arise for the lateral two lumbrical muscles. The cutaneous branches of the median nerve are placed in the palm between the superficial palmar arch and the flexor tendons. They become superficial at the roots of the fingers between the slips of the palmar aponeurosis, or, in the case of the nerves to the thumb and lateral side of the index finger, at the lateral edge of the palmar aponeurosis. In the fingers they are placed in front of the digital arteries, and are distributed to the sides and palmar surfaces of the fingers. Those palmar branches, as in the case of the ulnar nerve, are beset with numerous lamellated corpuscles. Each nerve supplies one or more *dorsal branches,* distributed to the skin and fascia on the back of the distal phalanx of the thumb and the distal two phalanges of the first two and a half fingers, thus making up for the deficiency of the radial nerve in those situations.

Articular branches can be traced to the interphalangeal joints, and usually also to the metacarpo-phalangeal joints of the thumb and index and middle fingers. Numerous **vascular** branches are distributed to the neighbouring arteries by the palmar cutaneous nerve and its branches.

Communications.—(1) The median nerve sometimes receives a communicating branch from the musculo-cutaneous nerve in the upper arm. (2) It communicates in some cases, in the proximal part of the forearm, with the ulnar nerve behind the flexor muscles. (3) It communicates by means of its cutaneous branches with the ulnar nerve in the palm of the hand.

ULNAR NERVE

The **ulnar nerve** arises from the medial cord of the brachial plexus, and contains fibres from the eighth cervical and first thoracic nerves. In over half the number of cases it has also a root from the lateral cord of the plexus or from the lateral root of the median nerve (seventh cervical nerve). This additional root is subject to great variation in size. In the axilla the ulnar nerve lies between the axillary artery and vein, and behind the medial cutaneous nerve of the forearm ; in the proximal half of the upper arm it lies on the medial side of the brachial artery anterior to the triceps muscle. In the distal half of the upper arm it separates from the brachial artery, and, passing behind the intermuscular septum and in front of the medial head of the triceps in company with the ulnar collateral artery, it reaches the interval between the medial epicondyle of the humerus and the olecranon. It is there protected by an arch of aponeurosis stretching between the epicondyle and the olecranon. It enters the forearm between the humeral and ulnar origins of the flexor carpi ulnaris, and descends between the flexor carpi ulnaris and flexor digitorum profundus. In the distal half of the forearm it becomes comparatively superficial, lying on the medial side of the ulnar artery (to which it furnishes branches) overlapped by the tendon of the flexor carpi ulnaris. Just proximal to the flexor retinaculum [lig. carpi transversum], and lateral to the pisiform bone, it pierces the deep fascia, in company with the artery, and passes on to the front of the retinaculum, where it divides, under cover of the palmaris brevis muscle, into its two terminal branches—superficial and deep.

Branches.—The ulnar nerve usually gives off no branches until it reaches the forearm.

In the forearm it gives off articular, muscular, and cutaneous branches.

The **articular branch** is distributed to the elbow joint and arises as the nerve passes behind the medial epicondyle of the humerus.

The **muscular branches** arise as soon as the nerve enters the forearm. They are distributed to the muscles between which the nerve lies—the flexor carpi ulnaris and the medial half of the flexor digitorum profundus. The flexor carpi ulnaris usually receives, just below the elbow joint, two branches, one each to its olecranon and condylar heads; the latter head may receive a secondary supply at a lower level, and a fourth branch to the muscle may be found. Only in exceptional cases does one of the branches arise proximal to the elbow joint (Linell).

The **cutaneous branches** are two in number, palmar and dorsal.

The **palmar cutaneous branch** is variable in size and position. It pierces the deep fascia in the distal third of the forearm and passes to the hypothenar eminence and palm of the hand, to the skin and fascia over which it is distributed. It gives branches to the ulnar artery, and often communicates with the medial cutaneous nerve of the forearm and the palmar cutaneous branch of the median nerve.

The **dorsal branch of the ulnar** is much larger. It arises from the ulnar nerve at a variable point in the middle third of the forearm; and, directed obliquely downwards and backwards, under cover of the tendon of the flexor carpi ulnaris and in contact with the ulna, it becomes cutaneous on the medial side of the forearm in its distal fourth. It passes on to the back of the hand, and, after giving off branches to the skin and fascia of the dorsum of the wrist and hand which communicate with the radial nerve, it terminates in three *dorsal digital nerves* to supply the little finger, the ring finger, and half of the middle finger in the following way: one branch courses along the ulnar side of the dorsum of the hand and supplies the little finger as far as the root of the nail; another branch subdivides at the cleft between the little and ring fingers to supply their adjacent sides to the same extent; a third branch bifurcates at the cleft between the ring and middle fingers, and supplies their adjacent sides, but only as far as the level of the proximal interphalangeal joints, the distal part of the surfaces being supplied by branches of the median overlapping from the palmar aspect. The last branch communicates with the radial nerve. The ulnar nerve sometimes supplies only the little finger and half of the ring finger on their dorsal surfaces.

In the **palm** the ulnar nerve supplies a small muscular branch to the palmaris brevis, and then subdivides into its terminal branches, which are named superficial and deep.

Terminal Branches.—The **superficial terminal branch** passes downwards deep to the palmar aponeurosis, and subdivides into a medial and a lateral branch. The medial branch proceeds along the medial border of the little finger, which it supplies on its palmar surface. The lateral branch becomes superficial at the cleft between the fourth and fifth digits, between the slips of the palmar aponeurosis, and subdivides into two branches (*palmar digital nerves*) which supply the adjacent sides of those fingers on their palmar surface. It communicates with the adjacent digital branch of the median nerve, and it usually supplies the metacarpo-phalangeal and interphalangeal joints of the ring and little fingers. The digital nerves supply the neighbouring arteries also.

The ulnar nerve, therefore, usually supplies one and a half fingers on their palmar surfaces and two and a half fingers on their dorsal surfaces, the remaining digits being supplied by the median nerve on the palmar surface, and the radial nerve on the dorsal surface. The median nerve further extends on to the dorsal surface of the distal phalanx of the thumb and the distal two phalanges of the first two and a half fingers, so making up for the deficiency of the radial nerve in those regions. Clinical observations show this to be a much more common arrangement than the classical description of the distribution of the ulnar nerve to one and a half fingers on both their surfaces.

The **deep terminal branch** is distributed mainly to muscles, but receives some fibres from afferent end organs in the deep structures of the palm. It separates from the superficial branch, and passes deeply between the flexor and abductor digiti minimi muscles; it supplies those muscles and the opponens digiti minimi, and, turning laterally along the line of the deep palmar arch and under cover of the deep flexor tendons, it supplies branches to the following muscles: interossei, third and fourth lumbricales (on their deep surfaces), the adductor pollicis (oblique and transverse heads), and the deep part of the flexor pollicis brevis. Vascular branches are given to the deeper vessels of the palm.

Communications.—The ulnar nerve communicates (1), in some cases, with the median nerve in the forearm; (2) with the medial cutaneous nerve of the forearm, and sometimes with the median nerve, by its palmar branch; (3) with the cutaneous part of the median nerve in the palm, by means of its terminal cutaneous branches; (4) with the radial nerve on the dorsum of the hand, by means of its dorsal branch.

Medial Cutaneous Nerve of Forearm

The **medial cutaneous nerve of the forearm** arises from the medial cord of the brachial plexus, and contains fibres of the eighth cervical and first thoracic nerves (Figs. 875 and 878). In the axilla and proximal half of the upper arm it lies superficial to the main artery. It becomes cutaneous by piercing the deep fascia about the middle of the upper arm on its medial side, and, accompanying the basilic vein through the distal half, it divides at the front of the elbow into its two terminal branches.

Branches.—In the upper arm, as soon as it becomes superficial, the nerve gives off a branch which supplies the skin and fascia of the distal half of the anterior surface of the upper arm on its medial side. At the elbow it divides into two terminal branches—anterior and posterior, which, crossing superficial or deep to the median basilic vein, are distributed to the medial side of the forearm.

The **anterior branch** can be followed to the wrist and supplies the whole of the front of the forearm in the medial half; the **posterior branch** is not so large, and, passing obliquely backwards and downwards over the origins of the pronator and flexor muscles, it is distributed to the proximal two-thirds or three-fourths of the back of the forearm on the medial side.

Communication.—The medial cutaneous nerve of the forearm communicates with the ulnar nerve in the distal part of the forearm.

Medial Cutaneous Nerve of Arm

The **medial cutaneous nerve of the arm** arises from the medial cord of the brachial plexus, and ultimately from the first thoracic nerve (Fig. 875, p. 1010). It lies at first between the axillary artery and vein; and after descending over, under, or even, in some cases, through the axillary vein, it perforates the deep fascia and is distributed to the skin and fascia of the upper arm for the proximal half or more on its medial side.

The nerve varies considerably in size. It may be absent, its place being taken by branches of the intercosto-brachial or by branches from the posterior cutaneous branch of the radial nerve. It generally bears a distinct relation in size to the intercosto-brachial, due to the fact that the size of the latter depends upon the size of the part of the second thoracic nerve connected with the first in the thorax. If an intra-thoracic connexion occurs between the first and second thoracic nerves, the intercosto-brachial may be deprived of a certain number of its fibres, which in that case reach the upper limb through the medial cutaneous nerve of the arm.

When traced up to the plexus the medial cutaneous nerve of the arm is found to have an origin from the posterior part of the cord formed by the eighth cervical and first thoracic nerves, and usually receives fibres from the first thoracic nerve only. In cases where "*axillary arches*" are present they may be supplied by this nerve.

CIRCUMFLEX NERVE

The **circumflex nerve** [N. axillaris] is a terminal branch of the posterior cord, and contains fibres of the fifth and sixth cervical nerves. At first it lies behind the axillary artery, but, at the lower border of the subscapularis, it leaves the axilla by passing backwards, in company with the posterior circumflex humeral artery, through a quadrilateral space bounded by the humerus, subscapularis, triceps (long head), and teres major. It winds round the back of the surgical neck of the humerus from medial to lateral side, and divides into an anterior and posterior branch. The anterior branch follows the artery round the humerus and is distributed to the deltoid through its deep surface. A few filaments pierce the muscle and become cutaneous. The posterior branch supplies the teres minor, and, after giving a few twigs to the posterior part of the deltoid, curves round the posterior border of that muscle to become the *upper lateral cutaneous nerve of the arm* (Fig. 879).

Branches.—**Muscular**

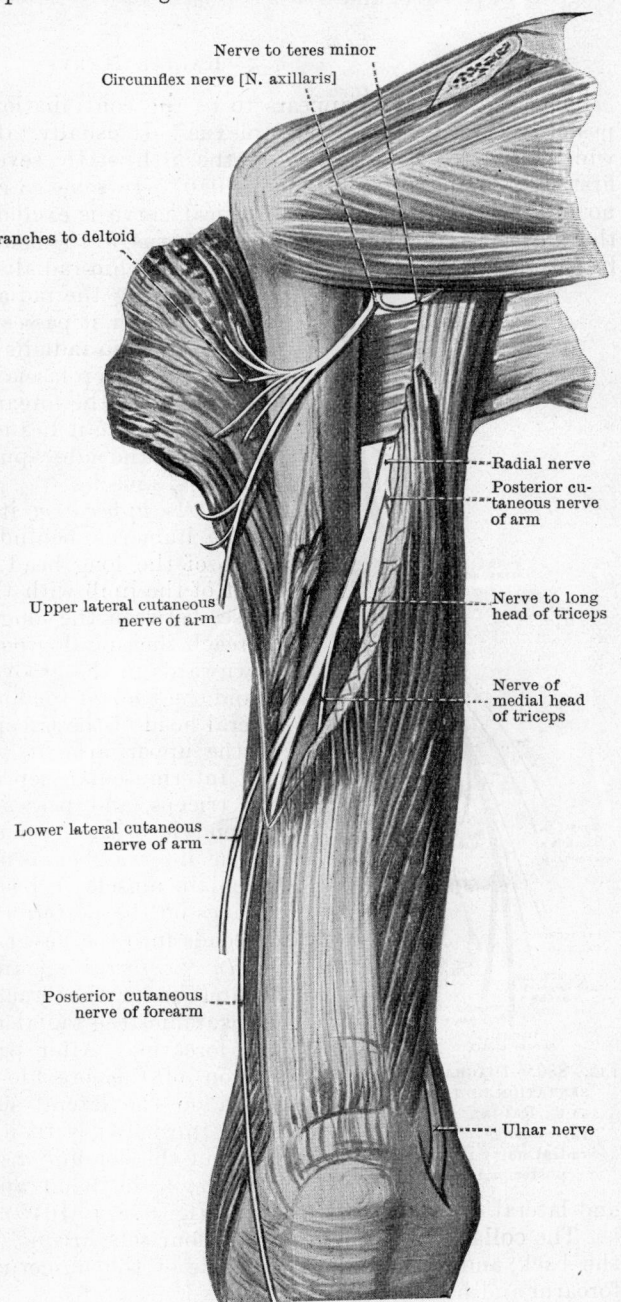

Nerve to teres minor

Circumflex nerve [N. axillaris]

Branches to deltoid

Radial nerve

Posterior cutaneous nerve of arm

Upper lateral cutaneous nerve of arm

Nerve to long head of triceps

Nerve of medial head of triceps

Lower lateral cutaneous nerve of arm

Posterior cutaneous nerve of forearm

Ulnar nerve

FIG. 879.—THE CIRCUMFLEX AND RADIAL NERVES.

branches are supplied to the teres minor and deltoid muscles. It often gives off the lower subscapular nerve. The nerve to the teres minor enters the lateral margin of the muscle ; it has a pseudo-ganglionic thickening of fibrous tissue on its trunk.

Articular branches enter the posterior part of the capsule of the shoulder joint.

A **cutaneous branch** of considerable size—*the upper lateral cutaneous nerve of the arm*—becomes superficial at the posterior border of the deltoid muscle, and passing obliquely downwards and forwards supplies the skin and fascia over its lower half (Figs. 878, p. 1015, and 879).

RADIAL NERVE

The **radial nerve** appears to be the continuation into the upper limb of the posterior cord of the brachial plexus. It usually takes origin from all the nerves which form the posterior cord—the fifth, sixth, seventh, and eighth cervical and first thoracic nerves (Fig. 875, p. 1010). In some cases the first thoracic contributes no fibres, and often the fifth cervical nerve is excluded from it. It extends from the axilla, round the back of the humerus, to the bend of the elbow, where it passes into the forearm under cover of the brachio-radialis [ramus superficialis]. After accompanying the radial artery in the middle third of the forearm, it passes backwards under the tendon of the brachio-radialis and becomes cutaneous by piercing the deep fascia on the lateral surface of the distal third of the forearm.

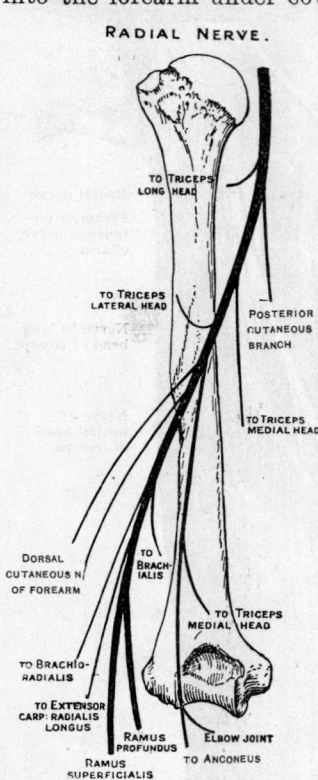

RADIAL NERVE.

TO TRICEPS LONG HEAD

TO TRICEPS LATERAL HEAD

POSTERIOR CUTANEOUS BRANCH

TO TRICEPS MEDIAL HEAD

DORSAL CUTANEOUS N OF FOREARM

TO BRACHIALIS

TO TRICEPS MEDIAL HEAD

TO BRACHIO-RADIALIS

TO EXTENSOR CARP: RADIALIS LONGUS

RAMUS PROFUNDUS

ELBOW JOINT

TO ANCONEUS

RAMUS SUPERFICIALIS

FIG. 880.—DIAGRAMMATIC REPRESENTATION OF THE BRANCHES OF THE RADIAL NERVE. *Ramus superficialis* = continuation of radial nerve; *Ramus profundus* = posterior interosseous nerve.

In the axilla it lies behind the axillary artery, and in front of the subscapularis, teres major, and latissimus dorsi muscles.

In the upper arm it first lies to the medial side of the humerus, behind the brachial artery, and in front of the long head of the triceps. Leaving the front of the limb with the profunda brachii artery, it passes between the long and medial heads of triceps to reach the spiral groove. It extends laterally and downwards in the groove, accompanied by the artery, round the back of the humerus and under cover of the lateral head of the triceps. Reaching the distal third of the upper arm, it pierces the proximal part of the intermuscular septum at the lateral border of the triceps, and passes to the front of the lateral epicondyle of the humerus, where it is deeply placed in the interval between the brachio-radialis and the brachialis muscles. Under cover of the former muscle it gives off the posterior interosseous nerve and then descends into the forearm.

In the forearm [ramus superficialis] it descends at first under the brachio-radialis and accompanies and supplies the radial artery in the middle third of the forearm. After passing backwards under the tendon of the brachio-radialis it pierces the deep fascia on the lateral surface of the forearm in the distal third. It is then distributed to the skin and fascia of the dorsum of the wrist, the lateral side and dorsum of the hand, and the dorsum of the thumb and lateral two and a half fingers (Fig. 878, p. 1015).

The **collateral branches** are in four sets, arising (*a*) on the medial side, (*b*) on the back, and (*c*) on the lateral side of the humerus (Fig. 880); and (*d*) in the forearm and hand.

I. **Branches arising medial to the Humerus.**—1. The **posterior cutaneous nerve of the arm**, arising in common with one of the following, or independently, pierces the fascia on the medial side of the limb near the axilla. It supplies the skin and fascia of the posterior surface of the upper arm in the proximal third, above and behind the area supplied by the medial cutaneous nerve of the arm and intercosto-brachial (Fig. 878, p. 1015). It varies in size, according to the bulk of these two nerves.

2. The **muscular branches** supply the triceps and the anconeus. The triceps receives four distinct branches in the following order: (i.) to the long head,

arising from the nerve in the axilla; (ii.) to the distal part of the medial head, arising near the lower border of the teres major, and sometimes termed the *ulnar collateral nerve* because it accompanies the ulnar nerve in the middle third of the arm; (iii.) to the lateral head, arising just distal to the last-mentioned branch; and (iv.) the main supply to the medial head, arising from the nerve just prior to its entry into the spiral groove of the humerus. The last branch, after supplying the medial head of the triceps, passes through the muscle and behind the lateral epicondyle of the humerus to terminate in the anconeus muscle. All those branches arise above the spiral groove or just as the nerve enters it; the only branches of any consequence that arise in the groove are the lower lateral cutaneous nerve of the arm and the posterior cutaneous nerve of the forearm.

II. **Branches arising on the Posterior Surface of the Humerus.** — The **lower lateral cutaneous nerve of the arm** arises before the radial passes through the lateral intermuscular septum, and, piercing the deep fascia a little below the deltoid, it supplies the skin and fascia of the lateral surface and back of the distal third of the upper arm and a small portion of the back of the forearm. The **posterior cutaneous nerve of forearm** arises with the preceding or immediately below it, and pierces the deep fascia about an inch lower down; it descends into the back of the forearm, where it supplies the skin and fascia, medial to the area innervated by the musculocutaneous nerve (Fig. 878, p. 1015). The extent of this area is variable; sometimes

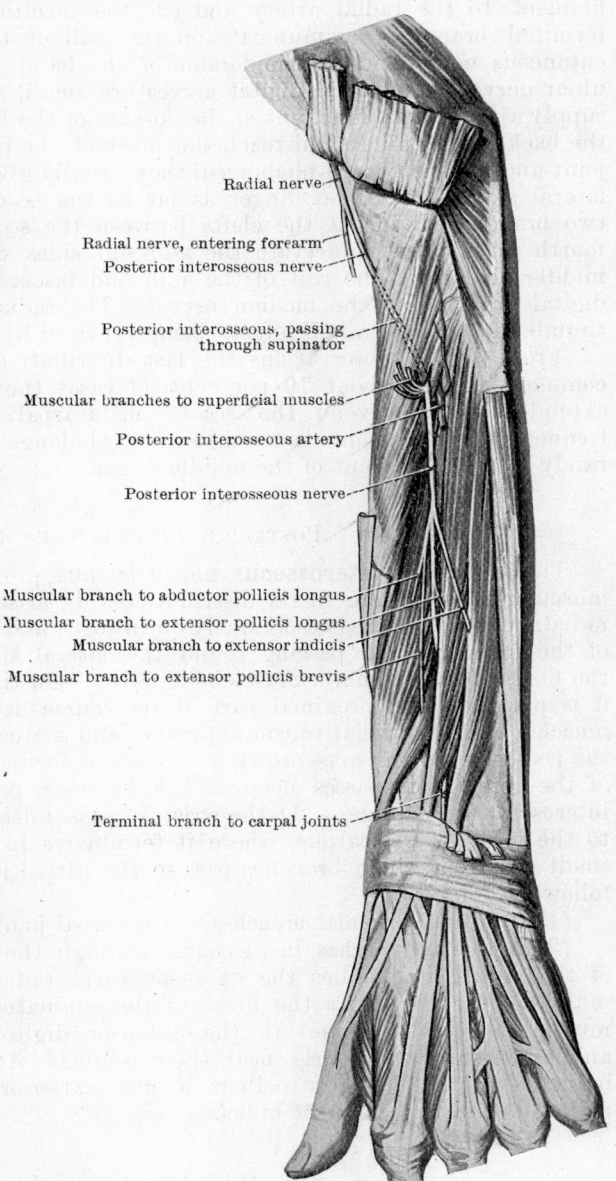

Radial nerve

Radial nerve, entering forearm
Posterior interosseous nerve

Posterior interosseous, passing through supinator

Muscular branches to superficial muscles

Posterior interosseous artery

Posterior interosseous nerve

Muscular branch to abductor pollicis longus
Muscular branch to extensor pollicis longus
Muscular branch to extensor indicis
Muscular branch to extensor pollicis brevis

Terminal branch to carpal joints

FIG. 881.—DISTRIBUTION OF THE POSTERIOR INTEROSSEOUS NERVE.

it approaches or reaches the level of the wrist, whilst in others it extends on to the dorsum of the hand and supplements the supply from the terminal part of the radial nerve itself.

III. **Branches arising at the Lateral Side of the Humerus.**—In the interval between the brachialis and brachio-radialis muscles, the radial nerve supplies **muscular branches** to the brachio-radialis (often double) and extensor carpi radialis longus. It may also provide the nerve to the extensor carpi radialis brevis. An inconstant branch is given to the brachialis, but it would appear from the negative results of electrical stimulation to be an afferent path.

IV. **Branches in the Forearm and Hand.**—The only branches which arise from the radial nerve in this part of its course [ramus superficialis] are: (1) some filaments to the radial artery and (2) the terminal **dorsal digital nerves**. The terminal branches communicate on the ball of the thumb with the musculo-cutaneous nerve, and on the dorsum of the hand, with the dorsal branch of the ulnar nerve. The **dorsal digital nerves** are small, and are five in number. They supply a very variable extent of the dorsum of the hand and fingers. Two pass to the back of the thumb and reach the level of the interphalangeal joint, to which joint and the metacarpo-phalangeal they usually give filaments. One supplies the lateral side of the index finger as far as the second phalanx. The remaining two branches divide at the clefts between the second and third and third and fourth fingers, and innervate the adjacent sides of those fingers as far as the middle phalanx. The rest of the skin and fascia of those digits is supplied by digital branches of the median nerve. The radial nerve may supply only the thumb and one and a half fingers, being replaced by branches from the ulnar nerve.

From clinical observations the last distribution would appear to be the more common, since in about 70 per cent. of cases the radial has been found not to extend medially beyond the second metacarpal bone. The digital branches frequently give filaments to the metacarpo-phalangeal joints of the index, and more rarely to the same joint of the middle finger.

POSTERIOR INTEROSSEOUS NERVE

The **posterior interosseous nerve** [ramus profundus n. radialis] is entirely muscular and articular in its distribution. It arises under cover of the brachio-radialis muscle. Directed obliquely downwards and backwards, it reaches the back of the forearm, after passing round the lateral side of the radius by piercing the fibres of the supinator muscle (Fig. 881). On the dorsal surface of the forearm it is placed in the proximal part of its course deep to the superficial extensor muscles, and superficial to the supinator and abductor pollicis longus, along with the posterior interosseous artery, to which it furnishes twigs. In the distal half of the forearm it passes deep to the extensor pollicis longus, and lies on the interosseous membrane. At the wrist it passes deep to the extensor tendons on to the back of the carpus, where it terminates in a gangliform enlargement of small size from which branches pass to the carpal joints. The nerve supplies the following branches:—

(1) Terminal **articular branches** to the carpal joints.

(2) **Muscular branches**, in its course through the forearm. On the lateral side of the radius, it supplies the extensor carpi radialis brevis and the supinator muscles before it enters the fibres of the supinator. After emerging from that muscle, it gives branches to the extensor digitorum, extensor digiti minimi, and extensor carpi ulnaris, near their origins. At a more distal level it gives branches to the abductor pollicis longus, extensor pollicis longus and extensor pollicis brevis, and extensor indicis.

SUBSCAPULAR NERVES

There are two subscapular nerves (Figs. 875 and 877)—upper and lower.

The **upper subscapular nerve** is often represented by two or three branches. It arises from the posterior cord of the plexus behind the axillary artery and contains fibres from the fifth and sixth cervical nerves (often from the fourth and seventh in addition). It passes downwards to supply the subscapularis muscle.

The **lower subscapular nerve** also arises behind the axillary artery from the posterior cord of the plexus (from the fifth and sixth cervical nerves) and it often arises in common with the circumflex nerve. It courses downwards behind the subscapular vessels to the teres major muscle, in which it ends. It supplies the lateral part of the subscapularis muscle and the teres major.

Nerve to Latissimus Dorsi

The **nerve to the latissimus dorsi** [n. thoracodorsalis] arises from the back of the posterior cord of the plexus, and receives fibres from the sixth, seventh, and eighth cervical nerves, or from the seventh and eighth nerves only. It is directed downwards and laterally between the two subscapular nerves, behind the axillary artery and over the posterior wall of the axilla, in company with the subscapular artery, to the latissimus dorsi muscle, which it supplies on its anterior (deep) surface.

THORACIC NERVES

The anterior primary rami of the **thoracic nerves** are twelve in number, each nerve emerging below the corresponding vertebra and rib. Eleven of the series are **intercostal**, the twelfth lies below the last rib and is called therefore the **subcostal** nerve. The first, second, third, and twelfth nerves present peculiarities in their course and distribution. The other thoracic nerves, as already stated, are simple, and may be regarded as types both in course and distribution.

The anterior primary ramus of the **first thoracic nerve** is the largest of the series. It emerges from the vertebral canal below the neck of the first rib, and divides in the first intercostal space into two very unequal parts. The *superior* and larger part ascends obliquely across the neck of the first rib, lying lateral to the superior intercostal artery, and enters the neck behind the subclavian artery. It proceeds laterally across the scalenus medius muscle and enters into the formation of the brachial plexus, as already described.

The *inferior* or *intercostal part* of the nerve is much smaller. It courses forwards on the pleural surface of the first rib and enters the first intercostal space near the costal cartilage; it supplies the intercostal muscles. After crossing the internal mammary artery the nerve usually turns forward to terminate in the superficial fascia as the anterior cutaneous branch. A lateral cutaneous branch is inconstant: when present this branch may communicate with the intercosto-brachial nerve or, more rarely, with the medial cutaneous nerve of the arm.

Communications.—Besides its junction with the eighth cervical to enter the brachial plexus, the first thoracic nerve effects the following communications: (*a*) The inferior cervical or the first thoracic ganglion of the sympathetic sends a *grey ramus communicans* to join the nerve on its appearance in the thorax. (*b*) The second thoracic nerve in a majority of cases communicates with the first. That communication varies considerably in size and distribution. It may reinforce the intercostal branch of the nerve, it may send one branch to the intercostal portion and another to the part of the nerve joining the brachial plexus, or it may consist of a nerve proceeding solely to join the brachial plexus by a junction in the first intercostal space with the part of the first thoracic nerve which is engaged in forming the plexus. (*c*) The first *white ramus communicans* in the thoracic region usually connects the first thoracic nerve with the first thoracic ganglion of the sympathetic trunk.

The **second intercostal nerve** is of large size, though much smaller than the first. It passes forwards through the second intercostal space, lying in the costal groove, between the external and internal intercostal muscles. At the level of the mid-axillary line it gives off a large lateral branch; continuing its course, it pierces the internal intercostal muscle and lies upon the pleura; finally, at the lateral border of the sternum, having crossed in front of the internal mammary artery, it passes forwards through the internal intercostal muscle, anterior intercostal membrane and pectoralis major, and ends in the front of the chest over the second intercostal space.

The nerve supplies the following branches :—

1. **Muscular branches** to the muscles of the second intercostal space.
2. **Cutaneous branches.** (*a*) Terminal **anterior cutaneous branches** to the skin and fascia over the second intercostal space (Fig. 883). (*b*) A large *lateral cutaneous branch* called the **intercosto-brachial nerve** (Fig. 875, p. 1010). That nerve pierces the intercostal

and serratus anterior muscles, and, crossing the axilla, extends to the upper arm. It pierces the deep fascia just beyond the posterior fold of the axilla, and can be traced as far as the interval between the medial epicondyle of the humerus and the olecranon. It supplies an area of skin and fascia stretching across the axilla and along the posterior surface of the upper arm on the medial side as far as the elbow (Fig. 878, p. 1015). It may supply the *axillary arches* when they are present.

The intercosto-brachial nerve varies in size. It may emerge through the first intercostal space, and it is often divisible into anterior and posterior branches, like the lateral cutaneous branch of an ordinary intercostal nerve.

Communications.—(1) The intercosto-brachial nerve communicates with two adjacent nerves. Either before or after piercing the fascia of the axilla it is joined by the medial cutaneous nerve of the arm. It also communicates with the posterior part of the lateral

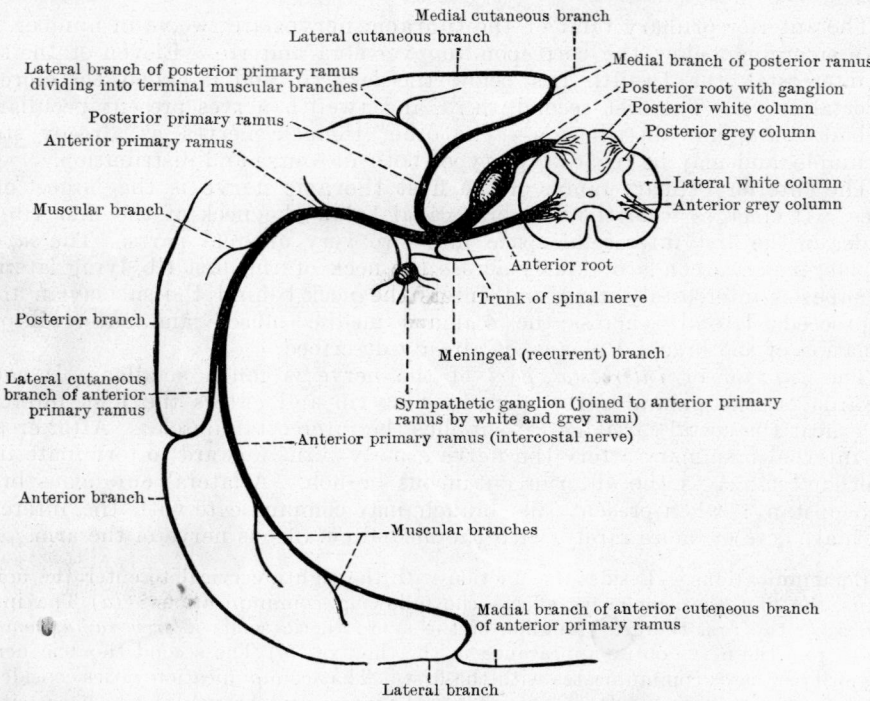

FIG. 882.—DIAGRAM OF THE ORIGIN AND DISTRIBUTION OF A TYPICAL SPINAL NERVE.

Note that the medial branch of the posterior primary ramus is represented as distributed to skin, whilst the lateral branch terminates at a deeper level in muscle. Both branches, however, supply muscles ; and in the lower half of the body it is the lateral branch that supplies skin and fascia.

cutaneous branch of the third intercostal nerve by means of the branches distributed to the floor and boundaries of the axilla. Sometimes it communicates with the lateral cutaneous branch of the first intercostal nerve. (2) Besides the branches referred to, the second thoracic nerve in many cases transmits a nerve to the brachial plexus which becomes incorporated with the first thoracic nerve after passing over the neck of the second rib. That branch is inconstant. As already mentioned, it may join only the intercostal part of the first thoracic nerve, it may join the brachial plexus only, or it may send branches to both parts of the first thoracic nerve. (3) Besides the communications effected by branches of the second thoracic nerve in its course, it also receives a *grey ramus communicans* from the second thoracic ganglion of the sympathetic trunk. It also sends a *white ramus communicans* to the sympathetic.

The **third intercostal nerve** differs from a typical thoracic nerve only in one respect. Its **lateral cutaneous branch** divides in the usual way into anterior and posterior parts, of which the latter is carried to the upper arm and supplies an area of skin and fascia on the medial side near the root of the limb. It effects a junction with the intercosto-brachial nerve (Fig. 875, p. 1010).

The **fourth, fifth, and sixth intercostal nerves** have a course and distribution

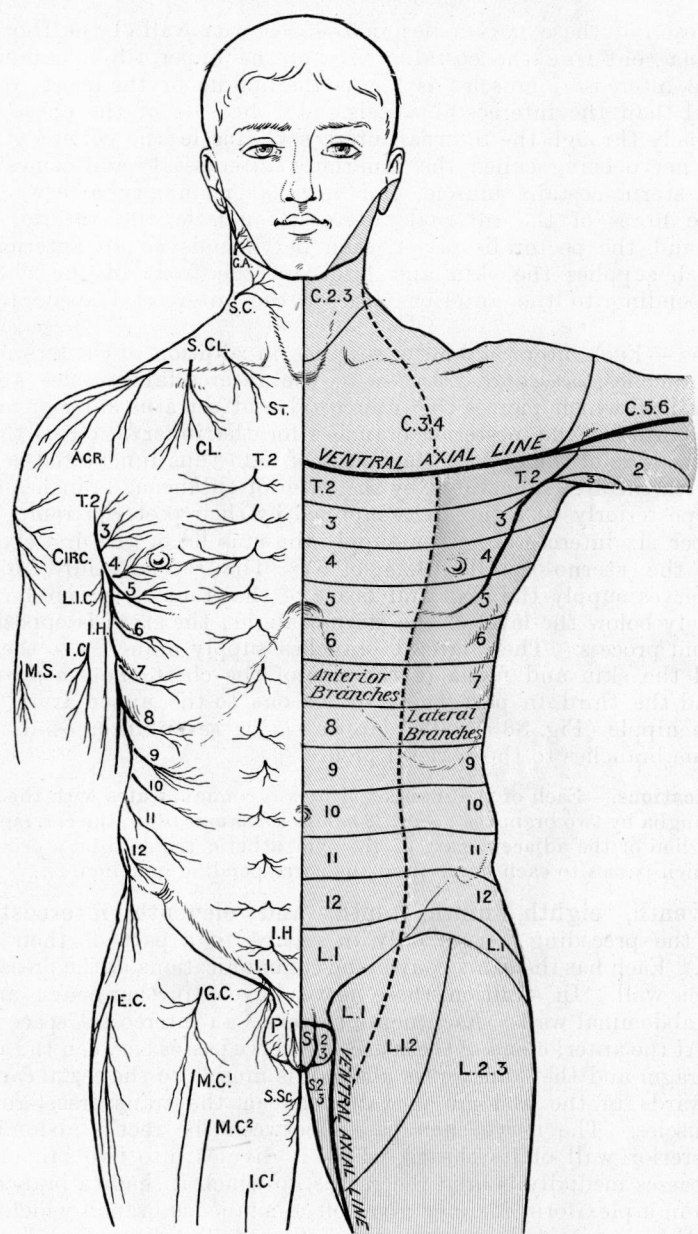

FIG. 883.—THE DISTRIBUTION OF CUTANEOUS NERVES ON THE FRONT OF THE TRUNK.

On one side the distribution of the several named nerves is represented.

G.A., Great auricular nerve ; S.C., Anterior cutaneous nerve of the neck ; S.CL., Supra-clavicular nerves :—
ACR., Lateral ; CL., Intermediate ; ST., Medial. T.2-12, Lateral and anterior branches of thoracic
nerves ; I.H., (below) Ilio-hypogastric nerve ; I.I., Ilio-inguinal nerve ; CIRC., Cutaneous branch of
circumflex nerve ; L.I.C., Medial cutaneous nerve of the arm ; I.H., (above) Intercosto-brachial ; I.C.,
Medial cutaneous nerve of the forearm ; M.S., Cutaneous branch of radial nerve ; E.C., Lateral
cutaneous nerve of thigh ; G.C., Femoral branch of genito-femoral nerve ; M.C.[1],[2], Branches of intermediate cutaneous nerve of thigh ; I.C.[1], Branch of medial cutaneous nerve of thigh ; P., Branches of
pudendal nerve ; S.Sc., Branches of posterior cutaneous nerve of the thigh.

On the other side a schematic representation is given of the areas supplied by the above nerves, the numerals
indicating the spinal origin of the branches of distribution to each area.

which are simple and typical. Except for the peculiarities above mentioned, the
second and third intercostal nerves have a similar distribution.

At first each of these nerves lies in the posterior wall of the thorax between the ribs; then, entering the costal groove of the upper rib, it extends forwards between the intercostal muscles as far as the middle of the chest wall, lying at a lower level than the intercostal vessels. At the side of the chest each nerve passes obliquely through the internal intercostal muscle (the portion of the muscle deep to the nerve being called the innermost intercostal), and comes to lie upon the pleura, sterno-costalis muscle, and internal mammary artery. Thereafter, piercing the fibres of the internal intercostal muscle, the anterior intercostal membrane, and the pectoralis major, each nerve ends as an **anterior cutaneous branch,** which supplies the skin and fascia of the front of the chest over an area corresponding to the anterior part of the intercostal space to which it belongs.

Branches.—Each intercostal nerve supplies, in addition to the terminal anterior cutaneous branches, *muscular branches* to the intercostal muscles and a **lateral cutaneous branch,** which pierces the intercostal and serratus anterior muscles, and divides into anterior and posterior branches for the innervation of the skin and fascia over the side of the chest. Each area of skin thus innervated is continuous anteriorly with the area innervated by the anterior cutaneous branches of the same nerves, and posteriorly with the areas supplied by their posterior rami.

The upper six intercostal nerves supply the muscles of the first six intercostal spaces and the sterno-costalis (3, 4, 5, 6). The second, third, fourth, fifth, and sixth nerves supply the skin and fascia of the front of the chest: the second is immediately below the level of the sternal angle; the sixth is opposite the base of the xiphoid process. Their lateral branches supply branches to the intercostal muscles and the skin and fascia of the side of the chest, the second (intercosto-brachial) and the third, in part, being drawn out to the upper arm. The fourth supplies the nipple (Fig. 883). The upper six or seven intercostal nerves give numerous fine branches to the parietal pleura.

Communications.—Each of the intercostal nerves communicates with the sympathetic trunk and ganglia by two branches—a *white ramus communicans* to the corresponding sympathetic ganglion or the adjacent part of the sympathetic trunk; and a *grey ramus communicans,* which passes to each nerve from the corresponding ganglion.

The **seventh, eighth, ninth, tenth, and eleventh intercostal nerves** differ from the preceding nerves only in regard to a part of their course and distribution. Each has the same course and communications as the preceding nerves in the thoracic wall. In addition, those nerves have a further course and distribution in the abdominal wall. Each nerve traverses an intercostal space in the way described. At the anterior end of the space, the nerve passes between the attachments of the diaphragm and the transversus abdominis muscle to the costal cartilages, and courses forwards in the abdominal wall between the transversus and obliquus internus muscles. The nerve then passes between the rectus abdominis muscle and the posterior wall of its sheath, where it divides into two branches (Wood). The larger passes medially behind the rectus, to which it sends a branch, and after breaking up in a plexiform manner gives off a cutaneous branch which pierces the muscle and the anterior wall of its sheath. The smaller division ends in the more lateral part of the rectus muscle.

Muscular Branches.—The lower intercostal nerves supply the intercostal muscles of the spaces in which they lie; and in the abdominal wall they innervate the transversus, obliquus internus and externus, and rectus abdominis. The branches arise from the main trunk as well as from its lateral and anterior branches. (The ninth, tenth, and eleventh nerves are described as assisting in the innervation of the diaphragm by communications with the phrenic nerve, but those fibres are probably afferent in function.)

Cutaneous Branches.—These are lateral and anterior. The **lateral cutaneous branches** divide into anterior and posterior parts, and, becoming superficial along the line of inter-digitation of the obliquus externus muscle with the serratus anterior and latissimus dorsi, they are directed more obliquely downwards than the lateral branches of the higher intercostal nerves, and are distributed to the skin and fascia of the loin as far down as the iliac crest. The lateral branch of the eleventh nerve can be traced over the iliac crest into the gluteal region.

The **anterior cutaneous branches** are small. That of the seventh nerve innervates the skin and fascia at the level of the xiphoid process. The eighth and ninth appear between the xiphoid process and the umbilicus; the tenth nerve supplies the region of the umbilicus; and the eleventh, the area immediately below the umbilicus.

The cutaneous branches of these nerves, including those of the posterior rami, thus supply continuous belts of skin which can be mapped out on the body from the vertebral column behind to the median plane in front. Those areas are not placed horizontally, but tend to be drawn downwards anteriorly as the series is followed from the upper to the lower nerves.

The lower six intercostal nerves supply many fine branches to the parietal peritoneum and extra-peritoneal tissue.

The anterior primary ramus of the twelfth thoracic nerve is the **subcostal nerve**, and is peculiar in its course and distribution. It emerges below the last rib (Fig. 885), and passes laterally and downwards behind the upper part of the psoas muscle and sometimes behind the lowest part of the pleura. It enters the abdomen below the lateral arcuate ligament [arcus lumbo-costalis lateralis], and crosses in front of the quadratus lumborum muscle. Behind the kidney it pierces the transversus abdominis muscle, and courses forwards in the interval between it and the obliquus internus as far as the sheath of the rectus muscle. After piercing the posterior wall of the sheath, the rectus muscle, and the anterior wall of the sheath, it ends by supplying the skin and fascia of the anterior abdominal wall midway between the umbilicus and the os pubis. The branches of the nerve are **muscular** to the transversus, obliqui, rectus, and pyramidalis muscles of the abdominal wall; and **cutaneous branches**, two in number—a terminal *anterior cutaneous branch*, which supplies the skin and fascia of the anterior abdominal wall midway between the umbilicus and the pubis, and a large *lateral cutaneous branch*, which, passing obliquely downwards through the lateral muscles of the abdominal wall, becomes superficial above the iliac crest, two inches behind the anterior superior spine. It supplies the skin and fascia of the gluteal region as far down as a point below and anterior to the greater trochanter of the femur (Fig. 683).

The subcostal nerve, in many cases, receives a **communicating branch** from the eleventh intercostal near its origin, and still more frequently sends a fine branch to join the first lumbar nerve in the psoas muscle. It may communicate also with the ilio-hypogastric nerve, as they lie near each other in the abdominal wall.

Intercommunications of the Thoracic Nerves.—It has been noted already that the belts or areas of skin supplied by the branches of the thoracic nerves are innervated also by adjacent nerves on either side which invade the area supplied by a given nerve. Communications also take place between the branches of the nerves supplying the intercostal muscles, whereby the muscles of a given space derive their innervation from more than one intercostal nerve.

LUMBAR, SACRAL, AND COCCYGEAL PLEXUSES

These plexuses are formed by the union of the anterior primary rami of the remaining spinal nerves (five lumbar, five sacral, and one coccygeal), and are united with one another—the lower lumbar nerves passing into the sacral plexus and the lower sacral into the coccygeal plexus. Frequently a fine communicating branch of the twelfth thoracic nerve joins the first lumbar nerve near its origin.

Of the nerves in question the first sacral is generally the largest in size, the nerves diminishing gradually above that nerve and rapidly below it. The nerves destined for the supply of the lower limb spring from the lumbar and sacral plexuses; in addition, nerves arise at their upper limit to be distributed to the trunk above the level of the limb; and near the lower limit nerves arise for the supply of the perineum.

Lumbar Plexus.—The lumbar plexus is formed by the anterior primary rami of the first four lumbar nerves, and is often joined by a branch from the twelfth thoracic nerve. It is limited below by the fourth lumbar nerve (*n. furcalis*), which enters also into the composition of the sacral plexus. The nerves of the lumbar plexus are formed in the loin, and supply that region as well as part of the lower limb.

Sacral Plexus.—The sacral plexus is formed by the anterior primary rami of the fourth and fifth lumbar, and the upper four sacral nerves, the fourth sacral nerve dividing to take part in the coccygeal plexus also. The nerves of the sacral

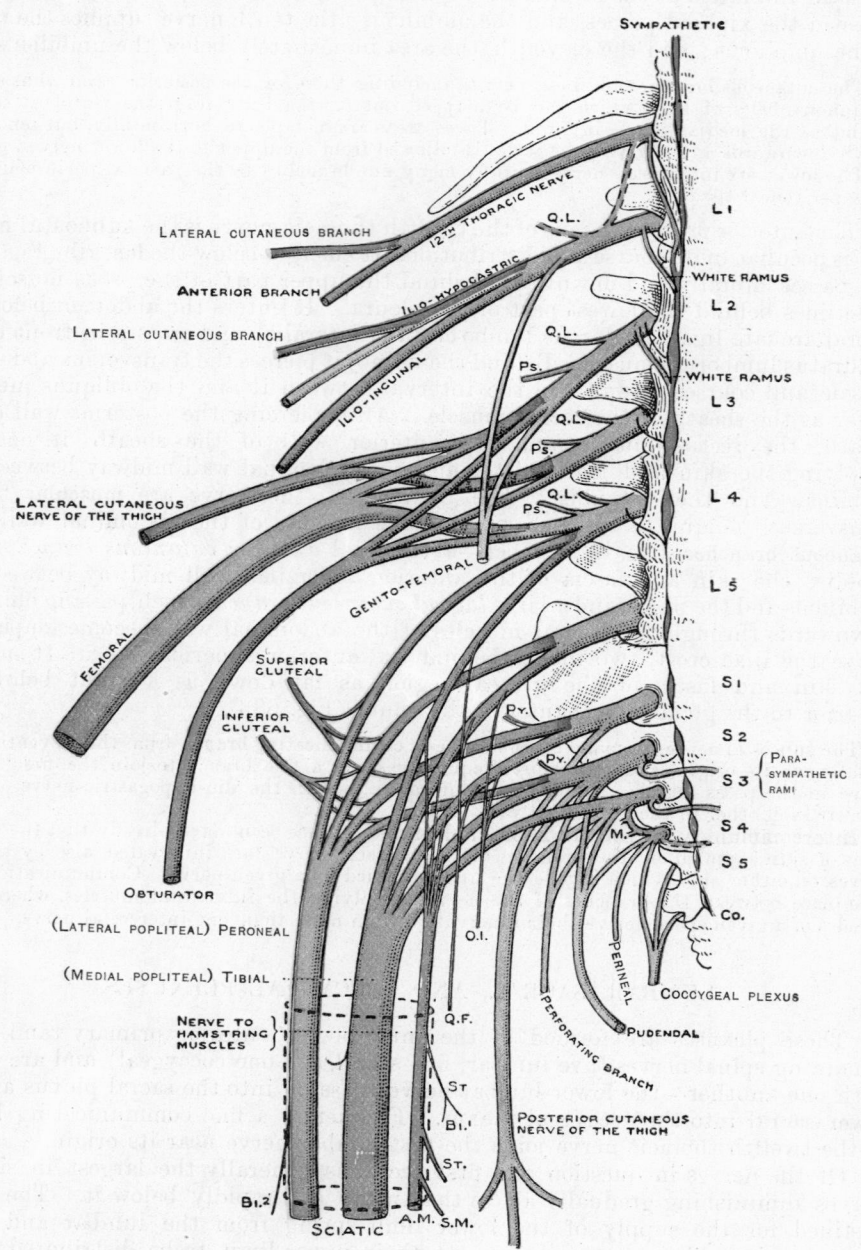

FIG. 884.—NERVES OF THE LUMBAR, SACRAL, AND COCCYGEAL PLEXUSES.

plexus are placed on the dorsal wall of the true pelvis, and are destined for the lower limb and the perineum.

Coccygeal Plexus.—The coccygeal plexus is formed by the anterior primary rami of the coccygeal and fifth sacral nerves and a portion of the fourth. It lies on the coccygeus muscle in the dorsal wall of the pelvis, and its branches are fine filaments to the coccygeus and levator ani and to the skin over the coccyx.

Communications with the Autonomic System.—Each of the nerves has communications with the sympathetic trunk in the abdomen and pelvis by means of grey **rami communicantes.** From the lumbar and sacral ganglia long slender *grey rami communicantes* are directed backwards and laterally over the bodies of the vertebræ, and (in the lumbar region) behind the origins of the psoas muscle, to reach the spinal nerves. Those branches are irregular in their arrangement. A given nerve may receive branches from two ganglia, or one ganglion may send branches to two nerves. The grey rami are longer in the loin than in the pelvis, owing to the position of the sympathetic trunk.

Certain lumbar nerves are connected with the sympathetic by means of *white rami communicantes* also. From the first two, and possibly in some cases also the third and fourth lumbar nerves, white rami are directed forwards, either independently or incorporated with the corresponding grey rami, to join the upper part of the lumbar sympathetic trunk. The fifth lumbar nerve and the first sacral nerves are unprovided with white rami.

From the anterior primary rami of the second and third or third and fourth sacral nerves parasympathetic fibres pass medially, and, crossing over (without joining) the sympathetic trunk, enter the pelvic plexuses of the autonomic system. The fifth sacral and coccygeal nerves have no white rami communicantes.

Variations in Position of the Lumbar and Sacral Plexuses

These plexuses show a very considerable variability in position and constitution. Eisler records concomitant variations in 18 per cent. of the cases examined by him. The variations occur within wide limits. The lumbar plexus may begin at the eleventh or twelfth thoracic or first lumbar nerve. The last nerve in the sciatic cord may be either the second or the third, or the fourth sacral nerve. The position of the *nervus furcalis* is a guide to the arrangement of the plexus. It may be the third, third and fourth, fourth, fourth and fifth, or fifth lumbar nerves. The resulting variations are illustrated by the following extreme cases :—

	(1) *Prefixed Variety.*	(2) *Normal.*	(3) *Postfixed Variety*
Nervus furcalis	L. 3 and 4 (double).	L. 4.	L. 5.
Obturator	L. 1, 2, 3.	L. 2, 3, 4.	L. 2, 3, 4, 5.
Femoral	T. 12, L. 1, 2, 3, 4.	L. 2, 3, 4.	L. 2, 3, 4, 5.
Med. popliteal [Tibial]	L. 3, 4, 5, S. 1, 2.	L. 4, 5, S. 1, 2, 3.	L. 5, S. 1, 2, 3, 4.
Lat. popliteal [Peroneal]	L. 3, 4, 5, S. 1.	L. 4, 5, S. 1, 2.	L. 5, S. 1, 2, 3.

The variations in the constitution of the lumbar and sacral plexuses which are most numerous are those due to the inclusion of nerves more caudally placed. Thus, out of twenty-two variations in the position of the *n. furcalis*, in nineteen Eisler found it to be the fifth lumbar nerve; in two cases only, the third lumbar nerve. There is further evidence that these variations in position are accompanied by variations in the vertebral column itself. Out of the twenty-two abnormal plexuses examined by Eisler, sixteen were coincident with abnormal arrangement of the associated vertebræ.

LUMBAR PLEXUS

The **lumbar plexus** is formed by the anterior primary rami of the first three lumbar nerves and a part of the fourth, with the addition, in half the number of cases, of a small branch from the subcostal (twelfth thoracic) nerve. The nerves increase in size from above downwards (Fig. 884).

Position and Constitution.—The plexus is formed in the substance of the psoas major muscle, in front of the transverse processes of the lumbar vertebræ. The nerves, on emerging from the intervertebral foramina, are connected as above described with the sympathetic system, and then divide in the following manner in the substance of the psoas major muscle. The first and second nerves divide into superior and inferior branches. The superior branch of the first nerve (which may be joined by the branch from the subcostal nerve) forms two nerves, the **ilio-hypogastric** and **ilio-inguinal.** The inferior branch of the first joins the superior branch of the second nerve, to form the **genito-femoral nerve.** The inferior branch of the second nerve, the whole of the third, and that part of the fourth nerve engaged in the constitution of the plexus divide each into two unequal parts—smaller *anterior* and larger *posterior parts.* The anterior portions combine together to form the **obturator nerve** ; the root from the second nerve is not always present.

65 *b*

The posterior portions of the same nerves combine together to form the **femoral nerve.** From the back of the posterior parts of the second and third nerves the **lateral cutaneous nerve of the thigh** arises. The nerves also provide, near their origins, irregular **muscular branches** for the psoas and quadratus lumborum muscles.

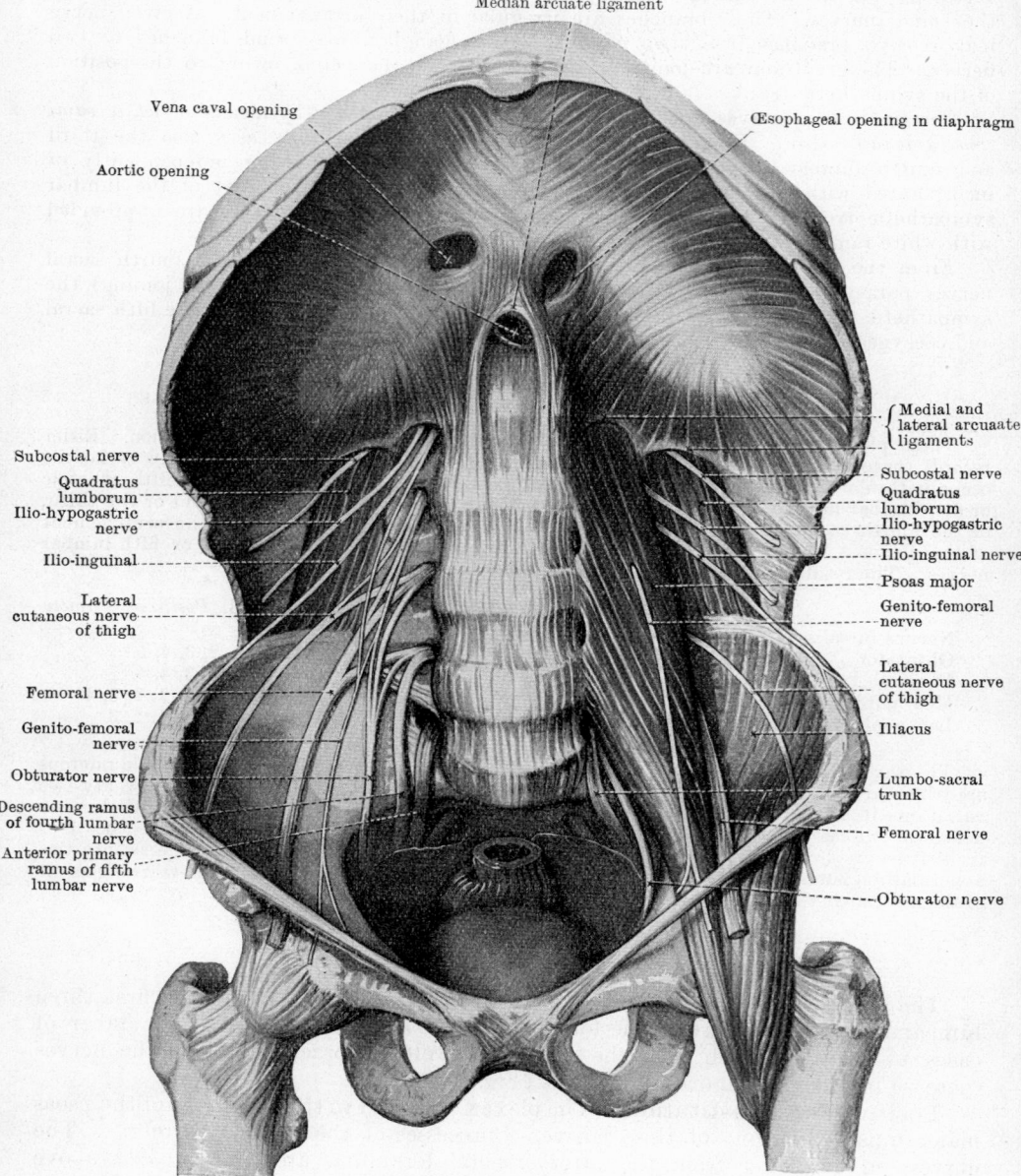

Median arcuate ligament

Vena caval opening

Œsophageal opening in diaphragm

Aortic opening

Medial and lateral arcuate ligaments

Subcostal nerve

Quadratus lumborum

Ilio-hypogastric nerve

Ilio-inguinal

Lateral cutaneous nerve of thigh

Femoral nerve

Genito-femoral nerve

Obturator nerve

Descending ramus of fourth lumbar nerve

Anterior primary ramus of fifth lumbar nerve

Subcostal nerve

Quadratus lumborum

Ilio-hypogastric nerve

Ilio-inguinal nerve

Psoas major

Genito-femoral nerve

Lateral cutaneous nerve of thigh

Iliacus

Lumbo-sacral trunk

Femoral nerve

Obturator nerve

FIG. 885.—THE MUSCLES AND NERVES ON THE POSTERIOR ABDOMINAL WALL.

The following is a list of the nerves which spring from the lumbar plexus, together with their origins :—

(1) Muscular branches to the quadratus lumborum (L. 1-4) and psoas muscles (L. 2, 3).

(2) Ilio-hypogastric (? T. 12, L. 1).

(3) Ilio-inguinal (? T. 12, L. 1).

(4) Genito-femoral (L. 1, 2).

(5) Lateral cutaneous (L. 2, 3).

(6) Obturator (L. 2, 3, 4).

(7) Femoral (L. 2, 3, 4).

Muscular Branches.—The nerves to the **quadratus lumborum muscle** arise independently from the first three or four lumbar nerves (and sometimes also from the subcostal nerve). The nerves to the **psoas major** arise from the second and third lumbar nerves, with additions, in some cases, from the first or fourth. They are often associated in their origin with the nerve to the iliacus from the femoral nerve. The **psoas minor**, when present, is innervated by the first or the second lumbar nerve.

The ilio-hypogastric and ilio-inguinal nerves closely resemble, in their course and distribution, the lower thoracic nerves, with which they are in series.

The **ilio-hypogastric nerve** is the highest branch of the first lumbar nerve. It receives fibres also from the subcostal, when that nerve communicates with the first lumbar nerve. After traversing the psoas major muscle obliquely, it appears at its lateral border, on the anterior surface of the quadratus lumborum and behind the kidney. It courses through the loin, lying between the transversus and obliquus abdominis internus muscles, above the iliac crest. About an inch in front of the anterior superior spine it pierces the obliquus internus, and continues its course in the groin deep to the aponeurosis of the obliquus externus. It finally becomes cutaneous in the anterior abdominal wall by piercing the aponeurosis of the obliquus externus about an inch and a half above the superficial inguinal ring (Fig. 883, p. 1025).

Its **branches** are—(1) *muscular* to the muscles of the abdominal wall; and (2) *cutaneous branches*, two in number. The **lateral cutaneous branch** corresponds with the lateral cutaneous branch of an intercostal nerve. It pierces the obliquus internus and obliquus externus, becomes cutaneous just above the iliac crest, below and behind the lateral cutaneous branch of the subcostal nerve. It is small, and may be absent. It is distributed to the skin and fascia over the upper part of the lateral side of the gluteal region, in contiguity with the cutaneous branch of the posterior primary ramus of the first lumbar nerve. The **anterior cutaneous branch** is the anterior terminal branch of the nerve. It supplies the skin and fascia of the anterior abdominal wall below the level of the subcostal nerve and above the os pubis.

The **ilio-inguinal nerve** is the second branch given off from the first lumbar nerve. It also may receive fibres from the subcostal nerve. Not infrequently the ilio-hypogastric and ilio-inguinal nerves are represented for a longer or shorter part of their course by a single trunk. When separate the nerve takes a course similar to that of the ilio-hypogastric nerve, but at a lower level, as far as the anterior abdominal wall. It appears at the lateral border of the psoas major, after traversing the muscle obliquely, and passes behind the kidney in front of the quadratus lumborum. It extends forwards between the transversus and obliquus internus, and pierces the latter muscle farther forward and lower down than the ilio-hypogastric; it continues forwards deep to the aponeurosis of the obliquus externus, just above the inguinal ligament, and becomes superficial after passing through the superficial inguinal ring and external spermatic fascia (Fig. 883, p. 1025). Whilst lying between the transversus and obliquus internus it usually communicates with the ilio-hypogastric nerve.

Its branches are *muscular* to the muscles of the abdominal wall among which it passes, and *cutaneous branches* which innervate the skin and fascia (1) of the anterior abdominal wall over the pubic symphysis, (2) of the thigh over the proximal and medial part of the femoral triangle, and (3) of the superior part of the scrotum, and root and dorsum of the penis in the male (*scrotal branches*), and of the mons pubis and labium majus in the female (*labial branches*). The last-named branches are contiguous to branches of the pudendal nerve. No lateral cutaneous branch arises from the ilio-inguinal nerve. It thus corresponds, like the anterior cutaneous part of the ilio-hypogastric nerve, to the anterior continuation of a typical thoracic nerve.

The **genito-femoral nerve** usually arises from the front of the first and second lumbar nerves, by two independent roots which unite in the substance of the psoas major. It appears on the posterior abdominal wall, lying on the front of the psoas major, medial to the psoas minor. It pierces the psoas fascia, and extends behind the ureter and along the lateral side of the common and external iliac arteries downwards, to the inguinal ligament (Fig. 885, p. 1030). At a variable point above that ligament it divides into two branches. 1. The **genital branch** [n. spermaticus ext.], a small nerve which crosses the lower part of the external iliac artery, and, along with the vas deferens, testicular artery and veins and vessels to cremaster, enters the inguinal canal through the deep inguinal ring. It ends by supplying small branches to the skin and fascia of the scrotum and adjacent part of the thigh. In the female it accompanies the round ligament to the labium majus. In its course it gives off the following small branches: (1) to the external iliac artery; (2) to the cremaster muscle; (3) to communicate with the testicular plexus of the autonomic system and the ilio-inguinal nerve. 2. The **femoral branch** [n. lumbo-inguinalis] continues the course of the parent nerve and passes into the thigh behind the inguinal ligament and then lies on the lateral side of the femoral artery. It becomes cutaneous by passing through the saphenous opening or through the fascia lata, and supplies an area of skin and fascia over the femoral triangle, lateral to that supplied by the ilio-inguinal nerve (Fig. 883, p. 1025). It communicates in the thigh with the intermediate cutaneous branch of the femoral nerve. Before piercing the deep fascia it gives a minute branch to the femoral artery.

The **lateral cutaneous nerve of the thigh** is distributed only to skin and fascia (Fig. 885). It arises from the back of the lumbar plexus, and usually from the second and third lumbar nerves. Emerging from the lateral border of the psoas major muscle, the nerve crosses the iliacus muscle, behind the fascia iliaca, to reach the anterior superior iliac spine. It enters the thigh behind the lateral end of the inguinal ligament, and either superficial or deep to the sartorius muscle, or through its upper part. It extends downwards in the front of the thigh for a few inches, lying at first deep to the fascia lata, and afterwards in a tubular investment of the fascia. It gives off small branches in this part of its course, and finally, piercing the fascia about four inches distal to the anterior superior iliac spine, it separates into anterior and posterior terminal branches. The **anterior branch** is the larger, and is distributed on the lateral part of the front of the thigh as far as the knee, where it may communicate with the patellar plexus. The smaller **posterior branch** supplies the skin and fascia of the lateral side of the buttock, distal to the greater trochanter, and the skin and fascia of the proximal two-thirds of the lateral side of the thigh (Fig. 887, p. 1036).

OBTURATOR NERVE

The **obturator nerve** supplies the muscles on the medial side of the thigh, gives articular branches to the hip and knee joints, and sometimes has also a cutaneous branch. It arises in the substance of the psoas major muscle by three roots placed in front of those of the femoral nerve, and derived from the second, third, and fourth lumbar nerves (Fig. 885, p. 1030). Sometimes the root from the second nerve is absent. Passing vertically downwards, the nerve emerges from the psoas major at its medial border, behind the common iliac vessels, and on the lateral side of the ureter and internal iliac vessels. It passes forwards below the pelvic brim in contact with the upper part of the obturator internus muscle and in company with the obturator artery to the obturator groove of the obturator foramen, through which it reaches the thigh. While in the obturator groove, where it lies above the obturator vessels, it separates into its two main branches, named anterior and posterior (Fig. 886).

In the thigh the **anterior branch** lies in front of the obturator externus and adductor brevis muscles, and behind the pectineus and adductor longus. In the middle third of the thigh it is found coursing along the medial border of the adductor longus; and it finally divides into two slender terminal filaments.

The branches of the **anterior part** of the nerve are:—

1. An **articular branch** to the hip joint which arises from the nerve as soon as it enters the thigh, and supplies the joint through the acetabular notch.

2. **Muscular branches** to the adductor longus, gracilis, adductor brevis (usually), and the pectineus (occasionally).

3. Two *terminal branches* : (*a*) **A cutaneous branch**, of very variable size and often absent, becomes superficial between the gracilis and adductor longus (Fig. 886), in the middle third of the thigh, and may supply the skin and fascia of the distal two-thirds of the thigh on its medial side. It is generally of small size, and is connected with branches of the medial cutaneous nerve of the thigh and the saphenous nerve behind the sartorius muscle to form a plexus. The branch from the saphenous nerve to the plexus passes medially behind the sartorius

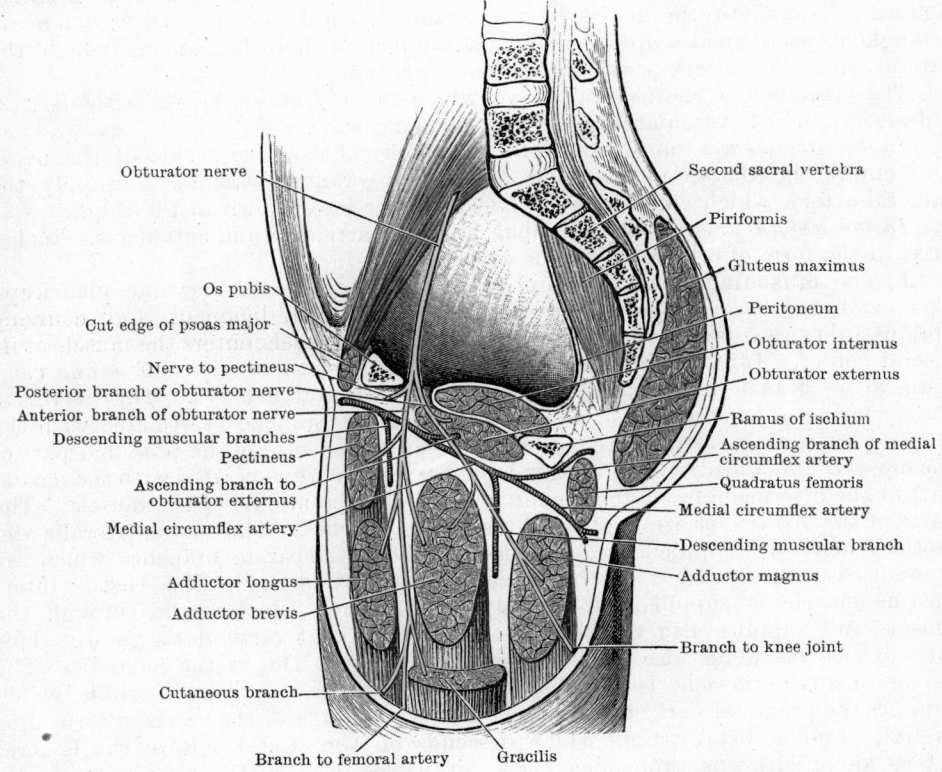

Obturator nerve

Os pubis

Cut edge of psoas major

Nerve to pectineus

Posterior branch of obturator nerve

Anterior branch of obturator nerve

Descending muscular branches

Pectineus

Ascending branch to obturator externus

Medial circumflex artery

Adductor longus

Adductor brevis

Cutaneous branch

Branch to femoral artery — Gracilis

Second sacral vertebra

Piriformis

Gluteus maximus

Peritoneum

Obturator internus

Obturator externus

Ramus of ischium

Ascending branch of medial circumflex artery

Quadratus femoris

Medial circumflex artery

Descending muscular branch

Adductor magnus

Branch to knee joint

FIG. 886.—SCHEME OF THE COURSE AND DISTRIBUTION OF THE OBTURATOR NERVE.

after piercing the fascial covering of the subsartorial canal [c. adductorius]. The branch from the medial cutaneous nerve is generally superficial at the point of formation of the plexus. (*b*) **A branch to the femoral artery** which enters the subsartorial canal along the medial border of the adductor longus, and ramifies over the distal part of the artery.

5. A fine **communicating branch** sometimes joins the femoral nerve in front of the hip joint.

The **posterior branch of the obturator nerve** reaches the thigh by piercing the obturator externus muscle. It descends between the adductor brevis and adductor magnus muscles. After passing obliquely through the adductor magnus, it enters the popliteal fossa on the popliteal artery, to which it furnishes twigs, and terminates by piercing the oblique posterior ligament of the knee joint.

Its branches are: (1) **muscular branches** to the obturator externus, adductor magnus, and the adductor brevis. The branch to the obturator externus arises before the nerve enters the muscle, in the obturator groove. The nerve to the adductor magnus is given off as the obturator nerve passes through the substance of the muscle. (2) The **articular terminal branch** to the posterior part of the knee joint.

Femoral Nerve

The **femoral nerve** is the large nerve of supply for the muscles of the front of the thigh; it gives articular branches to the hip and knee joints; and it has an extensive cutaneous distribution down the medial side of the limb to the foot. It arises in the substance of the psoas major muscle, from the back of the second, third, and fourth lumbar nerves, posterior to the obturator nerve. Passing obliquely through the psoas major muscle, it emerges from its lateral border a little below the iliac crest (Fig. 885, p. 1030), and passes downwards in the groove between the psoas and iliacus, to enter the thigh behind the inguinal ligament, lateral to the femoral sheath and femoral vessels. In the femoral triangle it soon breaks up into a large number of branches, among which the lateral circumflex artery passes in a lateral direction.

The **branches** of the femoral nerve, which are (1) muscular, (2) articular, (3) cutaneous, and (4) vascular, arise in the following way :—

In the abdomen a muscular branch arises from the lateral side of the nerve and enters the iliacus muscle, and a vascular branch descends to supply the femoral artery, which vessel also receives branches lower down in the thigh.

In the femoral triangle the terminal muscular, articular, and cutaneous branches arise in the form of a large bundle of nerves.

1. The **muscular branches** supply the pectineus, sartorius, and quadriceps. The nerve to the *pectineus* arises close to the inguinal ligament, and, coursing obliquely downwards and medially behind the femoral vessels, enters the muscle at its lateral border. It is not infrequently double. It sometimes gives off a fine communicating branch to the anterior part of the obturator nerve. The nerves to the *sartorius* are in two sets : a lateral set of short branches, associated with the lateral part of the intermediate cutaneous nerve, which supply the proximal part of the muscle; and a medial set of longer branches, which are associated with the medial part of the intermediate cutaneous nerve, and enter the middle of the muscle. The parts of the *quadriceps* are supplied by several branches. The vastus lateralis and rectus femoris are supplied on their deep surface by separate branches which are accompanied by branches of the lateral circumflex artery. The vastus intermedius muscle is supplied superficially by a branch which passes through the muscle, and supplies also the muscle of the knee joint (articularis genu). This muscle receives fibres also from one of the nerves to the vastus medialis. The vastus medialis muscle is supplied by two nerves : a proximal trunk, which supplies the proximal part of the muscle, and sends fibres to the vastus intermedius as well; and a distal trunk, which descends on the lateral side of the femoral artery along with the saphenous nerve; it passes deep to the sartorius, deep or superficial to the aponeurotic covering of the subsartorial canal, and enters the medial side of the muscle. That nerve gives off a small branch which enters the medullary canal of the femur.

2. The **articular branches** supply the hip and knee joints. The articular branch to the hip joint arises from the nerve to the rectus femoris, and is accompanied by branches from the lateral circumflex artery. The articular branches to the knee joint are four in number. Three of them arise from the nerves to the vastus lateralis, vastus intermedius, and vastus medialis, which, after the muscular nerves are given off, are continued downwards to the knee joint along the front of the femur. A fourth articular branch arises (sometimes) from the saphenous nerve.

3. The **cutaneous branches** are the intermediate and medial cutaneous nerves, and the saphenous nerve (Fig. 887).

The **intermediate cutaneous nerve of the thigh** arises in two parts, a *lateral* and a *medial branch*, in the proximal part of the femoral triangle. The two branches descend vertically and become cutaneous by piercing the fascia lata over the proximal third of the sartorius muscle. They carry muscular branches to the sartorius, and the lateral branch in many cases pierces the muscle. The two nerves supply the skin and fascia of the distal three-fourths of the front of the thigh, between the lateral cutaneous nerve of the thigh laterally and the medial cutaneous on the medial side. They reach to the front of the patella, and there assist in the formation of the patellar plexus. The lateral branch communicates, in the proximal third of the thigh, with twigs from the femoral branch of the genito-femoral nerve.

The **medial cutaneous nerve of the thigh** lies at first in the femoral triangle on the lateral side of the femoral vessels. At the apex of the triangle it crosses over the femoral vessels, and is directed downwards superficial to or through the sartorius muscle, and deep to the fascia lata, to the distal third of the thigh. It is distributed to the skin and fascia of the distal two-thirds of the thigh on the medial side by means of three branches—proximal, middle, and distal.

The *proximal branch* may be represented by two or more twigs. It arises from the main nerve near its origin, and pierces the fascia lata near the apex of the femoral triangle. It is distributed to the skin and fascia of the proximal part of the thigh along the line of the long saphenous vein. The *middle* or *anterior branch* is a larger nerve. It separates from the distal branch at the apex of the femoral triangle, and passing superficial to the sartorius muscle becomes cutaneous in the middle third of the thigh on the medial side. It supplies the skin and fascia of the distal half of the medial side of the thigh, extending as far as the knee, where it joins in the formation of the patellar plexus.

The *distal branch* represents the termination of the nerve. It passes along the medial side of the thigh superficial to the sartorius muscle, and communicates in the middle third of the thigh with the saphenous and obturator nerves to form a plexus. Piercing the fascia lata on the medial side of the thigh in the distal third, it ramifies over the medial side of the knee, and assists in the formation of the patellar plexus.

The size of the medial cutaneous nerve of the thigh varies with the size of the cutaneous part of the obturator, and of the saphenous nerve.

The **saphenous nerve** may be regarded as the terminal branch of the femoral nerve. It is destined for the skin and fascia of the leg and foot. From its origin in the femoral triangle it descends alongside the femoral vessels to the subsartorial canal. In the canal it crosses obliquely in front of the femoral artery from lateral to medial side. At the distal end of the canal, accompanied by the saphenous branch of the descending genicular artery, it passes anterior to the tendon of the adductor magnus, and opposite the medial side of the knee joint becomes cutaneous by passing between the sartorius and gracilis muscles. The nerve then extends downwards in the leg with the long saphenous vein, and passing over the front of the medial malleolus it terminates at the middle of the medial border of the foot.

Branches.—1. A **communicating branch** arises in the subsartorial canal [c. adductorius], and, passing medially behind the sartorius, joins with branches of the obturator nerve in forming a plexus.

2. The **infra-patellar branch** arises at the distal end of the subsartorial canal, and, piercing the sartorius muscle, is directed downwards and forwards below the patella, and over the medial condyle of the tibia to the front of the knee and proximal part of the leg. It enters into the formation of the patellar plexus.

3. An **articular branch** sometimes arises from the nerve at the medial side of the knee.

4. The **terminal branches** of the saphenous nerve are distributed to the skin and fascia of the front and medial side of the leg and the posterior half of the dorsum and medial side of the foot.

The **patellar plexus** consists of fine communications, beneath the skin in front of the knee, between the branches of the cutaneous nerves supplying that region. The nerves which enter into its formation are the infra-patellar branch of the saphenous, medial and intermediate cutaneous, and sometimes the lateral cutaneous nerve of the thigh.

The **accessory obturator nerve** is only occasionally present (29 per cent., Eisler). It arises from the third, or third and fourth lumbar nerves, between the roots of the obturator and femoral nerves. It is associated with the obturator nerve, from which, however, it is quite separable. It appears in the abdomen at the medial side of the psoas muscle and passes over the pelvic brim behind the external iliac vessels, leaves the obturator nerve, and enters the thigh in front of the os pubis.

In the thigh, behind the femoral vessels, it usually ends in three branches : a nerve which replaces the branch from the femoral nerve to the pectineus, a nerve to the hip joint, and a nerve which communicates with the anterior part of the obturator nerve. In some cases it only supplies the nerve to the pectineus ; more rarely it is of considerable size, and reinforces the obturator nerve in the innervation of the adductor muscles.

It is more closely associated with the femoral than with the obturator. Its origin is behind

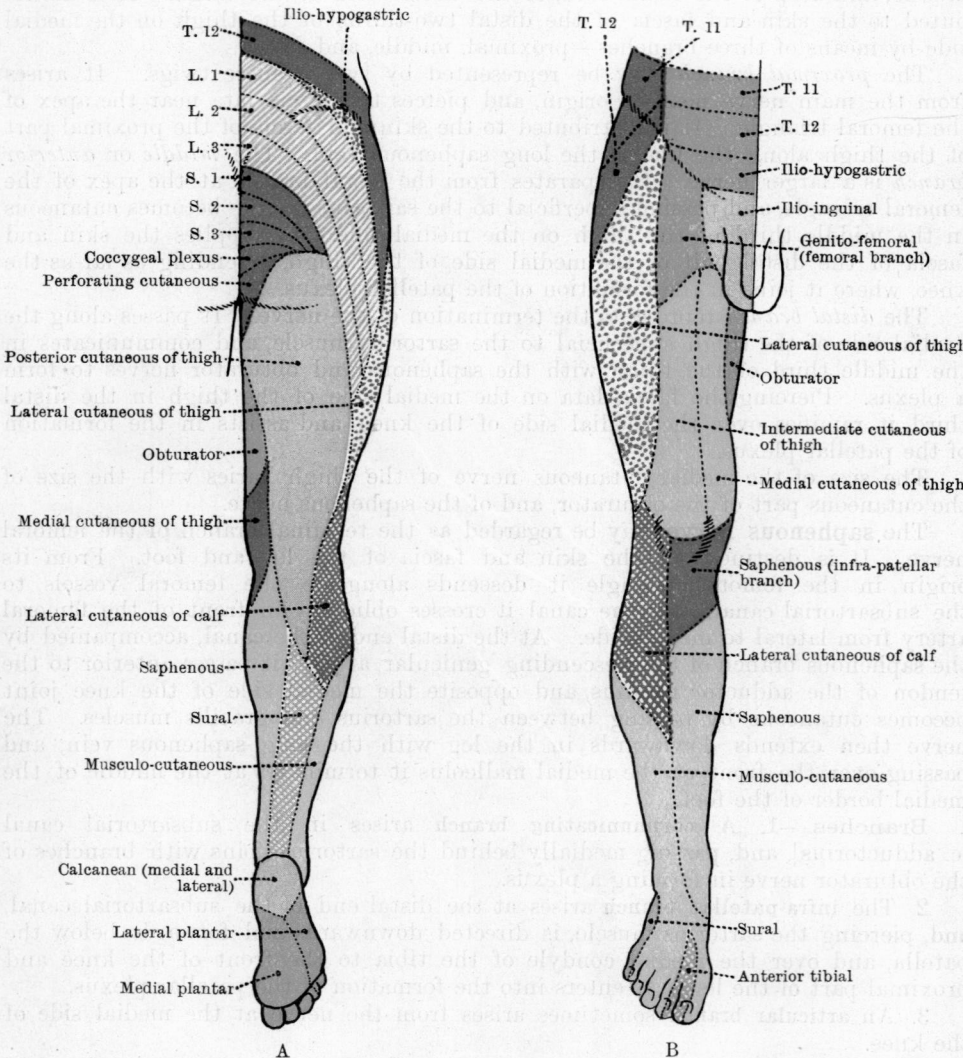

FIG. 887.—DISTRIBUTION OF CUTANEOUS NERVES : A, ON THE BACK ; B, ON THE FRONT OF THE LOWER LIMB.

the roots of the obturator : it is separated, like the femoral, from the obturator by the pubic bone ; and its chief branch—the branch to the pectineus muscle—replaces the normal branch from the femoral nerve. On the other hand, for a part of its course it accompanies the obturator, and in rare cases it may replace branches of that nerve.

The nerves which enter into the formation of the lumbar plexus are distributed to the ilio-hypogastric, ilio-inguinal and infero-medial cutaneous and some to the femoral cutaneous nerve of the thigh.

SACRAL PLEXUS

The sacral plexus is usually formed by the anterior primary rami of the following nerves—a part of the fourth lumbar nerve (n. furcalis), the fifth lumbar, the upper three sacral nerves and part of the fourth.

Communications with the Autonomic System.—Each of the nerves named is connected to the lumbar or the pelvic sympathetic trunk by *grey rami communicantes*, as already described; and parasympathetic fibres pass from the third and usually also from the second or the fourth sacral nerves to join the pelvic plexuses of the autonomic system.

Position and Constitution.—The plexus is placed on the dorsal wall of the

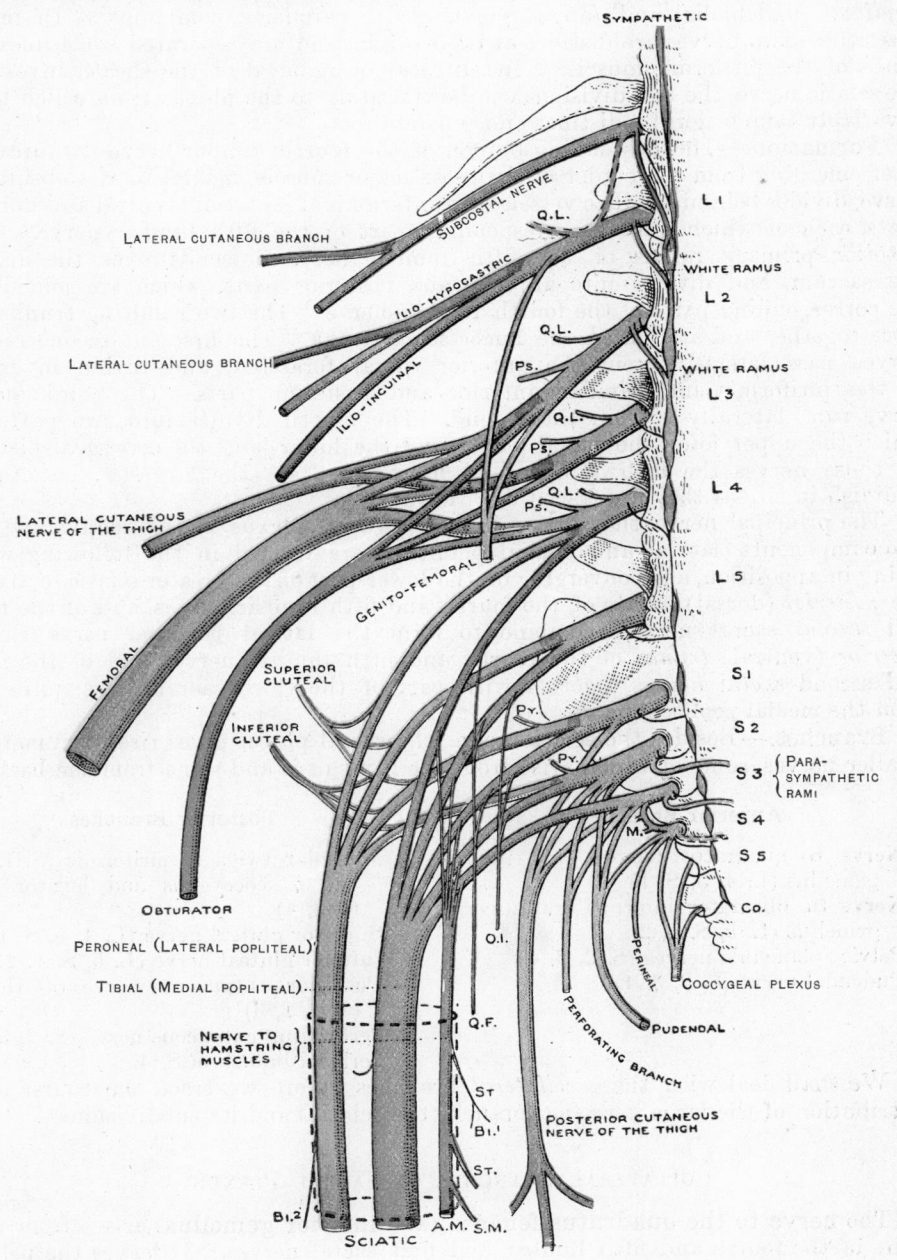

FIG. 888.—NERVES OF THE LUMBAR, SACRAL, AND COCCYGEAL PLEXUSES.

pelvis between the piriformis muscle and its fascia. In front of it there are the internal iliac vessels and the ureter, and, in addition, the pelvic colon on the left side, coils of the ileum on the right side.

The nerves which form the plexus converge towards the inferior part of the greater sciatic foramen, and unite to form a broad triangular band, the apex of

which is continued through the greater sciatic foramen below the piriformis
muscle into the gluteal region as the **sciatic nerve.** From the anterior and posterior
surfaces of the triangular band numerous small branches arise, which are distributed to the parts in the neighbourhood of the origin of the nerve.

The sciatic nerve ends in the thigh by dividing into two large nerves—the *medial
popliteal* [n. tibialis] and *lateral popliteal* [n. peronæus communis]. In many
cases these two nerves are distinct at their origin, and are separated sometimes by
fibres of the piriformis muscle. In all cases, on removal of the sheath investing
the sciatic nerve, the two divisions can be traced up to the plexus, from which they
invariably take origin by distinct and separate roots.

Formation.—The descending branch of the fourth lumbar nerve (n. furcalis)
after emerging from the border of the psoas major muscle, medial to the obturator
nerve, divides behind the iliac vessels into anterior and posterior (ventral and dorsal)
parts, each of which joins a corresponding part of the fifth lumbar nerve. The
anterior primary ramus of the fifth lumbar nerve descends over the ala of
the sacrum, and divides into anterior and posterior parts, which are joined by
the corresponding parts of the fourth lumbar nerve. The two resulting trunks lie
close together and are called the **lumbo-sacral trunk.** The first and second sacral
nerves pass laterally from the anterior sacral foramina, and divide in front
of the piriformis into similar anterior and posterior parts. The third sacral
nerve runs laterally to join the second. The fourth divides into two parts of
which the upper joins the sacral plexus and the lower joins the coccygeal plexus.
Of those nerves the fifth lumbar and first sacral are the largest; the others
diminish in size as they are traced downwards.

The principal nerve that arises from the sacral plexus is the sciatic, and its
two components (lateral and medial popliteal) are formed in the following way.
Lying in apposition, and converging on the lower part of the greater sciatic foramen,
the *posterior* (dorsal) *trunks* of the fourth and fifth lumbar nerves, and of the first
and second sacral nerves, combine to form the **lateral popliteal nerve.** The
anterior (ventral) *trunks* of the fourth and fifth lumbar nerves, and of the first
and second sacral nerves, together with part of the third sacral nerve, unite to
form the **medial popliteal nerve.**

Branches.—Besides the sciatic nerve, the sacral plexus gives rise to numerous
smaller nerves, some of which arise from the front of it and some from the back.

Anterior Branches.	Posterior Branches.
Nerve to quadratus femoris and inferior gemellus (L. 4, 5, S. 1)	Muscular twigs to piriformis (S. 1, 2) and to coccygeus and levator ani (S. 3, 4)
Nerve to obturator internus and superior gemellus (L. 5, S. 1, 2)	Superior gluteal nerve (L. 4, 5, S. 1)
Pelvic splanchnic nerves (S. 2, 3, 4)	Inferior gluteal nerve (L. 5, S. 1, 2)
Pudendal nerve (S. 2, 3, 4)	Posterior cutaneous nerve of thigh (S. 1, 2, 3)
	Perforating cutaneous nerve (S. 2, 3)
	Perineal branch of S. 4.

We shall deal with these *collateral* branches before we trace the course and
distribution of the large, *terminal* branch (the sciatic) and its subdivisions.

Collateral Branches of Sacral Plexus

The **nerve to the quadratus femoris** (and **inferior gemellus**) arises from the
front of the fourth and fifth lumbar and first sacral nerves. It leaves the pelvis
through the lower part of the greater sciatic foramen, passes downwards over the
back of the ischium near the capsule of the hip joint (to which it sends a fine
branch) deep to the sciatic nerve, gemelli, and obturator internus muscles. It
supplies a nerve to the inferior gemellus, and terminates in the deep surface of the
quadratus femoris. The branch to the hip joint may arise from the medial
popliteal part of the sciatic.

The **nerve to the obturator internus** (and **superior gemellus**) arises from the front of the fifth lumbar and first two sacral nerves. In the gluteal region it lies medial to the sciatic nerve on the lateral side of the internal pudendal vessels; crossing the ischial spine, it enters the ischio-rectal fossa through the lesser sciatic foramen. The nerve supplies, in the gluteal region, a branch to the superior gemellus, and it terminates by entering the pelvic surface of the obturator internus.

The **pelvic planchnic nerves**, as mentioned already, are composed of parasympathetic fibres. They are two slender filaments that spring from the second and third or third and fourth sacral nerves, and pass forwards to join the

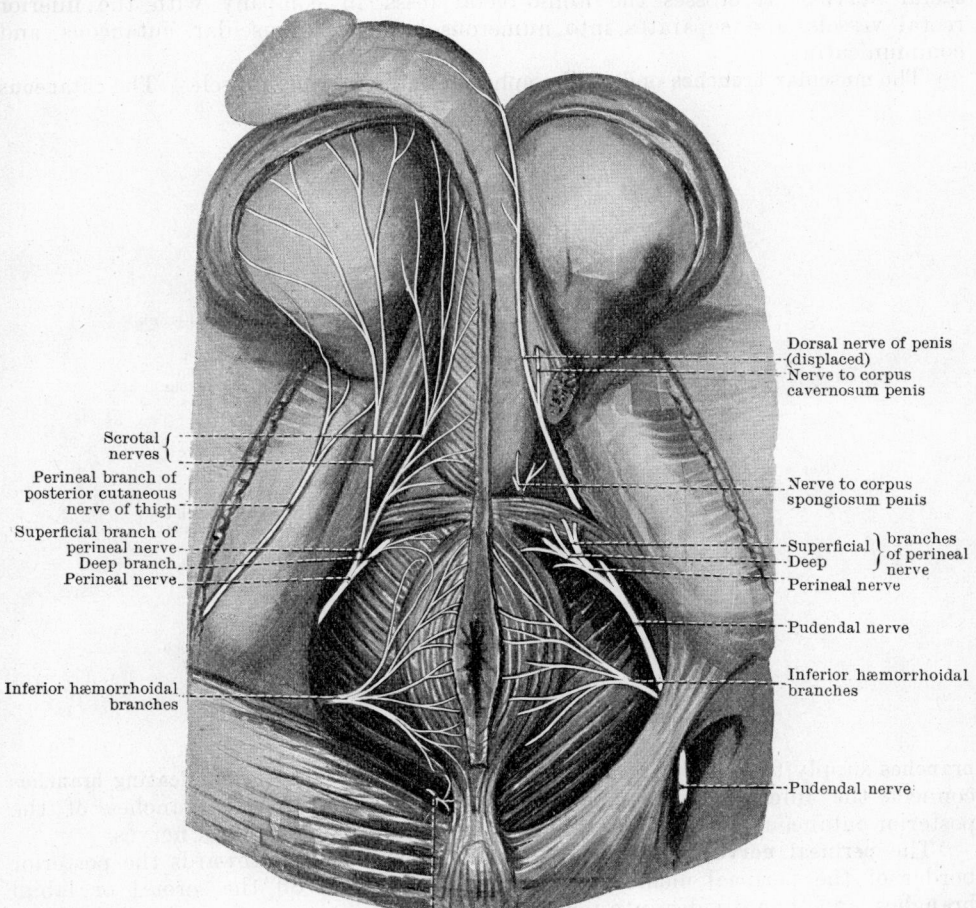

Scrotal
nerves

Perineal branch of
posterior cutaneous
nerve of thigh

Superficial branch of
perineal nerve
Deep branch
Perineal nerve

Inferior hæmorrhoidal
branches

Dorsal nerve of penis
(displaced)
Nerve to corpus
cavernosum penis

Nerve to corpus
spongiosum penis

Superficial } branches
Deep } of perineal
Perineal nerve } nerve

Pudendal nerve

Inferior hæmorrhoidal
branches

Pudendal nerve

Perineal branch of 4th sacral
FIG. 889.—DISTRIBUTION OF THE PUDENDAL NERVE.

sympathetic plexuses, by which they are distributed to viscera—urogenital organs and the lower part of the large intestine.

The **pudendal nerve** is the principal nerve for the supply of the perineum. It arises in the pelvis usually by three roots from the second, third, and fourth sacral nerves (Fig. 888, p. 1037). The nerve passes to the gluteal region through the greater sciatic foramen, medial to the sciatic nerve, and lies on the sacrospinous ligament, medial to the internal pudendal artery. With that artery, it passes through the lesser sciatic foramen into the perineum and enters the pudendal canal of the obturator fascia, which is deeply placed on the lateral wall of the ischio-rectal fossa. As the nerve enters the canal it gives off the inferior hæmorrhoidal nerve, and shortly afterwards it divides into its terminal branches—the perineal nerve and the dorsal nerve of the penis or clitoris—which runs forwards in the pudendal canal towards the posterior border of the perineal membrane [fascia inferior diaphragmatis urogenitalis].

The branches of the nerve are essentially the same in the two sexes. As a rule, it gives off no branches until it enters the perineum, but sometimes the inferior hæmorrhoidal nerve has a separate origin from the plexus, merely accompanying the pudendal nerve in the first part of its course; and in exceptional cases the perforating cutaneous nerve is a branch of the pudendal nerve.

The **inferior hæmorrhoidal nerve** arises from the pudendal nerve under cover of the gluteus maximus, at the posterior part of the ischio-rectal fossa. When it has an independent origin from the plexus, it arises from the third and fourth sacral nerves. It crosses the ischio-rectal fossa in company with the inferior rectal vessels, and separates into numerous branches—muscular, cutaneous, and communicating.

The **muscular branches** end in the sphincter ani externus muscle. The **cutaneous**

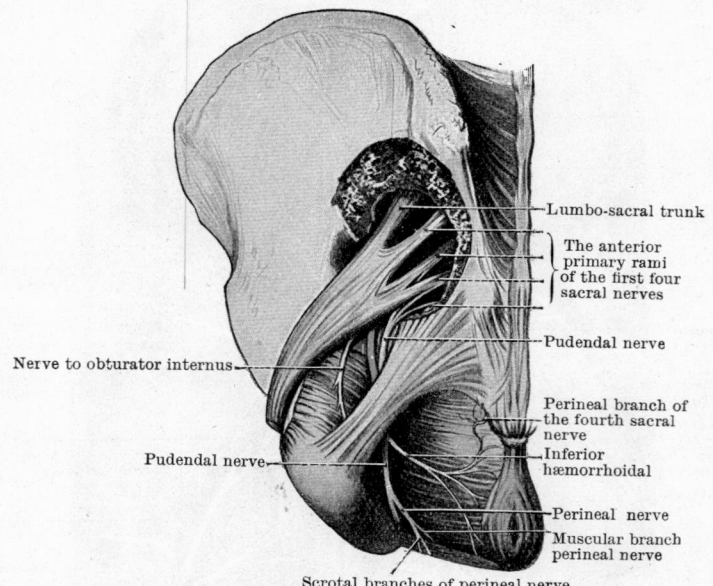

Nerve to obturator internus

Pudendal nerve

Lumbo-sacral trunk

The anterior primary rami of the first four sacral nerves

Pudendal nerve

Perineal branch of the fourth sacral nerve

Inferior hæmorrhoidal

Perineal nerve

Muscular branch perineal nerve

Scrotal branches of perineal nerve

FIG. 890.—THE ORIGIN AND COURSE OF THE PUDENDAL NERVE.

branches supply the skin and fascia around the anus. The **communicating branches** connect the inferior hæmorrhoidal nerve with the perineal branches of the posterior cutaneous nerve of the thigh, pudendal, and fourth sacral nerves.

The **perineal nerve** runs forwards in the pudendal canal towards the posterior border of the perineal membrane, near which it gives off the scrotal or labial branches, and then divides into terminal branches.

The *scrotal* or *labial branches* become superficial and are distributed to the skin and fascia of the perineum and the scrotum or the labium majus. They communicate with the perineal branches of the posterior cutaneous nerve of the thigh and with the inferior hæmorrhoidal nerve.

The *terminal branches* supply the muscles in the deep and superficial perineal pouches, and one of these enters the bulb of the penis and supplies the erectile tissue of the bulb and the corpus spongiosum penis, as well as the mucous membrane of the urethra, as far as the glans penis.

The **dorsal nerve of the penis** or **clitoris**, accompanies the internal pudendal artery through the pudendal canal into the deep perineal pouch. There, it passes forwards close to the side of the pubic arch, lying under cover of the crus and ischio-cavernosus and perineal membrane, and below the sphincter urethræ muscle. It sends a slender branch through the perineal membrane to supply the erectile tissue of the crus and corpus cavernosum penis; and then, piercing the perineal membrane near its anterior border at the lateral side of the dorsal artery of the penis (or clitoris), it passes on to the dorsum of the penis or clitoris, to which it is distributed in its distal two-thirds, sending branches round the sides of the organ to reach its under surface. In the female the nerve is much smaller than in the male.

The **nerve to the piriformis muscle** may be double. It arises from the back of the second, or first and second, sacral nerves, and at once enters the pelvic surface of the muscle.

The **nerves to coccygeus and levator ani** arise from a loop between the third and fourth sacral nerves and descend to these muscles. The **perineal branch of the fourth sacral nerve** arises from the lower part of the same loop; it descends through the coccygeus, appears in the posterior angle of the ischio-rectal fossa, and runs forwards to end in the posterior part of the external sphincter ani. It gives branches also to the overlying fascia and skin.

The **perforating cutaneous nerve** arises from the second and third sacral nerves (Fig. 888, p. 1037). At its origin it is associated with the lower roots of the posterior cutaneous nerve of the thigh. Passing downwards it pierces the sacro-tuberous ligament, and, after winding round the lower border of the gluteus maximus muscle or piercing its lower fibres, it becomes cutaneous a little distance from the coccyx, and supplies the skin and fascia of the lower part of the buttock and the medial part of the fold of the buttock.

The perforating cutaneous nerve is not always present. In a minority of cases it is associated at its origin with the pudendal nerve. When absent as a separate nerve, its place is taken by (1) gluteal branches of the posterior cutaneous nerve of the thigh, or (2) a branch from the pudendal nerve, or (3) a small nerve (n. perforans coccygeus major, Eisler) which arises separately from the third and fourth sacral nerves.

The **superior gluteal nerve** arises from the posterior surface of the fourth and fifth lumbar and first sacral nerves, and is directed backwards and laterally into the gluteal region above the piriformis muscle, along with the superior gluteal artery. Under cover of the gluteus maximus and gluteus medius, it passes over the gluteus minimus, along with the inferior branch of the deep division of the superior gluteal artery, to the deep surface of the tensor fasciæ latæ, in which it ends. On its way it supplies branches to the gluteus medius and gluteus minimus muscles.

The **inferior gluteal nerve** arises from the posterior surface of the fifth lumbar and upper two sacral nerves. It appears in the gluteal region at the lower border of the piriformis muscle, superficial to the sciatic nerve, and at once breaks up into a number of branches for the supply of the gluteus maximus. In its course in the buttock it is closely associated with the posterior cutaneous nerve of the thigh.

The **posterior cutaneous nerve of the thigh** (Fig. 888) is derived from the upper three sacral nerves or from the second and third. It is distributed to the lower limb and perineum, and is associated with other nerves belonging to both regions. Its higher roots from the first and second sacral nerves are intimately associated with the origin of the inferior gluteal nerve; its lowest root from the third sacral nerve is associated with the origins of the perforating cutaneous or of the pudendal nerve. It enters the gluteal region through the greater sciatic notch, below the piriformis, along with the inferior gluteal artery and nerve. Proceeding downwards, posterior to the sciatic nerve, it enters the thigh at the lower border of the gluteus maximus muscle, where it gives off considerable branches. Becoming gradually smaller as it descends over the hamstring muscles to the popliteal fossa, it finally pierces the deep fascia as one or more cutaneous branches which supply the skin and fascia over the calf of the leg for a variable distance (Fig. 887, p. 1036).

Branches.—The nerve is distributed *solely to skin and fascia*. It supplies branches to the perineum, buttock, thigh, and leg.

The *perineal branch* arises at the lower border of the gluteus maximus muscle (Fig. 889, p. 1039). It sweeps in a medial direction to the perineum, lying on the origin of the hamstring muscles, below the ischial tuberosity; and becoming subcutaneous after passing over the pubic arch, its terminal branches supply the skin and fascia of the scrotum and root of the penis, or, in the female, the labium majus and clitoris, communicating with branches of the ilio-inguinal nerve. Some of them pass backwards towards the anus and the perineal body and communicate with the inferior hæmorrhoidal and perineal branches of the pudendal nerve. In its course to the perineum the nerve gives off *collateral branches* to the proximal and medial part of the thigh.

The *gluteal branches*, large and numerous, arise from the nerve deep to the gluteus maximus, and become subcutaneous by piercing the fascia lata at different points along its lower border. They supply the skin and fascia of the lower half of the buttock. The most lateral branches, reaching to the back of the greater trochanter, overlap the terminal filaments of the gluteal branches of the lateral cutaneous nerve of the thigh, and the posterior primary rami of the upper three lumbar nerves. The most medial branches, which may pierce the sacro-tuberous ligament, reach nearly to the coccyx, and are co-extensive in their distribution with the branches of the perforating cutaneous nerve, which they reinforce and may replace.

The *branches to the thigh* pierce the fascia lata at intervals, and supply the skin and fascia of the back of the thigh.

The *branches to the calf* are two or more slender nerves which pierce the fascia over the popliteal fossa, and are distributed to the fascia and skin for a variable extent over the back of the leg. They may stop short over the popliteal fossa, or may reach as far as the ankle. Usually they extend as far as the middle of the calf and communicate with the sural nerve.

When the sciatic nerve is naturally divided at its origin into medial and lateral popliteal nerves (*e.g.*, by the piriformis muscle), the posterior cutaneous nerve also is separated into two parts : a **posterior part**, associated with the lateral popliteal nerve and arising in common with the lower roots of the inferior gluteal nerve (usually from the first and second sacral nerves), and comprising the branches to the gluteal region and lateral part of the back of the thigh and leg ; and an **anterior part**, associated with the medial popliteal nerve and arising usually from the second and third sacral nerves, along with the perforating cutaneous and pudendal nerves, and comprising the branches to the perineum and medial part of the limb.

SCIATIC NERVE

The **sciatic nerve** is the thickest nerve in the body. It consists of two nerves —the medial and lateral popliteal—bound together by an investing sheath, which contains, in addition to those nerves, a branch from each, viz., the nerve to the hamstring muscles, from the medial popliteal nerve, and the nerve to the short head of the biceps femoris, from the lateral popliteal nerve. From the account given of the origin of the fibres of the medial and lateral popliteal nerves, it follows that the fibres of the sciatic nerve are derived from the fourth and fifth lumbar and first, second, and third sacral nerves. A thick band about half an inch in breadth is formed, consisting, from the medial to the lateral side, of (1) the nerve to the hamstring muscles, (2) the medial popliteal nerve, (3) the lateral popliteal nerve, (4) the nerve to the short head of the biceps femoris.

The sciatic nerve leaves the pelvis and enters the gluteal region through the greater sciatic foramen between the piriformis and the superior gemellus. It runs laterally and then downwards through the gluteal region, in the hollow between the greater trochanter of the femur and the ischial tuberosity, accompanied by the inferior gluteal artery and the arteria comitans nervi ischiadici. It is covered posteriorly by the gluteus maximus, and is in relation anteriorly with the following structures, from above downwards : (1) the posterior surface of the ischium and the nerve to the quadratus femoris, (2) the superior gemellus, (3) the obturator internus, (4) the inferior gemellus, (5) the quadratus femoris.

The nerve enters the thigh at the lower border of the quadratus femoris and lies at first in the angle between the lower border of the gluteus maximus above and laterally, and the hamstring muscles medially. It then runs down the back of the thigh, on the posterior surface of the adductor magnus, and is covered by the long head of the biceps femoris, which crosses posterior to the nerve from the medial to the lateral side.

It usually terminates at the proximal angle of the popliteal fossa by dividing into the medial and lateral popliteal nerves; but the separation may occur at any higher level, and, as already noted, these two nerves may even be distinct at their origin, in which case the lateral popliteal usually pierces the piriformis.

The **nerve to the hamstring muscles** forms the most medial part of the sciatic trunk in the lower part of the buttock. It arises from all the roots of the medial popliteal nerve on their anterior aspect, viz., from the fourth and fifth lumbar and the first three sacral nerves. The fibres from the different roots unite to form a cord which is closely associated with the medial popliteal nerve— first in front of it and afterwards on its medial side. Extending into the thigh, the trunk is distributed to the hamstring muscles by means of two sets of branches. Just distal to the ischial tuberosity a proximal set of nerves enters the proximal part of the semitendinosus and the long head of the biceps. Lower down in the thigh the remaining portion of the nerve separates off from the medial popliteal part of the sciatic trunk and supplies branches to the semimembranosus, the distal part of the semitendinosus, and the adductor magnus.

The **nerve to the short head of the biceps** springs from the lateral side of the lateral popliteal trunk in the proximal part of the thigh. When traced to its origin, it is found to arise (sometimes in combination with the inferior gluteal nerve) from the fifth lumbar and first two sacral nerves. In its course it is closely applied to the lateral popliteal nerve, from which it separates in the middle third of the thigh, usually in combination with the articular branches of that nerve for the knee joint. In some cases it has an independent course in the thigh, and it may be associated in the buttock with the inferior gluteal nerve.

An **articular branch** for the lateral and anterior parts of the knee joint generally arises from the lateral popliteal nerve in common with the nerve to the short head of the biceps. When traced up to the plexus, it is found to arise from the posterior surface of the fourth and fifth lumbar and first sacral nerves. It passes through the proximal part of the popliteal fossa concealed by the biceps muscle, and separates into proximal and distal branches, which accompany the superior and inferior lateral articular arteries to the knee joint.

Terminal Branches of Sciatic Nerve.—The **lateral popliteal** and **medial popliteal nerves** are the two main trunks resulting from the combination of the posterior and anterior cords of the sacral plexus respectively. The lateral popliteal nerve is homologous with the radial nerve of the upper limb; the medial popliteal nerve represents a median-ulnar trunk.

LATERAL POPLITEAL NERVE

The **lateral popliteal nerve** [n. peronæus communis] arises from the posterior part of the sacral plexus from the fourth and fifth lumbar and first two sacral nerves. Incorporated in the sciatic nerve in the gluteal region and proximal part of the thigh, it descends from the bifurcation of that nerve through the popliteal fossa to its termination at a point about an inch distal to the head of the fibula. It is concealed at first by the biceps muscle. Following the tendon of that muscle, it passes obliquely through the proximal and lateral part of the popliteal fossa and over the lateral head of the gastrocnemius muscle to the back of the head of the fibula. In the distal part of its course it is quite superficial except at its termination, where it is covered by the peroneus longus muscle and lies between that muscle and the neck of the fibula, round which it winds.

Collateral Branches.—They are divided into two sets: (*a*) *Nerves arising while it is in combination with the medial popliteal nerve in the sciatic trunk.* They have been already described as a **muscular branch** to the short head of the biceps and an **articular branch** to the knee joint. (*b*) *Nerves arising in the popliteal fossa.* Those are **cutaneous branches**, viz., the lateral cutaneous nerve of the calf and the sural communicating branch.

The **lateral cutaneous nerve of the calf of the leg** is inconstant in size and distribution, and may be represented by two or more branches. It arises from the lateral popliteal nerve in the popliteal fossa, often in common with the succeeding nerve, pierces the deep fascia over the lateral head of the gastrocnemius, and is distributed to the skin and fascia on the lateral part of the back of the leg in the proximal two-thirds (Fig. 887, p. 1036). The extent of its distribution varies with that of the posterior cutaneous nerve of the thigh and the sural nerve.

The **sural communicating branch** [n. peronæus anastomoticus] begins in the popliteal fossa, passes over the lateral head of the gastrocnemius, deep to the deep fascia, to the middle third of the leg, where it joins the sural nerve. In many cases the two branches do not unite. In such cases the sural communicating branch may be limited in its distribution to the skin and fascia of the lateral side of the leg, or it may be distributed to the area usually supplied by the sural nerve.

A small *recurrent branch* arises immediately above the division of the lateral popliteal nerve into its two terminal branches. Passing forwards under cover of the origin of the peroneus longus muscle and through the extensor digitorum longus, the recurrent branch divides, distal to the lateral condyle of the tibia, into branches which supply the proximal fibres of the tibialis anterior muscle, the superior tibio-fibular joint, and the knee joint.

Terminal Branches.—The terminal branches of the lateral popliteal nerve are two in number: anterior tibial and musculo-cutaneous. They begin immediately below the head of the fibula, and are directed forwards, diverging in their course, under cover of the peroneus longus muscle.

ANTERIOR TIBIAL NERVE

The **anterior tibial nerve** [n. peronæus profundus] passes obliquely downwards, under cover of the peroneus longus, extensor digitorum longus, and extensor hallucis longus muscles, to the front of the leg. In its course it is deeply placed on the interosseous membrane and the distal part of the tibia, in company with the anterior tibial artery, lying first lateral, then anterior, and then lateral again, to the vessel. At the ankle it lies under cover of the superior extensor retinaculum [lig. transversum cruris] and the tendon of the extensor hallucis longus, and, crossing the ankle joint, it divides on the dorsum of the foot into its terminal branches.

1. **Collateral Branches** (in the leg).—These are given off to the muscles between which the nerve passes, namely: tibialis anterior, extensor hallucis longus, extensor digitorum longus, and peroneus tertius. A fine articular branch supplies the ankle joint.

2. **Terminal Branches** (on the foot).—The terminal branches are medial and lateral. The **medial (digital) branch** passes along the dorsum of the foot, on the lateral side of the dorsalis pedis artery, to the first interosseous space, where it divides into two *dorsal digital branches* for the supply of the skin and fascia of the lateral side of the big toe and the medial side of the second toe. Each of those branches communicates with branches of the musculo-cutaneous nerve. It gives off one or two branches which supply the medial tarso-metatarsal and metatarso-phalangeal joints, and enter the first dorsal interosseous muscle.

The **lateral branch** passes obliquely over the tarsus under cover of the extensor digitorum brevis, and ends in a gangliform enlargement (similar to the gangliform enlargement on the interosseous nerve of the forearm at the back of the wrist). From the enlargement, muscular branches arise for the supply of the extensor digitorum brevis, along with branches for the tarsal, tarso-metatarsal, and metatarso-phalangeal joints. Its *articular branches* may be as many as four in number. Of those the lateral two, extremely small, may only reach the tarso-metatarsal joints. The medial two are fine branches, which, besides supplying the joints, may give branches to the second and third dorsal interosseous muscles.

The branches from the nerve to the interosseous muscles must be afferent, since the motor supply of these muscles is derived from the lateral plantar nerve.

Musculo-Cutaneous Nerve

The **musculo-cutaneous nerve** [n. peronæus superficialis] passes downwards in front of the fibula, in a sheath in the intermuscular septum between the peronei and the extensor digitorum longus, to the distal third of the leg, where its two terminal branches pierce the deep fascia.

Its branches are: (1) *collateral* muscular branches distributed to the peroneus longus and peroneus brevis, as the nerve lies in relation to these muscles; (2) *terminal* cutaneous branches, medial and lateral.

The **medial branch** [n. cutaneus dorsalis medialis] courses downwards over the extensor retinacula, and after supplying offsets to the distal third of the leg and to the dorsum of the foot divides into three branches. (1) The most medial branch supplies the skin and fascia of the dorsum of the foot and the medial side of the big toe, and communicates with the saphenous nerve. (2) The intermediate branch passes to the interval between the big toe and the second, and divides into two branches which communicate with the medial branch of the anterior tibial nerve. (3) The lateral branch passes to the interval between the second and third toes, and divides into *dorsal digital branches* to supply the adjacent sides of these toes.

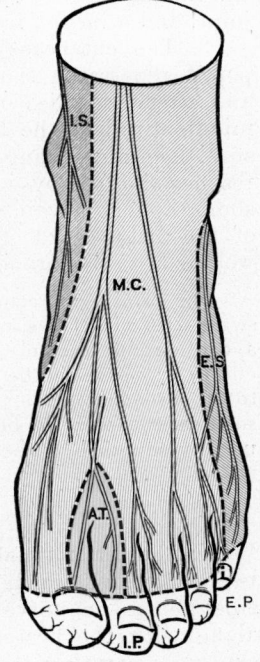

The **lateral branch** [n. cutaneus dorsalis intermedius] of the musculo-cutaneous nerve also passes over the extensor retinacula, and after supplying branches to the distal part of the leg and to the dorsum of the foot divides into two parts, which, passing to the intervals between the third and fourth, and fourth and fifth toes, divide into *dorsal digital branches* for the adjacent sides of these toes. The latter branches communicate with offsets of the sural nerve.

The arrangement of the cutaneous branches of the musculo-cutaneous nerve is liable to considerable variation. The lateral division of the nerve may be increased in size, and may supply the nerve to the adjacent sides of the second and third toes; or it may be reduced in size, in which case the sural nerve takes its place on the dorsum of the foot, often supplying as many as two and a half toes on the lateral side.

The cutaneous nerves on the dorsum of the toes are much smaller than the corresponding plantar digital nerves. They are reinforced on the dorsum of the terminal phalanges by twigs from the plantar nerves, which supply the tips of the toes and the nails.

Fig. 891.—Distribution of Cutaneous Nerves on the Dorsum of the Foot.

I.S., Saphenous nerve; M.C., musculo-cutaneous nerve; A.T., anterior tibial nerve; E.S., Sural nerve. The extremities of the toes are supplied by the medial and lateral plantar nerves (I.P., E.P.).

Medial Popliteal Nerve

The **medial popliteal nerve** [n. tibialis] arises from the anterior surface of the sacral plexus, usually from the fourth and fifth lumbar and first three sacral nerves (Fig. 888, p. 1037). It is incorporated in the sciatic trunk in the gluteal region and proximal part of the thigh. At the bifurcation of the sciatic nerve it passes onwards through the popliteal fossa and becomes the *posterior tibial nerve* at the lower border of the popliteus muscle. The course of the nerve through the gluteal region and thigh has already been described (p. 1042). In the popliteal fossa it is concealed at first by the semimembranosus and the other hamstring muscles. It passes behind the popliteal vessels from the lateral to the medial side, and is thereafter found behind the popliteus muscle, under cover of the gastrocnemius and plantaris.

The **collateral branches** are divided into two sets:—(a) *Nerves arising while it is incorporated in the Sciatic Nerve.*—They have been already described as *the nerve to the hamstring muscles*, and an occasional *articular branch* to the hip joint. (b) *Nerves arising in the Popliteal Fossa.*—These are in three sets—

articular, muscular, cutaneous. Vascular branches to the popliteal artery also are described.

1. The **articular branches** are slender nerves, variable in number. There are usually two, one of which pierces the oblique ligament of the knee joint, while the other, a long fine nerve, crosses the popliteal vessels, and descends to accompany the inferior medial articular artery to the knee joint. In its course it sometimes gives off a fine branch which accompanies the superior medial articular artery.

2. The **muscular branches** are five in number. Nerves for the two heads of the *gastrocnemius,* and for the *plantaris* enter those muscles at the borders of the popliteal fossa. A nerve for the *soleus* enters the superficial surface of the muscle. A nerve to the *popliteus* muscle passes behind that muscle, and, after winding round its distal border, supplies it on its anterior surface; as this nerve curves round the lower border of the popliteus it supplies branches to the *tibialis posterior,* a branch for the interosseous membrane, which can be traced as far as the inferior tibio-fibular joint, an *articular* branch for the superior tibio-fibular joint, and a *medullary* branch for the shaft of the tibia.

3. The **cutaneous branch** is the **sural nerve.** That nerve passes from the popliteal fossa in the groove between the two heads of the gastrocnemius muscle, and afterwards lies on the tendo calcaneus. It pierces the deep fascia in the middle third of the back of the leg, and is joined immediately afterwards by the sural communicating branch from the lateral popliteal nerve. The sural nerve reaches the foot by winding round the back of the lateral malleolus along with the short saphenous vein. It supplies cutaneous branches to the lateral side and back of the distal third of the leg, the ankle and heel (*lateral calcanean branches*) as well as articular branches to the ankle joint and the tarsal joints.

The sural nerve communicates on the foot with the musculo-cutaneous nerve, and its size varies with the size of that nerve. It may extend on to the dorsum of the foot for a considerable distance, and may either reinforce or replace the branches of the musculo-cutaneous nerve to the intervals between the fourth and fifth and the third and fourth toes. Frequently the sural communicating branch does not join the sural nerve, and in such cases the sural communicating branch may sometimes be distributed to the area usually supplied by the sural nerve

POSTERIOR TIBIAL NERVE

The **posterior tibial nerve** is a direct continuation of the medial popliteal, and begins at the distal border of the popliteus muscle. As it passes downwards from this point the nerve lies on the tibialis posterior muscle and the tibia, and, along with the posterior tibial vessels, occupies a sheath in the intermuscular septum separating the superficial and deep muscles of the back of the leg. In the proximal part of the leg the nerve is medial to the posterior tibial vessels, but, crossing behind them, it lies on their lateral side in the distal portion of its course. It terminates under cover of the flexor retinaculum [lig. laciniatum] by dividing into the lateral and medial plantar nerves.

The branches are muscular, cutaneous and terminal.

The **muscular branches** are four in number, comprising nerves to the soleus (entering its deep surface) and tibialis posterior, often arising by a common trunk, and nerves to the flexor digitorum longus and flexor hallucis longus, the latter generally accompanying (and supplying) the peroneal artery for some distance. The nerve to the tibialis posterior supplies twigs to the posterior tibial artery.

The **cutaneous branches** are the **medial calcanean branches,** which pierce the flexor retinaculum, and are distributed to the skin and fascia of the heel and posterior part of the sole of the foot.

In addition, a *medullary nerve* to the fibula and a small *articular branch* to the ankle joint are supplied by the posterior tibial nerve.

The **terminal branches of the posterior tibial nerve** are the *medial* and *lateral plantar nerves.*

MEDIAL PLANTAR NERVE

The **medial plantar nerve** is homologous with the median nerve in the hand (Fig. 892), and is rather larger than the lateral plantar. It courses forwards in the sole of the foot, under cover of the flexor retinaculum and abductor hallucis, to the interval between that muscle and the flexor digitorum brevis, in company with the medial plantar artery.

The **collateral branches** are muscular, cutaneous, articular and vascular. The *muscular* branches supply the abductor hallucis and the flexor digitorum brevis. The plantar *cutaneous* branches are small twigs which pierce the deep fascia in the interval between the above-mentioned muscles to supply the medial part of the sole of the foot. The *articular* branches are minute twigs which supply the tarsal and tarso-metatarsal joints. *Vascular branches* are given to the neighbouring arteries by the main nerve and its branches.

The **terminal branches** are four in number—the *plantar digital nerves*—and may be designated first, second, third, and fourth, from medial to lateral side.

The **first** (most medial) branch separates from the nerve before the others, and pierces the deep fascia behind the ball of the big toe. It supplies a muscular branch to the flexor hallucis brevis, and cutaneous branches to the medial side of the foot and ball of the big toe. It terminates as the plantar digital nerve for the medial side of the big toe.

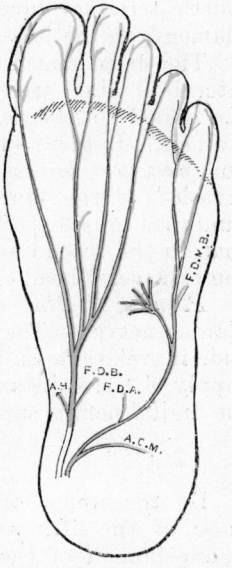

The **second branch** arises along with the third and fourth; after supplying a branch to the first lumbrical muscle, it becomes superficial in the interval between the first and second toes, and terminates by dividing into two digital nerves for the supply of the adjacent sides of these toes.

The **third** and **fourth branches** are distributed to skin and fascia and certain toe joints. They become superficial in the intervals between the second and third and the third and fourth toes, respectively, and there divide into branches for the supply of the adjacent sides of these toes.

LATERAL PLANTAR NERVE

The **lateral plantar nerve** is homologous with the ulnar nerve in the hand. From its origin, under cover of the flexor retinaculum, it extends forwards and laterally in the sole, along the medial side of the lateral plantar artery, between the flexor digitorum brevis and the flexor digitorum accessorius [m. quadratus plantæ], towards the base of the fifth metatarsal bone. There it ends by dividing into superficial and deep terminal branches.

Collateral Branches.—*Muscular branches* are given off from the undivided nerve to the flexor digitorum accessorius and abductor digiti minimi muscles. *Cutaneous branches* pierce the plantar fascia at intervals along the line of the intermuscular septum between the flexor digitorum brevis and abductor digiti minimi. *Vascular filaments* are given to neighbouring arteries by the lateral plantar nerve and its branches.

Terminal Branches.—The **superficial branch** is mainly cutaneous. Passing forwards between the flexor digitorum brevis and abductor digiti minimi, it divides into lateral and medial parts.

The lateral part, after supplying the flexor digiti minimi brevis muscle, and sometimes one or both interossei of the fourth space, becomes superficial behind the ball of the little toe, and supplies cutaneous twigs to the sole of the foot and ball of the toe.	It ends as the *plantar digital nerve* for the lateral side of the little toe.

The medial part passes forwards to the interval between the fourth and fifth toes, where it becomes cutaneous, and divides into two branches (*plantar digital nerves*) for the supply of the adjacent sides of those toes.	It communicates with the fourth terminal branch of the medial plantar nerve.	Both branches provide filaments to the joints of the toes to which they are distributed.

The **deep branch** of the lateral plantar nerve, passing deeply along with the lateral plantar artery, extends medially towards the big toe, under cover of (*i.e.* dorsal to) the flexor digitorum accessorius and oblique head of the adductor hallucis.	It gives off *articular branches* to the tarsal and tarso-metatarsal joints and *muscular branches* to the interossei of each space (except in some cases the muscles of the fourth space), to the adductor hallucis, and the lateral three lumbrical muscles.	The muscular branches enter the deep surfaces of the muscles, that to the second lumbrical reaching its muscle after passing forwards dorsal to the transverse head of the adductor hallucis.

Plantar digital nerves.—These nerves arise from both medial and lateral plantar nerves.	They supply the whole length of the toes on the plantar surface, and, in relation to the distal phalanges, furnish minute dorsal offsets for the supply of the nails and tips of the toes on their dorsal surfaces.	Filaments from the digital nerves supply the metatarso-phalangeal and interphalangeal joints.

COCCYGEAL PLEXUS

By the union of part of the anterior primary ramus of the fourth with those of the fifth sacral and coccygeal nerves, the **coccygeal plexus** is formed. A fine branch of the fourth sacral nerve descends to join the fifth sacral nerve, which then descends alongside the coccyx and is again joined by the coccygeal nerve, so that a plexiform cord results, homologous with the inferior caudal trunk of tailed animals.	Fine twigs arise from it, some of which enter the coccygeus and adjoining part of the levator ani, while others pierce the coccygeus and the overlying ligaments to supply the skin and fascia in the neighbourhood of the coccyx and behind the anus, medial to the branches of the perforating cutaneous nerve.

Communications with Autonomic System.—Like the other spinal nerves, the fourth and fifth sacral and coccygeal nerves are provided with fine *grey rami communicantes* from the sacral sympathetic trunk which join them after a short course on the front of the sacrum.

MORPHOLOGY OF THE NERVES OF THE PERINEUM

The structures which occupy the perineum are placed in the ventral axis of the body, and comprise, from before backwards, the penis and scrotum, or mons pubis and vulva, the perineal body, the anus and ischio-rectal fossa, and the coccyx.	They are placed on the medial side of the attachment of the lower limbs—the penis or mons pubis in relation to the preaxial border of the limb, the coccyx in relation to the postaxial border.

The nerves of the perineum, thus reaching the ventral axis of the trunk, are homologous with the anterior (ventral) terminations of other nerves.	They are separable into two series.	The perineum is supplied mainly by the lower four sacral nerves and the coccygeal nerve, but it is also innervated to a minor extent by the first lumbar nerve through the ilio-inguinal nerve, which reaches the root of the penis and the scrotum.	The region is thus supplied by two series of widely separated nerves which have their meeting-place on the dorsum and side of the penis and scrotum.	This junction of the ilio-inguinal and pudendal nerves constitutes the beginning of the **ventral axial line** (Fig. 893), which extends peripherally along the medial side of the lower limb.	Apart from this break in their distribution, a definite numerical order may be followed in the arrangement of the perineal nerves.	The higher parts of the perineum are innervated by the higher spinal nerves; the lower parts, by the lower nerves.	This is best exemplified in the distribution of the cutaneous nerves.	The base of the penis and scrotum (or mons pubis) is supplied by the first lumbar nerve (ilio-inguinal). The dorsal nerve of the penis (or clitoris), when traced back, is found to come from the second sacral nerve, and to a less extent from the third; the scrotal or labial nerves (perineal branches of the pudendal and posterior cutaneous nerve of the thigh) similarly arise from the third sacral nerve, and to a less extent from the second; the skin of the ischio-rectal fossa and anus is innervated by the inferior hæmorrhoidal (third and fourth sacral nerves), and the perineal branch of the fourth sacral nerve. The coccygeal plexus, lastly, supplies the skin and fascia round the coccyx (fourth and fifth sacral and coccygeal nerves).

Judged from its nerve-supply the perineum is to be regarded as occupying, for the most part, a position behind or more caudal than that of the lower limb in relation to the trunk, and there is a remarkable gap in the numerical sequence of the nerves that supply the ventral axis of the body. All the nerves between the first lumbar and the second sacral fail to reach the mid-ventral line of the trunk and are wholly concerned in the innervation of the lower limb.

At the preaxial border of the limb (groin) the first lumbar nerve —the highest nerve supplying the perineum—is concerned also in innervating the skin and fascia of the limb. At the postaxial border of the limb (fold of the buttock and back of the thigh), the second and third sacral nerves are also implicated in innervating that border of the limb. The fourth sacral nerve is concerned only to a very slight extent in the innervation of the limb by means of the perineal branch,

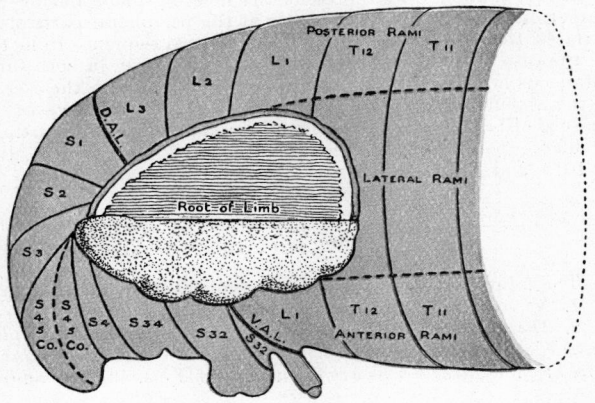

FIG. 893.—SCHEME of the innervation of the hinder portion of the trunk and of the perineum, and the interruption of the segmental arrangement of the nerves associated with the formation of the limb.

which reaches the beginning of its postaxial border; the last two spinal nerves are wholly unrepresented in the limb proper and end entirely in the trunk behind the limb.

DISTRIBUTION OF SPINAL NERVES TO MUSCLES AND SKIN OF THE LIMBS

By dissection, experiment, and clinical observation, it is conclusively proved that, as a rule, each nerve of distribution in the limb, whether to muscle or skin, is made up of fibres derived from more than one spinal nerve ; and, further, that in cutaneous distribution a considerable overlapping occurs in the course of the several peripheral nerves. Moreover, the arrangement of the distribution of the nerves to skin and to muscles is not identical. In the case of the skin of the limbs, by the covering of the limb being drawn on to it from adjacent parts in the process of growth, cutaneous nerves are engaged which are derived from sources not represented in the muscular innervation of the limbs. Again, among the muscles, some have undergone fusion, others have become rudimentary, and others again have altered their position in the limb.

INNERVATION OF THE SKIN OF THE LIMBS

While the scheme of cutaneous innervation of the limbs is fundamentally segmental, yet the arrangement is confused and complicated by various causes. The growth of the limb from the trunk has caused the skin to be drawn out over it like a stretched sheet of india-rubber (Herringham), and at the same time the extent of either the dorsal or the ventral area of the limb is increased at the expense of the other. The central nerves of the plexus remain buried deeply in the substance of the limb, coming to the surface only towards the periphery. The proximal parts of both surfaces of the limb thus become innervated by cutaneous nerves otherwise not necessarily concerned in the innervation of the limbs. Herringham has shown that—(A) *Of two spots on the skin, that nearer the preaxial border tends to be supplied by the higher nerve.* (B) *Of two spots in the preaxial area, the lower tends to be supplied by the lower nerve ; and of two spots in the postaxial area, the lower tends to be supplied by the higher nerve.* In other words, from the root of the limb along the preaxial border to its distal extremity, and along the postaxial border to the root of the limb again, there is a definite numerical sequence of spinal nerves supplying skin areas through nerves of the limb plexuses, as is illustrated, for example, in Fig. 887, p. 1036. A similar numerical sequence in the arrangement of the nerves is also found extending over the dorsal and ventral surfaces of the limbs from preaxial to postaxial border, except in certain situations.

On the dorsal and ventral surfaces of both upper and lower limbs there is a hiatus, for a certain distance, in the numerical sequence of the spinal nerves in their cutaneous distribution, explicable on the ground that the central nerves of the plexus, which fail to reach the surface in those situations, are replaced by cutaneous branches from neighbouring nerves. This hiatus has been named the *axial area* or *line.*

In the upper limb, *the dorsal axial area* or *line* extends from the median line of the back, opposite the vertebra prominens, to the insertion of the deltoid. *The ventral axial area* or *line* extends anteriorly from the median plane of the trunk, at the manubrio-sternal joint, across the chest, downwards along the front of the upper arm and forearm to the wrist.

In the lower limb, *the dorsal axial area* or *line* may be traced from the median plane of the back over the posterior superior iliac spine, across the gluteal region and thigh, to the head of the fibula. *A ventral axial area* or *line* can also be traced from the root of the penis along the medial side of the thigh and knee, and along the back of the leg to the heel.

Those areas or lines represent the meeting-place and overlapping of nerves which are not in numerical sequence; and it is only at the peripheral parts of the limbs, on the dorsal and ventral surfaces, that the nerves appear in numerical sequence from the preaxial to the postaxial border. In the case of the upper limb the hiatus is caused, in both surfaces of the limb, by the absence of cutaneous branches of the seventh cervical nerve; in the case of the lower limb the hiatus is due to the absence of branches from the fifth lumbar nerve on both surfaces of the limb, and the absence of branches from the fourth lumbar nerve, in addition, on the dorsal surface.

These points in the innervation of the skin of the limbs are illustrated by Fig. 878, p. 1015, and Fig. 887, p. 1036.

INNERVATION OF THE MUSCLES OF THE LIMBS

The following laws appear to be applicable to the upper and lower limbs alike :—

1. *No limb-muscle receives its nerve-supply from posterior primary rami.*

2. *The dorsal and ventral strata of muscles are always supplied by the corresponding dorsal and ventral branches of the nerves concerned. The ventral muscular stratum is more extensive than the dorsal; the ventral nerves are the more numerous, and the additional nerves are postaxially placed.*

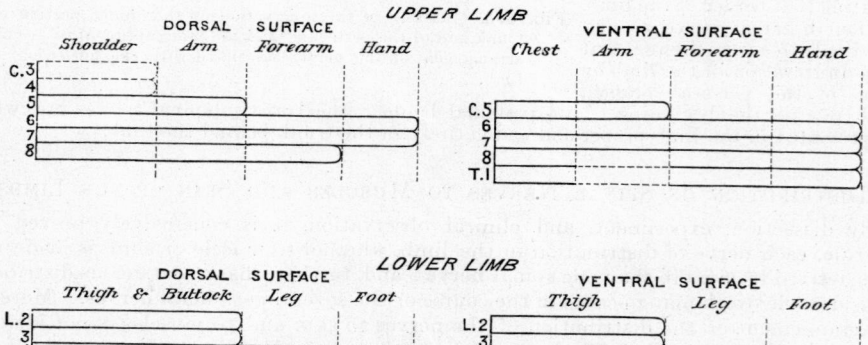

DIAGRAM of the segmental distribution of the muscular nerves of the upper and lower limbs.

The spinal nerves supplying muscles of the upper limb are C. 5, 6, 7, 8 (dorsal), and C. 5, 6, 7, 8, T. 1 (ventral); the nerves for the muscles of the lower limb are L. 2, 3, 4, 5, S. 1, 2 (dorsal), and L. 2, 3, 4, 5, S. 1, 2, 3 (ventral).

3. *The dorsal and ventral trunks of the nerves are distributed in the limb in a continuous, segmental manner;* so that, "of two muscles, that nearer the head end of the body tends to be supplied by the higher nerve, and that nearer the tail end by the lower nerve" (Herringham).

4. *The nerves placed most centrally in the plexus extend farthest into the limb, and the more preaxial nerves terminate sooner in the limb than the more postaxial nerves.*

The only exception to this rule is on the ventral (anterior) surface of the upper arm, where a suppression of the muscle elements leads to an absence of the regular series of segmental nerves (C. 8, T. 1) on its postaxial border. Those nerves reappear in the forearm, and the occasional "axillary arches" may be regarded as the muscular elements usually suppressed, and, when present, supplied by these nerves.

Muscles with a Double Nerve-Supply.—The existence of more than one nerve to a muscle indicates usually that the muscle is composite and is the representative of originally separate elements belonging to more than one segment or to both surfaces of the limb. In the case of the pectoralis major, subscapularis and flexor digitorum profundus, adductor magnus, and soleus, parts of the same (ventral or dorsal) stratum have fused, to form muscles innervated from the corresponding ventral or dorsal nerves. The other muscles having a double nerve-supply—biceps femoris, and (sometimes) pectineus—are examples of fusion at the preaxial or postaxial border of muscular elements derived from the dorsal and ventral surfaces of the limb, which are correspondingly innervated by branches from both dorsal and ventral series: *e.g.* the biceps femoris by the lateral popliteal (peroneal) (short head) and medial popliteal (tibial) nerves (long head); and the pectineus, by the femoral and (sometimes) obturator nerves. The brachialis commonly receives branches from both the musculo-cutaneous and the radial nerves, but electrical tests have shown that the fibres from the radial are afferent ones.

COMPOSITION OF THE LIMB PLEXUSES

In all mammals the same definite plan underlies the constitution of the limb plexuses. The nerves concerned are the anterior primary rami of certain segmental spinal nerves, which (with certain exceptions at the preaxial and postaxial borders) are destined wholly and solely for the innervation of the limb. Each of the anterior rami engaged divides into a pair of **secondary trunks**, named **dorsal** or posterior, **ventral** or anterior. The dorsal and ventral trunks again subdivide into **tertiary trunks** which combine with the corresponding subdivisions of neighbouring dorsal and ventral trunks to form the **nerves of distribution**. The combinations of *dorsal trunks* provide a series of nerves for the supply of that part of the limb which is derived from the *dorsal surface* of the embryonic limb bud ; the combinations of *ventral trunks* give rise to nerves of distribution to the regions corresponding to its *ventral surface*. Cutaneous nerves are less strictly dorsal and ventral than motor nerves. In the upper limb (Fig. 878, p. 1015) ventral offsets of the plexus tend to overlap the dorsal surface ; whilst in the lower limb (Fig. 887, p. 1036) the dorsal offsets tend to overlap the ventral (*i.e.* flexor) surface.

INTRANEURAL PLEXUSES

It has been proved that within the nerve trunks there are internal nerve plexuses which produce changes in the constitution of the bundles of fibres in peripheral nerves as they are followed through any distance. These internal plexuses are particularly evident in the neighbourhood of the origin of branches, but they are found in other parts also. It has been suggested that they serve to associate the afferent and efferent fibres of definite regions.

BLOOD SUPPLY OF PERIPHERAL NERVES

The arrangement of the blood supply to peripheral nerves is not constant, as was formerly believed, and the vessels always come from multiple sources. Each nerve receives a number of arteries ; for example, the ulnar may get from two to six in the upper arm, and from five to ten in the forearm (Ramage). On approaching the nerve each artery usually separates into proximal and distal divisions which enter the trunk and take part in the formation of a network composed of longitudinal and transverse or oblique anastomosing channels.

In certain regions the blood supply to nerves may be of importance in establishing a collateral circulation.

DEVELOPMENT OF THE SPINAL NERVES

I. **Origin of the Spinal Nerve Roots**.—Whilst both the posterior and anterior roots are developed from cells of the neural plate, they differ as regards their exact site of origin.

The **posterior roots** are derived entirely from the neural crest, the origin of which from the cells of the lateral margin of the neural plate is described in the section on Human Embryology (p. 42). At the time when they first appear, the neural crest is a flattened cellular band which extends from the auditory vesicle along the dorsal border of the neural tube to its caudal extremity. In the spinal region the crest shows segmental ganglionic enlargements along its ventral border, whilst its dorsal border shows a continuous cellular bridge throughout its length. Central processes are developed from the cells (neuroblasts) of the ganglionic enlargements, and, travelling upward through the crest, leave it along its dorsal border in segmental bundles to grow into the alar lamina of the neural tube. With the establishment of the dorsal root fibres the cellular bridge of the neural crest disappears, and the ganglionic enlargements thus become separated into individual spinal ganglia ; these grow ventrally and come into relation with the anterior roots. Peripheral processes are developed from the ganglionic neuroblasts and emerge from the ventral border of the ganglia to join the fibres of the anterior root, which they accompany as the posterior root fibres of the spinal nerves.

The **anterior roots**, on the contrary, are developed from the neural tube, which is a derivative of the neural plate. Processes from the neuroblasts situated in the mantle zone of the basal lamina grow out in small bundles which pierce the external limiting membrane and emerge in a continuous longitudinal series of rootlets from the ventro-lateral wall of the tube. Outside the tube the rootlets are grouped into segmental bundles—the anterior roots—which join the dorsal roots just peripheral to the spinal ganglia.

II. **Formation of the Spinal Nerve**.—The fibres of the posterior root ganglion and the anterior root grow by extension from the cells with which they are respectively connected, and meet in the space between the myotome and the side of the neural tube to form the **spinal nerve**. In the adult there is a fundamental primary division of the spinal nerve into posterior and anterior rami. In the process of development the separation is even more obvious. As the fibres of the posterior and anterior roots approximate, they separate at the same time, each into two unequal portions : the smaller parts of the two roots unite together to form the **posterior primary ramus** of the spinal nerve, and the larger parts unite to form the **anterior primary ramus**.

The **posterior primary ramus**, curving laterally and backwards, passes through the myotome and is connected with it. In the substance of the myotome it separates into branches as it proceeds towards the dorsal wall of the embryo. At a later stage, the branches are definitely arranged into a lateral and a medial series.

The **anterior primary ramus** grows gradually in a ventral direction under cover of the growing myotome towards the somato-splanchnic angle of the cœlom (Fig. 894). It spreads out at its distal end and eventually separates into two portions: a smaller, splanchnic or visceral; and a larger, somatic or parietal portion. (1) The smaller, **splanchnic** or **visceral portion** grows inwards to be connected through the sympathetic trunk with the innervation of organs in the splanchnic area. That branch of the spinal nerve becomes the **white ramus communicans** of the sympathetic. It is not present in the case of all the spinal nerves, but only in relation to the thoracic and upper lumbar and the third and second or fourth sacral nerves. It will be referred to again in connexion with the sympathetic system. (2) The larger, **somatic**

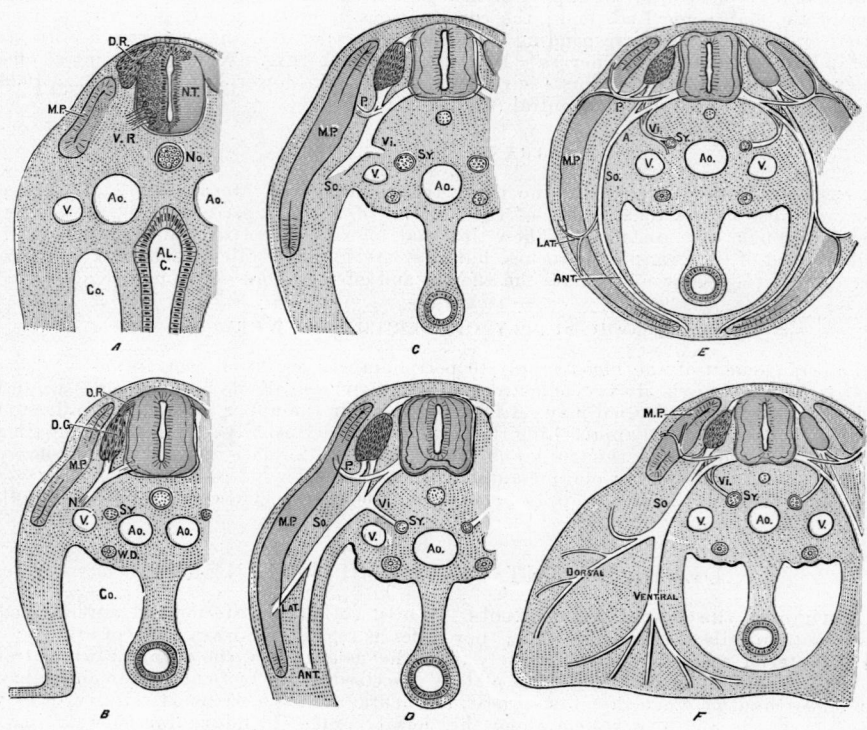

FIG. 894.—DEVELOPMENT OF THE SPINAL NERVES.

A, Formation of nerve roots.

		B, Formation of nerve trunk (N).
D.R., Posterior root.	Al.C., Alimentary canal.	D.G., Spinal ganglion.
V.R., Anterior root.	Ao., Aorta.	Sy., Sympathetic trunk.
N.T., Neural tube.	V., Cardinal vein.	W.D., Mesonephric duct.
No., Notochord.	M.P., Muscle plate.	Co., Cœlom.

C, Formation of nerves.

So., Somatic division.
Vi., Visceral branch.
P., Posterior ramus.

D, E, Formation of subordinate branches.

Lat., Lateral, and
Ant., Anterior, branches.

F, Formation of nerve trunks in relation to the limb: dorsal and ventral trunks corresponding to lateral and anterior trunks in D and E.

or **parietal portion** becomes the main part of the anterior primary ramus of the nerve. It continues the original ventral course of the nerve, and, reaching the body wall, subdivides into two terminal branches—a *lateral branch*, which grows laterally and downwards and reaches the side of the trunk, after piercing the myotome; and a ventral or *anterior branch*, which grows onwards in the body wall to reach the ventral axis. That arrangement is met with in the trunk between the limbs and in the neck.

III. **Formation of Limb Plexuses.**—The method of growth of the spinal nerves, just described, is modified in the regions where the limbs are developed. In relation to the limbs, which exist in the form of buds of undifferentiated cellular mesoderm before the spinal nerves have any connexion with them, the development of the anterior primary ramus of the nerve proceeds exactly in the way described, up to the point of formation of somatic and splanchnic branches. The **somatic branches** then stream out into the limb bud, passing into it below the ends of the myotomes and spreading out into a bundle of fibres at the basal attachment of the limb. Later, the nerves separate, each into a pair of definite trunks, named posterior or **dorsal** and anterior or **ventral**, which proceed into the limb bud on the dorsal and ventral surfaces respectively of the central core of mesoderm. While that process is going on, a *secondary union* takes place between parts of adjacent dorsal and ventral trunks. Dorsal trunks unite with dorsal trunks, ventral trunks unite with ventral trunks, to form the nerves distributed ultimately to the surfaces and periphery of the limb. These **dorsal and ventral trunks** are homologous with the **lateral** and **ventral branches** of the somatic nerves in other regions.

AUTONOMIC NERVOUS SYSTEM

The **autonomic nervous system** is that portion of the peripheral nervous system which serves functionally to distribute efferent impulses of central origin to the involuntary musculature of the viscera, heart, blood-vessels and skin, and the glandular epithelium generally ; and it further serves to collect afferent impulses from the viscera, and transmit them to the central nervous system. It consists of a

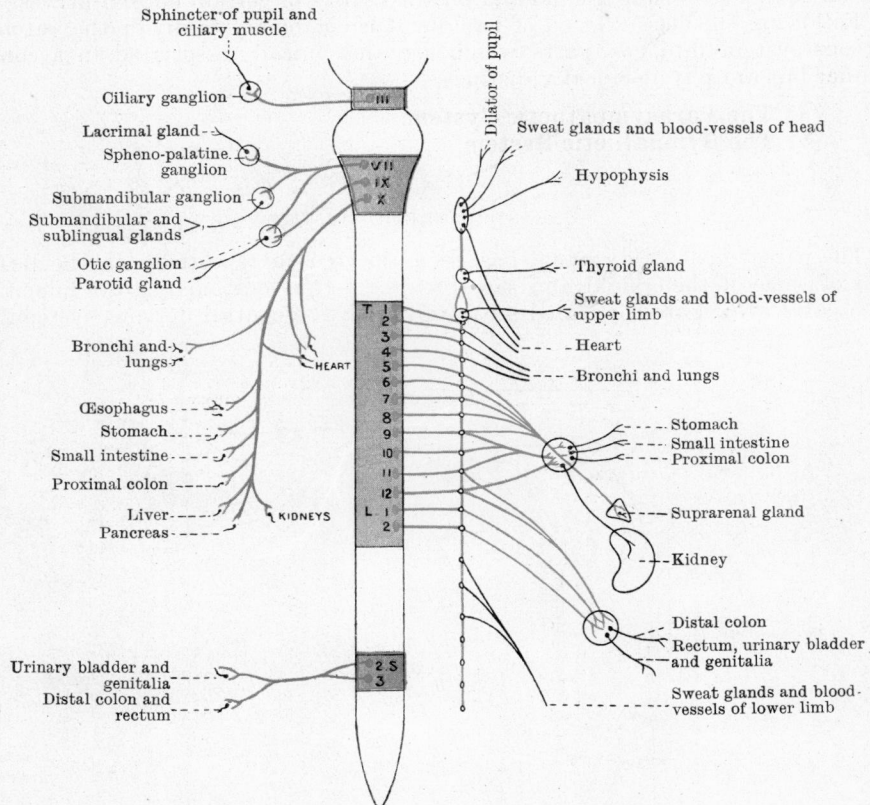

Fig. 895.—A Diagram to show the General Arrangement of the Autonomic Nervous System.
Preganglionic fibres of the parasympathetic system in blue and of the sympathetic system in red. Postganglionic fibres of both systems in black. (J. S. B. S.)

complex aggregation of ganglia, plexuses, and nerves, widely distributed throughout the whole body ; but since the tissues it supplies are most abundant in the visceral or splanchnic organs, the largest and most evident part of the system is found in the body-cavities.

The autonomic nervous system is essentially dependent upon and subservient to the central nervous system, from which it can no more be sharply separated, either anatomically or developmentally, than can the rest of the peripheral nervous system. For just as the cell bodies of the efferent neurones of the cerebro-spinal system lie in the brain stem and spinal cord, so do the efferent fibres of the autonomic system take origin in those parts, wherein they are connected with the central regulatory mechanisms of the viscera. Moreover, the two peripheral systems of fibres are closely related, especially in the first part of their course, since the fibres of the autonomic system emerge in the roots of certain cranial and spinal nerves. There is one marked difference, however, between the efferent fibres of the two systems. Those of the cerebro-spinal nerves pass continuously from their central origins to the tissues innervated; but those of the sympathetic system always enter and terminate in a ganglion, from a cell of which a new fibre arises and passes on to the periphery. Hence, in the autonomic system there are to be distinguished two series of fibres in the efferent path: **preganglionic** (medullated) fibres running from the central nervous system to the ganglia, and **postganglionic** (nearly all non-medullated) fibres passing from the ganglia onwards to their destinations (Fig. 898, p. 1056). The afferent fibres of the autonomic system, on the other hand, pass through the ganglia of their own system without interruption, and their cell stations are in the posterior root ganglia of some spinal nerves or the ganglia on the trunks of certain cranial nerves.

Following the classification of Langley it is customary to divide the autonomic nervous system into two parts, which are anatomically associated in a complex manner but are physiologically distinct:—

(*a*) **The Parasympathetic System.**
(*b*) **The Sympathetic System.**

PARASYMPATHETIC SYSTEM

The parasympathetic system has been referred to repeatedly in the descriptions of some of the cranial and sacral nerves. It is customary to divide it into three parts, which are connected separately with the central nervous system.

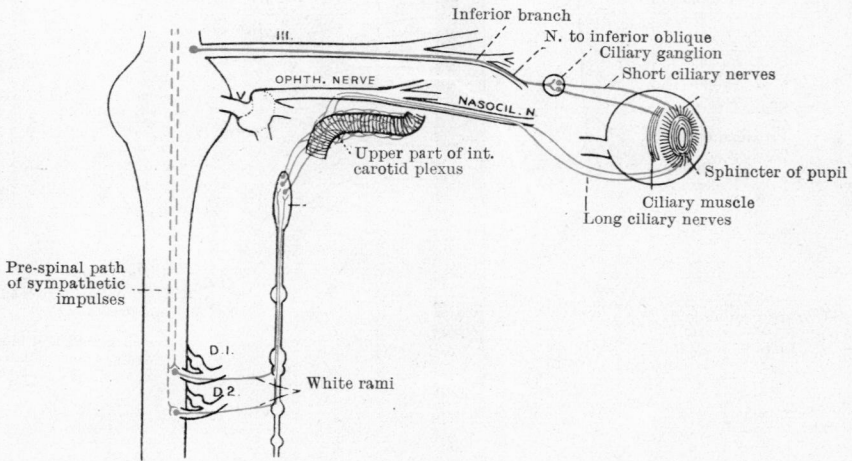

Fig. 896.—DIAGRAM TO SHOW THE CONNEXIONS OF THE AUTONOMIC NERVOUS SYSTEM WITH THE EYE.
Parasympathetic fibres blue, sympathetic fibres red. (J. S. B. S.)

(1) The **Mid-brain Outflow**, the fibres of which emerge in the oculomotor nerve.
(2) The **Medulla Oblongata** (Bulbar) **Outflow**, composed of fibres passing out in the facial, glosso-pharyngeal, and vagus nerves.
(3) The **Sacral** (or **Pelvic) Outflow**, consisting of fibres which pass out in the anterior primary rami of the second and third, or third and fourth sacral nerves.

1. The **Mid-brain Outflow** of preganglionic fibres passes out in the oculomotor nerve and reaches the ciliary ganglion by its parasympathetic root—a filament which springs from the branch of supply to the inferior oblique muscle. From the ganglion, postganglionic fibres (some of the short ciliary nerves) arise. They innervate the sphincter pupillæ and ciliary muscles of the eyeball.

2. The **Medulla Oblongata** (Bulbar) **Outflow** consists of three sets of pre-ganglionic fibres :—

  (a) The first set emerges from the brain stem with the sensory root of the **facial nerve** [nervus intermedius]. Some of those travel by the greater superficial petrosal nerve to end in the *spheno-palatine ganglion*. From that ganglion postganglionic fibres (rami orbitales) arise which supply secretory fibres to the lacrimal gland. Others reach the *submandibular ganglion* through the chorda tympani and lingual nerves. The postganglionic fibres from the sub-mandibular ganglion supply the submandibular and sublingual salivary glands.

  A small group of preganglionic fibres in the sensory root of the facial nerve terminate in the *otic ganglion*, which they reach through

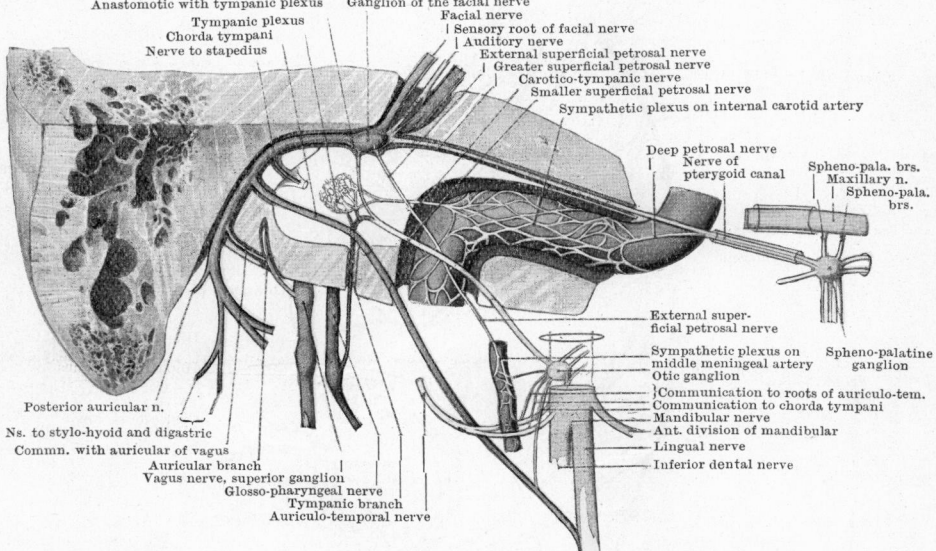

FIG. 897.—THE CONNEXIONS OF THE FACIAL NERVE IN THE TEMPORAL BONE.

the facial nerve, its communicating branch with the tympanic plexus and the lesser superficial petrosal nerve. The postganglionic fibres from the otic ganglion supply the parotid gland.

  (b) The second set leaves the brain stem in the trunk of the **glosso-pharyngeal nerve**. Those fibres traverse its tympanic branch and run to the *otic ganglion* in the lesser superficial petrosal nerve. As previously stated, postganglionic fibres from this ganglion innervate the parotid gland.

  (c) A third set emerges in the trunk of the **vagus**. They have a very wide distribution and are composed of afferent as well as efferent fibres. The efferent fibres in the vagus differ from the other preganglionic fibres of the autonomic nervous system in not passing to ganglia which can be isolated by dissection. They extend directly to ganglion cells to be found in the walls of the organs which they supply; in that way the postganglionic fibres have their origin, course, and distribution entirely within the walls of the organs concerned. Some of the preganglionic and afferent fibres in the trunk of the vagus are distributed to the respiratory passages, heart, and lungs, whilst in the abdomen fibres can be traced to the stomach, small intestine, proximal colon, liver, pancreas, and kidneys. The efferent fibres in the abdomen supply the smooth muscle in the viscera, blood-vessels and glands. In the complicated

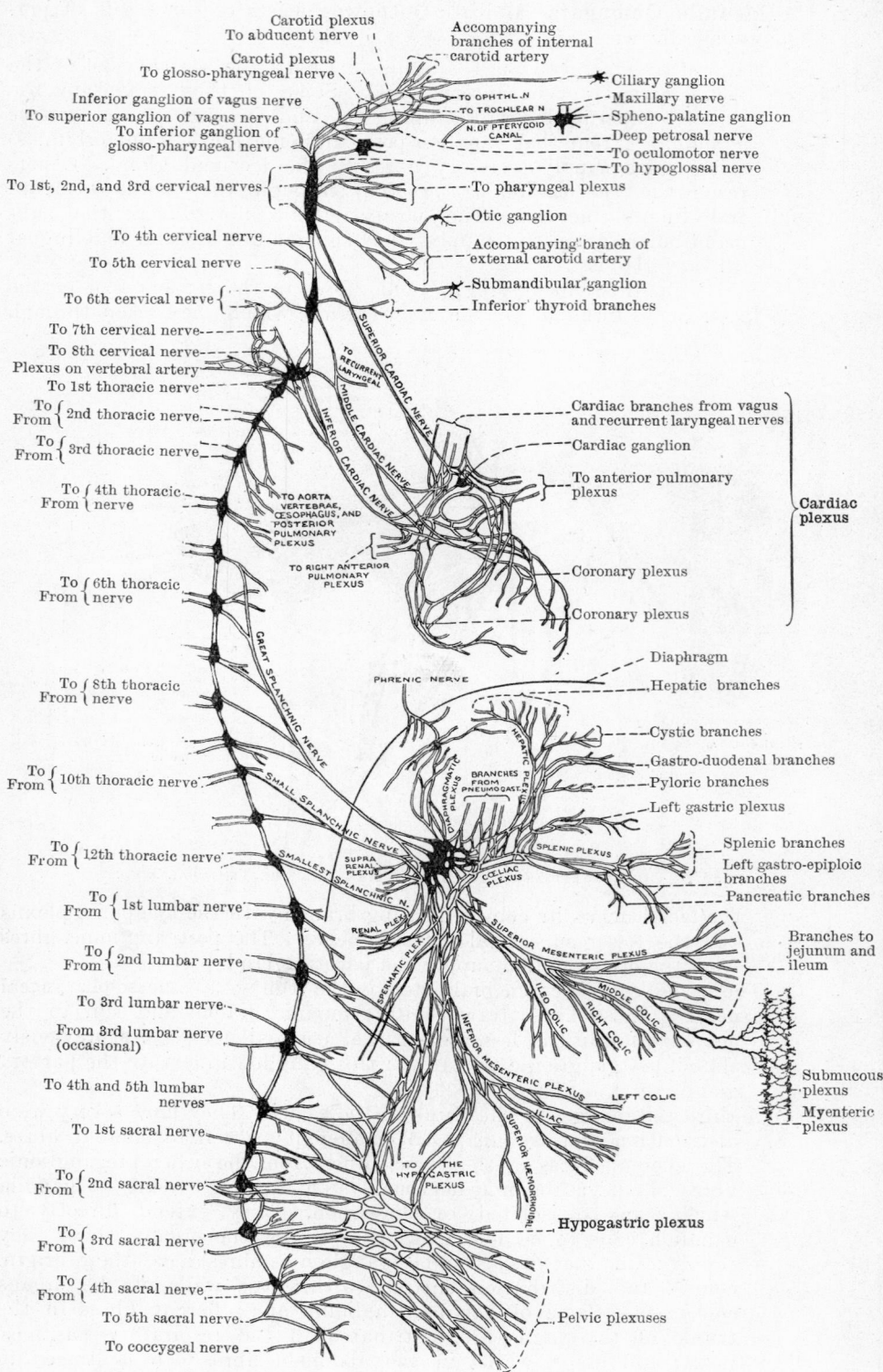

FIG. 898.—PLAN OF THE MAIN PARTS OF THE AUTONOMIC NERVOUS SYSTEM.
(After Flower, modified, with permission of Messrs. J. & A. Churchill.)

plexuses in the thorax and abdomen the parasympathetic fibres are inextricably mixed with sympathetic fibres. In recent studies (M'Crea) it has been shown, however, that the parasympathetic fibres in *both* vagi pass to the abdominal plexuses and so take part in the innervation of the small intestine, proximal colon, liver, pancreas, and kidneys.

3. The **Sacral Outflow** consists of preganglionic fibres which emerge in the anterior primary rami of the second and third or third and fourth sacral nerves. Those fibres form the pelvic splanchnic nerves on each side as they extend to the pelvic plexuses, in which they become associated with sympathetic fibres. The parasympathetic fibres are distributed to the distal colon, rectum, and the urogenital organs.

The general arrangement of the abdominal and pelvic plexuses will be described under the sympathetic system, but it is of primary importance to realise that those plexuses are formed by fibres from *both* divisions of the autonomic nervous system.

Sympathetic System

General Structure of the Sympathetic System.—The sympathetic system has been mentioned frequently in the descriptions of the cranial and spinal nerves. It is composed of two elements—ganglia and nerve fibres. The efferent fibres of the sympathetic part of the autonomic system arise from a limited part of the spinal cord—from the first thoracic to the second lumbar segments inclusive—and are sometimes referred to as the *thoracico-lumbar outflow*.

(A) A **ganglion** consists of a larger or smaller number of nerve-cells, almost all multipolar, though a few are unipolar or bipolar. Each cell is enclosed in a nucleated capsule of fibrous tissue, and is provided with one axon and a number of dendrites. Some of the dendrites ramify beneath the capsule, and hence are termed intracapsular; they may form a network around the cell or be localised in the form of a glomerulus. Other dendrites are extracellular; they pierce the capsule and run throughout the ganglion, taking part in the formation of an intercellular plexus, and making contact with the capsules of other cells. That plexus is joined by the ramifications of the entering preganglionic fibres, some of which also pierce the capsules of cells to meet the intracapsular dendrites. One preganglionic fibre can in that way directly influence many ganglionic neurones, which explains the difference between the comparatively small number of fibres which enter a ganglion and the large number that leave it. There appears to be no evidence of commissural neurones or sensori-motor synapses between the ganglion cells. The axon of a ganglion cell (a postganglionic fibre) is usually unmyelinated, though it may be myelinated at its origin from the parent cell. The ganglia may be classified as follows :—

(1) The **central ganglia** of the sympathetic trunks are variable in form and size, but they are more or less segmental in position. They are always connected together by narrow cords formed by ascending and descending fibres, and in that way a gangliated **sympathetic trunk** is formed on each side. There are 21 or 22 ganglia in each trunk, of which 3 are associated with the cervical nerves, 10 or 11 with the thoracic, 4 with the lumbar, and 4 with the sacral spinal nerves. At the cephalic end each sympathetic trunk is continued into the cranial cavity in the form of plexuses round the internal carotid artery, and thereby establishes relations with some of the cranial nerves. At their caudal ends the two sympathetic trunks unite in a single median ganglion placed in front of the coccyx—the *ganglion impar*. The sympathetic trunks provide a mechanism whereby the sympathetic fibres, having an origin from a limited part of the central nervous system, are widely distributed to all parts of the body.

(2) The intermediate or **collateral ganglia** (*ganglia plexuum sympathicorum*), which are found in connexion with the great prevertebral plexuses, permit fibres to be collected for distribution to one organ or to a group of organs physiologically related to one another.

(3) A **terminal group** of ganglia is commonly described, but recent research has shown that the ganglia which lie in close relation to the endings of the nerves in the viscera belong entirely or almost entirely to the parasympathetic system.

(B) The **nerve-fibres** in the sympathetic system are of two classes, medullated and non-medullated, though the distinction is not absolute. Those fibres which enter it from the central nervous system (**preganglionic**) are medullated, but are

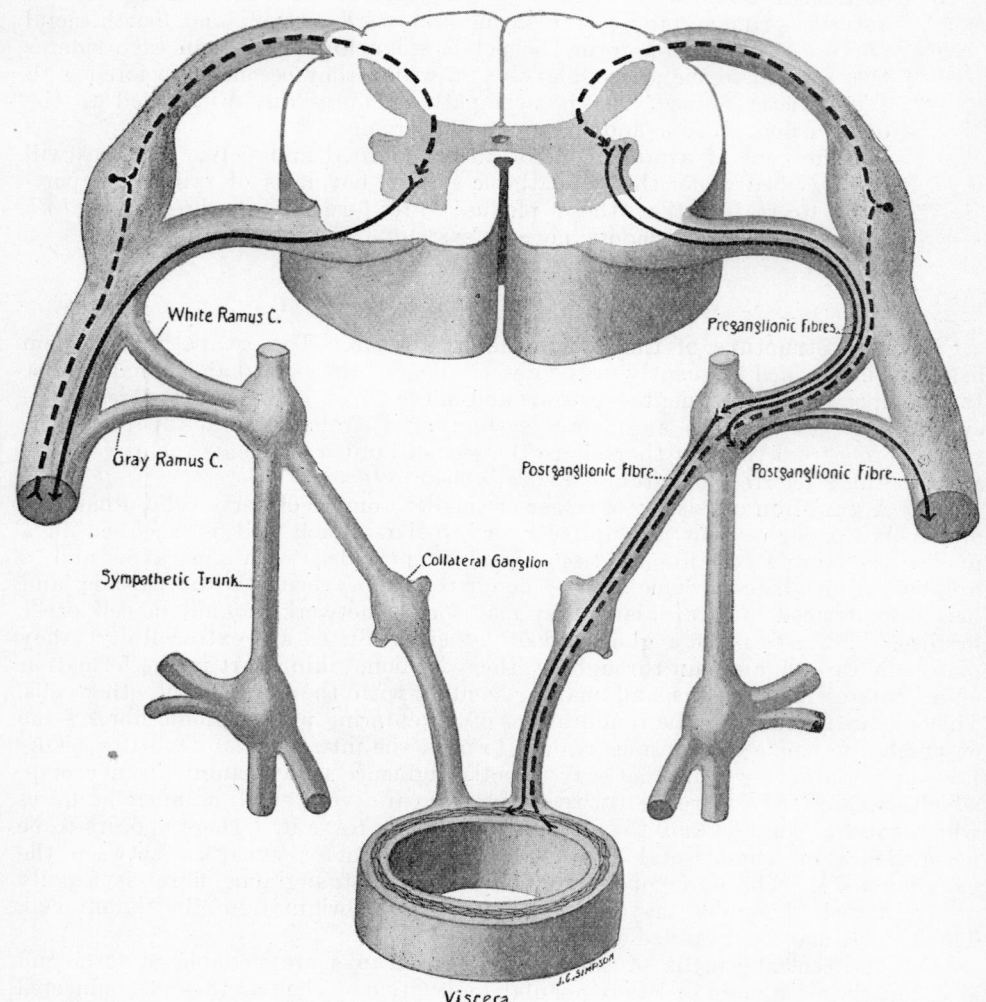

FIG. 899.—SCHEME SHOWING THE RELATION OF THE SYMPATHETIC SYSTEM TO THE SPINAL NERVES AND SPINAL CORD. (S. E. W.)

The main splanchnic fibres are shown on the right side, and, for contrast, the somatic on the left. Afferent fibres are indicated by broken lines, efferent fibres by continuous ones.

rather smaller than the somatic efferent fibres. The fibres which arise from cells situated in the sympathetic ganglia (**postganglionic**) are nearly all non-medullated or only partially medullated; a few possess delicate medullary sheaths. The nerve-fibres are aggregated to form the white and grey rami communicantes, the portions of the sympathetic trunk between the ganglia, and the peripheral branches of the trunk and ganglia.

(i.*a*) The **white rami communicantes** are all medullated fibres. They take origin from the anterior primary rami of the first thoracic to the second lumbar nerve inclusive. The cervical, lower lumbar, and sacral nerves do not give off white rami to the sympathetic system. The roots of the white rami communicantes arise from both posterior and anterior roots of the spinal nerves, but in largest numbers from the anterior root. The *fibres from the anterior root* are of very small size. They are the axons of nerve-cells within the spinal cord which enter the sympathetic trunk through the white ramus, and end by forming arborisations around the cells of a sympathetic ganglion; they are therefore preganglionic in position. There are three known courses for such a fibre to take in relation to the sympathetic system: (*a*) It may end in the ganglion with which the ramus is immediately related; (*b*) it may course upwards or downwards to reach a neighbouring ganglion; (*c*) it may pass beyond the sympathetic trunk to end in relation to cells of a collateral ganglion. All the fibres are *splanchnic efferent fibres*; they contain motor fibres for the unstriped muscular tissue of the vessels and viscera, and secretory fibres for the glands in the splanchnic area. The *fibres from the posterior root* of the spinal nerve which enter into the composition of the white ramus communicans are the axons of spinal ganglion cells. They constitute the *splanchnic afferent fibres,* and traverse the sympathetic trunk, passing upwards, downwards, and peripherally, without being connected with its cells. They are the afferent fibres from the viscera. It is not certain that fibres from the spinal ganglia are only found in connexion with nerves provided with distinct white rami. Similar medullated fibres are found also in the grey rami communicantes.

(i.*b*) The **grey rami communicantes** form a series of non-medullated fibres (with a small number of medullated fibres intermingled) which pass *from the ganglia to the spinal nerves*; they are therefore postganglionic in position. The grey rami are found in connexion with each and all of the spinal nerves. Their origins from the sympathetic trunk are quite irregular: they may come from the ganglia or the trunk between ganglia; they may divide after their origin, so that two spinal nerves are supplied from one ganglion; or two ganglia may supply branches to a single spinal nerve. The grey ramus is distributed with divisions of the spinal nerves and certain cranial nerves, supplying branches to unstriped muscular fibres (vaso-motor, pilo-motor) and glands (secretory). They also provide small recurrent branches that end in the membranes enveloping the spinal nerve-roots. Mingled with the non-medullated fibres of the grey rami there is a small number of medullated fibres, some of which may be regarded as afferent fibres—axons passing to the spinal ganglia which are incorporated with the grey rami.

(ii.) The **sympathetic trunks** are composed of white and grey fibres. The *white fibres* are: (1) splanchnic efferent fibres, passing to a ganglion above or below the point of entrance into the sympathetic system; (2) splanchnic afferent fibres, passing along the connecting cord and over or through the ganglia. The *grey fibres* are the axons of sympathetic ganglion cells; like the white fibres, they may pass along the sympathetic trunk for a certain distance upwards or downwards before they enter the splanchnic area as peripheral branches. There is no evidence of a purely associative neurone uniting one ganglion of the trunk with another.

(iii.) The **peripheral branches** of the sympathetic trunk are likewise composed of white and grey fibres. (1) The *white fibres* may be either splanchnic afferent fibres on their way from the viscera through the sympathetic trunk to the spinal ganglia, or splanchnic efferent fibres which, after traversing the trunk, without interruption (and being therefore still preganglionic in character), proceed to join and end in collateral ganglia in relation to viscera; (2) the *grey fibres* are postganglionic efferent branches—the axons of the ganglion cells—distributed on the one hand peripherally to the vessels and viscera of the splanchnic area, and on the other hand centrally, through the grey rami communicantes and the somatic divisions of the spinal nerves, to the glands and involuntary muscles in the somatic area as secretory and vaso-motor and pilo-motor fibres. A large proportion of the peripheral branches in the splanchnic area are eventually distributed to the viscera by accompanying the arteries which supply the various organs.

Description of the Sympathetic System.—For convenience of description the sympathetic trunks are dealt with first, in four regional parts, cephalic and cervical, thoracic, abdominal, and pelvic; and the great plexuses are described afterwards.

CEPHALIC AND CERVICAL PARTS OF SYMPATHETIC SYSTEM

The **cephalic** and **cervical part of each sympathetic trunk** is to be regarded as an upward prolongation of the primitive sympathetic system along the great vessels of the neck into the head region. It is characterised by the absence of **segmental ganglia** and by the absence of **white rami communicantes** joining it to the spinal nerves. Its connexion with the spinal nervous system is through the white rami communicantes of the upper thoracic nerves, which join the sympathetic trunk in the thorax, and travel upwards into its cervical portion. Its branches are distributed to structures belonging to head, neck, and thorax: (1) motor fibres to involuntary muscles (*e.g.* dilator of the pupil); (2) vaso-motor fibres for arteries of the head, neck, and upper limb; (3) pilo-motor fibres (along the cervical spinal nerves) to the skin of the head and neck and upper limb; (4) cardio-motor fibres; and (5) secretory fibres (*e.g.* to the submandibular gland).

Each trunk extends from the root of the neck, where it is continuous, in front of the neck of the first rib, with the thoracic portion of the trunk, to the base of the skull, and thus constitutes the **cervical** part of the system. It is then continued upwards into the skull in the form of plexiform branches upon the internal carotid artery to become the **cephalic** part of the system (p. 1062).

The **cervical part** of each sympathetic trunk is placed upon the prevertebral muscles and behind the carotid vessels. It consists of a narrow cord composed of medullated and non-medullated fibres, with two or three ganglia—a *superior* ganglion at the upper end, an *inferior* ganglion at the point of junction with the thoracic portion of the trunk, and a *middle* ganglion varying in position and often absent.

The **superior cervical ganglion** is situated below the base of the skull, and lies deeply behind the internal carotid artery. It is the largest of the sympathetic ganglia, measuring an inch or more in length. It is thought to be formed by the coalescence of four ganglia corresponding with the upper four cervical nerves.

The **middle cervical ganglion** is of small size, is frequently absent, and may be divided into two parts, indicating ganglia corresponding to the fifth and sixth cervical nerves. It is usually placed in front of the inferior thyroid artery as it passes behind the carotid sheath.

The **inferior cervical ganglion** is joined by the connecting cord to the middle (or superior) ganglion above, and is usually only imperfectly separated from the first thoracic ganglion below. Complete fusion occurs in about 50 per cent. (Sheehan). It is of considerable size, irregular in shape, and is placed above the pleura behind the first part of the vertebral artery and in front of the last cervical transverse process and the neck of the first rib. The superior intercostal artery is related to the lateral side of the lowest part of the ganglion.

The **branches** from the cervical sympathetic trunk and ganglia are divisible into two sets—(*A*) **Communicating branches** for other nerves; (*B*) **Peripheral** branches of distribution, which alone, or along with other nerves, form plexuses supplying vessels, glands, and viscera of the head, neck, and thorax, and the dilator of the pupil. Although this distinction is made, it is to be borne in mind that the branches of communication are as much nerves of distribution as the others.

SUPERIOR CERVICAL GANGLION

Numerous branches arise from the ganglion. They are all composed of post-ganglionic fibres, and comprise vaso-motor, pilo-motor, and secretory fibres to certain cranial and spinal nerves, vaso-motor fibres to the branches of the external and internal carotid arteries, and branches to the heart (accelerator), pharynx, certain glands, and the eye.

Communicating Branches.—1. *Grey rami communicantes* pass from the ganglion to the anterior primary rami of the first four cervical nerves.

2. Communications with Cranial Nerves.—Just outside the skull, in the deep part of the neck, communicating branches pass to the following cranial nerves : (*a*) to the inferior ganglion of the glosso-pharyngeal and the superior ganglion of the vagus (the *jugular nerve*); (*b*) to the inferior ganglion of the vagus; (*c*) to the hypoglossal nerve.

Peripheral Branches of Distribution.—1. Pharynx.—A **pharyngeal branch** passes behind the carotid sheath to reach the wall of the pharynx, where it joins with the pharyngeal branches of the glosso-pharyngeal and vagus nerves in the formation of the **pharyngeal plexus.**

2. Heart.—The **cardiac** branch is a slender nerve which, on the *right side*, descends behind the large vessels, but usually in front of the inferior thyroid

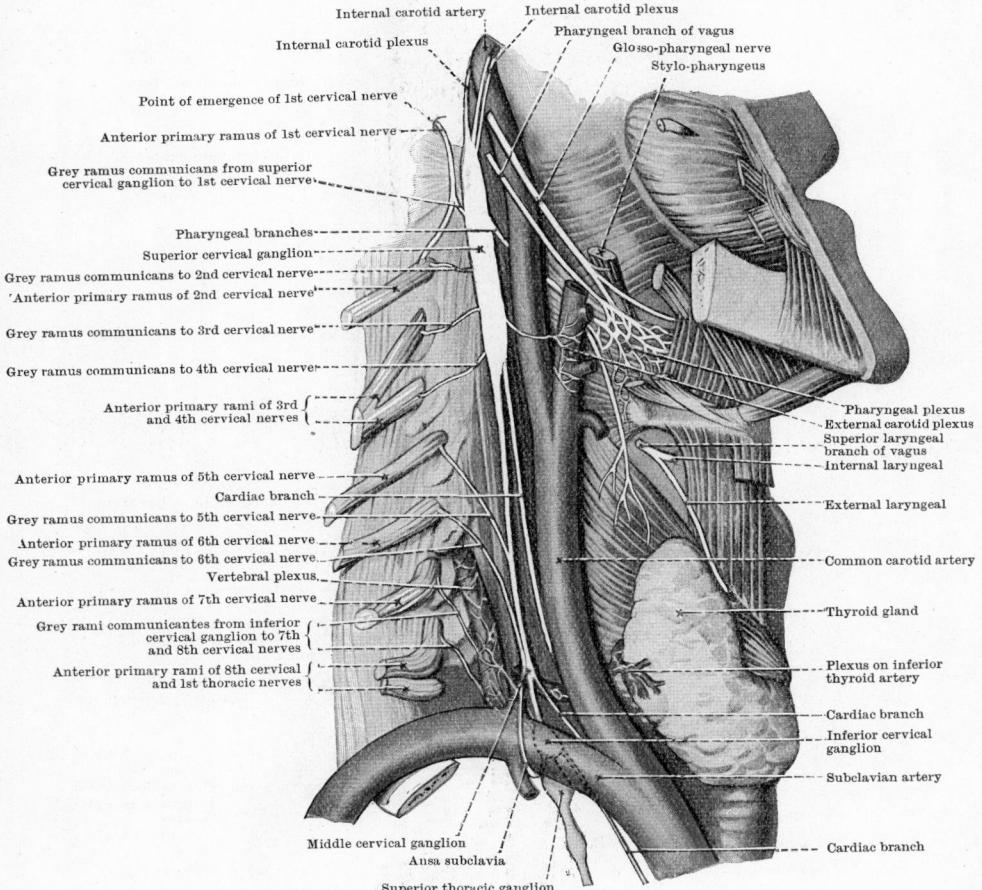

FIG. 900.—DISTRIBUTION OF BRANCHES OF SYMPATHETIC TRUNK AND GANGLIA IN THE NECK.

artery, and enters the thorax either in front of or behind the subclavian artery to join the deep cardiac plexus. On the *left side* the course of the nerve is similar in the neck, but in the superior mediastinum it passes between the left common carotid and subclavian arteries, and across the aortic arch, to join with the inferior cervical cardiac branch of the vagus in the formation of the superficial cardiac plexus. In their course both nerves form connexions with the other cardiac branches of the sympathetic, and with cardiac and other branches of the vagus (recurrent and external laryngeal), which contribute parasympathetic fibres.

3. Vessels.—(*a*) The **external carotid branches** pass forwards to the external carotid artery, and form the **external carotid plexus**, which supplies offsets to that

67 *b*

artery and its branches, as well as to the **carotid body**. From the subordinate plexuses on the facial and middle meningeal arteries sympathetic fibres pass

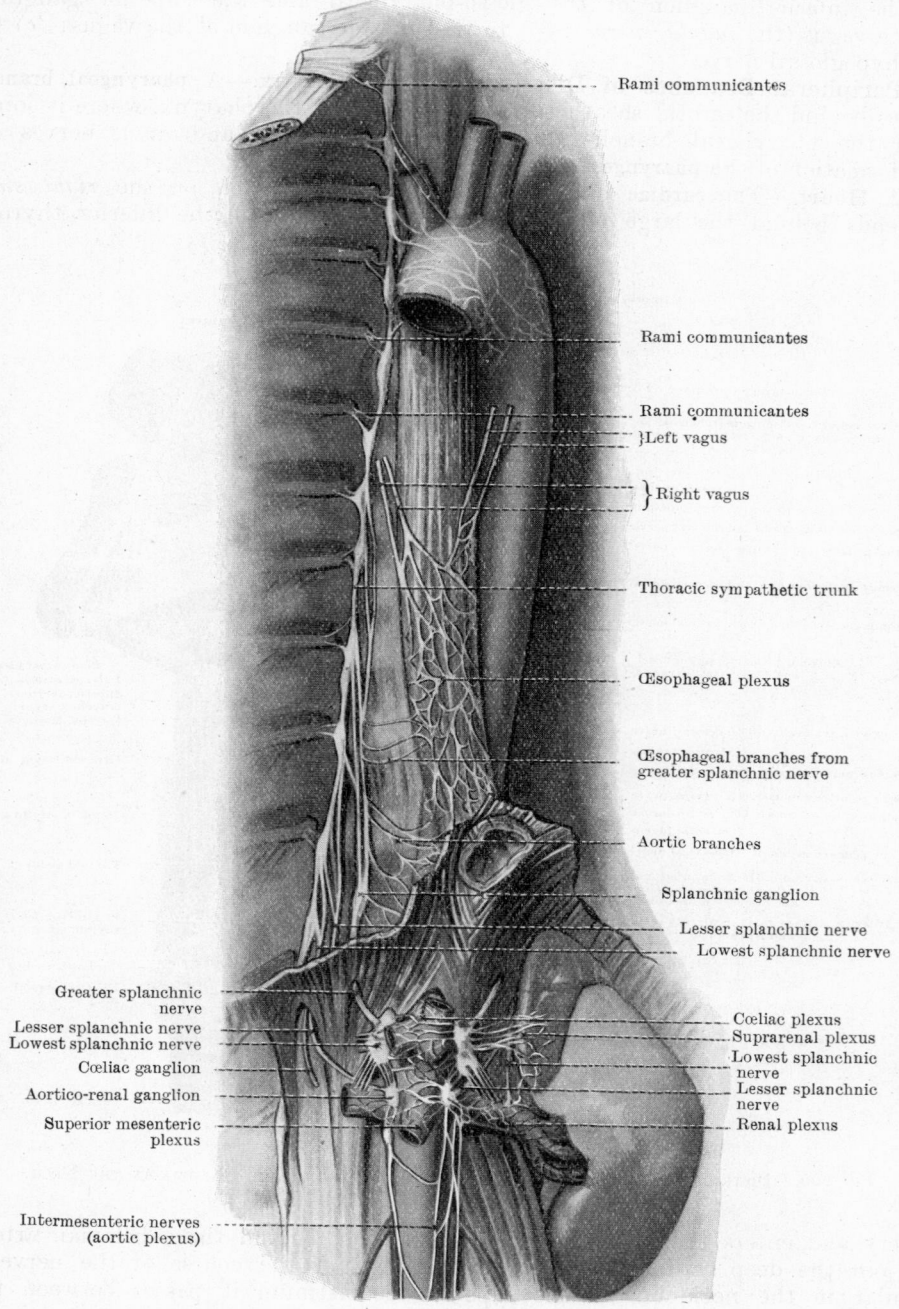

Rami communicantes

Rami communicantes

Rami communicantes
}Left vagus

} Right vagus

Thoracic sympathetic trunk

Œsophageal plexus

Œsophageal branches from greater splanchnic nerve

Aortic branches

Splanchnic ganglion

Lesser splanchnic nerve
Lowest splanchnic nerve

Greater splanchnic nerve
Lesser splanchnic nerve
Lowest splanchnic nerve
Cœliac ganglion
Aortico-renal ganglion
Superior mesenteric plexus

Cœliac plexus
Suprarenal plexus
Lowest splanchnic nerve
Lesser splanchnic nerve
Renal plexus

Intermesenteric nerves (aortic plexus)

FIG. 901.—THE SYMPATHETIC TRUNK AND THE PARASYMPATHETIC FIBRES FROM THE VAGI IN THE THORAX.

through the submandibular ganglion and otic ganglion, respectively, to supply the salivary glands.

(*b*) The **internal carotid branches** form an upward prolongation of the ganglion which applies itself in the form of bundles of nerve-fibres to the internal carotid artery as it enters the carotid canal in the temporal bone. The branches form the internal carotid plexus investing the artery, which supplies offsets to the vessel and its branches, and forms communications with certain cranial nerves.

The lower part of the internal carotid plexus communicates by fine branches with (*a*) the abducent nerve, and (*b*) the trigeminal ganglion, and gives off (*c*) the deep petrosal and (*d*) the carotico-tympanic nerves. The deep petrosal nerve joins the greater superficial petrosal nerve from the facial in the foramen lacerum. By their union the nerve of the pterygoid canal is formed, which, after traversing the pterygoid canal, can be traced to the spheno-palatine ganglion. The carotico-tympanic nerves, usually two in number (superior and inferior), pass to the tympanic plexus.

The upper part of the internal carotid plexus communicates with (*a*) the oculo-motor nerve, (*b*) the trochlear nerve, and (*c*) the ophthalmic division of the trigeminal nerve; it also (*d*) supplies twigs to the hypophysis and (*e*) forms the sympathetic root of the ciliary ganglion. The fibres joining the ophthalmic division of the trigeminal are transmitted by the naso-ciliary nerve and its long ciliary branches to the dilator of the pupil.

MIDDLE CERVICAL GANGLION

Communicating Branches.—1. *Grey rami communicantes* arise from the ganglion or from the connecting cord, and join the anterior primary rami of the fifth and sixth cervical nerves. 2. The ansa subclavia is a loop of communication from this ganglion which, after passing in front of and supplying offsets to the subclavian artery and its branches, joins the inferior cervical ganglion.

Peripheral Branches of Distribution.—1. Heart.—A cardiac branch, which may be the largest of the three cardiac branches of the cervical sympathetic trunk, descends, either separately or in company with other cardiac nerves, behind the large vessels into the thorax, where it ends in the deep cardiac plexus.

2. Thyroid Gland.—Branches extend medially along the inferior thyroid artery to supply the thyroid gland.

When the middle ganglion is absent the branches described arise from the sympathetic trunk.

INFERIOR CERVICAL GANGLION

Communicating Branches.—1. *Grey rami communicantes* arise from this ganglion for the anterior primary rami of the seventh and eighth cervical nerves. 2. The ansa subclavia already mentioned connects the middle and inferior ganglia over the front of the subclavian artery. 3. A communication frequently occurs with the recurrent laryngeal nerve.

Peripheral Branches of Distribution.—1. Heart.—A cardiac branch is given off to enter the deep cardiac plexus. On the left side it is often blended with the cardiac branch of the middle cervical ganglion.

2. Vessels.—(*a*) The vertebral plexus is a dense plexus of fibres surrounding the vertebral artery and accompanying its branches in the neck and in the cranial cavity. Branches are given to the 4th, 5th, and 6th cervical nerves from this plexus. (*b*) The subclavian plexus is derived from the ansa subclavia (subclavian loop), and supplies small offsets to the subclavian artery and its branches and the axillary artery. It gives branches also to the internal mammary artery, and communicates with the phrenic nerve.

THORACIC PART OF SYMPATHETIC SYSTEM

The thoracic part of the sympathetic trunk descends vertically under cover of the pleura, in front of the intercostal vessels; in the upper half of the thorax it lies first on the necks and then on the heads of the ribs, but, as the vertebral column widens, it comes to lie on the sides of the bodies of the vertebræ in the lower part of the thorax. It consists of a number of ganglia of an irregularly angular or fusiform shape, joined together by connecting bands of considerable thickness. The number of ganglia is usually ten or eleven; but the first—and sometimes others—may be so fused with the neighbouring ganglia as to reduce the number still further.

The thoracic part of the sympathetic trunk is characterised by its mode of union with the thoracic spinal nerves. Each thoracic nerve sends a **visceral branch** (white ramus communicans) to join the trunk in the thorax. The white rami separate into two main streams in relation to the sympathetic trunk. Those of the *upper five* nerves are for the most part directed upwards to be distributed through the cervical part of the sympathetic trunk in the manner already described. The white rami of the *lower thoracic* nerves are for the most part directed downwards in the inferior part of the sympathetic trunk and its branches, to be distributed in the abdomen; at the same time some of their fibres are directly supplied to certain thoracic viscera—lungs, aorta, œsophagus.

The white rami of the thoracic nerves are composed of: (1) **Splanchnic afferent fibres** passing from peripheral branches through the sympathetic trunk into the ganglia of the spinal nerves—medullated nerve-fibres unconnected with sympathetic ganglion cells. (2) **Somatic** and **splanchnic efferent fibres**—small medullated nerves which, after a longer or shorter course in the sympathetic trunk or its peripheral branches, become connected with the sympathetic ganglion cells, or with the cells of collateral ganglia, from which again (non-medullated) axons proceed to viscera and vessels.

The peripheral branches supplying *thoracic organs* contain vaso-motor fibres and efferent filaments for the innervation of the involuntary muscles of the lungs and aorta. The peripheral branches from the *lower* part of the sympathetic trunk in the thorax, receiving white rami from the lower thoracic nerves, are distributed mainly to structures below the diaphragm. They comprise (*a*) efferent fibres for the stomach and intestines; (*b*) pilo-motor fibres for the lower part of the body; (*c*) vaso-motor fibres for the abdominal aorta and its branches, and for the lower limbs; (*d*) secretory, and (*e*) afferent fibres from the abdominal viscera.

The **branches** from the trunk are, as in the neck, divisible into two sets—(*A*) Central branches, communicating with other nerves, and (*B*) peripheral branches, distributed in a plexiform manner to the thoracic and abdominal viscera.

(*A*) **Communicating Branches.**—The **white rami communicantes** from the thoracic nerves have already been described. Passing forwards from the anterior primary rami of the nerves, they become connected with the ganglia or the connecting cord of the sympathetic trunk.

The **grey rami communicantes** are branches that arise irregularly from each thoracic ganglion; they pass backwards along with the white rami, join the anterior primary rami of the thoracic nerves, and are distributed in a manner already described to the vessels, glands, and unstriped muscle in the skin.

(*B*) **Peripheral Branches of Distribution.**—These branches arise irregularly from the ganglia and the trunk. They are composed of non-medullated (splanchnic efferent) fibres derived from the ganglion cells, and medullated fibres (splanchnic efferent and afferent) derived directly from the white rami, without the intervention of the cells of the ganglia.

1. **Pulmonary Branches.**—From the trunk in the neighbourhood of the second, third, and fourth ganglia fine filaments arise which join the posterior pulmonary plexus.

2. **Aortic Branches.**—The upper part of the thoracic aorta receives fine branches from the upper five thoracic ganglia.

3. **Splanchnic Nerves.**—Three nerves arise from the inferior part of the gangliated trunk, partly from the ganglia themselves, and partly from the trunk between the ganglia. Actually they consist in greater part of fibres of the white rami which merely traverse the trunks on their way to their distribution. Passing downwards over the bodies of the thoracic vertebræ they pierce the diaphragm to end in the abdomen.

(*a*) The **greater splanchnic nerve** arises from the trunk between the fifth and ninth or tenth ganglia. By the union of several irregular strands a nerve of considerable size is formed, which descends over the bodies of the vertebræ, pierces the crus of the diaphragm, and joins the upper end of the *cœliac ganglion*.

In its course in the thorax the **splanchnic ganglion** is formed upon the nerve opposite the eleventh or twelfth thoracic vertebra; it appears larger in the fœtus than in the adult. From both nerve and ganglion branches arise in the thorax for the supply of the œsophagus and descending thoracic aorta (Fig. 901).

(*b*) The **lesser splanchnic nerve** arises from the trunk in the region of the ninth and tenth ganglia. It passes over the bodies of the lower thoracic vertebræ, pierces the diaphragm near to or along with the greater splanchnic nerve, and ends in the *cœliac ganglion*.

(*c*) The **lowest splanchnic nerve** arises from the last thoracic ganglion of the sympathetic, or it may be a branch of the lesser splanchnic nerve. It pierces the diaphragm, and ends in the *renal plexus*. It is not always present.

LUMBAR PART OF SYMPATHETIC SYSTEM

The **lumbar part of the sympathetic trunk** is placed upon the bodies of the lumbar vertebræ, along the medial margin of the psoas major muscle. On the right side it is covered by the inferior vena cava. The trunk usually descends in front of the lumbar vessels, but one or more lumbar veins may cross superficial to it and cause difficulty in the performance of the operation of "lumbar ganglionectomy." It is connected with the thoracic portion of the trunk by an attenuated cord which either pierces or passes behind the diaphragm; and it is continuous below with the pelvic portion of the trunk by means of a connecting cord which passes behind the common iliac artery.

It is joined by medullated fibres (white rami communicantes) from the first two (or three) lumbar spinal nerves, and it contains, as well, medullated fibres continued down from the lower part of the thoracic sympathetic trunk, and derived from the visceral branches (white rami communicantes) of the lower thoracic nerves.

This part of the trunk is characterised by great irregularity in the number of the ganglia. They are usually four in number, but there are frequently more (up to eight); and in extreme cases fusion may occur to such an extent that the separation of individual ganglia becomes impossible.

1. **Communicating Branches.**— **White rami communicantes.**—Only the first two (or three) lumbar nerves send visceral branches (white rami communicantes) to the upper lumbar ganglia or to the sympathetic trunk. These nerves form the lower limit of the thoraco-lumbar outflow of the spinal nerves.

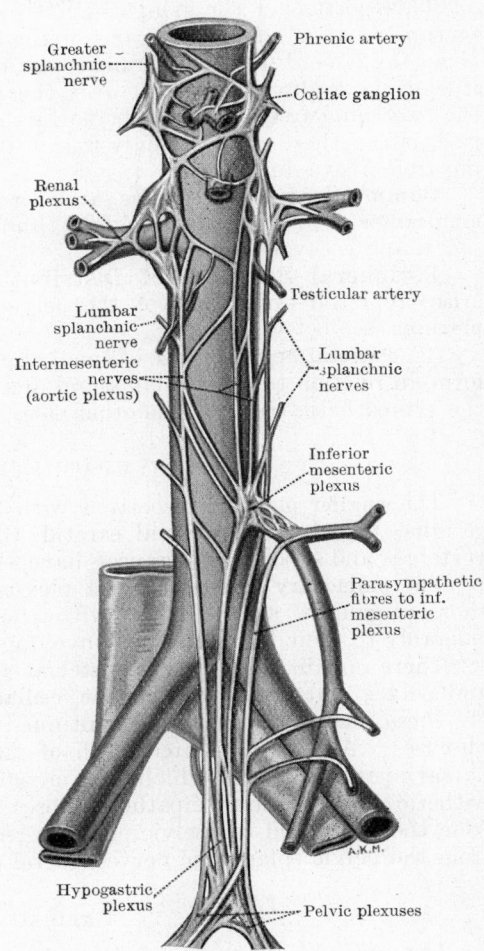

FIG. 902.—THE INTERMESENTERIC NERVES AND THE HYPOGASTRIC PLEXUS.

Grey rami communicantes pass from the sympathetic trunk to the anterior primary rami of the lumbar nerves in an irregular manner. One ramus may divide so as to supply branches to two adjacent spinal nerves; or one spinal nerve may be joined by several (two to five) grey rami from the sympathetic trunk.

The rami pass behind the psoas major muscle on the bodies of the vertebræ. They sometimes pierce the psoas muscle.

2. **Peripheral Branches of Distribution.**—A variable number of branches, sometimes termed the **lumbar splanchnic nerves,** arise from the medial side of the upper lumbar ganglia, or adjoining parts of the sympathetic trunk, and join the **intermesenteric nerves** (see p. 1070) of their own side. On the right side the lumbar splanchnic nerves approach the intermesenteric nerves from behind the inferior vena cava. Surgical experience has shown that the upper two lumbar splanchnic nerves on each side are the main source of sympathetic fibres for the innervation of the distal colon.

PELVIC PART OF SYMPATHETIC SYSTEM

The **pelvic part of the sympathetic trunk,** like the cervical and lower lumbar portions of this system, receives no *white rami communicantes* from the spinal nerves.

This portion of the sympathetic trunk is placed on the pelvic surface of the sacrum, crossing the medial parts of the anterior sacral foramina. It is connected above by a cord with the lumbar portion of the sympathetic trunk, and below it ends in a plexiform union over the coccyx with the trunk of the other side, the two being frequently connected by the **ganglion impar.** The number of ganglia is variable; there are commonly four. They are of small size, gradually diminishing from above downwards.

Communicating branches arise irregularly in the form of **grey rami communicantes** from the sacral ganglia, and join the anterior primary rami of the sacral and coccygeal nerves.

Peripheral Branches of Distribution.—(1) **Visceral branches** of small size arise from the upper part of the pelvic sympathetic trunk, and join the **pelvic plexuses** (see below).

(2) **Parietal branches,** also of small size, ramify over the front of the sacrum, and form, in relation to the median sacral artery, a plexiform union with branches from the sympathetic trunk of the other side.

SYMPATHETIC PLEXUSES

The **smaller plexuses** associated with the branches of the cervical sympathetic ganglia, namely, the internal carotid, the external carotid, pharyngeal, thyroid, vertebral and subclavian plexuses, have already been described.

The **pulmonary** and **œsophageal** plexuses, though receiving branches from the thoracic ganglia, are described with the vagus nerve, since it contributes considerably to their formation by conveying parasympathetic fibres to them.

There remain the great **prevertebral plexuses** situated in the thorax, abdomen, and pelvis, and named the **cardiac, cœliac, hypogastric,** and **pelvic** plexuses; each of those main networks is continued on into a large number of smaller plexuses. As already stated, each of the plexuses receives a large number of parasympathetic fibres which are mixed in a complex manner with the sympathetic fibres. Parasympathetic fibres reach the cardiac and cœliac plexuses from the vagi; and the pelvic plexuses receive their parasympathetic contribution from the pelvic splanchnic nerves (sacral outflow).

Cardiac Plexus

The cardiac branches of both sympathetic trunks combine with the cervical and thoracic cardiac branches of both vagus nerves to form the **cardiac plexus** which is situated above the base of the heart, and is divided into a superficial and a deep part.

The **superficial cardiac plexus** is placed in the concavity of the aortic arch, above the pericardium on the right side of the ligamentum arteriosum. It usually contains a small ganglion (**cardiac ganglion**). It is joined by two small nerves—(1) the cardiac branch from the superior cervical ganglion of the sym-

pathetic, and (2) the inferior cervical cardiac branch of the vagus (parasympathetic)—both of the left side—which reach it after passing over the arch of
the aorta.

Branches and **Communications.**—From the plexus branches of communication
pass (1) to the left half of the **deep cardiac plexus**, between the aortic arch and the

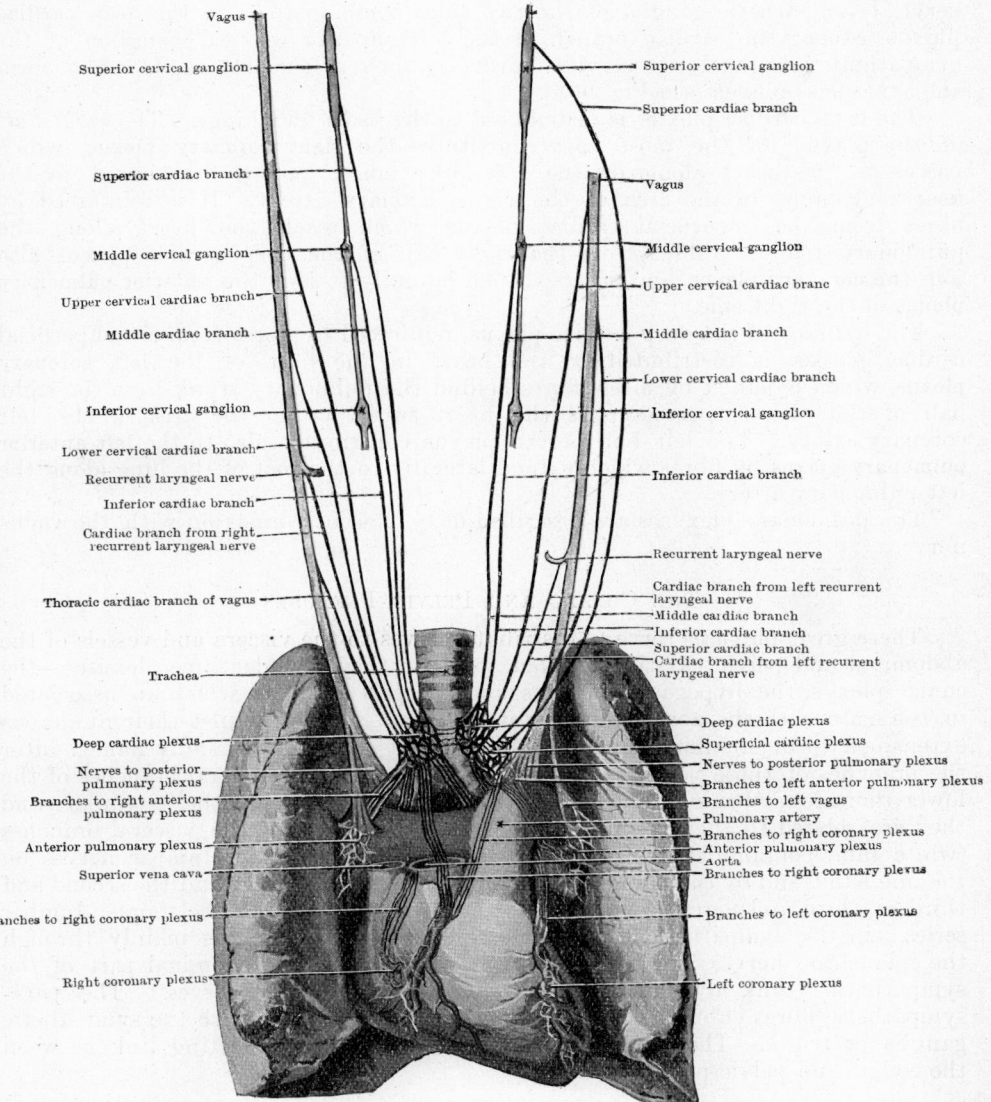

Vagus
Superior cervical ganglion
Superior cardiac branch
Middle cervical ganglion
Upper cervical cardiac branch
Middle cardiac branch
Inferior cervical ganglion
Lower cervical cardiac branch
Recurrent laryngeal nerve
Inferior cardiac branch
Cardiac branch from right
recurrent laryngeal nerve
Thoracic cardiac branch of vagus
Trachea
Deep cardiac plexus
Nerves to posterior
pulmonary plexus
Branches to right anterior
pulmonary plexus
Anterior pulmonary plexus
Superior vena cava
Branches to right coronary plexus
Right coronary plexus

Superior cervical ganglion
Superior cardiac branch
Vagus
Middle cervical ganglion
Upper cervical cardiac branc
Middle cardiac branch
Lower cervical cardiac branch
Inferior cervical ganglion
Inferior cardiac branch
Recurrent laryngeal nerve
Cardiac branch from left recurrent
laryngeal nerve
Middle cardiac branch
Inferior cardiac branch
Superior cardiac branch
Cardiac branch from left recurrent
laryngeal nerve
Deep cardiac plexus
Superficial cardiac plexus
Nerves to posterior pulmonary plexus
Branches to left anterior pulmonary plexus
Branches to left vagus
Pulmonary artery
Branches to right coronary plexus
Anterior pulmonary plexus
Aorta
Branches to right coronary plexus
Branches to left coronary plexus
Left coronary plexus

FIG. 903.—THE CARDIAC BRANCHES OF THE AUTONOMIC SYSTEM AND THE PULMONARY PLEXUSES.

bifurcation of the pulmonary trunk; (2) to the left **anterior pulmonary plexus**
along the left pulmonary artery; (3) the branches of distribution to the heart
extend along the pulmonary trunk to join the **right coronary plexus**, and supply
the substance of the heart.

The **deep cardiac plexus** is much larger. It is placed behind the arch of the
aorta, on the sides of the trachea, just above its bifurcation. It consists of two
lateral parts, joined together by numerous communications around the termination
of the trachea. The two portions of the plexus are different in their constitution
and distribution. The *right half* of the plexus is joined by both the cervical and
thoracic branches of the right vagus and by the branches of the right recurrent

larnygeal nerve, as well as by branches from the superior, middle, and inferior cervical ganglia of the sympathetic. The *left half* of the plexus is joined by the upper cervical cardiac branch of the left vagus, by branches from the left recurrent larnygeal nerve, and by branches from the middle and inferior cervical ganglia of the left sympathetic; it also receives a contribution from the superficial cardiac plexus. In other words, all the cardiac branches both from the vagi (parasympathetic) and cervical sympathetic ganglia of the two sides combine to form the deep cardiac plexus, except the cardiac branch of the left superior cervical ganglion of the sympathetic and the lower cervical cardiac branch of the left vagus, which form the superficial plexus (see Fig. 903).

The deep cardiac plexus is distributed to the heart and lungs. The *right half* of the plexus for the most part constitutes the **right coronary plexus**, which passes to the heart alongside the ascending aorta, and is distributed to the heart substance in the area of the right coronary artery. It is reinforced by fibres from the superficial cardiac plexus which reach the heart along the pulmonary trunk. Fibres from the right half of the deep cardiac plexus also join the **coronary plexus**, and others extend laterally to join the **anterior pulmonary plexus** of the right side.

The *left half* of the deep cardiac plexus, reinforced by fibres from the superficial cardiac plexus, is distributed to the heart in the form of the **left coronary plexus**, which is joined by a few fibres behind the pulmonary trunk from the right half of the plexus, and supplies the heart substance in the area of the left coronary artery. The left half of the plexus contributes also to the **left anterior pulmonary plexus** by fibres which extend laterally to the root of the lung along the left pulmonary artery.

The pulmonary plexuses are described on p. 984 in connexion with the vagus nerve.

The Cœliac and Pelvic Plexuses

These great plexuses serve to distribute nerves to the viscera and vessels of the abdominal and pelvic cavities. Taken together they include three plexuses—the cœliac plexus, the hypogastric plexus, and the pelvic plexus, which are associated in the main with the aorta and the internal iliac arteries, whilst their numerous extensions form smaller plexuses which invest and are generally named after the branches of those vessels. They are constituted by peripheral branches of the lower thoracic, abdominal, and upper pelvic parts of the sympathetic trunks; and they are related to the central nervous system by means of the visceral branches (white rami communicantes) of the lower thoracic and upper lumbar nerves on the one hand, and by the parasympathetic branches of the vagi and the second and third or third and fourth sacral nerves, on the other hand. The thoraco-lumbar series join the sympathetic trunk, and reach the cœliac plexus mainly through the splanchnic nerves, and to a lesser extent through the abdominal part of the sympathetic trunk by means of the lumbar splanchnic nerves. The parasympathetic fibres enter the pelvic plexus without connexion with the sympathetic ganglia or trunk. The hypogastric plexus serves as a connecting link between the cœliac and pelvic plexuses.

Cœliac Plexus

The **cœliac plexus**, the largest of the prevertebral plexuses, lies on the posterior abdominal wall in relation to the abdominal aorta. It is composed of three elements: the **cœliac plexus** surrounding the origin of the cœliac artery; and two **cœliac ganglia**, each lying on the corresponding crus of the diaphragm, and overlapped by the suprarenal gland, and on the right side by the inferior vena cava. The plexus is continuous with the phrenic, suprarenal, renal, and superior mesenteric plexuses. It is continued downwards by the **intermesenteric nerves**. These consist of one, two, or three fine bundles of nerve-fibres on each side, which descend on the antero-lateral aspect of the aorta. They are soon reinforced by the lumbar splanchnic nerves of their own side.

The **cœliac ganglia** constitute the chief ganglionic centres in the cœliac plexus. They are irregular in form, and are often partially subdivided. When subdivided the smaller lower segment is often referred to as the *aortico-renal ganglion*. At the upper end the cœliac ganglion receives the *greater splanchnic*

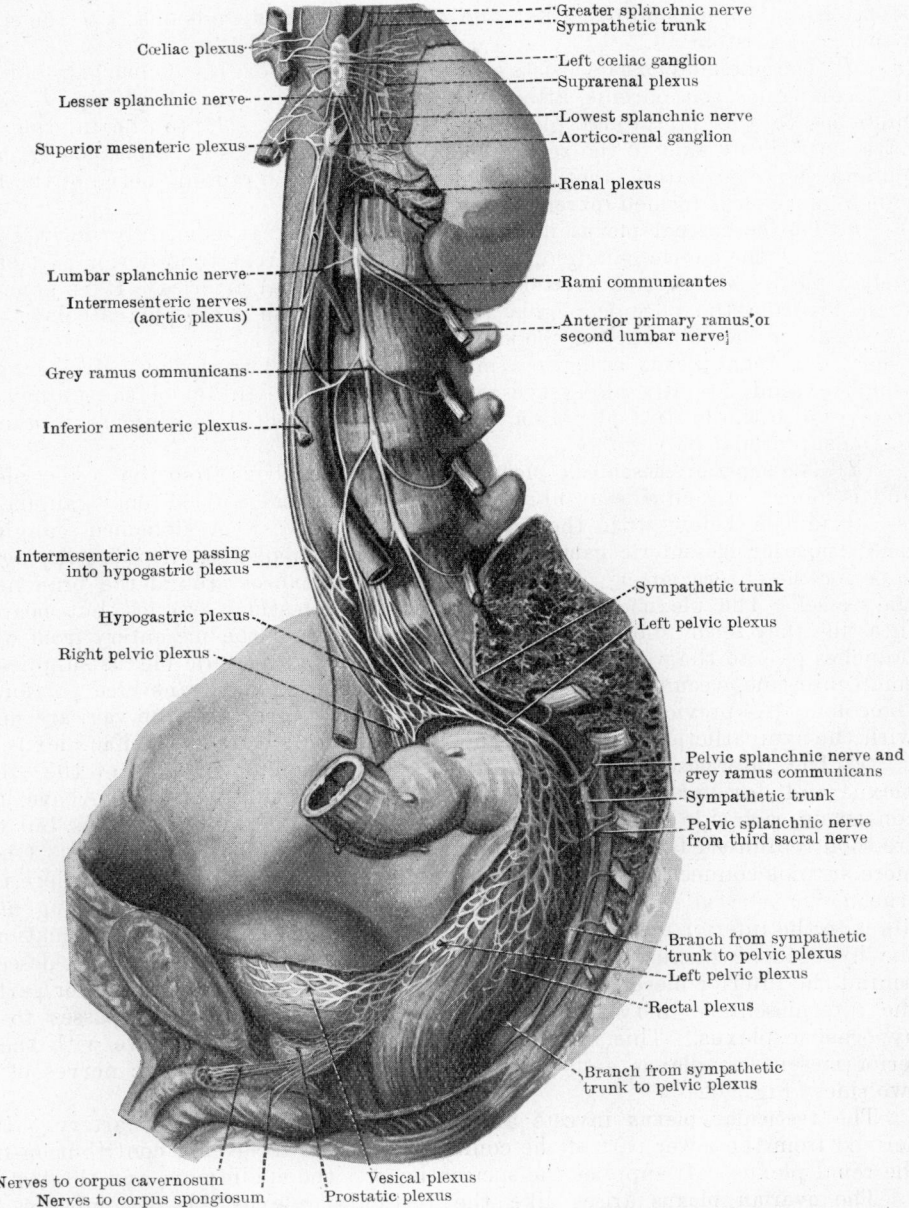

Cœliac plexus

Lesser splanchnic nerve

Superior mesenteric plexus

Greater splanchnic nerve
Sympathetic trunk
Left cœliac ganglion
Suprarenal plexus
Lowest splanchnic nerve
Aortico-renal ganglion
Renal plexus

Lumbar splanchnic nerve
Intermesenteric nerves
(aortic plexus)

Grey ramus communicans

Inferior mesenteric plexus

Rami communicantes
Anterior primary ramus of
second lumbar nerve

Intermesenteric nerve passing
into hypogastric plexus

Hypogastric plexus

Right pelvic plexus

Sympathetic trunk
Left pelvic plexus

Pelvic splanchnic nerve and
grey ramus communicans
Sympathetic trunk
Pelvic splanchnic nerve
from third sacral nerve

Branch from sympathetic
trunk to pelvic plexus
Left pelvic plexus
Rectal plexus

Branch from sympathetic
trunk to pelvic plexus

Nerves to corpus cavernosum
Nerves to corpus spongiosum

Vesical plexus
Prostatic plexus

FIG. 904.—THE PLEXUSES OF THE AUTONOMIC SYSTEM IN ABDOMEN AND PELVIS.

nerve, and at its lower end receives the *lesser splanchnic nerve*. Branches from the cœliac ganglia radiate in all directions—medially to join the cœliac plexus, upwards to form the phrenic plexus, laterally to the suprarenal plexus, downwards to the renal and superior mesenteric plexuses and to form the intermesenteric nerves. The **cœliac plexus** forms a considerable plexiform mass surrounding the cœliac artery. It consists of a dense meshwork of fibres with ganglia inter-mingled, joined by numerous branches from the cœliac ganglion on each side, and by parasympathetic branches from both vagi. It is continuous below with the superior mesenteric plexus and the intermesenteric nerves. Investing the cœliac artery, it is continuous with the plexuses which are distributed along the branches of the artery. The **left gastric plexus** supplies branches to the œsophagus and stomach; the **hepatic plexus** supplies branches to the liver and gall-bladder, stomach, duodenum, and pancreas; and the **splenic plexus** sends offsets to the spleen, pancreas, and stomach.

(*a*) The **phrenic plexus** consists of fibres that arise from the cœliac ganglion, and it accompanies the phrenic artery. Besides supplying the diaphragm, it gives branches to the suprarenal plexus, and on the right side to the inferior vena cava, on the left side to the œsophagus. It communicates on each side with the phrenic nerve. At the junction of the plexus and the phrenic nerve of the right side a ganglion is formed (**phrenic ganglion**).

(*b*) The **suprarenal plexus** is of considerable size. It is mainly derived from branches of the cœliac ganglion, reinforced by nerves from the inferior part of the cœliac plexus which stream laterally on the suprarenal arteries. It is joined by branches from the phrenic plexus above and from the renal plexus below. The nerves enter the substance of the suprarenal gland.

(*c*) The **renal plexus** is derived mainly from branches of the cœliac ganglion which extend laterally along the renal artery to the hilum of the kidney. It receives also the lowest splanchnic nerve, and is connected by numerous branches to the suprarenal plexus.

(*d*) The **superior mesenteric plexus** is inseparable above from the cœliac plexus, and is joined on each side by fibres from the cœliac and aortico-renal ganglia. It is continuous below with the intermesenteric nerves. A detached ganglionic mass (**superior mesenteric ganglion**) is present in the plexus. Accompanying the superior mesenteric artery it forms subordinate plexuses around the branches of the vessel. The plexuses at first surround the intestinal arteries, but near the intestine they form fine plexuses between the layers of the mesentery from which branches pass to the wall of the gut. The superior mesenteric plexus supplies the small intestine, cæcum, vermiform appendix, ascending and transverse portions of the colon. As previously stated, parasympathetic fibres from the vagi are mixed with the sympathetic fibres in this and other offshoots from the cœliac plexus.

(*e*) The **intermesenteric nerves** are a continuation downwards of the cœliac plexus and descend along the antero-lateral aspects of the aorta. Above, they consist on each side of one, two, or three slender bundles of nerve-fibres, but they are soon reinforced by the lumbar splanchnic nerves of their own side. One or more strands connect the intermesenteric nerves of the two sides, but there is no true *aortic plexus*. Below, the intermesenteric nerves, after contributing many fibres to the inferior mesenteric plexus, converge to take part in the formation of the hypogastric plexus. On the left side the trunk which they form descends behind the inferior mesenteric artery or its branches. Between the lower parts of the intermesenteric nerves is to be seen another bundle which passes to the hypogastric plexus. This intermediate bundle communicates above with the inferior mesenteric plexus and commonly with the intermesenteric nerves of the two sides (Fig. 902).

The **testicular plexus** invests and accompanies the testicular artery. It is derived from the lower part of the cœliac plexus, and receives a contribution from the renal plexus. It supplies the spermatic cord, the epididymis, and the testis.

The **ovarian plexus** arises like the testicular plexus. It accompanies the ovarian artery to the pelvis, and supplies the ovary, broad ligament, and uterine tube. It forms communications in the broad ligament with the **uterine plexus** (from the pelvic plexus), and sends fibres to the uterus.

The **inferior mesenteric plexus** is formed by a number of sets of fibres arising from the medial side of the right and left intermesenteric nerves. These fibres form a dense network around the inferior mesenteric artery, about half to three-quarters of an inch beyond its origin. Recent research has shown that the inferior mesenteric plexus receives sympathetic fibres from both sides and that the main source of these fibres is the upper lumbar splanchnic nerves. From the dense plexus around the stem of the inferior mesenteric artery perivascular fibres can be traced along all the branches of this vessel and these are distributed to the descending colon, pelvic colon, and upper part of the rectum. Descending from the inferior mesenteric plexus are fibres which join the hypogastric plexus. Probably these fibres are mainly sympathetic in origin, but it may be that some parasympathetic fibres ascend by this route to the inferior mesenteric plexus. The main path for parasympathetic fibres seems to be a small trunk, connected below with the pelvic splanchnic nerves (parasympathetic) on each side, which ascends on the left side of the hypogastric plexus over the left common iliac artery to join the inferior mesenteric plexus about one or one and a half inches distal to the origin of the artery from the aorta. Beyond this point the parasympathetic fibres are distributed with the sympathetic fibres.

PELVIC PLEXUS

The **hypogastric plexus** (the so-called "presacral nerve") is continued downwards in front of the sacral promontory and the sacrum and ends by dividing into the two pelvic plexuses.

The **pelvic plexuses** are formed by the separation of the hypogastric plexus into halves in front of the upper part of the sacrum. Each is joined by fibres from the upper portion of the pelvic part of the sympathetic trunk, and by the **pelvic splanchnic nerves** (parasympathetic) from the second and third or third and fourth sacral nerves. Accompanying the internal iliac artery and its branches, each pelvic plexus gives off subordinate plexuses for the pelvic viscera. Each subordinate plexus contains sympathetic and parasympathetic fibres.

(a) The **rectal plexus** supplies the rectum, and joins the superior rectal plexus from the inferior mesenteric plexus.

(b) The **vesical plexus** accompanies the vesical arteries to the bladder-wall. Besides supplying the muscular wall and mucous membrane of the bladder, it forms subordinate plexuses for the lower part of the ureter, the seminal vesicle, and the vas deferens.

(c) The **prostatic plexus** is of considerable size. It is placed on both sides of the organ, and, in addition to supplying its substance and the prostatic urethra, it sends offsets to the neck of the bladder and the seminal vesicle. It is continued forwards on each side to form the **cavernous plexus of the penis.** Bundles of nerves pierce the pelvic fascia and the perineal membrane, and, after supplying the membranous urethra, give off branches which enter and supply the corpus cavernosum penis. The cavernous nerves communicate with branches of the pudendal nerve and give offsets to the corpus spongiosum penis and the spongy portion of the urethra.

(d) The **uterine plexus** passes upwards with the uterine artery between the layers of the broad ligament, and is distributed to the surfaces and substance of the uterus. It communicates between the layers of the broad ligament with the plexus accompanying the ovarian artery.

The **vaginal plexus** is formed mainly by the visceral branches of the sacral nerves entering the pelvic plexus. It supplies the walls of the vagina and urethra, and provides a **cavernous plexus** for the clitoris. The uterine and vaginal plexuses correspond to the prostatic plexus.

INNERVATION OF THE BLOOD-VESSELS OF THE LIMBS

The mode of innervation of the proximal and distal vessels of the limbs is different.

The former are supplied with vaso-constrictor fibres (postganglionic and non-medullated) which arise directly from the sympathetic trunk or plexuses and ramify in the periarterial tissues in a plexiform manner. No ganglia occur in the periarterial plexuses (Woollard). In the case of the upper limb the filaments for the supply of the subclavian and axillary arteries arise from the ansa subclavia, whilst in the case of the lower limb they extend from the intermesenteric nerves along the common and external iliac arteries to the femoral artery.

The distal vessels in the limbs are provided with sympathetic fibres which are fine branches of the neighbouring nerve trunks (ulnar, anterior tibial, etc.). These peripheral nerves have, of course, received their sympathetic contribution as grey rami communicantes.

Recent research has shown that the more peripherally situated vessels in the limbs are also supplied with medullated fibres which send filaments to vessels and also to the neighbouring tissues; and it has been suggested that these fibres may be concerned in axon reflexes (Woollard).

The capillaries are provided with sympathetic fibres only.

DEVELOPMENT OF THE AUTONOMIC NERVOUS SYSTEM

Though primarily developed from cells which arise in the neural crest, the ganglia of the sympathetic system also contain cells which, in the trunk region at least, are derived from the neural tube. Embryologically, then, the sympathetic ganglia, plexuses, and nerves have a common origin with the remainder of the peripheral nervous system, and differ from it only in that the sympathetic cells have wandered farther from their place of origin than have those of the cerebro-spinal nerves.

When the neural tube detaches itself from the general ectodermal covering of the embryonic body, the neural crest becomes divided into right and left crests, each of which migrates ventro-laterally into the space between the neural tube and the myotomes. Those crests extend continuously on each side from the caudal end of the neural tube forwards to the auditory vesicle.

In the **spinal region** each crest becomes segmented into primitive ganglia which contain not only the primordia of the spinal ganglia but also cells destined for the sympathetic and chromaffin systems. From the ventral border of the primitive spinal ganglia the sympathetic neuroblasts detach themselves and individually migrate outwards along the paths of the developing dorsal roots of the spinal nerves. Meanwhile other cells have wandered out along the ventral roots from the neural tube to join the cells of neural-crest origin. Once the cells from each of the sources have mingled it is impossible to distinguish between them, nor is it possible to state precisely what part each plays in the subsequent development of the sympathetic system. Leaving the spinal nerves, the errant cells migrate into the neighbourhood of the aorta, where by rapid proliferation they form compact masses which fuse from segment to segment and produce a continuous longitudinal gangliated cord—the **sympathetic trunk.**

In the meantime, from the dorsal and ventral roots of the spinal nerves, centrifugal fibres grow out along the path previously followed by the cells. A little later, centripetal fibres are pushed out from the sympathetic trunk to join the spinal nerve trunk. The centrifugal fibres become myelinated and form the **white rami communicantes,** whilst the centripetal ones remain unmyelinated and form the **grey rami.** With the development of the fibres between the ganglia, the segmental character of the sympathetic trunks becomes evident throughout the thoracic and abdominal regions; the condensations which result in the three cervical ganglionic masses are also apparent.

The cells which form the ganglia of the **prevertebral plexuses** have the same origin as have those of the sympathetic trunks, differing only in that, instead of stopping in the neighbourhood of the aorta, they have migrated onwards in the loose mesoderm to come into closer relationship with the structures they supply. The cells of terminal plexuses, on the contrary, though arising from the neural crest, do not make any connexion with the sympathetic trunk; those of the cardiac, pulmonary, and greater part of the enteric plexuses migrate along the vagus nerve, whilst those of the enteric plexus in the terminal part of the digestive tube travel along the sacral nerves.

In the **head region** the sympathetic ganglia are not segmentally arranged, though, just as in the spinal region, they are developed primarily from cells which arise in the neural crest and migrate outwards through the cerebro-spinal ganglia on their way to the periphery. Moreover, just as the ganglia of the sympathetic trunk are connected with one another by longitudinal fibres, so are the cranial ganglia connected with one another and with the sympathetic trunk by means of the plexuses along the internal carotid artery. The four small **parasympathetic ganglia** in the head region arise from cells the majority of which are developed in connexion with the trigeminal ganglion, though there are probably added to the parasympathetic ganglia some few cells of either oculo-motor, facial, or glosso-pharyngeal origin.

The **ciliary ganglion** receives the majority of its cells from the trigeminal ganglion by way of the ophthalmic nerve, but a few are contributed *via* the oculo-motor nerve.

The **spheno-palatine ganglion** also is derived mainly from the trigeminal, its cells migrating along the maxillary nerve. The earliest cells, however, advance peripherally along the greater superficial petrosal branch of the facial nerve.

The **otic ganglion** arises from cells which migrate along the lesser superficial petrosal nerve from the inferior ganglion of the glosso-pharyngeal nerve, but it receives some also from the trigeminal ganglion through the mandibular nerve.

The **submandibular ganglion** arises from cells which have migrated along the mandibular and lingual nerves, but probably derives some cells from the facial also by way of the chorda tympani nerve.

ORGANS OF THE SENSES AND THE SKIN

Originally written by ROBERT HOWDEN, M.B., C.M., D.Sc., LL.D.,

Emeritus Professor of Anatomy, University of Durham

Revised and rewritten by C. M. WEST

ORGANS OF THE SENSES

THE **organs of the senses** constitute the apparatus by which man and other animals are made acquainted with their surroundings.

Every sense-organ consists of (*a*) a peripheral or receptive portion, where impulses are generated in response to external stimuli, (*b*) an intermediate or conducting portion, along which the impulses are conveyed, and (*c*) a central or perceptive portion, where the impulses are collected and transformed into sensations. The conducting and perceptive portions have been described in the chapter on the Nervous System; the receptive or peripheral portions form the subject matter of this chapter, and may be grouped under two headings: (1) those connected with the *special senses* of smell, sight, hearing, and taste, and situated in the nose, eye, ear, and mouth respectively; and (2) those of *general sensations* (the muscular sense, and the senses of pressure, heat, cold, and pain), which are widely distributed throughout the body.

ORGAN OF SMELL

The nose is the peripheral **organ of smell** and consists of: the external nose, which projects from the face; and the cavity of the nose, which is divided by a vertical septum into right and left chambers.

External Nose.—This resembles an irregular three-sided pyramid. Two sides of the pyramid are almost symmetrical and are the sides of the nose, which join the face at wide, open angles and are separated from each other by a more or less sharp margin named the **dorsum** of the nose. The dorsum is continuous with the forehead at the **root** of the nose and ends below in the **apex** of the nose, beyond which the nose is continued into the upper lip. The third side of the pyramid is the smallest, is directed downwards, and has in it two orifices called the **nostrils**. These are usually elliptical in shape in the adult but more circular in children; they are separated from each other by a median septum and are each bounded on the lateral side by the **ala** of the nose, which is the expanded lower part of the side of the nose. The upper part of the nose is fixed in position, being supported by the nasal bones and the frontal processes of the maxillæ, and it is covered with thin and movable skin; the lower part is movable, being supported only by pliable cartilages, and is covered with thick and closely adherent skin in which there are many large sebaceous glands.

Vessels and nerves.—The **arteries** are branches of the *facial artery* [a. maxillaris externa] and the *ophthalmic artery*. Its **veins** open into the *anterior facial vein* and also communicate with the *ophthalmic vein*. Its principal **lymph vessels** follow the course of the anterior facial vein and open into the *submandibular lymph glands*; but from the upper part of the nose one

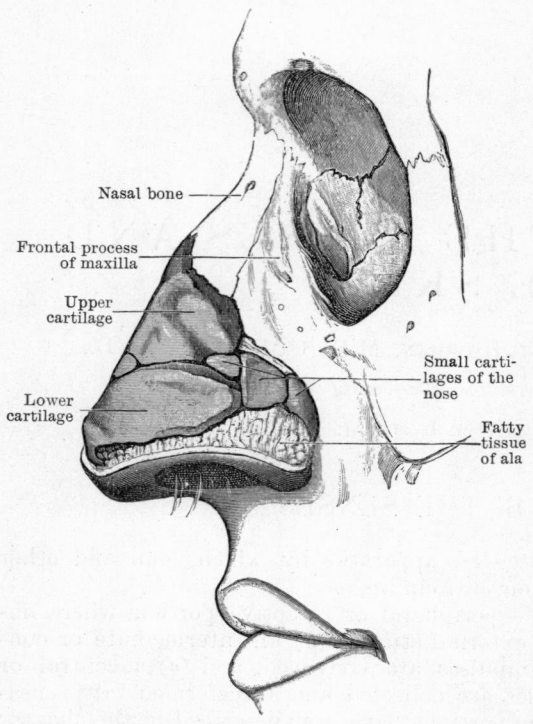

Nasal bone

Frontal process
of maxilla

Upper
cartilage

Lower
cartilage

Small carti-
lages of the
nose

Fatty
tissue
of ala

FIG. 905.—PROFILE VIEW OF THE BONY AND CARTI-
LAGINOUS SKELETON OF THE EXTERNAL NOSE.

or two lymph vessels run lateralwards
in the upper eyelid and end in the upper
parotid lymph glands, and a third group
runs below the orbit to the lower parotid
lymph glands. The **nerves** to the muscles
of the external nose come from the *facial
nerve,* and to the skin from the infra-
orbital branch of the *maxillary nerve*
and by the infratrochlear and external
nasal nerves, which are derived from
the naso-ciliary branch of the *ophthalmic
nerve.*

CARTILAGES OF THE NOSE

Five chief cartilages are concerned in the formation of the
nose; they are the upper and lower
cartilages on each side, and the
septal cartilage.

The **upper cartilage** [cartilago
nasi lateralis] (Figs. 905, 906) is
triangular in shape and is situated immediately below the nasal
bone. Its posterior edge is thin
and is attached to the maxilla
and to the nasal bone by fibrous
tissue. The anterior edge is
thick; its upper part is directly
continuous with the cartilage of
the septum, but its lower part is
separated from that cartilage by a
narrow fissure. The lower edge is joined, by fibrous tissue, to the lower cartilage.

The **lower cartilage of the nose**
[c. alaris major] (Figs. 905, 906)
is elliptical, with the long axis
directed downwards and forwards.
It supports the nostril on its
lateral side and from the lower
end, which helps to form the
apex of the nose, a small hook-
like process, called the *septal
process,* passes medially to support
the front of the nostril. The
lower cartilage is connected
above with the upper and septal
cartilages, and behind with the
maxilla by fibrous tissue in which
are imbedded two or three *small
cartilages of the nose*; in front it
is separated from its fellow by a
gap which is filled with fibrous
tissue and can easily be felt in
the living subject.

The **septal cartilage** (Fig. 907)
is of an irregular quadrilateral
form. Its postero-superior edge
is attached to the perpendicular
plate of the ethmoid bone; its
postero-inferior margin to the
vomer and to the nasal crests of

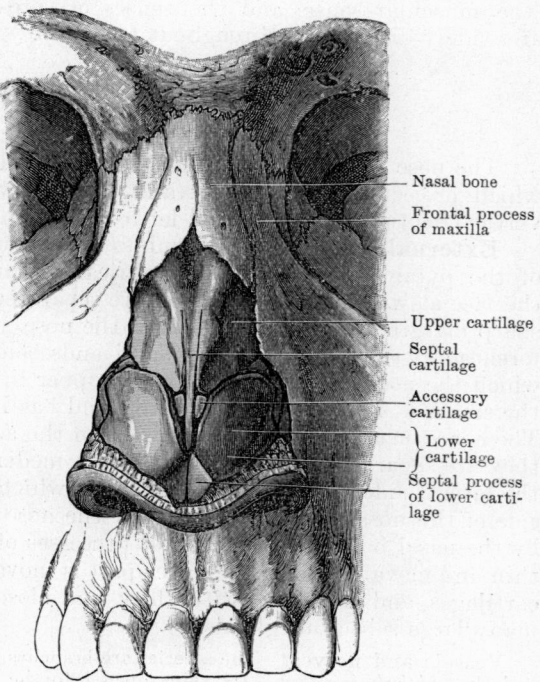

Nasal bone

Frontal process
of maxilla

Upper cartilage

Septal
cartilage

Accessory
cartilage

} Lower
} cartilage

Septal process
of lower carti-
lage

FIG. 906.—FRONT VIEW OF THE BONY AND CARTILAGINOUS
SKELETON OF THE EXTERNAL NOSE.

the maxillæ. Its antero-superior border is thick, and is fixed above to the back of the internasal suture; immediately below that suture it is directly continuous with the upper parts of the upper cartilages of the nose, which may be looked upon as its wing-like expansions. The lower part of each upper cartilage is separated from the septal cartilage by a fissure which is filled with fibrous tissue; in the fibrous tissue a small accessory cartilage is usually seen. The antero-inferior border of the septal cartilage is short, and is attached by fibrous tissue to the septal processes of the lower cartilages; its anterior angle is rounded and does not reach as far as the apex of the nose. The septal cartilage may be prolonged backwards (especially in children) as a narrow process, into the angle between the vomer and the ethmoid bone.

On each side of the postero-inferior edge of the septal cartilage there is a

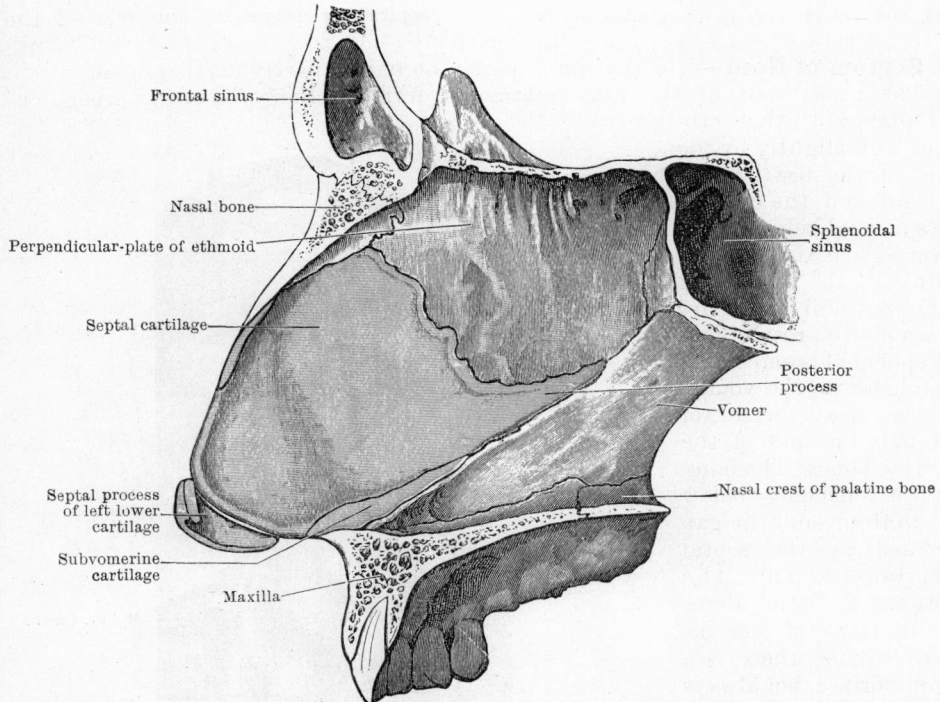

Frontal sinus

Nasal bone

Perpendicular-plate of ethmoid

Septal cartilage

Sphenoidal sinus

Posterior process

Vomer

Septal process of left lower cartilage

Subvomerine cartilage

Maxilla

Nasal crest of palatine bone

Fig. 907.—View of the Nasal Septum from the Left Side.

narrow band of cartilage, called the **subvomerine cartilage** (Fig. 907); it is attached to the vomer, and is seen best in a coronal section of the nose.

The lowest part of the nasal septum is not formed by the septal cartilage but by the septal processes of the lower cartilages and by the skin, and is therefore in reality double and, being freely movable, is termed the **movable part of the septum.**

CAVITY OF THE NOSE

The **cavity of the nose** extends from the *nostrils* in front to the *posterior apertures* of the nose behind; it is divided into right and left cavities by the *septum* of the nose, and opens through the posterior apertures into the nasal part of the pharynx. The medial or septal wall of each nasal cavity is smooth and flat, while the lateral wall is irregular owing to the presence of the nasal conchæ.

Immediately above the nostril there is a slightly expanded portion, called the **vestibule,** which is bounded laterally by the lower cartilage of the nose, and medially by the lower part of the septum. It is lined with skin, and is prolonged as a small recess towards the apex of the nose. The vestibule is partly subdivided by a curved ridge; and, in its lower part, there are hairs and sebaceous glands, the hairs being curved downwards to guard the entrance to the nostril; the upper part is smooth, and is limited superiorly by a slight, arched prominence which is caused by the lower edge of the upper cartilage.

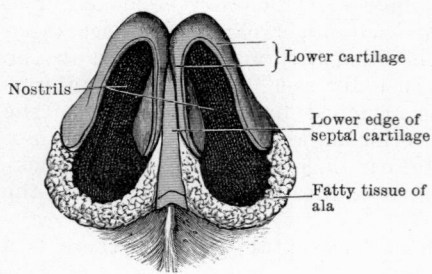

FIG. 908.—CARTILAGES OF NOSE FROM BELOW.

Each nasal cavity is divided into an upper or olfactory, and a lower or respiratory region. The **olfactory region**, to which alone the olfactory nerves are distributed, is a narrow slit-like space, bounded by the anterior part of the superior nasal concha and the corresponding part of the septum. The **respiratory region** is the rest of the cavity.

Septum of Nose.—The septum is partly bony and partly cartilaginous.

The upper part of the **bony septum** is formed chiefly by the perpendicular plate of the ethmoid, and slightly by the crest of the nasal bones in front and the crest of the sphenoid behind. The lower part is formed mainly by the vomer—in the upper and back part of which the rostrum of the sphenoid is embedded—and, below the vomer, by the nasal crests of the maxillæ and of the palatine bones. The bony part is deficient below and in front, and the gap is filled by the septal cartilage. In the septum, a little above and in front of the incisive canals, there is a minute orifice, not always recognisable, from which a blind pouch—the **vomero-nasal organ**—extends upwards and backwards for a distance of from 2 to 9 mm.; it is supported by the sub-vomerine cartilage. In Man the vomero-nasal organ is rudimentary (Fig. 911), but in many of the lower animals it is well developed and is lined with epithelium similar to that of the olfactory region, and is supplied by branches of the olfactory nerve.

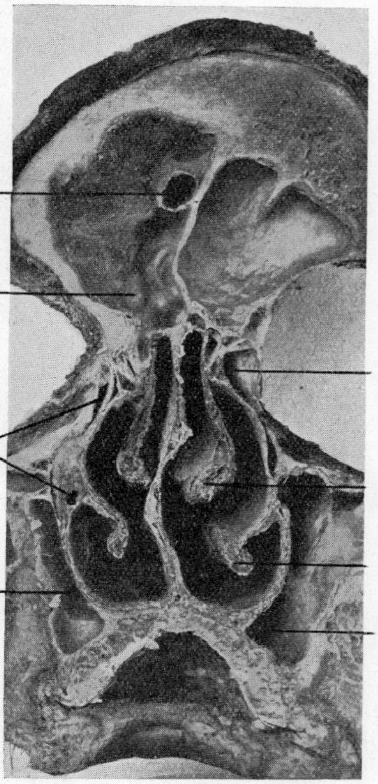

FIG. 909.—PHOTOGRAPH OF A CORONAL SECTION THROUGH THE NOSE, IN FRONT OF SECTION SHOWN IN FIG. 910. VIEWED FROM BEHIND. (C. M. W.)

Until the seventh year of life the nasal septum is, as a rule, in the median plane, but after that age it is very often bent to one or other side—more frequently to the right—the deflection being greatest usually along the line of junction of the vomer with the perpendicular plate of the ethmoid. Deflection of the septum is more common in European than in non-European skulls—occurring in about 53 per cent. of the former and in about 28 per cent. of the latter (Zuckerkandl). Associated with that deviation, or apart from it, crests or spurs of bone are found, projecting from the septum into one or other nasal cavity, in about 20 per cent. of skulls.

Lateral Wall (Fig. 912).—The lateral wall of the nasal cavity shows the three elevations caused by the superior, middle, and inferior conchæ and frequently

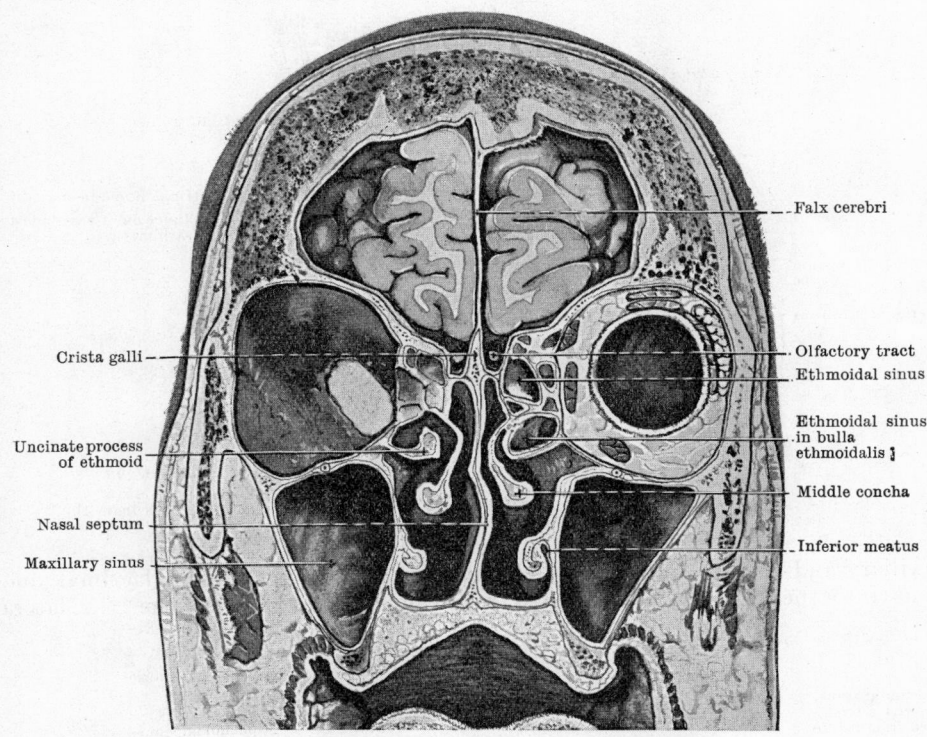

Falx cerebri

Crista galli

Olfactory tract

Ethmoidal sinus

Uncinate process
of ethmoid

Ethmoidal sinus
in bulla
ethmoidalis ¦

Middle concha

Nasal septum

Maxillary sinus

Inferior meatus

FIG. 910.—CORONAL SECTION OF THE HEAD ; BEHIND THE SECTION SHOWN IN FIG. 909.
VIEWED FROM THE FRONT. (C. M. W.)

a fourth due to a "highest" concha. Below and lateral to each concha there is a space or cleft—the superior, middle, and inferior meatus of the nose. Another

small space may be present below the "highest" concha ; and, above and behind the superior concha, there is a small space, called the **spheno - ethmoidal recess**, into which the sphenoidal sinus opens. Above and behind the vestibule and immediately in front of the middle meatus there is a slight concavity of the lateral wall known as the **atrium** of the **middle meatus** ; the atrium is limited above by a ridge, called the **agger nasi**, which is the representative

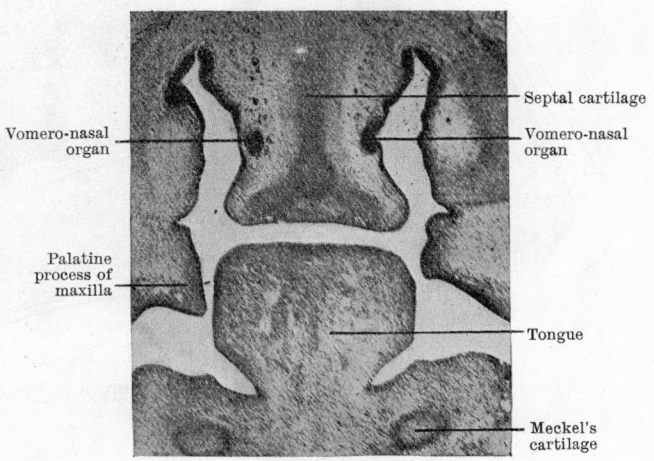

Septal cartilage

Vomero-nasal
organ

Vomero-nasal
organ

Palatine
process of
maxilla

Tongue

Meckel's
cartilage

FIG. 911.—SECTION THROUGH THE NOSE AND MOUTH OF A 20 MM. HUMAN
EMBRYO (×28). (A. R.)

of the naso-turbinal found in many mammals. Above the agger nasi, a groove known as the **olfactory sulcus** leads to the olfactory portion of the nose. Certain of the paranasal sinuses open into the various meatuses of the nose : the sphenoidal sinus into the spheno-ethmoidal recess, the posterior ethmoidal sinuses into the superior meatus, the anterior and middle ethmoidal sinuses and the

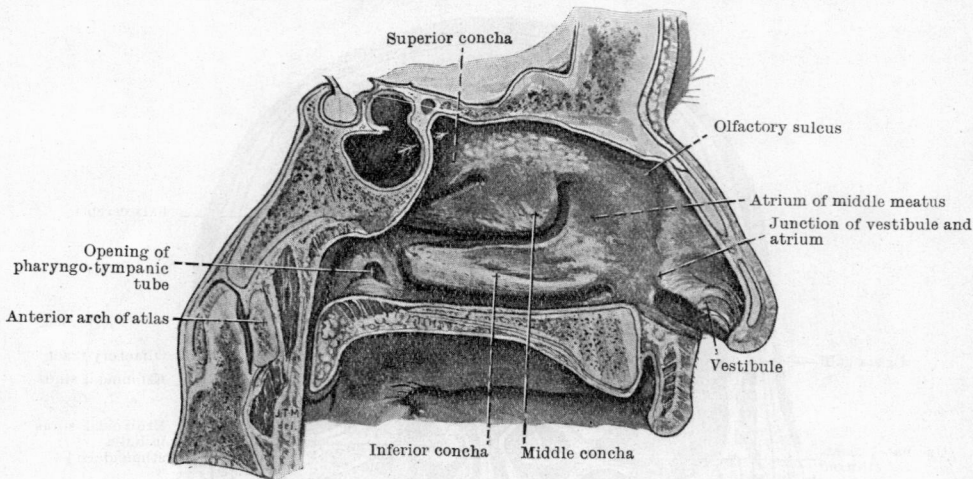

Fig. 912.—View of Lateral Wall of left Nasal Cavity. The arrow passes from the sphenoidal sinus to the spheno-ethmoidal recess. (C. M. W.)

maxillary and frontal sinuses into the middle meatus. The naso-lacrimal duct opens into the inferior meatus. On removal of the middle concha, the lateral

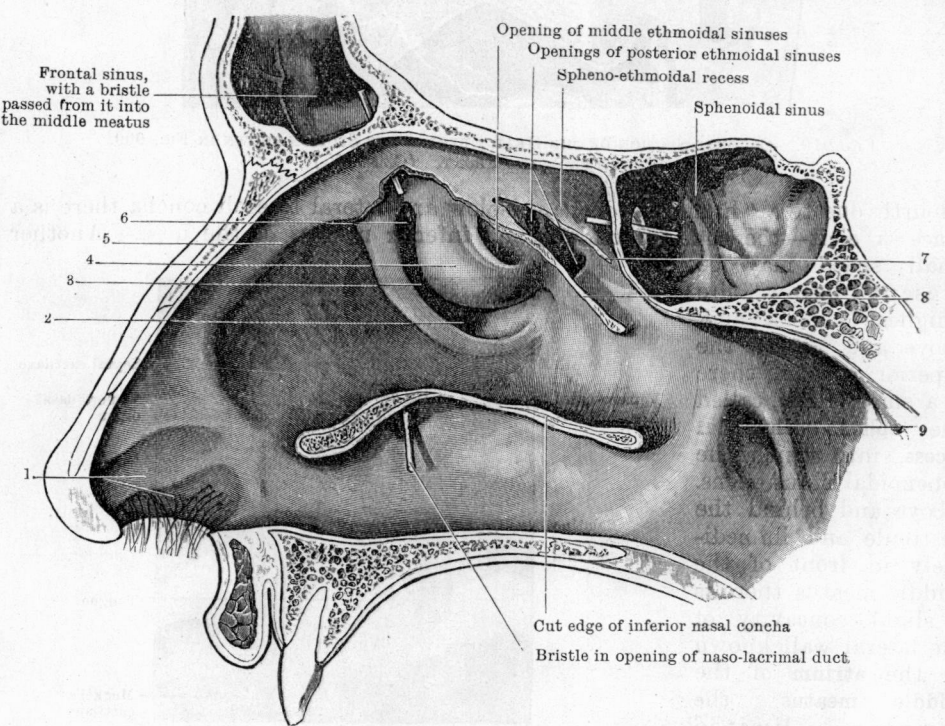

Fig. 913.—View of the Lateral Wall of the Nose—The Nasal Conchæ having been removed.

1. Vestibule.
2. Opening of maxillary sinus.
3. Hiatus semilunaris.
4. Bulla ethmoidalis.
5. Agger nasi.
6. Opening of anterior ethmoidal sinuses.
7. Cut edge of superior nasal concha.
8. Cut edge of middle nasal concha.
9. Opening of pharyngo-typanic tube.

wall is seen to be marked by a curved groove, called the **hiatus semilunaris**, which is limited above by an elevation—the **ethmoidal bulla**—due to the bulging of the middle ethmoidal sinuses, and below by the sharp edge of the **uncinate process** of the ethmoid bone; the anterior end of the hiatus semilunaris opens into the ethmoidal infundibulum, which leads to the frontal sinus; the openings of the middle ethmoidal sinuses are usually placed above the bulla; the anterior ethmoidal sinuses and the maxillary sinus open into the hiatus.

Roof.—The roof of the nasal cavity is very narrow, except at its posterior part, and is divisible into three portions—fronto-nasal, ethmoidal, and sphenoidal—in accordance with the bones which enter into its formation.

Floor.—The floor of the nasal cavity is formed by the palatine process of the maxilla and the horizontal plate of the palatine bone. In it, close to the lower margin of the septum and immediately over the incisive canal, a funnel-shaped depression called the *naso-palatine recess* is sometimes seen; it is directed downwards and forwards, and indicates the position of a communication which existed between the nasal and oral cavities in early intra-uterine life.

Mucous Membrane of Nose.—The mucous membrane lines the entire nasal cavity except the vestibule; it is firmly bound to the subjacent periosteum and perichondrium. It is continuous, through the posterior apertures of the nose with the mucous lining of the nasal part of the pharynx; through the naso-lacrimal duct and the lacrimal sac and canaliculi, with the conjunctiva; and through the apertures leading into the paranasal sinuses with the delicate lining of those cavities.

In the respiratory region the mucous membrane is thick

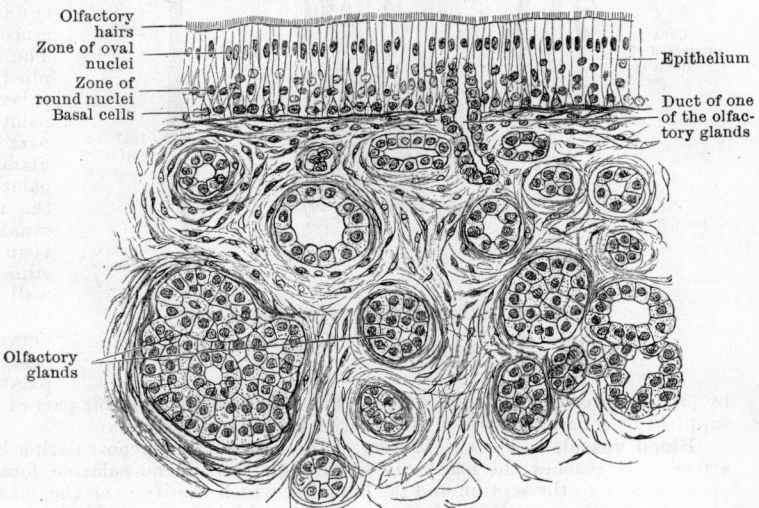

FIG. 914.—SECTION THROUGH THE OLFACTORY MUCOUS MEMBRANE.

and highly vascular and contains many acinous glands, especially in the posterior half of the cavity; in the olfactory region it is thin and yellow and contains the peripheral endings of the olfactory nerves.

Structure.—In the respiratory region the mucous membrane is covered with columnar, ciliated epithelium; between the bases of the columnar cells smaller pyramidal cells occur, and goblet or mucous cells also are found. In children a considerable amount of adenoid tissue is present. In the olfactory region the mucous membrane is covered with non-ciliated, columnar epithelium in which the cells may be divided into *supporting, olfactory* and *basal* cells.

The superficial parts of the **supporting cells** are columnar and contain fine granules of yellow pigment; the deep parts are continued for some distance as attenuated processes which may be branched. Their nuclei are elliptical or oval, and are situated at the deep ends of the columnar parts of the cells—forming the *zone of oval nuclei*.

The **olfactory cells** are bipolar nerve-cells, and their central processes are delicate and beaded filaments which are continued through the cribriform plate of the ethmoid to the brain. They are homologous with the nerve-cells of the spinal ganglia, but differ from them in that they retain their primitive position in the surface epithelium. The cell-bodies are spindle-shaped and are arranged in several rows between the deeper attenuated parts of the supporting cells. Their nuclei are large and spherical, and form a layer of some thickness termed the *zone of round nuclei*. The peripheral process of each olfactory cell is rod-like, and extends between the columnar portions of the supporting cells as far as their free surfaces, where it pierces the external limiting membrane and divides into a number of fine hair-like processes named **olfactory hairs**.

The **basal cells** are branched, and lie between the deep ends of the supporting and olfactory cells.

Olfactory Nerves.—The fibres of the olfactory nerves are devoid of medullary sheaths, but are provided with primitive sheaths; they arise, as stated, from the olfactory cells. They are collected into fasciculi which form a plexiform network under the mucous membrane and ascend on the medial and lateral walls of the olfactory region of the nasal cavity. They are lodged, near the base of the skull, in grooves or canals in the ethmoid bone, and pass into the cranial cavity through the foramina in the cribriform plate. They enter the olfactory bulb, in the glomeruli of which they subdivide and form synapses with the dendrites of the mitral cells of the bulb (Fig. 792).

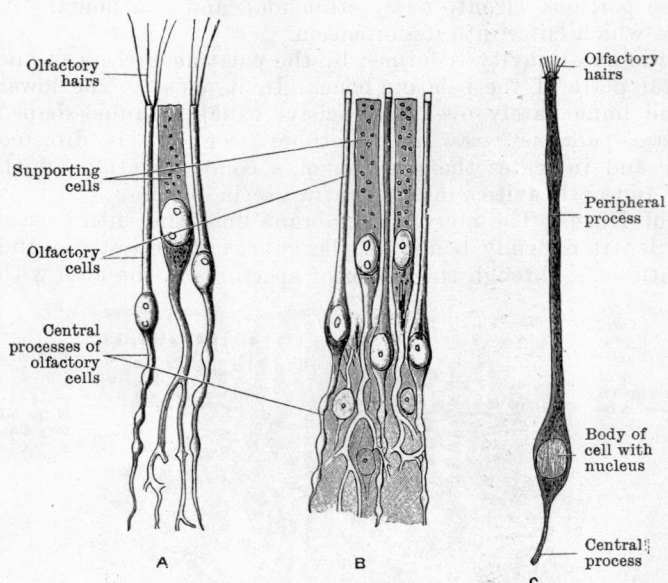

FIG. 915.—OLFACTORY AND SUPPORTING CELLS.

A. Frog } M. Schultze.   C. Human olfactory cell (v. Brunn).
B. Human

The trigeminal nerve supplies branches of ordinary sensation to the nasal mucous membrane as follows: The septum is chiefly supplied by the long spheno-palatine nerve [n. naso-palatinus], but its posterior part receives additional filaments from the spheno-palatine ganglion and from the nerve of the pterygoid canal, and its anterior portion from the anterior ethmoidal nerve. The lateral wall is supplied (1) by the short spheno-palatine nerves; (2) by the lower nasal branches of the greater palatine nerve; and in front by (3) the anterior ethmoidal nerve. The floor and the anterior part of the inferior meatus are supplied by a nasal branch of the anterior superior dental nerve.

Blood-vessels.—The chief artery of the nose is the spheno-palatine branch of the maxillary artery. It reaches the nasal cavity through the spheno-palatine foramen, and divides into (a) an artery to the septum and (b) branches which ramify over the meatuses and conchæ, and also supply the maxillary, frontal and ethmoidal sinuses. The upper portion of the cavity receives a supply from the ethmoidal arteries, and the posterior part some small branches from the greater palatine artery. The nostrils are supplied by a branch of the facial artery [a. maxillaris externa] and by the septal branch of the superior labial artery. The maxillary sinus is supplied by the infra-orbital and posterior superior dental arteries, and the sphenoidal sinus gets its chief supply from the spheno-palatine artery. The veins form a dense cavernous plexus which is well seen in the respiratory region, and especially so over the inferior nasal concha and the lower and posterior parts of the septum. The venous blood is carried in three chief directions, viz. *forwards* into the anterior facial vein, *backwards* into the pterygoid plexus through the spheno-palatine vein, and *upwards* into the ethmoidal veins. The ethmoidal veins communicate with the ophthalmic veins and the veins of the dura mater; one ethmoidal vein passes up through the cribriform plate, and opens either into the venous plexus of the olfactory bulb or directly into one of the veins on the orbital surface of the brain.

Lymph Vessels.—These form an irregular network in the superficial part of the mucous membrane and communicate with the lymph spaces which surround the branches of the olfactory nerve; they can be injected from the subdural and subarachnoid spaces. The chief lymph vessels are directed backwards towards the posterior apertures of the nose, and, on each side, are collected into two trunks, one passing to a lymph gland in front of the axis vertebra, the other to one or two lymph glands near the greater horn of the hyoid bone.

PARANASAL SINUSES

The paranasal sinuses are the frontal, ethmoidal, sphenoidal, and maxillary; they open into the nasal cavities, and are lined with mucous membrane which is continuous with that of the nasal cavities.

The **frontal sinuses** are two in number, and are placed behind the superciliary arches; they are rarely symmetrical because the septum which separates them frequently deviates from the median plane. Their average measurements are: height, 3·16 cm.; breadth, 2·58 cm.; depth from before backwards, 1·8 cm. Each opens, through the infundibulum, into the anterior part of the middle meatus of the nose.

The **ethmoidal sinuses** are the numerous, thin-walled air-cavities that occupy the labyrinth of the ethmoid bone; their walls are completed by the frontal, maxillary, lacrimal, sphenoid, and palatine bones, with which the labyrinth articulates. They are separated from the orbits by thin bony laminæ, and are arranged on each side in three groups—anterior, middle, and posterior. The anterior and middle groups open into the middle meatus of the nose, and the posterior group into the superior meatus.

The **sphenoidal sinuses** are a pair of cavities in the body of the sphenoid bone; they are rarely symmetrical, since the septum between them is often bent to one or other side. Their average measurements are: height, 2 cm.; width, 1·8 cm.; antero-posterior depth, 2·1 cm. Each opens into the spheno-ethmoidal recess of the nose.

The **maxillary sinuses** are pyramidal cavities in the bodies of the maxillæ. Their average measurements are: height, opposite the first molar tooth, 3·5 cm.; width, 2·5 cm.; antero-posterior depth, 3·2 cm. In the upper part of the medial wall of each sinus there is an opening through which it communicates with the lower part of the hiatus semilunaris in the middle meatus of the nose. An accessory opening is frequently seen above the posterior part of the inferior concha.[1]

The relations of the sinuses are given in the chapter on Osteology; and their appearance in radiographs may be studied in Plates V, VIII and LVII-LX.

ORGAN OF SIGHT

EYEBALL

The eyeball is the peripheral part of the **organ of sight**; associated with it are certain accessory structures, namely, the eyelids, the conjunctiva and the lacrimal apparatus.

The eyeball is situated in the anterior part of the orbit. It is not quite spherical, being composed of the segments of two unequal spheres, viz. a smaller anterior, corneal segment, and a larger posterior, scleral segment (Fig. 916). The anterior or corneal segment projects in front of the scleral portion, the union of the two parts being indicated, externally, by a slight groove called the **sulcus scleræ**. The central points of the anterior and posterior surfaces of the eyeball are its **anterior** and **posterior poles**; a straight line joining the two poles is termed the **optic axis**; and a line encircling the eyeball, midway between the poles, is named the **equator**. The axes of the two eyeballs are almost parallel, converging only slightly behind; but the axes of the optic nerves converge markedly behind, and, if prolonged backwards, would meet in the region of the dorsum sellæ of the sphenoid. The antero-posterior, horizontal and vertical diameters of the eyeball are nearly equal, being about one inch. The diameters are rather less in the female than in the male, but the size of the bulb is fairly constant in the same sex.

Fascial Sheath of Eyeball.—The fascial sheath is a thin fibrous coat which closely envelops the eyeball from the entrance of the optic nerve to the sclero-corneal junction; it forms a socket for the eyeball, and separates it from the other contents of the orbit. The sheath is separated from the eyeball merely by a potential space which, though it has sometimes been described as a lymph-space, is not lined with endothelium, but is traversed by a meshwork of fine areolar tissue. Posteriorly, around the entrance of the optic nerve the sheath is difficult to define, for here it is pierced by the ciliary nerves and the posterior ciliary vessels; it is not continued backwards to form a sheath for the optic nerve. It is pierced near the equator by the venæ vorticosæ, and farther forwards by the

---

[1] The measurements of the sinuses are those given by Logan Turner, *Accessory Sinuses of the Nose*, 1901.

orbital muscles on the way to their insertion into the sclera. The part of the sheath in front of the insertions of the recti muscles is thin; it lies between the ocular part of the conjunctiva and the sclera, and fuses with the sclera immediately behind the sclero-corneal junction. The sheaths of the orbital muscles are thin and almost invisible posteriorly, but they become thick anteriorly, and blend with the fascial sheath of the eyeball at the points where it is pierced by the muscles.

Offsets from the outer surfaces of the muscle-sheaths pass to the walls of the orbit, and, as they probably check the actions of the muscles, they are named **check ligaments**; they are developed best in association with the lateral and medial recti. The lateral part of the sheath of the lateral rectus is greatly thickened

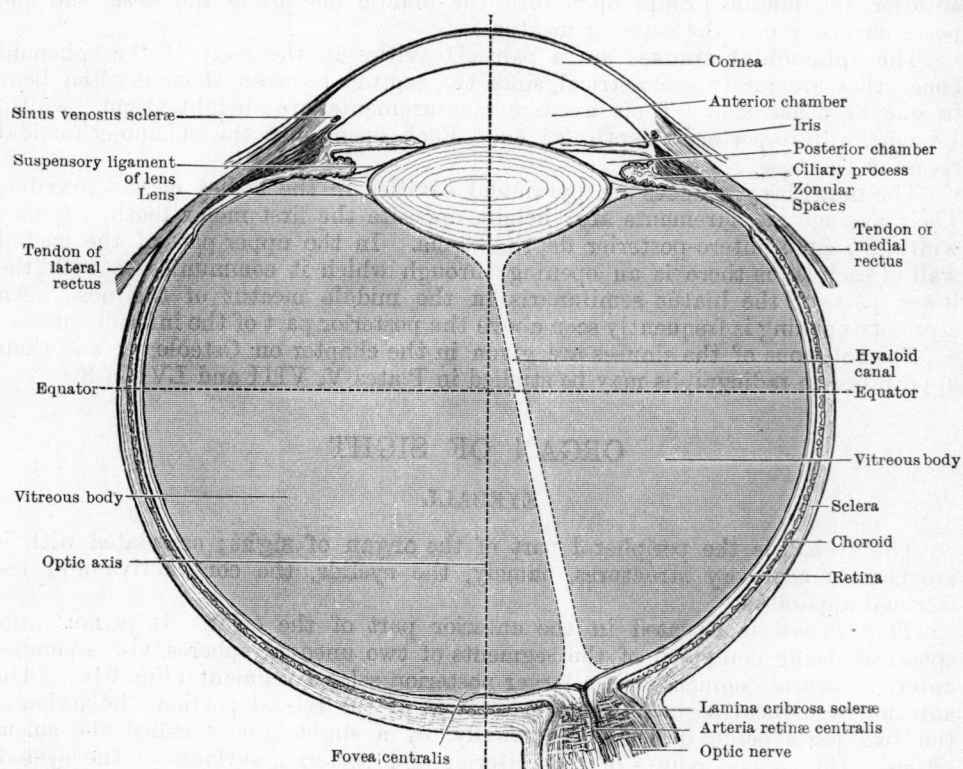

FIG. 916.—DIAGRAM OF A HORIZONTAL SECTION THROUGH LEFT EYEBALL
AND OPTIC NERVE (× 4).

anteriorly, and forms a triangular mass of tissue which constitutes the check ligament for that muscle; it is attached to a tubercle on the orbital surface of the zygomatic bone, and to the lateral palpebral ligament. The check ligament of the medial rectus also is triangular; it is fixed to the lacrimal bone, behind its crest, and to the lacrimal caruncle. The sheath of the superior rectus blends with that of the levator palpebræ superioris, and the sheet so formed is attached to the superior conjunctival fornix. The sheath of the inferior rectus is joined to those of the medial and lateral recti, and, as these are fixed to the medial and lateral walls of the orbit by the check ligaments, a continuous band, named the **suspensory ligament**, is slung from side to side like a hammock beneath the eyeball. The ends of the suspensory ligament blend not only with the check ligaments but also with the medial and lateral horns of the aponeurosis of the levator palpebræ superioris. The sheath of the superior oblique extends as far as the pulley through which the tendon passes and is attached to it. The sheath of the inferior oblique blends with that of the inferior rectus, and the united sheaths send forward one thin lamella into the lower eyelid, and another to unite with the fascial sheath of the eyeball.

The wall of the eyeball (Fig. 916) consists of three concentric coats; enclosed within it there are three transparent refracting media. The three coats are : (1) an outer, fibrous coat; (2) a middle, vascular, pigmented, and partly muscular coat; (3) an inner, nervous coat. The three refracting media are named, from behind forwards, the **vitreous body**, the **lens**, and the **aqueous humour**.

FIBROUS COAT OF THE EYEBALL

The fibrous coat of the eyeball is divided into an opaque, posterior part called the **sclera**, and a transparent, anterior part called the **cornea**.

Sclera.—The sclera is the firm, opaque, white coat of the eye. It has a blue tinge in childhood, since it is then thinner than in the adult and allows the pigment of the choroid to show through it; in old age it has a yellow hue. It is thickest anteriorly (0·6 mm.) and posteriorly (1 mm.), and is thinnest at the equator (0·5 mm.). At the back, 3 mm. to the nasal side of the posterior pole, the sclera is pierced by the optic nerve. The part of the sclera through which the nerve bundles pass is called the *lamina cribrosa scleræ*; the fibrous sheath of the nerve blends with the outer part of the sclera. Around the entrance of the optic nerve there are fifteen or twenty small apertures for the passage of the ciliary nerves and the short posterior ciliary arteries. On each side of the nerve, at a little distance from its entrance, the two long posterior ciliary arteries pierce the sclera. Near the equator there are four openings—two above and two below—for the exit of the venæ vorticosæ; and near the sulcus scleræ there are the openings for the anterior ciliary arteries. The deep surface of the sclera is of a brownish colour, and is lined with flattened endo-thelial cells. It is separ-ated from the proper tissue of the choroid by the **perichoroidal space**, which is traversed by the ciliary nerves and arteries just mentioned, and by a delicate meshwork of fine, pigmented areolar tissue, called the **suprachoroid lamina**, which loosely attaches the sclera to the choroid. At the sclero-corneal junction the fibrous tissue of the sclera passes continuously into that of the cornea, and in the deeper part of the junc-tion there is a circular canal called the **sinus venosus scleræ** (Fig. 917).

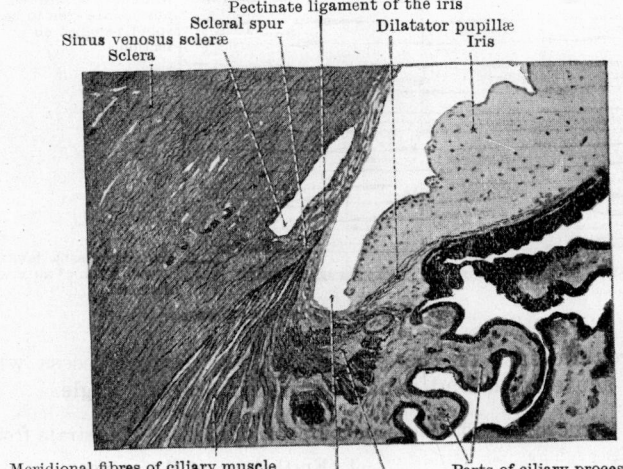

Fig. 917.—Section of Irido-corneal Angle. (A. Thomson.)

When seen in a meridional section, the sinus venosus scleræ appears as a narrow cleft; its outer wall is the compact tissue of the sclera and its inner wall is a projecting rim of sclera which appears triangular in section, and is directed forwards and is continuous with the posterior elastic lamina of the cornea. The sinus is lined with endothelium, and occasionally contains a few red blood-corpuscles. It communicates with the anterior ciliary veins, and, through the spaces of the irido-corneal angle, with the anterior chamber of the eye.

Structure.—The sclera consists of bundles of white fibrous tissue and some fine elastic fibres; the bundles form equatorial and meridional layers, which interlace with each other. Numerous spaces containing connective tissue cells exist between the fibres. Pigmented cells are plentiful in its innermost layer.

Vessels and Nerves.—The arteries of the sclera are branches of the anterior and short posterior *ciliary arteries*; its **veins** open into the *venae vorticosae* and anterior *ciliary veins*. The **nerves** of the sclera are derived from the ciliary nerves, which, after losing their medullary sheaths, pass between the fibrous bundles.

Cornea.—The **cornea** is transparent and forms the anterior part of the outer coat. It is slightly thicker than the sclera—being about 0·95 mm. at its centre, and 1·19 mm. at the periphery. Its anterior surface is covered with a stratified epithelium continuous with that of the conjunctiva; its posterior surface forms the anterior wall of the anterior chamber of the eye. The degree of curvature of the cornea varies in different persons, and is greater in youth than in old age; it is, as a rule, slightly greater in the vertical than in the horizontal plane, and diminishes from the centre to the circumference of the cornea. The arc of the cornea is equal to about one-sixth of the total circumference of the eyeball.

The cornea is continuous with the sclera, at the **sclero-corneal junction.** The sclero-corneal junction is not a perpendicular line of union; the sclera is bevelled on its posterior surface and the cornea on its anterior; the bevelling is most marked at the upper and lower parts of the junction, and thus the cornea, when seen from in front, is not quite circular in outline but slightly elliptical, the longer diameter being horizontal. Directly in front of the junction, the inner surface of the cornea projects in the form of a rounded rim, with the result that a circular groove or sulcus is seen behind the rim. Between the sclero-corneal junction and the front of the circumference of the iris there is a narrow recess which on section appears as an acute angle and is named the **irido-corneal angle.**

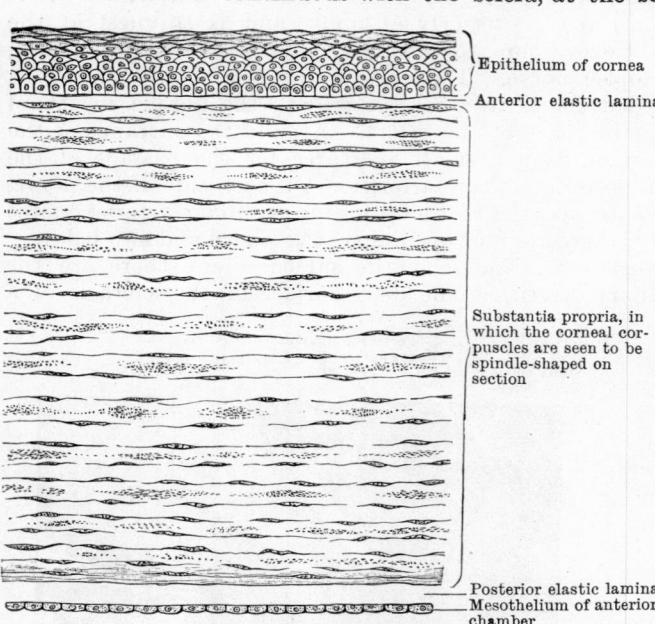

Epithelium of cornea

Anterior elastic lamina

Substantia propria, in which the corneal corpuscles are seen to be spindle-shaped on section

Posterior elastic lamina
Mesothelium of anterior chamber

FIG. 918.—SECTION OF CORNEA.

Structure.—The cornea is composed of the following strata from before backwards (Fig. 918):—

1. Epithelium of the cornea.
2. Anterior elastic lamina.
3. Substantia propria.
4. Posterior elastic lamina.
5. Mesothelium of anterior chamber.

1. The **epithelium of the cornea** is continuous with the epithelium on the free surface of the conjunctiva, and consists of six or eight strata of nucleated cells. Deepest of all is a single layer of columnar cells, the flattened bases of which rest on the anterior elastic lamina, while their opposite ends are round and contain the nuclei. Superficial to that layer there are three or four strata of polygonal cells, most of which exhibit finger-like processes which join with the corresponding processes of neighbouring cells; the more superficial layers consist of squamous cells.

2. The **anterior elastic lamina** is merely a differentiation of the anterior part of the substantia propria, from which it is separated only with difficulty; it differs from true elastic tissue in not being stained yellow by picrocarmine.

3. The **substantia propria** presents, in a fresh condition, a homogeneous appearance; but, with the assistance of reagents, it is seen to consist of modified fibrous tissue, with a few elastic fibres. An amorphous interstitial substance binds the fibres into bundles, and cements the bundles into lamellæ which are flattened from before backwards. The fibres of any one lamella cross those of adjacent lamellæ almost at right angles.

The cells of the cornea are very irregularly stellate bodies, and are situated between the lamellæ. In fixed preparations they appear to lie in spaces which they do not completely fill, and it has been suggested that the rest of the space is occupied by lymph, that the various spaces or lacunæ communicate with each other by means of fine canaliculi, and that a path is thus established for the circulation of nutritive fluids to the cornea. The matter is not definitely settled, but it seems probable that the cells do in reality completely fill the spaces, and that the canaliculi are artificial clefts between the bundles and lamellæ and may be due to increased intra-ocular tension during life or to the action of reagents in the preparation of microscopic specimens.

After middle age a greyish opaque ring, 1·5 to 2 mm. in breadth, is frequently seen near the periphery of the cornea ; it is termed the **arcus senilis**, and results from a deposit of fat granules in the lamellæ and in the corneal cells.

4. The **posterior elastic lamina** is a clear homogeneous membrane that covers the posterior surface of the substantia propria, to which it is less firmly attached than is the anterior elastic lamina. In the living eye it has the appearance of an olive-yellow, shining surface covered with small hexagonal dots ; in old age the hexagonal patterning becomes less distinct and regular and round dark patches appear in places. At the sclero-corneal junction the posterior elastic lamina splits into bundles of fine fibres which interlace and are continued towards the circumference of the iris as the **pectinate ligament of the iris**. The spaces between the interlacing fibres are termed the **spaces of the irido-corneal angle**, and are lined with mesothelium prolonged from that of the anterior chamber of the eye. They communicate internally with the irido-corneal angle and externally with the sinus venosus scleræ, and constitute important channels through which fluid may filter from the anterior chamber into the sinus and thence into the anterior ciliary veins. When the pectinate ligament is followed backwards most of its fibres are seen to be attached to the anterior surface of an inwardly directed rim of scleral tissue, but a few are carried past the edge of the rim, round the irido-corneal angle, and into the iris, where they are directly continuous with the fibres of the dilatator pupillæ muscle (Arthur Thomson).

5. The **mesothelium of the anterior chamber** consists of a single layer of polygonal cells ; it is continued as a lining to the spaces of the irido-corneal angle and is reflected on to the anterior surface of the iris.

Vessels and Nerves of the Cornea.—In the fœtus the cornea is traversed, almost as far as its centre, by capillaries ; but in the adult it is devoid of blood-vessels, except at its margin. The capillaries of the conjunctiva and sclera pass into this marginal area where they end in loops. The rest of the cornea is nourished by the lymph which percolates through the intercellular substance.

The **nerves** of the cornea are derived from the *ciliary nerves*. Around its periphery they form an annular plexus from which nerve-fibres pass into the cornea ; they then lose their medullary sheaths and ramify in the substantia propria, forming the fundamental or *stroma plexus*. Fibres extend from this plexus through the anterior elastic lamina and form a *sub-epithelial plexus* from which fine filaments ramify between the epithelial cells as far as the superficial layers.

VASCULAR COAT OF THE EYEBALL

The vascular and pigmented coat of the eyeball comprises, from behind forwards, the choroid, the ciliary body, and the iris (Fig. 916).

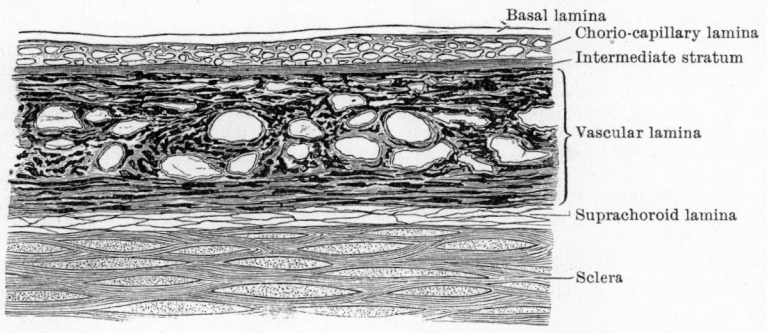

Basal lamina
Chorio-capillary lamina
Intermediate stratum

Vascular lamina

Suprachoroid lamina

Sclera

FIG. 919.—TRANSVERSE SECTION OF CHOROID AND INNER PART OF SCLERA.

Choroid.—The choroid is a dark brown membrane which intervenes between the sclera and the retina. It is loosely attached to the sclera by a layer of fine areolar tissue named the suprachoroid lamina, except at the point of entrance of the optic nerve and where the blood vessels pierce the sclera ; here the connexion is much closer. It extends as far forwards as the anterior limit of the nervous layer of the retina, and here it is succeeded by the ciliary body, which connects it with the circumference of the iris.

Structure.—The choroid is composed, from without inwards, of three layers, (a) the suprachoroid lamina; (b) the proper tissue of the choroid; and (c) the basal lamina (Fig. 919).

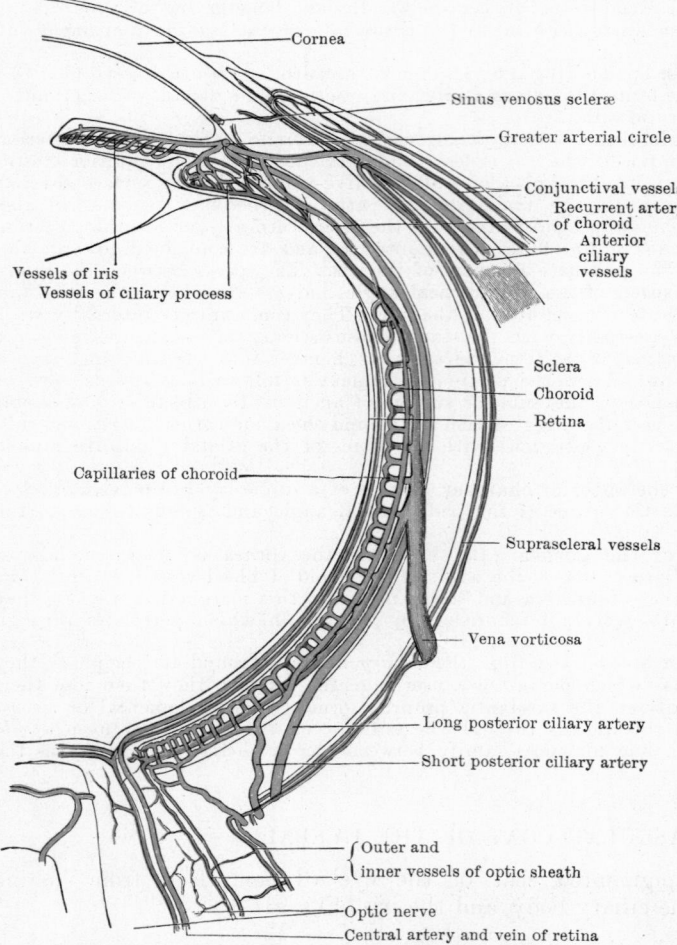

FIG. 920.—DIAGRAM OF THE CIRCULATION IN THE EYE. (Leber.)

The **suprachoroid lamina** is the tissue which occupies the perichoroidal space between the sclera and the proper tissue of the choroid; it consists of a series of fine non-vascular lamellæ, each containing a delicate network of elastic fibres, amongst which are stellate pigmented cells and some large phagocytic cells.

The **proper tissue of the choroid** consists of an outer layer containing larger blood vessels, and an inner which is composed of a close network of capillaries in a fine fibro-elastic intercellular substance. The outer layer is called the **vascular lamina**, and the inner the **chorio-capillary lamina**.

The **basal lamina** is the basement membrane of the choroid and separates it from the outer, pigmented layer of the retina; it appears as a thin glassy membrane in whose outer part very fine elastic fibres can be recognised.

Vessels of the Choroid.—The **arteries** of the choroid are derived from the *short posterior ciliary vessels*, which pierce the sclera around the entrance of the optic nerve, and form a wide-meshed plexus in the vascular lamina. The **veins** are superficial to the arteries and converge to form whorls which open into the venæ vorticosæ.

Tapetum.—In many animals, especially the ruminants and carnivores, there is seen on the postero-lateral part of the choroid a brilliant iridescence to which the name **tapetum** is applied. Absent in man, it may be due, as in the horse, to a thin fibrous layer between the two laminæ of the proper tissue of the choroid (tapetum fibrosum), or, as in the seal, to the presence of five or six layers of flattened iridescent cells (tapetum cellulosum) that lie immediately outside the chorio-capillary lamina.

Ciliary Body.—The ciliary body connects the choroid with the circumference of the iris (Fig. 916), and comprises three zones—(a) the ciliary ring, (b) the ciliary processes, and (c) the ciliary muscle.

The **ciliary ring** is a zone, about 4 mm. wide, immediately adjoining the choroid and extending from the level of the ora serrata of the retina to the posterior end of the ciliary processes; it is faintly marked on its inner surface by a series of radial ridges.

The **ciliary processes** are a series of about seventy prominent radial ridges arranged in a circle behind the periphery of the iris, against which they stand out sharply by their paler colour. They have an average measurement of about

2 mm. in length, and are much wrinkled; when traced backwards they merge into the ciliary ring, and when traced forwards to the periphery of the iris, they bulge inwards, overlapping its deep surface, and give attachment to some of the fibres of the suspensory ligament of the lens.

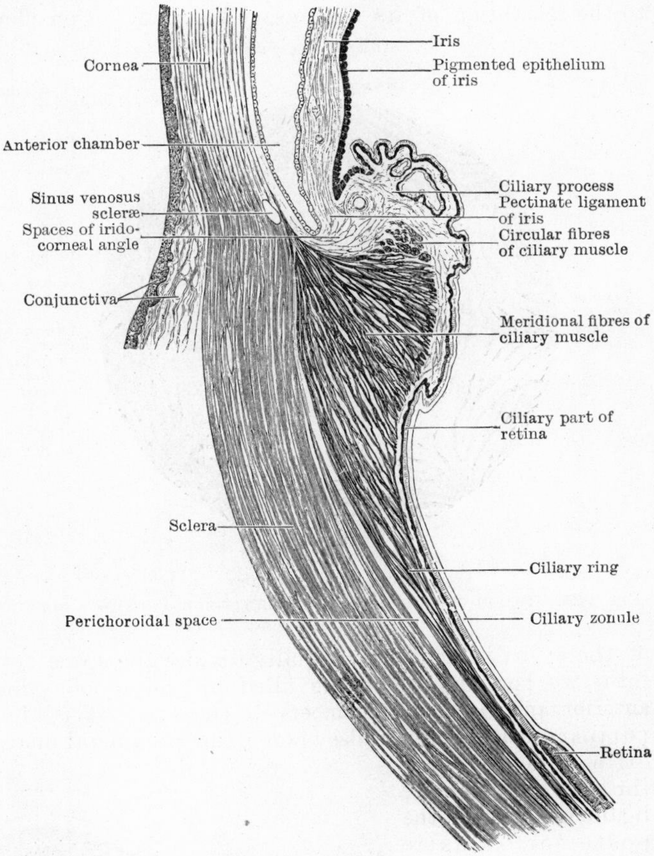

Structure.— The ciliary ring and processes are essentially similar in structure to the choroid, except that the chorio-capillary lamina is not present. Their inner surfaces are covered with two layers of epithelium, representing the original two layers of the embryonic optic cup, of which the outer is deeply pigmented. When the pigment is bleached away it is possible to recognise that the epithelium is invaginated into the substance of the processes so as to form tubular glands from which the aqueous humour may in part be derived. These two layers are continuous with the retina and are known as the **ciliary part of the retina.**

The **ciliary muscle** appears, in meridional sections, as a triangular mass of muscle tissue placed between the sclera laterally and the ciliary ring and processes medially.

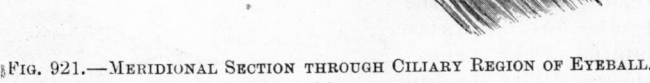

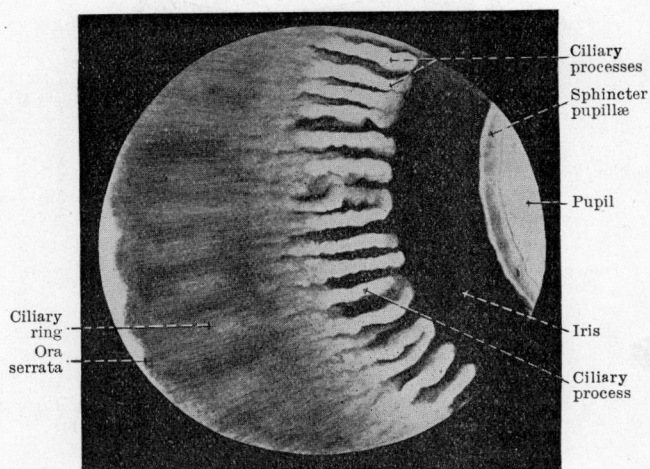

FIG. 921.—MERIDIONAL SECTION THROUGH CILIARY REGION OF EYEBALL.

The muscle is composed of meridional and circular fibres; the meridional fibres are attached anteriorly to the inwardly projecting rim of sclera which has been referred to (p. 1086) as giving attachment to most of the fibres of the pectinate ligament of the iris; from this point the fibres radiate backwards, to be attached to the ciliary processes and ciliary ring; the circular fibres form a small zone of muscular tissue to the medial side of the meridional fibres and behind the irido-corneal angle. The ciliary muscle, as a whole,

FIG. 922.—THE ANTERIOR PART OF THE EYEBALL SEEN FROM WITHIN. (C. M. W.)

lies in the plane of the suprachoroid lamina ; when it contracts it draws forward the ciliary ring and the ciliary processes and the lens becomes more convex, owing to the relaxation of its suspensory ligament.   Considerable individual differences

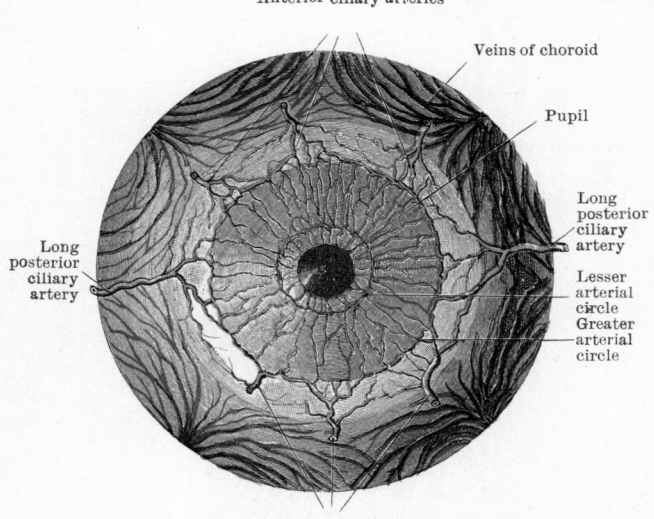

FIG. 923.—BLOOD-VESSELS OF IRIS AND ANTERIOR PART OF CHOROID VIEWED FROM THE FRONT (Arnold).

exist as to the degree of development of the two portions of the ciliary muscle ; the meridional fibres are always more numerous than the circular fibres, which are absent or rudimentary in myopic eyes, but are well developed, as a rule, in hypermetropic eyes.

Iris.—The iris is a contractile diaphragm situated in front of the lens, and it presents, a little to the nasal side of its centre, an almost circular aperture — the **pupil**—which, during life, is continually varying in size in order to regulate the amount of light admitted into the interior

of the eyeball.   The iris partially divides the space between the cornea and lens into two portions which are filled by the aqueous humour, and are named the **anterior and posterior chambers** of the eye.   It is thinner at its peripheral and pupillary margins than elsewhere ; the peripheral margin is continuous with the

ciliary body, and, through the pectinate ligament, with the posterior elastic lamina of the cornea ; the pupillary margin rests on the front of the capsule of the lens.

The colour of the eye depends on the arrangement of the pigment in the iris ; in the blue eye the pigment is limited to the posterior surface of the iris, but in the brown or black eye it is also scattered throughout its stroma ; in the albino the pigment is absent.

The pupil is covered, during the greater part of intra-uterine life, by the **pupillary membrane.**   This is a thin,

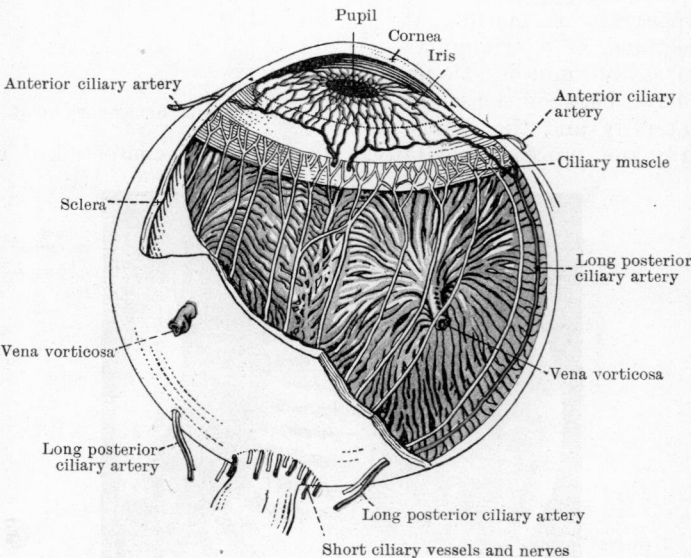

FIG. 924.—DISSECTION OF THE EYEBALL SHOWING THE VASCULAR COAT AND THE ARRANGEMENT OF THE CILIARY NERVES AND VESSELS.

highly vascular membrane of which the vessels are derived primarily from the hyaloid artery and later from the long posterior ciliary arteries.   The membrane is situated on the superficial surface of the iris and its vessels form a series of arcades converging towards the centre of the pupil.   At about the seventh month of intra-uterine life, atrophy begins in the central vessels and proceeds towards the circumference, more and more peripheral vessels becoming involved until the lesser arterial circle is reached ; here the process of atrophy ceases, and this circle comes therefore to be the most central part of the vascular arcades of the iris. At birth, atrophy of the membrane is usually complete, though fragments of it may remain into adult life.

Structure.—The main mass of the iris is known as the *stroma* and is composed of delicate white and elastic fibres, mingled with pigmented cells, blood-vessels, nerves, and non-striped muscular fibres.

The anterior surface of the stroma is covered with a layer of mesothelium continuous with that on the posterior surface of the cornea. The posterior surface of the iris is covered with a double layer of epithelium continuous with that on the inner surface of the ciliary ring and processes ; like that layer, it is derived from the two layers of the embryonic optic cup, and thus it is in reality a part of the retina ; the outer layer of epithelium is pigmented ; and the non-striped muscle fibres of the iris are developed from the inner layer. The involuntary muscles of the iris are the sphincter and the dilator of the pupil ; the sphincter muscle is arranged in a circular manner round the pupil and by its contraction it reduces the size of that aperture ; the dilator consists of fibres which radiate from the pupil to the periphery of the iris.

Vessels and Nerves.—The **arteries** of the iris come from the *long posterior ciliary* and the *anterior ciliary* branches of the ophthalmic artery. There are two long posterior ciliary arteries, a medial and a lateral ; they pierce the sclera by the sides of the optic nerve and run forwards between the sclera and the choroid as far as the periphery of the iris, where they are joined by the anterior ciliary arteries, which are usually arranged as two or three superior and two or three inferior branches ; by the union of all these vessels a vascular circle is formed round the margin of the iris and is known as the *greater arterial circle* of the iris. From this circle branches pass forwards towards the pupil, round which a second circle is formed, called the *lesser arterial circle* of the iris. The **veins** of the iris proceed towards its periphery, and communicate with the veins of the ciliary processes and with the sinus venosus scleræ. The convergence of the blood-vessels towards the pupil gives a striated appearance to the anterior surface of the iris.

The **nerves** of the choroid and iris (Fig. 924) are derived from the long and short *ciliary* nerves. The former, two or three in number, are branches of the naso-ciliary nerve ; the latter, from eight to fourteen in number, are derived from the ciliary ganglion. Piercing the sclera around the entrance of the optic nerve, the ciliary nerves traverse the perichoroidal lymph-space, where they form a plexus, rich in nerve-cells, from which filaments are supplied to the blood-vessels of the choroid. In front of the ciliary muscle a second plexus, also rich in nerve-cells, is formed ; it supplies the ciliary muscle and sends filaments into the iris, as far as its pupillary margin, for the supply of its muscular fibres and blood-vessels. The sphincter of the pupil and the ciliary muscle are supplied by the oculo-motor nerve, the dilator of the pupil by the sympathetic.

RETINA

The **retina**, or nervous coat of the eyeball, is a soft, delicate membrane in which the fibres of the optic nerve are spread out. It is composed of two layers— an outer, pigmented layer, attached to the choroid ; and an inner nervous layer, which is the retina proper, and is in contact with the vitreous body. Expanding from the entrance of the optic nerve, the retina appears to end at the posterior edge of the ciliary body in a wavy border, called the **ora serrata** of the retina. But it is, in reality, only the nervous elements of the retina which come to an end at this line ; the pigmented layer and a layer of columnar epithelium are prolonged over the posterior surface of the ciliary body and iris (Fig. 921). The portion of the retina behind the ora serrata is termed the **optic part of the retina**, and its thickness gradually diminishes from 0·4 mm. near the entrance of the optic nerve, to 0·1 mm. at the ora serrata. It presents, near the posterior pole of the eye, a small, oval yellowish spot, called the **macula lutea**, of which the central part is depressed and named the **fovea centralis**. About 3 mm. to the nasal side and slightly below the level of the posterior pole there is a whitish disc which corresponds with the point of entrance of the optic nerve, and has a diameter of about 1·5 mm. ; this is known as the *optic disc*, and its circumference is slightly raised to surround a central depression. The optic disc consists merely of nerve-fibres ; it is insensitive to light, and is named the " blind spot." At the optic disc and at the ora serrata the retina is much more firmly adherent to the choroid than elsewhere.

The nervous layer of the retina is transparent during life, but becomes opaque and of a greyish colour soon after death. If an animal is kept in the dark before the removal of its eyeball, the retina presents a purple tinge owing to the presence of a colouring matter, named **rhodopsin** or **visual purple**, which is rapidly bleached on exposure to sunlight. The visual purple is absent from the macula lutea, and over a narrow zone, 3-4 mm. in width, near the ora serrata.

Structure of the Retina (Figs. 925, 926, 927).—The nervous elements of the retina are supported by non-nervous or **sustentacular fibres**, and are arranged in the following seven layers from within outwards, *i.e.* from the vitreous body to the choroid :—

1. Layer of nerve-fibres.
2. Ganglionic or nerve-cell layer.
3. Inner plexiform layer.
4. Inner nuclear layer.
5. Outer plexiform layer.
6. Outer nuclear layer.
7. Layer of rods and cones.

An internal limiting membrane separates the nerve-fibre layer from the vitreous body, and an external limiting membrane separates the layer of rods and cones from the outer nuclear layer; next to the layer of rods and cones is the single non-nervous and pigmented layer.

1. **Layer of Nerve-fibres.**—Most of these fibres are centripetal and are the axons of cells in the ganglionic layer; they reach the brain by means of the optic nerve, of which they constitute the greater part. A few are centrifugal and are the axons of cells situated in the brain; they reach the retina by means of the optic nerve and they ultimately ramify in the inner plexiform layer.

2. **Ganglionic or Nerve-cell Layer.**—The cells of the ganglionic layer vary in size; they are oval or piriform in shape, and form a single layer, except at the macula lutea, where several strata are present. The axons of these nerve cells pass into the nerve-fibre layer; the dendrites form arborisations in the inner plexiform layer with the axons of cells in the inner nuclear layer.

3. **Inner Plexiform Layer.**—This is constituted chiefly by the interlacement of the dendrites of the cells of the ganglionic layer with the axons of those of the inner nuclear layer.

4. **Inner Nuclear Layer.**—This consists of numerous cells which may be divided into (*a*) bipolar cells, (*b*) horizontal cells, and (*c*) amacrine cells;

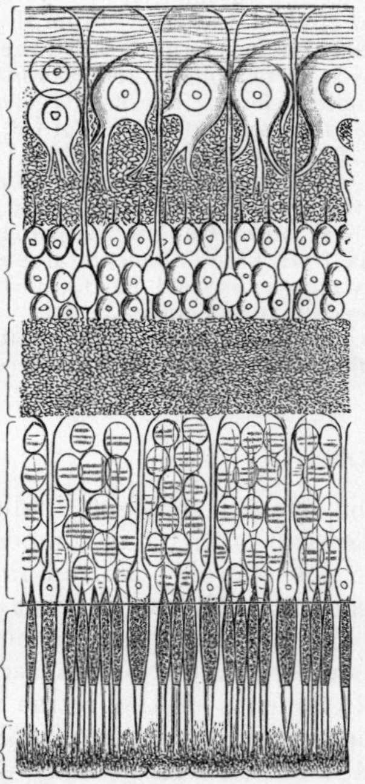

FIG. 925.—DIAGRAMMATIC SECTION OF THE HUMAN RETINA (modified from Schultze).

the nuclei of the sustentacular fibres also are present in this layer.

(*a*) The **bipolar cells** are by far the most numerous; they are fusiform in shape and are divided into rod bipolars and cone bipolars. The axons of each type arborise in the inner plexiform layer with the dendrites of the ganglion cells; the dendrites of the rod bipolars arborise round the ends of the rod fibres, and those of the cone bipolars round the ends of the cone fibres.

(*b*) The **horizontal cells** serve to connect various rod fibres or cone fibres to each other. There are small and large horizontal cells: the small cells are flattened and star-like and lie on the borderline between the outer plexiform and the inner nuclear layers; they send a tuft of dendrites outwards, towards the bases of the cone fibres; their axons are directed horizontally for a variable distance, and end round the bases of other cone fibres. The large cells are irregular in shape and are placed to the inner side of the small cells; their processes make connexion between various rod fibres. A third variety of horizontal cell sends short processes into the outer plexiform layer and a long process into the inner plexiform layer, where it arborises round the end of a centrifugal fibre.

(c) The **amacrine cells** are so called on account of the absence of an axon. They are situated in the innermost part of the inner nuclear layer; their processes ramify in the

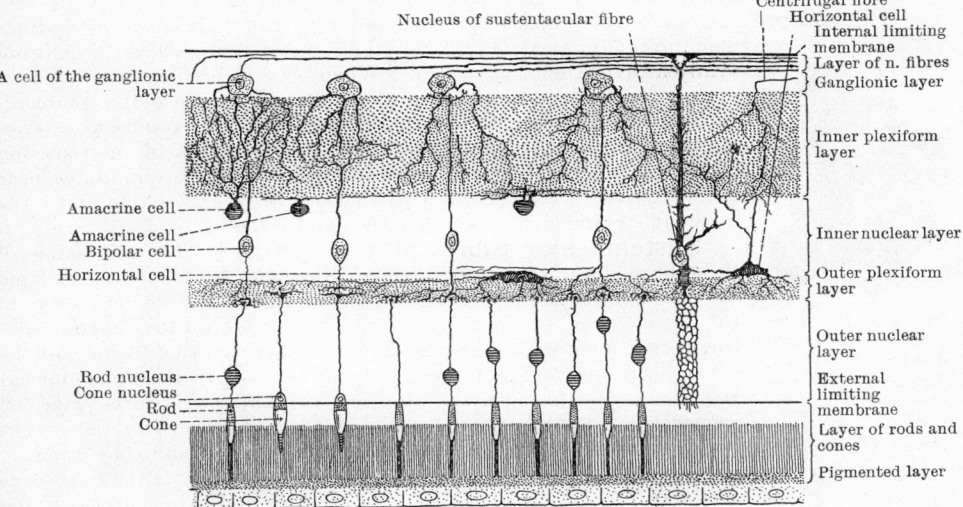

FIG. 926.—A PLAN OF THE RETINAL NEURONS. (After Cajal.)

inner plexiform layer, it may be in one stratum (stratified cells) or in several strata (diffuse cells).

5. Outer Plexiform Layer.
—This is constituted by the interlacement of the dendrites of the bipolar and horizontal cells, just described, with the spherules of the rod fibres and the ramifications of the foot-plates of the cone fibres.

6. Outer Nuclear Layer.
—This is chiefly made up of the nuclei of the rod and cone fibres; the nuclei of the rod fibres lie at different levels in the layer, but those of the cone fibres are all situated close against the external limiting membrane of the retina. The rod nuclei send a process into the outer plexiform layer where it ends in a small rounded knob, or spherule, in association with the dendrites of rod bipolar or horizontal cells; the cone nuclei send out processes which are similarly arranged but end in an expanded foot-plate instead of in a spherule. From their opposite ends the rod nuclei send inwards processes which pass through the external limiting membrane into the outer ends of the rods, whereas the cone nuclei, since they are placed close alongside the external limiting membrane, become directly continuous through the membrane with the outer ends of the cones.

7. Layer of Rods and Cones.
—The essential visual cells are the **rod cells** and the **cone cells**. Each rod cell and cone cell is composed of an inner part called the rod or the cone, and an outer part called the rod or cone fibre, of which an account has been given already. The layer under discussion contains the outer element of the rod and cone cells. At the fovea centralis, cones alone are present, and in this situation are more slender and elongated than elsewhere; as one passes forwards over the retina from the macula the rods appear and gradually outnumber the cones; near the ora serrata cones are again the more numerous; over the retina as a whole the rods are nearly twenty times as many as the cones. The rods are slender, cylindrical, and of almost uniform diameter throughout their length; the cones are spindle-shaped and taper to a fine point at the outer end. Each rod and cone has an outer and an inner segment; the outer segment of a rod is slightly more slender than the inner and it contains the rhodopsin; the outer segment of a cone is far smaller

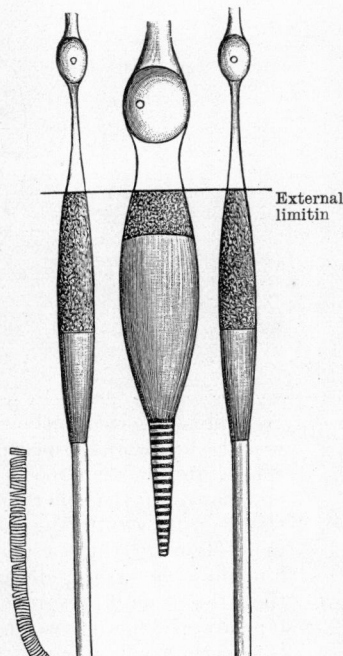

FIG. 927.

A, A cone and two rods from the human retina (modified from Max Schultze); B, Outer part of rod separated into discs.

than the inner and it rapidly tapers to a fine point. The inner segments of both rods and cones have an affinity for staining reagents, and each shows a homogeneous basal portion and a longitudinally striated outer part.

8. **Pigmented Layer.**—This consists of a single stratum of cells which, on surface view, are hexagonal (Fig. 928), their outer flattened surfaces being firmly attached to the choroid. When seen in profile the outer part of each cell contains a large oval nucleus and is devoid of pigment, while the inner portion is filled with pigment and extends as a series of thread-like processes amongst the outer segments of the rods and cones. When the eye is in the dark the pigment accumulates near the outer part of the cell, but when the eye is exposed to light the pigment streams in between the rods and cones.

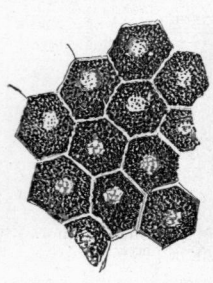

FIG. 928.—PIGMENTED LAYER OF HUMAN RETINA (viewed from the surface).

Sustentacular Fibres of the Retina.—The cell bodies of these fibres lie in the inner nuclear layer, and the fibres extend from the cell body inwards and outwards through the whole thickness of the retina from the internal to the external limiting membrane ; these two membranes are, in fact, formed by the fusion of the expanded inner and outer ends of the fibres. In the inner nuclear and inner plexiform layers the inwardly directed fibres give off numerous side branches, and in the outer nuclear layer the outwardly directed fibres form a delicate network which lodges the rod and cone nuclei.

Structure of the Macula Lutea and Fovea Centralis.—At the fovea centralis there are no rods ; the cones are closely packed, and are narrower and

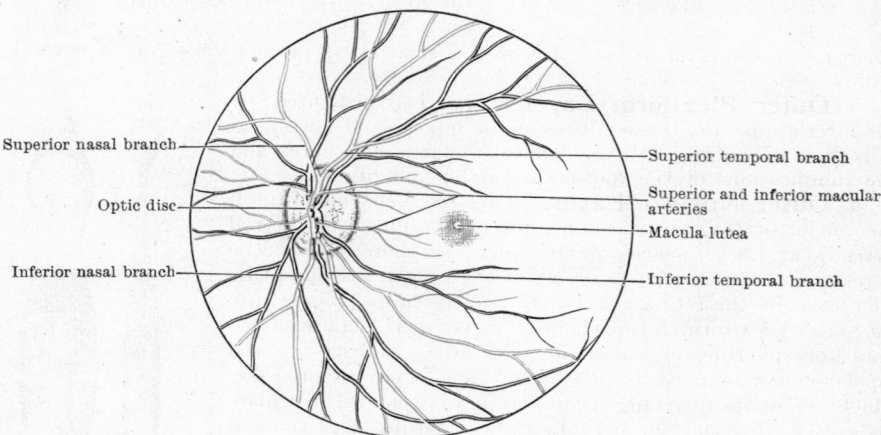

Superior nasal branch

Optic disc

Inferior nasal branch

Superior temporal branch

Superior and inferior macular arteries

Macula lutea

Inferior temporal branch

FIG. 929.—BLOOD-VESSELS OF THE RETINA.

are more elongated in their outer segments than they are elsewhere in the retina. Since the macula lutea, and especially the fovea centralis, are the regions of distinct vision, the cones are here almost bare, being covered only by the cone nuclei and fibres, and the light has therefore to pass through only a comparatively thin layer of retinal tissue on its way to the receptor cells. At the periphery of the macula there is a great increase in the thickness of the ganglionic layer and in that of the inner nuclear layer, but these layers rapidly come to an end as the fovea is approached. It thus happens that the cone fibres must pass obliquely from the fovea centralis to reach the cone bipolars which are nearer the periphery of the macula, and the cone nuclei and fibres thus form an obliquely directed stratum covering the cones in the region of the fovea.

At the ora serrata the nervous layers of the retina come to an end—first the rods and cones, then the other nervous layers. In front of the ora serrata the retina is prolonged over the back of the ciliary processes and iris, but is represented only by the pigmented layer and by a layer of columnar epithelium.

Vessels of the Retina (Fig. 929).—The retina is supplied by the **arteria retinæ centralis,** a branch of the ophthalmic artery ; it pierces the sheath of the optic nerve obliquely from below, and then appears at the centre of the optic disc. It then divides into an upper and a lower branch, each of which divides into a nasal branch and a temporal branch ; the resulting four branches are named the superior and inferior temporal arteries and the superior and inferior nasal arteries. The temporal arteries pass laterally above and below the macula lutea, to which they give small branches; these do not, however, extend as far as the fovea centralis, which is devoid of blood-vessels. The macula receives also two small arteries (superior and inferior macular) directly from the stem of the arteria centralis. The larger vessels run in the layer of nerve-fibres; they do not anastomose with each other except through the capillary plexuses, which extend as far as the inner nuclear layer. The **veins** follow the course of the arteries; they have no muscular coats, but consist merely of a layer of endothelial cells outside which there is a perivascular lymph-sheath surrounded by delicate retiform tissue.

REFRACTING MEDIA

Vitreous Body.—This is a transparent, jelly-like substance permeated by a meshwork of very fine fibrils. It fills the space between the lens and the retina and is hollowed out anteriorly for the reception of the lens. It is especially adherent in the region of the ora serrata, and here its fibrils show a condensation and are reinforced by the accession of radial fibres from the ciliary region; these fibres pass towards the margin of the lens. This thickened, flat ring is named the **ciliary zonule**, and in the region of the ciliary processes it is radially folded and thus shows a series of alternating ridges and grooves; into the grooves the ciliary processes are received, and the intimacy of their connexion may be recognised by the fact that when the ciliary processes are removed some of their pigment remains adherent to the zonule. On the other hand, the ridges of the zonule are not adherent to the depressions between the ciliary processes, but are separated from them by a series of lymph

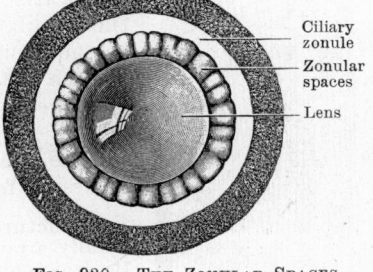

FIG. 930.—THE ZONULAR SPACES DISTENDED; VIEWED FROM THE FRONT.

spaces which may be regarded as diverticula of the posterior chamber, with which they communicate. As the fibres of the zonule approach the lens some pass in front of its margin and others behind it; those which pass in front of the lens form what is known as the *suspensory ligament* of the lens; those which pass behind the lens form a lining for the depression on the front of the vitreous into which the lens is received and which is called the *hyaloid fossa*. Round the margin of the lens, and between the two layers into which the ciliary zonule splits, there is a series of sacculated lymph spaces named the *zonular spaces*. The suspensory ligament covers the anterior surface of the lens and exerts a pressure upon it; when the ciliary muscle contracts it draws forward the ciliary processes, to which the fibres of the zonule are attached, and thus relaxes the suspensory ligament and thereby allows the anterior surface of the lens to become more convex; this is probably the sequence of events in the process of accommodation of the eye. A further condensation of the fibrils of the vitreous body marks out an irregular channel which extends from the optic disc to the middle of the posterior surface of the lens, and is named the *hyaloid canal*; this passage was traversed in the embryo by the hyaloid artery, the remains of which

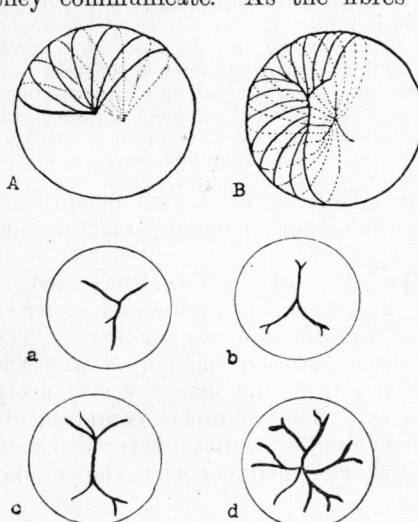

FIG. 931.—DIAGRAM SHOWING THE FORMATION OF THE RADII OF THE LENS. (Ida C. Mann.)

A, The simplest arrangement of lens fibres all of the same length and all extending from pole to pole, with resulting absence of radii. B, The manner in which lens radii develop when all the fibres are not of the same length and do not reach from pole to pole. a, b, c, d, Varieties of radii. (By permission of the Cambridge University Press.)

can be recognised in the living eye as a small corkscrew-like structure depending from the back of the lens. The hyaloid canal is not horizontal; after the fourth year it sags down in a curve and may be brought into view by sudden upward and downward movements of the eye (Mann).

The vitreous body has sometimes been described as being enclosed in a *hyaloid membrane*; if such a membrane exists, it is nothing more than a condensation of the fibrils in the anterior part of the vitreous and there is no definite structural formation separating the remainder of the vitreous from the retina.

Lens.—The lens lies in front of the vitreous body and behind the iris. It is a biconvex, transparent body (Fig. 916), enclosed in a thin, transparent, homogeneous *capsule*. The central points of its anterior and posterior surfaces are termed the **anterior** and **posterior poles**, and a line joining the poles is known as the **axis**; the peripheral circumference is named the **equator**. The axial measurement of the lens is 4 mm., and the transverse diameter from 9 to 10 mm. The anterior surface is in contact with the pupillary margin of the iris; the central part of that surface corresponds with the pupil; the peripheral part is separated from the iris by the aqueous humour of the posterior chamber. The posterior surface of the lens is more convex than the anterior, and occupies the hyaloid fossa of the vitreous body. The curvatures of the surfaces of the lens, especially that of the anterior surface, are constantly varying, during life, for the purpose of focussing near or distant objects on the retina.

Structure.—The lens is composed of a series of more or less concentrically arranged fibres enclosed within a thin capsule. The interior of the lens is of a firmer consistence than the outer part, and is named the *nucleus*. On the front of the lens, inside the capsule, is the *epithelium of the lens*, composed of cubical cells with nuclei at their inner ends. These cells retain their cubical form only on the front of the lens; at the equator they become more elongated and instead of covering the back of the lens they gradually approach its centre, and the cell bodies, becoming more and more attenuated, form the *lens fibres*. Since none of the fibres are long enough to reach from pole to pole, those which start, for example, at the anterior pole, meet adjacent fibres at some distance from the posterior pole, and *vice versa*; the lines along which the fibres meet can be seen on the front and back of the lens and are named the *radii of the lens*; in the fœtus there are three of these radii on the front and on the back of the lens, but they increase in number as age advances.

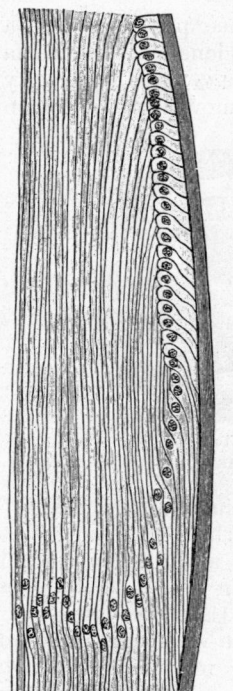

FIG. 932.

SECTION THROUGH THE EQUATOR OF THE LENS.

Showing the gradual transition of the epithelium into lens fibres. (After Babuchin.)

In the fœtus the lens is soft, of a pinkish colour, and nearly spherical; in old age it becomes flattened, and assumes a yellowish tint.

Chambers of the Eye (Fig. 916).—The front part of the eyeball is divided by the iris into *anterior* and *posterior chambers*, both of which contain *aqueous humour*. The anterior chamber is the space between the cornea and the iris, and the posterior chamber separates the iris from the lens, its suspensory ligament, and the front of the ciliary processes. The chambers communicate with each other through the pupil; the anterior chamber communicates also with the spaces of the irido-corneal angle, and the posterior chamber with the zonular spaces.

The aqueous humour has a refractive index of about 1·336, and consists of about 98 per cent. of water, with 1·4 per cent. of sodium chloride, and traces of albumin.

EYEBROWS AND EYELIDS

The **eyebrows** are a pair of arched eminences of thickened skin above the orbits, and are covered with short, stout hairs. Deep to the skin are the interlacing fibres of the orbicularis oculi and occipito-frontalis muscles; between these and the periosteum there is a layer of fatty and areolar tissue, which is thickest in the lower part of the eyebrow.

The **eyelids** or **palpebræ** are two movable curtains situated in front of the eyeball. The upper is the larger, and the more movable, being provided with an elevator muscle—the *levator palpebræ superioris*. The interval between the eyelids is termed the **palpebral fissure** and measures transversely about 30 mm., but varies considerably in different persons and in different races. When the lids are opened the fissure is elliptical in shape, but when they are closed in sleep it is a transverse slit which lies on a level with the lower margin of the cornea. The ends of the fissure are termed the *medial* and *lateral angles* of the eye. The edge of each lid is flat, and along its anterior border the eyelashes are attached, while behind them are the openings of the *tarsal glands*. About 6 mm. from the medial angle of the eye there is a small elevation on each lid, named the **lacrimal papilla**, on the summit of which there is a minute opening called the **punctum lacrimale**; from the papilla to the medial angle the margins of the lids are rounded and devoid of eyelashes, and they enclose a triangular area, termed the **lacus lacrimalis**, at the bottom of which a small raised island of modified skin, called the **lacrimal caruncle**, is seen. The deep surfaces of the lids are lined with the conjunctiva, and are in contact with the eyeball except near the medial angle, where there intervenes a vertical fold of conjunctiva, called the **plica semilunaris conjunctivæ**, which in many animals contains a plate of cartilage.

Structure.—The basis of each eyelid is a plate of condensed fibrous tissue called the *tarsus*. The superior, and larger, is semi-oval in shape with a thick and straight lower edge and a thin and arched upper edge; it measures about 10 mm. in its greatest vertical diameter. The inferior tarsus is a narrow strip with an almost uniform vertical measurement of 5 mm. In front of each tarsus there are the fibres of the orbicularis oculi, and in front of the superior tarsus there is also a part of the outspread tendon of the levator palpebræ superioris, and the deep lamella of this muscle is attached to the upper edge of the tarsus. Embedded in the back of each tarsus there is a row of from 20 to 30 modified sebaceous glands named the **tarsal glands**, of which the openings have already been noticed. The lateral ends of the tarsi unite to form the *lateral palpebral ligament*, which fixes them to a small tubercle on the orbital surface of the zygomatic bone; their medial ends join to form the *medial palpebral ligament*, which is attached to the frontal process of the maxilla immediately in front of the lacrimal fossa.

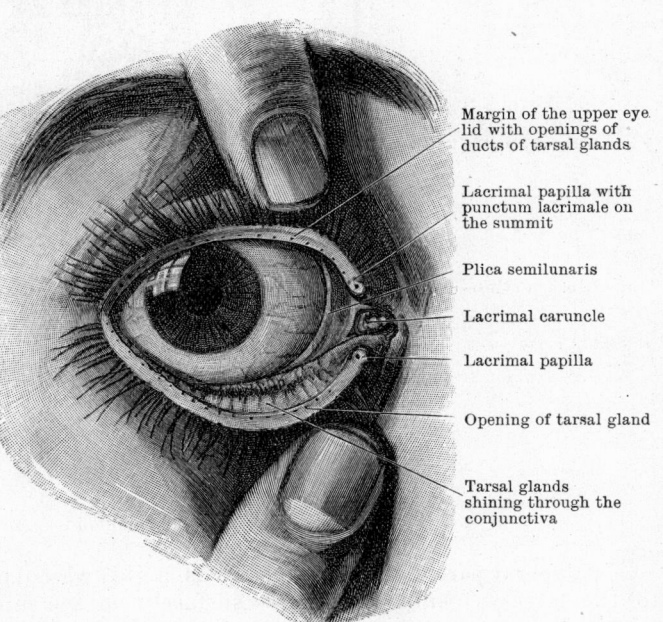

Margin of the upper eyelid with openings of ducts of tarsal glands

Lacrimal papilla with punctum lacrimale on the summit

Plica semilunaris

Lacrimal caruncle

Lacrimal papilla

Opening of tarsal gland

Tarsal glands shining through the conjunctiva

Fig. 933.—Eye with Lids slightly everted to show the Conjunctiva.

The eyelids are further strengthened by a membranous sheet, named the **palpebral fascia**, which extends into them from the margin of the opening of the orbit, along which it is continuous with the periosteum. In the upper eyelid the fascia fuses with the superficial lamella of the aponeurosis of the levator palpebræ superioris; in the lower eyelid it is thin, and blends with the anterior surface of the inferior tarsus.

The skin of the eyelids is thin, and is continuous, at their free margins, with the palpebral conjunctiva. The subcutaneous tissue is loose and devoid of fat, and in it are found the fibres of the orbicularis oculi muscle—a small separate slip of which occupies the margin of the lids behind the eyelashes.

Behind the roots of the eyelashes there are two or three rows of modified sweat glands termed the **ciliary glands**.

H. Müller described a layer of non-striped muscle in each eyelid: in the upper lid it extends from the deep lamella of the aponeurosis of the levator palpebræ superioris to the superior tarsus; in the lower lid it arises from the sheath of the inferior oblique and divides into two lamellæ, one ending in the ocular part of the conjunctiva, the other in the lower eyelid.

The eyelashes are short curved hairs, three or four rows deep, which project from the free margins of the eyelids. In the upper eyelid they are longer and more numerous than in the lower lid.

Conjunctiva.—The conjunctiva is the membrane which clothes the deep surfaces of the eyelids, and is reflected from them on to the front of the eyeball; the lines of reflection are known as the *superior* and *inferior* **conjunctival fornices.**

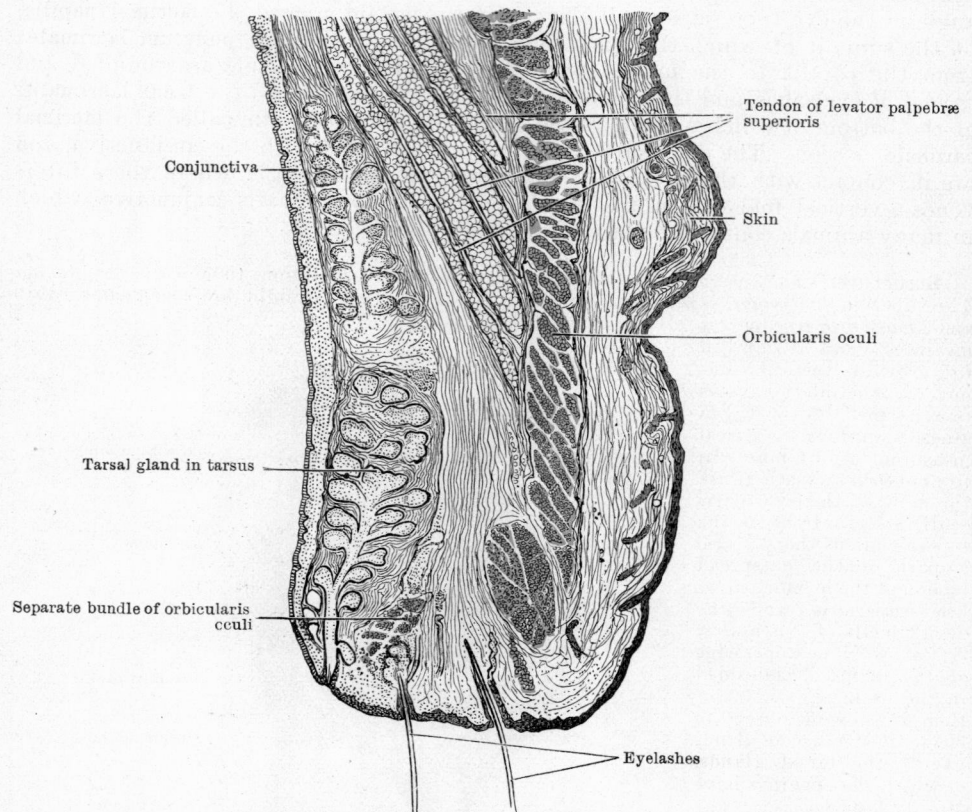

FIG. 934.—SAGITTAL SECTION THROUGH UPPER EYELID.

The palpebral part of the conjunctiva is highly vascular, and intimately adherent to the tarsi. Opening on its free surface, near the superior and inferior fornices, there is a number of acino-tubular glands which are more numerous in the upper lid than in the lower; they are identical in structure with the lacrimal gland. The ocular part of the conjunctiva is thinner; it covers the sclera but is not adherent to it, for the two structures are separated by the thinned-out fascial sheath of the eyeball; at the sclero-corneal junction the sheath comes to an end and the conjunctiva is continued forward over the cornea, to which it is firmly adherent, and, in fact, represented merely by the epithelium of the cornea.

Vessels and Nerves.—The chief **arteries** of the eyelids are the superior and inferior palpebral branches of the ophthalmic artery; they pierce the palpebral fascia above and below the medial palpebral ligament, and turn laterally in the corresponding lid near its free margin. The upper lid receives branches from the supra-orbital and supra-trochlear arteries also, and the lower lid from the facial artery. The **veins** are arranged in two sets: (*a*) subconjunctival, opening into the muscular tributaries of the ophthalmic veins, and (*b*) pretarsal, opening into the anterior facial and superficial temporal veins. The **lymph vessels** form networks in front of and behind the tarsal plates. The lymph is drained chiefly into the parotid lymph glands, but partly, by vessels which accompany the anterior facial vein, into the submandibular lymph glands. The **sensory nerves** of the eyelids are the supra-orbital and supra-trochlear for the upper lid, and the infra-orbital for the lower lid. The region of the lateral angle is supplied by the lacrimal nerve, and that of the medial angle by the infra-trochlear. The levator palpebræ superioris muscle is supplied by the oculo-motor nerve, and the non-striped fibres of the eyelids by the sympathetic.

LACRIMAL APPARATUS

The **lacrimal apparatus** consists of : (1) the lacrimal gland, which secretes the tears ; and (2) the lacrimal canaliculi, lacrimal sac, and naso-lacrimal duct, through which the tears are conveyed to the nasal cavity.

The **lacrimal gland** (Fig. 936) is of about the size and form of an almond, and is situated in the upper and lateral part of the orbit. It occupies the fossa on the medial surface of the zygomatic process of the frontal bone, and extends down almost as far as the lateral angle of the eye ; from this point a continuation of the gland, called the **palpebral process**, projects upwards, backwards, and medially in the root of the upper eyelid and along the line of the superior conjunctival fornix. Occasionally the palpebral process projects also in a downward and medial direction beyond the lateral angle of the eye, and for a considerable distance along the root of the lower lid. It is

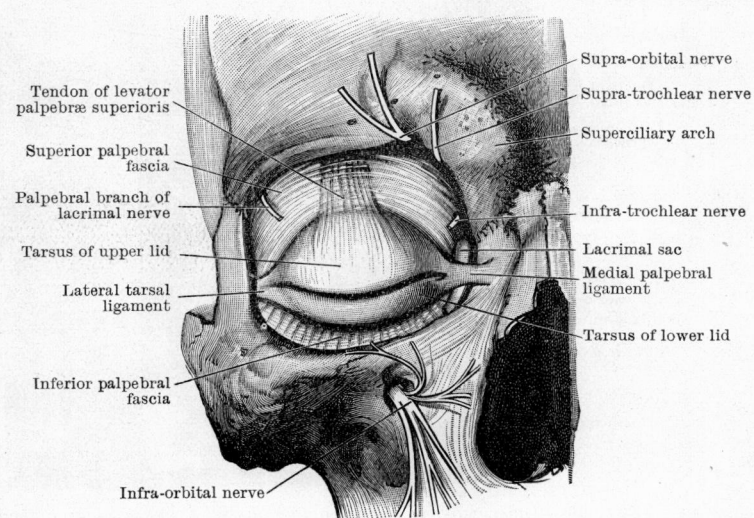

FIG. 935.—DISSECTION OF THE EYELID. The orbicularis oculi has been removed.

only at its lateral end that the palpebral process is connected with the main gland, and the two are separated from each other by the expanded insertion of the levator palpebræ superioris, which, until it is turned aside, completely hides the process. The ducts of the gland vary in number from three to nine, and open at the upper and lateral part of the superior fornix of the conjunctiva. In close relation with the conjunctival fornices (especially the superior fornix) there are numerous small *accessory lacrimal glands*, the secretion from which may serve to moisten the conjunctiva after the extirpation of the principal gland and its process.

Structure, Vessels, and Nerves.—The structure of the lacrimal gland resembles that of the parotid gland. It is supplied by the sympathetic, lacrimal, and facial **nerves**, and by the lacrimal **artery** ; its **veins** open into the ophthalmic vein.

The **lacrimal canaliculi** (Fig. 936), one in each eyelid, begin in minute orifices, termed *puncta lacrimalia*, situated on the summit of the lacrimal papillæ ; each canaliculus is about 10 mm. long. From the puncta lacrimalia they pass medially above and below the lacus lacrimalis ; the superior at first ascends for a short distance and then inclines downwards ; the inferior descends for a short distance and then runs horizontally ; where the canaliculi change their direction they are dilated into ampullæ. The two canaliculi open close together into the lateral and front part of the lacrimal sac, a little above its middle ; sometimes they open into a pouch-like dilatation of the sac. The canaliculi are lined with stratified epithelium, outside which there is a layer of striped muscular fibres continuous with the lacrimal part of the orbicularis oculi. The muscular fibres are arranged in a spiral manner round the canaliculi, but at the base of each lacrimal papilla the fibres are circular in direction.

The lacrimal sac and naso-lacrimal duct together form the passage by which the tears are conveyed from the lacrimal canaliculi to the nasal cavity.

The **lacrimal sac** (Figs. 935, 936) is the upper, blind part of the naso-lacrimal duct, and it occupies the lacrimal fossa on the medial wall of the orbit. A sheet of fascia, continuous with the orbital periosteum, stretches from the anterior to the posterior edge of the lacrimal fossa and thus covers the lateral side of the lacrimal sac. The medial palpebral ligament and some of the fibres of the orbicularis oculi muscle lie in front of the upper half of the lacrimal sac;

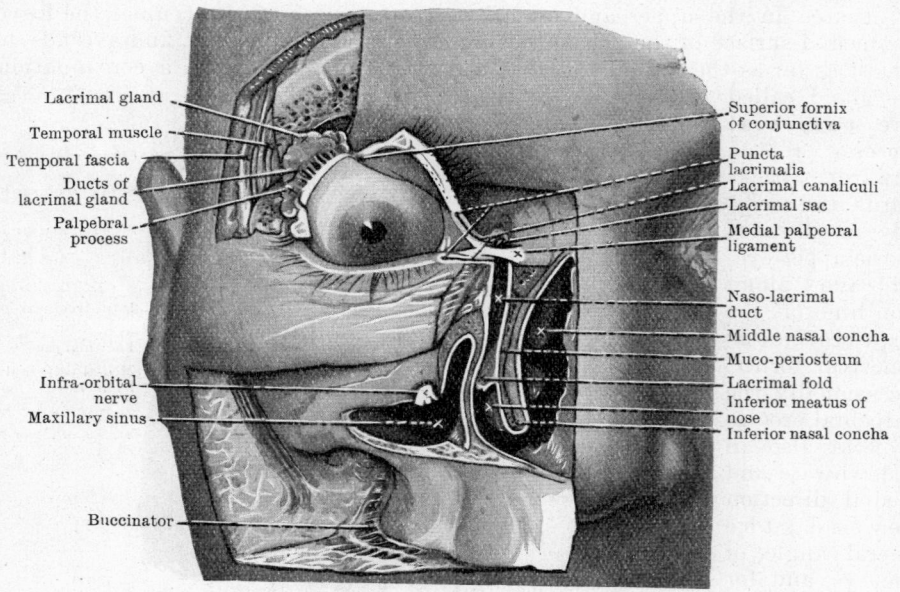

FIG. 936.—DISSECTION TO SHOW THE LACRIMAL APPARATUS (semi-diagrammatic).

the lacrimal part of this muscle lies behind and to the lateral side of the sac; the lower half of the sac is below these two structures.

The **naso-lacrimal duct** (Fig. 936) is about 18 mm. long, and has a diameter of from 3 to 4 mm. Rather narrower in the middle than at its ends, it is directed downwards and slightly backwards and laterally. It opens into the inferior meatus of the nose towards its anterior end, about 30 mm. behind the nostril. The opening is very variable in form and position, and is frequently guarded by a fold of mucous membrane termed the *lacrimal fold* (Fig. 936). The duct is lined with columnar epithelium.

Vessels and Nerves.—The arteries are derived from the palpebral arteries, from the terminal branch of the facial artery [a. maxillaris externa], and from the infra-orbital artery. The veins of the naso-lacrimal duct are large, and form a well-marked plexus. The nerves of the lacrimal canaliculi and sac are derived from the infra-trochlear nerve; the lower part of the naso-lacrimal duct receives a branch from the anterior superior dental nerve.

DEVELOPMENT OF THE EYE

The retina and optic nerve are developed from a hollow outgrowth of the fore-brain termed the **optic vesicle.** The vesicle extends towards the side of the head, and its connexion with the brain is gradually elongated to form the **optic stalk.** The ectoderm overlying the optic vesicle becomes thickened, invaginated, and finally cut off as a hollow island of cells named the **lens vesicle.** That vesicle indents the outer and lower part of the optic vesicle, converting it into a cup (**optic cup**), which thus consists of two layers of cells continuous with each other at the margin of the cup. The inner layer is the thicker, and becomes the nervous layer of the retina, while the outer forms the pigmented layer. The edge of the optic cup extends in front of the equator of the lens, and bounds the future pupil. In front of the lens, and also opposite its equator, the retinal layer is thin, and is represented only by a stratum of columnar cells which becomes closely applied to the pigmented layer, the two forming the ciliary part of the retina. The indentation of the optic cup extends along the postero-inferior aspect of the optic stalk in the form of a groove termed the **choroidal fissure** (Fig. 939). Through this fissure mesoderm passes inwards between the lens and the retina to form a part of the vitreous body, and the arteria retinæ centralis also becomes enclosed in it and so gains its future position in the optic nerve. This artery is prolonged forwards from the optic disc through the vitreous body, as a cone of branches, as far as the back of the lens. By the fifth or sixth month all those branches have disappeared except one—the **hyaloid artery**—which persists until the last month of intra-uterine life, when it also atrophies, leaving only the **hyaloid canal** (and its corkscrew-like anterior end adherent to the back of the lens) to indicate its position.

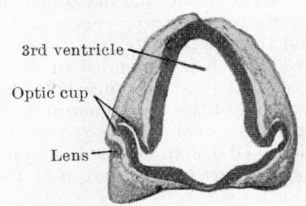

FIG. 937.—SECTION OF THE DEVELOPING EYE OF A 5-MM. HUMAN EMBRYO. × 20 (A. R.)

The vitreous body is developed between the optic cup and the lens, and is derived partly from ectoderm and partly from mesoderm. It consists primarily of a series of fine protoplasmic fibres which project from the cells of the retinal layer of the cup and from the back of the lens and form a delicate reticular tissue. At first the fibres are seen in relation to the whole of the optic cup, but later they become more condensed where they form the ciliary zonule and the walls of the hyaloid canal, though they can still be seen throughout the whole of the vitreous in the adult. The mesodermal element of the vitreous body is derived from the mesoderm which enters, through the choroidal fissure, into the optic cup, where it unites with these ectodermal fibres, to form the vitreous body.

The lens, at first in contact with the ectoderm from which it is derived, is soon separated from it by mesoderm, and is then a rounded vesicle with epithelial walls. The anterior wall remains as a single layer of cells—the anterior lens epithelium of the adult. The cells of the posterior wall become elongated into lens fibres, and by their forward growth the cavity of the vesicle is obliterated. The elongation of the cells into lens fibres is greatest at the centre of the lens, while near the equator the fibres are shorter, and here the gradual transition between the anterior epithelium and the lens

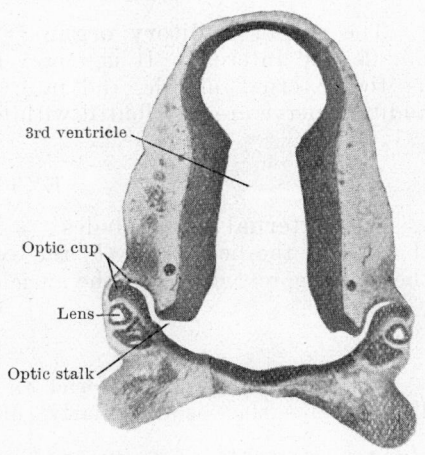

FIG. 938.—SECTION OF THE DEVELOPING EYE OF A 10-MM. HUMAN EMBRYO. × 20 (A. R.)

fibres is seen (Fig. 932). The lens becomes enveloped in a vascular tunic which receives its vessels from the arteria retinæ centralis and from the vessels of the iris. The front part of this tunic forms the pupillary membrane which disappears before birth (p. 1088).

The optic stalk, at first hollow, becomes solid by the thickening of its walls, and, acquiring nerve-fibres, is transformed into the optic nerve. The further development of the retina resembles, in certain respects, that of the spinal cord.

In the first stage in the development of the retina there are present an inner marginal layer and an outer neuro-epithelial layer; that is followed by the formation of an inner and outer neuroblast layer by a migration of cells from the primitive neuro-epithelial layer to the marginal layer. The new inner neuroblast layer ultimately gives rise to the ganglion cells, the amacrine cells, and the cells of the sustentacular fibres, while the outer neuroblast layer furnishes the bipolar and the horizontal cells of the inner nuclear layer, and the nuclei of the rods and cones. It will thus be seen that the inner nuclear layer of the fully formed eye, comprising amacrine, sustentacular, bipolar, and horizontal cells, is a composite structure derived in part from the inner primitive neuroblast layer and in part from the outer layer (Mann).

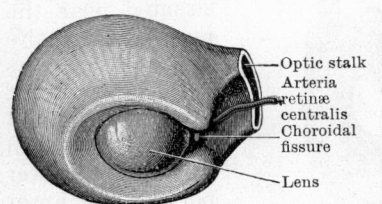

FIG. 939.—OPTIC CUP AND LENS VIEWED FROM BEHIND AND BELOW, to show formation of choroidal fissure and enclosure of the arteria retinæ centralis (from a model by Ziegler).

The condensed mesoderm around the optic cup becomes the sclera and choroid. The mesoderm in front of the lens becomes divided by a cleft into a thick anterior layer and a thin posterior layer. The cleft becomes the anterior chamber of the eye ; the anterior mesodermal layer becomes the substantia propria of the cornea ; the posterior mesodermal layer forms the stroma of the iris and anterior part of the temporary vascular tunic of the lens ; the deep surface of the iris is ectodermal in origin and is derived from the forward growth of the edge of the optic cup.

The **eyelids** arise as folds above and below the cornea, each being covered on both surfaces with ectoderm. By the third month the edges of the folds meet and unite, the eyelids being only permanently opened shortly before birth; in many animals they are not opened until after birth. The ectoderm forms the epithelium of the conjunctiva and the epithelium of the cornea. It is also invaginated at the margins of the eyelids to form the hair follicles and the lining cells of the tarsal and ciliary glands, and at the superior conjunctival fornix to form the lining cells of the ducts and alveoli of the lacrimal gland.

The **lacrimal sac** and **naso-lacrimal duct** are developed along the line of the furrow which separates the maxillary process from the lateral nasal process. The furrow is lined with ectodermal cells, and those cells, after the meeting and fusion of the lips of the furrow, proliferate and form a solid rod which is embedded in the mesoderm. By the breaking down and disintegration of its central cells, the rod becomes hollowed out to form the lacrimal sac and the naso-lacrimal duct—the lower end of the duct remaining closed until near the end of intra-uterine life. The **lacrimal canaliculi** are developed as secondary buds of cells which extend lateralwards from the upper end of the solid rod, and subsequently undergo canalisation. The **lacrimal caruncle** is formed from a small part of the margin of the lower eyelid which is cut off by the growth of the inferior lacrimal canaliculus.

ORGAN OF HEARING

The **ear** or **auditory organ** (Fig. 940) consists of three portions—external, middle, and internal. It is, however, customary to speak of these three portions as the external, middle, and internal ear; the peripheral terminations of the auditory nerve are distributed within the internal ear.

EXTERNAL EAR

The **external ear** includes—(a) the auricle, attached to and projecting from the side of the head; and (b) the external auditory meatus, leading inwards from the most depressed part of the auricle to the tympanic membrane.

AURICLE

The **auricle** (Fig. 941) forms an angle of about 30° with the side of the head. Its lateral surface is irregularly concave, but has several well-marked elevations and depressions. The deepest of the depressions—the **concha**—is situated near the middle of the auricle; it is divided by a ridge, called the **crus of the helix**, into an upper and a lower portion; the lower portion is the larger and leads into the external auditory meatus. Anteriorly, the crus helicis is continuous with the **helix** or margin of the auricle, which is incurved in the greater part of its

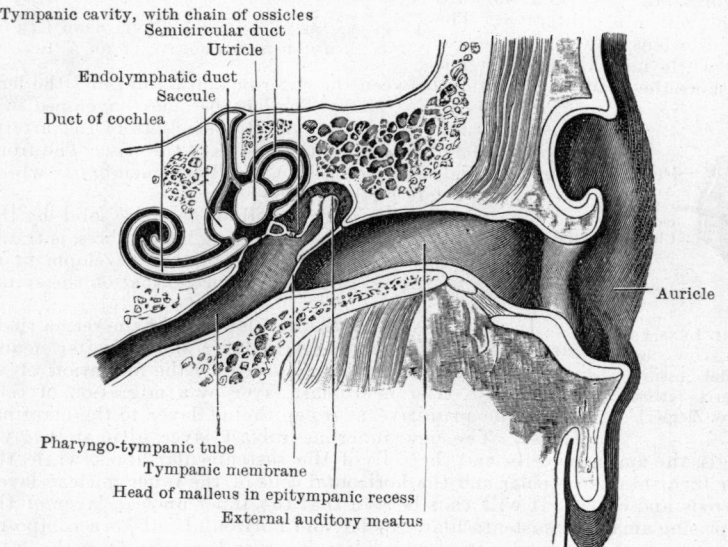

Tympanic cavity, with chain of ossicles
Semicircular duct
Utricle
Endolymphatic duct
Saccule
Duct of cochlea

Auricle

Pharyngo-tympanic tube
Tympanic membrane
Head of malleus in epitympanic recess
External auditory meatus

FIG. 940.—DIAGRAMMATIC SECTION OF THE ORGAN OF HEARING.

extent, and is directed at first upwards, and then backwards and downwards, to become gradually lost in the upper part of the lobule. Near the point where the helix begins to descend, a small **tubercle** is often seen. In front of the descending part of the helix there is a second elevation, called the **antihelix**, which bifurcates superiorly into two **crura** that enclose a depression called the **triangular fossa**. The elongated furrow between the helix and antihelix is named the **scaphoid fossa**. The concha is overlapped in front by a tongue-like process called the **tragus**, and below and behind by a triangular projection called the **antitragus** ; the notch, directed downwards and forwards between those two processes, is named the **incisura intertragica**. The tragus is often partially divided into two small tubercles, and it is separated from the helix by the **anterior notch of the auricle**. The **lobule** is situated below the incisura intertragica, and is the most dependent part of the auricle.

The medial or cranial surface of the auricle presents elevations corresponding to the depressions on its lateral surface, *e.g.* the **eminence of the concha**, the **eminence of the scaphoid fossa**, the **eminence of the triangular fossa**, etc.

The auricle, usually smaller and more finely modelled in women than in men, presents great variations in size and shape in different persons. In the new-born child its length is about one-third of that of the adult ; in old age it increases both in length and breadth.

The **tubercle of the ear** is a triangular prominence which projects usually forwards from the helix. It is more often present in men than in women. Its significance, which was recognised by Charles Darwin, is that it probably represents the point of the ear of lower animals ; it is well seen in the macaque monkey, the ear of which closely resembles that of a human fœtus of the sixth month. The **lobule** may be small and sessile or considerably elongated ; it may adhere to the skin of the cheek, or its lower end may be bifurcated.

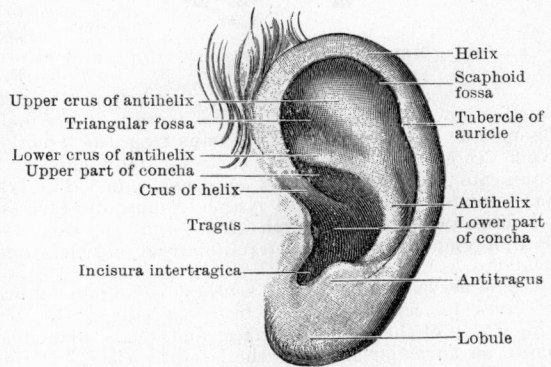

FIG. 941.—LATERAL SURFACE OF LEFT AURICLE.

Labels: Helix · Scaphoid fossa · Tubercle of auricle · Upper crus of antihelix · Triangular fossa · Lower crus of antihelix · Upper crus of concha · Crus of helix · Antihelix · Lower part of concha · Tragus · Incisura intertragica · Antitragus · Lobule

Structure of the Auricle.—The skin of the auricle is thin and smooth, and is prolonged, in the form of a tube, as a lining to the external auditory meatus. On the lateral surface of the auricle, it adheres firmly to the subjacent perichondrium. Strong hairs, named **tragi**, are often present in men on the tragus and antitragus, and also in the incisura intertragica ; soft downy hairs are found over the greater part of the auricle and point towards the tubercle. Sebaceous glands, present on both surfaces of the auricle, are most numerous in the concha and triangular fossa. Sweat glands are found on the medial surface ; few or none on the lateral surface.

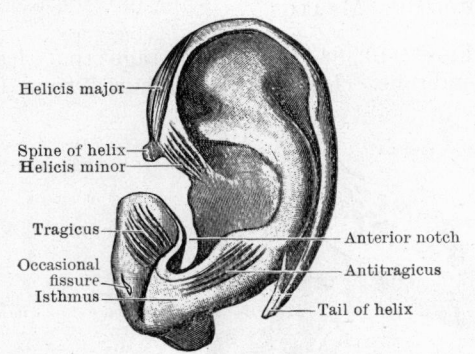

FIG. 942.—LATERAL SURFACE OF CARTILAGE OF THE AURICLE, WITH MUSCLES.

Labels: Helicis major · Spine of helix · Helicis minor · Tragicus · Occasional fissure · Isthmus · Anterior notch · Antitragicus · Tail of helix

The greater part of the auricle is supported by yellow fibro-cartilage ; the cartilage is, however, absent from the lobule, which is composed of fat and fibro-areolar tissue. When laid bare, the cartilage (Figs. 942, 943) presents, in an exaggerated form, all the inequalities of the auricle. It is continuous medially with the cartilaginous part of the external auditory meatus by a narrow **isthmus**, 8 or 9 mm. in breadth, which corresponds laterally with the deepest part of the incisura intertragica. The most anterior part of the cartilage of the helix projects forwards as the **spine**, and the most inferior part is called the **tail** of the helix.

Ligaments of the Auricle.—The cartilage of the auricle is fixed to the temporal bone by two extrinsic ligaments—an *anterior*, stretching from the spine of the helix and the tragus to the zygomatic process, and a *posterior*, stretching from the eminence of the concha to the mastoid part of the bone. Small intrinsic ligaments pass between individual parts of the auricle.

Muscles of the Auricle.—The muscles of the auricle are divisible into two groups, *extrinsic* and *intrinsic*. The extrinsic muscles connect the auricle to the skull and scalp, and are described in the chapter on Myology. The intrinsic muscles are confined to the auricle and are six in number, four on its lateral surface and two on its cranial or medial surface.

(*a*) *On the lateral surface* (Fig. 942)—

1. The **helicis major** muscle passes upwards from the spine of the helix along the ascending

part of the helix. 2. The **helicis minor** muscle covers the crus of the helix. 3. The **tragicus** muscle runs vertically over the greater part of the tragus. Some of its fibres are prolonged upwards to the spine of the helix and constitute the **pyramidalis** muscle. 4. The **antitragicus** muscle covers the antitragus and runs obliquely upwards and backwards to the antihelix and tail of the helix.

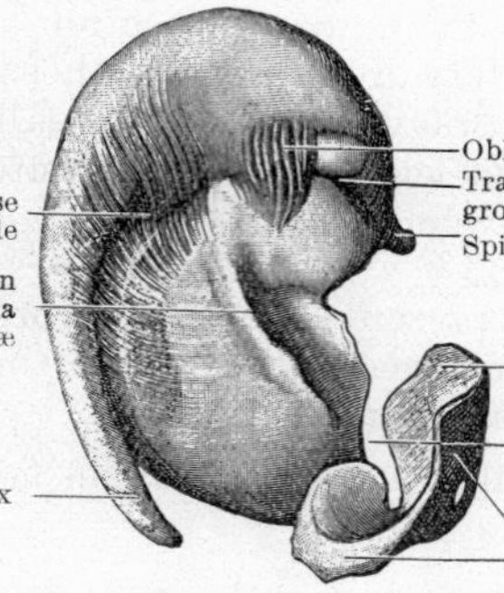

(b) On the medial surface (Fig. 943)—

1. The **transverse muscle of the auricle** consists of scattered fibres which stretch from the eminence of the concha to the eminence of the scaphoid fossa. 2. The **oblique muscle of the auricle** comprises a few fasciculi which run obliquely or vertically from the helix to the eminence of the concha.

Vessels and Nerves.—The **arteries** are derived—*(a)* from the superficial temporal artery, which sends two or three branches to the lateral surface; and *(b)* from the posterior auricular artery, which gives three or four branches to the medial surface. From the branches of the posterior auricular artery two sets of twigs pass to the lateral surface, one turning round the free margin of the helix, and the other passing through small fissures in the cartilage. The **veins** from the lateral surface open into the superficial temporal vein; those from the medial surface chiefly join the posterior auricular vein, but some communicate with the mastoid emissary vein. The **lymph vessels** take three directions, viz.: *(a)* forwards to the parotid lymph glands, and especially to the gland in front of the tragus; *(b)* downwards to the lymph glands that lie alongside the external jugular vein, and to the lymph glands under the sterno-mastoid muscle; and *(c)* backwards to the mastoid lymph glands.

The **nerves** are motor and sensory. The muscles are supplied by the facial nerve. The skin receives its sensory nerves from—*(a)* the great auricular nerve, which supplies nearly the whole of the medial surface, and sends filaments in company with the branches of the posterior auricular artery to the lateral surface; *(b)* the auriculo-temporal nerve, which supplies the tragus and ascending part of the helix; *(c)* the lesser occipital nerve, which sends a branch to the upper part of the medial surface.

Labels for Fig. 943: Transverse muscle — Ridge on eminentia conchæ — Tail of helix — Oblique muscle — Transverse groove — Spine of helix — Cartilage of tragus — Anterior notch — Cartilage of meatus

FIG. 943.—MEDIAL SURFACE OF THE CARTILAGE OF THE AURICLE.

EXTERNAL AUDITORY MEATUS

The **external auditory meatus** (Figs. 940, 944) is the passage that leads from the concha to the tympanic membrane. Its length, measured from the bottom of the concha, is 24 mm.; from the margin of the tragus it is 35 mm. On account of the obliquity of the tympanic membrane the anterior and inferior walls of the meatus are longer than the posterior and superior walls. The meatus consists of a lateral cartilaginous part, about 8 mm. in length; and a medial bony part about 16 mm. in length. The entire meatus makes a sinuous bend (Fig. 940) and may be divided into three portions—lateral, intermediate, and medial; each is directed medialwards, but, in addition, the lateral part is inclined forwards and slightly upwards; the intermediate, backwards; and the medial—the longest—forwards

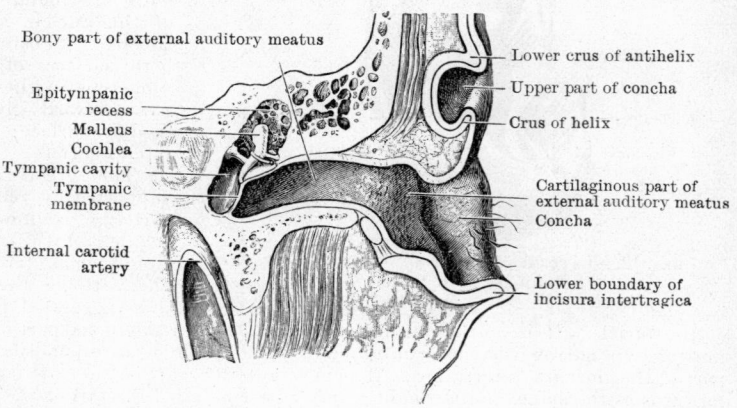

Labels for Fig. 944: Bony part of external auditory meatus — Epitympanic recess — Malleus — Cochlea — Tympanic cavity — Tympanic membrane — Internal carotid artery — Lower crus of antihelix — Upper part of concha — Crus of helix — Cartilaginous part of external auditory meatus — Concha — Lower boundary of incisura intertragica

FIG. 944.—CORONAL SECTION OF RIGHT EAR; ANTERIOR HALF OF SECTION, viewed from behind.

and slightly downwards. On transverse section the canal is seen to be elliptical—its greatest diameter being directed from above downwards and backwards. Widest at its lateral end, it becomes slightly narrower at the medial end of the cartilaginous part; once more expanding in the lateral portion of the bony part, it is again constricted near its medial end; this is the narrowest part or **isthmus**, and is 20 mm. from the bottom of the concha. The medial end of the meatus is nearly circular and is closed by the tympanic membrane.

The lumen of the cartilaginous part is influenced by the movements of the mandible, being widened when that bone is depressed. A large part of the head of the mandible lies in front of the bony part of the meatus, but a small portion lies in front of the cartilaginous part; between this part of the meatus and the mandible there is lodged a process of the parotid gland. Behind the bony part, and separated from it by a thin plate of bone, are the mastoid air-cells.

Structure of the Meatus.—The cartilage of the meatus is folded to form a groove, opening upwards and backwards, the margins of the groove being connected with each other by fibrous tissue. The medial end of the cartilaginous part of the meatus is firmly fixed to the lateral margin of the bony part; its lateral end is continuous with the cartilage of the tragus. Two fissures exist in the anterior portion of the cartilaginous part, and are filled with fibrous tissue. In the lateral part of the meatus the cartilage forms about three-fourths of the circumference of the tube; but near the medial end it forms only a part of the anterior and lower boundaries.

The bony part is described on pp. 149, 150. In the new-born child it is represented by an incomplete ring of bone —the **tympanic ring**— together with a small

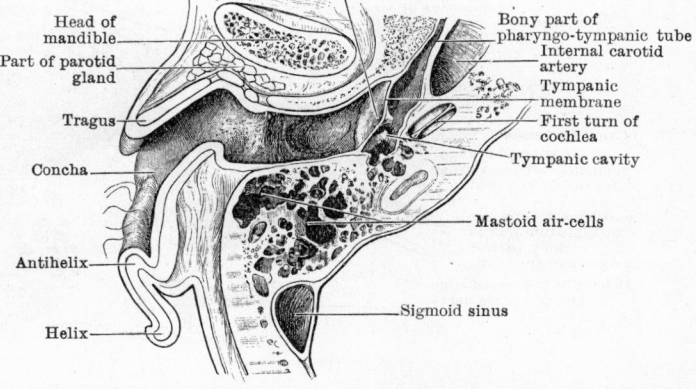

FIG. 945.—HORIZONTAL SECTION THROUGH RIGHT EAR; UPPER HALF OF SECTION, viewed from below

portion of the squamous part of the temporal bone, which articulates with the ring and completes it superiorly. Along the concavity of the ring there is a groove, called the **tympanic groove**, in which the circumference of the tympanic membrane is fixed. On the medial surface of the anterior part of the ring, a little below its free end, a groove, called the **malleolar sulcus**, is directed downwards and forwards. It transmits the anterior process and the anterior ligament of the malleus, the tympanic artery, and the chorda tympani nerve. A **fibrous tympanic plate** (Symington) intervenes between the tympanic ring and the cartilage of the meatus, and into that plate the bony ring extends. The bony outgrowth does not, however, proceed uniformly from the whole circumference of the ring but occurs most rapidly from its anterior and posterior parts, with the result that when the two outgrowths fuse, at about the end of the second year of life, a gap is left between them in the floor of the meatus; this gap is usually closed by the fifth year, but persists in about 19 per cent. of adult skulls (Bürkner).

The lumen of the meatus in the new-born child is extremely small: its lateral part is funnel-shaped; its medial part is a mere slit, bounded below by the fibrous tympanic plate and above by the tympanic membrane.

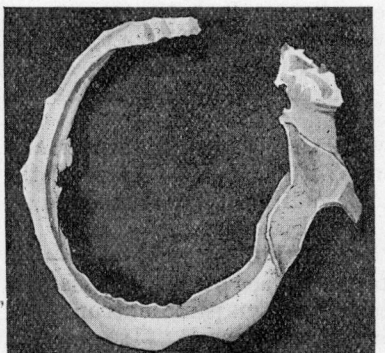

FIG. 946.—THE LEFT TYMPANIC RING SEEN FROM THE MEDIAL SIDE. (C. M. W.)

The meatus is lined with skin which covers also the lateral surface of the tympanic membrane. The skin is thick in the cartilaginous part, and contains fine hairs and sebaceous glands; the glands extend for some distance along the postero-superior wall of the bony part of the meatus. In the subcutaneous tissue of the cartilaginous part there are numerous enlarged sweat glands; they are named **ceruminous glands** because they secrete the ear wax or cerumen.

Vessels and Nerves.—The arteries of the external auditory meatus are branches of the posterior auricular and superficial temporal arteries, and of the deep auricular artery —the last distributing some minute twigs to the tympanic membrane. The **veins** open into the maxillary and external jugular veins, and into the pterygoid venous plexus. The **lymph-vessels** end like those of the auricle. **Sensory nerves** are supplied to the meatus by the auriculo-temporal nerve and by the auricular branch of the vagus nerve.

TYMPANUM OR MIDDLE EAR

The **tympanic cavity** is a small air-chamber in the temporal bone, between the tympanic membrane and the lateral wall of the internal ear or labyrinth (Figs. 940, 944). It is lined with mucous membrane, and contains a chain of ossicles—malleus, incus, and stapes—which reaches from its lateral wall to its medial wall, and transmits the vibrations of the tympanic membrane across the cavity to the internal ear. Several ligaments and two small muscles are attached to the ossicles.

The larger part of the tympanic cavity is opposite the tympanic membrane and is called the **tympanum proper**, but the cavity extends also above the level of

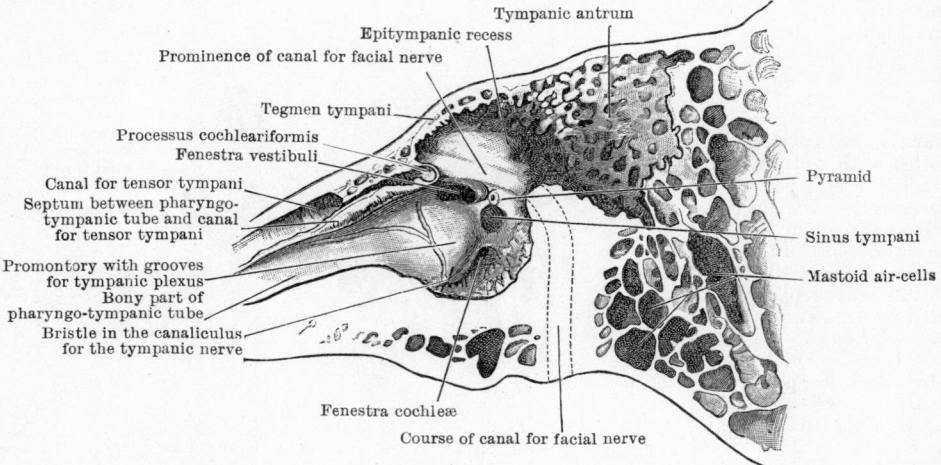

FIG. 947.—SECTION THROUGH LEFT TEMPORAL BONE, showing medial wall of tympanic cavity, etc.

the membrane and this extension is named the epitympanic recess; it contains the greater part of the incus and the upper half of the malleus. Including the recess, the vertical and antero-posterior diameters of the cavity are each about 15 mm. The distance between its lateral and medial walls is about 6 mm. in the upper part and 4 mm. in the lower, while at its central part, owing to the bulging of the two walls towards the cavity, it is only 1·5 or 2 mm.

The tympanic cavity communicates, behind, with the tympanic antrum, and through that with the mastoid air-cells; in front, with the nasal part of the pharynx, through the pharyngo-tympanic tube [tuba auditiva]. It is enclosed by a roof, a floor, and four walls—anterior, posterior, medial, and lateral.

The **roof** of the tympanic cavity (Fig. 947) is a thin plate of bone—the **tegmen tympani**—which forms a portion of the anterior surface of the petrous part of the temporal bone. It extends backwards to cover the tympanic antrum, and forwards to form a roof for the canal for the tensor tympani muscle. It separates the tympanic cavity and antrum from the middle cranial fossa; it may contain a few air-cells, and occasionally it is partly deficient. In the child its lateral edge corresponds with the petro-squamous suture, traces of which can generally be seen in the adult bone.

The **floor** is narrower than the roof, and consists of a thin plate of bone which separates the tympanic cavity from the jugular fossa; anteriorly, it ascends and is continuous with the posterior wall of the carotid canal. The inner orifice of the canaliculus which transmits the tympanic nerve—a branch of the glosso-pharyngeal—is placed near the junction of the floor and medial wall.

The **medial wall** of the middle ear is also the lateral wall of the internal ear (Fig. 947). It presents—(1) A rounded eminence, called the **promontory**, caused by the bulging of the first coil of the cochlea; its surface is marked by small grooves which lodge the tympanic plexus of nerves. (2) An oval or kidney-shaped opening, named the **fenestra vestibuli**, situated above and behind the promontory, with its long axis directed antero-posteriorly, and its concavity directed downwards. It measures 3 mm. in length and 1·5 mm. in breadth and, in the macerated bone, leads into the vestibule of the bony labyrinth, but, in the recent state, is closed by the base or footplate of the stapes, surrounded by its **annular ligament**. (3) An elevation—the **prominence of the facial nerve canal**—situated above the fenestra vestibuli, in the epitympanic recess. (4) The **processus cochleariformis**—a thin, narrow bony shelf which extends

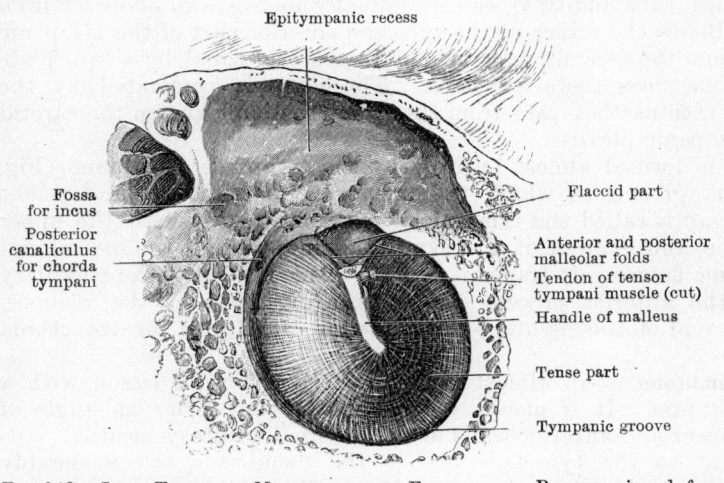

Epitympanic recess

Fossa for incus
Posterior canaliculus for chorda tympani

Flaccid part
Anterior and posterior malleolar folds
Tendon of tensor tympani muscle (cut)
Handle of malleus

Tense part

Tympanic groove

FIG. 948.—LEFT TYMPANIC MEMBRANE AND EPITYMPANIC RECESS, viewed from within. The head and neck of the malleus have been removed to show the flaccid part and the malleolar folds.

backwards above the anterior end of the fenestra vestibuli, where it makes a sharp lateral curve, and forms a pulley over which the tendon of the tensor tympani muscle plays. (5) A funnel-shaped recess, situated behind and below the promontory, and almost hidden by its overhanging edge, and which leads to an irregularly oval opening, termed the **fenestra cochleæ**; in the macerated bone the fenestra opens into the cochlea, but in the recent state is closed by the **secondary tympanic membrane**. This membrane consists of three layers: (*a*) a *lateral* layer, continuous with the mucous lining of the tympanum, and containing a network of capillaries; (*b*) an *intermediate* fibrous layer; (*c*) a *medial* layer, continuous with the epithelial lining of the labyrinth. (6) A small depression named the **sinus tympani**, situated behind the promontory and between the fenestra vestibuli and the fenestra cochleæ; it indicates the position of the ampullated end of the posterior semicircular canal.

The **posterior wall** of the tympanic cavity presents, from above downwards: (1) a round or triangular opening, called the **aditus**, which leads from the epitympanic recess into the **tympanic antrum** (Fig. 947); (2) a depression—the **fossa for the incus**—situated in the postero-inferior part of the epitympanic recess (Fig. 953), for the reception of the end of the short process of the incus; (3) a minute conical bony projection called the **pyramid** (Fig. 947), the summit of which is perforated by the tendon of the stapedius muscle. From the interior of the pyramid a small canal passes downwards and backwards in front of the facial canal, into which it usually opens; its walls give attachment to the stapedius, and it transmits the vascular and nervous supply to that muscle. This small canal sometimes opens independently on the base of the skull, immediately in front of the stylo-mastoid foramen; (4) a small aperture—the **posterior canaliculus of the chorda tympani**—situated close to the posterior edge of the tympanic membrane nearly on a level with the upper end of the handle of the malleus (Fig. 948).

The **anterior wall** is narrowed in its transverse diameter by the approximation of the lateral and medial walls of the tympanic cavity, and in its vertical diameter by the descent of the tegmen tympani and the ascent of the carotid canal (Fig. 947). It presents the openings of two parallel canals, one above the other, separated by a thin lamella of bone, the free posterior end of which is the processus cochleariformis. The two canals run forwards on the lateral wall of the carotid canal and open in the angle between the squamous and the petrous parts of the temporal bone. The higher and smaller canal is the **canal for the tensor tympani**, and lies immediately below the tegmen tympani. It has a diameter of about 2 mm., and extends on to the medial wall of the tympanic cavity above the anterior part of the fenestra vestibuli. The lower and larger canal is the **bony part** of the **pharyngo-tympanic tube** [tuba auditiva], and it gradually increases in diameter from before backwards. Below the orifice of the tube the anterior part of the tympanic cavity is separated from the ascending portion of the carotid canal by a thin plate of bone in which sometimes there are gaps. The plate is perforated by the carotico-tympanic nerves as they pass from the sympathetic plexus on the carotid artery to join the tympanic plexus.

The **lateral wall** is formed almost entirely by the tympanic membrane (Fig. 949). The tympanic groove, to which the membrane is attached, is deficient superiorly, and the gap is called the **tympanic notch**. On a level with the upper edge of the membrane, and in front of the tympanic ring, there is the medial end of the **squamo-tympanic fissure**. It transmits the tympanic branch of the maxillary artery, and lodges the anterior process and anterior ligament of the malleus. Close to the medial end of the fissure is the **anterior canaliculus for the chorda tympani**.

The **tympanic membrane** is an almost circular sheet of fibrous tissue, with a diameter of about 10 mm. It is placed very obliquely, and forms an angle of about 55° with the lower and anterior walls of the external auditory meatus.

At its attachment to the tympanic groove the membrane is considerably thickened. This thickened portion is named the **fibro-cartilaginous ring** and is prolonged from the anterior and posterior ends of the tympanic notch to the lateral process of the malleus as two ligamentous bands which raise up ridges, called the **anterior** and **posterior malleolar folds**, on the medial surface of the membrane. The small triangular portion of the membrane (Fig. 949) between the malleolar folds is thin and lax, and is its **flaccid part**, whilst the main portion of the membrane is tightly stretched and is termed the **tense part**. The handle of the malleus is firmly fixed to the tympanic membrane, the central portion of which is drawn towards the tympanic cavity so that the lateral surface of the membrane is concave. The point of greatest convexity of the membrane corresponds with the lower end of the handle of the malleus, and is named the **umbo of the tympanic membrane**.

Structure.—The tympanic membrane is in three layers—cuticular, fibrous, and mucous. The **cuticular layer** is continuous with the skin of the external auditory meatus.

Flaccid part
Anterior malleolar fold

Handle of malleus

Antero-superior quadrant

Antero-inferior quadrant

Posterior malleolar fold
Lateral process of malleus
Long process of incus

Postero-superior quadrant

Postero-inferior quadrant

Cone of light

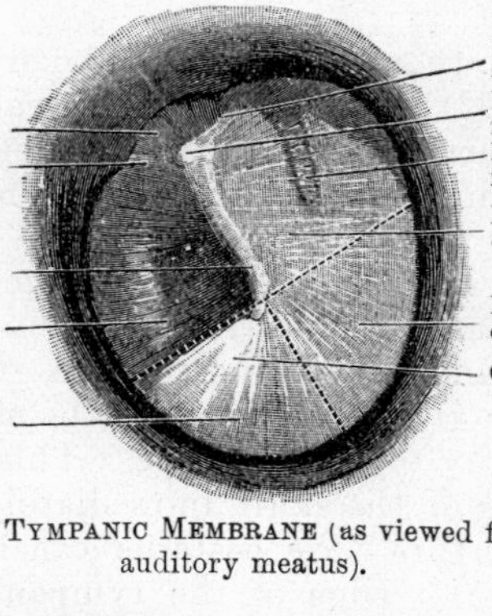

Fig. 949.—Left Tympanic Membrane (as viewed from the external auditory meatus).

The **fibrous layer** is composed of radial and circular fibres. The radial fibres pass from the handle of the malleus to the fibro-cartilaginous ring; the circular fibres are numerous near the circumference of the membrane, but scattered and few in number near its centre (Fig. 948). Both radial and circular fibres are absent from the flaccid part, which thus consists only of the cuticular and mucous layers.

The **mucous layer** is continuous with the mucous lining of the tympanic cavity and is thickest over the upper part of the membrane.

Otoscopic Examination of the Tympanic Membrane (Fig. 949).—The tympanic membrane, in the living, is of a "pearl-grey" colour, but may present a reddish or yellowish tinge; the posterior segment is usually clearer than the anterior. At the antero-superior part, close to its periphery, a whitish point appears as if projecting towards the meatus; this is the lateral process of the malleus. Passing downwards and backwards from that point to the umbo there is a ridge caused by the handle of the malleus, the lower end of which appears rounded. Two ridges, corresponding with the malleolar folds, extend from the lateral process of the malleus, one forwards and upwards, the other backwards and upwards. Behind, and near the lower end of the handle of the malleus, is a reddish or yellowish spot, due to the promontory of the medial wall shining through. If the membrane is very transparent, the long process of the incus may be visible behind the upper part of the handle of the malleus, reaching downwards as far as its middle. From the lower end of the handle, a bright area termed the "cone of light" radiates in a downward and forward direction.

For the purpose of precise localisation of any point on the membrane, its surface is divided into quadrants by the handle of the malleus and a line continued from it to the circumference and by a line drawn at right angles to this through the lower end of the handle.

Vascular and Nervous Supply of the Tympanic Membrane.—The **arteries** are arranged in two sets—one on the cutaneous surface and another on the mucous surface; they anastomose by means of small branches which pierce the membrane, especially near its periphery. The first set is derived chiefly from the deep auricular artery; the vessels on the mucous surface are small and proceed from the anterior tympanic artery and from the stylo-mastoid artery. The **veins** from the cutaneous surface open into the external jugular vein; those from the mucous surface partly end in the venous plexus on the pharyngo-tympanic tube, and partly in the sigmoid sinus and in the veins of the dura mater. The **lymph-vessels**, like the blood-vessels, are arranged in two sets, cutaneous and mucous, which, however, communicate freely with each other. The lateral surface of the membrane receives its **nerves** from the auriculo-temporal nerve and from the auricular branch of the vagus nerve; the medial surface, from the tympanic branch of the glosso-pharyngeal nerve.

TYMPANIC ANTRUM AND MASTOID AIR CELLS

The **tympanic antrum** is an air-space situated behind the epitympanic recess. In the adult its average length is from 12 to 15 mm., its height from

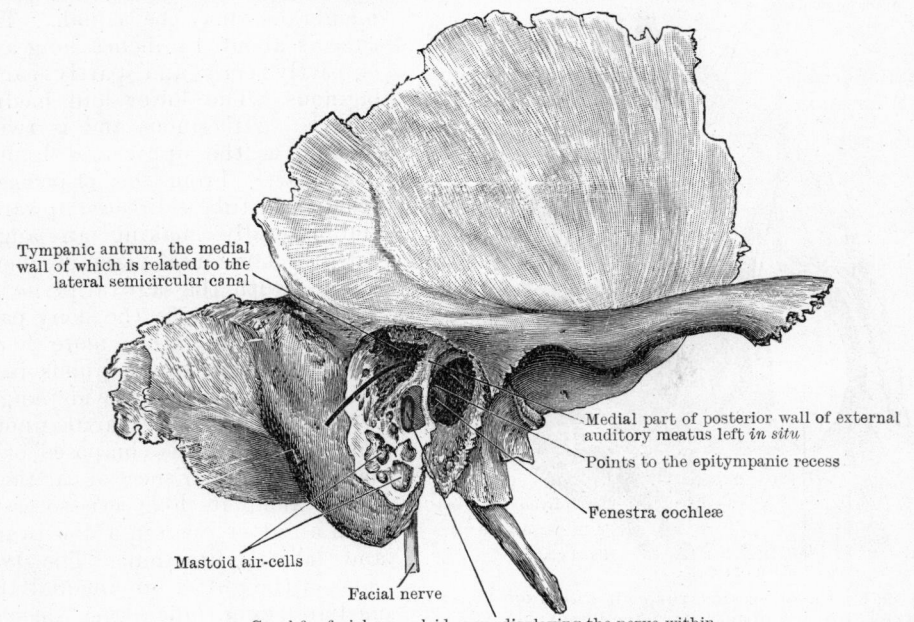

Tympanic antrum, the medial wall of which is related to the lateral semicircular canal

Medial part of posterior wall of external auditory meatus left *in situ*

Points to the epitympanic recess

Fenestra cochleæ

Mastoid air-cells

Facial nerve

Canal for facial nerve laid open, displaying the nerve within

FIG. 950.—PREPARATION DISPLAYING THE POSITION AND RELATIONS OF THE TYMPANIC ANTRUM. The greater part of the posterior wall of the external meatus has been removed, leaving only a bridge of bone at its medial end; under this a bristle passes from the tympanic antrum to the tympanic cavity.

8 to 10 mm., and its width from 6 to 8 mm. Its roof is the tegmen tympani, and its floor and medial wall are the mastoid and petrous parts of the temporal bone; laterally it is closed by the portion of the squamous part of the temporal bone which lies below the supramastoid crest. It communicates with the epitympanic recess through the aditus, on the medial wall of which, immediately above and behind the canal for the facial nerve, there is a smooth convexity that indicates the position of the ampullated ends of the superior and lateral semicircular canals.

70 *a*

At birth the lateral wall of the antrum has a thickness of only 1 or 2 mm., but it increases to about 10 mm. by the ninth year and to about 15 mm. in the adult. Coincident with the growth of the mastoid process the mastoid air-cells are developed downwards and backwards as diverticula from the antrum, and present the greatest possible variation in different skulls.

The **mastoid air-cells** may be large or small, numerous or few, and may involve all the mastoid part of the temporal bone or may not extend at all deeply into it ; when the cells are large and numerous the compact bone around them is thin, and the inner cells are separated from the posterior cranial fossa and the sigmoid sinus only by a thin sheet of bone which sometimes is perforated. When the cells are few and small the mastoid part is almost solid. The air-cells are not always limited to the mastoid part of the temporal bone, but may extend forwards into the roof of the meatus, upwards towards the squamous part, and medially towards the temporo-occipital suture ; occasionally they invade the jugular process of the occipital bone. The tympanic antrum and the mastoid air-cells are lined with thin mucous membrane continuous with that of the tympanic cavity ; it is firmly adherent to the endosteum, and its free surface is covered with a layer of flattened, non-ciliated epithelium.

PHARYNGO-TYMPANIC TUBE

The **pharyngo-tympanic tube** [tuba auditiva] is the passage through which air may pass from the pharynx to the tympanic cavity in order that the pressure

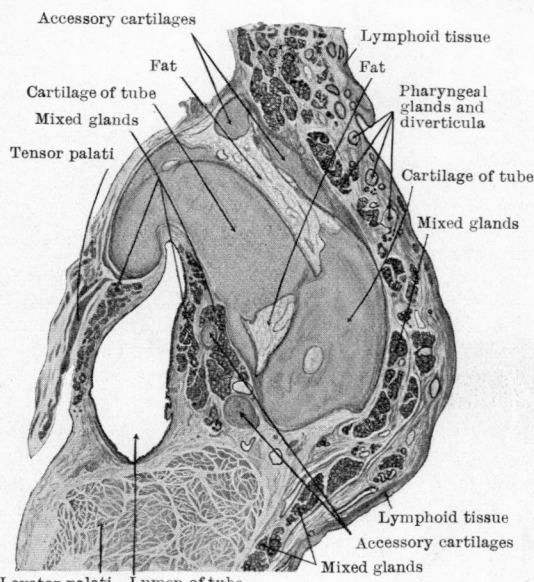

of air on each side of the tympanic membrane may be equal. The tube is about $1\frac{1}{2}$ inches long and is partly bony and partly cartilaginous. The lower and medial part is cartilaginous and is twice as long as the upper and lateral bony part. From the **pharyngeal opening** the tube is directed upwards and laterally, making an angle with the horizontal plane of about 40° and with the sagittal plane an angle of about 45° ; the bony part of the tube is rather more horizontal than the cartilaginous part and makes with it a wide angle —about 160°. The cartilaginous part of the tube is composed of a narrow triangular sheet of cartilage folded along its long axis so as to form a gutter, open in a downward and lateral direction. The two sides of the gutter are unequal, the medial being much the deeper. The gap between the sides of the gutter is bridged over by fibrous tissue, thus converting the gutter into a tube. The base of this triangular cartilage impinges on the wall of the pharynx and partially surrounds the *pharyngeal opening* of the tube ; the apex is firmly fixed to the bony part of the tube ; the amount of cartilage thus becomes gradually less as the bony part of the tube is approached. As can be easily demonstrated by a triangular piece of paper folded in the manner indicated above, it is only the medial and upper walls of the gutter that impinge on the pharyngeal wall ; in that situation they give rise to a hook-like ridge, named the **tubal elevation** (torus tubarius), from the posterior edge of which there is prolonged down the pharyngeal wall a fold of mucous membrane called the **salpingo-pharyngeal fold** ; this fold overlies the salpingo-pharyngeus muscle.

Accessory cartilages
Lymphoid tissue
Fat
Fat
Cartilage of tube
Pharyngeal glands and diverticula
Mixed glands
Tensor palati
Cartilage of tube
Mixed glands
Lymphoid tissue
Accessory cartilages
Mixed glands
Levator palati   Lumen of tube

FIG. 951.—CROSS SECTION THROUGH PHARYNGO-TYMPANIC TUBE [TUBA AUDITIVA] NEAR ITS PHARYNGEAL END.

The cartilaginous part of the tube is firmly fixed to the under surface of the skull in the groove between the greater wing of the sphenoid and the petrous part of the temporal bone. Close to its medial end it is supported by a small tubercle on the posterior edge of the medial pterygoid plate. The tensor palati muscle, which receives some fibres of origin from the cartilage, lies on the lateral side of the tube and separates it from the middle meningeal artery and the mandibular division of the trigeminal nerve; the levator palati and the mucous membrane of the pharynx are on its medial side. The bony part of the tube occupies the angle between the tympanic and petrous parts of the temporal bone, and it opens into the tympanic cavity below the canal for the tensor tympani muscle; the internal carotid artery ascends across its medial side.

The tube is opened, during deglutition, by the tensor palati and salpingo-pharyngeus muscles. When the tensor contracts, the lateral wall of the tube is drawn lateralwards and forwards. The salpingo-pharyngeus draws the medial part of the cartilage downwards and backwards, thus increasing the angle between it and the lateral part.

Mucous Membrane.—The mucous lining of the tube is continuous behind with that of the tympanic cavity, and in front with that of the nasal part of the pharynx. In the bony part it is thin and firmly fixed to the bony wall; in the cartilaginous part it is loose and thrown into longitudinal folds. Numerous mucous glands open into the tube near its pharyngeal end, and there also there is a considerable amount of adenoid tissue. The adenoid tissue is continuous with that of the nasal part of the pharynx, and, like it, is especially well developed in children. The mucous membrane is lined with ciliated columnar epithelium.

Vessels and Nerves.—The arteries of the tube come from the ascending pharyngeal and middle meningeal arteries and from the artery of the pterygoid canal. Its veins drain into the pterygoid venous plexus. Its sensory nerves are derived from the tympanic plexus and from the pharyngeal branch of the spheno-palatine ganglion.

The tube of the child differs considerably from that of the adult; its lumen is relatively wider, its direction more horizontal, and its bony part relatively shorter. The pharyngeal opening is below the level of the hard palate in the foetus; at birth it is level with the palate; at the fourth year it is 3 to 4 mm. above it, and still higher in the adult—10 mm. above it. In the child it is a narrow fissure, and the tubal elevation is less prominent.

AUDITORY OSSICLES.

The auditory ossicles, three in number, form an articulated column that connects the lateral wall of the tympanic cavity with the medial wall; they are

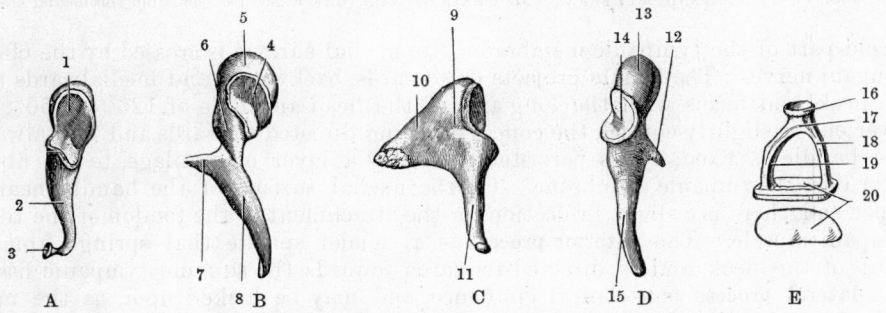

FIG. 952.—AUDITORY OSSICLES OF LEFT EAR (enlarged about three times).

A, Incus, seen from the front; B, Malleus, seen from behind; C, Incus, and D, Malleus, seen from medial side; E, Stapes.

1. Body of incus, with articular surface for head of malleus.	7. Lateral process of malleus.	14. Facet for incus.
	8. Handle of malleus.	15. Handle of malleus.
2. Long process of incus.	9. Body of incus.	16. Head of stapes.
3. Lentiform nodule of incus.	10. Short process of incus.	17. Neck of stapes.
4. Articular surface for incus.	11. Long process of incus.	18. Anterior limb of stapes.
5. Head of malleus.	12. Anterior process of malleus.	19. Posterior limb of stapes.
6. Neck of malleus.	13. Head of malleus.	20. Base of stapes.

named the malleus, the incus, and the stapes. The malleus is attached to the medial surface of the tympanic membrane; the stapes fits against the fenestra vestibuli; and the incus is in an intermediate position.

The **malleus** (Fig. 952, B, D)—the largest of the three—is from 8 to 9 mm. long, and has a head, a neck, a handle, and two processes—anterior and lateral.

The head and neck are situated in the epitympanic recess; the lateral process and the handle are fixed to the medial surface of the tympanic membrane; the anterior process is directed forwards towards the squamo-tympanic fissure, to the margin of which, in the adult, it is connected by ligamentous fibres. The **head** is smooth and convex above and in front; on its posterior surface there is a facet for articulation with the body of the incus. The facet is more or less elliptical, but is constricted near the middle; an oblique ridge, corresponding with the constriction, divides the facet into two parts—an upper and larger, directed backwards, and a lower and lesser, directed medialwards. Opposite the lower part of the constriction the inferior edge of the facet is very prominent, and is continued upwards into the oblique ridge just referred to and forms a tooth-like spur. On the back of the head, below this spur, there is an oblique crest, to which the lateral ligament of the malleus is attached. The **neck** is the slightly constricted portion immediately below the head. Its lateral surface is directed towards the

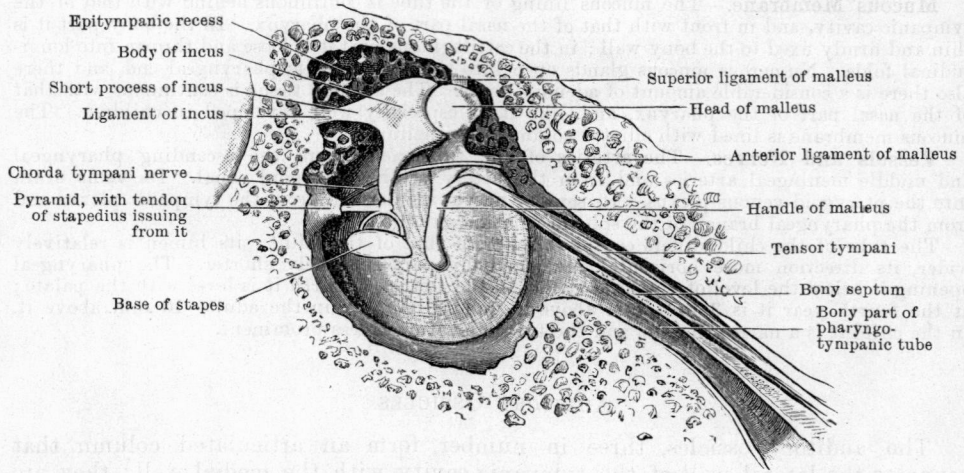

Epitympanic recess
Body of incus
Short process of incus
Ligament of incus
Chorda tympani nerve
Pyramid, with tendon of stapedius issuing from it
Base of stapes

Superior ligament of malleus
Head of malleus
Anterior ligament of malleus
Handle of malleus
Tensor tympani
Bony septum
Bony part of pharyngo-tympanic tube

FIG. 953.—LEFT TYMPANIC MEMBRANE AND CHAIN OF AUDITORY OSSICLES (seen from the medial side).

flaccid part of the tympanic membrane; its medial surface is crossed by the chorda tympani nerve. The **handle** projects downwards, backwards, and medialwards from the neck, and forms with the long axis of the head an angle of 126° to 150°; the lower end is slightly curved, the concavity being directed forwards and lateralwards. The handle is fixed, by its periosteum and by a layer of cartilage, to the fibrous layer of the tympanic membrane. On the medial surface of the handle, near its upper end, there is a slight projection for the attachment of the tendon of the tensor tympani muscle. The **anterior process** is a slender spicule that springs from the front of the neck and is directed forwards towards the squamo-tympanic fissure. The **lateral process** is a conical eminence, and may be looked upon as the upper end of the handle projected lateralwards; it is fixed to the upper part of the tympanic membrane by a layer of cartilage, and to the ends of the tympanic notch by the anterior and posterior malleolar folds.

The **incus** (Fig. 952, A, C) resembles a molar tooth with widely divergent roots. It has a body, a long process, and a short process; the processes form with each other an angle of 90° to 100°. The body and the short process are situated in the epitympanic recess. On the **body** there is a more or less saddle-shaped surface for articulation with the head of the malleus. That surface is directed forwards, and its lower part is hollowed out for the accommodation of the spur of the malleus; in front of this hollow it is prominent and spur-like. The long process projects downwards into the tympanic cavity, where it lies parallel with the handle of the malleus, but slightly posterior and medial to it. Its lower end is bent medialwards and narrowed to form a short neck, on the end of which there is a small knob of bone, called the **lentiform nodule,** for articulation with the head of the stapes. The short process is thick, pyramidal in shape, and projects horizontally backwards; its apex, covered with cartilage, is received into the fossa for the incus.

The **stapes** (Fig. 952, E) has a head, a neck, two limbs, and a base. The **head,** directed lateralwards, is concave for articulation with the lentiform nodule of the incus. The **neck** is slightly constricted, and from it the two limbs spring; the tendon of the stapedius is inserted into the posterior surface of the neck. The **anterior limb** is shorter and less curved than the **posterior limb.** Diverging from each other, the limbs are directed medialwards and are attached— one near the anterior end of the base, the other near its posterior end. The **base** is oval or kidney shaped, when seen from the medial side, and it fits against the fenestra vestibuli. In the recent condition an obturator membrane fills the arch formed by the limbs and the base, the limbs being grooved for its reception.

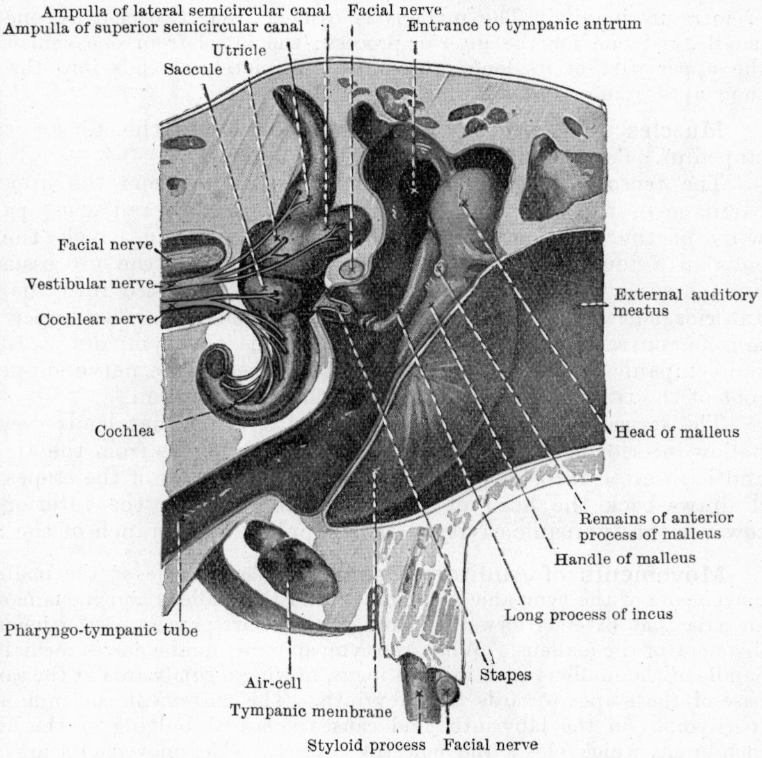

Joints of Auditory Ossicles.—The joint between the head of the malleus and the body of the incus is synovial, and may be described as a saddle-shaped

FIG. 954.—THE TYMPANIC CAVITY AND ADJACENT PARTS (SEMI-DIAGRAMMATIC).

joint. It is surrounded by an articular capsule, from the inner surface of which a wedge-shaped disc projects into the joint-cavity and incompletely divides it. The joint between the lentiform nodule and the head of the stapes is of the nature of a ball-and-socket joint, but some observers deny the presence of a synovial cavity and regard the articulation as a syndesmosis.

Ligaments of Auditory Ossicles.—The malleus is attached to the walls of the tympanic cavity by anterior, superior, and lateral ligaments (Fig. 953). The **anterior ligament** consists of two portions: one passes forwards from the anterior process through the squamo-tympanic fissure, to reach the spine of the sphenoid, from which it is continued to the spheno-mandibular ligament; the other extends from the anterior process to the anterior margin of the tympanic notch. The **superior ligament** stretches from the head of the malleus to the roof of the epitympanic recess. The **lateral ligament** is short and fan-shaped; its fibres radiate from the oblique crest of the malleus to the posterior edge of the tympanic notch. The posterior part of the ligament is strong, and, with the anterior ligament, it forms the axis around which the malleus rotates; and the two constitute what Helmholtz termed the "axis-ligament" of the malleus.

70 c

The posterior end of the short process of the incus is tipped with cartilage and fixed by means of a ligament to the fossa for the incus (Fig. 953).

The medial surface and the circumference of the base of the stapes are covered with hyaline cartilage; the cartilage encircling the base is joined to the circumference of the fenestra vestibuli by a ring of elastic fibres named the **annular ligament of the base of the stapes.**

Development of Auditory Ossicles.—The malleus and incus are developed from the upper end of the cartilage of the first (mandibular) arch; the stapes arises from an extension of the cartilage of the second (hyoid) arch in the region of the fenestra vestibuli, where it is developed around a small artery—the *stapedial artery*—which subsequently atrophies. Ossification begins in all three bones about the third month of intra-uterine life. The malleus is ossified from two centres, one for the head and handle, and one for the anterior process; the incus from one centre which appears in the upper part of its long process, and ultimately extends into the lentiform nodule; the stapes from one centre which appears in its base.

Muscles of Auditory Ossicles.—These are the tensor tympani and the stapedius.

The **tensor tympani**, the larger, takes origin from the upper surface of the cartilage of the pharyngo-tympanic tube, from the adjacent part of the greater wing of the sphenoid and from the bony canal in which the muscle lies. It ends in a tendon which bends lateralwards round the processus cochleariformis, and passes across the tympanic cavity to be inserted into the medial edge and anterior surface of the handle of the malleus, near its upper end. When the muscle contracts it draws the handle towards the tympanic cavity, and so makes the tympanic membrane more tense. It receives its nerve supply from the motor root of the trigeminal nerve, through the otic ganglion.

The **stapedius** arises from the walls of a canal that leads downwards from the hollow interior of the pyramid. Its tendon emerges from the apex of the pyramid and is inserted into the posterior surface of the neck of the stapes. On contraction it draws back the head of the stapes, and so tilts the anterior part of the base towards the tympanic cavity. It is supplied by a branch of the facial nerve.

Movements of Auditory Ossicles.—The handle of the malleus follows all the movements of the tympanic membrane; and the malleus and incus move together around an axis that extends forwards through the short process of the incus and the anterior ligament of the malleus. When the tympanic membrane moves medialwards it carries the handle of the malleus with it; the incus, moving medialwards at the same time, forces the base of the stapes towards the labyrinth. The movement is communicated to the fluid (perilymph) in the labyrinth, and causes a lateral bulging of the secondary tympanic membrane, which closes the fenestra cochleæ. The movements are reversed when the tympanic membrane is relaxed, unless the lateral movement of the membrane is excessive. When that occurs, the incus does not follow the full movement of the malleus, but merely glides on that bone at the incudo-malleolar joint, and thus the forcible dragging of the base of the stapes out of the fenestra vestibuli is prevented. The spur arrangement, already described, on the head of the malleus and body of the incus, causes the incudo-malleolar joint to become locked during the medial movement of the handle of the malleus, the joint becoming unlocked during its lateral movement.

Mucous Membrane of Tympanic Cavity.—The mucous lining is continuous, through the pharyngo-tympanic tube, with that of the nasal part of the pharynx; it extends backwards also and lines the tympanic antrum and the mastoid air-cells. Thin and transparent, it follows closely all the irregularities of the walls of the cavity, and is reflected over the ossicles, their ligaments and muscles, and the chorda tympani; there is thus formed a number of folds that enclose pouches in which pus may collect in inflammatory conditions of the middle ear.

Vessels and Nerves of Tympanic Cavity.—The arteries are: (1) The anterior tympanic artery, which reaches the cavity by way of the squamo-tympanic fissure. (2) The stylo-mastoid artery, which passes through the stylo-mastoid foramen; (3) a branch from the middle meningeal artery, which accompanies the greater superficial petrosal nerve. The veins drain into the pterygoid plexus and the superior petrosal sinus. The lymph vessels form a network in the mucous membrane and end mainly in the retro-pharyngeal and parotid lymph glands. The nerves supplying the muscles have already been referred to above. The mucous membrane receives its nerves from the tympanic plexus. The chorda tympani branch of the facial nerve passes from behind, upwards and forwards through the tympanic cavity; its course is described on p. 977.

Early Condition of Tympanic Cavity.—During the greater part of intra-uterine life the tympanic cavity is almost completely filled with a soft, reddish, jelly-like embryonic tissue in which there is a slit-like space lined with epithelium. By the time of birth that tissue has disappeared, and at birth the cavity is filled with fluid which becomes absorbed, after the entrance of air from the nasal part of the pharynx through the pharyngo-tympanic tube. At birth the tympanic membrane is close to the surface of the skull, and there is no bony external auditory meatus. All the parts of the middle and internal ear are relatively large and show little if any difference from the adult condition.

INTERNAL EAR

The **internal ear** is lodged within the petrous part of the temporal bone, and is composed of a series of delicate membranous chambers and passages—the *membranous labyrinth*—enclosed within corresponding cavities which are hollowed out of the bone and constitute the *bony labyrinth*. The component parts of the membranous labyrinth are, from before backwards, the **duct of the cochlea**, the **saccule** and **utricle**, and the three **semicircular ducts**; the corresponding parts of the

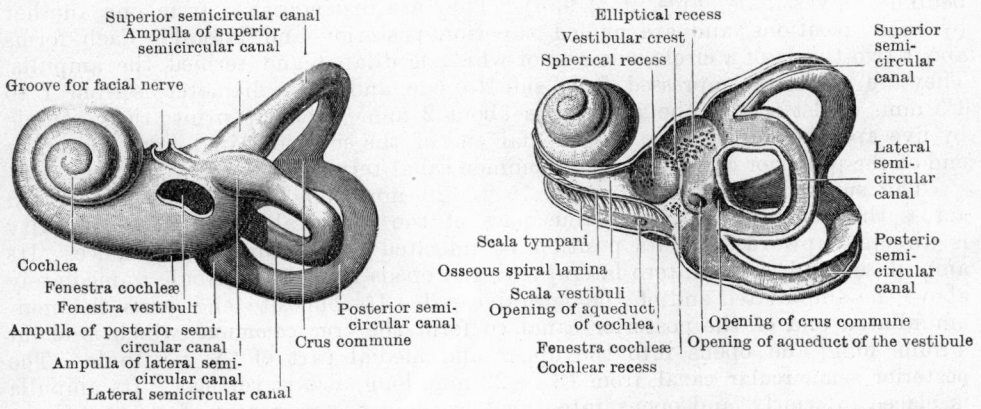

FIG. 955.—LEFT BONY LABYRINTH
(seen from the lateral side).

FIG. 956.—INTERIOR OF LEFT BONY LABYRINTH
(seen from below and from the lateral side).

bony labyrinth are the **cochlea**, the **vestibule**, and the three **semicircular canals**. The utricle and the saccule are both contained in the vestibule; and all the parts of the bony labyrinth are considerably larger than the parts of the membranous labyrinth.

BONY LABYRINTH

Vestibule.—The vestibule is the middle portion of the bony labyrinth, and communicates behind with the semicircular canals and in front with the cochlea. It is an oval cavity, with its long axis directed forwards and lateralwards, and it measures about 6 mm. antero-posteriorly, 4 or 5 mm. vertically, and about 3 mm. transversely. Its lateral wall is directed towards the tympanic cavity, and in it is the fenestra vestibuli, which is closed by the base of the stapes. Its medial wall corresponds with the bottom of the internal auditory meatus, and presents, at its antero-inferior part, a circular depression, called the **spherical recess**, which lodges the saccule. In the recess there are twelve or fifteen small foramina (**macula cribrosa media**) which transmit the filaments of the auditory nerve to the saccule. The spherical recess is limited above and behind by an oblique ridge, called the **vestibular crest**, the anterior end of which is triangular in shape and named the **pyramid of the vestibule**. Posteriorly the crest divides into two limbs, that enclose a small depression, called the **cochlear recess**, in which there are several small foramina for the passage of the nerves from the vestibular end of the duct of the cochlea. Above and behind the vestibular crest, in the roof and medial wall of the vestibule, there is an oval depression, called the **elliptical recess**, which lodges the utricle. The pyramid of the vestibule and adjacent part of the elliptical recess show twenty-five or thirty small foramina (**macula cribrosa superior**) for the passage of the nerves to the utricle and to the ampullæ of the superior and lateral semicircular ducts. Behind and below the elliptical recess there is a furrow, gradually deepening to form a canal, called the **aqueduct of the vestibule**, which passes backwards through the petrous part of the temporal bone, and opens into the posterior cranial fossa as a slit-like fissure, about midway between the internal auditory meatus and the groove for the sigmoid sinus. This aqueduct is from 8 to 10 mm. long, and gives passage to the endolymphatic duct and a small vein. At the posterior part of the vestibule there are five circular openings leading into the semicircular canals; at its anterior part there is an elliptical opening that leads into the scala vestibuli of the cochlea. The opening is bounded below by a thin bony plate, called the **osseous spiral lamina**, which springs from the floor of the vestibule immediately lateral to the spherical recess, and forms, in the cochlea, the bony part of the septum between the scala tympani and the scala vestibuli.

Semicircular Canals.—The three semicircular canals are situated above and behind the vestibule (Figs. 955, 956). They are distinguished from one another by their positions, and are named superior, posterior, and lateral. Each forms about two-thirds of a circle, one end of which is dilated and termed the ampulla. They are slightly compressed from side to side, and their diameter is from 1 to 1·5 mm., whilst that of the ampullæ is about 2 mm. They open into the vestibule by five apertures only, since the medial end of the superior canal joins the upper end of the posterior canal to form a common canal termed the *crus commune*.

The **superior semicircular canal**, 15 to 20 mm. long, is vertical and placed across the long axis of the petrous part of the temporal bone. Its convexity is directed upwards, and its position is indicated by the arcuate eminence. Its ampullated end is the antero-lateral end, and opens into the vestibule immediately above the ampullated end of the lateral canal. Its opposite end joins the non-ampullated end of the posterior canal to form the **crus commune**, which is about 4 mm. long, and opens into the upper and medial part of the vestibule. The **posterior semicircular canal**, from 18 to 22 mm. long, also is vertical. Its ampulla is placed inferiorly, and opens into the lower and posterior part of the vestibule, where there are six or eight small apertures (**macula cribrosa inferior**) for the transmission of the nerves to this ampulla. Its upper end joins the crus commune. The **lateral canal**, from 12 to 15 mm. long, arches nearly horizontally. Its lateral end is ampullated, and opens into the vestibule immediately above the fenestra vestibuli, close to the ampullated end of the superior canal, and causes an elevation on the medial wall of the tympanic antrum above the canal for the facial nerve. The lateral canal of one ear is very nearly in the same plane as that of the other; the superior canal of one ear is nearly parallel to the posterior canal of the other.

Cochlea.—When freed from its surroundings the **cochlea** has the form of a short cone (Fig. 957); the central part of its **base** corresponds with the bottom of the internal auditory meatus, whilst its apex or **cupola**, directed forwards and lateralwards, is in close relation with the canal for the tensor tympani muscle. [In the following description the cochlea is supposed to be placed on its base.] It measures about 9 mm. across the base and about 5 mm. from base to apex, and consists of a spirally arranged tube, which forms from 2½ to 2¾ coils around a central pillar termed the **modiolus**. The length of the tube is from 28 to 30 mm., and its diameter, near the base of the cochlea is 2 mm. Its coils are distinguished by the terms basal, middle, and apical; the basal coil bulges into the tympanic cavity, giving rise to the promontory on its medial wall.

The modiolus is about 3 mm. long, and its diameter diminishes rapidly from the base to the apex; it ends about 1 mm. from the cupola. Its **base** corresponds with the **cochlear area** on the fundus of the internal auditory meatus, and exhibits (1) the **tractus spiralis foraminosus**, which transmits the nerves from the basal and middle coils of the cochlea, and (2) a **central foramen**, which gives passage to the nerves from the apical coil. From the free edge of the osseous spiral lamina numerous small canals, for the transmission of vessels and nerves, pass to its attached edge, where they unite to form the **spiral canal** of the cochlea, which lodges the **spiral**

ganglion. From the spiral canal other small canals pass down the modiolus and open by the holes along the tractus spiralis foraminosus.

The **osseous spiral lamina** is a thin, flat shelf of bone which winds round the modiolus like the thread of a screw, and, projecting about half-way into the cochlear tube, incompletely divides it into two passages—an upper, the **scala vestibuli**, and a lower, the **scala tympani**. It begins at the floor of the vestibule, near the fenestra

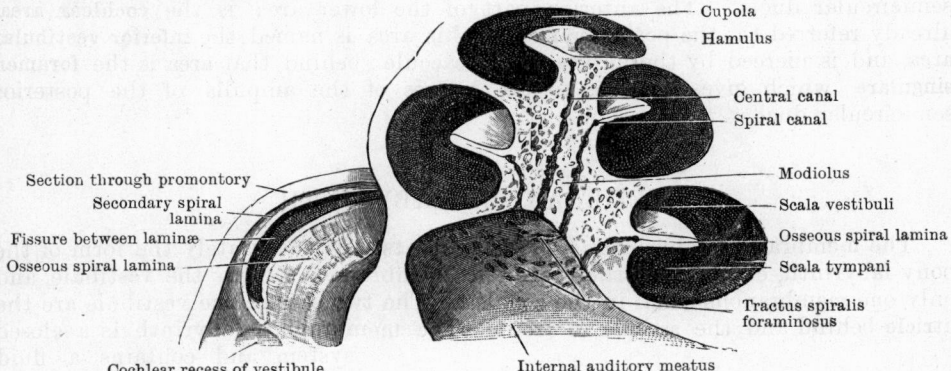

FIG. 957.—SECTION OF BONY COCHLEA.

cochleæ, and ends near the cupola of the cochlea in a sickle-shaped process, called the **hamulus of the spiral lamina,** which helps to bound an aperture named the **helicotrema,** through which the scala tympanic and scala vestibuli communicate with each other. In the basal coil the upper surface of the lamina forms almost a right angle with the modiolus, but the angle becomes more and more acute on ascending the tube. In the lower half of the basal coil a second smaller bony plate, called the **secondary spiral lamina,** projects from the outer wall of the cochlea towards the osseous spiral lamina, without, however, reaching it, so that a slit-like fissure is seen between the two laminæ, which are continuous with each other round the posterior end of the fissure. A membrane, called the **basilar lamina,** stretches from the free edge of the osseous spiral lamina to the outer wall of the cochlea, and completes the division of the cochlear tube into scala vestibuli and scala tympani; the two, however, communicate with each other through the opening of the helicotrema at the cupola of the cochlea. The scala tympani begins at the fenestra cochleæ, which is closed by the secondary tympanic membrane (p. 1105). Close to the beginning of the scala tympani and on its medial wall there is seen the inner orifice of the **aqueduct of the cochlea**; this is a canal, measuring from 10 to 12 mm. in length, which opens on the under surface

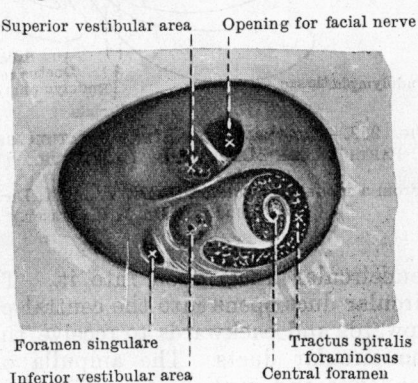

FIG. 958. — FUNDUS OF INTERNAL AUDITORY MEATUS DIVIDED INTO UPPER AND LOWER AREAS BY THE TRANSVERSE CREST.

of the petrous part of the temporal bone in the upper border of the jugular fossa. This aqueduct establishes a communication between the scala tympani and the subarachnoid space in the following manner; both dura mater and arachnoid are continued along the glosso-pharyngeal nerve to the jugular foramen, and here the dura mater becomes continuous with the pericranium on the outside of the skull, whereas a diverticulum of the arachnoid passes towards the scala tympani and unites with a corresponding outgrowth from that passage; the resulting communication between scala tympani and subarachnoid space is the aqueduct of the cochlea. The scala vestibuli, the higher of the two passages, begins in the vestibule; in the basal coil its diameter is less than that of the scala tympani, but in the upper coils it is greater.

The **fundus** of the **internal auditory meatus** has been referred to as forming the medial wall of the vestibule and the base of the modiolus. It is divided by a transverse crest into an upper and a lower area. In the anterior part of the upper area there is a single large opening for the transmission of the facial nerve; the posterior part is named the **superior vestibular area**, and is perforated by the nerves of the utricle and of the ampullæ of the superior and lateral semicircular ducts. The anterior part of the lower area is the **cochlear area**, already referred to; the posterior part of this area is named the **inferior vestibular area**, and is pierced by the nerves to the saccule; behind that area is the **foramen singulare**, which gives passage to the nerves of the ampulla of the posterior semicircular duct.

MEMBRANOUS LABYRINTH

The membranous labyrinth (Fig. 959) repeats fairly accurately the form of the bony labyrinth, except that there are two membranous sacs in the vestibule, and only one membranous canal in the cochlea. The two sacs in the vestibule are the **utricle** behind and the **saccule** in front. The membranous labyrinth is a closed system and contains a fluid called **endolymph**; the membranous labyrinth does not completely fill the bony labyrinth, and the resulting space is occupied by a fluid termed **perilymph**. Neither of these fluids has any connexion with the fluid of the lymphatic system. The perilymphatic space is closed except for the communication with the subarachnoid space, to which reference has already been made.

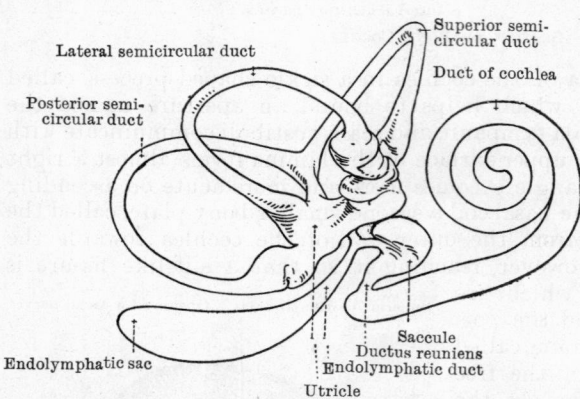

FIG. 959.—DIAGRAMMATIC REPRESENTATION OF THE DIFFERENT PARTS OF THE MEMBRANOUS LABYRINTH. (Milne Dickie.)

(From a model constructed by Dr. J. K. M. Dickie, from sections made by Dr. J. S. Fraser.)

The **utricle** (Fig. 959) occupies the postero-superior portion of the vestibule. Its highest part lies in the elliptical recess, and the ampullæ of the superior and lateral semicircular ducts open into it. The non-ampullated end of the lateral semicircular duct opens into the central part of the utricle, and that part is prolonged upwards and backwards to receive the crus commune of the superior and posterior semicircular ducts. The ampulla of the posterior semicircular duct opens into the lower and medial part. The floor and anterior wall of the highest part are thickened to form the **macula of the utricle**, to which the utricular fibres of the auditory nerve are transmitted through the foramina in the pyramid of the vestibule. Whitish in colour, and of an oval or nearly rhombic shape, this macula measures 3 mm. in length and 2·3 mm. in its greatest breadth.

The **saccule** is smaller than the utricle, and occupies the spherical recess in the lower and anterior part of the vestibule (Fig. 956). It is of an oval shape and measures 3 mm. in its longest diameter, and about 2 mm. in its shortest. It presents, anteriorly, an oval whitish thickening, called the **macula of the saccule**, which has a breadth of about 1·5 mm., and to which the saccular fibres of the auditory nerve are distributed. The upper end of the saccule is directed upwards and backwards, and comes into contact with the utricle, and there the utricle and saccule are separated by a common wall (Milne Dickie). From the lower part of the saccule a short canal—the **ductus reuniens**—descends and gradually widens into the vestibular end of the duct of the cochlea. A second small channel, named the **endolymphatic duct**, is continued from the posterior part of the saccule, and is joined by a small canal, called the **utriculo-saccular duct**, which arises from the medial side of the utricle. The endolymphatic duct then enters and traverses the aqueduct of the vestibule and ends, under the dura mater on

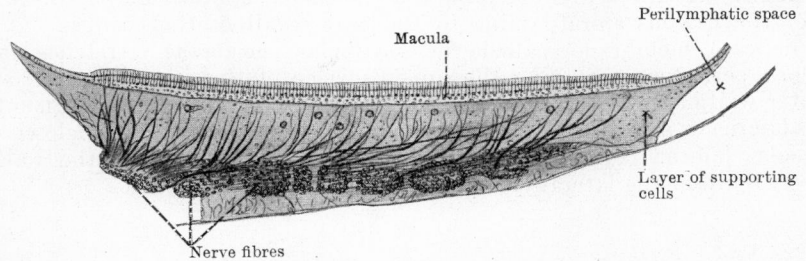

FIG. 960.—VERTICAL SECTION OF WALL OF HIGHEST PART OF UTRICLE WITH THE MACULA AND BUNDLES OF NERVE FIBRES.

the posterior surface of the petrous part of the temporal bone, in a dilated blind pouch termed the **endolymphatic sac**.

Structure.—The walls of the utricle and saccule are composed of (a) an external layer of fibrous tissue which blends with the endosteal lining of the vestibule, (b) a middle, transparent layer and (c) an internal epithelial layer. The walls are thickened at the maculæ and on them the epithelium is columnar, towards their periphery it is cubical, and elsewhere it is of the pavement type.

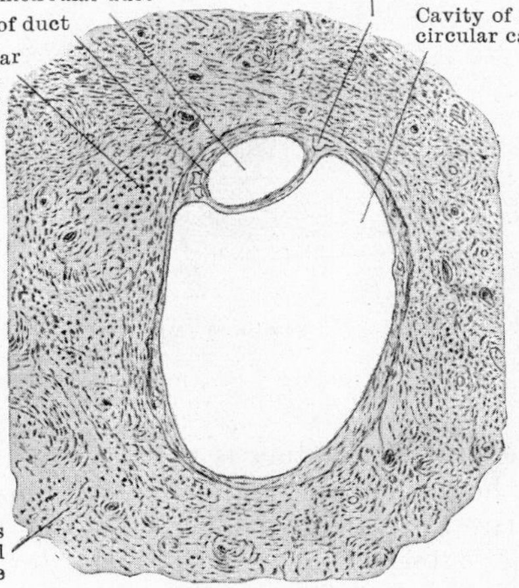

In the maculæ of the utricle and saccule two kinds of cells are found, (a) supporting cells, and (b) hair-cells. The **supporting cells** are fusiform, with the nucleus near the middle. Their deep ends are branched; their free ends lie between the hair-cells and form a thin inner limiting layer. The **hair-cells** are flask-shaped, their rounded ends lying between the supporting cells. Each hair-cell contains a large nucleus in its deepest part, the rest of the cell being granular and pigmented. From the free end of each there projects a stiff, hair-like process which, on the application of reagents, splits into several filaments. The nerve-fibres ramify around the deep ends of the hair-cells (Fig. 962). A collection of small crystals of carbonate of lime, termed *otoliths*, adheres to each of the maculæ.

FIG. 961.—SECTION OF A SEMICIRCULAR CANAL AND DUCT.

(From a section made by Dr. J. S. Fraser.)

The **semicircular ducts** are elliptical on transverse section (Fig. 961), and only about one-fourth of the girth of the bony canals which contain them. The convex wall of each duct is fixed to the endosteal lining of the canal, whilst the opposite part is connected by delicate fibrous bands with the bony wall. Like the bony canals, each of the semicircular ducts is dilated at one end into an ampulla which nearly fills the corresponding portion of the bony canal.

Structure.—Each semicircular duct has three layers: (a) an external vascular and partly pigmented fibrous layer which fixes the duct to the bony wall; (b) a middle transparent layer presenting a number of papilliform elevations which project towards the lumen; (c) an internal epithelial layer composed of pavement cells. In each ampulla the middle, transparent layer is thickened, and projects into the cavity as a transverse elevation which, when seen from above, is fiddle-shaped; the most prominent part of the elevation is named the *ampullary crest*. The cells covering the crest consist of **supporting cells** and **hair-cells**, and are similar in their arrangement to those in the maculæ of the utricle and saccule; the hairs of the hair-cells are, however, considerably longer, and project as far as the middle of the ampullary lumen.

The **duct of the cochlea** is a spirally arranged canal inside the bony cochlea. Its lower end occupies the cochlear recess of the vestibule and communicates with the saccule through the ductus reuniens; its upper end is closed, and is named the **cæcum cupulare**; it is fixed to the cupola of the cochlea, and partly bounds the helicotrema.   As already stated (p. 1115), the basilar lamina stretches from the free edge of the osseous spiral lamina to the outer wall of the cochlea.   A second, more delicate membrane, called the **vestibular membrane**, stretches from the thickened periosteum covering the upper surface of the osseous spiral lamina to the outer wall of the cochlea, some distance above the external attachment of the basilar lamina.   A tunnel, triangular in transverse section, is thus enclosed between the basilar lamina below, the vestibular membrane above, and the wall of the scala vestibuli on the lateral side; this is the *duct of the cochlea.*

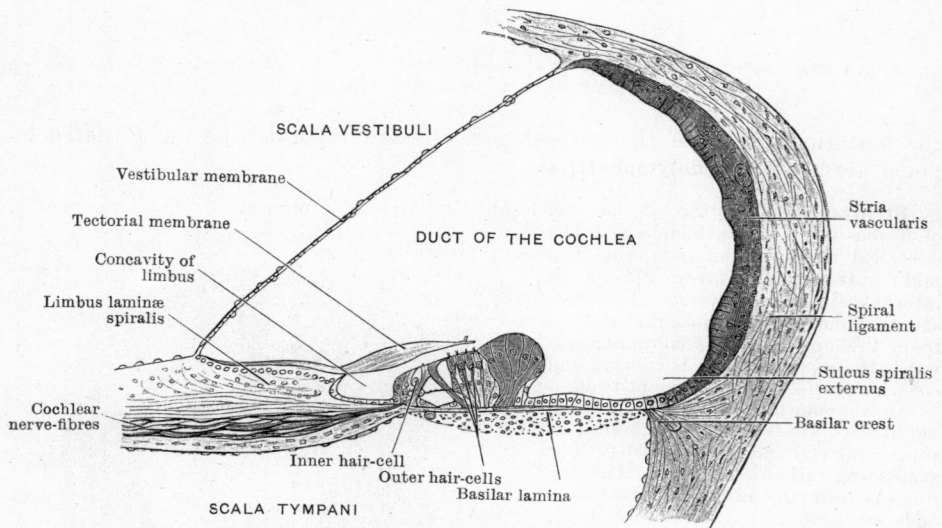

SCALA VESTIBULI

Vestibular membrane

Tectorial membrane

Concavity of limbus

Limbus laminæ spiralis

DUCT OF THE COCHLEA

Stria vascularis

Spiral ligament

Sulcus spiralis externus

Cochlear nerve-fibres

Basilar crest

Inner hair-cell

Outer hair-cells

Basilar lamina

SCALA TYMPANI

FIG. 962.—SECTION ACROSS THE DUCT OF THE COCHLEA.   (Retzius.)

The **roof** of the duct is the vestibular membrane, which is an extremely delicate, nearly homogeneous membrane, covered on both surfaces with a layer of epithelium. Its entire thickness is about 3 μ.

The **outer wall** is the endosteal lining of the bony cochlea, which is thickened and greatly modified to form the *spiral ligament of the cochlea.*   This ligament projects inwards inferiorly as a triangular crest to which the outer edge of the basilar lamina is attached.   The upper part of the spiral ligament contains, immediately under its epithelial lining, numerous small blood-vessels and capillary loops, forming the **stria vascularis.**   The lower limit of this stria is bounded by a prominence, called the *spiral prominence,* in which there is seen a vessel—the **vas prominens**—and below this prominence is a concavity, called the *spiral sulcus.* The height of the outer wall of the duct diminishes towards the apex of the cochlea.

The **floor** of the duct is formed by the lateral part of the upper surface of the osseous spiral lamina and by the basilar lamina.   On the inner part of the basilar lamina the complicated structure termed the *spiral organ* is situated.   The osseous spiral lamina consists of two plates of bone between which the canals for the branches of the cochlear nerve are placed.   On the upper plate the endosteum is thickened and modified to form the **limbus laminæ spiralis**, the outer border of which is concave, and appears, in radial sections, as a C-shaped indentation.   The portions of the limbus which project above and below this concavity are termed respectively the *vestibular lip* and the *tympanic lip.*   The tympanic lip is perforated by the peripherally directed branches of the cochlear nerves, and is continuous with the basilar lamina.   The upper surface of the limbus and of its vestibular lip is divided into a series of blocks or segments by furrows that intersect each other at right angles ; this gives to the free edge of the vestibular lip a dentated appearance, and here the segments are named the *auditory teeth*. The limbus is covered with a layer of apparently squamous epithelium ; the deeper protoplasmic portions of the cells, however, with their contained nuclei, lie in the intervals between the blocks, or segments, just mentioned.

The **basilar lamina** stretches from the tympanic lip of the limbus to the crest of the spiral ligament. Its inner part is thin, and supports the spiral organ. Its outer part is thicker and distinctly striated, owing to the presence of numerous fibres. The under surface of the basilar lamina is covered with a layer of fibrous tissue which contains, in its inner part, small blood-vessels ; one of them which lies below the more medial part of the spiral organ is considerably larger than any of the others. The width of the basilar lamina increases from 0·21 mm. in the basal coil to 0·36 mm. in the apical coil.

Spiral Organ.—This is an epithelial eminence of complicated structure, placed on the inner part of the basilar lamina. It extends throughout the entire length of the duct of the cochlea, and comprises the following structures : (1) Corti's rods or pillars, (2) hair-cells (inner and outer), (3) supporting cells of Deiters, (4) the cells of Hensen and Claudius, (5) the reticular lamina, and (6) the tectorial membrane.

The **rods of Corti** form two rows, **inner** and **outer**, of stiff, pillar-like structures, and each rod presents a base or foot-plate, an intermediate elongated portion, and an upper end or head. The bases of the rods are planted on the basilar lamina—those of the inner row at some little distance from those of the outer. The intermediate portions of the rods incline towards each other and the heads come into contact, so that, between the two rows and the basilar lamina, a triangular passage, called the **tunnel of Corti**, is enclosed ; this tunnel increases both in height and width on passing towards the apex of the cochlea. The **inner rods** number nearly 6000, and the head of each resembles the upper end of the ulna, presenting externally a deep

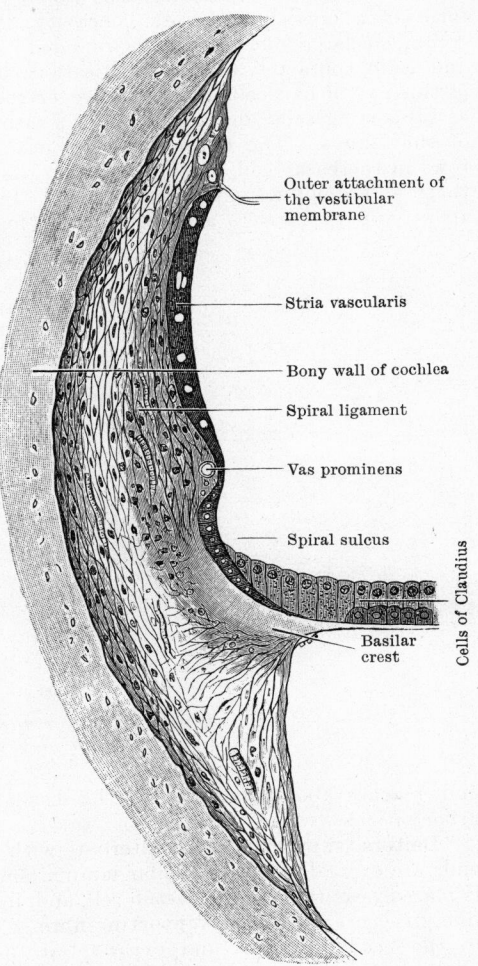

Outer attachment of the vestibular membrane

Stria vascularis

Bony wall of cochlea

Spiral ligament

Vas prominens

Spiral sulcus

Cells of Claudius

Basilar crest

FIG. 963.—TRANSVERSE SECTION THROUGH OUTER WALL OF DUCT OF THE COCHLEA. (Schwalbe.)

concavity for the reception of a corresponding convexity on the head of the outer rod. The part of the head which overhangs that concavity is prolonged outwards, under the name of the **head-plate**, and overlaps the head of the outer rod. The expanded bases of the inner rods are placed immediately on the outer side of the foramina for the cochlear nerves in the tympanic lip of the limbus ; the intermediate parts of these rods are sinuously curved, and form with the basilar lamina an angle of about 60°. The **outer rods** number about 4000, and are longer than the inner, especially in the upper turns of the cochlea. They are more inclined towards the basilar lamina, and form with it an angle of about 40°. The head of each is convex inwards, to fit the concavity on the head of the inner rod, and is prolonged outwards as a plate called the **phalangeal process**. The main part of each rod consists of a nearly homogeneous material which is finely striated. At the base of each rod, on the surface next Corti's tunnel, there is a nucleated mass of protoplasm which reaches as far as the head of the rod, and covers also a part of the floor of the tunnel ; this protoplasm may be regarded as the undifferentiated part of the cell from which the rod was developed. Slit-like intervals, for the transmission of nerves, exist between the intermediate portions of adjacent rods.

Hair-cells.—These, like Corti's rods, are arranged in two sets—**inner** and **outer**. The inner set is a single row lying immediately internal to the inner rods; the outer set is arranged in three or four rows placed to the outer side of the outer rods. The **inner hair-cells** are about 3500 in number; the diameter of each is greater than that of an inner rod, and so each inner hair-cell is supported by more than one rod. The free end of each hair-cell is surmounted by about twenty fine hair-like processes, arranged in the form of a crescent with its concavity directed inwards. The deep end of the cell contains a large nucleus and is rounded; it reaches only about half-way down the rod, and is in contact with the arborisations of the nerve terminations. To the inner side of this row of hair-cells there are two or three rows of elongated columnar cells which act as supporting cells, and are continuous with the low columnar cells that line the concavity of the limbus. The **outer hair-cells** number about 12,000, and are arranged in three rows in the basal coil and four rows in the upper two coils, although in the higher coils the rows are not so regularly arranged. The free, rounded end of each hair-cell supports about twenty hairlets arranged in the form of a crescent opening inwards; the deep

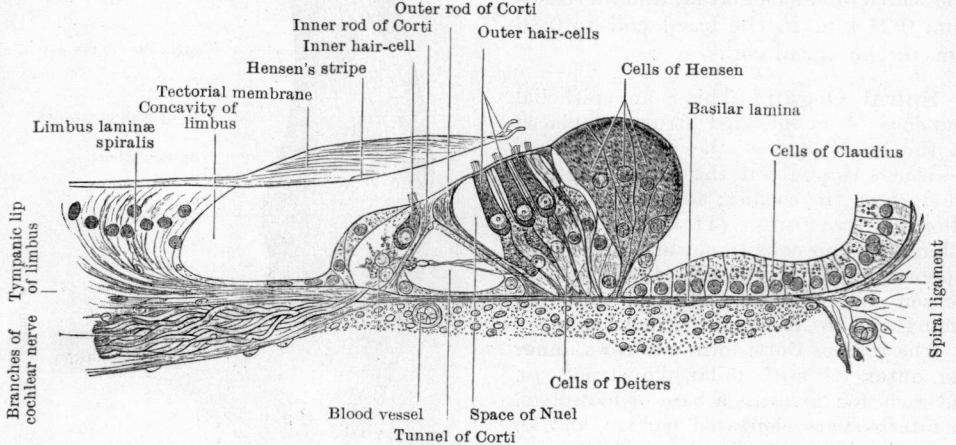

FIG. 964.—TRANSVERSE SECTION OF THE SPIRAL ORGAN FROM THE CENTRAL COIL OF THE DUCT OF THE COCHLEA. (Retzius.)

end reaches about half-way to the basilar lamina, and is in contact with the nerve arborisations.

Deiters' supporting cells alternate with the rows of the outer hair-cells; their lower ends are expanded on the basilar lamina, and their upper ends are tapered. The nucleus is placed near the middle of each cell, and, in addition, each cell contains a bright, thread-like structure called the **supporting fibre**. That fibre is attached by a club-shaped base to the basilar lamina, and expands, at the free end of the cell, to form one of the phalanges of the reticular lamina, which is described below.

The **cells of Hensen**, or outer supporting cells, are arranged in about half a dozen rows immediately outside Deiters' cells, and are the most elevated part of the spiral organ. Their lower ends are narrow and attached to the basilar lamina, whilst their free ends are expanded. The columnar cells situated to the outer side of the cells of Hensen, and covering the outer part of the basilar lamina, are named the **cells of Claudius**. An interval exists between the outer rods of Corti and the neighbouring row of hair-cells and is termed the **space of Nuel**; it communicates with Corti's tunnel, and extends outwards between the outer hair-cells as far as Hensen's cells.

The **reticular lamina** is a thin sheet that extends from the heads of the outer rods to Hensen's cells, and is formed from expansions of these two structures. These expansions are termed the **phalanges** of the lamina, and are arranged in rows corresponding with the heads of the outer rods, the cells of Hensen, and the cells of Deiters, which also contribute to its formation. The free ends of the hair-cells occupy the intervals between the phalanges.

The **tectorial membrane** is a projecting shelf, of jelly-like consistence, which overhangs the inner half of the spiral organ. Attached, by its inner border, to the limbus near the vestibular membrane, it reaches outwards as far as the outer row of hair-cells. Its inner portion is thin and overlies the auditory teeth of the limbus. Its outer part is thickened

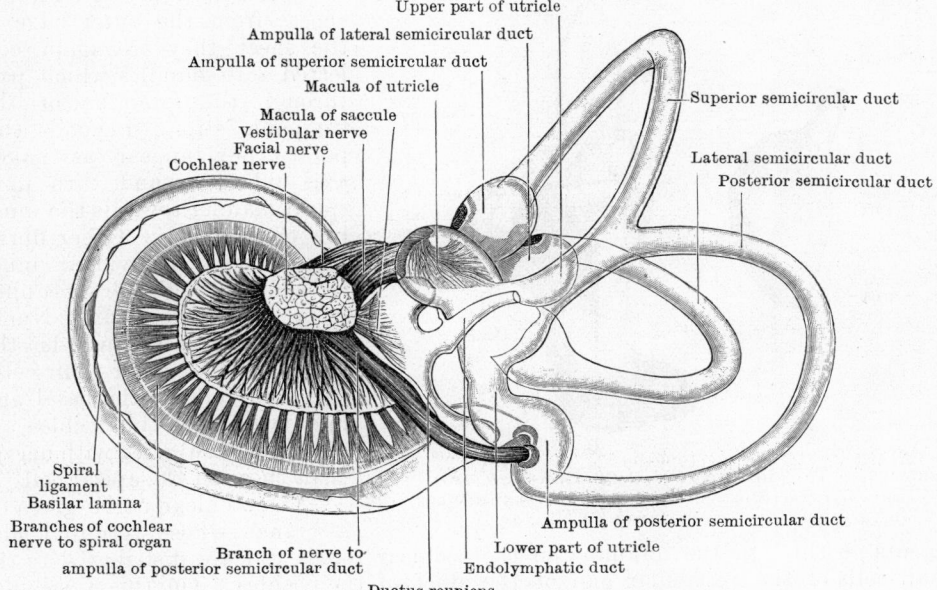

FIG. 965.—MEMBRANOUS LABYRINTH OF A FIVE MONTHS' FŒTUS.
Postero-medial aspect (Retzius).

but becomes attenuated near its free border, which is fringed. The hairs of the hair-cells project against the under surface of the membrane, and on this surface, opposite the interval between the inner and outer rows of hair-cells, there is a clear, spirally arranged band named **Hensen's stripe**.

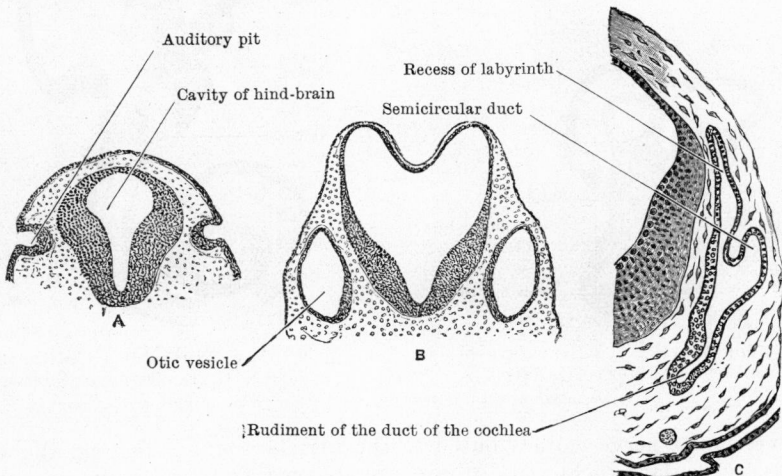

FIG. 966.—SECTIONS THROUGH THE REGION OF THE HIND-BRAIN OF FŒTAL RABBITS
(to illustrate the development of the membranous labyrinth).

Auditory Nerve [N. Acusticus] (Fig. 965).—This nerve divides in the internal auditory meatus into a cochlear nerve and a vestibular nerve.

The **cochlear nerve** is the nerve of hearing. Its fibres originate from the cells of the **spiral ganglion**. This ganglion is situated in the spiral canal of the modiolus; and from the ganglion the centrally directed fibres traverse the modiolus—those from the apical coil emerging through the central foramen and those from the basal coils through the holes in the tractus spiralis foraminosus. The peripherally directed fibres extend outwards, at first in bundles, and then in a more or less continuous sheet; from the outer edge of the sheet they are again collected into bundles which pass through the foramina of the tympanic lip. Beyond this point they appear as naked axis-cylinders, and turn in a spiral manner towards the inner row of hair-cells. Other fibrils run between individual inner rods and through Corti's tunnel, from which they enter Nuel's space, and pass towards the bases of the outer hair-cells. The hair-cells in the basal and middle coils of the cochlea are more richly supplied with nerves than those in the apical coil.

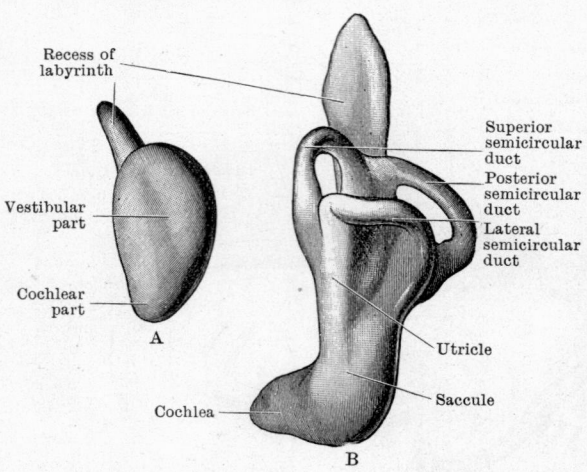

FIG. 967.—THE LEFT MEMBRANOUS LABYRINTH SEEN FROM THE LATERAL SIDE, A, AT ABOUT THE FOURTH WEEK, AND B, AT ABOUT THE FIFTH WEEK (W. His, Jr.).

The cochlear nerve gives off a branch whose terminal filaments go through the foramina in the cochlear recess and are distributed to the hair-cells of the vestibular end of the duct of the cochlea. On this vestibular branch there is a minute ganglion (Böettcher).

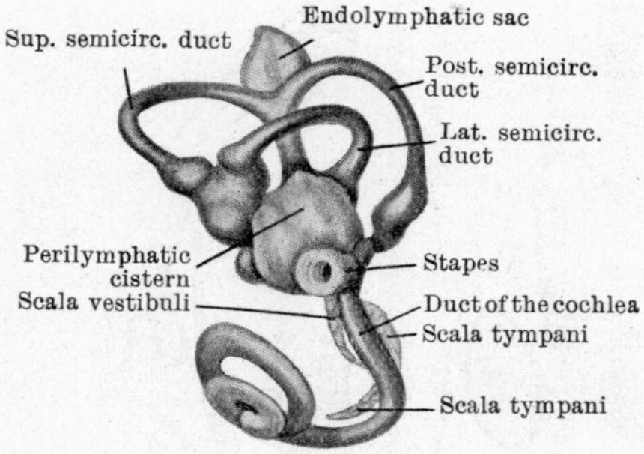

FIG. 968.—THE MEMBRANOUS LABYRINTH OF A 50 MM. HUMAN EMBRYO (Streeter).

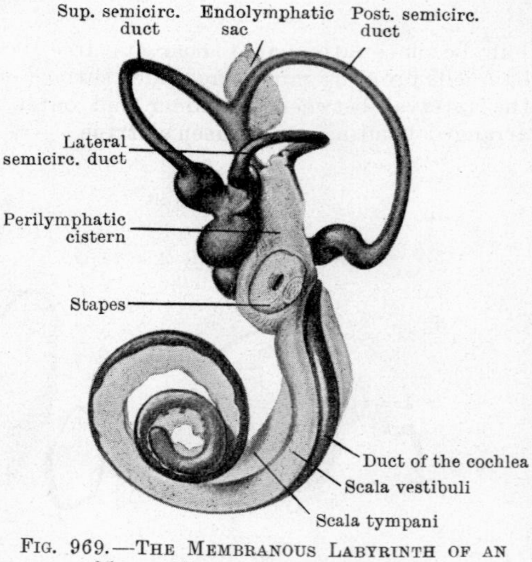

FIG. 969.—THE MEMBRANOUS LABYRINTH OF AN 85 MM. HUMAN EMBRYO (Streeter).

(By permission of the Carnegie Institution of Washington.)

The **vestibular nerve** is distributed to the utricle, the saccule, and the ampullæ of the semicircular ducts; its fibres are derived from cells in the **vestibular ganglion**, which is usually placed in the internal auditory meatus. From the ganglion three branches arise—superior, inferior, and posterior—and each of these splits into filaments which pass through foramina in the fundus of the internal auditory meatus. The filaments from the superior branch go through the foramina in the superior vestibular area and supply the macula of the utricle and the ampullary crests of the superior and lateral semicircular ducts; those from the inferior branch run through the foramina in the inferior vestibular area, and pass to the macula of the saccule. The posterior branch passes through the foramen singulare, and its filaments, six to eight in number, are distributed to the ampullary crests of the posterior semicircular duct. Sometimes the vestibular ganglion, instead of being a single structure, is split into three parts corresponding with the three branches of the nerve.

Vessels of Internal Ear.—The **arteries** are the internal auditory branch of the basilar artery, and the stylo-mastoid branch of the posterior auricular artery. The internal auditory artery enters the internal meatus and divides into vestibular and cochlear branches which are distributed to the structures supplied by the corresponding nerves. The **veins** from the cochlea and vestibule unite, at the bottom of the internal meatus, with the veins from the semicircular canals to form the **internal auditory vein,** which may open either into the posterior part of the inferior petrosal sinus or into the sigmoid sinus. A small vein passes through the aqueduct of the cochlea and opens into the inferior petrosal sinus or into the internal jugular vein. Another small vein traverses the aqueduct of the vestibule and ends in the superior petrosal sinus.

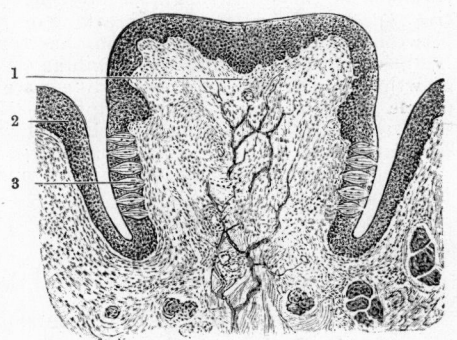

FIG. 970.—SECTION THROUGH A VALLATE PAPILLA OF HUMAN TONGUE.

1. Papilla. 2. Vallum. 3. Taste-buds.

DEVELOPMENT OF MEMBRANOUS LABYRINTH

The epithelial lining of the labyrinth is derived from an invagination of the head ectoderm, termed the **auditory pit**, which appears opposite the hind-brain immediately above the first pharyngeal groove. The mouth of the pit is closed by the growing together of its margins, and the pit then assumes the form of a vesicle—the **otic vesicle**—which severs its connexion with the ectoderm and sinks into the subjacent mesoderm. The vesicle soon becomes pear-shaped; and its middle part gives off a diverticulum which later forms the endolymphatic duct and sac. About the fifth week the anterior part of the vesicle is prolonged medialwards and forwards as a diverticulum—the future duct of the cochlea. The diverticulum is at first short and straight, but it elongates and curves on itself, so that at the twelfth week all three coils of the cochlear duct are differentiated.

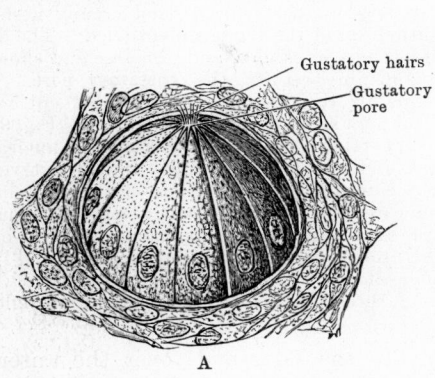

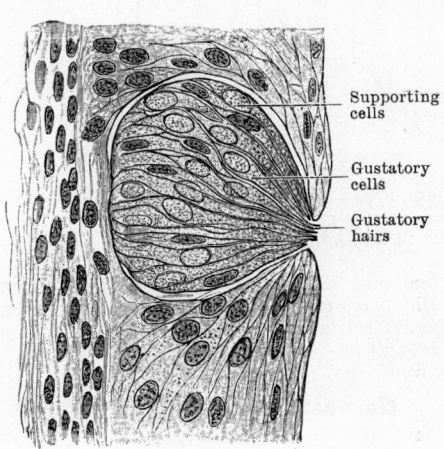

FIG. 971.

A, Three-quarter surface view of a taste-bud from the folia linguæ of a rabbit.

B, Vertical section of a taste-bud from the folia linguæ of a rabbit.

From the upper part of the vesicle the three semicircular ducts are developed, and appear as hollow, disc-like evaginations ; the central parts of the walls of each disc coalesce and disappear, leaving only the peripheral ring or canal. The three ducts are free about the beginning of the second month, and are developed in the following order, viz.: superior, posterior, and lateral. The part of the otic vesicle from which the endolymphatic duct arises becomes divided by a constriction into an anterior part—the saccule—communicating with the duct of the cochlea, and a posterior part—the utricle—communicating with the semicircular ducts. The constriction extends for some distance into the endolymphatic duct, and thus the utricle and saccule are connected by a Y-shaped tube. Another constriction makes its appearance between the saccule and the vestibular end of the duct of the cochlea and forms the ductus reuniens. The epithelial lining is at first columnar, but becomes cubical throughout the whole labyrinth, except opposite the terminations of the auditory nerve, where it forms the columnar epithelium of the maculæ of the utricle and saccule, of the ampullary crests and of the spiral organ. On the floor of the duct of the cochlea two ridges appear, of which the inner forms the limbus laminæ spiralis, whilst the cells of the outer become modified to form the rods of Corti, the hair-cells, and the supporting cells of Deiters and Hensen.

In the development of the perilymphatic spaces, the mesoderm surrounding the otic vesicle and its subsequent derivatives becomes differentiated into three layers—an inner reticular, a middle precartilaginous, and an outer cartilaginous. Room must be made in the enclosing cartilaginous labyrinth for the growing membranous portion, and this is brought about by a reversion of the precartilaginous layer next the membranous labyrinth into the more primitive type of reticular tissue; a breaking down of the fibrillæ of this tissue allows of a confluence between the enclosed spaces, which thus come to form the more or less completely open perilymphatic spaces enclosing the membranous labyrinth. The scala vestibuli appears as an outgrowth from the primitive cistern-like space which is developed in relation to the saccule and utricle, while the scala tympani appears independently a little earlier; these two spaces, or scalæ, follow along the turns of the cochlear duct and unite at the helicotrema about the sixteenth week.

The development of the external and middle parts of the ear are described in the section on Embryology.

ORGAN OF TASTE

The peripheral **organ of taste** consists of groups of modified epithelial cells, termed **taste-buds**, found on the tongue and in its immediate neighbourhood.

Taste-buds are present in large numbers around the circumference of the vallate papillæ, and some are found also on the opposing walls of the vallum (Fig. 970). They are very numerous over the folia linguæ, and are found also over the posterior part and sides of the tongue, on the fungiform papillæ, on the oral surface of the soft palate and on the posterior surface of the epiglottis.

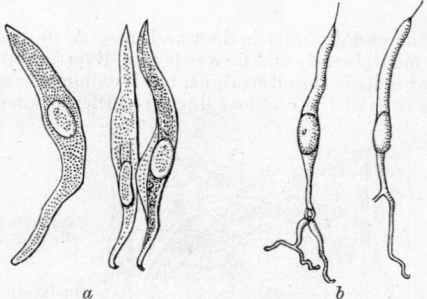

FIG. 972.—ISOLATED CELLS FROM THE TASTE-BUD OF A RABBIT (Engelmann).

a, Supporting cells.   *b,* Gustatory cells.

Structure of Taste-buds (Fig. 971).—The taste-buds are oval or flask-shaped, and occupy nests in the epithelium of the regions mentioned. The deep end of each is expanded and the free end shows a minute opening termed the **gustatory pore**. The taste-buds are composed of two kinds of epithelial cells—supporting cells and gustatory cells (Fig. 972). The **supporting cells** are elongated, nucleated spindles, and are mostly arranged like the staves of a cask to form the outer envelope of the taste-bud; but some are found in the interior amongst the gustatory cells. The **gustatory cells** occupy the centre of the taste-bud, and each has a nucleated cell-body which is prolonged into a peripheral and a central process. The peripheral process is rod-like, and terminates at the gustatory pore in a slender filament called the **gustatory hair**. The central process passes towards the deep extremity of the taste-bud, where it ends in a single or branched varicose filament.

Nerves of Taste.—The nerve of supply to the taste-buds over the anterior part of the tongue is the chorda tympani; that for the posterior part is the glossopharyngeal. The nerve-fibrils lose their medullary sheaths and ramify in the taste-buds, partly between the gustatory cells and partly among the supporting cells.

COMMON INTEGUMENT

The **skin** covers the body, and is continuous, at the orifices on its surface, with the mucous lining of the alimentary canal and other canals. It contains the peripheral terminations of many of the sensory nerves, and serves as a protection to the deeper tissues. It plays an important part in regulating the body temperature, and, by means of its sweat glands and sebaceous glands, acts as an excretory organ. Its superficial layers are modified in certain situations to form the hairs and nails.

The skin is very elastic, and its colour, determined partly by its own pigment and partly by that of the blood, is deeper on exposed parts and in the regions of the external genital organs, axillæ, and mammary areolæ, than elsewhere. The colour varies also with race and age. It is pink in childhood in the white races, but it assumes a yellowish tinge in old age.

The surface of the skin is perforated by the hair-follicles and by the ducts of the sweat glands and of the sebaceous glands; and on the palms, soles, and flexor surfaces of the digits it presents numerous permanent **ridges** which corre-spond with rows of underlying papillæ. Over the terminal phal-anges the ridges form distinctive patterns which are retained from youth to old age, and may be utilised for pur-poses of identifi-cation by means of finger-prints. Where subcutane-ous muscles exist the skin can be thrown into wrinkles by their contraction. Over the greater part of the body it is freely movable; but it is bound down to the underlying tissues on the scalp and lateral surfaces of the auricles, the palms and soles, and at the flexure lines of joints.

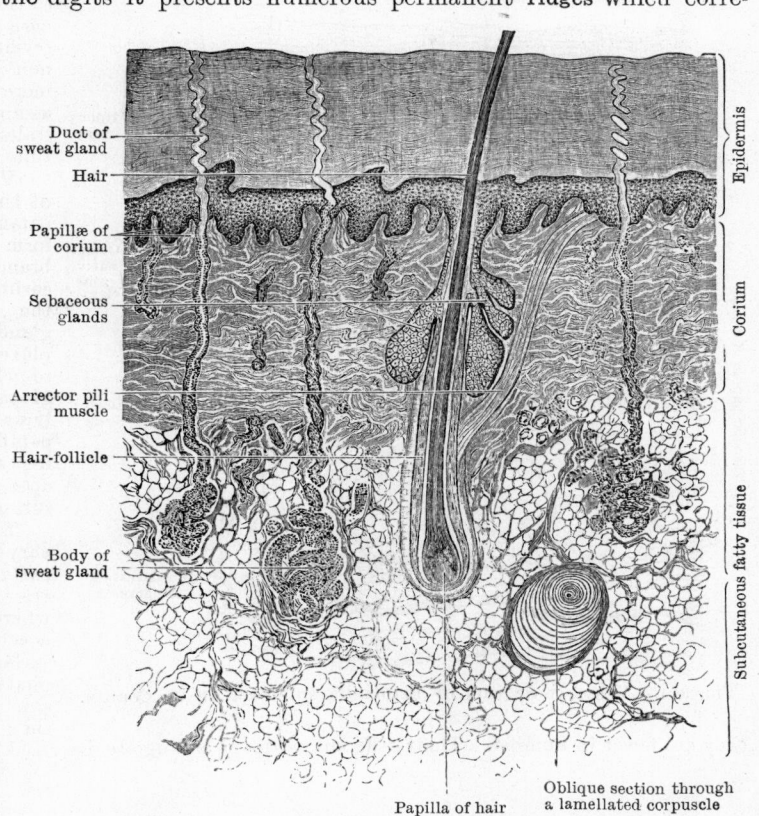

Fig. 973.—Vertical Section of the Skin (schematic).

Structure.—The skin is composed of a deep layer called the corium, and a superficial layer called the epidermis (Fig. 973).

The **corium** or **true skin** is derived from the embryonic mesoderm, and consists essentially of a felted interlacement of white and elastic fibres. In the deeper layers the fibrous bundles are coarse and form an open network in the meshes of which there are vessels, nerves, pellets of fat, hair-follicles, and glands. The deeper layer passes, as a rule, without any line of demarcation into the layer of subcutaneous fatty tissue, but in some parts it rests upon a layer of striped or unstriped muscular fibres—unstriped in the scrotum, striped in the other parts. In the superficial layer the fibrous tissue bundles are finer and form a close network, and projecting from the superficial surface of this network there are numerous finger-like, single, or branched elevations, termed **papillæ** (Fig. 974), which are received into corresponding depressions on the deep surface of the epidermis. These papillæ vary in size, being small on the eyelids, but large on the palms and soles, where they may attain a length of 225 μ, and produce the permanent ridges already referred to. Each ridge usually contains two rows of papillæ between which the ducts of the sweat glands pass to open on the surface. The papillæ consist of fine white and elastic fibres, mostly arranged parallel to the long axis of the papillæ; the majority contain capillary loops, but some contain the terminations of nerves. The superficial surface of the corium is covered with a thin, homogeneous basement-membrane.

The **epidermis** is derived from the embryonic ectoderm and covers the corium. Its thickness varies in different parts of the body and ranges from 0·3 mm. to 1 mm. or more; it is thickest on the palms of the hands and soles of the feet, and thinnest on the eyelids and penis. It is non-vascular and consists of stratified epithelium, and may be divided into two main zones, called the horny zone and the germinative zone. The **germinative zone** lies next the corium and receives its name from the fact that it is in this situation that regeneration of the epidermis takes place. The deeper layer of cells of the germinative zone are columnar or cylindrical and constitute the *basal cell layer*; the more superficial part of the germinative zone is composed of from six to eight layers of cells which are characterised by having peculiar spines or prickles, and this part of the zone is called therefore the *prickle-cell layer*. In the **horny zone** there are three layers called, from within outwards, the granular layer, the clear layer, and the horny layer. The *granular layer* is composed of three or four rows of cells containing irregularly shaped and shining granules; the *clear layer* is composed of several rows of cells which contain a clear shining substance, called *keratohyalin*, which causes this layer to stand out very clearly in sections of the skin; the *horny layer* is made up of several layers of flattened non-nucleated cells, the more superficial of which assume the form of horny scales, and are from time to time removed by friction.

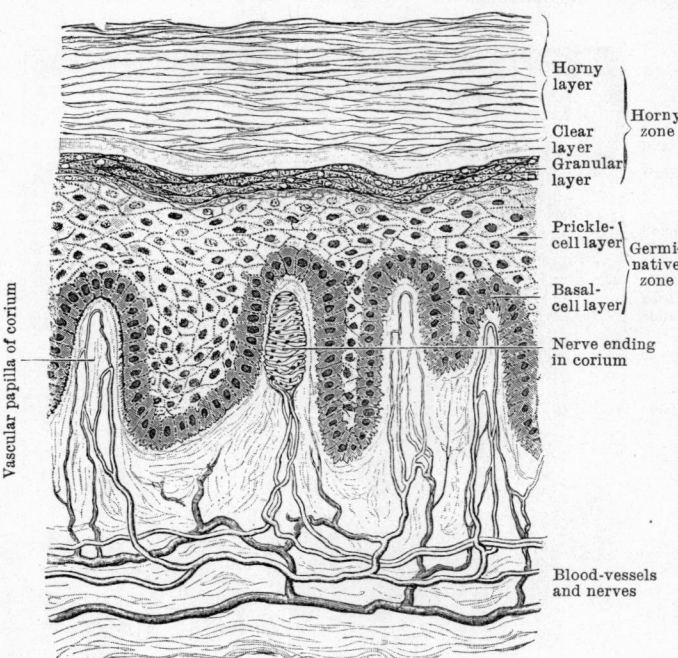

FIG. 974.—VERTICAL SECTION OF EPIDERMIS AND PAPILLÆ OF CORIUM.

Vessels and Nerves of the Skin.—In the subcutaneous tissue the **arteries** form a plexus from which branches extend into the corium, where they supply the hair-follicles and glands, and form a second plexus under the papillæ, to which small loops are given. The **veins** and the **lymph vessels** begin in the papillæ, and, after forming subpapillary plexuses, open into their respective subcutaneous vessels.

The **nerves** of the skin vary in number in different parts of the body; they are extremely numerous where the sense of touch is acute, *e.g.* on the palmar surfaces of the terminal phalanges, but in the skin of the back, where the sensibility is less, they are fewer in number. Their different modes of ending are described on pp. 1130-1132.

APPENDAGES OF THE SKIN

The appendages of the skin are the nails, the hairs, the sebaceous glands, and the sweat glands.

Ungues.—The **nails** (Figs. 975, 976) are epidermal structures, and represent the hoofs and claws of the lower animals. The body is the exposed part of the nail, and it rests on the corium. Its **free border** overhangs the tip of the digit; its **hidden border** is covered with a fold of skin at the **root** of the nail. The **collateral borders** are overlapped by folds of skin called the **nail walls**.

The corium under the nail is the **nail bed**, and it is marked by longitudinal grooves and ridges called the **grooves** and **ridges of the nail bed**. The horny zone and the germinative zone of the epidermis are represented in the nails by the superficial part of the nail and by the free edge of skin at the root, which are the **horny zone of the nail**, and by the deeper part of the nail, which is its **germinative zone**. The body of the nail has a pink colour, except at the free border and over a small semilunar area near the root, which is called the **lunula**. The whole of the body of the nail is slightly translucent, and thus has a pink colour from the light reflected from the underlying tissues; at the free border and at the lunula there is not the same intimate contact with the underlying tissues, and thus these portions of the nail appear to be white.

Pili.—**Hairs** are well developed on the external genital organs, scalp, and margins of the eyelids, in the axilla, the vestibule of the nose, and at the entrance to the concha of the auricle, and also on the face in men. Those on the genital organs and face appear about puberty. Rudimentary over the greater part of the body, hairs are absent from the flexor surfaces of the hands and feet, the dorsal surfaces of the distal phalanges, the glans penis, the inner surface of the prepuce, and medial surfaces of the labia pudendi. Marked variations, individual and racial, exist as to the colour of the hair, and also as to the manner of its growth, for which the terms straight, curly, woolly, etc., are employed. Straight hairs are coarser than curly ones, and have, moreover, a circular or oval outline on transverse section —curly hairs being flat and riband-like.

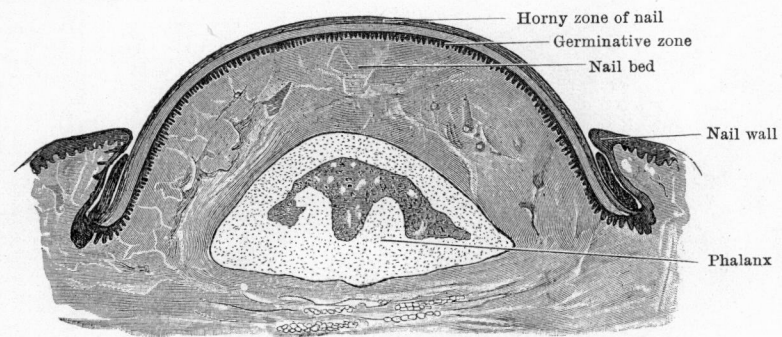

FIG. 975.—TRANSVERSE SECTION OF A NAIL.

The **root of the hair** is embedded in a depression of the skin termed the **hair-follicle** (Fig. 973); the *shaft* is the free portion of the hair, and consists from without inwards of cuticle, cortex, and medulla. The *cuticle* is formed of a layer of imbricated scales which overlap one another from below upwards. The *cortex* consists of longitudinally arranged fibres made up of elongated, closely applied, fusiform cells which contain pigment and sometimes air-spaces—the latter especially in white hairs. The *medulla*, absent from the fine hairs of the body generally

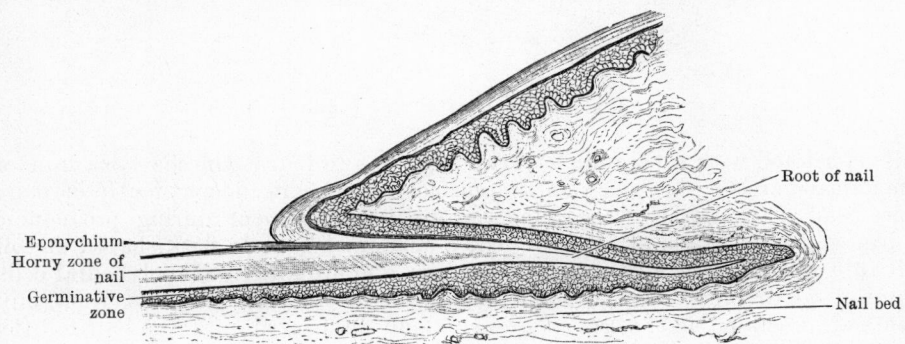

FIG. 976.—LONGITUDINAL SECTION THROUGH ROOT OF NAIL.

and from the hairs of young children, forms a central core which appears black by transmitted light, and white by reflected light, and is composed of polyhedral nucleated cells containing pigment, fat-granules, and air-spaces.

The **hair-follicle** is an oblique or curved invagination of the epidermis and corium—curved in curly hairs—and in the case of large hairs extends into the subcutaneous tissue (Fig. 973); the ducts of the sebaceous glands open into the hair-follicles a short distance below the opening of the follicle. The portion of the follicle derived from the corium consists of a sheath of fibrous tissue arranged as an external longitudinal layer and internal circular layer, the latter being lined with a hyaline layer directly continuous with the basement-membrane of the corium. The parts of the follicle derived from the epidermis are named the **inner and outer root-sheaths**. Below the orifices of the ducts of the sebaceous glands the outer root-sheath is formed by the germinative zone of the epidermis, while above these orifices all the epidermal layers contribute to it. The inner root-sheath surrounds the cuticle of the hair, and comprises from without inwards—(a) *Henle's layer*—a layer of nucleated cubical cells. (b) *Huxley's layer*—one or two layers of polyhedral nucleated cells. (c) A delicate *cuticle* composed of a layer of flattened imbricated cells, with atrophied nuclei. The bottom of the hair-follicle is moulded on a vascular papilla, derived from the corium and capped by the **bulb of the hair** or expanded part of the hair-root. The cells of the bulb are continuous round its edge with those of the outer root-sheath, and an upward growth from the bulb gives rise to the hair itself and the inner root-sheath. The vessels form capillary loops in the papilla of the hair, and send twigs into the outer layer of its fibrous sheath ; the inner and outer root-sheaths and the hair itself are non-vascular. The nerves end in longitudinal and annular fibrils below the level of the sebaceous glands and outside the hyaline layer of the follicle.

Sebaceous Glands.—These glands exist wherever there are hairs, and their ducts open into the superficial parts of the hair-follicles (Fig. 973); the number of

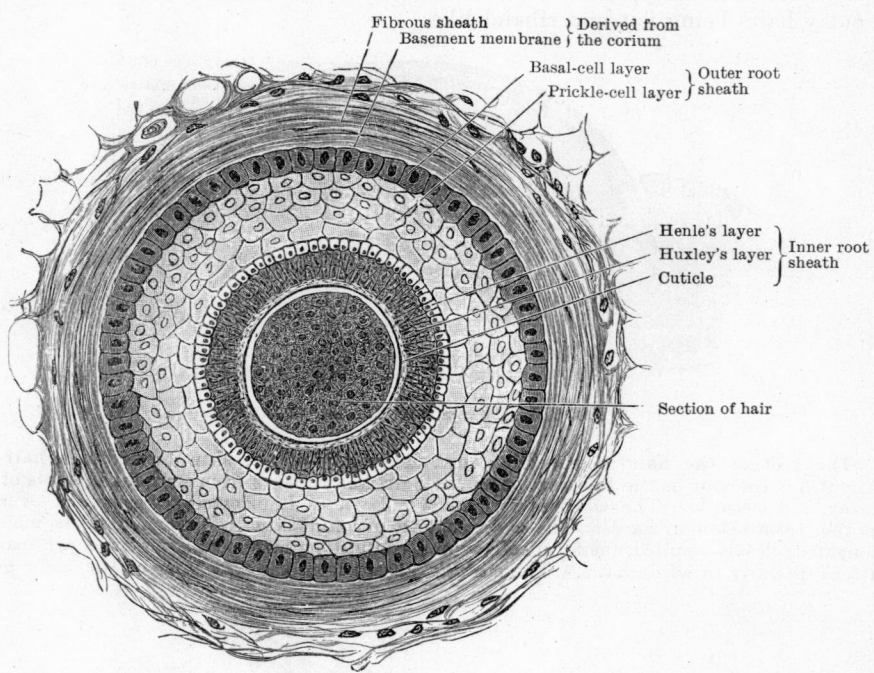

Fibrous sheath ⎱ Derived from
Basement membrane ⎰ the corium

Basal-cell layer ⎱ Outer root
Prickle-cell layer ⎰ sheath

Henle's layer ⎱
Huxley's layer ⎰ Inner root sheath
Cuticle

Section of hair

FIG. 977.—TRANSVERSE SECTION OF A HAIR-FOLLICLE WITH A CONTAINED HAIR (semi-diagrammatic).

glands associated with each follicle varies from one to four. On the labia minora and mammary areolæ they open on the surface of the skin independently of hair-follicles, and in the areolæ they undergo great enlargement during pregnancy. The deep end of each gland expands into a cluster of oval or flask-shaped **alveoli** which are surrounded by a basement-membrane, and are filled with polyhedral cells containing oil droplets. By the breaking down of the internal cells, their oily contents are liberated as the *sebum cutaneum* and discharged into the hair-follicle, whilst the deeper cells undergo proliferation. The size of the glands bears no proportion to that of the hairs, the glands being very large in the minute hair-follicles of the fœtus and new-born child, and also in the follicles of the rudimentary hairs of the nose and certain parts of the face.

Bundles of non-striped muscular fibres are associated with the hair-follicles, and are named the **arrectores pilorum muscles.** Attached to the deep part of the hair-follicle, and forming with it an acute angle, they pass outwards close to the sebaceous glands, and end in the papillary layer of the corium. They are situated on the side towards which the hair slopes, so that, on contraction, they diminish the obliquity of the hair-follicle and make the hair more erect, and, at the same time, compress the sebaceous glands and expel their contents. The condition of "goose-skin" is caused by the contraction of these slender muscles.

Sweat Glands.—The sweat glands are found in the skin of nearly every part of the body ; they are relatively few in number on the back of the trunk, but are very plentiful on the palms and soles, where they open on the summits of the curved ridges. Each consists of an elongated tube; the deeper portion of the tube forms its secretory part, and is coiled in the subcutaneous tissue or deep part of the corium to form an oval or spherical structure termed the **body** of the gland (Fig. 973). The superficial part of the tube, or **duct**, extends through the corium and epidermis, and opens on the surface by a funnel-shaped orifice called the **sweat pore**; where the epidermis is thick the duct is spirally coiled.

The bodies of the glands, as a rule, vary in diameter from 0·1 mm. to 0·5 mm., but in the axillæ they measure from 1 mm. to 4 mm. Each is surrounded by a capillary network and by a capsule of fibrous tissue inside which there is a homogeneous basement-membrane. The lumen of the tube is lined with a layer of nucleated, granular, and striated, columnar, epithelial cells, between the deep ends of which and the basement-membrane there is a layer of non-striped muscular fibres, the long axis of the fibres being more or less parallel with that of the tube. The excretory ducts are devoid of muscular fibres, and consist of a basement-membrane lined with two or three layers of polyhedral cells which are covered, next the lumen of the duct, with a thin cuticle.

The **ciliary glands**, at the margins of the eyelids, and the **ceruminous glands** of the external auditory meatus, are modified sweat glands. The ciliary glands are, however, not coiled, the cell-protoplasm of the ceruminous glands contains yellowish pigment, and their gland-ducts, in the fœtus, open into hair-follicles.

DEVELOPMENT OF THE SKIN AND ITS APPENDAGES

Skin.—The corium is developed from the mesoderm, the cells of which, immediately underlying the ectoderm, have, by the first month of intra-uterine life, become aggregated together and flattened parallel to the surface of the embryo. By the third month they form two layers, the superficial of which becomes the corium, and the deeper the subcutaneous tissue; the papillæ of the corium make their appearance in the fourth month. The epidermis, nails, hairs, sweat glands, and sebaceous glands are of ectodermal origin.

The epidermis at first consists of a single layer of cells, but by the end of the second month two layers are present—a superficial layer of flattened cells, and a deeper layer of cubical cells. By the third month three strata are seen, of which the two deeper layers come to form the future germinative zone, while the superficial layer is called the *epitrichium*, since it lies superficial to the emerging hairs, by which it is pushed off to help in the formation of the greasy covering of the child at birth, called the *vernix caseosa*. From the germinative zone cells arise and become pushed nearer and nearer to the surface, where they undergo gradual cornification and so form the various layers of the horny zone.

Nails.—The rudiments of the nails are seen about the beginning of the third month of intra-uterine life, as thickenings of the epitrichium over the ends of the digits. Owing to the greater growth of the palmar surfaces of the digits, the nail rudiments come to be placed dorsally, and, at the proximal edge of each, an ingrowth of the germinative zone occurs to form its root. The superficial cells of the germinative zone become cornified to form a part of the horny zone— the future nail proper—over the greater part of which the epitrichium disappears. The epitrichium persists in the adult, across the root of the nail, as the *eponychium*, which covers the proximal part of the lunula, and, until the fifth month, it also forms a thick mass over the distal edge of the nail, and is continued into the horny zone over the end of the digit; but that continuity is lost, and by the seventh month the nail has a free border. The nails grow in length, or are renewed in case of removal, by a proliferation of the cells of the germinative zone.

Hairs.—The hair-rudiments appear about the third month of intra-uterine life as solid downgrowths of the germinative zone which pass obliquely into the subjacent corium. The deep end of each downgrowth of cells expands to form the hair-bulb, and is moulded on a papilla derived from the corium; the epidermis immediately overlying the papilla is differentiated into the hair and its inner root-sheath, and the original peripheral cells form its outer root-sheath. The surrounding corium is condensed to form the fibrous sheath of the hair-follicle, the hyaline layer of which is continuous with the basement-membrane covering the corium. The hair gradually elongates, and, reaching the neck of the follicle, its extremity lies at first under the epitrichium, but becomes free by pushing off the epitrichium, at about the fifth month of intra-uterine life. The first crop of hairs is called the *down*, and is well developed by the seventh month; it consists of very delicate hairs, some of which are shed before birth and the remainder shortly after—the last to drop out being those of the eyelashes and scalp—and are replaced by stronger hairs. Shedding and renewal of the hairs take place during life; prior to the shedding of a hair active growth and proliferation of the cells of the hair-bulb cease, and the papilla becomes atrophied, while the hair-root, gradually approaching the surface, at last drops out. New hairs arise from epidermic buds which extend downwards from the follicle, and their development is identical with that of the original hairs.

Sebaceous Glands.—These appear about the fifth month of intra-uterine life as solid outgrowths from the sides of the hair-follicles, and consist of epidermal offshoots continued from the cells of the outer root-sheath. Their deep ends become enlarged and lobulated to form the secreting part of the gland, and the narrow neck which connects this with the follicle forms its duct. The sebaceous secretion helps in the formation of the *vernix caseosa*.

Sweat Glands.—These, like the hairs, arise as solid downgrowths of the germinative zone. They descend, however, perpendicularly, instead of obliquely, and are of a yellowish colour; they appear on the palms and soles early in the fourth month of intra-uterine life, but much later over the hairy parts of the body. The downgrowths extend through the corium, and, on reaching the subcutaneous tissue, become coiled up to form the body or secreting part of the gland. The ducts of the glands do not open on the surface until the seventh month.

ENDINGS OF NERVES OF GENERAL SENSATIONS

Under this heading will be described the terminations of those sensory nerves which are widely distributed throughout the body and are associated with the muscular sense and the senses of pressure, heat, cold, and pain. Those nerves may end (*a*) as fine ramifications of the naked axis-cylinders lying *free* amongst the tissues, or (*b*) in *special end-organs* where the terminations of the axis-cylinders are surrounded by capsules of fibrous tissue.

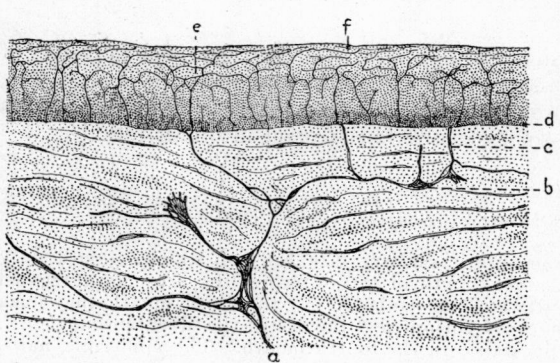

FIG. 978.—TRANSVERSE SECTION OF CORNEA STAINED WITH CHLORIDE OF GOLD (Ranvier).

a, b, Primary plexus in substantia propria of cornea; *c,* branch passing to subepithelial plexus, *d*; *e,* intra-epithelial plexus; *f,* terminations of fibrils.

FREE NERVE-ENDINGS

Free nerve-endings are found chiefly in the epithelium of the skin and mucous membranes, and constitute the peripheral pain end-organs.

The nerve-fibres, after subdividing in the subepithelial fibrous tissue, lose successively their medullary and primitive sheaths and are continued as naked axis-cylinders, which, if stained with gold chloride, are seen to consist of fine varicose filaments. The axis-cylinders subdivide and form primary and secondary plexuses, and from the secondary plexuses numerous fibrillæ pierce the subepithelial basement-membrane and ramify between the overlying epithelial cells, where they end in minute knobs or flattened discs. Free nerve-endings occur also around the sweat glands, in the papillæ and root-sheaths of the hair-follicles, in the subepithelial and intermuscular connective tissues, and in serous membranes.

Modifications of free nerve-endings are seen in the *tactile discs*; in which the neuro-fibrillæ end in the deeper layers of the epidermis as crescentic or cup-shaped expansions, in contact with large, modified epithelial cells. These tactile discs are well marked in the pig's snout (Fig. 979).

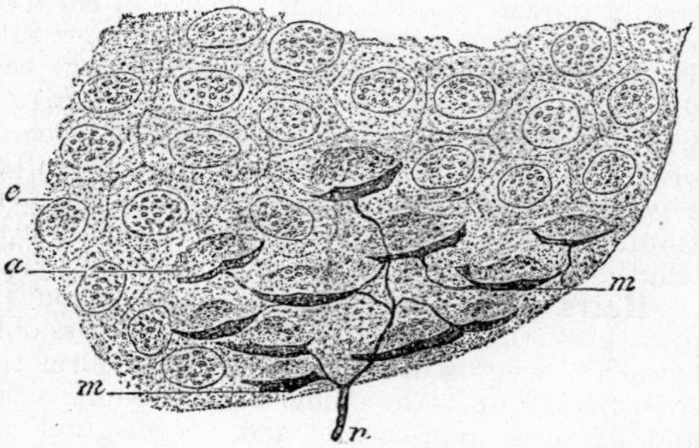

SPECIAL END-ORGANS

The special end-organs vary in size and form, but in all of them the termination of the axis-cylinder is enclosed within a capsule or sheath of varying thickness. The following are the different types of special nerve-endings: bulbous corpuscles, lamellated corpuscles, oval corpuscles, and the special sensory nerve-endings in muscle, known as neuro-muscular spindles and neuro-tendinous spindles.

Bulbous Corpuscles.—These are minute cylindrical or oval bodies, first described by Krause. Each consists of a thin capsule derived from the perineurium of the nerve and

FIG. 979.—ENDING OF NERVE IN TACTILE DISCS OF THE PIG'S SNOUT (Ranvier). (From Quain's *Anatomy*.)

n, Medullated fibre; *m,* terminal discs in muscle; *e,* cells of epidermis; *a,* modified cell to which a tactile disc is applied.

enclosing a core of homogeneous or nucleated semifluid substance.   As the nerve-fibre pierces the capsule it loses its medullary sheath, and the axis-cylinder is continued into the core, where it may pursue a rather tortuous course, but more frequently divides into minute varicose fibrils which form an intricate plexus. Bulbous corpuscles occur in the conjunctiva, the lips and tongue, in the synovial membrane of certain joints, along the course of some of the larger nerve trunks, and in the skin of the glans of the penis and of the clitoris; in the penis and clitoris they may attain a considerable size and have thicker capsules than elsewhere.

Lamellated Corpuscles.—These were described by Pacini, and consist of a fibrous tissue capsule, composed of a number of concentric layers, arranged round a central core of more or less clear protoplasm.   The deeper layers of the capsule are closely applied to each other, but those towards the circumference of the corpuscle are here and there separated by narrow lymph spaces. Each corpuscle is of an oval shape, and its capsule is pierced at one end by a medullated nerve-fibre which loses its sheath on reaching the core of the corpuscle; the naked axis-cylinder then passes to the other end of the core, where it terminates in one or more enlargements in which the neuro-fibrillæ form a dense network.   Lamellated corpuscles occur in the deeper parts of the body in general; in the deeper layers of the skin of the hands and feet, in the loose areolar tissue of the posterior abdominal wall, in the subcutaneous tissue near joints, and along the course of certain nerves.

Oval Corpuscles.—These corpuscles, which were described by Wagner and Meissner, are especially concerned with tactile impressions.   They are oval in shape and are pierced at one end by a medullated nerve-fibre which then loses its sheath; the axis-cylinders, which are frequently varicose, take a spiral or convoluted course towards the other end of the core, where they terminate in slight enlargements.   Running with the medullated nerve-fibres there are several fibres which have lost their sheaths at some distance from the corpuscle; they pierce the capsule and break up into a very complicated network of horizontal branches.   Oval corpuscles are most numerous in the deeper layers of the true skin of the palm of the hand and of the sole of the foot, and of the tips of the fingers and toes.

There also occur in the fingers rather different corpuscles, which were described by Ruffini.   They are oval or fusiform and are found in the subcutaneous tissue of the fingers, where

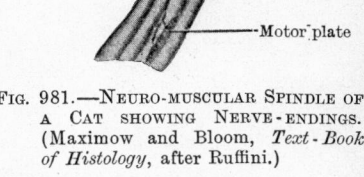

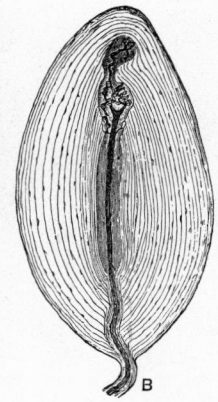
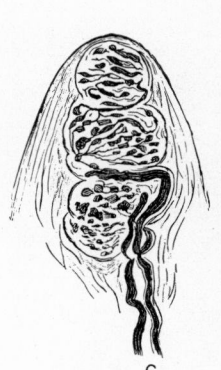

Motor plate

Branched endings

Spiral endings

Capsule

Branched endings

Motor nerve-fibres

Motor plate

Nerve bundle

Axial muscle fibres of the spindle

Motor plate

A   B   C

FIG. 980.

A, Bulbous corpuscle.
B, Lamellated corpuscle ⎰
C, Oval corpuscle   ⎱ (After Ranvier.)

FIG. 981.—NEURO-MUSCULAR SPINDLE OF A CAT SHOWING NERVE-ENDINGS. (Maximow and Bloom, *Text-Book of Histology*, after Ruffini.)

the axis-cylinders break up into a close-meshed network which lies between the smaller fasciculi of fibrous tissue or partly encircles them.

Neuro-muscular and Neuro-tendinous Spindles.—These special sensory nerve-endings occur in nearly all the voluntary muscles.   As the names imply they are spindle-shaped structures composed partly of nervous elements and partly of muscular or tendinous elements ; the neuro-tendinous spindles are always situated close to the junction of muscle and tendon. In each case there is a capsule of several layers of fibrous tissue surrounding an internal core of specialised muscle or tendon fibres ; since these fibres lie in the interior of the spindle-shaped or fusiform body, they are known as **intrafusal** fibres. In the case of the

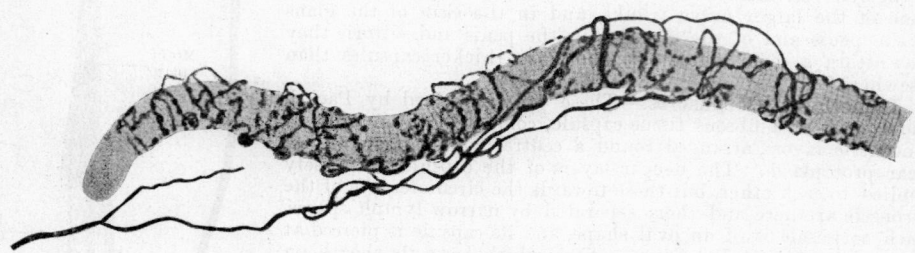

Fig. 982.—A Sensory Nerve-ending enveloping a Fibre of an Ocular Muscle.
(Maximow and Bloom, *Text-Book of Histology,* after Dogiel.)

neuro-muscular spindle the intrafusal fibres display many of the characteristics of embryonic muscle ; they are smaller in both length and diameter than ordinary muscle fibres, and they contain more protoplasm ; they have numerous nuclei near the middle of the spindle, and their cross striation is less distinct there. The intrafusal tendon fibres also are slightly modified. In each type of spindle there is a lymph space between the capsule and the axial core of fibres, which is largest in the middle of the structure and thus gives it its spindle-shape. The nerve-fibres pierce the side of the capsule (usually near its middle) and lose their medullary sheaths as they do so ; the axis-cylinders then divide and surround the muscle or tendon fibres in an annular or branching, or, as is more usual, in a spiral manner, forming a complicated plexus (Fig. 981).

In addition to these rather complicated modes of termination, sensory nerves may end by forming annular or spiral networks around non-specialised muscle fibres, the essential difference being that, in these simpler formations, there is no capsule (Fig. 982).

BLOOD VASCULAR

AND

LYMPHATIC SYSTEMS

Originally written by the late A. H. YOUNG, M.B., F.R.C.S.,
Professor of Anatomy, University of Manchester

and ARTHUR ROBINSON, M.D., LL.D., F.R.C.S.,
Emeritus Professor of Anatomy, University of Edinburgh

Revised and partly rewritten by J. C. BRASH

ALL the tissues of the body require that food and other materials necessary for their growth, maintenance, and work shall be carried to them in a fluid form, and that the products of their work shall be removed, also in a fluid form, either to the tissues by which they can be used, or to places where they can be eliminated, if they are residual or effete and would be dangerous if they accumulated in the body. It is to meet these necessities that the tubular vascular system is provided. It is filled with corpuscle-laden fluids called **blood** and **lymph** which are the media used for the transport of materials to and from the tissues.

It consists of the **heart, arteries, capillaries, veins**, and **lymph vessels**.

The heart is a rhythmically contractile muscular pump, and it is divided into receiving and ejecting chambers. During the intervals between its rhythmical contractions blood flows from vessels called **veins** into its receiving chambers, which are termed **atria**. As soon as the receiving chambers are full they contract and force their contents into ejecting chambers called **ventricles**; then the ventricles contract and project the blood into efferent vessels known as **arteries**.

The two stem arteries into which the blood is projected (the aorta and the pulmonary trunk) are necessarily large, but they break up into branches which again branch, and so, by repeated branchings, the arteries rapidly become smaller as they approach the tissue areas they supply. Ultimately the smallest branches, which are called **arterioles**, end in plexuses of vessels of extremely small calibre which are known as **capillaries**.

Capillary networks, whose meshes vary in size and form in different regions, are found in all tissues except cartilage. They are drained by the **veins**, which gradually unite with one another to form larger trunks, and through the terminal and largest trunks the blood is returned to the atria of the heart.

As the blood passes through the parts of the capillary plexuses into which the arterioles open, some of its fluid portion, which is termed **blood plasma**, passes through the thin walls of the capillaries and permeates the tissues, from which a part re-enters the capillaries towards their venous ends, and so is returned to the heart. The remaining part is collected from the tissues by another set of capillary vessels from which it passes into **lymph vessels**, which all ultimately end in the great veins at the root of the neck; thus, all the fluid which irrigates the tissues is eventually passed on to the heart.

It is, however, a well-known fact that much watery fluid containing effete products is removed from the body as urine by the action of the kidneys. The fluid passes from the renal blood capillaries into the renal tubules, and so by way of the ureters and urinary bladder to the exterior. A large quantity of fluid is also given off from the skin and in the breath from the lungs as watery vapour. The fluid thus passed out of the body is replenished by fluid taken in by the mouth and passed through the walls of the abdominal part of the alimentary canal into the blood and lymph capillaries which lie in the tissues of those walls.

For the proper performance of tissue work, an indispensable necessity, other than food in the ordinary sense, is **oxygen**; and one of the effete products which must be discharged is **carbonic acid**.

The lowest vertebrates obtain their oxygen from water by means of capillary plexuses in their gills through which the blood passes on its way from the heart to the tissues. In fishes, therefore, the heart is essentially a single tube, divided mainly into a single receiving and a single ejecting chamber.

Gills, however, are not well adapted for obtaining oxygen from air; therefore, as land animals were evolved from fish, other means for obtaining oxygen had to be adopted, and special organs called lungs were developed.

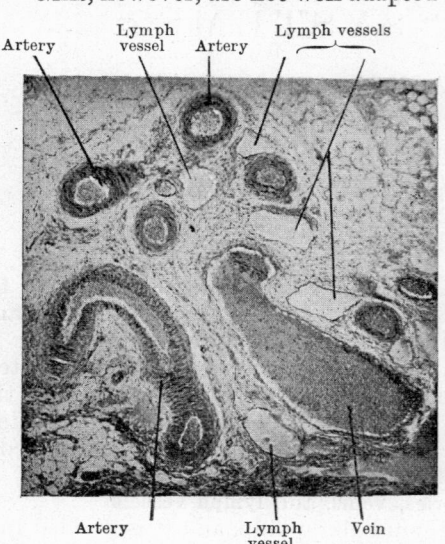

FIG. 983.—PHOTOGRAPH OF A SECTION OF ARTERIES, A VEIN, AND LYMPH VESSELS.

Since a certain amount of moisture is necessary for all active tissues, obviously the gills were ill adapted for transformation into lungs. They were placed too superficially and their surface epithelium, which would have had to play an active part, could not have been easily and regularly kept in a sufficiently moist and warm condition.

Another organ—the swim-bladder of certain fishes—was available. It was deeply situated and therefore could be kept warm and moist; further, it developed as a diverticulum from the alimentary canal, and consequently could be kept in communication with the external air through the mouth and nose. It was supplied, however, by branches of the aorta which contained oxygenated blood; consequently, its adoption for transformation into lungs necessitated an alteration of the circulation whereby it would be possible for the venous blood, returned to the heart by the veins, to be sent first through the lungs, where it could lose its carbonic acid and obtain oxygen, and then through the body generally.

The process of evolution whereby this object was attained was gradual during the period of transition from fish to mammal. It was fully achieved by the complete division of the single longitudinal tube of the primitive heart into right and left halves by the formation of septa, and by the connexion of the right ventricle with arteries passing to the lungs and of the left atrium with the veins returning blood from the lungs, whilst the left ventricle was connected with the arteries supplying the body generally and the right atrium with the veins returning blood from the body. In that way two circulations were established—the pulmonary and the systemic. The arteries, capillaries, and veins of the lungs constitute the **pulmonary circulation**, and those of the body generally the **systemic circulation**.

There is in addition the system of vessels called lymph vessels which return some of the fluid from the tissues to the systemic veins. Lymph glands are associated with the lymph vessels, and together they constitute the **lymphatic system**.

TISSUES OF THE VASCULAR SYSTEM

The tissues of which the various parts of the vascular system are composed are: endothelium, areolar tissues, white fibrous tissue, elastic tissue, unstriped muscle, and cardiac muscle. Of these, endothelium alone is found in all parts of the system. It lines the cavities of the heart, the arteries, the arterioles, the veins, and the lymph vessels, and it is almost the only constituent of the walls of the majority of the capillaries.

The **heart** consists mainly of cardiac muscle with a certain amount of areolar tissue, white fibrous tissue and elastic tissue; and its cavities are lined with a single layer of endothelial cells.

The cardiac muscle is peculiar, inasmuch as its cells are striated like voluntary muscle but are devoid of a cell membrane. They branch and anastomose with one another, and their nuclei are central.

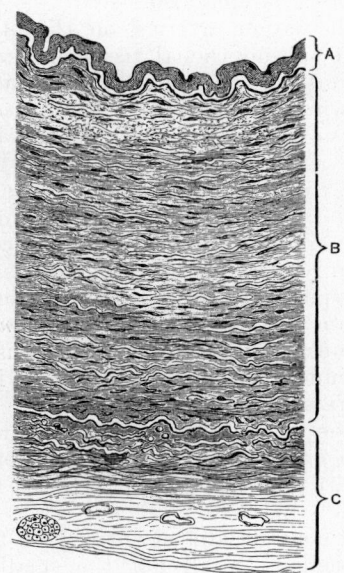

FIG. 984.—TRANSVERSE SECTION
THROUGH THE WALL OF A LARGE
ARTERY.

A, Inner Coat. B, Middle Coat.
C, Outer Coat.

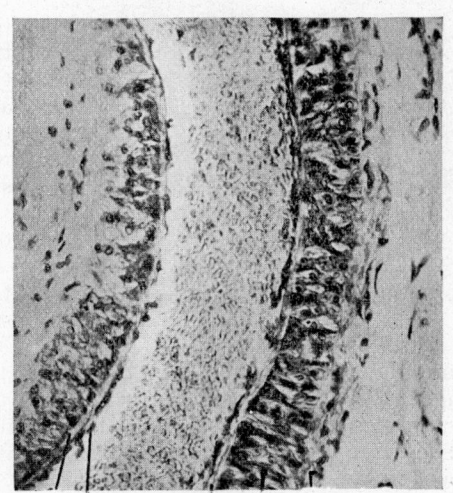

Elastic   Outer Coat
lamina Endothelium Inner Middle
                      Coat Coat

FIG. 985.—PHOTOGRAPH OF A LONGITUDINAL SECTION
OF A SMALL ARTERY.

The **arteries** are composed of unstriped muscle, areolar tissue, white fibrous tissue, elastic tissue, and endothelium. All the arteries are lined with a single layer of endothelial cells, but the other tissues are present in different amounts in different vessels. The tissues are arranged in three coats.

In arteries of the largest size elastic tissue predominates, so that by their distension, as blood is suddenly forced into them by the contractions of the heart, the smaller vessels may be preserved from sudden great strain, whilst the elastic recoil of the distended walls keeps up a steady onflow of blood in the arteries in the intervals between the contractions of the heart.

All parts of the body are not equally active at the same time, and it is obvious that an active part will require more blood during its activity than it does when it is quiescent. Therefore it is necessary that the flow of blood to any particular tissue or organ shall be capable of regulation. The regulation is obtained by means of unstriped muscle, which predominates in the arteries of medium and small size.

The muscle consists of spindle-shaped cells which, for the main part, are arranged in spiral bundles in the middle parts of the walls of the arteries, where they form, with a little intermingled areolar tissue, the middle coat (*tunica media*) of the artery.

The muscle fibres are not under control of the will, but they are under control of the nervous system. Therefore when there is a call from any area for more blood the muscle fibres relax, the calibres of the arteries enlarge, and more blood is permitted to flow through them, and when less blood is required the muscle fibres contract and the lumina of the arteries are diminished.

The constituent parts of the **inner coat** (*tunica intima*) in arteries of medium size are the *endothelial lining*, a thin *subendothelial layer* of fine areolar tissue

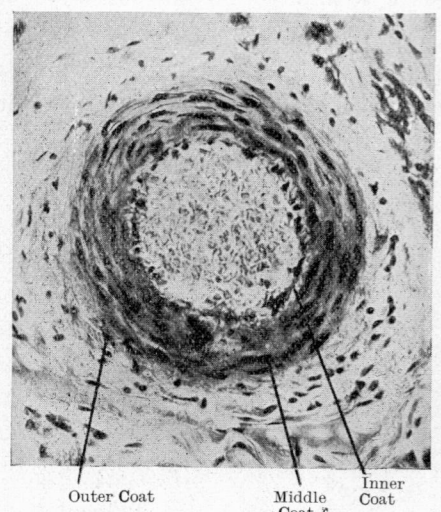

fibres and cells, and a layer of elastic fibrils, running more or less longitudinally, or an elastic fenestrated membrane called the *elastic lamina*. In the smaller arteries the subendothelial tissue disappears. The smallest arteries are devoid of the elastic lamina also.

In the larger arteries, on the other hand, the subendothelial tissue increases in amount and contains more elastic fibrils which merge into the elastic lamina, so that the boundary between the two is lost; whilst in the largest arteries the combined subendothelial tissue and elastic lamina are blended with the middle coat, which itself consists mainly of layers of elastic fibrils.

In typical arteries—that is, arteries of medium size—the **middle coat** (*tunica media*) consists mainly of unstriped muscle fibres bound together in more or less spiral strata by fine areolar tissue.

FIG. 986.—PHOTOGRAPH OF A TRANSVERSE SECTION OF A SMALL ARTERY.

As the arteries become smaller and the middle coat is reduced, the muscular strata become fewer and fewer until only a single layer of scattered fibrils remains (Fig. 987). In the largest arteries the muscle fibres are largely replaced by elastic fibrils.

The **outer coat** (*tunica adventitia*) of an artery consists almost entirely of fine fibrous tissue in which lie many fibrous tissue cells. In all but the smallest arteries numerous elastic fibres also are present. The elastic element is specially strong near the middle coat in small and medium-sized vessels, and is sometimes described as an external elastic membrane. The outer coat of some arteries contains also unstriped muscle fibres arranged longitudinally.

The outer coat is the strongest and least friable coat of the artery. It disappears from the smallest arteries as the muscle fibres disappear, but is very strong around small, medium, and large arteries.

In addition to their three coats, arteries are enclosed in a **sheath** of the surrounding fibro-areolar tissue.

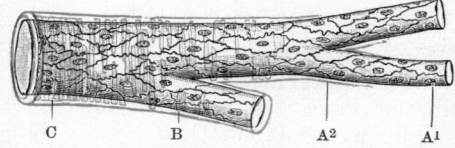

FIG. 987.—STRUCTURE OF BLOOD-VESSELS (diagrammatic).

A¹, Capillary—with simple endothelial walls. A², Larger capillary—with connective tissue sheath, "adventitia capillaris." B, Capillary arteriole—showing muscle cells of middle coat, few and scattered. C, Artery—muscular elements of the middle coat forming a continuous layer.

Capillaries measure from 8 μ to 12·5 μ in diameter, and about ·75 mm. in length. Their walls are simple, and, in the smallest capillaries, consist of elongated elastic and contractile endothelial cells, with sinuous edges, pointed extremities, and oval nuclei. The cells are cemented to one another along their margins by intercellular cement which readily stains with nitrate of silver. In places the cement substance appears to accumulate, forming minute spots indicative of the less perfect apposition of the edges of the cells. Here and there on the outer surfaces of the capillaries there are isolated cells called **Rouget cells.** They have been thought to be contractile, but their function is uncertain.

The larger capillaries are invested by an areolar tissue sheath consisting largely of branched cells which are united to one another and to the endothelial cells of the capillary wall.

Capillaries are arranged in networks, and there are great variations in the size and form of the meshes of these networks in different tissues.

In some organs (*e.g.* liver, suprarenal glands) the capillary-like spaces between the cells of the organ are not true capillaries. They have been developed by the growth of columns of cells of the organ into blood-spaces which are then broken up into narrow channels. These channels are not completely lined with endothelium and the cells of the organ are therefore in direct contact with the blood; they have been called **sinusoids** (Minot).

In erectile tissue also there are no true capillaries, since the small arteries open directly into cavernous spaces, lined with endothelium, from which the blood is drained by the small veins.

The walls of **veins** are similar in structure to those of arteries; they are, however, thinner—so much so that, although veins are cylindrical tubes when

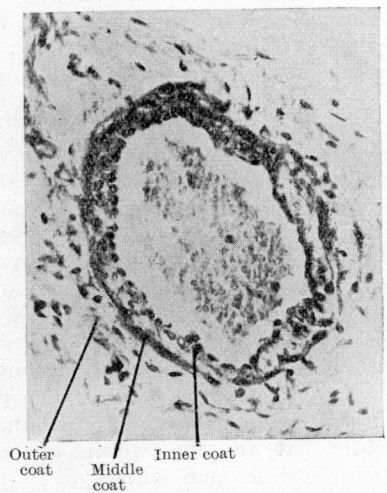

Outer coat   Inner coat
coat   Middle coat

FIG. 988.—PHOTOGRAPH OF A TRANSVERSE
SECTION OF A SMALL VEIN.

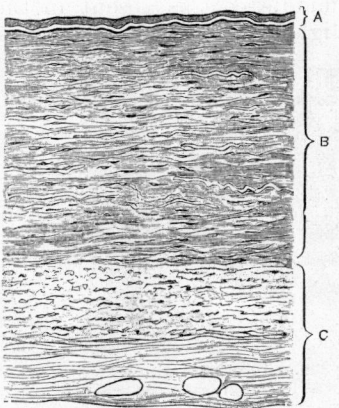

FIG. 989.—TRANSVERSE SECTION OF
THE WALL OF A VEIN.
A, Inner coat.   B, Middle coat.
C, Outer coat.

full of blood, they collapse when empty and their lumina almost disappear. The structural details of the three coats vary considerably in different veins. Like the arteries, the veins are enclosed in fibro-areolar sheaths.

In the majority of the veins the **inner coat** includes an internal endothelial layer, a middle layer of subendothelial areolar tissue, and an outer layer of elastic tissue. The inner coat of a vein is less brittle than the inner coat of an artery, and is more easily peeled off from the middle coat. The subendothelial tissue is a fine fibrillated areolar tissue, less abundant than in the arteries, and in many cases it is absent. The elastic layer consists of lamellæ of elastic fibres which are arranged longitudinally; it rarely has the appearance of a fenestrated membrane.

One of the chief peculiarities of the inner coat of veins is the presence of folds of its substance which constitute **valves** (Fig. 990). The cusps of the valves are of semilunar shape, and they are usually arranged in pairs. Their convex borders are continuous with the vessel wall, and their free borders are turned towards the heart; whilst, therefore, they do not interfere with the free flow of blood from the periphery, they prevent any backward flow towards it, and they help to sustain the column of blood in all vessels in which there is an upward flow. Each valve cusp consists of a fold of the endothelial layer, strengthened by a little areolar tissue. As a general rule, the wall of the vein is dilated on the cardiac side of each valve into a shallow pouch or sinus; consequently, when the veins are distended they assume a nodulated appearance. Competent valves do not occur in the large veins of the trunk. They are more numerous in the deep than in the superficial veins of the limbs, and in the veins of children than in the veins of adults.

The presence of valves in the superficial veins of the forearm is readily demonstrated by Harvey's simple classical experiment. The venous return being obstructed by pressure on the upper arm, a finger is placed on one of the distended veins, which is then emptied of its blood as far as the nearest valve by stroking it upwards. The column of blood will be sustained by the valve while the part of the vein below it remains empty. If the pressure of the finger is now removed, the vein fills from below, so that the flow of blood towards the heart is also demonstrated.

The **middle coat** is much thinner than the corresponding coat of an artery, and it contains a smaller amount of muscle and a larger amount of ordinary areolar tissue; indeed, so much does the latter preponderate that it separates the muscular fibres into a number of isolated bands, so that they do not form a continuous layer. In some of the veins the more internal muscular fibres do not retain the circular direction which is usual in arteries and veins; on the contrary, they run longitudinally. That arrangement is met with in the branches of the mesenteric veins, in the femoral and iliac veins, and in the umbilical veins. The middle coat is absent in the thoracic part of the inferior vena cava; it is but slightly developed in many of the larger veins, whilst in the internal jugular veins its muscular tissue is very small in amount.

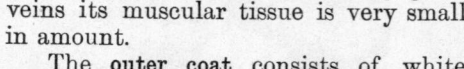

FIG. 990.—DIAGRAMS SHOWING THE VALVES OF VEINS (W. Sharpey).

A, Vein laid open showing the folds of the inner coat forming a valve; B, Longitudinal section of a vein through a valve; C, Distended vein showing the swellings opposite a valve. (*Essentials of Histology*, Sharpey-Schafer and Carleton.)

The **outer coat** consists of white fibrous and elastic tissue. In many of the larger veins a considerable amount of muscular tissue also is present; that is the case in the iliac and axillary veins, the abdominal part of the inferior vena cava, the azygos and hemiazygos veins, and in the renal, testicular, splenic, superior mesenteric, portal, and hepatic veins. The outer coat is frequently thicker than the middle coat, and the two are not easily separable from each other.

Vascular and Nervous Supply of Arteries and Veins.—The walls of the blood-vessels are supplied by numerous small **arteries**, called *vasa vasorum*, which are distributed to the outer and middle coats. They arise either from the vessels they supply or from adjacent arteries, and after a short course enter the walls of the vessels in which they end. The blood is returned by small **veins** to adjacent veins of larger size.

Cleft-like intercellular spaces are present in the inner and middle coats but definite **lymph vessels** are found only in the outer coat.

Arteries are well supplied with sympathetic **nerves**, both medullated and non-medullated, which form a plexus in the outer coat. The non-medullated fibres are *efferent* and supply the muscular tissue of the middle coat. The medullated fibres are probably *afferent* and end in the outer and inner coats. A few lamellated (Pacinian) corpuscles are present in the outer coat of the aorta. The veins also are supplied by nerves in a similar way but they are much less numerous than in the arteries.

THE HEART

The **heart** is a hollow muscular organ situated in the middle mediastinum enclosed in a fibro-serous sac called the pericardium. It receives blood from the veins, and propels it into and along the arteries. The cavity of the fully developed heart is completely separated into right and left halves by an obliquely placed longitudinal septum, and each half is incompletely divided into a posterior receiving chamber, the **atrium**, and an anterior ejecting chamber, the **ventricle**. Externally a comparatively shallow constriction, called the atrio-ventricular groove, indicates the separation of the atria from the ventricles; internally a wide aperture is left between the lower part of each atrium and the posterior part of the corresponding ventricle. Each **atrio-ventricular orifice** is provided with a valve which allows the free passage of blood from the atrium to the ventricle, but effectually prevents its return.

The **atrio-ventricular groove** [sulcus coronarius], which runs transversely to the long axis of the heart, separates a postero-superior or atrial portion from an antero-inferior or ventricular portion of the heart. The groove is interrupted in front by the roots of the pulmonary trunk and the aorta. The separation of the atrial portion into right and left chambers is marked, externally, only at the base of the heart where there is an indistinct interatrial groove. The division of the ventricular portion into right and left ventricles is more definitely marked on the surface by anterior and inferior interventricular grooves, which meet at the lower border of the heart to the right of the apex.

The **shape** of the heart is that of an irregular and slightly flattened cone; and

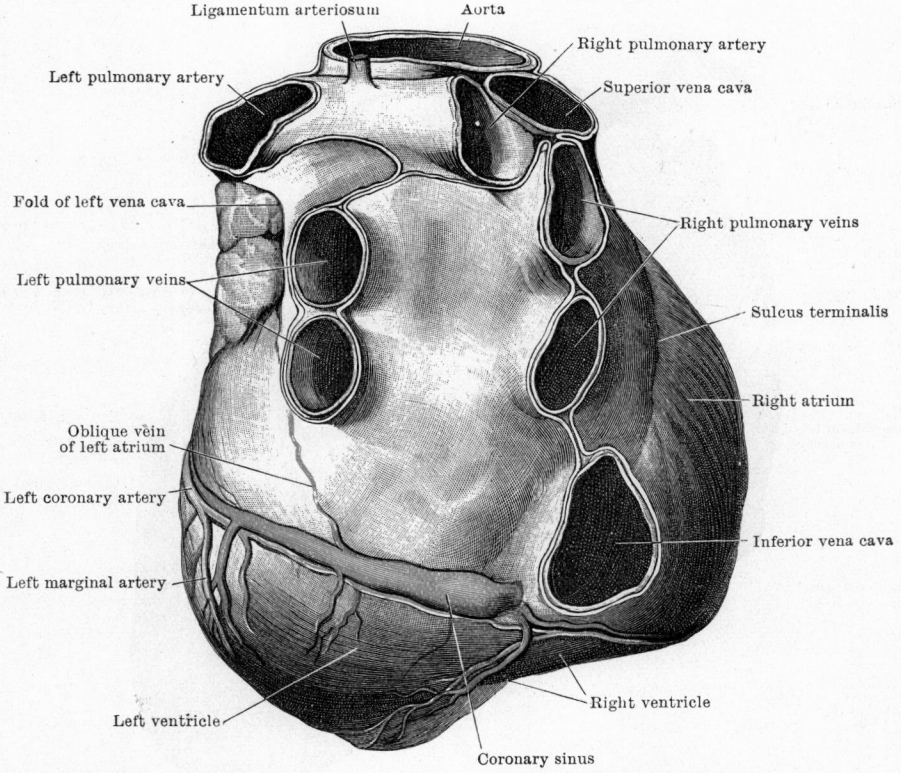

FIG. 991.—BASE AND DIAPHRAGMATIC SURFACE OF THE HEART, showing the openings of the great vessels and the line of reflexion of the serous pericardium in a formalin-hardened preparation.

a base, an apex, and three surfaces (sterno-costal, diaphragmatic, and left) are described. The sterno-costal surface is limited by four borders which are sometimes described as the borders of the heart. The axis of the heart, from base to apex, runs obliquely from behind forwards, to the left and downwards.

The **base of the heart** is formed by the atria—almost entirely by the left atrium—and is directed backwards. It is opposite the bodies of the fifth, sixth, seventh, and eighth thoracic vertebræ, from which it is separated by the lower right pulmonary vein, the descending thoracic aorta, the œsophagus and the vagi, the thoracic duct and the azygos veins.

The base is more or less flat. It is irregularly quadrilateral in outline, and the ends of the superior and inferior venæ cavæ and of the four pulmonary veins pass through it. The two left pulmonary veins pierce it near its left border. The superior vena cava enters the base at its right upper angle, and the inferior vena cava at its right lower angle. Between the two venæ cavæ the two right pulmonary veins pierce the wall of the left atrium immediately to the left of the indistinct interatrial sulcus. The portion of the surface which lies

72 *a*

between the right and left pulmonary veins forms the anterior boundary of a section of the pericardial cavity called the oblique sinus.

The base is limited below by the posterior part of the atrio-ventricular groove, in which the coronary sinus lies; its upper border is in relation with the pulmonary arteries. At the upper part of its left border a small fold of pericardium, called the *fold of the left vena cava*, descends from the left pulmonary artery to the upper left pulmonary vein (see p. 1154). From its lower end a small vein—*the oblique vein of the left atrium*—passes below the orifice of the lower left pulmonary vein, and descends to the coronary sinus. Further, it is from the base that the visceral layer of the pericardium, which elsewhere com-

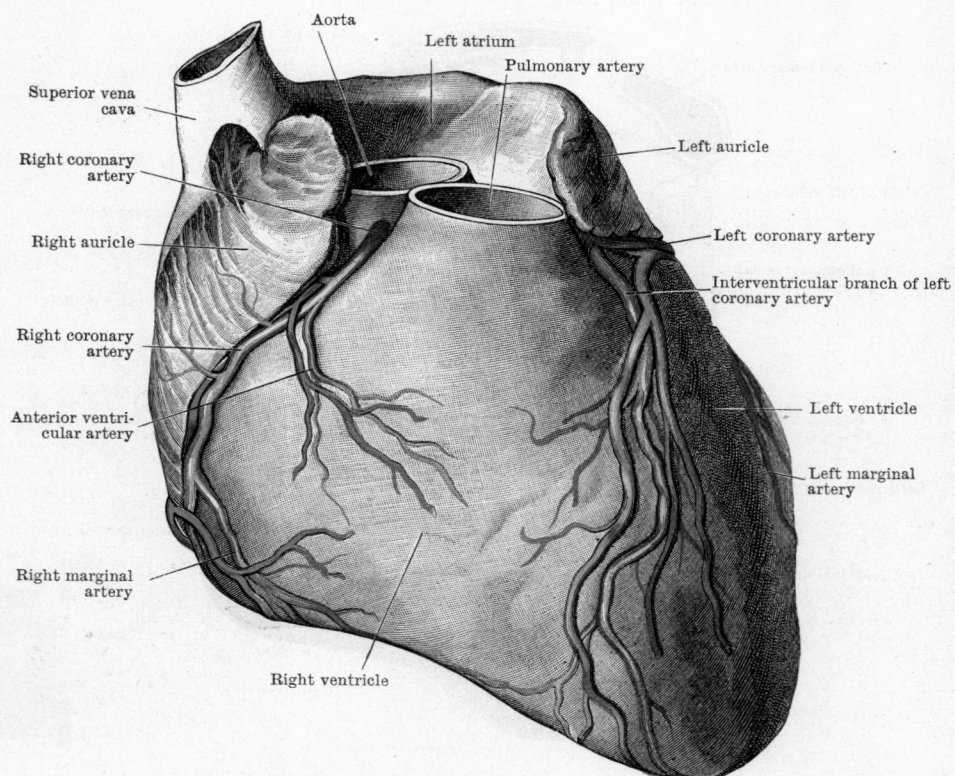

Aorta

Left atrium

Pulmonary artery

Superior vena cava

Left auricle

Right coronary artery

Left coronary artery

Right auricle

Interventricular branch of left coronary artery

Right coronary artery

Anterior ventricular artery

Left ventricle

Left marginal artery

Right marginal artery

Right ventricle

FIG. 992.—STERNO-COSTAL SURFACE OF FORMALIN-FIXED HEART.

pletely invests the heart, is reflected on to the fibrous layer, the lines of reflexion corresponding with the orifices of the great vessels.[1]

The **apex**, bluntly rounded, is formed entirely by the left ventricle. It is directed downwards, forwards, and to the left, and is situated, under cover of the left lung and pleura, behind the fifth left intercostal space, or behind the sixth rib, three or three and a half inches from the anterior median line.

The **sterno-costal surface** is directed upwards, forwards, and to the left. It lies behind the body of the sternum and the medial ends of the cartilages of the third, fourth, fifth, and sixth ribs of the right side, and a greater extent of the corresponding cartilages of the left side. That surface is separated into upper and lower sections by the anterior part of the atrio-ventricular groove, which runs obliquely from above downwards and from left to right, from the level of the third left costal cartilage to that of the sixth right. The upper section of the surface, which is concave forwards, is formed by the

[1] In the fœtus and young child the atrial portion of the heart forms not only the base, but also the posterior part of the inferior or diaphragmatic surface.

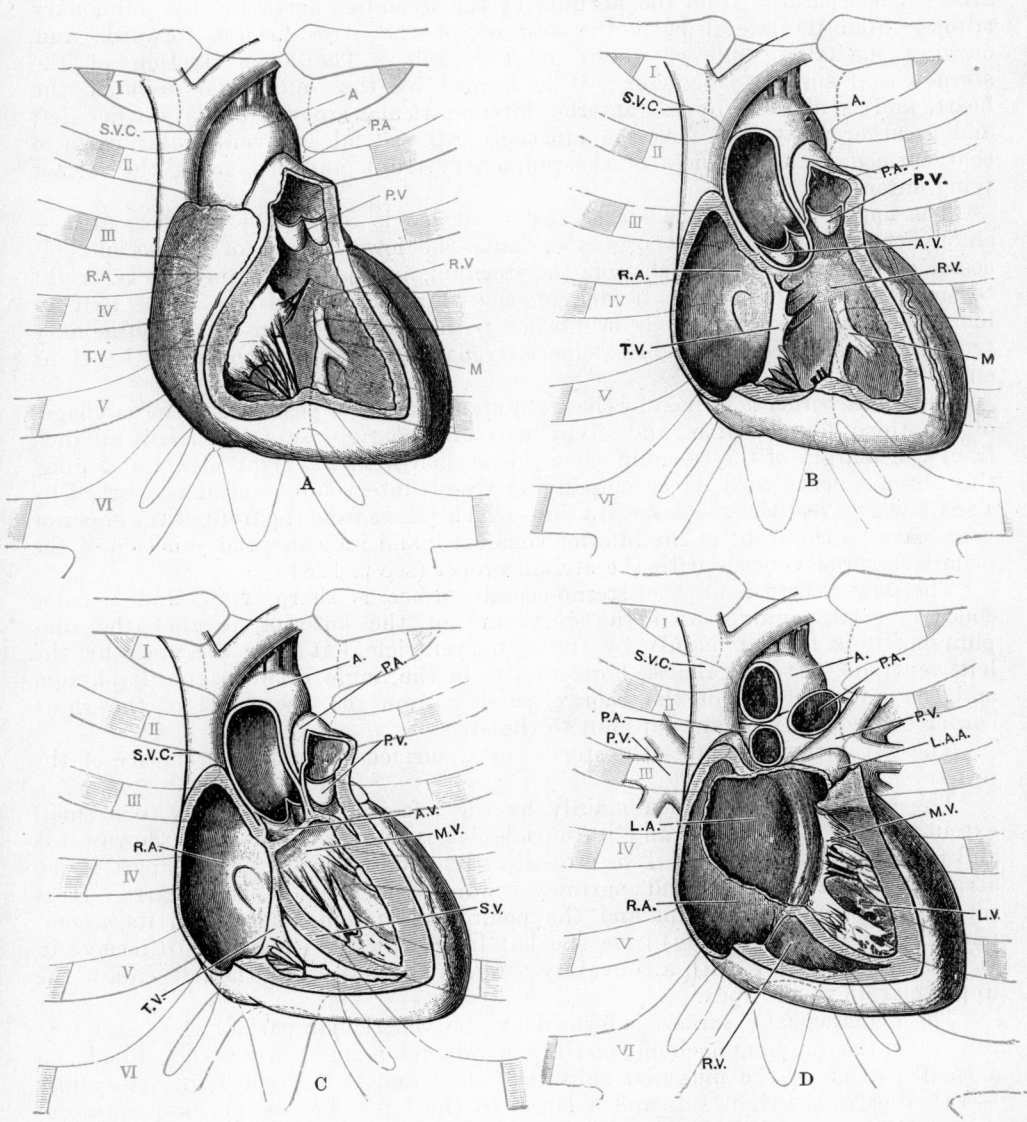

Fig. 993.—The Relations of the Cavities and Valves of the Heart to the Anterior Wall of the Thorax. (From photographs of a formalin-hardened subject, with the heart dissected *in situ*.)

In A the anterior wall of the right ventricle has been removed and the pulmonary trunk opened.

In B the anterior walls of the ascending aorta and of the right atrium have been removed ; also the anterior cusp of the tricuspid valve.

In C the greater part of the ventricular septum has been removed, and the anterior cusp of the mitral valve exposed.

In D the ascending aorta, anterior cusp of mitral valve, pulmonary trunk, and atrial septum have been removed ; the cavities of the left atrium and left ventricle are exposed.

A.	Aortic arch.	M.	Moderator band.	R.A.	Right atrium.
A.V.	Aortic valve.	M.V.	Mitral valve.	R.V.	Right ventricle.
L.A.	Left atrium.	P.A.	Pulmonary trunk.	S.V.	Ventricular septum.
L.A.A.	Left auricle.	**P.V.**	Pulmonary valve.	S.V.C.	Superior vena cava.
L.V.	Left ventricle.	P.V.	Pulmonary vein.	T.V.	Tricuspid valve.

atria; it is separated from the sternum by the ascending aorta and the pulmonary trunk; from its lateral parts the auricles of the atria project forwards and, curving medially, embrace those great vessels. The lower section of the sterno-costal surface is convex; it is formed by the ventricular part of the heart, and is divided, by an **anterior interventricular groove**, into a smaller left and a larger right part. At the junction of the atrial and ventricular parts of that surface are the orifices of the pulmonary trunk and the aorta, the former lying anterior to the latter.

The **upper border** of the sterno-costal surface is formed by the two atria—chiefly the left atrium. It begins opposite the lower border of the second left costal cartilage about an inch from the sternum, and passes obliquely to the right to end opposite the upper border of the third right cartilage about half an inch from the sternum. It is in relation with the bifurcation of the pulmonary trunk and its two branches; the superior vena cava enters the heart at its right end.

The **right border** is formed by the right atrium. It lies posterior to the cartilages of the third, fourth, fifth, and sixth ribs on the right side, about half an inch from the margin of the sternum; it is in relation with the right pleura and lung, the phrenic nerve with its accompanying vessels intervening, and it is marked by a shallow groove—the *sulcus terminalis*—which passes from the front of the superior vena cava to the front of the inferior vena cava, and indicates the junction of the primitive sinus venosus with the atrium proper (see p. 1281).

The **lower border** of the sterno-costal surface is sharp, thin, and usually concave, corresponding with the curvature of the anterior part of the diaphragm; it is formed mainly by the right ventricle, but near the apex by the left ventricle. It lies, almost horizontally, in the angle between the diaphragm and the anterior wall of the thorax, passing from the lower end of the right border behind the xiphisternal joint to the apex.

The **left border** separates the sterno-costal surface from the left surface of the heart.

The **left surface** is formed mainly by the left ventricle, and only to a small extent by the left atrium and its auricle; it is convex from above downwards and from before backwards. It is crossed at its widest part by the left part of the atrio-ventricular groove, and narrows towards the apex of the heart. It is separated by the pericardium and the pleura (the phrenic nerve and its accompanying vessels intervening) from the left lung, which is excavated to receive it. It descends obliquely, with a convexity towards the left, from the left end of the upper margin to the apex.

The **diaphragmatic surface** is formed by the ventricular part of the heart. It rests upon the diaphragm, chiefly on the central tendon, but, towards the left side, on a small portion of the muscular substance also; and it is divided into two areas—a smaller to the right side and a larger to the left side—by an oblique antero-posterior groove called the **inferior interventricular groove**. It is separated from the base by the posterior part of the atrio-ventricular groove.

CHAMBERS OF THE HEART

Atria.—The **atrial portion** of the heart is cuboidal in form, with an anterior concave surface. Its cavity is divided into two chambers—the right and left atria—by a septum which runs from the anterior wall backwards and to the right so obliquely that the right atrium lies anterior and to the right, and the left atrium posterior and to the left.

The long axis of each atrium is vertical, and each possesses a well-marked, ear-shaped prolongation, known as the **auricle**, which projects forwards from its anterior and upper angle.

The **right atrium** receives, posteriorly, the superior vena cava above and the inferior vena cava below. Between them, and a little above its middle, it is crossed behind by the lower right pulmonary vein on its way from the hilum of the lung to the left atrium. It is continuous below and in front with the right ventricle, at the atrio-ventricular orifice. Above and in front it is in relation with the ascending aorta, and from that part of the atrium the right auricle is prolonged forwards and to the left. Its right side forms the right border of the heart, and is separated by the pericardium from the right phrenic nerve and its accompanying vessels, and the right pleura and lung. Behind and on the left, the right atrium is limited by the oblique septum which separates it from the left atrium.

Interior of Right Atrium.—The walls are lined with a glistening membrane called **endocardium**, and are smooth except anteriorly and in the auricle, where muscular bundles, called the **musculi pectinati**, form a series of small vertical columns. The musculi pectinati end behind in a crest, called the **crista terminalis**,

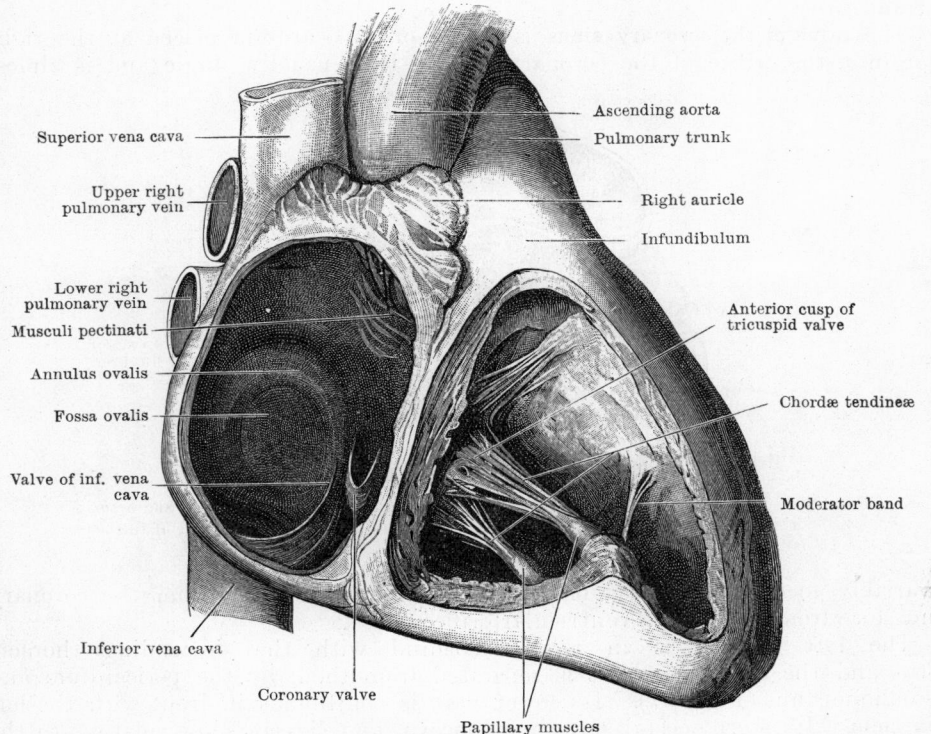

Superior vena cava

Upper right
pulmonary vein

Lower right
pulmonary vein

Musculi pectinati

Annulus ovalis

Fossa ovalis

Valve of inf. vena
cava

Inferior vena cava

Coronary valve

Ascending aorta

Pulmonary trunk

Right auricle

Infundibulum

Anterior cusp of
tricuspid valve

Chordæ tendineæ

Moderator band

Papillary muscles

Fig. 994.—Cavities of the Right Atrium and Right Ventricle of a Formalin-fixed Heart.

which corresponds in position with the sulcus terminalis (p. 1142) on the external surface.

At the upper and posterior part of the cavity is the opening of the superior vena cava, devoid of a valve. At the lower and posterior part is the orifice of the inferior vena cava, bounded, anteriorly, by the rudimentary **valve of the inferior vena cava**, and immediately in front and to the left of that valve, between it and the atrio-ventricular orifice, is the opening of the coronary sinus, guarded by the unicuspid **coronary valve**. The **right atrio-ventricular orifice**, guarded on the ventricular side by a tricuspid valve, is also known as the **tricuspid orifice**. It is situated in the inferior part of the anterior boundary, and admits the tips of three fingers. A number of small fossæ are scattered over the walls, and into some of them the **venæ cordis minimæ** open by minute orifices called *foramina venarum minimarum*. In the septal wall is an oval depression, called the **fossa ovalis**. It is bounded, above and in front, by a raised margin, called the **annulus ovalis** [limbus fossæ ovalis], which is continuous, below, with the valve of the inferior vena cava; the fossa is the remains of the **foramen ovale**, through which the right atrium

72 c

communicated with the left atrium before Lirth. Even in the adult a portion of the aperture persists at the upper part of the fossa in about one in five cases. A small eminence may be seen between the orifices of the superior and inferior venæ cavæ, and behind the upper part of the fossa ovalis; it is called the **intervenous tubercle**, and it probably directs the blood from the superior vena cava to the tricuspid orifice during fœtal life.

The **valve of the inferior vena cava** is a thin and sometimes fenestrated fold of endocardium and subendocardial tissue which extends from the anterior and lower margin of the orifice of the inferior vena cava to the anterior part of the annulus ovalis. It varies very much in size, and is usually of falciform shape; its apex is attached to the annulus ovalis and its base to the margin of the inferior caval orifice. It is an important structure in the fœtus, directing the blood from the inferior vena cava through the foramen ovale into the left atrium.

The **valve of the coronary sinus** is a fold of endocardium placed at the right margin of the orifice of the coronary sinus. It is usually single and is almost

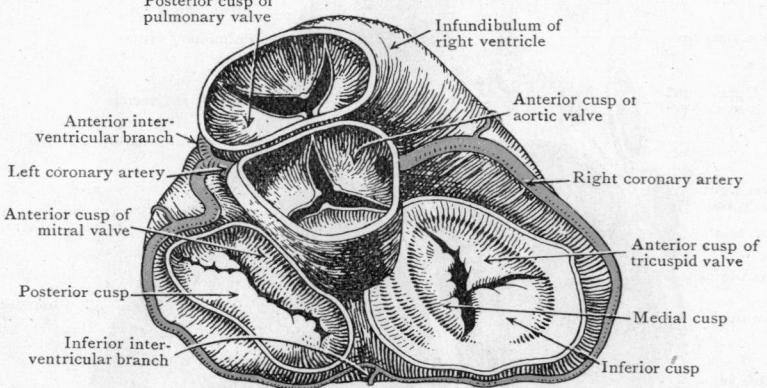

FIG. 995.—BASE OF THE VENTRICLES OF THE HEART, showing atrio-ventricular and arterial orifices with their valves, and the coronary arteries. The anterior surface of the heart is towards the right in the Figure.

invariably incompetent; but it serves to direct the blood from the coronary sinus forwards to the atrio-ventricular orifice.

The **left atrium** is in relation behind with the descending thoracic aorta and the œsophagus, but is separated from them by the pericardium and its oblique sinus (Fig. 997). Its lower part is continuous in front with the left ventricle. Its sterno-costal surface is concave, and lies in close relation to the ascending aorta, the pulmonary trunk, and the left coronary artery. Its right side, formed by the interatrial septum, is directed forwards and to the right. Its left side forms a very small portion of the left surface of the heart, and from it, at its junction with the antero-superior surface, the long and narrow left auricle is prolonged, forwards, round the left side of the ascending aorta and the pulmonary trunk. Four pulmonary veins enter the upper part of the posterior surface, two on each side.

Interior of Left Atrium.—The walls are lined with endocardium, and are smooth except in the auricle, where musculi pectinati are present, and on the septum, in a position corresponding with the upper part of the fossa ovalis on the right side, where there are several musculo-fibrous bundles radiating forwards and upwards. Those septal bundles are separated at their bases by small semilunar depressions, in the largest of which a remnant of the foramen ovale may be found. The apertures of venæ cordis minimæ (foramina venarum minimarum) are scattered irregularly over the wall, whilst in the inferior part of the anterior boundary is the **left atrio-ventricular** or **mitral orifice**. The orifice is oval in form; its long axis runs obliquely from above downwards and to the right. It is capable of admitting the tips of two fingers, and it is guarded on the ventricular side by a valve formed of two large cusps and known as the **left atrio-ventricular** or **mitral valve**.

Ventricles.—The **ventricular portion** of the heart is conical and slightly flattened. The base, directed upwards and backwards, is partly continuous with the atrial portion and partly free. It is perforated by four orifices—the two atrio-ventricular, the aortic, and the pulmonary. The atrio-ventricular orifices are placed posteriorly, one on each side; anteriorly and between them is the aortic orifice, whilst the orifice of the pulmonary trunk is still farther forward, and slightly to the left of the aortic orifice (Fig. 995).

In the triangle between the atrio-ventricular and the aortic orifices a mass of dense fibrous tissue is embedded—*fibrous trigone*—which is the representative of the os cordis of the ox. It is continuous with the upper part of the interventricular septum, and with fibrous rings which surround the apertures at the bases of the ventricles.

The ventricular portion of the heart is divided into right and left chambers by the **ventricular septum**, which is placed obliquely, with one surface directed forwards and to the right, and the other backwards and to the left; its lower end lies to the right of the apex of the heart. The margins of the septum are indicated on the two surfaces of the ventricular part of the heart by anterior and inferior interventricular grooves.

The **right ventricle** is triangular in form. Its base is directed upwards and to the right, and, in the greater part of its extent, it is continuous with the right

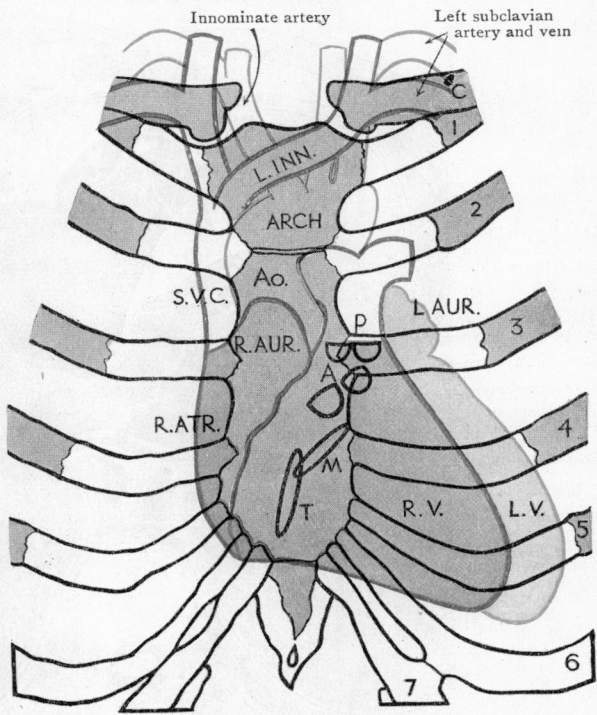

FIG. 996.—RELATION OF THE HEART AND GREAT VESSELS TO THE ANTERIOR WALL OF THE THORAX

1 to 7. Ribs and costal cartilages.
  A. Aortic orifice.
  Ao. Ascending Aorta.
  C. Clavicle.
  L.V. Left ventricle.

M. Mitral orifice.
P. Pulmonary orifice.
R.V. Right ventricle.
S.V.C. Superior vena cava.
T. Tricuspid orifice.

atrium, with which it communicates by the atrio-ventricular orifice; but its left and anterior angle is free from the atrium, and gives origin to the pulmonary trunk. Its inferior wall rests upon the diaphragm. The sterno-costal wall is posterior to the lower half of the sternum and the cartilages of the fourth, fifth, and sixth ribs of the left side. The left or septal wall bulges into its interior, and on that account the transverse section of the cavity has a semilunar outline.

Interior of Right Ventricle.—The cavity itself is a bent tube consisting of two parts:—an inferior portion or **body**, which communicates with the atrium through the atrio-ventricular orifice; and an antero-superior part—the **infundibulum** [conus arteriosus]—which ends in the pulmonary trunk. In the angle between the two limbs there is a thick ledge of muscle called the **infundibulo-ventricular crest** [crista supraventricularis].

The **right atrio-ventricular** or **tricuspid orifice** is guarded by the **right atrio-ventricular** or **tricuspid valve**. The three cusps are an *inferior*, a *medial* or septal, and an *anterior* which intervenes between the atrio-ventricular orifice and the infundibulum. Each cusp consists of a fold of endocardium, strengthened by a little enclosed fibrous tissue. The bases of the cusps are generally continuous with one another at the atrio-ventricular orifice, where they are attached to a fibrous ring, but they may be separated by small secondary cusps which fill the angles between the main segments. The apices of the cusps project into the ventricle. The margins, which are thinner than the central portions, are notched and irregular. The atrial surfaces are smooth. The ventricular surfaces are roughened, and, like the margins and apices, they give insertion to the **chordæ tendineæ.** The chordæ tendineæ are fine tendinous cords whose opposite ends

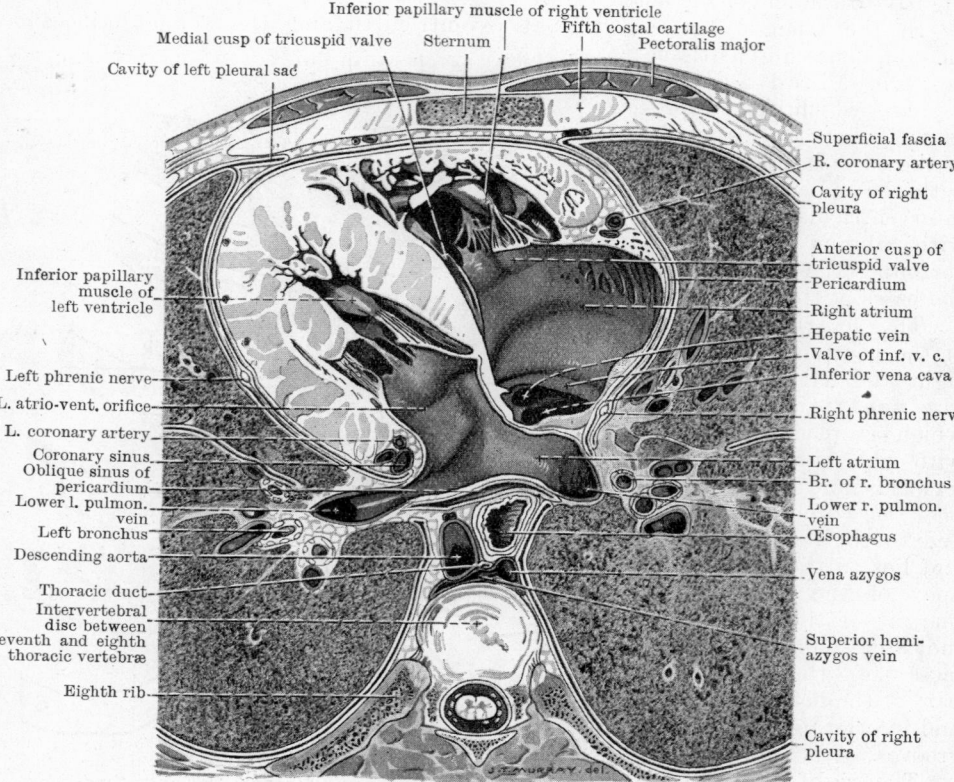

FIG. 997.—TRANSVERSE SECTION OF THE THORAX OF A YOUNG MAN SHOWING THE CAVITIES AND SOME OF THE RELATIONS OF THE HEART. The Section is in the Plane D—D, Fig. 1038, p. 1239.

are attached to conical muscular projections from the wall of the ventricle called the **papillary muscles** (Fig. 994).

The **pulmonary orifice** lies in front and to the left of the tricuspid orifice. It is guarded by a **pulmonary valve** composed of three semilunar segments, two of which are placed in front and one behind. The convexity or outer border of each semilunar segment is attached to the wall of the pulmonary artery at its root. The inner border is free, and it presents at its middle a small **nodule.** On each side of the nodule there is a small, thin marginal segment, of semilunar form, called the **lunule.** Each segment of the valve is composed of a layer of endocardium on its ventricular surface, an endothelial layer on its arterial surface, continuous with the inner coat of the artery, and an intervening stratum of fibrous tissue. Both the attached and the free margins of the cusps are strengthened by fibrous bands, and strands of condensed fibrous tissue radiate from the outer border of each cusp to the nodule, but they do not enter the lunules. When the valve closes the nodules are closely apposed, the lunules of the adjacent segments of the valve are pressed together, and both nodules and lunules project vertically upwards into the interior of the artery.

The walls are lined with endocardium. They are smooth in the infundibulum, but are made rugose and sponge-like in the body by the inward projection of numerous muscular bundles called the **trabeculæ carneæ**. The fleshy trabeculæ are of three kinds : the simpler are merely columns raised in relief on the wall of the ventricle. The second class are rounded bundles, free in the middle, but attached at each end to the wall of the ventricle. One special bundle of the second group, called the **moderator band**, is attached by one end to the septum, and by the other to the sterno-costal wall, at the base of the anterior papillary muscle ; it tends to prevent over-distension of the cavity ; but its chief importance is that it conducts the right septal division of the atrio-ventricular bundle from the septum to the anterior wall of the ventricle (see p. 1149). The third variety are the **papillary muscles** which project into the cavity of the ventricle. The bases of the papillary muscles are continuous with the wall of the ventricle, and their apices give origin to numerous chordæ tendineæ which are attached to the apices, the borders, and ventricular surfaces of the cusps of the tricuspid valve.

The papillary muscles of the right ventricle are—(1) a large *anterior* muscle, from which the chordæ pass to the anterior and inferior cusps of the valve ; (2) a smaller and more irregular *inferior* muscle, sometimes represented by two or more segments, from which chordæ pass to the inferior and medial cusps ; and (3) a group of small *septal* muscular cones, varying in size and number, which project from the septum and are united by chordæ to the anterior and medial cusps.

The walls of the right ventricle, other than the septal, are much thinner than those of the left, but the trabeculæ carneæ are coarser and less numerous in the right ventricle than in the left.

The **left ventricle** is a conical chamber, and its cavity is oval in transverse section. The base is directed upwards and backwards, and in the greater part of its extent it is continuous with the corresponding atrium, with which it communicates through the mitral orifice ; but in front and to the right of its communication with the atrium it is continued into the ascending aorta. Its apex is the **apex of the heart**. The inferior wall is related to the diaphragm ; it is flat, and it forms two-thirds of the diaphragmatic surface of the heart. The sterno-costal wall is convex, and lies behind the third, fourth, and fifth costal cartilages of the left side near their junction with the ribs ; it forms nearly one-third of the ventricular part of the sterno-costal surface of the heart. The right or septal wall is concave towards the interior. The walls of the left ventricle are three times as thick as those of the right ventricle. They are thickest round the widest part of the cavity, and that is about one-fourth of its length from the base. The muscular part is thinner at the apex than elsewhere ; but the thinnest part of the wall is the membranous upper and posterior part of the septum.

Interior of Left Ventricle.—The cavity is separable into two parts. The lower part is the **body**, which communicates with the left atrium through the atrio-ventricular orifice. The upper and anterior part is called the **aortic vestibule**, for it leads into the aorta ; its walls consist of tough fibrous tissue, and are therefore non-contractile.

The **left atrio-ventricular** or **mitral orifice** is oval ; its long axis runs obliquely from above downwards and to the right ; it is guarded by a bicuspid valve known as the **left atrio-ventricular** or **mitral valve**. The two cusps are triangular and of unequal size. The smaller *posterior cusp* is placed behind and to the left of the orifice ; and the larger *anterior cusp* is placed in front and to the right, between the mitral and aortic orifices. The bases of the cusps are either continuous with each other at their attachments to the fibrous ring around the mitral orifice, or they are separated by small secondary cusps of irregular form and size. The apices of the cusps project into the cavity of the ventricle. The atrial surfaces are smooth ; the ventricular surfaces are roughened by the attachments of the chordæ tendineæ, which are connected also with the irregular and notched margins and with the apices. The structure is the same as that of the cusps of the tricuspid valve (p. 1145) ; but the ventricular surface of the anterior (*aortic*) cusp is relatively smooth, and therefore the blood flow into the aorta is not impeded.

The **aortic orifice** is circular; it lies immediately in front and to the right of the mitral orifice, from which it is separated by the anterior cusp of the mitral valve, and it is guarded by the **aortic valve**, formed of three semilunar segments, one of which is placed in front and the other two behind. The structure and attachments of the cusps of the aortic valve are similar to those of the cusps of the pulmonary valve (see p. 1146).

The walls of the left ventricle are lined with endocardium. The septum and the upper part of the sterno-costal wall are relatively smooth. The rest is sponge-like owing to numerous fine **trabeculæ carneæ**. There are two **papillary muscles**—a *superior* and an *inferior*. They are much larger than the papillary muscles of the right ventricle; and each is connected by chordæ tendineæ with both cusps of the mitral valve. Two or three fine strands, corresponding in position to the moderator band in the right ventricle, are usually to be found passing across the cavity from the septum to the superior papillary muscle (see p. 1150).

The **ventricular septum** is a strong musculo-membranous partition. It is placed obliquely, so that one surface looks forwards and to the right, and bulges into the right ventricle, whilst the other looks backwards and to the left, and is concave towards the left ventricle. It extends from the right of the apex to the interval that separates the pulmonary and tricuspid orifices from the aortic and mitral. Its sterno-costal and inferior borders correspond respectively with the anterior and inferior interventricular grooves. The larger part of the septum is muscular, and is developed from the wall of the ventricular part of the primitive heart. The upper and posterior part is developed from the septum of the truncus arteriosus. It is called the **pars membranacea septi**, for it is entirely fibrous; and it is the thinnest portion of the ventricular walls. It separates the aortic vestibule not only from the upper part of the right ventricle, but also from the lower part of the right atrium. Occasionally it is defective or absent; the two ventricles then communicate with each other directly.

STRUCTURE OF THE HEART

The walls of the heart consist mainly of peculiar striped muscle, called the myocardium, which is enclosed between the visceral layer of the pericardium, or epicardium, externally, and the endocardium internally.

The **epicardium**, or visceral layer of the pericardium, consists of white fibrous and of elastic tissue, the latter forming a distinct reticulum in the deeper part. The surface which looks towards the pericardial cavity is covered with flat polygonal endothelial plates.

The **endocardium** lines the cardiac cavities and is continuous with the inner coats of the vessels. It is much thinner than the epicardium. It consists, like the inner coat of the blood-vessels, of an inner lining of flat endothelial cells, a layer of fine subendo-thelial areolar tissue, and an external elastic layer which usually assumes the form of a fenestrated membrane.

The fibres of the **myocardium** differ from those of ordinary voluntary striped muscle in several ways: they are shorter, many of them being oblong cells, with forked extremities which are closely cemented to similar processes of adjacent cells; they form a reticulum; and the nuclei lie in the centres of the cells. Moreover, still more peculiar fibres, the **fibres of Purkinje**, are found immediately subjacent to the subendocardial tissue. The fibres of Purkinje are large cells which unite with one another at their extremities; their central portions consist of granular protoplasm, in which sometimes one but more frequently two nuclei are embedded, and the peripheral portion of each cell is transversely striated. Those cells present, in a per-manent form, a condition which is transitory in all other striped muscle cells.

The reticulating cardiac muscle cells are grouped in sheets and strands which have a more or less characteristic and definite arrangement in different parts of the heart; they are separated and at the same time bound together by intervening lamellæ of fine areolar tissue. By careful dissection, and after special methods of preparation, it is possible to recognise many layers and bundles, some of which are, however, probably artificially produced.

The heart also possesses a fibrous skeleton which strengthens its orifices, is continuous with the roots of the aorta and the pulmonary trunk, and gives attachment to the valves and the muscular layers. *Fibrous rings* surround the atrio-ventricular, pulmonary and aortic orifices, and in the interval between the atrio-ventricular and aortic orifices is situated the *fibrous trigone* that has already been mentioned (p. 1145). The back of the infundibulum is also connected to the aorta by a fibrous band which is continuous with the membranous part of the ventricular septum.

In the **atria** the muscular fasciculi fall naturally into two groups: (*a*) superficial fibres common to both atria; (*b*) deep fibres special to each atrium.

The superficial fibres are most numerous on the sterno-costal aspect and in the neighbourhood of the atrio-ventricular sulcus. They run transversely across the atria and a few of them dip into the atrial septum.

The deep fibres are—(1) Looped fibres ; the ends of the looped fibres are attached to the fibrous rings around the atrio-ventricular orifices and the fibres pass antero-posteriorly over the atria. (2) Annular fibres which surround (a) the extremities of the large vessels which open into the atria ; (b) the auricles ; (c) the fossa ovalis.

In the **ventricles** the muscular fasciculi form more or less definite V-shaped loops which begin and end at the fibrous rings which surround the large orifices at the bases of the ventricles. These loops embrace the cavities of either one or both ventricles, one stem of each loop lying on the outer surface of the heart and the other in the interior, and some of the loops possess very acute whilst others have very open bends.

The superficial fibres on the sterno-costal surface pass towards the left, those on the inferior surface towards the right. At the apex all are coiled into a whorl or *vortex* through which they pass into the interior of the ventricular walls and run towards the base, some in the septum and others in the papillary muscles. The various bundles which have been described can, according to Mall, be resolved into two main systems. One system arises from the infundibulum and the root of the aorta, that is, from the remains of the primitive aortic trunk : it is called the "bulbo-spiral" system. The other springs from the region of the primitive venous sinus and is termed the "sino-spiral." Both systems are separable into superficial and deep portions, and the general plan of more or less spirally curved V-shaped loops is retained in each, but the details of the arrangement are too complicated for consideration within the limits of an ordinary text-book (see *Amer. Journ. Anat.*, 1910–1911, vol. xi.).

Conducting System of the Heart (Neuro-myocardium).

—It would appear from the description of the muscular structure of the heart that the atrial and ventricular muscle fibres are entirely separated from each other by the fibrous rings which surround the atrio-ventricular orifices ; that, however, is not the case, for the two groups are connected by a bundle of muscle fibres of pale colour and rudimentary structure, which lies immediately subjacent to the endocardium and constitutes the atrio-ventricular bundle This, however, is only part of the conducting system of the heart.

The function of initiating the sequence of events in the cycle of heart action, of controlling its regularity, and of transmitting the impulses from atria to ventricles, resides in certain special parts of the myocardium. Heart muscle has the power of rhythmic contraction. One collection of the special myocardial tissue, situated in the wall of the right atrium, sets the pace of the rhythm ; another part, beginning in the wall of the right atrium and extending across the otherwise fibrous atrio-ventricular junction, and spreading out to form a sub-endocardial network in the walls of the ventricles, propagates the rhythm of the atrial contraction to the ventricles. If the connecting link is severed, experimentally or by disease, the remarkable result follows that the ventricles contract independently of the atria, and with a much slower rhythm. This condition is known as "heart block."

The parts concerned in this controlling and conducting mechanism are composed of myocardial tissue, distinguished from the ordinary cardiac muscle not only because it is less highly differentiated from the original cells, but also because the muscle fibres are intimately associated with numerous nerve cells and fibrils, which probably have a share in the initiation and transmission of the rhythmic heart contraction. The functional connexion between the parts of the heart has thus a neuro-muscular basis ; and the system as a whole may therefore be distinguished as the "neuro-myocardium." Its parts are named the *sinu-atrial node*, the *atrio-ventricular node*, and the *atrio-ventricular bundle* with its right and left septal divisions, which end in the *terminal subendocardial network*.

The **sinu-atrial node** (Keith and Flack) is a small collection of vascular neuro-myocardium situated in the wall of the right atrium at the upper end of the crista terminalis.

The **atrio-ventricular node** (Tawara) is a nodule of the same kind of vascular tissue, situated in the septal wall of the right atrium immediately above the opening of the coronary sinus.

The **atrio-ventricular bundle** (Kent, His) is a pale bundle, about the thickness of a match, of the special muscle fibres, with which nerve fibres are associated. It springs from the node, runs forward on the septum, passes through the fibrous atrio-ventricular junction, and appears beneath the endocardium of the right ventricle under cover of the medial (septal) cusp of the tricuspid valve. There it swells out a little, and then passes forwards along the posterior and lower border of the membranous upper part of the ventricular septum to the upper end of the muscular part of that septum, where it divides into right and left branches (Figs. 998, 999).

The *right septal division* continues the course of the main bundle on the muscular part of the septum towards the moderator band, along which it passes from the septum to the anterior wall of the ventricle, which it reaches at the base of the anterior papillary muscle. Fine branches arise from it as it reaches the moderator band, and these continue along the septum to the base of the inferior papillary muscle. One or two of them occasionally appear as free threads passing across the cavity of the ventricle.

The *left septal division* pierces the ventricular septum between its membranous and muscular parts, and appears on the left side of the septum, down which it runs, as a flattened band, to the base of the inferior papillary muscle of the left ventricle. As it passes down the septum, two or three fine strands usually spring from it and pass across the cavity of the ventricle to the base of the superior papillary muscle. These strands are very distinct in the hearts of the sheep and calf, in which both septal branches and the network in which they end can be recognised very easily by the naked eye as whitish structures beneath the endocardium.

The **terminal sub-endocardial network** (Purkinje) is spread out beneath the endocardium

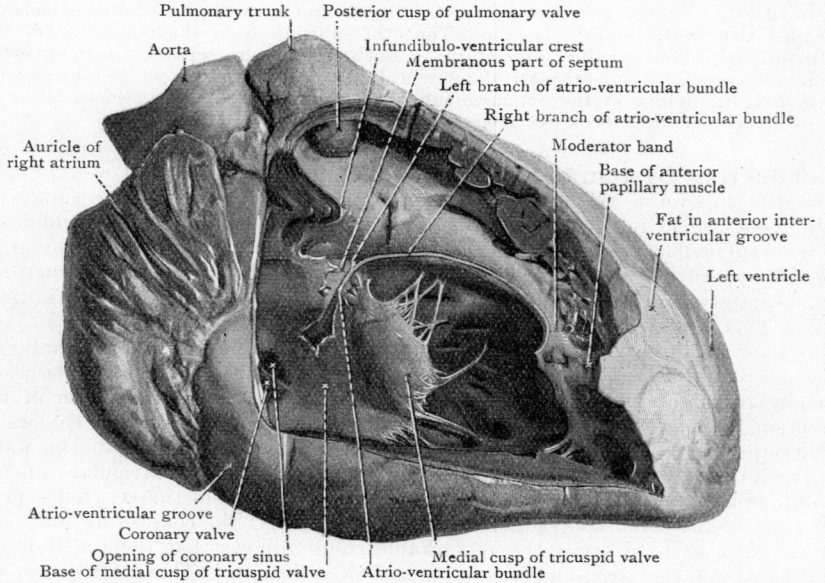

Pulmonary trunk   Posterior cusp of pulmonary valve

Aorta   Infundibulo-ventricular crest
                              Membranous part of septum
                              Left branch of atrio-ventricular bundle

                              Right branch of atrio-ventricular bundle

                              Moderator band

Auricle of
right atrium   Base of anterior
                              papillary muscle

                              Fat in anterior inter-
                              ventricular groove

                              Left ventricle

Atrio-ventricular groove
Coronary valve
Opening of coronary sinus   Medial cusp of tricuspid valve
Base of medial cusp of tricuspid valve   Atrio-ventricular bundle

FIG. 998.—DISSECTION OF THE RIGHT VENTRICLE SHOWING THE COURSE AND DIVISION OF THE
ATRIO-VENTRICULAR BUNDLE.

of the greater part of both ventricles. It receives the branches of the bundle at the bases of the papillary muscles, which are consequently the first parts of the ventricles to contract. The network forms a characteristic collar around each papillary muscle, the apex of the muscle being free of the network. The meshes of the network become finer, and then disappear, towards the atrio-ventricular and arterial orifices of the ventricles. A striking picture of the distribution of the subendocardial network and of the course of the bundle and its branches may be obtained by the injection of Indian ink or other suitable coloured liquid into the sheath which surrounds the whole system. Good results are most easily obtained in the heart of an ungulate (Fig. 999).

Action of the Heart.—The differences between the various parts of the heart, *e.g.* the relative thickness of the walls of the chambers, are associated with the functions of the various chambers, and with the action of the heart in the maintenance of the circulation of the blood. The heart is a muscular pump, provided with receiving and ejecting chambers. It has three phases of action ; (1) a period of atrial *systole* or contraction ; (2) a period of ventricular contraction, which immediately succeeds the atrial contraction ; (3) a period of *diastole* or rest.

During the period of rest the chambers, previously contracted, expand as the muscular fibres of the heart relax. The expansion is aided by the respiratory movements of the thorax, and, as it progresses, blood flows into the right atrium from the venæ cavæ and the coronary sinus, and into the left atrium through the four pulmonary veins. As the blood enters the atria, it begins at once to flow into the ventricles through the open atrio-ventricular orifices, and the onward movement is completed by the contraction of the atria. The atrial systole begins with the contraction of the circular fibres which surround the mouths of the veins entering the atria, and thus the blood is prevented from passing back into the veins. As the contraction spreads, the atria are emptied and the ventricles become distended. Then the ventricular systole begins, the atrio-ventricular valves close, the arterial valves open, and, as the contraction proceeds, the blood is driven out of the ventricles through the arterial orifices—from the right ventricle into the pulmonary trunk, and from the left ventricle into the aorta.

When the ventricular contraction is completed, the period of systole is at an end and the period of diastole begins; and, as long as the heart remains alive, the cycle is repeated.

The work of the atria is merely to complete the discharge of the blood through the widely open atrio-ventricular orifices into the ventricles and to expand the ventricles.

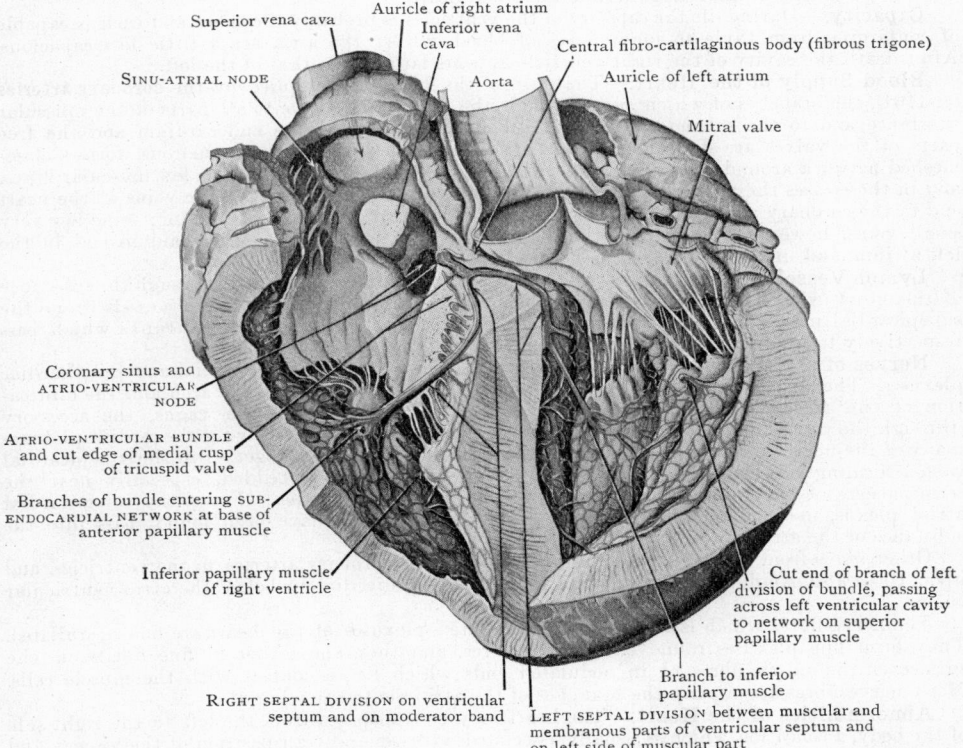

FIG. 999.—THE CONDUCTING SYSTEM OF A SHEEP'S HEART; FROM DISSECTED AND INJECTED SPECIMENS.

For that purpose no great force is required; the walls of the atria are therefore thin. The work of the ventricles is much more severe; their walls are therefore thicker. The right ventricle, however, has only to exert sufficient force to drive the blood through the lungs to the left atrium—that is, through a comparatively short distance and against a relatively small resistance. Its walls are therefore thin as compared with the walls of the left ventricle, which have to be sufficiently strong to force the blood through the whole body. The pressure created in the aorta (150 mm. Hg.) is about three times as great as that in the pulmonary arteries; corresponding to the relation between these pressures is the fact that the left ventricular wall is about three times as thick as the right.

Size of the Heart.—The heart is about five inches (125 mm.) long, three and a half inches (85 mm.) broad; its greatest depth from its sterno-costal to its diaphragmatic surface is two and a half inches (60 mm.), and it is roughly estimated as being about the same size as the closed fist. The size, however, is variable even in health, the volume increasing at first rapidly, and then gradually, with increasing age, from 22 cc. at birth to 155 cc. at the fifteenth year, and to 250 cc. by the twentieth year. From that period to the fiftieth year, when the maximum volume (280 cc.) is attained, the increase is much more gradual, and after fifty a slight decrease sets in. The volume is the same in both sexes up to the period of puberty, but thereafter it preponderates in the male.

Weight.—The average weight of the heart in the male adult is 11 ounces (310 grms.), and in the female adult 9 ounces (255 grms.) ; but the weight varies greatly, always, however, in definite relation to the weight of the body, the relative proportions changing at different periods of life. Thus at birth the heart weighs 13½ drachms (24 grms.), and its relation to the body weight is as 1 to 130, whilst in the adult the relative proportion is as 1 to 205. The heart is said to increase rapidly in weight up to the seventh year, then more slowly up to the age of puberty, when a second acceleration sets in ; but after the attainment of adult life the increase, which continues till the seventieth year, is very gradual.

These changes affect the whole heart, but the several parts also vary in their relation to one another at different periods of life. During fœtal life the right atrium is heavier than the left ; in the first month after birth the two become equal ; at the second year the right again begins to preponderate, and it is heavier than the left during the remainder of life. In the latter part of fœtal life the two ventricles are equal ; after birth the left grows more rapidly than the right, until, at the end of the second year, a position of stability is gained, when the right is to the left as 1 to 2, and this proportion is maintained until death.

Capacity.—During life the capacity of the ventricles is probably the same, and each is capable of containing from three to four ounces of blood, whilst the atria are a little less capacious. After death the cavity of the right ventricle appears larger than that of the left.

Blood Supply of the Heart.—The walls of the heart are supplied by the **coronary arteries** (p. 1161), the branches of which pass through the interstitial tissue to all parts of the muscular substance and to the subendocardial and subepicardial tissues ; the endocardium and the free parts of the valves are devoid of vessels. The capillaries, which are numerous, form a close-meshed network around the muscular fibres. Sometimes the valves contain a few muscular fibres, and in those cases they also receive some minute vessels. The majority of the veins of the heart end in the coronary sinus, which opens into the lower part of the right atrium ; some few very small veins, however, open directly into the right atrium, and others are said to end in the left atrium, and in the cavities of the ventricles.

Lymph Vessels of the Heart.—A subendocardial plexus communicates through the substance of the heart with a superficial network beneath the epicardium. Efferent vessels from the subepicardial network follow the coronary arteries and end in right and left trunks which pass respectively to innominate and tracheo-bronchial glands.

Nerves of the Heart.—The heart receives its nerves from the superficial and deep cardiac plexuses. The former lies below the aortic arch and the latter between the arch and the bifurcation of the trachea. Through the plexuses it is connected with the vagus, the accessory (through the vagus), and the sympathetic nerves (see p. 1066). After leaving the cardiac plexuses many of the nerve-fibres enter the walls of the atria and anastomose together in the subepicardial tissue, forming a plexus in which many ganglion cells are embedded, especially near the terminations of the inferior vena cava and the pulmonary veins. From the subepicardial atrial plexus, nerve filaments, on which nerve ganglion cells have been found, pass into the substance of the atrial walls.

Other fibres from the cardiac plexuses accompany the coronary arteries to the ventricles, and upon those also ganglion cells are found in the region immediately below the atrio-ventricular sulcus.

The nerve-fibres which issue from the gangliated plexuses of the heart are non-medullated. They form fine plexuses round the muscle fibres, and they end either in fine fibrils on the surfaces of the muscle fibres, or in nodulated ends which lie in contact with the muscle cells. Many nerve fibres accompany the branches of the atrio-ventricular bundle.

Abnormalities of the Heart.—The **heart** may be transposed from the left to the right side of the body, a condition which is usually associated with general transposition of the viscera, and with the presence of a right aortic arch instead of a left.

The external form of the heart does not as a rule vary much, but occasionally the apex is slightly bifid, a character it normally possesses at an early stage of its development, and which is retained in the adult in many cetaceans and sirenians. The internal conformation of the heart deviates from the normal much more frequently ; more particularly is this the case with regard to the septa which separate the right from the left chambers. The interatrial septum may be entirely absent, as in fishes ; it may be fenestrated and incomplete, as in some amphibians ; or the foramen ovale may remain patent, as in amphibians and reptiles.

The ventricular septum may be absent, as in fishes and amphibians, or incomplete, as in reptiles ; when incomplete, it is usually the "pars membranacea septi" which is deficient, but perforations are occasionally found in the muscular portion.

The communication between the infundibulum of the right ventricle and the body of the ventricle may be constricted or the infundibulum may be entirely cut off from the remainder of the cavity. In such cases of "pulmonary stenosis" there is always an interventricular foramen, and the pulmonary arteries receive their blood from the aorta *via* a patent ductus arteriosus. Many congenital malformations of the heart are incompatible with life.

PERICARDIUM

The **pericardium** is a fibro-serous sac which surrounds the heart. It lies in the middle mediastinum. It is attached below to the diaphragm, and above and behind to the roots of the great vessels. In front and behind it is in relation with structures in the anterior and posterior mediastina; laterally it is in close apposition with the pleural sacs.

The **fibrous pericardium** is a strong fibrous sac of conical form; its base is attached to the central tendon and to the adjacent part of the muscular substance of the diaphragm, and it is pierced by the inferior vena cava. At its apex and posteriorly it is gradually lost upon the great vessels which enter and emerge from the heart, and it gives sheaths to them—namely, the aorta, the two branches of the pulmonary trunk, the superior vena cava, the four pulmonary veins, and the

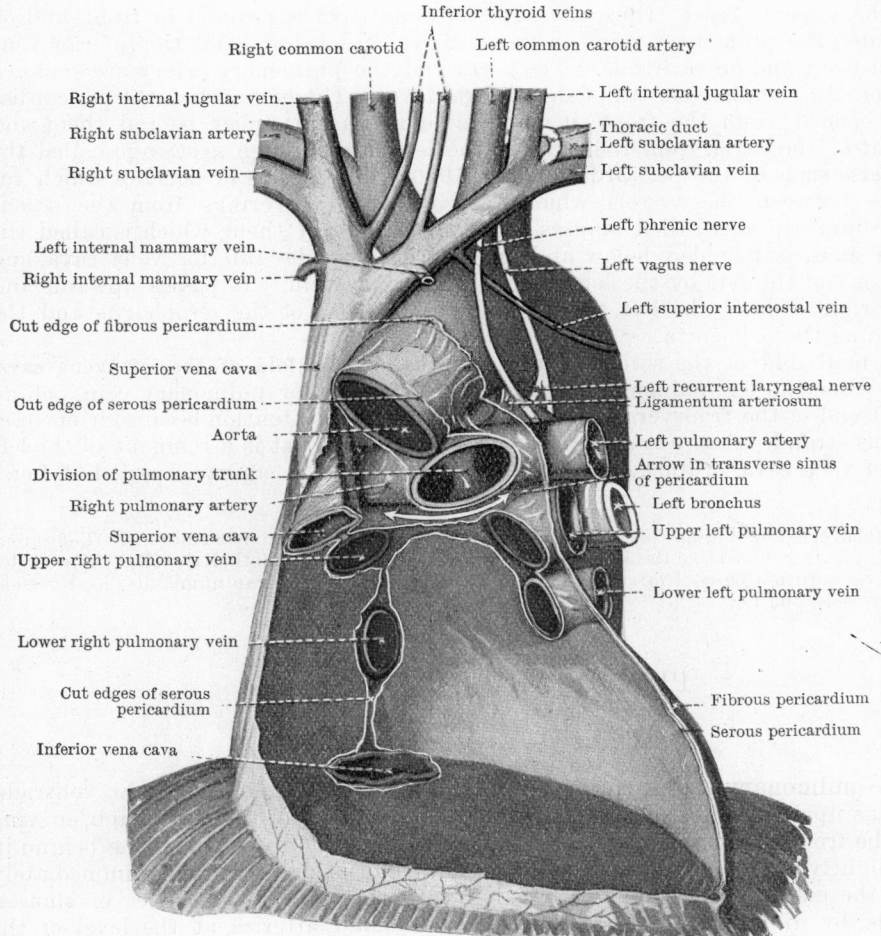

Inferior thyroid veins
Right common carotid
Left common carotid artery
Right internal jugular vein
Left internal jugular vein
Right subclavian artery
Thoracic duct
Left subclavian artery
Right subclavian vein
Left subclavian vein
Left phrenic nerve
Left internal mammary vein
Right internal mammary vein
Left vagus nerve
Left superior intercostal vein
Cut edge of fibrous pericardium
Superior vena cava
Left recurrent laryngeal nerve
Ligamentum arteriosum
Cut edge of serous pericardium
Aorta
Left pulmonary artery
Division of pulmonary trunk
Arrow in transverse sinus of pericardium
Right pulmonary artery
Left bronchus
Superior vena cava
Upper left pulmonary vein
Upper right pulmonary vein
Lower left pulmonary vein
Lower right pulmonary vein
Cut edges of serous pericardium
Fibrous pericardium
Serous pericardium
Inferior vena cava

Fig. 1000.—Posterior Wall of the Pericardium after the Removal of the Heart.
Showing the relation of the serous pericardium to the great vessels.

ligamentum arteriosum. Its anterior surface forms the posterior boundary of the anterior mediastinum, and it is attached, above and below, by the sterno-pericardial ligaments to the sternum. In the greater part of its extent it is separated from the anterior wall of the thorax by the anterior parts of the lungs and pleural sacs, but it is in direct relation with the left half of the lower portion of the body of the sternum and often with the medial ends of the cartilages of the fourth, fifth, and sixth ribs of the left side and the left sterno-costalis [transversus thoracis] muscle. Its posterior surface forms the anterior boundary of the posterior mediastinum; it is in relation with the œsophagus and the descending aorta, both of which it separates from the back of the left atrium. Each lateral surface is in close contact with the mediastinal portion of the parietal pleura, the phrenic nerve and its accompanying vessels intervening. The inner surface of the fibrous sac is lined with and is closely attached to the parietal part of the serous pericardium.

The **serous pericardium** is a closed sac containing a little lubricating fluid. It is surrounded by the fibrous pericardium and invaginated by the heart. It is, therefore, separable into two portions—the parietal, which lines the inner surface of the fibrous sac, and the visceral, which ensheathes, or partially ensheathes, the heart and the great vessels; but the two portions are, of course, continuous with each other where the serous layer is reflected on to the great vessels as they pierce the fibrous layer. The majority of the great vessels receive only partial coverings from the visceral layer : thus, the superior vena cava is covered in front and on each side; the pulmonary veins in front, above, and below; and the inferior vena cava in front and on each side. The aorta and the pulmonary artery are enclosed together in a complete sheath of the visceral layer. Therefore, when the pericardial sac is opened from the front, it is possible to pass a finger behind them and in front of the atria, from the right to the left side, through a passage called the **transverse sinus** of the pericardium (Fig. 1000). The spaces or pouches which intervene between the vessels which receive partial coverings from the serous pericardium are also called sinuses; and the largest of them, which is called the **oblique sinus**, is bounded below and on the right by the inferior vena cava, and above and on the left by the left inferior pulmonary vein. It passes upwards and to the right behind the left atrium, and lies in front of the œsophagus and the descending thoracic aorta.

A small fold of the serous pericardium, called the **fold of the left vena cava**, passes from the left pulmonary artery to the left superior pulmonary vein, behind the left end of the transverse sinus. It merits special attention because it encloses a fibrous strand—the *ligament of the left vena cava*. That is a remnant of the left superior vena cava, or duct of Cuvier, which atrophied at an early period of fœtal life.

Structure.—The fibrous pericardium is a dense unyielding fibrous membrane. The serous pericardium is covered on its inner aspect by a layer of flat endothelial cells. The endothelium rests upon a basis of mixed white and elastic fibres in which run numerous blood-vessels, lymph vessels, and nerves.

PULMONARY CIRCULATION

PULMONARY ARTERIES

The **pulmonary trunk** springs from the infundibulum of the right ventricle, and runs upwards and backwards, towards the concavity of the aortic arch, curving from the front round the left side of the ascending aorta to reach a plane behind it. It is slightly wider at its origin than the aorta, and is slightly dilated, immediately above the cusps of the pulmonary valve, into three shallow pouches or **sinuses**. It ends, by dividing into right and left pulmonary arteries, at the level of the sternal end of the second left costal cartilage. Its length is a little more than two inches.

Relations.—The pulmonary trunk is enclosed within the fibrous pericardium, and is enveloped, along with the ascending aorta, in a common sheath of the visceral layer of the serous pericardium (Fig. 1000). It lies behind the anterior end of the second left intercostal space, from which it is separated by the anterior margins of the left lung and pleural sac.

Its posterior relations are first the ascending aorta, and then the anterior wall of the left atrium (Figs. 992, 995). To the right it is in relation with the auricle of the right atrium, and the ascending aorta, and to the left with the auricle of the left atrium. Immediately above its bifurcation, between it and the aortic arch, is the superficial cardiac plexus.

Both the coronary arteries are in relation to its root—the right coronary artery on its right, the left at first behind and then on its left.

The **right pulmonary artery** is longer and wider than the left. It passes to the right lung, in its root, enters the hilum and descends, with the main bronchus, to the lower end of the lung (Fig. 1002).

Relations.—Before it enters the lung the right pulmonary artery passes behind the ascending aorta, the superior vena cava, and the upper right pulmonary vein. At first, it lies below the arch of the aorta and the right bronchus, in front of the œsophagus, and above the left atrium and the lower right pulmonary vein; then it crosses in front of the right bronchus, immediately below its eparterial branch, and reaches the hilum of the lung. In the lung the artery descends posterior and lateral to the main bronchus and between its anterior and posterior branches.

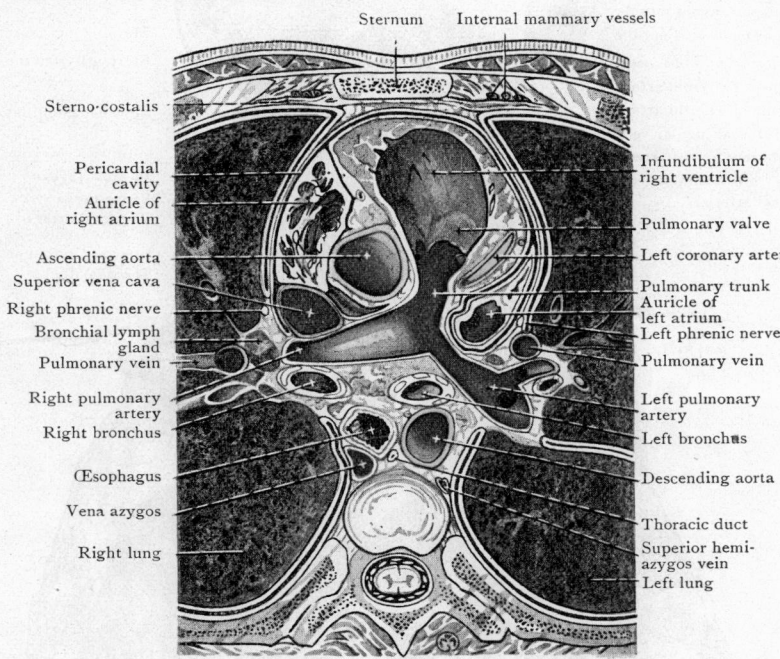

FIG. 1001.—TRANSVERSE SECTION OF THE THORAX OF A YOUNG MAN ALONG THE PLANE C–C, Fig. 1038, p. 1239, seen from below.

Branches.—Before entering the hilum it gives off a large branch which accompanies the eparterial bronchus to the upper lobe of the right lung. In the substance of the lung it gives off numerous branches which accompany the anterior, posterior, and accessory branches of the right bronchus. (See Respiratory System, p. 684.)

The **left pulmonary artery**, shorter, narrower, and a little higher in position than the right, passes laterally and backwards from the bifurcation of the pulmonary trunk, and runs, in the root, to the hilum of the left lung; it then descends, in company with the main bronchus, to the lower end of the lung.

Relations.—Before it enters the lung it is crossed, *anteriorly*, by the upper left pulmonary vein; *posterior to* it, are the left bronchus and the descending aorta; *above*, are the aortic arch (to which it is connected by the ligamentum arteriosum) and the left recurrent laryngeal nerve; *below*, it is in relation with the lower left pulmonary vein. After entering the lung it descends, like the right pulmonary artery, posterior and lateral to the stem bronchus, and between its ventral and dorsal branches.

Branches.—Just before it passes through the hilum it gives off a branch to the upper lobe of the left lung, and in the substance of the lung its branches correspond with the anterior, posterior, and accessory branches of the left bronchus.

PULMONARY VEINS

The terminal **pulmonary veins** (Figs. 991, 997 and 1000), two on each side, open into the left atrium of the heart. Their tributaries arise in capillary plexuses in the walls of the pulmonary alveoli. By the union of the smaller veins larger vessels

73 *a*

are formed which run in front of the bronchial tubes, and unite to form in each lobe a single efferent vessel which passes into the root of the lung. Thus there are five main pulmonary veins, but, immediately after entering the root of the lung, the vessels from the upper and middle lobes of the right lung join together, and so

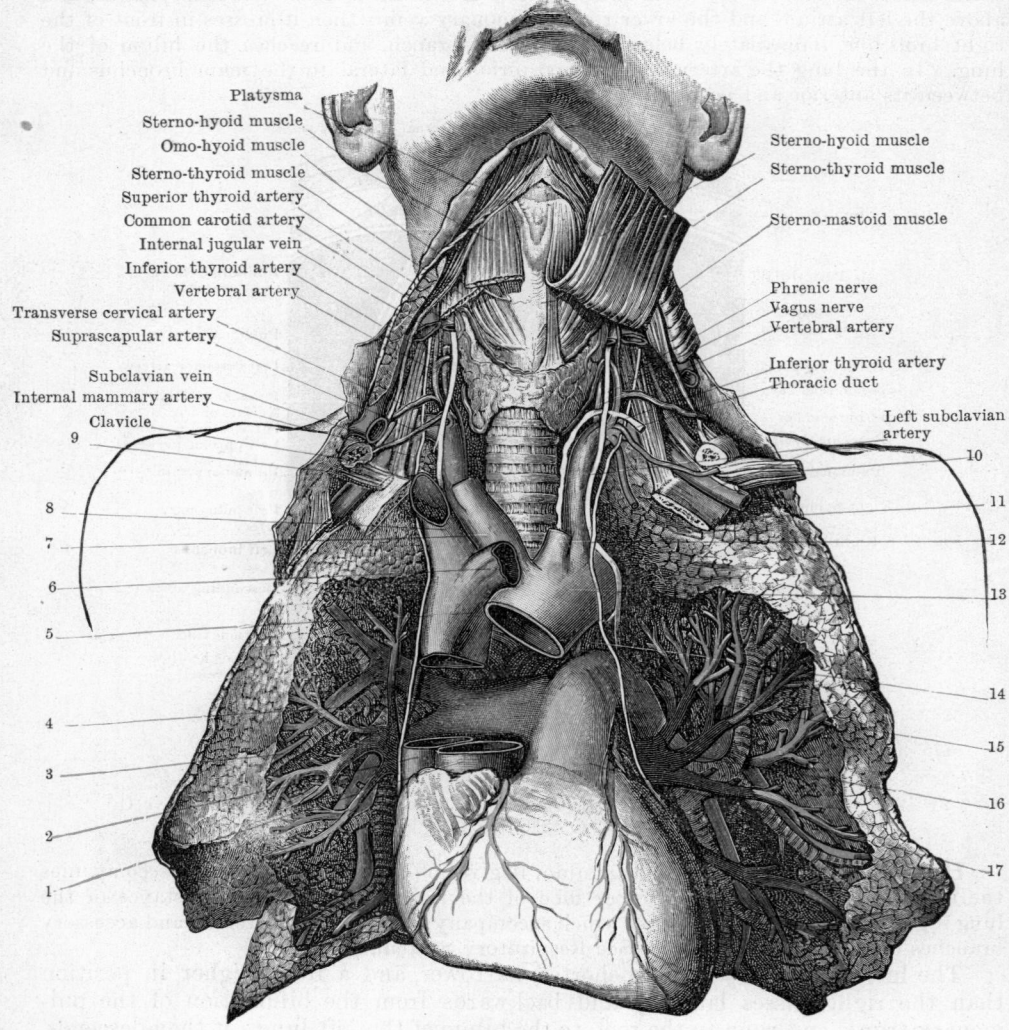

FIG. 1002.—THE PULMONARY ARTERIES AND VEINS AND THEIR RELATIONS IN A FORMALIN-HARDENED PREPARATION.

The ascending aorta and part of the superior vena cava have been removed.

1. Ascending aorta.
2. Superior vena cava.
3. Upper right pulmonary vein.
4. Right pulmonary artery.
5. Superior vena cava.
6. Left innominate vein.
7. Innominate artery.
8. Right innominate vein.
9. Subclavius muscle.
10. Subclavius muscle.
11. First rib.
12. Left common carotid artery.
13. Arch of aorta.
14. Ligamentum arteriosum.
15. Left pulmonary artery.
16. Upper left pulmonary vein.
17. Pulmonary trunk.

only four terminal pulmonary veins open into the left atrium. Neither the main stems nor their tributaries possess valves.

Relations.—In the root of each lung the upper pulmonary vein lies below and in front of the pulmonary artery. The lower pulmonary vein is in the lowest part of the root, and also in a plane posterior to the upper vein.

On the right side the upper pulmonary vein passes behind the superior vena cava, and the lower passes behind the right atrium. They both end in the upper and posterior part of the left atrium close to the atrial septum. *On the left side* both upper and lower pulmonary veins cross in front of the descending aorta, and they end in the upper and posterior part of the left atrium near its left border.

All four pulmonary veins perforate the fibrous layer of the pericardium, and receive partial coverings of the serous layer before they enter the atrium.

SYSTEMIC CIRCULATION
AORTA

The **aorta** is the main trunk of the general arterial system. It begins at the base of the left ventricle and runs upwards (**ascending aorta**), with an inclination to the right and forwards, to the level of the second right costal cartilage; continuing upwards it curves first to the left and then backwards and downwards, until it reaches the left side of the lower border of the fourth thoracic vertebra (**arch of aorta**); from that level it runs downwards (**descending aorta**) through the thorax into the abdomen, where it ends, on the left of the median plane, at the level of the fourth lumbar vertebra, by bifurcating into the two common iliac arteries. The descending portion of the aorta is, for convenience, divided into the *descending thoracic aorta*, and the *abdominal aorta*.

Ascending Aorta.—The ascending aorta lies in the middle mediastinum. It springs from the base of the left ventricle, behind the left margin of the sternum, opposite the lower border of the third left costal cartilage. From its origin it passes upwards, forwards, and to the right, and ends by becoming the arch of the aorta, behind the right margin of the sternum, at the level of the second costal cartilage. Its *length* is from 2 to 2¼ inches (about 55 mm.) and its diameter is a little over 1 inch (about 28 mm.). In the adult it is a little narrower at its origin than the pulmonary artery, but as age advances it enlarges and exceeds that vessel in size. The diameter, however, is not uniform throughout the whole length of the ascending aorta. Its root is dilated owing to

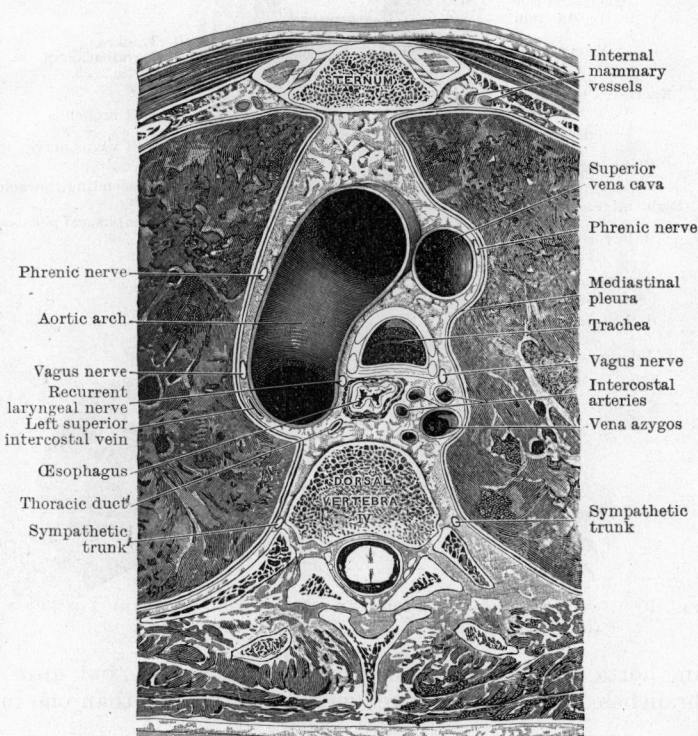

FIG. 1003.—TRANSVERSE SECTION THROUGH THE SUPERIOR MEDIASTINUM AT THE LEVEL OF THE FOURTH THORACIC VERTEBRA.

three bulgings in its wall—the **sinuses of the aorta**. The sinuses are immediately opposite the cusps of the aortic valve. One is therefore anterior in position, and two posterior. At a higher level a diffuse bulging of the right wall is sometimes known as the *great sinus* of the aorta.

Relations.—The ascending aorta is completely enclosed within the fibrous pericardium which blends above with the sheath of the vessel, and it is enveloped, together with the pulmonary trunk, in a tube of the serous pericardium. At its origin it has the infundibulum of the right ventricle and the pulmonary trunk in front, the transverse sinus of the pericardium and the anterior wall of the left atrium behind, and the right atrium on its right side. In the upper part of its course the ascending aorta is overlapped by the anterior margins of the right lung and right pleural sac, whilst posterior to it are the right atrium, the right pulmonary artery, the right bronchus, and the left margin of the superior vena cava. The superior vena cava lies on the right side, and partly behind the upper part of the ascending aorta, whilst the pulmonary trunk is at first in front and then, at a higher level, on its left side.

Branches.—Two branches arise from the ascending aorta, viz., the right and the left coronary arteries (p. 1161). The right coronary artery springs from the anterior sinus of the aorta, and the left artery from the left posterior sinus (Fig. 995).

Arch of Aorta.—The arch of the aorta lies in the superior mediastinum behind the lower part of the manubrium sterni. It begins behind the right margin of the sternum, at its union with the second costal cartilage, and ends at the left side of the lower border of the fourth thoracic vertebra. The arch makes two curves, one with the convexity upwards (Fig. 1000), and the other with the convexity to the left and slightly forwards. From its origin it runs for a short distance upwards and to the left anterior to the trachea; then it passes backwards, round the left side of the trachea to the left side of the body of the fourth thoracic vertebra (Fig. 1003). Finally it turns downwards to become continuous with the descending aorta.

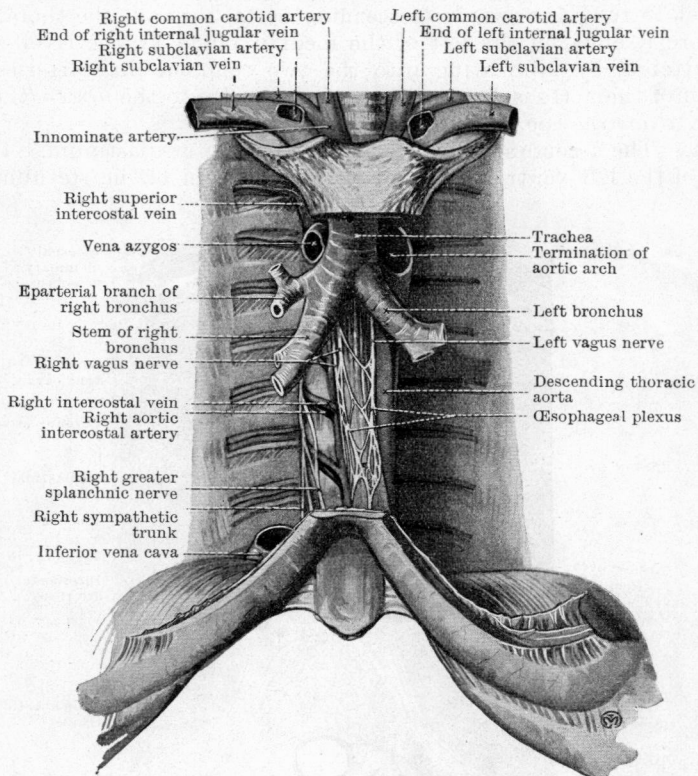

Right common carotid artery
End of right internal jugular vein
Right subclavian artery
Right subclavian vein

Left common carotid artery
End of left internal jugular vein
Left subclavian artery
Left subclavian vein

Innominate artery

Right superior intercostal vein

Vena azygos

Eparterial branch of right bronchus

Stem of right bronchus
Right vagus nerve

Right intercostal vein
Right aortic intercostal artery

Right greater splanchnic nerve
Right sympathetic trunk
Inferior vena cava

Trachea
Termination of aortic arch

Left bronchus

Left vagus nerve

Descending thoracic aorta
Œsophageal plexus

Fig. 1004.—Dissection of the Posterior Mediastinum and the Posterior Part of the Superior Mediastinum, from the Front.

The arch has at first the same diameter as the ascending aorta, a little more than one inch (28 mm.), but after giving off three large branches, the diameter is reduced to a little less than one inch (23 mm.).

Relations.—*In front*, it is related to the remains of the thymus, and is overlapped, almost equally, by the right and left pleuræ and lungs. *On its left*, it is very closely related to the left pleura and lung. Under cover of the pleura, its left side is crossed vertically by four nerves in the following order from before backwards : the left phrenic, the inferior cervical cardiac branch of the left vagus, the cardiac branch of the left superior cervical ganglion of the sympathetic, and the trunk of the left vagus. The left superior intercostal vein passes obliquely upwards and to the right, across it, superficial to the left vagus nerve and deep to the left phrenic nerve.

Behind, and *on the right* of the arch, are the deep cardiac plexus, the trachea, the left recurrent laryngeal nerve, the left border of the œsophagus, and the thoracic duct. *Above* are its three large branches—the innominate, the left common carotid, and the left subclavian arteries ; and crossing anterior to them is the left innominate vein. *Below* are the bifurcation of the pulmonary trunk and the root of the left lung ; the ligamentum arteriosum, which also is below, attaches it to the left pulmonary artery, whilst to the right of the ligament lies the superficial cardiac plexus, and to its left and behind it the left recurrent laryngeal nerve.

Branches.—The three great vessels which supply the head and neck, part of the thoracic wall, and the upper limbs—the innominate, the left common carotid, and the left subclavian arteries—arise from the aortic arch (p. 1162).

Descending Aorta.—The **descending thoracic aorta** lies in the posterior mediastinum ; it extends from the end of the arch, at the lower border of the left side of the fourth thoracic vertebra, to the aortic opening in the diaphragm, where, opposite the twelfth thoracic vertebra, it becomes continuous with the abdominal aorta. Its length is from seven to eight inches (17·5 to 20 cm.), and its diameter diminishes slightly as it gives off branches.

Relations.—Its *posterior* relations are: the vertebral column and the anterior longitudinal ligament ; the superior and inferior hemiazygos veins, which cross behind it ; the posterior intercostal arteries, which spring from its posterior surface ; and the left pleura and lung, which are behind its left margin—especially in its upper part.

In front it is in relation, from above downwards, with the root of the left lung, the pericardium, which separates it from the back of the left atrium, the œsophagus with the œsophageal plexus of nerves, and the diaphragm, which separates it from the caudate lobe of the liver. On the *left side* are the left lung and pleura. On the *right side* the thoracic duct and the vena azygos are in relation to it along its whole length. The vertebral bodies and the œsophagus also lie to the right of the upper part of the descending thoracic aorta, whilst the right lung and pleura are in relation below.

Branches.—Nine pairs of posterior intercostal arteries, one pair of subcostal arteries, two left bronchial arteries, four or five œsophageal, some small pericardial, and a few mediastinal and phrenic branches, usually arise from the descending thoracic aorta (p. 1203).

The **abdominal aorta** lies in the epigastric and umbilical regions of the abdomen. It extends from the middle of the lower border of the last thoracic vertebra to the body of the fourth lumbar vertebra, where, to the left of the median plane, it bifurcates into the right and left common iliac arteries. The point of division is usually a little below and to the left of the umbilicus, opposite a line drawn transversely across the abdomen on a level with the highest points of the iliac crests.

At first it is about 21 mm. in diameter, but after the origin of two large branches—the cœliac and the superior mesenteric arteries—it diminishes considerably, and then retains a fairly uniform diameter to its termination.

Relations.—*Behind*, it is related to the upper four lumbar vertebræ and the intervertebral discs between them, the anterior longitudinal ligament, and the third and fourth left lumbar veins ; four pairs of lumbar arteries and a single median sacral artery also spring from the posterior surface of the vessel. *In front* are the intermesenteric nerves (aortic plexus), and also in close relation with it from above downwards are the cœliac artery and cœliac plexus, the pancreas and splenic vein, the superior mesenteric artery, the left renal vein, the third part of the duodenum, the inferior mesenteric artery, the root of the mesentery, and the peritoneum and coils of small intestine. More superficially the stomach, the transverse colon, and the greater and lesser omenta are in front. On the *right side*, in the upper part of its extent, are the thoracic duct and cisterna chyli, the vena azygos, and the right crus of the diaphragm—the latter separating it from the right cœliac ganglion and from the upper part of the inferior vena cava. Its lower part is in direct relation, on the right side, with the inferior vena cava. On the *left side*, the left crus of the diaphragm with the left cœliac ganglion, and the terminal portion of the duodenum, are in close relation with its upper part, whilst in the lower portion of its extent the peritoneum and some coils of the small intestine are in contact with it. Aortic lymph glands lie in front and on both sides of it.

Branches.—The branches form two groups—visceral and parietal—and each group consists of paired and unpaired vessels, as follows :—*Visceral*—Cœliac, superior mesenteric, inferior mesenteric ; pairs of suprarenal, renal, and testicular or ovarian : *Parietal*— Median sacral (which is the original continuation of the aorta) ; one pair of phrenic, four pairs of lumbar, and a terminal pair of common iliac arteries (p. 1205).

Abnormalities of the Pulmonary Trunk and Aorta.—The pulmonary trunk and the aorta may arise by a common stem, as in fishes and some amphibians, and the common stem may spring from either the right or the left ventricle, or from both. In those cases the truncus

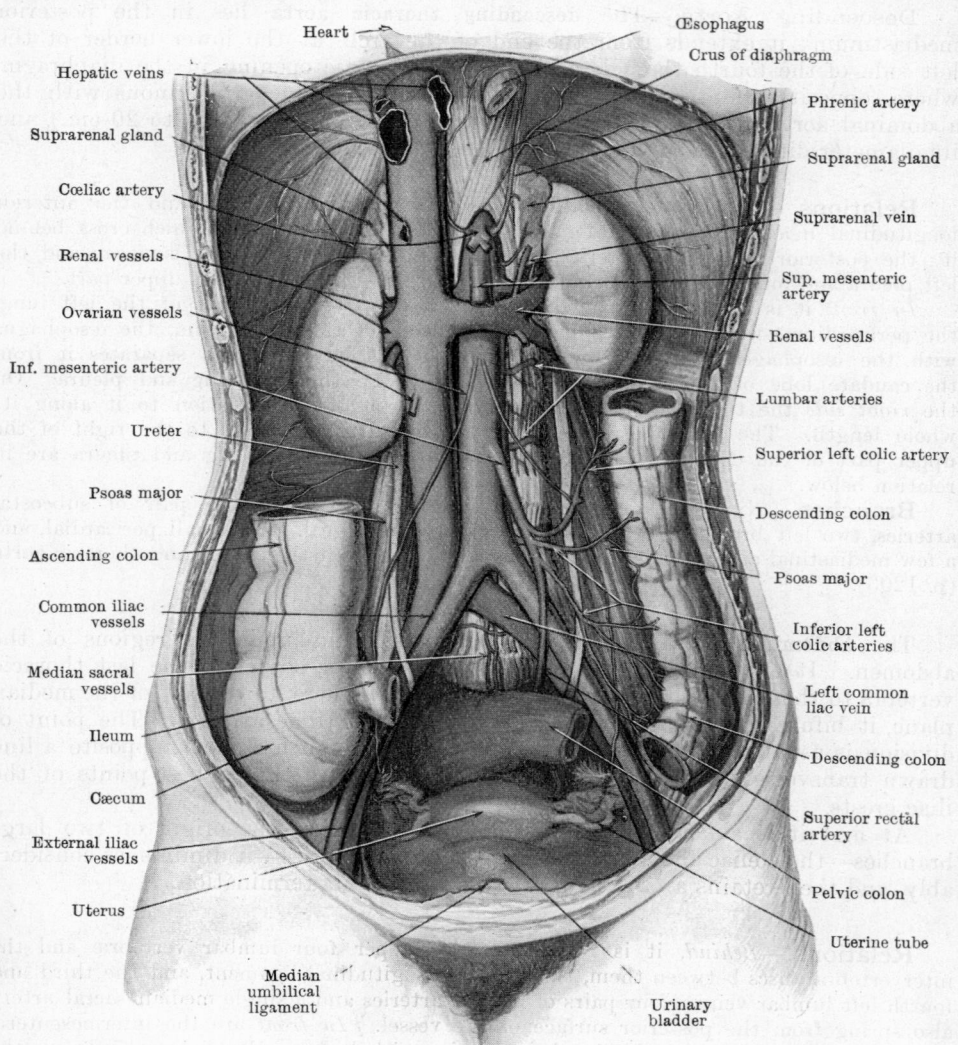

Fig. 1005.—The Abdominal Aorta and its Branches in a Formalin-hardened Preparation.

arteriosus has remained undivided, and the normal position of the ventricular septum in relation to the lower orifice of the bulbus cordis has been altered.

Again, owing to malposition of the aortic septum, the pulmonary trunk may spring from the left ventricle and the aorta from the right ventricle. In some cases the root of the pulmonary trunk is obliterated, and the blood passes to the lungs along the patent ductus arteriosus.

Occasionally the arch of the aorta is on the right side instead of the left, a condition which is normal in birds. More rarely there are two permanent aortic arches, right and left, as in reptiles ; the œsophagus and trachea are then enclosed in a vascular collar, the two arches unite dorsally, and the descending aorta has a double origin. Quite independent of that condition, however, the two primitive dorsal aortæ sometimes fail, either altogether or partially, to unite together, and the descending aorta is accordingly represented, to a corresponding extent, by two tubes. A more common, though still rare, form of double aorta is that due to the persistence, in whole or in part, of the septum formed by the fused walls of the primitive dorsal aortæ from which the descending aorta is developed.

The length of the descending aorta is determined largely by the extent to which fusion of the two primitive aortæ takes place. Accordingly, when that deviates from the normal, the end of the descending aorta is at a correspondingly higher or lower level than usual, and the lengths of the common iliac arteries are almost invariably proportionately modified. The bifurcation of the aorta may be as low as the fifth lumbar vertebra; less frequently it is higher than usual; it is rare, however, to find it as high as the third lumbar vertebra, and still more rare to find it at the level of the second.

The aorta, instead of bifurcating into two common iliac arteries, may end in a common iliac artery on one side and an internal iliac artery on the opposite side, the external iliac artery on the irregular side arising, at a higher level, as a branch of the aortic stem. That arrangement approaches the condition met with in carnivores and many other mammals, in which the aorta bifurcates into two internal iliac arteries, the external iliacs arising from the aorta at a higher level as collateral branches; it is probably due either to a fusion of the secondary roots of the umbilical arteries of opposite sides or to a caudal continuation of the fusion of the primitive dorsal aortæ.

BRANCHES OF ASCENDING AORTA

CORONARY ARTERIES

The coronary arteries are two in number, a right and a left; they are distributed almost entirely to the heart, but give also some small branches to the roots of the great vessels, and to the pericardium (Figs. 991, 992, and 995). The branches of the coronary arteries anastomose freely in the substance of the heart, but form no anastomoses with any other arteries. For detailed information the reader should consult *The Blood-Supply of the Heart*, Gross, 1921.

The **right coronary artery** springs from the anterior aortic sinus. It runs forwards, between the root of the pulmonary trunk and the auricle of the right atrium, to the atrio-ventricular groove, in which it passes downwards and to the right to the junction of the right and lower borders of the heart. There it turns backwards into the posterior part of the groove, together with the small cardiac vein, and runs as far as the posterior end of the inferior interventricular groove, where it gives off its interventricular branch and then ends by anastomosing with the left coronary artery. It is accompanied by branches from the cardiac plexus and lymph vessels, and in the second part of its course by the small cardiac vein.

Branches.—The **interventricular** branch runs forwards in the inferior interventricular groove; it supplies both ventricles, and anastomoses, at the apex of the heart, with the interventricular branch of the left coronary artery.

Twigs are distributed to the roots of the aorta and pulmonary trunk. Branches pass upwards on the anterior surface of the right atrium, and downwards on the anterior surface of the right ventricle; a larger **marginal** branch runs along the lower border of the heart and gives branches to both surfaces of the right ventricle.

The **left coronary artery** arises from the left posterior aortic sinus. Its short trunk runs to the left and then forwards, between the root of the pulmonary trunk and the auricle of the left atrium, to the upper end of the anterior interventricular groove, where it gives off an interventricular branch. It then runs round the left surface of the heart, in the left part of the atrio-ventricular groove, where it comes into relation with the coronary sinus, and ends by anastomosing with the right coronary artery.

Branches.—The **interventricular branch** passes down the anterior interventricular groove to the lower border of the heart, where it anastomoses with the interventricular branch from the right coronary; it supplies both ventricles, and is accompanied by cardiac nerves and lymph vessels and by the great cardiac vein.

Branches of small size pass to the wall of the left atrium, the left surface of the heart, and the posterior part of the inferior surface of the left ventricle; and small twigs are also given to the roots of the aorta and pulmonary trunk.

Variations.—The two **coronary arteries** may arise by a single stem. When arising separately both may spring from the same aortic sinus; or, again, an interventricular branch may arise as a distinct vessel from the same aortic sinus as the coronary to which it belongs. The variability is not very remarkable, seeing that the arteries in question are merely enlarged "vasa vasorum" raised to a position of special importance by the development of the heart.

BRANCHES OF ARCH OF AORTA

The branches which arise from the arch of the aorta supply the head and neck, the upper limbs, and part of the body wall.

They are three in number—the **innominate**, the **left common carotid**, and the **left subclavian arteries**. The innominate is a short but wide trunk, from the termination of which the right common carotid and the right subclavian arteries spring (Figs. 1000 and 1002); thus there is, at first, a difference between the stem vessels of opposite sides, but their branches are distributed to similar areas.

Variations.—The **branches of the arch** may be increased or decreased in number.

The highest number recorded is six—right subclavian, right vertebral, right common carotid, left common carotid, left vertebral, and left subclavian. Apparently that condition is the result of the absorption into the arch of the innominate artery and of the roots of the subclavian arteries, to points beyond the origins of the vertebrals. By variations of that process of absorption other combinations may be produced ; thus, instead of the roots of the subclavian arteries being absorbed, the right common carotid and innominate arteries may alone be absorbed, in which case the five following branches spring separately from the arch of the aorta : right subclavian, right external carotid, right internal carotid, left common carotid, and left subclavian. The trunk most commonly absorbed is the initial part of the left subclavian ; the number of branches then arising from the arch of the aorta is four, the additional vessel being the left vertebral, which arises between the left common carotid and the left subclavian. Occasionally the usual three branches from the arch are increased to four by the formation of a new vessel, the "thyroidea ima." That may be placed between the innominate and left carotid trunks, in which case it represents a persistent ventral visceral branch from the ventral root of the fourth left aortic arch ; in other cases the thyroidea ima springs from the innominate artery and represents a ventral visceral branch of the ventral root of the fourth *right* arch. Very rarely the right vertebral artery arises separately, and forms a fourth branch of the arch of the aorta, the rest of the branches being normal. That condition cannot be accounted for by any modification of the ordinary developmental processes. It may possibly be due to the persistence of an irregular or unimportant anastomosis between the ventral root of an aortic arch and the seventh somatic segmental artery.

Decrease in the number of branches from the arch of the aorta is most frequently due to fusion of the ventral roots of the fourth aortic arches, the result being that a stem is formed common to the right subclavian and the right and left common carotid arteries ; whilst the left subclavian, arising separately, is the only other branch which springs from the arch of the aorta.

If the fusion of the ventral roots proceeds further and includes those of the third arches, the result, as regards the branches given off from the arch of the aorta, is the same, *i.e.*, there is a common stem for the right subclavian and both carotids, and a separate left subclavian trunk ; but the common stem then gives off the right subclavian artery, and afterwards continues for some distance before it divides into the two common carotids, of which the left crosses in front of the trachea. That arrangement is common in many quadrumana and in some other mammals.

When the number of branches from the arch of the aorta is reduced to two, it is only rarely that they are a right subclavian artery and a single stem common to the two carotids and the left subclavian artery. In such cases, however, the right common carotid crosses in front of the trachea, and the variation is one of practical importance, but it does not appear to exist as a normal condition in any mammal. Probably it is due to fusion of the ventral roots of the fourth aortic arches, with absorption of the left fourth arch and the left subclavian into the stem so formed, whilst the right subclavian is relatively displaced. The two common carotids may arise by a common stem, and the left subclavian arise separately from the arch of the aorta, whilst the right subclavian springs from the descending aorta, and passes upwards and to the right behind the œsophagus. That arrangement probably results from the disappearance of the fourth right arch, the fusion of the ventral roots of the fourth arches of opposite sides and the persistence of the dorsal roots of the right fourth and sixth arches. (See Development of Vascular System, p. 1282.)

Sometimes two innominate arteries, right and left, replace the usual three branches of the arch of the aorta. That is the normal arrangement in bats, moles, and hedgehogs. It is obviously the result of the disappearance of that portion of the arch which intervenes between the left carotid and left subclavian arteries, and the consequent fusion of these two vessels.

In a similar way may be explained the rarer condition in which the three ordinary branches of the arch arise by one single stem, which divides into right and left innominate arteries. In most ruminants, in the horse and in the tapir, that arrangement is constant.

Other combinations and modifications may be met with in the branches of the arch of the aorta as the result of fusions and absorption. Other arteries also—internal mammary, inferior thyroid, bronchial—may occasionally arise from it.

INNOMINATE ARTERY

The **innominate artery** (Fig. 1002) arises, behind the middle of the manubrium sterni, as the first branch from the convexity of the arch of the aorta and it ends behind the upper part of the right sterno-clavicular joint, where it divides into the right subclavian and right common carotid arteries.

Course.—The trunk (from 35 to 50 mm. in length) runs upwards, backwards, and to the right, in the superior mediastinum, to the root of the neck.

Relations.—*Posterior*—It is in contact behind, with the trachea below and with the right pleural sac above. *Anterior*—The left innominate vein crosses in front of the lower part of the artery, and the remains of the thymus are in front of that vein ; above that level, the sterno-thyroid muscle separates it from the sterno-hyoid and the right sterno-clavicular joint. *Right Side*—The right innominate vein and the upper part of the superior vena cava are on the right side of the artery. *Left Side*—On its left side is the origin of the left common carotid artery, whilst at a higher level the trachea is in contact with it.

Branches.—As a rule the innominate artery does not give off any branches except its two terminals, but occasionally it furnishes an additional branch—the thyroidea ima.

Variations.—The innominate artery may be absent. On the other hand there may be two innominate arteries, a right and a left, each ending in corresponding common carotid and subclavian trunks, and the two vessels may themselves arise by a common stem. The branches of the innominate artery may be increased in number ; or the innominate may vary from the normal only in length. As a consequence of such modifications in length, the origins of the right common carotid and right subclavian arteries may be at a higher or lower level than usual, whilst, in the absence of the innominate artery, both these arteries may arise directly from the aorta.

The **thyroidea ima** is an inconstant and slender vessel. When present it may arise from the arch of the aorta, but it springs usually from the lower part of the innominate. It passes upwards, on the front of the trachea, and is distributed to the thyroid gland and the trachea.

ARTERIES OF THE HEAD AND NECK

The vessels distributed to the Head and Neck are derived chiefly from the carotid trunks ; there are, however, in addition, other vessels which arise from the main arterial stems of the Upper Limbs, and it will be advantageous to describe the most important of those, namely, the vertebral arteries, with the carotid system. The smaller additional branches will be considered along with the remaining branches of the subclavian arteries.

The **carotid system of arteries** consists, on each side, of a **common carotid** trunk, which divides into **internal** and **external carotid arteries**, from which numerous branches are given off (Figs. 1000, 1006, 1008, 1009).

The internal carotid arteries are distributed, almost entirely, to the contents of the cranial cavity that lie internal to the dura mater, and to the structures in the cavity of the orbit. The external carotid arteries, on the other hand, supply structures of the head and neck more externally situated.

It is to be noted, however, that the vascular supply of the brain is not wholly derived from the internal carotid vessels, but that the vertebral arteries also make an important contribution to it.

COMMON CAROTID ARTERIES

The two **common carotid arteries** are of unequal length. The *right common carotid artery* begins at the bifurcation of the innominate artery behind the right sterno-clavicular joint ; the *left common carotid* arises, in the superior mediastinum, from the arch of the aorta ; but each terminates at the level of the upper border of the thyroid cartilage. The left artery has thus a short intra-thoracic course, and, so far, its relations call for separate consideration ; whilst in the rest of its course it passes upwards in the neck, like the right common carotid, and has almost similar relations.

Left Common Carotid Artery.—The **left common carotid artery** springs from the upper aspect of the aortic arch, immediately behind and to the left of the origin of the innominate artery, and its *thoracic portion* extends to the left sterno-clavicular joint, where the cervical portion begins. It is from 1 to 1½ inches

(25–37 mm.) in length, and it runs upwards and slightly laterally through the upper part of the superior mediastinum.

Relations.—*Posterior.*—The vessel is in contact behind, and from below upwards, with the trachea, the left recurrent laryngeal nerve, the œsophagus, and the thoracic duct ; and the thoracic part of the left subclavian artery is a postero-lateral relation. *Anterior.*— The left innominate vein runs obliquely across the artery, in front of which cardiac branches from the left vagus and sympathetic descend vertically. Those structures, together with the remains of the thymus and the anterior margins of the left lung and pleura, separate the artery from the manubrium sterni, and from the origins of the sterno-hyoid and sterno-thyroid muscles. *Medial.*—The innominate artery

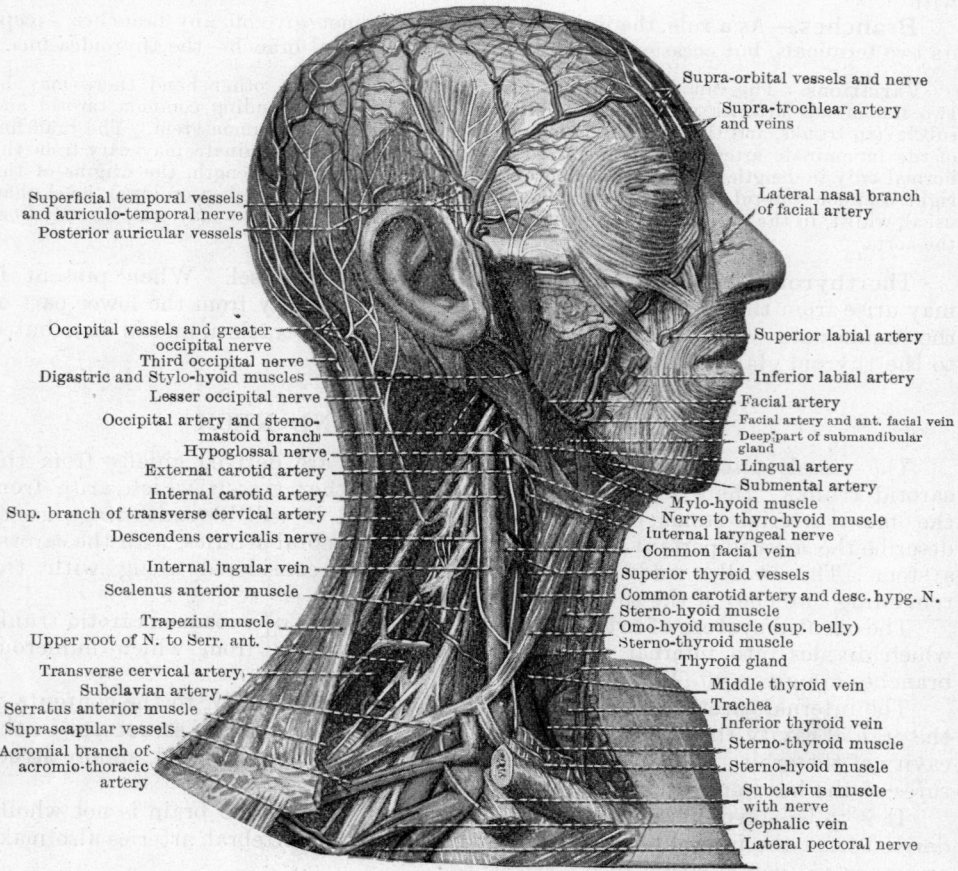

Supra-orbital vessels and nerve

Supra-trochlear artery and veins

Lateral nasal branch of facial artery

Superficial temporal vessels and auriculo-temporal nerve

Posterior auricular vessels

Occipital vessels and greater occipital nerve

Third occipital nerve

Digastric and Stylo-hyoid muscles

Lesser occipital nerve

Occipital artery and sterno-mastoid branch

Hypoglossal nerve

External carotid artery

Internal carotid artery

Sup. branch of transverse cervical artery

Descendens cervicalis nerve

Internal jugular vein

Scalenus anterior muscle

Trapezius muscle

Upper root of N. to Serr. ant.

Transverse cervical artery

Subclavian artery

Serratus anterior muscle

Suprascapular vessels

Acromial branch of acromio-thoracic artery

Superior labial artery

Inferior labial artery

Facial artery

Facial artery and ant. facial vein

Deep part of submandibular gland

Lingual artery

Submental artery

Mylo-hyoid muscle

Nerve to thyro-hyoid muscle

Internal laryngeal nerve

Common facial vein

Superior thyroid vessels

Common carotid artery and desc. hypg. N.

Sterno-hyoid muscle

Omo-hyoid muscle (sup. belly)

Sterno-thyroid muscle

Thyroid gland

Middle thyroid vein

Trachea

Inferior thyroid vein

Sterno-thyroid muscle

Sterno-hyoid muscle

Subclavius muscle with nerve

Cephalic vein

Lateral pectoral nerve

FIG. 1006.—DISSECTION OF THE HEAD AND NECK SHOWING THE CAROTID ARTERIES.

below, and the trachea above, are on the right side. *Lateral.*—The left pleura, and, on a posterior plane, the left phrenic and vagus nerves and the left subclavian artery are on its left side.

The *cervical portion* of the **left common carotid artery** is about three and a half inches (85 mm.) long ; it extends from the left sterno-clavicular joint to the level of the upper border of the thyroid cartilage and the lower border of the third cervical vertebra, where it ends by dividing into external and internal carotid arteries.

Course.—It runs upwards, laterally, and backwards, through the anterior triangle of the neck. Below it is separated from its fellow of the opposite side by the trachea and the œsophagus, and above by the relatively wide larynx and pharynx.

Relations.—It is enclosed, together with the internal jugular vein and the vagus nerve, in a sheath of cervical fascia—the **carotid sheath**.

Posterior.—The longus cervicis and scalenus anterior, below, and the longus capitis, above, are separated from the posterior surface of the artery and its sheath by the prevertebral fascia and the sympathetic trunk. The vertebral artery and the thoracic duct are posterior to it at the level of the seventh cervical vertebra; the inferior thyroid artery crosses behind it, between it and either the vertebral artery or the transverse process of the sixth cervical vertebra; and the vagus nerve lies postero-lateral to it.

Superficial.—The descending branch of the hypoglossal nerve lies superficial to the artery, usually outside the sheath, but sometimes enclosed in it (Fig. 1006). Opposite the sixth cervical vertebra the omo-hyoid muscle and the sterno-mastoid branch of the superior thyroid artery cross superficial to the common carotid artery, which is overlapped, above the omo-hyoid muscle, by the anterior border of the sterno-mastoid and by deep cervical lymph glands. It is frequently crossed, in that part of its extent, by the superior thyroid vein. Below the omo-hyoid the artery is covered by the sterno-thyroid, the sterno-hyoid, and the sterno-mastoid muscles, and it may be overlapped by the lobe of the thyroid gland; it is also crossed, deep to the muscles, by the middle thyroid vein, whilst occasionally a communication between the common facial and anterior jugular veins descends in front of the artery along the anterior border of the sterno-mastoid. Just above the sternum the anterior jugular vein is in front of the artery, but separated from it by the sterno-hyoid and sterno-thyroid muscles.

Medial.—The trachea and œsophagus, with the recurrent laryngeal nerve in the angle between them, are medial to the lower part of the artery; the larynx and pharynx are medial to its upper part. The carotid body lies on the medial side of the termination of the artery.

Lateral.—The internal jugular vein occupies the lateral part of the carotid sheath. The vein lies not only to the lateral side of the artery, but also slightly in front of it, especially in the lower part of the neck.

Branches.—As a rule no branches are given off from either of the common carotid arteries, except the terminal branches and some minute twigs to the carotid sheath and carotid body. But occasionally one or more of the branches usually given off by the external carotid may arise from the common carotid; the most frequent is the superior thyroid artery.

Right Common Carotid Artery.—The **right common carotid artery**, as already stated, differs as regards origin from the left common carotid. In length and general position it corresponds with the cervical portion of the left common carotid, and its relations also are very similar. Such differences as exist may be briefly summarised as follows: The internal jugular vein lies lateral to the artery on each side; on the left side in the lower part of the neck it is also anterior to the artery, whilst on the right side the vein is separated from the lateral surface of the artery, at its lower end, by a well-marked interval in which the vagus nerve appears. The thoracic duct does not come into relation with the right common carotid. There is also a difference in the relations of the recurrent laryngeal nerves to the arteries on the two sides. The left nerve is posterior to the mediastinal part of the left artery, and lies medial to its cervical part, whilst the right nerve passes posterior to the lower part of the corresponding artery in the neck to reach its medial side. The œsophagus has a less intimate relation with the right common carotid artery than with the left.

Carotid Sinus.—The terminal portion of the common carotid artery and the root of its internal carotid branch are dilated to form the *carotid sinus*. This sinus is part of the mechanism that regulates blood pressure; its walls are more elastic than adjacent parts of the arteries, and it is specially innervated by the glosso-pharyngeal nerve, which supplies the carotid body also (see Fig. 655, p. 769).

Variations.—The right common carotid artery may arise separately from the arch of the aorta; then it may be the first, or, much more rarely, the second branch. In the former case the fourth right aortic arch has been obliterated, and the right subclavian artery springs from the descending aorta; in the latter case either the innominate stem has been absorbed into the arch of the aorta, or the ventral root of the fourth right aortic arch has fused with part of an elongated fourth left arch.

Whether the artery arises as the first or second branch, the origin may be to the left of the median plane, and the trunk may pass in front of the trachea, or behind the œsophagus, before it ascends into the neck.

The left common carotid artery varies, as regards its origin, much more frequently than the right vessel; not uncommonly, and apparently because of the fusion of the ventral roots of the fourth aortic arches, it arises from a stem common to it and to the right common carotid and right subclavian arteries.

Both common carotids may vary as regards their termination. They may divide at a higher or lower level than usual, the former more commonly than the latter; whilst in a few exceptional cases the common carotid does not divide, but is continued directly into the internal carotid; then the branches usually given off by the external carotid spring from it. That arrangement is probably due to obliteration of the ventral roots of the first and second aortic arches, the arches persisting and being divided into the branches which generally arise from their ventral extremities.

EXTERNAL CAROTID ARTERY

The **external carotid artery** (Figs. 1006, 1008) is the smaller of the two terminal branches of the common carotid; its length is about $2\frac{1}{2}$ inches (62 mm). It extends from the upper border of the thyroid cartilage to the back of the neck of the mandible, where it ends by dividing into the superficial temporal and the maxillary arteries.

Course.—It begins in the carotid triangle, passes upwards, medial to the posterior belly of the digastric and the stylo-hyoid muscles and the lower part of the parotid gland; then it grooves the medial border of the gland, and passes through its substance to the upper part of its antero-medial surface behind the neck of the mandible, where it ends.

At first it lies anterior and medial to the internal carotid artery, but it inclines backwards as it ascends, and thus becomes superficial to the internal carotid. Its course is indicated by a line drawn from the tip of the greater horn of the hyoid bone to the lobule of the ear.

Relations.—*Posterior.*—Its lower part is in close relation with the internal carotid, and its upper part with the parotid gland.

Medial.—At first the inferior constrictor muscle is in relation with its medial side, but at a higher level the structures which intervene between it and the internal carotid—the stylo-pharyngeus muscle, the tip of the styloid process, the stylo-glossus muscle, the glosso-pharyngeal nerve, and the pharyngeal branch of the vagus—separate it from the wall of the pharynx; whilst medial both to it and to the internal carotid artery are the external and internal laryngeal branches of the superior laryngeal nerve.

Superficial.—In the carotid triangle it is overlapped by the anterior border of the sterno-mastoid. Immediately below the level of its occipital branch, it is crossed by the hypoglossal nerve; and it is crossed by the lingual and common facial veins also, and sometimes by the superior thyroid vein. At the level of the angle of the mandible it passes under cover of the posterior belly of the digastric and the stylo-hyoid muscles, which separate it from the medial surface of the medial pterygoid muscle. As it emerges from under cover of the stylo-hyoid it grooves the parotid gland, and as it passes through the gland the posterior facial vein descends superficial to the artery, and both the artery and the vein are crossed, usually superficially, by the branches of the facial nerve.

Branches.—Eight branches arise from the external carotid artery; of those, three—the superior thyroid, the lingual, and the facial—spring from the front of the artery in the carotid triangle; two arise from the back of the artery, namely, the occipital and the posterior auricular, the former below the posterior belly of the digastric and the latter above it; one from its medial side, namely, the ascending pharyngeal, which arises in the carotid triangle. The external carotid ends by dividing into the superficial temporal and the maxillary arteries.

Variations.—The external carotid artery may be absent, or it may, in rare cases, arise directly from the arch of the aorta. The number of its branches may be diminished either by fusion of their roots or by transference to the internal or common carotid arteries. On the other hand, the number of its branches may be increased; thus, the sterno-mastoid artery, or the infra-hyoid branch usually given off by the superior thyroid artery, or the ascending palatine branch of the facial artery, may arise directly from the external carotid.

Branches of External Carotid Artery

(1) The **superior thyroid artery** (Figs. 1002 and 1006) springs from the front of the lower part of the external carotid artery, just below the tip of the greater

horn of the hyoid bone, and it ends at the apex of the corresponding lobe of the thyroid gland by dividing into glandular branches.

Course.—From its origin, in the carotid triangle, the artery runs downwards and forwards to its termination.

Relations.—*Medially* it is in relation with the inferior constrictor muscle and the external laryngeal branch of the superior laryngeal nerve.

Superficially it is covered, at its origin, by the anterior border of the sterno-mastoid; afterwards, for a short distance, by fascia, platysma, and skin, and in the lower part of its extent by the omo-hyoid, the sterno-hyoid, and the sterno-thyroid muscles, and it is overlapped by an accompanying vein.

Branches.—*In the carotid triangle.*—A small **infra-hyoid artery** runs along the lower border of the hyoid bone, under cover of the thyro-hyoid muscle, to anastomose with its fellow of the opposite side and with the supra-hyoid branch of the lingual artery. It supplies the thyro-hyoid muscle and membrane.

The **superior laryngeal artery** runs forwards, deep to the thyro-hyoid muscle. It pierces the thyro-hyoid membrane and enters the lateral wall of the piriform fossa, in company with the internal laryngeal nerve, supplies the muscles, ligaments, and mucous membrane of the larynx, and anastomoses with its fellow of the opposite side, with the crico-thyroid branch, and with the inferior thyroid artery.

The **sterno-mastoid branch** passes downwards and backwards, along the upper border of the superior belly of the omo-hyoid muscle and across the common carotid artery, to the deep surface of the sterno-mastoid muscle. It anastomoses, in the sterno-mastoid, with branches of the occipital and suprascapular arteries.

In the muscular triangle.—A **crico-thyroid branch** passes forwards, either superficial or deep to the sterno-thyroid. It crosses the crico-thyroid muscle to anastomose, in front of the crico-thyroid ligament, with its fellow of the opposite side, and, by branches which perforate the ligament, with laryngeal branches of the superior and inferior thyroid arteries. It supplies the adjacent muscles and membrane.

The terminal **glandular branches** are anterior, medial, and lateral. The *anterior glandular branch* descends along the anterior border of the lobe of the thyroid gland, and runs along the upper border of the isthmus, to anastomose with its fellow of the opposite side. The *medial glandular branch* is the largest; it is distributed to the medial surface of the lobe. The *lateral glandular branch*, which ramifies in the lateral surface of the lobe, is the smallest. All three branches anastomose with one another and with branches from the inferior thyroid artery.

(2) The **lingual artery** (Figs. 1006 and 1008) springs from the front of the external carotid, opposite the tip of the greater horn of the hyoid bone, and becoming the *arteria profundae lingua*, it ends beneath the tip of the tongue, where it anastomoses with its fellow of the opposite side.

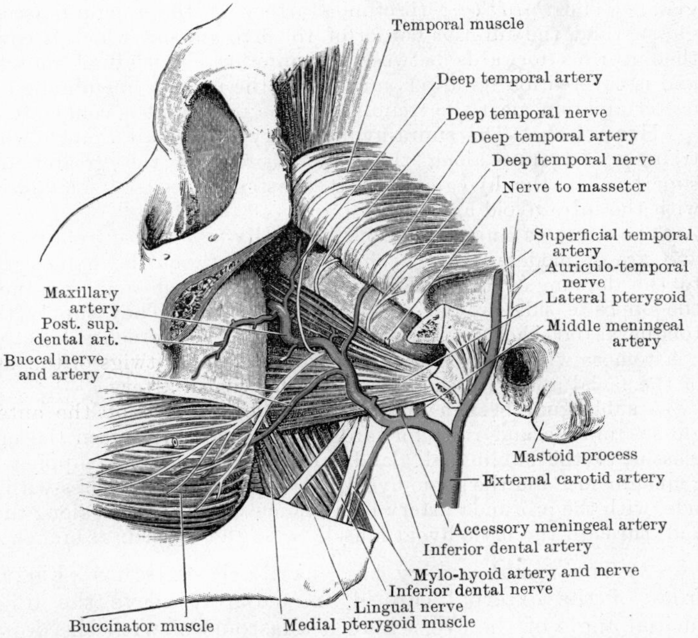

FIG. 1007.—DISSECTION SHOWING THE TERMINATION OF THE EXTERNAL CAROTID ARTERY AND THE FIRST AND SECOND PARTS OF THE MAXILLARY ARTERY.

Temporal muscle
Deep temporal artery
Deep temporal nerve
Deep temporal artery
Deep temporal nerve
Nerve to masseter
Superficial temporal artery
Auriculo-temporal nerve
Lateral pterygoid
Middle meningeal artery
Mastoid process
External carotid artery
Accessory meningeal artery
Inferior dental artery
Mylo-hyoid artery and nerve
Inferior dental nerve
Lingual nerve
Medial pterygoid muscle
Buccinator muscle
Buccal nerve and artery
Post. sup. dental art.
Maxillary artery

Course.—Whilst in the carotid triangle, the *first part of the artery* forms a loop with the convexity upwards. The *second part* passes forwards, medial to the hyo-glossus muscle immediately above the greater horn of the hyoid bone, to the anterior border of the hyo-glossus, where it gives off a sublingual branch and becomes the third part or profunda artery of the tongue. The **profunda artery of the tongue** passes obliquely upwards and forwards, under cover of the anterior border of the hyo-glossus, and then takes a tortuous course forwards on the under surface of the tongue to the tip.

Relations.—The *first part* of the lingual artery is crossed superficially by the hypo-glossal nerve, and is covered by skin, fascia, and the platysma; it rests medially against the middle constrictor of the pharynx. The *second part* is deeper. It lies between the middle constrictor medially and the hyo-glossus laterally, and is separated by the latter from the hypoglossal nerve and its vena comitans, and the lower part of the submandibular gland. The *third part* (profunda artery of the tongue) ascends between the genio-glossus and the anterior border of the hyo-glossus, which is covered by the mylohyoid; then it runs forwards between the inferior longitudinal muscle and the genio-glossus, and is covered, on its lower surface, by the mucous membrane of the tongue. Thus, at its termination, near the frenulum of the tongue, it is comparatively superficial.

Branches.—The **supra-hyoid artery** is a small branch which arises in the carotid triangle and runs along the upper border of the greater horn of the hyoid bone superficial to the hyo-glossus. It anastomoses with its fellow of the opposite side and with the infra-hyoid artery.

The **dorsales linguæ branches**—usually two—arise from the second part of the artery and are of moderate size. They ascend, between the hyo-glossus and the genio-glossus, to the dorsum of the tongue, where they branch and anastomose with their fellows of the opposite side around the foramen cæcum. They supply the posterior part of the tongue as far back as the epiglottis, and send branches backwards to the tonsil which anastomose with the tonsillar artery and tonsillar twigs of the ascending palatine branch of the facial and with the ascending pharyngeal artery.

A **sublingual branch** arises at the lower part of the anterior border of the hyo-glossus muscle and runs forwards and upwards, between the mylo-hyoid and the genio-glossus, to the sublingual gland, which it supplies; it supplies also the mylo-hyoid, the genio-glossus, and the genio-hyoid muscles. It anastomoses with its fellow of the opposite side, with the profunda artery by a branch which it sends along the frenulum of the tongue, and, through the mylo-hyoid muscle, with the submental branch of the facial artery.

(3) The **facial artery** [A. maxillaris externa] (Fig. 1006) arises from the front of the external carotid, immediately above the lingual. It ends at the medial angle of the eye, where it anastomoses with the dorsal nasal and palpebral branches of the ophthalmic artery.

Course.—The course of the facial artery is very tortuous. It begins in the carotid triangle, immediately above the lingual, and passes *upwards* to the angle of the mandible, on the lateral surface of the middle constrictor muscle. Still ascending, it lies between the posterior belly of the digastric and the stylo-hyoid muscles laterally, and the superior constrictor medially. When it reaches the upper border of the stylo-hyoid it enters a groove in the posterior part of the submandibular gland and runs *downwards* and *forwards*, between the lateral surface of the gland and the medial pterygoid muscle, to the lower border of the mandible. There it pierces the deep cervical fascia, turns round the inferior border of the mandible at the anterior border of the masseter, enters the face, and continues *upwards* and *forwards* in a tortuous manner to its termination.

Relations.—In the carotid triangle the artery is comparatively superficial, except just at its origin, which is overlapped by the anterior fibres of the sterno-mastoid muscle. As it ascends it is in relation, on the medial side, with the middle and superior constrictor muscles, and the superior constrictor separates it from the tonsil. Its relations between the point where it passes medial to the posterior belly of the digastric and the point where it turns round the lower border of the mandible have been given in the description of its course.

After turning round the lower border of the body of the mandible, which it grooves slightly, the artery becomes more superficial than in any other part of its course, being covered only by platysma, fascia, and skin. At that point the anterior facial vein is immediately posterior to the artery, lying on the surface of the masseter. As it passes upwards in the face the artery lies between the platysma, the risorius, the zygomaticus major, and the levator labii superioris, which, with skin and fascia, are superficial to it, and the buccinator and the levator anguli oris, which are deeper; it then enters the substance of the levator labii superioris alaeque nasi.

The anterior facial vein is posterior to the artery in the face, is situated at some little distance from it, and runs a straighter course.

Branches.—Four named branches are given off in the neck and several in the face.

In the Neck.—The **ascending palatine artery** (Fig. 1013) is a small branch which arises under cover of the posterior belly of the digastric. It ascends, and, after passing between the stylo-glossus and the stylo-pharyngeus muscles, reaches the apex of the petrous portion of the temporal bone, where it turns downwards over the upper border of the superior constrictor of the pharynx, accompanying the levator palati muscle, and enters the soft palate (Fig. 1009).

It supplies the lateral wall of the upper part of the pharynx, the soft palate, the tonsil, and the pharyngo-tympanic tube [tuba auditiva]. It anastomoses with the tonsillar branch of the facial, the dorsales linguæ, the greater palatine branch of the maxillary, and with the ascending pharyngeal artery, which sometimes replaces it.

The **tonsillar artery** is a small branch which arises close to the ascending palatine. It passes upwards between the medial pterygoid and the styloglossus, pierces the superior constrictor, and ends in the tonsil. It supplies the middle and superior constrictor muscles, and it anastomoses with the dorsales linguæ, with the ascending palatine and the ascending pharyngeal arteries.

The **glandular branches** are two or three small twigs which pass directly into the submandibular gland.

The **submental artery** arises from the facial just as the latter vessel turns round the inferior border of the mandible. It is the largest branch given off in the neck; it runs forwards, on the lateral surface of the mylo-hyoid muscle, and medial to the upper part of the submandibular gland, to the symphysis menti; there it turns upwards, round the margin of the mandible, and it ends by anastomosing with branches of the mental and inferior labial arteries. In the neck the submental artery supplies the mylo-hyoid muscle, and the submandibular and sublingual glands, the latter by a branch which perforates the mylo-hyoid muscle. It anastomoses with the mylo-hyoid branch of the inferior dental and with the sublingual branch of the lingual artery.

In the Face.—The **inferior labial arteries** arise from the front of the facial below the level of the angle of the mouth. There are usually two, the lower arising below the level of the alveolar border of the mandible. They run medially, under cover of the muscles of the lower lip, supply the skin, muscles, mucous membrane, and glands of the lip, and anastomose with each other, with the mental artery, and with their fellows of the opposite side. The upper of the two arteries pierces the orbicularis oris and runs close to the mucous membrane near the margin of the lip.

The **superior labial artery** springs from the front of the facial about the level of the angle of the mouth. It runs medially, between the orbicularis oris and the mucous membrane of the upper lip, to the median plane, supplying the skin, muscles, mucous membrane and glands of the upper lip, and, by a *septal branch*, the lower and anterior part of the nasal septum. It anastomoses with its fellow of the opposite side, with the *lateral nasal* branch of the facial, and with the septal branch of the spheno-palatine artery.

Numerous other small branches arise from the facial artery in the face; through these it anastomoses also with the transverse facial artery, and with the buccal and infra-orbital branches of the maxillary artery.

The *lateral nasal* is a constant branch that ramifies on the side of the nose (Fig. 1006).

(4) The **occipital artery** (Figs. 1006, 1008) arises from the back of the external carotid artery, below the posterior belly of the digastric muscle, and ends, near the medial end of the superior nuchal line of the occipital bone, by dividing into medial and lateral terminal branches.

Course.—It begins in the carotid triangle and runs upwards and backwards, parallel with and under cover of the posterior belly of the digastric, to the interval between the transverse process of the atlas and the base of the skull; there it turns backwards, in a groove on the lower surface of the mastoid portion of the temporal bone; as it leaves the groove it alters its direction and runs upwards and medially, on the superior oblique muscle, to the junction of the medial and intermediate

74

thirds of the superior nuchal line of the occipital bone, where it pierces the deep fascia of the neck and enters the superficial fascia of the scalp.

Relations.—In the first part of its course the occipital artery crosses successively the internal carotid artery, the hypoglossal nerve (which hooks round it), the vagus nerve, the internal jugular vein, and the accessory nerve ; it is covered by the lower fibres of the posterior belly of the digastric, and the anterior part of the sterno-mastoid muscle. In the second and more horizontal part of its course it is still under cover of the sterno-mastoid and digastric, and lies, medially, against the rectus capitis lateralis, which separates it from the vertebral artery. In the third part of its course it rests upon the superior oblique and semispinalis capitis, under cover of the sterno-mastoid and the splenius capitis muscles, and either superficial or deep to the longissimus capitis. Near its termination it is crossed by the greater occipital nerve, and it passes either through the trapezius or between the trapezius and the sterno-mastoid.

Branches.—**Muscular branches** go to the surrounding muscles. There are usually two **sterno-mastoid branches** ; one springs from the occipital near its origin, is looped downwards across the hypoglossal nerve, and is continued downwards and backwards, below and anterior to the accessory nerve, into the sterno-mastoid muscle, where it anastomoses with the sterno-mastoid branch of the superior thyroid artery. The other arises higher up and accompanies the accessory nerve into the muscle.

The **descending branch** is given off from the occipital upon the surface of the superior oblique and supplies the muscles of the back of the neck. It passes medially, and divides at the lateral border of the semispinalis capitis into superficial and deep branches. The superficial branch runs between the semispinalis and the splenius capitis, and anastomoses with the superficial branch of the transverse cervical artery. The deep branch descends between the semispinalis capitis and the underlying semispinalis cervicis, and anastomoses with branches of the deep cervical artery.

The **meningeal** are irregular branches given off anterior to the mastoid process. They enter the skull through the condylar canals, or through the jugular foramen ; they supply the dura mater in the posterior fossa of the skull, and anastomose with the middle meningeal and with meningeal branches of the ascending pharyngeal artery.

The **mastoid** is a small and inconstant branch which arises behind the mastoid process. It enters the posterior fossa of the skull through the mastoid foramen, supplies the dura mater, and anastomoses with branches of the middle meningeal artery.

The **auricular** is an inconstant branch which is given off from the occipital, as a rule, only when the posterior auricular artery is absent. It ramifies over the mastoid process, and supplies the medial surface of the auricle.

The terminal **occipital branches** are medial and lateral. They ramify in the superficial fascia of the posterior part of the scalp, where they anastomose with the posterior auricular and superficial temporal arteries. Both branches are accompanied by branches of the greater occipital nerve. The medial branch gives off a *meningeal* twig, which passes into the skull through the parietal foramen to supply the walls of the superior sagittal sinus and to anastomose with the middle meningeal artery.

(5) The **posterior auricular artery** (Figs. 1006, 1008, 1013) springs from the back of the external carotid immediately above the posterior belly of the digastric muscle, and it ends between the mastoid process and the back of the auricle by dividing into occipital and auricular branches.

Course and Relations.—From its origin it runs upwards and backwards, superficial to the styloid process under cover of the parotid gland, to the interval between the mastoid process and the auricle. It is accompanied in the terminal part of its course by the posterior auricular branch of the facial nerve.

Branches.—In addition to twigs of supply to the parotid gland and *muscular* branches to the sterno-mastoid, the digastric, and the styloid group of muscles, there are three named branches.

The **stylo-mastoid artery** is given off at the lower border of the external auditory meatus, runs upwards by the side of the facial nerve, and enters the stylo-mastoid foramen. It accompanies the facial nerve in its canal to the upper part of the medial wall of the tympanum, where it ends by anastomosing with the superficial petrosal branch of the middle meningeal artery ; other branches anastomose with tympanic branches from the internal carotid and the ascending pharyngeal arteries, and with the internal auditory branch of the basilar.   It supplies the tympanic cavity and antrum, the vestibule, and semicircular canals, *mastoid* branches to the mastoid air-cells and a *stapedial* to the stapedius muscle; and it gives off a *posterior tympanic branch*, which anastomoses with the anterior tympanic branch of the maxillary artery, forming, in young subjects, a vascular circle around the membrana tympani.

The **auricular branch** ascends medial to the posterior auricular muscle.   It gives branches to the auricle and to the scalp in the posterior part of the temporal region, which anastomose with the superficial temporal and occipital arteries.   The auricular branches supply both surfaces of the auricle, piercing or turning round the margins of the cartilage

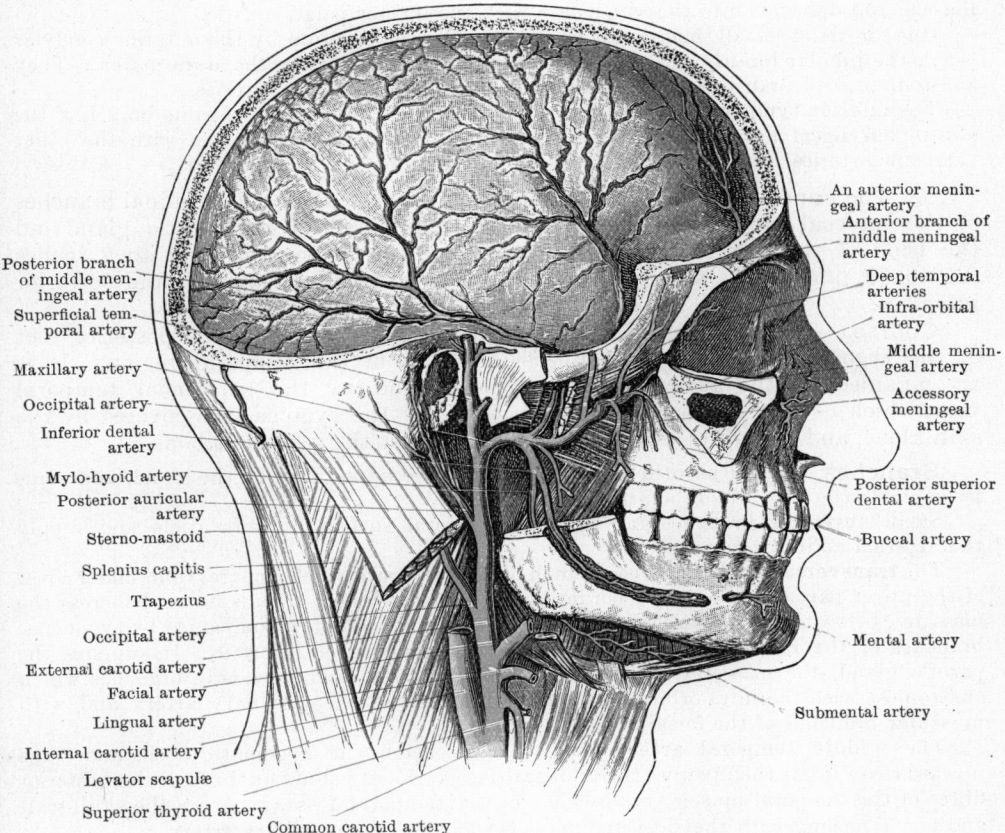

FIG. 1008.—EXTERNAL CAROTID, MAXILLARY, AND MENINGEAL ARTERIES.

to gain the lateral surface; and they anastomose with the auricular branches of the superficial temporal artery.

The **occipital branch** runs upwards and backwards along the insertion of the sterno-mastoid muscle.   It supplies the sterno-mastoid muscle, the occipital belly of the occipito-frontalis, and the skin; and it anastomoses with the occipital artery.

(6) The **ascending pharyngeal artery** (Fig. 1013) arises from the medial surface of the lower part of the external carotid, and its terminal branches are distributed to the wall of the pharynx and in the soft palate.

Course.—It begins in the carotid triangle, usually as the first or second branch of the external carotid, and it ascends on the wall of the pharynx to the apex of the petrous portion of the temporal bone.

Relations.—*Medially* it is in relation with the constrictor muscles of the pharynx. *Posterior* to it is the longus capitis.   *Laterally* it is in relation with the internal carotid artery, and it is crossed by the stylo-pharyngeus muscle, the glosso-pharyngeal nerve, and the pharyngeal branch of the vagus.

74 *a*

Branches.—The branches of this artery are very irregular and inconstant; in addition to those named, small branches are distributed to the prevertebral muscles and fascia, the deep cervical lymph glands, and the large nerve trunks. They anastomose with branches of the ascending cervical and vertebral arteries.

Small **pharyngeal branches** ramify on the walls of the pharynx and supply the middle and superior constrictor muscles, the tonsil, and the lower part of the pharyngo-tympanic tube [tuba auditiva]. They anastomose with branches of the superior thyroid, lingual, and facial arteries. A small inconstant branch sometimes replaces the ascending palatine branch of the facial artery. When present it springs from the upper part of the ascending pharyngeal artery, pierces the pharyngo-basilar fascia above the superior constrictor muscle, and descends into the soft palate with the levator palati muscle.

One or more small **meningeal** branches enter the cranium by the anterior condylar canal, the jugular foramen, or the foramen lacerum, and supply the dura mater. They anastomose with branches of the middle meningeal and vertebral arteries.

The **inferior tympanic** is a small artery which accompanies the tympanic branch of the glosso-pharyngeal nerve to the tympanic cavity, where it anastomoses with the other tympanic arteries.

(7) The **superficial temporal artery** (Fig. 1006), one of the terminal branches of the external carotid, begins between the upper part of the parotid gland and the back of the neck of the mandible, and ends in the scalp, from 1 to 2 inches (25 to 50 mm.) above the zygomatic arch, by dividing into anterior and posterior branches.

Course.—The artery ascends, pierces the deep fascia, crosses the posterior root of the zygoma, and enters the superficial fascia of the temporal region. It is accompanied by the auriculo-temporal nerve and by the superficial temporal vein, which usually lies behind it. As it crosses the zygoma it is covered by the skin alone, and it may be easily compressed against the subjacent bone.

Branches.—Small **parotid** branches supply the upper part of the gland, and some twigs go to the *mandibular joint*.

Small **auricular** branches ramify on the lateral surface of the auricle and supply the external auditory meatus.

The **transverse facial artery** is a branch of moderate size which emerges from under cover of the upper part of the anterior border of the parotid gland. It runs forwards across the masseter, below the zygomatic arch and above the parotid duct, accompanied by zygomatic branches of the facial nerve, which may lie either above or below it. It supplies the parotid gland, the masseter, parotid duct, and the skin, and it ends in branches which anastomose with the infra-orbital and buccal branches of the maxillary artery and with muscular branches of the facial artery.

The **middle temporal artery** usually arises below the zygomatic arch, and runs upwards over it; it then pierces the temporal fascia, passes behind or through the posterior fibres of the temporal muscle, and ascends in the temporal fossa, grooving the skull wall and anastomosing with the deep temporal branches of the maxillary artery.

The **zygomatic** branch may spring directly from the superficial temporal, but it is frequently a branch of the middle temporal. It runs forwards, above the zygomatic arch between the two layers of the temporal fascia. It supplies branches to the orbicularis oculi, and anastomoses, through the zygomatic bone and round the lateral orbital margin, with the lacrimal and palpebral branches of the ophthalmic artery.

The **anterior** [frontal] **branch** runs forwards and upwards, in a tortuous course, through the superficial fascia of the scalp towards the frontal eminence, lying at first upon the temporal fascia, and then upon the epicranial aponeurosis. It supplies the frontal belly of the occipito-frontalis and the orbicularis oculi, and anastomoses with the lacrimal and supra-orbital branches of the ophthalmic artery, with the posterior terminal branch of the superficial temporal, and with its fellow of the opposite side.

The **posterior** [parietal] **branch,** less tortuous than the anterior, runs upwards and backwards in the superficial fascia of the scalp. It anastomoses in front with the anterior terminal branch, behind with the posterior auricular and occipital arteries, and across the median line with its fellow of the opposite side. It supplies the skin and fascia, and the anterior and superior muscles of the auricle.

(8) The **maxillary artery** [A. maxillaris interna] begins between the upper part of the parotid gland and the back of the neck of the mandible and ends in the pterygo-palatine fossa (Figs. 1008, 1009).

Course and Relations.—The maxillary artery has many important relations, in the consideration of which it is convenient to divide the vessel into three parts. The **first part** extends from the back of the neck of the mandible into the infratemporal fossa, as far as the lower border of the lateral pterygoid muscle. It lies between the spheno-mandibular ligament and the neck of the mandible, along with the auriculo-temporal nerve and the maxillary vein. The **second part** is in the infratemporal fossa, and runs upwards and forwards. It may lie on the lateral or the medial side of the lower head of the lateral pterygoid muscle either between the temporal and lateral pterygoid muscles or between the lateral pterygoid and the branches of the mandibular nerve. The **third part** passes between the upper and the lower heads of the lateral pterygoid, and through the pterygo-maxillary fissure into the pterygo-palatine fossa.

Branches.—*From the first part.*—The **deep auricular artery** passes upwards in the parotid gland to the external auditory meatus. It supplies also the mandibular joint and the superficial surface of the tympanic membrane. It anastomoses with branches of the superficial temporal and posterior auricular arteries.

The **anterior tympanic artery** is a variable and small branch. It runs upwards and backwards, traverses the squamo-tympanic fissure, and enters the tympanum near its lateral wall. In the tympanic cavity it anastomoses with tympanic branches from the internal carotid and ascending pharyngeal arteries, and with the posterior tympanic branch of the stylo-mastoid artery, forming with the latter, in young subjects, a circular anastomosis around the tympanic membrane.

Middle Meningeal Artery.—This is the largest of the meningeal arteries; it is also by far the most important branch of the maxillary artery as it is a frequent source of haemorrhage following injury to the skull. It ascends between the lateral pterygoid muscle and the spheno-mandibular ligament and lies on the lateral surface of the tensor palati, which separates it from the pharyngo-tympanic tube; it passes between the two roots of the auriculo-temporal nerve and through the foramen spinosum, and enters the middle cranial fossa. Before it enters the skull it lies behind the mandibular nerve, and is accompanied by a vein which descends through the foramen spinosum. In the middle cranial fossa it passes for a short distance forwards, in a groove on the greater wing of the sphenoid, in the outer layer of the dura mater, and divides into anterior and posterior terminal branches.

Branches.—A small **superficial petrosal** branch arises from the middle meningeal soon after it enters the cranium. It passes through the hiatus for the greater superficial petrosal nerve and anastomoses with the stylo-mastoid branch of the posterior auricular artery; it gives branches to the facial nerve and the wall of the tympanic cavity.

Minute branches supply the ganglion and the roots of the trigeminal nerve.

A small **superior tympanic artery** reaches the tympanic cavity through the canal for the tensor tympani, which muscle it supplies, or through the petro-squamous suture.

The **anterior terminal branch**, the larger and more important of the two, passes upwards along the greater wing of the sphenoid to the antero-inferior angle of the parietal bone, where it is often enclosed in a bony canal; it is continued upwards, a short distance behind the anterior border of the parietal bone, almost to the vertex of the skull, sending branches forwards and backwards. An occasional branch from the anterior terminal branch enters the orbit through the superior orbital fissure and anastomoses with the lacrimal artery.

The **posterior terminal branch** passes backwards from the greater wing of the sphenoid to the squamous part of the temporal bone, whence it sends branches upwards to the vertex, and backwards to the occiput.

The anterior and posterior branches of the middle meningeal artery and their ramifications are separated from the bone by corresponding veins.

By means of its various branches the middle meningeal artery anastomoses—with its fellow of the opposite side; with the accessory meningeal artery; with meningeal branches from the occipital, ascending pharyngeal, ophthalmic, and lacrimal arteries; with the stylo-mastoid branch of the posterior auricular, in the temporal bone; and, through the skull wall, with the middle and deep temporal arteries.

An **accessory meningeal artery** may arise either directly from the first part of the maxillary or from the middle meningeal artery. It enters the middle fossa of the skull through the foramen ovale, and supplies the trigeminal ganglion and the dura mater.

The **inferior dental [alveolar] artery** is a branch of moderate size which passes downwards, between the spheno-mandibular ligament and the ramus of the mandible, to the mandibular foramen. It is accompanied by the inferior dental nerve, which lies in front of it. Entering the foramen it descends with the nerve in the mandibular canal and, after giving off the mental artery, is continued in the bone to the median plane, where it anastomoses with its fellow of the opposite side.

Branches.—Before it enters the mandibular foramen it gives off a small **lingual** twig, which accompanies the lingual nerve and supplies the buccal mucous membrane, and also the **mylo-hyoid artery**, a small branch which arises immediately above the foramen. It pierces the spheno-mandibular ligament, and descends, with the mylo-hyoid nerve, in the mylo-hyoid groove to the floor of the mouth, where it anastomoses, on the superficial surface of the mylo-hyoid muscle, with the submental branch of the facial artery.

In the mandibular canal branches are given off to the molar teeth, to the premolar teeth, and, beyond the point of origin of the mental artery, to the canine and incisor teeth. The **mental artery**, which passes through the mental foramen, emerges beneath the depressor labii inferioris and anastomoses with its fellow of the opposite side, with the inferior labial, and with the submental arteries.

From the second part.—The **masseteric artery** is a small branch which passes laterally, through the mandibular notch, to the deep surface of the masseter muscle. It anastomoses in the substance of the muscle with branches of the facial and transverse facial arteries.

There are two **deep temporal arteries**—anterior and posterior. They ascend, in the temporal fossa, between the temporal muscle and the squamous part of the temporal bone, supplying the muscle and anastomosing with the middle temporal and lacrimal arteries, and, through the substance of the temporal bone, with the middle meningeal artery.

Small **pterygoid branches** supply the medial and lateral pterygoid muscles.

The **buccal artery** is a long, slender branch which passes obliquely forwards and downwards with the buccal nerve. It supplies the buccinator muscle, the skin and mucous membrane of the cheek, and it anastomoses with branches of the facial artery.

From the third part.—One or more **posterior superior dental** [alveolar] **arteries** descend, in the infratemporal fossa, on the posterior surface of the maxilla, and end in branches which supply the molar and premolar teeth and the mucous lining of the maxillary sinus; they also give twigs to the gums and to the buccinator muscle.

An **infra-orbital artery** arises in the pterygo-palatine fossa. It enters the orbit through the inferior orbital fissure and runs forwards, in the infra-orbital groove and canal, to the infra-orbital foramen, through which it emerges on the face, deep to the levator labii superioris. In the infra-orbital groove it gives branches to the inferior rectus and inferior oblique muscles of the orbit and to the lacrimal gland. In the infra-orbital canal it gives small twigs to the canine and incisor teeth (*ant. sup. dental* [alveolar] *arteries*) and to the walls of the maxillary sinus. In the face it sends branches upwards to the lower eyelid, to the lacrimal sac, and to the frontal process of the maxilla; those anastomose with branches of the ophthalmic and facial arteries; other branches run downwards to the upper lip, where they anastomose with the superior labial artery, and laterally into the cheek to unite with the transverse facial and the buccal arteries.

The **greater palatine artery** runs downwards, through the pterygo-palatine fossa and the greater palatine canal, to the roof of the mouth. As it descends it gives off the artery of the pterygoid canal and several small twigs (*lesser palatine arteries*) which pass through the lesser palatine canals to supply the soft palate, and to anastomose with the ascending palatine and tonsillar branches of the facial and with the ascending pharyngeal artery. The greater palatine artery runs forwards in the roof of the mouth, medial to the alveolar process and lateral to the accompanying nerve. Its delicate terminal portion ascends through the incisive canal and anastomoses in the nasal septum with a branch of the spheno-palatine artery. In its course forwards in the roof of the mouth the greater palatine artery supplies the gums and the mucous membrane of the hard palate, and also the palatine and maxillary bones.

The **artery of the pterygoid canal** is a long, slender branch, usually given off from the greater palatine; it runs backwards through the pterygoid canal with the corresponding nerve and supplies branches to the upper part of the pharynx, to the levator and tensor palati muscles, and to the pharyngo-tympanic tube. One of the latter branches passes along the wall of the tube to the tympanic cavity, where it anastomoses with the other tympanic arteries.

The **pharyngeal branch** is a small artery which runs backwards, with the pharyngeal branch of the spheno-palatine ganglion, through the palatino-vaginal [pharyngeal] canal to the roof of the pharynx. It supplies the mucous lining of the upper and posterior part of the roof of the nose, the roof of the pharynx, the sphenoidal sinus, and the lower part of the pharyngo-tympanic tube.

The **spheno-palatine artery** is the continuation of the maxillary artery. It passes medially, through the spheno-palatine foramen, into the nose, where it gives off (a) a branch to the sphenoidal sinus, and (b) a branch which may replace the pharyngeal artery. Then it divides into nasal branches. The *posterior lateral nasal* branches supply the lateral wall of the nasal cavity and the sinuses which open through it, and they anastomose with the posterior and anterior ethmoidal arteries and the lateral nasal branch of the facial. The *posterior septal nasal* branch accompanies the long spheno-

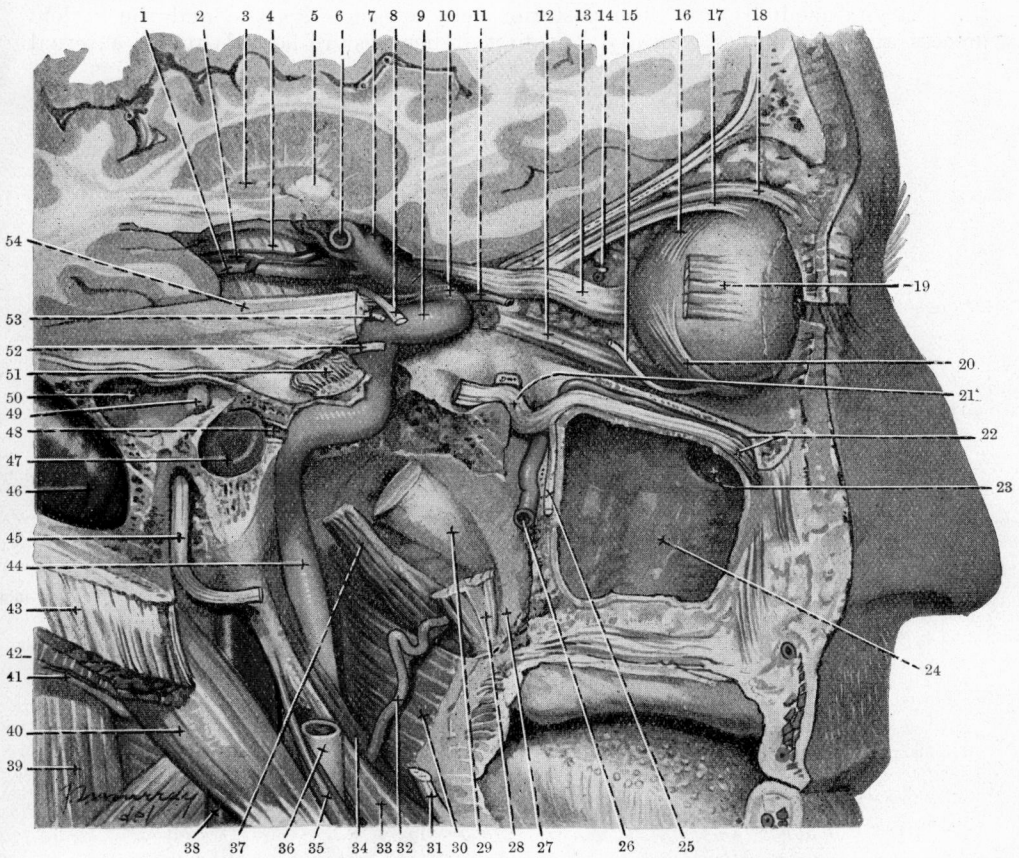

Fig. 1009.—Dissection showing the Course and Relations of the Upper Part of the Internal Carotid Artery.

1. Posterior cerebral artery.
2. Basal vein.
3. Lentiform nucleus.
4. Cerebral peduncle.
5. Anterior commissure.
6. Middle cerebral artery.
7. Anterior cerebral artery.
8. Oculo-motor nerve.
9. Internal carotid artery.
10. Interclinoid ligament.
11. Ophthalmic artery.
12. Inferior rectus muscle.
13. Optic nerve.
14. Naso-ciliary nerve (cut).
15. Nerve to inf. oblique muscle.
16. Tendon of sup. oblique muscle.
17. Superior rectus muscle.
18. Levator palpebræ muscle.
19. Lateral rectus muscle.

20. Inferior oblique muscle.
21. Maxillary nerve.
22. Infra-orbital nerve and artery.
23. Opening from maxillary sinus into nose.
24. Maxillary sinus.
25. Posterior superior dental nerve.
26. Maxillary artery.
27. Medial pterygoid lamina.
28. Tensor palati muscle.
29. Pharyngo-tympanic tube.
30. Superior constrictor muscle.
31. Lingual nerve.
32. Ascending palatine branch of facial artery.
33. Stylo-glossus muscle.
34. Stylo-pharyngeus muscle.
35. Stylo-hyoid muscle.
36. External carotid artery.

37. Levator palati muscle.
38. Internal jugular vein.
39. Longissimus capitis muscle.
40. Posterior belly of digastric muscle.
41. Occipital artery.
42. Splenius capitis muscle.
43. Sterno-mastoid muscle.
44. Internal carotid artery.
45. Facial nerve.
46. Sigmoid sinus.
47. Tympanic membrane.
48. Pharyngo-tympanic tube (osseous part).
49. Head of malleus.
50. Tympanic antrum.
51. Trigeminal ganglion.
52. Abducent nerve.
53. Trochlear nerve.
54. Tentorium cerebelli.

palatine nerve across the roof of the nasal cavity and downwards and forwards in the groove on the vomer. It anastomoses with the greater palatine artery and the septal branch of the superior labial.

INTERNAL CAROTID ARTERY

The **internal carotid artery** (Figs. 1006, 1008, 1009, and 1010) springs from the common carotid, opposite the upper border of the thyroid cartilage, and ends in

74 c

the middle fossa of the skull, in the vallecula of the cerebrum below the anterior
perforated substance close to the stem of the lateral sulcus, where it divides
into the anterior and middle cerebral arteries (Fig. 1009).

Course.—From its origin in the carotid triangle it ascends to the base of the
skull, lying first in the carotid triangle, medial to the anterior border of the
sterno-mastoid, and then between the areolar tissue behind the lateral border of
the pharynx medially, and the posterior belly of the digastric and the styloid
process and its muscles laterally. At first it lies postero-lateral to the external

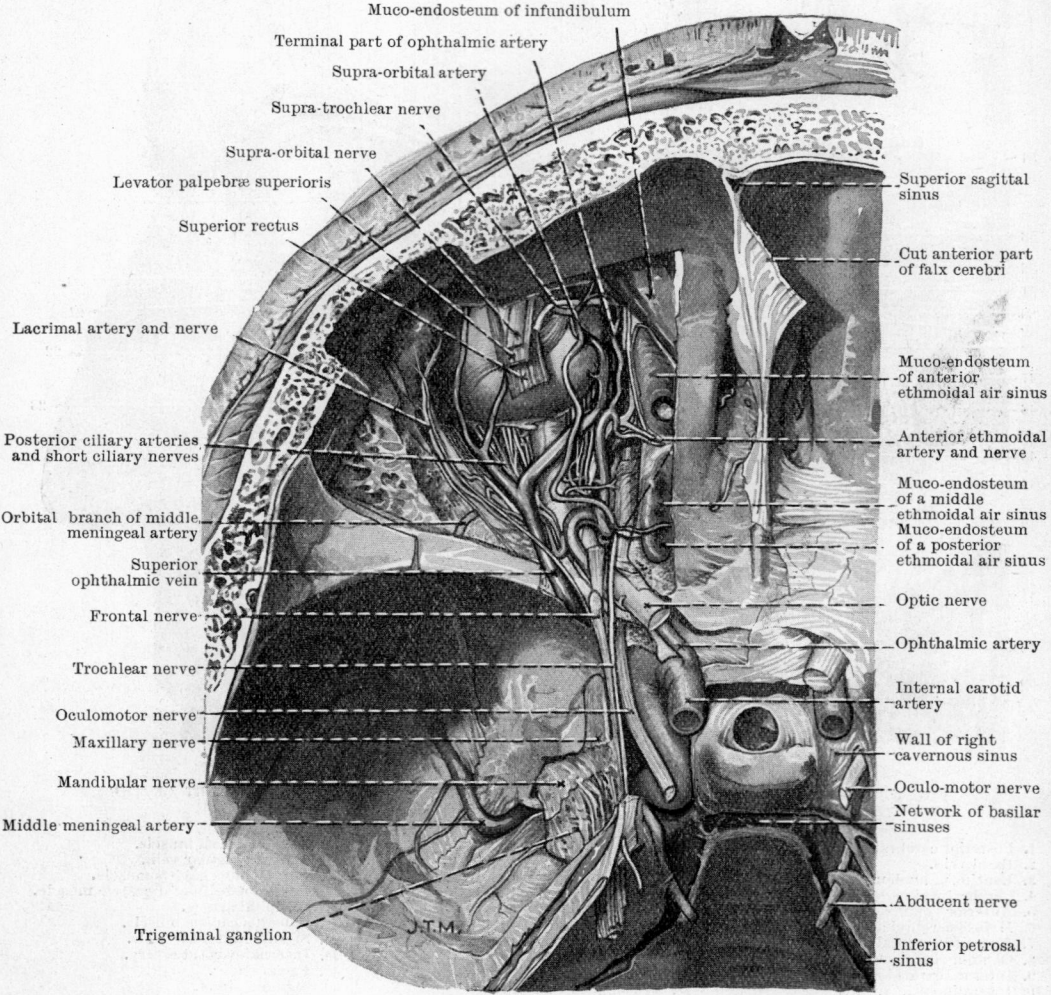

FIG. 1010.—DISSECTION OF THE ORBIT AND MIDDLE CRANIAL FOSSA. On the right side the trochlear
nerve has been removed, and in the left orbit portions of the structures above the ophthalmic artery
have been taken away. (E. B. J.)

carotid, but as it ascends it gradually passes to the medial side of that artery,
from which it is separated by the styloid process, the stylo-pharyngeus muscle,
the glosso-pharyngeal nerve, the pharyngeal branch of the vagus and a portion of
the parotid gland.

At the base of the skull it enters the carotid canal, in which it ascends, anterior
to the tympanum and the cochlea; then it turns antero-medially to the apex of
the petrous temporal bone, where it enters the foramen lacerum, through which it
ascends, along the side of the body of the sphenoid, into the middle cranial fossa.

In the middle fossa it runs forwards, in the lateral wall of the cavernous sinus, to the lesser wing of the sphenoid; there it turns backwards along the medial border of the anterior clinoid process, which it grooves. At the tip of the process it turns upwards and laterally to the point where it divides below the anterior perforated substance (Fig. 1009).

Relations.—Three main parts of the artery require separate consideration.

In the Neck.—*Posterior* to the artery are the longus capitis, the prevertebral fascia, and the sympathetic trunk, which separate it from the transverse processes of the cervical vertebræ. *Postero-lateral* to it are the internal jugular vein and the vagus nerve; the accessory and glosso-pharyngeal nerves also are postero-lateral to the artery for a short distance in the upper part of the neck, where they intervene between it and the internal jugular vein. *Medial* or deep to the internal carotid is the external carotid artery for a short distance below, and afterwards the wall of the pharynx, the areolar tissue behind the wall of the pharynx, the ascending pharyngeal artery, the pharyngeal plexus of veins, and the external and internal laryngeal nerves. Just before it enters the temporal bone the levator palati muscle is antero-medial to it. *Lateral* or superficial to it are the sterno-mastoid, skin, and fasciæ, and it is crossed under cover of the sterno-mastoid, from below upwards, by the hypoglossal nerve, the occipital artery, and the posterior auricular artery. It is also crossed superficially, between the last-mentioned arteries, by the digastric and stylo-hyoid muscles, which separate it from the parotid gland, and below the digastric it is covered by the lower part of the gland. Passing obliquely across its antero-lateral surface, and separating it from the external carotid artery, are the following structures—the stylo-pharyngeus, the styloid process (or the stylo-glossus muscle), and the glosso-pharyngeal nerve, the pharyngeal branch of the vagus, and some sympathetic twigs.

In the Carotid Canal.—The artery, as it passes upwards, is antero-inferior to the cochlea and the tympanum, postero-medial to the pharyngo-tympanic tube and the canal for the tensor tympani, and below the trigeminal ganglion. The thin lamina of bone which separates it from the tympanum is frequently perforated, and the lamina between it and the trigeminal ganglion is frequently absent. In its course through the canal it is accompanied by small veins and sympathetic nerves. The veins receive tributaries from the tympanum, and communicate above with the cavernous sinus and below with the internal jugular vein. The nerves are branches of the superior cervical ganglion and constitute the internal carotid plexus.

As it enters the cranial cavity the internal carotid artery pierces the external layer of the dura mater and passes between the lingula and the sixth cranial nerve laterally, and the petrosal process of the body of the sphenoid medially.

In the Cranial Cavity.—The artery runs forwards, in the lateral wall of the cavernous sinus, in relation with the oculo-motor, trochlear, the ophthalmic division of the trigeminal, and the abducent nerves laterally, and with the endothelial wall of the sinus medially. When it reaches the lower root of the lesser wing of the sphenoid it turns upwards to the medial side of the anterior clinoid process, pierces the inner layer of the dura mater, and comes into close relation with the inferior surface of the optic nerve immediately behind the optic foramen. It then turns abruptly backwards below the optic nerve, and on the medial side of the anterior clinoid process which it frequently grooves; inclining laterally, it runs between the optic and oculo-motor nerves, and below the anterior perforated substance, to the medial end of the stem of the lateral sulcus, where it turns upwards, at some distance from the corresponding lateral border of the optic chiasma, and, after piercing the arachnoid, divides into its two terminal branches— the anterior and middle cerebral arteries.

Carotid sinus.—The carotid sinus includes the root of the internal carotid artery, and may be limited to it (see p. 1165).

Variations.—The internal carotid artery is rarely absent, but its absence has been noted upon one side (more commonly the left) and upon both sides. Occasionally it springs from the arch of the aorta, and in its course through the neck it may vary in length and in tortuosity. One or more of the branches usually derived from the external carotid artery may arise from it, and it sometimes gives off a large meningeal branch to the posterior fossa of the skull. Its posterior communicating branch may replace the posterior cerebral artery; on the other hand, the upper part of the internal carotid may be absent, and the posterior communicating artery, springing from the posterior cerebral, may become the middle cerebral artery.

BRANCHES OF INTERNAL CAROTID ARTERY

Branches are given off from the internal carotid in the temporal bone and in the cranium, but no constant branches are given off in the neck.

In the Temporal Bone.—(1) A **carotico-tympanic branch**, very small, perforates the posterior wall of the carotid canal, and anastomoses in the tympanum with the tympanic branches of the stylo-mastoid, maxillary, and ascending pharyngeal arteries.

A small, inconstant branch accompanies the nerve of the pterygoid canal and anastomoses with the artery of the canal.

In the Cranium.—Small branches are distributed to the walls of the cavernous sinus, to the oculo-motor, trochlear, trigeminal, and abducent nerves, to the trigeminal ganglion and to the dura mater of the middle cranial fossa.

One or two small branches supply the *hypophysis cerebri* (see p. 778).

(2) The **ophthalmic artery** (Figs. 1009, 1010) springs from the antero-medial side of the internal carotid as it turns upwards on the medial side of the anterior clinoid process. It passes forwards and laterally, below the optic nerve, through the optic foramen into the orbital cavity. In the orbit it runs forwards, for a short distance, on the lateral side of the optic nerve, and it is in relation laterally with the ciliary ganglion and the lateral rectus muscle; turning upwards and medially, it crosses, between the optic nerve and the superior rectus, to the medial wall of the orbit, where it turns forwards to end near the front of the orbit by dividing into the supratrochlear and dorsal nasal arteries. It is accompanied at first by the naso-ciliary nerve and then by the infratrochlear nerve.

Variations.—The ophthalmic artery, as it traverses the orbit, may pass either above or below the optic nerve. It (or its lacrimal branch) is occasionally replaced by a branch of the middle meningeal artery.

Branches.—The branches of the ophthalmic artery are numerous. The **posterior ciliary arteries**, usually six to eight in number, run forwards at the sides of the optic nerve; they soon divide into numerous branches which pierce the fascial sheath of the eyeball and the posterior part of the sclera; the majority terminate in the choroid coat of the eye as the *short posterior ciliary arteries*, but two of larger size, the *long posterior ciliary arteries*, run forwards, one on each side of the eyeball almost in the horizontal plane, between the sclera and the choroid, to the periphery of the iris, where they divide. The resulting branches anastomose with anterior ciliary arteries to form the *greater arterial circle* at the periphery of the iris, from which secondary branches run inwards and anastomose together in a *lesser arterial circle* near the pupillary border of the iris.

The **central artery of the retina** arises in, or close to, the optic foramen. It pierces the infero-medial aspect of the optic nerve almost at once, and runs in its centre to the retina where it breaks up into terminal branches (see p. 1092).

Small **meningeal branches**, of which one arises from the lacrimal artery, pass backwards through the superior orbital fissure into the middle fossa of the cranium, where they anastomose with the middle and accessory meningeal arteries and with meningeal branches of the internal carotid and lacrimal arteries.

The **lacrimal artery** arises from the ophthalmic on the lateral side of the optic nerve. It runs forwards with the lacrimal nerve, along the upper border of the lateral rectus, to the upper lateral corner of the orbit, where it gives off branches to the lacrimal gland. In its course it gives off *muscular branches* to the lateral and superior recti, and twigs which accompany the zygomatico-temporal and zygomatico-facial branches of the zygomatic nerve to the temporal fossa and the face respectively. The lacrimal artery gives off also *anterior ciliary arteries* to the eyeball, and it ends in the *lateral palpebral arteries* which supply the conjunctiva and the eyelids.

The **muscular** branches are arranged in two sets; one supplies the upper lateral, the other the lower and medial orbital muscles. They anastomose with muscular branches from the lacrimal and the supra-orbital arteries, and they give off *anterior ciliary arteries*.

The **anterior ciliary arteries** arise from muscular branches of the ophthalmic and from the lacrimal artery. They pierce the sclera behind the corneo-scleral junction and join the greater arterial circle of the iris. They give off small *episcleral arteries* which pass forwards on the surface of the sclera to the corneo-scleral junction, and give off in turn minute *anterior conjunctival arteries*, which loop back in the conjunctiva to anastomose with posterior conjunctival branches of the palpebral arteries. (For the circulation in the Eye and its accessory organs, see the chapter on Organs of the Senses and Fig. 920).

The **supra-orbital artery** is given off as the ophthalmic artery crosses above the optic nerve. It passes round the medial borders of the superior rectus and levator palpebræ muscles, and runs forwards, between the levator and the periosteum, to the supra-orbital notch or foramen, accompanying the frontal nerve and its supra-orbital branch. Passing through the notch it reaches the scalp, and, after it has perforated the frontalis muscle, it anastomoses with the supra-trochlear and superficial temporal arteries.

Anterior and **posterior ethmoidal arteries** arise from the ophthalmic as it runs forwards along the medial wall of the orbit. They pass medially, between the superior oblique and the medial rectus. The posterior, which is much the smaller of the two, traverses the posterior ethmoidal canal and supplies the posterior ethmoidal sinuses and the posterior and upper part of the lateral wall of the nasal cavity. The anterior ethmoidal artery passes through the anterior ethmoidal canal with the anterior ethmoidal nerve, enters the anterior fossa of the skull, and crosses the cribriform plate of the ethmoid to the nasal slit, passes through an aperture at the lateral side of that slit into the nasal cavity, where it descends, with the nasal continuation of the anterior ethmoidal nerve, in a groove on the inner surface of the nasal bone, and, finally, passes between the lateral cartilage and the lower border of the nasal bone to the tip of the nose. It gives off meningeal branches in the anterior cranial fossa and supplies the anterior and middle ethmoidal cells, the frontal sinus, the nasal muco-periosteum, and the skin on the dorsum of the nose.

Medial palpebral arteries, upper and lower, are given off near the termination of the ophthalmic. They are distributed to the upper and lower eyelids, and they anastomose with the supra-orbital and infra-orbital arteries, and with the **lateral palpebral arteries,** which arise from the lacrimal, to form the *superior* and *inferior palpebral arches.* The palpebral arteries give off *posterior conjunctival arteries,* which anastomose with the anterior conjunctival branches of the anterior ciliary arteries.

The **dorsal nasal artery** passes out of the orbit above the medial palpebral ligament. It pierces the palpebral fascia and ends on the side of the nose by anastomosing with the terminal part of the facial artery.

The **supratrochlear artery** [A. frontalis] pierces the palpebral fascia at the upper and medial

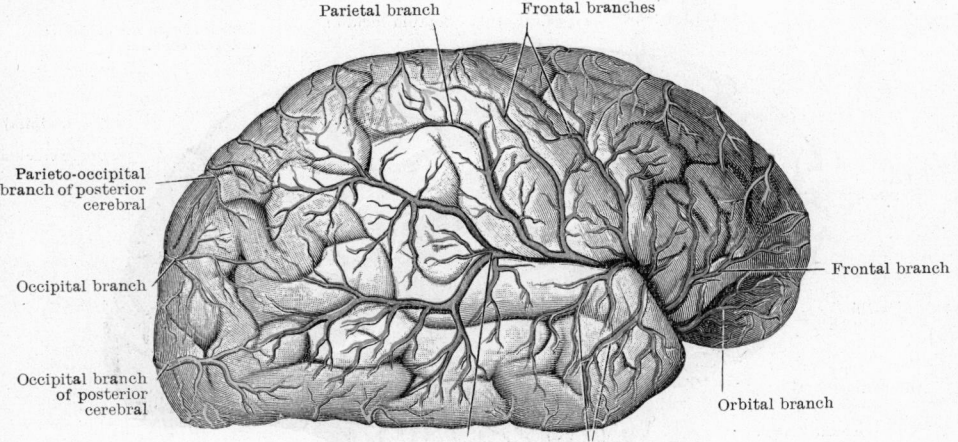

Parietal branch   Frontal branches

Parieto-occipital branch of posterior cerebral

Occipital branch

Occipital branch of posterior cerebral

Frontal branch

Orbital branch

Parieto-temporal branch   Temporal branches of middle cerebral

FIG. 1011.—DISTRIBUTION OF CEREBRAL ARTERIES ON THE SUPERO-LATERAL SURFACE OF THE RIGHT CEREBRAL HEMISPHERE.

The anterior cerebral artery is coloured green, the middle cerebral red, and the posterior cerebral orange.

part of the orbit, and ascends, with the supratrochlear nerve, in the superficial fascia of the anterior and medial part of the scalp, anastomosing with its fellow of the opposite side and with the supra-orbital artery.

(3) The **posterior communicating artery** arises from the internal carotid near its termination, and forms part of the *circulus arteriosus.* It runs backwards, below the optic tract and anterior to the cerebral peduncle, and, passing above the oculo-motor nerve, joins the posterior cerebral artery. It gives branches to the optic chiasma, the optic tract, the cerebral peduncle, the interpeduncular region, the internal capsule, and the thalamus. The posterior communicating artery varies much in size; it may be small on one or both sides, and sometimes it is very large on one side. Occasionally it replaces the origin of the posterior cerebral artery from the basilar; and it sometimes arises from the middle cerebral artery.

(4) The **anterior choroid artery** is a small branch which also arises near the termination of the internal carotid; it passes backwards and laterally, between the cerebral peduncle and the uncus, to the lower and anterior part of the choroid fissure, which it enters; and it ends in the choroid plexus of the lateral ventricle. It supplies the optic tract, the cerebral peduncle, the uncus, the posterior part of the internal capsule, the tail of the caudate nucleus, part of the lentiform nucleus, and the amygdaloid nucleus.

(5) The **anterior cerebral artery** is the smaller of the two terminal branches of the internal carotid. It passes forwards and medially, above the optic chiasma and in front of the lamina terminalis, to enter the longitudinal fissure of

the cerebrum; it continues upwards and forwards along the rostrum of the corpus callosum, turns round the genu, and runs backwards in the longitudinal fissure on the upper surface of the corpus callosum or in the sulcus cinguli; and it ends by turning upwards on the medial surface of the hemisphere in front of the parieto-occipital sulcus and dividing into branches which pass over the supero-medial margin of the hemisphere. As it enters the longitudinal fissure it is closely connected with its fellow of the opposite side by a wide but short **anterior communicating artery**, and from that point the two arteries run side by side, though separated by the arachnoid mater and, in the posterior part of their course, by the edge of the falx cerebri.

Branches.—Branches of all the cerebral arteries are distributed both to the interior of the cerebrum and to the cerebral cortex; they therefore form two distinct groups which do not communicate with one another—(a) **central**; (b) **cortical**.

The branches of the anterior cerebral are as follows:

Central Branches.—These are a small group of slender arteries which pass upwards into the base of the brain, in front of the optic chiasma; they pierce the lamina terminalis and the rostrum of the corpus callosum, and supply the head of the caudate

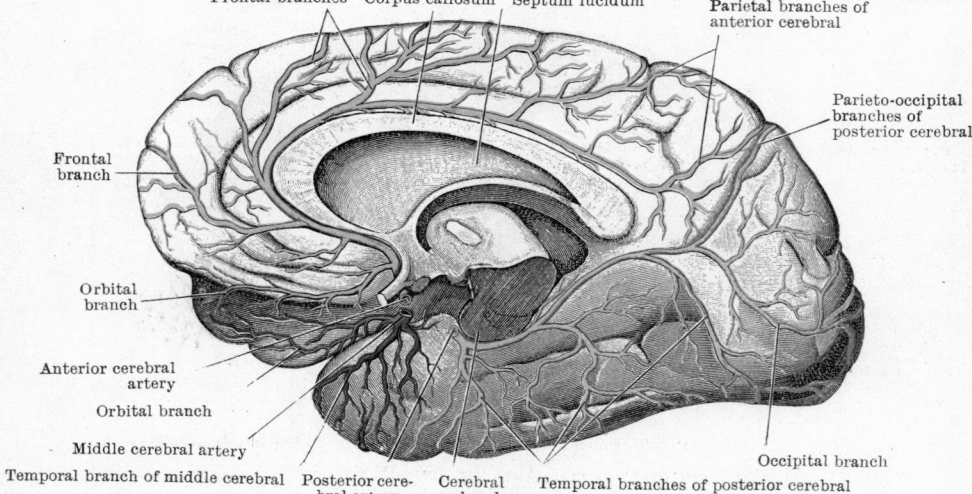

FIG. 1012.—DISTRIBUTION OF CEREBRAL ARTERIES ON THE MEDIAL AND TENTORIAL SURFACES OF THE RIGHT CEREBRAL HEMISPHERE.

The anterior cerebral artery is coloured green, the middle cerebral red, and the posterior cerebral orange.

nucleus, the anterior part of the lentiform nucleus and internal capsule, the anterior columns of the fornix, the septum lucidum, and the anterior commissure. These branches are known as the **antero-medial central arteries**.

Cortical Branches.—The area supplied by these is seen in Figs. 1011, 1012; it includes the corpus callosum. One or more small **orbital branches** supply the medial half of the orbital surface and the olfactory lobe.

Several **frontal branches** are distributed to the medial surface of the frontal lobe, to the gyrus cinguli, to the superior and middle frontal gyri on the supero-lateral surface of the hemisphere, and to the upper part of the pre-central gyrus.

Parietal branches supply the præcuneus, and the upper parts of the post-central gyrus and the superior parietal lobule.

Branches of the anterior cerebral artery thus supply the upper parts of the motor and sensory areas of the cortex.

Variations.—The anterior cerebral may arise from the corresponding artery of the opposite side by enlargement of the anterior communicating artery; or there may be an additional anterior cerebral artery, the third vessel arising from the anterior communicating artery.

(6) The **middle cerebral artery** is the larger of the two terminal branches of the internal carotid artery and is in more direct continuation with it. It passes laterally, in the stem of the lateral sulcus, to the surface of the insula, where it divides into numerous parietal and temporal branches.

Branches.—*Central branches* are numerous and very variable in size. They arise at the base of the brain, and pierce the anterior perforated substance. They constitute the **antero-lateral central arteries**, and are arranged in two sets, known as the medial and the lateral striate arteries.

The **medial striate arteries** pass upwards through the globus pallidus of the lentiform nucleus and the internal capsule to end in the caudate nucleus. They supply the anterior parts of the lentiform and caudate nuclei and of the internal capsule.

The **lateral striate arteries** pass upwards through the putamen of the lentiform nucleus, or between it and the external capsule, and they form two sets—an anterior and a posterior ; both sets traverse the lentiform nucleus and the internal capsule, but the anterior arteries terminate in the caudate nucleus, and the posterior in the thalamus. One of the anterior set, which passes in the first instance round the lateral side of the

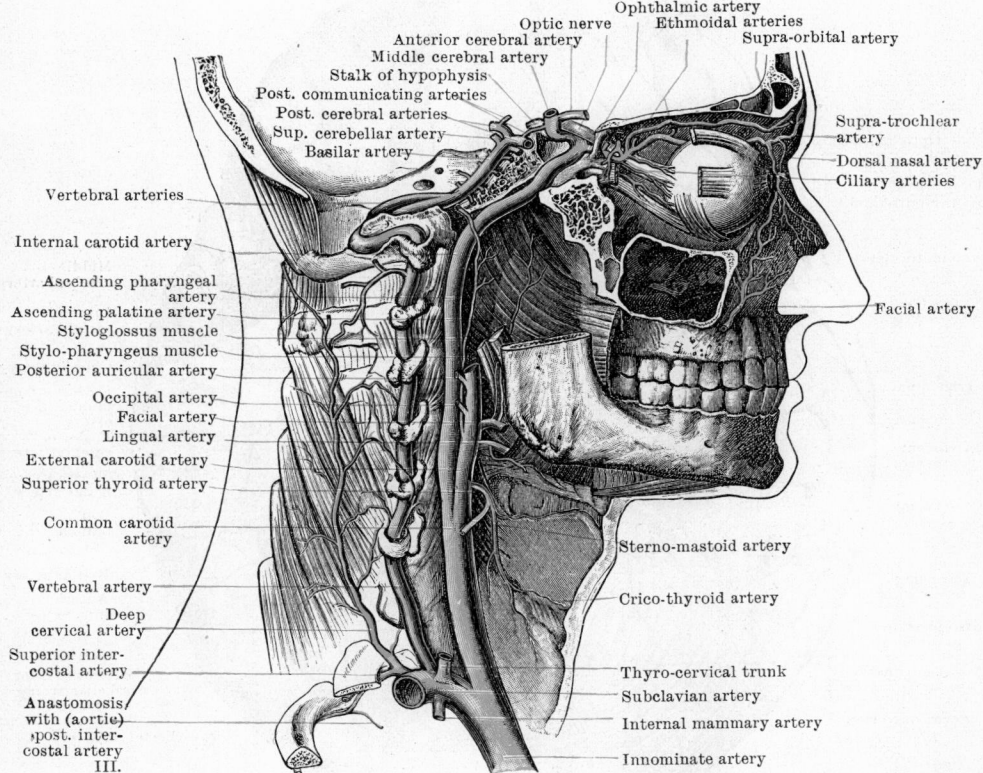

FIG. 1013.—THE CAROTID, SUBCLAVIAN, AND VERTEBRAL ARTERIES AND THEIR MAIN BRANCHES.

lentiform nucleus and afterwards through its substance, is larger than its companions ; it is said to be the one that most frequently ruptures, and is known as the "artery of cerebral hæmorrhage."

Cortical branches are given off as the middle cerebral artery passes over the surface of the insula at the bottom of the lateral sulcus. They supply the gyri of the insula, the deep surfaces of its opercula, and a considerable area of the frontal, parietal, and temporal lobes (Figs. 1011, 1012).

One or two **orbital branches** run forwards and laterally, and are distributed to the lateral part of the orbital surface of the frontal lobe and to the inferior frontal gyrus.

Several **frontal branches** turn round the upper margin of the lateral sulcus, and are distributed to the inferior and middle frontal gyri, and to the greater part of the pre-central gyrus.

Two main **parietal branches** emerge from the lateral sulcus and pass upwards and backwards, supplying the post-central gyrus and the superior and inferior parietal lobules.

The **temporal branches** pass out of the lateral sulcus, and turn downwards to supply the greater part of the lateral surface of the temporal lobe.

A common parieto-temporal branch, continuing the main stem of the middle cerebral artery, emerges, as a rule, from the posterior end of the lateral sulcus ; and divides into parietal and temporal branches (Fig. 1011).

VERTEBRAL ARTERY

The **vertebral artery** (Figs. 1013 and 1014) is the first branch given off from the subclavian trunk ; it arises from the upper and posterior part of the parent stem, opposite the interval between the scalenus anterior 'and the longus cervicis

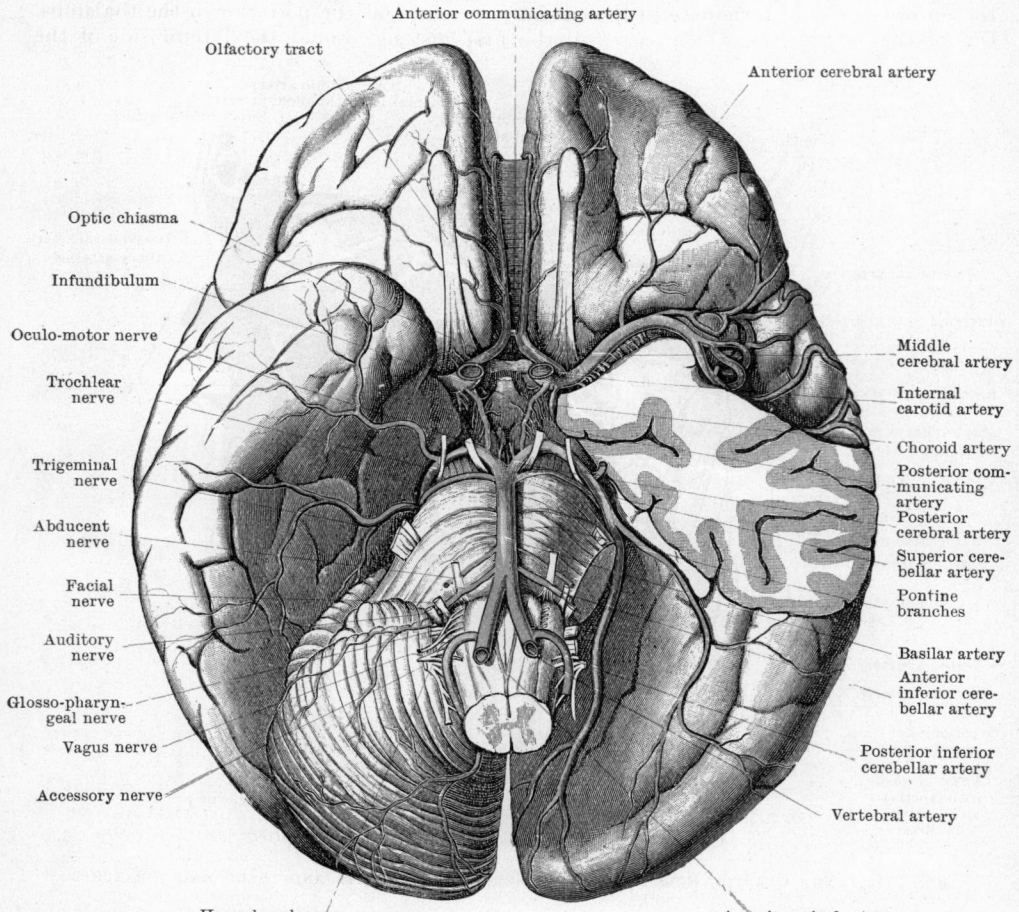

Anterior communicating artery

Olfactory tract

Anterior cerebral artery

Optic chiasma

Infundibulum

Oculo-motor nerve

Trochlear nerve

Trigeminal nerve

Abducent nerve

Facial nerve

Auditory nerve

Glosso-pharyn-geal nerve

Vagus nerve

Accessory nerve

Middle cerebral artery

Internal carotid artery

Choroid artery

Posterior com-municating artery

Posterior cerebral artery

Superior cere-bellar artery

Pontine branches

Basilar artery

Anterior inferior cere-bellar artery

Posterior inferior cerebellar artery

Vertebral artery

Hypoglossal nerve

Anterior spinal artery

FIG. 1014.—ARTERIES OF THE BASE OF THE BRAIN SHOWING THE CIRCULUS ARTERIOSUS.

muscles, and terminates at the lower border of the pons by uniting with its fellow of the opposite side to form the basilar artery.

Course and Relations.—The vertebral artery is divisible into four parts.

The **first part** runs upwards and backwards, between the scalenus anterior and the lateral border of the longus cervicis, to the foramen in the transverse process of the sixth cervical vertebra. It is surrounded by a plexus of sympathetic nerve fibres, is covered by the vertebral and internal jugular veins, and it may be crossed in front by the inferior thyroid artery. On the left side the terminal part of the thoracic duct also passes anterior to it. The **second part** runs upwards through the foramina in the transverse processes of the upper six cervical vertebræ. As far as the second cervical vertebra its course is almost vertical ; as it passes through the transverse process of the axis, however, it is directed obliquely upwards and laterally to the atlas. It is surrounded by a plexus of sympathetic nerve fibres, and also by a plexus of veins. The artery lies anterior to the trunks of the cervical nerves, and medial to the intertransverse muscles. The **third part** emerges from the foramen transversarium of the atlas, between the anterior primary ramus of the first cervical nerve medially and the rectus capitis lateralis laterally, and runs almost horizontally backwards and medially, behind the lateral mass of the atlas. In that part of its course it enters the sub-occipital triangle, where it lies in the groove on the upper surface of the posterior arch of the atlas. It is separated from the bone by the first cervical nerve, and is overlapped super-ficially by the adjacent borders of the superior and inferior oblique muscles. It leaves the triangle by passing anterior to the thickened (sometimes ossified) edge of the posterior atlanto-occipital membrane and enters the vertebral canal.

The **fourth part** pierces the spinal dura mater and runs upwards into the cranial cavity through the foramen magnum. Behind it are the roots of the hypo-glossal nerve, and in front of it is the first dentation of the ligamentum denticu-latum. Then it pierces the arachnoid, and, inclining to the front of the medulla oblongata, reaches the lower border of the pons, where it unites with its fellow of the opposite side to form the basilar artery (Fig. 1014).

Variations.—The vertebral artery may have a double origin—one from the subclavian, and one from the inferior thyroid artery or from the aorta.

The right vertebral may arise from the common carotid or from the arch of the aorta. Occasionally it springs from the descending aorta, an arrangement associated with the persistence of the dorsal roots of the fourth and fifth right arches.

The left vertebral artery not infrequently springs from the arch of the aorta, arising between the left common carotid and left subclavian arteries ; that is evidently due to the absorption of the stem of the seventh segmental artery into the aortic arch. Very exceptionally the left vertebral is a branch of an intercostal artery.

In its course upwards either vertebral artery may enter the foramen transversarium of any of the lower six cervical vertebræ. If it does not enter one of the lowest of those foramina, it has probably been formed in part from the precostal instead of from the postcostal anastomosing channels.

The artery may enter the vertebral canal with the second cervical nerve instead of with the first, or, after leaving the foramen transversarium of the third vertebra, it may divide into two branches, one of which accompanies the second and the other the first cervical nerve ; the two branches unite together again in the vertebral canal to form a single trunk.

Sometimes, though rarely, it gives off superior intercostal and inferior thyroid branches. The upper end of one of the vertebrals is sometimes very small, or it may end in small terminal branches ; in the latter case the basilar artery is formed by the direct continuation of the opposite vertebral.

Branches.—**Muscular branches** which vary in number and size arise from the vertebral artery in the cervical part of its course. They supply the deep muscles of the neck and the suboccipital muscles, and anastomose with the deep and ascending cervical arteries and with the descending branch of the occipital artery.

Spinal branches pass, from the medial side of the *second part* of the vertebral artery, through the intervertebral foramina, into the vertebral canal, where they give off twigs which run along the roots of the spinal nerves to reinforce the anterior and posterior spinal arteries ; they supply the bodies of the vertebræ and the intervertebral discs and anastomose with corresponding arteries above and below.

One or two small **meningeal branches** are given off before the vertebral artery pierces the dura mater. They ascend into the posterior fossa of the skull, where they anastomose with meningeal branches of the occipital and ascending pharyngeal arteries, and occasion-ally with branches of the middle meningeal artery.

The **posterior spinal artery** springs most commonly from the posterior inferior cerebellar branch of the vertebral (Stopford), but occasionally it arises from the vertebral directly. It runs downwards upon the side of the medulla oblongata, giving branches to the fasciculi cuneatus and gracilis, and then on the spinal cord, either in front of or behind the posterior nerve-roots. It is a slender artery, but is continued to the lower part of the spinal cord by means of reinforcements from the spinal branches of the vertebral and posterior intercostal arteries. It gives off branches to the pia mater which form more or less regular anastomoses on the medial and lateral sides of the posterior nerve-roots. It ends by joining the anterior spinal artery.

The **anterior spinal artery** arises near the termination of the vertebral. It runs obliquely downwards and medially, in front of the medulla oblongata, and unites with its fellow of the opposite side in front of the decussation of the pyramids to form a single trunk, which descends along the anterior median fissure of the spinal cord, and is continued as a fine vessel along the filum terminale. The median anterior spinal artery is reinforced as it descends by anastomosing twigs from the spinal branches of the vertebral, posterior intercostal, and lumbar arteries, and it gives off branches which pierce the pia mater and supply the spinal cord. Branches from the right and left arteries and from the median vessel supply the anterior and medial parts of the medulla oblongata, including the hypoglossal nucleus and the hypoglossal triangle on the floor of the fourth ventricle (Stopford, Shellshear).

The **posterior inferior cerebellar artery** is the largest branch of the vertebral. It arises near the lower end of the olive and pursues a very tortuous course backwards round the medulla oblongata, at first between the rootlets of the hypoglossal nerve, and then upwards behind the rootlets of the vagus and glosso-pharyngeal nerves, loops backwards and downwards from the lower border of the pons along the infero-lateral boundary of the fourth ventricle, and then turns outwards into the vallecula of the cerebellum, where it divides into lateral and medial terminal branches. The trunk of the artery gives branches to the medulla oblongata and to the choroid plexus of the fourth ventricle. Some of these branches supply the nuclei of the glosso-pharyngeal, the vagus, and the accessory nerves, the spino-thalamic, spino-cerebellar, rubro-spinal, and olivo-cerebellar tracts, and possibly also the vestibular root of the auditory and the spinal tract of the fifth nerve (Bury and Stopford). A special branch goes to supply the dentate nucleus of the cerebellum (Shellshear). The medial terminal branch runs backwards between the inferior vermis and the hemisphere of the cerebellum; it supplies the vermis, and anastomoses with its fellow of the opposite side. The lateral terminal branch passes to the lower surface of the hemisphere and anastomoses with the superior cerebellar artery.

Basilar Artery.— The basilar artery is formed by the junction of the two vertebral arteries; it begins at the lower border of the pons and ends at its upper border by bifurcating into the two posterior cerebral arteries.

Course and Relations.—It runs upwards, in the median part of the cisterna pontis, in a shallow groove on the front of the pons, behind the sphenoidal section of the basi-cranial axis and between the two abducent nerves.

Variations.—The basilar artery may be double in part of its extent, or its lumen may be divided by a more or less complete septum. It may end in one instead of two posterior cerebral arteries, the missing vessel being supplied by the enlargement of the posterior communicating branch of the internal carotid.

Branches.—A series of pairs of small **pontine branches** supply the pons, the middle cerebellar peduncles [brachia pontis], and the roots of the trigeminal nerves.

The **internal auditory arteries** are a pair of long slender branches. Each internal auditory may spring either from the basilar or from the anterior inferior cerebellar artery of the same side (Stopford). It enters the corresponding internal auditory meatus with the facial and auditory nerves, and is distributed to the internal ear.

The **anterior inferior cerebellar arteries** arise, one on each side, from the middle of the basilar artery. They pass backwards, on the anterior parts of the lower surfaces of the hemispheres of the cerebellum, and anastomose with the posterior inferior cerebellar arteries.

The **superior cerebellar arteries** arise near the termination of the basilar. Each passes laterally, at the upper border of the pons, directly below the oculo-motor nerve of the same side, and, after turning round the lateral side of the cerebral peduncle, below the trochlear nerve, it reaches the upper surface of the cerebellum, where it divides into a medial and a lateral branch. The medial branch supplies the upper part of the vermis, and the superior medullary velum. The lateral branch is distributed over the upper surface of the cerebellar hemisphere; it anastomoses with the inferior cerebellar arteries.

The **posterior cerebral arteries** (Figs. 1009 and 1014) are the two terminal branches of the basilar. Each runs backwards and upwards between the cerebral peduncle and the uncus and parallel to the superior cerebellar artery, from which it is separated by the oculo-motor and trochlear nerves. It is connected with the internal carotid by the posterior communicating artery; it gives branches to the inferior surface of the cerebrum, and is continued backwards beneath the splenium of the corpus callosum to the calcarine sulcus, where it divides into occipital and parieto-occipital branches. It supplies the tentorial surface of the hemisphere, the medial and lateral surfaces of the occipital lobe, and the inferior temporal gyrus (Figs. 1011, 1012).

Variations.—The size of the origin of the posterior cerebral artery from the basilar and the size of the posterior communicating artery vary inversely, and the posterior cerebral may arise entirely from the internal carotid. It may be double, the extra vessel arising from either the basilar or the posterior communicating artery.

Branches.—*Central.*—A set of small **postero-medial central arteries** pass, on the medial side of the corresponding cerebral peduncle, to the posterior perforated substance. They supply the peduncle, the posterior part of the thalamus, the mamillary bodies, and the walls of the third ventricle.

A set of small **postero-lateral central arteries** pass round the lateral side of the peduncle. They supply the quadrigeminal and geniculate bodies, the pineal body, the peduncle, and the posterior part of the thalamus.

A set of small **posterior choroid branches** pass through the upper part of the choroid fissure ; they enter the posterior part of the tela chorioidea of the third ventricle, and end in the choroid plexus. They supply also the adjacent parts of the fornix.

Cortical.—Several **temporal branches** supply the uncus, the hippocampal gyrus, the medial and lateral occipito-temporal gyri, and the lingual gyrus.

The **occipital branches**, one of which continues the line of the main artery along the calcarine sulcus, supply the cuneus, the lingual gyrus, and the occipital pole ; they are especially associated with the supply of the visual area of the cortex of the brain.

The **parieto-occipital branch** passes along the corresponding sulcus and supplies the cuneus and precuneus.

Circulus Arteriosus (Fig. 1014).—The cerebral arteries of opposite sides are intimately connected together at the base of the brain by anastomosing channels. Thus, the two anterior cerebral arteries are connected with each other by the anterior communicating artery, whilst the two posterior cerebral arteries are in continuity through the basilar artery, from which they arise. There is also a free anastomosis on each side between the carotid system of cerebral arteries and the vertebral system by means of the posterior communicating arteries, which connect the internal carotid trunks and posterior cerebral arteries. It is stated that this free anastomosis equalises the flow of blood to the various parts of the cerebrum, and provides for the continuation of a regular blood-supply if one or more of the main trunks should be obstructed.

These vessels form the so-called **circulus arteriosus** (long known as the "circle of Willis"), which is situated at the base of the brain in the inter-peduncular cistern. It encloses the following structures : the posterior perforated substance, the mamillary bodies, the tuber cinereum, the infundibulum, and the optic chiasma. The "circle" is irregularly polygonal in outline, and is formed behind by the termination of the basilar and by the two posterior cerebral arteries, postero-laterally by the posterior communicating arteries and the internal carotids, antero-laterally by the anterior cerebral arteries, and in front by the anterior communicating artery.

Variations.—The posterior communicating artery is the most variable part of the "circle." It may be absent on one side or it may be larger than usual, so that the posterior cerebral artery arises mainly or even entirely from the internal carotid. The anterior communicating artery (which may be double or triple) also varies in size, and there may be corresponding reduction in size of the origin of one of the anterior cerebral arteries from the internal carotid.

ARTERIES OF THE UPPER LIMB

The main arterial stem of each upper limb passes through the root of the neck, traverses the axilla, and is continued through the upper arm to the forearm. In the forearm its extent is short, for it ends opposite the neck of the radius by bifurcating into the radial and ulnar arteries, which run through the forearm to the hand. That portion of the common trunk which lies in the root of the neck is known as the **subclavian artery**, the part in the axilla is termed the **axillary artery**, whilst the remaining part is called the **brachial artery**.

SUBCLAVIAN ARTERIES

On the right side the subclavian artery (Figs. 996, 1000, 1002, and 1006) is one of the two branches of the innominate artery, and begins behind the sterno-clavicular joint, but on the left side it arises from the arch of the aorta, behind the upper half of the manubrium sterni.

The right artery is about 3 inches (75 mm.) long; it lies in the root of the neck. The left artery is about 4 inches (100 mm.) long, and is situated not only in the root of the neck but also in the superior mediastinum of the thorax. In the root of the neck each artery arches laterally, across the front of the apex of the lung and behind the scalenus anterior muscle, and is divided into three parts, which lie respectively to the medial side, behind, and to the lateral side of the muscle. The extent to which the arch rises above the level of the clavicle varies; not uncommonly it reaches the level of the lower part of the thyroid gland. The first parts of the subclavian arteries differ from each other both in extent and relations. The relations of the second and third parts are similar on the two sides.

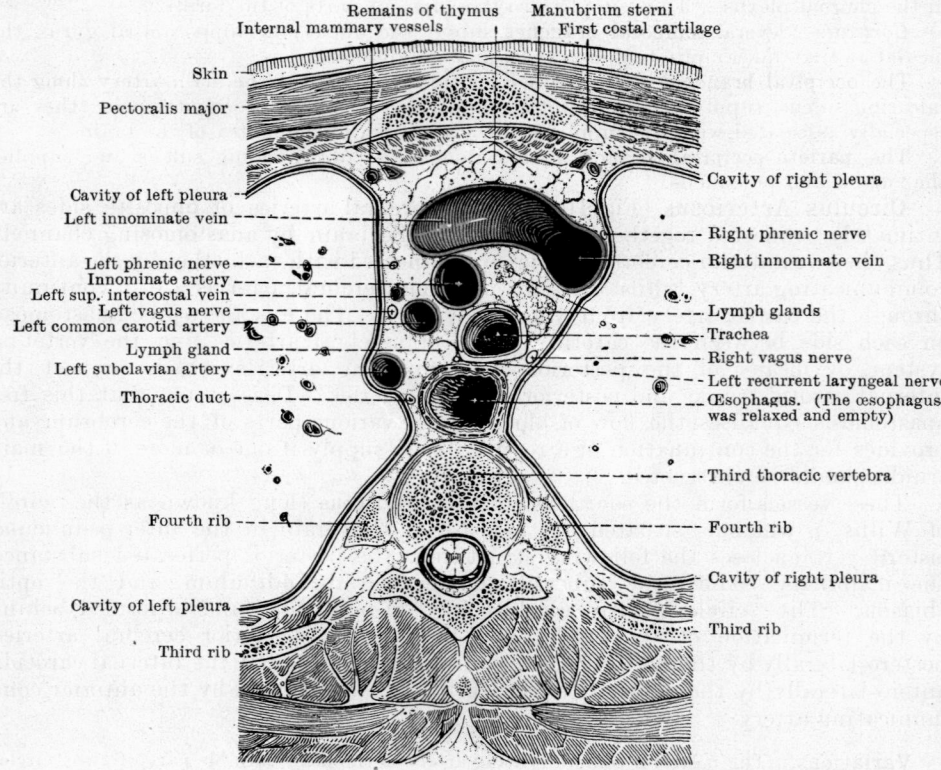

FIG. 1015.—TRANSVERSE SECTION OF THE THORAX OF A YOUNG MAN ALONG THE PLANE A-A, FIG. 1038, p. 1239.

The **first part of the left subclavian artery** springs from the arch of the aorta, behind the origin of the left common carotid and on the left side of the trachea. It ascends almost vertically, in the superior mediastinum, to the root of the neck, where it arches upwards and laterally to the medial border of the scalenus anterior muscle.

Relations.—(A) **As it ascends.**—*Posterior.*—Left pleura and lung, laterally; medially, first the œsophagus and the thoracic duct, and then fatty tissue and the longus cervicis muscle. *Anterior.*—The left vagus, the cardiac branch of the left superior cervical sympathetic ganglion, the inferior cardiac branch of the left vagus, the left phrenic nerve, and the left common carotid artery, in front of which there is the left innominate vein. It is overlapped by the left lung and pleura. *Medial.*—From below upwards, the trachea, and, some fatty areolar tissue intervening, the left recurrent laryngeal nerve, the œsophagus, and the thoracic duct. *Lateral.*—The left pleura and lung, the lung being grooved by it.

(B) **As it runs laterally.**—*Posterior.*—The apex of the left lung and the cervical pleura covered by the suprapleural membrane. *Anterior.*—The vertebral and internal jugular veins; the phrenic nerve and the thoracic duct; the sterno-thyroid and sterno-hyoid muscles; the anterior jugular vein; and the sterno-mastoid.

The **first part of the right subclavian artery** (Fig. 1002) extends from the back of the right sterno-clavicular joint to the medial border of the scalenus anterior. Thus it is limited to the root of the neck.

Relations.—*Posterior.*—Behind that part of the artery are the recurrent laryngeal nerve, the posterior part of the ansa subclavia, and the apex of the right lung covered by cervical pleura. *Inferior.*—The recurrent laryngeal nerve curves backwards *below* it and intervenes between it and the pleural sac. *Anterior.*—In front it is in relation with the right vagus, the cardiac branches of the vagus and the sympathetic, the anterior portion of the ansa subclavia, the internal jugular and vertebral veins, and more superficially the sterno-hyoid and sterno-thyroid muscles, the anterior jugular vein, and the sterno-mastoid muscle. The right common carotid artery also is in front of it at its origin.

The **second part of the subclavian artery**, on *each side*, extends from the medial to the lateral border of the scalenus anterior, behind which it lies.

Relations.—*Posteriorly* and *below* it is in relation with the pleural sac. *Anteriorly* it is covered by the scalenus anterior and the sterno-mastoid muscles. The scalenus anterior separates it from the subclavian vein, which lies at a slightly lower level, from the transverse cervical and suprascapular arteries, from the anterior jugular vein, and, on the right side, from the phrenic nerve.

The **third part of the subclavian artery** is the most superficial portion. It extends from the lateral border of the scalenus anterior to the outer border of the first rib, lying partly in the posterior triangle of the neck and partly behind the clavicle and the subclavius muscle.

Relations.—It rests upon the upper surface of the first rib. Immediately *posterior* to it is the lowest trunk of the brachial plexus, which separates it from the scalenus medius muscle. *Anterior* to it, and at a slightly lower level, lies the subclavian vein. The external jugular vein crosses the medial part of that portion of the artery, and receives the transverse cervical and suprascapular veins; those vessels also pass in front of the artery, which is thus covered superficially by venous trunks; it is also crossed vertically, behind the veins, by the nerve to the subclavius muscle. The lateral section of that part of the artery lies behind the clavicle and the subclavius muscle. It is crossed in front by the suprascapular artery, but the layer of deep cervical fascia which binds the inferior belly of the omo-hyoid to the posterior border of the subclavian groove intervenes between the two vessels. More superficially the third part of the artery is covered by the superficial layer of the deep fascia, the superficial fascia (containing the supraclavicular nerves and the platysma), and the skin.

Variations.—The variations in origin of the subclavian arteries have already been mentioned (p. 1162). Other interesting modifications are met with in respect of its position and branches.

The subclavian artery may reach as high as one and a half inches (4 cm.) above the clavicle, though as a rule it does not reach more than half that distance. On the other hand, it may not rise even to the level of the upper border of the clavicle. The differences appear to be associated with descent of the clavicle and sternum, which occurs as age increases.

The artery may pass in front of or through the scalenus anterior instead of behind it, or the vein may accompany it behind the muscle.

The branches of the subclavian artery may be modified with reference to their points of origin; thus, those of the first part may be farther medial or lateral than usual, the suprascapular or some other branch of the thyro-cervical trunk may arise separately from the third part of the subclavian, and not uncommonly the deep branch of the transverse cervical artery is a branch of that part. The variations of the vertebral artery have already been described; those of the thyro-cervical trunk and its branches are numerous but not important.

BRANCHES OF SUBCLAVIAN ARTERY

(1) The **vertebral artery** is distributed almost entirely to the head and neck, and its chief function is to supply the posterior part of the brain. Its description has therefore been given with that of the other cerebral arteries (see p. 1182).

(2) The **thyro-cervical trunk** (Figs. 1002 and 1013) arises close to the medial border of the scalenus anterior, from the upper and front part of the subclavian

artery, directly above the origin of the internal mammary artery. After a very short upward course, it ends, under cover of the internal jugular vein, by dividing into three branches—the inferior thyroid, the transverse cervical, and the supra-scapular.

(A) The **inferior thyroid artery** (Fig. 1002) ascends along the anterior border of the scalenus anterior, and turns medially, opposite the cricoid cartilage, to the middle of the posterior border of the corresponding lobe of the thyroid gland; it then curves medially and downwards, and descends to the lower end of the lobe, where it divides into ascending and inferior terminal branches.

Relations.—*Posterior* are the vertebral artery, and the longus cervicis muscle; the recurrent laryngeal nerve passes either in front of or behind the vessel, behind the thyroid gland. It is covered *anteriorly* by the carotid sheath, which contains the common carotid artery, the internal jugular vein, and the vagus nerve; the middle cervical ganglion of the sympathetic lies in front of the artery as it runs medially; and on the left side the thoracic duct also passes in front of it.

Branches.—Numerous small **muscular** branches pass to adjacent muscles.

The **ascending cervical artery** usually springs from the inferior thyroid as it turns medially, but it may arise separately from the thyro-cervical trunk. It ascends, parallel with and medial to the phrenic nerve, in the groove between the longus capitis and the scalenus anterior, to both of which it gives *muscular branches*. It also gives off *spinal branches* which pass through the intervertebral foramina to the vertebral canal. It anastomoses with branches of the vertebral, occipital, ascending pharyngeal, and deep cervical arteries.

Small **pharyngeal branches** supply the lower part of the pharynx; small **œsophageal branches** anastomose with the œsophageal branches of the thoracic aorta; and **tracheal branches** anastomose on the trachea with branches of the superior thyroid and with the bronchial arteries.

An **inferior laryngeal artery** accompanies the recurrent laryngeal nerve to the lower part of the larynx. It enters the larynx, at the lower border of the inferior constrictor, gives branches to the laryngeal muscles and mucous membrane, and anastomoses with the laryngeal branch of the superior thyroid artery.

Inferior and ascending terminal **glandular branches** supply the posterior and lower parts of the thyroid gland, and anastomose with branches of the superior thyroid artery and with their fellows of the opposite side. Small branches are given to the parathyroid glands.

(B) The **transverse cervical artery** (Figs. 1006 and 1017) arises from the thyro-cervical trunk and runs upwards and backwards across the posterior triangle of the neck to the anterior border of the trapezius; there it divides into a superficial and a deep branch. It is very variable in size.

Immediately after its origin, under cover of the internal jugular vein, it crosses the scalenus anterior, lying superficial to the phrenic nerve and under cover of the sterno-mastoid muscle; on the left side it is also crossed, superficially, by the terminal part of the thoracic duct. Passing from beneath the sterno-mastoid, it enters the lower part of the posterior triangle of the neck, where it lies upon the trunks of the brachial plexus, and as it runs upwards and backwards to its termination it passes deep to the inferior belly of the omo-hyoid.

The superficial branch may be a separate vessel which springs from the thyro-cervical trunk and takes the course described, whilst the deep branch arises from the third part of the sub-clavian artery and lies at a lower level. In such cases the upper of the two vessels is called the *superficial cervical artery* and the lower the *descending scapular artery*.

Branches.—The **superficial branch** [R. ascendens], usually a slender branch, passes beneath the trapezius; it sends branches upwards and downwards on the deep surface of the trapezius, where they anastomose with twigs from the descending branch of the occipital artery.

The **deep branch** [R. descendens] runs downwards, deep to the levator scapulæ and the rhomboid muscles, close to the medial border of the scapula. It runs parallel with and a short distance away from the nerve to the rhomboids, and it sends branches into the supraspinous, the infraspinous, and the subscapular fossæ, which anastomose with branches of the suprascapular and subscapular arteries. It also sends branches backwards, through and between the rhomboid muscles, which anastomose with the posterior branches of posterior intercostal arteries.

The **suprascapular artery** [A. transversa scapulæ] springs from the thyro-cervical trunk and ends in the infraspinous fossa of the scapula. As a rule it is smaller than the transverse cervical artery.

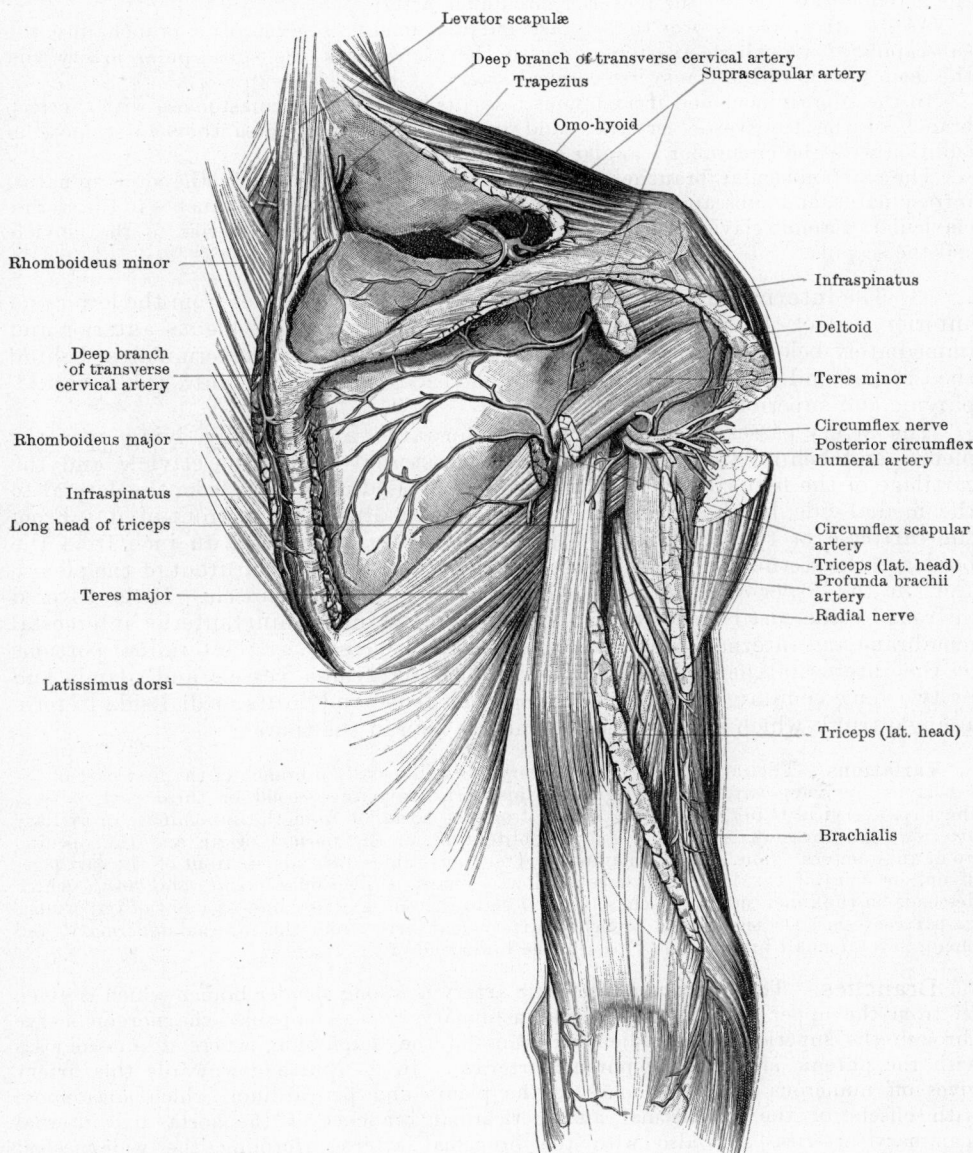

FIG. 1016.—DISSECTION OF THE BACK OF THE SHOULDER AND ARM, showing the anastomosing vessels on the dorsum of the scapula, and the posterior humeral circumflex and the profunda brachii arteries.

It begins behind the internal jugular vein, crosses the scalenus anterior and the phrenic nerve, and is covered superficially by the sterno-mastoid; on the left side it lies behind the thoracic duct also. Continuing laterally behind the clavicle and crossing superficial to the third part of the subclavian artery and the cords of the brachial plexus, it reaches the suprascapular notch and passes over the suprascapular ligament. Then it descends, with the suprascapular nerve, through the supraspinous fossa and deep to the supraspinatus muscle, and after passing through the great scapular notch, deep to the spino-glenoid ligament, it ends in the infraspinous fossa.

Branches.—The trunk of the artery gives branches to the adjacent muscles, a branch that passes superficial to the sternal end of the clavicle and an **acromial branch,** which ramifies over the acromion, anastomosing with the acromial branches of the acromio-thoracic and the posterior circumflex arteries.

As the artery passes over the suprascapular ligament, it gives off a branch into the subscapular fossa, which anastomoses with the branches of the subscapular artery and the deep branch of the transverse cervical artery.

In the supraspinous and infraspinous fossæ its branches also anastomose with the deep branch of the transverse cervical; and in the infraspinous fossa they anastomose in addition with the circumflex scapular artery.

The chief **muscular branches** of the suprascapular artery supply the supraspinatus, infraspinatus, and subscapularis muscles. The artery also supplies branches to the sterno-clavicular, acromio-clavicular, and shoulder joints, and nutrient arteries to the clavicle and the scapula.

(3) The **internal mammary artery** (Figs. 1002, 1013) arises from the lower and anterior part of the subclavian, at the medial border of the scalenus anterior and immediately below the origin of the thyro-cervical trunk. It terminates, behind the sternal end of the sixth intercostal space, by dividing into the musculo-phrenic and superior epigastric arteries.

The artery passes at first downwards, forwards, and medially, lying upon the pleura, and behind the innominate vein, the sternal end of the clavicle, and the cartilage of the first rib; the right artery is crossed obliquely, from the lateral to the medial side, by the phrenic nerve, which usually passes in front of it. From the cartilage of the first rib it descends vertically, about half an inch from the border of the sternum, and lies, in the upper part of its course, in front of the pleura, and, in the lower part, in front of the sterno-costalis muscle. It is covered in front by the cartilages of the upper six ribs, the intervening anterior intercostal membrane and internal intercostal muscles, and is crossed by the terminal portions of the intercostal nerves. It is accompanied by lymph vessels and glands and by two venæ comitantes, which unite together above and on its medial side to form a single trunk which ends in the innominate vein in the thorax.

Variations.—The internal mammary artery, though usually a branch of the first part of the subclavian, is very variable in origin. It may arise from the second or third part, or from the thyro-cervical trunk, or it may spring from the aorta, or from the innominate or axillary arteries. All these variations are due to obliteration of the normal origin and the opening up of anastomoses. The internal mammary artery sometimes descends in front of the cartilages of one or more of the lower true ribs; and occasionally it gives off a *lateral costal branch* which descends on the inner side of the chest wall, close to the mid-axillary line—a point of importance in paracentesis. Occasionally a bronchial artery may arise from the internal mammary, and one or several small branches may pass to the lower end of the trachea.

Branches.—The **pericardiaco-phrenic artery** is a long slender branch which is given off from the upper part of the internal mammary. It accompanies the phrenic nerve through the superior and middle mediastina to the diaphragm, where it anastomoses with the phrenic and musculo-phrenic arteries. In its course downwards this artery gives off numerous small branches to the pleura and pericardium, which anastomose with offsets of the mediastinal and pericardial branches of the aorta and internal mammary arteries, and also with the bronchial arteries, forming the wide-meshed *subpleural plexus* of Turner.

Numerous small **mediastinal branches** pass into the mediastinum and supply the back of the sternum, the areolar tissue and lymph glands, the thymus and the pericardium. The *thymic branches* are larger and more important in the child.

The **anterior intercostal arteries** are two in number in each of the upper six inter-costal spaces. They pass laterally and lie for a short distance between the pleura (or the sterno-costalis) and the internal intercostal muscles; they then pass between the internal intercostal muscles and the intercostales intimi (see p. 422), and end by anastomosing with the posterior intercostal arteries and their collateral branches.

The **perforating branches,** one in each of the upper six intercostal spaces, are small vessels which pass forwards, with the anterior cutaneous branches of the intercostal nerves, piercing the internal intercostal muscle, the anterior intercostal membrane, and the pectoralis major. They end in the skin and subcutaneous tissue. They supply twigs to the sternum, and those in the second, third, and fourth spaces, usually the largest of the series, give off *mammary branches* which are of special importance in the female as arteries of supply to the mammary gland.

The **musculo-phrenic artery**, the lateral terminal branch of the internal mammary, runs downwards and laterally, from the sixth intercostal space to the tenth costal cartilage. In the upper part of its course it lies upon the thoracic surface of the diaphragm, but it pierces the diaphragm about the level of the eighth costal cartilage, and ends on its abdominal surface. It gives off *muscular branches* to the diaphragm which anastomose with phrenic branches of the thoracic aorta and with the phrenic arteries ; and it supplies two **anterior intercostal arteries** to each of the seventh, eighth, and ninth intercostal spaces. These are distributed in the same manner as the corresponding branches of the internal mammary artery, and end by anastomosing with the posterior intercostal arteries and their collateral branches.

The **superior epigastric artery**, the medial terminal branch of the internal mammary, descends into the anterior wall of the abdomen. It leaves the thorax, between the sternal and costal origins of the diaphragm, and enters the sheath of the rectus abdominis muscle, lying first behind the muscle and then in its substance. It ends by anastomosing with branches of the inferior epigastric artery. It gives *muscular branches* to the rectus, to the other muscles of the abdominal wall, and to the diaphragm. Small cutaneous branches pierce the rectus and the anterior wall of its sheath ; these accompany the anterior terminal branches of the lower intercostal nerves, and end in the subcutaneous tissues and skin of the middle portion of the anterior abdominal wall. A small branch which supplies adjacent muscle and skin crosses the front of the xiphoid process to anastomose with its fellow of the opposite side, and branches of small size pass backwards in the falciform ligament to the liver, where they anastomose with branches of the hepatic artery.

(4) The **costo-cervical trunk** (Fig. 1013) springs from the back of the second part of the subclavian artery on the right side and from the first part on the left side. It runs upwards and backwards, over the cervical pleura and the apex of the lung, to the neck of the first rib, where it divides into the deep cervical and superior intercostal arteries.

Branches.—The **deep cervical artery** springs from the costo-cervical trunk at upper border of the neck of the first rib. It runs backwards, into the back of the neck, passing below the eighth cervical nerve, and between the transverse process of the seventh cervical vertebra and the neck of the first rib. In the back of the neck it ascends between the semispinalis capitis and semispinalis cervicis muscles, and it ends by anastomosing with the descending branch of the occipital artery ; it anastomoses also with branches of the ascending cervical and vertebral arteries. It supplies the adjacent muscles ; and it sends a *spinal* branch, through the intervertebral foramen between the last cervical and the first thoracic vertebræ, into the vertebral canal ; this branch anastomoses with the spinal branches of the vertebral and posterior intercostal arteries.

The **superior intercostal artery** descends, in front of the neck of the first rib, between the first thoracic nerve laterally and the sympathetic trunk medially. At the lower border of the neck of the rib, it gives off the posterior intercostal artery of the first space ; then, after crossing in front of the neck of the second rib, it becomes the posterior intercostal artery of the second intercostal space. The **first two posterior intercostal arteries** run laterally, each in its own space, lying first between the pleura and the posterior intercostal membrane, and then between the intercostalis intimus and the internal intercostal muscle (see p. 422). Their branches end by anastomosing with anterior intercostal branches of the internal mammary artery. Each gives off *muscular* branches to the intercostal muscles, a *nutrient branch* to the rib below which it lies, and a *collateral branch* which runs along the lower border of the corresponding space. They also have *posterior branches* which are distributed in the same manner as the posterior branches of the other posterior intercostal arteries (p. 1204).

Variations.—The **deep cervical artery** may arise directly from the subclavian trunk and the **superior intercostal artery** may be absent, its place being taken by branches from the aorta. The superior intercostal is sometimes formed from a postcostal instead of a precostal primitive channel. In such cases it passes between the necks of the ribs and the transverse processes of the vertebræ instead of, as usual, in front of the necks of the ribs.

AXILLARY ARTERY

The **axillary artery** is the direct continuation of the subclavian artery, and it becomes the brachial artery.

It begins at the outer border of the first rib, at the apex of the axilla. It passes downwards along the lateral wall of the space, *i.e.* along the medial side of the shoulder-joint and the humerus, to the lower border of the teres major, where it becomes the brachial artery. A line drawn from the middle of the clavicle to the medial border of the prominence of the coraco-brachialis muscle, when the

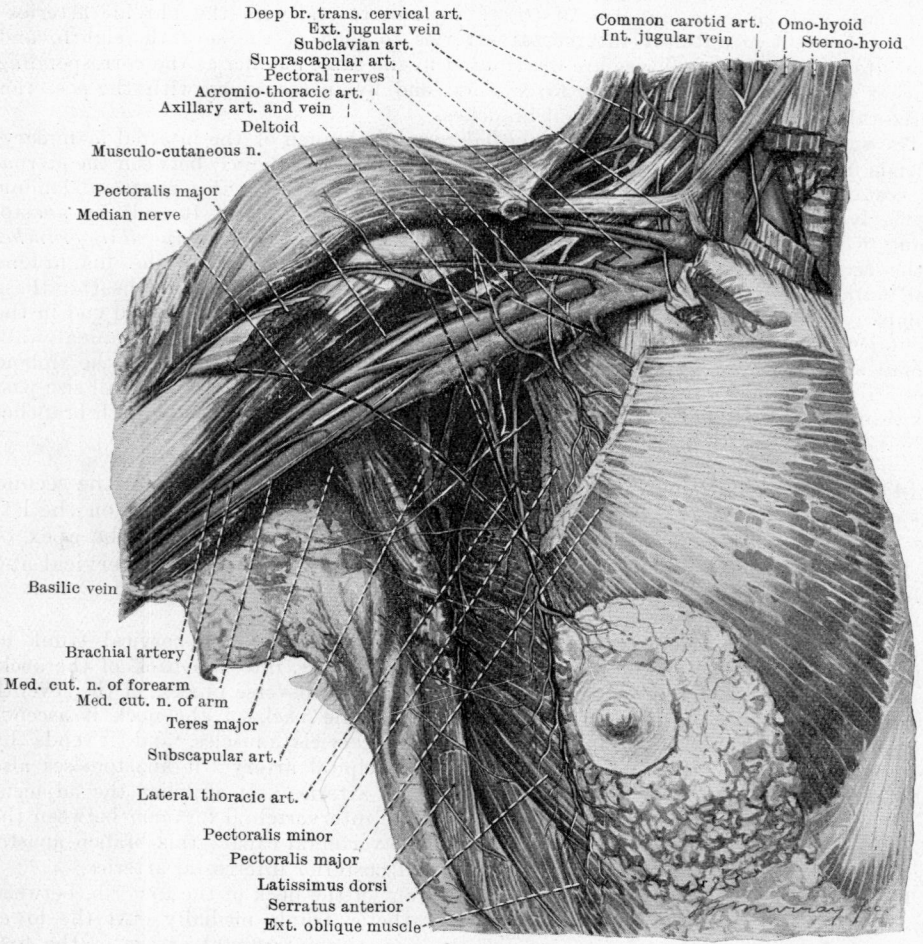

Deep br. trans. cervical art.
Ext. jugular vein
Subclavian art.
Suprascapular art.
Pectoral nerves
Acromio-thoracic art.
Axillary art. and vein
Deltoid
Musculo-cutaneous n.
Pectoralis major
Median nerve

Common carotid art.   Omo-hyoid
Int. jugular vein   Sterno-hyoid

Basilic vein
Brachial artery
Med. cut. n. of forearm
Med. cut. n. of arm
Teres major
Subscapular art.
Lateral thoracic art.
Pectoralis minor
Pectoralis major
Latissimus dorsi
Serratus anterior
Ext. oblique muscle

FIG. 1017.—AXILLARY ARTERY AND ITS BRANCHES.

NOTE.—The middle third of the clavicle has been removed ; and the arm has been slightly abducted and rotated laterally. Parts of the pectoralis major and minor have been removed ; the positions of the lower border of the pectoralis major and both borders of the pectoralis minor are indicated by broken black lines.

arm is abducted until it is at right angles with the side, indicates the position and direction of the artery.

The position and direction, and to a certain extent the relations of the axillary artery, are modified however by changes in the position of the upper limb. With the arm hanging by the side the axillary artery describes a curve with the concavity directed downwards and medially, and the vein lies along its medial side. When the arm is at right angles with the side, the axillary artery is almost straight ; it lies closer to the lateral wall of the axilla, and the vein overlaps it antero-medially. When the arm is raised above the level of the shoulder the axillary artery is curved over the head of the humerus, with the convexity of the curve below, and the vein lies still more in front of it.

For descriptive purposes the artery is divided into three parts: the first part lies above the pectoralis minor, the second behind, and the third part below it.

Though it is the usual custom to describe three parts of the axillary artery —a division which is of practical interest in so far as it emphasises the fact that the axillary artery is surgically accessible above the pectoralis minor—it is to be noted that the upper border of the pectoralis minor may be so nearly in line with the outer border of the first rib, at the point where the axillary artery begins, that the first part of the artery is exceedingly short.

Relations of the First Part.—*Posterior.*—The first part of the artery is enclosed, together with the vein and the cords of the brachial plexus, in a prolongation of the cervical fascia known as the *axillary sheath.* Posterior to the sheath are the upper serration of the serratus anterior, the contents of the first intercostal space, and the nerve to serratus anterior, which descends vertically between the artery and the muscle; whilst, within the sheath, the medial pectoral nerve and the medial cord of the brachial plexus lie behind the artery. *Anterior.*—It is covered in front by the clavi-pectoral fascia. This fascia intervenes between the artery and the cephalic vein, the branches of the lateral pectoral nerve, the branches of the acromio-thoracic artery with their accompanying veins, and the clavicular part of the pectoralis major muscle, superficial to which are the deep fascia, the supra-clavicular nerves descending from the cervical plexus, the platysma in the superficial fascia, and the skin. Posterior to the clavi-pectoral fascia the artery is crossed by a loop of communication between the lateral and medial pectoral nerves. *Lateral.*—Above and to the lateral side are the lateral and posterior cords of the brachial plexus and the lateral pectoral nerve. Below and to the medial side is the axillary vein, the medial pectoral nerve intervening.

Relations of the Second Part.—*Posterior.*—Behind the second part of the artery are the posterior cord of the brachial plexus and the fatty areolar tissue which separates it from the subscapularis muscle. *Anterior.*—In front is the pectoralis minor, and, more superficially, the pectoralis major, the fasciæ and skin. *Lateral.*—To the lateral side lies the lateral cord of the brachial plexus. *Medial.*—On the medial side the medial cord of the plexus lies in close relation to the artery, and intervenes between it and the axillary vein.

Relations of the Third Part.—*Posterior.*—The third part of the artery rests upon the lower part of the subscapularis, the latissimus dorsi, and the teres major. It is separated from the fibres of the subscapularis by the circumflex [axillary] and radial nerves, and from the latissimus dorsi and teres major by the radial nerve alone. *Anterior.*— It is crossed in front by the medial head of the median nerve. In its upper half it lies under cover of the lower part of the pectoralis major, the fasciæ and skin, whilst its lower part, which is superficial, is covered by skin and fasciæ only. *Lateral.*—To the lateral side lie the median and musculo-cutaneous nerves and the coraco-brachialis muscle. *Medial.*—To the medial side is the axillary vein. The two vessels are, however, separated by two of the chief branches of the medial cord of the brachial plexus, for between the vein and the artery in front lies the medial cutaneous nerve of the forearm; and between them behind is the ulnar nerve. The medial cutaneous nerve of the arm lies medial to the vein, and the venæ comitantes of the brachial artery ascend along the medial side to end in the axillary vein at the lower border of the subscapularis muscle.

Variations.—The **axillary artery** does not vary much in its origin or course. Its relations may be modified by the existence of a muscular or tendinous "axillary arch," which, passing from the latissimus dorsi to the pectoralis major, crosses the distal part of the artery superficially; and there may be an anomalous arrangement of its branches. Occasionally the subscapular, circumflex humeral, profunda brachii and ulnar collateral arteries arise from the axillary by a common stem. In those cases the chief branches of the brachial plexus are grouped round the common stem instead of round the axillary artery. The arrangement is due to the persistence of a different part of the original vascular plexus.

Sometimes the axillary artery divides into the radial and ulnar arteries, and more rarely the common interosseous artery may spring from it. Obviously there is no brachial artery when the radial and ulnar arteries are formed by the division of the axillary; its place is taken by the two abnormal vessels which, as a rule, are separated by the median nerve as they run through the arm; the radial is usually more superficial than the ulnar, and crosses laterally in front of it at the bend of the elbow.

BRANCHES OF AXILLARY ARTERY

(1) The **superior thoracic artery** [A. thoracalis suprema] is a small branch which arises from the first part of the axillary at the lower border of the sub-clavius. It runs downwards and medially, across the first intercostal space, and pierces the medial part of the clavi-pectoral fascia. It supplies branches to the adjacent muscles; and it anastomoses with branches of the suprascapular, the internal mammary, and the acromio-thoracic arteries.

(2) The **acromio-thoracic artery** [A. thoraco-acromialis] (Fig. 1017) arises near the upper border of the pectoralis minor, from the second part of the axillary artery. It is a very short trunk, of considerable size, which passes forwards, pierces the clavi-pectoral fascia, and ends, deep to the clavicular portion of the pectoralis major, by dividing into four terminal branches—acromial, clavicular, deltoid, and pectoral.

The **acromial branch** runs upwards and laterally, across the tip of the coracoid process, to the acromion; it anastomoses with the deltoid branch, with the acromial branches of the suprascapular, and with the posterior circumflex humeral artery.

The **clavicular branch** is a long slender artery which runs upwards and medially, to the sterno-clavicular joint, anastomosing with the superior thoracic, with branches of the suprascapular, and with the first perforating branch of the internal mammary artery. It supplies the adjacent muscles and the sterno-clavicular joint.

The **deltoid branch** descends, in the groove between the pectoralis major and the deltoid, where it lies by the side of the cephalic vein, as far as the insertion of the deltoid. It anastomoses with the acromial branch and with the anterior circumflex humeral artery; and it gives branches to the pectoralis major and deltoid muscles and to the skin.

The **pectoral** is a large branch which descends between the two pectoral muscles, to both of which it gives branches, and it anastomoses with the intercostal and lateral thoracic arteries.

(3) The **lateral thoracic artery** arises from the second part of the axillary, and descends, along the lateral border of the pectoralis minor, to anastomose with the intercostal and subscapular arteries and with the pectoral branch of the acromio-thoracic. It supplies the adjacent muscles, and sends *external mammary branches* to the lateral part of the mammary gland.

(4) The **subscapular artery** is the largest branch of the axillary. It arises from the third part of the artery, opposite the lower border of the subscapularis, along which it descends, giving branches to the muscle and to the medial wall of the axilla. After a short course it gives off the circumflex scapular artery, and then, accompanied by the nerve to the latissimus dorsi, continues along the lateral border of the scapula to the wall of the thorax, where it anastomoses with the lateral thoracic artery, with branches of the intercostal arteries, and with the deep branch of the transverse cervical.

The **circumflex scapular artery** is frequently larger than the continuation of the parent trunk. It arises about one and a half inches from the origin of the subscapular, and passes backwards into the triangular space which lies between the subscapularis above, the teres major below, and the long heads of the triceps laterally. Turning round and usually grooving the lateral border of the scapula, under cover of the teres minor, it enters the infraspinous fossa, where it breaks up into branches which anastomose with the deep branch of the transverse cervical artery and the suprascapular artery. In the triangular space the artery gives off two branches; one passes into the subscapular fossa and anastomoses there with the same two arteries; the other runs downwards, to the inferior angle of the scapula, between the teres major and minor muscles. Small branches are given also to the deltoid and long head of triceps.

(5) The **posterior circumflex humeral artery** arises from the third part of the axillary artery and passes backwards, accompanied by the circumflex [axillary] nerve, through an intermuscular cleft, the so-called quadrangular space, which is bounded by the teres minor and the subscapularis above, the teres major below, the long head of the triceps medially, and the humerus laterally. It turns round the surgical neck of the humerus, under cover of the deltoid muscle, and ends in numerous branches which supply a large portion of the deltoid and anastomose

with the anterior circumflex humeral and the acromio-thoracic arteries. As a rule it is an artery of large size, only slightly smaller than the subscapular.

Branches.—**Muscular branches** are given to the adjacent muscles, and a branch ascends, through the deltoid, to the acromion, where it anastomoses with the acromial branches of the suprascapular and the acromio-thoracic arteries. A *descending branch* runs downwards along the lateral head of the triceps to anastomose with the profunda brachii artery; frequently this branch is enlarged so that the posterior circumflex humeral arises from the profunda brachii. The artery also supplies articular branches to the shoulder-joint, and nutrient branches to the proximal end of the humerus.

(6) The **anterior circumflex humeral artery** is a small branch; it is given off from the third part of the axillary close to, or in common with, the posterior circumflex. It passes laterally, posterior to the coraco-brachialis and the two heads of the biceps, round the front of the surgical neck of the humerus, and it ends by anastomosing with the posterior humeral circumflex. It gives muscular branches to the adjacent muscles, one of which runs downwards along the tendon of insertion of the pectoralis major. At the bicipital groove it gives off a well-marked branch which ascends with the tendon of the long head of the biceps to the shoulder joint.

BRACHIAL ARTERY

The **brachial artery** is the direct continuation of the axillary. It begins at the lower border of the teres major, and ends, in the cubital fossa, opposite the neck of the radius, by dividing into the radial and ulnar arteries.

The brachial artery runs downwards along the *medial* side of the arm, at first on the medial side and then in front of the humerus. Its position and that of the axillary artery may be indicated on the surface, when the arm is abducted, by a line drawn from the middle of the clavicle to the centre of the bend of the elbow.

Relations.—*Posterior.*—It lies, successively, anterior to the long head of the triceps, the radial nerve and the profunda vessels intervening; the medial head of the triceps; the insertion of the coraco-brachialis; and the brachialis.

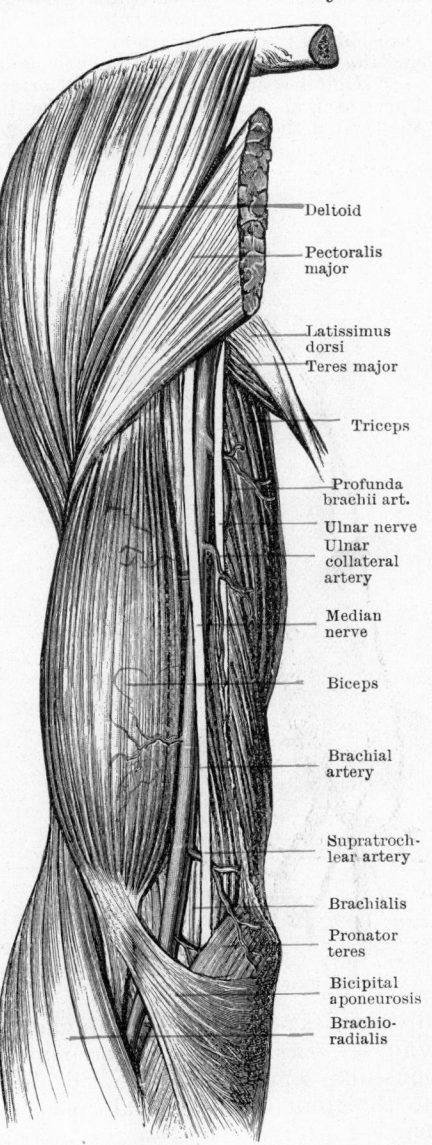

FIG. 1018.—THE BRACHIAL ARTERY AND ITS BRANCHES.

Anterior.—It is overlapped *anteriorly* by the medial border of the biceps; it is crossed, at the middle of the arm, by the median nerve, and, in addition, it is covered by deep and superficial fascia and skin. In the cubital fossa a thickened portion of the deep fascia, called the bicipital aponeurosis [lacertus fibrosus], separates it from the median cubital vein and the anterior branch of the medial cutaneous nerve of the forearm, both of which lie in the superficial fascia. *Lateral.*—To the *lateral side* it is in relation, proximally, with the median nerve, and, distally, with the biceps. *Medial.*—To the *medial side* it is in relation, in the proximal part of its extent, with the basilic vein, the medial cutaneous nerve of the forearm, the medial cutaneous nerve of the arm, and the ulnar nerve, and in the distal part with the median nerve.   Two venæ comitantes, a medial and a lateral, accompany the artery, and communications between them pass across the vessel.

Variations.—The **brachial artery** is rarely prolonged beyond its usual point of bifurcation; not uncommonly, however, it bifurcates at a higher level.   Of the two terminal branches of the brachial, one may divide into radial and common interosseous, the other forming the ulnar; or one may divide into radial and ulnar, whilst the other is the common interosseous. Occasionally the brachial artery ends by dividing into three branches—viz., the radial, the ulnar, and the common interosseous.   The common interosseous was the original trunk.

" High division " of the brachial artery occurs most commonly in the proximal third of the upper arm, and least commonly in the distal third; the resulting trunks are often united near the bend of the elbow by a more or less oblique anastomosis.

When there is high division of the brachial artery the radial branch may pierce the deep fascia of the arm near the bend of the elbow, and descend in the forearm in the superficial fascia; or it may run deeper, and pass behind the tendon of the biceps.   The ulnar branch sometimes runs, on the medial intermuscular septum, towards the medial epicondyle, and then laterally towards the middle of the bend of the elbow, behind a band of fascia from which the proximal fibres of the pronator teres arise, or behind the supracondylar process of the humerus if it is present. More commonly the ulnar branch descends towards the medial epicondyle, and crosses superficial to the flexor muscles or deep to the palmaris longus; and in a few cases it is subcutaneous.   Rarely the ulnar artery accompanies the ulnar nerve behind the medial epicondyle; it has then obviously been formed by enlargement of the ordinary ulnar collateral and posterior ulnar recurrent arteries.

Instead of following its usual course along the brachialis muscle, the brachial artery may accompany the median nerve behind a supracondylar process, or ligament, as in many carnivora; it may pass in front of the median nerve instead of behind it.   It may give off a "vas aberrans" or a median artery, and any of its ordinary branches may be absent.

The vas aberrans given off from the brachial artery usually ends in the radial artery, sometimes in the radial recurrent, and rarely in the ulnar artery.

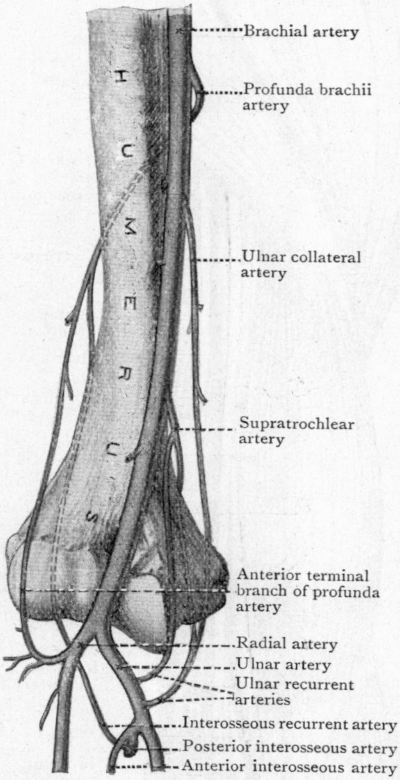

FIG. 1019.—DIAGRAM OF ANASTOMOSIS AROUND THE ELBOW JOINT.

Labels on figure:
Brachial artery
Profunda brachii artery
Ulnar collateral artery
Supratrochlear artery
Anterior terminal branch of profunda artery
Radial artery
Ulnar artery
Ulnar recurrent arteries
Interosseous recurrent artery
Posterior interosseous artery
Anterior interosseous artery

BRANCHES OF BRACHIAL ARTERY

(1) The **profunda brachii artery** is a large branch which arises from the postero-medial side of the brachial, soon after its origin. It runs downwards and laterally in the groove for the radial nerve, and divides, at the back of the humerus, into two descending branches, anterior and posterior.   Not infrequently the division takes place at a higher level, and the artery appears double.   The *anterior descending branch* accompanies the radial nerve through the lateral intermuscular septum, and descends, between the brachio-radialis and the brachialis, to the front of the lateral epicondyle, where it anastomoses with the radial recurrent artery.   The *posterior descending branch* continues downwards, behind the lateral intermuscular septum to the back of the lateral epicondyle, where it anastomoses with the interosseous recurrent and supratrochlear arteries.

Behind the humerus one of the descending branches gives off—(*a*) a slender twig, which descends with the nerve to the anconeus muscle in the medial head of the triceps to the back of the elbow, where it anastomoses with the supratrochlear artery; (*b*) a *nutrient branch*, which enters a foramen on the posterior surface of the humerus; and (*c*) an *ascending branch* [R. deltoideus], which anastomoses with the descending branch of the posterior circumflex humeral artery.

(2) **Muscular branches** are given to the adjacent muscles.

(3) A small **nutrient branch** arises from the middle of the brachial and enters the nutrient foramen on the antero-medial surface of the humerus.

(4) The **ulnar collateral artery** [A. collateralis uln. sup.] is smaller than the profunda, with which it sometimes arises by a common trunk ; usually, however, it springs from the postero-medial side of the middle of the brachial artery. It runs downwards and backwards, with the ulnar nerve, through the medial intermuscular septum, and then, passing more vertically, reaches the back of the medial epicondyle of the humerus, where it ends by anastomosing with the posterior ulnar recurrent and supratrochlear arteries.

(5) The **supratrochlear artery** [A. collateralis uln. inf.] arises from the medial side of the brachial artery about two inches above its bifurcation. It runs medially between the median nerve and the brachialis. Then it pierces the medial intermuscular septum, and turns laterally, between the medial head of the triceps and the posterior surface of the bone, to the lateral epicondyle. It supplies the adjacent muscles, and anastomoses, in front of the medial epicondyle with the anterior ulnar recurrent, behind the medial epicondyle with the posterior ulnar recurrent and the ulnar collateral, on the back of the humerus with the twig from the profunda which follows the nerve to the anconeus, and behind the lateral epicondyle with the posterior descending branch of the profunda and with the interosseous recurrent artery.

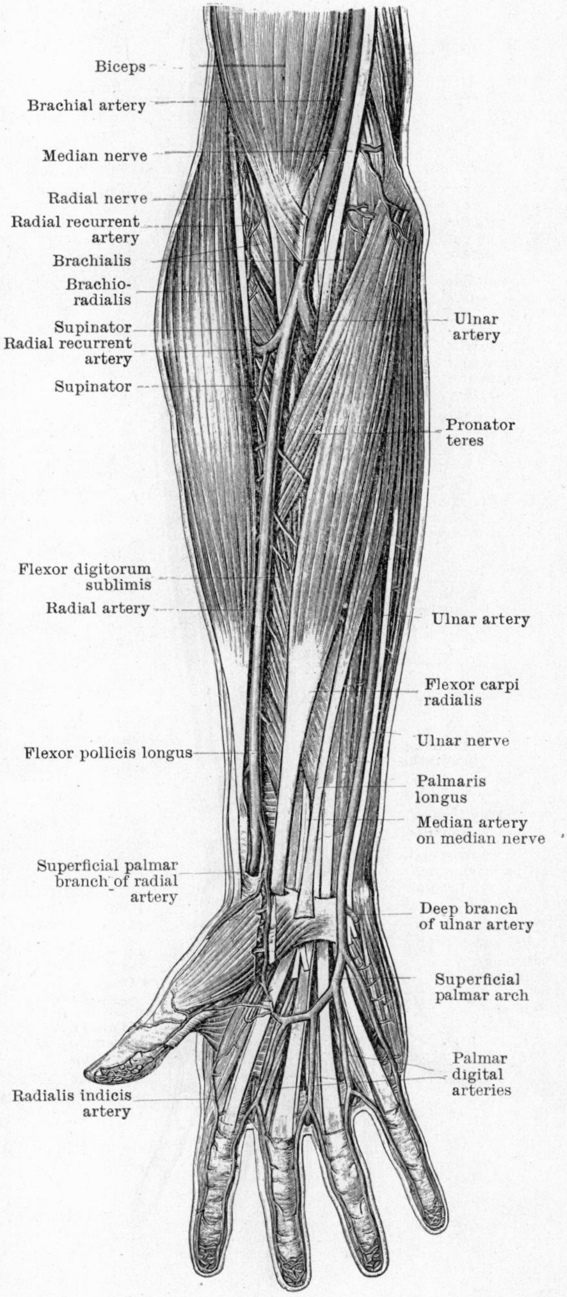

RADIAL ARTERY

The **radial artery** (Figs. 1020 and 1021) is the smaller of the two terminal branches of the brachial artery, but it is in more direct line with the parent trunk. It begins in the cubital fossa, opposite the neck of the radius, and ends in the palm of the hand, by anastomosing with the deep branch of the ulnar artery, and thus completing the deep palmar arch.

The trunk is divisible into **three parts**. The *first part* lies in the forearm. It runs downwards and slighty laterally to the apex of the styloid process of the radius.

FIG. 1020.—SUPERFICIAL DISSECTION OF THE FOREARM AND HAND, showing the radial and ulnar arteries and the superficial palmar arch with its branches.

The *second part* curves round the lateral side of the wrist, and across the scaphoid and trapezium, to reach the proximal end of the first interosseous space. The *third part* passes forwards, through the first interosseous space, to the palm of the hand, where it joins the deep branch of the ulnar artery.

Relations of the First Part—*Posterior.*—It passes successively across the following structures : the tendon of insertion of the biceps, the supinator, the pronator teres, the radial portion of the flexor digitorum sublimis, the flexor pollicis longus, the pronator quadratus, and the lower end of the radius.

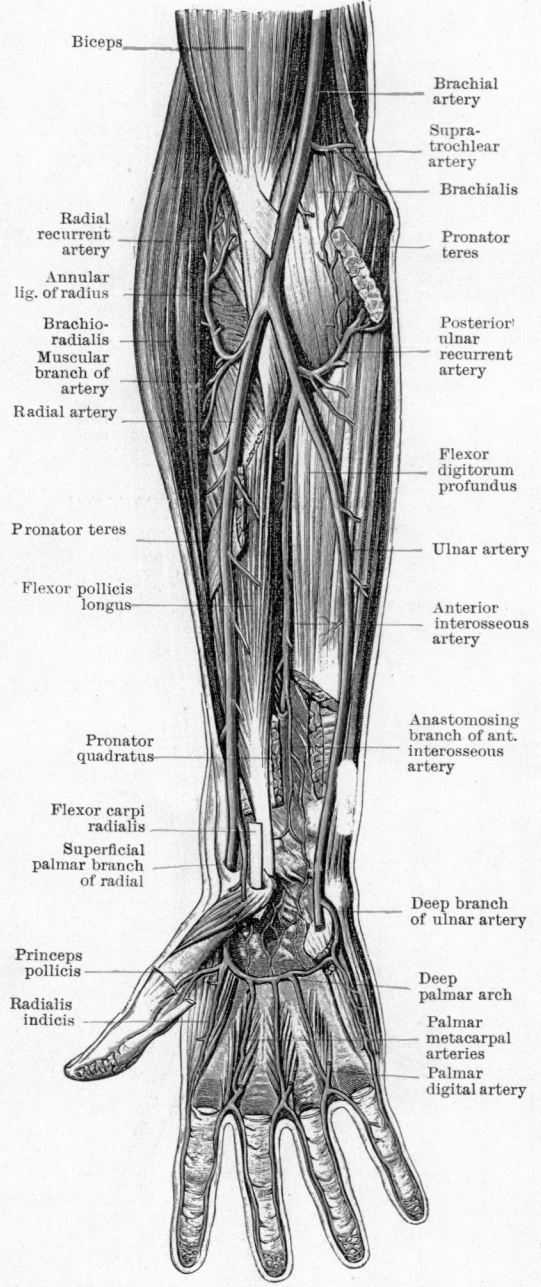

Anterior.—The artery is covered superficially, in the proximal half, by the border of the brachio-radialis ; in the remainder of its extent it is covered only by skin and fasciæ.

To the *radial side* are the brachio-radialis and the radial nerve. The nerve lies near to the middle third of the artery. To the *ulnar side* are the pronator teres, proximally, and the flexor carpi radialis, distally. Two venæ comitantes lie along the sides of the artery.

Branches of the First Part.

—The **radial recurrent artery** arises in the cubital fossa, where it springs from the lateral side of the radial, on the surface of the supinator. It runs towards the radial border of the forearm, passes between the radial nerve and its posterior interosseous branch, and then runs upwards to the lateral epicondyle of the humerus, where it anastomoses with the anterior descending branch of the profunda brachii. The radial recurrent supplies numerous branches to the adjacent muscles.

Muscular branches supply the muscles on the radial side of the forearm.

The **superficial palmar branch** (Fig. 1020) is a slender vessel which arises a short distance above the wrist and runs downwards across the ball of the thumb. It usually pierces the superficial muscles of the thenar eminence, and ends either in their substance or by uniting with the ulnar artery to complete the *superficial palmar arch.*

An **anterior carpal branch** passes medially, between the synovial sheaths of the flexor tendons and the radial attachment of the anterior radio-carpal ligament. It anastomoses with the anterior carpal branch of the ulnar artery to form the *anterior carpal arch,* and it receives communications from the anterior interosseous artery and from the deep palmar arch.

Relations of the Second Part.

—As it curves round the radial side and the dorsum of the wrist, the radial artery lies upon the lateral ligament of the wrist, and upon the scaphoid

Fig. 1021.—Deep Dissection of the Forearm and Hand, showing the radial and ulnar arteries and their branches and the deep palmar arch and its branches.

bone and the trapezium. It is crossed by the tendons of the abductor pollicis longus, the extensor pollicis brevis, and the extensor pollicis longus ; more superficially it is covered by skin, and by fascia, which contains the cephalic vein and some filaments of the radial nerve.

Branches of the Second Part (Fig. 1022).—The **posterior carpal branch** runs medially on the dorsal intercarpal ligaments, deep to the extensor tendons, and joins the posterior carpal branch of the ulnar artery to complete the *posterior carpal arch*. From the arch three **dorsal metacarpal arteries** run downwards on the second, third, and fourth dorsal interosseous muscles, and divide, opposite the heads of the metacarpal bones, each into two **dorsal digital arteries** which supply the adjacent sides of the fingers and anastomose with the palmar digital arteries.

Two *dorsal digital arteries of the thumb* and a *radial dorsal digital artery of the index* take independent origin from the radial artery; the former run along the dorsal borders of the thumb and anastomose with the palmar digital branches of the princeps pollicis; the latter, from which the adjacent vessel of the thumb may arise, runs downwards, on the ulnar head of the first dorsal interosseous muscle to reach the radial border of the index finger.

Each dorsal metacarpal artery is connected with the deep palmar arch by a *proximal perforating branch* which passes through the proximal part of the corresponding interosseous space, and with a digital branch from the superficial palmar arch by a *distal perforating branch* which passes through the distal part of the space. The first dorsal metacarpal (which runs on the second dorsal interosseous muscle) may arise direct from the radial or in common with the posterior carpal branch.

Relations of the Third Part.—The third part of the radial artery passes between the two heads of the first dorsal interosseous muscle to reach the palm, where it turns medially, deep to the oblique head of the adductor pollicis, and, after passing through the proximal fibres of the transverse head, or between the two heads of that muscle, it unites with the deep branch of the ulnar artery, completing the *deep palmar arch*.

Branches of the Third Part.—The **princeps pollicis artery** is given off as soon as the radial artery enters the palm. It runs downwards, on the palmar aspect of the first metacarpal bone, between the adductor and the opponens pollicis, and under cover of the long flexor tendon. Near the distal end of the bone, it divides into two *palmar digital arteries*, which run along the sides of the thumb and anastomose with the dorsal digital arteries.

The **radialis indicis artery** is a branch which descends between the ulnar head of the first dorsal interosseous muscle and the adductor pollicis and along the radial side of the index finger to its tip. It supplies the adjacent tissues, and not uncommonly it anastomoses with the superficial palmar arch.

Variations.—The **radial artery** may be absent, its place being taken by branches of the ulnar or interosseous arteries. Its origin may be higher than usual, from the axillary, or from the brachial. It may end in muscular branches in the forearm, or as the superficial palmar, or in carpal branches; the distal portion of the artery is then usually replaced by branches of the ulnar or interosseous arteries. Occasionally the radial divides some distance proximal to the wrist into two terminal branches, one of which gives off the carpal branches, and becomes the superficial palmar, whilst the other crosses superficial to the extensor tendons and passes to the back of the wrist.

The radial artery may run a superficial course, or, and especially when it arises at a more distal level than usual, it may pass deep to the pronator teres and the radial origin of the flexor digitorum sublimis. Sometimes it passes to the back of the wrist across the brachio-radialis, and it may lie superficial to the extensor tendons of the thumb, instead of deep to them.

Its branches may be diminished or increased in number. The radial recurrent may spring from the brachial or ulnar arteries, or may be represented by several branches from the proximal part of the radial. The radial dorsal digital artery of the index finger may be large, and may replace the princeps pollicis and the radialis indicis. The posterior carpal branch and dorsal metacarpal arteries may be replaced—the former by branches of the interosseous arteries of the forearm, and the latter by the proximal perforating branches of the deep palmar arch.

The princeps pollicis and radialis indicis arteries may be absent, their places being taken either by branches of the superficial palmar arch or by the radial dorsal digital artery of the index.

ULNAR ARTERY

The **ulnar artery** (Figs. 1020 and 1021) is the larger terminal branch, but is in less direct line with the brachial artery. It begins in the cubital fossa, opposite the neck of the radius, and ends in the palm of the hand, where it anastomoses with the superficial palmar branch of the radial artery to form the superficial palmar arch.

From its origin it runs obliquely, downwards and medially, deep to the muscles that arise from the medial epicondyle, to the junction of the proximal and middle thirds of the forearm, where it comes into relation with the ulnar nerve. It then runs straight, on the radial side of the ulnar nerve, to the wrist, crosses in front of the flexor retinaculum [lig. carpi transversum], on the radial side of the pisiform bone, and enters the palm of the hand.

Relations—*Posterior.*—In succession it lies in front of the distal part of the brachialis, the flexor digitorum profundus, and the flexor retinaculum. *Anterior.*—It is crossed, in the oblique part of its course, by the pronator teres, the median nerve (which is separated from the artery by the ulnar head of the pronator teres), the flexor digitorum sublimis, the flexor carpi radialis, and the palmaris longus. In the middle third of the forearm it is overlapped by the flexor carpi ulnaris, and in the distal third it is covered by skin and fasciæ only. For a short distance above the wrist the palmar cutaneous branch of the ulnar nerve lies in front of it. As it crosses the flexor retinaculum, it may be bound down by a fascial slip from the superficial surface of the retinaculum to the pisiform bone and the tendon of the flexor carpi ulnaris. Two communicating venæ comitantes lie one on each side of the artery. On the *radial side* there is also, in its distal two-thirds, the flexor digitorum sublimis. On its *ulnar side* are the flexor carpi ulnaris and the ulnar nerve.

Branches.—The **anterior ulnar recurrent artery** is a small branch which arises in the cubital fossa, frequently in common with the posterior ulnar recurrent. It runs upwards, under cover of the pronator teres, to the front of the medial epicondyle, and anastomoses with branches of the supratrochlear artery.

The **posterior ulnar recurrent artery**, larger than the anterior, arises in the cubital fossa from the ulnar side of the ulnar artery, and ascends, on the flexor profundus and under cover of the muscles which arise from the medial epicondyle, to the back of that prominence, where it passes between the humeral and ulnar heads of the flexor carpi ulnaris, and anastomoses with the ulnar collateral and supratrochlear arteries. It gives branches to the adjacent muscles and to the elbow joint.

The **common interosseous artery** is a short trunk which springs from the postero-lateral side of the ulnar artery, in the distal part of the cubital fossa. It passes backwards towards the proximal border of the interosseous membrane, and divides into anterior and posterior interosseous branches.

The **anterior interosseous artery** runs downwards, on the anterior surface of the interosseous membrane, between the adjacent borders of the flexor pollicis longus and the flexor digitorum profundus, to the proximal border of the pronator quadratus; there it pierces the interosseous membrane, and continues downwards, first on the posterior surface of the membrane, deep to the extensor pollicis longus and extensor indicis, and then on the distal end of the radius, in the groove for the extensor digitorum; and it ends, on the back of the carpus, by joining the posterior carpal arch. It is accompanied on the front of the interosseous membrane by the anterior interosseous nerve, and on the back of the membrane by the posterior interosseous nerve.

Branches.—It supplies **muscular branches** to the adjacent muscles, and gives *nutrient* branches to the radius and ulna. A slender *communicating* branch passes distally, deep to the pronator quadratus and on the interosseous membrane, to anastomose with the anterior carpal arch. After it has passed to the back of the forearm, it anastomoses with the posterior interosseous artery. The **median artery** is a long slender branch which arises from the proximal part of the anterior interosseous and runs with the median nerve to the palm, where it anastomoses with recurrent branches of the superficial palmar arch.

The **posterior interosseous artery** is usually smaller than the anterior interosseous. It passes to the back of the forearm between the proximal border of the interosseous membrane and the oblique cord, and then between the supinator and the abductor pollicis longus, after which it descends, between the superficial and deep muscles on the back of the forearm, to the wrist. At the wrist it anastomoses with the anterior interosseous artery and with the posterior carpal arch. As it crosses the abductor pollicis longus it is accompanied by the posterior interosseous nerve, but in the remainder of its course it is separated from the nerve by the deep muscles.

Branches.—An **interosseous recurrent artery** is given off at the distal border of the supinator. It runs upwards, on the posterior surface of the supinator, under cover of the anconeus, to the back of the lateral epicondyle of the humerus, where it anastomoses with the posterior descending branch of the profunda brachii and with branches of the supratrochlear artery. **Muscular branches** supply the adjacent muscles, and the artery also supplies the skin on the back of the forearm and the wrist.

The **anterior carpal branch** of the ulnar artery is a small branch, given off above the flexor retinaculum; it passes towards the radial side, deep to the flexor tendons and their sheaths, on the anterior radio-carpal ligament, and anastomoses with the anterior carpal branch of the radial to form the anterior carpal arch.

The **posterior carpal branch** arises from the ulnar side of the ulnar artery, immediately proximal to the pisiform bone. It passes, deep to the tendons of the flexor and extensor carpi ulnaris, to the back of the carpus, where it unites with the posterior carpal branch of the radial to form the posterior carpal arch.

The **deep branch of the ulnar artery** [R. volaris profundus] descends between the abductor and flexor digiti minimi, and, turning towards the radial side, deep to the flexor, the opponens, and the long flexor tendons and their sheaths, it joins the radial artery to complete the *deep palmar arch.*

Variations.—The **ulnar artery** may be absent, being replaced by the median artery or the anterior interosseous artery, and it may end in the deep palmar arch instead of in the superficial. It rarely arises more distally than usual, and when it arises higher up it most commonly passes superficial to the muscles which spring from the medial epicondyle. Moreover, it then frequently has no interosseous branch, the latter vessel springing from the radial artery. In explanation it may be noted that the anterior interosseous artery is the original continuation of the brachial. Even when it begins at the usual level the ulnar artery may pass superficial to the muscles that arise from the medial epicondyle, and its interosseous and recurrent branches then spring from the radial artery.

The **interosseous arteries** may arise separately from the ulnar instead of by a common interosseous trunk. The recurrent branches of the ulnar may spring from the common interosseous, which itself may be a branch of the radial.

The small **median artery**—the companion artery of the median nerve—usually a branch of the anterior interosseous, may spring from the axillary, brachial, or ulnar arteries; it may be much larger than usual, and it may end either by breaking up into digital arteries, or by joining one or more digital branches of the superficial palmar arch or the arch itself.

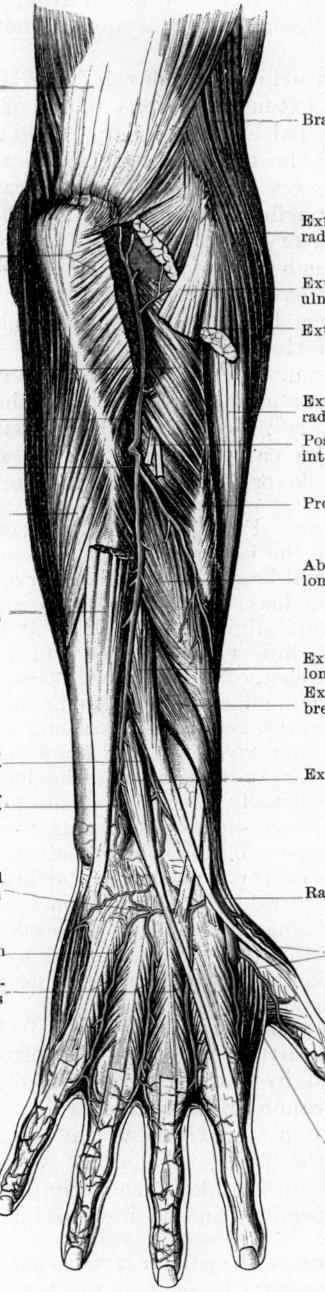

FIG. 1022.—POSTERIOR INTEROSSEOUS ARTERY AND SECOND PART OF THE RADIAL ARTERY, WITH THEIR BRANCHES.

ARTERIAL ARCHES OF WRIST AND HAND

The **anterior carpal arch** (Fig. 1021) lies on the radial attachment of the anterior radio-carpal ligament, deep to the long flexor tendons and their synovial sheaths.

It is formed by the union of the anterior carpal branches of the radial and ulnar arteries, and it receives a communicating branch from the anterior interosseous artery and recurrent branches from the deep palmar arch. Branches from it supply the ligaments and synovial membranes of the radio-carpal and intercarpal joints.

The **posterior carpal arch** (Fig. 1022) lies on the dorsal intercarpal ligaments deep to the extensor tendons and their sheaths. It is formed by the union of the posterior carpal branches of the radial and ulnar arteries, and receives the terminal branches of the anterior and posterior interosseous arteries. It supplies adjacent joints and gives off three **dorsal metacarpal arteries.**

The **superficial palmar arch** (Fig. 1020) includes the terminal portion of the ulnar artery, and is usually completed on the radial side by the superficial palmar branch of the radial, or by the radialis indicis or the princeps pollicis artery. It extends from the ball of the little finger to the ulnar border of the flexor pollicis brevis, and reaches distally to a line drawn across the palm at the level of the distal border of the fully abducted thumb. It is accompanied by venæ comitantes and it is covered by the skin and the central portion of the palmar aponeurosis, and, on the ulnar side of the palm, by the palmaris brevis. It is in contact dorsally with the flexor and opponens digiti minimi, and with the palmar digital branches of the ulnar and median nerves, as well as with the flexor tendons and the lumbrical muscles.

Branches.—Four **palmar digital arteries** arise from the convex side of the arch. The most ulnar of the four passes along the ulnar border of the little finger, accompanied by a palmar digital branch of the ulnar nerve ; the other three pass downwards each between two flexor tendons and superficial to a palmar digital nerve and a lumbrical muscle, towards the interdigital clefts, where, at the level of the base of the proximal phalanges, each divides into two branches which supply the contiguous sides of the fingers bounding the cleft. As the branches pass along the sides of the fingers they lie behind the corresponding digital nerves, and supply branches to the joints, to the flexor tendons and their sheaths, and to the skin and subcutaneous tissues on the palmar surfaces of the fingers ; they give off dorsal branches also which anastomose with the dorsal digital arteries and supply the tissues on the dorsal surfaces of the middle and distal phalanges. Some of the dorsally directed branches form a plexus in the matrix of the nail. In the pulp of the finger-tips anastomosing twigs join to form arches from which numerous branches are given off to the skin and subcutaneous fat.

Each of the three palmar digital arteries which pass to interdigital clefts is joined, just before it divides, by a palmar metacarpal artery from the deep palmar arch and a distal perforating branch from a dorsal metacarpal artery. The digital artery to the ulnar side of the little finger is joined by a branch which arises either from the medial palmar metacarpal artery or from the deep palmar arch.

The **deep palmar arch** (Fig. 1021) extends from the base of the metacarpal bone of the little finger to the proximal end of the first interosseous space. It is formed by the terminal part of the radial artery and its anastomosis with the deep branch of the ulnar. It is from half to three-quarters of an inch (12 to 18 mm.) proximal to the level of the superficial palmar arch. It lies deeply in the palm, in contact with the proximal ends of the shafts of the metacarpal bones and on the origin of the interossei muscles, and deep to the long flexor tendons and their synovial sheaths.

Branches.—The **palmar metacarpal arteries** are three vessels which pass downwards, on the interosseous muscles of the three ulnar interosseous spaces, deep to the flexor tendons. They end by joining the palmar digital arteries immediately before these vessels divide.

Three small **perforating branches** pass backwards, through the interosseous spaces, between the heads of the second, third, and fourth dorsal interosseous muscles, and join the dorsal metacarpal arteries.

Small *recurrent branches* pass upwards to join the anterior carpal arch, and other small branches are distributed to the adjacent joints.

Variations.—The **superficial palmar arch** is sometimes absent ; its branches are then given off from the deep arch. Or it may be larger than usual, and it may be completed on the radial side by the radialis indicis, the princeps pollicis, or the median artery.

The **deep palmar arch** is much more rarely absent than the superficial arch. When absent its branches are supplied by the superficial arch, the proximal perforating arteries, or the anterior carpal arch.

BRANCHES OF DESCENDING THORACIC AORTA

The branches given off from the descending thoracic aorta are distributed chiefly to the walls of the thorax and to the thoracic viscera. They contribute also to the supply of the spinal cord and its membranes, of the vertebral column, and of the upper part of the abdominal wall. The branches, which are numerous and for the most part arranged in pairs, are as follows :—

Visceral { Bronchial / Œsophageal / Pericardial / Mediastinal

Parietal { Posterior intercostal / Subcostal / Phrenic / The vas aberrans

VISCERAL BRANCHES OF DESCENDING THORACIC AORTA

The **bronchial arteries** are usually two in number—an upper and a lower— and both pass to the left lung. The *upper left bronchial artery* arises from the front of the aorta opposite the fifth thoracic vertebra ; the *lower left bronchial artery* usually takes origin at a slightly lower level. Both vessels are directed downwards and laterally to the back of the bronchus which they accompany, and, dividing similarly, they follow its ramifications in the lung. They not only supply the walls of the bronchial tubes and the substance of the lungs, but also give branches to the broncho-pulmonary lymph glands, the pulmonary vessels, the pericardium, and the œsophagus.

As a rule there is only one *right bronchial artery*. It arises either from the third right posterior intercostal artery (*i.e.* the first right intercostal branch of the aorta) or from the upper left bronchial artery. More rarely it springs directly from the aorta. In its course and distribution it corresponds to the bronchial arteries of the left side.

Variations.—The **bronchial arteries** obviously correspond to splanchnic arteries and their continuations to diverticula from the walls of the gut ; therefore the usual origin of the right bronchial artery must result from the persistence of an anastomosis between a splanchnic artery and the first part of a somatic intersegmental artery ; the origin of the right from the upper left bronchial artery, which sometimes occurs, is due to the fusion of the roots of two splanchnic arteries. The occasional origin of a bronchial vessel from an internal mammary artery can result only from the persistence and enlargement of an anastomosis between a splanchnic artery and the ventral branch of a somatic segmental artery. The origin of a bronchial branch from a subclavian artery may have the same or a different significance on opposite sides of the body. A bronchial artery which arises from the left subclavian artery corresponds with the origin of the right bronchial artery from the third right posterior intercostal artery ; it is due to the persistence of an anastomosis between a splanchnic artery and the root of a somatic intersegmental artery. The origin of a bronchial artery from a right subclavian artery may be due to a similar cause ; it may, on the other hand, be due to the enlargement of an anastomosis between a splanchnic branch of the descending aorta and a splanchnic branch of the fourth right aortic arch. A bronchial artery occasionally arises from the inferior thyroid ; that is due to the persistence and enlargement of an anastomosis between splanchnic arteries.

The **œsophageal branches** are variable ; usually four or five small branches spring from the front of the aorta and pass forwards to the œsophagus, in the walls of which they ramify, anastomosing above with branches of the left bronchial and inferior thyroid arteries, and below with œsophageal branches of the left gastric and the phrenic arteries.

The **pericardial branches** are three or four small irregular vessels which are distributed on the surface of the pericardium.

Small **mediastinal branches** pass to the areolar tissue and glands in the posterior mediastinum.

PARIETAL BRANCHES OF DESCENDING THORACIC AORTA

Posterior Intercostal Arteries.—Nine pairs of posterior intercostal arteries (III-XI) arise from the back of the aorta—usually separately but, not uncommonly, a pair may take origin by a common trunk. They are distributed to the lower nine intercostal spaces, to the vertebral column, to the contents of the vertebral canal, and to the muscles and skin of the back. The first three on each side give branches to the mammary gland also. The arteries of opposite sides closely correspond, but, since the upper part of the descending thoracic aorta lies on the left of the vertebral column, most of the right posterior intercostal arteries cross the front of the column, behind the œsophagus, the thoracic duct, and the vena azygos, and are longer than the left arteries. In other respects the course of each artery is almost identical. As each artery runs backwards and laterally, across the side of the vertebral column, to an intercostal space, it passes behind the pleura, and is crossed by the sympathetic trunk. The lower arteries are crossed by the splanchnic nerves also, and those on the left side are crossed by the superior or inferior hemiazygos vein.

As each artery passes laterally, between the necks of two adjacent ribs, it gives off a posterior branch. Then it ascends to the upper border of the space to which it belongs, and, passing either behind or in front of the corresponding intercostal nerve, is continued along the space, in the costal groove. In the space, as far as the angle of the rib, it lies between the pleura and the posterior intercostal membrane. Then it is continued forwards between the intercostalis intimus and the internal intercostal muscle (see p. 442). In the costal groove the artery lies between the corresponding vein above and the intercostal nerve below, and it ends by anastomosing with an anterior intercostal branch of the internal mammary or of the musculo-phrenic artery. The lower two posterior intercostal arteries, on each side, extend beyond their spaces into the abdominal wall, and anastomose with branches of the superior epigastric, subcostal, and lumbar arteries. The first right intercostal branch of the aorta (posterior intercostal artery III) frequently gives off the right bronchial artery.

Branches.—The **posterior branch** passes backwards, between the necks of the ribs which bound the space, medial to the superior costo-transverse ligament, and then, accompanied by the posterior primary ramus of a spinal nerve, between the adjacent transverse processes, to the vertebral groove, where it divides into medial and lateral terminal branches. The medial branch passes backwards and medially, either over or through the multifidus, giving branches to the muscles between which it passes and to the vertebral column. The lateral branch runs laterally under cover of the longissimus thoracis to the interval between it and the costalis. *Muscular branches* supply the muscles and *cutaneous branches* pass to the skin of the back. A *spinal branch* passes through the corresponding intervertebral foramen, and enters the vertebral canal, to the contents and walls of which it is distributed. Twigs from the spinal branches run medially, on the roots of the spinal nerve, to supply the membranes of the spinal cord and reinforce the anterior and posterior spinal arteries. Others anastomose with twigs from adjacent arteries on the backs of the bodies of the vertebræ to form a series of vertical arches connected by short transverse anastomoses. Similar though less regular anastomoses are formed on the posterior wall of the vertebral canal.

A **collateral branch** arises near the angle of the rib. It descends and runs forward along the lower border of the intercostal space, to anastomose in front with an anterior intercostal branch of the internal mammary or musculo-phrenic artery. The collateral branches of the lower two intercostal arteries, on each side, are inconstant; when present they are small, and end in the abdominal wall.

Muscular branches to the adjacent muscles are given off both by the main trunk and its collateral branch.

A **lateral cutaneous** branch accompanies the lateral cutaneous branch of the intercostal nerve. Those of the third, fourth, and fifth spaces give a *mammary branch* to the mammary gland; these branches anastomose with branches of the lateral thoracic and internal mammary arteries.

In addition to the secondary branches above named, the trunk of the third posterior intercostal artery anastomoses with the superior intercostal, and may supply the whole or the greater part of the second intercostal space. Longitudinal anastomoses between adjacent trunks and also between adjacent posterior branches of posterior intercostal arteries sometimes exist near the necks of the ribs, or near the transverse processes.

The **subcostal arteries** are in series with the posterior intercostal arteries, and are distributed in the same manner. The trunk runs along the lower border of the twelfth rib in company with the subcostal nerve. It passes below the lateral arcuate ligament [arcus lumbo-costalis lateralis] to the abdomen, and there crosses in front of the quadratus lumborum, and behind the kidney and the adjacent part of the colon. It next pierces the aponeurosis of origin of the transversus abdominis, and runs between the transversus and the internal oblique muscles, anastomosing with the lower intercostal arteries, with the lumbar arteries, and with branches of the superior epigastric artery.

Variations.—Variations of the **posterior intercostal arteries** are not very common, but they are significant and interesting. Corresponding vessels of opposite sides may arise from a common stem which has been formed by the fusion of the roots of two somatic intersegmental arteries after or simultaneously with the fusion of the primitive dorsal aortæ. The number of intercostal arteries may be reduced, one artery supplying two or more intercostal spaces; in such cases the roots of origin of some of the somatic intersegmental arteries in the thoracic region have disappeared, and the precostal anastomoses between their ventral branches have persisted.

Occasionally the number of the intercostal arteries is increased, an additional artery being given to the second intercostal space, which is usually supplied by the superior intercostal artery; that is brought about by the persistence of the root of the tenth somatic intersegmental artery and the disappearance of the precostal anastomosis between the ventral branches of the ninth and tenth somatic intersegmental arteries. Very rarely the third posterior intercostal artery sends a branch upwards between the necks of the ribs and the transverse processes of the upper thoracic region; that branch supplies the upper intercostal spaces, the superior intercostal artery being small or absent, and it ends by becoming the deep cervical artery. It is due to the persistence of the postcostal anastomoses in the upper thoracic region, and is a repetition of a condition regularly present in some carnivores.

Phrenic branches [Aa. phrenicæ superiores] are given off from the lower part of the thoracic aorta. They are small vessels which ramify on the upper and posterior surfaces of the diaphragm, and anastomose with the pericardiaco-phrenic and musculo-phrenic branches of the internal mammary arteries.

The **vas aberrans** is a variable and inconstant branch of the thoracic aorta; it represents the dorsal roots of the fourth and sixth right aortic arches of the embryo. When present it arises from the front and right side of the upper part of the descending aorta near the upper left bronchial artery, and passes upwards and to the right behind the œsophagus; it frequently anastomoses with the right superior intercostal artery, and it may be enlarged and form the first part of the right subclavian artery.

BRANCHES OF ABDOMINAL AORTA

The branches of the abdominal portion of the aorta are distributed almost entirely to the walls and contents of the abdominal cavity, but some supply small branches to the vertebral column, and to the contents of the vertebral canal, and others are prolonged into the true pelvis. They are divisible into visceral and parietal groups, both of which include paired and single (unpaired) vessels.

Visceral
- Paired
  - Suprarenal
  - Renal
  - Testicular or Ovarian
- Single
  - Cœliac
  - Superior mesenteric
  - Inferior mesenteric

Parietal
- Paired
  - Phrenic
  - Lumbar
  - Common iliac
- Single
  - Median sacral

PAIRED VISCERAL BRANCHES OF ABDOMINAL AORTA

There are three pairs of **suprarenal arteries**—the superior, middle, and inferior. Of these only the middle arise directly from the aorta; the superior spring from the phrenic arteries, and the inferior from the renal arteries.

The **middle suprarenal arteries** are a pair of small branches which arise, behind the pancreas, from the sides of the aorta, close to the origin of the superior mesenteric artery. They run, one on each side, laterally and upwards, upon the crura of the diaphragm just above the renal arteries, to the suprarenal glands, to which they are distributed. They anastomose with the superior and inferior suprarenal arteries.

The **renal arteries** (Fig. 1025) arise, one on each side, from the aorta, about half an inch below the origin of the superior mesenteric artery and opposite the second lumbar vertebra.

Both arteries are of large size, and the right is frequently slightly lower in position than the left. Each artery runs almost transversely to the hilum of the corresponding kidney. It passes anterior to the crus of the diaphragm and the upper part of the psoas muscle. The left artery lies posterior to the pancreas; the right vessel passes behind the inferior vena cava, the head of the pancreas, and the second part of the duodenum. The renal vein usually lies below and anterior to the artery, but near the kidney the vein not infrequently occupies a posterior position.

On reaching the hilum of the kidney each artery divides into three branches, two of which pass in front of the pelvis of the ureter, and between it and the renal vein, and the third behind the pelvis. In the renal sinus these primary branches break up into numerous secondary branches which enter the kidney substance between the pyramids (see p. 697).

Branches.—Each renal artery gives off small **ureteric branches** to the upper part of the ureter, which anastomose with branches of the testicular or ovarian arteries, and an **inferior suprarenal artery**, which passes upwards to the lower part of the suprarenal gland.

Small branches, which anastomose with the lumbar arteries, are also given to the aortic lymph glands and to the renal fat.

Variations.—The **renal arteries** frequently deviate from the normal arrangement. They may spring from a common stem, or there may be two or more renal arteries on one or both sides. The *accessory arteries* are more common on the left than on the right side, and an accessory artery arising below the ordinary vessel is more common than one arising above it.

Accessory renal arteries may be derived not only from the aorta, but also from the common iliac or internal iliac arteries; they have been described as arising also from the phrenic, testicular, lumbar, and median sacral arteries, and even from the external iliac artery. As the kidney is developed in the region of the first sacral vertebra, and afterwards ascends to its permanent position, it is not surprising that it occasionally receives arteries from the main stem of more than one of the segments of the body through which it has passed, and it is usually found that the lower the position of the kidney in the abdomen the more likely it is to receive its arteries from the lower part of the aorta or from the common iliac arteries. The accessory renal arteries which spring from the phrenic, the testicular, and lumbar arteries can only be the result of the persistence and enlargement of anastomosing channels between the renal and either another intermediate visceral artery, or a somatic artery.

The **testicular** or **ovarian arteries** are long slender vessels which spring from the front of the aorta a short distance below the origins of the renal arteries.

Each **testicular artery** runs downwards, on the anterior surface of the psoas major, to the deep inguinal ring, where it comes into relation with the vas deferens. It accompanies the vas deferens through the inguinal canal to the testis, to which it is distributed.

Relations.—*Posterior.*—The right artery passes in front of the inferior vena cava, and as each artery descends, on the anterior surface of the psoas major, it passes in front of the corresponding genito-femoral nerve and the ureter.

Anterior.—Each artery is in relation anteriorly with the peritoneum to which it is attached; but crossing in front of the right artery and intervening between it and the peritoneum are the third part of the duodenum, the right colic and the ileo-colic arteries, and the terminal part of the superior mesenteric artery; and the cæcum may overlap it. Crossing anterior to the left artery are the superior and inferior left colic branches of the inferior mesenteric artery and the terminal part of the descending colon.

In the lower part of the abdominal portion of its course each testicular artery is accompanied by two veins, which issue from the pampiniform plexus in the inguinal canal and enter the abdomen through the deep inguinal ring, but at a higher level the two veins usually fuse into a single stem which is usually lateral to the artery.

As it approaches the inguinal canal each testicular artery passes in front of the lower end of the external iliac artery and the inferior epigastric artery; and as it runs downwards and medially, in the canal, it is accompanied by the vas deferens, and is more or less enclosed in the meshes of the pampiniform venous plexus. At the lower end of the canal it passes through the superficial inguinal ring and descends in the scrotum, lying antero-lateral to the vas deferens and in close association with the anterior group of testicular veins. At the upper end of the testis it breaks up into branches, some of which are distributed to the testis and others to the epididymis.

Branches.—In the abdominal part of its course each testicular artery gives off **ureteric branches** to the abdominal part of the ureter, and twigs to the peri-nephric fat, the peritoneum, and the aortic lymph glands.

The course and the relations of each **ovarian artery**, as far as the level of the brim of the true pelvis, are the same as the relations of the corresponding testicular artery; but at the level of the upper end of the external iliac artery each ovarian artery turns medially, crosses anterior to the upper part of the corresponding external iliac artery and vein, and enters the upper part of the broad ligament of the uterus. In the broad ligament it runs medially, below the uterine tube, to the level of the ovary. There it turns backwards and passes between the layers of the mesovarium, where it breaks up into terminal branches which enter the ovary through the hilum in its anterior border. As it lies in the broad ligament each ovarian artery is accompanied by the pampiniform plexus of ovarian veins. In the lower portion of the abdominal part of its course it is accompanied by two veins which issue from the pampiniform plexus at the brim of the true pelvis and unite at a higher level into a single trunk.

Branches.—In the abdominal part of its course the branches of the ovarian artery are the same as those of the testicular artery.

In the pelvic part of its course it gives branches to the walls of the uterine tube, to the round ligament of the uterus, and it ends by anastomosing with the uterine artery.

Variations.—The **testicular or ovarian arteries** may be double on one or both sides; the arteries of the two sides may spring from a common trunk, or each may arise from the renal, accessory renal, or suprarenal arteries. The right artery may pass behind the inferior vena cava instead of in front of it. The testicular and ovarian arteries arise from the upper lumbar portion of the aorta, because the testes and ovaries are developed in and obtain their arterial supply in that region, and the vessels are elongated as the testes and ovaries descend to their permanent positions.

Single Visceral Branches of Abdominal Aorta

The **cœliac artery** (Figs. 1023 and 1025) arises from the front of the abdominal aorta, immediately below the aortic orifice of the diaphragm and between its crura. It is a short but wide vessel which runs almost horizontally forwards, below the caudate lobe of the liver, for a distance of about half an inch (12 mm.). It ends by dividing into three branches—the left gastric, the hepatic, and the splenic.

Relations.—As the short trunk lies behind the lesser sac of the peritoneum it runs forwards, below the caudate lobe of the liver and above the upper border of the pancreas and the splenic vein. It is surrounded by the cœliac plexus of the sympathetic.

Branches.—The **left gastric** is the smallest branch of the cœliac artery. It runs obliquely upwards and to the left, and reaches the lesser curvature of the stomach close to the œsophagus. It then turns sharply forwards, downwards, and to the right, and runs towards the pyloric end of the stomach to anastomose with the right gastric branch of the hepatic artery. In the first part of its course the artery lies on the left crus behind the lesser sac; it then passes into the left gastro-pancreatic fold, and is continued between the layers of the lesser omentum.

When the left gastric artery reaches the stomach it gives off **œsophageal branches** which pass upwards on the œsophagus to anastomose with œsophageal branches of the thoracic aorta and with the phrenic artery. Branches are distributed to both surfaces of the stomach. They anastomose with the short gastric branches of the splenic, and with branches of the gastro-epiploic arterial arch on the greater curvature of the stomach.

The **splenic artery** (Fig. 1023) is the largest branch of the cœliac artery. It runs a tortuous course behind the stomach and the lesser sac of peritoneum along the upper border of the pancreas. It lies in front of the left suprarenal gland and the upper part of the left kidney, and passes forwards between the two layers of the lieno-renal ligament, in which it divides into five to eight terminal **splenic branches** which enter the hilum of the spleen and supply the splenic substance. It is accompanied by the splenic vein, which lies below it.

Branches.—Numerous small **pancreatic** branches are given off to the pancreas. A larger branch (*pancreatica magna*), occasionally present, enters the upper border of the pancreas, about the junction of its middle and left thirds, and runs from left to right in the substance of the pancreas, a little above and posterior to the pancreatic duct. The pancreatic branches anastomose with one another and with branches of the pancreatico-duodenal arteries.

The **short gastric arteries**, four or five in number, are given off either from the end of the splenic artery or, more commonly, from some of its terminal branches. They

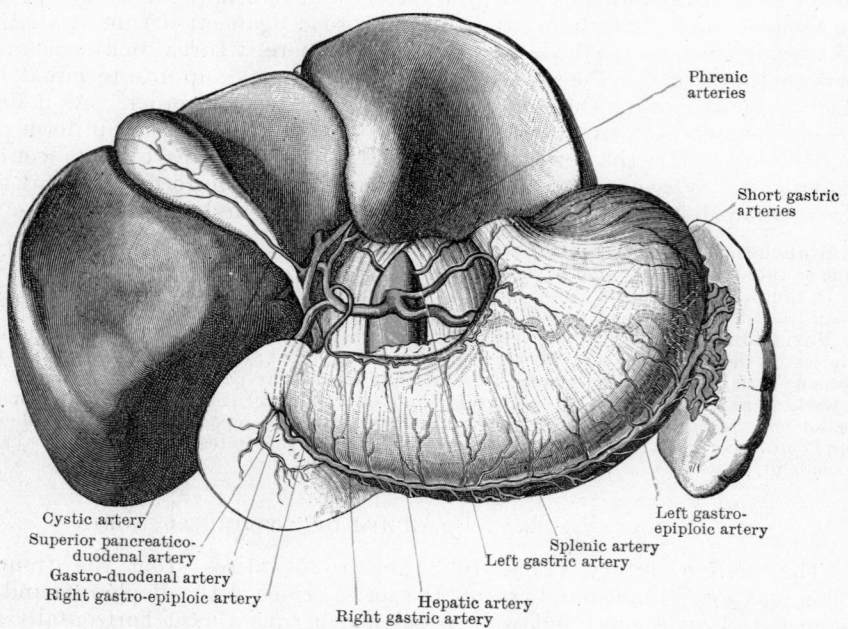

FIG. 1023.—THE CŒLIAC ARTERY AND ITS BRANCHES.

pass between the layers of the gastro-splenic ligament to the left part of the greater curvature of the stomach, and anastomose with the œsophageal, the left gastric, and the left gastro-epiploic arteries.

The **left gastro-epiploic artery** arises from the front of the splenic, close to its termination, and passes forwards, between the layers of the gastro-splenic ligament, to the left end of the lower part of the greater curvature of the stomach, along which it is continued, from left to right, between the anterior two layers of the greater omentum. It ends by anastomosing with the right gastro-epiploic artery. It gives off numerous branches to both surfaces of the stomach; they anastomose with the short gastric and with branches of the left and right gastric arteries. Long slender *omental branches* pass to the omentum.

The **hepatic artery** (Fig. 1023) runs along the upper border of the head of the pancreas to the right gastro-pancreatic fold of peritoneum, in which it turns forwards to the upper border of the first part of the duodenum. It then passes upwards, between the layers of the lesser omentum, anterior to the portal vein and to the left of the bile duct, and reaches the porta hepatis, where it divides into right and left terminal branches.

Branches.—The **right gastric artery** is a small branch which arises opposite the upper border of the first part of the duodenum. It runs between the layers of the lesser omentum to the pylorus, and then along the lesser curvature of the stomach. It gives branches to both surfaces of the stomach, and ends by anastomosing with the left gastric artery. It also gives a branch to the first part of the duodenum.

The **gastro-duodenal artery** arises just above the upper border of the first part of the duodenum, descends behind it and ends opposite its lower border. In its course it lies between the neck of the pancreas and the first part of the duodenum, and anterior to the portal vein. The bile duct is on its right side. The vessel ends by dividing into the right gastro-epiploic and superior pancreatico-duodenal arteries. The **right gastro-epiploic artery** is the larger ; it passes from right to left, along the greater curvature of the stomach, between the layers of the greater omentum, and unites with the left gastro-epiploic branch of the splenic artery. From the arterial arch so formed branches pass upwards on both surfaces of the stomach, to anastomose with branches of the right and left gastric arteries. *Omental branches* pass downwards in the greater omentum. The **superior pancreatico-duodenal artery** runs a short course to the right, between the duodenum and the head of the pancreas, and divides into anterior and posterior terminal branches, which descend, the former in front of and the latter behind the head of the pancreas, to anastomose with similar branches of the inferior pancreatico-duodenal artery. They supply the head of the pancreas, anastomosing in it with the pancreatic branches of the splenic artery ; branches are given also to the second part of the duodenum and to the bile duct.

Terminal Branches. — The **right branch** passes, either in front of or behind the common hepatic duct and behind the cystic duct, to the right end of the porta hepatis ; there it divides into two or more branches which enter the substance of the liver and accompany the branches of the portal vein and the hepatic duct. As it crosses the junction of the hepatic and cystic ducts, the right branch gives off the cystic artery. The **cystic artery** runs downwards and forwards, along the cystic duct, to the gall-bladder, where it divides into anterior and posterior branches ; the anterior passes downwards between the gall-bladder and the visceral surface of the liver, to both of which it gives offsets ; the posterior branch is distributed on the posterior surface of the gall-bladder, and lies between it and the peritoneum. The **left branch** is longer and narrower than the right. It runs to the left end of the porta hepatis, gives one or two branches to the caudate lobe, crosses the fissure for the ligamentum teres, and breaks up into branches which terminate in the substance of the left lobe of the liver.

Variations. — The **cœliac artery** may be absent, its branches arising separately from the aorta or from some other source. Sometimes it gives off only two branches, usually the left gastric and splenic, and occasionally it gives four branches, the additional branch being either a second left gastric artery or a separate gastro-duodenal artery. The **left gastric artery** is occasionally double ; it may spring directly from the aorta, and it may give off the left hepatic or an accessory hepatic artery. The **splenic artery** may arise from the middle colic, from the left hepatic, or from the superior or inferior mesenteric artery. The **hepatic artery** may spring directly from the aorta or from the superior mesenteric artery ; the left hepatic artery arises occasionally from the left gastric artery. Accessory hepatic arteries are not uncommon, and they originate either from the left gastric, superior mesenteric, renal, or inferior mesenteric artery.

The **superior mesenteric artery** (Figs. 1024 and 1025) springs from the front of the aorta, about half an inch (12 mm.) below the origin of the cœliac artery and opposite the first lumbar vertebra.

It passes obliquely downwards and forwards, crossing anterior to the left renal vein, the uncinate process of the head of the pancreas, and the third part of the duodenum ; on the duodenum it enters the root of the mesentery, in which it continues to descend, curving obliquely from above downwards and to the right, to the right iliac fossa, and crossing, in this part of its course, in front of the aorta, the inferior vena cava, the right ureter, and the right psoas major muscle. At its origin it lies behind the pancreas and the splenic vein ; where it passes in front of the duodenum it is crossed anteriorly by the transverse colon ; and in the lower part of its extent it is behind the coils of small intestine. It ends by anastomosing with the ileo-colic artery.

Branches. — The branches of the superior mesenteric artery supply the duodenum and the pancreas in part, the whole of the small intestine below the duodenum, and the large intestine nearly as far as the left colic flexure.

The **inferior pancreatico-duodenal artery** arises either from the trunk of the superior mesenteric, at the upper border of the third part of the duodenum, or from the first jejunal branch. It runs to the right, between the head of the pancreas and the third part of the duodenum, and ends by dividing into two branches, anterior and posterior, which ascend, the former in front, the latter behind the head of the pancreas; they supply the head of the pancreas and the duodenum, and they anastomose with the similar branches of the superior pancreatico-duodenal artery.

The branches to the small intestine, varying from ten to sixteen in number, are separable into two groups—**jejunal** and **ileal**. They spring from the convexity of the

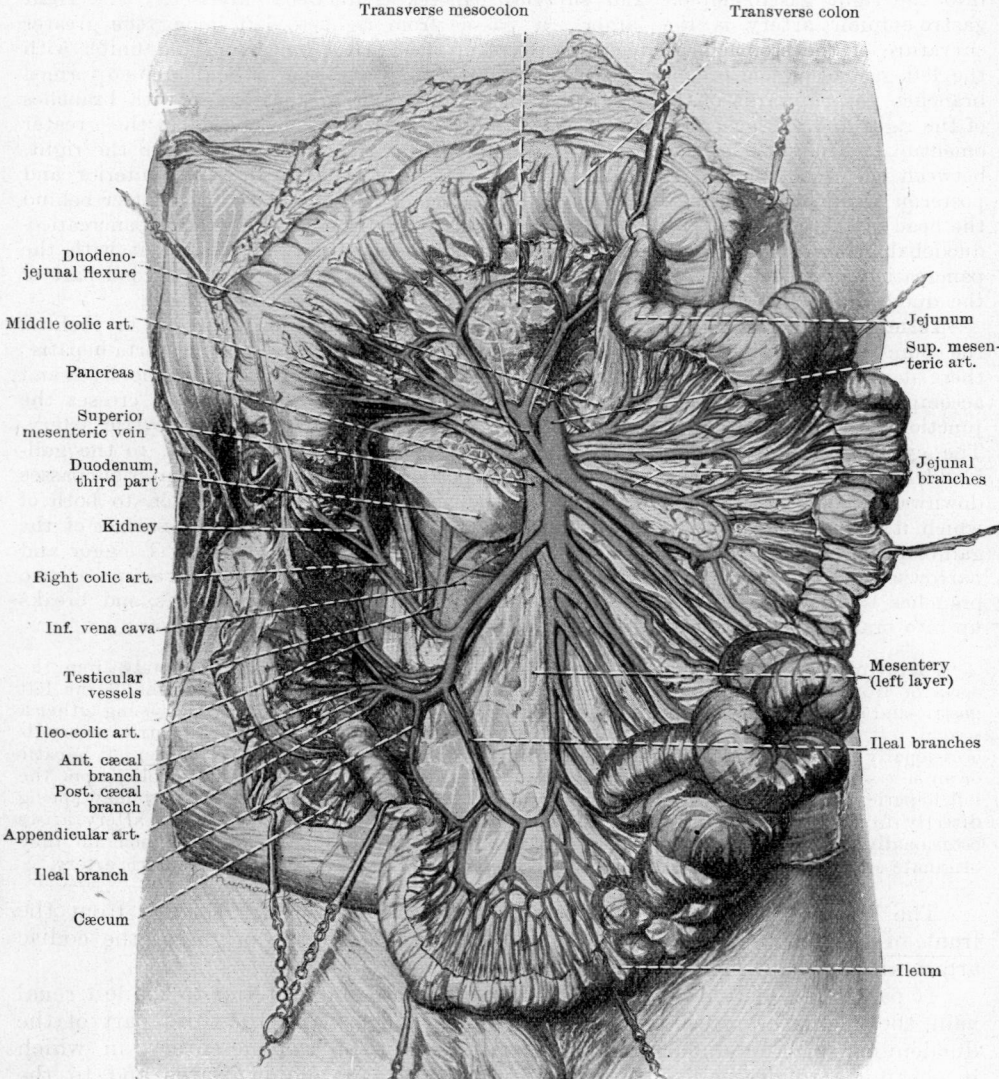

Transverse mesocolon — Transverse colon

Duodeno-jejunal flexure

Middle colic art.

Pancreas

Superior mesenteric vein

Duodenum, third part

Kidney

Right colic art.

Inf. vena cava

Testicular vessels

Ileo-colic art.

Ant. cæcal branch
Post. cæcal branch

Appendicular art.

Ileal branch

Cæcum

Jejunum

Sup. mesenteric art.

Jejunal branches

Mesentery (left layer)

Ileal branches

Ileum

FIG. 1024.—THE SUPERIOR MESENTERIC ARTERY AND ITS BRANCHES.
Note the difference in the number and arrangement of the loops formed by the jejunal as contrasted with the ileal branches.

superior mesenteric artery, and pass obliquely forwards and downwards, between the layers of the mesentery, each dividing into two branches which anastomose with adjacent arteries to form a series of arcades from which secondary branches are given off. The upper jejunal branches form only one or two arches, but the process of division and union is repeated three or four times in the case of the ileal branches; thus four or five tiers of arches are formed, in the longer, lower part of the mesentery. The branches from the terminal arcades pass to the wall of the gut, generally to one or other side, but occasionally a terminal branch divides and passes to both sides. The terminal branches from any one terminal arcade neither anastomose with one another nor with the branches of adjacent terminal arcades (A. J. Cokkinis, *Journ. Anat.* vol. xliv., 1930).   Branches from the successive arcades are given off also to the mesenteric lymph glands.

The **ileo-colic artery** arises by a common trunk with the right colic, or separately from the right side of the superior mesenteric, and passes downwards and to the right, behind the peritoneum, towards the lower part of the ascending colon.   It ends by dividing into an ascending branch which anastomoses with the lower branch of the right colic, and a descending branch which supplies the lower part of the ascending colon, sends branches to the front and back of the cæcum, gives off the appendicular artery, and ends in a branch to the lower part of the ileum which anastomoses with the superior mesenteric trunk.

The *anterior cœcal* branch passes across the front of the ileo-colic junction in the fold of peritoneum called the vascular fold of the cæcum; the *posterior cœcal* branch crosses the back of the ileo-colic junction.   The **appendicular artery** passes behind the terminal part of the ileum into the mesentery of the vermiform appendix; it runs near the free margin of the mesentery to the tip of the appendix and gives off a series of short branches which supply the apex of the cæcum and the appendix from its root to its tip.

The **right colic artery** springs from the right or concave side of the superior mesenteric, either alone or in the form of a common trunk which divides into right colic and ileo-colic branches.   It runs to the right, behind the peritoneum on the posterior wall of the abdomen, and in front of the right psoas major, the ureter, and the testicular or ovarian vessels, towards the ascending colon, near which it divides into an ascending and a descending branch.   The former passes upwards, and anastomoses, in the transverse mesocolon, with the middle colic artery; the latter descends to anastomose with the upper branch of the ileo-colic.   From the loops thus formed branches are distributed to the walls of the ascending colon and the beginning of the transverse colon.

The **middle colic artery** is a large branch which springs from the front of the superior mesenteric as it escapes from behind the pancreas.   It runs downwards and forwards, in the transverse mesocolon, and ends by dividing into two branches which anastomose with the right and left colic arteries, forming arcades.   Secondary and tertiary loops are sometimes formed and the terminal branches are distributed to the walls of the transverse colon.

Variations.—The superior mesenteric artery may be double, and it may supply the whole of the alimentary canal from the second part of the duodenum to the end of the rectum, the inferior mesenteric artery being absent.   In addition to its ordinary branches it may give off a hepatic, a splenic, a pancreatic, a gastric, a gastro-epiploic, or a gastro-duodenal branch.

The **inferior mesenteric artery** (Fig. 1025) arises from the front of the aorta towards the left side, about an inch and a half (3-4 cm.) above the bifurcation; it passes downwards and slightly to the left, lying behind the peritoneum and in front of the left psoas major muscle, to the upper and left border of the left common iliac artery, where it becomes the superior rectal artery.

Branches.—The **superior left colic artery** [A. colica sinistra] arises from the left side of the inferior mesenteric near its origin, and almost immediately divides into an upper and a lower branch.   The *upper branch* runs upwards and to the left towards the left colic flexure, and to the lower pole of the left kidney, where it divides into a branch which enters the transverse mesocolon to end by joining the left branch of the middle colic artery, and a descending branch to the upper part of the descending colon.   The *lower branch*, which may arise separately, passes to the left, behind the peritoneum, and divides into ascending and descending divisions; the ascending anastomoses with the descending division of the upper branch and supplies the descending colon above the iliac crest.   The descending division supplies the descending colon below the iliac crest, and anastomoses with branches of the inferior left colic arteries.   Both branches of the superior left colic artery lie immediately behind the peritoneum, and cross anterior to the ureter and the testicular or ovarian vessels.

The **inferior left colic arteries** [Aa. sigmoideæ], usually two in number, arise from the convexity of the inferior mesenteric, and pass downwards and to the left to the lower part of the descending colon and to the pelvic colon.   They lie behind the peritoneum, and in front of the psoas major, the ureter, and the upper part of the iliacus. They end by dividing into branches which anastomose with the terminal twigs of the lower branch of the superior left colic above and with branches of the superior rectal below, forming a series of arches from which branches are distributed to the colon.

The **superior rectal artery** [A. hæmorrhoidalis sup.] is the direct continuation of the inferior mesenteric. It enters the mesentery of the pelvic colon, crosses the front of the left common iliac artery, descends into the true pelvis as far as the third piece of the sacrum, or, in other words, to the junction between the pelvic colon and the rectum, and divides into two branches which pass downwards on the sides of the rectum. Half-way down the rectum each of the two terminal branches of the superior rectal artery divides into two or more branches which pass through the muscular coats into the sub-mucous tissue, where they divide into numerous small branches which pass vertically downwards, anastomosing with one another, with offsets from the middle rectal branches of the internal iliac arteries, the inferior rectal branches of the internal pudendal arteries, and with branches from the median sacral artery.

The superior rectal artery supplies the mucous and the muscular coats of the pelvic colon and the mucous coat of the rectum.

Variations.—The **inferior mesenteric artery** may give hepatic, renal, or middle colic branches; occasionally it is absent, being replaced by branches of the superior mesenteric, and sometimes, as in ruminants and some rodents, its left colic branch does not anastomose with the middle colic artery.

PARIETAL BRANCHES OF ABDOMINAL AORTA

The **phrenic arteries** [Aa. phrenicæ inferiores] (Fig. 1025), right and left, are of small size; they arise, either separately or by a common trunk, from the aorta immediately below the diaphragm, to which they are distributed. Diverging from its fellow, each artery runs upwards and laterally, on the corresponding crus of the diaphragm—that on the right side passing behind the inferior vena cava, that on the left side behind the œsophagus—and just before reaching the central tendon of the diaphragm each divides into medial and lateral terminal branches. The *medial branch* runs forwards, and anastomoses with its fellow of the opposite side, forming an arch, convex forwards, along the anterior border of the central tendon of the diaphragm. Offsets from this arch anastomose with the pericardiaco-phrenic and musculo-phrenic arteries. The *lateral branch* passes laterally towards the lower ribs, and anastomoses with the musculo-phrenic and lower intercostal arteries.

In addition to supplying the diaphragm, each phrenic artery gives off a **superior suprarenal artery** to the suprarenal gland of its own side. The right artery sends small hepatic branches into the liver through the bare area, and minute branches pass to the inferior vena cava. The left artery gives œsophageal branches which anastomose with œsophageal branches of the aorta and of the left gastric artery.

Variations.—The **phrenic arteries** are very variable; they may arise by a common trunk either from the cœliac artery or from the aorta; they may arise separately either from the aorta or from the cœliac artery and more commonly from the latter vessel; or again, one may spring from the aorta or cœliac artery, and the other from the left gastric, renal, or even from the superior mesenteric artery.

The **lumbar arteries** are in series with the posterior intercostal arteries; their distribution is very similar; and, like the intercostals, they arise, either separately or by common trunks, from the back of the aorta. There are usually four pairs of lumbar arteries, but occasionally a fifth pair arises from or in common with the median sacral artery. From their origins the lumbar arteries pass laterally and backwards, across the front and sides of the bodies of the upper four lumbar vertebræ, to the intervals between the adjacent transverse processes, beyond which they are continued into the lateral part of the abdominal wall.

Each artery in its backward course, and while still in relation with the vertebral body, is crossed by the sympathetic trunk, and then, after passing medial to and being protected by one of the fibrous arches from which the psoas major muscle arises, it runs behind the muscle and the lumbar plexus. The upper two arteries, on each side, pass behind the crus of the diaphragm also. Beyond the interval between the transverse processes of the vertebræ each artery turns laterally and crosses the quadratus lumborum—the last usually passing in front of the muscle and the others behind it; it then pierces the aponeurosis of origin of the transversus, and proceeds forwards in the lateral abdominal wall, in the interval between the transversus and internal oblique muscles. The lumbar arteries anastomose with one another, with the lower posterior intercostal and the subcostal arteries, and with branches of the superior and inferior epigastric and of the deep circumflex iliac and ilio-lumbar arteries. Fine twigs also pass from the lumbar arteries to the extra-peritoneal fat; those anastomose with corresponding branches

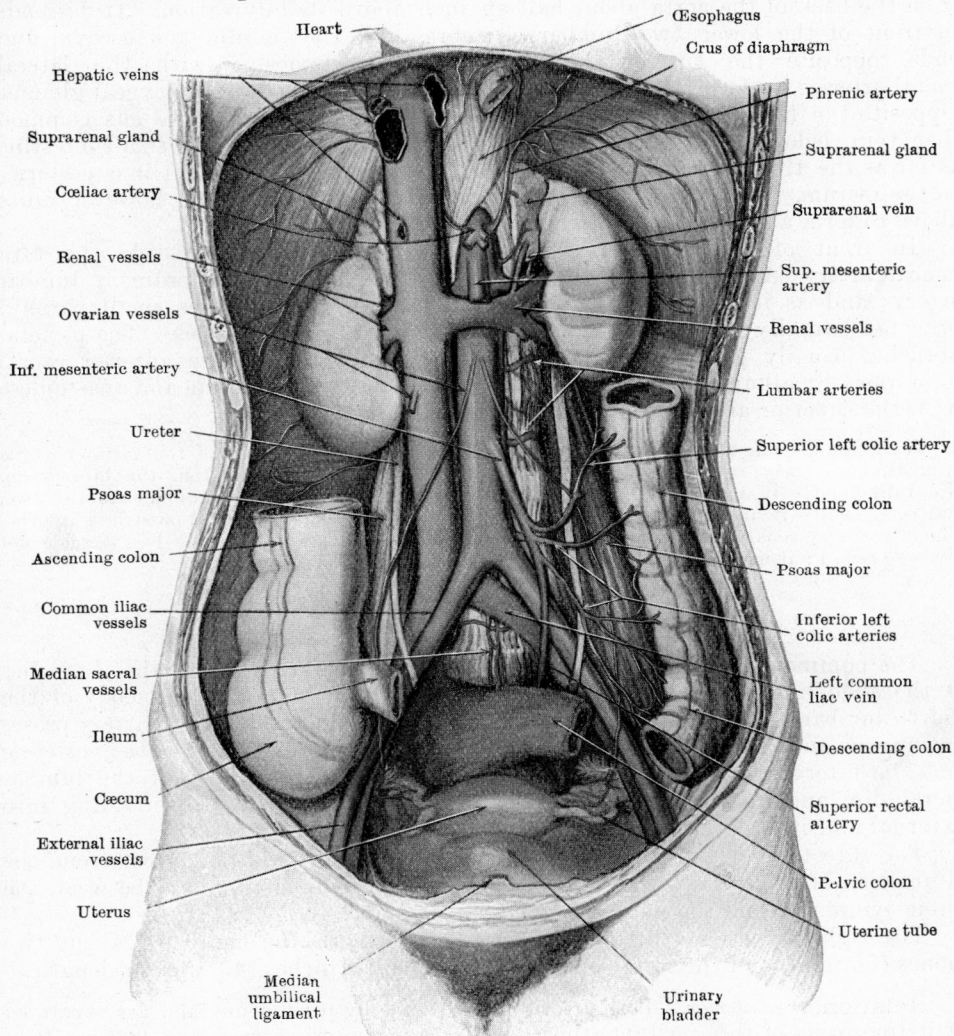

Heart — Œsophagus
Crus of diaphragm
Hepatic veins
Phrenic artery
Suprarenal gland
Suprarenal gland
Cœliac artery
Suprarenal vein
Renal vessels
Sup. mesenteric artery
Ovarian vessels
Renal vessels
Inf. mesenteric artery
Lumbar arteries
Ureter
Superior left colic artery
Psoas major
Descending colon
Ascending colon
Psoas major
Common iliac vessels
Inferior left colic arteries
Median sacral vessels
Left common liac vein
Ileum
Descending colon
Cæcum
Superior rectal artery
External iliac vessels
Uterus
Pelvic colon
Uterine tube
Median umbilical ligament
Urinary bladder

FIG. 1025.—THE ABDOMINAL AORTA AND ITS BRANCHES IN A FORMALIN-HARDENED PREPARATION.

from the phrenic and ilio-lumbar arteries, and with small branches from the hepatic, renal, and colic arteries, to form the *subperitoneal plexus* of Turner.

The abdominal aorta is almost median in position; consequently the right lumbar arteries are scarcely longer than the left. On the right side the arteries pass behind the inferior vena cava; but the upper two are separated from the vena cava by the cisterna chyli and the right crus of the diaphragm.

Branches.—Each lumbar artery gives off, opposite the interval between the vertebral transverse processes, a **posterior branch** of considerable size. It is homologous with and is distributed like the posterior branch of a posterior intercostal artery (p. 1204); a *spinal branch* enters the vertebral canal through the corresponding vertebral foramen. **Muscular branches** are given off both from the main trunk and its posterior branch.

Variations.— Variations of the **lumbar arteries** are very similar to those of the posterior intercostal arteries (p. 1205), and they are due to similar causes. Further, a lumbar artery may have its area of distribution extended into the adjacent segment.

The **median sacral artery** (Fig. 1025) is a single median vessel. It is commonly regarded as a caudal aorta and as the direct continuation of the abdominal aorta. It is, however, of small size, and almost invariably arises from the back of the aorta about half an inch above its bifurcation. It descends in front of the lower two lumbar vertebræ and the sacrum and coccyx, and ends, opposite the tip of the coccyx, by anastomosing with the lateral sacral arteries to form loops from which branches pass to the coccygeal glomus. Opposite the fifth lumbar vertebra it is crossed, anteriorly, by the left common iliac vein, below which it is covered by peritoneum and coils of small intestine as far as the third piece of the sacrum, and in the rest of its extent it is posterior to the rectum. It is accompanied below by venæ comitantes, which, however, unite above to form a single median sacral vein.

In front of the last lumbar vertebra it gives off on each side the **fifth lumbar artery** [A. lumbalis ima], which is distributed like an ordinary lumbar artery; and as it descends in front of the sacrum it distributes small parietal branches laterally which anastomose with the lateral sacral arteries. The parietal branches usually give off small *spinal* offsets which enter the anterior sacral foramina. Small and irregular visceral branches pass to the rectum and anastomose with the superior and middle rectal arteries.

Variations.—The **median sacral artery** usually springs from the back of the aorta above its bifurcation; it may arise considerably above, or more rarely directly from the bifurcation. Not infrequently it arises from a fourth lumbar artery or from a stem common to the two, and occasionally it arises from a common iliac or internal iliac artery. Sometimes it gives off an accessory renal artery, and occasionally a rectal branch arises from it. The vessel is not always present; it may be double, entirely or in part.

COMMON ILIAC ARTERIES

The **common iliac arteries** (Figs. 1025 and 1029) are the terminal branches of the abdominal aorta. They commence opposite the middle of the body of the fourth lumbar vertebra a little to the left of the median plane. Each artery passes downwards and laterally, across the bodies of the fourth and fifth lumbar vertebræ and the intervening intervertebral disc, and it ends, at the level of the lumbo-sacral disc and anterior to the corresponding sacro-iliac joint, by dividing into external and internal iliac branches.

The direction of each common iliac is indicated by a line drawn from the bifurcation of the aorta to a point on the inguinal ligament midway between the pubic symphysis and the anterior superior iliac spine.

The right artery is a little longer than the left, the former being about two inches (50 mm.) and the latter one and three-quarter inches (43 mm.) in length.

Relations.—*Anterior.*—Both arteries are covered by peritoneum, and are separated by it from coils of the small intestine. The intermesenteric nerves (Fig. 902, p. 1065) run downwards into the hypogastric plexus in front of the upper ends of the arteries, and each of them is often crossed, near its termination, by the corresponding ureter.

The left artery is crossed, in addition, by the superior rectal vessels.

Posterior.—Behind the artery, of each side, are the bodies of the fourth and fifth lumbar vertebræ and the intervening intervertebral disc, the sympathetic trunk, and the psoas major muscle. Those relationships, however, are much closer on the left side than on the right. The right common iliac, except at its lower end, where it is in contact with the psoas major, is separated from the structures named by the terminations of the right and left common iliac veins and the commencement of the inferior vena cava. More deeply placed, in the areolar tissue between the psoas major and the lumbar vertebræ, are the obturator nerve, the lumbo-sacral trunk, and the ilio-lumbar artery, which form distant posterior relations to the common iliac artery of the corresponding side.

Lateral.—The lateral relations of each artery are coils of small intestine, the ureter, testicular or ovarian vessels, and the genito-femoral nerve.

Medial.—The medial side of each artery is clothed with peritoneum. The left vein is medial to and below its artery, but on a posterior plane. The right vein is at first postero-medial to its artery, but at its upper part it is directly behind the artery and is joined there by the left vein.

Branches.—The external and internal iliac arteries are the only branches.

Variations.—The **common iliac artery** may be longer or shorter than usual, a modification which is determined largely, though not altogether, by the point at which the bifurcation of the aorta takes place. If exceptionally long, it is usually tortuous. In Man the artery is very rarely absent. It occasionally gives off the median or a lateral sacral artery, and ilio-lumbar, testicular, or accessory renal branches may arise from it.

INTERNAL ILIAC ARTERY

The **internal iliac artery** [A. hypogastrica] (Figs. 1026 and 1029) in the fœtus is the direct continuation of the common iliac trunk. It supplies numerous branches to the pelvis, runs upwards on the anterior abdominal wall to the umbilicus as the umbilical artery, and is prolonged through the umbilical cord to the placenta. One of its pelvic branches—the inferior gluteal—is at first the main artery of the lower limb, but subsequently another branch is given off which becomes the chief arterial trunk. That branch is the external iliac artery; it soon equals and ultimately exceeds the internal iliac in size, and it is into those two vessels that the common iliac appears to bifurcate.

When the placental circulation ceases after the umbilical cord is severed at birth, the umbilical part of the internal iliac trunk, which extends from the pelvis to the umbilicus, atrophies, and is afterwards represented almost entirely by a fibrous cord, known as the *lateral umbilical ligament*. The proximal part of the obliterated artery remains pervious to convey blood to its superior vesical branch. The permanent internal iliac artery is a comparatively short vessel. Owing to the arrangement of some of its branches it appears to end in an anterior and a posterior division, the former of which is to be regarded as the continuation of the vessel, whilst the latter is simply a common stem of origin for some of the branches.

With this explanation the artery may be described in the usual manner.

It arises from the common iliac opposite the sacro-iliac joint and at the level of the lumbo-sacral disc, and descends into the true pelvis, to end, as a rule, opposite the upper border of the greater sciatic notch, in two divisions—anterior and posterior—from each of which branches of distribution are given off. The artery measures about one and a half inches (35 mm). in length.

Relations.—*Antero-medial.*—Each internal iliac artery is covered antero-medially by peritoneum, under cover of which the corresponding ureter descends along the anterior border of the artery. The pelvic colon crosses from the front to the medial side of the left artery, and the terminal part of the ileum bears the same relation to the right artery.

Posterior to it are the internal iliac vein and the commencement of the common iliac vein ; behind these are the lumbo-sacral trunk and the sacro-iliac joint.

Lateral.—On its lateral side the external iliac vein separates it from the psoas major muscle, above. At a lower level the obturator nerve, embedded in a mass of fat, and, lower still, the obturator vein intervene between the artery and the side wall of the pelvis.

Branches.—The internal iliac artery supplies the greater part of the pelvic wall and contents, and branches are distributed also to the gluteal region and thigh and to the external genital organs.

All the branches may be given off separately from a single undivided parent trunk, but as a rule they arise in two groups corresponding to the two divisions in which the artery, under these circumstances, appears to end. The branches are usually classified as parietal and visceral.

Posterior Division	Anterior Division		
Parietal	Parietal	Visceral	
Ilio-lumbar	Obturator	Umbilical	Inferior vesical (male)
Lateral sacral	Internal pudendal	Superior vesical	Uterine ⎫ (female)
Superior gluteal	Inferior gluteal	Middle rectal	Vaginal ⎭

Branches of Posterior Division of Internal Iliac Artery

The **ilio-lumbar artery** runs upwards and laterally, out of the true pelvis, to the iliac fossa. It passes anterior to the sacro-iliac joint, between the lumbo-sacral trunk and the obturator nerve, and posterior to the lower part of the common iliac vessels and the psoas major muscle.

In the iliac fossa it divides into an iliac and a lumbar branch. The **iliac branch** ramifies in the iliac fossa and anastomoses with branches of the deep circumflex iliac and obturator arteries; it gives offsets to the iliacus, and supplies a large

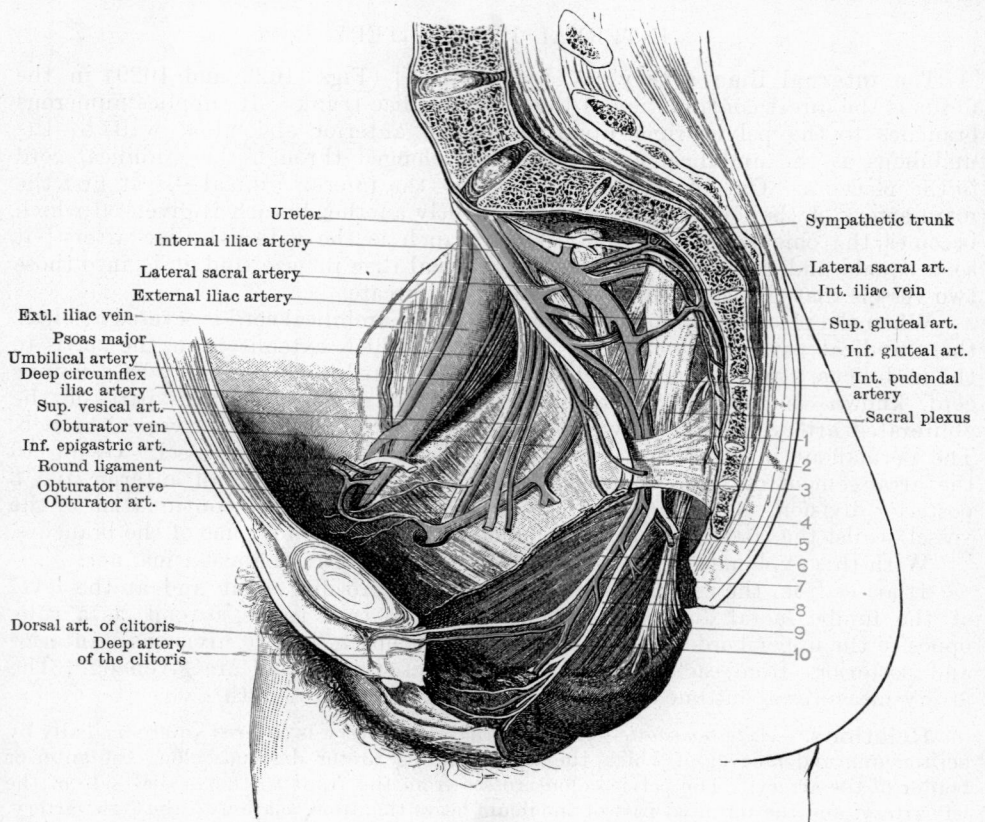

FIG. 1026.—INTERNAL ILIAC ARTERY AND ITS BRANCHES IN THE FEMALE.

1. Sacro-spinous ligament.
2. Uterine artery.
3. Vaginal artery.
4. Inferior hæmorrhoidal nerve.
5. Inferior rectal [hæmorrhoidal] artery.

6. Dorsal nerve of clitoris.
7. Internal pudendal artery.
8. Perineal nerve.
9. Labial artery.
10. Artery of bulb of the vestibule.

nutrient branch to the ilium. The **lumbar branch** ascends, behind the psoas major, to the iliac crest. It supplies the psoas and quadratus lumborum, and anastomoses with the lumbar and deep circumflex iliac arteries; it also gives off a *spinal branch*, which enters the intervertebral foramen between the fifth lumbar vertebra and the sacrum, and is distributed like the spinal branches of the lumbar and posterior intercostal arteries.

There are usually two **lateral sacral arteries**—superior and inferior—but they may arise by a common stem.

Both run downwards and medially, on the front of the sacrum. The *inferior* passes anterior to the piriformis and the sacral nerves, and descends, on the lateral side of the sympathetic trunk, to the coccyx, where it ends by anastomosing with the median sacral. The *superior* reaches only as far as the first or the second anterior sacral foramen; then it enters the sacral canal. It anastomoses with the lower lateral sacral and with the median sacral artery. Branches are given off by the lateral sacral arteries to the piriformis and to the sacral nerves. Spinal offsets are also given off, which pass through the anterior sacral foramina into the sacral canal; they supply the sacral dura mater and the arachnoid, the roots of the sacral nerves, and the filum terminale, and anastomose with other spinal arteries. They then pass through the posterior sacral foramina, to supply muscles on the back of the sacrum and anastomose with branches of the superior and inferior gluteal arteries.

The **superior gluteal artery** (Figs. 1026 and 1028) is the continuation of the posterior division of the internal iliac artery after it has given off its ilio-lumbar and lateral sacral branches. It is a large vessel which pierces the pelvic fascia, and passes backwards, between the lumbo-sacral trunk and the first sacral nerve. It leaves the pelvis through the upper part of the greater sciatic foramen, above the piriformis muscle, and enters the gluteal region, where it divides, under cover of the gluteus maximus and between the adjacent borders of the piriformis and gluteus medius muscles, into superficial and deep branches.

The **superficial branch** divides at once into numerous secondary branches, some of which supply the gluteus maximus, whilst others pass through it, near its origin, to the overlying skin. The branches freely anastomose with branches of the inferior gluteal, internal pudendal, medial circumflex, deep circumflex iliac, and lateral sacral arteries.

The **deep branch** runs forwards between the gluteus medius and minimus, and, after giving a nutrient branch to the ilium, subdivides into upper and lower branches. The *upper branch* runs forwards along the upper border of the gluteus minimus and passes beyond the anterior margins of the gluteus medius and minimus to anastomose, under cover of the tensor fasciæ latæ, with the ascending branch of the lateral circumflex artery. It anastomoses with the deep circumflex iliac artery also, and it supplies muscular branches to the adjacent muscles. The *lower branch*, accompanied by the superior gluteal nerve and its branch to the tensor fasciæ latæ, passes more directly forwards, across the gluteus minimus, towards the greater trochanter. It supplies the gluteal muscles, and anastomoses with the ascending branch of the lateral circumflex artery.

Before leaving the pelvis the gluteal artery gives **muscular branches** to the pelvic diaphragm and the obturator internus, nutrient branches to the hip bone, and supplies the roots of the sacral plexus.

Parietal Branches of Anterior Division of Internal Iliac Artery

The **obturator artery** (Figs. 1026 and 1029) runs forwards and downwards along the side wall of the true pelvis, near its brim, to the obturator foramen, through the upper part of which it passes. It ends immediately on entering the thigh, by dividing into anterior and posterior terminal branches, which skirt round the margin of the obturator foramen deep to the obturator externus muscle. It is accompanied, in the whole of its pelvic course, by the obturator nerve and vein, the nerve being above the artery and the vein below it.

To its lateral side is the obturator fascia, which intervenes between it and the upper part of the obturator internus muscle, whilst on its medial side it is covered by peritoneum. The ureter intervenes between the posterior part of the artery and the peritoneum. When the bladder is distended it also comes into close relation with the lower and anterior part of the artery. In the female the ovarian vessels and the broad ligament are medial relations of the obturator artery.

Branches.—All the branches except the terminal are given off before the artery leaves the pelvis. *Muscular* branches supply the adjacent muscles; a *nutrient* branch to the ilium passes deep to the ilio-psoas muscle, supplies the bone, and anastomoses with the ilio-lumbar artery; and a *vesical* branch or branches pass medially to the bladder. A **pubic branch**, given off just before the artery leaves the pelvis, ascends on the pelvic surface of the pubis; it anastomoses with its fellow of the opposite side and with the pubic branch of the inferior epigastric, which, in its downward course, may pass on either the lateral or medial side of the femoral ring. In the latter position the branch of the inferior epigastric is important in relation to femoral hernia; the importance is emphasised when, as sometimes happens, the obturator artery arises as an enlarged pubic branch of the inferior epigastric artery instead of from the internal iliac. The *anterior terminal branch* runs forwards, and the *posterior* backwards around the margin of the obturator foramen. They lie on the obturator membrane, under cover of the obturator externus, and they anastomose together at the lower margin of the foramen. Both give off offsets which anastomose with the medial circumflex artery, and supply the adjacent muscles. The posterior branch gives also an **acetabular branch** to the hip joint, which passes upwards, through the acetabular notch, to supply the head of the femur and its ligament.

The **internal pudendal artery** (Figs. 1026 and 1027) arises in common with the inferior gluteal artery. It runs downwards and backwards, to the lower part of the greater sciatic foramen, lying anterior to the piriformis muscle and the sacral plexus, from both of which it is separated by the pelvic fascia. At the lower border of the piriformis it pierces the pelvic fascia, passes between the piriformis and coccygeus muscles, and leaves the pelvis to enter the gluteal region. It is accompanied by venæ comitantes, the inferior gluteal vessels and nerve, the pudendal nerve, and the nerve to the obturator internus. In the gluteal region it lies on the ischial spine under cover of the gluteus maximus, and between the pudendal nerve and the nerve to the obturator internus, the former being medial to it. It next passes through the lesser sciatic foramen and enters the perineum, in the anterior part of which it ends by dividing into the deep and dorsal arteries of the penis or of the clitoris.

In the first part of its course *in the perineum* the artery lies in the lateral fascial wall of the ischio-rectal fossa, where it is enclosed in a canal in the obturator fascia —the pudendal canal. This canal, which is situated about one and a half inches above the lower margin of the ischial tuberosity, contains also the pudendal veins and the terminal parts of the pudendal nerve, *i.e.* the dorsal nerve of the penis, which lies above the artery, and the perineal nerve, which lies below it. From the ischio-rectal fossa the internal pudendal artery is continued forwards in the deep perineal pouch close to the ramus of the pubis. About half an inch below the pubic symphysis it turns somewhat abruptly downwards, pierces the perineal membrane, and immediately divides into its terminal branches—the deep artery and the dorsal artery. The division sometimes takes place while the artery is still within the deep perineal pouch.

Branches.—*In the pelvis.*—Small branches to muscles and to the sacral plexus.

In the gluteal region.—*Muscular* branches are distributed to the adjacent muscles and anastomose with branches of the gluteal and medial circumflex arteries.

In the ischio-rectal fossa.—The **inferior rectal artery** [A. hæmorrhoidalis inferior] pierces the wall of the fascial canal, and runs obliquely forwards and medially. It soon divides into two or three main branches, which may arise separately from the pudendal ; they pass across the fossa to the anal canal. The branches of the artery anastomose with the transverse perineal and, in the walls of the anal canal, with their fellows of the opposite side, and with the middle and superior rectal arteries ; they supply cutaneous twigs to the region of the anus, and send others round the lower border of the gluteus maximus to supply the lower part of the buttock.

Two **scrotal** or **labial branches** arise in the anterior part of the ischio-rectal fossa, either separately or by a common trunk [A. perinei], and pierce the posterior border of the perineal membrane. They are continued forwards, in the urogenital triangle, to the scrotum or labium majus according to sex, deep to the superficial fascia. They anastomose with their fellows of the opposite side, with the transverse perineal and the external pudendal arteries, and supply the muscles and subcutaneous structures of the urogenital triangle.

The **transverse perineal artery** is a small branch which arises from one of the scrotal or labial branches or from the common trunk ; it may arise directly from the internal pudendal. It runs medially along the superficial transversus perinei to the perineal body, where it anastomoses with its fellow of the opposite side, and with the inferior rectal arteries. It supplies adjacent muscles.

In the urogenital triangle.—The **artery of the bulb of the penis**, usually of relatively large size, is given off in the deep perineal pouch. It runs transversely along the posterior border of the sphincter urethræ, and then, turning forwards, it pierces the perineal membrane a short distance from the side of the urethra, and enters the substance of the bulb. It passes onwards in the corpus spongiosum to the glans, where it anastomoses with its fellow and with the dorsal arteries of the penis.

It supplies the sphincter urethræ, the bulbo-urethral gland, the corpus spongiosum penis, and the spongy part of the urethra. In the female the corresponding artery supplies the bulb of the vestibule.

The **deep artery of the penis (of the clitoris** in the female) is usually the larger of the two terminal branches. Immediately after its origin it enters the crus, and runs forwards in the corpus cavernosum of the penis (or clitoris), which it supplies.

The **dorsal artery of the penis (of the clitoris** in the female) passes forwards between the layers of the suspensory ligament of the penis (or clitoris), and runs along the dorsal surface of the organ, with the dorsal nerve immediately lateral to it, and

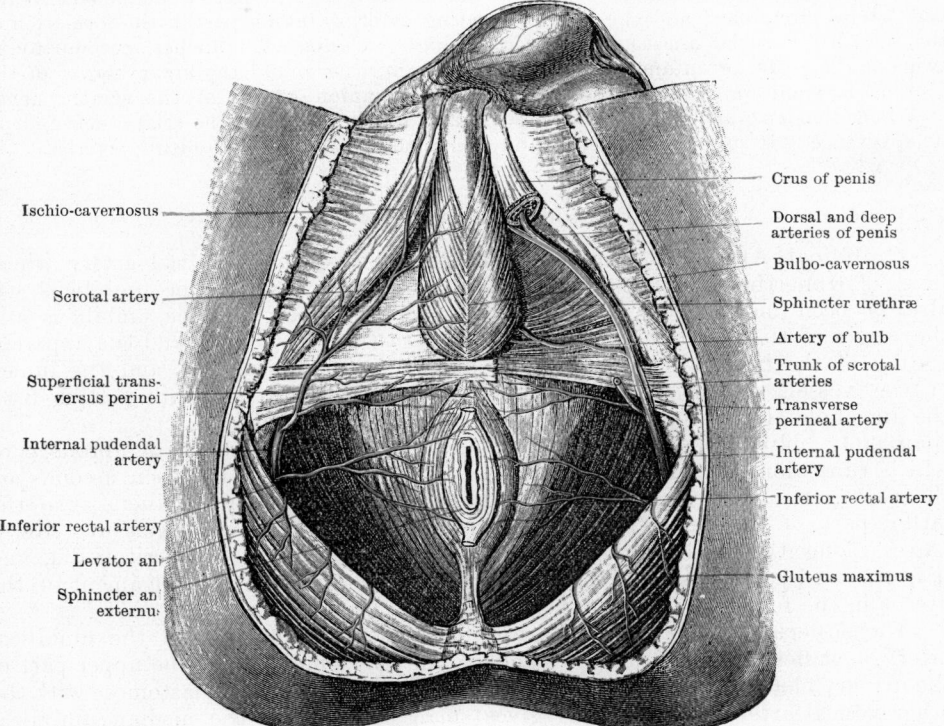

Ischio-cavernosus

Scrotal artery

Superficial transversus perinei

Internal pudendal artery

Inferior rectal artery

Levator ani

Sphincter ani externus

Crus of penis

Dorsal and deep arteries of penis

Bulbo-cavernosus

Sphincter urethræ

Artery of bulb

Trunk of scrotal arteries

Transverse perineal artery

Internal pudendal artery

Inferior rectal artery

Gluteus maximus

FIG. 1027.—PERINEAL DISTRIBUTION OF THE INTERNAL PUDENDAL ARTERY IN THE MALE.

separated from its fellow of the opposite side by the deep dorsal vein, which lies in the median plane. It supplies the superficial tissues on the dorsal aspect of the penis, sends branches into the corpus cavernosum to anastomose with the deep artery, and its terminal branches enter the glans, where they anastomose with the arteries to the bulb. It anastomoses also with the external pudendal branches of the femoral.

The **inferior gluteal artery** (Figs. 1026 and 1028) arises by a common trunk with the internal pudendal artery. It descends a little postero-lateral to the internal pudendal vessels, pierces the pelvic fascia, runs backwards and laterally between the first and second, or second and third sacral nerves, and, passing between the piriformis and coccygeus muscles, leaves the pelvis through the lower part of the greater sciatic foramen, and enters the gluteal region just below the piriformis. In the gluteal region it descends along the postero-medial side of the sciatic nerve, deep to the gluteus maximus, and behind the obturator internus, the two gemelli, the quadratus femoris, and upper part of the adductor magnus muscles, to reach the proximal part of the thigh.

Below the lower border of the gluteus maximus the artery is comparatively superficial, and, having given off its largest branches, it descends, as a long slender vessel, with the posterior cutaneous nerve of the thigh.

Branches.—*In the pelvis.*—Small and irregular branches supply the adjacent viscera and muscles and the sacral nerves; they anastomose with branches of the internal pudendal and lateral sacral arteries.

In the buttock.—**Muscular branches** are given off to the muscles of the buttock and to the proximal parts of the hamstring muscles. They anastomose with the internal pudendal, medial circumflex, and obturator arteries. One or two **coccygeal branches** arise immediately after the artery leaves the pelvis. They run medially, pierce the sacro-tuberous ligament and the gluteus maximus, and end in the soft tissues over the posterior surface of the coccyx and of the lower part of the sacrum. They supply twigs to the gluteus maximus, and anastomose with branches of the gluteal and lateral sacral arteries. An *anastomosing* branch passes laterally, superficial or deep to the sciatic nerve, towards the greater trochanter of the femur. It gives a branch to the back of the hip joint and anastomoses with branches of the gluteal, internal pudendal, medial and lateral circumflex, and the first perforating arteries, taking part in the formation of the so-called "crucial anastomosis" of the thigh. *Cutaneous* branches, accompanying twigs of the posterior cutaneous nerve of the thigh, pass round the lower border of the gluteus maximus muscle to the skin. The **companion artery of the sciatic nerve** is a long slender branch which runs downwards on the surface of the sciatic nerve, or in its substance. It supplies the nerve, and anastomoses with the perforating arteries.

Visceral Branches of the Anterior Division

Umbilical Artery.—Atrophy of that portion of the **umbilical artery** which extends from the anterior division of the internal iliac to the umbilicus has already been mentioned. The atrophy is complete between the umbilicus and the origin of the superior vesical artery, but between that origin and the apparent ending of the internal iliac in its two divisions it is incomplete, and the lumen of the vessel, though greatly diminished in size, remains patent. It is from the incompletely obliterated portion that the superior vesical artery arises. The completely obliterated part of the umbilical artery is reduced to a fibrous cord which runs along the side of the bladder almost to its apex, and then ascends, on the posterior surface of the anterior abdominal wall, to the umbilicus. In the latter part of its course it is known as the **lateral umbilical ligament**. As it passes along the wall of the true pelvis it is external to the peritoneum, and it is crossed by the vas deferens in the male, and by the round ligament of the uterus in the female.

The **superior vesical artery** arises from the pervious part of the umbilical artery, as it lies at the side of the bladder. It passes medially to the upper part of the urinary bladder and divides into numerous branches which anastomose with the other vesical arteries, and it also gives small branches to the median umbilical ligament (urachus), and often to the lower part of the ureter. Not infrequently the long slender *artery of the vas deferens* arises from it.

The **inferior vesical artery** runs medially, upon the upper surface of the levator ani, to the lower part of the bladder. It gives branches also to the seminal vesicle, the vas deferens, the lower part of the ureter and the prostate, and it anastomoses with its fellow of the opposite side, with the other vesical arteries, and with the middle rectal artery.

The **artery of the vas deferens** may arise from either the superior vesical or the inferior vesical artery. It is a long slender vessel which accompanies the vas deferens to the testis, where it anastomoses with the testicular artery. It anastomoses also with the artery of the cremaster.

The **middle rectal artery** [A. hæmorrhoidalis media] arises either directly from the anterior division of the internal iliac or from the inferior vesical; more rarely it springs from the internal pudendal. It runs medially, and is distributed to the rectum; it gives branches also to the prostate, the seminal vesicle, and the vas deferens; and it anastomoses with its fellow of the opposite side, with the inferior vesical, and with the other rectal arteries.

The **vaginal artery** may arise either directly from the anterior division of the internal iliac or from a stem common to it and the uterine artery, and it may be represented by several branches.

It runs downwards and medially, on the floor of the pelvis, to the side of the vagina, and divides into numerous branches which ramify on its anterior and posterior walls. The corresponding branches of opposite sides anastomose and form anterior and posterior longitudinal vessels—the so-called *azygos arteries*. They also anastomose above with the vaginal branches of the uterine arteries, and below with the perineal branches of the internal pudendal. In addition to supplying the vagina, it gives small branches to the bulb of the vestibule, to the base of the bladder, and to the rectum.

The **uterine artery** arises either separately or in common with the vaginal or middle rectal artery. It runs medially and slightly forwards, upon the upper surface of the levator ani, to the lower border of the broad ligament, between the two layers of which it passes medially, and arches above the ureter about three-quarters of an inch from the uterus. It passes above the lateral fornix of the vagina to the side of the neck of the uterus, and then ascends in a tortuous manner towards the fundus, but at the level of the uterine tube it turns laterally, below the tube and between the layers of the broad ligament, and ends as an *ovarian branch* which anastomoses with the ovarian artery. It supplies the uterus, the ligament of the ovary, and the round ligament of the uterus, and gives off *vaginal* and *tubal branches* to the upper part of the vagina and the medial part of the uterine tube. It anastomoses with its fellow of the opposite side, with the vaginal and ovarian arteries, and, along the round ligament of the uterus, with the inferior epigastric arteries.

Variations.—The **internal iliac artery** varies in length. It is longer and arises at a higher level when the common iliac is short. In rare cases it arises from the aorta without the intervention of a common iliac. Frequently, as in the fœtus, it does not end in anterior and posterior divisions, but forms a single trunk from which the branches are given off.

The visceral branches vary much in number and size, and the **middle rectal** may not be present, its place being taken by branches from the vesical arteries. A renal branch sometimes arises from the internal iliac artery.

The **ilio-lumbar branch** often arises from the common iliac instead of the internal iliac; the **superior gluteal** and **inferior gluteal** arteries may arise by a common stem, or the superior gluteal may be absent, and its place taken by a branch from the femoral artery; the inferior gluteal artery may, as in the fœtus, constitute the main artery of the lower limb, and run distally to become continuous with the popliteal artery. Probably the companion artery of the sciatic nerve represents the original continuity of the two vessels.

In some instances the **obturator artery** arises from the inferior epigastric artery instead of from the internal iliac. The condition is apparently due to obliteration of the usual origin of the obturator artery and the subsequent enlargement of the anastomosing pubic branches of the obturator and inferior epigastric arteries. The course of the abnormal obturator artery is of importance. From its origin it descends into the true pelvis, on the medial side of the external iliac vein, and usually on the lateral side of the femoral ring; but in three-tenths of examples, and more often in males than in females, it descends on the medial side of the ring.

The obturator artery sometimes gives off an accessory pudendal branch which passes along the side of the prostate, pierces the sphincter urethræ, and ends by dividing into the deep and dorsal arteries of the penis. When that occurs the internal pudendal artery is small, and it ends as the artery to the bulb. Occasionally the accessory pudendal arises from the internal pudendal artery within the pelvis, or from one of the vesical arteries.

EXTERNAL ILIAC ARTERY

The **external iliac artery** (Figs. 1025, 1029) extends from a point opposite the sacro-iliac joint, at the level of the lumbo-sacral disc, to a point at the inguinal ligament, midway between the anterior superior iliac spine and the pubic symphysis, where it becomes the femoral artery. Its length is about three and a half to four inches (85 to 100 mm.), and in the adult it is usually slightly wider than the internal iliac artery.

It runs downwards, forwards, and laterally, along the brim of the pelvis, resting upon the fascia iliaca, which separates it above from the medial border of the psoas major muscle, and below from its anterior surface; and it is enclosed, with its accompanying vein, in a thin fascial sheath.

Relations.—*Anterior.*—It is covered in front by peritoneum, which separates it on the right side from the terminal portion of the ileum, and sometimes from the vermiform appendix, and on the left side, from small intestine, except where the termination of the descending colon crosses it. Several branches of the lower of the two inferior left colic arteries also cross it on the left side. The ureter sometimes crosses the artery near its origin, and in the female the ovarian vessels cross the upper part of the artery. Near

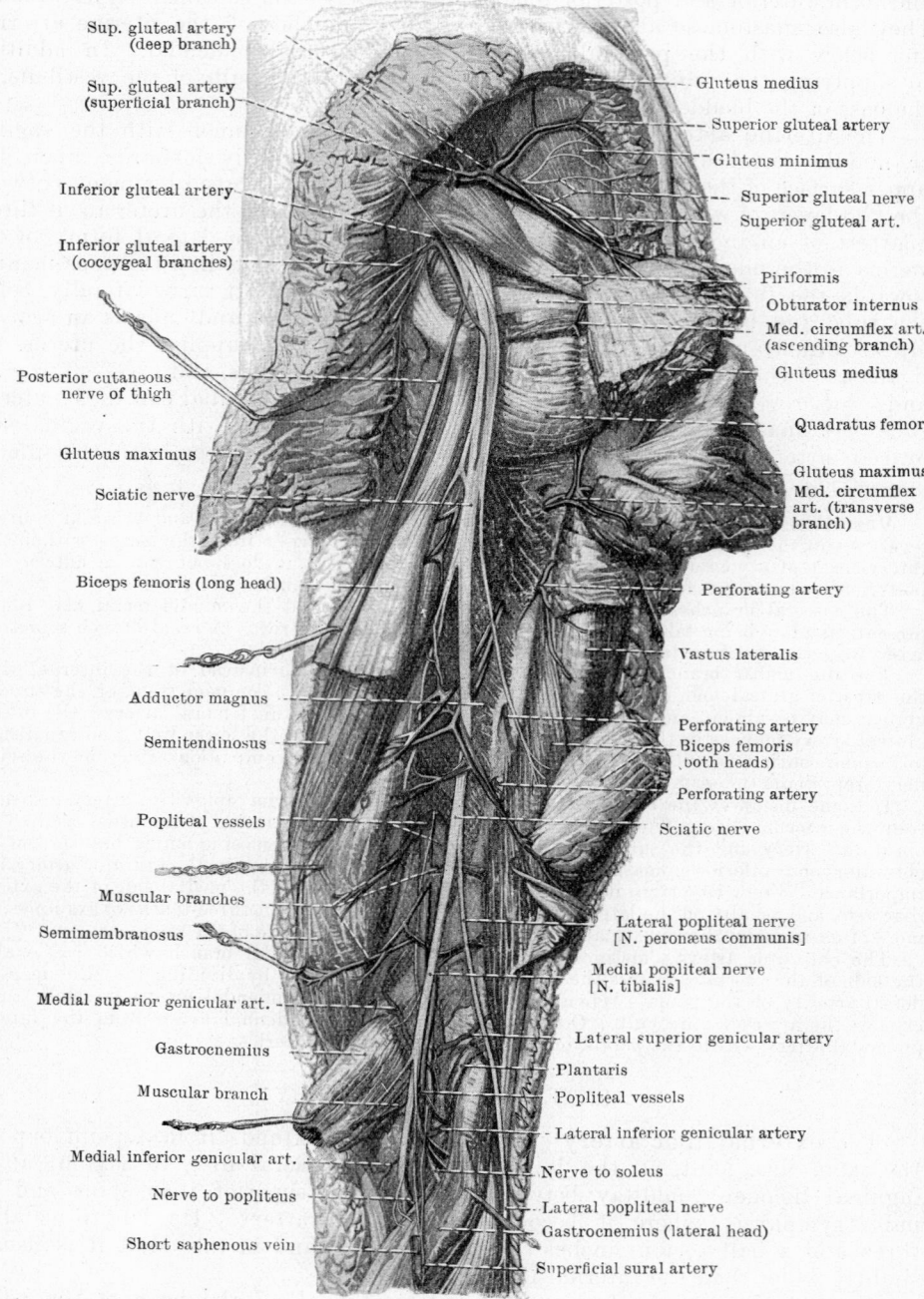

FIG. 1028.—ARTERIES OF THE BUTTOCK AND THE POSTERIOR ASPECT OF THE THIGH AND KNEE.
NOTE.—In the specimen there was no anastomotic branch of the inferior gluteal artery, and the transverse terminal branch of the medial circumflex artery pierced the upper part of the adductor magnus.

its lower end the testicular vessels and the genital branch of the genito-femoral nerve lie on the artery, and they are all crossed by the deep circumflex iliac vein. In the male that part of the artery is crossed also by the vas deferens, and in the female by the round ligament of the uterus.   External iliac lymph glands lie in front and at the sides of the artery, and almost invariably one of these is directly in front of its termination.

Posterior.—The fascia iliaca and psoas major muscle lie behind the artery.   Near its upper end the obturator nerve and the external iliac vein are posterior to the vessel.

Lateral.—On its lateral side is the genito-femoral nerve.   *Medial.*—To the medial side is the peritoneum, and at its lower part the external iliac vein.

Branches.—In addition to small branches to the psoas major muscle and to the lymph glands, two named branches of considerable size spring from the external iliac artery—the inferior epigastric and the deep circumflex iliac.

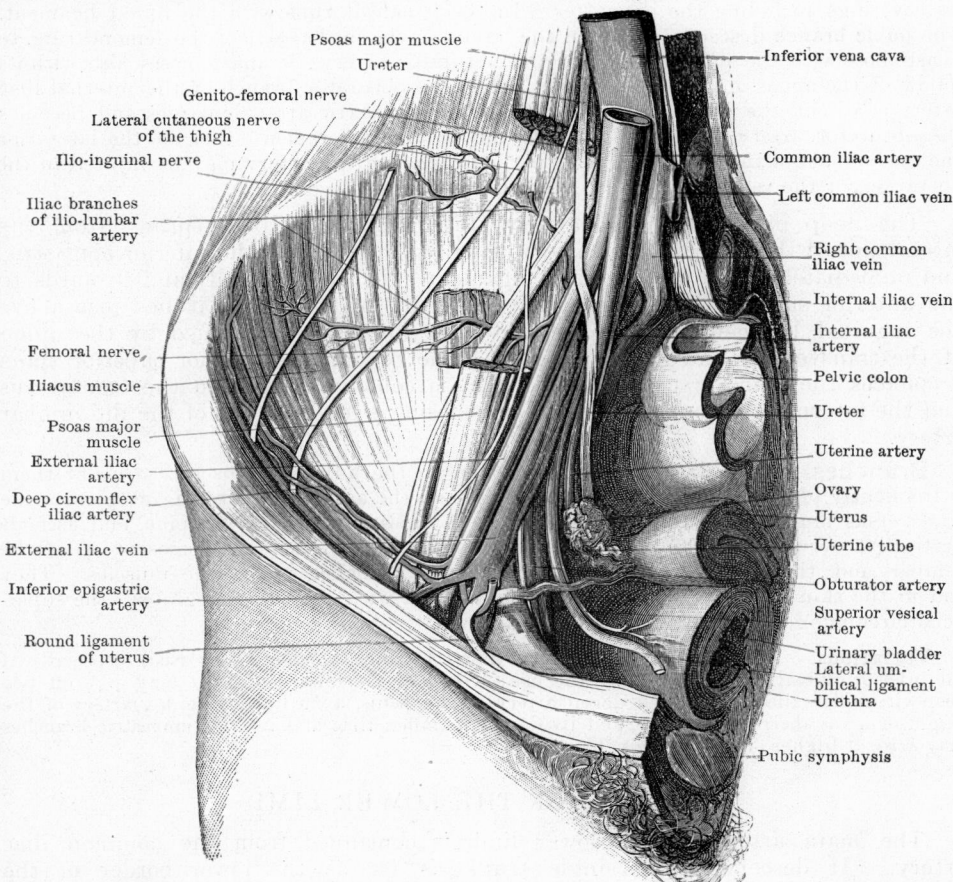

Psoas major muscle
Ureter
Genito-femoral nerve
Lateral cutaneous nerve of the thigh
Ilio-inguinal nerve
Iliac branches of ilio-lumbar artery
Femoral nerve
Iliacus muscle
Psoas major muscle
External iliac artery
Deep circumflex iliac artery
External iliac vein
Inferior epigastric artery
Round ligament of uterus

Inferior vena cava
Common iliac artery
Left common iliac vein
Right common iliac vein
Internal iliac vein
Internal iliac artery
Pelvic colon
Ureter
Uterine artery
Ovary
Uterus
Uterine tube
Obturator artery
Superior vesical artery
Urinary bladder
Lateral umbilical ligament
Urethra
Pubic symphysis

Fig. 1029.—The Iliac Arteries and Veins in the Female.

The **inferior epigastric artery** (Figs. 1026 and 1029) arises, immediately above the inguinal ligament, from the front of the external iliac.   It lies in the extra-peritoneal fat; it curves forwards from its origin, turns round the lower border of the peritoneal sac, and runs upwards and medially, along the medial side of the deep inguinal ring and along the lateral border of the medial inguinal fossa raising a fold of the peritoneum; it then pierces the transversalis fascia, passes over the arcuate line [linea semicircularis] and enters the sheath of the rectus abdominis muscle.   For a short distance it ascends posterior to the rectus, but it soon penetrates into the substance of the muscle, and breaks up into branches which anastomose with terminal offsets of the superior epigastric branch of the internal mammary artery and with the lower posterior intercostal arteries.   At the deep inguinal ring, the vas deferens in the male, or the round ligament of the uterus in the female, hooks round the artery and passes medially behind it towards the pelvis.

Branches.—**Muscular branches** supply the muscles of the abdominal wall, and anastomose with branches of the deep circumflex iliac, the lumbar, and the lower posterior intercostal arteries.   **Cutaneous branches** pierce the rectus abdominis and the ant of its sheath, and end in the subcutaneous tissues of the anterior abdomin where they anastomose with corresponding branches of the opposite side and branches of the superficial epigastric artery.   The **artery of the cremaster** [A. spern external] in the male (**artery of the round ligament of the uterus** in the female) is sm It descends through the inguinal canal and anastomoses with the external puden arteries and the scrotal or labial branches of the pudendal artery, and in the male wi the testicular artery also.   In the male it accompanies the spermatic cord, supplying its coverings, including the cremaster.   In the female it runs with the round ligament. The **pubic branch** descends, either on the lateral or the medial side of the femoral ring, to anastomose with the pubic branch of the obturator artery ; it anastomoses also with its fellow of the opposite side.   Sometimes, when the obturator branch of the internal iliac artery is absent, the pubic branch of the inferior epigastric artery enlarges and becomes the obturator artery, which descends to the obturator foramen either on the lateral or the medial side of the femoral ring.   In the latter case the artery may be injured in the operation for the relief of a strangulated femoral hernia.

The **deep circumflex iliac artery** (Figs. 1029 and 1030) springs from the lateral side of the external iliac artery, usually a little below the inferior epigastric, and immediately above the inguinal ligament.   It runs laterally and upwards to the anterior superior iliac spine.   In that part of its course it lies just above the inguinal ligament, and is enclosed in a fibrous canal formed by the union of the transversalis and iliac fasciæ.   A little beyond the anterior superior spine it pierces the transversus abdominis, and is continued between the transversus and the internal oblique, to end by anastomosing with branches of the ilio-lumbar artery.

Branches.—**Muscular branches** are given to the adjacent muscles.   One of them is frequently of considerable size and is known as the **ascending branch** ; it pierces the transversus muscle a short distance in front of the anterior superior spine, and ascends vertically, between the transversus and the internal oblique, anastomosing with the lumbar and the epigastric arteries.   **Cutaneous branches** pierce the muscles.   They end in the skin over the iliac crest, and anastomose with the superior gluteal, the superficial circumflex iliac, and the ilio-lumbar arteries.

Variations.—The **external iliac artery** may be much smaller than usual, especially if the inferior gluteal artery persists as the main vessel of the lower limb.   It may give off two deep circumflex iliac branches, a dorsal artery of the penis, a medial circumflex artery of the thigh, or a vas aberrans (p. 1230), and its deep circumflex iliac and inferior epigastric branches may arise at higher or lower levels than usual.

ARTERIES OF THE LOWER LIMB

The main artery of the lower limb is continued from the common iliac artery.   It descends as a single trunk as far as the lower border of the popliteus, and ends there by dividing into the anterior and posterior tibial arteries. Distinctive names are, however, applied to different parts of the artery, corresponding to the several regions through which it passes.   Thus in the abdomen it is called the **external iliac artery**, in the proximal two-thirds of the thigh it receives the name of the **femoral artery**, whilst its distal part, which is situated on the flexor aspect of the knee, is termed the **popliteal artery**.

FEMORAL ARTERY

The **femoral artery** (Figs. 1030 and 1031) is the continuation of the external iliac into the thigh.   It begins at the lower border of the inguinal ligament, passes through the proximal two-thirds of the thigh, and ends at the opening in the adductor magnus.

Course.—Its general direction is indicated by a line drawn from the inguinal ligament, midway between the anterior superior iliac spine and the pubic symphysis, to the adductor tubercle, the thigh being flexed, abducted, and rotated laterally.

In its proximal half the femoral artery lies in the femoral triangle and is comparatively superficial; at the apex of the triangle it passes deep to the sartorius, enters the subsartorial [adductor] canal (Hunter's), and is then more deeply placed.

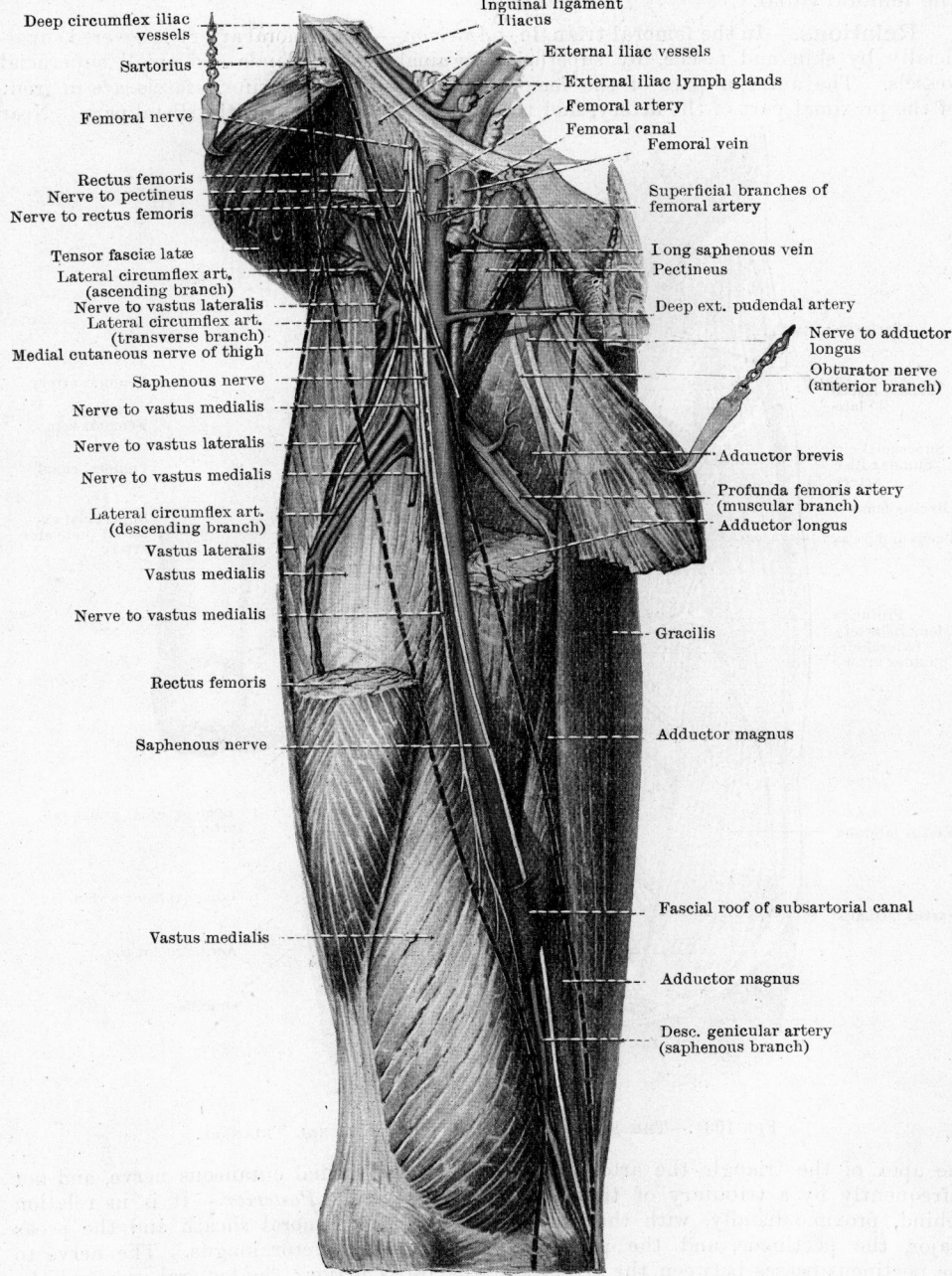

FIG. 1030.—THE FEMORAL ARTERY AND ITS BRANCHES.

NOTE.—The outlines of the sartorius, the upper part of the rectus femoris, and the adductor longus are indicated by broken black lines.

At their entry into the femoral triangle both the artery and its vein are enclosed, for a distance of one and a quarter inches (30 mm.), in a funnel-shaped fascial sheath formed of the fascia transversalis in front and the fascia iliaca behind. That sheath is called the **femoral sheath**; it is divided by antero-posterior septa into three compartments. The lateral compartment is occupied by the femoral artery and the femoral branch of the genito-femoral nerve; the intermediate compartment contains the femoral vein; and the medial compartment is the femoral canal.

Relations.—In the femoral triangle—*Anterior.*—The femoral artery is covered superficially by skin and fasciæ, by superficial inguinal lymph glands and small superficial vessels. The anterior part of the femoral sheath and the cribriform fascia are in front of the proximal part of the artery, and the fascia lata is in front of the distal part. Near

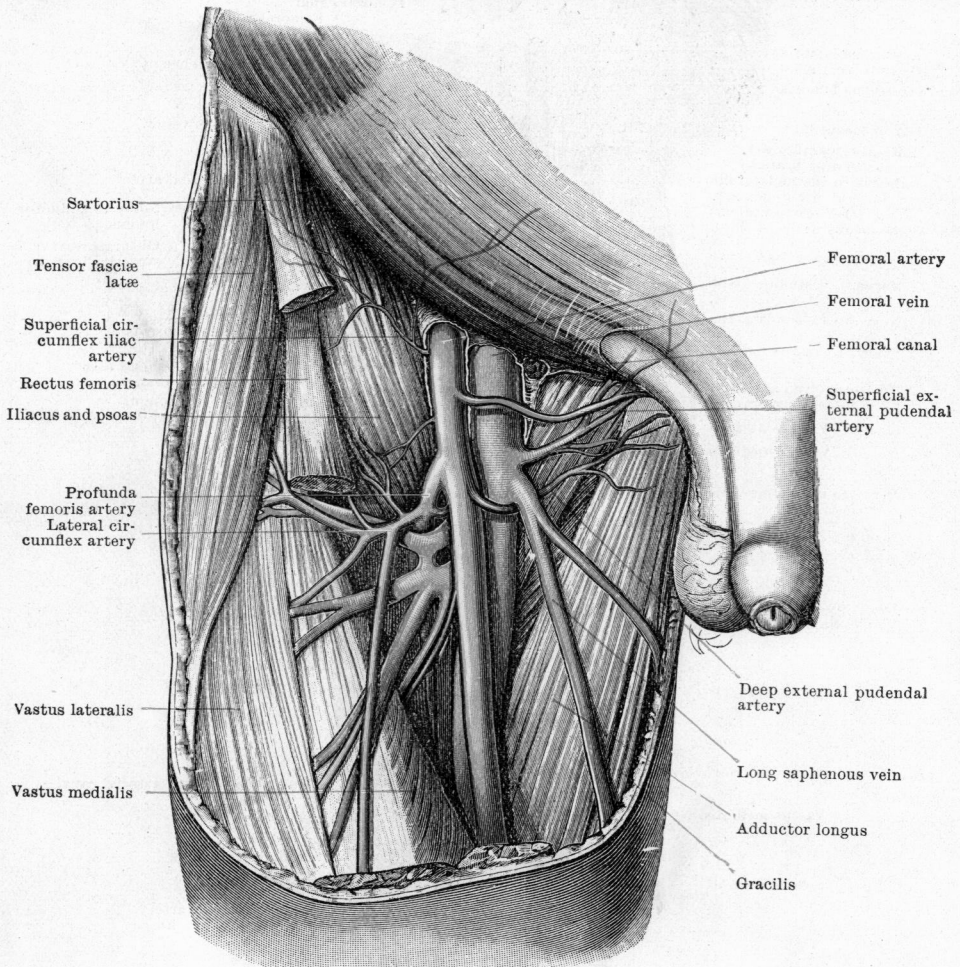

FIG. 1031.—THE FEMORAL VESSELS IN THE FEMORAL TRIANGLE.

the apex of the triangle the artery is crossed by the medial cutaneous nerve, and not infrequently by a tributary of the long saphenous vein. *Posterior.*—It is in relation behind, proximo-distally, with the posterior part of the femoral sheath and the psoas major, the pectineus, and the proximal part of the adductor longus. The nerve to the pectineus passes between the artery and the psoas major; the femoral vein and the profunda artery and vein intervene between it and the pectineus, and the femoral vein also separates it from the adductor longus.

The femoral vein, which lies on a plane posterior to the artery in the lower part of the femoral triangle, passes to its *medial side* above, where it is separated from the artery by the lateral septum of the femoral sheath. On the *lateral side* of the artery are the femoral branch of the genito-femoral nerve, the femoral sheath, and the femoral nerve proximally; more distally the saphenous nerve and the nerve to the vastus medialis are continued on the lateral side.

In the subsartorial canal—*Posterior.*—The adductors longus and magnus are behind the artery, but are separated from it by the femoral vein, which is posterior to the artery proximally, and postero-lateral distally. The vastus medialis is *antero-lateral.* The fascial roof of the canal, the subsartorial plexus of nerves and the sartorius are *antero-medial.* The saphenous nerve enters the canal with the artery, and runs first on its lateral side, then anterior, and lastly on its medial side.

Branches.—The femoral artery gives off the following branches :—

(1) Superficial branches.
  (*a*) Superficial circumflex iliac.
  (*b*) Superficial epigastric.
  (*c*) Superficial external pudendal.

(2) Muscular.
(3) Deep external pudendal.
(4) Profunda femoris.
(5) Descending genicular.

The **superficial circumflex iliac artery** springs from the front of the femoral artery, just below the inguinal ligament. It pierces the femoral sheath and the fascia lata, lateral to the saphenous opening of the fascia lata, and runs in the superficial fascia as far as the anterior superior iliac spine. It supplies the lateral set of inguinal lymph glands and the skin of the groin ; and it sends branches, through the fascia lata, to anastomose with branches of the deep circumflex iliac artery, and supply the upper parts of the sartorius and tensor fasciæ latæ muscles.

The **superficial epigastric artery** arises near the preceding. It pierces the femoral sheath and the cribriform fascia, and passes upwards and medially towards the umbilicus between the superficial and deep layers of the superficial fascia of the abdominal wall. It supplies the inguinal lymph glands and the skin ; it anastomoses with its fellow of the opposite side, with the inferior epigastric, and with the superficial circumflex iliac and superficial external pudendal arteries.

The **superficial external pudendal artery** also springs from the front of the femoral artery, and, after piercing the femoral sheath and the cribriform fascia, runs upwards and medially towards the pubic tubercle, where it crosses superficial to the spermatic cord or the round ligament of the uterus and divides into terminal *scrotal* or *labial branches* according to the sex. It supplies the skin of the lower part of the abdominal wall, the root of the dorsum of the penis in the male, and the region of the mons pubis in the female, and it anastomoses with its fellow of the opposite side, with the deep external pudendal, with the dorsal artery of the penis or clitoris, and with the superficial epigastric artery.

The **muscular branches** are distributed to the adjacent muscles.

The **deep external pudendal artery** arises from the medial side of the femoral. It runs medially, anterior to the pectineus, and either anterior or posterior to the adductor longus, to the medial side of the thigh ; it then pierces the deep fascia, and ends in the scrotum or the labium majus, where it anastomoses with the scrotal or labial branches of the superficial external and the internal pudendal arteries, and with the artery of the cremaster or of the round ligament.

The **profunda femoris artery** (Fig. 1031) is the largest branch of the femoral artery. It arises about an inch and a half distal to the inguinal ligament, from the lateral side of the femoral artery. It curves backwards and medially, passes posterior to the femoral artery, and runs downwards, close to the medial aspect of the femur, to the distal third of the thigh, where it perforates the adductor magnus and passes to the back of the thigh. Its termination is known as the *fourth perforating artery.* As the profunda artery descends it lies anterior to the iliacus, the pectineus, the adductor brevis, and the adductor magnus. It is separated from the femoral artery by its own vein, by the femoral vein, and by the adductor longus muscle.

Branches.—**Muscular branches** are given off from the profunda, both in the femoral triangle and between the adductor muscles ; many of them end in the adductors, others pass through the adductor magnus, and end in the hamstring muscles, where they anastomose with the transverse branch of the medial circumflex and with the proximal muscular branches of the popliteal artery.

The **lateral circumflex artery** (Figs. 1030 and 1031) springs from the lateral side of the profunda, or occasionally from the femoral artery proximal to the origin of the profunda. It runs laterally, anterior to the iliacus and among the branches of the femoral nerve, to the lateral border of the femoral triangle; then, passing posterior to the sartorius and the rectus femoris, it ends by dividing into three terminal branches — the ascending, the transverse, and the descending. Before its termination it supplies branches to the muscles mentioned and to the proximal part of the vastus intermedius.

The **ascending branch** runs upwards and laterally, posterior to the rectus femoris and the tensor fasciæ latæ, along the trochanteric line, to the adjacent anterior borders of the gluteus medius and gluteus minimus, between which it passes to anastomose with the deep branches of the superior gluteal artery. It supplies twigs to the neighbouring muscles, anastomoses with the gluteal, the deep circumflex iliac, and the transverse branch of the lateral circumflex arteries, and, as it ascends along the trochanteric line, it gives off a branch which passes between the two limbs of the ilio-femoral ligament into the hip joint. The **transverse branch** is small; it runs laterally, between the vastus intermedius and the rectus femoris, passes into the substance of the vastus lateralis, winds round the femur, and anastomoses with the ascending and descending branches, with the perforating branches

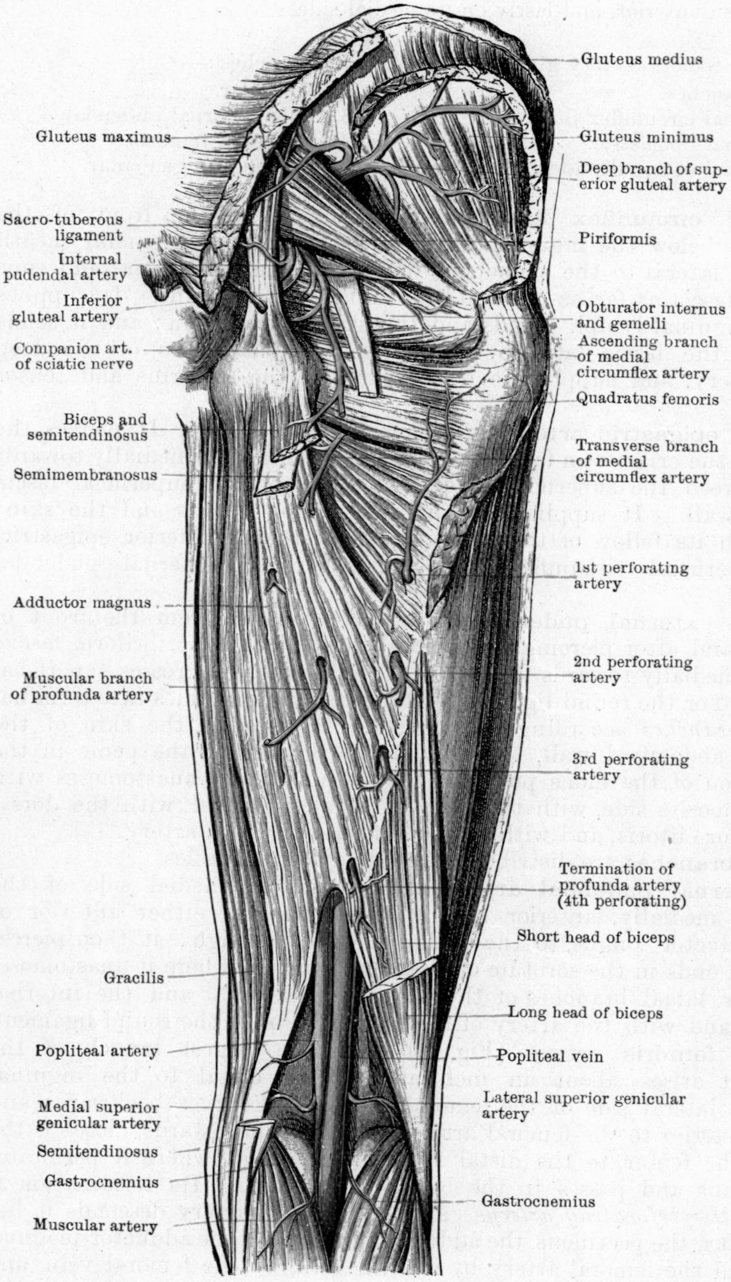

FIG. 1032.—ARTERIES OF GLUTEAL REGION AND BACK OF THIGH AND KNEE.

of the profunda, and with the inferior gluteal and medial circumflex arteries. The **descending branch** runs downwards, posterior to the rectus and along the anterior border of the vastus lateralis, accompanied by the nerve to the latter muscle. It anastomoses with the transverse branch, with twigs of the inferior perforating arteries, with the descending genicular branch of the femoral, and with the lateral superior genicular branch of the popliteal artery.

The **medial circumflex artery** springs from the medial and posterior part of the profunda, at the same level as the lateral circumflex, and runs backwards through the floor of the femoral triangle, passing between the psoas major and the pectineus; then it crosses the upper border of the adductor brevis, and continuing backwards, below the neck of the femur, it passes between the adjacent borders of the obturator externus and the adductor brevis to the upper border of the adductor magnus, where it divides into two terminal branches—a transverse and an ascending branch.

Branches.—An **acetabular branch** is given off as the artery passes below the neck of the femur. It ascends to the acetabular notch where it anastomoses with twigs from the posterior branch of the obturator artery, and it sends branches into the acetabular fossa and along the ligament of the head of the femur to supply the bone. **Muscular branches** are given off to the neighbouring muscles. The largest of those branches usually arises immediately before the termination of the artery; it runs downwards, on the anterior surface of the adductor magnus, and anastomoses with the muscular branches of the profunda artery. The **ascending branch** passes upwards and laterally, between the obturator externus and the quadratus femoris to the trochanteric fossa of the femur, where it anastomoses with branches of the superior and inferior gluteal arteries. The **transverse branch** runs backwards to the hamstring muscles—usually between the lower border of the quadratus femoris and the upper border of the adductor magnus, but it may pierce the upper part of the adductor magnus. It anastomoses, in front of the distal part of the gluteus maximus, with the inferior gluteal and first perforating arteries and with the transverse branch of the lateral circumflex, and, in the substance of the hamstrings, with the muscular branches of the profunda.

The **perforating arteries** (Fig. 1032), including the terminal branch of the profunda, are usually described as four in number; but they are often irregular. They curve backwards and laterally, round the back of the femur, lying close to the bone and anterior to the well-marked tendinous arches which interrupt the continuity of muscular attachments; their terminal branches enter the vastus lateralis and anastomose in its substance with one another, with the descending branch of the lateral circumflex, with the descending genicular artery, and with the lateral superior genicular branch of the popliteal.

The **first perforating artery** pierces the insertions of the adductors brevis and magnus. Its branches anastomose, anterior to the gluteus maximus, with the inferior gluteal, and with the transverse branches of the medial and lateral circumflex arteries, forming what is known as the *crucial anastomosis of the thigh.*

The **second perforating artery** pierces the adductors brevis and magnus, and then passes between the gluteus maximus and the short head of the biceps femoris into the vastus lateralis. It anastomoses with its proximal and distal fellows, and with the medial circumflex and the proximal muscular branches of the popliteal artery.

The **third** and **fourth perforating arteries** pass through the adductor magnus and the short head of the biceps femoris into the vastus lateralis. Their anastomoses are similar to those of the second perforating.

A **nutrient branch** to the femur is given off from either the second or third perforating artery, usually the former; an additional nutrient branch may be supplied also by the first or fourth perforating arteries.

The **descending genicular artery** [A. genu suprema] arises near the termination of the femoral artery, in the distal part of the subsartorial canal, and divides almost immediately into a superficial (saphenous) and a deep (musculo-articular) branch; indeed, very frequently the two branches arise separately from the femoral trunk.

The **saphenous branch** passes through the distal end of the subsartorial canal with the saphenous nerve, and appears superficially, on the medial side of the knee, between the gracilis and the sartorius. It gives twigs to the skin of the proximal and medial part of the leg, and it anastomoses with the medial inferior genicular artery. The **musculo-articular branch** runs towards the knee, in the substance of the vastus medialis, along the anterior aspect of the tendon of the adductor magnus. It anastomoses with the medial superior genicular artery; and it sends branches laterally, one on the surface of the femur and another along the proximal border of the patella, to anastomose with the descending branch of the lateral circumflex, the fourth perforating artery, the lateral superior genicular, and the anterior tibial recurrent.

Variations.—The **femoral artery** is small, and ends in the profunda and circumflex branches, when the inferior gluteal artery forms the principal vessel of the lower limb. The **profunda** branch, which arises usually from the lateral side of the femoral trunk, about 1½ in. (35 mm.) distal to the inguinal ligament, may begin at a more proximal or a more distal level, and from the back or the medial side of the femoral trunk. In rare cases when the profunda arises at a more proximal level than usual it may cross anterior to the femoral vein, above the entrance of the long saphenous vein, after which it passes downwards and laterally behind the femoral vessels (Johnston, *Anat. Anz.*, Bd. 42, 1912). Absence of the profunda has been noted, and in those cases the branches usually given off by it spring directly from the femoral artery.

The femoral artery may be double for a portion of its extent, or it may be joined by a vas aberrans given off from the external iliac artery. In addition to its ordinary branches, it may furnish one or both of the circumflex arteries of the thigh, and sometimes it gives off, near the origin of the profunda, a *long saphenous artery*, such as exists normally in many mammals. This vessel runs downwards through the femoral triangle and the subsartorial canal, and accompanies the saphenous nerve to the medial side of the foot.

The deep circumflex iliac, the obturator, and the inferior epigastric arteries are occasionally given off from the femoral.

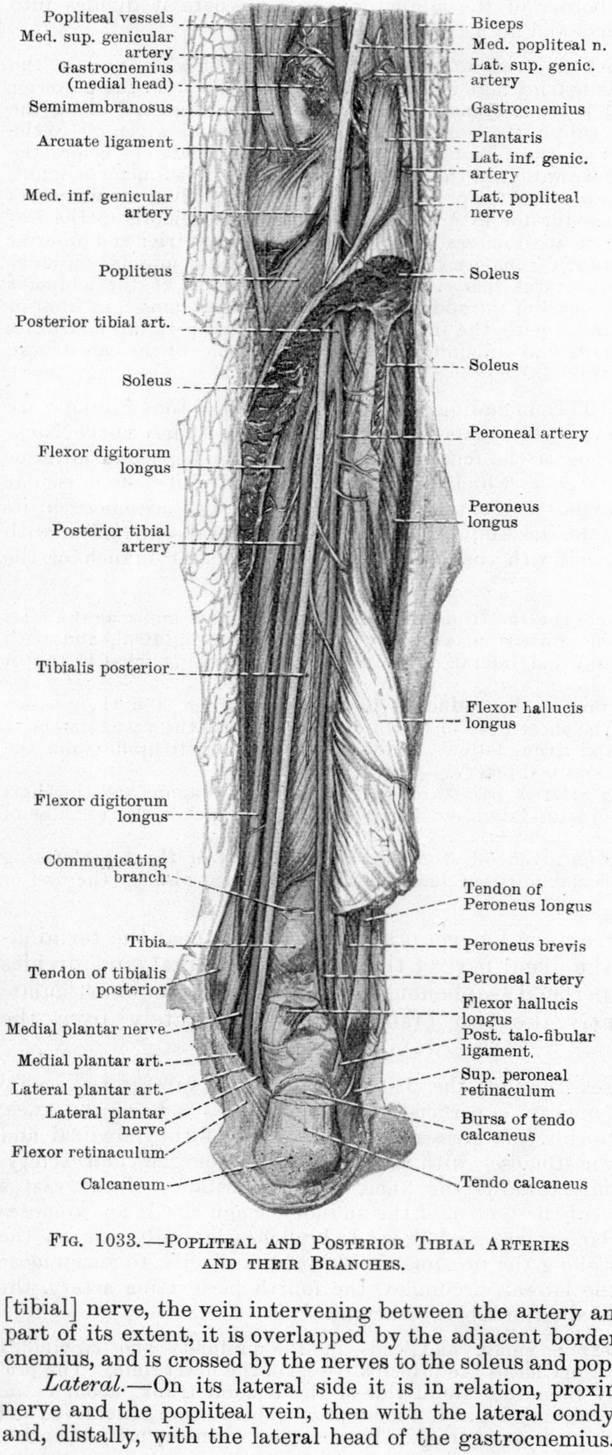

Popliteal vessels
Med. sup. genicular artery
Gastrocnemius (medial head)
Semimembranosus
Arcuate ligament
Med. inf. genicular artery
Popliteus
Posterior tibial art.
Soleus
Flexor digitorum longus
Posterior tibial artery
Tibialis posterior
Flexor digitorum longus
Communicating branch
Tibia
Tendon of tibialis posterior
Medial plantar nerve
Medial plantar art.
Lateral plantar art.
Lateral plantar nerve
Flexor retinaculum
Calcaneum
Biceps
Med. popliteal n.
Lat. sup. genic. artery
Gastrocnemius
Plantaris
Lat. inf. genic. artery
Lat. popliteal nerve
Soleus
Soleus
Peroneal artery
Peroneus longus
Flexor hallucis longus
Tendon of Peroneus longus
Peroneus brevis
Peroneal artery
Flexor hallucis longus
Post. talo-fibular ligament.
Sup. peroneal retinaculum
Bursa of tendo calcaneus
Tendo calcaneus

FIG. 1033.—POPLITEAL AND POSTERIOR TIBIAL ARTERIES AND THEIR BRANCHES.

POPLITEAL ARTERY

The **popliteal artery** is the direct continuation of the femoral. It begins at the medial and proximal side of the popliteal fossa, under cover of the semimembranosus, and ends at the distal border of the popliteus muscle, and on a level with the distal part of the tubercle of the tibia, by dividing into the anterior and the posterior tibial arteries. The artery passes obliquely from its origin to the interspace between the condyles of the femur, and then descends vertically.

Relations.— *Anterior.*—It is closely related to the popliteal surface of the femur, the posterior part of the capsule of the knee joint, and the fascia covering the posterior surface of the popliteus in that order from above downwards.

Posterior.— The artery is overlapped behind, in the proximal part of its extent, by the lateral border of the semimembranosus; it is crossed, about its middle, by the popliteal vein and the medial popliteal [tibial] nerve, the vein intervening between the artery and the nerve; whilst, in the distal part of its extent, it is overlapped by the adjacent borders of the two heads of the gastrocnemius, and is crossed by the nerves to the soleus and popliteus and by the plantaris muscle.

Lateral.—On its lateral side it is in relation, proximally, with the medial popliteal nerve and the popliteal vein, then with the lateral condyle of the femur and the plantaris, and, distally, with the lateral head of the gastrocnemius.

Medial.—On the medial side it is in relation, proximally, with the semimembranosus, then with the medial condyle of the femur, and distally with the medial popliteal nerve, the popliteal vein, and the medial head of the gastrocnemius. Popliteal lymph glands are arranged irregularly around the artery.

Branches.—**Muscular branches** are given off in two sets, proximal and distal.

The *proximal muscular branches* are distributed to the distal parts of the hamstring muscles, in which they anastomose with branches of the profunda artery.

The distal muscular or *sural arteries* enter the proximal parts of the muscles of the calf, and they anastomose with branches of the posterior tibial artery and the lower genicular arteries.

There are five **genicular arteries**—namely, lateral superior and inferior, medial superior and inferior, and a middle.

The **lateral superior genicular artery** passes laterally, proximal to the lateral condyle, behind the femur and in front of the biceps tendon, into the vastus lateralis, where it anastomoses with the descending genicular artery, the descending branch of the lateral circumflex, and the fourth perforating artery; it also sends branches distally to anastomose with the lateral inferior genicular and with the anterior recurrent branch of the anterior tibial.

The **medial superior genicular artery** passes medially, proximal to the medial condyle, behind the femur, and anterior to the tendon of the adductor magnus, into the vastus medialis. It anastomoses with branches of the descending genicular artery and of the lateral superior genicular artery.

The **lateral inferior genicular artery** runs laterally, across the popliteus muscle and anterior to the plantaris and the lateral head of the gastrocnemius; then, turning forwards, it is joined by an articular branch of the lateral popliteal nerve, and passes deep to the lateral ligament of the knee. It ends by anastomosing with its fellow of the opposite side, with the lateral superior genicular and the anterior recurrent branch of the anterior tibial artery.

The **medial inferior genicular artery** passes medially, distal to the medial condyle of the tibia, along the proximal border of the popliteus and in front of the medial head of the gastrocnemius, to the medial side of the knee, where it turns forwards, between the bone and the medial ligament of the knee, and ends anteriorly by anastomosing with its fellow of the opposite side, with the anterior recurrent branch of the anterior tibial artery, and with the medial superior genicular artery.

The **middle genicular artery** passes directly forwards from the front of the popliteal artery, pierces the central part of the posterior surface of the capsule of the knee joint, and enters the intercondylar notch. It supplies branches to the cruciate ligaments and to the synovial membrane, and is accompanied by an articular branch of the medial popliteal nerve, and sometimes by the articular branch of the obturator nerve.

Cutaneous branches are distributed to the skin over the popliteal fossa. One of these, the *superficial sural artery*, runs along the middle of the back of the calf with the short saphenous vein.

Variations.—The **popliteal artery** may exceptionally form the direct continuation of the inferior gluteal artery. It sometimes divides at a more proximal or more distal level than usual, and the division may be into either two or three branches; if three terminal branches are present, they are the anterior and posterior tibial and the peroneal arteries, and if only two, either the anterior and posterior tibial, or the anterior tibial and the peroneal arteries.

Occasionally the artery is double for a short portion of its course, and it has been found to cross, first posterior to the medial head of the gastrocnemius to the medial side of the knee, and then anterior to the medial head of the gastrocnemius to regain the popliteal fossa. The number of its branches may be reduced, or they may be increased by the addition of a vas aberrans which connects it with the posterior tibial artery. Its superficial sural branch may enlarge to form a well-marked short saphenous artery.

POSTERIOR TIBIAL ARTERY

The **posterior tibial artery**, the larger of the two terminal branches of the popliteal, begins at the distal border of the popliteus and ends midway between the tip of the medial malleolus and the most prominent part of the heel, at the distal border of the flexor retinaculum [lig. laciniatum]. It ends by dividing into the medial and the lateral plantar arteries, which pass onwards to the sole of the foot (Fig. 1034).

The posterior tibial artery runs downwards and medially, in the posterior part of the leg, between the superficial and deep layers of muscles and covered, posteriorly, by the intermuscular fascia which intervenes between them.

Relations.—*Anterior.*—It is in contact, proximo-distally, with the tibialis posterior, the flexor digitorum longus, the posterior surface of the tibia, and the posterior ligament of the ankle joint.

Posterior.—The artery is crossed about an inch and a half distal to its origin by the posterior tibial nerve. Elsewhere it is in contact with the intermuscular fascia which binds down the deep layer of muscles. More superficially the proximal half of the artery is covered by the fleshy parts of the soleus and gastrocnemius muscles, between which is the plantaris; the distal half of the artery is much nearer the surface, and is covered only by skin and fasciæ. At its termination it lies deep to the flexor retinaculum.

Lateral and Medial.—The artery is accompanied by two venæ comitantes, one on each side. The posterior tibial nerve lies at first on the medial side of the vessel, then crosses posterior to it, and is continued downwards on its lateral side. In the most distal part of its course the artery is separated from the medial malleolus by the tendons of the tibialis posterior and the flexor digitorum longus, whilst the tendon of the flexor hallucis longus lies lateral to it.

Branches.—The posterior tibial gives off numerous branches, the largest of which, the peroneal, is one of the chief arteries of the leg. The branches include—

Large **muscular branches** to the adjacent muscles. They anastomose with the sural branches of the popliteal artery and the medial inferior genicular artery.

Cutaneous branches are distributed to the skin of the medial and posterior part of the leg.

A **circumflex fibular branch** passes laterally round the neck of the fibula through the fibres of the soleus, and anastomoses with the lateral inferior genicular and the sural arteries, and supplies the adjacent muscles. Occasionally it springs from the lower end of the popliteal artery, or from the anterior tibial.

The **peroneal artery** (Fig. 1033) is the largest branch of the posterior tibial. It arises about an inch (25 mm.) below the distal border of the popliteus, curves laterally across the proximal part of the tibialis posterior to the medial crest of the fibula, along which it passes to the distal part of the interosseous space. About an inch proximal to the ankle joint it gives off a perforating branch and then passes, behind the inferior tibio-fibular joint and lateral malleolus, to the lateral side of the heel and the foot. It supplies the ankle, the inferior tibio-fibular and talo-calcanean joints, and anastomoses with a calcanean branch of the lateral plantar artery, and with the tarsal and arcuate branches of the dorsalis pedis.

As the peroneal artery passes laterally from its origin it lies behind the tibialis posterior, and is covered posteriorly by the deep intermuscular fascia and by the soleus. As it descends along the medial crest of the fibula it lies in a fibrous canal between the tibialis posterior in front and the flexor hallucis longus behind. It is accompanied by two venæ comitantes which anastomose around it.

Branches.—**Muscular branches** are distributed to the adjacent muscles. Some pass through the interosseous membrane and supply the anterior muscles of the leg.

The **nutrient artery to the fibula** enters the nutrient foramen of that bone.

The **communicating branch** passes across the back of the tibia, about an inch above the inferior tibio-fibular joint, to anastomose with the posterior tibial artery.

The **perforating branch** passes forwards at the junction of the distal border of the interosseous membrane and the interosseous tibio-fibular ligament, and runs, in front of the ankle joint, to the dorsum of the foot, where it anastomoses with the lateral malleolar branch of the anterior tibial artery and with the tarsal branch of the dorsalis pedis; it also supplies branches to the inferior tibio-fibular joint, to the ankle joint, and to the peroneus tertius.

A **malleolar branch** and **calcanean branches** take part in the anastomoses on the lateral side of the ankle and heel.

The **nutrient artery to the tibia**, the largest of the nutrient group of arteries to long bones, springs from the proximal part of the posterior tibial, pierces the tibialis posterior, and enters the nutrient foramen on the posterior surface of the bone. Before it enters the tibia the nutrient artery gives small muscular branches.

The **communicating branch** unites the posterior tibial to the peroneal artery about an inch above the inferior tibio-fibular joint. It passes posterior to the shaft of the tibia and anterior to the flexor hallucis longus.

Calcanean branches arise from the artery just before it divides. They pierce the flexor retinaculum, supply the medial side of the heel, and anastomose with the peroneal and the malleolar arteries.

A **malleolar branch** is distributed to the medial surface of the medial malleolus, anastomosing with malleolar branches of the anterior tibial and peroneal arteries.

Variations.—The **posterior tibial artery** may be small or altogether absent, its place being taken by branches of the peroneal artery; again, it may be longer or shorter than usual, in conformity with the more proximal or more distal division of the popliteal trunk. The peroneal artery is large, if either the anterior or the posterior tibial artery is small. The perforating branch of the peroneal is almost invariably large when the anterior tibial artery is small; in some cases it replaces the whole of the dorsalis pedis continuation of the latter vessel; in others, however, only the tarsal and arcuate branches are so replaced. The peroneal sometimes arises from a stem common to it and the anterior tibial artery.

PLANTAR ARTERIES

The **medial** and **lateral plantar arteries** are the terminal branches of the posterior tibial artery. They arise, under cover of the flexor retinaculum midway between the tip of the medial malleolus and the most prominent part of the medial side of the heel (Figs. 1033, 1034).

The **medial plantar artery** is the smaller of the two terminal branches of the posterior tibial artery. It passes forwards, on the medial side of the medial plantar nerve, along the medial side of the foot in the interval between the abductor hallucis and the flexor digitorum brevis, to the head of the first metatarsal bone, where it ends by uniting with the digital branch of the first plantar metatarsal artery which is distributed to the medial side of the big toe. In its

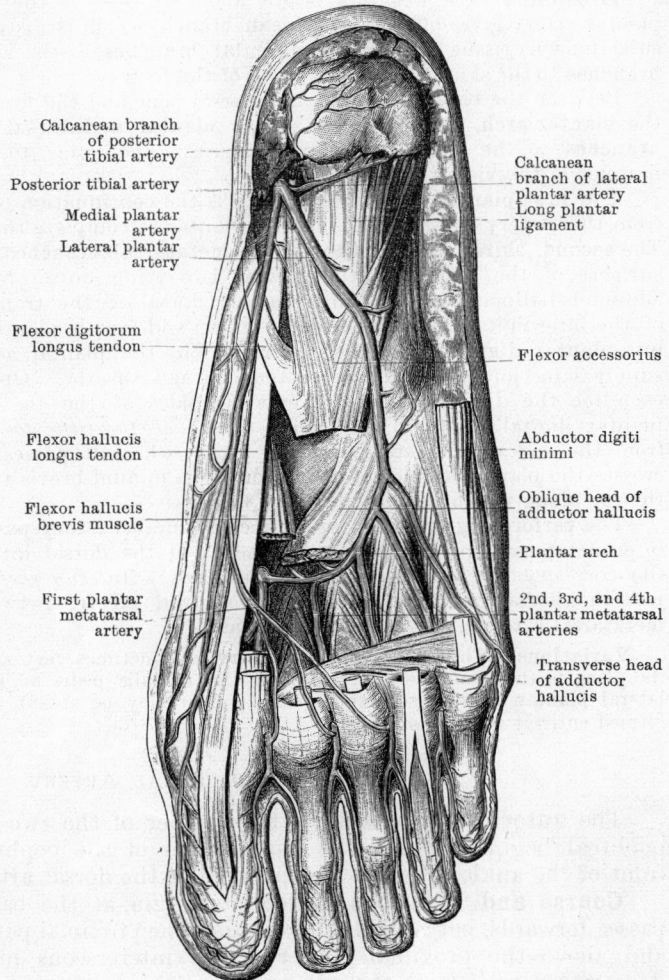

Calcanean branch of posterior tibial artery
Posterior tibial artery
Medial plantar artery
Lateral plantar artery
Flexor digitorum longus tendon
Flexor hallucis longus tendon
Flexor hallucis brevis muscle
First plantar metatarsal artery

Calcanean branch of lateral plantar artery
Long plantar ligament
Flexor accessorius
Abductor digiti minimi
Oblique head of adductor hallucis
Plantar arch
2nd, 3rd, and 4th plantar metatarsal arteries
Transverse head of adductor hallucis

FIG. 1034.—THE PLANTAR ARTERIES AND THEIR BRANCHES.

course forwards it gives off a branch which ramifies on the superficial surface of the abductor hallucis, branches to the adjacent muscles and articulations, and branches to the skin; it also gives three *digital branches* which anastomose, at the roots of the medial three interdigital clefts, with the medial plantar metatarsal arteries. Some of the cutaneous branches of the medial plantar artery anastomose, round the medial border of the foot, with cutaneous branches of the dorsalis pedis artery.

The **lateral plantar artery** is the larger of the two terminal branches of the posterior tibial artery. It runs forwards across the sole on the lateral side of the lateral plantar nerve, first between the flexor digitorum brevis superficially and the flexor accessorius [quadratus plantæ] deeply, and then, in the interval between the flexor digitorum brevis and the abductor digiti minimi, to the medial side of the base of the fifth metatarsal bone. There it turns abruptly medially and, gaining a deeper plane, passes across the bases of the metatarsal bones and the origins of the interossei, and above the oblique head of the adductor hallucis, to the lateral side of the base of the first metatarsal bone, where it ends by anastomosing with the dorsalis pedis artery. The last part of the artery is convex forwards and forms the *plantar arch*, which is completed by its junction with the dorsalis pedis.

Branches.—Between its origin and the base of the fifth metatarsal the lateral plantar artery gives off:—A **calcanean branch**, which is distributed to the skin and the subcutaneous tissue of the heel; **muscular branches** to the adjacent muscles; **cutaneous branches** to the skin of the lateral side of the foot.

Between the base of the fifth metatarsal bone and the first interosseous space it forms the **plantar arch**, and gives off:—Four **plantar metatarsal arteries**; three **perforating branches** to the dorsal metatarsal arteries; and twigs to the tarsal joints and the muscles in the vicinity.

The **first plantar metatarsal artery** is the continuation of the dorsalis pedis, arising from that artery as it joins the lateral plantar to complete the plantar arch (see p. 1237). The **second, third,** and **fourth plantar metatarsal branches** run forwards on the plantar surfaces of the interossei, the medial two lying dorsal to the oblique head of the adductor hallucis, and all three passing dorsal to the transverse head. At the bases of the interdigital clefts the second, third, and fourth plantar metatarsal arteries divide into **plantar digital arteries** which run along the plantar aspects of adjacent toes, and supply skin, joints, and the flexor tendons and sheaths. Opposite the distal phalanx of each toe the digital arteries of opposite sides of the toe anastomose together. The plantar digital artery *to the lateral border of the little toe* has an independent origin from the end of the lateral plantar artery where it passes into the plantar arch. It crosses the plantar surface of the flexor digiti minimi brevis to reach the lateral border of the toe along which it runs.

The **perforating branches** are three in number; they pass through the lateral three inter-metatarsal spaces, between the heads of the dorsal interosseous muscles, and join the corresponding dorsal metatarsal arteries. *Anterior perforating branches*, which also join the dorsal metatarsal arteries, are given off from two or three of the plantar metatarsal arteries just before they divide.

Variations.—The **medial plantar artery** is sometimes very small. It may be absent and its place is then taken by branches of the dorsalis pedis or lateral plantar arteries. The **lateral plantar artery** also may be small; or it may be absent, the plantar arch being then formed entirely by the dorsalis pedis.

Anterior Tibial Artery

The **anterior tibial artery**, the smaller of the two terminal divisions of the popliteal, begins opposite the distal border of the popliteus muscle, and ends in front of the ankle, where it is continued as the dorsal artery of the foot.

Course and Relations.—From its origin, at the back of the leg, the artery passes forwards, between the two slips of the proximal part of the tibialis posterior and above the proximal border of the interosseous membrane. It then runs downwards, resting, in the proximal two-thirds of its course, against the anterior surface of the interosseous membrane and, subsequently, on the distal part of the tibia and the anterior ligament of the ankle-joint. In the proximal third of the anterior compartment of the leg it lies between the extensor digitorum longus laterally and the tibialis anterior medially; in the middle third it is between the extensor hallucis longus and the tibialis anterior; in the distal third the extensor hallucis longus crosses in front of the artery and reaches its medial side, and the most distal part of the vessel lies between the tendon of the extensor hallucis longus on the medial side and the most medial tendon of the extensor digitorum longus on the lateral side. Two venæ comitantes, with numerous intercommunications, lie along the sides of the artery.

The anterior tibial nerve [N. peronæus profundus] is at first well to the lateral side of the artery, but it approaches the vessel and lies in front of its middle third; more distally the nerve is usually found on the lateral side again, and at the ankle it intervenes between the artery and the most medial tendon of the extensor digitorum longus.

The proximal part of the anterior tibial artery is deeply placed and the adjacent muscles overlap it. In the distal two-thirds of its extent it is easily accessible from the surface ; and beyond being covered by the nerve and crossed by the tendon, as already described, is covered, in addition, only by skin, fascia, and the superior extensor retinaculum [lig. transversum cruris].

Branches.—Close to its origin the artery gives off a posterior recurrent and sometimes a circumflex fibular branch ; after it reaches the front of the leg it gives off anterior recurrent, muscular, cutaneous, and medial and lateral anterior malleolar branches.

The **circumflex fibular branch** is a small vessel that may arise from the posterior tibial or the popliteal artery (See p. 1232).

The **posterior recurrent branch**, also small, and not always present, runs upwards, anterior to the popliteus muscle, to the back of the knee-joint. It anastomoses with the inferior genicular branches of the popliteal, and gives branches to the popliteus muscle and the superior tibio-fibular joint.

The **anterior recurrent branch** arises from the anterior tibial artery in front of the interosseous membrane. It runs upwards and medially, between the proximal part of the tibialis anterior and the lateral condyle of the tibia, accompanied by the recurrent articular branch of the lateral popliteal [common peroneal] nerve, and, after supplying the tibialis anterior and the superior tibio-fibular joint, it pierces the deep fascia of the leg ; it is connected with the anastomoses round the knee-joint, formed by the genicular branches of the popliteal artery, the descending branch of the lateral circumflex artery, and the descending genicular artery.

The **muscular branches** are distributed to the adjacent muscles of the front and back of the leg.

The **cutaneous branches** supply the skin of the front of the leg.

The **medial anterior malleolar artery** arises from the lower part of the anterior tibial

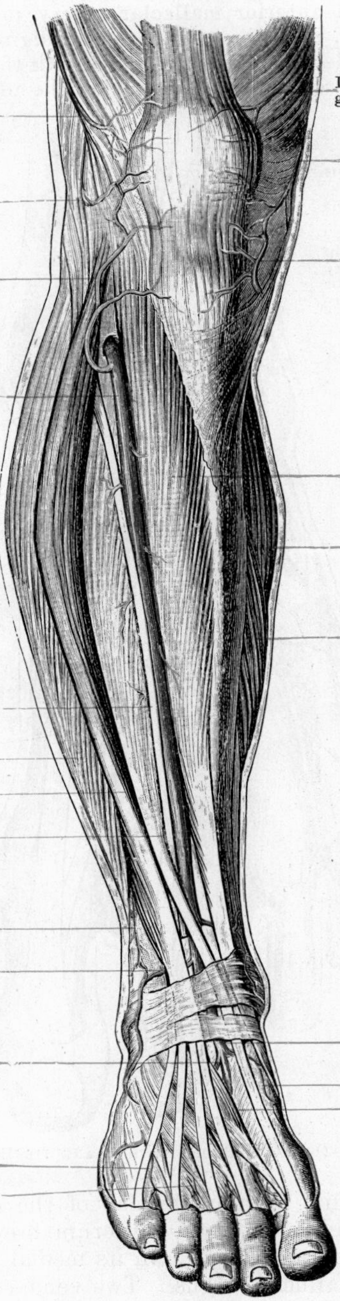

Fig. 1035.—Anterior Tibial Artery and its Branches.

Labels on figure:
- Lateral superior genicular artery
- Lateral inferior genicular artery
- Anterior recurrent branch of ant. tibial artery
- Anterior tibial artery
- Anterior tibial [deep peroneal] nerve
- Peroneus brevis
- Extensor digitorum longus
- Extensor hallucis longus
- Perforating branch of peroneal artery
- Lateral anterior malleolar artery
- Tarsal artery
- Dorsal metatarsal arteries
- Descending genicular artery
- Medial superior genicular artery
- Medial inferior genicular artery
- Tibialis anterior
- Gastrocnemius
- Soleus
- Dorsalis pedis artery
- Cutaneous branch Extensor digitorum brevis

78 a

artery, and is smaller than its companion on the lateral side. It runs medially, posterior to the tibialis anterior tendon, ramifies over the medial malleolus, anastomosing with branches of the posterior tibial artery, and is distributed to the skin and to the ankle-joint.

The **lateral anterior malleolar artery**, more constant and larger than the medial, passes laterally, posterior to the extensor digitorum longus and peroneus tertius, towards the lateral malleolus. It anastomoses with the perforating branch of the peroneal artery and with the tarsal artery, and supplies the ankle joint and the adjacent joints.

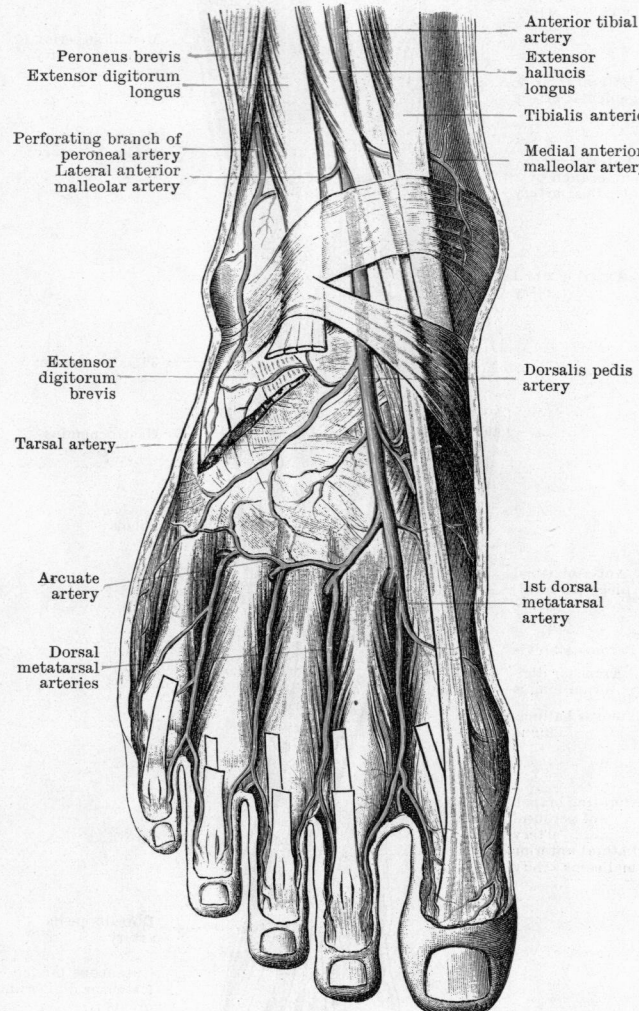

Peroneus brevis

Extensor digitorum longus

Perforating branch of peroneal artery
Lateral anterior malleolar artery

Extensor digitorum brevis

Tarsal artery

Arcuate artery

Dorsal metatarsal arteries

Anterior tibial artery

Extensor hallucis longus

Tibialis anterior

Medial anterior malleolar artery

Dorsalis pedis artery

1st dorsal metatarsal artery

FIG. 1036.—DORSALIS PEDIS ARTERY AND ITS BRANCHES.

Dorsalis Pedis Artery.—The dorsal artery of the foot is the direct continuation of the anterior tibial; it begins on the front of the ankle-joint, and runs to the posterior end of the first interosseous space, where it gives off the first dorsal metatarsal artery and then passes into the sole of the foot between the two heads of the first dorsal interosseous muscle to unite with the lateral plantar artery in the formation of the plantar arch.

It is covered superficially by skin and fasciæ, including the inferior extensor retinaculum [lig. cruciatum cruris], and it is crossed, just before it reaches the first interosseous space, by the tendon of the extensor hallucis brevis. It rests upon the anterior ligament of the ankle, the head of the talus, the talo-navicular ligament, the dorsum of the navicular bone, and the dorsal cuneo-navicular and the inter-cuneiform ligaments between the medial and intermediate cuneiform bones. On its lateral side is the medial terminal branch of the anterior tibial nerve, which intervenes between it and the extensor digitorum brevis and the most medial tendon of the extensor digitorum longus. On its medial side it is in relation with the tendon of the extensor hallucis longus. Two venæ comitantes, one on each side, accompany the artery.

Branches.—**Cutaneous branches** are distributed to the skin on the dorsum and medial side of the foot; they anastomose with branches of the medial plantar artery.

The **tarsal artery** arises opposite the head of the talus; it runs laterally, deep to the extensor digitorum brevis, supplying that muscle and the tarsal joints, and it anastomoses with the perforating branch of the peroneal, the arcuate, and lateral plantar arteries, and with the lateral anterior malleolar artery. Other smaller tarsal branches are given off on both lateral and medial sides of the artery.

The **arcuate artery** arises opposite the medial cuneiform bone. It runs laterally, on the bases of the metatarsal bones, deep to the long and short extensor tendons, supplies the extensor digitorum brevis, and anastomoses with branches of the tarsal and lateral plantar arteries. It gives off three **dorsal metatarsal arteries,** second, third, and fourth, which run forwards on the muscles which occupy the lateral three interosseous spaces to the clefts of the toes, where each divides into two *dorsal digital arteries* for the adjacent sides of the toes bounding the cleft to which it goes. The lateral side of the little toe receives a branch from the most lateral dorsal metatarsal artery. Each dorsal metatarsal artery gives off a *posterior perforating branch*, which passes through the posterior part of the intermetatarsal space, between the heads of the dorsal interosseous muscle, to anastomose with the plantar arch, and an *anterior perforating branch*, which passes through the anterior part of the space to anastomose with the corresponding plantar metatarsal artery.

The **first dorsal metatarsal artery** is continued forwards from the dorsalis pedis and runs on the dorsal surface of the first dorsal interosseous muscle. It ends by dividing into dorsal digital branches for the adjacent sides of the first and second toes. Before it divides it usually gives off a *dorsal digital branch* which passes, deep to the tendon of the extensor hallucis, to the medial side of the big toe.

As the dorsalis pedis unites with the lateral plantar artery to complete the plantar arch it gives off the **first plantar metatarsal artery,** which passes forwards, along the first intermetatarsal space, to the base of the first interdigital cleft, where it divides into *plantar digital arteries* for the adjacent sides of the first and second toes ; before it divides it gives off a *plantar digital artery* to the medial side of the big toe.

Variations.—The **anterior tibial artery** may be absent, its place being taken by branches of the posterior tibial and peroneal arteries. It is longer than normal when the popliteal artery divides at a higher level than usual, and in those cases it may pass either posterior or anterior to the popliteus muscle. Occasionally the anterior tibial artery and its dorsalis pedis continuation are larger than normal, and the terminal part of the dorsalis pedis takes the place, more or less completely, of the lateral plantar artery.

VEINS

Veins commence in the networks of capillaries. They converge towards the heart, and unite with one another to form larger and still larger vessels, until, finally, seven large trunks are formed which open into the atria of the heart. Three of the trunks—the **superior vena cava,** the **inferior vena cava,** and the **coronary sinus**—belong to the *systemic circulation* ; they contain venous blood, and open into the right atrium. The remaining four—the **pulmonary veins**—belong to the *pulmonary circulation* ; they return oxygenated blood from the lungs, and open into the left atrium. They are described on p. 1155.

In addition to the systemic and pulmonary veins, there is also a third group of veins, constituting the **portal system,** in which blood from the abdominal part of the alimentary canal, and from the spleen and pancreas, is conveyed to the liver. The portal system is peculiar in that it both begins and ends in capillaries. From the sinusoidal capillaries in the liver the *hepatic veins* arise, and as those open into the inferior vena cava the blood of the portal system is finally poured into the general systemic circulation. The hepatic veins receive also the blood supplied to the liver by the hepatic arteries.

SYSTEMIC VEINS

The **systemic veins** return blood to the right atrium of the heart through the superior vena cava, the inferior vena cava, and the coronary sinus. The two venæ cavæ receive blood from the head and neck, the body wall, the limbs, and from the abdominal and pelvic viscera. The coronary sinus receives blood from the veins of the walls of the heart alone.

General Arrangement.—The veins of the head and neck, the body wall and limbs, form two groups—(1) the superficial veins ; (2) the deep veins.

The **superficial veins** lie in the superficial fascia ; they begin in the capillaries of the skin and subcutaneous tissues, and are very numerous. They freely

78 *b*

anastomose with one another, and they also communicate with the deep veins, in which they end after piercing the deep fascia. They may or may not accompany superficial arteries.

The **deep veins** accompany arteries, and are known as *venae comitantes*. The large arteries have only one accompanying vein, but with the medium-sized and small arteries there are usually two venæ comitantes, which anastomose freely with each other by short transverse channels of communication.

Visceral veins usually accompany the arteries which supply viscera in the head, neck, thorax, and abdomen. As a rule there is only one vein with each visceral artery, and, with the exception of those which enter into the formation of the portal system, they end in the deep systemic veins.

CORONARY SINUS AND VEINS OF THE HEART

The **coronary sinus** (Fig. 991) is a short, but relatively wide, venous trunk which receives the majority of the veins of the heart. It lies in the lower part of the atrio-ventricular groove, between the left atrium and the left ventricle, and it is covered superficially by some of the muscular fibres of the atrium.

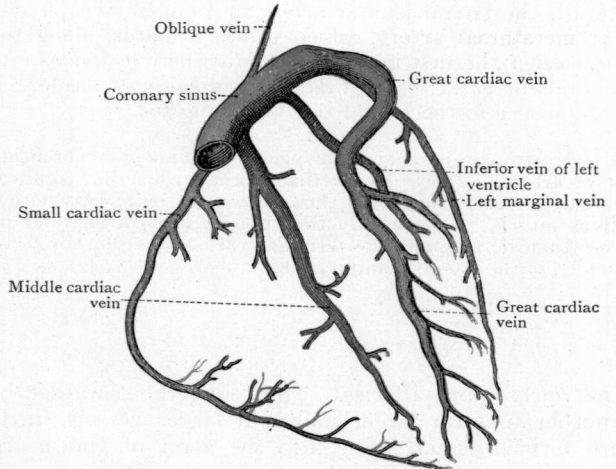

It terminates in the lower and posterior part of the right atrium, between the orifice of the inferior vena cava on the right, and the right atrio-ventricular orifice in front; an imperfect valve, consisting of one cusp, called the **valve of the coronary sinus**, is situated at the right margin of the opening of the sinus into the atrium.

The apertures of the tributaries of the coronary sinus are not provided with

FIG. 1037.—DIAGRAM OF VEINS ON THE SURFACE OF THE HEART.

valves, except those of the great and small cardiac veins, and their valves are often incompetent.

Tributaries.—The **great cardiac vein** (Fig. 992) begins at the apex of the heart. It ascends, in the anterior interventricular groove, to the atrio-ventricular groove; it then turns to the left, and, passing round the left surface of the heart into the lower part of the atrio-ventricular sulcus, ends in the left extremity of the coronary sinus. It receives tributaries from the walls of both ventricles and from the wall of the left atrium. It receives also the *left marginal vein* which ascends from the apex of the heart along its left border.

The **small cardiac vein** is very variable; as a rule it begins at the lower border of the heart near the apex and passes to the right to the atrio-ventricular groove, in which it turns to the left, and ends in the right extremity of the coronary sinus. It receives tributaries from the walls of the right atrium and the right ventricle.

The **oblique vein of the left atrium** (Fig. 991) is a small venous channel which descends obliquely on the posterior wall of the left atrium, and ends in the coronary sinus. It is of special interest inasmuch as it represents the left superior vena cava of some other mammals, and is developed from the left duct of Cuvier. It is continuous above with the *ligament of the left vena cava* (see Pericardium, p. 1154).

The **inferior vein of the left ventricle** runs backwards along the lower surface of the left ventricle and ends in the coronary sinus.

The **middle cardiac vein** begins at the apex of the heart, and passes backwards in the inferior interventricular groove to end in the coronary sinus near its right extremity. It receives tributaries from the walls of both ventricles.

Veins of the Heart which do not end in the Coronary Sinus.—The **anterior cardiac veins** are two or three small vessels which ascend on the anterior wall of the right ventricle to the atrio-ventricular groove across which they pass to end directly in the right atrium. The **venæ cordis minimæ** are a number of small veins

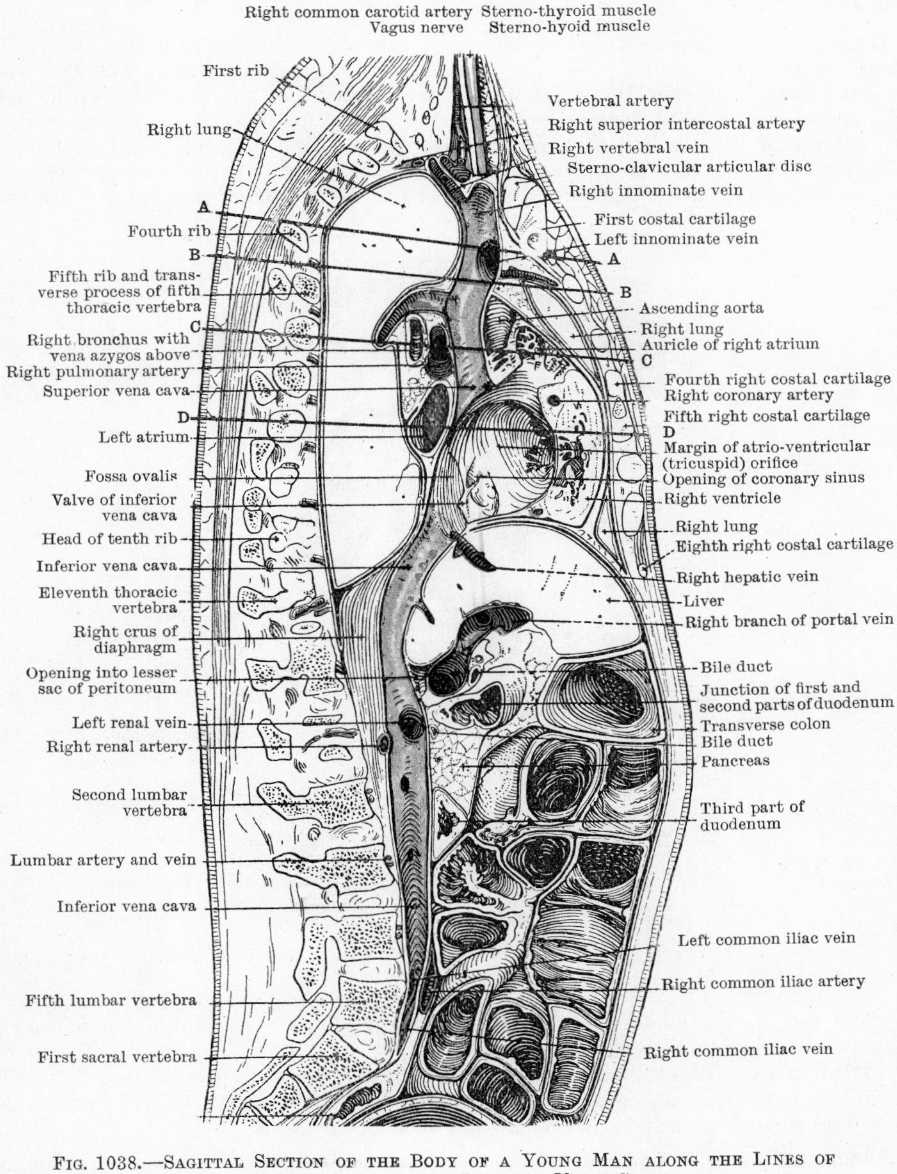

FIG. 1038.—SAGITTAL SECTION OF THE BODY OF A YOUNG MAN ALONG THE LINES OF THE SUPERIOR AND THE INFERIOR VENÆ CAVÆ.

A-A. Plane of section of Fig. 1015. C-C. Plane of section of Fig. 1001.
B-B. Plane of section of Fig. 1039. D-D. Plane of section of Fig. 997.

which begin in the substance of the walls of the heart and end directly in its cavities, principally in the atria.

SUPERIOR VENA CAVA

The **superior vena cava** (Figs. 1002 and 1038) returns the blood from the head and neck, the upper limbs, the thoracic wall, and a portion of the upper part of the wall of the abdomen. It is formed, at the lower border of the first right costal cartilage, by the union of the two innominate veins, and it descends to the level of the third right costal cartilage, where it opens into the upper and posterior part

78 c

of the right atrium. It is about three inches (75 mm.) long; in the lower half of its extent it is enclosed within the fibrous layer of the pericardium, and it is covered in front and on each side by the serous layer.

Relations.—It is overlapped *anteriorly* by the margins of the right lung and pleura and by the ascending aorta. The lung and pleura intervene between it and the second and third costal cartilages, the internal intercostal muscles in the first and second intercostal spaces, and the internal mammary vessels. It is in relation *posteriorly* with the right margin of the trachea, the vena azygos, which opens into it at right angles, the right bronchus, the right pulmonary artery, and the upper right pulmonary vein. On its *left side* are the ascending aorta and the origin of the innominate artery, whilst on

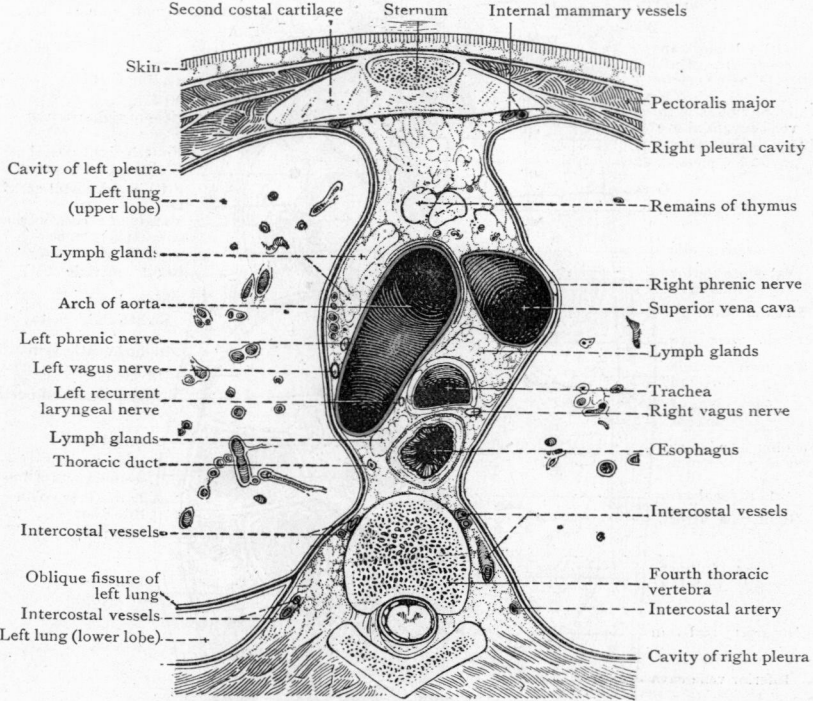

Fig. 1039. Transverse Section of the Thorax of a Young Man along the Plane B-B, Fig. 1038.

the *right side* it is in close relation with the right pleura—the phrenic nerve and the pericardiaco-phrenic vessels intervening.

Tributaries.—In addition to the two innominate veins, by the union of which it is formed, the superior vena cava receives only one large tributary, viz., the vena azygos; but several small pericardial and mediastinal veins open into it.

Abnormalities.—The superior vena cava may develop on the left side instead of on the right. That peculiarity is due to the persistence of the left duct of Cuvier instead of the right, and it is associated with absence of the coronary sinus, which is replaced by the lower part of the left superior vena cava. An exceptional case is recorded in which the opening of the coronary sinus into the heart was obliterated, and the cardiac veins terminated in a trunk which passed upwards to the left innominate vein. That trunk was obviously formed by enlargement of the left duct of Cuvier and the lower part of the left anterior cardinal vein. Not very uncommonly, as the result of the persistence of both ducts of Cuvier, there are two superior venæ cavæ, the transverse anastomosis which usually forms the left innominate vein being small or absent. In such cases the left innominate vein descends in the left part of the superior mediastinum, crosses the aortic arch, is joined by the left superior intercostal vein, and becomes the left superior vena cava, which descends anterior to the root of the left lung, and ends in the lower and back part of the right atrium. It receives the great cardiac vein, and, turning to the back of the heart, replaces the coronary sinus. This arrangement is normal in many mammals. Occasionally in Man the left superior vena cava terminates in the left atrium, and the coronary sinus, which represents a part of the sinus venosus, has been seen to have a similar ending; both these abnormal endings are the result of malposition of the atrial septum.

Vena Azygos and its Tributaries

The **vena azygos** is variable in its origin. It usually springs from the back of the inferior vena cava at the level of the renal veins (see *right lumbar azygos vein,* below), and enters the thorax through the aortic opening of the diaphragm, but may begin, between the diaphragm and the body of the twelfth thoracic vertebra, as the continuation of the right subcostal vein, or from the junction of that vein and the right ascending lumbar vein. It ascends through the posterior mediastinum to the upper part of the fifth thoracic vertebra. There it enters the superior mediastinum, arches forwards above the root of the right lung, and ends, opposite the second costal cartilage, by entering the back of the superior vena cava just before the vena cava pierces the pericardium. It frequently possesses imperfect valves.

Relations—In the posterior mediastinum.—*Posteriorly,* it rests upon the lower eight thoracic vertebræ, the intervertebral discs, and the anterior longitudinal ligament; and it crosses the posterior intercostal arteries of the right side. *Medial* to it are the thoracic duct and the descending aorta. *Lateral* to it there are the diaphragm, the greater splanchnic nerve, and the right pleura and lung. *Anteriorly,* it is related, in succession, to the diaphragm, the overlapping right pleura and lung, and the œsophagus. **In the superior mediastinum.**—The root of the lung is *below.* The trachea and the right vagus are *medial.* The right pleura and lung are *lateral.* The vein grooves the lung deeply above its hilum, and therefore the pleura and lung are also *above.*

Tributaries.—(1) Right bronchial veins. (2) Œsophageal, pericardial and phrenic veins. (3) Mediastinal veins. (4) Right ascending lumbar vein. (5) Right subcostal vein. (6) Right posterior intercostal veins of the lower eight spaces. (7) Right superior intercostal vein formed by the union of the posterior intercostal veins of the second and third spaces. (8) Inferior vena hemiazygos and superior vena hemiazygos, which convey much of the blood of the left side of the thoracic and abdominal walls to the vena azygos.

The **superior vena hemiazygos** [V. hemiazygos accessoria] begins, at the vertebral end of the fourth intercostal space of the left side, as the continuation of the fourth posterior intercostal vein. It runs downwards and forwards on the body of the fourth thoracic vertebra to reach the aorta, and descends close along the left side of the descending aorta as far as the eighth thoracic vertebra. There it bends abruptly to the right, and crosses behind the aorta and the thoracic duct to end in the vena azygos. Till it bends to the right it is under cover of the pleura, and crosses superficial to the upper left posterior intercostal arteries. Its **tributaries** are:—(1) the left bronchial veins; (2) some mediastinal veins; and (3) the left posterior intercostal veins of the fourth, fifth, sixth, and seventh spaces, and, sometimes, the eighth. Its upper part is often connected with the left superior intercostal vein.

The **inferior vena hemiazygos** [V. hemiazygos] usually springs from the back of the left renal vein (see *left lumbar azygos vein*) and enters the thorax by piercing the left crus of the diaphragm; but it may begin, between the diaphragm and the left side of the body of the twelfth thoracic vertebra, as the continuation of the left subcostal vein or from the junction of that vein and the left ascending lumbar vein. It runs upwards on the vertebral bodies to the ninth vertebra, where it turns abruptly to the right, and crosses behind the aorta and the thoracic duct to end in the vena azygos. In its upward course it is under cover of first the diaphragm and then the left pleura, and it crosses superficial to the lower left posterior intercostal arteries; the greater splanchnic nerve descends close along its lateral side; and the descending aorta is on its medial side and overlaps it anteriorly. Its **tributaries** are:—(1) some mediastinal veins; (2) the left ascending lumbar vein; (3) the left subcostal vein; (4) the left posterior intercostal veins of the eleventh, tenth, and ninth spaces, and, sometimes, the eighth.

The azygos and inferior hemiazygos veins are the morphological continuations of the "lumbar azygos veins." These veins, when present, may receive the upper two (or more) of the lumbar veins, but in the adult they are often reduced to mere fibrous cords or may not be found. The *right lumbar azygos vein* is the usual origin of the vena azygos and springs from the back of the inferior vena cava at the level of the renal veins. It passes upwards between the crura of the diaphragm (or pierces the right crus), and enters the thorax through the aortic opening (or to the right of that opening). The *left lumbar azygos vein* is the usual origin of the inferior vena hemiazygos; it arises from the back of the left renal vein, and pierces the left crus.

The **bronchial veins** do not quite correspond to the bronchial arteries, and they are not found on the walls of the smallest bronchi. On each side the tributaries run in front of or behind the bronchial tubes to reach the root of the lung, where they unite, as a rule, into two small trunks; those of the right side open into the vena azygos, and those of the left into the superior vena hemiazygos, or into the left superior intercostal vein. On both sides they receive tracheal and mediastinal veins. Some small bronchial veins, including most of those from the smaller tubes, open into the pulmonary veins.

The œsophageal, pericardial, and phrenic veins are small, irregular vessels that drain blood from the œsophagus, the back of the pericardium, and the posterior part of the diaphragm; and they end in the vena azygos.

The mediastinal veins are small, irregular vessels that drain blood from the fat and the lymph glands of the posterior mediastinum. They end in the azygos vein, in the two hemiazygos veins, and in the bronchial veins.

The ascending lumbar vein (p. 1266) is a longitudinal, anastomosing channel that connects the lateral sacral, ilio-lumbar and lumbar veins. The upper two lumbar veins may end in it or may be merely connected by it. It ends in the vena azygos on the right side and the inferior vena hemiazygos on the left side.

The intercostal veins are in two sets—an anterior and a posterior. The anterior intercostal veins are described on pp. 1243, 1244.

The posterior intercostal veins are eleven on each side. Each lies in the posterior part of an intercostal space, in the costal groove, above the corresponding artery. It is provided with valves, both near its termination and along its course, which prevent the blood from flowing towards the anterior wall of the chest. It receives small unnamed tributaries from the adjacent muscles and bones, and at the vertebral end of the intercostal space it receives a *posterior tributary*, which passes forwards between transverse processes from the back. That tributary is formed by the union of small veins from the muscles of the back, from the plexuses on the fronts and backs of the vertebræ, and from the plexuses inside the vertebral canal. It also receives a *lateral cutaneous tributary* corresponding to the branch of the artery.

The first posterior intercostal vein ascends across the front of the neck of the first rib on the lateral side of the superior intercostal artery, and arches forwards over the summit of the pleura to end either in the innominate vein or in the vertebral vein. The second and third (and sometimes the fourth) unite to form the superior intercostal vein. The right superior intercostal vein inclines downwards and forwards to join the vena azygos where that vein begins to arch forwards. The left vein runs downwards and forwards to the aorta, and then forwards and upwards on the left side of the aortic arch, superficial to the left vagus and deep to the left phrenic nerve, and joins the lower border of the left innominate vein. The lower portion is part of the azygos venous line (p. 1292); its upper portion is a remnant of the left posterior and anterior cardinal veins. The remaining posterior intercostal veins curve forwards over the bodies of the vertebræ; those of the right side end in the vena azygos; those of the left side end in the superior and inferior hemiazygos veins.

Variations.—The vena azygos may be formed on the left side; it then arches over the root of the left lung, and ends in the coronary sinus. This is the normal arrangement in some mammals, and it is due to the persistence of the cephalic end of the left posterior cardinal vein, the thoracic part of the left supracardinal vein, and the left duct of Cuvier.

Occasionally the azygos vein is the only vessel by which blood is returned to the heart from the lower limbs and the lower parts of the body walls. In such cases that portion of the inferior vena cava which usually extends from the right renal vein to the heart is absent and the azygos vein is the direct continuation of the inferior vena cava. This condition probably results from the absence of those parts of the inferior vena cava which are formed from the right vitelline and the right subcardinal veins, and the enlargement of the azygos venous line (see p. 1263).

The vena azygos is occasionally enclosed in a fold of pleura and sunk deeply into the right lung, cutting off an accessory lobe—the *lobe of the vena azygos*.

The superior and inferior hemiazygos veins may be absent. In such cases each left intercostal vein opens separately into the vena azygos. On the other hand, the hemiazygos veins may form a continuous trunk which may open by a transverse anastomosis into the azygos vein, or it may join the left innominate vein. When the hemiazygos veins form a single trunk, which receives the left posterior intercostal veins and opens into the left innominate vein, the condition is due to the persistence of the whole of the thoracic part of the azygos venous line, the upper part of the left posterior cardinal vein, and the lower part of the left anterior cardinal vein.

Cases also occur in which the thoracic part of the azygos venous line is represented by three instead of two stems, either the superior or the inferior hemiazygos vein being represented by two vessels.

INNOMINATE VEINS

The **innominate veins** (Figs. 1000 and 1002) are two in number, right and left. They return blood from the head and neck, the upper limbs, the upper part of the posterior wall of the thorax, the anterior wall of the thorax, and the upper part of the anterior wall of the abdomen. Each innominate vein commences behind the medial end of the clavicle of the corresponding side, and is formed by the union of the internal jugular and subclavian veins; the two innominate veins terminate by uniting together, at the lower border of the first costal cartilage of the right side, to form the superior vena cava. To reach that point the left vein has to pass from left to right behind the manubrium sterni, and it is therefore about three times as long as the right vein. The innominate veins do not possess valves.

The **right innominate vein** is a little more than 1 inch (25 mm.) in length. It descends almost vertically to the lower border of the first costal cartilage.

Relations.—In the root of the neck.—The innominate artery is *medial*. The clavicle and the sterno-hyoid and sterno-thyroid muscles are *anterior*. The cervical pleura is *posterior and lateral*; and the internal mammary artery and the phrenic nerve are between it and the pleura. **In the thorax.**—The innominate artery is *medial*. The trachea and the vagus nerve are *postero-medial*. The lung and pleura are *lateral*, but overlap it in front and behind; the phrenic nerve and pericardiaco-phrenic vessels, descending along its right side, are between it and the pleura.

Tributaries.—In addition to the veins by the union of which it is formed, the right innominate vein receives the right vertebral and internal mammary veins, the first right posterior intercostal vein, and sometimes the right inferior thyroid vein or a common trunk of the two veins. The *right lymphatic duct* (or separate lymph trunks) also opens into it.

The **left innominate vein** passes from left to right, with a slight obliquity downwards, behind the upper half of the manubrium sterni, to the lower border of the first right costal cartilage. It is about 3 inches (60 to 75 mm.) long.

Relations.—In the root of the neck.—*Posteriorly*, it rests first upon the cervical pleura and the internal mammary artery, and next upon the fat surrounding the phrenic and vagus nerves, the cervical cardiac branches of the vagus and sympathetic, and the ascending part of the subclavian artery. *Anteriorly*, the sterno-thyroid and sterno-hyoid muscles separate it from the clavicle and the sterno-clavicular joint. **In the thorax.**—The left common carotid artery and the innominate artery are *posterior* to it, and separate it from the trachea. *Anterior* to it there are the manubrium, the origins of the sterno-hyoid and sterno-thyroid, the remains of the thymus, and, at its termination, the overlapping margin of the right pleura and lung. Its *lower* border is in relation with the arch of the aorta, and on its *upper* border it receives the inferior thyroid vein of one or both sides, or a common trunk.

Tributaries.—It receives the *thoracic duct*, which opens into it at the angle of junction of the internal jugular and subclavian veins and is its most important tributary. It also receives the vertebral, internal mammary, inferior thyroid, and superior intercostal veins of its own side, the first left posterior intercostal vein, and some pericardial, thymic, and mediastinal veins. Sometimes the right inferior thyroid vein joins it, but not uncommonly that vessel ends in the right innominate vein or in the commencement of the superior vena cava.

Internal Mammary Veins.—Each internal mammary artery is accompanied by venæ comitantes; they begin by the union of the venæ comitantes of the superior epigastric and musculo-phrenic arteries, between the sixth costal cartilage and the sterno-costalis [transversus thoracis]; and at the upper part of the thorax they fuse into a single vessel which enters the superior mediastinum and ends in the innominate vein of the same side.

The tributaries of the internal mammary veins are—(*a*) The **venæ comitantes** of the **superior epigastric** and **musculo-phrenic arteries**, which in their turn receive the veins that accompany the branches of those arteries. (*b*) Six **anterior perforating veins**, which accompany the corresponding arteries, one in each of the upper six intercostal spaces. (*c*) Twelve **anterior intercostal veins** from the upper six intercostal spaces, two veins lying in each space with the corresponding branches of the internal mammary artery. (*d*) Small and irregular **pleural, muscular, mediastinal, pericardial,** and **thymic veins.** (*e*) the **pericardiaco-phrenic veins.**

The internal mammary veins are provided with numerous valves which prevent the blood from flowing downwards.

Superior Epigastric Veins.—The venæ comitantes of the superior epigastric artery receive tributaries from the substance of the rectus abdominis, the sheath of the muscle, and the *subcutaneous veins* of the upper part of the abdominal wall; they pass, with the artery, between the sternal and costal origins of the diaphragm, and end in the internal mammary veins.

Musculo-phrenic Veins.—The venæ comitantes of the musculo-phrenic artery begin in the abdomen, pass through the diaphragm with the musculo-phrenic artery, and end in the internal mammary veins. They receive as tributaries the **anterior intercostal veins** of the seventh, eighth, and ninth intercostal spaces, and venules from the substance of the diaphragm and walls of the abdomen.

The **vertebral veins** correspond only to the extra-cranial parts of the vertebral arteries. Each begins between the skull and the atlas by the union of offsets from the internal vertebral venous plexuses, as they issue from the vertebral canal. It passes across the posterior arch of the atlas, with the vertebral artery, to the foramen in the transverse process of the atlas. In the foramina in the cervical transverse processes, a plexus of venous channels surrounds the artery. At the lower part of the neck efferents from the plexus unite to form a single trunk which issues from the foramen in the transverse process of the sixth cervical vertebra, and descends, between the longus cervicis and scalenus anterior muscles, to end in the back of the upper part of the innominate vein; near its termination there is a unicuspid or bicuspid valve.

Relations.—In the first part of its course the vein lies in the sub-occipital triangle. The second, plexiform portion, is in the canal formed by the foramina in the transverse processes of the cervical vertebræ, and it lies anterior to the trunks of the cervical spinal nerves with the vertebral artery, which it surrounds. The third part, in the root of the neck, is between the longus cervicis and scalenus anterior muscles, in front of the first part of the vertebral artery, and behind the internal jugular vein.

Tributaries.—In addition to the offsets from the internal vertebral plexuses by the union of which it is formed, each vertebral vein receives the following tributaries. Small veins join it from the muscles, ligaments, and bones of the deeper parts of the neck, and the lower and posterior part of the head. Tributaries from the internal vertebral plexuses pass out of the vertebral canal by the intervertebral foramina. The **anterior vertebral vein** is formed by the union of tributaries which issue from a venous plexus on the front of the bodies of the cervical vertebræ and the roots of their transverse processes. It lies alongside the ascending cervical artery, and ends in the vertebral vein, immediately after that vein has issued from the foramen in the sixth cervical transverse process. The **deep cervical vein** begins in the sub-occipital triangle from a venous plexus with which the vertebral and occipital veins communicate. It descends, behind the cervical transverse processes, in company with the deep cervical artery, turns forwards at the root of the neck, between the transverse processes of the sixth and seventh cervical vertebræ or between the latter and the neck of the first rib, and opens into the vertebral vein. It receives blood from the muscles, ligaments, and bones of the back of the neck. The **first posterior intercostal vein** sometimes opens into the vertebral vein.

Occasionally the venous plexus around the vertebral artery ends below in two terminal trunks—anterior and posterior—instead of one. In those cases the second terminal vessel lies behind the lower part of the vertebral artery, passes through the foramen in the transverse process of the seventh cervical vertebra, and turns forwards on the lateral side of the artery to join the anterior trunk, thus forming a common terminal vein which ends in the usual manner.

The **inferior thyroid veins** are formed by the union of tributaries which issue from the isthmus and the lobes of the thyroid gland. The two veins descend, along the front of the trachea, into the superior mediastinum, where the right inferior thyroid vein ends either in the right innominate vein or in the junction of the two innominate veins, and the left in the upper border of the left innominate vein; or the two veins unite to form a single trunk, which ends usually in the left innominate vein, but occasionally in the right. As they descend in the neck the inferior thyroid veins anastomose together, and sometimes the anastomoses are so frequent that a venous plexus is formed in front of the lower cervical portion of the trachea.

VEINS OF THE HEAD AND NECK

Internal Jugular Vein (Figs. 1000, 1002, 1006, 1017, and 1043).—Each internal jugular vein begins in the posterior compartment of the jugular foramen, as the direct continuation of the sigmoid [transverse] sinus, and ends behind the medial part of the clavicle by uniting with the subclavian vein of the same side to form the innominate vein.

Its commencement, which is dilated, forms the *upper bulb* of the jugular vein. In the upper part of the neck it lies postero-lateral to the internal carotid artery and the last four cranial nerves. As it descends it accompanies first the internal and then the common carotid artery. It inclines forwards as it descends, and gradually passes from its original position, behind and to the lateral side of the internal carotid artery, until it lies more completely to the lateral side of the internal and common carotid arteries, and it overlaps the latter in front. That is more especially the case on the left side, for both internal jugular veins trend slightly towards the right as they descend; consequently, at the root of the neck, the right vein is separated from the right common carotid artery by a small interval filled with areolar tissue in which the vagus nerve lies, whilst the left vein is more directly in front of the corresponding common carotid artery.

A dilatation, called the *lower bulb,* is present at the lower end of the vein; it is bounded, either above or below, by a valve of two or three semilunar cusps. Sometimes this bulb is bounded by valves both above and below.

Relations.—The vein lies anterior to the transverse processes of the cervical vertebræ, the rectus capitis lateralis, longus capitis, and scalenus anterior muscles, the ascending cervical artery, and the phrenic nerve; the suprascapular and the transverse cervical arteries intervene between it and the scalenus anterior. At the root of the neck the vein lies in front of the first part of the subclavian artery and the origins of the vertebral artery and the thyro-cervical trunk, and on the left side it is anterior to the terminal part of the thoracic duct.

On the antero-medial side of the internal jugular vein, immediately below the skull, are the internal carotid artery and the last four cranial nerves; in the rest of its extent it is in relation, medially, first with the internal and then with the common carotid artery, whilst to its medial side and behind, between it and the large arteries, lies the vagus nerve.

Each internal jugular vein is covered superficially, in the whole of its length, by the sterno-mastoid muscle; near its upper end it is crossed by the styloid process, the stylo-pharyngeus and stylo-hyoid muscles, and the posterior belly of the digastric, whilst in its lower half, the omo-hyoid, the sterno-hyoid, and the sterno-thyroid muscles are superficial to it, under cover of the sterno-mastoid. Just below the transverse process of the atlas, and under cover of the sterno-mastoid, the vein is crossed, on its lateral side, by the accessory nerve and by the occipital artery; about the middle of its course it is crossed by the descendens cervicalis nerve, and near its lower end by the anterior jugular vein; the latter vessel, however, is separated from it by the sterno-hyoid and sterno-thyroid muscles. Superficial to the vein are numerous deep cervical lymph glands.

Variations.—The internal jugular vein may be either smaller or larger than usual. In either case, compensatory changes in size occur in the transverse and sigmoid sinuses and internal jugular vein of the opposite side, or in the external and anterior jugular veins of the same side.

Tributaries.—The **inferior petrosal sinus** joins it near its commencement, and the **vein of the cochlear canaliculus** is also a direct tributary if it does not join that sinus. **Pharyngeal veins** drain the *pharyngeal venous plexus* on the wall of the pharynx. The **common facial vein** receives the anterior and posterior facial veins. The common terminal trunk of the **lingual veins** returns part of the blood from the tongue, and the **vena comitans n. hypoglossi** accompanies the hypoglossal nerve. The **superior thyroid vein** accompanies the corresponding artery and its sterno-mastoid branch and receives the **superior laryngeal vein.** The **middle thyroid vein** passes backwards from the lobe of the thyroid gland and crosses the common carotid artery. The **occipital vein** occasionally terminates in the internal jugular vein, but most frequently it ends in the *sub-occipital* plexus, which is drained by the vertebral and deep cervical veins (see p. 1244).

The **common facial vein** is formed by the union of the **anterior** and **posterior facial**

veins. It crosses the external and internal carotid arteries, and ends in the internal jugular vein. Just before it disappears beneath the sterno-mastoid, the common facial vein frequently gives off a large branch which descends along the anterior border of the sterno-mastoid to the supra-sternal fossa, where it joins the anterior jugular vein.

The **anterior facial vein** (Fig. 1040) begins at the medial angle of the eye by the union [v. angularis] of the supra-orbital and supra-trochlear veins. It passes downwards and backwards in the face, to the lower and anterior part of the masseter muscle, which it crosses, lying in the same plane as the facial [external maxillary] artery, but following a much straighter course. After crossing the lower border of the mandible it passes across the submandibular triangle, superficial to the submandibular gland, and separate from the facial artery, which there lies in a deeper plane. It ends, a short distance below the angle of the mandible, by uniting with the posterior facial vein to form the common facial vein.

The anterior facial vein receives tributaries corresponding with all the branches of the facial artery, except the ascending palatine and the tonsillar, which have no accompanying veins, the blood from the region which they supply being returned for the most part through the pharyngeal plexus. The anterior facial vein also communicates with the pterygoid plexus around the lateral pterygoid muscle by means of an anastomosing channel, called the **deep facial vein**, which passes backwards, between the masseter and buccinator muscles, into the infra-temporal fossa.

The **posterior facial vein** is described on p. 1249.

Subclavian Vein.—The subclavian vein, of each side, is the direct continuation of the main vein of the upper limb, *i.e.* the axillary vein; but through its tributary, the external jugular vein, it receives blood both from the head and from the superficial parts of the neck.

From its commencement, at the outer border of the first rib, it runs medially, below and anterior to the corresponding artery, from which it is separated by the lower part of the scalenus anterior muscle, and it ends behind the medial end of the clavicle, by joining the internal jugular vein to form the innominate vein of the corresponding side. As it passes medially it forms a slight curve the convexity of which is directed upwards.

Each subclavian vein possesses a single bicuspid valve which is situated immediately to the lateral side of the opening of the external jugular vein.

Relations.—The subclavian vein is in relation *anteriorly* with the posterior layer of the clavi-pectoral fascia, which separates it from the subclavius muscle, and the nerve to the subclavius, and with the back of the medial part of the clavicle.

It is closely attached to the posterior surface of the clavi-pectoral fascia; consequently it is expanded when the clavicle is moved forwards, an arrangement which constitutes a distinct danger when operations are being performed in the neighbourhood of the vein; for, in the event of the vessel being wounded, forward movement of the clavicle may cause air to be sucked into the vein, with fatal results.

Posterior to the vein, and on a higher plane, is the third part of the subclavian artery, but it is separated from the second part by the scalenus anterior. As soon as it reaches the medial border of the muscle it unites with the internal jugular vein.

The upper surface of the first rib is *below* the vein.

Tributaries.—Whilst the subclavian vein is the direct continuation of the axillary vein, and receives, therefore, the blood from the upper limb, it has, as a general rule, only one named tributary—the external jugular vein.

The **external jugular vein** (Fig. 1040) is formed on the superficial surface of the sterno-mastoid muscle, a little below and behind the angle of the mandible, by the union of the posterior auricular vein with a branch from the posterior facial vein. In many cases the branch from the posterior facial vein is so preponderantly large that it is more correct to describe the external jugular vein as its continuation. After its formation the external jugular vein descends across the sterno-mastoid, with a slight obliquity backwards, to the supraclavicular part of the posterior triangle of the neck, where it pierces the deep fascia, crosses in front of the third part of the subclavian artery, and ends in the subclavian vein.

As it passes across the sterno-mastoid muscle it is covered by the superficial fascia and platysma muscle, and it lies parallel with the great auricular nerve; after crossing the anterior cutaneous nerve of the neck it reaches the posterior border of the sterno-mastoid, where it receives a tributary called the **posterior external jugular vein**, which drains the superficial tissues of the upper and back part of the neck, and runs downwards and forwards, across the roof of the upper part of the posterior triangle.

As the external jugular vein pierces the deep cervical fascia above the clavicle, its wall is closely attached to the margin of the opening through which it passes;

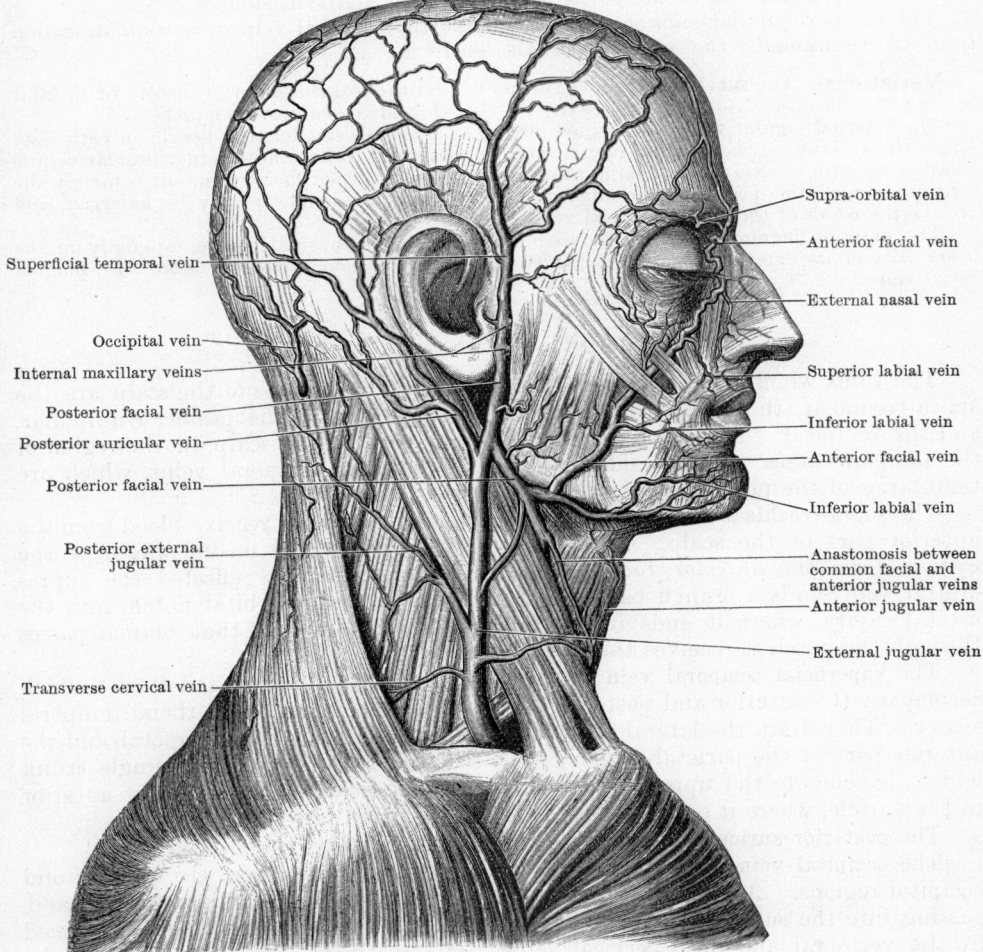

Superficial temporal vein

Occipital vein
Internal maxillary veins
Posterior facial vein
Posterior auricular vein
Posterior facial vein

Posterior external
jugular vein

Transverse cervical vein

Supra-orbital vein
Anterior facial vein
External nasal vein
Superior labial vein
Inferior labial vein
Anterior facial vein
Inferior labial vein
Anastomosis between
common facial and
anterior jugular veins
Anterior jugular vein
External jugular vein

FIG. 1040.—SUPERFICIAL VEINS OF HEAD AND NECK.

and as it is crossing in front of the third part of the subclavian artery it is joined by the suprascapular, transverse cervical, and anterior jugular veins.

There are usually two valves in the lower part of the vein—one, which is generally incompetent, at or near its termination, and a second at a higher level.

Tributaries.—The **posterior auricular vein** (Fig. 1040) receives tributaries from the posterior parts of the parietal and temporal regions and from the medial surface of the auricle. It is considerably larger than the posterior auricular artery, which it accompanies only in the scalp. At the base of the scalp it leaves the artery and descends in the superficial fascia, over the upper part of the sterno-mastoid, to join the external jugular vein.

The **transverse cervical** and **suprascapular veins** accompany the corresponding arteries; not infrequently they open directly into the subclavian vein.

The **anterior jugular vein** begins in the submental region, and is formed by the union of small veins from the lower lip and chin. It descends, in the superficial fascia, at a variable distance from the median plane, perforates the outer layer of the deep fascia, a short distance above the sternum, and enters the suprasternal space between the first and second layers of the deep fascia. In the space it sometimes receives a communication from the common facial vein, and it is connected with its fellow of the opposite side by a transverse channel which lies in front of the trachea and is called the **jugular arch.** Then it turns laterally, between the sterno-mastoid superficially and the sterno-hyoid, sterno-thyroid, and scalenus anterior muscles deeply, and ends in the external jugular vein at the posterior border of the sterno-mastoid.

The external jugular vein sometimes receives the occipital vein or a communication from it. Occasionally the cephalic vein also opens into it.

Variations.—The **subclavian vein** may pass behind the scalenus anterior instead of in front of it; and it has been seen passing between the clavicle and the subclavius muscle.

The **external jugular vein** is sometimes absent, or it may be smaller than usual; in both cases either the anterior or the internal jugular vein is enlarged. When the external jugular vein is small it sometimes receives no communication from the posterior facial vein, but is merely the continuation of the posterior auricular vein. On the other hand, it may be enlarged, and receive the whole of the posterior facial vein.

The **anterior jugular vein** may be absent, or it may be unusually large, especially in the lower part of its extent, and after it has received the occasional tributary from the common facial vein.

VEINS OF THE SCALP

The veins which drain the blood from the superficial parts of the scalp are the supra-trochlear, the supra-orbital, the superficial temporal, the posterior auricular, and the occipital. The blood from the deeper part of the scalp, in the region of the temporal fossa, on each side, passes into the deep temporal veins, which are tributaries of the pterygoid plexus.

The **supra-trochlear** [Vv. frontales] and **supra-orbital veins** receive blood from the anterior part of the scalp. They unite together, near the medial angle of the eye, to form the *anterior facial vein*; before the union is effected the supra-orbital vein sends a branch backwards, through the supra-orbital notch, into the orbital cavity, where it ends in the ophthalmic vein, and as that branch passes through the notch it receives the frontal diploic vein (p. 1250).

The **superficial temporal vein** (Figs. 1006, 1040) is formed by tributaries which accompany the anterior and posterior terminal branches of the superficial temporal artery. They drain the lateral frontal, the superficial part of the temporal, and the anterior part of the parietal region of the scalp, and unite to form a single trunk which descends to the upper border of the zygomatic arch, immediately anterior to the auricle, where it ends in the posterior facial vein (see p. 1249).

The **posterior auricular vein** has been described already (see p. 1247).

The **occipital vein** (Figs. 1006, 1040) receives tributaries from the parietal and occipital regions. As a rule it pierces the occipital origin of the trapezius, and, passing into the sub-occipital triangle, ends in a plexus of veins which is drained by the vertebral and deep cervical veins. It sometimes communicates with the external jugular vein, and occasionally an offset from it accompanies the corresponding artery and ends in the internal jugular vein.

It usually receives the mastoid emissary vein; one of its tributaries receives the parietal emissary vein, and occasionally an emissary vein from the *confluence of the sinuses* opens into it.

VEINS OF ORBIT, NOSE, AND INFRA-TEMPORAL REGION

The veins of those three regions are closely associated together; for although the orbital blood is returned, for the most part, to the cavernous sinus by the ophthalmic veins, these veins are closely connected with the pterygoid plexus, which lies in the infra-temporal region.

Veins of the Orbit.—The veins of the orbit, with the exception of the supra-orbital and supra-trochlear veins, correspond with the branches of the ophthalmic artery, and they gradually converge, as they pass backwards in the orbit, until they form two main trunks, a **superior ophthalmic vein** and an **inferior ophthalmic vein.**

The two trunks terminate separately, or by a single stem, in the anterior end of the cavernous sinus, to which they pass through the superior orbital fissure, and between the two heads of the lateral rectus muscle.

The superior ophthalmic vein communicates, at the supero-medial angle of the orbit, with the commencement of the anterior facial vein [v. angularis]. The inferior ophthalmic vein communicates, through the inferior orbital fissure, with the pterygoid plexus.

Veins of the Nose.—The veins of the walls of the nasal cavity end partly in the ethmoidal tributaries of the superior ophthalmic vein, partly in the septal tributaries of the superior labial and in the *external nasal veins,* all of which pass to the anterior facial vein; but the majority of the *internal nasal veins,* both from the septal and lateral walls, join together to form a spheno-palatine vein, which passes through the spheno-palatine foramen and the pterygo-palatine fossa to the pterygoid plexus.

Pterygoid Plexus and **Maxillary Vein.** — The **pterygoid plexus** of veins lies in the infra-temporal fossa. It covers the lateral surface of the medial pterygoid muscle, and surrounds the lateral pterygoid. It receives tributaries which correspond with and accompany the branches of the maxillary artery— namely, spheno-palatine, pharyngeal, veins of pterygoid canal, infra-orbital, posterior superior dental, greater palatine, buccal, two or three deep temporal, pterygoid, masseteric, and inferior dental veins, and the middle meningeal vein. It communicates above with the cavernous sinus by emissary veins through the foramen ovale; in front with the inferior ophthalmic vein through the inferior orbital fissure; and between the masseter and the buccinator with the anterior facial vein by the deep facial anastomosing branch. It also communicates behind and medially, on the medial side of the medial pterygoid, with the pharyngeal plexus, and it drains behind into the maxillary vein.

The **maxillary vein** is a short vessel which accompanies the first part of the maxillary artery, between the spheno-mandibular ligament and the neck of the mandible. Between the neck of the mandible and the antero-medial surface of the parotid gland it joins the upper part of the posterior facial vein. Occasionally the maxillary vein is double, and sometimes it is represented by several channels.

The **posterior facial vein** is formed, immediately above the zygomatic arch, by the union of the superficial temporal vein with the middle temporal vein, which accompanies the middle temporal artery (p. 1172). It crosses the zygomatic arch, dips deep to the upper part of the parotid gland, and, between the antero-medial surface of the gland and the posterior border of the mandible, receives the maxillary vein or veins. Then it descends, through the substance of the parotid and divides into two parts—anterior and posterior—which emerge from its lower end.

The **anterior division** passes forwards and downwards and unites with the anterior facial vein to form the common facial vein.

The **posterior division** forms one of the two tributaries of origin of the external jugular vein.

Variations.—The **posterior facial vein** may end entirely in the common facial vein, or in the external or the internal jugular vein. It may be very small or absent.

VENOUS SINUSES AND VEINS OF THE CRANIUM AND OF ITS CONTENTS

The venous channels met with in the cranial walls and cranial cavity are :—

(1) The diploic veins, which lie in the spongy tissue of the cranial bones.

(2) The meningeal veins, which accompany the meningeal arteries in the outer layer of the dura mater.

(3) The veins of the brain, which lie in the folds of pia mater and in the subarachnoid space.

(4) The cranial venous sinuses, which are channels situated between the outer and inner layers of the dura mater; they receive blood chiefly from the brain,

but also from the membranes and bones, and cerebro-spinal fluid is transmitted into them from the arachnoid villi and granulations.

DIPLOIC AND MENINGEAL VEINS

Diploic veins are anastomosing spaces in the diploë of the flat bones of the skull; they are lined with endothelium. The number of efferent vessels which emerge from the diploic spaces is not constant, but usually there are at least four on each side—a frontal, two parietal (anterior and posterior), and an occipital.

The **frontal diploic vein** is one of the most constant; it drains the anterior part of the frontal bone, passes through a small aperture in the upper margin of the supra-orbital notch, and ends in the supra-orbital vein.

The **anterior parietal diploic vein** drains the posterior part of the frontal bone

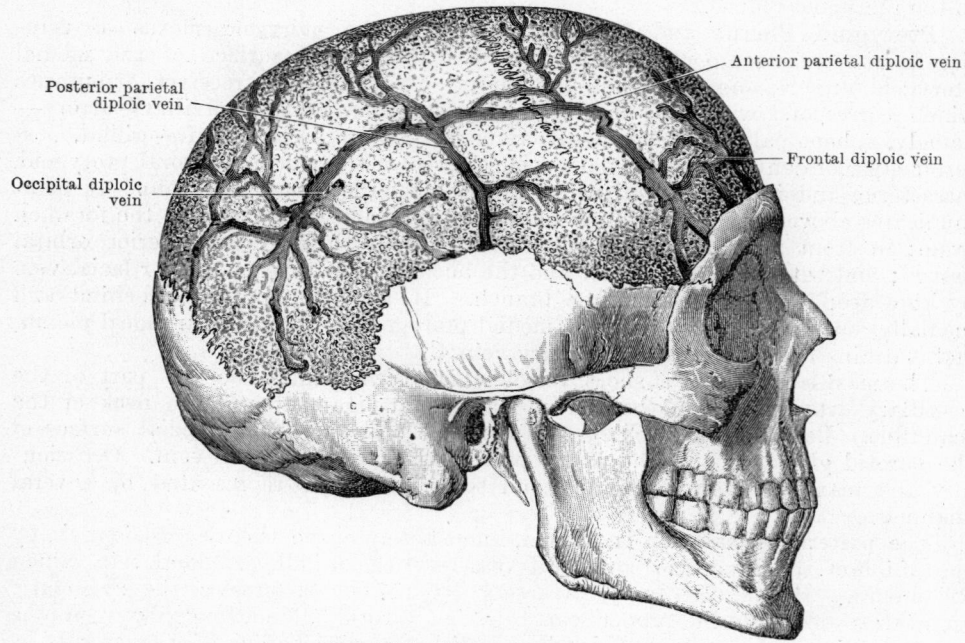

Posterior parietal diploic vein

Occipital diploic vein

Anterior parietal diploic vein

Frontal diploic vein

FIG. 1041.—VEINS OF THE DIPLOË.

and the anterior part of the parietal bone; it emerges from the great wing of the sphenoid, and ends either in the spheno-parietal sinus or in the anterior deep temporal vein.

The **posterior parietal diploic vein** drains the posterior part of the parietal bone; it runs downwards through the posterior inferior angle of the parietal bone and ends either in the transverse sinus, or, more commonly, in the mastoid emissary vein.

The **occipital diploic vein** is usually the largest of the series; it drains the occipital bone, and ends either in the occipital emissary vein or internally in the transverse sinus.

The **meningeal veins** commence in two capillary plexuses, a deep and a superficial. The deep plexus is a wide-meshed network in the inner layer of the dura mater. Its efferent vessels pass to the superficial plexus. The superficial plexus lies in the outer layer of the dura mater. It consists of numerous vessels of uniform calibre which frequently anastomose together and terminate in two sets of efferents; of those, one set ends in the cranial blood sinuses, and the other accompanies the meningeal arteries. The efferent meningeal veins are peculiar inasmuch as they do not alter much in size as they approach their terminations. They lie external to the arteries in the grooves in the bones, and are very liable to be torn when the bones are fractured (Wood Jones).

VEINS OF THE BRAIN

The veins of the brain include the veins of the cerebrum, mid-brain, cerebellum, pons, and medulla oblongata. They do not possess valves.

Veins of the Cerebrum.—The **cerebral veins** are arranged in two groups— deep and superficial.

The deep veins issue from the substance of the brain. The superficial veins lie upon its surface in the pia mater and the subarachnoid space. The terminal trunks of both sets pierce the arachnoid membrane and the inner layer of the dura mater, and open into the cranial venous sinuses.

The **deep cerebral veins** are the choroid veins, the thalamo-striate veins, the internal cerebral veins, the great cerebral vein, and the striate veins.

Each **choroid vein** is formed by the union of tributaries which issue from the choroid plexus in the central part and inferior horn of a lateral ventricle. It passes along the lateral border of the tela chorioidea of the third ventricle to the interventricular foramen, where it receives efferents from the choroid plexus of the third ventricle, and unites with the thalamo-striate vein to form the internal cerebral vein.

The **thalamo-striate vein** [vena terminalis] on each side, is formed by the union of tributaries which issue from the corpus striatum and from the thalamus. It runs forwards between the thalamus and the caudate nucleus, in a groove in the floor of the central part of the lateral ventricle, and, after receiving tributaries from the walls of the anterior horn of the ventricle and the septum lucidum, it ends at the apex of the tela chorioidea, where it joins the choroid vein to form the internal cerebral vein.

Each **internal cerebral vein** begins at the apex of the tela chorioidea, near the interventricular foramen, by the union of the thalamo-striate with the choroid vein. The two veins run backwards between the layers of the tela, receiving tributaries from the choroid plexuses of the third ventricle and from the fornix and corpus callosum, and end beneath the splenium of the corpus callosum, by uniting to form the great cerebral vein.

The **great cerebral vein** (Galen) passes backwards and slightly upwards from its origin, round the splenium of the corpus callosum. It ends in the anterior extremity of the straight sinus. In addition to the two internal cerebral veins, by the union of which it is formed, it receives tributaries from the posterior part of the gyrus cinguli of each side, from the pineal and quadrigeminal bodies, from the medial and inferior surfaces of the occipital lobes of the cerebral hemispheres, and from the upper surface of the cerebellum. It receives also the basal vein of each side (see p. 1252).

One or two **striate veins** descend from the substance of the corpus striatum, through the anterior perforated substance, and end in the basal vein.

The **superficial cerebral veins** are more numerous and of larger calibre than the cerebral arteries. They lie upon the surface of the cerebrum, drain blood from the cerebral cortex, and they are divisible into two sets—the superior and the inferior.

The **superior cerebral veins**, six to twelve in number on each side, lie in the pia mater and subarachnoid space on the upper and lateral aspect of the cerebral hemispheres. They run upwards and medially to the margin of the longitudinal fissure where they receive tributaries from the medial surface of the hemisphere. They end in the superior sagittal sinus, and those that encounter the *lacunae laterales* pass beneath them to reach the sinus. The anterior veins of that set are small and run transversely, but the posterior are large and run obliquely forwards and medially; they are embedded for some distance in the wall of the sinus, and their orifices are directed forwards against the blood stream.

The **inferior cerebral veins** lie on the lower and lateral aspects of the cerebral hemispheres; they end in the sinuses which lie at the base of the skull— the cavernous, the superior petrosal, and the transverse sinuses. One of these veins, the **superficial middle cerebral vein**, runs along the posterior ramus and the stem of the lateral sulcus to the cavernous sinus; occasionally it is united by an anastomotic loop, known as the **superior anastomotic vein** (Trolard), with the superior sagittal sinus, and sometimes by the **inferior anastomotic vein** with the transverse sinus.

Each **anterior cerebral vein** lies in the longitudinal fissure, and accompanies the corresponding anterior cerebral artery; it receives tributaries from the corpus callosum and the gyrus cinguli. Turning downwards, round the genu of the corpus callosum, it reaches the base of the brain, and ends in the basal vein.

The **deep middle cerebral vein** lies deeply in the lateral sulcus; it anastomoses freely with the superficial middle vein, receives tributaries from the insula and the opercula, and ends in the basal vein.

The **basal vein** begins at the anterior perforated substance; it is formed by the union of the anterior cerebral vein with the deep middle cerebral vein and

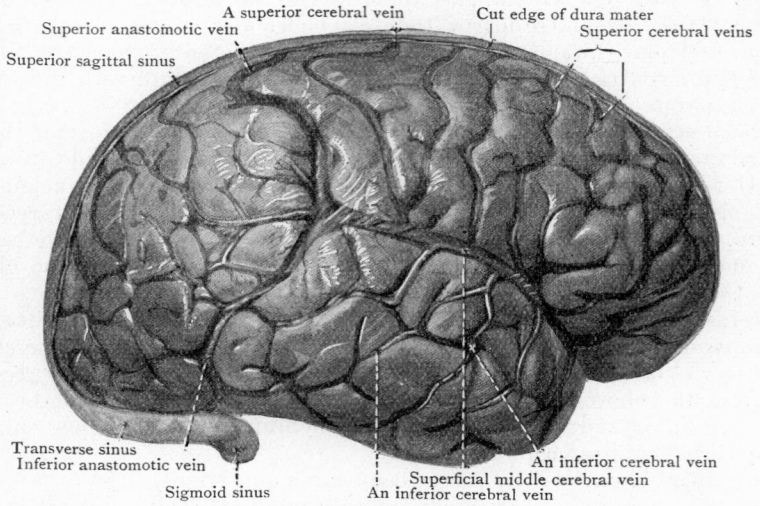

A superior cerebral vein · Cut edge of dura mater · Superior cerebral veins · Superior anastomotic vein · Superior sagittal sinus · Transverse sinus · Inferior anastomotic vein · Sigmoid sinus · An inferior cerebral vein · Superficial middle cerebral vein · An inferior cerebral vein

FIG. 1042.—VEINS OF THE SUPERO-LATERAL SURFACE OF THE HEMISPHERE, SEEN THROUGH THE ARACHNOID MATER.

receives the striate vein or veins. Passing backwards around the cerebral peduncle, it ends in the great cerebral vein. Its tributaries are derived from the walls of the tuber cinereum, the mamillary body, the posterior perforated substance, the uncus, the inferior horn of the lateral ventricle, and the cerebral peduncle.

Veins of the Mid-brain.—The veins of the mid-brain end for the most part either in the great cerebral vein or in the basal veins.

Cerebellar Veins. — Those veins also are divisible into two groups, the superficial and the deep. The former are quite independent of and much more numerous than the arteries. They form two sets, the superior and the inferior.

The **superior cerebellar veins** end in a median efferent vessel which is sometimes double, and in several lateral efferents. The median efferent vein runs forwards on the superior vermis and ends in the great cerebral vein. The lateral efferents end in the transverse sinuses or in the superior petrosal sinuses.

The **inferior cerebellar veins** also form a small median efferent and numerous lateral efferents; the former runs backwards on the inferior vermis and joins either the straight sinus or one of the transverse sinuses, and the latter end in the inferior petrosal and occipital sinuses.

The **deep cerebellar veins** issue from the substance of the cerebellum and join the superficial veins.

Veins of the Pons.—The deep veins from the substance of the pons pass forwards to its anterior surface, where they become superficial and anastomose to form a plexus which is drained by superior and inferior efferent veins. The superior efferent veins join the basal vein; the inferior efferent veins either unite with the cerebellar veins, or they open into the superior petrosal sinus.

Veins of the Medulla Oblongata.—Deep veins of the medulla oblongata issue from its substance and end in a superficial plexus. This plexus is drained by an anterior and a posterior median vein and by radicular veins.

The *anterior median vein* is continuous below with the corresponding vein of the spinal cord; it communicates above with the plexus on the surface of the pons.

The *posterior median vein* is continuous below with the posterior median vein of the spinal cord, from which it ascends to the lower end of the fourth ventricle, where it divides into two branches which join the inferior petrosal sinus or the network of basilar sinuses.

The *radicular veins* issue from the lateral parts of the plexus and run with the roots of the last four cranial nerves; they end in the inferior petrosal and occipital sinuses or in the upper part of the internal jugular vein.

Venous Sinuses of Dura Mater

The **venous sinuses** of the cranium are spaces between the layers of the dura mater and they are lined with an endothelium which is continuous with the endothelium of the veins. They receive the veins of the brain, communicate frequently with the meningeal veins and with veins external to the cranium, and end directly or indirectly in the internal jugular vein. Some of the cranial blood sinuses are unpaired, others are paired.

Unpaired Sinuses.—These are the superior sagittal, the inferior sagittal, the straight, the intercavernous, and the basilar sinuses.

The **superior sagittal sinus** begins at the crista galli, where it communicates, through the foramen cæcum, frequently with the veins of the frontal sinus, sometimes with the veins of the nasal cavity, and more rarely with the anterior facial vein. It passes backwards in the convex margin of the falx cerebri, grooving the cranial vault. As it descends along the occipital bone it usually deviates slightly to the right, and it ends at the internal occipital protuberance by becoming the right transverse sinus. Instead of passing to the right, it occasionally turns to the left, and ends in the left transverse sinus, and sometimes it bifurcates and ends in both transverse sinuses. When it ends wholly in the right or the left transverse sinus its termination is associated with a well-marked dilatation, called the *confluence of the sinuses*, which is lodged in a depression at one side of the internal occipital protuberance. The confluence is connected, across the protuberance, by an anastomosing channel, with a similar dilatation which marks the junction of the straight sinus with the lateral sinus of the opposite side. Opening into the superior sagittal sinus are the superior cerebral veins; and it communicates on each side by small openings with a series of spaces in the dura mater, called the **lacunæ laterales**, into which the arachnoid granulations project (see p. 953). It also communicates, by emissary veins which pass through the parietal foramina, with the veins on the exterior of the cranium. Its cavity, which is triangular in transverse section, is crossed by several fibrous strands.

The **inferior sagittal sinus** runs in the posterior two-thirds of the free part of the lower margin of the falx cerebri. It ends behind by joining with the great cerebral vein to form the straight sinus. It receives tributaries from the falx cerebri and from the medial surface of the middle third of each cerebral hemisphere.

Around the lower part of the hypophysis cerebri in the region of the sella turcica, there are intercommunicating channels which connect the two cavernous sinuses together. Two of these **intercavernous sinuses** lie in the anterior and posterior margins of the diaphragma sellæ and, together with the intervening parts of the cavernous sinuses, constitute the *circular sinus*; others pass across the floor of the hypophyseal fossa.

The **network of basilar sinuses** is situated in the dura mater on the clivus of the skull. It connects the cavernous and the inferior petrosal sinuses together, and communicates below with the anterior longitudinal vertebral sinuses.

The **straight sinus** is formed by the union of the inferior sagittal sinus with the great cerebral vein. It runs downwards and backwards along the line of union between the falx cerebri and the tentorium cerebelli, and receives some of the superior cerebellar veins and a few tributaries from the occipital lobes and the falx cerebri. As a general rule it turns to the left at the internal occipital protuberance, dilates slightly, and becomes continuous with the left transverse sinus, its dilatation being united with the corresponding dilatation on the lower

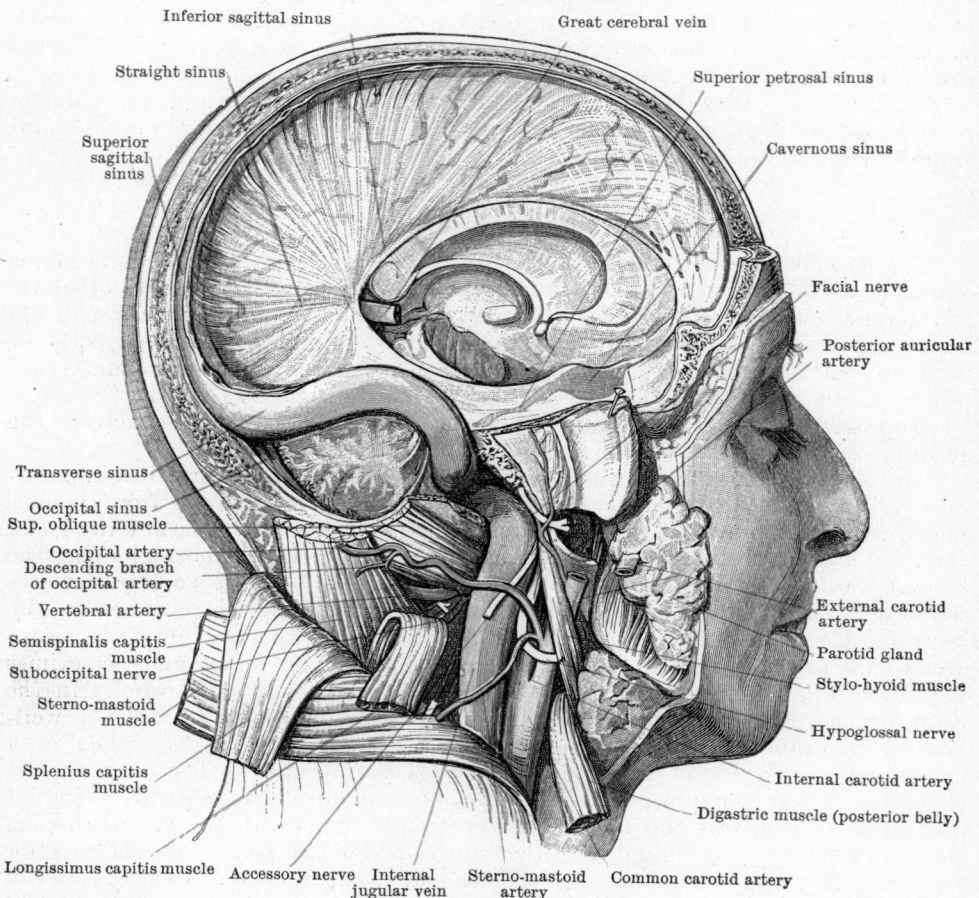

FIG. 1043.—DISSECTION OF THE HEAD AND NECK, SHOWING THE VENOUS SINUSES OF THE DURA MATER AND THE UPPER PART OF THE INTERNAL JUGULAR VEIN.

end of the superior sagittal sinus (the "confluence of the sinuses") by a transverse anastomosing channel. Occasionally the straight sinus ends in the right transverse sinus; in that case the superior sagittal sinus ends in the left transverse sinus; and sometimes it bifurcates to join both transverse sinuses.

Paired Sinuses.—There are six pairs of sinuses, viz., the transverse, the occipital, the cavernous, the superior petrosal, the inferior petrosal, and the spheno-parietal.

Each **transverse sinus** begins at the internal occipital protuberance, the right usually as the continuation of the superior sagittal, and the left as the continuation of the straight sinus. Each passes laterally in the postero-lateral part of the attached border of the tentorium cerebelli and in a groove on the occipital bone. From the lateral angle of the occipital bone it passes to the posterior inferior angle of the parietal bone, which it grooves; then it leaves the tentorium and turns downwards on the cerebral surface of the mastoid portion of the temporal bone;

from the latter it passes to the upper surface of the jugular process of the occipital bone; there it turns forwards and then downwards into the jugular foramen, where it becomes continuous with the internal jugular vein. The part which descends on the temporal bone and turns forwards on the jugular process of the occipital is called the **sigmoid sinus** (Fig. 1043).

Its tributaries are some of the inferior cerebral and superior and inferior

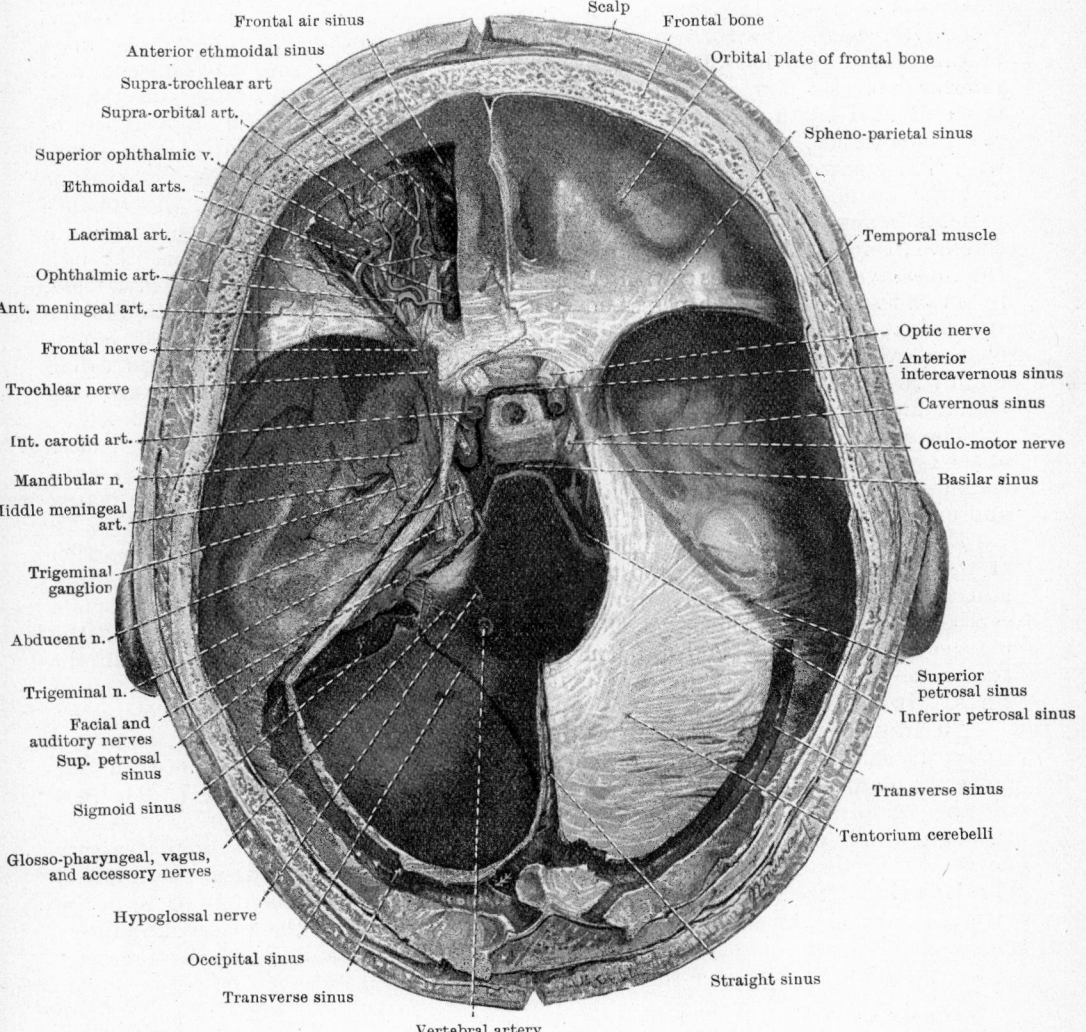

Frontal air sinus — Scalp — Frontal bone
Anterior ethmoidal sinus — Orbital plate of frontal bone
Supra-trochlear art
Supra-orbital art. — Spheno-parietal sinus
Superior ophthalmic v.
Ethmoidal arts.
Lacrimal art. — Temporal muscle
Ophthalmic art.
Ant. meningeal art. — Optic nerve
Frontal nerve — Anterior intercavernous sinus
Trochlear nerve — Cavernous sinus
Int. carotid art. — Oculo-motor nerve
Mandibular n. — Basilar sinus
Middle meningeal art.
Trigeminal ganglion
Abducent n.
Trigeminal n. — Superior petrosal sinus
Facial and auditory nerves — Inferior petrosal sinus
Sup. petrosal sinus
Sigmoid sinus — Transverse sinus
Glosso-pharyngeal, vagus, and accessory nerves — Tentorium cerebelli
Hypoglossal nerve
Occipital sinus
Transverse sinus — Straight sinus
Vertebral artery

FIG. 1044.—THE LOWER VENOUS SINUSES OF THE DURA MATER.

In the specimen represented the superior sagittal sinus opened into both transverse sinuses and chiefly into the left. The straight sinus also opened into both transverse sinuses. The medial part of the left transverse sinus was divided by a horizontal septum into upper and lower parts. The arrow in the figure passes below the septum.

cerebellar veins, a posterior parietal diploic vein, and the superior petrosal sinus. It is connected with the veins outside the cranium by emissary veins which pass through the mastoid foramen and the posterior condylar canal.

The **occipital sinuses** lie in the attached border of the falx cerebelli and in the dura mater along the postero-lateral boundaries of the foramen magnum; frequently they unite above and open by a single channel into the commencement of either the right or the left transverse sinus, but their upper extremities may remain separate, and then each communicates with the transverse sinus of its own side. On the other hand, either the right or the left sinus may be absent. Each opens below into the corresponding sigmoid sinus, and both communicate with the posterior longitudinal vertebral sinuses. Each occipital sinus is an anastomosing channel between the transverse and sigmoid sinuses of the same side, and each receives a few inferior cerebellar veins.

The **cavernous sinuses** lie at the sides of the body of the sphenoid bone. Each sinus begins in front at the medial end of the superior orbital fissure, where it receives the corresponding ophthalmic veins, and it ends at the apex of the petrous portion of the temporal bone by dividing into the superior and inferior petrosal sinuses. Its cavity, which is irregular in size and shape, is so divided by numerous fibrous strands that it assumes the appearance of cavernous tissue; and in its lateral wall are embedded the internal carotid artery with its sympathetic plexus, the oculo-motor, the trochlear, the ophthalmic and the abducent nerves. Its tributaries are the ophthalmic vein, the spheno-parietal sinus, and inferior cerebral veins, including the superficial middle cerebral vein. It communicates with the opposite cavernous sinus through the intercavernous sinuses; with the pterygoid plexus, in the infra-temporal fossa, by an emissary vein which passes either through the foramen ovale or through the sphenoidal emissary foramen; with the internal jugular vein by small venous channels which accompany the internal carotid artery through the carotid canal, and by the inferior petrosal sinus; with the transverse sinus by the superior petrosal sinus; and through the superior ophthalmic vein with the supra-orbital vein.

The **spheno-parietal sinuses** are lodged in the dura mater on the under surfaces of the lesser wings of the sphenoid bone close to their posterior borders. Each sinus communicates with the middle meningeal veins, receives veins from the dura mater, and ends in the anterior part of the corresponding cavernous sinus.

Each **superior petrosal** sinus begins at the apex of the petrous portion of the temporal bone in the posterior end of the corresponding cavernous sinus, and it runs backwards and laterally, in the attached margin of the tentorium cerebelli, above the trigeminal nerve. It grooves the superior margin of the petrous portion of the temporal bone, at the lateral end of which it ends in the transverse sinus at the point where it is turning down to become the sigmoid sinus. It receives inferior cerebral, superior cerebellar, tympanic, and diploic veins.

An **inferior petrosal sinus** begins at the posterior end of each cavernous sinus; it runs backwards, laterally, and downwards, in a groove between the posterior margin of the petrous part of the temporal bone and the basilar part of the occipital bone, to the anterior compartment of the jugular foramen, through which it passes. It crosses the glosso-pharyngeal, vagus and accessory nerves either on their lateral or on their medial side, and it ends in the internal jugular vein. Its tributaries include inferior cerebellar veins and veins from the internal ear; the **internal auditory vein** reaches it through the internal auditory meatus, and small venules emerge from the cochlear canaliculus and the aqueduct of the vestibule to join it or the internal jugular vein.

Variations.—Variations of the **venous sinuses** are not numerous. One transverse sinus may be absent or very small, when, as a rule, that of the opposite side is enlarged. The inferior sagittal, the occipital, or the spheno-parietal sinuses may be absent, and there may be an additional petro-squamous tributary to the transverse sinus. The *petro-squamous sinus*, when present, runs in a groove (the posterior part of which may be a canal) along the line of the petro-squamous suture and opens behind into the transverse sinus. It is the remains of a fœtal channel which joined the primitive head vein; and in the human adult, in rare cases, it pierces the skull just above the posterior root of the zygoma (squamosal foramen) or through the root (post-glenoid foramen) above the lateral end of the squamo-tympanic fissure and ends in the external jugular *via* the posterior facial vein. That is the normal arrangement in some mammals.

EMISSARY VEINS

The **emissary veins** are veins which convey blood from the venous sinuses of the dura mater to the veins which lie outside the walls of the cranium. They may be single veins, or plexiform channels surrounding other structures which are passing through the walls of the cranium ; individual emissary veins vary greatly in size and are not always present. They frequently communicate with the diploic veins.

In the child, and sometimes in the adult, a **frontal emissary vein** passes from the anterior end of the superior sagittal sinus through the foramen cæcum. Its lower end divides into two channels which either end in the veins of the frontal sinus or those of the roof of the nasal cavities, or they perforate the nasal bones and join the anterior facial veins.

The **parietal emissary veins**, one on each side, pass through the parietal foramina, from the superior sagittal sinus to a tributary of the occipital vein.

An **occipital emissary vein** is only occasionally present. It passes from the confluence of the sinuses through the occipital protuberance to one of the tributaries of an occipital vein, and, when present, it receives the occipital diploic vein.

A **mastoid emissary vein** connects the sigmoid sinus, through the mastoid foramen, with the occipital or the posterior auricular vein.

A **posterior condylar emissary vein** passes through the posterior condylar canal when present, and connects the lower end of the sigmoid sinus with the plexus of veins in the sub-occipital triangle.

Emissary veins of the foramen ovale surround the mandibular nerve, as it passes through the foramen ovale, and connect the cavernous sinus with the pterygoid plexus in the infra-temporal fossa. If the *sphenoidal emissary foramen (Vesalii)* is present, the plexus of the foramen ovale is replaced or supplemented by an emissary vein which passes through that foramen.

Emissary veins of the carotid canal accompany the internal carotid artery and connect the cavernous sinus either with the pharyngeal plexus or with the upper part of the internal jugular vein. A few small emissary veins also pass through the foramen lacerum to the pterygoid plexus.

As the hypoglossal nerve passes through the anterior condylar foramen it is accompanied either by a venous plexus or by a large **anterior condylar emissary vein** which connects the veins of the medulla oblongata and the lower part of the occipital sinus with the upper end of the internal jugular vein, or with the extra-cranial part of the inferior petrosal sinus.

Not uncommonly there is a venous connexion between the cavernous sinus and the veins in the facial canal of the temporal bone.

Veins of Vertebral Column

The veins of the vertebral column consist of rich venous plexuses which extend along the whole length of the column both inside and outside the vertebral canal. All the plexuses anastomose freely with one another ; they are united by longitudinal channels ; and they are drained by the series of intervertebral veins. They are described under the following heads :—

Internal vertebral plexuses   External vertebral plexuses
Basi-vertebral veins   Anterior
Longitudinal vertebral sinuses   Posterior

Internal Vertebral Plexuses.—The veins in the interior of the vertebral canal form a continuous venous network which lies between the dura mater and the walls of the vertebral canal. The network communicates laterally with the inter-vertebral veins, behind with the posterior external venous plexuses, whilst in front it receives the basi-vertebral veins. It receives veins from the spinal cord also.

The **basi-vertebral veins** are venous channels, enclosed by endothelial walls, which lie in the substance of the bodies of the vertebræ. They communicate with the plexuses of veins on the anterior surfaces of the bodies of the vertebræ, and they converge towards the posterior surfaces of the bodies of the vertebræ where they open into transverse anastomoses between the anterior longitudinal vertebral sinuses.

In the anterior part of the internal plexus, on the posterior surfaces of the bodies of the vertebræ and the intervertebral discs, at the sides of the posterior longitudinal ligament, there are two wide longitudinal channels, called the *anterior longitudinal vertebral sinuses*. They extend the whole length of the vertebral canal, are united together by transverse channels under cover of the posterior longitudinal ligament, and communicate above with the network of basilar sinuses, the terminal parts of the sigmoid sinuses, and with the plexus of veins which accompanies each hypoglossal nerve through the anterior condylar canal. Two less obvious longitudinal channels, called the *posterior longitudinal vertebral sinuses*, can sometimes be distinguished on the internal surfaces of the vertebral arches and the ligamenta flava. When they are well established, they communicate above with the occipital sinuses.

External Vertebral Plexuses.—The **anterior external vertebral plexuses** are formed by anastomosing venous channels which lie on the anterior surfaces of the bodies of the vertebræ. They communicate with the basi-vertebral veins and with the intervertebral veins.

The **posterior external vertebral plexuses** lie on the postero-lateral surfaces of the vertebræ, in the vertebral grooves, around the spines, the articular and the transverse processes of the vertebræ. They communicate with the internal plexuses and with the intervertebral veins, and they open into the vertebral, intercostal, and lumbar veins.

Intervertebral Veins.—The internal vertebral plexuses are drained not only above into the cranial venous sinuses by the longitudinal vertebral sinuses, but also by a series of **intervertebral veins** which pass through the intervertebral foramina. In the cervical region the intervertebral veins open externally into the vertebral veins, in the thoracic region into the intercostal veins, in the lumbar region into the lumbar veins, and in the sacral region into the lateral sacral veins. The intervertebral veins convey blood both from the internal and the external vertebral plexuses.

Veins of Spinal Cord

The **veins of the spinal cord** issue from its substance, and end in a plexus in the pia mater. In that plexus there are six longitudinal channels—one *antero-median*, along the anterior fissure; two *antero-lateral*, immediately behind the anterior nerve-roots; two *postero-lateral*, immediately behind the posterior nerve-roots; and one *postero-median*, behind the posterior septum. Radicular efferent vessels issue from the plexus, and pass along the nerve-roots to communicate with the internal vertebral venous network. The veins of the spinal cord vary very much in size, but they are largest on the lower part of the cord and on its posterior surface.

The postero-median and antero-median veins are continued above into the corresponding veins of the medulla oblongata.

The antero-lateral and postero-lateral veins pour their blood partly into the median veins and partly into the radicular veins; the greater part of the blood from the spinal cord is returned by the radicular veins.

VEINS OF UPPER LIMB

The veins of the upper limb are divisible into two sets — **superficial** and **deep**. Both sets open eventually into a common terminal trunk which is known as the **axillary vein**. That vein is, therefore, the chief efferent vein of the upper limb. It is continued as the subclavian vein to the innominate vein, through which its blood, together with that from the corresponding side of the head and neck, reaches the superior vena cava.

Deep Veins of Upper Limb

The deep veins of the upper limb, with the exception of the axillary vein, are arranged in pairs (**venæ comitantes**) which accompany the various arteries and are similarly named. So far as those veins are concerned it is sufficient to state that they are provided with valves, that they are situated one on each side of the artery with which they are associated, and that they are usually united together by numerous transverse anastomoses which cross the artery. The axillary vein, however, requires more detailed consideration.

The **axillary vein** (Figs. 1017 and 1100) begins, as the direct continuation of the basilic vein, opposite the lower border of the teres major muscle. It passes upwards and medially, through the axilla, along the medial side of the axillary artery, and ends, at the outer border of the first rib, by becoming the subclavian vein. It possesses one or more bicuspid valves, of which one is usually situated opposite the lower border of the subscapularis muscle.

Relations.—Its *anterior* relations are similar to those of the axillary artery, but, in addition, the vein is crossed in front, under cover of the clavicular part of the pectoralis major, by the pectoral branches of the acromio-thoracic artery, and by branches of the medial pectoral nerve, and it receives anteriorly the cephalic vein.

Posterior to it are the muscles which form the posterior wall of the axilla, the axillary fat, and the first serration of the serratus anterior. The nerve to the serratus anterior intervenes between it and that muscle, and the subscapular nerves, the nerve to the latissimus dorsi, and the subscapular artery pass between it and the subscapularis.

It is separated from the third part of the axillary artery by the ulnar nerve and the medial cutaneous nerve of the forearm; from the second part of the axillary artery by the medial cord of the brachial plexus; and in the proximal part of the axilla, behind the clavi-pectoral fascia, it is separated from the first part of the artery by the medial pectoral nerve. To its medial side lie the lateral set of axillary lymph glands and, in the distal part of the axilla, the medial cutaneous nerve of the arm.

Tributaries.—Its tributaries correspond with the branches of the axillary artery, except the acromio-thoracic. It receives the venæ comitantes of the brachial artery at the lower border of the subscapularis; and the cephalic vein joins it above the upper border of the pectoralis minor muscle.

SUPERFICIAL VEINS OF UPPER LIMB

The superficial veins of the upper limb commence in the superficial fascia of the palm and dorsum of the hand and of the digits.

Veins of the Digits and Hand.—The **palmar digital veins** are two or more fine longitudinal channels which lie in the superficial fascia of the palmar surfaces of the digits. They communicate, proximally, with a fine venous network which lies in the superficial fascia of the palm, and, at the proximal ends of the inter-digital clefts, by

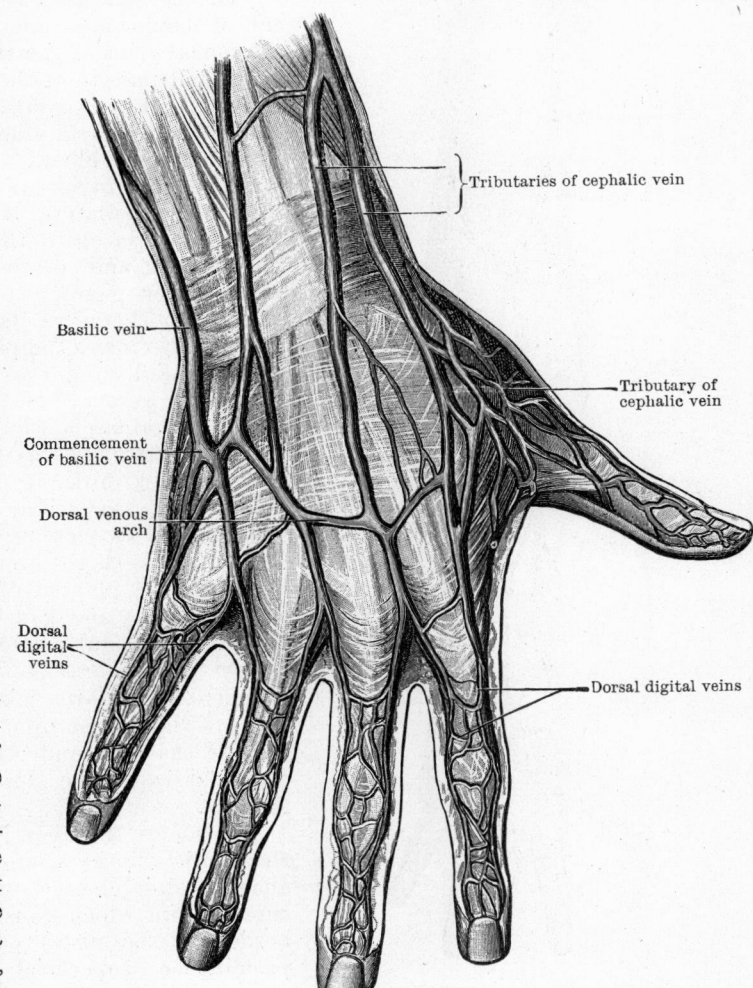

FIG. 1045.—SUPERFICIAL VEINS ON THE DORSUM OF THE HAND AND DIGITS.

means of anastomosing channels which pass backwards between the heads of the metacarpal bones, they open into the *dorsal digital veins.*

The **dorsal digital veins,** two in each digit, anastomose freely together on the dorsal surfaces of the digits. At the proximal ends of the interdigital clefts they communicate with the palmar digital veins, and then they unite together to form an indefinite series of *dorsal metacarpal veins* which again unite on the lower part of the back of the hand in a **dorsal venous arch** which, however, is extremely variable in position and shape.

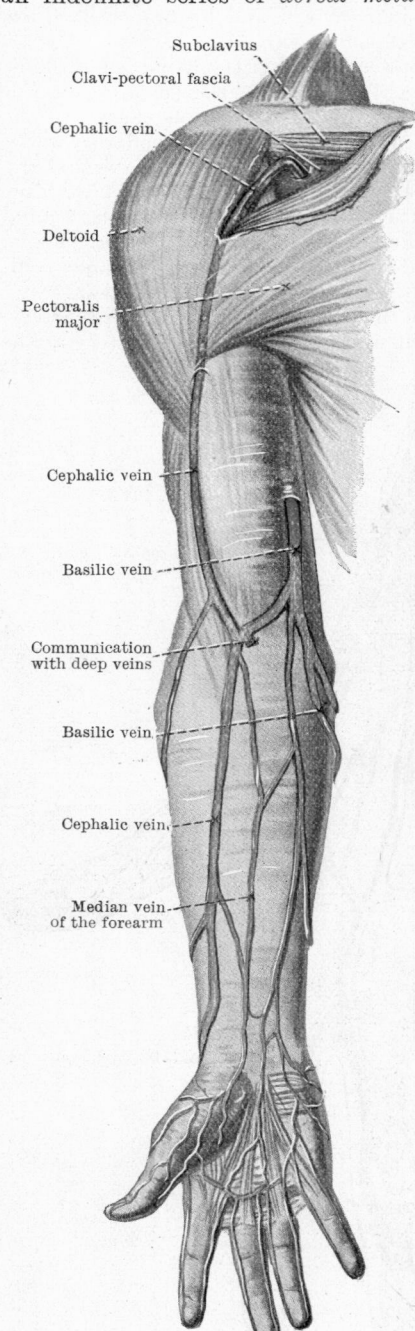

Subclavius

Clavi-pectoral fascia

Cephalic vein

Deltoid

Pectoralis major

Cephalic vein

Basilic vein

Communication with deep veins

Basilic vein

Cephalic vein

Median vein of the forearm

FIG. 1046.—SUPERFICIAL VEINS ON THE FLEXOR ASPECT OF THE RIGHT UPPER LIMB.

Veins of Forearm and Upper Arm.— The veins of the forearm emerge from the dorsal venous arch and from the palmar venous plexus, and they vary considerably in number and in size. As a rule there are two main longitudinal channels—the *cephalic vein* on the radial side and the *basilic vein* on the ulnar side. Sometimes there is a definite *median vein* on the front of the forearm.

The **cephalic vein** begins in the radial end of the dorsal venous arch. It receives the dorsal veins of the thumb, turns round the radial margin of the distal part of the forearm, and runs parallel with the anterior border of the brachio-radialis muscle to the front of the elbow. There, frequently much reduced in size, it turns laterally and runs along the lateral border of the prominence of the biceps to the interval between the deltoid and pectoralis major, along which, after piercing the deep fascia, it ascends to the infra-clavicular fossa. In the fossa it crosses the pectoralis minor and passes medially under cover of the clavicular part of the pectoralis major in front of the clavi-pectoral fascia, which separates it from the first part of the axillary artery; then, turning backwards, it pierces that fascia and ends in the axillary vein. Occasionally, instead of piercing the clavi-pectoral fascia, it crosses the front of the clavicle, deep to the platysma, pierces the deep cervical fascia, and joins the lower part of the external jugular vein.

On the flexor aspect of the forearm a number of tributaries join its lateral border. Some of these arise from the dorsal venous arch of the hand and others in the superficial fascia of the dorsal aspect of the forearm.

In front of the elbow it is connected with the basilic vein by a large obliquely placed anastomosing channel, called the *median cubital vein*, which runs along the medial border of the distal part of the biceps prominence, superficial to the bicipital aponeurosis [lacertus fibrosus] which separates it from the distal part of the brachial artery. In the infra-clavicular fossa it is joined by tributaries which correspond with the branches of the acromio-thoracic artery.

The **median cubital vein** not only connects together the cephalic and basilic veins but it receives also a communicating tributary from the deep veins of the forearm, and one or more superficial veins of varying size, which ascend on the front of the forearm.

Frequently the median cubital vein is relatively very large, and the more proximal part of the cephalic vein is then a comparatively small vessel.

The **basilic vein** begins in the ulnar end of the dorsal venous arch of the hand. It runs along the back of the forearm to the junction of the proximal and middle thirds, where it turns round the ulnar border of the forearm, and runs in front of the medial epicondyle of the humerus to the medial bicipital groove. At the middle of the upper arm it pierces the deep fascia. After piercing the fascia it runs along the medial border of the brachial artery to the axilla, and there becomes the axillary vein.

It is joined by tributaries from both surfaces of the forearm, and in front of the elbow by the median cubital vein, which connects it with the cephalic vein.

Median Vein of the Forearm. The median vein of the forearm, which begins in the palmar venous plexus and runs along the middle of the front of the forearm to the elbow, is occasionally a large vessel. At the bend of the elbow it receives the communication from the deep veins and then divides into two branches—the median cephalic and the median basilic veins (Fig. 1047). The *median cephalic vein* runs along the lateral bicipital sulcus and joins the cephalic vein. The *median basilic* passes along the medial bicipital sulcus and joins the basilic vein; it thus takes the place of the median cubital vein.

When venesection is performed in the forearm it is either the median cubital vein or the median basilic vein which is opened.

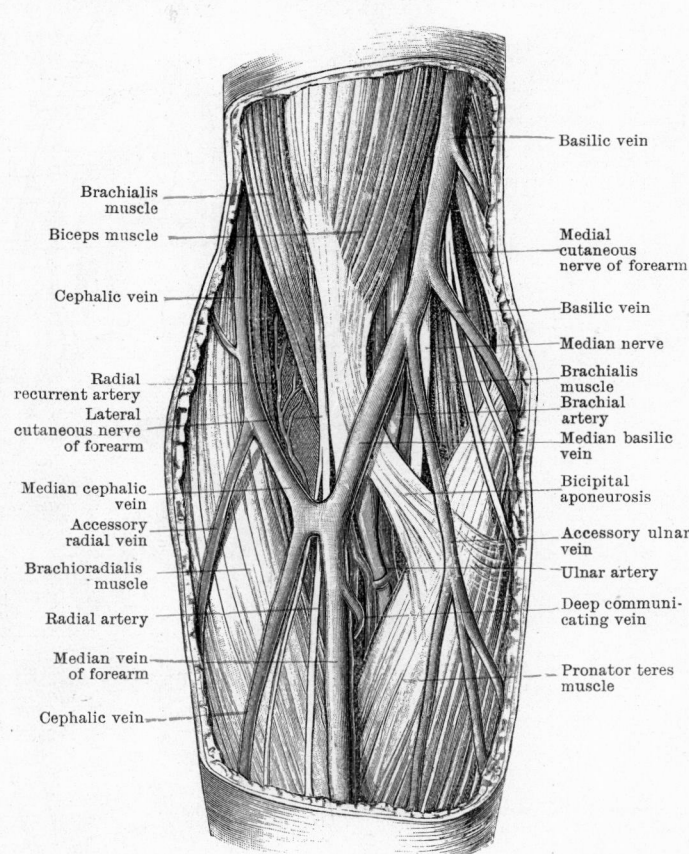

FIG. 1047.—SUPERFICIAL VEINS AT THE BEND OF THE ELBOW IN A SPECIMEN IN WHICH THE MEDIAN VEIN WAS LARGE.

Variations.—The superficial veins of the forearm are extremely variable; any of them may be absent, but most commonly it is the median or the cephalic vein which is wanting. The median cephalic and the cephalic veins may be small or absent, and, on the other hand, the cephalic vein may be larger than usual. The cephalic vein may end in the external jugular vein, which was its original termination; or it may be connected with the external jugular vein by an anastomosing channel which sometimes passes over the clavicle and sometimes through it. The basilic vein varies in size and in the level at which it pierces the deep fascia.

The **venæ comitantes** of the brachial artery usually end at the lower border of the subscapularis, where they join the axillary vein, but they may end above or below that level.

INFERIOR VENA CAVA

The **inferior vena cava** (Figs. 1048, 1049) is a large venous trunk which receives all the blood from the lower limbs, and the greater part of the blood from the walls and contents of the abdomen and pelvis.   It commences on the body of

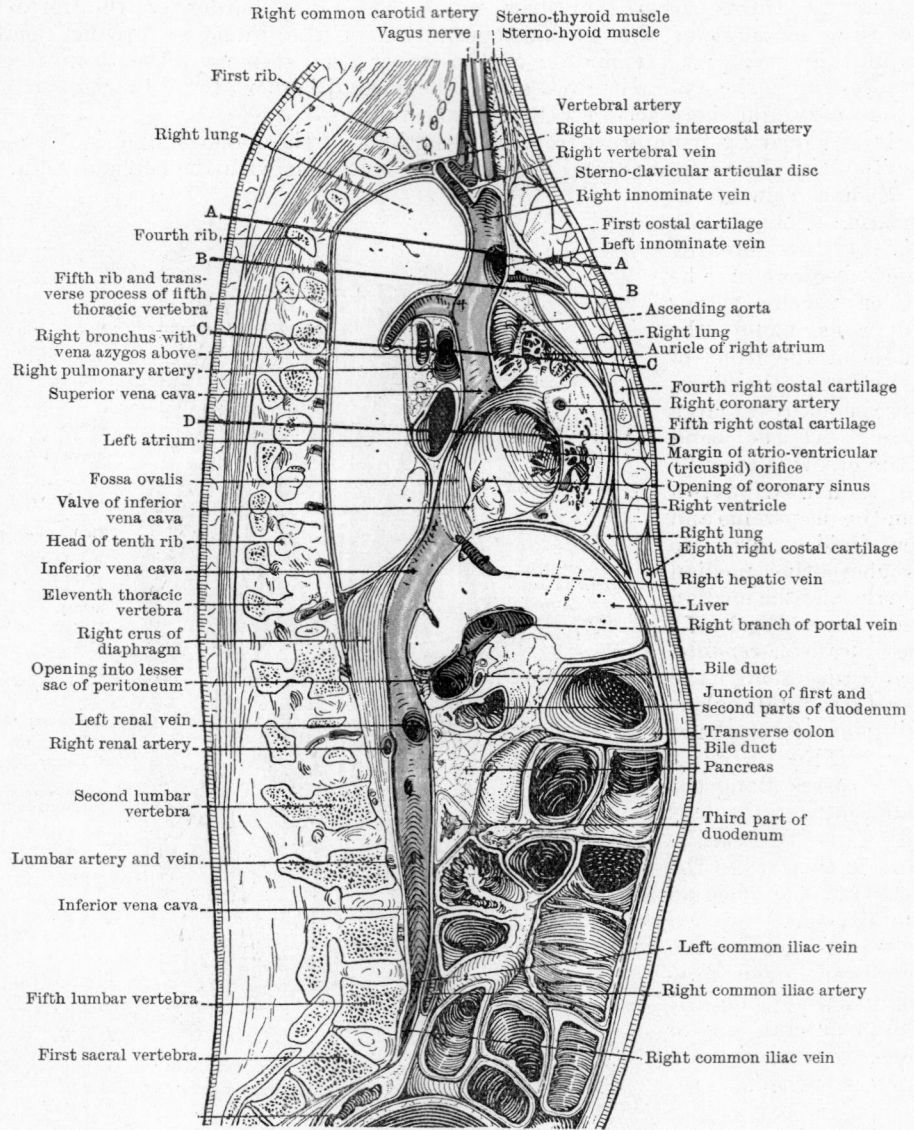

FIG. 1048.—SAGITTAL SECTION OF THE BODY OF A YOUNG MAN ALONG THE LINES OF THE SUPERIOR AND THE INFERIOR VENÆ CAVÆ.

A-A. Plane of section of Fig. 1015.   C-C. Plane of section of Fig. 1001.
B-B. Plane of section of Fig. 1039.   D-D. Plane of section of Fig. 997.

the fifth lumbar vertebra, to the right of the median plane, behind and to the right of the right common iliac artery.   It ascends through the abdomen, over the front of the vertebral column and the right crus of the diaphragm on the right of the median plane, and it pierces the central tendon of the diaphragm, between its middle and right leaflets, at the level of the lower part of the eighth thoracic vertebra.   It then enters the middle mediastinum, pierces the fibrous pericardium, and terminates in the lower and posterior part of the right atrium of the heart. Its intra-thoracic portion is very short, and its intra-pericardial portion is covered in front and on its right and left sides by the parietal serous pericardium. Attached to the inferior and anterior margin of its atrial orifice is the *valve of the inferior vena cava*; it is a remnant of an important fold of endocardium by which, in the fœtus, the blood from the inferior vena cava was directed through the foramen ovale into the left atrium.

Relations.—The inferior vena cava is in relation, *posteriorly*, with the bodies of the lower lumbar vertebræ and the corresponding part of the anterior longitudinal ligament, the anterior portion of the right psoas major muscle, the right lumbar sympathetic trunk, the trunks of the lower right lumbar arteries, the right crus of the diaphragm, the right renal artery, the right suprarenal artery, the right cœliac ganglion, the right phrenic artery, and the medial portion of the right suprarenal gland.

Anterior to it, from below upwards, are the following structures : the right common iliac artery, the lower end of the mesentery and the superior mesenteric vessels, the ileocolic and right colic vessels, the right testicular or ovarian artery and the third part of the duodenum, the head of the pancreas and the bile duct, the portal vein and the first part of the duodenum, the opening into the lesser sac of the peritoneum, and the liver—the vena cava being embedded in a deep groove on the back of the liver, so that the liver is to the right and left of it as well as in front. More superficially are coils of small intestine, the greater omentum, and the transverse colon and mesocolon.

To its *left side* are the aorta, the right crus of the diaphragm, and the caudate lobe of the liver.

On its *right side*, from below upwards, there are the right ureter, the right kidney, the right suprarenal gland (which is also behind), and the main part of the right lobe of the liver.

Variations and Abnormalities.—The lower part of the inferior vena cava is sometimes absent, in which case the common iliac veins ascend, one on the right and the other on the left of the aorta, to the level of the second lumbar vertebra, where the left common iliac vein receives the left renal vein, and then crosses in front of or behind the aorta to join the corresponding vein of the right side ; in such cases, therefore, the inferior vena cava begins at the level of the second lumbar vertebra, and it represents only the upper and last-formed part of the ordinary vessel ; the common iliac veins, each of which receives the lumbar veins of its own side, are exceptionally long, and they may or may not be united at the pelvic brim by a small transverse anastomosing channel. Cases of this kind are sometimes described as partial doubling of the inferior vena cava.

Occasionally the inferior vena cava does not end in the right atrium but is continuous with the vena azygos, which is much enlarged, and all the inferior caval blood is then carried to the superior vena cava. In such cases the hepatic veins open into the right atrium by a channel which represents the upper end of the inferior vena cava.

The lower part of the inferior vena cava sometimes lies to the left instead of to the right of the aorta ; that condition is associated with a long right common iliac vein, which crosses obliquely from right to left to join the shorter left common iliac vein. After receiving the left renal vein the misplaced inferior vena cava crosses in front of the aorta, reaching the right side at the level of the second or first lumbar vertebra. In other cases, however, the left inferior vena cava continues upwards through the left crus of the diaphragm, usurping the place of the inferior hemiazygos vein ; having entered the thorax, it may cross to the opposite side and terminate in the vena azygos, or it may continue upwards on the same side, arch over the root of the left lung, and descend behind the left atrium to end in the right atrium in the situation of the coronary sinus. In that group of cases also the hepatic veins open separately into the right atrium.

The inferior vena cava may lie ventral instead of dorsal to the right testicular or ovarian artery.

The tributaries of the inferior vena cava are also subject to variation. Additional renal, testicular, ovarian, or suprarenal veins may be present. Two or three lumbar veins of one or both sides may unite into a common trunk which ends in the inferior vena cava, and the hepatic veins may open separately, or after fusing into a common trunk, into the right atrium near the opening of the inferior vena cava.

The variations of the inferior vena cava and its tributaries are due to persistence of portions of the posterior cardinal, the subcardinal, and supracardinal veins and the azygos venous lines, which usually disappear, and to the persistence of transverse anastomoses and tributaries which usually atrophy, or to other modifications of the embryonic veins which ordinarily take part in the formation of the inferior vena caval system (see p. 1292).

Tributaries.—In addition to the two common iliac veins, by the union of which it is formed, and through which it receives blood from the pelvis and from the lower limbs, the inferior vena cava receives the following main tributaries : the hepatic veins, the right phrenic vein, the right suprarenal vein, the right and left renal veins, the right testicular or ovarian vein, and the third and fourth lumbar veins of both sides. It receives also a number of smaller tributaries, including one or two direct from the right ureter.

The **hepatic veins** (Fig. 1049) convey blood which has passed through the liver from the portal vein and from the hepatic artery, and they open into that portion of the inferior vena cava which lies immediately below the diaphragm and in the back of the right lobe of the liver. They form two groups, an upper group of two or three large trunks, and a lower group of smaller veins.

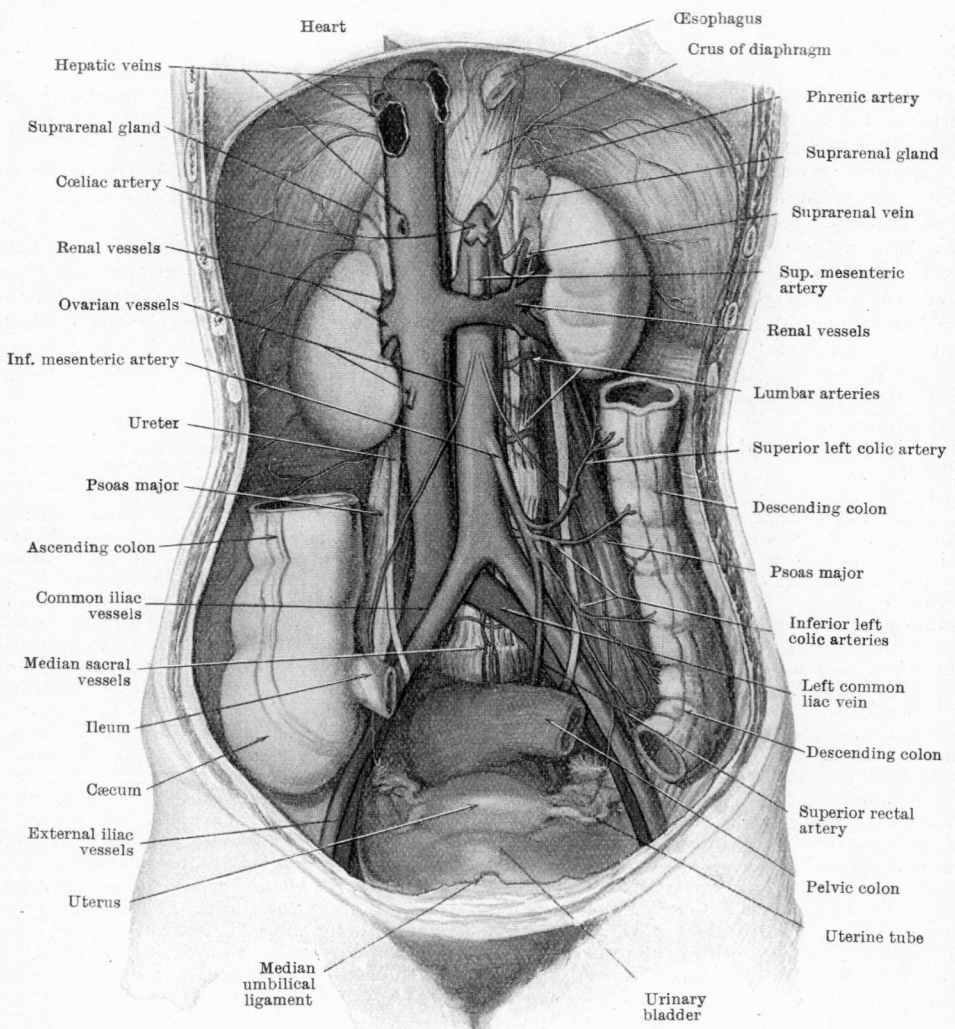

FIG. 1049.—THE INFERIOR VENA CAVA AND ITS TRIBUTARIES.

The upper group occasionally consists of only two veins, a right and a left; more frequently there are three vessels, a right, a left, and a middle vein, and in the latter case the middle vein issues from the caudate lobe.

The veins of the lower group vary in number from six to twenty; they return blood from the right and caudate lobes.

The hepatic veins begin as the *central* or *intralobular veins* of the lobules of the liver; the central veins issue from the lobules, and unite together to form *sublobular veins*; and the sublobular veins unite with one another, as they converge towards the posterior surface of the liver, to form the larger hepatic veins.

The **phrenic veins** are formed by tributaries from the diaphragm and correspond to the phrenic [inferior phrenic] arteries. The **right** vein ends in the upper part of the inferior vena cava. The **left** vein either descends to end in the left suprarenal or renal vein, or crosses behind or in front of the œsophagus to end in the inferior vena cava.

A single **suprarenal vein** issues from the hilum of each suprarenal gland; the *right* vein ends in the inferior vena cava; the *left* usually ends in the left renal vein, but sometimes it opens directly into the inferior vena cava.

The **renal veins** are formed by the union of five or six tributaries which issue from the hilum of each kidney, where they lie anterior to or are intermingled with the corresponding arteries.

The **right renal vein** is about one inch (25 mm.) long; it lies behind the second part of the duodenum, and ends in the right side of the inferior vena cava.

The **left renal vein** is about three inches (75 mm.) long. It crosses in front of the left psoas major, the left crus of the diaphragm, and the aorta immediately below the superior mesenteric artery. It lies behind the pancreas and the fourth part of the duodenum, and runs above the third part of the duodenum to end in the left side of the inferior vena cava. The left testicular or ovarian vein, according to the sex, and, almost invariably, the left suprarenal vein, open into it.

The **testicular veins**, on each side, issue from the testis and epididymis and form the *pampiniform plexus*. The plexus is one of the constituents of the spermatic cord, and consists of from eight to ten veins, most of which lie in front of the vas deferens; it passes upwards through the scrotum and inguinal canal, and ends near the deep inguinal ring in two main trunks which ascend with the corresponding testicular artery, receiving tributaries from the ureter; ultimately the two veins unite together and a single terminal vein is formed. The terminal testicular vein on the right side opens into the inferior vena cava, that on the left side into the left renal vein. The left testicular vein is longer than the right, the left testis being lower than the right, and the termination in the left renal vein being at a higher level than the termination of the right vein in the inferior vena cava. The testicular veins, on each side, lie anterior to the psoas major muscle and the ureter. They are covered by peritoneum, and they are crossed on the right side by the termination of the ileum and the third part of the duodenum, and on the left side by the iliac part of the descending colon, the end of the duodenum, and the lower part of the pancreas. They are provided with valves, one of which usually lies near the termination of each vein, but occasionally the valve near the orifice of the left testicular vein is absent.

The **ovarian veins**, on each side, issue from the hilum in the mesovarian border of the ovary. They pass between the layers of the broad ligament, where they anastomose freely and form the *pampiniform plexus*, which extends, laterally, towards the brim of the pelvis. From the plexus two veins issue which accompany the corresponding ovarian artery; they pass in front of the external iliac artery, and then upwards, behind the peritoneum and in front of the psoas major muscle and the ureter. The veins of the right side, like the corresponding testicular veins, also pass behind the termination of the ileum and the third part of the duodenum; whilst the left veins, near the inlet of the pelvis, pass behind the pelvic colon.

The two veins on each side ultimately fuse together to form a single terminal vein which ends, on the right side in the inferior vena cava, and on the left side in the left renal vein.

There are usually four **lumbar veins** on each side, one with each aortic lumbar artery. By their anterior and posterior tributaries the lumbar veins drain the lateral and posterior walls of the abdomen. The anterior tributaries commence in the lateral walls of the abdomen, where they communicate with the tributaries of the superior and inferior epigastric veins. The posterior tributaries issue from the muscles of the back, in the lumbar region, and receive the intervertebral veins draining the internal vertebral plexuses. The main stems pass forwards on the bodies of the vertebræ postero-medial to the psoas major muscle.

The terminations of the lumbar veins are very variable. Usually the lower two, on each side, end in the inferior vena cava, those of the left side passing on their way behind the aorta. The upper two on each side may end in the corresponding ascending lumbar vein, or in the azygos or hemiazygos vein. The lumbar veins of each side may all end in a median longitudinal channel (in the external vertebral plexus) which ascends behind the aorta in front of the vertebral bodies and branches to join the azygos and inferior hemiazygos veins; and they are all united together by a longitudinal anastomosing vessel—the ascending lumbar vein.

Each **ascending lumbar vein** passes upwards, between the psoas major and the roots of the transverse processes of the lumbar vertebræ. It begins in the lateral sacral vein of the same side, anastomoses with the ilio-lumbar vein, connects the lumbar veins together, receives tributaries from the anterior external vertebral plexus, and anastomoses with the inferior vena cava and the renal vein. The right ascending lumbar vein ends in the azygos vein and the left in the inferior hemiazygos vein.

Common Iliac Veins

The **common iliac veins** (Figs. 1026 and 1049), right and left, are formed by the union of the corresponding external and internal iliac veins. Each begins at the brim of the pelvis, immediately behind the upper part of the internal iliac artery, and both veins pass upwards to the body of the fifth lumbar vertebra, at the right half of which, posterior and lateral to the right common iliac artery, they unite to form the inferior vena cava.

The **right common iliac vein** is much shorter than the left; it passes anterior to the obturator nerve and the ilio-lumbar artery, and posterior to the corresponding common iliac artery.

The **left common iliac vein** is much longer than the right, and is placed more obliquely. It passes upwards and to the right, anterior to the body of the fifth lumbar vertebra and the median sacral artery. For some distance it runs along the medial side of the left common iliac artery, and then ends behind the right common iliac artery. Near its origin, it passes behind the mesentery of the pelvic colon and the superior rectal vessels.

Variations.—The left common iliac vein is short and the right long when the inferior vena cava lies on the left side. The common iliac veins may be absent, the internal iliac veins uniting to form the inferior vena cava, into which the external iliac veins open as lateral tributaries.

Tributaries.—Each common iliac vein receives the corresponding external iliac, internal iliac, and ilio-lumbar veins. The left common iliac vein receives, in addition, the median sacral vein.

The **ilio-lumbar vein** receives the fifth lumbar vein and tributaries from the iliac fossæ, from the lower parts of the vertebral muscles, and from the vertebral canal. It accompanies the corresponding artery only in the abdomen proper, for it passes behind the psoas major muscle and ends in the back of the corresponding common iliac vein.

The venæ comitantes of the median sacral artery begin by the union of tributaries which issue from the venous plexus on the pelvic surface of the sacrum, through which they communicate with the lateral sacral veins and receive blood from the interior of the sacral canal. They unite above into a single **median sacral vein**, which ends in the left common iliac vein.

The **internal iliac vein** [V. hypogastrica] (Fig. 1026) is a short trunk formed by the union of tributaries which correspond to all the branches of the internal iliac artery, with the exception of the umbilical and the ilio-lumbar arteries.

It begins at the upper border of the greater sciatic notch and ascends to the brim of the pelvis; there it unites with the external iliac vein to form the common iliac vein. It lies immediately behind the internal iliac artery, is crossed laterally by the obturator nerve, and is in relation medially, on the left side with the pelvic colon, and on the right side with the lower part of the ileum.

Tributaries.—The tributaries, which are numerous, are conveniently divided into extra-pelvic and intra-pelvic groups.

The *extra-pelvic tributaries* are all **parietal**, and include the superior and inferior gluteal, the obturator, and the internal pudendal veins.

The **superior gluteal veins** are the venæ comitantes of the superior gluteal artery, formed by tributaries which issue from the muscles of the gluteal region. They accompany the artery through the greater sciatic foramen, and end in the internal iliac vein, often as a single trunk.

The **inferior gluteal veins** are the venæ comitantes of the inferior gluteal artery which begin in the subcutaneous tissues on the back of the thigh; they ascend with the artery, and pass into the buttock on the deep aspect of the gluteus maximus, where they receive numerous tributaries from the surrounding muscles. Entering the pelvis through the greater sciatic foramen, they unite into a single vessel, which ends in the lower and anterior part of the internal iliac vein below the termination of the obturator vein.

The **obturator vein** is formed by the union of tributaries which issue from the hip joint and from the muscles of the proximal and medial part of the thigh. It enters the true pelvis through the obturator canal, runs backwards and upwards along the side wall of the pelvis, medial to the obturator fascia, immediately below the corresponding artery, and passes lateral to the ureter and the descending branches of the internal iliac artery to end in the internal iliac vein.

The **internal pudendal veins** are the venæ comitantes of the internal pudendal artery; in the male they emerge from the lower part of the *prostatic plexus*, which lies below and behind the inferior pubic ligament. They follow the course of the internal pudendal artery, and usually join together into a single vessel which ends in the internal iliac vein. They receive blood from the corpus cavernosum by the deep vein of the penis or clitoris, veins from the bulb, perineal and inferior rectal veins, and veins from the muscles of the gluteal region.

The **inferior rectal [hæmorrhoidal] veins** begin in the substance of the external sphincter of the anus and in the walls of the anal canal; they anastomose through the *rectal plexus* with the middle and superior rectal veins, and consequently connect the portal and vena caval systems together.

The *intra-pelvic tributaries* of the internal iliac vein are **parietal** and **visceral**: the former are represented by the lateral sacral veins; the latter include the efferent vessels from the plexuses around the several pelvic viscera.

Lateral sacral veins accompany the lateral sacral arteries, and end on each side in the corresponding internal iliac vein. They are connected together by an *anterior sacral venous plexus*.

The **pelvic venous plexuses** form dense networks of thin-walled veins associated with the rectum, bladder, prostate, uterus, and vagina. They communicate freely with one another, and from them the visceral tributaries of the internal iliac veins arise.

The rectal plexuses lie in the submucous coat of the rectum and anal canal and on the outer surface of their muscular coats. They are drained by the superior, middle, and inferior rectal veins; the superior rectal vein joins the portal system; the middle and inferior are tributaries of the systemic veins. The rectal plexuses, therefore, form a link between systemic and portal veins.

The **middle rectal [hæmorrhoidal] veins** are very irregular; sometimes they cannot be distinguished. When present they are formed by tributaries which begin in the submucous tissue of the rectum, where they communicate with the superior and inferior rectal veins in the rectal plexus; they pass through the muscular coat, and fuse together to form two middle rectal veins, right and left, each of which runs laterally beneath the peritoneum, on the upper surface of the levator ani, to end in the corresponding internal iliac vein. In the male each middle rectal vein receives tributaries from the seminal vesicle and vas deferens of its own side.

The **vesical plexus** *in the male* lies on the outer surface of the muscular coat of the bladder. It is densest round the neck of the bladder where it is continuous with the prostatic plexus, and at the base where it extends around the seminal vesicles, and around the ends of the ureters and the vasa deferentia. Several **vesical veins** pass from it on each side to the internal iliac vein.

The **prostatic plexus** is situated between the proper fibrous capsule of the prostate and its sheath of fascia. In front it receives the deep dorsal vein of the penis; behind it communicates with the vesical plexus, and its extension around the seminal vesicles and vasa deferentia. One or more efferent vessels pass from it on each side and open into the corresponding internal iliac vein.

The **vesical plexus** *in the female*, which represents the vesical and prostatic plexuses of the male, surrounds the upper part of the urethra and the neck of the bladder. It communicates with the vaginal plexus and receives the dorsal vein of the clitoris; and its efferent vessels end in the internal iliac vein.

The uterine plexuses lie along the borders of the uterus; they receive tributaries, which are entirely devoid of valves, from the uterus; and they communicate above with the ovarian pampiniform plexuses, and below with the vaginal plexuses.

The **uterine veins**, usually two on each side, issue from the lower parts of the uterine plexuses, above their communications with the vaginal plexuses. At first the uterine veins, on each side, lie in the medial part of the root of the broad ligament, above the lateral fornix of the vagina and the ureter; then they pass backwards, accompanying the corresponding artery, in a fold of peritoneum which lies between the back of the broad ligament and the recto-uterine fold; finally they ascend in the floor of the ovarian fossa, and end in the corresponding internal iliac vein.

The **vaginal plexuses** lie at the sides of the vagina. They receive tributaries from the walls of the vagina. They communicate with the uterine plexuses above; with the veins of the bulb below; in front with the vesical plexus; and behind with the veins which issue from the middle and lower parts of the rectal plexus. A single **vaginal vein** issues from the upper part of the vaginal plexus on each side; it accompanies the corresponding artery, and ends in the internal iliac vein.

Dorsal Veins of the Penis and Clitoris.—There are two dorsal veins of the penis—the superficial and the deep.

The **superficial dorsal vein** receives tributaries from the prepuce, and runs backwards, immediately beneath the skin, to the pubic symphysis, where it divides into right and left branches which end in the superficial external pudendal veins.

The **deep dorsal vein** lies on the dorsum of the penis, deep to the deep fascia. It begins in the sulcus behind the glans, by the union of numerous tributaries from the glans and the anterior parts of the corpora cavernosa; and it runs backwards in the mid-dorsal line, in the sulcus between the corpora cavernosa, from which it receives many additional tributaries. At the root of the penis the vein passes between the two layers of the suspensory ligament, and then between the inferior pubic ligament and the thickened anterior border of the perineal membrane (transverse ligament of the perineum), where it lies above the membranous part of the urethra. It ends by dividing into two branches which join the lower part of the prostatic plexus.

The **dorsal vein of the clitoris** in the female has a similar course to that of the deep dorsal vein of the penis in the male. It ends in the lower part of the vesical plexus and communicates with the internal pudendal veins.

The **external iliac vein** (Figs. 1026, 1029, and 1049) is the upward continuation of the femoral vein. It begins, on the medial side of the end of the external iliac artery, immediately behind the inguinal ligament, and ascends along the brim of the pelvis to a point opposite the sacro-iliac joint at the level of the lumbo-sacral disc, where it ends, immediately behind the internal iliac artery, by joining the internal iliac vein to form the common iliac vein. It lies, at first, on the medial side of the external iliac artery, but on a slightly posterior plane, and then directly posterior to the artery, whilst just before its termination it crosses the lateral side of the internal iliac artery, and separates that vessel from the medial surface of the psoas major muscle. In its whole course the vein lies anterior to the obturator nerve. It is usually provided with one, or sometimes two bicuspid valves; but both are usually incompetent. Its tributaries correspond to the branches of the external iliac artery; that is, the deep circumflex iliac and inferior epigastric veins open into it, close to its commencement. In addition, it frequently receives the pubic vein.

The **pubic vein** forms a communication between the obturator vein and the external iliac vein. It varies in size, and may form the main termination of the obturator vein, from which it arises. It begins in the obturator canal and ascends alongside the pubic branch of the inferior epigastric artery to reach the external iliac vein.

VEINS OF LOWER LIMB

The veins of the lower limb, like those of the upper limb, are arranged in two groups, the **superficial** and the **deep**; and in the lower as in the upper limb the deep veins are associated with the arteries as venæ comitantes, whilst the trunks of the superficial veins, which lie at first in the subcutaneous tissues, ultimately end in the deep veins. There is therefore a general similarity in the arrangement of the veins of the upper and lower limbs, but there are differences in detail which are of some importance. Thus, in the upper limb, there are two deep veins with each artery from the fingers to the root of the limb, where a single trunk, the axillary vein, is formed; but in the lower limb each main artery has two venæ comitantes only as far as the knee, where a single trunk is frequently formed. That vessel, the **popliteal vein,** is the commencement of the main venous stem of the lower limb; it is continued upwards through the thigh, as the **femoral vein,** and along the brim of the pelvis as the **external iliac vein,** which ends by uniting with the internal iliac to form the common iliac vein.

In the upper limb all the blood which passes through the superficial veins is poured into the efferent trunk vein at the root of the limb—the axillary vein; but in the lower limb the superficial veins of the lateral parts of the leg and foot join the popliteal vein at the knee, whilst those of the medial part of the limb join the femoral vein near the root of the limb in the femoral triangle.

In addition to these differences in the general arrangement of the veins of the limbs, it must be noted also that in the upper limb all the blood, from the shoulder-girdle region as well as from the free portion of the limb, is returned to the main efferent vein; but in the lower limb the greater part of the blood from the region of the pelvic girdle, and a considerable portion from the thigh, is returned by the gluteal, obturator, and internal pudendal veins to the internal iliac vein, which is not the main efferent vein of the limb.

Deep Veins of Lower Limb

Two *venæ comitantes* accompany all the arteries of the lower limb, except the popliteal and femoral trunks and the profunda femoris. They usually lie one on each side of the artery; they are connected with one another by transverse channels which pass across the artery, and they are provided with numerous valves.

The **popliteal vein** (Figs. 1028, 1032, 1033) is formed, at the distal border of the popliteus muscle, by the union of the venæ comitantes of the anterior and posterior tibial arteries. At its commencement it lies to the medial side of and slightly superficial to the popliteal artery, and to the lateral side of the medial popliteal [tibial] nerve. As it runs through the popliteal fossa it inclines laterally, and in the middle of the space it is directly posterior to the artery, separating the artery from the nerve which is still more posterior, whilst at the proximal part of the space it is postero-lateral to the artery, and still between it and the nerve. It then passes through the opening in the adductor magnus muscle and becomes the femoral vein.

The popliteal vein, which is provided with two or three bicuspid valves, is closely bound to the artery by a dense fascial sheath. Not uncommonly there are one or more additional satellite veins which anastomose with the popliteal vein, and in those cases the artery is more or less completely surrounded by venous trunks.

Tributaries.—In addition to venæ comitantes of the anterior and posterior tibial arteries, it receives tributaries which correspond with the branches of the popliteal artery, and it receives also one of the superficial veins of the leg—the short saphenous vein.

The **femoral vein** is the direct continuation of the popliteal vein. It begins at the junction of the middle and distal thirds of the thigh, at the opening in the adductor magnus muscle. It then ascends, through the subsartorial canal and through the femoral triangle, and ends, a little medial to the middle of the inguinal ligament, by becoming the external iliac vein.

In the subsartorial canal it lies at first postero-lateral to the femoral artery and then posterior to it, and it is anterior to the adductors magnus and longus, which separate it from the profunda vessels. In the distal part of the femoral triangle it is still behind the artery, and immediately in front of the profunda vein which separates it from the profunda artery, but in the proximal part of the femoral triangle it is on the medial side of the femoral artery. About one and a quarter inches (30 mm.) below the inguinal ligament it enters the middle compartment of the femoral sheath, through which it ascends to its termination, lying between the compartment for the femoral artery on the lateral side and the femoral canal on the medial side. It usually contains two bicuspid valves—one near its termination and the other just proximal to the entrance of its profunda tributary.

Tributaries.—It receives—(1) venæ comitantes of small unnamed arteries, of the descending genicular artery [arteria genu suprema], of the lateral and medial circumflex arteries (branches of the profunda femoris), and of the deep external pudendal artery; (2) the profunda femoris vein; (3) the long saphenous vein, which enters the femoral vein where that vessel lies in the middle compartment of the femoral sheath.

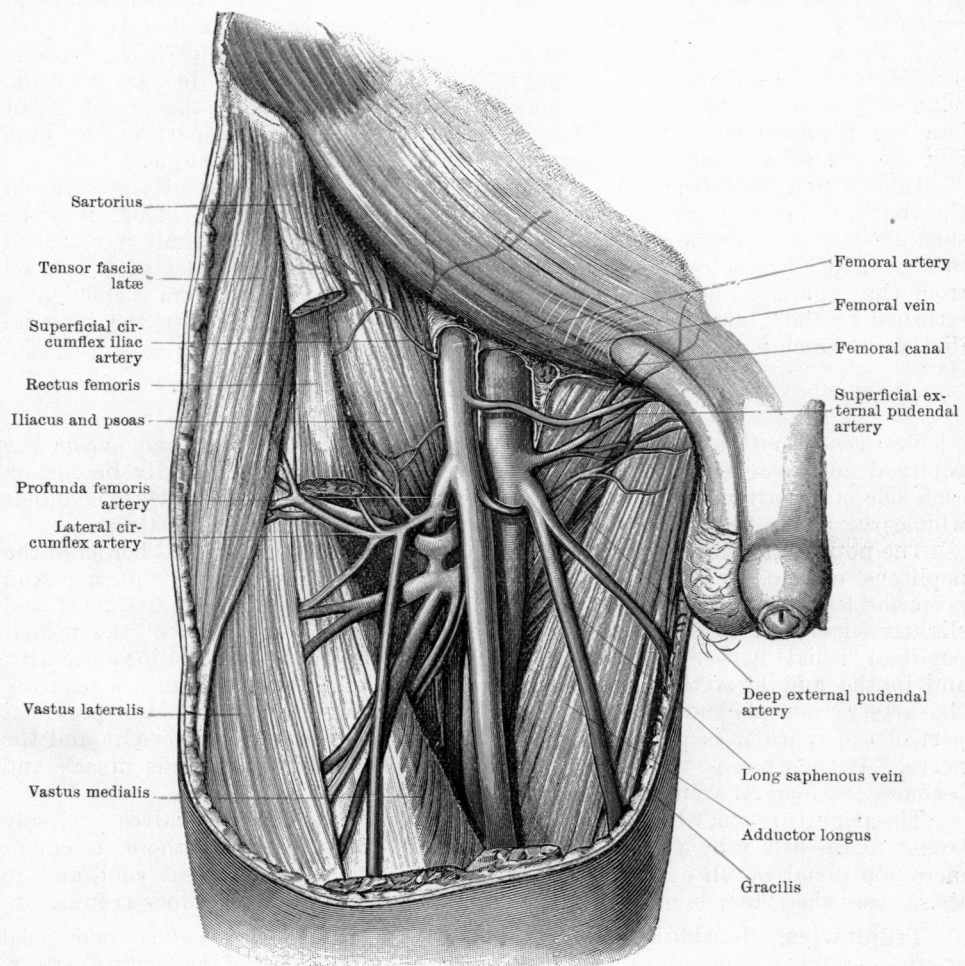

FIG. 1050.—THE FEMORAL VESSELS IN THE FEMORAL TRIANGLE.

The **profunda femoris vein** lies in front of its artery and separates it from the adductor longus and the femoral vein. It receives the venæ comitantes of the muscular and perforating branches of its artery, but only occasionally those of the circumflex arteries which usually join the femoral vein direct. It is connected through the *perforating veins* with the veins of the back of the thigh.

SUPERFICIAL VEINS OF LOWER LIMB

The superficial veins of the lower limb terminate in two trunks, one of which, the **short saphenous vein**, passes from the foot to the back of the knee; whilst the other, the **long saphenous vein**, extends from the foot to the groin.

The superficial veins of the sole of the foot form a fine plexus, immediately under cover of the skin, from which anterior, medial, and lateral efferents pass. The anterior efferents end in a transverse **plantar venous arch** which lies in the furrow at the roots of the toes, and the medial and lateral efferents pass round the sides of the foot to the long or short saphenous vein. The venous arch receives also small *plantar digital veins* from the toes, and it communicates between the heads of the metatarsals with the veins on the dorsum of the foot.

The superficial veins on the dorsal aspect of each toe unite to form two **dorsal digital veins**, which run along the borders of the dorsal surface. The dorsal digital veins of the adjacent borders of the interdigital clefts unite, at the apices of the clefts, to form four **dorsal metatarsal veins** which end in the dorsal venous arch of the foot. The dorsal digital vein from the medial side of the big toe ends in the long saphenous, and that from the lateral side of the little toe in the short saphenous vein.

The **dorsal venous arch** lies in the subcutaneous tissue, between the skin and the dorsal digital branches of the musculo-cutaneous nerve, opposite the anterior parts of the shafts of the metatarsal bones. It ends, medially, by uniting with the medial dorsal digital vein of the big toe to form the long saphenous vein, and laterally by joining the lateral dorsal digital vein of the little toe to form the short saphenous vein. The dorsal venous arch receives the dorsal metatarsal veins and interdigital efferents from the plantar venous arch; and numerous tributaries from the dorsum of the foot, which anastomose freely together forming a wide-meshed *dorsal venous network*, open into it from behind.

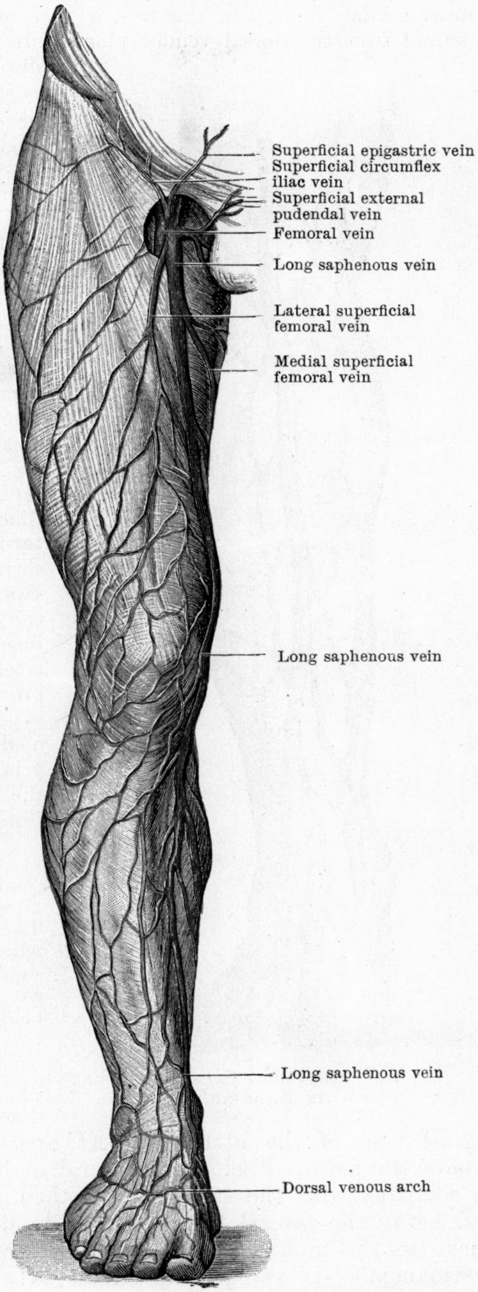

The **long saphenous vein** is formed by the union of the medial end of the dorsal venous arch with the medial dorsal digital vein of the big toe. It passes in front of the medial malleolus, crosses the medial surface of the distal third of the shaft of the tibia obliquely, and ascends, immediately behind the medial margin of the tibia, to the knee, where it lies medial to the posterior end

Superficial epigastric vein
Superficial circumflex iliac vein
Superficial external pudendal vein
Femoral vein

Long saphenous vein

Lateral superficial femoral vein

Medial superficial femoral vein

Long saphenous vein

Long saphenous vein

Dorsal venous arch

FIG. 1051.—THE LONG SAPHENOUS VEIN AND ITS TRIBUTARIES.

of the medial condyle of the femur; continuing upwards, with an inclination forwards and laterally, it gains the proximal part of the femoral triangle, where it perforates the cribriform fascia and the femoral sheath and ends in the femoral vein. In the foot and leg it is accompanied by the saphenous nerve, and for a short distance distal to the knee by the saphenous branch of the descending genicular artery. In the thigh, branches of the medial cutaneous nerve lie in close relation with it. It has from eight to twenty bicuspid valves.

Tributaries.—It communicates freely, through the deep fascia, with the deep intermuscular veins. In the foot it receives tributaries from the medial part of the sole and from the dorsal venous plexus. In the leg it is joined by tributaries from the dorsum of the foot, the medial and posterior parts of the heel, the front of the leg, and the back of the calf; and it anastomoses freely with the short saphenous vein. In the thigh it receives numerous tributaries, and amongst them are two veins of some size. Of those, the *lateral* ascends from the lateral side of the knee and ends in the long saphenous vein at the distal part of the femoral triangle; the *medial* ascends from the posterior aspect of the thigh, along its medial side, and ends in the long saphenous vein near the saphenous opening [fossa ovalis]. In many cases the medial superficial vein communicates distally with the short saphenous vein, and it is then called the *accessory saphenous vein.*

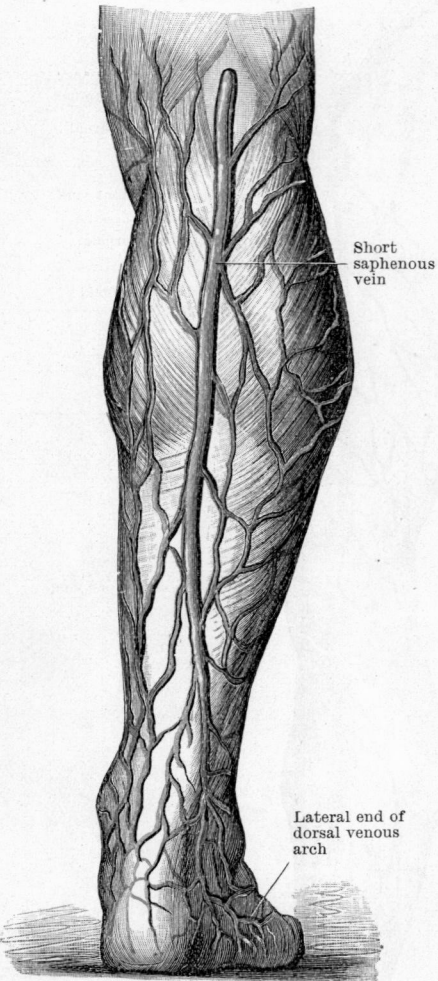

Short saphenous vein

Lateral end of dorsal venous arch

Fig. 1052.—The Short Saphenous Vein and its Tributaries.

The last tributaries to enter the long saphenous vein are the **superficial circumflex iliac, superficial epigastric,** and **superficial external pudendal veins.** They accompany the corresponding arteries, and end in the long saphenous vein immediately before it perforates the cribriform fascia. The superficial circumflex iliac vein receives blood from the lower and lateral part of the abdominal wall and the proximal and lateral parts of the thigh. The superficial epigastric vein drains the lower and medial part of the abdominal wall. The superficial external pudendal vein receives blood from the dorsum of the penis and the scrotum or from the labium majus.

The tributaries of the superficial epigastric vein communicate above with the tributaries of the lateral thoracic veins which join the axillary vein. These communications thus unite main vessels which pass to the inferior vena cava and the superior vena cava respectively; and they may enlarge if there is any obstruction to the flow of blood in either of the venæ cavæ.

The **short saphenous vein** is formed by the union of the lateral end of the dorsal venous arch with the lateral dorsal digital vein of the little toe. At first it passes backwards, along the lateral side of the foot and below the lateral malleolus, lying on the peroneal retinacula, in company with the sural nerve; then it ascends behind the lateral malleolus, and along the lateral border of the tendo calcaneus, still in company with the nerve, to the middle of the calf, whence it proceeds between the heads of the gastrocnemius to the popliteal fossa, where it pierces the deep fascia, and ends in the popliteal vein. It communicates, round the medial side of the leg, with the long saphenous vein, and through the deep fascia with the deep veins. It contains from six to twelve bicuspid valves.

Tributaries.—It receives tributaries from the lateral side of the foot, the lateral side and back of the heel, the back of the leg, and, occasionally, a descending tributary from the back of the thigh. Just before it pierces the popliteal fascia it frequently gives off a small branch which ascends round the medial side of the thigh and unites with the medial superficial vein to form the *accessory saphenous vein*. In that way a communication is established between the long and short saphenous veins, which may become enlarged, and constitute the main continuation of the short saphenous vein.

Variations.—The **venæ comitantes** are generally described as ending at the distal part of the popliteal fossa, but they may ascend as far as the femoral triangle; one or more small additional veins usually accompany the popliteal and femoral arteries, although, as a rule, there is only one large popliteal and one large femoral vein. In a few cases the popliteal vein does not pass through the opening in the adductor magnus, but ascends behind that muscle and becomes continuous with the profunda vein, the femoral artery being unaccompanied by any large vein during its passage through the subsartorial canal.

The **long saphenous vein** is not subject to much variation, but the **short saphenous vein** may end by joining the long saphenous, or, after piercing the deep fascia in the distal part of the thigh, it may ascend and join the inferior gluteal vein or one of the tributaries of the profunda vein.

PORTAL SYSTEM OF VEINS

The veins which form the **portal system** are the portal, the superior and inferior mesenteric and the splenic veins and their tributaries. They convey blood to the liver—(1) from the whole of the abdominal and pelvic parts of the alimentary canal, except the terminal part of the anal canal, (2) from the pancreas, and (3) from the spleen. The right branch of the portal vein receives the vein from the gall-bladder; and its left branch receives para-umbilical veins which pass along the round ligament of the liver and constitute one of the anastomoses between the portal and systemic veins. The tributaries of origin of the portal vein correspond with the branches of the splenic and the superior and inferior mesenteric arteries, after which they are named and which they accompany for a considerable distance. The larger or terminal veins leave their associated arteries; the **inferior mesenteric vein** joins the **splenic vein**, and the latter unites with the **superior mesenteric vein** to form the **portal vein,** which passes to the liver. All the larger vessels of this system, including the superior rectal vein, are devoid of valves, but valves are present in the tributaries in the fœtus, and some of them may remain in an imperfect condition in the smaller tributaries in the adult.

Unlike other veins, the portal vein ends like an artery by breaking up into branches which ultimately terminate in the sinusoidal capillaries in the substance of the liver; from the capillaries, which also receive the blood conveyed to the liver by the hepatic artery, the hepatic veins arise; and, as the hepatic veins open into the inferior vena cava, the portal blood ultimately reaches the general systemic circulation.

The portal vein conveys products of digestion to the liver, and in addition to this important function the whole portal system also acts as a reservoir of blood for the needs of the general circulation. It has been calculated that the portal system can contain about one-third of the total amount of blood in the body; and the amount of blood present can be varied by contraction or relaxation of the arteries by which it enters the system and of the terminal parts of the hepatic veins by which it leaves it. The spleen may be regarded as a specialised portion of the portal reservoir.

The **portal vein** is a wide venous channel, about three inches long (75 mm.). It begins by the union of the superior mesenteric and the splenic veins, behind and to the left of the neck of the pancreas, and either anterior to the left border of the inferior vena cava, at the level of the body of the first lumbar vertebra, or in front of the upturned extremity of the uncinate process of the head of the pancreas. It ascends in front of the inferior vena cava and behind the neck of the pancreas and the first part of the duodenum, to the lower border of the opening into the lesser sac of the peritoneum, where it passes forwards, in the right gastro-pancreatic fold of peritoneum, and enters the lesser omentum. Continuing its upward course, it lies behind the bile-duct and hepatic artery, and in front of the opening into the lesser sac; it ultimately reaches the right end of the porta hepatis, where it ends by dividing into a short and wide right branch and a longer and narrower left branch. Just before its termination it enlarges and the enlargement is called the *sinus of the portal vein*.

The **right branch** generally receives the **cystic vein** and then enters the right lobe of the liver, in which it breaks up into numerous branches which end as *interlobular veins* which are connected to the *sublobular* rootlets of the hepatic veins by the sinusoidal capillaries in the substance of the liver lobules (Fig. 534, p. 632).

The **left branch** runs from right to left, in the porta hepatis, giving off branches to the caudate and quadrate lobes; it crosses the fissure for the liga-

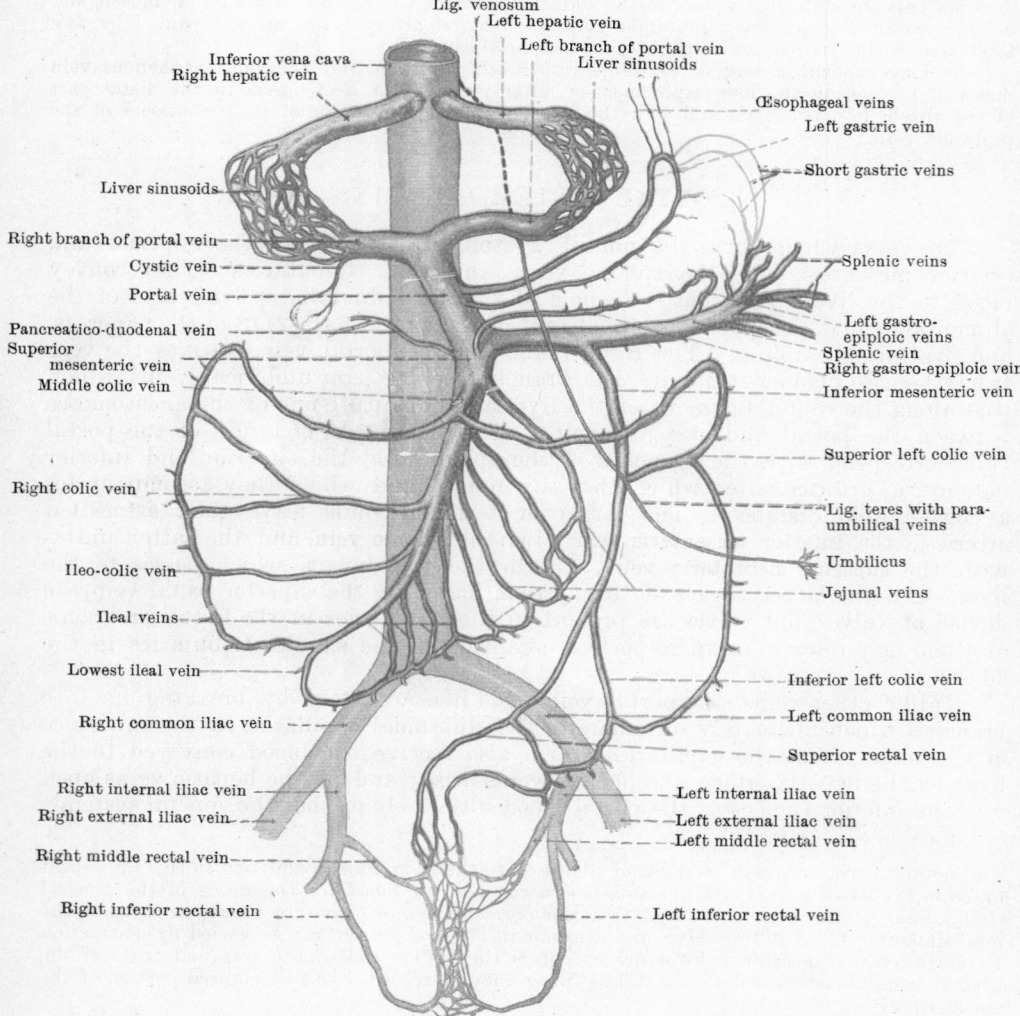

FIG. 1053.—SCHEMA OF THE PORTAL SYSTEM OF VEINS AND ITS CONNEXIONS WITH THE SYSTEMIC SYSTEM.—It must be remembered that systemic blood carried by the hepatic artery also enters the liver capillaries; therefore the hepatic veins contain both portal and systemic blood.

mentum teres, and ends in the left lobe of the liver in the same manner as the right branch.

As it crosses the fissure, the left branch of the portal vein is joined in front by the **round ligament** of the liver and some small accompanying veins, and behind by the **ligamentum venosum**. The round ligament is a fibrous cord which passes from the umbilicus to the left branch of the portal vein. It is the remains of the left umbilical vein of the fœtus. The small *para-umbilical veins* which accompany it connect the left branch of the portal vein with the superficial veins round the umbilicus. The ligament venosum connects the left branch of the portal vein with the upper part of the inferior vena cava. It is the remains of a fœtal blood-vessel—the **ductus venosus**—through which blood, carried from the placenta by the left umbilical vein, passed to the inferior vena cava without going through the liver. The portal vein is accompanied by numerous lymph vessels, and it is surrounded, in the lesser omentum, by filaments of the hepatic plexus of nerves.

Tributaries.—Soon after its formation the portal vein receives the left and right gastric veins, and the cystic vein opens into its right branch.

The **left gastric vein** [V. coronaria] begins in the lesser omentum by the union of tributaries from both surfaces of the stomach. It runs with the left gastric artery along the lesser curvature of the stomach to the œsophagus, from which it receives tributaries. It then turns backwards, in the left gastro-pancreatic fold, and reaches the posterior wall of the abdomen, where it again changes its direction to run from left to right behind the lesser sac of the peritoneum to the right gastro-pancreatic fold, at the root of which it opens into the portal vein.

The **right gastric vein** is a small vessel which is formed by the union of tributaries from the upper parts of both surfaces of the pyloric portion of the stomach. It runs from left to right along the lesser curvature, between the layers of the lesser omentum, and ends in the portal vein after that vessel has entered the lesser omentum. It receives the **pre-pyloric vein** which marks the position of the pylorus (see p. 583).

The **cystic vein** is formed by the union of tributaries which accompany the branches of the cystic artery on the anterior and posterior surfaces of the gall-bladder; it ascends along the cystic duct and ends as a rule in the right branch of the portal vein. Some small veins pass directly from the gall-bladder into the substance of the liver.

The **superior mesenteric vein** begins in the right iliac fossa, and ascends along the right side of the superior mesenteric artery. In the greater part of its course it lies in the root of the mesentery, and crosses the right ureter and testicular or ovarian vessels, the inferior vena cava and the third part of the duodenum. There it leaves the mesentery, ascends in front of the uncinate process of the pancreas, and, crossing behind the root of the transverse mesocolon, it ends behind the neck of the pancreas by uniting with the splenic vein to form the portal vein.

Tributaries.—It receives the veins that accompany the branches of the superior mesenteric artery, and also the right gastro-epiploic vein and pancreatico-duodenal veins, which enter it near its termination. The **appendicular** and **anterior** and **posterior cæcal** veins unite to form it. The **ileal** and **jejunal** veins run from the small intestine to the root of the mesentery to join it. The **ileo-colic** and **right colic** veins enter it below the duodenum. It receives the **middle colic** vein where it crosses the root of the mesocolon.

The **right gastro-epiploic vein** runs from left to right along the greater curvature of the stomach, between the anterior two layers of the greater omentum. It receives tributaries from both surfaces of the stomach. Near the pylorus it turns backwards, and ends in the superior mesenteric vein.

The **pancreatico-duodenal veins** receive tributaries from the head of the pancreas and the adjacent parts of the duodenum; the lower vein may join the right gastro-epiploic; the upper vein ascends along the superior pancreatico-duodenal artery, and ends in the upper part of the superior mesenteric vein or in the portal vein.

The **splenic vein** is formed by the union of five or six tributaries which issue from the hilum on the gastric surface of the spleen. It passes backwards and medially, in the lieno-renal ligament, to the kidney, turns to the right and runs behind the body of the pancreas and below the splenic artery; it crosses the front of the abdominal aorta immediately below the origin of the cœliac artery, and ends behind the neck of the pancreas by joining the superior mesenteric vein to form the portal vein.

Tributaries.—It receives the short gastric veins, the left gastro-epiploic vein, the pancreatic veins, and the inferior mesenteric vein. Occasionally the left gastric vein ends in it.

The **short gastric veins** are a series of small vessels which gather blood from the region of the left portion of the greater curvature of the stomach; they pass backwards towards the spleen, in the gastro-splenic ligament, and end either in the trunk of the splenic vein or in one of its main tributaries.

The **left gastro-epiploic vein** runs from right to left along the greater curvature of the stomach between the anterior two layers of the greater omentum. It enters the gastro-splenic ligament, through which it passes towards the hilum of the spleen, and ends by joining the commencement of the splenic vein. It receives tributaries from both surfaces of the stomach.

The **pancreatic veins** issue from the pancreas, and end at once in the splenic vein.

The **inferior mesenteric vein** is the continuation of the **superior rectal vein**, and it receives the **inferior left colic** [sigmoid] **veins** from the pelvic colon and iliac portion of the descending colon, and the **superior left colic vein** from the upper part of the descending colon and the left flexure. It begins on the middle of the left common iliac artery. It runs upwards along the left side of its own artery and the aorta, to the right of the ureter, on the front of the left psoas major muscle, crossing superficial to the left testicular or ovarian vessels, and superficial or deep to the inferior and superior left colic arteries. In most of its course it is directly behind the peritoneum, but near its upper end it passes behind the duodeno-jejunal flexure, and then, crossing in front of the left renal vein, it ends in the splenic vein behind the pancreas. Occasionally it bends to the right to end in the junction of the splenic and superior mesenteric veins. It is longer than its companion artery, as it ascends to a higher level than the origin of the artery.

The **superior rectal** [hæmorrhoidal] **vein** drains the greater part of the blood from the rectum. It arises by the union of tributaries from the rectal venous plexus, which lies between the mucous and muscular coats of the rectum, and through which it communicates with the middle and inferior rectal veins. It ascends, in company with the superior rectal artery and between the layers of the pelvic mesocolon, to the inlet of the pelvis, where it ends on the front of the left common iliac artery by becoming the inferior mesenteric vein.

Communications between Portal and Systemic Veins.—Important venous anastomoses take place between the outlying tributaries of the portal system and systemic veins. The most notable of these communications occur at the lower end of the œsophagus (between the left gastric vein and œsophageal veins which join the azygos system) and in the rectal plexus of veins (between the superior rectal vein and the middle and inferior rectal veins, which pass to the internal iliac). In both of these situations the communicating veins may enlarge ; in the region of the anal canal such varicose enlargements of the veins are known as *haemorrhoids* or piles.

The communication with superficial veins around the umbilicus by para-umbilical veins which reach the left branch of the portal vein along the round ligament of the liver has been mentioned already. Obstruction to the passage of blood through the liver is often indicated by the appearance of enlarged superficial veins radiating from the umbilicus—the so-called *caput medusae*. Enlarged veins may also appear in the falciform ligament or on the "bare area" of the liver and communicate with the veins of the diaphragm and the internal mammary veins. Other communications occur on the posterior wall of the abdomen between intestinal tributaries of the portal vein and the renal or lumbar veins or small retroperitoneal tributaries of the inferior vena cava.

DEVELOPMENT OF BLOOD VASCULAR SYSTEM

DEVELOPMENT OF THE HEART AND THE ARTERIES

In the general account of the development of the embryo (pp. 77-80) it has been pointed out that the primitive vascular system, from which the main blood-vessels of the adult are derived, consists of—

(1) A tubular heart, separated by constrictions into six parts named, from the caudal to the cephalic end, the sinus venosus, the atrium, the atrio-ventricular canal, the ventricle, the bulbus cordis, and the truncus arteriosus.

(2) Two ventral aortæ.

(3) Two dorsal aortæ fused in parts of their extent to form a median descending aorta.

(4) Six pairs of aortic arches, of which four pairs, the first to the fourth, connect the ventral aortæ with the unfused portions of the dorsal aortæ ; one pair, the fifth, connects the ventral aortæ, for a short time, with the dorsal parts of the sixth arches ; and the remaining pair, the sixth, connects the truncus arteriosus with the unfused parts of the dorsal aorta.

(5) Seven pairs of venous trunks, the vitelline, the umbilical, the anterior cardinal, the posterior cardinal, the ducts of Cuvier, the subcardinals, and the supracardinals, of which only three pairs—the vitelline veins, the umbilical veins, and the ducts of Cuvier—open directly into the venous sinus of the heart (Fig. 93).

It was also noted (a) that the dorsal aortæ give off a series of paired branches through which blood passes from the aortæ to networks of capillary vessels from which it is collected into the veins ; (b) that the venous trunks are connected with their fellows of the opposite side, across the median plane, by transverse anastomoses ; and (c) that anastomoses are formed between the posterior cardinal, the subcardinal, and the supracardinal veins (p. 80).

The further changes in the development of the heart and the blood-vessels have now to be considered.

Development of the Heart.—In the early part of the fourth week, when the embryo is about 2 mm. long, the heart is formed, in the septum transversum and the dorsal wall of the pericardium, by the fusion of the caudal parts of the ventral aortæ (Figs. 1054, 1055).

The sinus venosus lies for a time in the septum transversum. There it receives the ducts of Cuvier, the vitelline veins, and the umbilical veins ; and after a short period it is projected out of the septum transversum into the dorsal part of the pericardium.

After its formation the heart elongates more rapidly than the pericardium and therefore bends into the form of a loop, of which the cephalic limb is formed by the truncus arteriosus and the bulbus cordis, the apex, which lies ventrally, by the ventricle, and the caudal limb by the atrium and the sinus venosus (Fig. 1056). The interval between the cephalic and caudal limbs is filled by a fold of the lining pericardium which constitutes the mesocardium.

As the heart folds longitudinally it is also bent in the transverse plane, so that for a time the more cephalic part of the ventricle, with the bulbus cordis and the truncus arteriosus, lies towards the right of the more caudal part of the ventricle and the atrium and sinus venosus, and the atrio-ventricular orifice enters what, for a period, is the left limb of the ventricle (Fig. 1056).

Afterwards, as the ventricle enlarges mainly ventrally, laterally, and headwards, the atrio-ventricular orifice is transposed to the middle of its dorsal wall, the right segment of the sinus venosus is absorbed into the atrium, and the atrium, thus reinforced, expands round the sides of the bulbus cordis and the truncus arteriosus (Fig. 1056).

Subsequently the bulbus cordis is absorbed; partly into the ventricle and partly into the truncus arteriosus, and thereafter the truncus itself is divided into the pulmonary trunk and the ascending part of the aorta, whilst the mesocardium, which lay in the angle between the

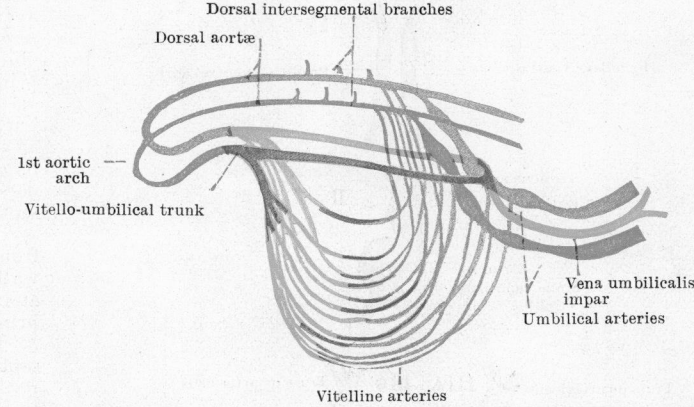

FIG. 1054.—SCHEMA OF CIRCULATION OF AN EMBRYO, 1·35 MM. LONG, WITH SIX SOMITES. (After Felix, modified.)

truncus arteriosus and the atrium, disappears, leaving an aperture—the transverse sinus of the pericardium—through which the right and left halves of the pericardial cavity communicate with each other on the dorsal and cephalic side of the ventricle, on the dorsal side of the ascending aorta and the pulmonary trunk, and on the ventral side of the atrium.

While the changes in position and shape of the heart, the disappearance of the mesocardium, and the division of the truncus arteriosus are taking place, the cavities of the atrium, the atrio-ventricular canal, and the cavity of the ventricle are all being divided into right and left halves by means of septa, which it is convenient to consider separately although they are formed simultaneously and fuse with one another in parts of their extent.

Division of the Atrio-ventricular Canal.—After the longitudinal folding of the primitive cardiac tube has occurred, the atrio-ventricular canal runs dorso-ventrally (from behind forwards in the erect posture) from the atrium to the ventricle. At first it is cylindrical in form, but gradually its cephalic and caudal walls are thickened to form *endocardial cushions*, which project into the middle of the lumen of the canal and convert it into a cleft (Figs. 1057, 1059). Finally the cushions fuse, forming an atrio-ventricular septum but leaving the right and left margins of the canal intact as the *right* and *left atrio-ventricular orifices*.

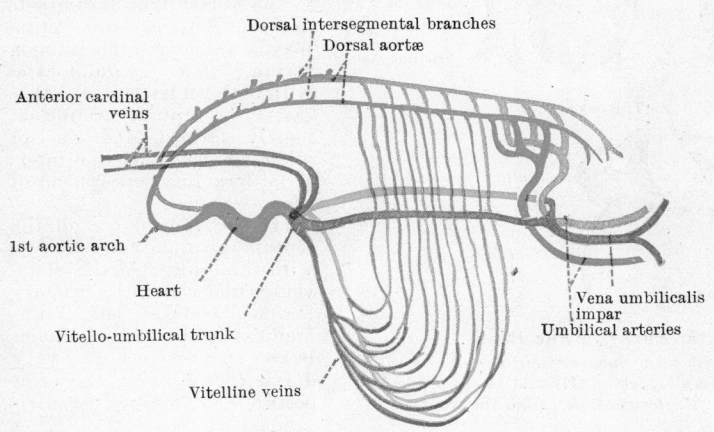

FIG. 1055.—SCHEMA OF VASCULAR SYSTEM OF AN EMBRYO, 2·6 MM. LONG, WITH FOURTEEN SOMITES. (Arteries after Felix, modified.)

Later, partly by invagination into the ventricle and partly by the growth of the margins of the atrio-ventricular orifices into the ventricles, the cusps of the atrio-ventricular valves are formed (Fig. 1059).

Occasionally the atrio-ventricular cushions obliterate not only the middle of the lumen of the atrio-ventricular canal but also one of its margins. In such cases only a single atrio-ventricular orifice is found in the later stages, right or left as the case may be. When such an abnormality occurs it is usually associated with incomplete formation of the atrial and ventricular septa.

Division of the Atrium.—The division of the primitive atrium into right and left atria is brought about by the formation and fusion of two septa—the septum primum and the septum secundum—and the fusion of both with the atrial end of the septum of the atrio-ventricular canal.

The *septum primum* is so called because it appears and partially disappears before the septum secundum is developed. It grows ventrally from the dorsal and cephalic walls of the atrium until it meets and fuses with the septum of the atrio-ventricular canal, and, as it grows, the area of communication between the right and left parts of the atrium is gradually reduced to an aperture. The aperture is called the *primary foramen ovale* (Fig. 1057). It is obliterated when the septum primum fuses with the septum of the atrio-ventricular canal; but before that fusion occurs an aperture called the *secondary foramen ovale* appears in the dorsal and caudal part of the septum primum (Fig. 1057).

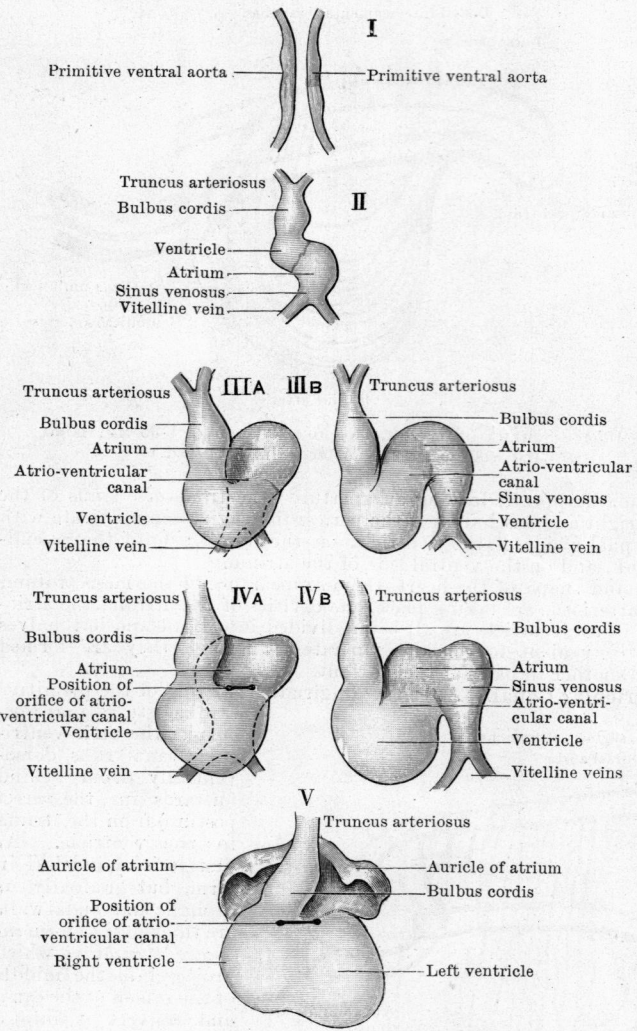

The *septum secundum* grows from the cephalic and ventral walls of the atrium, immediately to the right of the septum primum.

When the growth of the septum secundum has caused its dorsal margin to pass beyond the dorsal margin of the secondary foramen ovale, the latter margin acts as a flap valve which permits blood to pass through the secondary foramen ovale, from the right to the left atrium, but prevents its return. That condition is retained until a short time after birth, when the right surface of the septum primum fuses with the left surface of the septum secundum and the orifice is permanently closed.

As a result of incomplete development the atrial septum may be absent and the common atrium then communicates with both ventricles. In other cases the septum is incompletely formed, and one or other, or both, of the interatrial foramina persist to adult life.

If the ventral end of the septum primum fails to fuse with the septum of the atrio-ventricular canal, the primary foramen ovale persists, and is found as an aperture which lies between and immediately dorsal (posterior in the erect posture) to the atrio-ventricular apertures.

Fig. 1056.—Development of the Heart.
Diagram showing the changes in form and relation of parts at different stages. Modified from His's models. IIIB and IVB are side views; the other figures represent the heart as seen from the front.

If the right surface of the septum primum fails to fuse with the left surface of the septum secundum, a more or less reduced secondary foramen ovale persists. Such a condition is found in 10 per cent. of adults examined in the post-mortem room.

Division of the Truncus Arteriosus and the Cranial Part of the Bulbus Cordis.—It has already been noted that the bulbus cordis is absorbed partly into the truncus arteriosus and partly into the ventricular segment of the heart. As the absorption proceeds endocardial cushions develop in the truncus arteriosus and pass spirally along its inner wall into the ventricle. At the apex of the truncus, where it gives off the ventral aortæ and the sixth aortic arches, four endocardial cushions are found. They are placed ventrally, dorsally, and right and left.

The ventral and dorsal cushions disappear in normal cases, but the right and left cushions pass spirally along the vessel into the ventricle, and they fuse together to form a septum which divides the lumen of the truncus arteriosus into two passages.

At the apex of the truncus, the septum (formed from right and left cushions) divides the arterial trunk into a ventro-cranial (anterior in the erect posture) or aortic passage, which communicates with the ventral aortæ, and a dorso-caudal or pulmonary passage, which remains continuous with the sixth pair of aortic arches, which become parts of the pulmonary arteries.

At that level the septum has ventro-cephalic and dorso-caudal surfaces and right and left borders. But as it passes towards the ventricle it twists like a right-handed spiral, its right border first becoming dorsal, next left lateral, and finally ventral; consequently the surface which was originally dorso-caudal becomes ventro-cephalic, and as a result, when the ventricular end of the septum passes into the ventricle the blood from the right part of that chamber is directed into the sixth pair of aortic arches, which become parts of the pulmonary arteries, and that from the left part into the ventral aortæ and the four anterior aortic arches, which help to form the main arterial trunks of the head, neck, and upper limbs of the adult.

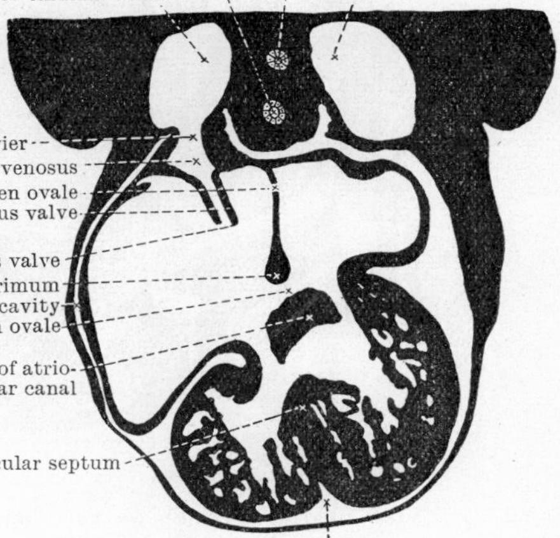

After the septum is completed it is split longitudinally, and so the truncus arteriosus is divided into the ascending aorta and the pulmonary trunk.

Division of the Ventricle.— As the bulbus cordis is absorbed (p. 1277), and the cavities of the truncus arteriosus and the atrium are divided by the formation of septa, the septum which divides the ventricle into right and left parts also appears.

It begins as a fold of the ventricle wall, immediately to the right of its most ventral point, and its position is indicated on the surface by a sulcus (Fig. 1057) which sometimes remains to produce a bifid apex of the heart. The fold takes form mainly as a result of the active outgrowth of the right and left ventricles; it consists of the muscular substance as well

FIG. 1057.—SECTION OF THE HEART OF A HUMAN EMBRYO.
(Edinburgh University collection.)

as the endocardial lining, and it projects into the cavity not only from its ventral but also from its cephalic and caudal walls; hence the septum, in the early stages, is semilunar in form.

The cephalic horn of the semilune advances along the wall of the ventricle until it meets the cephalic margin of the ventricular part of the septum of the truncus arteriosus, with which it fuses. The caudal margin travels along the caudal wall of the ventricle until it meets and fuses with the septum of the atrio-ventricular canal (Fig. 1060). The concave margin of the semilunar septum lies ventral to the aperture leading into the truncus arteriosus;

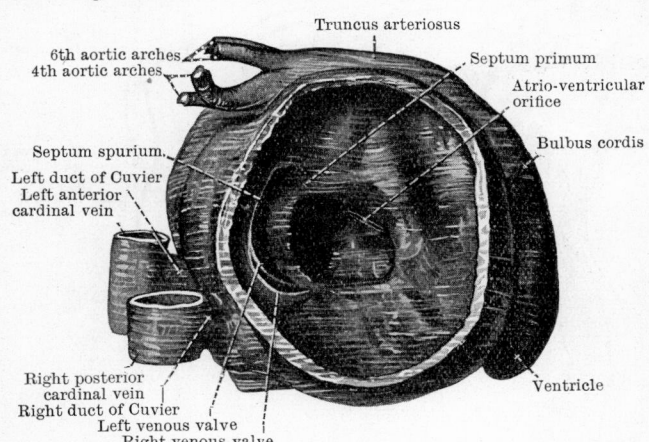

FIG. 1058.—MODEL SHOWING THE INTERIOR OF THE RIGHT ATRIUM OF A HUMAN EMBRYO 5·5 MM. LONG. (Edinburgh University collection. Reconstruction model by C. C. Wang.)

therefore, for a time, there exists an aperture, ventral to the truncus, through which the right and left ventricles communicate with each other. The aperture is closed by the extension of the septum of the truncus arteriosus into the ventricular area until it meets and fuses with the dorsal concave margin of the ventricular septum.

The ventricular septum of the adult consists, therefore, of two parts—a ventral and larger muscular part, formed from the wall of the ventricle, and a dorsal and smaller membranous part (pars membranacea), formed from the ventral extension of the septum of the truncus arteriosus.

The more common abnormalities which result from the non-completion or the modification of the developmental processes in the ventricular area are:—

(1) The septum of the truncus arteriosus may fail to descend into the ventricular area, in which case the pars membranacea septi is absent and an interventricular foramen exists through which the cavities of the two ventricles communicate with each other, and each ventricle opens into both the aorta and the pulmonary artery.

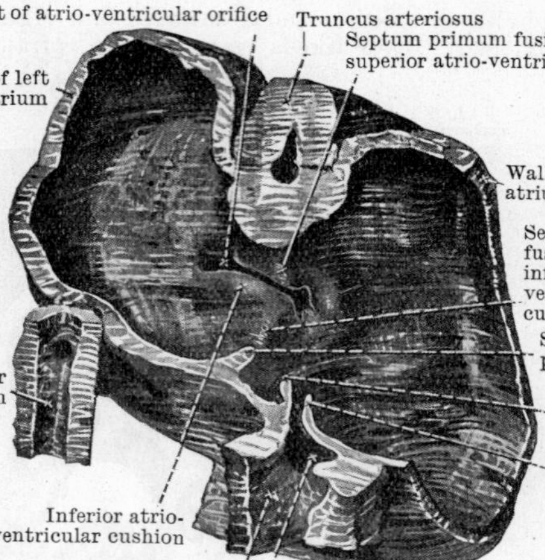

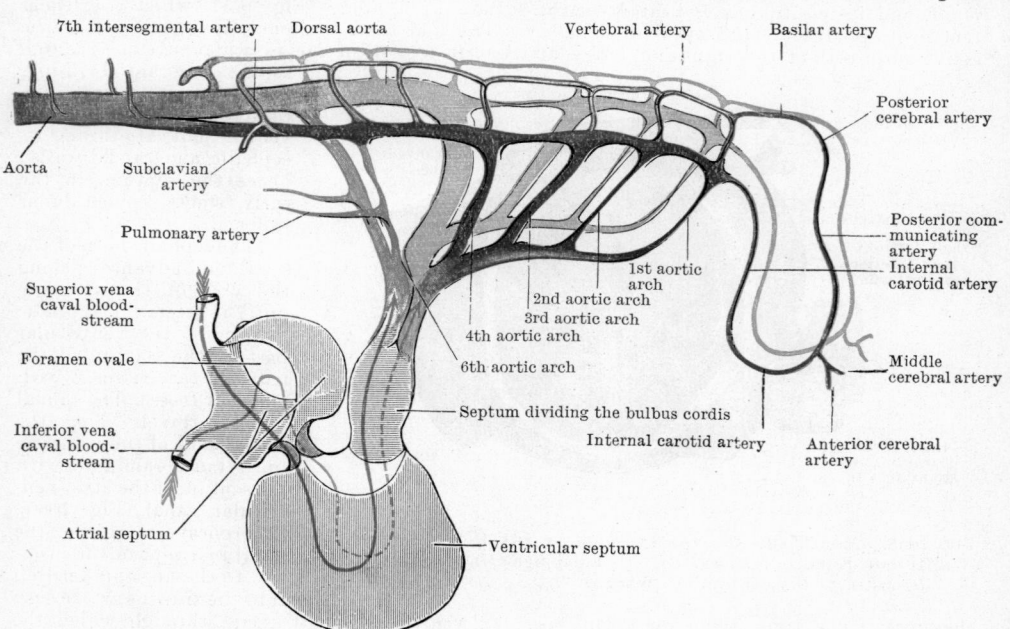

Left part of atrio-ventricular orifice
Truncus arteriosus
Septum primum fusing with superior atrio-ventricular cushion
Wall of left atrium
Wall of right atrium
Septum primum fusing with inferior atrio-ventricular cushion
Septum primum
Left posterior cardinal vein
Left venous valve
Right venous valve
Inferior atrio-ventricular cushion
Right posterior cardinal vein
Right duct of Cuvier opening into right horn of sinus venosus

FIG. 1059.—VIEW OF THE INTERIOR OF THE RIGHT AND LEFT ATRIA OF A HUMAN EMBRYO 5·5 MM. LONG. (Edinburgh University collection. Reconstruction model by C. C. Wang.)

(2) The muscular part of the ventricular septum may be absent. There is then only one ventricular cavity, which receives blood from both atria and projects it into both the pulmonary trunk and the aorta.

(3) The septum of the truncus arteriosus may form a left-handed instead of a right-handed spiral, with the result that the pulmonary trunk communicates with the left ventricle and the aorta with the right ventricle.

(4) The spiral twist of the septum of the truncus arteriosus may be incomplete, so that its ventral margin meets the dorsal margin of the ventricular septum more or less at right angles, then the pulmonary trunk and the aorta both communicate with each of the ventricles.

Many other abnormalities, due to interference with or alterations of the ordinary processes of development, occur; for accounts of them readers who are interested must consult monographs on malformations of the heart.

Fate of the Sinus Venosus.—The sinus venosus, which constituted the most caudal part

7th intersegmental artery   Dorsal aorta   Vertebral artery   Basilar artery
                                                                               Posterior cerebral artery
Aorta   Subclavian artery
           Pulmonary artery   Posterior communicating artery
                                                            1st aortic arch   Internal carotid artery
Superior vena caval blood-stream   2nd aortic arch
                                                            3rd aortic arch
Foramen ovale   4th aortic arch
                                                            6th aortic arch   Middle cerebral artery
Inferior vena caval blood-stream
                                 Septum dividing the bulbus cordis
                                 Internal carotid artery   Anterior cerebral artery
Atrial septum
                                 Ventricular septum

FIG. 1060.—DEVELOPMENT OF THE HEART AND THE MAIN ARTERIES.
Diagram of the heart, showing the formation of its septa, and of the cephalic portion of the arterial system.

of the primitive heart, was formed, in the septum transversum, by the fusion of the terminal parts of the common vitello-umbilical trunk veins. It consists of a single chamber possessing a right and a left horn and a middle section.

Each horn, at that time, receives a duct of Cuvier, a vitelline and an umbilical vein. Later, as the longitudinal folding of the cardiac tube occurs, the sinus venosus emerges from the septum transversum and appears in the caudal part of the pericardium. There it lies dorsal to the atrium into which its right horn opens, through an orifice guarded by right and left venous valves (Figs. 1058, 1059) which fuse with each other at their cephalic and caudal ends.

As development proceeds, the right horn of the sinus venosus is absorbed into the right atrium, the whole of the left and the cranial part of the right venous valves disappearing, whilst the caudal part of the right valve becomes the valve of the inferior vena cava, which is the modified termination of the right vitelline vein (see Development of the Portal System, p. 1285).

The left horn of the sinus venosus remains as the coronary sinus of the fully developed heart, and the dorsal wall of the middle section is projected ventrally towards the right atrium, to form the valve of the coronary sinus, which lies at the right margin of the opening through which the coronary sinus communicates with the right atrium (Fig. 994, p. 1143).

Fate of the Ventral Aortæ, the Aortic Arches, and the Unfused Parts of the Dorsal Aortæ.—It has already been pointed out (see p. 80) that when the embryo is 5 mm. long it possesses five pairs of aortic arches, of which the first and second pairs connect the ventral aortæ with the unfused parts of the dorsal aortæ, whilst the third, fourth, and sixth pairs, which also pass to the unfused parts of the dorsal aortæ, arise from a common stem which springs from the apex of the truncus arteriosus (Fig. 1061).

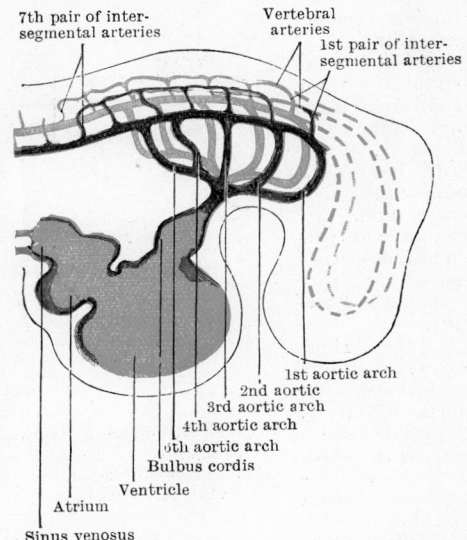

Fig. 1061.—Schema of the Stage of Five Aortic Arches. The cardinal veins and ducts of Cuvier are not shown.

As the embryo increases from 5 mm. to 9 mm. in length—(1) the third and fourth pairs of arches are transferred to the ventral aortæ; (2) a transitory fifth pair of arches appears and for a time connects the ventral aortæ with the dorsal parts of the sixth pair of arches; (3) the first two pairs of arches have begun to disappear; and (4) the right and left pulmonary arteries have grown from the corresponding sixth pair into the rudiments of the lungs (Fig. 1062).

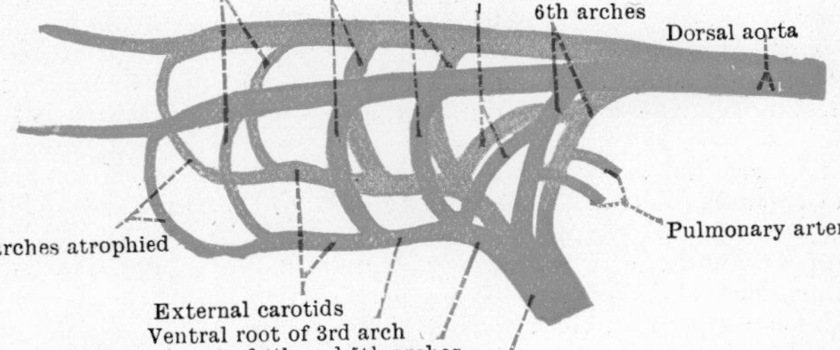

As soon as two or more arches arise from the ventral aortæ it is customary, for convenience of description, to speak of the parts of the ventral aortæ which lie caudal to the various arches as the ventral roots of those arches, and the corresponding parts of the dorsal aortæ are called the dorsal roots of the arches; therefore, at the 9 mm. stage, if the fifth pair of arches are left out of consideration on account of their very transitory and unimportant nature, it may be said that the first four pairs of arches have ventral roots. The sixth pair of arches spring from the apex of the truncus arteriosus, and therefore are devoid of ventral roots; but all the arches have dorsal roots, and the dorsal roots of the sixth pair end in the descending aorta, which was formed by the fusion of the more caudal portions of the primitive right and left dorsal aortæ.

Fig. 1062.—Schema of Aortic Arches of an Embryo 9 mm. long. (After Tandler, modified.) The second and third arches have atrophied and the transitory fifth has appeared.

The main events of the subsequent changes which occur before the embryo is 15 mm. long may be summarised as follows :—

(1) The following parts have disappeared :—

  (a) The dorsal roots of the third pair of arches.
  (b) The dorsal roots of the right fourth and sixth arches.
  (c) The dorsal part of the right sixth arch.

(2) In the meantime the truncus arteriosus has been divided into the ascending aorta, which passes from the left ventricle to the ventral roots of the fourth pair of arches, and the pulmonary trunk which con- nects the right ventricle with the sixth pair.

(3) The ventral root of the right fourth arch has be- come the innomin- ate artery.

(4) The ventral root of the left fourth arch and the fourth arch it- self have been con- verted into part of the arch of the aorta.

(5) The right fourth arch has become the right subclavian artery.

(6) The ventral roots of the third pair have be- come the common carotid arteries.

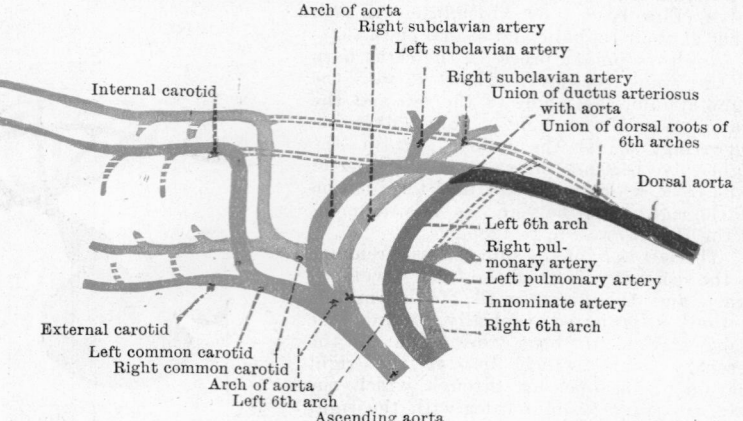

FIG. 1063.—SCHEMA OF PART OF THE ARTERIAL SYSTEM OF A FŒTUS SEEN FROM THE LEFT SIDE. Parts of the first and second arches, the dorsal roots of the third arches, the dorsal part of the right sixth arch, and the dorsal roots of the right fourth and fifth arches have atrophied. The position of the fifth arch is not indicated ; see Fig. 1062.

(7) The ventral roots of the first and second pair have become the external carotid arteries.

(8) The third pair of arches and the dorsal roots of the first and second pairs of arches have formed the internal carotid arteries.

(9) The dorsal root of the left fourth arch has become part of the arch of the aorta.

(10) The dorsal root of the left sixth arch has become the first part of the descending aorta.

(11) The dorsal part of the left sixth arch has become the ductus arteriosus, through which blood, which has passed from the right ventricle into the pulmonary trunk, is transmitted into the aortic arch until birth ; then the dorsal part of the left sixth arch becomes the ligamentum arteriosum ; the ventral part of the left sixth arch becomes the extra-pulmonary part of the left pulmonary artery.

(12) The dorsal part of the right sixth arch disappears and the ventral part becomes the extra-pulmonary portion of the right pulmonary artery.

Many variations of the main stems of the adult arterial system are the result of modifications of the ordinary developmental changes which have been noted. Parts which usually disappear may remain ; parts which usually remain may disappear ; and fusions and absorptions of parts which usually remain distinct may occur.

If the dorsal roots of the right fourth and sixth arches persist, in addition to the persistence of the same parts of the left side, both right and left aortic arches are formed, and the more cephalic part of the descending aorta is doubled, an arrangement which is found in adult reptiles.

If the dorsal roots of the right fourth and sixth arches persist and the corresponding parts on the left side disappear, the arch of the aorta is transposed from the left to the right side. That is the regular occurrence in birds.

If the right fourth arch disappears, and the dorsal roots of the right fourth and sixth arches persist—a not uncommon variation—then the right subclavian artery arises from the descending aorta caudal to the origin of the left subclavian artery.

If the ventral roots of the fourth pair of arches fuse, a common stem is formed, which arises from the arch of the aorta and gives origin to the right subclavian and both common carotid arteries.

If the ventral roots of the third and fourth pairs of arches all fuse, a common stem is formed, which springs from the arch of the aorta ; it gives off the right subclavian artery and the external and internal carotid arteries of both sides.

High division of the common carotid, on either side, may be due to the disappearance of the third arch and the dorsal roots of the second and third arches, and the persistence of the second arch.

Branches of the External Carotid Artery.—All the typical branches of the external carotid artery are present in embryos about 15 mm. long ; little is known, however, regarding the details of their development. It is probable that the maxillary artery and its branches are evolved partly from the ventral part of the first aortic arch and partly from an anastomosis with the branches of a temporary *stapedial artery*, which develops from the dorsal end of the second arch ; but it is not known whether the other branches of the external carotid spring as offsets from the ventral roots of the first or second arches or from the ventral parts of the arches themselves.

Descending Aorta.—The greater part of the descending aorta is formed by the fusion of the primitive dorsal aortæ. In embryos with twenty-three mesodermal somites the primitive dorsal aortæ are fused together from the tenth to the sixteenth segment (Fig. 93, p. 78). At a later period the fusion is continued caudalwards to the twenty-third body segment—the level of the fourth lumbar vertebra—where the common iliac arteries arise. Still later the small terminal portions of the primitive dorsal aortæ fuse together to form the median sacral artery, which runs to the end of the coccygeal region.

If the three somites which lie nearest the head-end, in embryos possessing twenty-three somites, are cephalic somites, then the point of commencement of the median aorta would be situated at the level of the seventh body somite, that is, at the situation of the future seventh cervical vertebra. The position of the anterior point of fusion of the primitive dorsal aortæ is indicated in the adult by the origin of the abnormal right subclavian artery, and is situated at the level of the fifth thoracic vertebra; therefore the anterior end of that part of the descending aorta which is formed by the fusion of the primitive dorsal aortæ must move caudalwards during the developmental period.

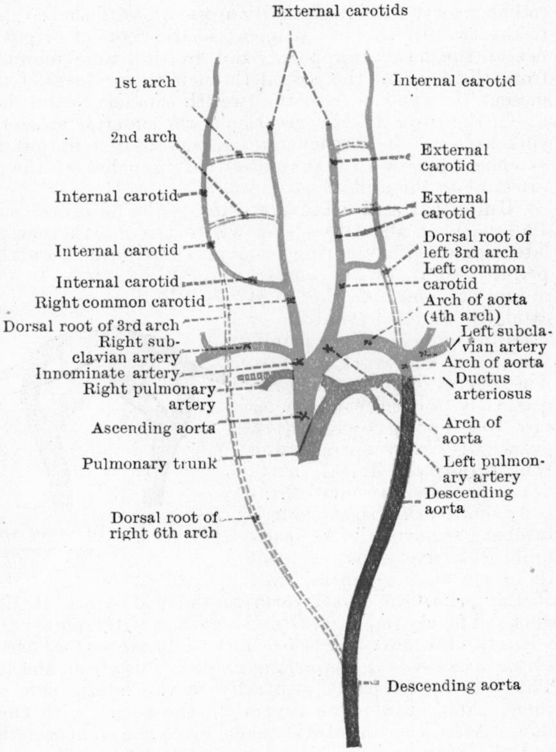

Branches of the Dorsal Aortæ.— The branches given off from the primitive dorsal aortæ are dorsal, lateral, and ventral.

Some of the **dorsal branches** arise in the head region, cephalic to the point where the first mesodermal somite is formed, and hence are presegmental. The others arise more caudally in the head, and in the neck and trunk regions, where they lie opposite the intervals between the mesodermal somites, and are therefore *intersegmental*.

They supply the neural tube and its surroundings, the tissues of the head and neck, the body wall and the limbs. But they do not send branches to the viscera; therefore they are somatic arteries. They anastomose with one another by a series of longitudinal channels which lie ventral and dorsal to the dorsal portions of the costal elements of the skeleton, and dorsal to the transverse processes of the vertebræ.

FIG. 1064.—Schema of Part of the Vascular System of a Fœtus seen from the Front. The positions of the first and second arches, the dorsal roots of the third arches on both sides, and the dorsal roots of the fourth and sixth arches on the right side are shown in dotted lines. The positions of the fifth arches are not shown.

An account of their branches and anastomoses and the transformations which affect them, and more especially of those which result in the formation of the vertebral arteries and the arteries of the limbs, is given in the description of the morphology of the vascular system (see pp. 1294 ff.). But it may be stated here that the main arteries of the adult which are derived from the dorsal branches of the primitive dorsal aortæ and their anastomoses and branches, are : (1) the intercostal and lumbar arteries and their posterior (dorsal) branches; (2) parts of the subclavian arteries; (3) the axillary arteries and their continuations in the upper limbs; (4) the vertebral arteries; (5) the spinal arteries; (6) the basilar artery; (7) the superior intercostal arteries; (8) the internal mammary and the superior and inferior epigastric arteries.

As a rule, the dorsal branches of the primitive dorsal aortæ remain separate from each other, even in the regions where the primitive dorsal aortæ themselves fuse, but occasionally in the thoracic and lumbar regions they fuse, with the result that intercostal and lumbar arteries of opposite sides arise from common stems.

The **lateral branches of the dorsal aortæ** are distributed to organs developed from the intermediate cell tracts—that is : to the pronephros and mesonephros [Wolffian body], which form the temporary kidneys ; to the metanephros, which becomes the permanent kidney ; and to the suprarenal and genital glands. They become the renal, testicular, and ovarian arteries.

The **ventral branches of the dorsal aortæ** are neither definitely segmental nor intersegmental. They pass to the walls of the entodermal portion of the alimentary canal and its diverticula, and also, in the early stages of development, to the walls of the yolk sac and the chorion and its placental derivative. They are connected together by longitudinal anastomosing channels which lie in the dorsal mesentery of the gut and also upon the wall of the gut itself. As the yolk sac atrophies, the prolongations of the ventral branches to its walls disappear, and simultaneously the portions of the corresponding vessels of opposite sides, which lie in the mesentery, dorsal to the gut, and the longitudinal anastomoses which connect them, fuse together to form unpaired stem-trunks from which the three great vessels of the abdominal part of the alimentary canal are derived, namely, the cœliac, the superior mesenteric, and the inferior mesenteric arteries. But the original stem of each of these three important vessels is not that which eventually forms its origin from the abdominal part of the aorta ; for the cœliac artery, which originally arose opposite the seventh cervical segment, wanders caudalwards to the twelfth thoracic segment as the roots of origin of the ventral vessels which are situated nearer the head disappear ; and in the same manner the superior mesenteric is transposed from the level of the second thoracic to the level of the first lumbar segment, and the inferior mesenteric wanders from the twelfth thoracic to the third lumbar segment.

Of the three arteries mentioned the superior mesenteric retains longest its connexion with the yolk sac, and it occasionally happens that a fibrous strand representing the original channel extends from one of the intestinal branches of the superior mesenteric past the side of the intestine to the umbilicus.

Umbilical and Iliac Arteries.—The umbilical arteries arise, when the embryo is less than 1·5 mm. long, about the level where the fourth cervical mesodermal somite is developed at a later stage. They spring from plexuses formed, on the lateral walls of the caudal part of the primitive gut, by the anastomoses of some of the most caudally situated ventral or vitelline branches of the primitive dorsal aorta (Fig. 1054). The origins of the arteries are gradually moved caudally as the embryo grows, until, eventually, they spring from the primitive dorsal aorta opposite the twenty-third body somite, that is, the fourth lumbar segment. As each umbilical artery passes from its origin on the ventral wall

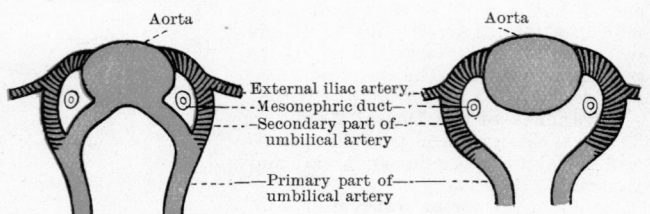

FIG. 1065.—DIAGRAM SHOWING THE FORMATION OF THE SECONDARY PART OF THE PRIMITIVE UMBILICAL ARTERY.

of the primitive dorsal aorta to the body-stalk it lies to the medial side of the pronephric duct. The ventral origin is, however, but temporary ; for, by the time the embryo has attained a length of 5 mm., and the primitive dorsal aortæ have fused to form the single descending aorta, a new vessel has arisen, on each side, from the lateral part of the caudal end of the aorta. This new vessel passes ventrally to the lateral side of the mesonephric [Wolffian] duct, and then unites, on a plane ventral to the aorta, with the primitive umbilical artery of the same side. After the union has taken place the ventral origin of the umbilical artery disappears, and the primitive umbilical artery then arises from the side of the caudal end of the aorta. From the newly formed vessel, which now constitutes the only origin of the umbilical artery, the **inferior gluteal artery**, which is the primitive main artery of the lower limb, arises. At a later period, and at a more dorsal level, a second branch arises from the dorsal root of origin of the umbilical artery ; this is the second main vessel of the lower limb, which becomes the **external iliac** and the **femoral arteries** of the adult. As soon as the external iliac artery is formed, that portion of the umbilical stem which lies dorsal to it becomes the **common iliac artery,** and the more ventral part, which descends into the true pelvis, becomes the **internal iliac [hypogastric] artery.** But that portion of the original umbilical artery which runs along the side of the true pelvis to the ventral wall of the abdomen, then to the umbilicus and through the umbilicus to the placenta, is still called the umbilical artery. After birth, when the placental circulation ceases, the greater part of the intra-abdominal portion of the umbilical artery atrophies and becomes converted into the **lateral umbilical ligament** ; but a portion of the part which lies in the pelvis remains pervious, and from it springs the **superior vesical artery.**

Arteries of the Upper Limbs.—It appears probable that, in the earliest stages of development, a number of branches arise from the sides of the primitive dorsal aortæ and pass to the rudiments of the upper limbs, where they end in vascular plexuses which are drained into the anterior cardinal veins.

At a later period the number of connexions with the aorta, on each side, is reduced to one, and that is transferred from the aorta to the ventral branch of the seventh intersegmental artery, whilst, at the same time, the original plexus in the limb is reduced to a single trunk, which is divisible into subclavian, axillary, brachial, and anterior interosseous segments. At a later period a median branch arises from the anterior interosseous artery, and still later radial and ulnar branches are formed, the portion of the ulnar artery which lies between the bifurcation of the brachial and the origin of its anterior interosseous branch being part of the original stem vessel.

Arteries of the Lower Limbs.—The development of the arteries of the lower limbs has been investigated by Senior, and readers who wish to follow the details of an intricate process, or those who desire to understand the evolution of the arterial variations met with in the lower limbs, should refer to Senior's *Communications* ;[1] only a general outline of the phenomena can be given here.

[1] H. D. Senior, *Amer. Journ. Anat.*, 1919 ; *Anat. Rec.*, 1920.

It is not possible from the knowledge so far attained to assign to the arteries of the lower limbs any segmental or intersegmental relationship.

In the first place, a primary axial artery is developed. It springs from the secondary umbilical artery, leaves the pelvis through the greater sciatic foramen, descends through the thigh between the rudiments of the hamstring and adductor muscles, passes through the popliteal fossa, where its distal part is in front of the rudiment of the popliteus muscle, and descends along the interosseous membrane to the foot, where it ends in a capillary plexus.

The remnants of the primitive axial artery usually present in the adult are—the inferior gluteal artery and its sciatic branch (which becomes the companion artery of the sciatic nerve), the proximal or femoral part of the popliteal artery, and the distal part of the peroneal artery.

After the axial artery is established, a new branch springs from the secondary umbilical artery above the origin of the axial artery. The new vessel runs along the inlet of the pelvis, passes above the superior pubic ramus, and enters the front part of the thigh, where it divides into two branches.

The two branches end in a capillary plexus which is joined distally by a recurrent branch of the axial artery which pierces the rudiment of the adductor magnus.

That part of the new vessel which lies in the abdomen becomes the external iliac artery. The part which lies in the thigh, with one of its branches, part of the capillary plexus and the recurrent branch of the axial artery, is converted into the femoral artery of the adult.

The other terminal branch and the remainder of the capillary plexus disappear, or they are utilised in the formation of some of the branches of the femoral artery.

All the arteries of the leg and foot of the adult, except the distal part of the peroneal artery, are formed either by rami of the primitive axial artery, or their branches, or anastomosing channels, or by combinations of some of the three groups of vessels.

DEVELOPMENT OF THE VEINS

During the period of embryonic life many venous plexuses and veins appear ; some of them are represented in the adult as parts of permanent vessels, others by fibrous cords, and some disappear leaving, in ordinary circumstances, no trace of their existence.

Those which appear may be classified in two groups : (1) Those which are partly extra-embryonic and partly intra-embryonic. (2) Those which are entirely intra-embryonic. The main features of the history of the first group are well established, but there is considerable difference of opinion regarding the history of those members of the second group, which lie in the lower part of the thorax and in the abdomen. It must be understood, therefore, that the account here given is merely a tentative summary of present-day knowledge and opinion.

Veins Partly Intra-Embryonic and Partly Extra-Embryonic

It has previously been noted (p. 77) that the earliest veins to appear are the *vitelline veins*, which return blood from the yolk sac, and the *umbilical veins*, which return purified blood from the placenta. Their further history may now be considered. They are paired veins, right and left, and between them there are transverse anastomoses.

Vitelline and Umbilical Veins, Portal Vein, Hepatic Veins, and the Cardiac End of the Inferior Vena Cava.—In the early stages of development the vitelline veins, right and left, convey blood from the yolk-sac part of the entodermal vesicle first to the caudal ends of the corresponding primitive ventral aortæ, and next, after the caudal parts of the primitive ventral aortæ have fused, to the sinus venosus of the primitive heart.

After the entodermal vesicle is separated into the embryonic alimentary canal, the yolk sac, and the vitello-intestinal duct, each vitelline vein passes along the duct to the corresponding side of the cephalic margin of the umbilical orifice, where it enters the embryo, passing at once into a mass of mesoderm called the septum transversum ; there it unites, for a time, with the cardiac end of the corresponding umbilical vein to form a common vitello-umbilical trunk, which terminates in the sinus venosus (Figs 1054, 1055). At that period the sinus venosus also is situated in the septum transversum.

Subsequently, as the sinus venosus leaves the septum transversum and passes into the pericardial cavity, the common vitello-umbilical trunk is absorbed into it, and each vein thus acquires its own separate opening into the sinus.

The septum transversum is a mass of mesoderm which intervenes between the pericardium and the ventral portion of the abdominal cavity along the line of the cephalic border of the umbilical orifice. From it are derived the caudal (lower) wall of the pericardium, the ventral part of the central and lateral parts of the diaphragm, the falciform ligament of the liver, the areolar tissue and vascular parts of the liver, and the lesser omentum.

The liver is developed from the branchings of a diverticulum from the ventral wall of the duodenum in the mesoderm of part of the septum transversum. Therefore the portions of the vitelline and umbilical veins which lie in the liver area of the septum transversum are expanded as the liver tissue grows, and at the same time broken up into a great number of anastomosing channels, which form for a period the main part of the liver substance and constitute what is called **sinusoidal tissue.**

The sinusoidal tissue consists of relatively wide anastomosing blood-vessels whose walls are formed at first of endothelium surrounded by areolar tissue. Intervening between the channels of adjacent sinuses, and spreading through the areolar tissue, there are ramifying strands of liver cells which multiply and increase in size and invade the sinusoidal blood spaces until they are, for the main part, reduced to the size of capillaries, and the liver becomes a comparatively solid organ. At the same time the endothelial lining of the spaces loses its continuity so that liver cells come into direct contact with the blood.

While the formation of the sinusoidal spaces is taking place in the liver area the parts of the fore-gut are defined, and as the duodenal and gastric parts recede from the liver the lesser omentum is evolved from the caudal part of the septum transversum. As the duodenum is delimited, the vitelline veins pass along its sides on their way to the liver, and become connected around the duodenum by three transverse anastomoses, two of which lie ventral and one dorsal to it. On the liver side of the anastomoses each vitelline vein is broken up into: a caudal part, the *vena advehens*, which enters the liver substance; an area of sinusoidal channels in the liver substance; and a cephalic part, the *vena revehens*, which passes from the liver to the heart. After a time the **left vena revehens** loses its direct connexion with the heart, moves across towards the right, and opens into the cephalic end of the right vena revehens. When that change has occurred all the blood passing to the liver by the vitelline veins reaches the heart by the **right vena revehens**, which now becomes the terminal part of the inferior vena cava. This also receives the ductus venosus—a new channel, which is evolved from the sinusoidal spaces, and which carries the major part of the blood from the left umbilical vein to the inferior vena cava.

In the meantime degeneration takes place in the ventral and caudal parts of the vitelline veins and in parts of the two loops formed by the three transverse anastomoses between them. The ventral parts of the veins disappear with the degeneration of the yolk sac, and the right half of the caudal loop and the left part of the cephalic loop also disappear (Fig. 1066). Simultaneously the superior mesenteric vein, which has been evolved in association with the formation of the intestine from the mid-gut, opens into the left vitelline vein, caudal to the dorsal transverse anastomosis, and, a little later, the splenic vein enters at the same point. The final result is the formation of the permanent **portal vein**, which is formed from—(1) the cephalic end of the left limb of the caudal loop between the vitelline veins; (2) the dorsal anastomosis between the vitelline veins; (3) the right limb of the cephalic loop formed by the vitelline veins. The right branch of the portal vein is the right vena advehens. The left branch of the portal vein is formed from the left vena advehens, and the more cephalic of the two ventral anastomoses between the vitelline veins. It is connected with the ligamentum teres of the liver, because the left umbilical vein, which opened at one time into the left horn of the sinus venosus of the heart, and afterwards into the sinusoids of the liver, finally becomes connected with the left vena advehens, at the level of the cephalic ventral anastomosis between the two vitelline veins; at the same point it is connected with the ductus venosus so that a channel may exist by which the blood from the placenta can pass to the right vena revehens without much admixture with the venous blood passing to the liver through the left branch of the portal vein and the left vena advehens. The ductus venosus is developed from the sinusoidal spaces of the liver as the left umbilical vein is transferred to the left vitelline vein.

The **venæ revehentes**, which transfer the blood from the liver to the heart, are the cephalic ends of the primitive vitelline veins. The left vena revehens, as already stated, eventually loses its connexion with the heart and ends in the right vena revehens, which receives the ductus venosus also. The right vena revehens thus becomes the only channel by which blood is returned to the heart from the alimentary canal and from the placenta: that is, it becomes the anterior or cephalic end of the inferior vena cava. The intrahepatic part of the stem of the right vena revehens becomes the **right hepatic vein**, and the left vena revehens becomes the **left hepatic vein**, which are the two vessels which pour, into the inferior vena cava, the blood which was carried from the alimentary canal to the liver by the portal vein and its branches.

As the cephalic part of the right vitelline vein is transformed from the right vena revehens into the anterior end of the inferior vena cava, some of the sinusoids in the dorsal part of the liver are fused together to form the hepatic part of the inferior vena cava, from the caudal end of which an outgrowth passes caudally to anastomose with the right subcardinal vein and to take part in the formation of the pre-renal part of the inferior vena cava (see p. 1292).

Umbilical Veins.—In the earliest stages of development there are three umbilical veins, the vena umbilicalis impar and its branches the left and right umbilical veins. The vena umbilicalis impar and the left umbilical vein persist until birth; the right umbilical vein disappears entirely at an early stage of development.

The vena umbilicalis impar passes from the placenta to the caudal boundary of the umbilical orifice, where it divides into the left and right umbilical veins. Each of the latter unites, for a time, with the corresponding vitelline vein in the septum transversum; then it becomes directly connected with the corresponding horn of the sinus venosus of the heart, and still later with sinusoidal spaces of the liver. The right umbilical vein has also a temporary secondary connexion with the right vitelline vein, but at an early period it undergoes atrophy and all parts of it completely disappear.

The left umbilical vein, which is connected first with the left vitelline vein, next with the heart, still later with the liver, and finally with the left vitelline again, at the point where the latter becomes the left vena advehens, persists until birth, and, after the disappearance of the right umbilical vein, it conveys the blood from the placenta to the liver, where part of the placental blood passes into the left vena advehens and so through the left vena revehens to the inferior vena cava, and part passes into the ductus venosus, by which it reaches that portion of the cephalic part of the right vena revehens which becomes the cephalic or anterior end of the permanent inferior vena cava.

After birth, when the placental circulation ceases, the left umbilical vein becomes the ligamentum teres of the liver.

Ductus Venosus.—The ductus venosus is developed as the left umbilical vein loses its direct connexion with the liver and becomes united to the left vena advehens. It is formed from the sinusoidal spaces of the rudimentary liver and connects the commencement of

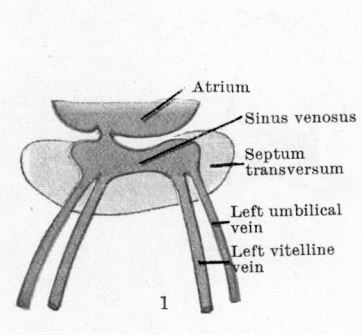

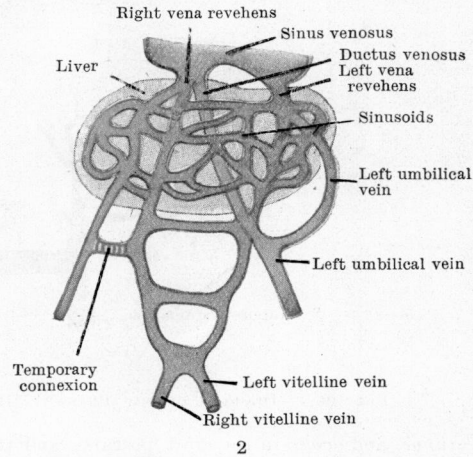

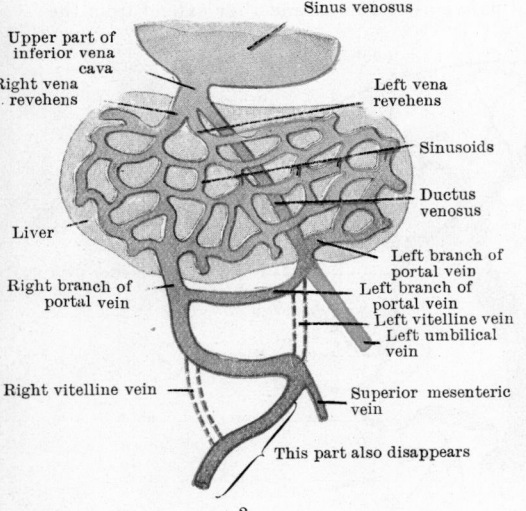

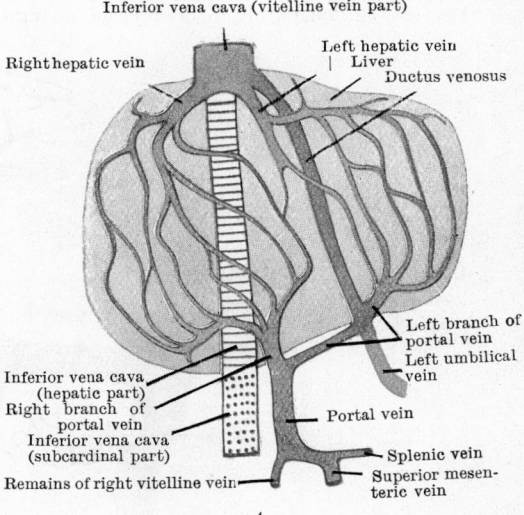

FIG. 1066.—SCHEMATA, showing four stages of the development of the portal system and parts of the inferior vena cava.

the left vena advehens with the cephalic part of the right vena revehens. It forms the more direct channel by which the greater part of the blood from the placenta is passed to the heart through that part of the right vena revehens which becomes the upper end of the inferior vena cava. After birth it is converted into the fibrous *ligamentum venosum*, which connects the left branch of the portal vein with the upper end of the inferior vena cava.

INTRA-EMBRYONIC VEINS

The consideration of the history of the veins of the second group—the intra-embryonic veins—and especially of those members of the group which appear in the lower part of the thorax and in the abdomen, is complicated by the names which have been given to them, and by insufficient definition of the exact positions of the vessels to which the names are applied;

it is thus sometimes difficult to decide whether or not the vessel which two different observers describe under the same term is really the same vessel, and whether or not the same vessel has been described under different names.

The main terms used to indicate the vessels which have been noted are *anterior cardinal veins*, *posterior cardinal veins*, *subcardinal veins*, *supracardinal veins*, *thoraco-lumbar veins*, the *prevertebral (subvertebral) plexus*, and the *azygos venous lines*.

In the subsequent account the embryo and fœtus are considered as being in the quadruped position. Therefore the terms *anterior* and *posterior* are equivalent to *cephalic* and *caudal*, and to

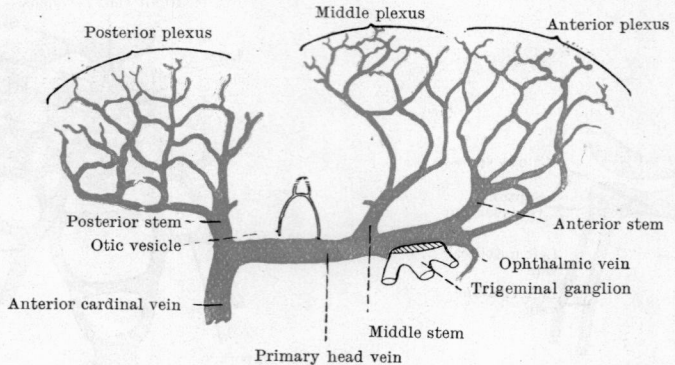

FIG. 1067.—DIAGRAM OF THE PRIMARY HEAD VEIN AND ITS TRIBUTARIES.   (After Streeter.)

upper and *lower* in the erect posture ; and the prefixes *sub-* and *supra-* are equivalent to *ventral* and *dorsal*, and to *anterior* and *posterior* in the erect posture.

Anterior Cardinal Veins.—The history of the anterior cardinal veins is relatively simple ; they are the first purely intra-embryonic longitudinal veins to appear, and they extend from the

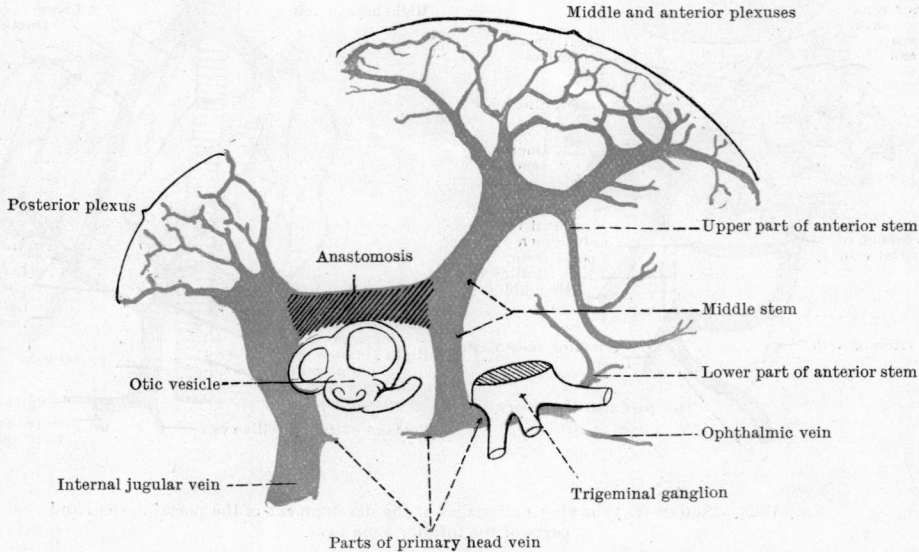

FIG. 1068.—DIAGRAM OF THE HEAD VEINS OF A 21 MM. EMBRYO.   (After Streeter.)

region of the eye to the sinus venosus of the heart, one on each side. Each anterior cardinal vein is separable into three parts — a cephalic part, and nuchal and thoracic parts. In the earliest stages the *cephalic part* extends from the optic stalk, along the medial side of the trigeminal ganglion, the otic vesicle, and the 7th to the 11th cranial nerves into the neck. At a later period the part which lies medial to the otic vesicle and the 7th to the 11th cranial nerves disappears and is replaced by a new vessel which lies lateral to the vesicle and the nerves. The new vessel follows the course of the facial nerve, and in part of its course is extracranial. At the anterior end of the neck it ends in the nuchal portion of the anterior cardinal vein which has now become the internal jugular vein. After the secondary channel is established the stem vessel of the head is termed the **primary head vein**. Its anterior part, which lies medial to the trigeminal ganglion, becomes the cavernous sinus ; its posterior part disappears, but before that disappearance occurs many changes take place in the tributaries of the primary head vein.

The most anterior tributaries of the primary head vein are derived from the region of the optic vesicle and remnants of them become converted into the ophthalmic vein. But in addition to the anterior tributaries there are numerous dorsal or upper tributaries which become arranged in three main groups: an *anterior plexus* associated with the regions of the fore-brain and the mid-brain; a *middle plexus* associated with the cerebellar region of the hind-brain; and a *posterior plexus* associated with the region of the medulla oblongata (Fig. 1067).

The vessels of each plexus tend to run together as they approach the stem of the primary head vein and so three *stems* are formed, the *anterior, middle,* and *posterior* (Fig. 1067); they were described by Mall in 1904. That condition persists until the embryo attains a length of about 18 mm. when an anastomosis forms, above the otic vesicle, between the stems from the middle and posterior plexuses (Fig. 1068), and at the same time that part of the primary head vein which lay lateral to the otic vesicle and the 7th, 8th, 9th, 10th, and 11th cranial nerves disappears (Fig. 1068).

By the time the embryo has become 21 mm. long the anastomosis mentioned has become very important, and a separation has occurred between the lower and the upper portions of

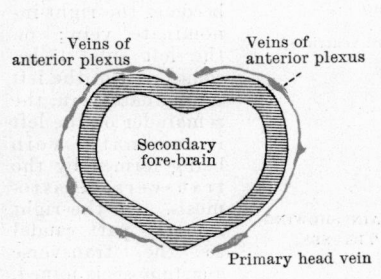

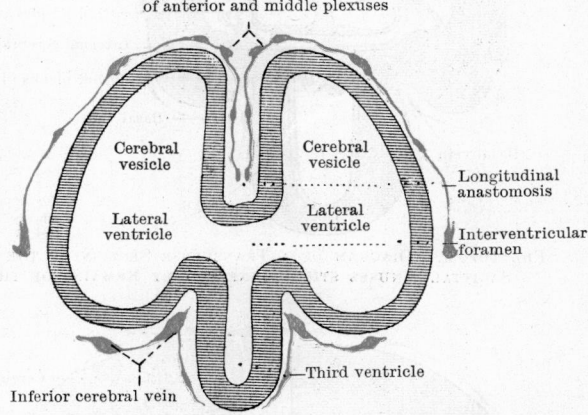

FIG. 1069 A.—DIAGRAM OF A TRANSVERSE SECTION OF THE SECONDARY FORE-BRAIN AND THE VENOUS PLEXUSES.

FIG. 1069 B.—DIAGRAM OF A TRANSVERSE SECTION OF THE BRAIN SHOWING THE FOLDING OF THE UPPER PARTS OF THE PLEXUSES BETWEEN THE CEREBRAL HEMISPHERES.

the anterior stem tributary; therefore, at that period, the blood from the eye region flows backwards to the anterior end of the primary head vein, then upwards along what was the lower part of the middle stem tributary, next backwards along the anastomosis above the otic region to the posterior stem tributary, down which it passes to the nuchal portion of the anterior cardinal vein which has now become the internal jugular vein (Fig. 1068). At this time the blood from the anterior and middle plexuses reaches the supra-otic anastomosis through the upper or dorsal part of the middle stem tributary (Fig. 1068).

With the formation of the subdural and subarachnoid spaces the main parts of the venous plexuses are carried away from the brain, with the membrane which will be transformed into the dura mater; but in part the plexuses still retain their connexions with the pia mater on the brain surface, and they afterwards establish new connexions with the veins which appear on the surfaces of the developing cerebral hemispheres. In the meantime, on each side, the upper or dorsal tributaries of the anterior and the middle plexus anastomose together (Fig. 1069 B).

When the cerebral hemispheres increase in size the dura-matral tissue is compressed between them, and between the cerebral hemispheres above and the mid- and hind-brain below, in the form of folds (Figs. 1070 A and B). As the folds are formed the conjoined anterior and middle plexuses of one side are carried into relation with those of the opposite side in the median plane of the head; there the vessels of opposite sides unite together and are finally resolved into the superior and inferior sagittal sinuses and the straight sinus (Figs. 1070 A and B); at the same time some of the smaller vessels of the plexuses which retain their connexion with the pia mater are transformed into the internal cerebral veins and the great cerebral vein; and from some of the lower or ventral tributaries, on each side, is produced the inferior cerebral vein of the embryo which probably becomes the basal vein of the adult (Figs. 1070 A and B).

While the changes last mentioned are taking place, the growth of the hemispheres forces the upper part of the middle stem tributary on each side backwards and then downwards until it becomes the transverse sinus (Fig. 1071); and the anastomosis above the otic region and the posterior stem tributary are converted into its continuation—the sigmoid sinus (Fig. 1071).

By the time this stage is attained the anterior portion of the primary head vein which lies to the medial side of the trigeminal ganglion has become the cavernous sinus, and the lower or ventral part of the middle stem tributary has been converted into the superior petrosal sinus (Fig. 1071).

The inferior petrosal sinus appears to be an independently formed anastomosis which connects the posterior end of the cavernous sinus with the upper end of the internal jugular vein across the medial side of the otic region (Fig. 1071).

The history of the *nuchal* and *thoracic* parts of the anterior cardinal veins is different, to a certain extent, on opposite sides. On both sides the anterior cardinal vein is joined, at the root of the neck, by the chief vein of the upper limb. The part cephalic to the junction becomes the internal jugular vein. Caudal to the junction, in the cephalic part of the thorax, a transverse anastomosis forms between the two anterior cardinal veins. The part cephalic to the anastomosis and caudal to the junction with the vein of the limb, on the right side, becomes the right innominate vein; on the left side it becomes part of the left innominate vein, the remainder of the left innominate vein being formed by the transverse anastomosis. On the right side the part caudal to the transverse anastomosis is joined, after a time, by the posterior cardinal vein of that side. The part cephalic to that junction becomes the extrapericardial part of the superior vena cava. The part caudal to the junction is called the *duct of Cuvier*; it becomes the intrapericardial part of the superior vena cava. On the left side the part of the anterior cardinal vein caudal to the transverse anastomosis opens, at first, into the left horn of the sinus venosus of the heart; after the anterior cardinal is joined by

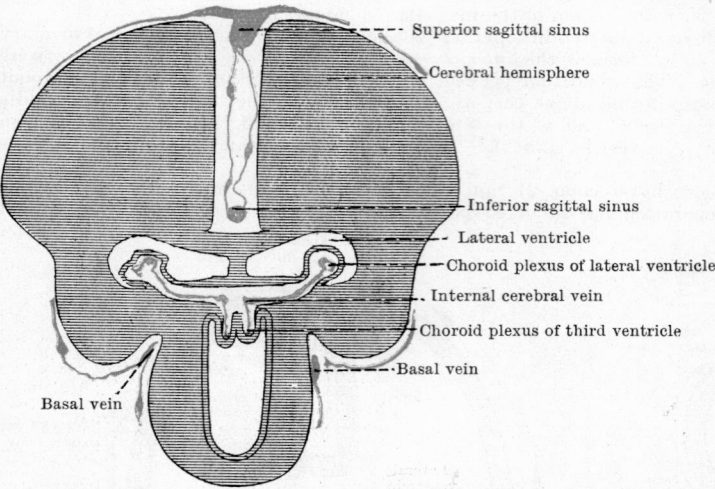

FIG. 1070 A.—DIAGRAM OF A TRANSVERSE SECTION OF THE BRAIN SHOWING SAGITTAL SINUSES STILL CONNECTED BY REMAINS OF THE PLEXUSES.

Labels: Superior sagittal sinus; Cerebral hemisphere; Inferior sagittal sinus; Lateral ventricle; Choroid plexus of lateral ventricle; Internal cerebral vein; Choroid plexus of third ventricle; Basal vein; Basal vein

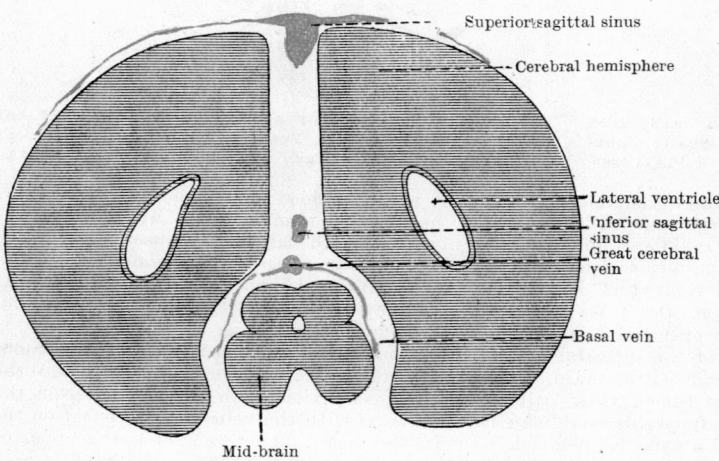

FIG. 1070 B.—DIAGRAM OF A TRANSVERSE SECTION OF THE BRAIN AFTER COMPLETION OF THE SAGITTAL SINUSES.

Labels: Superior sagittal sinus; Cerebral hemisphere; Lateral ventricle; Inferior sagittal sinus; Great cerebral vein; Basal vein; Mid-brain

the posterior cardinal its caudal part becomes the left duct of Cuvier (represented by the oblique vein of the left atrium), whilst the cephalic part becomes part of the left superior intercostal vein, which opens into the left innominate vein.

The **external jugular vein** is a new formation which receives for a time the cephalic vein of the upper limb; but the cephalic vein, which is a secondary vessel, is eventually transposed to the axillary vein, which is a part of the primitive upper limb vein.

Posterior Cardinal, Subcardinal, and Supracardinal Veins, Thoraco-lumbar Veins, Prevertebral Venous Plexus, Azygos Venous Lines, and the Inferior Vena Cava.

All the above veins extend from the abdomen into the thorax; and all of them, with the exception of the posterior cardinals, are evolved from more or less well-marked venous plexuses. They communicate freely with one another, and they receive in turn, as they supplant one another, the intersegmental veins which open first into the posterior cardinals, and finally in the thoracic region and in some cases, and to a variable extent, in the lumbar region into the adult representatives of the azygos venous lines.

The **Posterior Cardinal Veins** appear shortly after the anterior cardinals. They extend from the pelvic region along the dorsal wall of the abdomen, dorsal to the mesonephros and the remnants of the pronephros, into the septum transversum, where they unite with the anterior cardinals. They receive the intersegmental veins and the veins from the mesonephros, and, for a time, the veins of the upper limbs. When the subcardinal veins appear they form numerous anastomoses with the posterior cardinals; but the two most important anastomoses are situated —(1) near the cephalic ends, and (2) near the caudal ends, of the posterior cardinals; thereafter, between those two points, the posterior cardinals disappear. Their remaining caudal parts on both sides become the common iliac and internal iliac veins, the transverse part of the left common iliac vein being the remains of a transverse anastomosis between the two posterior cardinals. The cephalic part of the right posterior cardinal vein remains in the adult as the terminal portion of the vena azygos; and the cephalic part of the left posterior cardinal becomes the caudal part of the left superior intercostal vein.

The **Subcardinal Veins** appear later than the posterior cardinals, and in the dorsal part of the thorax and abdomen, ventro-lateral to the aorta and ventro-medial to the mesonephros. They anastomose freely together dorsal to the superior mesenteric artery, and ventral to the aorta, that is between the two kidneys, which by this time have attained their abdominal position. At each end they anastomose also with the posterior cardinals (see above). After the appearance of the subcardinals the posterior cardinals begin to disappear, and the intersegmental and

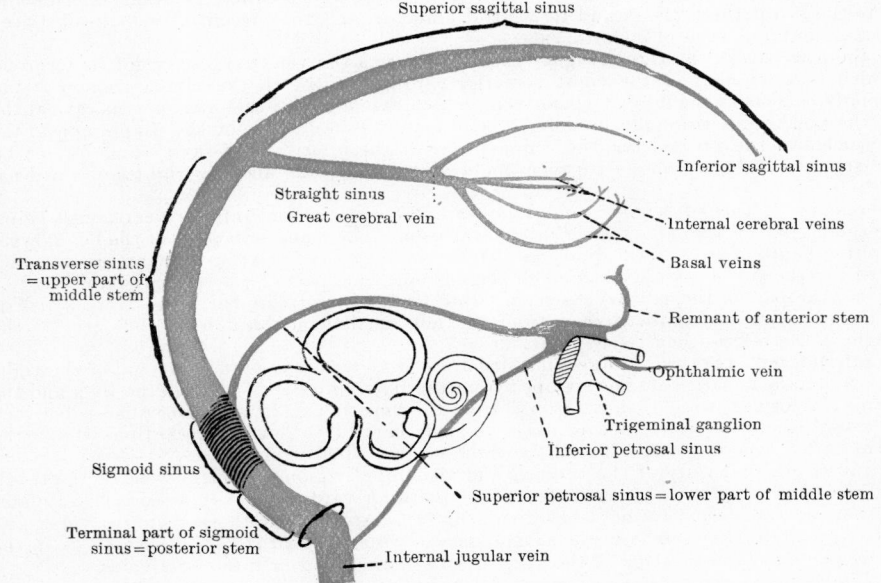

Superior sagittal sinus

Inferior sagittal sinus

Straight sinus
Great cerebral vein

Internal cerebral veins

Basal veins

Transverse sinus = upper part of middle stem

Remnant of anterior stem

Ophthalmic vein

Trigeminal ganglion
Inferior petrosal sinus

Sigmoid sinus

Superior petrosal sinus = lower part of middle stem

Terminal part of sigmoid sinus = posterior stem

Internal jugular vein

FIG. 1071.—DIAGRAM OF THE VENOUS SINUSES.

mesonephric veins which previously passed to them are transferred to the subcardinals. The right subcardinal forms a junction also with a downgrowth from the hepatic part of the inferior vena cava, and each receives the vein from the corresponding kidney.

The thoracic parts of the subcardinals disappear. The cephalic abdominal portion of each of them becomes the corresponding suprarenal vein. The anastomosis between the right sub-cardinal and the downgrowth from the hepatic part of the inferior vena cava and a part of the right subcardinal itself become part of the pre-renal and inter-renal part of the inferior vena cava. The transverse anastomosis between the two subcardinal veins dorsal to the superior mesenteric artery, becomes part of the left renal vein. The remaining parts of both subcardinals disappear.

Supracardinal Veins.—These veins have been defined, by Huntington and M'Clure, as bilateral and originally symmetrical venous channels which develop "dorso-medial to the primitive postcardinal veins by longitudinal anastomosis between somatic postcardinal tributaries." In the opinion of the observers quoted, the right takes part in the formation of the post-renal portion of the inferior vena cava, and both, in their thoracic sections, become converted into parts of the azygos system of veins. Unfortunately, the relationship of the supra-cardinal veins to the sympathetic trunks and their ventral branches (splanchnic and aortic) was not stated, and, as Reagan has pointed out, the inferior vena cava lies lateral to the nervous structures mentioned and the azygos vein lies medial, therefore the inferior vena cava is not in the azygos venous line, and if the right supracardinal is in the inferior caval line, it cannot be a forerunner of the azygos vein.

It may, however, be stated that each supracardinal vein, when fully formed, anastomoses— (1) with the corresponding posterior cardinal vein in the upper thoracic and lower abdominal regions; (2) with the corresponding subcardinal vein at the caudal border of the intersubcardinal anastomosis; (3) with its fellow of the opposite side; and (4) with the prevertebral plexus. Further, in the abdominal part of its extent it receives the intersegmental veins. As a rule the left supracardinal disappears almost entirely, but a considerable part of the right supracardinal and the anastomosis between it and the subcardinal persists and becomes the post-renal part of the inferior vena cava.

The **Thoraco-lumbar Veins** are described, by Reagan, as bilateral longitudinal venous channels which lie lateral to the sympathetic trunks and parallel with the azygos venous line. They are transitory structures which serve as transmitters of blood from the intersegmental veins, "caudally to the inferior vena cava pending the establishment of an azygos line." When their function terminates they disappear, leaving no adult derivative.

Prevertebral Plexus and the Azygos Veins.—The prevertebral plexus lies ventral to the bodies of the vertebræ and dorsal to the aorta, in the thoracic and lumbar regions, and to a less extent at the sides of and ventral to the aorta. Its lateral components have been termed *prevertebral* and *circumganglionic* and its median part *subcentral*. It communicates with the subcardinals, precardinal, and thoraco-lumbar venous channels and, as the major parts or the whole of those vessels disappear, their intersegmental tributaries open into it. Simultaneously its lateral parts become transformed into the rudiments of the azygos and hemiazygos veins, and its median part, not uncommonly and especially in the lumbar region, becomes a pre- or sub-central vein. The azygos venous line, on each side, lies lateral to the intersegmental arteries and medial to the sympathetic trunk and its ventral branches, and the precentral vein lies between the intersegmental arteries of opposite sides.

The thoracic part of the right azygos venous line forms the vena azygos, except its terminal part which is a remnant of the right posterior cardinal vein. In the lumbar region it not uncommonly persists as the lumbar azygos vein, which extends from the inferior vena cava at the level of the renal veins through the aortic opening in the right crus of the diaphragm to the commencement of the azygos vein, the connexion with the inferior vena cava being formed by the persistence of an anastomosis between the azygos venous line and the right supracardinal vein.

The remains of the left azygos venous line are the superior and inferior hemiazygos veins, and the caudal part of the left superior intercostal vein. The transverse parts of the hemiazygos veins are remnants of the intermediate part of the subvertebral plexus; they are occasionally connected together by a median anastomosis which represents part of a precentral vein.

The lumbar part of the left azygos venous line forms the left lumbar azygos vein which is frequently found, in the adult, passing from the left renal vein, through the left crus of the diaphragm to the inferior hemiazygos vein.

The **inferior vena cava** is a compound structure. Its terminal part is the end of the right vitelline vein; the hepatic part is developed from the liver sinusoids; between the liver and the renal veins it is formed from (1) an outgrowth from the hepatic part; (2) an anastomosis between the outgrowth and the right subcardinal vein; (3) part of the right subcardinal vein; the post-renal part is a persistent portion of the right supracardinal vein.

The intersegmental veins of the thoracic and abdominal regions drain the wall of the trunk and, in the earliest stages, they terminate in the posterior cardinal veins; at successively later periods they are transferred to the subcardinal, the supracardinal, the thoraco-lumbar veins, and finally to a greater or less extent to the azygos lines of veins. Eventually those which lie in the thoracic region enter one or other of the azygos veins or the superior intercostal veins.

The lumbar intersegmental veins have various terminations. The lower lumbar veins on the right side frequently end in the inferior vena cava, the connexion with the right supra-cardinal vein being retained; the upper right lumbar veins end, not uncommonly, in the right lumbar azygos vein; but cases occur in which all the right lumbar veins end in a vessel, called the right ascending lumbar vein, which connects the right ilio-lumbar vein with the azygos vein; it is a precostal anastomosis between the lumbar intersegmental veins. In such cases the connexions with the right supracardinal and the right lumbar azygos have been obliterated.

The left lumbar intersegmental veins may end (1) in a left ascending lumbar vein which connects the left ilio-lumbar vein with the inferior hemiazygos vein; (2) in a precentral vein which ends in the azygos vein, or the hemiazygos vein or both; (3) the lower lumbar veins may end in the inferior vena cava, reaching it by transverse anastomoses developed from the prevertebral plexus, and the upper left lumbar veins may end in the left lumbar azygos vein.

The above account of the development of the thoracic and abdominal parts of the venous system is a personal and tentative summary of present-day knowledge (A. Robinson, 1931). The reader who wants to form his own opinion on disputed points should consult Huntington and M'Clure, *Anat. Rec.* vol. vi., and *Amer. Anat. Memoirs*, No. 15, 1929; E. G. Butler, *Amer. Journ. Anat.* vol. xxxix., 1927; F. P. Reagan, *Anat. Rec.* vol. xxxv., 1927; *Quart. Rev. Biol.* vol. iv., 1929; and R. J. Gladstone, *Journ. Anat.* vol. lxiv., 1929. These communications contain references to all the literature to date dealing with the development of the posterior thoracic and abdominal veins.

THE FŒTAL CIRCULATION

During fœtal life, food and oxygen are transmitted from the maternal blood to the fœtal blood in the placenta, where the maternal blood flows in near relation to the walls of the fœtal blood-vessels; and the effete products produced by the cells of the fœtal tissues, including carbonic acid, are passed from the fœtal blood to the maternal blood in the same place. The umbilical arteries and the left umbilical vein persist therefore till birth in order to carry the blood from the fœtus to the placenta and back again.

Lungs are present in the fœtus, but they do not function as respiratory organs until birth; and, although the blood-vessels necessary for pulmonary respiration are present, the only blood that flows through them is that which is necessary for their nutrition and growth, the bronchial vessels being apparently, as yet, insufficient for the purpose. The foramen ovale and the ductus

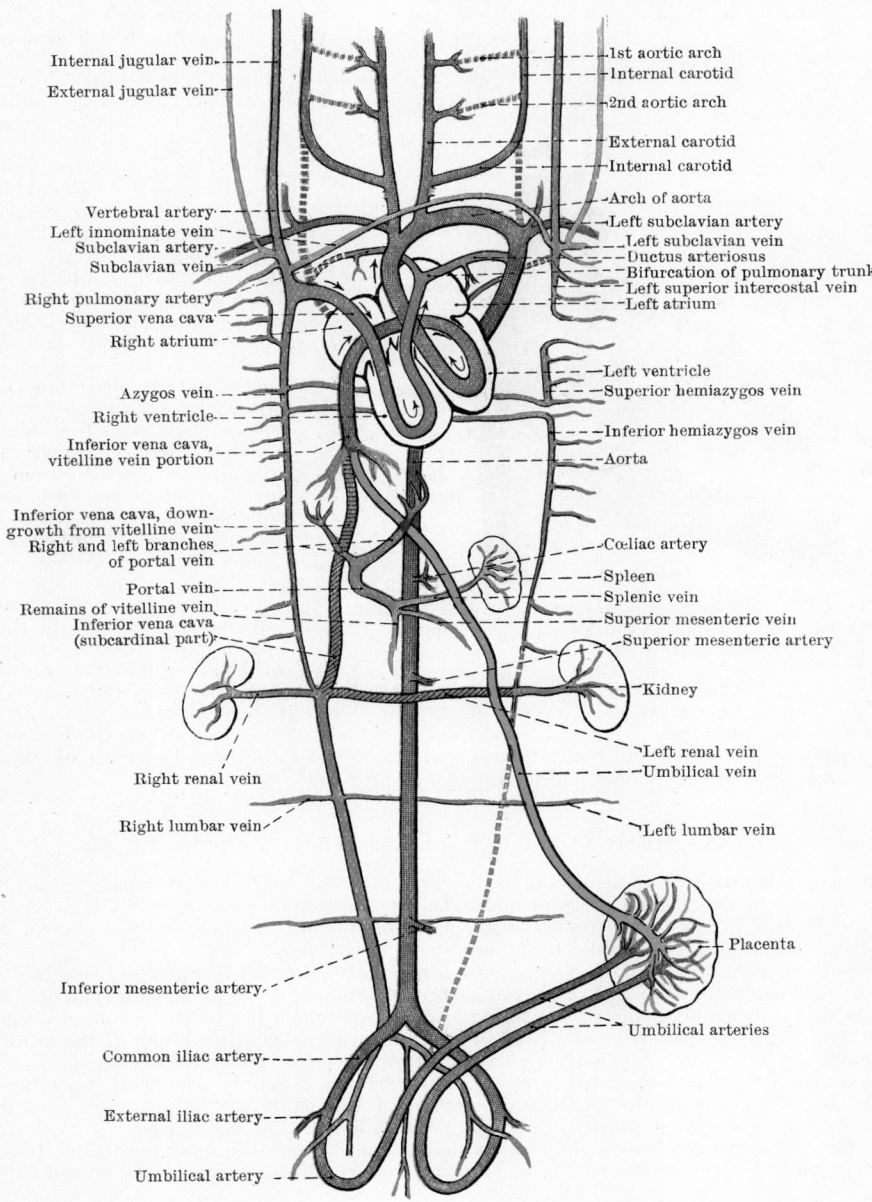

Internal jugular vein

External jugular vein

Vertebral artery
Left innominate vein
Subclavian artery
Subclavian vein

Right pulmonary artery
Superior vena cava
Right atrium

Azygos vein
Right ventricle
Inferior vena cava, vitelline vein portion

Inferior vena cava, downgrowth from vitelline vein
Right and left branches of portal vein
Portal vein
Remains of vitelline vein
Inferior vena cava (subcardinal part)

Right renal vein

Right lumbar vein

Inferior mesenteric artery

Common iliac artery

External iliac artery

Umbilical artery

1st aortic arch
Internal carotid
2nd aortic arch

External carotid
Internal carotid

Arch of aorta
Left subclavian artery
Left subclavian vein
Ductus arteriosus
Bifurcation of pulmonary trunk
Left superior intercostal vein
Left atrium

Left ventricle
Superior hemiazygos vein

Inferior hemiazygos vein
Aorta

Cœliac artery
Spleen
Splenic vein
Superior mesenteric vein
Superior mesenteric artery

Kidney

Left renal vein
Umbilical vein

Left lumbar vein

Placenta

Umbilical arteries

FIG. 1072.—DIAGRAM OF THE COURSE OF THE FŒTAL CIRCULATION.

arteriosus therefore remain patent till birth so that the blood that will pass through the lungs after birth may be transmitted to the aorta before birth.

As a consequence, the course of the circulation is different before and after birth.

After birth, blood passes from the body as a whole into the right atrium, which passes it on into the right ventricle, whence it is forced, through the lungs, to the left atrium, and thence to the left ventricle, by which it is propelled through the systemic vessels back to the right atrium.

In the fœtus, on the other hand, food- and oxygen-laden blood is carried from the placenta by the umbilical vein, and transmitted to the inferior vena cava, partly directly through the ductus venosus, and partly indirectly through the liver. In the inferior vena cava it mixes with venous blood returning from the lower limbs, the lower parts of the trunk, the renal organs, and the genital glands; and so it becomes mixed blood. The mixed stream passes from the inferior vena cava through the right atrium and the foramen ovale to the left atrium, thence to the left ventricle, which forces it through the aorta into all parts of the body.

The blood from the head and neck, the upper limbs, and the upper parts of the trunk returns by the superior vena cava to the right atrium, through which it passes into the right ventricle, which ejects it, through the pulmonary trunk and the ductus arteriosus, into the aorta, beyond the origin of the left subclavian artery, where it mixes with the blood from the left ventricle; only a small quantity enters the lungs.

In the fœtus, therefore, pure oxygenated blood is found only in the left umbilical vein and the ductus venosus. In the upper part of the inferior vena cava the blood becomes a mixture by blending with the blood returning from the lower limbs and the lower part of the trunk. The mixed stream, directed by the valve of the inferior vena cava, passes through the right into the left atrium, and thence through the left ventricle into the aorta. From the aorta, some of it passes into the head and neck and the upper limbs; the remainder passes into the descending aorta and is joined, beyond the origin of the left subclavian artery, by the venous stream from the head and neck and the upper limbs, which has passed from the superior vena cava through the right atrium, the right ventricle, the pulmonary trunk, and the ductus arteriosus.

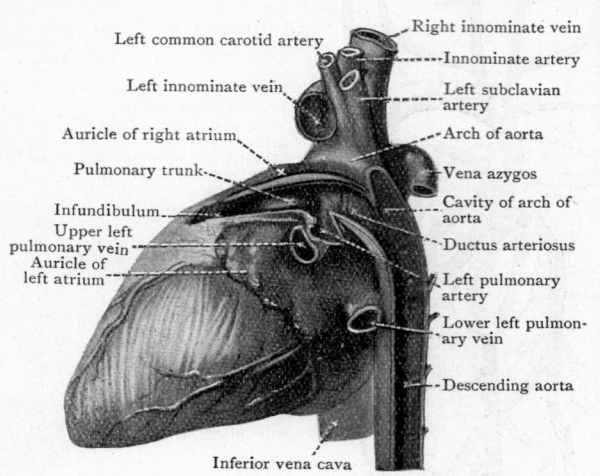

Left common carotid artery

Left innominate vein

Auricle of right atrium

Pulmonary trunk

Infundibulum
Upper left
pulmonary vein
Auricle of
left atrium

Right innominate vein

Innominate artery

Left subclavian artery

Arch of aorta

Vena azygos

Cavity of arch of aorta

Ductus arteriosus

Left pulmonary artery

Lower left pulmonary vein

Descending aorta

Inferior vena cava

FIG. 1073.—DISSECTION OF THE HEART AND GREAT VESSELS OF A FŒTUS, SHOWING THE ANGULAR JUNCTION OF THE DUCTUS ARTERIOSUS WITH THE AORTA.

From the descending aorta part of the blood passes to the walls of the thorax, to the abdomen and its contents, and to the lower limbs; the remainder passes through the internal iliac arteries and their umbilical branches to the placenta.

It is obvious, from what has been stated, that the blood in the descending aorta, which is supplied to the lower part of the trunk and the lower limbs, contains relatively less oxygen and food material and more effete matters than that in the ascending aorta and the arch of the aorta, which is transmitted to the head and neck and the upper limbs.

MORPHOLOGY OF THE BLOOD-VESSELS

In conformity with the general plan of the vertebrate body, the vascular system is essentially segmental and intersegmental in character. The intersegmental character of the intercostal and lumbar vessels is obvious; that of the vessels of the head, neck, and pelvis is less obvious but is still distinguishable in the vessels of the head.

The intersegmental arteries and veins form a series of bilaterally symmetrical vessels. Each of those intersegmental vessels is connected with its neighbour in front (cephalic) and its neighbour behind (caudal) by a portion of a longitudinal vessel which lies in the region of a segment and, therefore, may be called a segmental channel. Consequently, in a sense in the adult, the segmental channels anastomose with one another, through the intersegmental vessels which they connect together. The longitudinal trunks of the body are mainly, though not exclusively, segmental. From them the main stem vessels of the adult are formed, and the intersegmental vessels appear to proceed from or to them as branches or tributaries.

In the course of development the longitudinal trunks become the most important trunks in the body, and they are formed before the branches and tributaries make their appearance.

SEGMENTAL ARTERIES AND THEIR ANASTOMOSES

The main longitudinal trunks are the primitive aortæ. The descending aorta is formed, in the greater part of its extent, by the fusion of the dorsal parts of the primitive aortæ, and from it the intersegmental, lateral, and ventral arteries arise in pairs.

In a typical portion of the body of the embryo there are three arteries on each side. One arises from the dorsal surface of the primitive dorsal aorta, i.e. from the dorsal longitudinal trunk, and runs laterally and ventrally in the tissues developed from the somatic mesoderm; it is distributed to the body wall, including the vertebral column and its contents, and is termed a **somatic inter-segmental artery**. A second vessel arises from the side of the primitive dorsal aorta; it is distributed to the structures developed from or in the region of the intermediate cell mass—the suprarenal gland, the kidney, and the ovary or the testis—and it is accordingly termed a **lateral** or **intermediate visceral artery**. The third artery, which is known as the **splanchnic artery**, springs from the ventral surface of the aorta. It runs in the tissues developed from the splanchnic mesoderm, and supplies the wall of the alimentary canal.

The **somatic intersegmental arteries** form, in the early embryo, a regular series of paired vessels throughout the cervical, thoracic, lumbar, and sacral regions. It is, however, only in the thoracic and lumbar regions that their original characters are retained. The paired vessels pass dorsally, by the sides of the vertebræ, and divide into dorsal and ventral branches which accompany the corresponding posterior and anterior primary rami of the spinal nerves.

The **ventral branches** run ventro-laterally, between the ribs, in the thoracic region, and in corresponding positions in the lumbar region, and together with the stems they form the main parts or trunks of the vessels in the thoracic and lumbar regions. They are connected together, near their commencements, by a series of pre-costal anastomoses which pass in front of the necks of the ribs ; and they are also connected together, near their terminations, by ventral anastomos-

ing channels which run, in the thoracic region behind the costal cartilages, and in the lumbar region behind or in the substance of the rectus abdominis muscle. Each ventral branch gives off a lateral offset which is distributed like the lateral cutaneous branch of a spinal nerve. The ventral branch together with the stem of the intersegmental artery forms the trunk of an intercostal or lumbar artery in the adult.

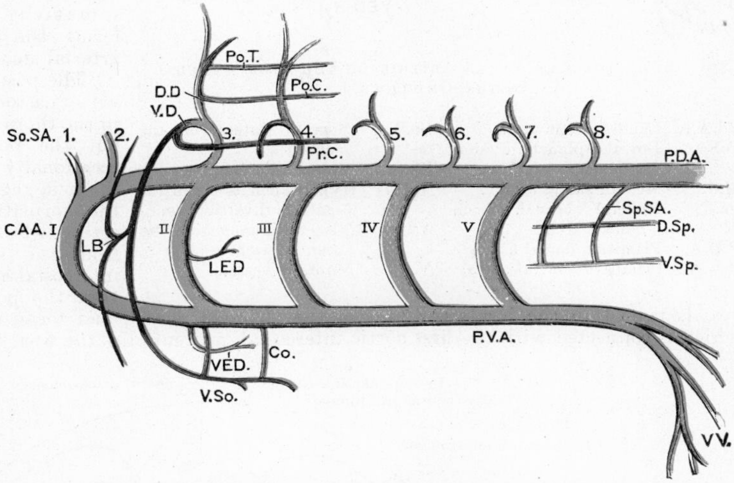

The **dorsal branches**, which are present before the ventral branches, run backwards between the transverse processes of the vertebræ, and form the posterior branches of the intercostal and lumbar arteries of the adult ; they are connected, behind the necks of the ribs, by postcostal anastomoses, and again, behind the transverse processes of the vertebræ, by posttransverse anastomos-

Fig. 1074.—Diagram of the Aortic Arches, and of the Segmental and Intersegmental Arteries Cephalic to the Umbilicus.

C.A.A. I, II, III, IV, V. The cephalic aortic arches.
Co.   Anastomosing vessel between the primitive ventral aorta and the ventral somatic anastomosis.
D.D.   Dorsal division of a somatic intersegmental artery.
D.Sp.   Dorsal splanchnic anastomosis.
L.B.   Lateral branch of ventral division of somatic intersegmental artery.
L.E.D.   Branch to lateral enteric diverticulum.
P.D.A.   Primitive dorsal aorta.

Po.C.   Post-costal anastomosis.
Po.T.   Post-transverse anastomosis.
Pr.C.   Pre-costal anastomosis.
P.V.A.   Primitive ventral aorta.
So.S.A. 1, 2, 3, 4, 5, 6, 7, 8. Somatic intersegmental arteries.
Sp.S.A. Splanchnic arteries.
V.D.   Ventral division of a somatic intersegmental artery.
V.E.D.   Branch to ventral enteric diverticulum.
V.V.   Vitelline vessels.
V.So.   Ventral somatic anastomosis.
V.Sp.   Ventral splanchnic anastomosis.

ing channels. Moreover, each dorsal branch, as it passes by the corresponding intervertebral foramen, gives off a spinal offset which enters the vertebral canal, along the corresponding nerve-root, and divides into a dorsal, a ventral, and a neural branch. The dorsal branches of those spinal arteries are connected together along the ventral surfaces of the laminæ by pre-laminar anastomoses, and the ventral branches are united on the dorsal surfaces of the vertebral bodies (or centra) with their fellows above and below by post-central anastomoses ; they are also united with their fellows of the opposite side by transverse communicating channels. The neural branches of the spinal arteries divide similarly into dorsal and ventral branches ; the dorsal branches of each side are connected together by post-neural anastomoses, which form the posterior spinal arteries ; and the ventral branches unite, in the median line, both with their neighbours above and below and with their fellows of the opposite side, forming a single longitudinal pre-neural trunk—the anterior spinal artery.

In the thoracic and lumbar regions of the body the somatic intersegmental arteries persist, and form the posterior intercostal and lumbar arteries. Those vessels spring from the dorsal aspect of the descending aorta, usually in pairs. The corresponding vessels of opposite sides occasionally fuse together at their origins, simultaneously with the fusion of the dorsal longitudinal trunks to form the descending aorta, and then the arteries of opposite sides arise by common stems.

The pre-costal anastomoses between the ventral branches of the somatic intersegmental arteries persist only in the thoracic region, where they are represented by the superior intercostal arteries; in the lumbar region they disappear entirely. The anastomoses between the anterior ends of the ventral branches of the somatic intersegmental arteries persist as the internal mammary and superior and inferior epigastric arteries.

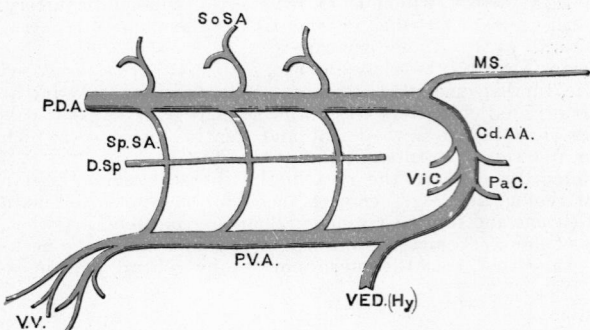

FIG. 1075.—DIAGRAM OF THE ARTERIES IN THE REGION CAUDAL TO THE UMBILICUS.

Cd.A.A.   Caudal aortic arch.
D.Sp.   Dorsal splanchnic ana-
          stomosis.
M.S.   Median sacral artery.
Pa.C.   Parietal branch from
          caudal arch.
P.D.A.   Primitive dorsal aorta.
P.V.A.   Primitive ventral aorta.

So.S.A.   Somatic intersegmental
          arteries.
Sp.S.A.   Splanchnic arteries.
V.E.D. (Hy). Branch to a ventral
          enteric diverticulum.
Vi.C.   Visceral branch from the
          caudal arch.
V.V.   Vitelline vessels.

The lateral offsets of the ventral branches are represented by the cutaneous arteries which accompany the lateral cutaneous branches of the spinal nerves; the lateral branch of the seventh somatic intersegmental artery forms the greater part of the arterial stem of the upper limb.

The post-costal and post-transverse anastomoses usually disappear in the thoracic and lumbar regions, but the post-costal anastomoses occasionally persist in the upper thoracic region, and take part in the formation of the vertebral artery, which in such cases arises from the first or second aortic intercostal artery. In some carnivora the post-costal longitudinal vessels persist in the headward part of the thoracic region, and form, on each side, a trunk which is connected with the first aortic intercostal, and supplies the first five intercostal spaces.

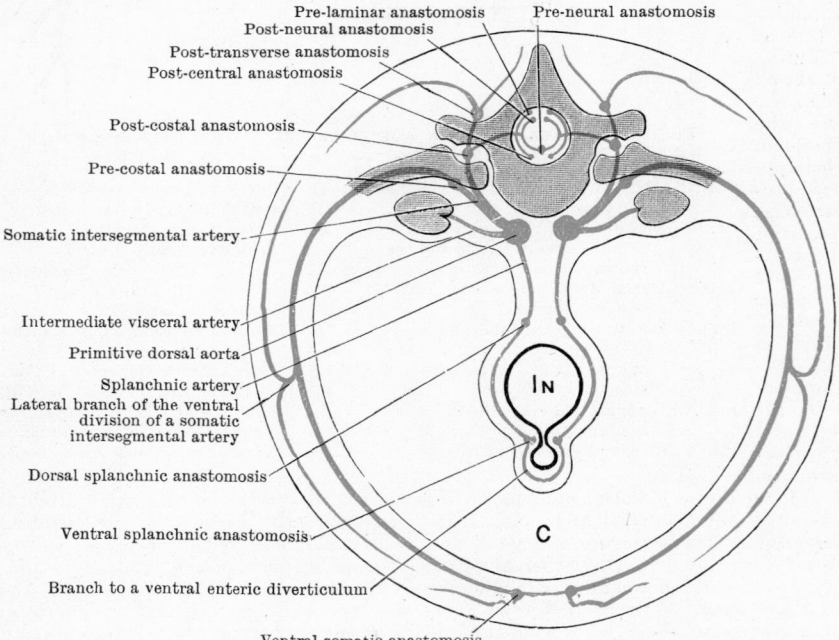

FIG. 1076.—DIAGRAM SHOWING THE ARRANGEMENT AND COMMUNICATIONS OF THE SEGMENTAL AND INTERSEGMENTAL ARTERIES AT AN EARLY STAGE OF DEVELOPMENT.

C, Cœlom ; IN, Intestine.

The pre-laminar, the post-central, and the pre- and post-neural anastomoses persist, the latter two aiding in the formation of the thoracic and lumbar portions of the anterior and posterior spinal arteries respectively.

It is in the cervical region, however, that the most interesting changes occur. The first six pairs of somatic intersegmental arteries lose their connexions with the dorsal roots of the aortic arches, *i.e.*, in other words, with the longitudinal anastomosing channels in that region. The seventh pair, however, persist in their entirety ; and from them are formed, on the right side, a portion of the subclavian trunk, and, on the left side, the whole of the subclavian stem from its commencement up to the origin of the vertebral artery. On each side the ventral branch of the seventh intersegmental artery forms that portion of the subclavian artery which lies between the origins of the vertebral and internal mammary arteries, and also the trunk of the internal mammary artery as far as the upper border of the first costal cartilage. The remainder of the internal mammary artery represents the ventral longitudinal anastomoses between the ventral branches of the seventh and the following somatic intersegmental arteries. The continuation of the subclavian artery, beyond the inner margin of the first rib, is the persistent and enlarged lateral offset of the ventral branch of the seventh somatic intersegmental artery, which is continued into the upper limb, caudal or postaxial to the shoulder girdle. The thyro-cervical trunk and the superior intercostal artery are both derived from the subclavian artery, are persistent pre-costal anastomoses, and the ascending cervical artery belongs to the same series of vessels. The vertebral artery, which appears as a branch of the subclavian in the adult, is, morphologically, somewhat complex. The first part represents the dorsal branch of the seventh somatic intersegmental artery ; the second part—that passing through the cervical transverse processes— consists of the persistent post-costal anastomoses between the dorsal branches of the first seven intersegmental arteries ; a third part, that lying on the arch of the atlas, is the spinal branch of the first somatic intersegmental artery and its neural continuation ; whilst, finally, the upper part of the vertebral artery—the part in the cranial cavity—appears to represent a prolongation of the pre-neural anastomoses, which still farther upwards are probably represented by the basilar artery. As already stated, the post-costal anastomoses below the seventh intersegmental artery occasionally persist, and in such cases the vertebral may lose its connexion with the subclavian, and spring from one or other of the posterior branches of the upper intercostal arteries.

The deep cervical artery is to be regarded as a remnant of the post-transverse longitudinal anastomoses.

The origin of the seventh somatic intersegmental artery from the dorsal longitudinal trunk is, at first, some distance caudal to the sixth aortic arch, but, simultaneously with the elongation of the

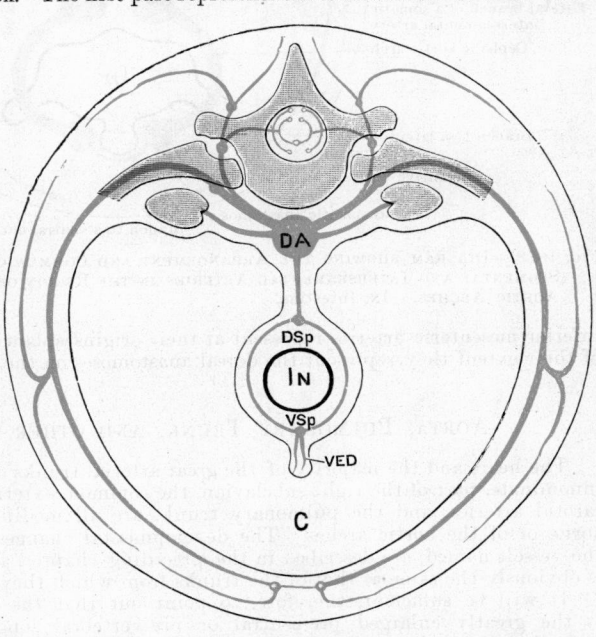

Fig. 1077.—Diagram of the Segmental and Intersegmental Arteries at a later Period of Development than in Fig. 1076.

C, Cœlom ; D.A, Dorsal aorta ; D.Sp, Dorsal splanchnic anastomosis ; In, Intestine ; V.E.D, Branch to ventral enteric diverticulum ; V.Sp, Ventral splanchnic anastomosis.

neck and the retraction of the heart into the thoracic region, it is shifted headwards until it is opposite the dorsal end of the fourth aortic arch.

The median sacral artery is formed by the fusion of two vessels, each of which springs from the dorsal surface of the aorta. It is regarded as the direct continuation of the descending aorta.

The **lateral** or **intermediate visceral arteries** supply the organs developed in the region of the intermediate cell mass. They form a somewhat irregular series of vessels in the adult, but presumably in the primitive condition there was a pair in each segment of the body ; many of these disappear, however, and the series is represented in the adult only by the suprarenals, the renals, and the testicular or ovarian arteries—possibly, also, by some of the branches of the internal iliac arteries.

The **splanchnic arteries** arise in the embryo from the ventral aspects of the primitive dorsal aortæ, and are not strictly either segmental or intersegmental in arrangement. They are distributed to the walls of the alimentary canal. Each anastomoses with its immediate neighbours on both the dorsal and the ventral walls of the gut.

After the fusion of the dorsal longitudinal trunks to form the descending aorta, the roots of each pair of the splanchnic arteries fuse into a common stem, or either the right or left artery altogether disappears. At a later period the majority of the splanchnic arteries lose their direct connexion with the descending aorta ; those which retain their connexion are the cœliac artery and the superior and inferior mesenteric arteries.

The bronchial and œsophageal arteries are later formations. They appear to correspond morphologically with the more primitive splanchnic arteries, but the developmental history is not known.

The left gastric branch of the cœliac artery, as it passes from its origin to the lesser curvature of the stomach, represents a right splanchnic artery; the remainder of the left gastric artery and the right gastric branch of the hepatic are remnants of the ventral anastomoses between the splanchnic arteries headwards of the umbilicus.

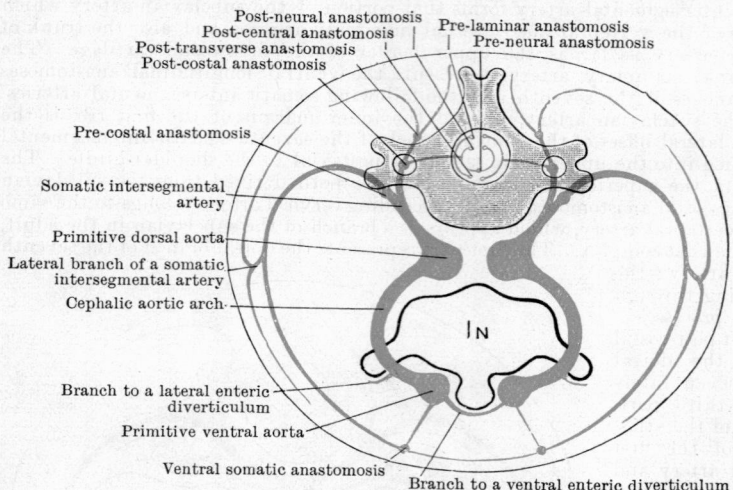

The splenic artery is a branch given off from a splanchnic artery to an organ developed in the mesogastrium; and the hepatic is a branch from the ventral splanchnic anastomoses to the hepatic diverticulum of the duodenal portion of the fore-gut.

FIG. 1078.—DIAGRAM SHOWING THE ARRANGEMENT AND COMMUNICATIONS OF THE SEGMENTAL AND INTERSEGMENTAL ARTERIES IN THE REGION OF THE CEPHALIC AORTIC ARCHES. IN, Intestine.

The superior and inferior mesenteric arteries represent at their origins splanchnic branches, and in the remainder of their extent they represent the dorsal anastomoses on the gut wall.

AORTA, PULMONARY TRUNK, AND OTHER CHIEF STEM VESSELS

The heart and the majority of the great arterial trunks of the body, including the aorta, the innominate, part of the right subclavian, the common, external, and greater parts of the internal carotid arteries, and the pulmonary trunk, are all modified portions either of the primitive aortæ or of the aortic arches. The developmental changes, which result in the formation of the vessels named, are described in the preceding chapter, and the morphology of these vessels is obviously the same as that of the trunks from which they are derived.

It will be sufficient, therefore, to point out that the primitive aortæ may be regarded as the greatly enlarged pre-central or pre-vertebral longitudinal anastomoses between the successive intersegmental arteries of each side; obviously, therefore, each primitive aorta, like the rest of the longitudinal anastomoses, consists chiefly of segmental elements. The origins of the intersegmental vessels enter into its formation only in so far as they connect the segmental vessels together, and so complete the longitudinal anastomoses.

The first cephalic aortic arches are simply portions of the primitive aortæ. The other aortic arches have possibly a different morphological significance, but their exact nature is not definitely settled.

The second, third, fourth, fifth, and sixth cephalic aortic arches of each side are developed in the undivided mesoderm of the head region, caudal to the first arch. They spring from the part of the primitive aorta which, after the head fold is formed, lies on the ventral aspect of the fore-gut, and they extend, at the side of the pharyngeal part of the fore-gut, to the dorsal aorta. Thus in some respects they may be looked upon as segmental vessels. In addition to the vessels already mentioned, there are given off from the ventral aortæ and the aortic arches a series of branches which supply ventral and lateral diverticula from the alimentary canal; these are represented in the adult by the superior thyroid and the thyroidea ima arteries.

Iliac Arteries and their Branches.—The common iliac arteries are formed from the secondary roots of the umbilical arteries, and their exact morphological position is uncertain. The true morphological position of the internal iliac [hypogastric] arteries is not yet defined. They also are parts of the secondary roots of the umbilical arteries, and they give off both somatic and splanchnic branches; therefore they do not correspond either with somatic intersegmental or with splanchnic arteries. The branches of the internal iliac artery are arranged in two groups—(1) a visceral set which supplies the walls of the hind-gut and the genital organs, and (2) a parietal set which is distributed to the body wall and to the hind-limbs. The branches distributed to the gut probably represent the splanchnic vessels, more or less homologous with ordinary splanchnic branches of the primitive aortæ, and the parietal branches are possibly the homologues of intersegmental arteries.

ARTERIES OF THE LIMBS

In all probability the vessels of both the upper and the lower limbs are derived originally from several somatic intersegmental arteries, the majority of which, however, have atrophied. The upper limb is supplied in man by the lateral offset from the ventral branch of the seventh somatic intersegmental artery. It passes into the limb caudal to the shoulder girdle, courses through the arm, enters the cubital fossa, and is continued through the forearm, in the early stages, as the anterior interosseous artery, which ends in the deep palmar arch. At a later period, ontogenetically, a median artery appears as a branch of the parent stem, and it ends in a superficial palmar arch ; still later the radial and ulnar branches are formed. The latter grow rapidly, soon exceeding in size the parent stem, and they terminate in the superficial and deep palmar arches. The interosseous and median arteries decrease, and generally lose their direct connexions with the palmar arches. The posterior interosseous artery also is a secondary branch from the parent stem, and the digital arteries are offsets from the palmar arterial arches.

The chief arteries of the lower limbs spring directly from the secondary roots of the umbilical arteries, and may be looked upon as being essentially intersegmental ; whether they represent the whole or only parts of typical somatic intersegmental arteries, however, is not clear.

The arteries of the lower limbs certainly show no very obvious indications of division into dorsal and ventral branches, though such indications are not entirely wanting. In their comparative absence it is supposed that the dorsal branches have been either suppressed or incorporated with the common stems ; that similarly the ventral branches and their lateral offsets are indistinguishably fused, and that probably both are represented in a limb artery.

The original stem vessel of the lower limb is the inferior gluteal artery, which is continued distally, posterior to the pelvic girdle, into the popliteal and peroneal arteries, and so to the sole of the foot, where it ends in a vascular plexus. Subsequently the external iliac artery is given off from the secondary root of the umbilical artery, dorsal to the origin of the inferior gluteal, and, passing into the limb anterior to the pelvic girdle, it becomes the greater part of the femoral artery. That vessel ultimately unites with the proximal part of the popliteal artery, and after the communication is established the distal part of the inferior gluteal atrophies and loses its connexion with the popliteal, which henceforth appears to be the direct continuation of the femoral trunk ; therefore, whilst the main artery of the upper limb is formed by the prolongation of the lateral branch of one segmental artery, the corresponding vessel of the lower limb is developed from representatives of, probably, two somatic segmental arteries, the external iliac and femoral trunks being the representatives of one, whilst the popliteal and its continuation, the peroneal, are parts of another.

The first main artery of the leg, ontogenetically, is the peroneal, which is continued into the plantar arch ; after a time, however, the posterior and anterior tibial branches are evolved. As a rule, they soon preponderate in size, and they terminate in the plantar arch, whilst the original trunk diminishes and loses its direct connexion with the arch.

The peroneal artery corresponds in position and development with the common interosseous trunk and the anterior interosseous artery in the forearm. The posterior tibial apparently corresponds with the median artery ; it develops in a similar way, and has similar relations to homologous nerves, the posterior tibial nerve representing the combined median and ulnar nerves of the upper limb.

The anterior tibial artery represents the posterior interosseous, whilst the radial and ulnar arteries of the upper limb are not represented in the lower limb.

MORPHOLOGY OF THE VEINS

The formation of the chief adult veins from the various longitudinal trunks which appear in the embryo has been described in the account of the development of the veins (pp. 1285, 1292) ; and the transference of the terminations of the intersegmental veins from one position to another was noted.

In the discussion of the morphology of the arteries it was shown that the ventral branches of the intersegmental arteries are primitively connected by pre-costal and ventral anastomoses ; the dorsal branches by post-costal and post-transverse anastomoses ; the spinal offsets of the dorsal branches are linked together by post-central and pre-laminar anastomoses, and their neural branches by pre- and post-neural anastomoses.

Similar anastomoses are formed between the corresponding veins, but they tend in many cases to be plexiform as in the case of the vertebral veins.

Remnants of pre-costal venous anastomoses are found in the adult as the ascending lumbar and lateral sacral veins ; and ventral anastomoses are represented by the internal mammary, and the superior and inferior epigastric veins.

Post-costal anastomoses are represented by the vertebral veins, and post-transverse anastomoses by the deep cervical veins.

Pre-laminar and post-central anastomoses form the adult posterior and anterior longitudinal vertebral sinuses ; and pre- and post-neural anastomoses give rise to the antero-lateral and postero-lateral veins of the spinal cord.

The morphology of the splanchnic veins corresponds closely with that of the splanchnic arteries, and does not require separate consideration.

82 a

Veins of the Limbs.—The veins of the limbs, like the arteries, were probably at one time intersegmental in character, but we have no indisputable proof that this was the case. Looked at from an embryological standpoint, the most primitive limb veins are a superficial distal arch and a post-axial trunk vein in each limb; at a later period digital veins are connected with the distal arch, and a pre-axial trunk is formed. In the upper limb the distal arch and its tributaries remain as the dorsal venous arch and the digital veins, and the post-axial vein becomes the basilic, axillary, and subclavian veins. The pre-axial vein of the upper limb is represented in the adult by the cephalic vein; the latter vessel originally terminated in the external jugular vein, above the clavicle, the union with the axillary portion of the post-axial vessel being a secondary condition; the primary condition is, however, frequently retained in man, and is constant in many monkeys. The anastomosis between the pre-axial and post-axial veins in the region of the elbow, and the connexion of the anastomosing channels, are brought about by newly formed vessels of secondary character.

The distal arch in the lower limb and the tributaries connected with it remain in the adult as the dorsal venous arch of the foot and the digital veins. The post-axial vein becomes the short saphenous vein, which was originally continued proximally as the popliteal and inferior gluteal veins to the internal iliac portion of the posterior cardinal vein.

The pre-axial vein of the lower limb becomes the long saphenous vein, which is continued proximally to the posterior cardinal portion of the left common iliac vein as the proximal part of the femoral and the external iliac veins.

The venæ comitantes of the arteries in both the upper and lower limbs are secondarily developed vessels which become connected with the upper portions of the pre-axial venous trunks.

VARIATIONS AND ABNORMALITIES OF THE VASCULAR SYSTEM

Variations are of special interest to the anatomist because of their morphological significance, and the vascular system is, perhaps more than any other, rich in such variations, many of which are of great practical importance.

With the exception of those irregularities which are directly due to the effect of morbid conditions and external influences, all variations are the result of modifications of normal developmental processes. The exceptions referred to are, however, very numerous; thus disease and external influences may lead to the obliteration of vessels, a condition which is invariably associated with the enlargement of collateral vessels; and it will be obvious that abnormalities so produced may occur in almost any situation.

Variations which are determined by, or are dependent upon, modifications of the usual developmental processes are of greater interest. In the human subject they are generally due either to the retention of conditions which, normally, are only transitory in ontogenetic development, or to the acquirement of conditions which, though not as a rule present at any time in man, occur normally in some animals.

There are, in addition, other variations from the normal, such as the division of the axillary artery into radial and ulnar branches; the higher or lower division of the brachial artery; the formation of "vasa aberrantia," e.g., of long slender vessels connecting the axillary or brachial to the radial, ulnar, or interosseous arteries; the altered position of certain vessels, e.g., the transference of the subclavian artery to the front of the scalenus anterior, or of the ulnar artery to the front of the superficial flexor muscles; all of which, though undoubtedly due to alterations of ordinary developmental processes, still do not represent any known conditions met with, either temporarily or permanently, in man or in other animals. Their occurrence cannot at present be adequately explained, and their retention in the adult is dependent entirely upon their utility.

To the first and the last of these different groups of abnormalities it is not necessary to refer further, whilst with regard to the rest they have been already sufficiently indicated after the account of the heart and vessels. They cannot, however, be fully understood and explained except on the basis of a comprehensive knowledge of the development and morphology of the vascular system, to the chapters on which the reader is referred. Those who require more detailed information should consult special monographs.[1]

Abnormalities or variations of veins are more frequently met with than those of arteries, and they are due to similar causes.

[1] Quain, R., *The Anatomy of the Arteries of the Human Body*. Dubrueil, I. M., *Des Anomalies artérielles*. Adachi, B., *Das Arteriensystem* (1928), and *Das Venensystem* (1933), *der Japaner*.

LYMPHATIC SYSTEM

While the arterial system is the sole distributing agent, the veins are assisted by another set of absorbent vessels—the lymph vascular system. The fluid absorbed by it—called **lymph**—contains numerous white corpuscles and is colourless except that from the intestinal canal, which may be milky because of its fatty content.

In structure the **lymph vessels** resemble veins, but differ in the following ways: (*a*) the capillaries are wider and more irregular in calibre; (*b*) beyond the stage corresponding with venules the vessels are smaller than veins and have their valves

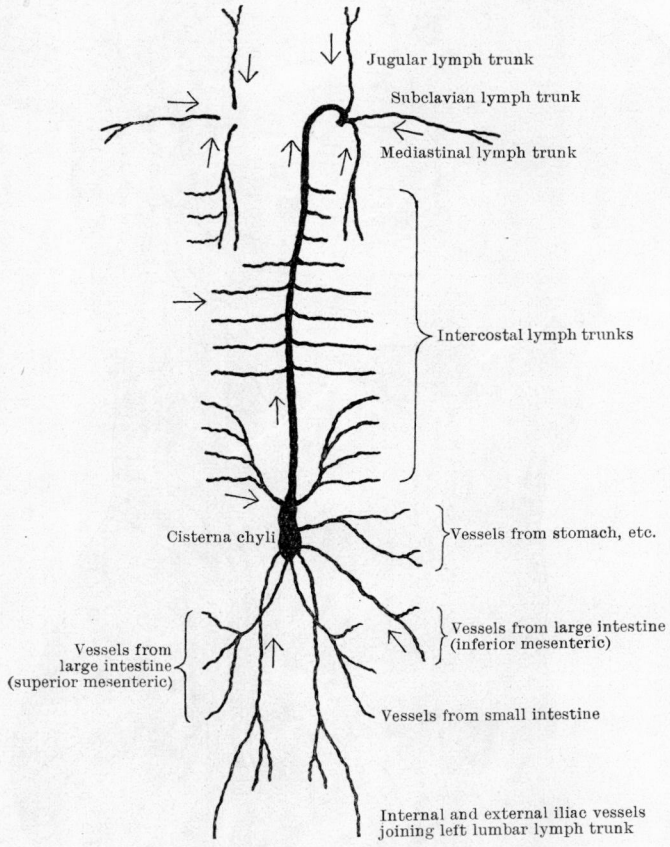

Jugular lymph trunk

Subclavian lymph trunk

Mediastinal lymph trunk

Intercostal lymph trunks

Cisterna chyli

Vessels from stomach, etc.

Vessels from large intestine (inferior mesenteric)

Vessels from large intestine (superior mesenteric)

Vessels from small intestine

Internal and external iliac vessels joining left lumbar lymph trunk

FIG. 1079.—DIAGRAM OF THE MAIN LYMPH VESSELS.

so closely and regularly set that in distension they have a uniform beaded appearance—a distinguishing characteristic; (*c*) they run in streams with little tendency to form large trunks; (*d*) they are invariably interrupted by nodular aggregations of lymphoid tissue called **lymph glands**; (*e*) their distribution is limited, for they are absent not only from avascular tissues but also from the entire central nervous system, and possibly from muscle and bone.

The lymph vessels merely collect and convey lymph; the lymph glands probably serve in part as filters and in part as the sources of origin of those lymph corpuscles which are called **lymphocytes** and become white blood corpuscles when they enter the blood stream. In its course from the tissues to the blood-vessels most of the lymph passes through at least one, and generally more than one, lymph gland; direct delivery of lymph into the veins is very exceptional (see p. 1343).

Lymph vessels are essentially sub-epithelial in position and are found abundantly in the skin, mucous membranes, all glands (including ductless glands), all serous membranes and synovial membranes.

The *superficial lymph vessels* lie in the skin and subcutaneous tissues; they

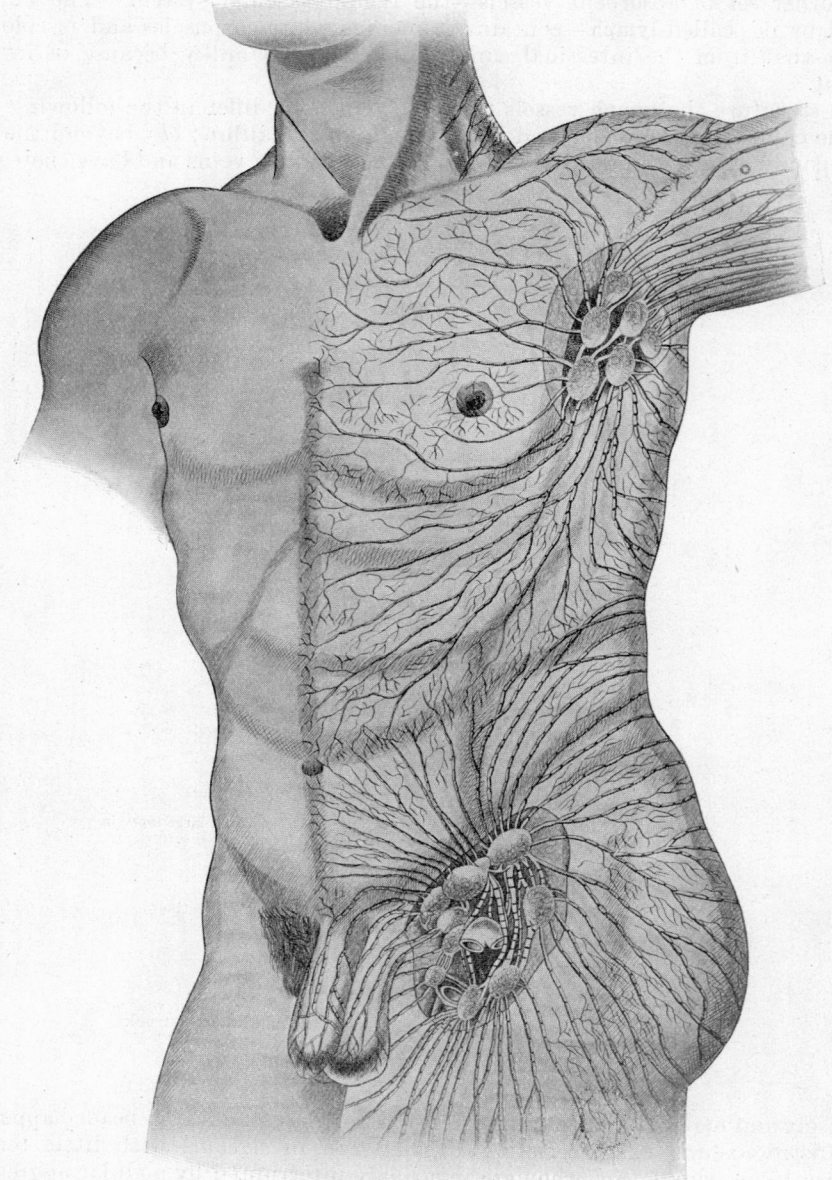

FIG. 1080.—CUTANEOUS LYMPH VESSELS OF THE ANTERIOR SURFACE OF THE TRUNK (after Sappey). Note the "lymph-shed" between the vessels that pass to the axillary and to the inguinal lymph glands.

frequently accompany the superficial veins and, in the limbs, they join the deep vessels in definitely localised situations.

On each side of the body the cutaneous lymph vessels converge from three large areas upon three groups of lymph glands (Figs. 1080, 1081, 1107): (*a*) from the skin of the lower limb, perineum, external genital organs and the trunk below the level of the umbilicus—to empty into the lymph glands in the groin;

(*b*) from the skin of the upper limb and the trunk above the umbilicus to the level of the clavicle in front and halfway up the back of the neck behind—to the lymph glands in the axilla; (*c*) from the scalp, face, and the rest of the neck—to the cervical glands.

The *deep lymph vessels* drain the lymph from parts of the body which lie deep

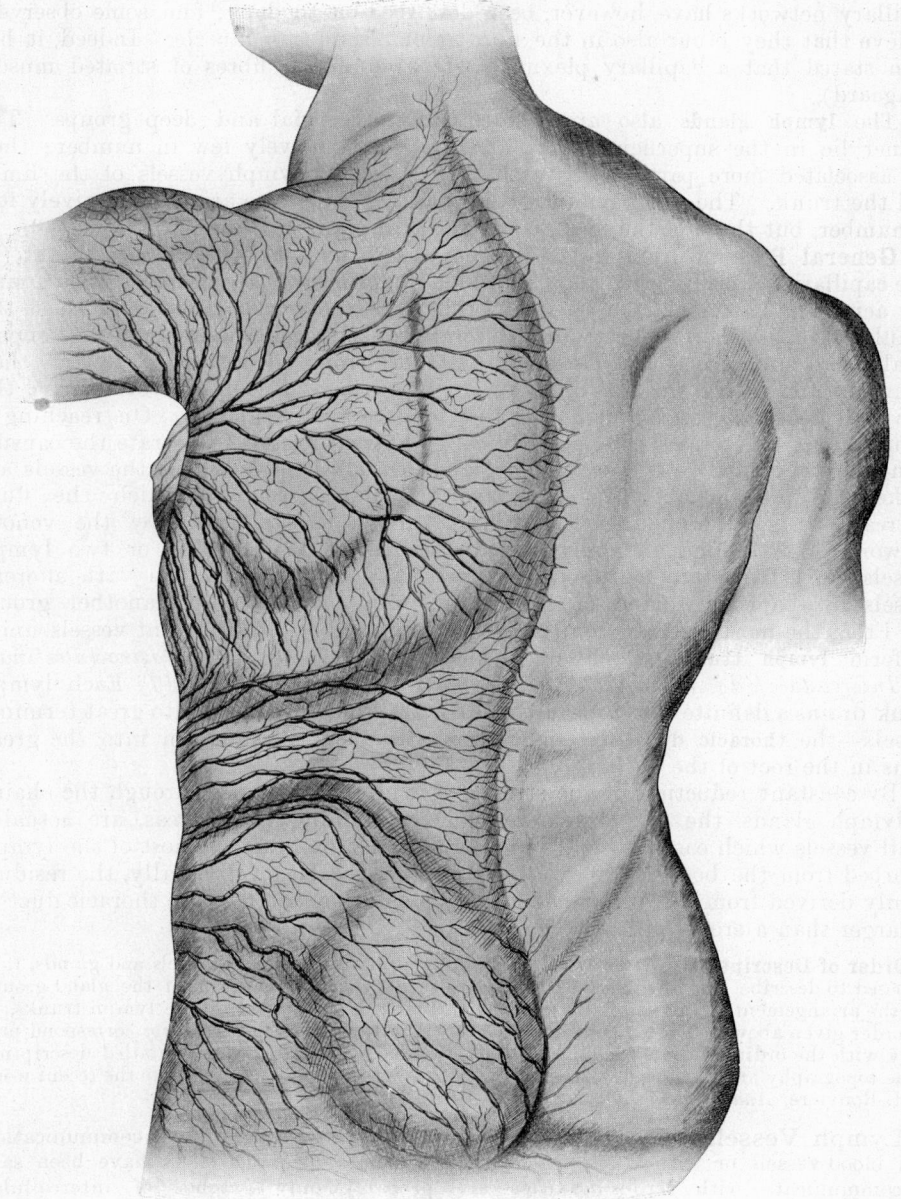

FIG. 1081.—CUTANEOUS LYMPH VESSELS OF THE POSTERIOR SURFACE OF THE TRUNK (after Sappey). Note the "lymph-shed" between the vessels that pass to the axillary and to the inguinal lymph glands, and on the buttock between vessels that pass to the inguinal glands by lateral and by medial routes.

to the deep fascia. They tend to accompany the blood-vessels of the various parts and organs; those of the viscera, however, frequently take unexpected courses to reach the nearest lymph glands.

The deep vessels of the limbs and trunk are relatively scanty and arise primarily

82 *c*

in the synovial membranes of the joints. As cutaneous lymph vessels may penetrate the deep fascia with the veins and run between muscles to join the deep stream, and as the lymph vessels of mucous membranes have to burrow through the muscular structure of the organs from the tongue downwards, it may appear that lymph vessels take origin in muscular tissue; but it should be noted that in relation to muscle lymph vessels are mainly passengers. Lymph-capillary networks have, however, been described on tendons; and some observers believe that they occur also in the fibro-areolar tissues of muscle. Indeed, it has been stated that a capillary plexus exists around the fibres of striated muscle (Aagaard).

The **lymph glands** also are divided into superficial and deep groups. The former lie in the superficial fascia and are comparatively few in number; they are associated more particularly with the superficial lymph vessels of the limbs and the trunk. The deep lymph glands of the limbs also are comparatively few in number, but those of the head, neck, and trunk are very numerous.

General Plan of Lymphatic System.—This may be set out as follows: (1) The capillaries of origin form plexuses which underlie surface epithelia and surround the acini and ducts of glands. (2) From these networks larger vessels of the venule type pass more deeply and penetrate the subjacent tissue—whether superficial fascia, submucous and muscular coats, or stroma of a gland—in which they communicate freely in networks. (3) From these deeper networks arise the valved collecting vessels which run towards the lymph glands. On reaching a lymph gland the vessels, conveniently called **afferent vessels**, penetrate the capsule at numerous points. (4) The lymph glands are stations in which the vessels are broken up into a labyrinth of active reticular tissue by which the fluid is treated in such a manner that a large part of it is absorbed by the venous network in the gland and only a residue is passed out by one or two lymph vessels. (5) These are called **efferent vessels**, and they may run with afferent vessels into another gland of the same group or pass on to another group. (6) From the most central group of each chain of glands the efferent vessels unite to form **lymph trunks** which are named: (*a*) *Lumbar*; (*b*) *Gastro-intestinal*; (*c*) *Intercostal*; (*d*) *Mediastinal*; (*e*) *Subclavian*; (*f*) *Jugular*. (7) Each lymph trunk drains a definite territory of the body, and they all empty into great terminal vessels—the **thoracic duct** and **right lymphatic duct**—which open into the great veins in the root of the neck.

By constant reduction of the stream of lymph as it passes through the chains of lymph glands, the *lymph trunks*, though draining large areas, are actually small vessels which easily escape notice in a dissection; and as most of the lymph absorbed from the body is thus restored to the circulation gradually, the residue, mainly derived from the intestines (*chyle*), is accommodated in the thoracic duct—no larger than a crow quill.

Order of Description.—After the following paragraphs on lymph vessels and glands, it is proposed to describe first the main lymph vessels and then the position of the gland groups and the arrangement of the vessels in each of the territories drained by the lymph trunks, in the order given above. The student should note that these territories do *not* correspond precisely with the ordinary divisions of the body. Readers who desire a more detailed description of the topography and variations of the lymph glands and vessels are referred to the recent work by H. Rouvière, *Anatomie des Lymphatiques de l'Homme*, Masson et Cⁱᵉ, 1932.

Lymph Vessels.—The *capillaries* of origin are *closed*, having no communication with blood-vessels or with tissue-spaces. The stomata by which they have been said to communicate with serous cavities are probably only patches of intercellular substance, and though fluid readily passes through serous membranes into the tissue spaces, from which it is absorbed by the lymph capillaries, there is no proof of a direct connexion. Lymph capillaries are wider than blood capillaries and more irregular in calibre; but they have the same structure, consisting of a single layer of endothelial cells through which lymph is absorbed from the tissue fluid. Wandering phagocytic cells carry in solid particles (*e.g.*, carbon dust and germs) which have entered the body through the skin or mucous membranes.

From their subepithelial position lymph capillaries are well placed to absorb the elements which form chalky, keratinous, and chitinous deposits and thus prevent their deposition in the skin, and in mucous, synovial and serous membranes. With the development of the lymph vascular system in the animal scale the exoskeleton disappears; and nails and horns are formed only in the positions which are the last to be reached by the lymph vessels in the development of individuals.

Although the lymph capillaries form an extensive network, it is probable that this is not continuous over large areas but arranged in more or less discrete patches from which there is selective absorption by larger vessels of the venule type. These vessels form wider-meshed networks in the skin, mucous membranes, etc., and from them vessels coalesce to form the collecting vessels.

The *collecting vessels*, as they run towards the lymph glands, receive tributaries from a narrow area. They are small vessels, white in colour, and are distinguished by their characteristic beaded appearance due to valves of the venous type placed at close and regular intervals. They are joined by smaller tributary vessels and frequently communicate with neighbouring collecting vessels, but, unlike the veins, they always run in streams of individual vessels rather than by confluence into larger trunks (see Fig. 1101). On reaching a gland each afferent vessel usually breaks up into smaller branches which penetrate the capsule. The issuing efferent vessels are only slightly larger than the afferent vessels and have the same structure. Owing to the valves the collecting lymph vessels can be injected only by thrusting a hollow needle into the plexus of origin and pumping in metallic mercury or colouring fluid. Small patches only are injected from each puncture, and thus an enormous number of injections is required for a picture such as is given by a single injection into the artery of a limb or viscus.

As the lymph vessels attain a larger size their walls are strengthened by a layer of elastic fibres on the outer surface of the endothelial coat. The fibres run longitudinally, and in some cases fuse together to form a fenestrated elastic membrane.

The walls of all the largest lymph vessels resemble those of veins and have three coats. The **inner coat** is a layer of endothelium covered externally by elastic fibres or a fenestrated elastic membrane. The **middle coat** is formed of transverse and oblique unstriped muscle fibres, intermingled with elastic fibres. The **outer coat** consists of longitudinal fibrous tissue elements with which oblique and longitudinal unstriped muscle fibres are intermingled; the latter feature is not met with in the blood vascular system, except in the walls of the large veins.

The bicuspid valves of lymph vessels are semilunar folds of the inner coat similar to those of veins. They are extremely numerous in the collecting vessels and are present also near the entrances of the great lymph channels into the venous system.

Lymph Glands.—These are nodules varying in size from a pin head to an almond; they are usually ovoid but may be globular, flattened, or irregular in shape. The larger glands show a depressed area, known as the *hilum*, through which the blood-vessels enter and the efferent lymph vessel emerges. The consistence is firm and the colour is usually greyish pink, but the tint varies with the position, vascularity, and state of activity of the gland. The lymph glands of the lungs are commonly blackened by deposit of carbon particles and those of the liver and spleen are often brownish; those of the mesentery are creamy or white while the chyle is passing through in quantities.

The lymph glands lie in loose areolar tissue, generally in groups but occasionally single. As they develop, the great majority are found in association with the primitive digestive canal in the pelvis, abdomen, thorax, and neck, and in the roots of the limb buds (axilla and groin). With the exception of the superficial inguinal glands, very few lie in the plane of the superficial fascia. A few small lymph glands stray along the blood-vessels into the limbs, into the intercostal spaces and the intervals between the lumbar transverse processes, along the internal mammary artery behind the costal cartilages, and along the occipital, posterior auricular, and facial arteries; but all these are outposts of the main groups which lie deeply in the neck and trunk for the most part by the sides of the great blood-vessels.

Structure of Lymph Glands.—Lymph glands consist essentially of : (1) Masses of lymphoid tissue, supported by (2) a fibrous framework including an external capsule and internal trabeculæ separated from the lymphoid tissue by (3) spaces called lymph sinuses. Each gland is separable also into cortex and medulla. The *cortex* lies immediately internal to the capsule, except at the hilum, where it is absent. The *medulla* forms the internal part of the gland, and reaches the surface at the hilum.

The **capsule** is formed of white fibrous tissue interspersed with elastic fibres; it contains some unstriped muscle fibres which extend into the trabeculæ.

The **trabeculæ** spring from the deep surface of the capsule and radiate through the cortex into the medulla, where they are broken up to form a coarse supporting network.

The **lymph sinuses** lie internal to the capsule and around the trabeculæ; and they separate both from the lymphoid tissue. The afferent lymph vessels of the gland pierce the capsule and enter the subcapsular sinus, from which branches pass inwards along the sides of the trabeculæ. The sinuses are traversed by fine fibrous tissue strands, and their channels are thus converted into a kind of sponge-work through which the lymph percolates into and through the lymphoid tissue. The lymph is ultimately collected by one or two efferent vessels which emerge from the medulla at the hilum.

The **lymphoid tissue** is continuous throughout the gland; but in the cortex it appears as rounded masses—*lymphoid nodules*—and in the medulla as branching and uniting strands known as *lymphoid cords*. Capillary-like lymph spaces pass from the lymph sinuses into the lymphoid tissue; and the endothelial lining becomes gradually converted into a *reticulum* of active phagocytic cells. It is through the meshes of this reticulo-endothelial tissue that the lymph has to pass on its way from afferent to efferent vessels, taking up *lymphocytes* from the masses of these cells with which the meshes of the reticulum are crowded.

In principle the structure of a lymph gland is similar to that of the spleen, in which the capillary system is broken up into an active reticulum from which the veins reform. Insoluble particles carried by the lymph to a gland are taken up by the phagocytic reticular cells, and may be permanently encapsuled in the gland.

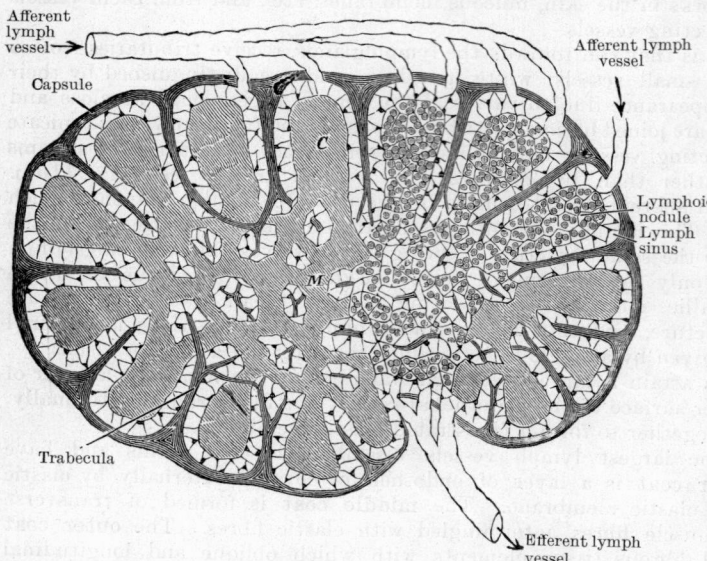

Fig. 1082.—Diagram of a Section of a Lymph Gland (W. Sharpey). C, Cortex; M, Medulla. (*Essentials of Histology*, Sharpey-Schafer and Carleton.)

Labels: Afferent lymph vessel; Capsule; C; Afferent lymph vessel; Lymphoid nodule; Lymph sinus; M; Trabecula; Efferent lymph vessel.

Blood-Vessels of Lymph Glands.—Small arteries are distributed to the capsule and through the capsule to the trabeculæ of the glands; but the main artery enters the hilum and breaks up into branches which follow the trabecular network of the medulla and enter the lymphoid nodules and cords, where they end in capillaries. The veins emerge at the hilum.

Hæmal Lymph Glands.—In various parts of the body, but more particularly in the retro-peritoneal region, and especially along the line of the abdominal aorta, a number of glands may be found which differ from ordinary lymph glands in that some of their sinuses contain blood. They are called hæmal lymph glands; the sinuses which contain lymph are in continuity with lymph vessels, whilst the blood-filled sinuses open into blood-vessels. It is stated that communications exist between the sinuses that contain blood and those filled with lymph, but the evidence on that point is not quite satisfactory.

Solitary Lymphatic Nodules.—Pin-head collections of lymphoid tissue, consisting of a reticulum enmeshing lymphocytes, are found in the mucous coat of the alimentary canal. They appear to be set in the path of lymph vessels proceeding from the capillary plexus of origin and may be deemed to be lymph glands in miniature. These *solitary lymphatic nodules* resemble the lymphoid nodules in the cortex of lymph glands. In the pharynx there are great aggregations of units which form tonsils; in the ileum many of the nodules coalesce to form elongated raised patches (*aggregated lymphatic nodules*); and in the vermiform appendix they form masses which constitute the most striking feature of its structure.

Rudimentary Lymph Glands.—In the path of lymph vessels before they reach the regional glands there are frequently minute nodules (schaltdrüsen) which interrupt one or two vessels only. They are tiny lymph glands in which only a few lymphoid units are involved: examples are the glands on the tibial vessels, deep vessels of forearm, tongue, etc. In some situations these minute glands become recognisable only during functional activity, *e.g.*, in the axilla during lactation.

TERMINAL LYMPH VESSELS

The terminal lymph vessels are the **thoracic duct** and the **right lymphatic duct.** The **thoracic duct** is by far the wider and the longer of the two. It begins in the abdomen as an elongated ovoid dilatation—the **cisterna chyli**—which measures $\frac{1}{4}$ to $\frac{1}{3}$ of an inch (6 to 8 mm.) in its broadest diameter, and from 2 to 3

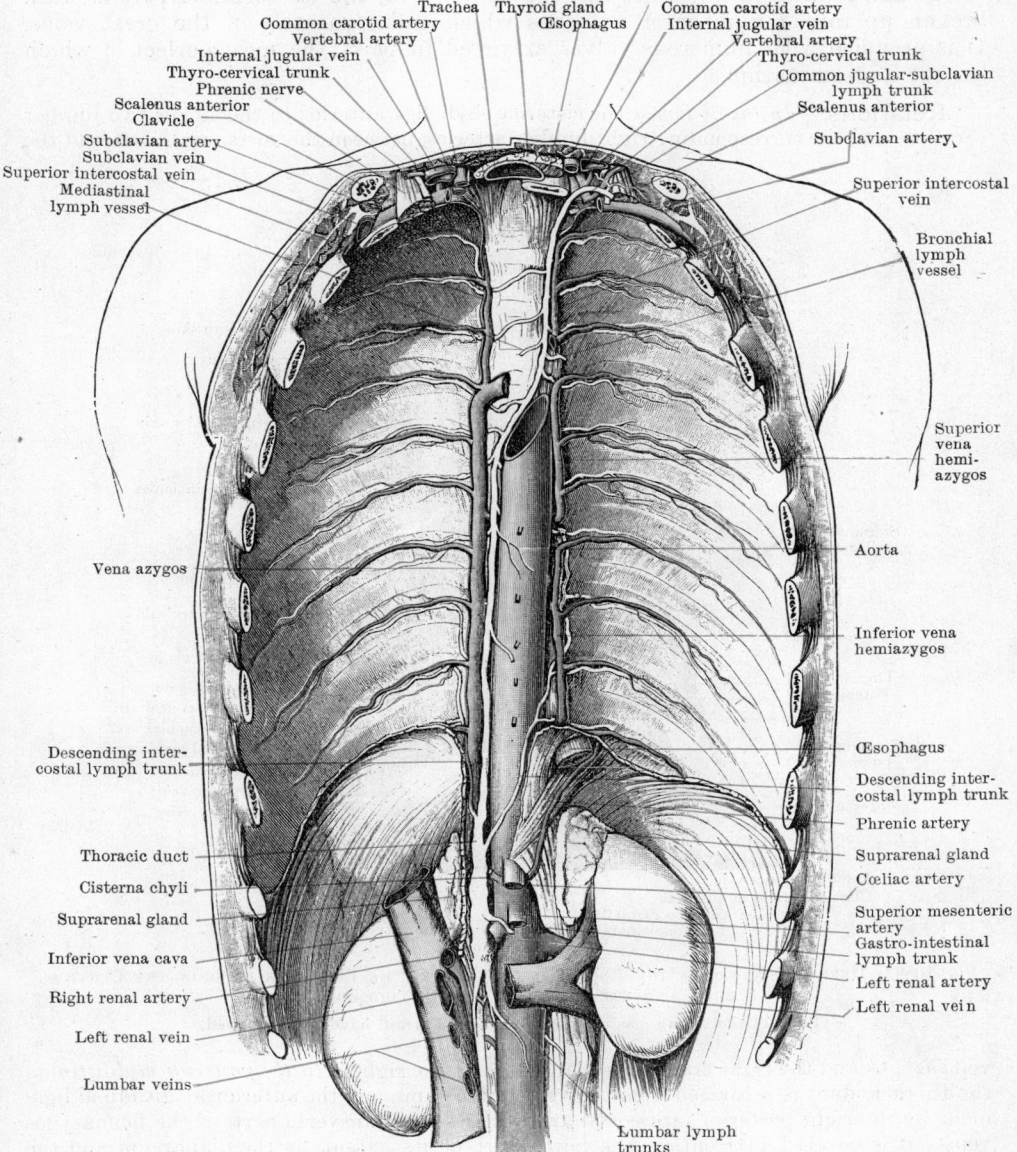

FIG. 1083.—THE THORACIC DUCT AND ITS TRIBUTARIES.

inches (50 to 75 mm.) in length. The cisterna chyli lies between the aorta and the right crus of the diaphragm, and opposite the first and second lumbar vertebræ. Passing upwards from the cisterna, through the aortic opening of the diaphragm, the thoracic duct enters the posterior mediastinum, and ascends, on the front of the vertebral column, to the right of the median plane, to the level of the fifth thoracic vertebra; there it crosses from the right to the left of the median plane, and ascends through the superior mediastinum to the root of the neck, where it turns laterally, between the vertebral and common carotid arteries; descending across the subclavian artery, it ends at the medial border of the left scalenus anterior, by joining the left innominate vein in the angle of junction of the internal jugular and the left subclavian veins.

The thoracic duct is about 18 inches (45 cm.) long, and about a line (2 mm.) in diameter, but it is rather wider at its origin from the cisterna. It may divide and reunite in its course through the thorax, and its terminal part is often broken up into a number of branches which end separately in the great veins. It is provided with numerous valves arranged in pairs, the most perfect of which is near its termination.

Relations.—*In the abdomen* the cisterna chyli lies anterior to the upper two lumbar vertebræ and the corresponding right lumbar arteries, between the aorta on the left and the

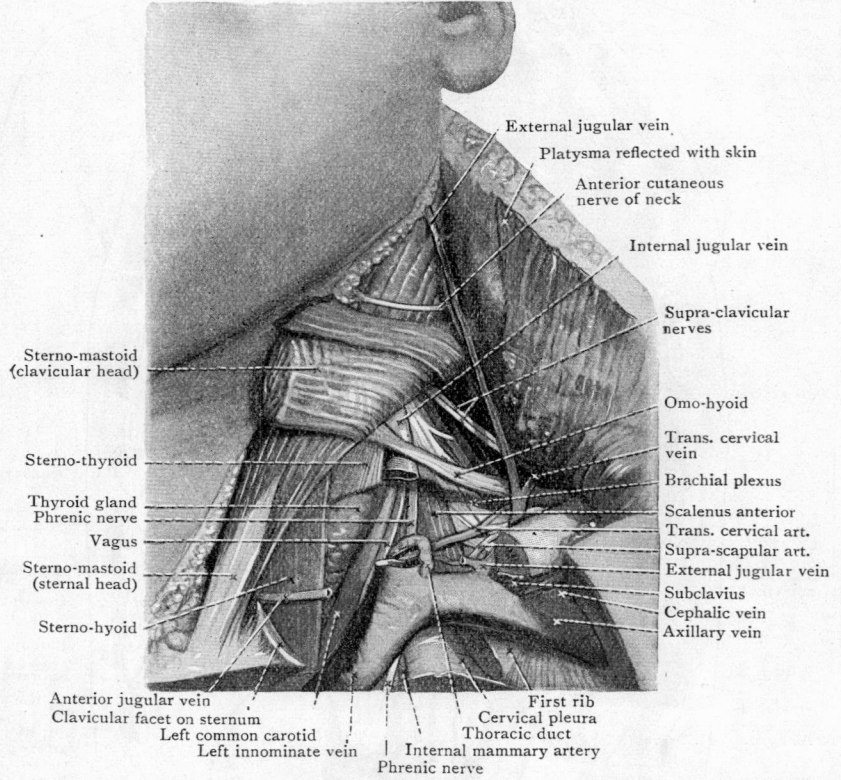

FIG. 1084.—DEEP DISSECTION OF THE ROOT OF THE NECK ON THE LEFT SIDE TO SHOW THE CERVICAL PLEURA AND THE RELATIONS OF THE THORACIC DUCT.

Parts of the sterno-mastoid and the sterno-thyroid have been removed.

vena azygos and the right crus of the diaphragm on the right. *In the posterior mediastinum* the thoracic duct is separated from the vertebral column and the anterior longitudinal ligament by the right posterior intercostal arteries and the transverse parts of the hemiazygos veins; it is covered, in front, in the lower part of its extent by the diaphragm and the right pleural sac, and in the upper part by the œsophagus; to its right is the vena azygos, and to its left the descending aorta. *In the superior mediastinum* it passes forwards from the vertebral column, and it is separated from the left longus cervicis muscle by a mass of fatty tissue; the œsophagus lies in front of it in that region, but the left margin of the duct projects beyond the œsophagus, and is in relation anteriorly, and from below upwards, with the arch of the aorta, the left subclavian artery and the pleura. As the duct enters the root of the neck it passes behind the left common carotid artery, whilst to its right and a little in front is the œsophagus, and the left pleura is still in association with its left border.

At the root of the neck it arches laterally above the apex of the pleural sac and then downwards across the first part of the left subclavian artery. It passes in front of the vertebral artery and vein, the roots of the inferior thyroid, transverse cervical, and suprascapular arteries, the medial border of the scalenus anterior and the left phrenic nerve, and behind the left carotid sheath and its contents.

Tributaries. — The cisterna chyli commonly receives five tributaries:— (1) The **gastro-intestinal trunk**, which is formed by the efferents of the superior mesenteric and cœliac groups of lymph glands, and conveys lymph from the lower and anterior part of the liver, the spleen, the pancreas, the stomach, the small intestine and the greater part of the large intestine. (2) A pair of **lumbar trunks**, formed by the efferents of the aortic [lumbar] glands, carry lymph from the whole of the skin below the level of the umbilicus, from the deep portions of the lower limbs, the lower abdominal and the pelvic walls, from the rest of the large intestine and the pelvic viscera, and from the kidneys, suprarenal glands, and genital glands. (3) A pair of **descending intercostal lymph trunks**, formed by the efferent vessels from the lower intercostal glands (see p. 1327), descend to the cisterna through the aortic opening of the diaphragm. Occasionally they unite to form a single trunk, and sometimes they, or some of the tributaries from which they are usually formed, open directly into the thoracic duct (Fig. 1083).

In its course through the posterior mediastinum the thoracic duct receives efferents from the posterior mediastinal glands and such of the intercostal glands as do not send their efferents into the descending trunk; through the posterior mediastinal glands it receives lymph from the œsophagus and the back of the pericardium, and also some from the upper and posterior part of the liver.

In the superior mediastinum the efferents of the upper intercostal glands of both sides open into it; it may receive also communications from the mediastinal lymph trunks of both sides.

At the root of the neck, immediately before its termination, it may receive (1) the efferents from the glands of the left upper limb, which frequently unite to form a **subclavian trunk**, and (2) the **left jugular trunk**, which conveys the lymph from the left side of the head and neck; but either of those vessels or both of them may end separately in the innominate or the subclavian vein. The **left mediastinal trunk** is rarely a tributary of the thoracic duct in the neck; almost invariably it has an independent entrance into the left innominate vein. It collects lymph from the deeper parts of the anterior thoracic wall and of the upper part of the anterior abdominal wall and from the anterior part of the diaphragm on the left side, from the left half of the mediastinum, the left side of the heart and the left lung.

The **right lymphatic duct** (Fig. 1085) is not always present. Indeed, it rarely exists as such, since the three vessels which occasionally unite to form it usually open separately into the right internal jugular, subclavian, and innominate veins. These vessels are (1) the **right jugular trunk**, (2) the **right subclavian trunk**, and (3) the **right mediastinal trunk**. It is not uncommon for the jugular and subclavian trunks (conveying lymph from the right side of the head and neck and from the right upper limb respectively) to unite, as on the left side, before entering the veins at the point corresponding to that at which the thoracic duct enters on the left side ; and this is the commonest form of "right lymphatic duct." The right mediastinal trunk, which collects lymph from an area corresponding to that drained by the left vessel, but including also the upper part of the right lobe of the liver, almost invariably enters the right innominate vein separately ; but even in the rare event of its union with the other two trunks the resulting *right lymphatic duct* does not correspond to the thoracic duct but only to the united tributaries which the thoracic duct also receives.

Variations.—The **cisterna chyli** may be very irregular or may be replaced by a plexus of vessels, formed by the gastro-intestinal and lumbar lymph trunks, from which the thoracic duct takes origin by several roots.

The **thoracic duct** in its course through the thorax frequently divides into two unequal branches which may run side by side for some distance before reuniting ; or it may even be broken up into a plexiform arrangement of lymph vessels. It may end in a number of branches which enter the great veins separately; and it sometimes divides in the upper part of the thorax into two stems, of which the right joins the right jugular trunk to form one variety of the right lymphatic duct (Fig. 1085). The thoracic duct may end in either the internal jugular or the subclavian vein, or even in the vertebral vein; whilst very rarely it may open into the vena azygos.

The arrangement and mode of termination of the **three lymph trunks—subclavian, jugular, mediastinal**—found in the

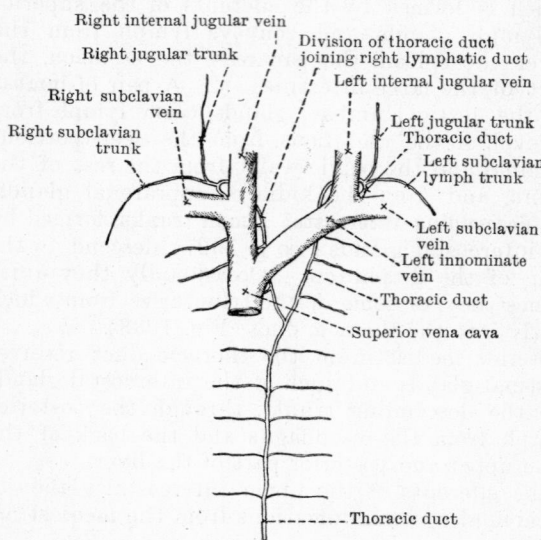

Right internal jugular vein

Right jugular trunk

Right subclavian vein

Right subclavian trunk

Division of thoracic duct joining right lymphatic duct

Left internal jugular vein

Left jugular trunk
Thoracic duct

Left subclavian lymph trunk

Left subclavian vein

Left innominate vein

Thoracic duct

Superior vena cava

Thoracic duct

FIG. 1085.—DIAGRAM SHOWING VARIATION IN ENDING OF THORACIC DUCT.

The mediastinal lymph trunks are not represented.

root of the neck on each side are very variable indeed. They may all open separately into one or other of the great veins; or they may unite together in a variety of ways. Their number may be increased by division of one of them, or by some of their tributaries ending independently—for example, the main efferent of the internal mammary lymph glands may fail to join the mediastinal trunk. On the left side, the mode of ending is influenced, in addition, by the presence of the thoracic duct, which, as noted, may itself break up into several divisions. The following statement may thus be taken as indicating only what are probably the commonest arrangements of the trunks.

On the left side, the jugular trunk ends in the thoracic duct, and the other two trunks may do so also; but the subclavian trunk often ends in the subclavian vein, and the mediastinal trunk usually ends in the innominate vein.

On the right side, the subclavian, jugular, and mediastinal trunks usually have separate entrances into the subclavian, internal jugular, and innominate veins respectively. But it is not uncommon for the subclavian and jugular trunks to unite at the medial margin of the scalenus anterior above the subclavian artery. The resulting vessel is called the *right lymphatic duct*. In rare cases the mediastinal trunk also joins the duct; and its internal mammary tributary may have independent entrance into the innominate vein.

LUMBAR LYMPH TRUNKS

The **lumbar lymph trunks** receive the lymph from the lower limbs, the perineum and external genital organs, the abdominal wall below the plane of the umbilicus, the urogenital system in the pelvis and abdomen, and the part of the digestive tract supplied by the inferior mesenteric artery. In maintaining the idea of the continuity of this great lymph stream it is necessary to trespass over the boundaries of the usual divisions of the body, since, for example, a true picture of the lymph drainage of the skin of the area cannot be obtained by a description of the lymph vessels of the lower limb alone.

SUPERFICIAL LYMPH GLANDS OF LOWER LIMB

The **superficial inguinal lymph glands** (Figs. 1080, 1086) lie in the subcutaneous fat below the inguinal ligament, and extend downwards on each side of the long saphenous vein for a few inches. They are arranged in a *proximal* set (5-6) below and parallel with the ligament and a *distal* set (4-5) associated with the vein. Each set may be divided into medial and lateral parts but as all these glands are freely interconnected they are best considered as one T-shaped group. Their *afferents* are derived from the skin of the whole body below the level of the umbilicus and from the lining membranes of the anal canal and of the penile portion of the spongy part of the urethra, or, in the female, of the vulva and lower end of the vagina. In the female they receive also one or two vessels from the uterus which run along the round ligament through the inguinal canal. The *efferents* pass deeply through the cribriform fascia and, though some enter the deep inguinal lymph glands, most of them pass upwards through the compartments of the femoral sheath to end in the lymph glands on the external iliac artery.

SUPERFICIAL LYMPH VESSELS OF LOWER LIMB AND TRUNK

The **superficial lymph vessels of the lumbar trunk territory** arise in the capillary network of the skin, from which the collecting vessels stream from a wide area towards

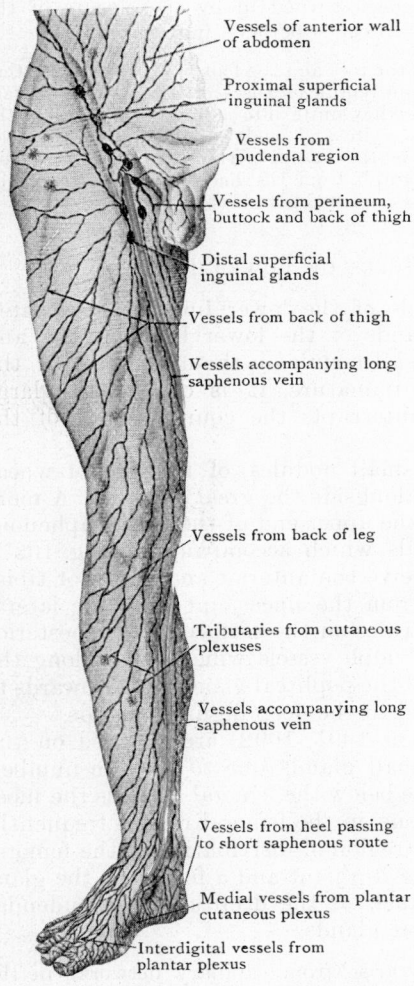

Vessels of anterior wall of abdomen

Proximal superficial inguinal glands

Vessels from pudendal region

Vessels from perineum, buttock and back of thigh

Distal superficial inguinal glands

Vessels from back of thigh

Vessels accompanying long saphenous vein

Vessels from back of leg

Tributaries from cutaneous plexuses

Vessels accompanying long saphenous vein

Vessels from heel passing to short saphenous route

Medial vessels from plantar cutaneous plexus

Interdigital vessels from plantar plexus

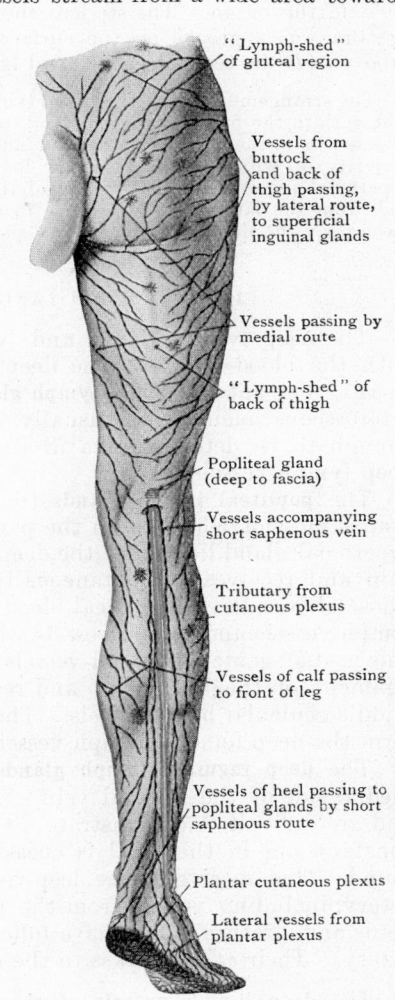

"Lymph-shed" of gluteal region

Vessels from buttock and back of thigh passing, by lateral route, to superficial inguinal glands

Vessels passing by medial route

"Lymph-shed" of back of thigh

Popliteal gland (deep to fascia)

Vessels accompanying short saphenous vein

Tributary from cutaneous plexus

Vessels of calf passing to front of leg

Vessels of heel passing to popliteal glands by short saphenous route

Plantar cutaneous plexus

Lateral vessels from plantar plexus

FIG. 1086.—SUPERFICIAL LYMPH VESSELS OF THE FRONT OF THE LOWER LIMB.

FIG. 1087.—SUPERFICIAL LYMPH VESSELS OF THE BACK OF THE LOWER LIMB.

the groin. The main stream begins in the foot, follows the direction of the long saphenous vein, and is constantly reinforced by vessels which incline upwards around the lateral and medial borders of the leg and thigh from the back and sides of the limb. Towards the root of the limb the vessels run almost horizontally; the lateral vessels of the buttock sweep round below the iliac crest and are succeeded by a descending stream from the back, sides, and front of the abdominal wall below the level of the umbilicus: on the medial side a stream descends from the back of the sacrum and the natal cleft, is joined by some vessels from the medial third of the buttock, by the perineal, anal, and scrotal or vulvar lymph vessels, and turns laterally in the superficial fascia overlying the adductor longus : and lastly the lymph vessels of the penis, including those of the penile urethra, complete the great whorl (Figs. 1080, 1081, 1086, 1087).

Certain exceptions and peculiarities must be noted : (*a*) a few lymph vessels on the skin overlying the short saphenous vein accompany that vessel into the popliteal glands ; (*b*) at several points lymph vessels leave the superficial stream and are conducted along the blood-vessels through the deep fascia to join the deep stream ; (*c*) the lymph vessels of the skin of the penis accompany those of the scrotum but those of the glans follow the deep dorsal vein till in contact with the pubis ; there the majority turn laterally to reach the superficial inguinal glands, but a few accompany the vein under the pubic arch into the pelvis. As the lymph vessels of the glans run towards the pubis they receive numerous tributaries which emerge from the urethra along the ventral median line and encircle the organ. The student should note that these vessels were formed when the urethra was a groove on the surface, and have been turned in by the closure of the groove ; (*d*) the testis does *not* send lymph vessels to the superficial inguinal glands.

The arrangement of the superficial lymph vessels of the toes and the foot is very similar to that met with in the fingers and the hand (p. 1333). From lymph plexuses on the plantar surface vessels pass to the dorsum of the foot and toes, where they unite into a number of vessels, the majority of which accompany the long saphenous vein and end in the distal group of superficial inguinal glands. Some of the lymph from the lateral part of the plantar surface and from the lateral border of the foot, and the lymph from the heel, enter vessels which accompany the short saphenous vein ; these end in the popliteal glands (Fig. 1087).

DEEP LYMPH GLANDS AND VESSELS OF LOWER LIMB

The deep lymph glands and lymph vessels of the lower limb are associated with the blood-vessels. The deep lymph glands of the lower limb are few and small. The **anterior tibial lymph gland** is a small nodule on the upper part of the interosseous membrane ; usually minute or immature, it is occasionally large enough to be detected in a dissection. It interrupts the course of one of the deep lymph vessels.

The **popliteal lymph glands** (6 or 7) are small nodules, of the size of wheat grains, most of which lie in the popliteal fat alongside the great vessels. A more superficial gland lies under the deep fascia on the upper end of the short saphenous vein and receives the cutaneous lymph vessels which accompany it (Fig. 1087). Those alongside the popliteal blood-vessels receive the anterior and posterior tibial lymph vessels and lymph vessels which issue from the knee joint with the lateral and medial genicular blood-vessels : one gland lies on the surface of the posterior ligament of the knee joint and receives the lymph vessels which issue along the middle genicular blood-vessels. The *efferents* of the popliteal glands pass upwards to form the deep femoral lymph vessels which end in the deep inguinal glands.

The **deep inguinal lymph glands** (Figs. 1089, 1091, 1092) are situated on the medial side of the femoral vein. They are small glands, one to three in number, and are difficult to demonstrate. Of these, one below the femoral canal is the most constant, one in the canal is occasional, and one in the femoral ring is frequently found. They receive all the deep vessels in the region of distribution of the femoral artery, including vessels from the front of the hip joint and a few from the glans penis and urethra which have followed the track of the deep external pudendal artery. Their *efferents* pass to the external iliac glands.

The **deep lymph vessels** of the lower limb arise from capillary networks in the synovial membranes of joints and tendon sheaths, and follow the main blood-vessels. They are joined by some cutaneous lymph vessels from the limb and penis which have passed deeply along the cutaneous blood-vessels. Many of the vessels from the leg and foot end in the popliteal glands, but some pass directly to the deep inguinal glands in which also deep vessels of the more proximal parts end. The deep lymph vessels of the gluteal region and perineum accompany branches of the internal iliac artery into the pelvis and will be noted in the next section.

LYMPH VESSELS OF ANTERIOR WALL OF ABDOMEN

The **lymph vessels of the anterior wall of the abdomen** may be briefly reviewed at this point. Since they pass in different directions and ultimately discharge not only into the *lumbar* but also into the *subclavian* and *mediastinal* lymph trunks, their description is to be found in the sections dealing with these respective trunks.

The *superficial lymph vessels* of the upper part of the anterior wall of the abdomen go mainly to the anterior or pectoral group of axillary glands; but some pierce the wall of the lower part of the thorax and end in the internal mammary glands. Those of the lower part of the abdominal wall end in the proximal group of superficial inguinal glands.

The *deep lymph vessels* of the upper part of the anterior abdominal wall accompany the superior epigastric blood-vessels and end in the internal mammary glands. Those of the lower part accompany the inferior epigastric and deep circumflex iliac vessels, and end in the inferior external iliac glands (see below). Small lymph glands are often found interrupting these deep lymph vessels.

Lymph Vessels of External Genital Organs

The **lymph vessels of the scrotum** or of the **vulva** pass to the proximal superficial inguinal glands, and mostly to the medial group.

The **superficial lymph vessels of the penis** go to the medial glands of the proximal superficial inguinal group. The **deep lymph vessels of the penis**, including those of the penile portion of the urethra, end either in the medial glands of the proximal superficial inguinal group or in the deep inguinal glands. A few vessels follow the deep dorsal vein, and join the rich outflow of the prostate to the internal iliac glands. The **lymph vessels of the clitoris** end like those of the penis.

Lymph Glands of the Pelvis

The lymph glands of the pelvis may be grouped according to their position in association with blood-vessels: (1) *External iliac* in succession to the inguinal lymph glands; (2) *internal iliac* with sub-groups associated with the branches of the artery; and (3) *common iliac*. (Figs. 1088, 1089, 1091.)

The **external iliac lymph glands** (8-10) form three incomplete chains—lateral, intermediate, and medial—which lie along the external iliac vessels. The largest members are found on the lower end of the blood-vessels—usually one in front, one on the medial, and one on the lateral side; each of these may be single or may be accompanied by smaller glands. A few are scattered along the blood vessels at higher levels. They receive the efferents of the inguinal glands, superficial and deep, the deep lymph vessels of the lower part of the anterior abdominal wall— interrupted by small outlying members of the group, *inferior epigastric glands* and *circumflex iliac glands*—and a number of afferents direct from the pelvic viscera. Their *efferents* pass to the common iliac glands.

The **internal iliac lymph glands** lie along the trunk and branches of the internal iliac [hypogastric] vessels on the pelvic wall and in the fatty tissue around the organs. They receive *afferents* from all the pelvic viscera, and also from the perineum and the gluteal region. Their *efferents* pass to the common iliac glands. On the pelvic wall some of the glands around the stem of the internal iliac artery merge into the medial external iliac chain above; others may be found on the stems of the parietal branches of the artery—*gluteal, pudendal, obturator*—and they may be so named; but only one group need be specially designated—the **sacral lymph glands**, which lie in the hollow of the sacrum.

In the fatty tissue near the viscera there are usually a number of small outlying glands:—

(*a*) **Ano-rectal lymph glands** (2-8) in relation with the ampulla of the rectum and the back of the bladder or the vagina; (*b*) a **middle rectal lymph gland** on each side of the rectum about its middle; (*c*) **vesical lymph glands**—*anterior* (occasional) in the retropubic fat, and *lateral* along the side of the bladder in relation with the obliterated umbilical artery; (*d*) in the female the **para-uterine lymph glands** in the root of the broad ligament close to the cervix.

The **common iliac lymph glands** (4-6) continue the internal and external iliac groups upwards; those on the lateral side and behind each common iliac artery may be regarded as the successors of the external iliac chain, but they all communicate freely. Their *efferents* pass to the aortic glands. As the medial members of the two common iliac groups come together in the angle between the iliac vessels they form a median group of glands; some of these have been (unnecessarily) named *lymph glands of the promontory* and *sub-aortic glands*.

The nominal groups of pelvic glands are in reality quite artificial. The important facts are that a number of lymph glands are situated in the fat round the internal iliac blood vessels and their branches—**lymph glands of the cavity**; and that a number on the external and common iliac vessels form a collar on the brim—**lymph glands of the brim.**

The glands of the brim (external iliac and common iliac) receive the efferent vessels from the glands of the cavity (internal iliac and all sub-groups) and also

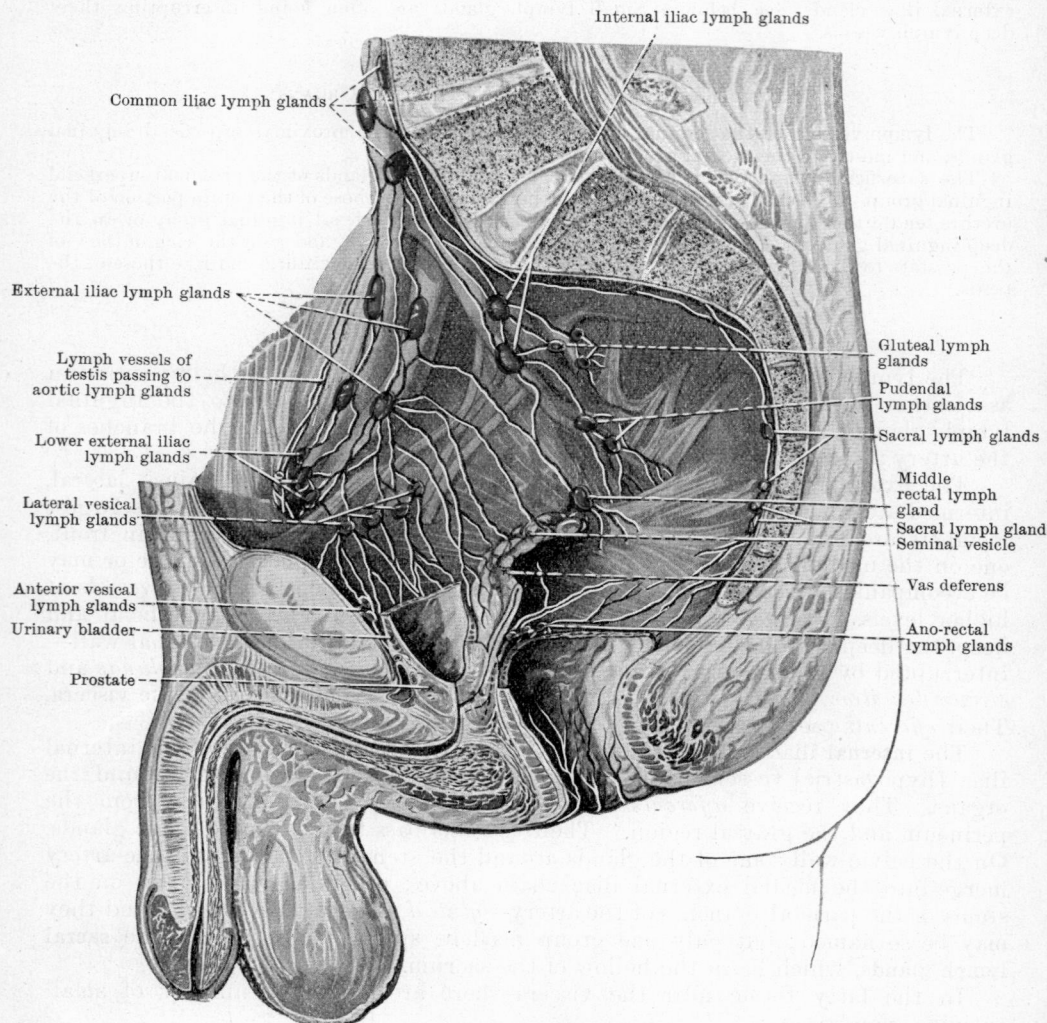

Fig. 1088.—The Lymph Glands of the Pelvis.

numerous direct afferent vessels from *all the pelvic organs* and from the peritoneum of the lower abdominal wall. Moreover, vessels from the upper part of the rectum, from the upper part of the uterus, and from the uterine tube and ovary, escape even the glands of the brim and pass into the abdomen to end in the aortic glands.

PARIETAL AFFERENT LYMPH VESSELS OF PELVIC GLANDS

The deep lymph vessels from the anterior and lateral abdominal wall below the umbilicus and from the iliac fossa arise from a subperitoneal capillary network, and follow the superior epigastric and deep circumflex iliac arteries to the lowest external iliac glands.

Lymph vessels that arise from the medial side of the hip joint follow the obturator artery, and from the back of the joint others pass along the gluteal vessels, with deep lymph vessels of the gluteal region, to reach internal iliac glands situated on these branches of the main artery. Deep lymph vessels from the perineum, arising in the bulbar and membranous parts of the urethra, from the bulbo-urethral glands (from the greater vestibular glands in the female), and some from the anal canal, follow the internal pudendal artery to the internal iliac glands, and thence to the lymph glands of the brim.

LYMPH VESSELS OF THE PELVIC VISCERA

Although the lymph glands of the pelvis are for the most part situated along the blood vessels, it is important to note that the lymph vessels of pelvic organs do not

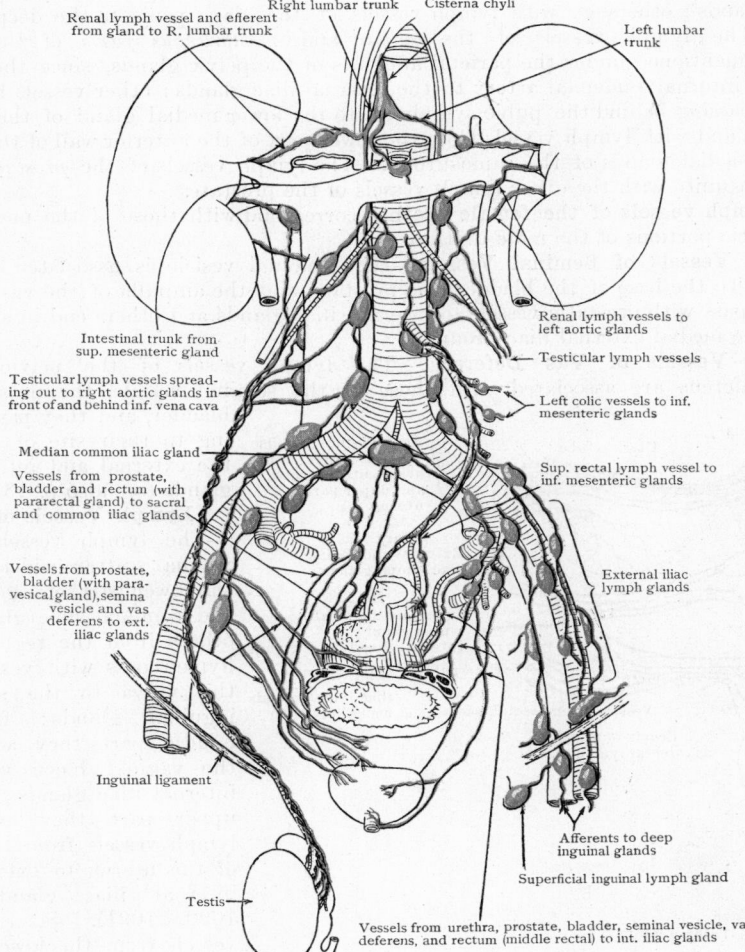

Right lumbar trunk   Cisterna chyli

Renal lymph vessel and efferent from gland to R. lumbar trunk

Left lumbar trunk

Intestinal trunk from sup. mesenteric gland

Renal lymph vessels to left aortic glands

Testicular lymph vessels

Testicular lymph vessels spreading out to right aortic glands in front of and behind inf. vena cava

Left colic vessels to inf. mesenteric glands

Median common iliac gland

Vessels from prostate, bladder and rectum (with pararectal gland) to sacral and common iliac glands

Sup. rectal lymph vessel to inf. mesenteric glands

Vessels from prostate, bladder (with para-vesical gland), semina vesicle and vas deferens to ext. iliac glands

External iliac lymph glands

Inguinal ligament

Afferents to deep inguinal glands

Superficial inguinal lymph gland

Testis

Vessels from urethra, prostate, bladder, seminal vesicle, vas deferens, and rectum (middle rectal) to int. iliac glands

FIG. 1089.—DIAGRAM OF LYMPH VESSELS AND GLANDS OF MALE PELVIS AND ABDOMEN.

necessarily follow only the paths of the blood vessels that supply them. Many of them take other paths (*e.g.*, to the external iliac glands) and the drainage of pelvic organs is therefore to some extent along unexpected lines. On the other hand the lymph vessels of the ovary and of the upper part of the rectum do follow their blood vessels out of the pelvis to end in glands in the abdomen.

Lymph Vessels of Urinary Bladder.—The lymph vessels of the urinary bladder arise from a submucous plexus (Albarran) and pierce the muscular coat. From the superior and infero-lateral surfaces of the bladder, the vessels, some of which are interrupted in the anterior and lateral vesical glands, pass to the external iliac lymph glands. From the base of the bladder also vessels pass to the external iliac glands, but some end in internal iliac glands. Lymph vessels from the neck of the bladder are associated with those from the prostate that run to the sacral and the median common iliac glands.

Lymph Vessels of Ureter.—The lymph vessels of the *pelvic part* of the ureter are associated with those of the urinary bladder (see also p. 1320).

Lymph Vessels of the Prostate.—The prostatic lymph vessels mainly follow the inferior vesical artery and end in the anterior and lateral vesical glands, and in the internal iliac glands; some, however, pass backwards to the sacral glands, and others follow the vas deferens to external iliac glands; one or two may run downwards to join the vessels of the membranous urethra.

Lymph Vessels of Male Urethra.—It has been pointed out that the lymph vessels of the greater part of the *spongy part* of the urethra pass to the superficial inguinal glands; others go with lymph vessels of the glans penis to the deep inguinal glands. The lymph vessels of the *bulbar* and *membranous parts* of the urethra have been mentioned under the parietal afferents of the pelvic glands, since they mainly follow the internal pudendal artery to the internal iliac glands; other vessels have been described passing behind the pubic symphysis to the lower medial gland of the external iliac group, and with lymph vessels from the lower part of the anterior wall of the bladder to higher medial glands of the same group. The lymph vessels of the *prostatic part* of the urethra unite with the other lymph vessels of the prostate.

The **lymph vessels of the female urethra** correspond with those of the membranous and prostatic portions of the male urethra.

Lymph Vessels of Seminal Vesicle.—The seminal vesicle is associated in lymph drainage with the base of the bladder, the prostate, and the ampulla of the vas deferens. Collectors pass with prostatic vessels to internal iliac glands and others end in a posterior gland of the medial external iliac group.

Lymph Vessels of Vas Deferens.—The lymph vessels of the pelvic part of the vas deferens are associated with those of the seminal vesicle, the prostate, and bladder, and they pass, according to their site of origin, to the external and internal iliac glands (see also p. 1320).

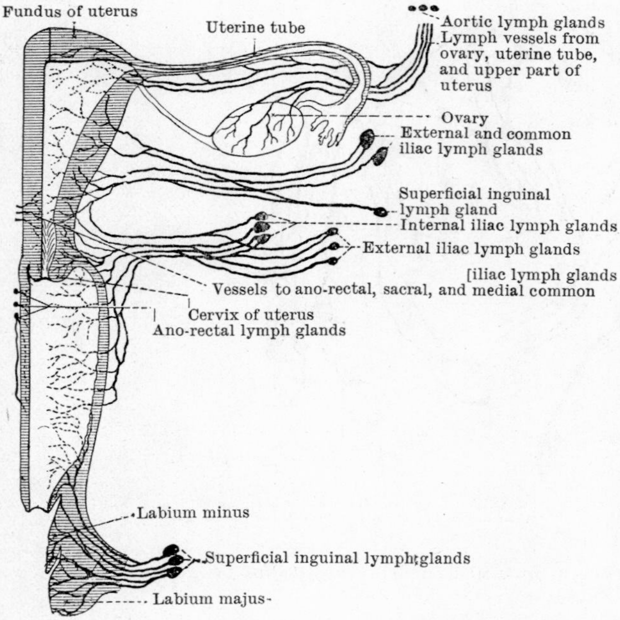

Lymph Vessels of Vagina.—The lymph vessels of the vagina scatter widely. From the lower part some go to sacral and common iliac glands, and others from the region of the hymen pass with vessels from the vulva to the superficial inguinal glands; from the middle part they accompany the vaginal blood vessels to internal iliac glands; from the upper part they accompany lymph vessels from the cervix of the uterus to external and internal iliac glands (Figs. 1090, 1091). Some of the vessels from the lower part of the posterior wall of the vagina may be interrupted in the small ano-rectal lymph glands.

Lymph Vessels of Uterus.—The capillary plexus in the mucous coat of the uterus communicates with a voluminous

Fundus of uterus
Uterine tube
Aortic lymph glands
Lymph vessels from ovary, uterine tube, and upper part of uterus
Ovary
External and common iliac lymph glands
Superficial inguinal lymph gland
Internal iliac lymph glands
External iliac lymph glands
[iliac lymph glands
Vessels to ano-rectal, sacral, and medial common
Cervix of uterus
Ano-rectal lymph glands
Labium minus
Superficial inguinal lymph glands
Labium majus

FIG. 1090.—DIAGRAM OF LYMPH VESSELS OF FEMALE GENITAL ORGANS.

subserous plexus from which the collecting vessels arise. They run to widely separated groups of lymph glands—superficial inguinal, external and internal iliac, sacral and common iliac, and aortic (Figs. 1090, 1091).

From the *cervix* vessels pass to both external and internal iliac glands, and also to the sacral and median common iliac glands. From the *lower part of the body* some may pass with vessels from the cervix to internal iliac glands, but most of them go to external iliac glands.   From the *upper part of the body* and the *fundus* the most important outflow is with the vessels of the uterine tube and ovary upwards over the pelvic brim to aortic lymph glands (see p. 1320).   The aortic glands that receive lymph vessels from the uterus are situated near the origin of the inferior vena cava on the right side and of the inferior mesenteric artery on the left.   In addition, one or two vessels from the fundus and the body run along the round ligament of the uterus to the superficial inguinal lymph glands.   Some of the uterine lymph vessels are interrupted in the para-uterine lymph glands.

Lymph Vessels of Uterine Tube.—The main lymph drainage of the uterine tube is with the lymph vessels of the fundus of the uterus and of the ovary to aortic lymph glands (see p. 1320); but a vessel may occasionally pass to an external iliac or even to an internal iliac gland.

Lymph Vessels of Ovary.—The lymph vessels of the ovary pass entirely out of the pelvis to aortic lymph glands (see p. 1320).

Lymph Vessels of Rectum and Anal Canal.—Like those of the uterus and vagina, the lymph vessels of the anal canal and rectum end in widely separated groups of glands. They arise mainly from a plexus in the mucous coat continuous through the plexus of the anal canal with the cutaneous plexus of the perineum.   Most of the collecting vessels end in pelvic lymph glands —sacral, internal iliac, and common iliac—but from the lower end of the anal canal some pass with cutaneous vessels to superficial inguinal glands, and from the upper part of the rectum the lymph drainage is continuous with that of the pelvic colon and the vessels pass upwards out of the pelvis to the inferior mesenteric glands.

From the lower end of the anal canal vessels run, with those of the skin around the anus, forwards in the perineum and ascend to the superficial inguinal glands. From the greater part of the anal canal the lymph vessels run either across the ischio-rectal fossa or upwards with those of the lower part of the rectum along the middle rectal [haemorrhoidal]

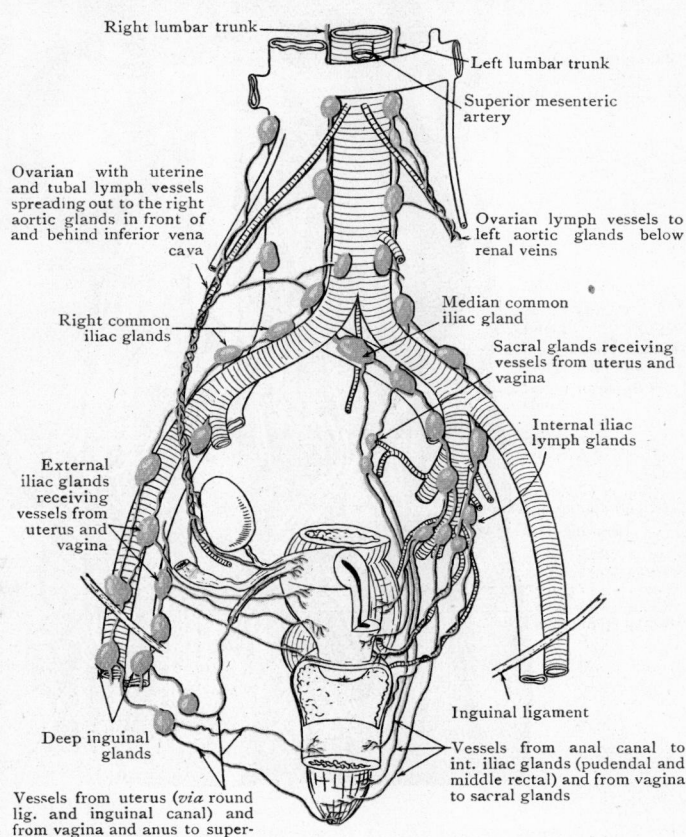

Fig. 1091.—Diagram of Lymph Vessels and Glands of Female Pelvis and Abdomen.

blood vessels to internal iliac glands.   Other vessels from the rectum end in the sacral and median common iliac glands; and a very important group ascends along the superior rectal blood vessels to reach glands about the stem of the inferior mesenteric artery.   Vessels from the anal canal and lower part of the rectum may be interrupted in the small ano-rectal lymph glands; and others from the middle and upper parts of the rectum pass through para-rectal glands.

Aortic and Inferior Mesenteric Lymph Glands

The **aortic lymph glands** [Lg. lumbales] (Figs. 1089, 1092) are arranged in a number of chains which lie in the loose tissue around the aorta and inferior vena cava. Below they are in continuity with the common iliac glands; and from the upper members of the aortic group behind the pancreas the right and left lumbar lymph trunks emerge. The lymph glands lie at the sides of the great vessels, between them, in front of and behind them: they have, therefore, been subdivided into *right lateral* (pre-venous, retro-venous), *left lateral, pre-aortic,* and *retro-aortic* :

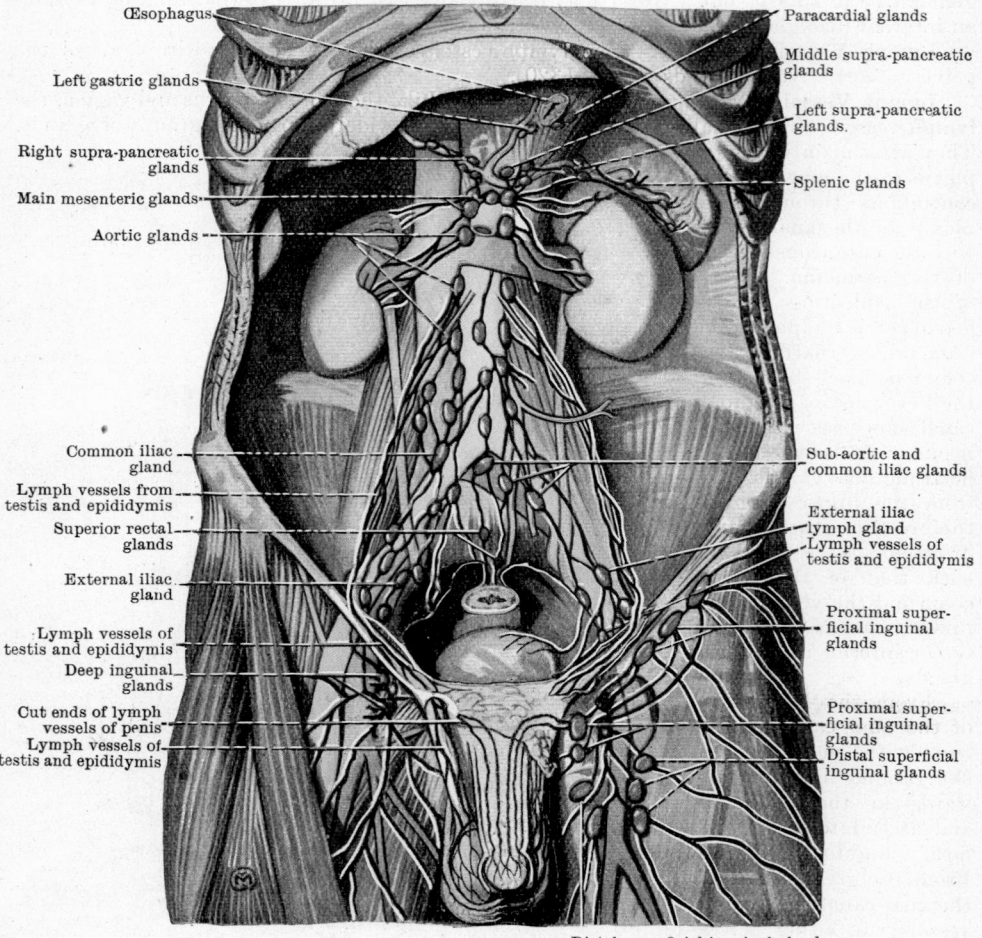

Œsophagus

Left gastric glands

Right supra-pancreatic
glands

Main mesenteric glands

Aortic glands

Common iliac
gland

Lymph vessels from
testis and epididymis

Superior rectal
glands

External iliac
gland

Lymph vessels of
testis and epididymis

Deep inguinal
glands

Cut ends of lymph
vessels of penis

Lymph vessels of
testis and epididymis

Paracardial glands

Middle supra-pancreatic
glands

Left supra-pancreatic
glands.

Splenic glands

Sub-aortic and
common iliac glands

External iliac
lymph gland

Lymph vessels of
testis and epididymis

Proximal super-
ficial inguinal
glands

Proximal super-
ficial inguinal
glands

Distal superficial
inguinal glands

Distal superficial inguinal glands

Fig. 1092.—Semi-diagrammatic view of the Lymph Glands and Vessels of the Inguinal Region, the Pelvis and the Posterior Wall of the Abdomen.

but as they are freely interconnected such subdivision is scarcely necessary. They are most numerous on the left side of the aorta, where they are tightly packed from the common iliac artery up to the renal artery. Their concentration in this situation may be explained, first by the fact that the corresponding members on the right side have to be disposed round the vena cava, and secondly by the fact that the upper end of the inferior mesenteric lymph gland chain is not separated from the aortic glands. Above the level of the renal vessels the aortic group is represented by a few small glands not easily distinguished from the cœliac and superior mesenteric groups. In the process of development a large number of glands are formed in the primitive mesentery. Those at the root of the mesentery drain the body wall and the abdominal organs developed in the region of the intermediate cell mass—suprarenal, kidney, and testis or ovary—and receive the efferents from lower limbs and pelvis. Those in the primitive mesentery are associated with the three great visceral vessels—cœliac, superior mesenteric, and inferior mesenteric arteries—and drain the abdominal part of the fore-gut, the mid-gut, and the hind-gut. Each of these great groups may be regarded as offshoots of the aortic glands, but while the inferior mesenteric group does not dissociate itself from the lumbar trunks, the efferent lymph vessels of the cœliac and superior mesenteric groups open separately into the cisterna chyli by the gastro-intestinal trunk.

Some outlying small members of the aortic group of glands are separated from the main body by the psoas and lie in the intervals between the lumbar transverse processes; they are in series with the sacral glands below and the intercostal glands above; they may be called the *lateral lumbar lymph glands*.

The *afferent* vessels of these lateral glands are derived from the lumbar synovial joints, the dura mater of the vertebral canal and some cutaneous vessels from the lumbar region which have followed the posterior branches of the lumbar arteries; their *efferents* pass along the lumbar blood vessels to the aortic glands. The main aortic glands receive (*a*) the efferents of the common iliac glands (lymph of whole lower limb, abdominal wall below umbilical level, perineum, external genital organs and pelvis; (*b*) efferents of the lateral lumbar glands; (*c*) efferents of the inferior mesenteric chain; (*d*) afferents from the testis and epididymis (ovary, uterine tube, and upper part of uterus in the female); and (*e*) afferents from the abdominal part of the ureter, the kidneys and suprarenal glands, and from the under surface of the diaphragm. The territory of drainage corresponds to the distribution of the paired branches of the aorta, with that of the inferior mesenteric artery added.

The **inferior mesenteric system of lymph glands** is an extension of the aortic group of glands along the inferior mesenteric artery and its branches. The main **inferior mesenteric lymph glands** lie along the stem of the artery. They receive lymph from the outlying glands of the system that are scattered along the branches of the artery as far as the wall of the intestine. The outlying glands are known as the lymph glands of the colon, and are arranged in subsidiary groups. The same arrangement of lymph glands is found along the branches of the *superior mesenteric artery* that supply part of the large intestine (see p. 1323).

The **lymph glands of the colon** may be considered as forming four groups—epicolic, paracolic, intermediate and main colic (Jamieson and Dobson) (Fig. 1095).

(*a*) The **epicolic glands** are small nodules which lie in the appendices epiploicæ and in relation with the wall of the gut. (*b*) The **paracolic glands** lie along the medial borders of the ascending and descending parts of the colon, along the upper border of the transverse colon, and on the mesenteric border of the pelvic colon. (*c*) The **intermediate colic glands** lie along the branches of the colic arteries. (*d*) The **main colic glands** are situated around the stems from which the colic arteries arise.

The lymph gathered by the lymph plexuses in the walls of the gut passes through one or more of these subsidiary groups of glands before it reaches the lymph glands situated on the stems of the main blood vessels. In addition to the drainage of the rectum by lymph vessels that pass upwards out of the pelvis with the superior rectal [hæmorrhoidal] artery, *afferents* of the main inferior mesenteric glands convey lymph from the descending and pelvic parts of the colon; their *efferents* pass to the aortic lymph glands which drain mainly into the left lumbar lymph trunk.

Lymph Vessels of Testis and Epididymis.—A rich capillary network surrounds the tubules in the testis and gives origin to collecting vessels which traverse the mediastinum testis to emerge through the back of the organ; they are joined by the vessels of the epididymis and a superficial set from the serous covering. These vessels

(6-8) ascend in the spermatic cord, pass through the deep inguinal ring and then follow the testicular blood vessels upwards on the psoas. About the level of the iliac crest they curve medially and spread out like a fountain spray to end in the lower aortic lymph glands, from the bifurcation of the aorta to the level of the renal veins (Fig. 1089). One vessel (probably from the tunica vaginalis) usually diverges into an external iliac gland. The student should note that the lymph vessels of the testis were developed while the organ lay on the posterior abdominal wall, and that the scrotum is merely a diverticulum of the lower abdominal wall: hence the difference in the destination of the lymph vessels of the scrotum (inguinal lymph glands) and of the testis and epididymis (aortic lymph glands).

Lymph Vessels of Vas Deferens.—As far as the brim of the pelvis these join the testicular lymph vessels; from the pelvic portion (as already noted, p. 1316) they pass upwards to the external iliac glands and backwards to the internal iliac glands.

Lymph Vessels of Ovary.—Like the lymph vessels of the testis those of the ovary end in aortic lymph glands; their destination depends on the development of the organ in the abdomen. They emerge through the hilum of the ovary, are joined by lymph vessels from the fundus of the uterus and the uterine tube and ascend over the pelvic brim with the ovarian blood vessels. On the posterior wall of the abdomen they spread out to end in aortic glands from the bifurcation of the aorta to the level of the renal veins (Fig. 1091).

Lymph Vessels of Ureter.—The vessels of the ureter are believed to arise from a scanty plexus in the mucous coat. The collecting vessels are not numerous. From the pelvic part of the ureter, vessels pass to the internal, external, and common iliac glands; from the middle part to the aortic glands; and from the upper end, including the pelvis and calyces, they run with the renal lymph vessels.

Lymph Vessels of Kidney.—These vessels are injected with difficulty and, like those of the bladder and ureter, appear to be scanty.

In addition to the subserous plexus on the parts of the kidney covered with peritoneum, there is a plexus of lymph vessels in the renal fat from which collectors pass to aortic glands. In the fibrous capsule of the kidney there is another plexus which receives communications from the vessels in the cortex of the organ and gives origin to collecting vessels which pass medially to join those emerging from the hilum.

The lymph vessels of the cortical and medullary parts of the substance of the kidney unite in the region of the bases of the pyramids and traverse the renal columns to appear in the sinus. They emerge from the hilum both in front of and behind the blood vessels and run medially to end in aortic glands at and below the level of the hilum. On the right side some of the glands in which they end are situated behind the inferior vena cava.

From the back of the upper end of the kidney a few vessels may pass with some from the suprarenal glands through the diaphragm (with the communications between the renal and suprarenal veins and the azygos veins) into the lowest lymph glands in the posterior mediastinum.

Lymph Vessels of Suprarenal Gland.—Lymph vessels emerge from the surface of the suprarenal gland with the arteries and through the hilum with the vein. These vessels drain the cortex and the medulla respectively, but they arise from a continuous capillary plexus. They end mainly in cœliac and upper aortic lymph glands; but some of them have been noted above as passing through the diaphragm into the posterior mediastinal lymph glands.

Lymph Vessels of the Peritoneum.—The lymph vessels of the serous coats of the viscera are described with the lymph drainage of each organ. Those from the parietal peritoneum arise from a subserous network—specially rich on the diaphragm—and tend to converge on the blood vessels which run in the extra-peritoneal tissue in the different regions. In the pelvis they pass to the nearest glands in the cavity or on the brim. On the anterior abdominal wall and in the iliac fossa they accompany the superior and inferior epigastric and the deep circumflex iliac blood vessels. On the posterior wall of the abdomen in the lower part they join the vessels that run from the ascending and descending colon and are thus conveyed to the gland groups on the superior and inferior mesenteric arteries. Laterally they accompany the lumbar blood vessels to the lateral aortic glands. Higher up they join the vessels from the kidneys. Above, the diaphragmatic lymph vessels mainly pierce the diaphragm to join the rich sub-pleural plexus on its upper surface; the stream which accompanies the phrenic blood vessels to reach the uppermost aortic glands is therefore small.

GASTRO-INTESTINAL LYMPH TRUNK

The **gastro-intestinal lymph trunk** enters the cisterna chyli and is formed by the union of the efferents of the proximal members of great groups of lymph glands situated on the cœliac and superior mesenteric arteries and their branches. The efferents of the proximal lymph glands of the group associated with the inferior mesenteric artery empty into the aortic glands on the left side of the aorta, and so mainly into the left lumbar lymph trunk.   These three sets of glands are developed in the parts of the primitive mesentery associated with the fore-gut, mid-gut, and hind-gut respectively.

The student will note that the term "aortic glands" is applied to those which lie on the great vessels at the root of the primitive mesentery, and the terms "cœliac," "superior mesenteric," and "inferior mesenteric" to those originally *in* that mesentery.   Above the level of the renal vessels, where the superior mesenteric and cœliac glands merge and communicate with the upper aortic glands, it is impossible to distinguish clearly between the two sets.   The distinctions in that region are rather artificially made to facilitate description.

CŒLIAC AND SUPERIOR MESENTERIC LYMPH GLANDS

The **cœliac system of lymph glands** presents descriptive difficulties.   The main group extends along the upper border of the pancreas in association with the cœliac artery and its hepatic and splenic branches.   For convenience of appellation and because they found all the glands on the hepatic and splenic arteries to be stations for the lymph vessels of the stomach and less importantly associated with the liver and spleen, Jamieson and Dobson subdivided and named them the *right, middle, and left supra-pancreatic glands*; to each set certain lymph streams converge from well defined territories.   The term "gastric" glands for any particular group is apt to be misleading, as *all* the groups in the cœliac system receive lymph vessels from the stomach.   The following table indicates the relation of the different groups of glands in the cœliac system :

CŒLIAC LYMPH GLANDS

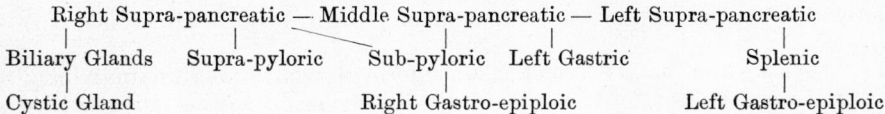

Right Supra-pancreatic — Middle Supra-pancreatic — Left Supra-pancreatic

Biliary Glands   Supra-pyloric   Sub-pyloric   Left Gastric   Splenic

Cystic Gland   Right Gastro-epiploic   Left Gastro-epiploic

The **splenic lymph glands** are a few small glands situated above the tail of the pancreas at the hilum of the spleen.   They receive the lymph vessels of the spleen and also vessels, which accompany the left gastro-epiploic artery, from the lower border of the stomach ; in the course of some of these one or two small **left gastro-epiploic lymph glands** may be found in the gastro-splenic ligament near the spleen.

The **left supra-pancreatic lymph glands** [Lg. pancreatico-lienales] lie on the stem of the splenic artery.   They receive the efferents of the splenic glands, lymph vessels from the body of the pancreas, and an abundant stream from the fundus and body of the stomach with the short gastric arteries.

The **left gastric lymph glands** [Lg. gastricae superiores] form a long chain. The most distal members—lower left gastric—lie on the lesser curvature of the stomach to the left of the angular notch.   Above this, the cardiac end of the stomach is surrounded by the glands like a string of beads round the neck of the organ (*paracardial lymph glands*).   Beyond that the chain lies around the trunk of the left gastric artery—upper left gastric glands.   Finally the chain merges with the middle supra-pancreatic group.   The left gastric glands receive the lymph vessels from an area of the stomach, front and back, between the lesser curvature and a line from the summit of the fundus downwards along the junction of the middle and lower thirds of the surfaces as far as the pyloric canal.   From any part of this surface some of the vessels skirt past the lower and paracardial glands and reach the upper group. This behaviour is characteristic of the lymph vessels of the alimentary canal (see Figs. 1095, 1096).

The **middle supra-pancreatic lymph glands** [Lg. cœliacæ] surround the stem of the cœliac artery and receive the efferents of the left gastric glands, of the left and right supra-pancreatic glands, and some efferents of the sub-pyloric glands (see below).

The **right supra-pancreatic lymph glands** lie along the horizontal part of the

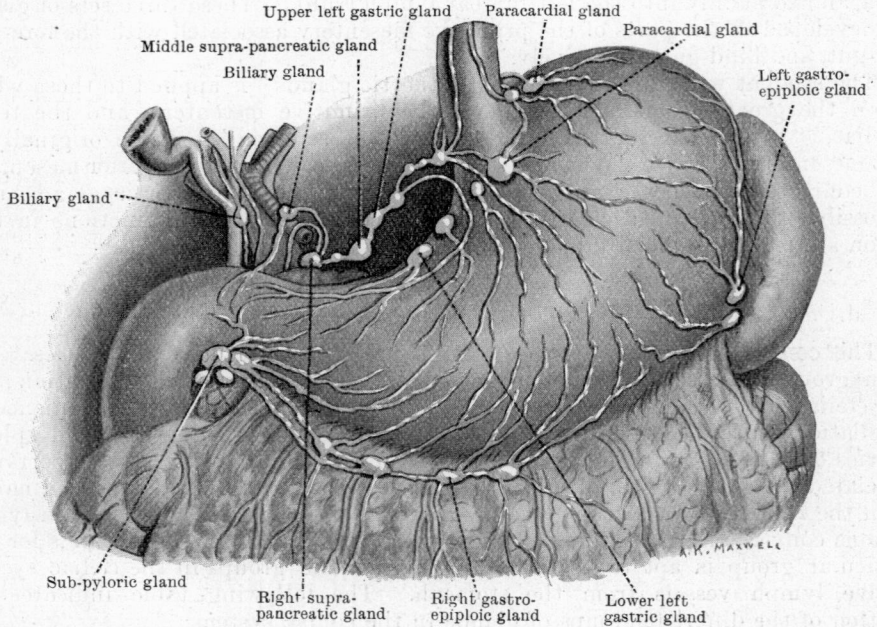

Upper left gastric gland Paracardial gland Paracardial gland

Middle supra-pancreatic gland

Biliary gland

Left gastro-epiploic gland

Biliary gland

Sub-pyloric gland

Right supra-pancreatic gland

Right gastro-epiploic gland

Lower left gastric gland

A. K. MAXWELL

FIG. 1093.—LYMPH VESSELS AND LYMPH GLANDS OF THE STOMACH (Jamieson and Dobson, redrawn).

stem of the hepatic artery and are continuous in various directions with the following subgroups.

The **hepatic** and **biliary lymph glands** form a continuous chain which runs along the ascending part of the stem of the artery as far as the porta hepatis and downwards behind the duodenum and head of the pancreas with the bile duct ; a constant member of this group lies in the curve of the neck of the gall-bladder— the **cystic lymph gland**. The lower end of this chain receives *afferents* from the head of pancreas, the back of the duodenum, and a few from the pyloric end of the stomach ; the upper members of the chain (hepatic glands) receive numerous afferent vessels from the liver (lower margin of the parietal surface and the whole of the visceral surface), and from the gall-bladder and the bile ducts. The *efferents* end in the right supra-pancreatic group.

The **sub-pyloric lymph glands** form an important group which lies on the head of the pancreas below the beginning of the duodenum, and after a short interval is continued in a chain of single glands in the course of the right gastro-epiploic artery between the layers of the great omentum—**right gastro-epiploic lymph glands** [Lg. gastricae inferiores]. These glands together drain the lower part of the pyloric portion of the stomach, and the sub-pyloric *efferents* run in various directions, some to the nearest main group—the superior mesenteric root glands, some obliquely over the pancreas to the middle supra-pancreatic group, and some to the right supra-pancreatic glands (Fig. 1094).

The **supra-pyloric lymph glands** are a small group found in the lesser omentum along the right gastric branch of the hepatic artery ; they interrupt a few vessels from the pyloric canal, and send *efferents* to the right supra-pancreatic group.

The *efferent* vessels of the middle and right supra-pancreatic glands combine with the superior mesenteric ultimate efferents to form the single or multiple *gastro-intestinal trunk.* Some efferent vessels pass to communicate with glands in the superior mesenteric and aortic groups.

The **superior mesenteric system of lymph glands** extends into the primitive mesentery of the mid-gut loop, and the glands belonging to it are scattered along the stem of the artery and all its branches as far as the intestinal wall. Little

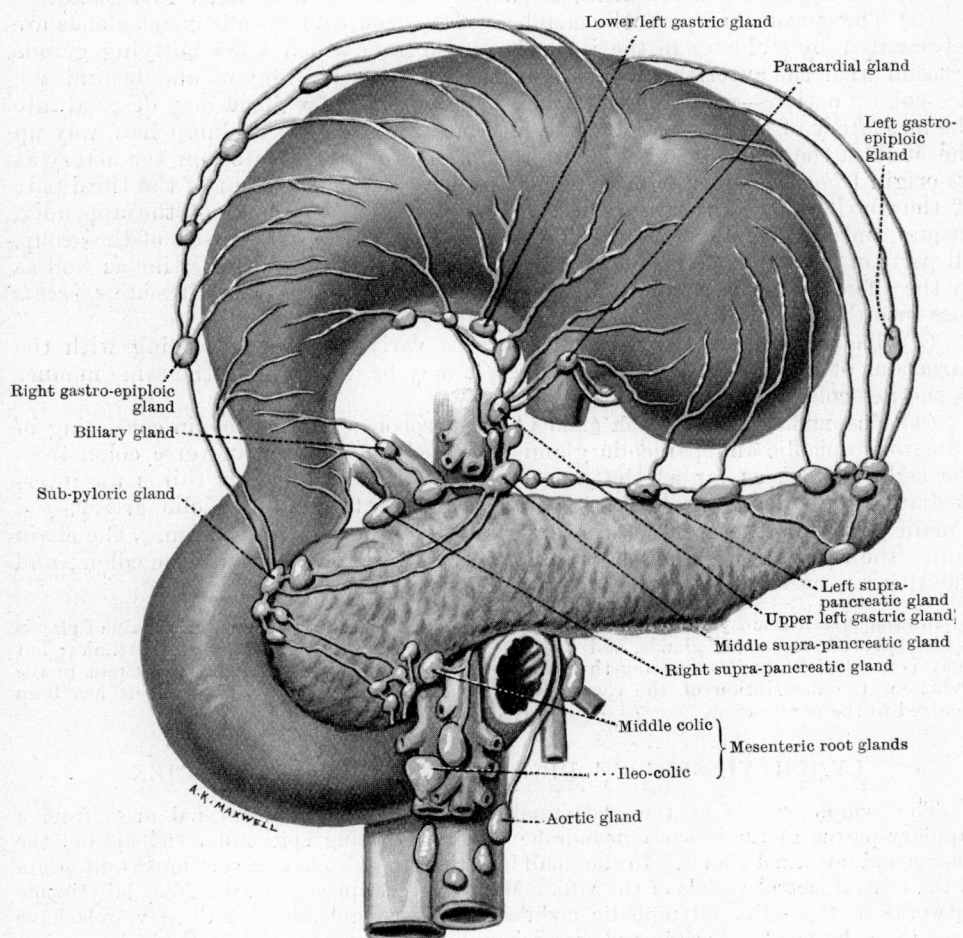

Lower left gastric gland

Paracardial gland

Left gastro-
epiploic
gland

Right gastro-epiploic
gland

Biliary gland

Sub-pyloric gland

Left supra-
pancreatic gland
Upper left gastric gland
Middle supra-pancreatic gland
Right supra-pancreatic gland

Middle colic
Mesenteric root glands
Ileo-colic

Aortic gland

A·K·MAXWELL

FIG. 1094.—LYMPH VESSELS AND LYMPH GLANDS OF POSTERIOR SURFACE OF STOMACH. The Stomach has been turned upwards to show the Supra-Pancreatic and other Groups of Glands. (Jamieson and Dobson, redrawn.)

order can be introduced by descriptive grouping, but it is customary to indicate the following subdivisions: (*a*) mesenteric root glands; (*b*) subsidiary chains with the branches of the artery—(1) the glands of the mesentery, (2) ileo-colic group, (3) right colic group, (4) middle colic group.

(*a*) The **mesenteric root glands** are large and numerous, clustered round the stems of the main blood vessels as they lie in front of the duodenum and the head of the pancreas. They receive the ultimate efferents of all the subsidiary groups as well as some efferents from the sub-pyloric glands and direct afferents from the head of the pancreas and the duodenum, and also some efferents from the upper left colic group (see p. 1324).

(*b*) In the subsidiary groups related to the drainage of the large intestine the same arrangement obtains as in the inferior mesenteric group (p. 1319). Some glands lie on the intestinal wall (*epicolic*), some along the arcades of the colic vessels (*paracolic*) and some form irregular chains along the colic vessels and tend to group themselves into *intermediate* and *main* sets. There is no such regular order in the lymph glands of the mesentery.

(1) The **lymph glands of the mesentery** (100-200 in number) are scattered in the fatty tissue of the mesentery without order : they receive the *afferent* vessels from the jejunum and the ileum (excepting the lowest few inches); the *efferents* pass from gland to gland and the ultimate efferents enter the mesenteric root glands.

(2) The epicolic and paracolic members of the group of **ileo-colic lymph glands** are represented by a cluster in the ileo-colic angle from which a few outlying glands descend with the anterior and posterior cæcal vessels in front of and behind the ileo-colic junction—**cæcal lymph glands**. One **appendicular gland** may descend into the mesentery of the appendix. The intermediate group is a clump half way up the stem of the ileo-colic artery, and the main group is situated on the artery at its origin from the superior mesenteric, and may lie on the front of the third part of the duodenum. The vessels of the lower end of the ileum, of the appendix, cæcum, and lower end of the ascending colon form the *afferent* vessels of the group, all parts of the chain being entered by direct vessels from the intestine as well as by the efferent vessels of the earlier members of the chain. The ultimate *efferents* pass into the mesenteric root glands.

(3) The **right colic lymph glands** form a variable group according with the variations of the artery. When distinct, it may be described in the same manner as the ileo-colic group.

(4) The **middle colic lymph glands** [Lg. mesocolicæ] form a chain consisting of numerous epicolic and paracolic glands disposed along the transverse colon from the right flexure as far as the junction of its middle and left thirds, an intermediate group about the point of bifurcation of the middle colic artery, and a main group on the stem of the artery as it enters the mesocolon. The chain drains the right flexure and the proximal two-thirds of the transverse colon ; and the ultimate *efferents* enter the mesenteric root glands.

Inferior Mesenteric Lymph Glands.—As already noted, the inferior mesenteric chain of glands is blended with the aortic glands, and its vessels contribute to the lumbar lymph trunks ; but as it is convenient to describe together all the lymph vessels of the digestive system in the abdomen, the description of the course of the inferior mesenteric lymph vessels has been deferred to the next section.

LYMPH VESSELS OF DIGESTIVE SYSTEM IN ABDOMEN

The lymph vessels of the abdominal part of the alimentary canal arise from a capillary plexus in the mucous membrane under the lining epithelium and around the gastric and intestinal glands. In the small intestine they also have a very important origin in the central lacteal vessels of the villi. Many vessels appear to arise from labyrinthic networks in the solitary lymphatic nodules, but it is probable that these vessels have come from the plexus of origin and are broken up in the solitary nodules—which are thus lymph glands in miniature. The lymph vessels from the mucous membrane perforate the muscular coats, between which they communicate freely, and on emerging are joined by the tributaries from the subserous network : they then pass away with the blood-vessels. In the small intestine they may run longitudinally on the surface for some inches before turning into the mesentery. The vessels are not all trapped by the glands nearest the wall of the alimentary canal ; from all parts of the canal many run directly to glands at any point along the course of the blood-vessels.

Lymph Vessels of Large Intestine.—In the area of distribution of the inferior mesenteric artery, the lymph vessels of the large intestine pass to the epicolic, paracolic, and intermediate and main groups of glands associated with the branches of the artery. Those which follow the inferior left colic arteries from the **descending** and **pelvic colon** are joined by the stream which passes upwards from the rectum on the superior rectal [hæmorrhoidal] artery (p. 1317). The lymph drainage from the *left third* of the **transverse colon** and the **left flexure** must be specially mentioned because the vessels, none of which are "direct vessels" beyond the intermediate gland group, divide at that group (Fig. 1095) and follow two paths—one leading along the superior left colic artery to the inferior mesenteric main group on the left side of the aorta, the other along the curve of the inferior mesenteric vein to the superior mesenteric root glands. Some small peritoneal lymph vessels from the flexure run up in the greater omentum and thence through the gastro-splenic ligament to the glands at the hilum of the spleen.   The vessels from the *right two-thirds* of the **transverse colon** and from the *right flexure* run to the middle colic group; from the upper and middle parts of the **ascending colon** to the right colic group; from the lower part of the ascending colon, **cæcum, appendix,** and **end of the ileum** to the ileo-colic group.   The course of the lymph vessels from the cæcum and appendix is shown from the front in Fig. 1095, and is specially illustrated from behind in Fig. 1096.   Many collecting vessels leave the appendix and enter its mesentery where they unite to form four or five main lymph vessels.   These follow the appendicular

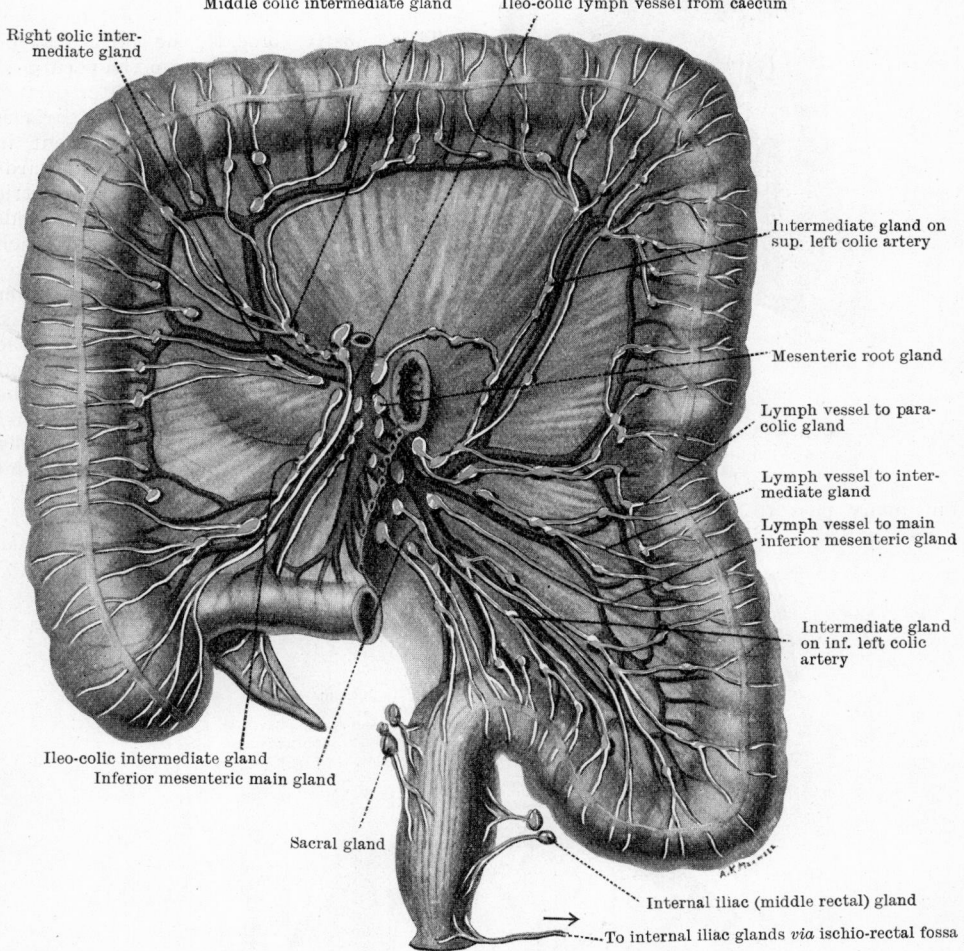

FIG. 1095.—LYMPH VESSELS AND GLANDS OF THE LARGE INTESTINE (Jamieson and Dobson, redrawn).

blood-vessels behind the lower end of the ileum and end in glands along the whole length of the ileo-colic chain.

Lymph Vessels of Small Intestine.—From the lower end of the ileum to the duodeno-jejunal flexure—**ileum** and **jejunum**—the lymph vessels run to the glands of the mesentery.   From the lower half of the **duodenum** the vessels run directly to the mesenteric root glands, from the upper half to the sub-pyloric glands in front and to the biliary glands behind.

Lymph Vessels of Stomach.—These run in three streams: (*a*) from the front and back of the fundus and body over an area indicated by a line (nearer the greater than the lesser curvature) from the fundus to the pyloric canal, to the left gastric glands; (*b*) from the area below the line as far as the angular notch, to the splenic and left supra-pancreatic glands; (*c*) from the pyloric canal, by vessels descending to the right gastro-epiploic and sub-pyloric glands, and upwards in the right end of the lesser omentum to the supra-pyloric glands, lower members of the biliary chain and the right supra-pancreatic glands (Figs. 1093, 1094).

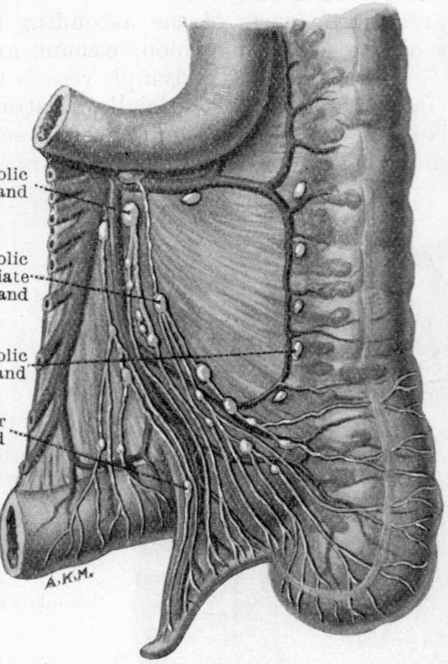

Lymph Vessels of Pancreas.—The pancreas is drained by vessels which enter the supra-pancreatic glands above, the superior mesenteric root glands below, and the aortic glands behind.

Lymph Vessels of Liver. — Interlobular collecting vessels are formed from capillaries in the lobules of the liver. They mostly come to the surface at innumerable points and form the peritoneal lymph vessels. From the greater part of the right, superior, and anterior surfaces they run to the falciform ligament in large numbers, enter it, turn upwards and pass along the superior epigastric blood-vessels into the retro-sternal glands (see p. 1327). Those from the lower inch or so of the right and anterior surfaces turn round the lower edge of the liver and sweep towards the porta hepatis, where they pick up the vessels of the visceral surface and the **gall-bladder,** and a deep stream of vessels from the interior of the liver, some of which end in the hepatic glands of the porta. They pass into the lesser omentum and descend in it to end in the biliary chain of glands;

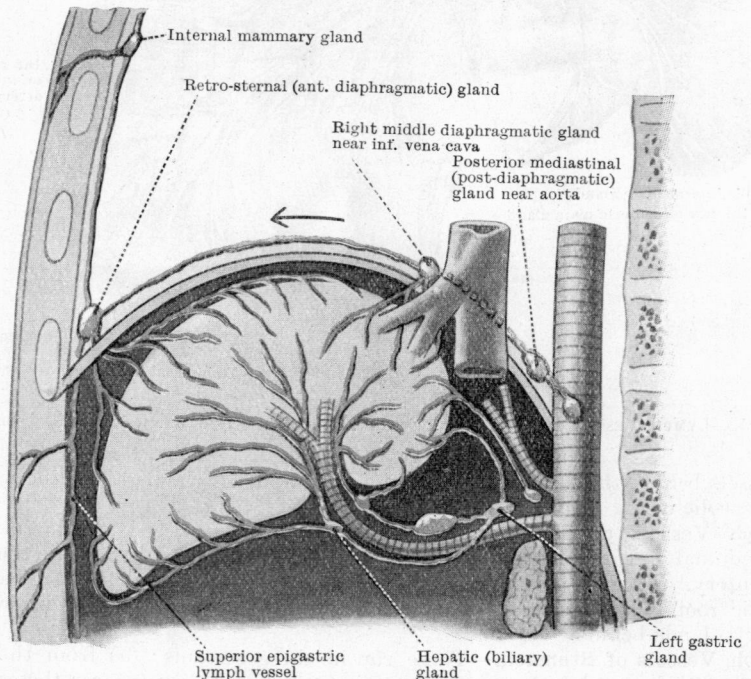

Ileo-colic main gland

Ileo-colic intermediate gland

Paracolic gland

Appendicular gland

A.K.M.

FIG. 1096.—LYMPH VESSELS AND GLANDS OF THE CÆCUM AND APPENDIX FROM BEHIND (Jamieson and Dobson, redrawn).

but many pass to the left to reach the left gastric glands. Other vessels emerge from the back of the liver and follow the right phrenic vessels to the cœliac

Internal mammary gland

Retro-sternal (ant. diaphragmatic) gland

Right middle diaphragmatic gland near inf. vena cava

Posterior mediastinal (post-diaphragmatic) gland near aorta

Superior epigastric lymph vessel

Hepatic (biliary) gland

Left gastric gland

FIG. 1097.—DIAGRAMMATIC SAGITTAL SECTION SHOWING THE LYMPH DRAINAGE OF THE LIVER.

glands. Deep vessels, from the interior of the liver in the region of the main hepatic veins, emerge with these veins and pass up with the inferior vena cava to middle diaphragmatic glands in the thorax (see below).   It will be noted that there are two main lymph currents from the liver—one ultimately passing into the cisterna, the other *via* the internal mammary route to the mediastinal trunks of both sides (Fig. 1097).

Lymph Vessels of Spleen.—The vessels of the spleen pass to the splenic lymph glands, which lie near the hilum of the spleen, and to the left supra-pancreatic lymph glands.

INTERCOSTAL AND MEDIASTINAL LYMPH TRUNKS

There are numerous lymph trunks in the thorax.   A large **mediastinal lymph trunk** [tr. bronchomediastinalis] is the chief pathway of both the parietal and visceral lymph vessels; it receives the efferents of the glands associated with the internal mammary artery as well as those situated in the mediastinum.   It may unite in various ways with other trunks in the root of the neck (see pp. 1309, 1310), but usually opens separately into the corresponding innominate vein.

In addition to the *descending intercostal lymph trunks,* there are a number of independent **intercostal lymph trunks** which join the thoracic duct directly (see below and p. 1309).   The thoracic duct receives directly a number of efferent vessels from posterior mediastinal lymph glands also.

Lymph Glands of the Thorax

The groups of lymph glands in the thorax are (*a*) intercostal, (*b*) diaphragmatic, (*c*) posterior mediastinal, (*d*) internal mammary, (*e*) innominate, and (*f*) tracheo-bronchial.

The **intercostal lymph glands** are small nodules (1 or 2) situated in the vertebral end of each intercostal space in series with the lateral lumbar glands.   They receive *afferents* from (*a*) the parietal pleura of the posterior thoracic wall; (*b*) vessels which accompany the intercostal arteries, mainly derived from the costo-vertebral and intervertebral synovial joints, and such cutaneous vessels from the posterior and lateral chest wall as have penetrated deeply with the posterior and lateral cutaneous blood vessels.

The *efferents* of the glands of the upper six or seven spaces run independently to the thoracic duct on both sides.   Those of the glands of the lower four or five spaces join on each side to form a **descending intercostal trunk** which, after receiving the efferents of the glands in the lowest part of the posterior mediastinum, passes through the aortic opening to enter the upper part of the cisterna chyli.

The **posterior mediastinal lymph glands**, few and variable, lie around the lower thoracic part of the œsophagus.   They receive *afferents* from the œsophagus, the back of the pericardium and the back of diaphragm, on which their lowest members rest.   Their *efferents* pass directly to the thoracic duct and to the descending intercostal lymph trunks; and they are connected above with the paratracheal glands.

The **diaphragmatic lymph glands** (Figs. 1097, 1098) may be subdivided into: (1) a *posterior* group, better considered as the lowest members of the posterior mediastinal group; (2) an *anterior* group better considered under the name "retro-sternal" as part of the internal mammary chain; (3) a *middle* group, which on the left side is found as a small cluster around the phrenic nerve as it enters the diaphragm.   The middle diaphragmatic glands receive *afferents* from the lateral portion of the diaphragm, and send *efferents* forwards to the retro-sternal and backwards to the lower posterior mediastinal glands.   On the right side the group is larger, lies in near relation to the inferior vena cava, and receives in addition a certain number of afferents from the liver which issue with the hepatic venous trunks (p. 1326).

The **retro-sternal lymph glands** (Fig. 1098) are the lowest members of the internal mammary chain and consist of a number (3-6) of relatively large glands situated on the sternal and costal origins of the diaphragm behind the base of the xiphoid process and seventh costal cartilages.   Their *afferents* are the lower anterior intercostal lymph vessels, vessels from the front of the pericardium and the anterior part of the diaphragm, and a very large stream which accompanies the superior epigastric blood-vessels not only from the perforating lymph vessels of the anterior abdominal wall (few) but a liberal stream of vessels which pass from the upper and anterior surfaces of the liver through the falciform ligament and account for the number and size of the retro-sternal group of glands. The *efferents* pass up to the next group.

The **internal mammary lymph glands** [Lg. sternales] (Fig. 1098) form a chain consisting of one or two glands in each of the upper four intercostal spaces close to the sternum: they receive the efferents of the retro-sternal glands and the lymph vessels which accompany the intercostal and perforating branches of

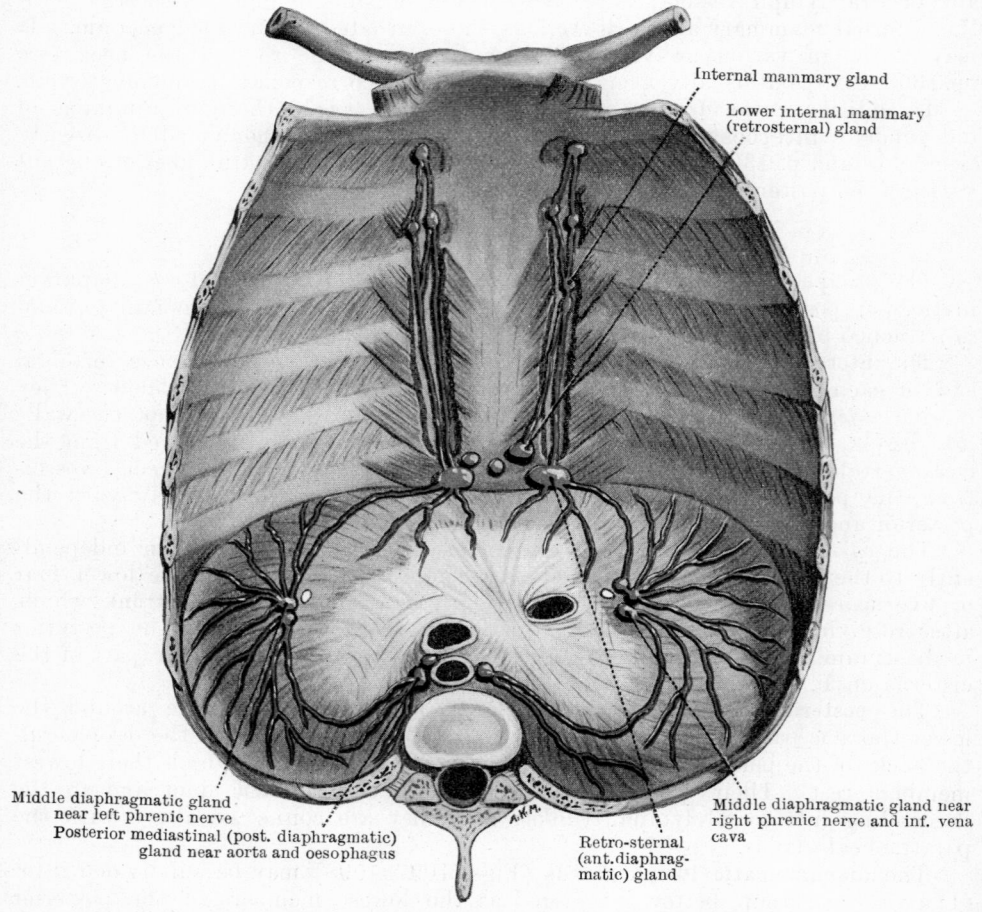

Internal mammary gland

Lower internal mammary (retrosternal) gland

Middle diaphragmatic gland near left phrenic nerve

Posterior mediastinal (post. diaphragmatic) gland near aorta and oesophagus

Retro-sternal (ant.diaphragmatic) gland

Middle diaphragmatic gland near right phrenic nerve and inf. vena cava

FIG. 1098.—INTERNAL MAMMARY AND DIAPHRAGMATIC LYMPH GLANDS FROM BEHIND.
The Lymph Drainage of the Thoracic Surface of the Diaphragm is shown also.

the internal mammary artery. These vessels require special mention: the anterior intercostal afferents of the internal mammary chain drain the parietal pleura almost as far back as the angles of the ribs; and along the perforating arteries some cutaneous lymph vessels come from the skin of the mamma and from the stroma of the medial part of the mammary gland. Hence the great surgical importance of the internal mammary chain.

The *efferents* of the internal mammary glands usually join to form a single vessel which unites with the efferents of the tracheo-bronchial and innominate glands to form the mediastinal lymph trunk. An *internal mammary trunk* may also open independently into the veins (see p. 1310).

The lymph glands associated with the pulmonary system and the heart lie in the superior and middle mediastina. A rather irregular arrangement may be reduced for descriptive purposes to the following scheme :—(*a*) Glands of the roots of the lungs: (1) Broncho-pulmonary; (2) Inferior tracheo-bronchial; (3) Superior tracheo-bronchial. (*b*) Paratracheal glands; (*c*) Innominate glands.

The **broncho-pulmonary lymph glands** are embedded in the hilum of the lung and in the intervals between the pulmonary vessels and the bronchus as they enter the root. Small outlying *pulmonary glands* may be found on the larger bronchi in the substance of the lung.

The **inferior tracheo-bronchial lymph glands** are situated in the angle of bifurcation of the trachea, and unite the other groups of glands of the two sides.

The **superior tracheo-bronchial lymph glands** are continuous with the upper broncho-pulmonary glands in the open angle between the trachea and the bronchus on each side.

The glands of the root of the lung receive on each side the lymph vessels of the lung (including the visceral pleura), and from the bronchi and lower end of the trachea ; and vessels from the left side of the heart end in the inferior tracheo-bronchial group. Their *efferents* pass upwards on the trachea.

The **paratracheal lymph glands** extend upwards along each side of the trachea into the neck. They drain the trachea and the corresponding part of the œsophagus.

The **innominate lymph glands** [Lg. mediastinales anteriores] are a few small glands scattered in the superior mediastinum in the vicinity of the innominate veins and the aortic arch.

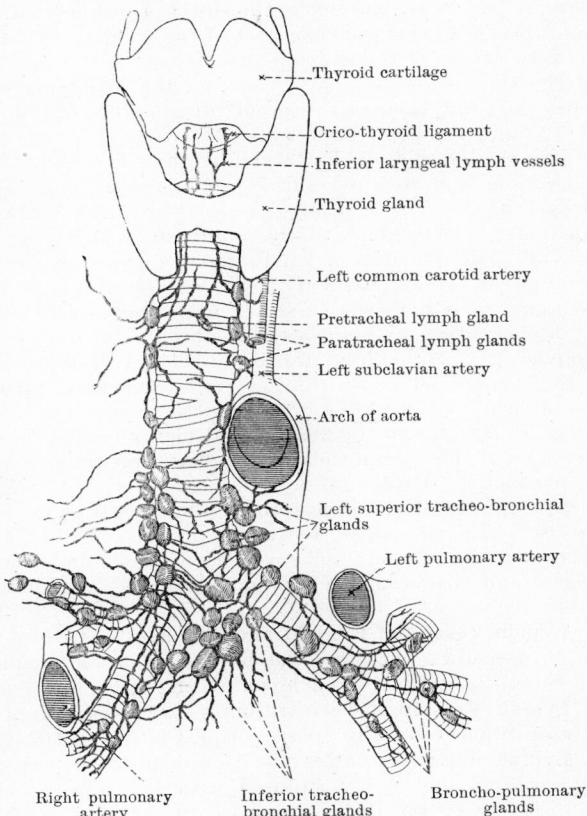

Thyroid cartilage

Crico-thyroid ligament

Inferior laryngeal lymph vessels

Thyroid gland

Left common carotid artery

Pretracheal lymph gland
Paratracheal lymph glands
Left subclavian artery

Arch of aorta

Left superior tracheo-bronchial glands

Left pulmonary artery

Right pulmonary artery   Inferior tracheo-bronchial glands   Broncho-pulmonary glands

Fig. 1099.—The Glands in relation to the Trachea and the Main Bronchi.

They receive lymph vessels from the thymus and the upper part of the pericardium, and also from the right side of the heart.

The ultimate *efferents* of all these lymph glands unite to form a single vessel on each side of the trachea which usually joins the single efferent of the internal mammary glands to form the **mediastinal lymph trunk**. This trunk usually enters the front of the junction of the subclavian and internal jugular veins, but the left trunk may join the thoracic duct and the right may join the jugular or the subclavian lymph trunk or unite with them to form a right lymphatic duct (see pp. 1309, 1310).

LYMPH VESSELS OF THE DIAPHRAGM AND THORAX

Lymph Vessels of Diaphragm (Fig. 1098).—An extensive lymph plexus is present on each surface—abdominal and thoracic—of the diaphragm. The subserous parts of the plexuses (beneath the parts of the diaphragm covered by peritoneum and pleura) are most voluminous, but on each surface of the middle lobe of the central tendon the plexus is very scanty or absent. The two plexuses are united by numerous vessels that pierce the diaphragm, and many of the collecting vessels from the anterior part of the abdominal surface also pierce the diaphragm to join with vessels from the thoracic surface on their way to the retro-sternal (anterior diaphragmatic) lymph glands. From the lateral and posterior parts of the abdominal surface vessels may take a similar course through the diaphragm to reach the middle diaphragmatic glands, and a comparatively small number follow the course of the phrenic arteries to end in upper aortic glands on the crura of the diaphragm.

Lymph vessels from the thoracic surface of the diaphragm run in three directions to glands situated within the thorax : (1) from the anterior part to the retro-sternal lymph glands ; (2) from the lateral part to the middle diaphragmatic glands ; and (3) from the posterior part of the surface to the posterior mediastinal (posterior diaphragmatic) glands. Some vessels of the posterior part of the thoracic surface may pierce the diaphragm and run with vessels of the abdominal surface to aortic glands.

The lymph vessels that pass from the abdominal surface of the diaphragm to the middle and anterior (retro-sternal) diaphragmatic lymph glands are in communication with lymph vessels of the liver.

Lymph Vessels of Parietal Pleura.—The parietal pleura is drained by vessels which issue from its outer surface and form larger collecting vessels in the extra-pleural areolar tissue. The collecting vessels from the **costal pleura** in general run in two directions—backwards with the intercostal blood vessels to the intercostal glands, and forwards to the retro-sternal and internal mammary glands. But vessels from the pleural lining of the axillary parts of the second and third intercostal spaces usually—and from the fourth and fifth spaces sometimes—pierce the intercostal muscles and emerge with the lateral cutaneous branches of the intercostal nerves to end in axillary lymph glands (Rouvière). Vessels from the costal pleura of the first space run upwards through the thoracic inlet and end with those of the **cervical pleura** in lower deep cervical glands. One of them may cross the first rib with the subclavian vein and end in an apical axillary gland. Vessels from the **mediastinal pleura** pass to the tracheo-bronchial and mediastinal glands ; and those from the **diaphragmatic pleura** run with the vessels of the corresponding parts of the diaphragm.

Lymph Vessels of Lungs and Pulmonary Pleura.—Each lung possesses a plexus of vessels on the bronchial tree as far as the smallest bronchioles : there are no lymph vessels on the alveoli. The vessels of the pulmonary (visceral) pleura penetrate the lung to join the bronchial lymph vessels, and all emerge at the hilum and end in the glands of the root.

Lymph Vessels of Bronchi and Trachea.—The bronchi and the intrathoracic part of the trachea drain into the lymph glands that lie around them in the roots of the lungs and the mediastinum—broncho-pulmonary, tracheo-bronchial, and paratracheal.

Lymph Vessels of Pericardium.—The pericardium drains into the nearest glands in front of and behind it—posterior mediastinal, retro-sternal, innominate.

Lymph Vessels of Heart.—A wide-meshed plexus of minute vessels under the endocardium—not to be confused with the injected sheath of the Purkinje network, see p. 1150 and Fig. 999—gives rise to efferents which pierce the myocardium to join others from the richer plexus under the epicardium. The subepicardial plexus of the ventricles is easily injected, but on the atria the plexus is relatively scanty and not easily demonstrated. In consequence, the destination of the lymph vessels of the **atria** is not well known ; only a few seem to pass into the atrio-ventricular groove and join the vessels of the ventricles ; it is probable that the chief drainage is from the upper parts of the atria to tracheo-bronchial glands. The collecting vessels from the **ventricles** pass into the atrio-ventricular groove and follow the coronary arteries towards their origin. Those associated with the right coronary artery usually form a single trunk which passes upwards in front of the ascending aorta to the innominate glands ; those associated with the left coronary artery (draining a part of the right ventricle, as well as the whole of the left) also usually end in a single vessel which passes on the left of and behind the pulmonary trunk to one or other of the tracheo-bronchial glands—usually a member of the right superior group (Shore).

Lymph Vessels of Œsophagus.—The œsophagus is drained into different groups of lymph glands according to the situation of its parts. Its lymph vessels run (a) from the *abdominal part* to the left gastric glands, (b) from the *lower thoracic part* to the posterior mediastinal glands, and (c) from the *upper thoracic* and *cervical parts* to the paratracheal glands with the vessels of the trachea.

Lymph Vessels of Thymus.—The thymus sends vessels to the innominate glands and to the internal mammary glands of both sides.

SUBCLAVIAN LYMPH TRUNKS

The area of drainage of the **subclavian lymph trunk** comprises the upper limb and a cutaneous area of the trunk extending from the umbilical plane to the level of the clavicle in front and half-way up the neck behind; the vessels of the mammary gland also are included. The subclavian trunk ends in a variety of ways (see p. 1310), but very often it enters the corresponding subclavian vein directly.

SUPERFICIAL AND DEEP LYMPH GLANDS OF UPPER LIMB

The glands in the territory of the subclavian lymph trunk comprise a few superficial glands and a greater number of deep glands including the important axillary group.

The **superficial glands** are (*a*) supra-trochlear, (*b*) infra-clavicular (including delto-pectoral and inter-pectoral): the **deep glands** are (*a*) small and inconstant nodules in the cubital fossa and on the upper parts of the arteries of the forearm, (*b*) brachial, (*c*) axillary.

Superficial Lymph Glands of Upper Limb.—The **supra-trochlear lymph glands** [Lg. cubitales superficiales] (1-2) are found on the medial side of the basilic vein a little above the medial epicondyle of the humerus: they receive *afferents* from the fingers and hand on the medial side of the mid-finger line and from a strip on the ulnar side of the forearm: their *efferents* join the deep stream along the basilic vein.

The **infra-clavicular lymph glands** (1-2) lie in the infra-clavicular fossa on the upper end of the cephalic vein and drain some vessels from the skin of the "vaccination area" and of the shoulder, and from the upper part of the mammary gland: their *efferents* perforate the clavi-pectoral fascia to join the apical axillary glands. Outlying members of this group are found in two situations. A **delto-pectoral lymph gland** is occasionally found in the groove between the deltoid and the pectoralis major muscles. It receives *afferents* from the skin of the lateral part of the upper arm and of the shoulder, and gives *efferents* to the infra-clavicular glands and to the subclavian trunk. Small, more deeply placed, **inter-pectoral lymph glands** are sometimes found between the great and small pectoral muscles. They lie in the path of the lymph vessels which pass from the upper part of the mammary gland to the infra-clavicular glands (Fig. 1100).

Deep Lymph Glands of Upper Limb.—The **deep lymph glands of the forearm** are small, inconstant, immature nodules on the radial, ulnar, and interosseous arteries and in the cubital fossa; they interrupt a few of the deep lymph vessels. The **brachial lymph glands** are merely outlying members of the axillary glands found occasionally along the upper part of the brachial artery. The *efferents* of all these glands pass to the lateral axillary group.

The **axillary lymph glands** are very numerous and widely distributed in the axillary fatty tissue. They may be divided into groups below and above the pectoralis minor tendon. The lower group is subdivided into (*a*) lateral, (*b*) pectoral, (*c*) subscapular, (*d*) central. The upper group is called (*e*) apical.

The **lateral axillary glands** lie in the fatty tissue along the axillary vein. From this group the **anterior** or **pectoral** and the **posterior** or **subscapular glands** radiate along the lower border of the pectoralis minor on the chest wall with the lateral thoracic artery, and along the lateral border of the scapula with the subscapular artery. The **central group** is composed of loose members of the former three groups; they lie under the axillary fascia, and one of them frequently projects through an opening in that fascia.

The *afferents* of the lower axillary glands are (*a*) the deep vessels of the whole limb, (*b*) the cutaneous vessels of the limb and trunk above the umbilical plane, (*c*) the vessels of the mammary gland. It must be noted that all the sub-groups of the axillary glands receive vessels from all these sources. The **apical axillary glands** are in continuity with the lateral group and receive the efferents of all the lower groups and of the infra-clavicular glands. They are also in continuity with the lateral lower deep cervical glands (see p. 1337), so that some of the lymph from the axilla may go through these glands to the jugular lymph trunk; but their *efferents* go mainly to form the **subclavian lymph trunk**, which enters inde-

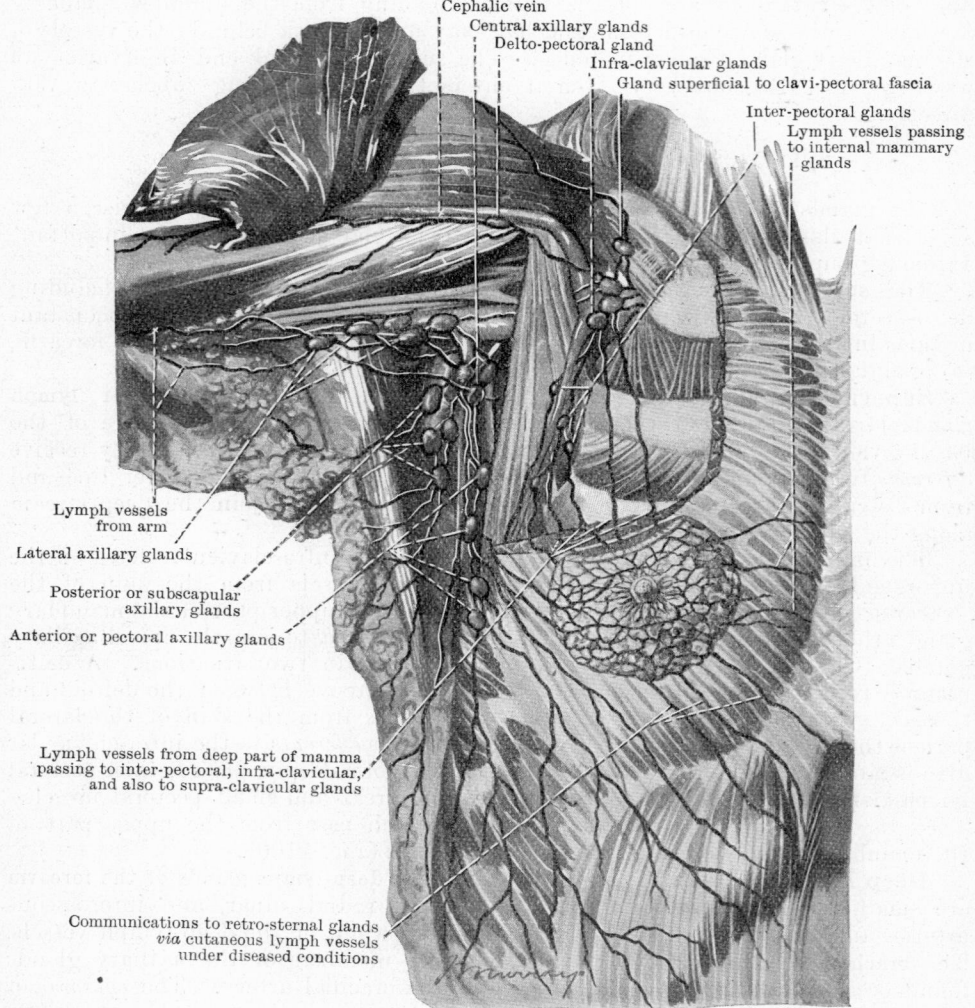

Cephalic vein
Central axillary glands
Delto-pectoral gland
Infra-clavicular glands
Gland superficial to clavi-pectoral fascia

Inter-pectoral glands
Lymph vessels passing
to internal mammary
glands

Lymph vessels
from arm
Lateral axillary glands

Posterior or subscapular
axillary glands

Anterior or pectoral axillary glands

Lymph vessels from deep part of mamma
passing to inter-pectoral, infra-clavicular,
and also to supra-clavicular glands

Communications to retro-sternal glands
via cutaneous lymph vessels
under diseased conditions

FIG. 1100.—DISSECTION OF AXILLA AND ANTERIOR PART OF THORACIC WALL, SHOWING LYMPH GLANDS
AND VESSELS. (Semi-diagrammatic.)

pendently into the junction of the great veins or may join the thoracic duct on the left side or unite with either the jugular or the mediastinal trunk or with both on the right side.

SUPERFICIAL LYMPH VESSELS OF UPPER LIMB AND TRUNK

The **superficial lymph vessels of the subclavian trunk territory** must be considered as a whole, those of the upper limb being taken with those of the trunk above the umbilicus (including the mammary gland).

The **superficial lymph vessels of the upper limb** begin in a rich cutaneous plexus from which vessels stream upwards irrespective of the veins. On the front of the forearm they run almost parallel to one another but with an inclination towards the axilla, and they are reinforced by vessels that slope upwards and forwards from the back of the limb round its margins. As they ascend into the upper arm some vessels on the medial side are interrupted by the supra-trochlear glands, and some pass through the deep fascia with the basilic vein to join the deep stream; but nearly all run to the axilla before they pierce the deep fascia. The vessels from the front and back of the upper arm become more and more horizontal as they join the main stream, and some take a descending course from the front and back of the shoulder region (Figs. 1101, 1102). On the back

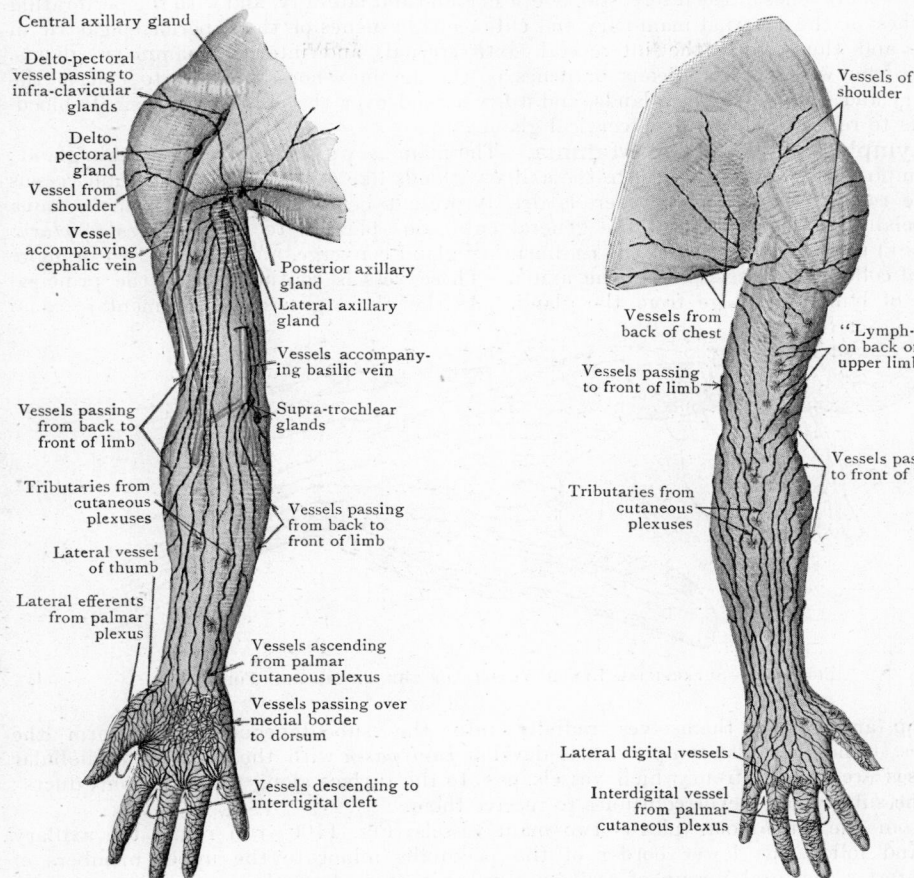

FIG. 1101.—SUPERFICIAL LYMPH VESSELS AND GLANDS OF FRONT OF UPPER LIMB.

FIG. 1102.—SUPERFICIAL LYMPH VESSELS OF BACK OF UPPER LIMB.

of the upper arm and of the elbow there is a "lymph-shed" from which vessels pass round the lateral and medial margins to the front. A few vessels from the skin over the upper part of the cephalic vein follow that vein to the infra-clavicular glands, and may be interrupted in delto-pectoral glands.

The cutaneous plexuses are finest and most dense on the palmar surfaces of the fingers and hand. The efferents from the palmar digital plexus of each finger pass to the dorsum of the digit. There they unite to form dorsal digital vessels, 2-4, which run to the dorsum of the hand, where they unite together to form new vessels.

The efferents from the palmar plexus of the hand run upwards, downwards, and to the lateral and medial margins of the hand. The lateral efferents, as they turn round the lateral border of the hand, join the efferents of the thumb. The medial efferents turn round the medial border of the hand, and join the efferents of the little finger. The efferents which run upwards are few and variable; when they are present they lie along the line of the median vein of the forearm. The efferents which run downwards pass to the interdigital clefts, where they turn backwards and join the vessels on the dorsum of the hand (Figs. 1101, 1102).

The **superficial lymph vessels of the trunk** are arranged in a great whorl which begins at the shoulder. Behind, the vessels run downwards from the lower part of the neck, horizontally from the scapular region, and upwards from the back above the iliac crest (Fig. 1081), to converge round the posterior fold of the axilla. The vessels from the side of the trunk ascend vertically, whilst those in front gradually incline more and more horizontally until the whorl is completed by the vessels over the upper part of the pectoral region as they descend to curve round the anterior axillary fold (Fig. 1080). The plexus of origin is continuous over the median line, and many of the vessels of one side begin on the other side. There are also several vagrant vessels which penetrate deeply along the cutaneous branches of the intercostal arteries behind and laterally, and with the perforating branches of the internal mammary and cutaneous branches of the superior epigastric in front, and thus reach the intercostal, retro-sternal, and internal mammary glands. Others run with the cutaneous branches of the acromio-thoracic artery to end in the axillary and infra-clavicular glands, and a few ascend over the clavicle with small blood-vessels to reach the lower deep cervical glands.

Lymph Vessels of the Mamma.—The mammary gland is a modified skin gland ; its lymph vessels therefore run to the axillary glands like other cutaneous lymph vessels of the region. In the infant there is already present beneath the areola of the mamma a specially developed part of the general cutaneous plexus ; to this *sub-areolar plexus* (Sappey) the lymph vessels of the rudimentary gland converge, and from it two or more special collecting vessels pass to the axilla. These vessels continue to be the principal route of lymph drainage from the gland. As the gland grows, its rudimentary acini

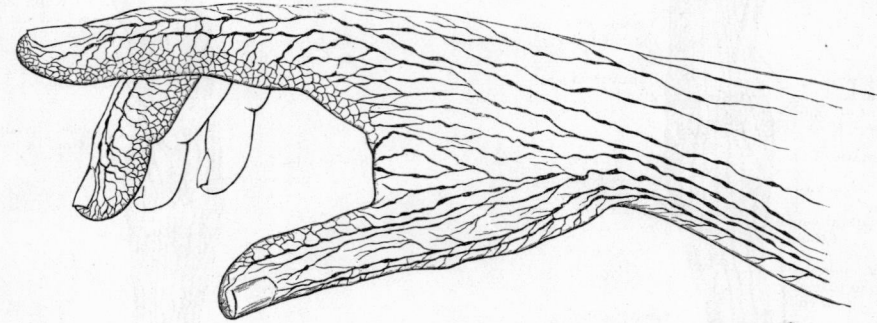

FIG. 1103.—SUPERFICIAL LYMPH VESSELS OF THE THUMB AND FOREFINGER.

develop and thrust themselves radially into the subcutaneous fat to form the lobules. The glandular lymph vessels develop *pari passu* with the lobules ; perilobular plexuses are formed from which vessels pass to the surface along the lactiferous ducts ; and the sub-areolar plexus continues to receive them.

From the sub-areolar plexus two main vessels (Fig. 1100) run round the axillary fold and follow the lower border of the pectoralis minor to the upper members of the anterior (pectoral) group of axillary glands situated along the lateral thoracic vein. The greater part of the mammary gland is drained by this route, but from the peripheral lobules other vessels pass in different directions to other groups of lymph glands. From the lower part of the gland some follow the route taken by the principal vessels to the axilla. They end also in the anterior group of lymph glands ; but it should be noted again that all the sub-groups of axillary lymph glands are interconnected, and that lymph vessels from the mamma may pass *directly* to any sub-group, even to the lateral group along the axillary vein. From the upper part of the gland and from its deep surface vessels run, over or through the pectoral muscles, to the apical axillary lymph glands, either directly or *via* the infra-clavicular group ; some of these vessels are interrupted in the small inter-pectoral lymph glands (see p. 1331). From the medial part of the mammary gland a few vessels pierce the pectoralis major and pass through the anterior ends of the intercostal spaces to reach the internal mammary chain of lymph glands.

The cutaneous vessels must be remembered as an important part of the lymph drainage of the mamma. These are included in the account already given of the superficial lymph vessels of the trunk ; and it should be noted that some of them pass deeply between the lobules of the gland. They may thus appear to issue from its substance and give the impression that the direct drainage from the periphery of the gland is more extensive than it really is. These cutaneous vessels pass to the axillary, infra-clavicular, and internal mammary lymph glands, and a few ascend from the skin of the upper part of the mamma to the lower deep cervical glands. From the skin of the medial part of the mamma, vessels may pass across the median plane to internal mammary and axillary lymph glands of the opposite side. No path has been found from the mamma *via* the superior epigastric vessels to the retro-sternal glands in health ;

but when diseased conditions have spread into the cutaneous plexus below the gland, these lymph glands may be affected (Fig. 1100).

Deep Lymph Vessels of Upper Limb

The **deep lymph vessels of the upper limb** accompany the deeper blood-vessels. Some of the deep lymph vessels of the hand and forearm may be interrupted in the deep glands which are occasionally present in the forearm, but most of them either end in the cubital or brachial glands, or pass directly to the lateral group of axillary glands.

JUGULAR LYMPH TRUNKS

The area of drainage of the **jugular lymph trunk** comprises the head and neck— except the skin of the lower part of the back of the neck—and the parts drained by such deep lymph vessels as may accompany the transverse cervical artery. The trunk is formed by the union of the efferents of the superior and inferior deep cervical lymph glands; the right trunk enters the angle of union of the internal jugular and subclavian veins, and the left trunk joins the thoracic duct.

Lymph Glands of Head and Neck

The arrangement of lymph glands and vessels in the head and neck is less simple than in other parts of the body, and there is some added difficulty of description from the facts that the apical group of axillary glands merges with

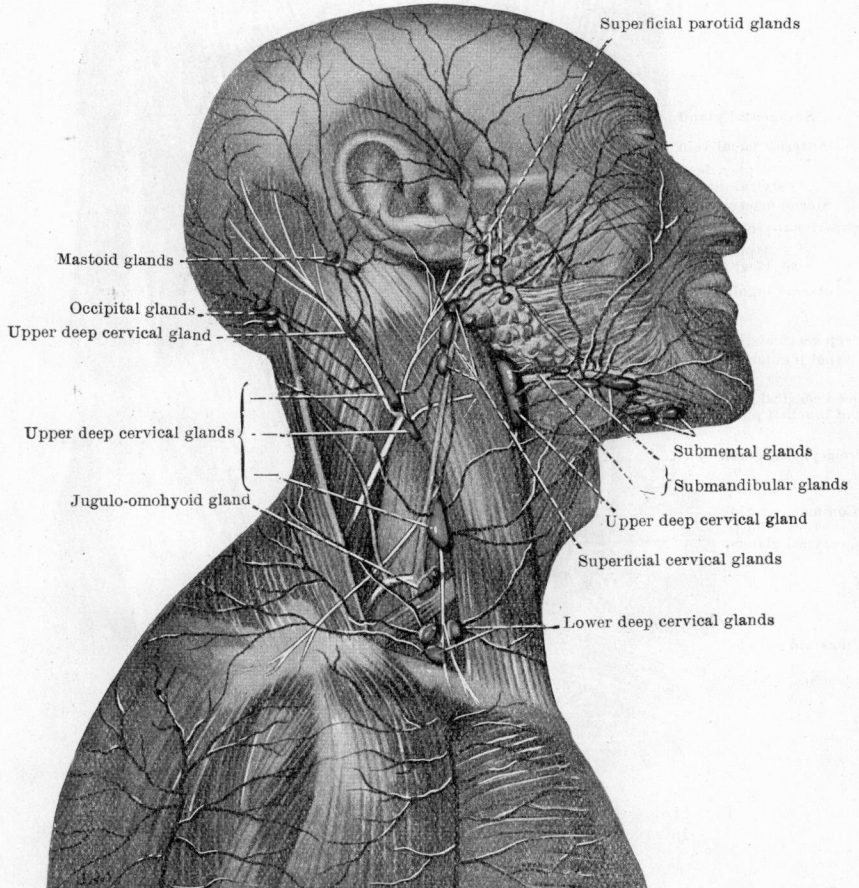

FIG. 1104.—LYMPH GLANDS OF HEAD AND NECK AS SEEN WITH THE STERNO-MASTOID IN POSITION. The occipital, mastoid, and superficial parotid glands are inserted in accordance with descriptions. The other glands were present in one or other of the two bodies from which the drawing was made. Compare Fig. 1106.

the glands in the root of the neck, and that the paratracheal group extends upwards from the thorax into the neck, and sends its upper efferents to join the jugular lymph trunk. Further, the lymph glands of the neck in reality form one continuous group with numerous offshoots. It is convenient, however, in order that a bird's-eye view of the whole system may be obtained, to describe a main chain of glands along the great vessels of the neck and subsidiary groups along the course of the branches of the external carotid artery and on the inferior thyroid artery.

The glands thus arranged are—

(1) Deep cervical glands (jugular chain).

(2) Glands associated with the scalp and face, forming a "collar chain" between the head and the neck: (*a*) occipital; (*b*) mastoid; (*c*) parotid and superficial cervical; (*d*) submandibular with facial glands; (*e*) submental.

(3) Anterior cervical glands: (*a*) infra-hyoid; (*b*) prelaryngeal; (*c*) pretracheal; (*d*) paratracheal.

Deep Cervical Lymph Glands.—The deep cervical lymph glands extend from the base of the skull to the root of the neck, along the path of the great vessels

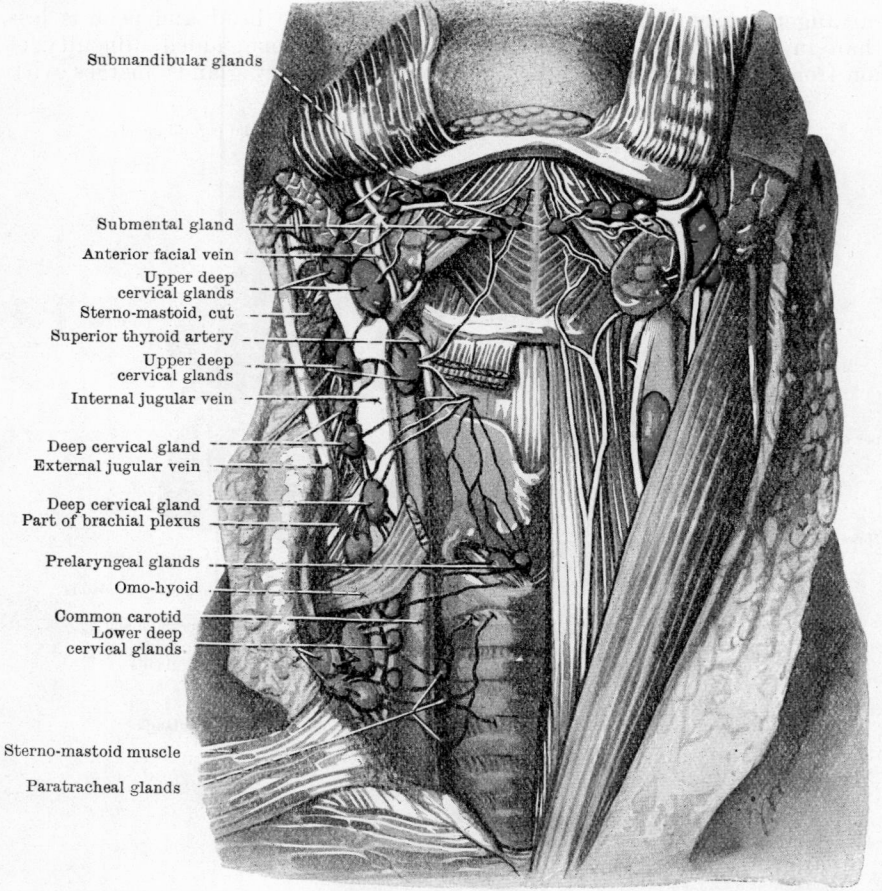

Submandibular glands

Submental gland
Anterior facial vein
Upper deep cervical glands
Sterno-mastoid, cut
Superior thyroid artery
Upper deep cervical glands
Internal jugular vein

Deep cervical gland
External jugular vein

Deep cervical gland
Part of brachial plexus

Prelaryngeal glands
Omo-hyoid

Common carotid
Lower deep cervical glands

Sterno-mastoid muscle

Paratracheal glands

FIG. 1105.—LYMPH GLANDS OF THE NECK SEEN FROM THE FRONT.
Infra-hyoid glands and pretracheal glands were not present.

on each side of the pharynx and gullet. Most of them are concealed by the sterno-mastoid, but the oblique direction of the muscle leaves uncovered the lower end of the chain, which thus invades the lower part of the posterior triangle of the neck. Numerous members also project at the posterior border of the sterno-mastoid and stray backwards into the posterior triangle. When enlarged by disease the row of projecting glands forms an obvious swelling along the posterior border of the sterno-mastoid. It is customary to divide the chain into superior and inferior parts, but only for the same reason as in the axilla—the fact that a muscle (omo-hyoid) crosses the chain. Nevertheless, the chain is continuous: its division into groups is a topographical convenience only. It is likewise convenient to subdivide each part of the chain into medial and lateral groups.

Superior Deep Cervical Lymph Glands.—(1) The *medial group* of upper deep cervical lymph glands lies on the superficial surface of the internal jugular vein and in the carotid triangle of the neck. The highest members of the group are slightly separated from the rest; they are known as **retro-pharyngeal glands,** and lie behind the lateral border of the naso-pharynx on the prevertebral fascia in front of the rectus capitis anterior. They receive *afferents* from the naso-pharynx, the pharyngo-tympanic [auditory] tube and the atlanto-occipital and atlanto-axial joints. Below these a few small **deep parotid lymph glands** are embedded in the deep surface of the parotid salivary gland and even in its substance (see p. 1339). Below the parotid the chain becomes exuberant; its numerous members are mainly associated with the internal jugular vein under the sterno-mastoid; but they stray forwards so as to appear in the anterior triangle of the neck—notably one group, the largest member of which is frequently palpable below the angle of the jaw. This gland lies under the common facial vein in the interval between the digastric muscle and the internal jugular vein, and hence it has been named the *jugulo-digastric lymph gland* (Leaf) (Fig. 1106); it is specially associated with the lymph drainage of the tongue and of the tonsil. The lowest gland of the group projects beyond the posterior border of the sterno-mastoid immediately above the tendon of the omohyoid muscle—the *jugulo-omohyoid gland* (Jamieson and Dobson) (Fig. 1104); it receives efferents from the submental glands and also a direct lymph vessel from the tip of the tongue. (2) The members of the *lateral group* of upper deep cervical lymph glands lie under cover of the posterior part of the upper portion of the sterno-mastoid, and in the upper part of the posterior triangle of the neck. They are embedded in the fat-laden fascia which covers the roots of the cervical plexus and the upper part of the brachial plexus, and the levator scapulæ and the scalene muscles, and several of them are in close relation with the accessory nerve (Fig. 1006).

The upper deep cervical glands receive *afferent* vessels from various subsidiary groups of glands (see pp. 1338, 1339). They receive lymph, directly or indirectly, from the skin of the head and neck, from the nose, the mouth, the tongue, the pharynx and larynx, the tonsil, the upper part of the thyroid gland, the sub-mandibular, sublingual, and parotid salivary glands. Their *efferents* pass either to the lower deep cervical glands or to the jugular lymph trunk.

Inferior Deep Cervical Lymph Glands (Figs. 1105, 1106).—These glands are situated below the level of the omohyoid muscle. They are mainly under cover of the sterno-mastoid, the trapezius and the clavicle, but some of them appear in the lower part of the posterior triangle of the neck. (1) The members of the *medial group* lie in relation with the lower part of the internal jugular vein, opposite the interval between the sternal and clavicular heads of the sterno-mastoid. They receive *afferents* from some of the upper deep cervical glands and from the pretracheal and the paratracheal glands. Their *efferents* unite with some of the efferents of the upper medial group and pass with them to the jugular lymph trunk.

(2) The members of the *lateral group* of lower deep cervical glands lie in the fatty tissue superficial to the brachial plexus and the third part of the subclavian artery, and extend beneath the trapezius along the transverse cervical blood-vessels. They receive lymph from the skin of the back of the neck and a few vessels which ascend over the clavicle from the skin of the pectoral region, including the upper part of the mamma. They are in communication with the apical group of axillary glands, and their *efferents* join the jugular lymphatic trunk.

The subsidiary offshoots of the deep cervical glands are found in the tract of the smaller arteries.

The **anterior cervical lymph glands** include the following outlying small groups—

(1) With the superior thyroid artery: (*a*) the *infra-hyoid glands* on the thyro-hyoid membrane; (*b*) *prelaryngeal glands* on the crico-thyroid ligament.

(2) With the inferior thyroid artery: (*a*) *pretracheal glands* at the lower end of the thyroid gland; (*b*) the upper *paratracheal glands* in the groove between trachea and œsophagus. These glands receive lymph from the larynx, the trachea and œsophagus in the neck and the thyroid gland, and transmit it to the lower deep cervical glands.

(3) With the lingual artery in relation to the hyo-glossus a few small occasional

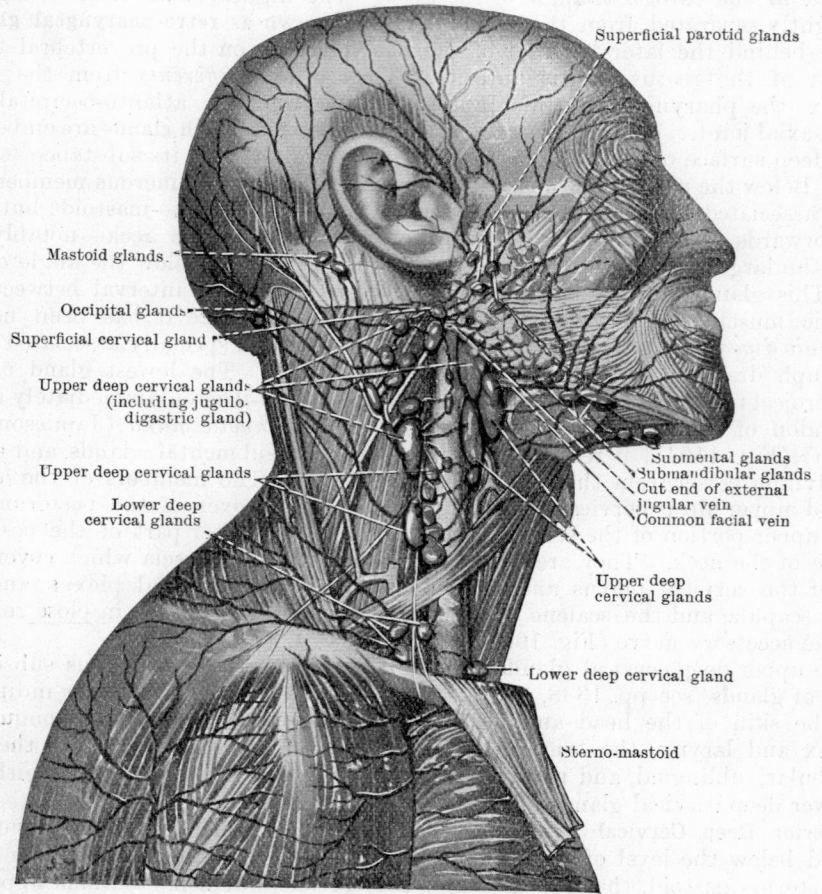

FIG. 1106.—LYMPH GLANDS OF HEAD AND NECK AS SEEN AFTER THE REMOVAL OF THE STERNO-MASTOID
MUSCLE. The occipital, mastoid, and superficial parotid glands are inserted in accordance with descriptions. The other glands were present in one or other or in both the bodies from which the figure was made. Compare Fig. 1104.

lingual glands on the course of some of the lymph vessels of the tongue; and with the maxillary artery occasional small glands in the infra-temporal region.

The "collar" glands in the course of the facial, superficial temporal, posterior auricular and occipital blood-vessels require particular description.

The **occipital lymph glands** (1-2) are situated on the occipital vessels as they emerge through the trapezius; their *afferents* come from the scalp and their *efferents* pierce the deep fascia to join the deep cervical glands.

The **mastoid lymph glands** [Lg. auriculares posteriores] (2-3) lie on the mastoid process; the largest is a flat coin-like gland frequently palpable. Their *afferents* come from the scalp and the back of the auricle, and the *efferents* run round or through the sterno-mastoid muscle to the deep glands.

The **parotid lymph glands** are embedded partly in the superficial surface of the parotid salivary gland under the deep fascia and partly in its substance. The more superficial (pre-auricular) glands receive numerous afferents from the front of the auricle and from the scalp, forehead, eyebrows, eyelids and the cheek, and their *efferents* pass to the deeper glands and to the upper deep cervical glands (jugulo-digastric). The deeper parotid lymph glands receive *afferents* from the external auditory meatus, the pharyngo-tympanic tube and the tympanum, the soft palate, the posterior part of the nasal cavity and the deeper portions of the cheek. Their *efferents* pass to the upper deep cervical glands.

The **superficial cervical lymph glands** (Fig. 1104) are merely the lower end of the superficial parotid group and may stray some distance down along the external jugular vein; they are small and become conspicuous only when diseased.

The **submandibular lymph glands** [Lg. submaxillares] (4-6) lie in the chink between the jaw and the submandibular salivary gland; the larger members are in contact with the facial vessels, and one may be placed between the salivary gland and the digastric. They receive the cutaneous vessels of the face below the eye, and many of the vessels of the tongue; the *efferents* run to the deep cervical glands, notably the jugulo-digastric and jugulo-omohyoid.

Minute glands are not infrequently found on the course of the vessels of the face, and may be named *infra-orbital, buccal,* and *mandibular* according to their position (Fig, 1107).

The **submental lymph glands** (1-4) form a median group that lies on the mylo-hyoid muscles midway between the symphysis and the hyoid bone; their *efferents* are derived from the lower lip and chin, mingled with those passing to the submandibular lymph glands, and from the tip of the tongue; their *efferents* run to the deep cervical glands as far down as the jugulo-omohyoid gland.

Lymph Vessels of Head and Neck

The **superficial lymph vessels** of the **scalp** and **forehead** run on the general lines of the occipital, posterior auricular, and superficial temporal blood-vessels to the *occipital, mastoid,* and *parotid* lymph glands; from the **eyelids** and **cheeks** they pass to the *parotid* and *submandibular* lymph glands; from the **nose, lips,** and **chin** to the *submandibular* and *submental* glands (Figs. 1104, 1107). These glands constitute the "collar chain" of glands; but it is important to note that it is not a complete barrier; many vessels from all parts of the scalp and face slip past these glands and run into the deep cervical chain (Fig. 1107). The superficial vessels of the **neck** perforate the deep fascia at numerous points to enter the deep cervical glands; a few on the upper part of the back of the neck are interrupted first by a few minute nodules that lie on the trapezius; and those from the lower part of the back of the neck join the stream which runs to the axillary glands around the posterior fold of the axilla.

Lymph Vessels of Eyelids and Conjunctiva.—These vessels arise from cutaneous and sub-conjunctival plexuses, and form two groups, a medial and a lateral; some run superficial, and others deep to the orbicularis oculi. (*a*) The *medial vessels* drain a very small part of the skin only of the upper eyelid, and about one half of the skin and conjunctiva of the lower eyelid; they follow the course of the anterior facial vein to the submandibular lymph glands, and some of them may be interrupted in the infra-orbital and buccal glands. (*b*) The *lateral vessels* (6-7) drain the greater part of the skin of the upper eyelid and the whole of its conjunctiva, and about one half of the skin and conjunctiva of the lower eyelid. They pass backwards, more or less along the line of the transverse facial vessels, and end in the parotid and superficial cervical lymph glands.

Lymph Vessels of the Orbit.—It is doubtful if any true lymph vessels exist in the **eyeball.** Lymph spaces have been described in the coats of the eyeball, and lymph vessels are stated to exist in the chorioid coat, but their existence is uncertain.

The lymph vessels of the **lacrimal gland** run with the lateral palpebral lymph vessels to the parotid lymph glands (Orts). Those of the **lacrimal sac** separate, one running laterally beneath the conjunctiva to pass to a parotid lymph gland, others joining medial palpebral vessels to reach the submandibular lymph glands.

Lymph Vessels of Ear.—The lymph vessels from the anterior portion of the lateral surface of the upper part of the **auricle** end in the parotid glands. Those from the lower part of the auricle go to the superficial cervical glands. Those from the medial surface and from the posterior portion of the upper part of the lateral surface of the auricle end in the mastoid glands, but some of them may establish direct communication with the upper deep cervical glands. The lymph vessels of the **external auditory meatus** are associated with those of the auricle and end in the parotid and mastoid glands.

The lymph vessels of the **middle ear** pass in two directions. Those from the lateral wall of the cavity join the vessels of the **tympanic membrane** and of the external auditory meatus and end in the parotid glands. The lymph vessels which drain the medial wall and the **pharyngo-tympanic** [auditory] **tube** end in the retro-pharyngeal and upper deep cervical glands.

It is doubtful if any lymph vessels exist in the **internal ear**. It is possible that the

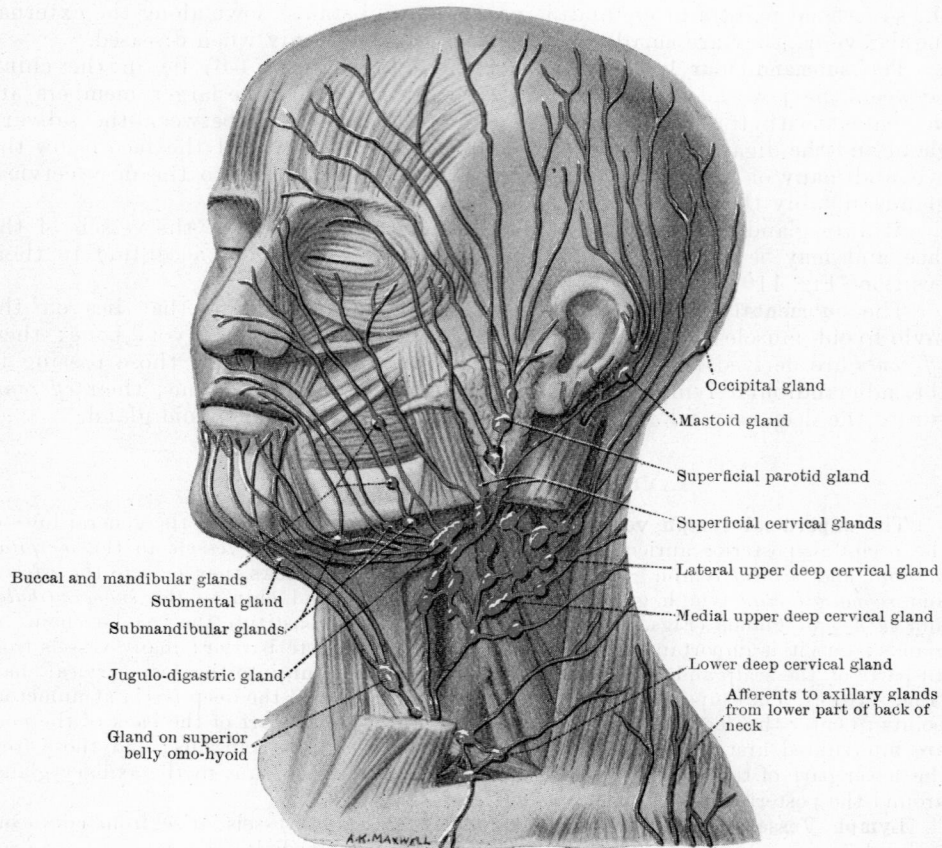

Occipital gland

Mastoid gland

Superficial parotid gland

Superficial cervical glands

Lateral upper deep cervical gland

Medial upper deep cervical gland

Lower deep cervical gland

Afferents to axillary glands from lower part of back of neck

Buccal and mandibular glands

Submental gland

Submandibular glands

Jugulo-digastric gland

Gland on superior belly omo-hyoid

A.K.MAXWELL

FIG. 1107.—SUPERFICIAL LYMPH VESSELS OF THE SCALP AND FACE.

perilymph drains into the subarachnoid space of the posterior fossa of the skull along the line of the ductus endolymphaticus, and that the endolymph reaches the subarachnoid space along the fibres of the auditory nerve.

Lymph Vessels of Nose.—The lymph vessels from the **external nose** pass mainly to the submandibular lymph glands, but a vessel from the root of the nose may pass with those of the upper eyelid to a parotid gland. The vessels of the **nasal cavity** arise from a plexus in the muco-periosteum. Those from the anterior part of the cavity accompany the vessels of the lower portion of the external nose and end in the submandibular glands. Those from the posterior part end partly in the medial upper deep cervical glands and partly in the retro-pharyngeal glands.

There is little definite knowledge regarding the lymph vessels of the **paranasal sinuses**, but it is probable that they follow the vessels of the nasal cavities and end in the same glands. Spaces of lymphatic character accompany the olfactory nerves into the cranium.

Lymph Vessels of Lips.—The lymph vessels of the lips arise from cutaneous and mucous plexuses. Those from the skin of the medial part of the lower lip pass to the submental glands and often cross the median plane. The cutaneous vessels from the lateral part of the lower lip unite with those from the upper lip and end in the sub-mandibular glands, but some from the upper lip may end in the superficial cervical glands.

The lymph vessels from the mucous membrane of the lips take the same course and end in the same glands as those of the skin ; but they tend to spread more widely.   Those of the upper lip, though ending mainly in the submandibular glands, may reach parotid and submental glands ; and those from the medial part of the lower lip pass to sub-mandibular as well as to submental lymph glands.

Lymph Vessels of Cheeks.—Most of the superficial and deep lymph vessels of the cheeks pass to the submandibular glands, but some of them may reach the superficial cervical or the upper deep cervical glands.   They may be interrupted in the buccal glands.

Lymph Vessels of Gums.—The vessels from the outer parts of both mandibular and maxillary gums end in the submandibular glands.   Occasionally a vessel from the anterior part of the mandibular gum ends in a submental gland.   The vessels from the inner part of the mandibular gum end in the submandibular and upper deep cervical glands ; those of the inner part of the maxillary gum run with the vessels of the hard and the soft palate, and end mainly in the upper deep cervical glands.

Lymph Vessels of Teeth.—Lymph vessels have been injected in the pulp of the teeth (Schweitzer, Dewey and Noyes).   Those of the lower teeth run in the mandibular canal and end in the submandibular or the upper deep cervical glands.   Those of the upper teeth emerge from the infra-orbital foramen and pass with vessels of the face to the submandibular glands.

Lymph Vessels of Palate.—These vessels run backwards to join those of the inner parts of the maxillary gums and end mainly in upper deep cervical glands.   But vessels from the palate may occasionally continue backwards to reach the retro-pharyngeal glands or pass downwards in the cheek to the submandibular glands.

Lymph Vessels of Tongue.—The lymph vessels of the tongue arise from a rich capillary plexus in the mucous membrane ; and they end in the submental, submandibular

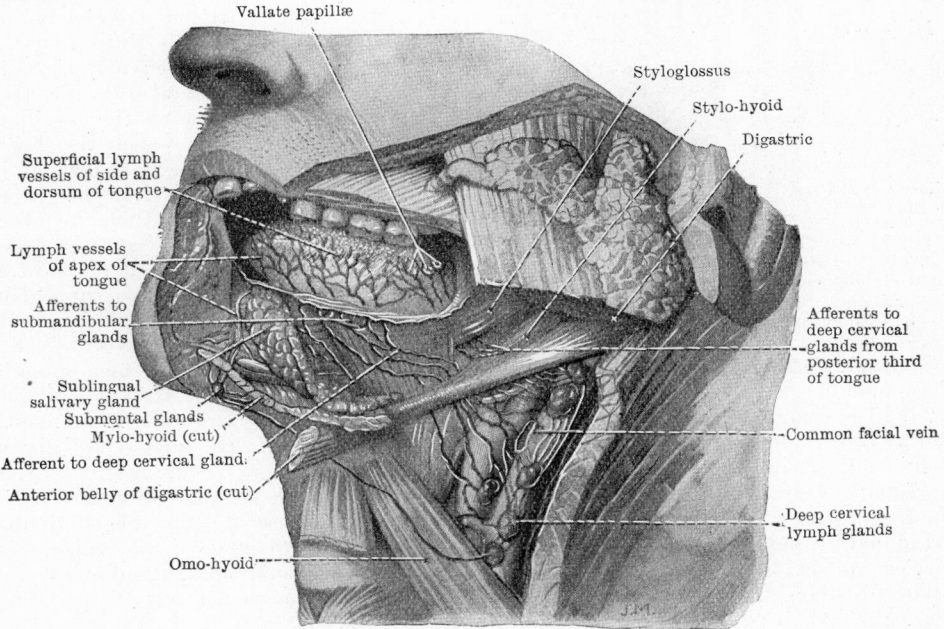

FIG. 1108.—LYMPH VESSELS OF THE TONGUE.

and upper deep cervical lymph glands.   The vessels are arranged in four groups—anterior, middle, posterior, and central.

The *anterior vessels* drain the tip and the inferior (free) surface.   They pierce the mylo-hyoid muscle and end in the submental lymph glands—all except one vessel which passes the submental glands, crosses the hyoid bone and ends in the jugulo-omohyoid gland.

The *middle vessels* drain the anterior two-thirds of the dorsum and margins (except the tip). They pass downwards, at different depths, to end in the submandibular and upper deep cervical glands. Those that end in the submandibular glands pass superficial to the sublingual salivary gland, and pierce the mylo-hyoid muscle. Others run in a deeper plane, over both surfaces of the hyo-glossus, and end in any of the deep cervical glands between the digastric muscle and the omo-hyoid.

The *posterior vessels*—larger than the others—drain the posterior third of the dorsum. They first run backwards beneath the mucous membrane, and then turn laterally to pierce the wall of the pharynx below the tonsil ; they also end in the deep cervical chain —principally in the jugulo-digastric gland.

The *central vessels* arise in the dorsal plexus near the median plane. They descend between the genio-glossi, and are joined by vessels from the deep parts of the tongue. They then run laterally and backwards, with the veins of the tongue, and end in upper deep cervical glands below the digastric muscle.

It is important to note that any of the upper deep cervical glands below the digastric may receive lymph vessels direct from the tongue ; and that, in general, the farther forward the origin of the vessel the lower down is the gland in which it ends. Note also that some members of the anterior, posterior, and central groups cross the median plane to end in glands of the opposite side.

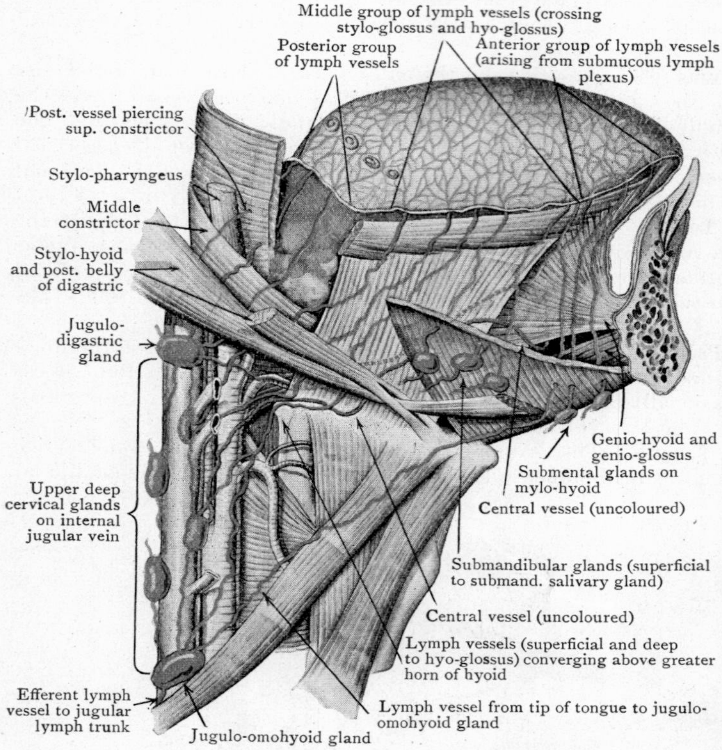

FIG. 1109.—DIAGRAM OF THE COURSE OF THE LYMPH VESSELS OF THE TONGUE. Only one central vessel is shown (uncoloured). Central vessels and one or more of the posterior group may cross the median plane and end in deep cervical glands of the opposite side.

Lymph Vessels of Floor of Mouth.—The capillary plexus of the mucous membrane of the tongue is continuous across the floor of the mouth with the plexus of the mandibular gum. The lymph vessels that arise from that part of the mucous membrane of the mouth run with the anterior, middle and posterior vessels of the tongue to the same lymph glands —submental, submandibular, and upper deep cervical.

Lymph Vessels of Salivary Glands.—The lymph vessels of the **parotid gland** end in the neighbouring parotid lymph glands. One or two lymph vessels of the **submandibular gland** end in the submandibular lymph glands, but most of them go to the upper deep cervical glands. Lymph vessels from the anterior part of the **sublingual gland** end in the submandibular lymph glands, and others from the posterior part run to upper deep cervical glands between the digastric and the omo-hyoid.

Lymph Vessels of Pharynx.—From the nasal part of pharynx, including the **naso-pharyngeal tonsil**, and from the posterior wall and lateral borders of the oral and laryngeal parts, the lymph stream flows to the median line posteriorly. There the larger vessels pierce the walls of the pharynx ; they then turn laterally and end in the retro-pharyngeal and upper deep cervical glands.

From the anterior wall of the laryngeal part of the pharynx, that is, from the region of the piriform fossæ and the posterior surface of the larynx, the lymph vessels pass along the course of the superior laryngeal artery, pierce the thyro-hyoid membrane, and end in the upper deep cervical glands.

The lymph vessels of the **tonsil** and the adjacent parts of the palato-glossal and palato-pharyngeal arches pierce the lateral wall of the pharynx and end in upper deep cervical glands immediately below the posterior belly of the digastric—many of them in the jugulo-digastric gland.

Lymph Vessels of Thyroid Gland.—These vessels arise in the intervesicular tissue of the gland and form a dense subcapsular plexus on its surface (Figs. 657, 658, p. 773), common to both lobes and the isthmus; therefore the lymph can pass from the lobe of one side to the terminal glands of the opposite side. The collecting vessels from the upper part of each lobe and of the isthmus end in the upper deep cervical glands and one of them may pass to a retro-pharyngeal gland; those from the lower part of the isthmus and of each lobe end in the pretracheal and paratracheal glands and one of them may pass down to an innominate gland; those from the side of each lobe pass to the deep cervical glands. It has been stated that a lymph vessel from the right lobe occasionally ends directly in the right subclavian vein (Mahorner, *Anat. Rec.*, 1927), and that one from the left lobe may end in the thoracic duct without the intervention of a lymph gland (Rouvière).

Lymph Vessels of Larynx.—The lymph plexus of the larynx is separable into upper and lower portions; they are connected together on the posterior wall of the cavity, but are separated, laterally and anteriorly, by the vocal folds, which contain extremely few fine capillary vessels only. The lymph vessels of the upper part pass mainly along the superior larnygeal artery; they pierce the thyro-hyoid membrane with lymph vessels of the pharynx, and end in the upper deep cervical glands; some of them may be interrupted in the infra-hyoid glands. The efferent vessels from the lower part of the larynx emerge in two groups. Those from the anterior region pierce the crico-thyroid ligament and end in the prelaryngeal, the pretracheal, and the deep cervical glands. The efferents from the postero-lateral region pierce the crico-tracheal membrane and end in the paratracheal and lower deep cervical glands (Fig. 1105).

Lymph Vessels of Cervical Part of Trachea and Œsophagus.—The collecting vessels of the cervical parts of the trachea and œsophagus end in the paratracheal and the inferior deep cervical glands. From the upper part of the trachea some vessels pass to the prelaryngeal glands also.

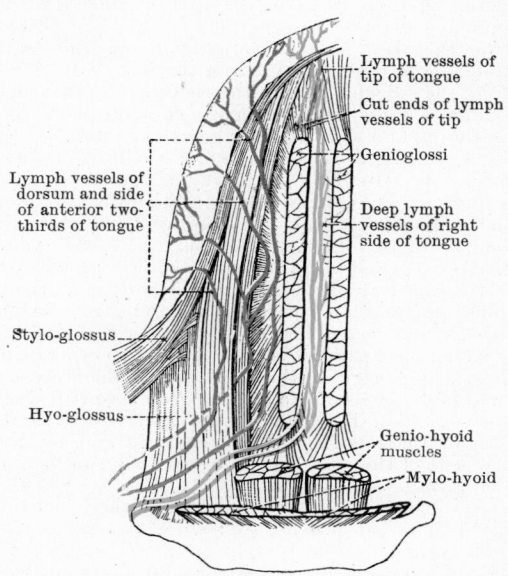

FIG. 1110.—DIAGRAM OF LYMPH VESSELS OF ANTERIOR TWO-THIRDS OF TONGUE, SEEN FROM BELOW. (After Poirier, modified.) Anterior vessels, red; middle vessels, blue; central vessels, green.

DEVELOPMENT OF LYMPHATIC SYSTEM

The lymphatic system is an adjunct of the venous system, sharing its absorbent function and emptying into the great veins in the root of the neck. The main question in the development of lymph vessels is whether they were originally independent formations which secondarily acquired connexions with the veins, or were derived primarily from the veins as endothelial outgrowths which spread into the body from one or more definite sites.

The first obvious sign of the development of the lymphatic system is the appearance of the structures known as **lymph sacs** which are closely related to the veins in certain situations. The first of these to appear is the jugular lymph sac, which is present in the human embryo of 10-11 mm., and six of them are present in the 30 mm. embryo (Sabin). Whatever the origin of these sacs, there is agreement about their position and their subsequent history.

An *anterior* or *jugular lymph sac* is found at the union of the chief vein of the upper limb with the anterior cardinal vein; a *posterior lymph sac* appears at the union of the chief vein of the lower limb with the posterior cardinal vein; a *retro-peritoneal lymph sac* develops at the root of the primitive mesentery; and another on the posterior wall of the abdomen is identified with the *cisterna chyli*. It may be noted that the anterior and posterior lymph sacs are developed in the same positions as the "lymph hearts" of the Amphibia.

Four of the lymph sacs are thus situated at the junctions of the limbs with the trunk and the other two on the back of the abdomen. All of them—with the exception of the anterior part of the sac from which the cisterna chyli is developed—become broken up into anastomosing channels and converted later into groups of lymph glands; and the jugular sacs acquire secondary connexions with the veins, which remain as the permanent terminations of the lymph trunks.

According to Sabin, the lymph sacs are developed as outgrowths of the endothelium of the veins near which they appear, and from the sacs all the lymph vessels of the body sprout—radiating from them to the parts drained by the principal lymph trunks. Thus, from the jugular sacs vessels spread into the head and neck, the upper limbs and upper part of the trunk; from the posterior sacs they spread into the lower part of the trunk and the lower limbs; and from the retroperitoneal sac at the root of the mesentery they grow towards the intestines, and from the sac which forms the cisterna to other abdominal organs. According to this view, the lymph sacs lose their primary connexions with the veins, and only later at the root of the neck do the jugular sacs acquire connexions again.

According to Huntington and McClure, on the other hand, all lymph vessels are originally formed as clefts in the mesenchyme exactly as blood vessels are formed (see p. 77). These clefts acquire an endothelial lining and unite into plexuses of capillary vessels. At first they are indistinguishable from developing veins, and indeed contain blood cells. Later the blood content of those vessels destined to become lymph channels disappears or is discharged into the veins. According to this view, the lymph sacs are formed by the running together of parts of the capillary plexuses which develop along the primitive venous trunks, the thoracic duct is developed by the formation of channels in these plexuses, and all the peripheral lymph vessels arise locally by the fusion of mesenchymal spaces.

There is a parallel between these two contrasting views and the older conflict on the single or multiple origin of the blood-vessels themselves. Formerly it was maintained (His) that all the blood-vessels of the embryo grow into it from those primarily developed in the wall of the yolk-sac; but it is now agreed that blood-vascular channels arise from the mesenchyme not only on the yolk-sac, in the body stalk and in the chorion, but in exactly the same manner in the body of the embryo also, where they run together to form anastomosing channels from which the primitive blood-vessels take form. The essential feature of Huntington and McClure's view of the origin of lymph vessels is the belief that endothelium may be formed directly from mesenchyme anywhere; and since that is true in the case of blood-vascular channels, it is difficult to deny that lymph-vascular channels also may arise independently in the mesenchyme. The technique of the investigation of these questions is admittedly difficult, but it may be that the chief difficulty is in the interpretation of results. The injection methods on which Sabin relied certainly appear to show that lymph vessels radiate from the lymph sacs; but they demonstrate only those vessels that are in communication with the sacs; they do not prove that there are no developing lymph channels farther afield that have not yet acquired their central connexions. It is true that endothelium grows, so that capillary plexuses may sprout; but it is probable that the apparent spread of lymph vessels from centres is due to progressive fusion rather than to peripheral outgrowth.

Lymph Glands.—Lymph glands are developed by the aggregation of lymphocytes in the mesenchymal strands of plexuses of lymph vessels. As the lymphocytes accumulate they form a nodule of lymphoid tissue, and the vessels around it are transformed into the peripheral portion of the lymph sinus. The lymphoid tissue is then broken up into cords by anastomosing lymph channels which grow into it from the sinus, mainly on the side of the efferent vessels. The capsule is formed by condensation of areolar tissue on the surface of the peripheral sinus, and the trabeculæ of the larger glands grow inwards from it.

The great majority of lymph glands are developed in central positions, and those that form in relation to peripheral lymph vessels are smaller and often rudimentary. Groups of numerous glands develop in the plexuses formed by the breaking up of the lymph sacs, including the lower part of the cisterna chyli from which cœliac and aortic glands are thus derived.

In early stages of development lymph glands possess blood-vascular as well as lymph capillary networks, and if the blood-vascular network preponderates over the lymph-vascular, the developing gland has a reddish appearance and is known as a hæmal gland. Such glands are found in Man as well as in other mammals, and it would appear from the observations of Swale Vincent and Harrison that hæmal glands are merely rudimentary forms of true lymph glands (*Journ. Anat. and Physiol.*, 1897, vol. xxxi.).

Thoracic Duct.—A rich plexus of lymph vessels is formed in the thorax around the aorta but principally behind and at its sides. The plexus, whether developed *in situ* or as anastomosing outgrowths from the sacs, communicates below with the lymph sac that forms the *cisterna chyli* and above with both jugular lymph sacs. From the plexus two longitudinal vessels, with numerous transverse anastomoses, are developed. Each of these vessels may persist and terminate above in the innominate vein of its own side, and there are then two thoracic ducts. Usually the continuity of each vessel is broken at the level of the 5th thoracic vertebra, where one of the transverse anastomosis enlarges. The lower part of the left vessel and the upper part of the right disappear. The component parts of the thoracic duct are, therefore, the lower part of the right longitudinal vessel, the upper part of the left longitudinal vessel, and a transverse anastomosis between them. Its origin from the cisterna chyli may remain plexiform or double.

It is obvious that from the primitive condition many varieties of the thoracic duct might be evolved and the majority of the various possible variations have been found in adult bodies (see H. K. Davis, *Amer. Journ. Anat.*, 1915, vol. xvii.).

SURFACE AND SURGICAL ANATOMY

Originally written by SIR HAROLD J. STILES, K.B.E., LL.D., D.Sc., F.R.C.S.ED.

Formerly Regius Professor of Clinical Surgery, University of Edinburgh

Revised and partly rewritten by JOHN FRASER

HEAD AND NECK

CRANIUM

Scalp.—The first and third layers of the scalp, namely, the **skin** and the **occipito-frontalis muscle**, are firmly united by fibrous processes which pass from the one to the other through the second or subcutaneous **fatty layer**. Those three layers are separated from the pericranium by a **layer of loose areolar tissue** which supports the small vessels passing between the scalp proper and pericranium. The **pericranium**, although regarded anatomically as periosteum, possesses limited bone-forming properties; over the vertex it is readily separated from the skull-cap except along the lines of the sutures, where it is united by sutural ligaments to the external layer of the dura mater.

The free **blood-supply of the scalp** nourishes its abundant hair follicles and glands. The main vessels lie in the dense subcutaneous tissue, and are therefore superficial to the occipito-frontalis muscle (Fig. 1111). The arteries that supply the frontal region are derived from the internal carotid, and those for the remainder of the scalp spring from the external carotid. The two groups of vessels anastomose with one another, and also with those of the opposite side—hence the failure of ligature of the external carotid to cure cirsoid aneurysm of the superficial temporal artery.

Wounds of the scalp bleed freely, and the vessels are difficult to ligature on account of the fixation of their walls to the dense subcutaneous tissue. In extensive flap wounds and in diffuse suppuration deep to the occipito-frontalis muscle there is little danger of sloughing of the scalp. **Abscesses and hæmorrhages** superficial to the occipito-frontalis muscle are usually limited on account of the density of the subcutaneous tissue. Hæmorrhage deep to the occipito-frontalis muscle is seldom extensive on account of the small size of the vessels, but suppuration in that situation may rapidly undermine the whole muscle and its aponeurosis —the epicranial aponeurosis [galea aponeurotica]. The area under cover of the occipito-frontalis is sometimes termed "the dangerous area," and in cases of extensive infection the swelling may extend from the superior nuchal lines to the superciliary arches, and reach laterally to the level of the zygoma. Incisions to evacuate the pus should be made early, and parallel to the main vessels of the scalp. Extravasation of blood deep to the pericranium leads to a hæmatoma which is limited by the sutures (cephalhæmatoma).

The **veins** of the scalp communicate with the intracranial venous sinuses:— (1) directly through their anastomoses with the large emissary veins—the parietal, which open into the superior sagittal sinus, and the mastoid and condylar, which open into the sigmoid sinus; (2) through the anastomoses of the supra-trochlear and supra-orbital veins with the ophthalmic vein, which opens into the cavernous sinus; (3) through the veins of the diplöe, which connect the veins of the scalp and the pericranium with those of the dura mater and the venous sinuses; (4) through small veins which pass from the pericranium through the bones and the sutural ligaments to the dura mater. It is along these various channels that pyogenic infection may extend from the scalp and pericranium, through the bone, to the dura mater and venous sinuses, and from the sinuses to the cerebral veins, the pia-arachnoid, and the substance of the brain. More rarely the infection spreads from the cranial cavity along the emissary veins to the scalp.

The **lymph vessels** of the anterior part of the scalp join the facial lymph vessels; those of the temporal and parietal regions end in the parotid lymph glands, situated in front of and below the ear, and in the mastoid glands on the insertion of the sterno-mastoid muscle. The lymph vessels of the occipital region end in the occipital glands, which lie close to the occipital artery and the greater occipital nerve where they become superficial in the scalp at the upper end of the trapezius. Occipital neuralgia may result from pressure on the nerve by enlargement of one of those glands.

Bony Landmarks of Cranium.—At the root of the nose there is the fronto-nasal suture, the mid-point of which is the **nasion**; and immediately above is the **glabella**—a slight prominence which connects the superciliary arches. About an inch below the posterior pole of the cranium, and 2 inches above the spine of the

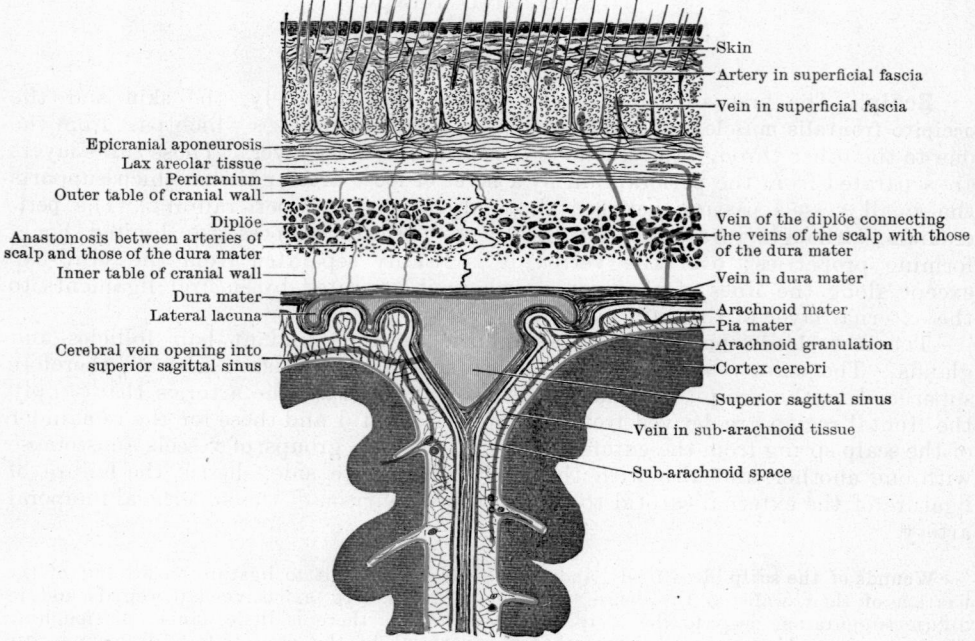

Fig. 1111.—Diagrammatic Representation of a Coronal Section through the Scalp, Cranium, Meninges, and Cortex Cerebri.

axis vertebra, is the external occipital protuberance (the centre of which is the **inion**). In the child this protuberance is not developed; but its position is identified as a point at the junction of the upper and middle thirds of a line extending from the posterior pole of the skull to the spine of the axis vertebra.

About a third of the distance from the nasion to the inion is the **bregma** or junction of the coronal and sagittal sutures; with the head in the natural erect posture the bregma is at, or close to, the middle of a line carried across the vertex from one tragus to the other. At birth the position of the bregma is occupied by the **anterior fontanelle**—a rhomboidal membranous area which is usually completely ossified towards the end of the second year. The size and date of closure of the fontanelle, as well as its tension and pulsation, are points to be carefully noted in the clinical examination of children (Fig. 155 and Pl. IV, Fig. 2).

The **lambda**, or junction of the sagittal and lambdoid sutures, situated 2½ inches above the inion, can generally be felt through the scalp as a slight depression; a line drawn from it to the asterion—the articulation of the postero-inferior angle of the parietal bone with the temporal and occipital bones—corresponds to the **lambdoid suture**.

The **parietal eminence**, which varies considerably in the definiteness with which it can be recognised, overlies the **termination of the posterior ramus** of the **lateral sulcus** of the cerebrum. The **frontal eminence** (better marked in the child) overlies the **middle frontal gyrus**.

Crossing the supra-orbital margin, a finger's-breadth from the median line, are the **supra-trochlear nerve** and **vessels**; the artery nourishes the flap in the operation of rhinoplasty. On the supra-orbital margin, two finger-breadths from the median line, is the **supra-orbital notch** or **foramen**—the guide to the **supra-orbital nerve** and **vessels**. A little above the level of the lateral angle of the eye is the **fronto-zygomatic suture**, immediately above which is the **zygomatic process** of the frontal bone. At the posterior end of the suture, the **zygomatico-temporal nerve** pierces the temporal fascia to reach the skin; and half an inch above the suture is the **lower margin** of the **cerebral hemisphere**. The **temporal line** marks the upper limit of the temporal muscle. It begins at the zygomatic process of the frontal bone, arches upwards between the temple and the forehead; then curving backwards, it skirts the lower part of the parietal eminence, and finally, turning downwards, it joins the supra-mastoid crest near the top of the root of the auricle; the anterior part of the line is the only part easily felt. The **supra-mastoid crest** curves upwards and backwards from the external auditory meatus for an inch, but it is obscured by the auricle.

The **zygomatic arch**, an important landmark, is horizontal when the head is in the natural position, and is on the same level as the inferior margin of the orbit and the inion; its upper border is at, or not infrequently a little above, the level of the infero-lateral margin of the cerebral hemisphere. The upper border of the zygoma may be traced backwards immediately above the tragus and the external auditory meatus to become continuous with the supra-mastoid crest. The **superficial temporal vessels** and the **auriculo-temporal nerve** cross the zygoma immediately in front of the tragus, and it is there that the pulsations of the superficial temporal artery may be felt during the administration of an anæsthetic, or the vessel compressed for the purpose of checking bleeding from the temporal region of the head. The termination of the auriculo-temporal nerve in the neighbourhood of the parietal eminence is often the seat of a neuralgic pain in irritative conditions at the external auditory meatus—the meatus being in part supplied by that nerve.

Two inches vertically above the middle of the zygomatic arch is the **pterion**. This is a point which cannot be felt, but is nevertheless of topographical importance, as it overlies the point where the lateral sulcus of the cerebrum breaks up into its three rami and the point where the **anterior branch** of the **middle meningeal artery** is most deeply embedded in the bone.

The thickness of the skull-cap varies at different parts and in different subjects. The inner table is only half the thickness of the outer table, but both possess the same degree of elasticity. When the vault is fractured from direct violence, the inner table is more extensively fissured than the outer table, because the elements of the outer table are compressed, while those of the inner table are stretched apart. The weak areas at the base of the skull through which fractures are liable to extend are: (1) In the anterior cranial fossa—the orbital plates of the frontal bone, and the cribriform plate of the ethmoid. (2) In the middle cranial fossa—the region of the articular fossa, and of the foramen ovale. (3) In the posterior fossa—the fossæ of the occipital bone. The petrous part of the temporal bone, though strong, is weakened by the tympanic cavity and by the jugular fossa.

Cranio-Cerebral Topography.—While there are methods by which cranio-cerebral topography is indicated in considerable detail, it is better to employ a scheme by which the primary sulci of the brain may be outlined on the skull, and then to outline the position of the more important gyri and the secondary sulci. It should be pointed out that the position of the cerebral landmarks may vary within normal limits, and it is impossible therefore to delineate them with absolute accuracy. The lines which are used to indicate their position are only approximate, though they are sufficiently reliable for clinical and operative purposes. The following scheme is recommended. A **base line** is drawn from the lower margin of the orbit backwards through the upper border of the external auditory meatus to the occipital region ; the cerebrum lies above the level of this line, while the cerebellum occupies a position below the level of the posterior third of the line.

Primary Sulci.—The position of the **central sulcus** is now outlined by a line which begins half an inch behind the mid-point of a sagittal line passing from the root of the nose to the external occipital protuberance and extends downwards and forwards for a distance of 3½ inches at an angle of 67·5°. For ordinary purposes the situation of the sulcus may be indicated by the following simple and practical method. A piece of paper folded to a right angle is again folded to an angle of 45° and once more to an angle of 22·5° ; reopen two of the folds to obtain an angle of 67·5° ; place the point of the folds half an inch behind the mid-point already named, and one edge along the median plane in front of that—the other edge will indicate the position of the central sulcus (see Pl. LXI).

The stem of the **lateral sulcus** reaches the lateral surface of the cerebrum opposite the *pterion*—that point being about 1¼ inches behind the zygomatic process of the frontal bone and half an inch up. It divides there into three rami ; the **anterior two rami** are short, and pass forwards and upwards, diverging from each other ; the **posterior ramus** is the most important part of the sulcus. It is indicated by a line that begins at the pterion, is drawn backwards and slightly upwards to a point below the parietal eminence, and is curved sharply upwards to end at that eminence.

The upper end of the **parieto-occipital sulcus** is half an inch or less above the lambda in the adult, and a line drawn laterally from this point for a distance of half an inch or an inch indicates the position of the part of the sulcus which appears on the supero-lateral surface of the cerebral hemisphere. In a child, the sulcus may be as much as an inch above the lambda.

Lobes.—By means of the lines for these sulci, the position of the lobes can be gauged roughly. The **frontal lobe** is the part in front of the central sulcus ; the **temporal lobe** is below the posterior ramus of the lateral sulcus and extends from the margin of the orbit to a line drawn to the back of the root of the auricle from the point for the parieto-occipital sulcus. The **occipital lobe** is behind that line ; the **parietal lobe** is between the central sulcus and the upper half of that line.

Gyri and Secondary Sulci.—Each lobe is divided into gyri by secondary sulci. In the frontal lobe the **pre-central sulcus** runs parallel to the central sulcus three-fifths of an inch in front of it, cutting off the **pre-central gyrus**. The remainder of the frontal lobe is divided into the *superior, middle,* and *inferior frontal gyri* by two sulci—*superior* and *inferior frontal*. The lower part of the inferior frontal gyrus is divided into three portions by the anterior rami of the lateral sulcus. Those three portions, together with the lower part of the pre-central gyrus, comprise the **motor speech centre**, which is developed on the left side of the brain in right-handed people.

In the parietal lobe the **post-central sulcus** is three-fifths of an inch behind and parallel to the central sulcus, and cuts off the **post-central gyrus**. The *intra-parietal sulcus* runs backwards from the post-central sulcus, and divides the rest of the lobe into two parts named the *superior* and *inferior parietal lobules*. The inferior lobule is divided into three parts that surround the upturned ends of the lateral sulcus and the temporal sulci. These parts contain centres for the interpretation of printed and written words ; and it should be noted that the anterior part underlies the parietal eminence of the skull.

The **motor area** for individual movements occupies the anterior wall of the central sulcus and the adjoining free surface of the pre-central gyrus ; it also extends into the para-central lobule on the medial surface. The body is inverted in this area, and the relative position of the parts as represented in the cortex is shown in Fig. 1114. In an adult, the highest part of the temporal line is opposite the area for the upper limb ; but in a child ,the temporal muscle is relatively small, and the temporal line is only a little above the squamous suture—opposite the area for the head. The **sensory area**—that is the centre for the reception of common sensation—is in the posterior wall of the central sulcus and the adjoining free surface of the post-central gyrus; in it also the body is inverted.

The lateral surface of the temporal lobe is divided into *superior, middle,* and *inferior temporal gyri* by the *superior* and *inferior temporal sulci,* which are parallel to the posterior ramus of the lateral sulcus. The **auditory area**—that is the centre for the mere reception of sound—is in the middle of the superior temporal gyrus. The posterior ramus separates it from the lower end of the sensory area, and it is opposite a point on the skull a little above and in front of the top of the auricle.

The arrangement of sulci and gyri in the lateral surface of the occipital lobe is very inconstant. The **visual area**—the centre for the reception of impressions of light—is on the medial surface of the lobe in relation to the calcarine and post-

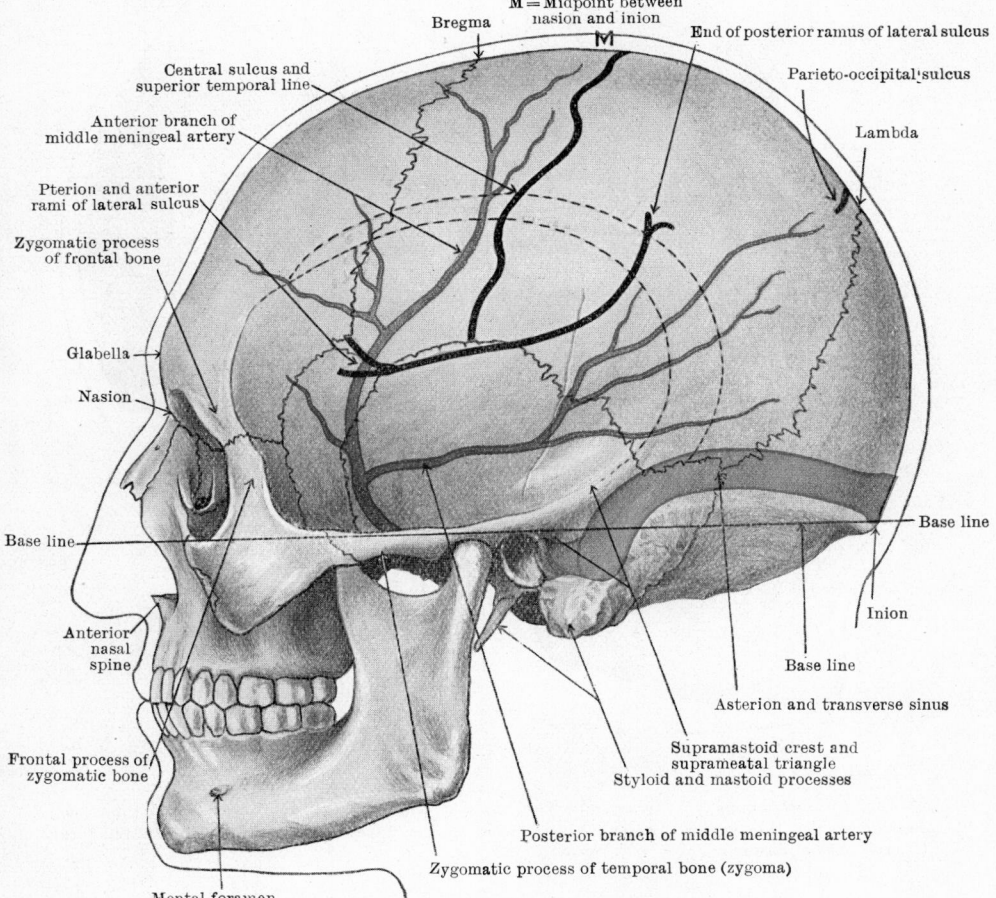

FIG. 1112.—CRANIO-CEREBRAL TOPOGRAPHY I : Landmarks of skull ; chief sulci of cerebrum ; transverse and sigmoid venous sinuses ; middle meningeal artery.

calcarine sulci, but in some hemispheres the post-calcarine sulcus extends on to the lateral surface, carrying a portion of the centre for light with it. This portion is opposite the finger tip placed immediately above the external occipital protuberance.

Lateral Ventricle.—The central part of the lateral ventricle occupies a level between the posterior ramus of the lateral sulcus and the middle part of the temporal line. The anterior horn of the ventricle is immediately above the level of the pterion; the posterior horn is opposite the posterior part of the temporal line but is very variable both in length and width; the inferior horn corresponds to the middle temporal gyrus.

The **lateral ventricle** may be tapped or drained through its posterior horn at a point 1¼ inches above the superior nuchal line and ¾ inch from the median line. The cavity of the ventricle at this point is at a depth of about 2½ inches from the surface. The procedure of ventriculography has been introduced by Dandy in the investigation of hydrocephalus and cerebral tumours. Following puncture of the lateral ventricle, a percentage of the cerebro-spinal fluid is removed,

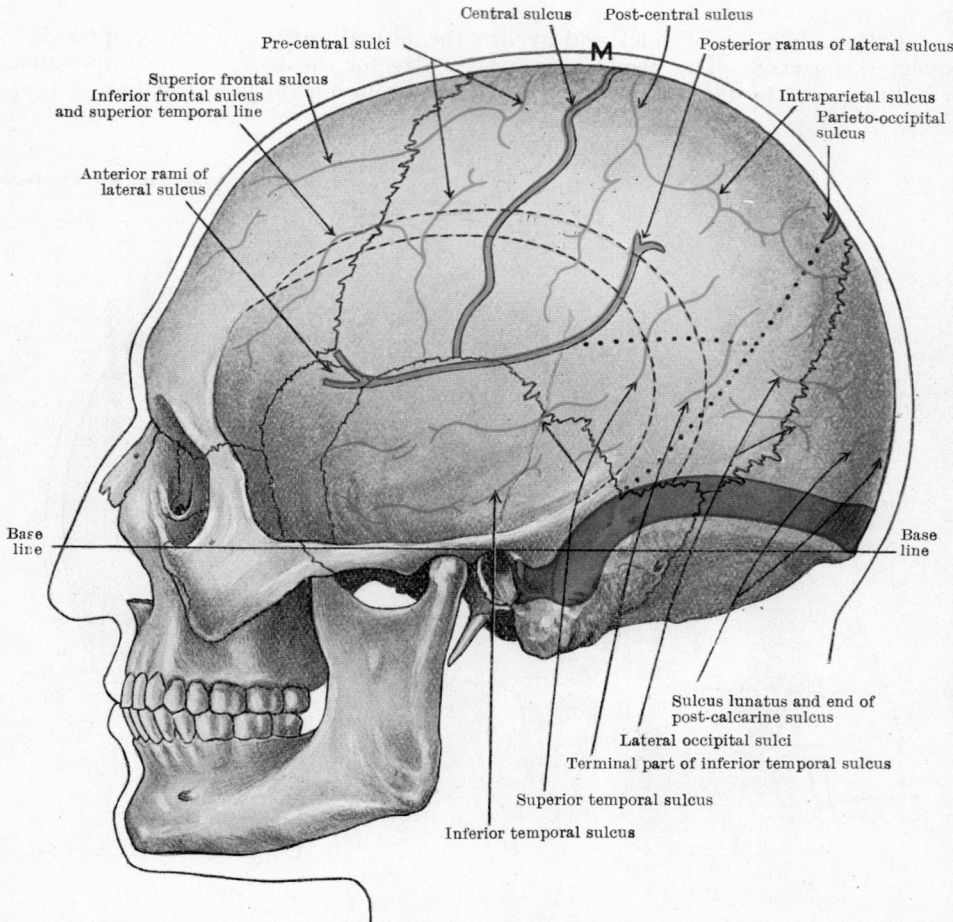

Fig. 1113.—Cranio-cerebral Topography II : Venous sinuses (blue) ; chief sulci (thick yellow) ; secondary sulci (thin yellow) ; artificial boundaries between lobes (lines of round dots) ; temporal lines (curved lines of dashes).

and its bulk replaced by an equal proportion of oxygen. The skull is then X-rayed in such positions as to permit a demonstration of the circulation of the gas through the various cavities and channels of the ventricular system (Pls. LX and LXI).

The **cerebello-medullary cistern** is situated between the under surface of the cerebellum and the medulla oblongata ; it may be tapped by suboccipital puncture—the needle passing through the posterior atlanto-occipital membrane. The needle is inserted close to the median line immediately above the atlas vertebra, and its direction is from the point of insertion towards the root of the nose.

To expose a **hemisphere** of the **cerebellum,** trephine over the middle of a line drawn from the tip of the mastoid process to the external occipital protuberance.

To expose both hemispheres of the cerebellum, reflect two flaps by an anchor-shaped incision. The curved, horizontal limb is made a little above and parallel to the superior nuchal lines, and, if possible, the ends of the incision should not reach the mastoid emissary vein (a finger's breadth behind the root of the auricle at the level of the meatus), for it may give rise to troublesome bleeding. The occipital arteries (an inch lateral to the inion) are divided. The vertical limb of the incision descends in the median line. If more room is required, the opening in the bone may be extended above the level of the transverse sinuses without wounding them, as they can be displaced along with the dura. The occipital sinus is divided between two ligatures. After division of the dura displace a hemisphere of the cerebellum towards the median plane to enable the finger to be passed between it and the posterior surface of the petrous portion of the temporal bone and in that way reach a tumour of the auditory nerve, which occupies the angle between the cerebellum and the pons.

Meningeal Arteries.—When the calvaria is removed the **meningeal arteries** are left with the dura mater, for they are in its outer layer. Of those vessels the middle meningeal **artery** is the only one of surgical importance. It is frequently

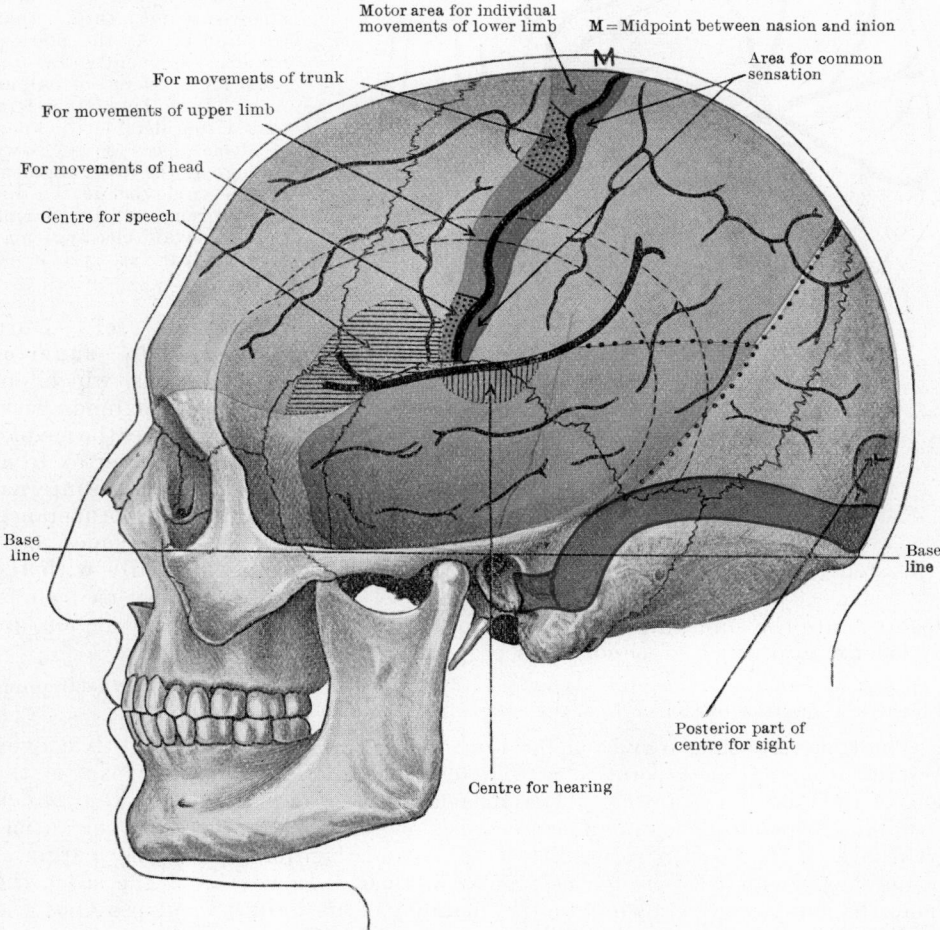

Fig. 1114.—Cranio-cerebral Topography III : Lobes of cerebrum ; motor and sensory areas ; centres for speech, hearing, and sight. *Frontal* and *occipital* lobes red ; *parietal* lobe, blue ; *temporal* lobe, purple.

lacerated in fractures of the skull; the blood is generally extravasated between the dura and the bone, and the bleeding point lies deep to the clot. After entering the cranial cavity through the foramen spinosum, the *main trunk* runs laterally and slightly forwards to divide into anterior and posterior branches at or a little above the level of the zygomatic arch, midway between the orbit and the auditory meatus.

The *anterior and larger branch* passes upwards (with a slight forward convexity) to the pterion and then upwards and backwards towards the mid-point between the nasion and the inion, giving off branches on its way. Its main trunk is opposite and parallel to the motor area and is therefore encountered in operations on that part (Pl. LXIII).

The *posterior branch* passes backwards towards the lambda.

To expose the *trunk* of the vessel and its bifurcation, apply the trephine immediately above the middle of the zygomatic arch. To expose the *anterior branch,* apply the pin of the trephine at a point 1½ inches behind the zygomatic process of the frontal bone and 1⅖ inches above the zygoma. This leads to exposure of the vessel as it crosses the pterion and grooves the bone deeply. The lower segment of the disc of bone removed is much thicker than the upper. At the pterion, the artery frequently runs in a canal for a distance of half an inch. It follows, therefore, that a considerable thickness of bone has to be sawn through at the lower segment of the circle before the disc can be removed, and during the removal bleeding may occur from the artery as it lies in the canal.

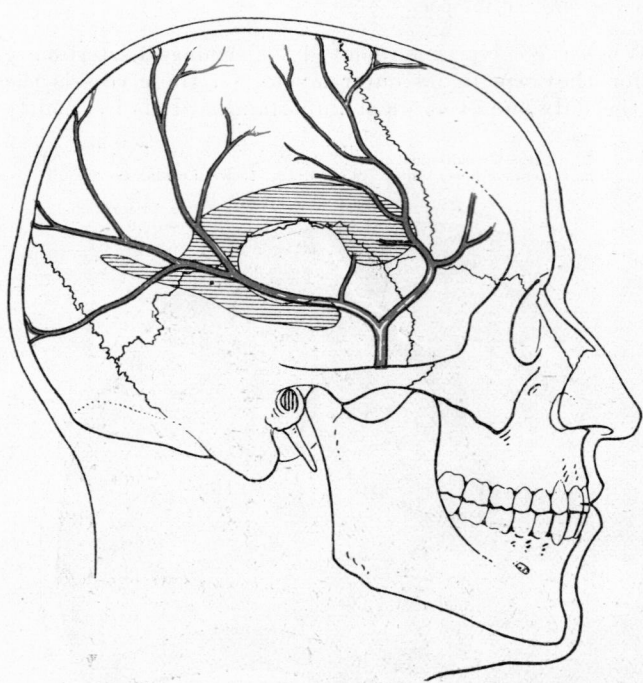

FIG. 1115.—TOPOGRAPHY OF THE NORMAL LATERAL VENTRICLES. (By permission of the *Brit. Journ. of Surg.*) See also Pls. LX and LXI.

Sinuses of Dura Mater.—The superior sagittal sinus, which enlarges as it extends backwards, occupies the median plane of the vertex from the glabella to the internal occipital protuberance, where it becomes continuous usually with the right transverse sinus.

Opening into the sinus, especially in the posterior part of the parietal region, are the lacunæ, into which arachnoid villi project.

In opening the skull over the posterior part of the vertex, keep the edge of the trephine at least three-quarters of an inch from the median plane to avoid the lacunæ.

The **transverse sinus** may be mapped out on the surface by a line, slightly convex upwards, *drawn* from a point a little above the inion to the upper part of the back of the root of the auricle. The **sigmoid sinus** is indicated by a line which begins at this point and is drawn downwards along the back of the root of the auricle to the level of the lower margin of the meatus, and then forwards to the margin of the meatus, which is opposite the jugular foramen. In wounds of the sinus the hæmorrhage is very free, owing to the inability of its walls to collapse; but the bleeding is easily controlled by plugging.

Cerebral Arteries.—Of the **cerebral arteries**, the *middle* supplies almost the whole of the motor area, and one of its striate branches, which enter the brain at the anterior perforated substance, is called "*the artery of cerebral hæmorrhage*" from the frequency of its rupture in apoplexy. The extravasated blood involves the motor part of the internal capsule. The postero-medial central branches of the *posterior cerebral* artery, which enter the brain at the posterior perforated substance, supply the thalamus and walls of the third ventricle; hæmorrhage from one of those branches is apt to rupture into the ventricle. The postero-lateral central branches of the posterior cerebral artery supply the thalamus, and when one of those vessels ruptures the hæmorrhage is apt to invade the posterior part of the internal capsule, where the fibres for *sight* and *hearing* are situated. (For radiography of internal carotid artery in the living head, see Pl. LXI, Fig. 2.)

PLATE LXI

Upper end of Central Sulcus

Posterior horn of
Lateral Ventricle

Anterior horn of Lateral Ventricle

Inferior horn of Lateral Ventricle

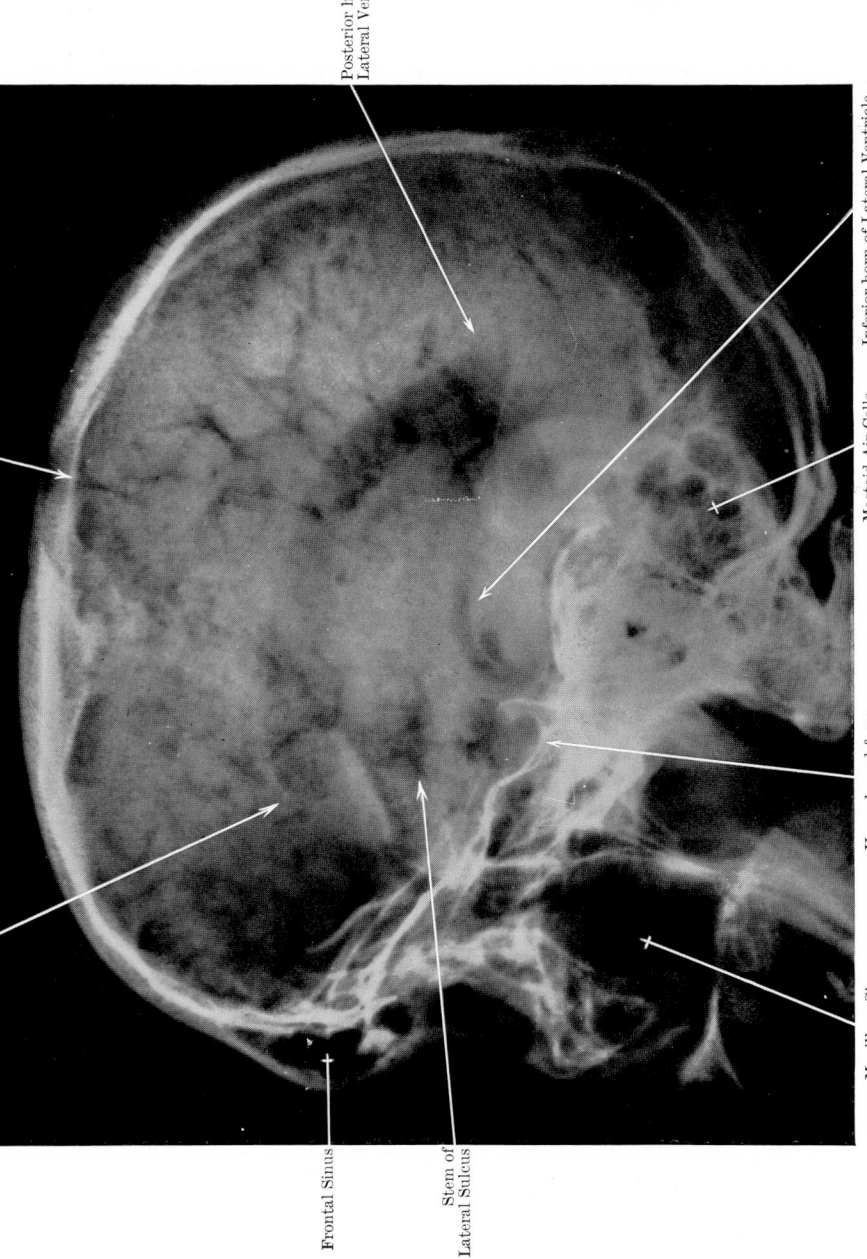

Frontal Sinus

Stem of
Lateral Sulcus

Maxillary Sinus

Hypophyseal fossa

Mastoid Air Cells

PLATE LXI.—LATERAL RADIOGRAPH OF LIVING HEAD OF MAN AGED 24, AFTER INJECTION OF OXYGEN INTO THE SPINAL SUBARACHNOID SPACE BY LUMBAR PUNCTURE (Encephalograph : Mr. Norman M. Dott).

The Sulci of the Cerebral Hemisphere appear in the radiograph on account of the relative translucency to the X-Rays of the oxygen-filled subarachnoid spaces. The oxygen has entered the Ventricular System also, and the form, size and position of a Lateral Ventricle are well shown. Compare with Plate LX in which the Lateral Ventricles, directly injected, are more obvious but considerably enlarged.

[Facing p. 1352

PLATE LXII

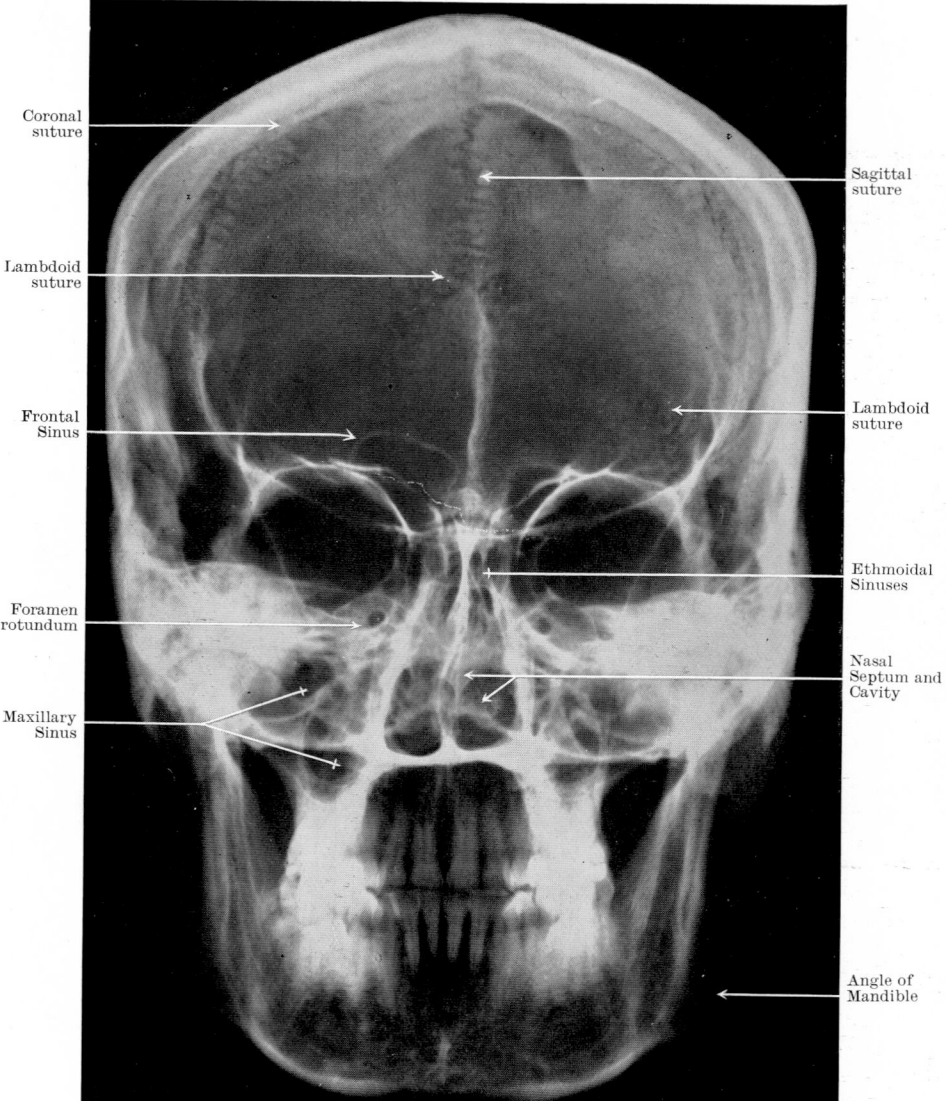

Coronal suture

Sagittal suture

Lambdoid suture

Lambdoid suture

Frontal Sinus

Ethmoidal Sinuses

Foramen rotundum

Nasal Septum and Cavity

Maxillary Sinus

Angle of Mandible

PLATE LXII.—ANTERO-POSTERIOR RADIOGRAPH OF THE SAME MALE
SKULL AS IN PLATE V.

Compare with Fig. 137, p. 141 ; Fig. 148, p. 181 ; and, for variations in the extent of the frontal sinuses, with Plate LVIII, Fig. 1. Note that in this skull the septum between the two frontal sinuses is broad, which accounts for the fact that their cavities are not well seen in Plate V.

PLATE LXIII

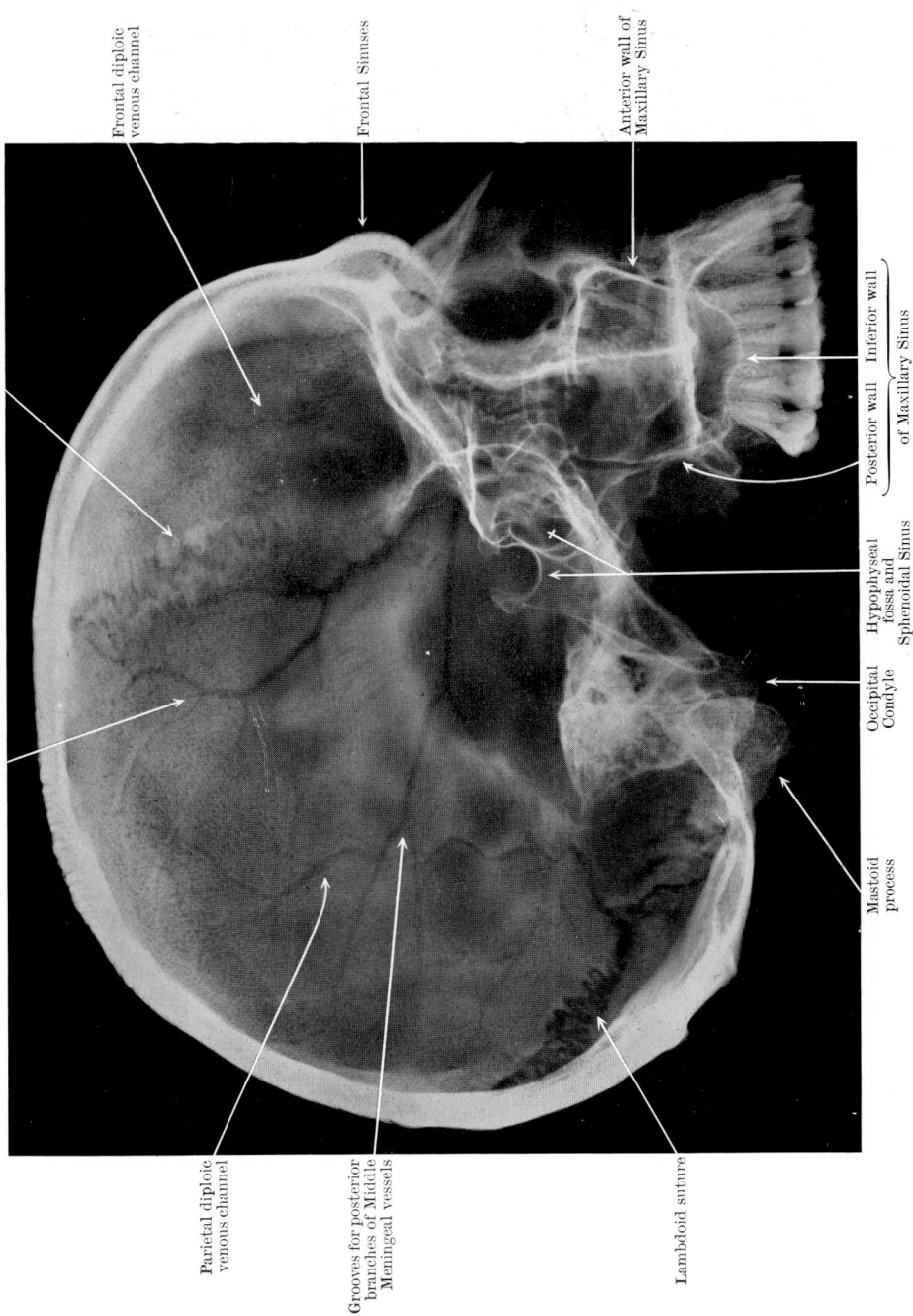

Frontal diploic venous channel

Coronal suture

Grooves or anterior branches of Middle Meningeal vessels

Frontal Sinuses

Anterior wall of Maxillary Sinus

Inferior wall

Posterior wall } of Maxillary Sinus

Hypophyseal fossa and Sphenoidal Sinus

Occipital Condyle

Mastoid process

Parietal diploic venous channel

Grooves for posterior branches of Middle Meningeal vessels

Lambdoid suture

PLATE LXIII.—LATERAL RADIOGRAPH OF RIGHT HALF OF MALE SKULL.

Compare with Fig. 138, p. 147 ; Fig. 147, p. 179 ; with Plate V (radiograph of the same skull complete), and with radiographs of the living head (Plates LVII, LVIII, LVIII (Fig. 2), and LX)

PLATE LXIV

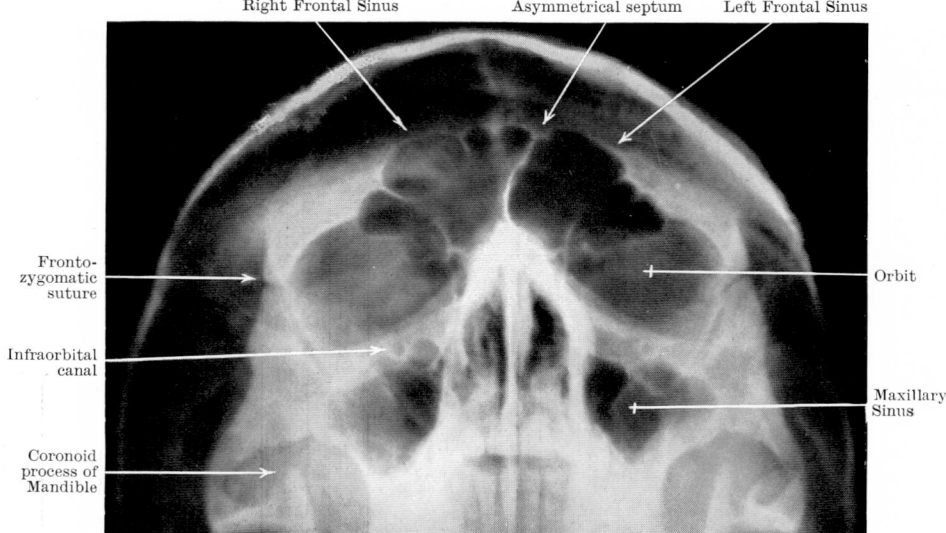

Right Frontal Sinus   Asymmetrical septum   Left Frontal Sinus

Fronto-
zygomatic
suture

Infraorbital
canal

Coronoid
process of
Mandible

Orbit

Maxillary
Sinus

FIG. 1.—RADIOGRAPH OF THE FRONTAL SINUSES OF MAN AGED 34. (Dr. J. F. Brailsford.)

Note the asymmetrical position of the septum, and the extension of the sinuses into the roofs of the orbits. Compare with Plate VIII, and for lateral views of the Frontal Sinuses see Fig. 2 and Plates V, LVII, LIX and LX.

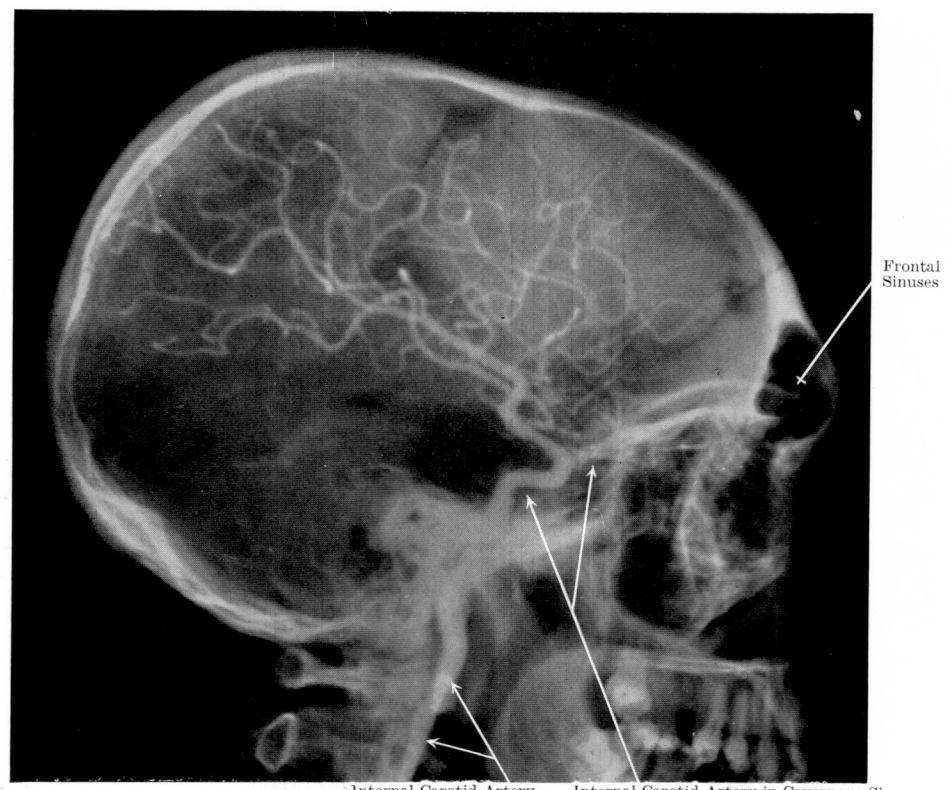

Frontal
Sinuses

Internal Carotid Artery   Internal Carotid Artery in Cavernous Sinus
in Neck   and Ophthalmic Artery

FIG. 2.—LATERAL RADIOGRAPH OF LIVING HEAD OF MAN AGED 24, AFTER INJECTION OF THORIUM DIOXIDE (THOROTRAST) INTO THE RIGHT INTERNAL CAROTID ARTERY (Cerebral Arteriograph: Mr. Norman M. Dott).

The Internal Carotid Artery is seen in the upper part of the Neck, in the Carotid Canal, and in the Cavernous Sinus. Note its division into Anterior and Middle Cerebral Arteries and the appearance of their branches. The Ophthalmic Artery is also seen leaving the internal carotid and ramifying in the orbit.

[Facing p. 1353

Trigeminal Ganglion [G. Semilunare].—The topography of the trigeminal ganglion is important in relation to the operation of division of its sensory root for the cure of trigeminal neuralgia. The ganglion is situated between the layers of the dura mater in the middle cranial fossa, at the apex of the petrous portion of the temporal bone.

The surgeon reaches it by an extra-dural route through an opening immediately above the zygomatic arch. The bone is removed down to the level of the infra-temporal crest, which forms the boundary line between the lateral wall and floor of the middle cranial fossa. The dura mater is separated from the floor of the fossa so as to admit of the ligature of the middle meningeal artery immediately after its entrance through the foramen spinosum. The dura mater is separated from the bone still farther in a medial and backward direction till the cavity between its layers occupied by the ganglion is reached. The outer layer of the dura is then incised horizontally, and the postero-lateral border of the ganglion is exposed. The sensory root passes backwards from the ganglion, and is enclosed in a tube of arachnoid mater. Incise the arachnoid behind the ganglion. Some drops of subarachnoid fluid will escape; and then the root can be seen and followed back to the aperture in the dura mater immediately below the attachment of the tentorium cerebelli, between it and the upper margin of the petrous temporal bone. The sensory root

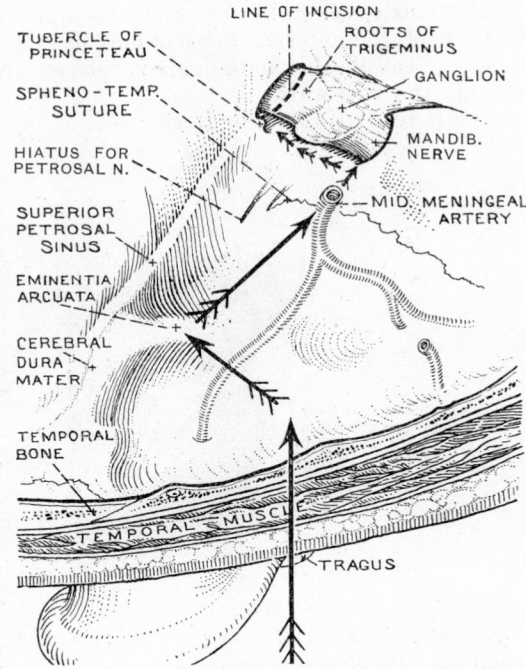

FIG. 1116. THE TEMPORAL ROUTE OF ACCESS TO THE TRI-GEMINAL [SEMILUNAR] GANGLION. (Victor Pauchet, by permission of Ernest Benn, Ltd.)

is then gently raised on a hook and its bundles must be carefully divided without injury to the motor root, which lies below the sensory root. The ganglion has a greyish-red colour and a felted surface, while the sensory root of the trigeminal nerve is almost white, and is striated longitudinally.

Ear.—The skin of the lateral surface of the **auricle** is tightly bound down to the perichondrium; and inflammations of it are attended therefore with little swelling but much pain. The **posterior auricular artery**, which ascends along the groove at the posterior attachment of the auricle, is immediately in front of the incision for opening the tympanic antrum.

The general direction of the **external auditory meatus** is medially, forwards, and downwards, and the meatus has various curves of practical importance. The highest part of the upward convexity, which is also the narrowest part of the canal, is situated at the middle of its osseous portion; beyond that the floor sinks to form a recess in which foreign bodies are apt to be imprisoned. Of the two horizontal curves the lateral is convex forwards, the medial concave forwards. The skin of the osseous portion of the canal is thin and fused with the periosteum. Boils in the canal are extremely painful; when situated on the posterior wall and associated with cellulitis the condition may be difficult to distinguish from mastoiditis.

The relations of the osseous walls of the meatus are of importance to the surgeon. The whole of the upper wall and the upper half of the posterior wall, developed from the squamous portion of the temporal bone, consist of two layers of compact bone, an upper and a lower, which are continuous with the inner and outer tables of the skull. The upper plate passes medially to the petro-squamosal suture, where it becomes continuous with the lateral edge of the tegmen tympani, which roofs over the epitympanic recess and the tympanic antrum; the lower plate bends downwards and medially at its deepest part to form the infero-lateral wall of the recess and the anterior part of the lateral wall of the antrum. On the upper and posterior segment of the external auditory margin is the **suprameatal spine**. It occupies the middle of the base of a small depression, called the **supra-meatal triangle**, which lies between the supra-mastoid crest and the postero-superior quadrant of the external osseous meatus. The spine can sometimes be felt in the living subject if the forefinger is placed in the external meatus and pressed upwards and backwards.

The lower half of the posterior wall of the osseous meatus (posterior part of the

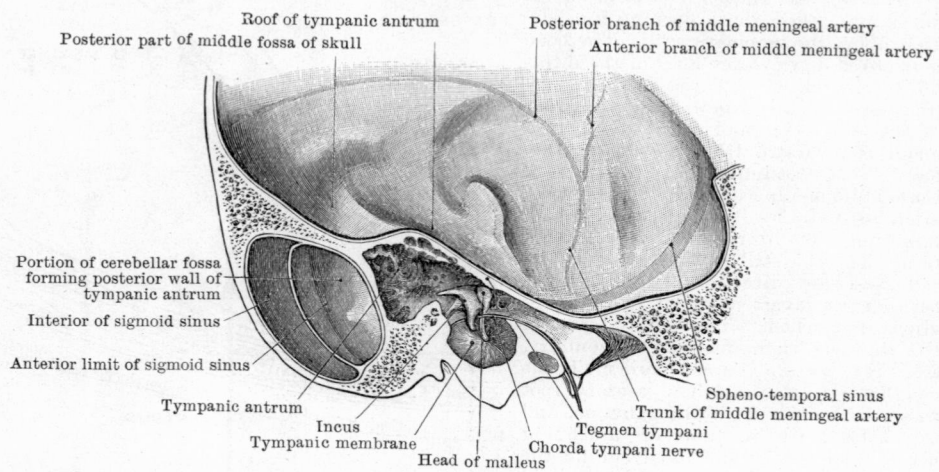

Roof of tympanic antrum
Posterior part of middle fossa of skull
Posterior branch of middle meningeal artery
Anterior branch of middle meningeal artery
Portion of cerebellar fossa forming posterior wall of tympanic antrum
Interior of sigmoid sinus
Anterior limit of sigmoid sinus
Tympanic antrum
Incus
Tympanic membrane
Head of malleus
Spheno-temporal sinus
Trunk of middle meningeal artery
Tegmen tympani
Chorda tympani nerve

FIG. 1117.—VIEW OF THE LATERAL WALL OF THE MIDDLE EAR.
Section through the left temporal bone of a child, to show the relations of the tympanum and tympanic antrum to the middle and posterior fossæ of the skull.

tympanic plate) is fused with the anterior part of the mastoid portion of the temporal bone, and closes the lower and anterior set of mastoid air-cells (border cells).

Anteriorly and inferiorly the osseous meatus is related respectively to the **mandibular joint** and the **parotid gland**. Hence it follows: that blows upon the chin may fracture the tympanic plate as well as the base of the skull; that pain on mastication is usually complained of in acute inflammatory affections of the meatus and middle ear; and that in young children, in whom the tympanic plate is incompletely ossified, suppurative inflammation is apt to extend from the parotid region into the external auditory meatus.

Clinically, to obtain a view of the **tympanic membrane** a speculum and a reflecting mirror are employed; the auricle is pulled upwards, backwards, and laterally in order to straighten the cartilaginous part of the meatus. The healthy membrane is pearly grey, semi-opaque, slightly concave, and obliquely placed, the upper and posterior portion being nearer to the observer than the anterior and inferior part.

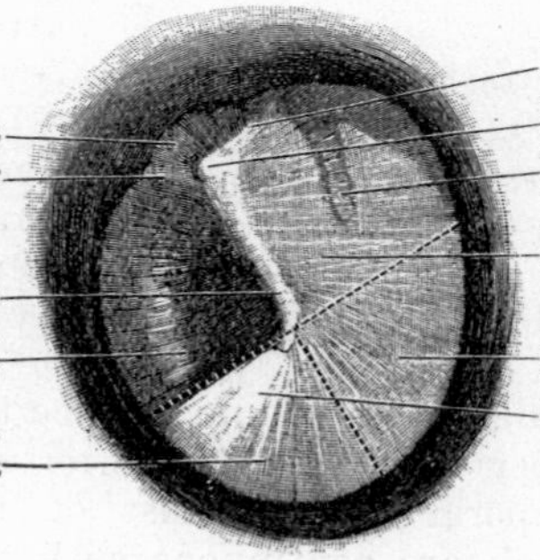

The handle and lateral process of the malleus, both embedded in the tympanic membrane, are the only objects distinctly seen when the healthy ear is examined with the speculum. The lateral process of the malleus projects laterally, and presents itself, therefore, as a distinct knob-like projection at the upper part of the membrane; passing forwards and backwards from that process are

Flaccid part
Anterior malleolar fold
Handle of malleus
Antero-superior quadrant
Antero-inferior quadrant
Posterior malleolar fold
Lateral process of malleus
Long process of incus
Postero-superior quadrant
Postero-inferior quadrant
Cone of light

FIG. 1118.—LEFT TYMPANIC MEMBRANE (as viewed from the external auditory meatus). ×3. (From Howden.)

the **anterior** and **posterior malleolar folds** of the membrane; they form the lower limit of the *flaccid part* of the membrane, and correspond to the line of the chorda tympani nerve. The handle of the malleus, situated at the junction of the two upper quadrants, is seen passing downwards and backwards to the point of maximum convexity of the membrane (umbo), situated a little below its centre (Fig. 1118); passing downwards and forwards from the umbo is the *triangular cone of reflected light*, to which too much importance must not be attached, since its appearances vary considerably in healthy ears. Normally, the long process of the incus is but faintly visible, and still less so are the promontory and fenestra cochleæ; in the condition of obstruction of the pharyngo-tympanic tube [tuba auditiva], however, in which the membrane is indrawn, those structures, along with the malleolar folds, become more distinct.

In the operation of *paracentesis of the tympanic membrane* the incision is made

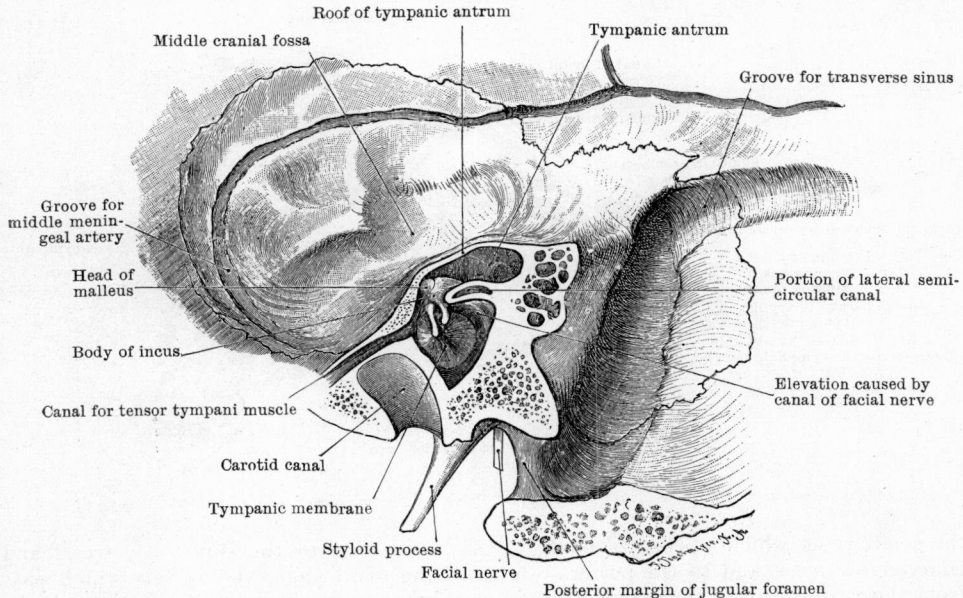

Roof of tympanic antrum

Middle cranial fossa

Tympanic antrum

Groove for transverse sinus

Groove for middle meningeal artery

Head of malleus

Portion of lateral semicircular canal

Body of incus

Canal for tensor tympani muscle

Elevation caused by canal of facial nerve

Carotid canal

Tympanic membrane

Styloid process

Facial nerve

Posterior margin of jugular foramen

FIG. 1119.—SECTION THROUGH PETROUS PORTION OF TEMPORAL BONE OF ADULT.

Showing the relation of the tympanum to the middle and posterior fossæ of the skull.

through the two posterior quadrants, as, in addition to good drainage being provided, they are farthest removed from important structures such as the chorda tympani nerve.

In order that the clinical importance of the parts seen through the translucent membrane may be understood, it is necessary to study the relative position of the structures in that part of the tympanum which lies opposite the tympanic membrane. If the tympanic plate and the tympanic membrane are carefully removed so as to leave the ossicles and chorda tympani nerve in position, it will be seen that the head of the malleus and the body and short process of the incus are altogether above the tympanic membrane, and that they occupy the **epitympanic recess** (Fig. 1119). At the junction of the upper two quadrants of the membrane is the **handle** of the **malleus**, which is directed downwards, backwards, and medially; the tendon of the tensor tympani muscle crosses the tympanic cavity from its medial wall to be attached to the upper part of the handle. The **lateral process** of the **malleus** is directed laterally a little below the deepest part of the roof of the osseous external auditory meatus. Opposite the postero-superior quadrant are the **long process** of the **incus**, which descends behind and almost parallel to the handle of the malleus, and the **stapes**, which is directed medially and also slightly upwards and backwards to the fenestra vestibuli. The **chorda tympani nerve** runs from behind forwards between the lateral surface of the upper part of the long process of the incus and the medial surface of the neck of the malleus. At the deepest part of the roof of the osseous canal, above the chorda tympani nerve and the lateral process of the malleus, is the **tympanic notch**, which is occupied by the flaccid, highest portion of the tympanic membrane; the notch is due to a deficiency in the tympanic ring, which forms only about five-sixths of a circle. Opposite the postero-inferior quadrant of the drum-head is the **promontory** caused by the first coil of the **cochlea**, below and behind which is the **fenestra cochleæ**. Opposite the antero-superior quadrant are the **cochleariform process**, the **tendon** of the **tensor tympani**, and the passage leading towards the **pharyngo-tympanic tube**.

The *medial wall* of the tympanic cavity is related to the internal ear. The *roof* separates the tympanic cavity (epitympanic recess) from the middle cranial fossa and the brain. It is formed by the **tegmen tympani**—a thin plate of bone which is continued backwards to roof over the tympanic antrum, and forwards to form the roof of the canal for the tensor tympani immediately above the osseous portion of the pharyngo-tympanic tube. Laterally the tegmen is limited by the **petro-squamous suture**, which may persist for some years after birth, thus affording a channel along which pyogenic infection may spread from the middle ear to the meninges and brain. Infection may spread also along

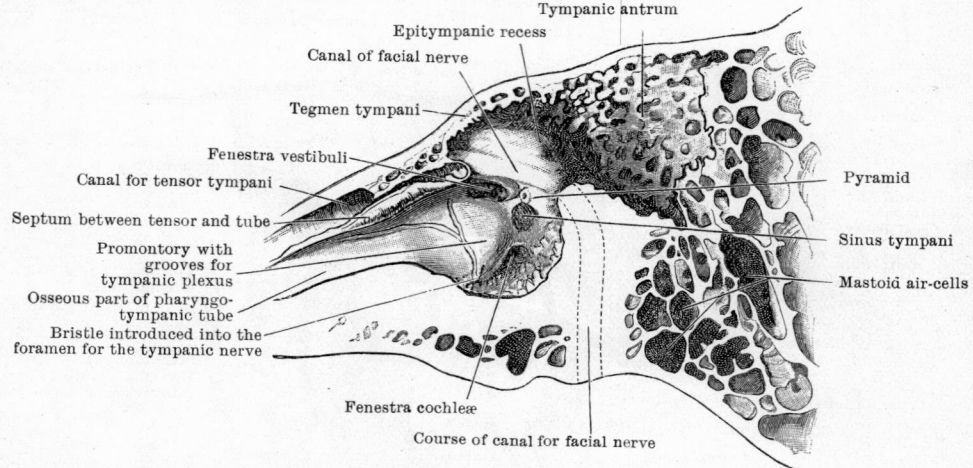

Tympanic antrum
Epitympanic recess
Canal of facial nerve
Tegmen tympani—
Fenestra vestibuli—
Canal for tensor tympani —
Septum between tensor and tube —
Promontory with grooves for tympanic plexus
Osseous part of pharyngo-tympanic tube
Bristle introduced into the foramen for the tympanic nerve
Pyramid
Sinus tympani
Mastoid air-cells
Fenestra cochleæ
Course of canal for facial nerve

FIG. 1120.—SECTION THROUGH LEFT TEMPORAL BONE, showing medial wall of tympanic cavity, etc.

the small veins which convey blood from the tympanum to the superior petrosal and transverse sinuses, and to the posterior fossa of the skull along the vessels which pass from the medial wall of the tympanic antrum through the subarcuate fossa, beneath the dome of the superior semicircular canal.

The floor of the tympanum is constituted mainly by the bone bounding the **jugular fossa**, which is occupied by the upper bulb of the internal jugular vein. When the sigmoid sinus is large and unusually far forward the bulb also is large; the fossa is consequently deeper, and arches up into the floor of the tympanic cavity, from which it may be separated merely by a thin and translucent plate of bone which occasionally shows an osseous deficiency. In cases where that condition existed the jugular bulb has been wounded in the operation of paracentesis of the tympanic membrane.

Anteriorly the tympanic cavity leads into the **pharyngo-tympanic tube** [tuba auditiva], which brings it into communication with the nasal part of the pharynx. In the child the tube is shorter and wider than in the adult; inflammations of the pharynx are therefore more apt to reach the tympanum along this route in an infant than in an adult.

Above the level of the tympanic membrane is the **epitympanic recess**, which communicates posteriorly by means of a triangular opening (*aditus ad antrum*) with the tympanic antrum. The epitympanic recess contains, from before backwards, the head of the malleus, the body and short process of the incus—the process being attached by a ligament to the floor of the aditus. When those structures are covered with inflamed mucous membrane or granulations, drainage from the tympanic antrum into the tympanum is interfered with. The *boundaries of the aditus*, important surgically, are as follows: superiorly, the tegmen tympani; medially, an eminence of compact bone containing the lateral semicircular canal; below and in front of them is a second smaller prominence, corresponding to that portion of the canal for the facial nerve which curves immediately above and behind the fenestra vestibuli. The wall of the facial canal in that situation is thin or even deficient, so that inflammation may readily spread from the tympanum to the facial nerve. The lateral wall of the aditus is formed by the deepest part of the upper wall of the osseous external auditory meatus.

The *posterior wall* of the tympanum, below the aditus ad antrum, is formed by diplöic bone which contains the descending portion of the canal for the facial nerve. Immediately below the floor of the aditus, on the posterior wall of the tympanum, is the pyramid, through which the tendon of the stapedius muscle emerges to be attached to the head of the stapes.

The **tympanic antrum** is a backward and upward extension of the tympanum (Fig. 1120) and it is relatively larger in the child than in the adult. Situated above and behind the tympanic cavity proper, its *lateral wall* is a triangular plate of bone which descends, behind the external auditory meatus, from the squamous temporal. Posteriorly, that triangular plate is separated in the child from the petro-mastoid element by the **squamo-mastoid suture**, which overlies the posterior part of the antrum and transmits small veins to the surface. The suture does not disappear until a year or two after birth, and remains of it may frequently be detected in the adult bone. The anterior and upper portion of the triangular plate turns medially at an angle to form the upper and posterior wall of the rudimentary osseous meatus, as well as the floor of the epitympanic recess.

In the adult the lateral wall of the tympanic antrum is a plate of bone, from $\frac{1}{2}$ to $\frac{3}{4}$ in. in thickness, that separates the antrum from the suprameatal triangle, and may therefore be felt through the skin as a slight depression. It occupies the centre of a triangle formed by the supra-mastoid crest, the posterior-superior quadrant of the auditory meatus and an imaginary line drawn vertically through the posterior margin of the meatus. The supra-mastoid crest, which varies considerably in its obliquity, is sometimes situated a little above the level of the roof of the antrum; it is safer, therefore, when operating on the antrum, to take the level of the upper border of the osseous meatus as the guide, in order to avoid opening the middle fossa of the skull. In children the supra-mastoid crest is not developed, so that if the operator mistakes the posterior root of the zygoma for the crest he will open into the middle cranial fossa immediately in front of the epitympanic recess. The postero-superior quadrant of the osseous meatus is therefore the only reliable guide to the antrum in the child.

The *medial wall* of the antrum is a thick plate of spongy bone which separates the antrum from that portion of the posterior fossa which lies between the aqueduct of the vestibule and the groove for the sigmoid sinus, and contains the posterior semicircular canal.

The *roof* slopes downwards and forwards, and is the posterior and thinnest part of the tegmen tympani.

The *floor* is on a lower level than the aditus, and is therefore unfavourably placed for natural drainage.

The **mastoid process** begins to develop in the second year. As development advances the diplöe surrounding the antrum in the child becomes excavated to form the **mastoid air cells**, which radiate from the antrum, and either directly or indirectly communicate with it by small openings. In the pneumatic type of mastoid the whole of the mastoid part of the temporal bone is occupied by those cells ; and they extend also upwards into the squamous portion, forwards to the posterior wall of the osseous meatus (border-cells), and backwards into the occipital bone. Pus retained within the "*border-cells*" may penetrate the posterior wall of the osseous meatus, and rupture through it. Less frequently the mastoid cells are absent, the bone consisting either of osseous tissue similar to that of the diplöe, or of dense bone (sclerosed type).

In the infant the mastoid portion of the temporal bone is composed of sclerotic or sclero-diploëtic bone. The tympanic antrum is always present and there are a few small air cells in its lateral wall. In the adult the sclerotic or sclero-diploëtic type of bone persists in about 20 per cent. of skulls; that is to say, that the lateral wall of the antrum is formed either of dense bone, or of bone whose spaces are filled with marrow. In the remaining 80 per cent. the mastoid part of the temporal bone is cellular or pneumatic, owing to the extension of the air cells from the antrum. The difference in anatomical structure is of great importance in cases of mastoiditis because, if a patient with a pneumatic mastoid suffers from severe otitis media and mastoiditis, the inflammatory process extends to all those air cells and usually comes to the surface on the lateral surface of the mastoid-temporal, giving rise to a subperiosteal abscess. On the other hand, if the patient has a sclerotic or sclero-diploëtic mastoid—the so-called "persistent infantile" form of mastoid—the inflammatory process is confined to the tympanic antrum and does not manifest itself on the surface. It is in the latter cases that an attack of acute suppurative otitis media, with infection of the tympanic antrum, is specially liable to become chronic or to result in infection of the labyrinth or an intracranial complication. In operating on cases of chronic middle ear suppuration the surgeon almost invariably meets with the persistent infantile type of mastoid temporal, for the reason given above. Formerly it was erroneously supposed that the chronic infection of the mastoid resulted in sclerosis of the bone. We now know that cause and effect were transposed and that it is the sclerotic type of mastoid which has resulted in the chronic inflammatory condition and not the chronic inflammatory condition which has resulted in sclerosis of the mastoid.

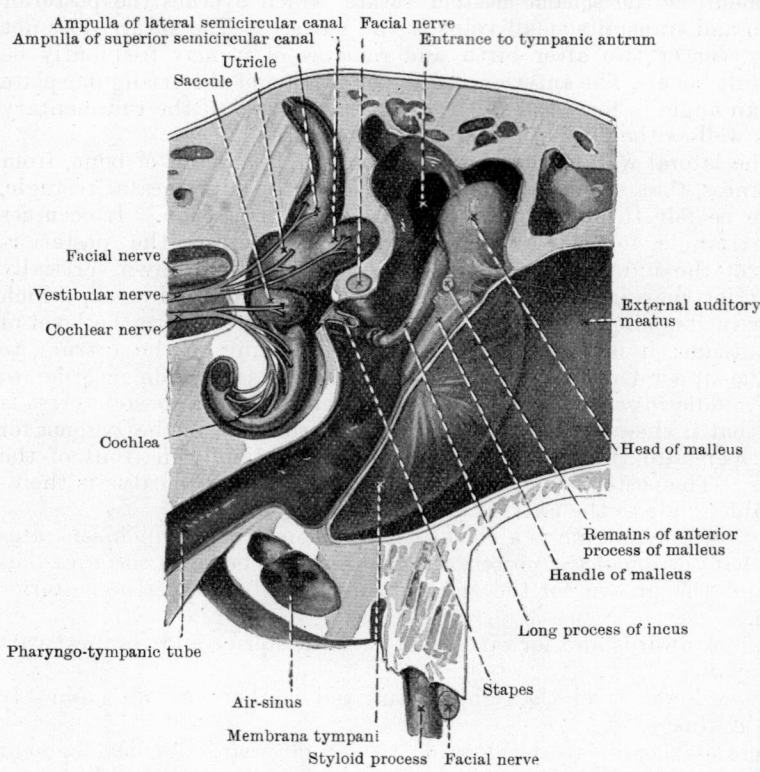

Ampulla of lateral semicircular canal — Facial nerve
Ampulla of superior semicircular canal — Entrance to tympanic antrum
Utricle
Saccule
Facial nerve
Vestibular nerve
Cochlear nerve
External auditory meatus
Cochlea
Head of malleus
Remains of anterior process of malleus
Handle of malleus
Long process of incus
Pharyngo-tympanic tube
Air-sinus
Stapes
Membrana tympani
Styloid process — Facial nerve

FIG. 1121.—THE TYMPANIC CAVITY AND ADJACENT PARTS (SEMI-DIAGRAMMATIC).

The **labyrinth** may become infected in cases of suppurative otitis media. In acute cases the infective process may pass into the inner ear through the fenestra vestibuli or fenestra cochleæ. In the former case the annular ligament is infiltrated by pus cells, while in the latter the secondary tympanic membrane is similarly affected. In chronic cases, on the other hand, the route of infection is by way of the prominence of the lateral semicircular canal, which not infrequently becomes eroded in cases of chronic purulent otitis media associated with accumulation of cast-off epithelium in the tympanic antrum—a condition known as *cholesteatoma*. If the labyrinth contains pus it is unsafe to operate on the mastoid unless the inner ear is opened up at the same time. If that is not done the mastoid operation is likely to be followed by purulent meningitis, owing to the passage of infective material from the labyrinth to the subarachnoid space. The hollow spaces of the labyrinth may be drained after removal of the promontory (see Fig. 1120) by means of a small gouge and two or three blows of the hammer. Apply the gouge immediately below and in front of the fenestra vestibuli, in order to remove the bone between the two fenestræ. In addition, the prominence of the lateral semicircular canal on the medial wall and floor of the aditus is usually removed and the canal opened up (Hinsberg's operation). A more radical method is that described by Neumann, in which the sigmoid sinus is exposed with the large gouge and hammer. A small, blunt periosteum elevator is then passed in between the sigmoid sinus and its bony wall, in a medial and forward direction, so as to separate the dura mater from the bone in the region of the saccus endolymphaticus. Stacke's protector is then introduced between the dura mater and the bone, and the bone is removed with the gouge in the direction of the internal auditory meatus. In that way first the posterior semicircular canal is opened up and later the lateral canal is reached. The smooth end of the lateral canal is then followed up to the vestibule, in order that the vestibule may be freely drained from behind. In addition, the lateral wall of the promontory is chipped off according to the method described above in Hinsberg's operation.

The mastoid portion of the temporal bone is grooved, on its medial surface, by the **sigmoid sinus**. The average distance of the foremost part of the sinus from the supra-meatal triangle is 1 cm. The right sinus usually receives the superior sagittal sinus, and it is then larger and farther forward than the left; in extreme cases it may reach to within 2 or 3 mm. of the meatus. The average minimum distance of the sigmoid sinus from the *lateral* surface of the mastoid temporal is about 10 mm., but when the sinus is large and far forward the thickness may be reduced to 1 or 2 mm.

The **facial nerve**, after entering the facial canal at the bottom of the internal auditory meatus, lies immediately above and behind the fenestra vestibuli, between it and the prominence of the lateral semicircular canal; thence it descends almost vertically in the posterior wall of the tympanum $\frac{1}{8}$ in. behind and medial to the lower half of the deepest part of the posterior wall of the external osseous meatus, and it emerges through the stylo-mastoid foramen (Fig. 1121).

In the infant, in consequence of the absence of the mastoid process, the exit of the facial nerve from the stylo-mastoid foramen is exposed on the lateral surface of the skull rather than on the base, at a point immediately behind the posterior segment of the tympanic horse-shoe. It follows, therefore, that, in infancy, the incision to expose the antrum should not be curved too far downwards and forwards, else the facial nerve may be divided. In the infant the position of the tympanic antrum is relatively higher than in the adult, because in the infant the upper wall of the auditory meatus inclines towards the vertical plane instead of being horizontal.

The lymph vessels from the auricle and external meatus open into the mastoid and parotid lymph glands—the latter receiving also the lymph from the middle ear. The efferent vessels from those glands open into the glands that lie deep to the upper part of the sterno-mastoid muscle; hence it is that those groups of glands are so frequently found to be diseased secondary to tuberculosis of the middle ear; and care must be taken not to mistake an abscess in one of the mastoid glands for subperiosteal mastoid suppuration associated with middle-ear disease.

To open the **tympanic antrum** the surgeon makes a curved incision a little behind the attachment of the auricle, and removes, with a hammer and gouge, the bone immediately above and behind the postero-superior quadrant of the external osseous meatus. The operator avoids (1) the *middle fossa* of the *skull* by keeping below the supra-mastoid crest; (2) the *sigmoid sinus* by keeping close to the external auditory meatus and by directing the chisel slightly forwards as well as medially in opening the mastoid cells; (3) the descending portion of the *facial nerve* by not encroaching upon the inferior half of the deepest part of the posterior wall of the osseous meatus. If the operation is extended from the tympanic antrum through the aditus into the epitympanic recess, care must be taken not to injure either the *lateral semicircular canal* or the *facial nerve*, both of which lie in relation to the medial wall of the aditus.

Paranasal Sinuses.—The **frontal sinuses** are a pair of cavities situated immediately above the root of the nose between the two tables of the frontal bone (Fig. 1122). Each sinus at its most dependent part communicates, by means of the infundibulum, with the middle meatus of the nose. A bony septum, rarely incomplete, separates the two sinuses; it is usually median below, but it may deviate to one or other side above (Pl. LXIV. Fig. 1.)

The sinuses vary considerably in their size and shape, independently of the degree of development of the glabella and superciliary arches. Average dimensions are approximately an inch in height and in breadth and over an inch in depth along its floor. But the sinus may exist merely as a small recess above the nose, or it may extend upwards into the forehead for more than two inches, laterally to the side of the skull, and its inferior part may extend backwards, in the orbital roof, as far as the optic foramen. The anterior wall is the thickest, but the thickness may vary from 1 to 5 mm. The floor is the thinnest wall; when pus is retained within the cavity it tends to point therefore at the upper and medial angle of the orbital opening. Intra-cranial suppuration may arise in connexion with sinus disease by extension through the cerebral wall of a sinus. The muco-endosteal lining is thin and pale and readily strips from the bone.

In many subjects, by the aid of *trans-illumination*, the extent of the sinuses and the position of the intervening septum may be mapped out upon the forehead. For that purpose a small electric lamp is placed against the floor of the sinus, beneath the medial third of the supra-orbital margin.

The radiographic appearances of the frontal sinuses are of importance clinically and give more information than trans-illumination. Antero-posterior radiographs (Pls. LXII and LXIV, Fig. 1) show the vertical extent of the sinuses, the degree of asymmetry, and the presence or absence of recesses, and their intervening septa. An orbital expansion is indicated by a well-defined shadow with a sharply-defined upper margin, extending laterally parallel to and immediately above the medial half or more of the supra-orbital margin. Lateral radiographs (Pls. LXI, LXIII, LXIV, Fig. 2) show not only the height of the

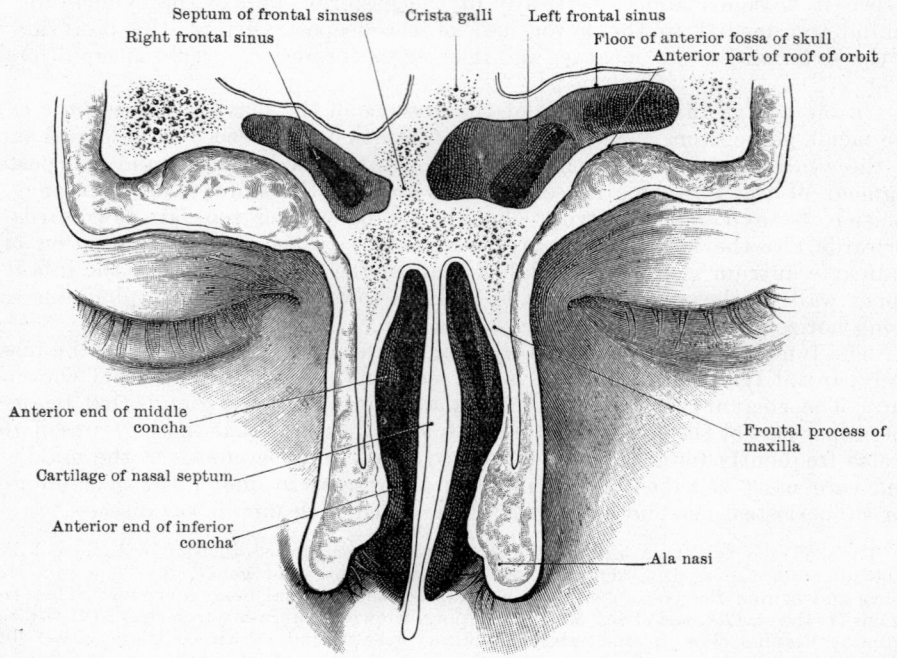

Fig. 1122.—Coronal Section through the Nose and Frontal Sinuses.

sinuses but also their antero-posterior diameter, as well as the degree to which their lower parts extend backwards in the roof of the orbit and the relation of the sinus to the underlying ethmoid sinuses. It is exceptional to meet with frontal sinuses before the age of five years, but they are almost invariably present by the seventh or eighth year.

When the sinus is explored the opening in the bone should be made close to the median plane, immediately above the root of the nose. In marked cases of deviation of the septum one sinus may extend so far beyond the median plane as to reduce the other to a mere slit; in such cases the surgeon may fail to open the diseased sinus when the operation is performed through the anterior wall. The sinus frequently contains incomplete partitions which cut off pockets and recesses usually found towards the lateral angle of the sinus; in chronic suppuration of the sinuses, special attention should be paid to those recesses as well as to the backward extension into the orbital roof. The anterior ethmoidal sinuses are closely related to the medial or nasal portion of the floor of the sinus and its passage of exit; hence suppuration very frequently co-exists in both cavities. In some cases pus may flow from the frontal sinus along the infundibulum into the hiatus semilunaris and so into the maxillary sinus, which opens into the lower part of the hiatus. Killian's operation for the cure of chronic suppuration in the sinus consists in removing its anterior and inferior walls—the supra-orbital margin being left to prevent the falling in of the eyebrow. By the removal of the frontal process of the maxilla good access may at the same time be obtained to the ethmoidal sinuses, and free drainage established between the frontal sinus and the nasal cavity.

In an antero-posterior radiograph of the skull (Pl. LXII), the light shadows formed by the **ethmoidal sinuses** are seen to occupy the well-defined area bounded on each side by the still lighter shadow of the orbital cavity and above by the dense horizontal shadow of the cribriform plate, which occupies the frontier line between those sinuses and the frontal sinuses. Anteriorly the ethmoidal area is overlapped by the vertical shadow caused by the frontal processes of the maxillæ and by the ridges of the lacrimal bones. Not infrequently the ethmoidal sinuses will be seen to extend into the roof of the orbit, while inferiorly and laterally they come into close relation to the upper and medial angle of the shadow caused by the maxillary sinus. The comparative transparency of the area of the ethmoidal sinuses is accounted for by the fact that it is superimposed upon that of the sphenoidal sinuses.

In a lateral radiograph the ethmoidal area is seen to extend from the frontal process of the maxilla backwards across the orbits to the sphenoidal sinuses, with which they are contiguous (Pl. LXIII). The area is crossed about its middle by the vertical shadow caused by the lateral margin of the orbit. In front of that, and occupying, therefore, the light area of the orbital cavity, are the *anterior ethmoidal sinuses*; and behind it are the *posterior ethmoidal sinuses*. In a profile view of the skull, the posterior ethmoidal sinuses, the sphenoidal sinuses, and the hypophyseal fossa all lie, from before backwards, in the axis of those rays which pass through the thinnest portion of the cranial box, namely, the anterior part of the temporal fossa; hence the possibility of identifying them in a radiograph taken even from a living subject (Pl. LX).

The **sphenoidal sinuses** are so far behind the upper half of the anterior bony apertures of the nose that their outlines cannot be identified in an antero-posterior radiograph. If the sinuses are filled with bismuth before the radiograph is taken, it will be seen that they produce a well-defined and slightly oval black shadow, about the size of a shilling, situated opposite the upper half of these apertures, the upper limit of the shadow reaching just up to the transverse curvilinear line already referred to, while laterally the shadow reaches 5 mm. medial to the lower half of the medial margin of the orbit (Logan Turner).

In lateral radiographs of the skull the slight shadow caused by the sphenoidal sinus is seen immediately below and in front of the characteristic well-defined cup-shaped shadow thrown by the floor of the hypophyseal fossa (Pls. LX, LXI, LXIII). Inferiorly, the sinus area is bounded and to some extent overlapped and obliterated by the dense shadow which corresponds to the articular eminence and the horizontal portion of the greater wing of the sphenoid—that is to say, to the floor of the middle cranial fossa. That dark shadow is continuous, posteriorly, with that caused by the petrous portion of the temporal bone. Anteriorly is the shadow of the posterior ethmoidal sinuses (blurred by that produced by the vertical portion of the greater wing of the sphenoid), while posteriorly it is limited by the shadow produced by the part of the body of the sphenoid that lies below the dorsum sellæ.

HYPOPHYSIS CEREBRI

The topography of the *hypophyseal fossa*, which lodges the hypophysis cerebri, is of importance now that surgery has succeeded in dealing with certain tumours and enlargements of the hypophysis. The hypophyseal fossa is immediately behind the upper part of the sphenoidal sinuses; and, in a median section of the skull, the anterior half of the fossa is seen to project into what would correspond to the supero-posterior angle of the sinuses (Fig. 147). The more the sphenoidal sinuses project backwards, below the hypophyseal fossa, the thinner is that part of the floor of the posterior cranial fossa which separates the sinus from the basilar artery and the pons. When, on the other hand, the sphenoidal sinuses are small and do not extend backwards below the hypophyseal fossa, it may be difficult to identify the fossa during an operation.

The sphenoidal sinuses are the surgeon's guide to the hypophysis. To reach them he traverses the upper portions of both nasal cavities, removing, from before backwards, the upper portion of the septum nasi, the superior and middle conchæ, and, if necessary, the ethmoidal sinuses. The rostrum of the sphenoid, situated at the upper and most posterior part of the nasal septum, serves as a guide to the anterior wall of the sphenoidal sinuses; after its removal the operator opens up the sinuses by removing their anterior and inferior walls and the septum. He then exposes the hypophysis by breaking down the anterior portion of the floor of the hypophyseal fossa, which bulges into the upper and posterior part of the sinuses. In making the opening from the sinuses into the fossa, the surgeon must keep strictly to the median plane, in order to avoid opening into the cavernous sinus; if the roof of the sinus is penetrated in front of the fossa and the cranial cavity opened, the optic chiasma is liable to be injured; and if the posterior wall of the sinus is penetrated below the level of the fossa the spongy tissue of the body of the sphenoid will be opened into, and if the sinus happened to extend unusually far back, the anterior part of the posterior cranial fossa would be entered, and the basilar artery, on the front of the pons, might sustain damage.

The average distance from the nasion to the anterior superior margin of the sphenoidal sinus is $1\frac{3}{4}$ inches, while the distance from the anterior superior boundary of the sinus to the anterior superior margin of the hypophyseal fossa is a little more than $\frac{1}{2}$ inch; the total distance from the nasion to the hypophysis is therefore from $2\frac{1}{4}$ to $2\frac{1}{2}$ inches. The average distance from the anterior nasal spine to the hypophysis is almost 3 in. while that from the temporal fossa to the hypophysis is 2 inches. The floor of the hypophyseal fossa occupies a plane half an inch above the upper border of the zygoma, and is on a level also with a plane projected backwards from the nasion to the inion. The normal fossa varies considerably in size.

In lateral radiographs of the skull (Pls. LX, LXI, LXIII), the outline of the hypophyseal fossa is marked out by a crescentic linear shadow, the anterior and posterior horns of the crescent being the shadows of the anterior and posterior clinoid processes. Below and in front of the fossa the outlines of the sphenoidal sinuses may be distinctly traced. In front of the fossa the shadow which outlines the roof of the sphenoidal sinus is formed from before backwards by (1) the tuberculum sellæ, (2) the optic groove, (3) the plane of the lesser wing of the sphenoid. Above the lesser wing there is a second horizontal shadow caused by the roof of the orbit. Below the sphenoidal sinus there is a curved shadow produced by the floor of the middle cranial fossa; and behind the dorsum sellæ a dense triangular shadow corresponds to the petrous portion of the temporal bone.

Enlargements of the hypophysis cerebri can often be clearly demonstrated by an increase in the depth and antero-posterior diameter of the radiographic outline of the hypophyseal fossa, by the unusual extent to which the fossa encroaches on the sphenoidal sinus, by pressure atrophy of the clinoid processes, and by the thinning and backward inclination of the dorsum sellæ.

Adenomata and cysts of the anterior (glandular) lobe of the hypophysis frequently enlarge upward through the diaphragma sellæ towards the brain. After emerging from the fossa the tumour bulges upwards through the space bounded in front by the anterior segment of the circulus arteriosus, and behind by the optic nerves and the chiasma. The resulting blindness—temporal, homonymous, or complete—is due to the pressure of the growth on the optic nerves.

When enlargement of the hypophysis necessitates surgical interference, the possible routes of access vary according to the position and extent of the swelling. Supra-hypophyseal tumours and hypophyseal tumours which have extended above the level of the hypophyseal fossa are approached by the trans-frontal route. Tumours confined to the fossa or extending sideways are dealt with most appropriately by the naso-sphenoidal route.

THE FACE

The skin of the face is thin, vascular, and rich in sebaceous and sweat glands; it is intimately connected with the subcutaneous tissue, in which the facial muscles and the main blood-vessels are embedded. Owing to its elasticity and to the presence of the main blood-vessels in the lax subcutaneous tissue, the face is an admirable site for plastic operations, as the flaps do not necrose in spite of considerable tension. The laxity of the tissues accounts for the marked swelling which attends œdematous and inflammatory conditions about the face. Whenever possible, incisions should be made along the line of the natural furrows and creases of the skin, in order that the resulting cicatrix may be less noticeable.

The bony landmarks of the face which can be readily palpated are: the **superciliary arches** and the **glabella**, the **nasion**, the **bridge of the nose**, the **bony anterior aperture of the nose** and the **anterior nasal spine**, the **supra- and infra-orbital margins**, the **zygomatic process** of the **frontal bone**, the **medial angular process**, the anterior part of the **temporal line**, the **zygomatic bone**, the **zygomatic arch**, and the region of the **canine fossa** of the maxilla.

Immediately below the root of the zygoma, and in front of the upper part of the tragus, is the **head of the mandible**. If the finger-tip is pressed on the head while the mouth is being widely opened, the bone will be felt to glide forwards, while the finger sinks deeply into the hollow corresponding to the **articular fossa**. The close relation of the first part of the **maxillary artery** to the medial side of the neck of the mandible must be kept in mind in operations calling for disarticulation or excision of the head. The **ramus of the mandible** is sandwiched between the masseter and the pterygoid muscles, and can be removed without opening into the cavity of the mouth. Below the head, one can palpate the borders of the ramus and the **angle** and **body of the mandible**. The anterior border of the **coronoid process** is felt in front of the upper part of the anterior border of the masseter, immediately below the anterior part of the zygomatic arch.

The pulsation of the **facial artery** [a. maxillaris externa] may be felt as the vessel crosses the lower margin of the mandible at the anterior border of the masseter, $1\frac{1}{4}$ in. in front of the angle of the mandible. To map out the course of the artery on the face, draw a line from that point to a point $\frac{1}{2}$ in. lateral to the angle of the mouth, and thence to a point a little behind the ala nasi and along the side of the nose to the medial angle of the eye. The **anterior facial vein** is behind the facial artery, and takes a straighter course from the medial angle of the eye to the anterior inferior angle of the masseter. The vessel is devoid of valves; infective phlebitis and thrombosis are therefore apt to spread along it to the cavernous sinus by way of the ophthalmic and pterygoid veins.

A line dropped vertically from the supra-orbital notch to the lower border of the mandible opposite the interval between the two lower premolar teeth, will cross the **infra-orbital** and **mental foramina**—the former $\frac{1}{4}$ in. below the infra-orbital margin, the latter midway between the borders of the mandible. In the operation of neurectomy for the relief of trigeminal neuralgia, those foramina furnish the guides to the correspondingly named branches of the fifth nerve. It should be remembered that these nerves, after emerging from their foramina, lie, at first, deep to the facial muscles. The supra-orbital and infra-orbital nerves are not infrequently represented each by two branches, one of which passes through an accessory foramen situated lateral to the normal opening. In neurectomy of the **inferior dental nerve**, the ramus of the mandible is trephined midway between its anterior and posterior borders, in line with the crown of the last molar tooth, the nerve being reached as it enters the mandibular canal; the **lingual nerve**, which lies a little in front of the inferior dental, can be exposed through the same opening.

The relations of the maxillary and mandibular divisions of the trigeminal nerve have become of increased importance to the surgeon since the introduction of the treatment of trigeminal neuralgia by the injection of alcohol into those nerves immediately after their exit from the cranial cavity. To reach the maxillary nerve as it lies in the pterygo-palatine fossa, puncture the skin immediately below the zygomatic arch, about 4 cm. in front of the anterior wall of the external auditory meatus. The needle should be directed medially with a slight inclination upwards and backwards. After perforating the masseter and temporal muscles, the instrument enters the fatty tissue of the infra-temporal fossa, embedded in which there are the maxillary artery and some veins. The needle, penetrating still more deeply, is made to pass between the two heads of the lateral pterygoid muscle through the pterygo-maxillary fissure into the pterygo-palatine fossa. If the instrument is passed too far forwards it will strike the maxilla; if too far backwards, the lateral pterygoid lamina. The œdema of the eyelids which not infrequently follows the operation is due to some of the fluid passing upwards into the orbit through the inferior orbital fissure. The distance from the skin to the nerve is about 5 cm. (2 in.). The patient's mouth should be open while the introduction of the needle is proceeding : otherwise the needle may come into contact with the coronoid process of the mandible.

The mandibular nerve is injected immediately below the foramen ovale, which is 4 cm. from the skin in the same coronal plane as the articular eminence. When the mouth is opened widely the head of the mandible travels forwards and can be distinctly felt immediately below the eminence. To avoid the mandibular joint introduce the needle through the skin immediately below the zygoma, a little in front of the eminence, an inch in front of the external auditory meatus. Push it medially and slightly backwards through the mandibular notch, and thence through, or immediately above, the lateral pterygoid muscle, into the nerve. Symington pointed out that the chief dangers connected with this operation are dependent upon the needle being passed in too far. Thus, if it is directed straight medially beyond the depth of the nerve (4 cm.) it will penetrate the tensor palati and the pharyngo-tympanic tube and open on the side wall of the naso-pharynx ; or, if directed a little upwards, it may pass through the foramen ovale, and even reach the cavernous sinus and the internal carotid artery, as the medial boundary of the foramen slopes upwards and medially.

The **facial nerve**, after emerging from the stylo-mastoid foramen, enters the substance of the parotid gland, nearly an inch deep to the middle of the anterior border of the mastoid process. It is superficial to the external carotid artery. Branches of the nerve can be rolled under the finger as they cross the neck and head of the mandible ; incisions continued along the mandible above that point should be only skin-deep if the branches are to be avoided. To expose the trunk of the nerve make an incision from the middle of the anterior border of the mastoid process to the angle of the mandible. Incisions on the cheek should, whenever possible, be planned so as to run parallel with the branches of the nerve, which radiate from the lower end of the tragus. The nerve may be paralysed by wounds of the cheek and by malignant tumours of the parotid, as also by intra-cranial and middle-ear lesions.

The **parotid gland** (Fig. 1129) is surrounded by a fascial envelope, the strongest portion of which is continued from the deep cervical fascia over its lateral surface to become attached to the zygoma ; hence abscesses in the parotid tend to burrow deeply towards the pterygo-palatine fossa and the upper part of the pharynx ; the pus should therefore be evacuated early by Hilton's method through an oblique incision a little behind and below the angle of the mandible. A study of the relations of the gland explains the surgical difficulties which attend its complete removal.

The **parotid duct** can be rolled beneath the finger as it crosses the masseter, rather less than a finger's-breadth below the zygoma. After winding round the anterior border of the muscle it pierces the buccinator, and opens into the mouth opposite the second upper molar tooth. The duct corresponds to the middle third of a line drawn from the lower margin of the concha of the auricle to a point midway between the ala nasi and the margin of the upper lip.

Superficial to the parotid and a little in front of the tragus there is a **parotid lymph gland** which is frequently found to be inflamed in children suffering from eczematous conditions of the eyelids, face, scalp, and external ear. When an abscess connected with that gland is opened, make the incision as low down as possible, in order to avoid the parotid duct.

The deep parotid lymph glands, which lie partly in the substance of the parotid and partly deep to it, are especially liable to become infected secondary to tuberculous disease of the middle ear and to malignant affections about the root of the tongue, the throat, and the naso-pharynx. In their removal it is generally impossible to avoid the cervical branch of the facial nerve, which pierces the cervical fascia immediately below and behind the angle of the mandible. The cervical branch supplies the platysma and the depressor labii inferioris muscles ; its division therefore gives rise to inability to depress the lower lip on the affected side. At the same operation some trouble may be caused by bleeding from the posterior facial vein and its divisions, which traverse the substance of the parotid gland.

Eyelids.—The skin of the **eyelids**, more especially of the upper, is very thin and is connected with the orbicularis oculi muscle by delicate, lax subcutaneous tissue destitute of fat ; hence the marked swelling which occurs in a " black eye " and in œdema of the lids. Along the anterior edge of the free margin of each lid are the eyelashes and the orifices of the sebaceous glands, suppurative inflammation of which gives rise to a "*stye*"; along the posterior edge are the minute orifices of the **tarsal glands**. Those glands, embedded in the deep surface of the tarsi, are seen through the palpebral conjunctiva as a row of parallel, yellowish, granular-looking streaks. From the deep position of the glands it follows that the skin over a Meibomian cyst—a retention cyst resulting from occlusion of the orifice of a tarsal gland—is freely movable, and that to reach the cyst an incision should be made through the conjunctival surface of the lid.

The **palpebral conjunctiva** is closely adherent to the ocular surface of the tarsi; at the fornix it is loose and contains small lymph follicles, which become hypertrophied in the condition known as granular conjunctivitis. The **ocular conjunctiva** is thin, transparent, and loosely attached to the sclera, so that in an operation on the eye a fold of the membrane can be picked up with forceps to steady the eyeball.

In inflammatory affections of the eye the state of the visible vessels gives important information as to the seat of the mischief. For example, in inflammation of the *conjunctiva* the posterior conjunctival vessels (derived from the palpebral arteries)—scarcely visible normally—appear as a close network which fades away towards the corneal margin; those vessels move freely with the conjunctiva, and disappear under pressure. · In superficial inflammations of the *cornea* the anterior conjunctival vessels (the most superficial of the terminal branches of the anterior ciliary arteries) are seen to spread in a freely branching manner into its superficial layers. In *iritis* and deep inflammations of the cornea there is a pink circumcorneal zone of vascular dilatation consisting of delicate straight vessels which do not disappear under pressure and do not move with the conjunctiva; they are the subconjunctival (episcleral) terminations of the anterior ciliary arteries; in health they are invisible.

Lacrimal Apparatus.—The **lacrimal gland**, situated behind the lateral part of the supra-orbital margin, cannot be felt unless enlarged. If the upper eyelid is raised and everted, the palpebral process of the gland is seen to bulge below the lateral third of the fornix, in which situation also the minute orifices of the lacrimal ducts may be detected. When the lower lid is drawn gently downwards, the **punctum lacrimale** is seen on a slight papillary elevation of its margin about 4 mm. from the medial angle of the eye; the corresponding orifice of the upper lid is a little more medial. Normally the puncta are directed towards the ocular conjunctiva, and are accurately applied to it, immediately lateral to the lacrimal caruncle. Drawing the lids laterally puts the **medial palpebral ligament** on the stretch, and it can be felt as a narrow tense band passing medially to be attached to the frontal process of the maxilla. The ligament is a guide to the position of the **lacrimal sac**, which it crosses a little above its middle. Continuous with the lower end of the lacrimal sac is the **naso-lacrimal duct**, which passes downwards and slightly backwards and laterally to open into the inferior meatus of the nose under cover of the anterior part of the inferior concha. The lacrimal sac and naso-lacrimal duct each measure about $\frac{1}{2}$ in. in length; the duct is slightly contracted at its beginning and end, and it is in those situations that pathological strictures of the duct are most common. Spontaneous rupture of an abscess of the lacrimal sac occurs almost invariably immediately below the medial palpebral ligament; it is in that situation that the abscess should be opened, the incision being made a little lateral to the terminal part of the facial artery.

The **lacrimal canaliculi**, which convey the tears from the puncta to the lacrimal sac, run for the first 1-2 mm. almost vertically from the free margins of the lids, and then parallel to them. The **lacrimal caruncle** is placed between those portions of the lids in which the canaliculi lie. In the various morbid conditions which give rise either to misdirection of the puncta or to stricture at any part of the lacrimal drainage apparatus, overflow of the tears (*epiphora*) is the chief sign. When a probe is passed along a lacrimal canaliculus, the instrument, in consequence of the bend of the canaliculus, is passed at first vertically from the margin of the lid, and afterwards parallel to it, until the point is felt to strike against the medial wall of the lacrimal sac; to pass the instrument onwards along the naso-lacrimal duct rotate the handle forwards and upwards through a quarter of a circle, and then push it gently downwards and slightly backwards and laterally into the inferior meatus of the nose.

The **tarsi** are attached to the periosteum of the orbital margins by the *palpebral fascia,* which shuts off the communication between the subcutaneous tissue of the eyelids and the fatty tissue of the orbital cavity. In fracture of the floor of the anterior cranial fossa involving the roof of the orbit, the blood extends forwards between the periosteum and the musculo-fascial envelope of the orbit, and appears under the conjunctiva.

To obtain free access to the cavity of the orbit, the surgeon first enlarges the palpebral fissure by making a horizontal incision from the lateral angle of the eye to the lateral margin of the orbit, and then, after everting the eyelid, divides the conjunctiva along the fornix of the upper or of the lower lid, or of both, as may be necessary.

Nose.—To examine the cavity of the nose from the front (*anterior rhinoscopy*), dilate the nostril with a nasal speculum and illuminate the interior by means of strong reflected light. The **anterior end of the inferior concha** appears as a rounded body projecting from the side wall of the nose; when its muco-periosteum is turgescent it is apt to come into contact with the nasal septum and so occlude the cavity. The **inferior meatus** is between the inferior concha and the side wall of the nasal cavity; bring it into view by tilting the head backwards. The **lower end of the naso-lacrimal duct** is concealed by the anterior part of the inferior concha. The **floor** of the nose is horizontal and is on a slightly lower level than the nostrils. The **septum**, generally more or less deviated to one or other side, is seen when the head is slightly rotated away from the side to be examined. The **anterior end of the middle concha**, which lies a little behind and medial to the infero-medial angle of the orbital margin, is seen when the patient's head is thrown well back; it is separated from the septum only by a slit-like interval. Rotate the patient's head towards the shoulder to bring the **anterior part** of **the middle meatus** of that side into view; pus in that situation may originate from the frontal sinus, the anterior ethmoidal sinuses, or the maxillary sinus, all of which open into the middle meatus.

When epistaxis occurs it usually proceeds from the small vessels of the septum. Arrest the bleeding by compressing the superior labial arteries, by plugging the nostrils, or by grasping the cartilaginous part of the nose firmly between the finger and thumb.

The **maxillary sinus** is a pyramidal cavity with its base formed by the side wall of the nose and its apex directed towards the zygomatic bone. The cavity is lined with a thin muco-endosteum, easily separable from the bone and in which mucous cysts may develop. The floor of the sinus, which is a little below the level of the floor of the nose, is separated from the roots of the premolar and molar teeth by a plate of bone of varying thickness. When that plate is thin and devoid of spongy bone, suppuration at the roots of one of the teeth is very apt to extend to the sinus. The *orifice* is situated at the highest part of the sinus, and is therefore unfavourably placed for natural drainage; it opens into the middle meatus of the nose through the lower part of the *hiatus semilunaris.* In a varying percentage of persons a second communication exists between the sinus and middle meatus, the opening being situated behind and below the normal orifice; when that accessory aperture exists, pus from the sinus may drain backwards into the nasal part of the pharynx (Logan Turner).

In *empyema of the sinus* the opening to evacuate and drain the cavity may be made—(1) Through the canine fossa. (2) Through the side wall of the inferior meatus of the nose.

In an antero-posterior radiograph of the skull (Pl. LXII), the shadow of the maxillary sinus presents a pyramidal outline, the base corresponding to the floor of the orbit and the rounded apex to the alveolar recess of the sinus. Sometimes the floor of the sinus extends medially, below the floor of the nose, into the palatine process of the maxilla so as to form a distinct palatine recess. The medial outline of the sinus area is the foreshortened shadow of the nasal wall of the sinus and the lateral pterygoid lamina; laterally it is outlined by the zygomatic bone. The petrous portion of the temporal bone throws a deep shadow across the upper half of the sinus. When the radiograph is taken, the head should therefore be placed in such a position that that shadow is raised as much as possible into the orbits. In the living subject the lower and medial portion of the outline of the sinus is considerably obscured by the shadow caused by the cervical portion of the vertebral column (Killian).

In a lateral radiograph of the facial region of the dried skull (Pls. LXIII and LXVI, Fig. 1), the shadow of the outline of the maxillary sinus is well defined. It is represented below by the dense, horizontal shadow of the bony palate, which crosses the tips of the roots of the molar teeth. Above it is limited anteriorly by the dark, curved shadow of the floor of the orbit; while above and posteriorly is the shadow of the posterior ethmoidal-sinus area. Behind the maxillary area are the vertical linear shadows of the pterygoid laminæ, overlapped by that of the coronoid process of the mandible. The anterior part of the sinus area is overlapped and, to a considerable extent, obscured, by the dense and more or less triangular shadow caused by the zygomatic bone.

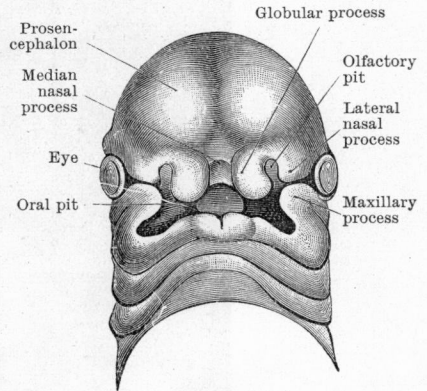

FIG. 1123.—HEAD OF HUMAN EMBRYO ABOUT 29 DAYS OLD, showing the division of the lower part of the median nasal process into the two globular processes, the intervention of the olfactory pits between the median and lateral nasal processes, and the approximation of the maxillary and lateral nasal processes, which, however, are separated by the oculo-nasal sulcus. (From His.)

Lips.—In compressing the **labial arteries**, remember that they run under cover of the mucous membrane, a short distance from the free margins of the lips. The lips are abundantly supplied with **mucous glands** which can be felt nearer their attached than their free borders immediately outside the mucous membrane; the glands are a frequent seat of mucous cysts; occasionally they undergo a congenital enlargement which results in one form of hypertrophy of the lip.

Hare-lip is due to failure of the union of the superficial parts of the maxillary process with the median nasal subdivision of the fronto-nasal process (Fig. 1123). The deformity is spoken of as complete or incomplete according to whether the cleft extends into the nostril or involves merely a portion of the lip. The fissure may involve the lip only, or it may include the alveolar process of the maxilla; in the latter case the cleft may or may not be associated with a cleft of the palate. Lastly, the hare-lip may be single or double; when single, it is usually on the left side.

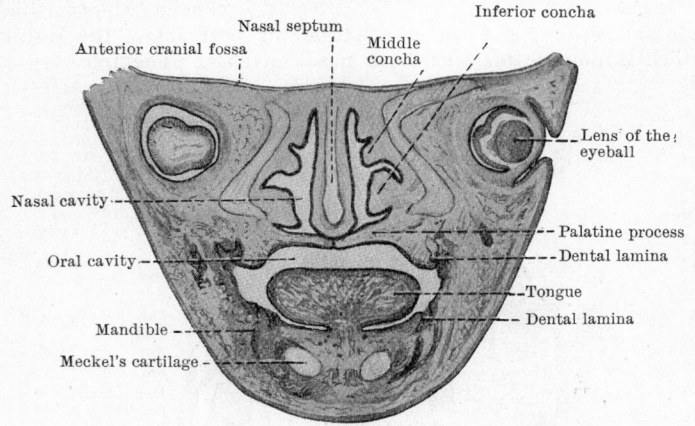

FIG. 1124.—CORONAL SECTION THROUGH THE FACE OF A HUMAN EMBRYO AT THE SEVENTH WEEK.

Palate.—Fig. 1124 shows how the mouth is shut off from the nasal cavities by the growth inwards from the deep surface of the maxillary process of a pair of horizontal plates (palatine processes) which unite in the median plane with each other and with the lower border of the septum of the nose; the septum, which develops as a downgrowth from the primitive basis cranii, is continuous anteriorly with that portion of the fronto-nasal process which forms the premaxillæ and the median portion of the upper lip. The various degrees of *cleft palate* are due to the more or less complete failure of union of the palatine processes with each other and with the premaxillary part of the median nasal processes. The cleft in the soft palate, which is always median, may be either partial or complete, and may or may not extend forwards into the hard palate. The cleft in the hard palate is spoken of as single or double according to whether the palatine processes have failed to unite with the lower edge of the nasal septum on one side or on both sides. When the cleft extends forwards through the alveolar process to become continuous with a cleft of the lip, the medial (premaxillary) edge of the cleft is usually projected forwards in advance of the lateral (maxillary) edge. The projecting premaxillary edge is forced back into line with the maxillary edge when the lip cleft is closed.

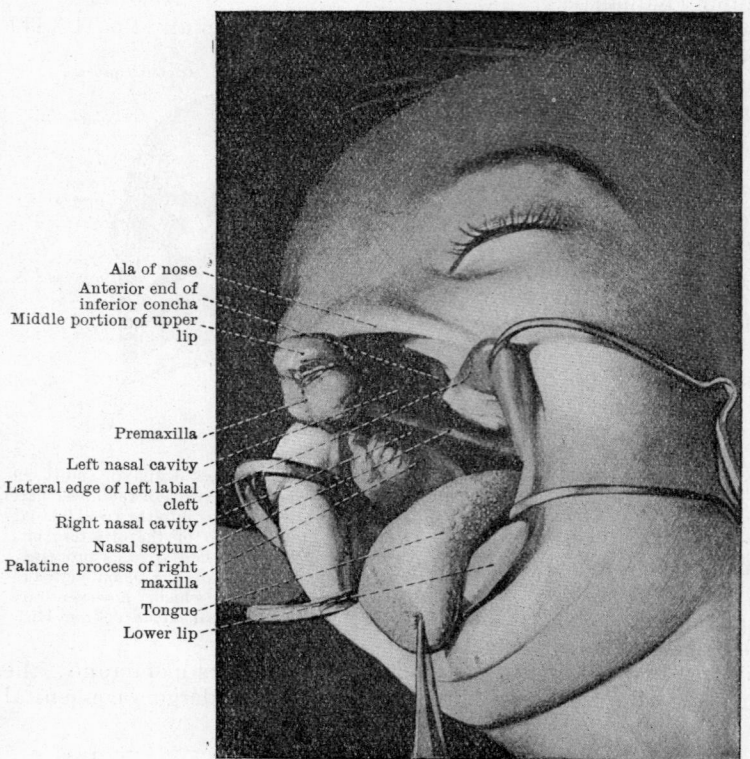

Ala of nose
Anterior end of inferior concha
Middle portion of upper lip

Premaxilla
Left nasal cavity
Lateral edge of left labial cleft
Right nasal cavity
Nasal septum
Palatine process of right maxilla
Tongue
Lower lip

FIG. 1125.—FROM A PHOTOGRAPH SHOWING DOUBLE COMPLETE HARE-LIP AND CLEFT PALATE.

In what is known as a complete double cleft palate, the palatine processes fail to join the nasal septum and the premaxillæ on both sides; the result is a wide median cleft which communicates with both nasal cavities. The free, lower border of the vomer extends along the middle of the cleft to be continuous anteriorly with the rounded premaxillary mass; that mass, along with the central portion of the upper lip, is projected forwards between the two labial clefts, often to such an extent that it appears to spring from the tip of the nose (Fig. 1125). In an operation on such a double hare-lip the first step is to correct the premaxillary projection. That is achieved by the removal of a triangular portion of the nasal septum immediately behind the attachment of the vomer to the

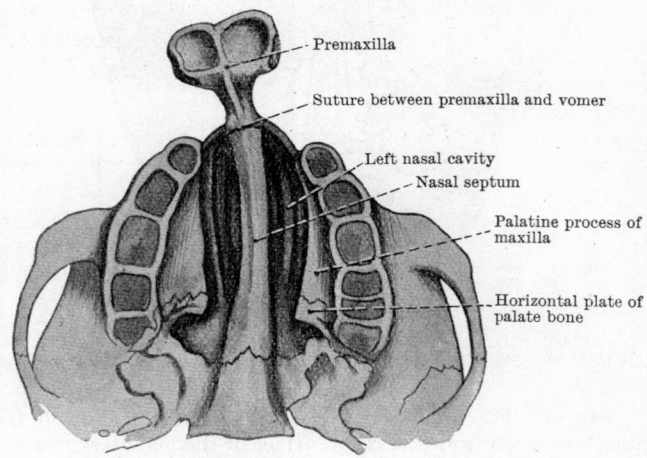

Premaxilla
Suture between premaxilla and vomer
Left nasal cavity
Nasal septum
Palatine process of maxilla
Horizontal plate of palate bone

FIG. 1126.—SHOWS ARRANGEMENT OF BONES IN DOUBLE CLEFT PALATE. (*Handbook of Practical Surgery*, Bergmann, Bruns, and Mikulicz.)

premaxilla, in order that the premaxilla may be displaced backwards into line with the alveolar margins of the maxilla. The base of the triangular piece of bone should not be taken from the constricted portion of the neck of the premaxillary projection, but should consist of the olive-shaped thickening situated immediately behind the neck. That thickening is crossed by the transverse suture that unites the premaxilla with the anterior extremity of the vomer (Fig. 1126). If the premaxillary projection is removed altogether, there is nothing left to support the upper lip, and the result is an ugly deformity, due to the comparative protrusion and redundancy of the lower lip.

Teeth.—The **milk teeth** begin to appear about the sixth month—the first to emerge being usually the lower central incisors. The first dentition is completed about the thirtieth month. Delayed dentition is due generally to rickets. Of the **permanent set** the first to erupt are the first molars, which appear about the end of the sixth year; the third molars—the last to appear—may erupt any time between the seventeenth and the twenty-fifth year, or even later. As the permanent teeth push their way towards the surface, absorption of the roots of the first set takes place, and the first set either fall out of their own accord or are easily removed. Loss of the permanent teeth is followed by absorption of the alveolar margin of the jaw. The tooth sockets are lined with a thin periosteum which is anatomically continuous both with the tissue of the teeth and with the dense fibrous tissue of the deep layer of the gum.

The upper incisors and canines and the lower premolars have *cylindrical* roots; hence in extracting those teeth, loosen them first by a slight rotatory movement; the roots of the lower incisors and canines and of the upper premolars are *flattened*, and must therefore be loosened by a side-to-side movement. The roots of the third molars are *convergent*, generally welded together and curved backwards, especially in the mandible. The first and second upper molars have three roots, and they are often *divergent*.

Tongue.—For practical purposes, as well as on developmental and structural grounds, it is convenient to divide the tongue into an anterior two-thirds (the **oral part**) and a posterior third (the **pharyngeal part**) (Fig. 1129). At the junction of the two portions, immediately behind the median vallate papilla, is the **foramen cæcum**, which represents the remains of the pharyngeal end of the **thyro-glossal duct**. *Congenital cysts* and *fistulæ* which develop from persistent remains of that duct are always median, and are met with both above and below the hyoid bone.

The mucous membrane of the pharyngeal part of the tongue is much more sensitive than that of the oral part; hence, when a tongue depressor is used, the instrument should, except under special circumstances, rest only upon the oral region; otherwise a reflex arching of the tongue will be set up which prevents the operator from obtaining a satisfactory view of the throat. Scattered over the pharyngeal part are clusters of **lymphoid follicles** (**lingual tonsil**) which appear on the surface as a number of nodular umbilicated elevations provided with little crypts into which mucous glands open (Fig. 461). The lingual tonsil is liable to chronic inflammation and hypertrophy—conditions which are often accompanied by a varicose condition of the veins that lie immediately outside the mucous membrane containing the palato-glossus muscle. To obtain a satisfactory view of the lingual tonsil in the living subject, use a laryngoscopic mirror.

The pair of mucous glands situated in the lower part of the tongue a little behind its tip, and known as the **anterior lingual glands**, are of interest in that they occasionally give rise to mucous cysts similar to those which develop in connexion with the labial glands (Fig. 1128).

The muscular bundles of the tongue are separated by a quantity of loose areolar tissue, rich in blood-vessels and lymph vessels (Fig. 1127); hence acute inflammatory œdema of the tongue may be attended with a degree of swelling sufficient to obstruct the respiratory passage.

The main **blood-vessels** of the tongue run from behind forwards, nearer its lower surface than its upper surface (Fig. 1127); incisions into the substance of the tongue to reduce swelling and tension should therefore be made longitudinally on the dorsum. Bleeding from the lingual artery, divided in the substance of the tongue, is temporarily arrested by the finger passed behind the tongue to hook it well forward, and compress the vessel against the lingual surface of the mandible. On account of the very slender anastomosis between the vessels of the two halves of the tongue, scarcely any bleeding occurs when it is split in the median plane.

The collecting **lymph vessels** which arise from the lymph net-works in the mucous membrane and muscular substance of the tongue may be divided into four groups: (1) **Apical trunks**, which open partly into the submental glands and partly into a gland (jugulo-omohyoid) that lies immediately above the superior belly of the omo-hyoid muscle. (2) **Marginal trunks**, some of which pass lateral to the sublingual gland and through the mylo-hyoid muscle to join the most anterior of the submandibular lymph glands, while others pass medial to the sublingual gland, in front of and behind the hyo-glossus muscle, to join the glands in the carotid triangle. The more *anterior* their lingual origin the *lower* is the gland to which they pass. (3) The **basal trunks**, from the posterior third of the tongue, pass from before backwards towards the lower end of the tonsil, where they pierce the superior and middle constrictors of the pharynx, and, after surrounding the lingual artery, open into a gland (jugulo-digastric) placed on the internal jugular vein immediately below the

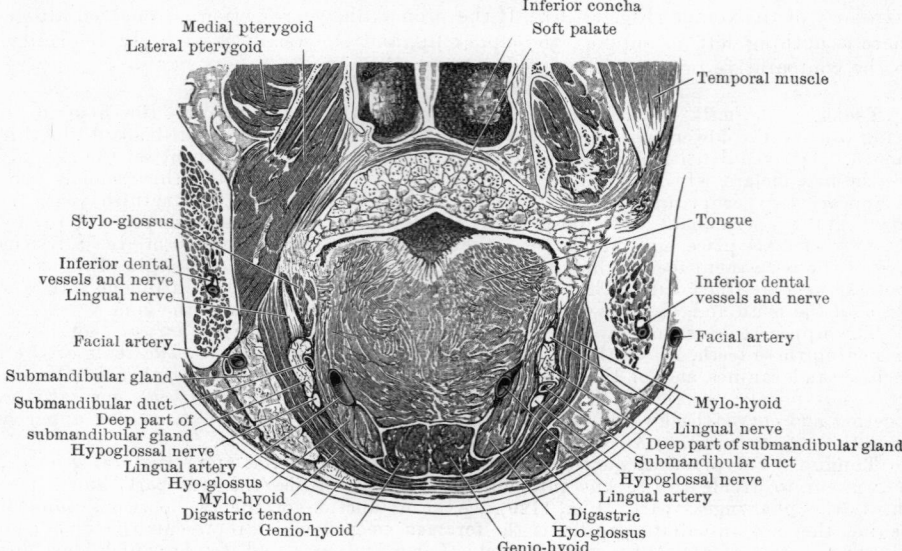

FIG. 1127.—Coronal Section through the Tongue and Submandibular Region in a Plane behind the Molar Teeth.

posterior belly of the digastric. (4) The **central trunks**, which descend in the middle line between the genio-glossi, pass deep to the hyo-glossus and mylo-hyoid muscles into the submandibular space, and thence in front of the hyoid bone (having embraced the tendon of the digastric) to join glands in the carotid triangle (Figs. 1109, 1110).

Cavity of Mouth.—The groove between the tongue and the gums is crossed in the median plane by the **frenulum linguæ** (Fig. 1128). At each side of the lower part of the frenulum is the **orifice of the submandibular duct.** A little to one side of the frenulum the **profunda vein** is seen through the thin mucous membrane; to the lateral side of the vein are the profunda artery and the lingual nerve, both of which lie deeper in the tongue than the vein and are therefore not visible.

The position of the profunda artery is indicated by the overlying edge-like fold of mucous membrane —the fimbriated fold.

The mucous membrane at the anterior part of the floor of the mouth is thrown into a slight elevation which overlies and is caused by the corresponding **sublingual salivary gland.** The duct of the submandibular gland and the lingual nerve lie below and to the medial side of the sublingual gland.

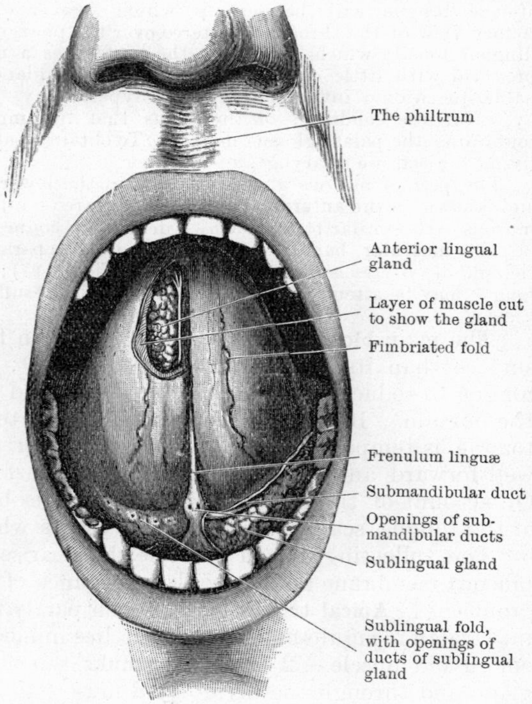

FIG. 1128.—Open Mouth with Tongue raised and the Sublingual and Anterior Lingual Glands exposed.

A branch of the lingual nerve is seen running on the medial side of the sublingual gland. (Birmingham.)

When a shortened frenulum is divided for "tongue-tie" the deep lingual vessels and the orifices of the submandibular ducts must be avoided. Behind the frenulum linguæ are the anterior borders of the **genio-glossus muscles,** which ascend from the superior genial tubercles. In operations necessitating the removal of the region of the symphysis of the mandible, or the separation of the origins of the genio-glossi, the tongue must be kept forward, otherwise the patient will be suffocated by the organ falling backwards over the entrance to the larynx. In removing a small salivary calculus from the floor of the mouth fix the calculus with the finger against the lingual surface of the mandible before cutting down upon it.

When the teeth are clenched the only communication between the vestibule of the mouth and the oral cavity proper is an opening behind the last molar

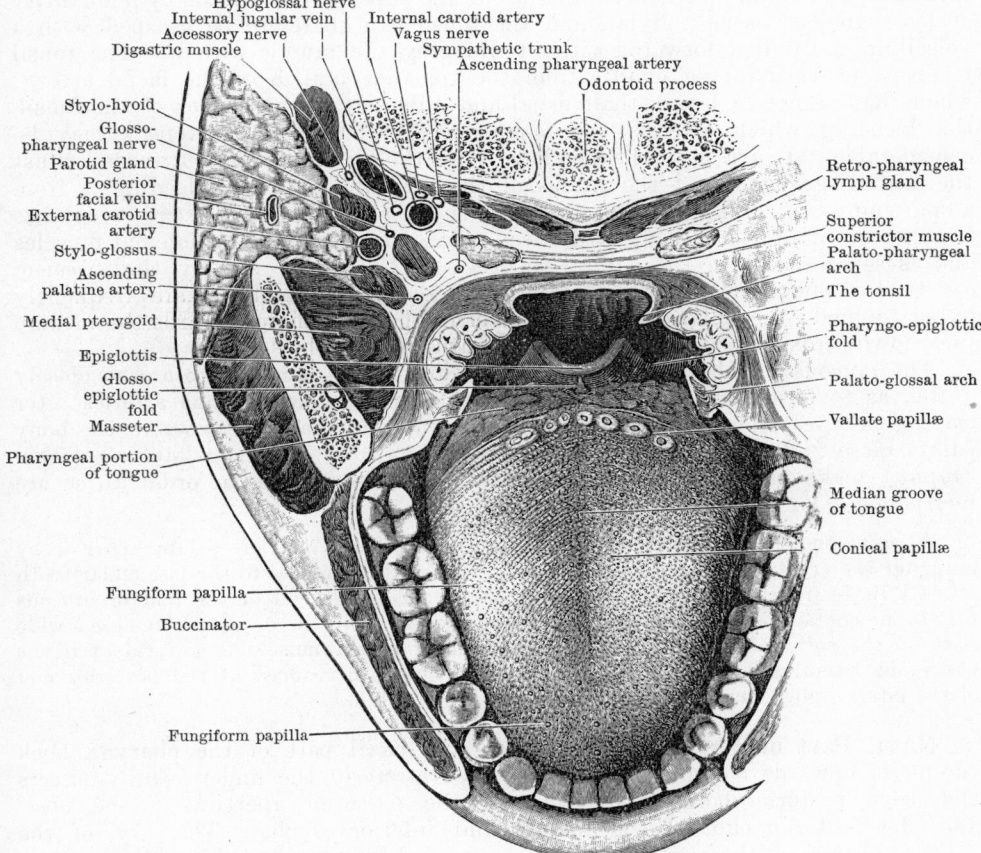

FIG. 1129.—HORIZONTAL SECTION THROUGH MOUTH AND PHARYNX AT THE LEVEL OF THE TONSILS.

The stylo-pharyngeus (which is seen on the medial side of the external carotid artery) and the prevertebral muscles are not indicated by reference lines. (Birmingham.)

tooth which can barely admit a medium-sized catheter. Therefore, when the jaws cannot be separated it is generally necessary to feed the patient through a tube passed along the floor of the nose.

When the mouth is opened widely and a deep inspiration is taken, the soft palate is elevated, and the palato-glossal and palato-pharyngeal arches are made prominent. The **palato-glossal arches** spring from the anterior surface of the soft palate, close to the base of the uvula, and arch downwards and laterally, in front of the tonsils, to end at the posterior part of the side of the tongue. The **palato-pharyngeal arches** are really the continuation of the free border of the soft palate downwards behind the tonsils to be lost upon the side wall of the pharynx. Together with the lower edge of the soft palate and the posterior wall of the pharynx, they bound an oblique opening (**pharyngeal isthmus**) through which the mucous membrane of the posterior wall of the nasal portion of the pharynx is visible.

In the *adult* the upper four cervical vertebræ can be explored from the mouth (Pl. XVII, Fig. 1); in the *child* the finger can reach still farther—down to the sixth vertebra and the back of the cricoid cartilage.

Tonsils.—The **tonsils** [tonsillæ palatinæ] (Fig. 1129) lie one in each side wall of the pharynx between the palatine arches, opposite a point a little above the angle of the mandible. Each tonsil is covered, on its free surface, with mucous membrane upon which are seen the orifices of the *tonsillar pits*; the lateral or deep surface is covered with a layer of fibrous tissue which forms an imperfect sheath for the organ and is separated from the superior constrictor by a quantity of loose areolar tissue and fat, and the tonsil can therefore be grasped with a volsellum and pulled forwards without dragging the muscle with it. The tonsil receives its *blood-supply* mainly from the tonsillar branch of the facial artery; when that branch is larger than usual and adherent to the sheath of the tonsil, the bleeding which attends the operation of removal of the tonsils may be considerable. To arrest the hæmorrhage press the bleeding point outwards against the medial pterygoid and the ramus of the mandible. If the bleeding is from a spurting vessel of larger size, its source is probably the *facial artery*, which has been wounded as it arches upwards deep to the digastric and stylohyoid muscles and is separated from the lateral surface of the tonsil only by the superior constrictor muscle. In children and adolescents the tonsils are frequently hypertrophied; the enlargement may be either general, more towards the median line, downwards along the pharynx, or upwards behind the soft palate.

The mucous membrane and the periosteum of the **hard palate** are so closely united as to form practically one membrane. The **greater palatine arteries**, after leaving the greater palatine foramina, run forwards in shallow grooves in the bony palate, close to its alveolar margin. In the operation for cleft palate (*staphylorrhaphy*), make the lateral incisions *lateral* to those vessels in order to secure nourishment for the muco-periosteal flaps.

When secondary hæmorrhage occurs after the operation for cleft palate, arrest it by plugging the **greater palatine foramen**, which lies a little medial to the last molar tooth about ⅓ in. in front of the pterygoid hamulus, at the upper end of the fold of mucous membrane containing the pterygo-mandibular ligament. In the operation to close a wide cleft of the soft palate the tension of the **tensor palati muscle** is got rid of if the **pterygoid hamulus** is chipped off with a small chisel introduced at the posterior end of the lateral relief incisions.

Nasal Part of Pharynx.—To explore the nasal part of the pharynx hook the finger upwards behind the soft palate. *Anteriorly*, the finger readily detects the sharp, posterior border of the vomer, the posterior aperture of the nose, and the posterior ends of the middle and inferior conchæ. The *roof* of the space is formed by the basilar part of the occipital bone, while behind the *posterior wall* there is a transverse bony ridge caused by the anterior arch of the atlas. On each *side wall* there is the opening of the **pharyngo-tympanic tube** [tuba auditiva] situated ½ in. behind the posterior end of the inferior concha. The orifice, bounded above and below by a prominent margin, is directed downwards and forwards, and therefore in a direction favourable to the passage of the Eustachian catheter. Behind the posterior margin of the orifice there is the *recess of the pharynx*, in which the point of the catheter is apt to become engaged. On the roof and posterior wall of the pharynx, down to the level of the foramen magnum (Fig. 473, p. 588), and extending laterally as far as the orifices of the tubes, there is a collection of adenoid tissue called the **naso-pharyngeal tonsil**. Hypertrophy of that tissue constitutes the condition known as "*adenoids*," the harmful effects of which are due to their interference with nasal respiration. On the centre of the nasopharyngeal tonsil there is an orifice leading into a small recess into which numerous mucous glands open. The structures felt in the naso-pharynx may be made visible by light reflected on a small mirror placed immediately behind and below the soft palate (*posterior rhinoscopy*).   The lower part of the inferior concha is obscured from view by the bulging of the upper surface of the soft palate.

If the posterior wall of the pharynx is observed during the pronunciation of vowels it will be noticed that a transverse ridge appears immediately below the naso-pharyngeal tonsil, opposite the anterior arch of the atlas (Passavant's ridge). It is produced by the contraction of certain fibres of the superior constrictor muscle, and may be regarded as a naso-pharyngeal valve or sphincter.

When the posterior apertures of the nose have to be plugged it is important to remember that these openings are rather more than one inch in height and about half an inch across. In the child, owing to the small size of the face, the vertical diameter of the naso-pharynx and the height of these apertures are relatively much smaller than in the adult.

The **retro-pharyngeal lymph glands** are one or two pairs of glands that lie opposite the hollow below the auricle at the junction of the posterior wall and side walls of the pharynx.   They are embedded in loose areolar tissue and are separated from the atlas by the prevertebral muscles and fascia.   They receive afferent lymphatics from the mucosa of the nasal cavities and the air sinuses, the naso-pharynx, the pharyngo-tympanic tubes, and the tympanic cavity.   Their efferent lymphatics empty into the glands in the upper part of the carotid triangle. After the first year of life they undergo retrogressive changes, but they persist as lymphatic nodes until the tenth or twelfth year.   In children, suppuration originating in one of them is the commonest cause of a retro-pharyngeal abscess.

THE NECK

The processes and partitions which proceed from the deep surface of the general envelope of **deep cervical fascia** subdivide the neck into compartments which limit and determine the spread of pus.   The most important compartment is the **visceral compartment**, bounded *anteriorly* by the pretracheal fascia, *posteriorly* by the prevertebral fascia, and *laterally* by the fascia forming the vascular compartment.   Inferiorly, the visceral compartment extends into the superior mediastinum ; superiorly, its posterior part extends to the base of the skull, but its anterior part reaches only to the hyoid bone   *Abscesses* in the compartment are either secondary to disease of the lymph glands or other organs which it contains, or are the result of a primary suppurative cellulitis.   A tubercular abscess originating in one of the retro-pharyngeal lymph glands (Fig. 1129) lies *in front of* the prevertebral fascia, and points into the pharynx ; abscesses secondary to disease of the cervical vertebræ lie *behind* the prevertebral fascia, and spread laterally behind the vascular compartment ; they point behind the sterno-mastoid, and should be opened through an incision at the posterior border of the muscle— the surgeon keeping close to the transverse processes in order to avoid the structures in the vascular compartment.

In front of the visceral compartment there is a **small muscular compartment** containing the infra-hyoid muscles ; in front of it again, in the region of the supra-sternal notch, is the small **supra-sternal compartment**, containing the anterior jugular veins, along with their transverse communicating branch (*jugular arch*), a little fat, and one or two lymph glands.

The **vascular compartment** contains the carotid arteries and the internal jugular vein, and the following nerves, viz. : the vagus, part of the hypoglossal nerve, the descendens hypoglossi, and part of the accessory nerve.   These structures are enveloped in an ill-defined fascial tube called the *carotid sheath*.   The sheath is surrounded by areolar tissue in which a chain of lymph glands is embedded ; normally, the glands may be readily separated from the sheath of the internal jugular vein, but they become adherent to it when they are inflamed.   The sympathetic trunk and the inferior thyroid artery lie in the areolar tissue between the posterior wall of the carotid sheath and the prevertebral fascia ; they can be reached through an incision along the posterior border of the sterno-mastoid muscle—that muscle, along with the carotid sheath and its contents, being pulled well forwards. In the approach to the trunk of the inferior thyroid artery from the front the sterno-mastoid and carotid sheath are pulled back and the dissection is continued through the areolar tissue between the carotid sheath and the sheath of the thyroid gland, which is formed by the pretracheal fascia.

A glandular abscess in the vascular compartment usually points on the surface, adhesions being formed, first, between the gland and the fascia, and, subsequently, between the fascia and the cutaneous structures. In diffuse suppurative cellulitis of the compartment the pus burrows towards the root of the neck, and may reach either the mediastinum or the axilla.

Median Line of Neck.—The body of the **hyoid bone** divides the median plane of the neck into **supra-hyoid** and **infra-hyoid portions.** Above the hyoid bone

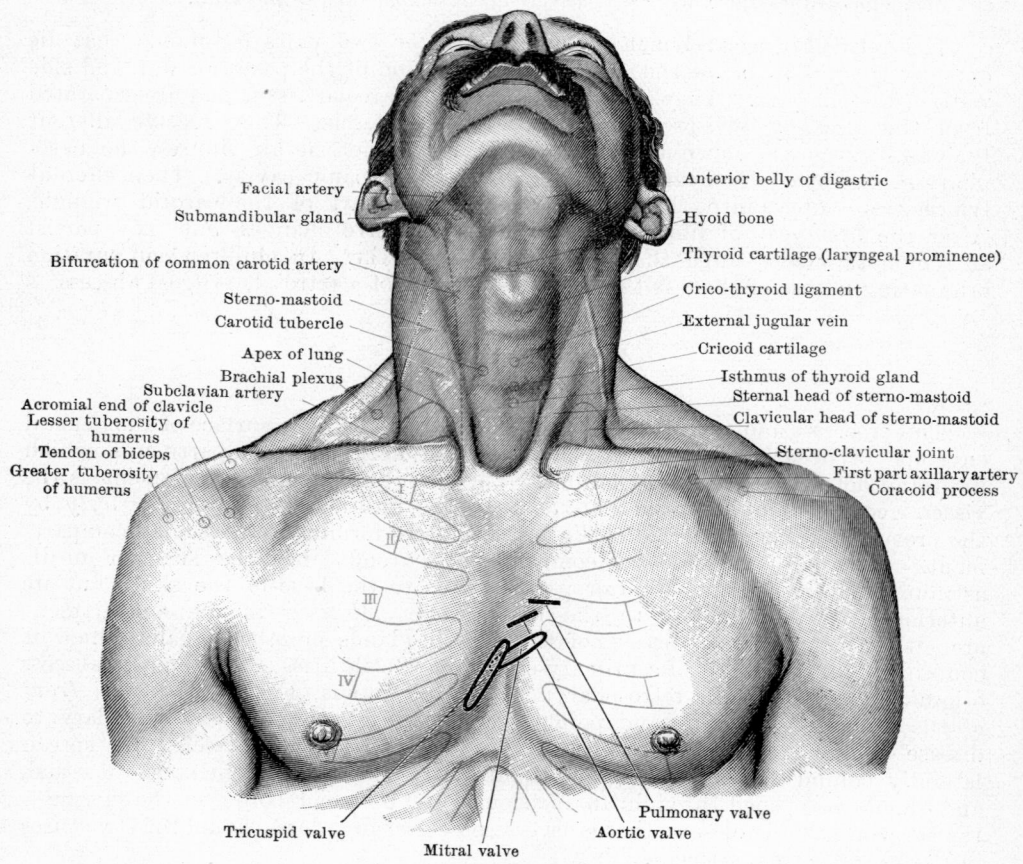

Facial artery
Submandibular gland
Bifurcation of common carotid artery
Sterno-mastoid
Carotid tubercle
Apex of lung
Brachial plexus
Subclavian artery
Acromial end of clavicle
Lesser tuberosity of humerus
Tendon of biceps
Greater tuberosity of humerus

Anterior belly of digastric
Hyoid bone
Thyroid cartilage (laryngeal prominence)
Crico-thyroid ligament
External jugular vein
Cricoid cartilage
Isthmus of thyroid gland
Sternal head of sterno-mastoid
Clavicular head of sterno-mastoid
Sterno-clavicular joint
First part axillary artery
Coracoid process

Tricuspid valve
Mitral valve
Aortic valve
Pulmonary valve

Fig. 1130.—Front of Neck and Shoulders.

is the **submental triangle**, with its apex at the symphysis menti and its sides formed by the anterior bellies of the digastrics. In the floor of the triangle **are** the anterior portions of the mylo-hyoid muscles, united by the median raphe (Fig. 1131). The most important structures in the triangle are the **submental lymph glands**, which can usually be felt a little above the body of the hyoid bone. In children they are a frequent seat of abscess secondary to impetigo of the lower lip and chin. About 1 in. below the hyoid bone is the **laryngeal prominence**— more prominent in men than in women. On each side of the prominence are the laminæ of the thyroid cartilage, while between that cartilage and the hyoid bone there is the **thyro-hyoid membrane.** In the operation of *sub-hyoid pharyngotomy*, the epiglottis and the inlet of the larynx are reached through the anterior wall of the pharynx at the level of the thyro-hyoid membrane. The structures divided are, from without inwards : (1) the skin and fasciæ, (2) the sterno-hyoid, omo-hyoid, and thyro-hyoid muscles, (3) the median thyro-hyoid ligament, along with a layer of fat between it and the lower part of the epiglottis, and, finally, (4) the glosso-epiglottic fold of mucous membrane. The incision must not be extended too far from the median plane for fear of wounding the **superior laryngeal vessels** and **internal laryngeal nerve**, which pierce the thyro-hyoid membrane.

The wound in suicidal *cut-throat* is generally at the level of the thyro-hyoid interval. The more important structures usually divided are: (1) more or less of the left sterno-mastoid muscle, (2) the superior thyroid vessels, (3) the thyro-hyoid membrane, (4) the stem of the epiglottis, and, less frequently, (5) the carotid vessels, the internal jugular vein, and the internal laryngeal nerve. When the wound is above the hyoid bone, the lingual and facial vessels and the muscles of the tongue are the more important structures injured.

The **rima glottidis** is opposite the middle of the anterior border of the thyroid cartilage.

In the operation of thyrotomy, care is taken to divide the thyroid cartilage exactly in the median plane in order that injury to the vocal folds may be avoided.

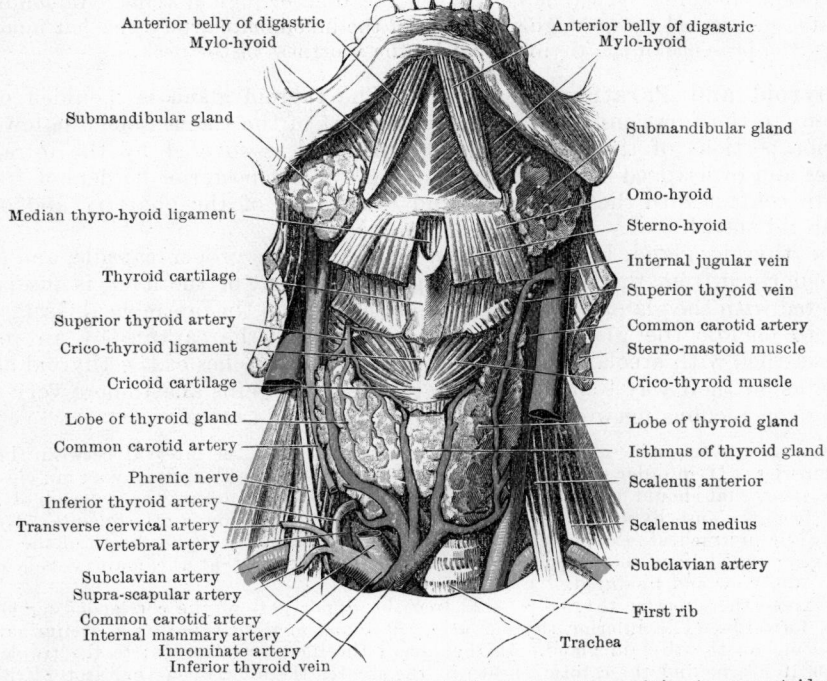

FIG. 1131.—DISSECTION OF THE FRONT OF THE NECK. The lower portions of the sterno-mastoid muscles and right common carotid artery have been removed to show the deeper parts.

A little more than an inch below the laryngeal prominence is the arch of the **cricoid cartilage**, which may be readily felt, and, when the neck is extended, often seen. Above the cricoid is the **crico-thyroid ligament**; in the operation of laryngotomy only the median portion of the ligament is divided, lest the crico-thyroid muscles be injured. The crico-thyroid branch of the superior thyroid artery lies close to the lower border of the thyroid cartilage. Below the cricoid cartilage is the **trachea**, which recedes as it descends, so that it lies 1½ in. from the surface at the level of the upper border of the sternum. The **isthmus** of the **thyroid gland** usually lies in front of the second, third, and fourth rings of the trachea (Fig. 1131), but may reach up to the cricoid. Immediately in front of the trachea, below the isthmus of the thyroid, is the pretracheal fat, containing one or two **lymph glands** and the **inferior thyroid veins**, each represented by one or more branches which converge as they descend. The pretracheal lymph glands receive afferent vessels from the larynx and thyroid gland, and their efferent vessels open into the glands along the lower part of the carotid sheath. In the adult the **innominate artery** crosses the front of the trachea at the level of the upper border of the sternum ; in the child, however, it often crosses half an inch higher—a relation which must be remembered in the operation of low tracheotomy.

In the operation of **high tracheotomy** the upper three rings of the trachea are divided by a median incision. The incision divides the skin, the superficial fascia and the tributaries of the anterior jugular veins, the general envelope of deep cervical fascia, and (after passing between the right and left infra-hyoid muscles) the pretracheal fascia, which descends from the cricoid to enclose the isthmus of the thyroid gland. If this fascia is divided transversely below the cricoid, the isthmus may be pulled downwards and the upper rings of the trachea exposed. In some cases it is necessary either to divide the isthmus or to extend the incision upwards through the cricoid cartilage. In opening the uppermost part of the trachea, the operator keeps the edge of the knife directed upwards to avoid injuring the vessels at the upper border of the isthmus. The anterior jugular veins are in danger of being wounded if the skin incision is not strictly median. In **low tracheotomy** the trachea below the isthmus is opened ; it is a more troublesome operation, on account of the depth of the trachea and the presence in front of it of the inferior thyroid veins and of the anastomosis between the anterior jugular veins. In children the difficulty is increased by the higher position of the innominate artery and left innominate vein, by the presence of the thymus, and by the shortness of the neck.

Thyroid and Parathyroid Glands.—The **thyroid gland** is moulded on and adherent to the front and sides of the upper part of the trachea and the lower and posterior portions of the sides of the larynx, and is covered by the infra-hyoid muscles and overlapped by the sterno-mastoid. The posterior borders of its lobes come in contact with the œsophagus and lower part of the pharynx, and overlap the carotid sheath.

The thyroid gland, like the prostate, has its own proper capsule, and also a sheath derived from the fascia. The capsule, like that of the liver, is inseparably connected with the gland. The sheath is derived from the pretracheal fascia, which splits to enclose the gland, and is separated from the capsule by an interval which is filled with areolar tissue and is crossed by branches of the thyroid arteries and veins on their way to and from the gland. The veins anastomose very freely, making conspicuous networks between the capsule and the sheath.

The surgeon reaches the gland in the median plane through the interval between the infra-hyoid muscles. If, in order to obtain more room, he has to divide the infra-hyoid muscles on one or both sides, that should be done towards their upper attachments, as their nerves of supply, derived from the ansa hypoglossi, enter the muscles nearer their lower attachments. By freely dividing the pretracheal fascia where it forms the anterior portion of the sheath of the thyroid, the surgeon can deliver the gland out of the wound so freed that the main vessels may be brought into view and ligatured.

To expose the superior thyroid vessels, free the upper part of the corresponding lobe and draw it forwards. The inferior thyroid artery is sometimes ligatured as a preliminary step to operating on the thyroid gland. In that event the ligature is applied to the trunk of the vessel as it lies behind the carotid sheath in the areolar tissue between the carotid artery and the prevertebral fascia (De Quervain). In the operation of partial thyroidectomy the posterior part of the capsule of the gland and a layer of thyroid substance are left behind so as to guard against injury to the parathyroids and the recurrent laryngeal nerve. In that procedure the branches of the inferior thyroid artery are ligatured after they have pierced the capsule of the gland. The recurrent laryngeal nerve, which also lies between the posterior part of the sheath and the postero-medial aspect of the corresponding lobe, ascends, either behind the inferior thyroid artery or between its main divisions.

The **parathyroid glands** can generally be distinguished from the thyroid tissue itself, and from the lymph glands, by their greyish-yellow colour and by their smooth and shining surfaces. Each superior parathyroid is embedded in the posterior border of the lobe opposite the cricoid cartilage. It is in close relation to the pharyngo-œsophageal junction, from which it is separated by the posterior part of the sheath of the thyroid gland. The inferior para-thyroid, on each side, is supplied by a small vessel from one of the branches of the inferior thyroid artery ; it also lies within the sheath and is on the back of the lower pole of the gland, a little lateral to the inferior thyroid artery and the recurrent laryngeal nerve. When the inferior thyroid artery has been ligatured, the medial glandular branch of the superior thyroid artery furnishes a sufficient blood-supply to the inferior parathyroid (see also p. 776).

Triangles of the Neck.—The side of the neck is divided into an **anterior** and a **posterior triangle** by the sterno-mastoid muscle; the anterior triangle is further subdivided into *digastric, carotid,* and *muscular triangles* by the digastric and omo-hyoid muscles.

The **sterno-mastoid muscle** is one of the most important superficial land-marks of the neck. The anterior border of the muscle, the more distinct of the two, may be felt along its whole extent. Between the prominent sternal origin

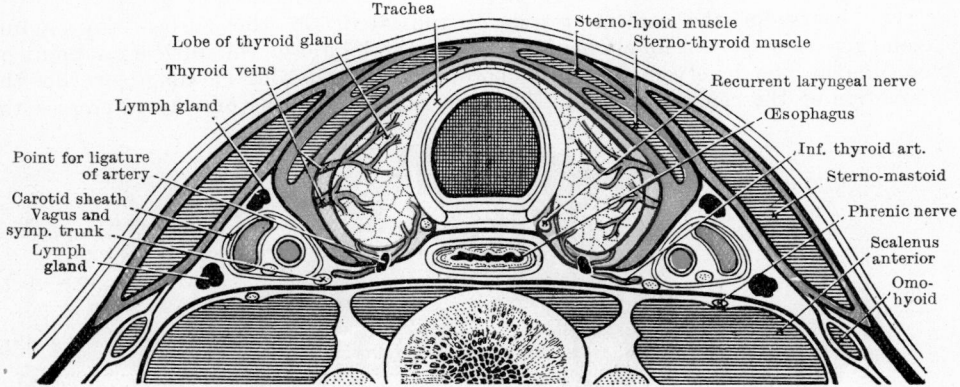

FIG. 1132.—A DIAGRAM OF THE RELATIONS OF THE CERVICAL FASCIA TO THE THYROID GLAND.

Blue = deep cervical fascia (sterno-mastoid layer). Red = sheath of thyroid gland (pretracheal fascia). Yellow = capsule of the thyroid gland. (Modified from De Quervain.)

and the broad ribbon-like clavicular origin there is a slight triangular depression which overlies the lowest part of the internal jugular vein.

By dividing the cervical fascia along the anterior and posterior borders of the muscle the surgeon is able to displace the muscle backwards and forwards and so obtain free access to the structures deep to it. If the posterior fibres of the muscle are divided at their clavicular and mastoid attachments the muscle is made still more freely movable. As the fascia along its posterior border is cut the cutaneous branches of the cervical plexus are usually divided, but care is taken not to injure the accessory nerve. Should it be necessary to remove the upper third or more of the muscle, the divided end is stitched to the levator scapulæ or to the scalenus medius, according to the amount resected. When the muscle is completely cut across at the lower part of the neck, as is done, for example, in congenital wry-neck, the close relation of the anterior and external jugular veins to its two borders must be kept in mind. After division of the muscle, the lower part of the superior belly of the omo-hyoid is seen, lying on that part of the carotid sheath which overlies the internal jugular vein.

Digastric Triangle.—The chief structure in this triangle is the **submandibular gland**, which is overlapped by the body of the mandible and reaches down to the greater horn of the hyoid bone. The **anterior facial vein** passes downwards and backwards, superficial to the gland, while the **facial artery**, embedded in its deep surface, arches upwards under cover of the angle of the mandible, where it approaches the tonsil, being separated from it, however, by the superior con-strictor of the pharynx. The **lingual artery** may be ligatured in the digastric triangle, though, in that triangle, it is deep to the hyo-glossus. It lies a little above the greater horn of the hyoid bone; the superficial guides to the vessel are the lower border of the submandibular gland, and the hypoglossal nerve and its vena comitans, which lie superficial to the hyo-glossus—that muscle being recognised by the vertical direction of its fibres. The *floor* of the digastric triangle is formed, from before backwards, by the mylo-hyoid, hyo-glossus, and superior constrictor of the pharynx. The **lymph glands** of the space receive their lymph from the face, lips, teeth and gums, tongue, and floor of the mouth; hence the frequency with which they become the seat of abscess formation and malignant enlargement. To palpate them the surgeon stands behind the patient and thrusts the fingers well up under cover of the mandible, the patient's chin being a little depressed so as to relax the cervical fascia.

Carotid Triangle.—The central landmark of the carotid triangle is the **greater horn** of the **hyoid bone**, the tip of which, when the fascia is relaxed, may be felt, at the anterior border of the sterno-mastoid, about an inch below the angle of the mandible. The deep cervical fascia holds the upper part of the sterno-mastoid forwards towards the angle of the mandible, so that, with the fascia undivided, the anterior border of the sterno-mastoid overlaps the internal jugular vein and the bifurcation of the common carotid artery.

The **course of the carotid vessels** is indicated, on the surface, by a line extending from the sterno-clavicular joint to the lobule of the auricle; a point on that line, at the level of the upper border of the thyroid cartilage, overlies the **bifurcation of the common carotid.** The **superior belly** of the **omo-hyoid** crosses the

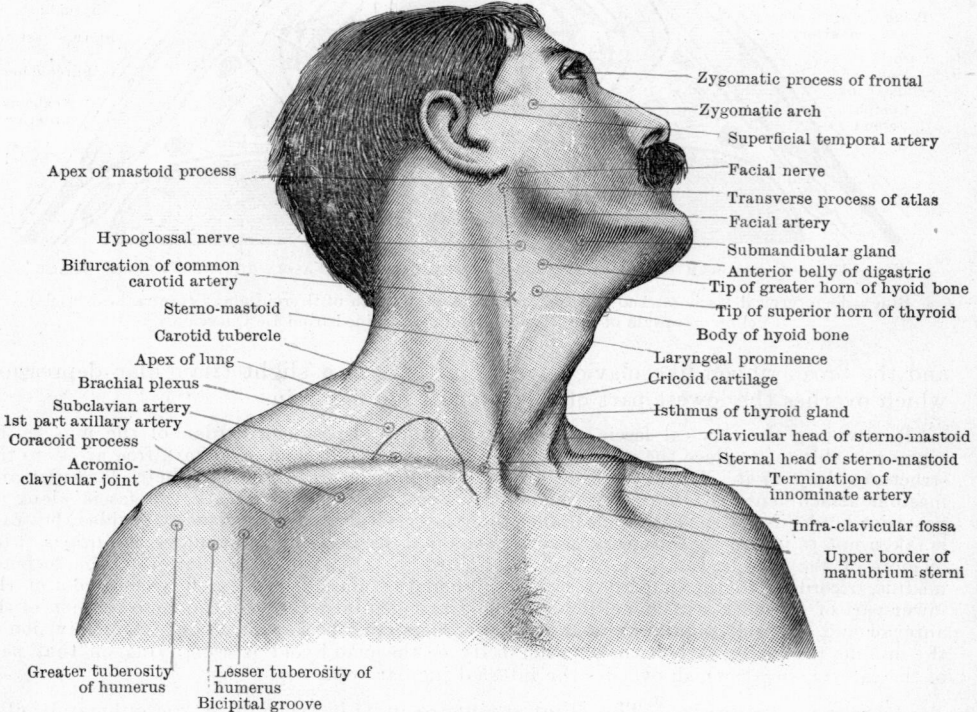

Zygomatic process of frontal
Zygomatic arch
Superficial temporal artery
Facial nerve
Transverse process of atlas
Facial artery
Submandibular gland
Anterior belly of digastric
Tip of greater horn of hyoid bone
Tip of superior horn of thyroid
Body of hyoid bone
Laryngeal prominence
Cricoid cartilage
Isthmus of thyroid gland
Clavicular head of sterno-mastoid
Sternal head of sterno-mastoid
Termination of innominate artery
Infra-clavicular fossa
Upper border of manubrium sterni

Apex of mastoid process
Hypoglossal nerve
Bifurcation of common carotid artery
Sterno-mastoid
Carotid tubercle
Apex of lung
Brachial plexus
Subclavian artery
1st part axillary artery
Coracoid process
Acromio-clavicular joint

Greater tuberosity of humerus
Lesser tuberosity of humerus
Bicipital groove

FIG. 1133.—SIDE OF THE NECK.

common carotid very obliquely at the level of the lower border of the larynx. The pulsations of the carotid vessels may be felt in the hollow between the larynx and the sterno-mastoid. In the carotid triangle the **external carotid** lies medial and anterior to the internal carotid. The seat of election for *ligation of the external carotid* is between its superior thyroid and lingual branches, a finger's-breadth below the tip of the greater horn of the hyoid bone; the difficulty in the operation is due to the plexus of veins (formed by the common facial, lingual, and superior thyroid veins) which overlies the artery. The lingual and facial arteries sometimes arise from a common trunk which must not be mistaken for the external carotid. The **superior thyroid artery** arises opposite the upper horn of the thyroid cartilage, which may be felt 1 in. or less below the tip of the greater horn of the hyoid bone. The vessel is the common source of arterial hæmorrhage in cut-throat. The guide to the **lingual artery**, in the carotid triangle, is the tip of the greater horn of the hyoid bone, above which it forms an arch crossed superficially by the hypoglossal nerve. The vessel enters the digastric triangle by passing forwards, deep to the hyo-glossus and the overlying stylo-hyoid and digastric muscles. When ligature of the artery is called for, it is usually necessary to secure it in the carotid triangle in order that the ligature may be applied on the proximal side of its dorsalis linguæ branches.

From a surgical point of view the **internal jugular vein** is the most important structure in the whole anterior triangle. In the carotid triangle it overlaps the carotid vessels, and its sheath is under cover of the general envelope of deep cervical fascia, from which it is separated by loose areolar tissue. About the level of the hyoid bone it receives the common facial vein, which is a large vessel; and at a lower level it receives the superior and middle thyroid veins, which are often greatly enlarged in goitre.

The term **deep cervical glands** includes a broad chain of lymph glands which is closely related to the internal jugular vein, and stretches from the transverse process of the atlas to the root of the neck.

The chain is divided into medial and lateral parts by the internal jugular vein. The medial division extends from the level of the posterior belly of the digastric muscle and the stylo-mandibular ligament to the lower border of the superior belly of the omo-hyoid muscle, the main group occupying a triangle bounded above by the posterior belly of the digastric muscle, in front by the common facial vein, and posteriorly by the internal jugular vein (the jugulo-digastric glands).

Lymph from the tonsil passes to this group, and, as the tonsil is one of the principal portals of entry of tuberculous infection, the jugulo-digastric glands are those most commonly affected by the disease.

The glands lying below the omo-hyoid muscle receive lymph from the back of the tongue, and they are therefore affected secondary to malignant disease of that organ.

The lateral chain lies postero-lateral to the internal jugular on the attachments of the scalenus medius and levator scapulæ muscles. They are smaller in size than the medial group, but when enlarged they may form a swelling which projects across the posterior triangle as far as the trapezius. They are embedded in a quantity of fibro-fatty tissue which encloses the accessory nerve and the cervical plexus. They receive lymph from the posterior and lateral walls of the pharynx and the posterior portion of the tongue.

The lowest glands of the group, viz. the supra-clavicular, are subdivided into a superficial and a deep cluster by the omo-hyoid muscle and the second layer of deep cervical fascia. They receive their afferent vessels from the sub-clavicular group of axillary glands.

The **hypoglossal nerve**, in the carotid triangle, is overlapped by the lower border of the posterior belly of the digastric muscle. It runs forwards, superficial to the occipital and internal and external carotid and lingual arteries, immediately below the origin of the inferior sterno-mastoid branch of the occipital artery. The **vagus nerve** descends vertically, within the carotid sheath, behind and between the carotid vessels and the internal jugular vein; care must be taken not to include it when ligaturing the common carotid artery or the internal jugular vein. Surgically, the **accessory** is the most important nerve in the anterior triangle; it enters the substance of the sterno-mastoid muscle 1½ in. below the tip of the mastoid process. A portion of the nerve is resected in the treatment of spasmodic wry-neck, and it is always exposed in the removal of the medial group of deep cervical glands. The course of the nerve in the carotid and posterior triangles may be mapped out by a line drawn from a point midway between the tip of the mastoid process and the angle of the mandible to a point little above the middle of the posterior border of the sterno-mastoid, and thence across the posterior triangle to the anterior border of the trapezius about two inches above the clavicle. The deeper guides to the nerve are the posterior belly of the digastric, which is superficial to it, and the internal jugular vein, which it crosses very obliquely, from above downwards and backwards, below and in front of the **transverse process of the atlas** (felt as a distinct bony resistance midway between the tip of the mastoid process and the angle of the mandible). The superior sterno-mastoid branch of the occipital artery lies in close relation to the nerve, and often serves as a guide to the nerve when it is obscured by diseased tissues.

In paralysis of the trapezius muscle from injury to the accessory nerve the shoulder droops and is pulled forwards and medially by the pectoralis major and minor muscles. If the paralysis occurs during childhood the chest on the same side becomes flattened in front, owing to the adaptive shortening of the pectorals and to their diminished pull on the ribs. Unless that mechanism is appreciated the infra-clavicular flattening of the chest is very liable to be erroneously attributed to pulmonary tuberculosis. The upper part of the accessory nerve is surrounded by the upper lateral group of deep cervical glands; it is in that situation, and again when it emerges from under cover of the posterior border of the sterno-mastoid muscle, that it is liable to be injured in operations for the removal of tuberculous glands.

The **cervical part of the sympathetic trunk** lies in the posterior wall of the vascular compartment of the neck, and may be reached by an incision along the posterior border of the sterno-mastoid: the anterior surfaces of the roots of the transverse processes of the vertebræ are the deep guides to the trunk.

The **cervical plexus** lies deep to the upper half of the sterno-mastoid on the levator scapulæ and scalenus medius muscles, and may be exposed through an incision along the posterior border of the upper half of the sterno-mastoid muscle. The **phrenic nerve**—the most important branch of the cervical plexus—arises one inch above the carotid tubercle and descends almost vertically towards the medial part of the clavicle; it is overlapped by the lateral margin of the internal jugular vein. Although the surgeon frequently exposes the phrenic nerve in removing the lower medial group of deep cervical glands, it is protected from injury by the fascia which binds it down to the scalenus anterior; it is here also that it is approached in the operation of **phrenic avulsion**.

The **muscular triangle** is an important triangular intermuscular space bounded by the sterno-mastoid, the superior belly of the omo-hyoid, and the median line of the neck. Behind that space, there is a deeper space which is bounded by the longus cervicis and scalenus anterior muscles, and whose apex is the anterior tubercle of the transverse process of the sixth cervical vertebra. By making an incision along the anterior border of the left sterno-mastoid muscle, and passing through the muscular triangle into the deeper space, the surgeon reaches the internal jugular vein, the common carotid artery, the vagus, the thoracic duct, the middle cervical ganglion of the sympathetic, the inferior thyroid artery, the vertebral vessels, the recurrent laryngeal nerve, and the œsophagus. The most important bony landmark in the space is the anterior tubercle of the transverse process of the sixth cervical vertebra. The common carotid artery may be compressed against that tubercle, which is therefore termed the "*carotid tubercle.*" It is the most important guide to the vertebral artery, for the artery enters the foramen in the transverse process of the sixth cervical vertebra.

The **cervical portion of the œsophagus** begins at the level of the cricoid cartilage, and descends behind the trachea, protruding a little beyond its left margin. To expose it, the surgeon, after passing through the muscular triangle, divides the pre-tracheal fascia, and passes between the trachea and the carotid sheath down to the longus cervicis muscle medial to the inferior thyroid artery and vertebral' vessels. The lower pole of the lobe of the thyroid gland is pulled medially along with the trachea. The œsophagus lies in the loose areolar tissue in front of the prevertebral fascia, and is therefore sufficiently movable to be brought to the surface. The œsophagus may be exposed also through an incision in the median plane—the trachea, which is freely movable, being displaced to the right side. If the œsophagus has to be opened care must be taken not to injure the **recurrent laryngeal nerve**, which ascends in the groove between it and the trachea; and also the loose submucous coat must not be mistaken for the lumen of the tube. The so-called "pulsion-diverticulum of the œsophagus" does not take origin from the upper part of the gullet, as frequently stated; it begins as a hernia-like protrusion of the posterior wall of the pharynx, between the oblique and the transverse fibres of the inferior constrictor muscle (Killian). During the act of swallowing the transverse fibres act as a sphincter, while the oblique fibres elevate the larynx. If the sphincter should fail to relax during the detrusor action of the pharynx it is not difficult to understand how a diverticulum might arise, and, when once produced, why it should undergo progressive enlargement.

The **thoracic duct,** after entering the left side of the root of the neck between the œsophagus and the pleura, ascends to about an inch above the clavicle. At that level it arches laterally behind the carotid sheath in front of the vertebral vessels. Great care must therefore be taken not to injure the duct during removal of the lymph glands which lie in the loose areolar tissue behind the lower part of the internal jugular vein, between it and the vertebral vein, at the medial border of the scalenus anterior. In addition to those glands a few small lymph glands lie along the sides of the cervical portions of the trachea and œsophagus. They receive their afferent vessels from the larynx, trachea, œsophagus, and thyroid gland.

POSTERIOR TRIANGLE

The roof of the posterior triangle is the general envelope of deep cervical fascia; the fascia which covers the muscles of its floor, as well as that which covers the brachial nerve trunks and the subclavian artery, is a lateral continuation of the prevertebral fascia. Numerous lymph glands are embedded in the areolar tissue between those two layers of fascia. During removal of these glands, every endeavour should be made to preserve the motor nerves. The **accessory nerve,** after entering the posterior triangle a little above the middle of the posterior border of the sterno-mastoid, crosses the triangle on the surface of the levator scapulæ and parallel to its fibres. It leaves the triangle by passing under cover of the anterior border of the trapezius, about two inches above the clavicle. The **lesser occipital nerve** curves round the accessory from below upwards, superficially, at the posterior border of the sterno-mastoid; it furnishes, therefore, a useful guide to the position of that important motor nerve.

The **nerve to the rhomboids** crosses the triangle, below the accessory, and enters the fascial septum between the levator scapulæ and scalenus medius muscles. The **nerve to the serratus anterior** arises from the fifth, sixth, and seventh cervical nerves. The roots from the fifth and sixth pierce the scalenus medius and join the root from the seventh (which runs superficial to the muscle) in the axilla. The **supra-scapular nerve** is seen arising from the lateral edge of the upper trunk of the brachial plexus, a little above the inferior belly of the omo-hyoid muscle.

The loops of the **cervical plexus** lie under cover of the upper part of the sterno-mastoid muscle, between it and the origins of the levator scapulæ and the upper part of the scalenus medius muscles, and are overlapped by the internal jugular vein.

The **inferior belly of the omo-hyoid** passes deep to the posterior border of the sterno-mastoid at a point about one inch above the clavicle. The **external jugular vein**—usually visible through the skin—runs in a line from the angle of the jaw to the junction of the medial and intermediate thirds of the clavicle; it is the vessel which is generally opened to relieve the right side of the heart in asphyxia. It pierces the deep fascia at the posterior border of the sterno-mastoid about an inch above the clavicle, and as its walls are adherent to the margins of the aperture its lumen is kept open at that point; hence a wound of the vein in that situation is liable to be followed by the suction of air into the blood during inspiration. The **third part** of the **subclavian artery** can be compressed against the first rib by pressure directed downwards and backwards, immediately above the clavicle, a little behind the posterior border of the sterno-mastoid muscle. To map out the *course* of the subclavian artery in the neck, draw a line, convex upwards, from the upper border of the sterno-clavicular joint to the middle of the clavicle, the highest part of the arch to reach from $\frac{1}{2}$ to 1 in. above the bone.

To *ligature the vessel* in the third part of its course, make an angular incision along the upper border of the middle of the clavicle and the lower part of the posterior border of the sterno-mastoid muscle. The most important guides to the vessel are the inferior belly of the omo-hyoid, the lateral border of the scalenus anterior, and the scalene tubercle of the first rib. The close relation of the vessel to the lowest trunk of the brachial plexus and to the cervical pleura must be kept in mind. In the rare instances in which a cervical rib is present the subclavian artery lies either in front of it, or arches above it, according to the degree of development of the rib. The **subclavian vein** lies below and in front of the artery, altogether under cover of the clavicle.

Entering the posterior triangle, from behind the lateral border of the scalenus anterior, are the roots of the **brachial plexus.** They unite to form the trunks of the plexus, which lie on the scalenus medius, and can be felt, through the skin, immediately above and behind the third part of the subclavian artery. The anterior primary ramus of the fifth cervical nerve—*i.e.* the uppermost root—supplies the rhomboids, the abductors and lateral rotators of the upper arm, and the flexors and supinators of the forearm; that of the sixth the adductors and medial rotators of the upper arm, and the extensors and pronators of the forearm; that of the seventh the flexors and extensors of the wrist; that of the eighth the flexors and extensors of the fingers; that of the first thoracic, the small muscles of the hand. The roots provided by the fifth, sixth, and seventh nerves contribute the fibres for the nerve to the serratus anterior. Each root of the brachial plexus contributes to the nerve supply of the pectoralis major muscle, and as the fibres of the muscle are supplied from above downwards by the roots in their numerical order, valuable information is obtained by careful testing of the action of the muscle in all suspected cases of injury to the brachial plexus.

When the first thoracic nerve is ruptured within or close to the vertebral canal, the sympathetic fibres which run in it on their way to join the inferior cervical ganglion are torn across. The result is that, among other signs, there will be (1) contraction of the pupil, due to paralysis of the dilator pupillæ; (2) narrowing of the palpebral fissure, due to paralysis of the involuntary fibres of the upper eyelid; (3) slight recession of the eyeball (enophthalmos), due to paralysis of the non-striated orbital muscle of Müller.

As regards the cutaneous distribution in the upper limb, the sensory fibres from the lateral (pre-axial) border of the upper arm enter the fifth nerve, while those from the lateral half of the forearm and hand enter the sixth nerve. The fibres from the centre of the surface of the hand on both ventral and dorsal surfaces and adjacent sides of middle and ring fingers enter the seventh nerve. The fibres from the medial (post-axial) part of the hand enter the eighth cervical nerve; those from the medial border of the forearm enter the first thoracic; and those from the medial side of the upper arm run in the second thoracic nerve. The carotid tubercle lies between the anterior primary rami of the sixth and seventh cervical nerves. The fifth and sixth cervical nerves are those which suffer most when the plexus is injured by forcible depression of the shoulder while the head is bent to the opposite side, such as occurs, for instance, in the "Obstetrical Paralyses" of Duchenne. The lowest trunk of the plexus is the one most liable to be overstretched when traction is applied either to the upper limb or to the rest of the body when the limb is elevated above the shoulder.

To expose the trunks of the brachial plexus make an incision from the junction of the middle and lower thirds of the posterior border of the sterno-mastoid downwards and laterally to the junction of the lateral and intermediate thirds of the clavicle.

The relation of the lowest trunk of the brachial plexus to the first rib is important in relation to those forms of brachial neuritis in which the motor and sensory symptoms indicate pressure on the anterior primary ramus of the first thoracic nerve.

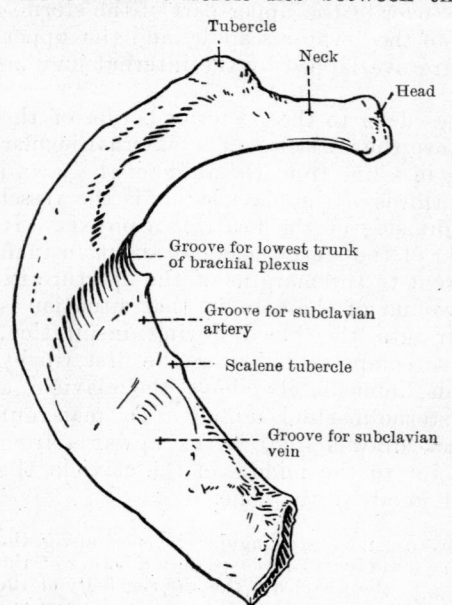

Tubercle

Neck

Head

Groove for lowest trunk of brachial plexus

Groove for subclavian artery

Scalene tubercle

Groove for subclavian vein

Fig. 1134.—THE FIRST RIB, SEEN FROM ABOVE.

The lowest trunk of the brachial plexus lies immediately behind the third part of the subclavian artery in such close relation to the upper surface of the first rib that it may groove the bone, especially if the part contributed by the first thoracic nerve is large and is supplemented by a branch from the second thoracic.

Several cases of neuralgia and partial paralysis of the intrinsic muscles of the hand supplied by the first thoracic nerve have been cured by removal of the portion of the first rib grooved by the trunk. The symptoms were due to the portion of the first thoracic nerve which goes to join the brachial plexus being stretched and pressed upon by the first rib as it crosses the inner edge of the rib to join the eighth cervical nerve. Although similar symptoms may be produced by the first thoracic nerve being stretched across a cervical rib, the surgeon must not expect to find that anomaly in all cases; and when a radiograph has been obtained, do not mistake a well-developed posterior tubercle of the transverse process of the seventh cervical vertebra for a foreshortened view of a rudimentary cervical rib.

In cases in which the first rib produces neuritis from pressure on the first thoracic nerve, it is necessary to remove the portion of the bone between its tubercle and the scalene tubercle. In order to expose and detach the scalenus medius muscle from its insertion into the first rib between the groove for the subclavian artery and the tubercle of the rib, free the plexus from the anterior surface of this muscle and then pull it downwards and medially. In doing that, take care not to injure either of the roots of the nerve to the serratus anterior which pierce the muscle or the trunk of that nerve; the trunk descends behind the lateral edge of the plexus and then crosses the upper digitation of the serratus anterior to enter the axilla. That muscle and the muscles of the first intercostal space are detached from the outer border of the rib, while the supra-pleural membrane is separated from the inner border of the rib, and in doing that take care not to injure the pleura.

In the posterior median line of the neck is the **nuchal furrow**, at the bottom of which are the cervical spines and the ligamentum nuchæ. At the upper part of the furrow, about two inches below the external occipital protuberance, is the **spine of the second cervical vertebra**, which is large and can be distinctly felt; a line drawn from it to the transverse process of the atlas corresponds to the position of the inferior oblique muscle and, therefore, to the inferior margin of the **sub-occipital triangle**. The course of the deep part of the **greater occipital nerve** may be mapped out by a line from the middle of the above-mentioned line to a point one inch lateral to the external occipital protuberance. In the floor of the sub-occipital triangle is the posterior arch of the atlas, upon which the **vertebral artery** lies.

THORAX

In the male the **nipple** is placed usually over the fourth inter-space, or fifth rib, four inches from the median plane. In the child the nipple may be as high as the lower border of the third rib. In the female the position of the nipple is so variable that it is of no topographical value.

In muscular subjects there is a well-marked median furrow between the sternal origins of the right and left **pectoralis major muscles**. The medial part of the lower border of each of those muscles forms a curved prominence which lies over the fifth rib. Below that prominence there is a more or less flat surface that corresponds to the upper part of the rectus abdominis muscle. In the axillary and infra-axillary regions there are the prominences caused by the digitations of origin of the **serratus anterior**, the first to appear below the pectoralis major being that which springs from the fifth rib.

The **upper border** of the **sternum** lies in the same horizontal plane as the lower border of the body of the second thoracic vertebra, the distance between the two being about two inches. The manubrium and the body of the sternum form a slight angle at their junction, known as the *sternal angle*. At the angle there is a horizontal ridge which, although not always visible, can always be felt. The angle is in the same plane as the upper border of the body of the fifth thoracic vertebra.

The **xiphi-sternal joint** is opposite the ninth thoracic vertebra, and is felt as a short, transverse ridge between the seventh pair of costal cartilages, immediately

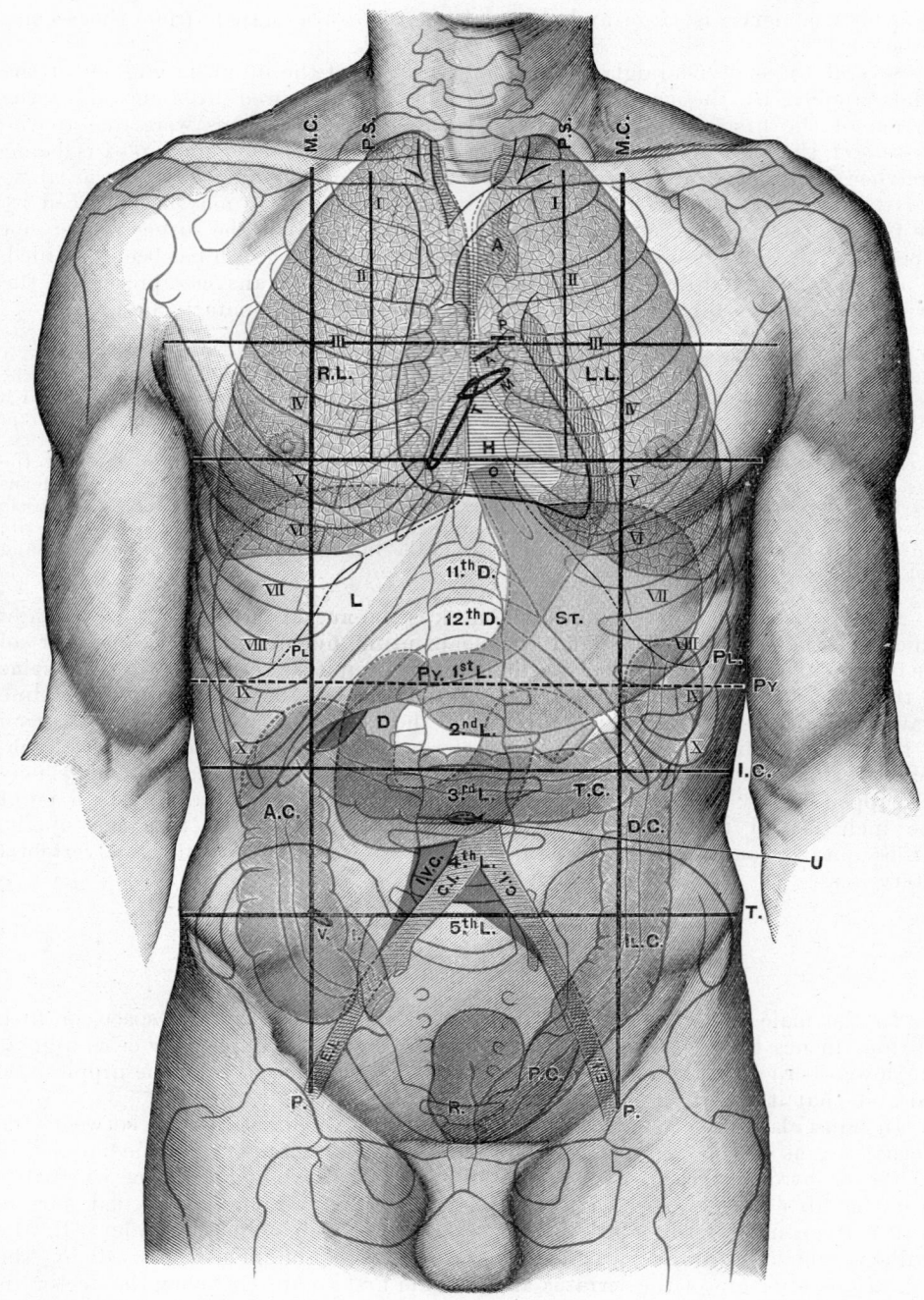

FIG. 1135.—ANTERIOR ASPECT OF TRUNK, SHOWING SURFACE TOPOGRAPHY OF VISCERA.

A.	Aorta.	Il.C.	Lower part of descending	Pl.	Pleura.
A.	Aortic orifice.		colon.	P.S.	Para-sternal line.
A.C.	Ascending colon.	I.V.C.	Inferior vena cava.	Py.	Pylorus and transpyloric plane.
C.I.	Common iliac artery.	L.	Liver.	R.	Rectum.
D.	Duodenum.	L.L.	Left lung.	R.L.	Right lung.
D.C.	Descending colon.	M.	Mitral orifice.	St.	Stomach.
E.I.	External iliac artery.	M.C.	Mid-clavicular line.	**T.**	Intertubercular plane.
H.	Heart.	O.	Œsophagus.	T.	Tricuspid orifice.
I.	Ileum.	**P.**	Inguinal vertical line.	T.C.	Transverse colon.
I.C.	Sub-costal plane.	P.	Pulmonary orifice.	U.	Umbilicus.
		P.C.	Pelvic colon.	V.	Ileo-colic valve.

PLATE LXV

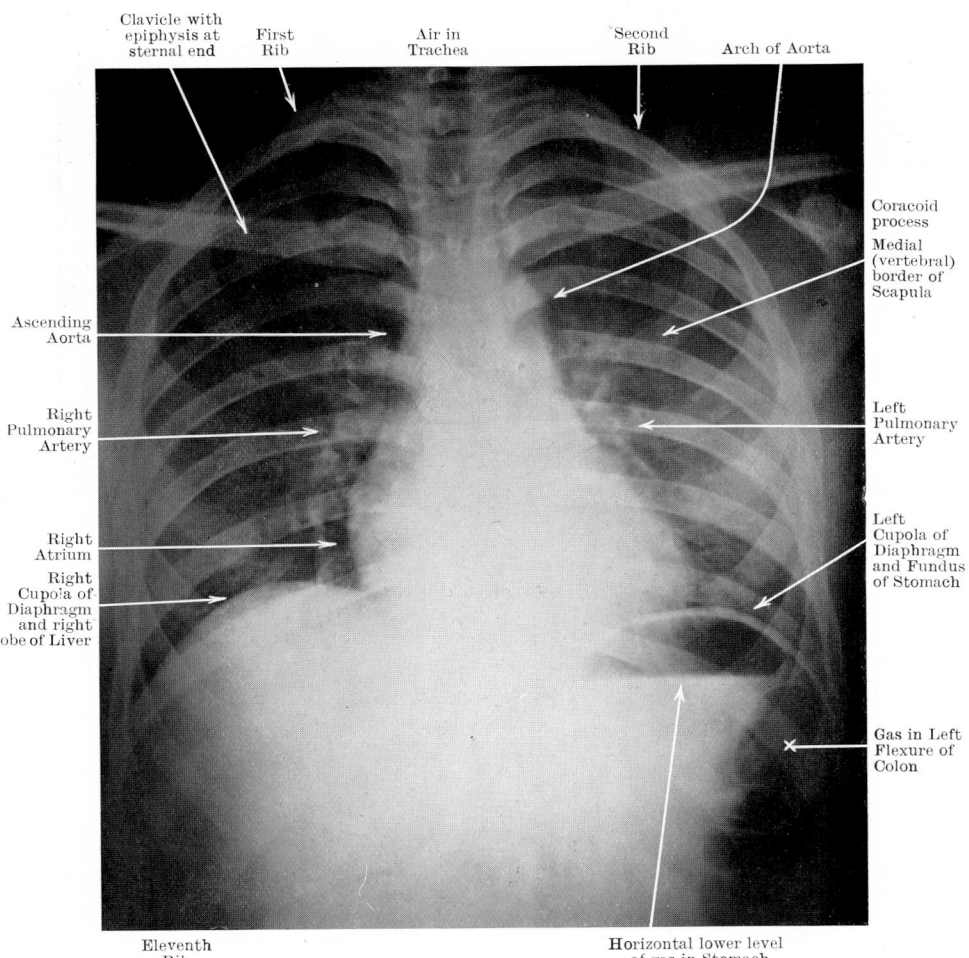

Clavicle with epiphysis at sternal end — First Rib — Air in Trachea — Second Rib — Arch of Aorta

Coracoid process

Medial (vertebral) border of Scapula

Ascending Aorta

Right Pulmonary Artery

Left Pulmonary Artery

Right Atrium

Left Cupola of Diaphragm and Fundus of Stomach

Right Cupola of Diaphragm and right lobe of Liver

Gas in Left Flexure of Colon

Eleventh Rib

Horizontal lower level of gas in Stomach

PLATE LXV.—RADIOGRAPH OF THORAX OF YOUTH AGED 18, IN
POSITION OF SEMI-INSPIRATION.

Compare with Figs. 1 and 2, Plate LXVIII, noting the differences in level of the
Diaphragm and in the shape of the Heart.   Cf. also Plate L.

PLATE LXVI

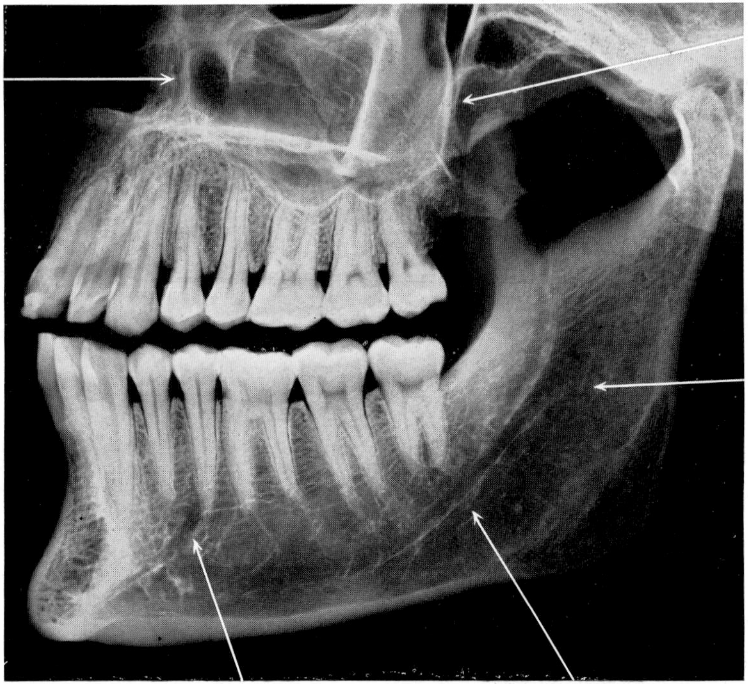

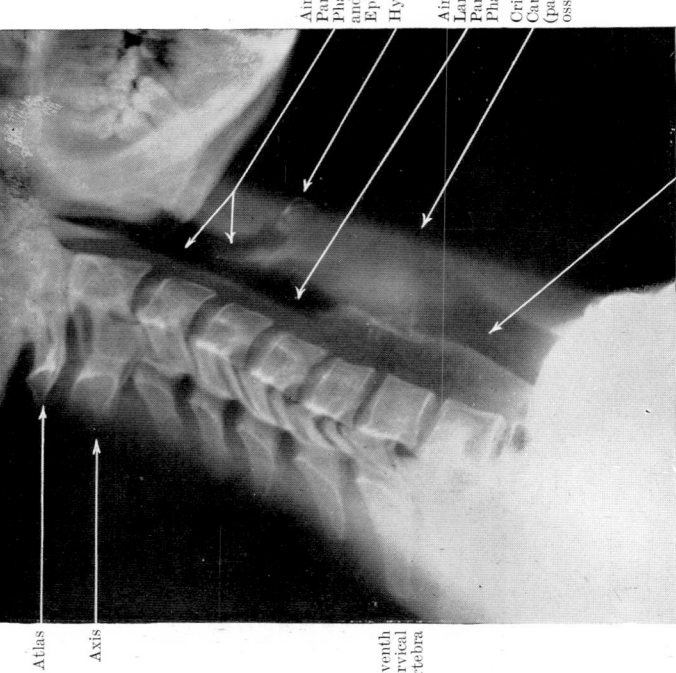

Air in Oral Part of Pharynx: and Epiglottis

Hyoid bone

Air in Laryngeal Part of Pharynx

Cricoid Cartilage (partly ossified)

Air in Trachea

Atlas

Axis

Seventh Cervical Vertebra

FIG. 2.—LATERAL RADIOGRAPH OF NECK OF MAN AGED 36.
(Dr. J. F. Brailsford.)

The positions of the Pharynx and the Trachea are shown, like air-sinuses of the head, by the relative translucency to the X-Rays of their air-filled cavities. Note the closure of the post-cricoid portion of the Laryngeal Part of the Pharynx. Cf. Plate XLIX.

Posterior wall of Maxillary Sinus

Mandibular foramen

Anterior wall of Maxillary Sinus

Mental foramen

Mandibular canal

FIG. 1.—LATERAL RADIOGRAPH OF LEFT HALF OF JAWS OF MALE SKULL WITH COMPLETE SET OF TEETH.

Note the details of the Tooth Cavities and Root Canals, and of the structure of the bone around the Tooth Sockets. The usual relation of the Roots of the Upper Teeth to the Maxillary Sinus (see p. 183) is well shown; see also Plate LIX.

PLATE LXVII

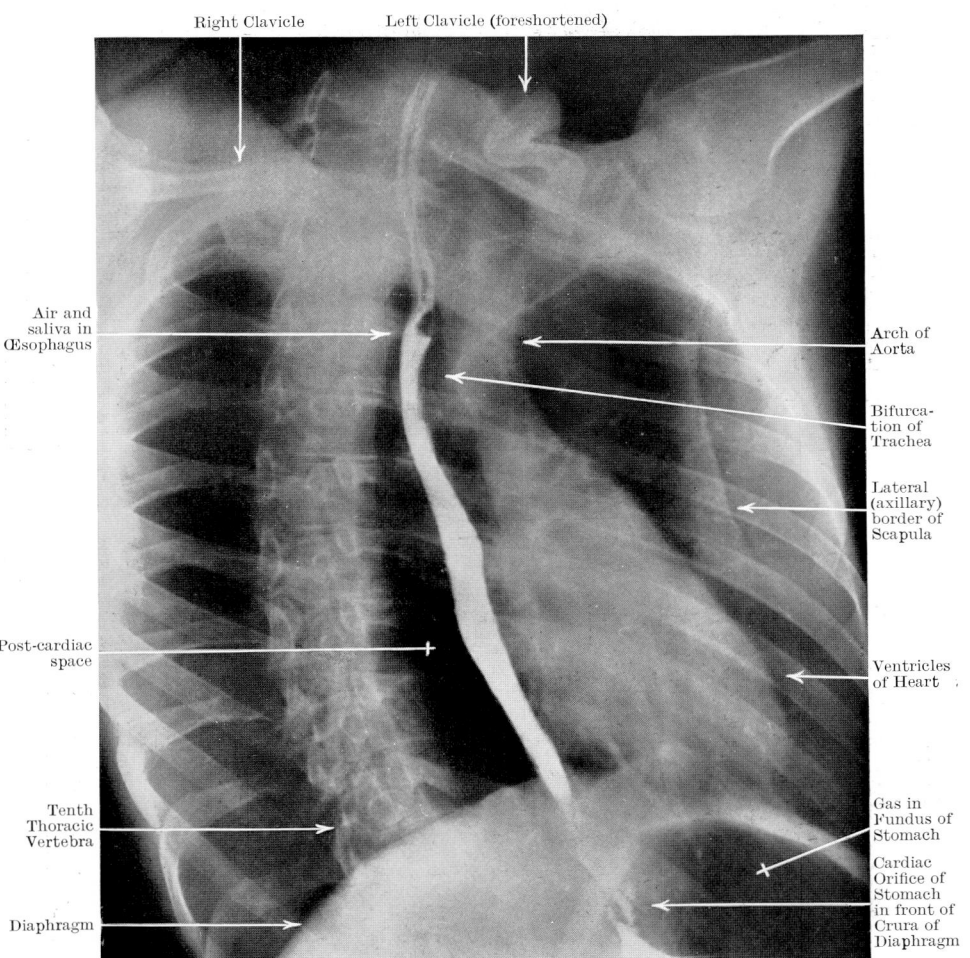

Right Clavicle   Left Clavicle (foreshortened)

Air and
saliva in
Œsophagus

Post-cardiac
space

Tenth
Thoracic
Vertebra

Diaphragm

Arch of
Aorta

Bifurca-
tion of
Trachea

Lateral
(axillary)
border of
Scapula

Ventricles
of Heart

Gas in
Fundus of
Stomach

Cardiac
Orifice of
Stomach
in front of
Crura of
Diaphragm

PLATE LXVII.—OBLIQUE LATERAL RADIOGRAPH OF THORAX OF YOUTH
AGED 18, DURING THE PASSAGE OF " BISMUTH PASTE " THROUGH
THE ŒSOPHAGUS.

For the relation of the Œsophagus to the Vertebral Column and the back of the
Pericardium, see Fig. 480, D and E, p. 566 ; and note that the " post-cardiac space " is part
of the posterior mediastinum occupied mainly by the Œsophagus and the Descending Aorta.

PLATE LXVIII

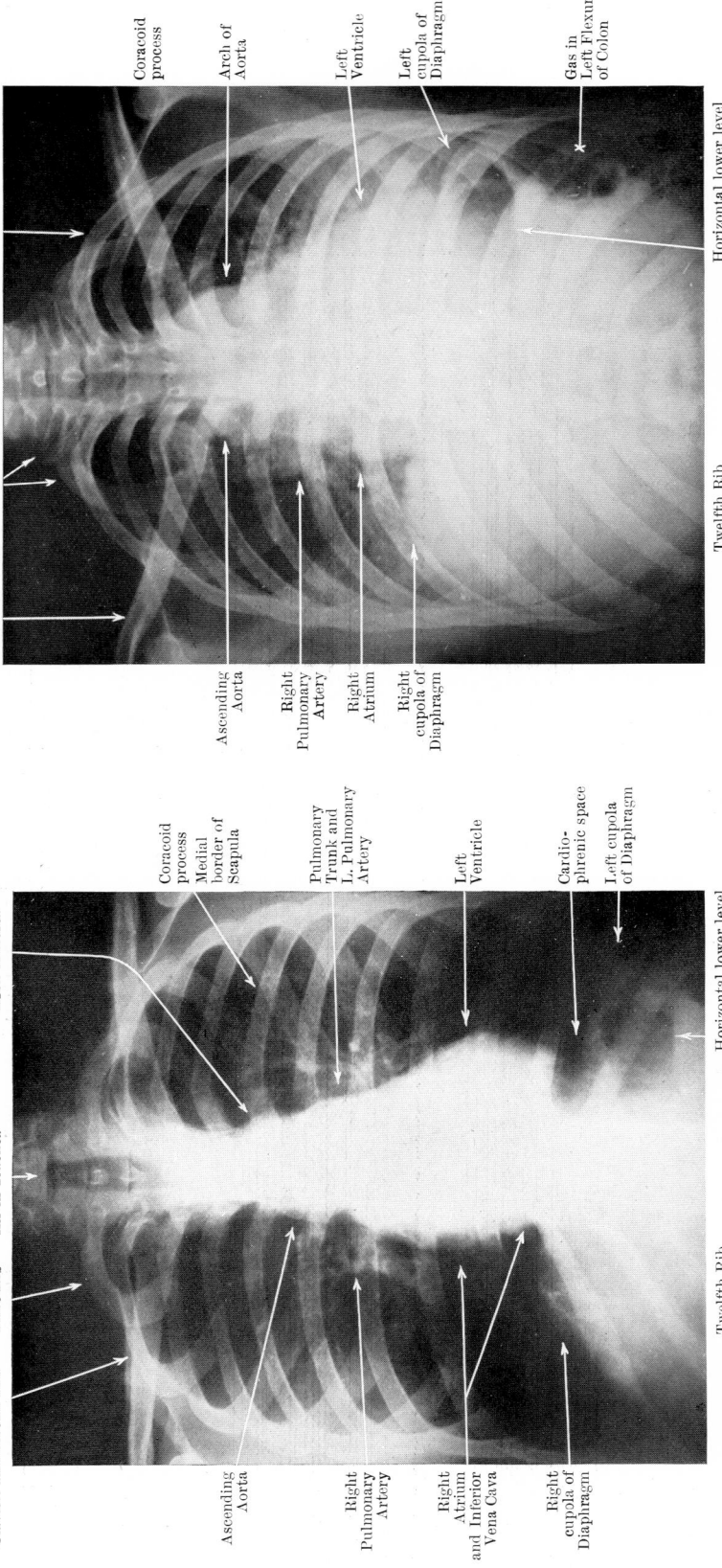

Coracoid process

Arch of Aorta

Left Ventricle

Left cupola of Diaphragm

Gas in Left Flexure of Colon

Second Rib

First Rib and transverse process of Seventh Cervical Vertebra

Clavicle

Horizontal lower level of gas in Stomach

Twelfth Rib

Ascending Aorta

Right Pulmonary Artery

Right Atrium

Right cupola of Diaphragm

Fig. 2.—Radiograph of the same Thorax in position of Full Expiration.

Note the descent of the medial parts of the Clavicles, the rise of the Diaphragm, the broadening of the Heart and Great Vessels, the greater obliquity of the Ribs, and the greater density of the Lungs. Compare with Fig. 1.

Arch of Aorta

Coracoid process
Medial border of Scapula

Pulmonary Trunk and L. Pulmonary Artery

Left Ventricle

Cardio-phrenic space

Left cupola of Diaphragm

Sixth Cervical Vertebra: Air in Trachea

First Rib

Clavicle and Second Rib

Horizontal lower level of gas in Plate LXV

Twelfth Rib

Ascending Aorta

Right Pulmonary Artery

Right Atrium and Inferior Vena Cava

Right cupola of Diaphragm

Fig. 1.—Radiograph of the same Thorax as in Plate LXV (Youth aged 18) in position of Full Inspiration.

Note the rise of the Clavicles, the descent of the Diaphragm, the narrowing and better definition of the Heart and the more horizontal position of the Ribs. Compare with Fig. 2.

above a shallow depression called the **epigastric fossa**, in whose floor the xiphoid process can be felt.

The xiphoid process lies in the wall of the abdomen in front of the liver, for the xiphi-sternal joint marks the junction between the thorax and abdomen in the median plane, and in that situation it is the guide to the diaphragm, the lower border of the heart, and the upper surface of the liver.

Fracture of the sternum is rare, and generally occurs at or close to the junction of the manu-brium and the body ; it may occur either from direct violence, or indirectly along with fracture of the vertebral column. The periosteum of the sternum, unlike that of the ribs, is firmly adherent to the bone.

The **ribs**, which in well-nourished subjects cause no surface prominences, are visible in thin persons ; in the obese it is very difficult even to feel them. When the ribs are counted from the front, the *second* may always be identified by its relation to the sternal angle. The *first rib* is to a large extent under cover of the clavicle. The lower border of the pectoralis major and the first visible digita-tion of the serratus anterior afford reliable guides to the *fifth rib*. The *seventh costal cartilage* is the one felt on the costal margin nearest the sternum (though occasionally the eighth cartilage, and not the seventh, is the lowest to reach the sternum). The second and third costal cartilages are almost horizontal ; below that the cartilages ascend with increasing obliquity, that of the sixth being the first to present a distinct angle. The anterior end of the second intercostal space is the widest, while those of the fifth and sixth are very narrow.

The **costo-chondral junctions** may be indicated, on the surface, by a line drawn from the sterno-clavicular joint to a point a finger's-breadth behind the angle of the tenth costal cartilage ; the first junction, however, is lateral to that line.

The **internal mammary artery** crosses behind the medial ends of the upper five intercostal spaces, about half an inch from the edge of the sternum. The vessel is accompanied by two veins which unite opposite the third interspace to form a single vein which ends in the innominate vein at the inlet of the thorax.

This artery is occasionally injured in punctured wounds of the chest. At the second or third intercostal space it is easily ligatured through a transverse incision, but at a lower level it is generally necessary to resect a portion of one of the costal cartilages.

LUNGS AND PLEURÆ

The **apex** of the lung and the cervical pleura extend upwards into the root of the neck for a distance of about an inch above the sternal third of the clavicle and are intimately related to the subclavian artery anteriorly ; they are mapped out by a curved line drawn from the upper border of the sterno-clavicular joint across the sterno-mastoid to the junction of the medial and intermediate thirds of the clavicle, the highest part of the curve reaching from $\frac{1}{2}$ to $1\frac{1}{2}$ in. above the clavicle.

Both the **cervical pleura** and the **subclavian artery** may be injured by one of the fragments in a fracture of the clavicle ; the scalene muscles, however, afford considerable protection to the pleura. When the third part of the subclavian artery is ligatured, care must be taken not to injure the cervical pleura.

To mark in the **anterior border** of the **right lung**, draw a line from the upper border of the sterno-clavicular joint to the centre of the manubrium sterni, and from there vertically downwards, in or slightly to the left of the median plane to the xiphi-sternal joint (Fig. 1136).

The **anterior border** of the **left lung** is mapped out by a corresponding line as far as the fourth costal cartilage ; thence it is directed along the lower border of the fourth costal cartilage for an inch and a half or two inches and then curved downwards and medially to a point a little below and to the left of the xiphi-sternal joint. The lower part of the front of the right ventricle is therefore un-covered by lung and gives a completely dull note on percussion; that area is spoken of as the area of "*complete cardiac dullness.*"

The level of the **lower border** of the lung is practically the same on both sides; it is mapped out by a line that begins at or near the xiphi-sternal joint and is drawn in a slightly curved direction, with the convexity downwards, across the side of the chest towards the tenth thoracic spine. The line crosses

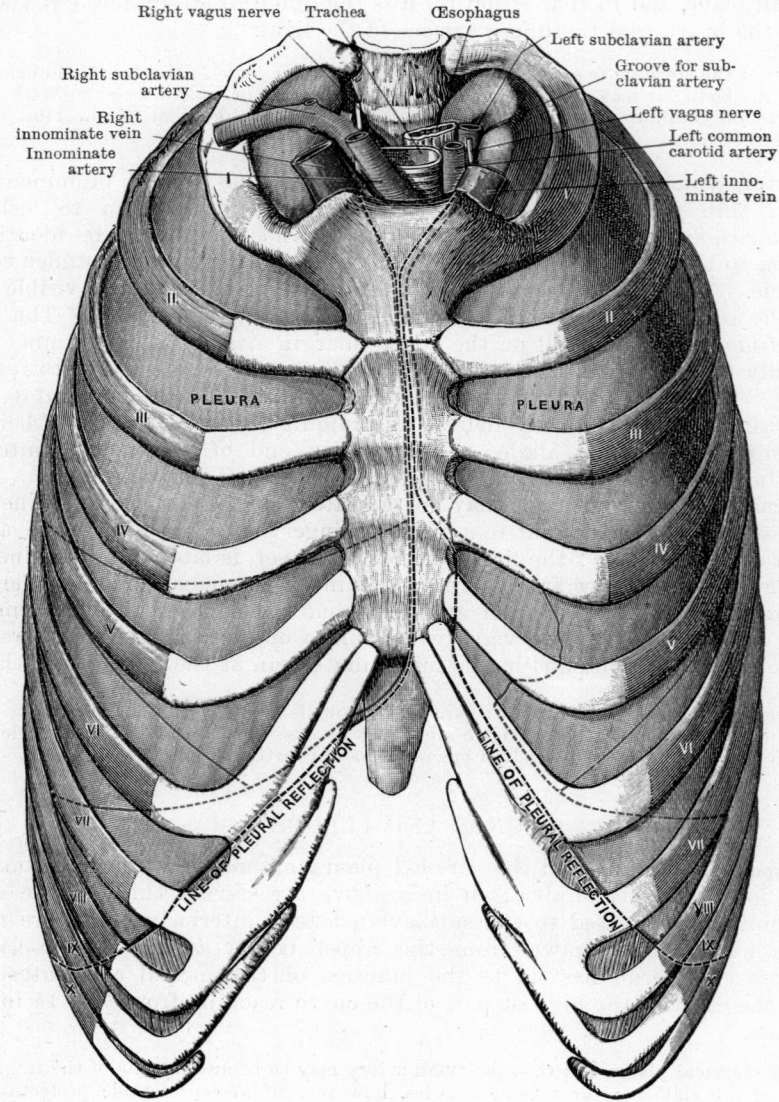

Fig. 1136.—Dissection of a Subject hardened by Formalin Injection, to show the pleural sacs from the front. The anterior and diaphragmatic lines of pleural reflexion are indicated by black dotted lines, and the outlines of the lungs and their fissures by the blue lines. (D. J. C.)

the eighth rib in the mid-axillary line about a hand's-breadth above the costal margin (Figs. 1136-1139).

To indicate the position of the **oblique fissure** a line is drawn from the second thoracic spine to the root of the spine of the scapula, and thence downwards, laterally and forwards to end at the sixth or seventh costal cartilage about three finger-breadths from the median plane. When the arm is raised above the level of the shoulder, and the hand placed on the back of the head, the inferior angle of the scapula is rotated upwards and forwards so that the medial margin practically corresponds with the line of the oblique fissure.

The **horizontal fissure** of the right lung is mapped out by a line drawn from the median line of the sternum, at the level of the fourth costal cartilage, towards the right and slightly upwards to the mid-axillary line.

Pleuræ.—The **line of reflexion** of the **right pleura** from the back of the sternum may be said to correspond to the anterior border of the right lung.

On the **left side**, the pleural reflexion corresponds to the anterior border of the left lung as far as the lower edge of the fourth chondro-sternal junction, at which point it leaves the lung and descends, behind the left border of the sternum, to the xiphi-sternal joint (Figs. 1136, 1145).

The **costo-diaphragmatic reflexion** or lower border of the pleura (see Figs. 1137 and 1144) is indicated on the surface by a line drawn from the xiphi-sternal joint towards the twelfth thoracic spine. The line is markedly convex downwards and crosses the tenth rib on the mid-axillary line about two finger-breadths above the costal margin.

The **relations** of the **pleura** to the **twelfth rib** are of importance to the surgeon, especially in connexion with operations on the kidney (Figs. 1138–1140). When the rib is not abnormally short, the pleural reflexion crosses it opposite the lateral border of the sacro-spinalis muscle; hence an incision may be carried deeply as far as the apex of the angle between the twelfth rib and the lateral border of the sacro-spinalis without risk to the pleura. When, however, the twelfth rib does not reach the lateral border of the sacro-spinalis, the rib felt there is the eleventh; an incision carried upwards to that level is certain to wound the pleura (Melsom). Therefore, count the ribs from the second downwards, in order not to mistake the eleventh for the twelfth, when the twelfth is rudimentary.

Medial to the lateral edge of the sacro-spinalis the pleural reflexion lies below the level of the twelfth rib, and not infrequently descends as far as the transverse process of the first lumbar vertebra. This must be borne in mind by the surgeon when he is carrying out a dissection to expose the kidney from the back.

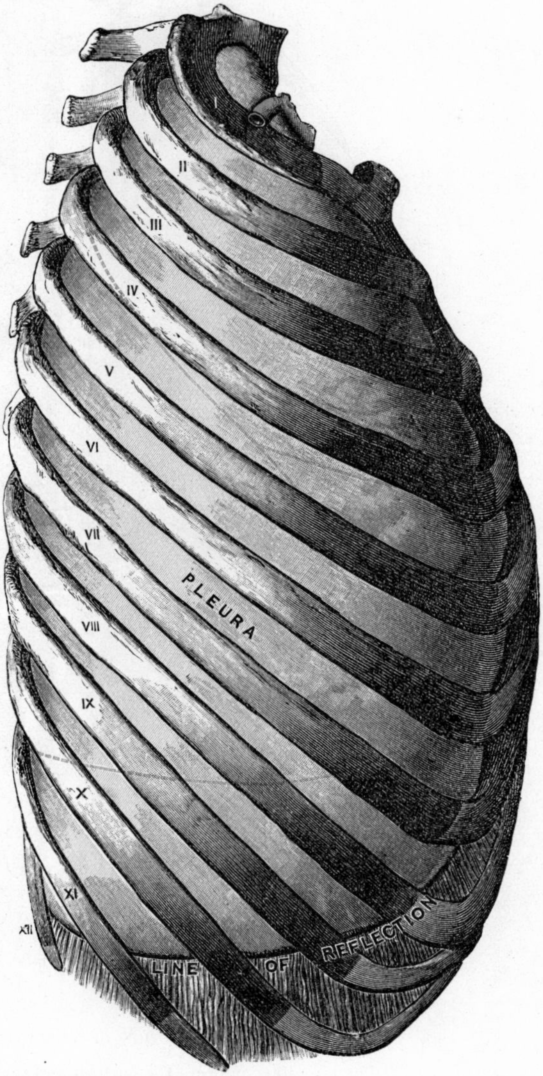

On the *right side* of the posterior mediastinum, the **mediastinal pleura**, as it passes backwards from the pericardium to the vertebral column, sweeps over the right side of the œsophagus; malignant ulcers of the

Fig. 1137.—Lateral View of the Right Pleural Sac in a Subject hardened by Formalin Injection. The blue lines indicate the outline of the right lung, and also the position of its fissures. (D. J. C.)

œsophagus are therefore more likely to invade the right pleura than the left. On the *left side* it passes from the bodies of the vertebræ on to the left side of the aorta. Hence, in the operation to evacuate pus from the posterior mediastinum, there is less risk of opening the pleura if the space is entered from the left side of the vertebral column.

The seat of election for *tapping the pleura* (*paracentesis pleuræ*) is the sixth or seventh intercostal space, a little in front of the posterior axillary fold. To allow of the introduction of a tube to drain away the pus from the pleural cavity in empyema, resect a portion of one of the ribs (sixth to ninth). The intercostal vessels and nerve, which lie in the costal groove, are avoided if the rib is removed subperiosteally. If the chest is opened in a line dropped from the lower end of the scapula, care must be taken not to resect either the seventh or the eighth ribs, for though they are exposed when the arm is elevated, they are overlapped by the lower part of the scapula when the arm is lowered.

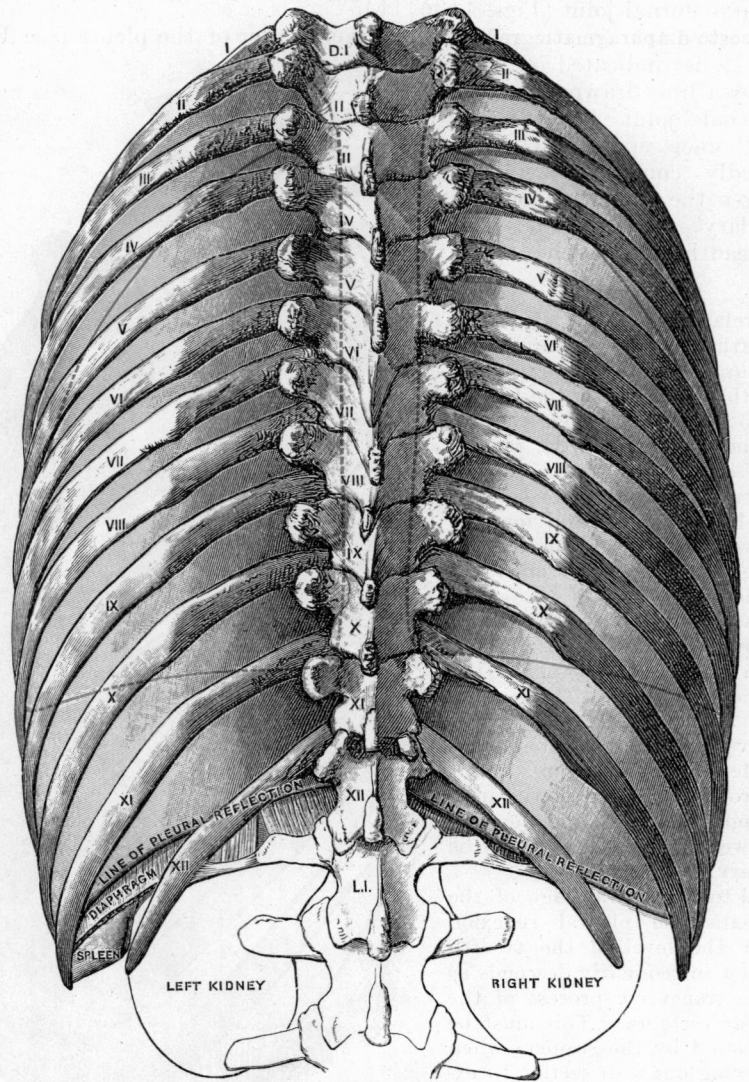

FIG. 1138.—DISSECTION OF THE PLEURAL SACS FROM BEHIND.

The blue lines indicate the outlines and the fissures of the lungs. (D. J. C.)

Anteriorly, the **bifurcation** of the **trachea** is opposite the *sternal angle*, while posteriorly it is a little below the level of the root of the spine of the scapula, opposite the fourth thoracic spine. The bifurcation takes place one vertebra higher in the infant than in the adult (Symington).

The septum between the right and the left bronchus is a little to the left of the middle of the trachea, and the right bronchus is wider and more nearly in a line with the trachea than the left bronchus; hence the greater tendency of foreign bodies to enter the right bronchus.

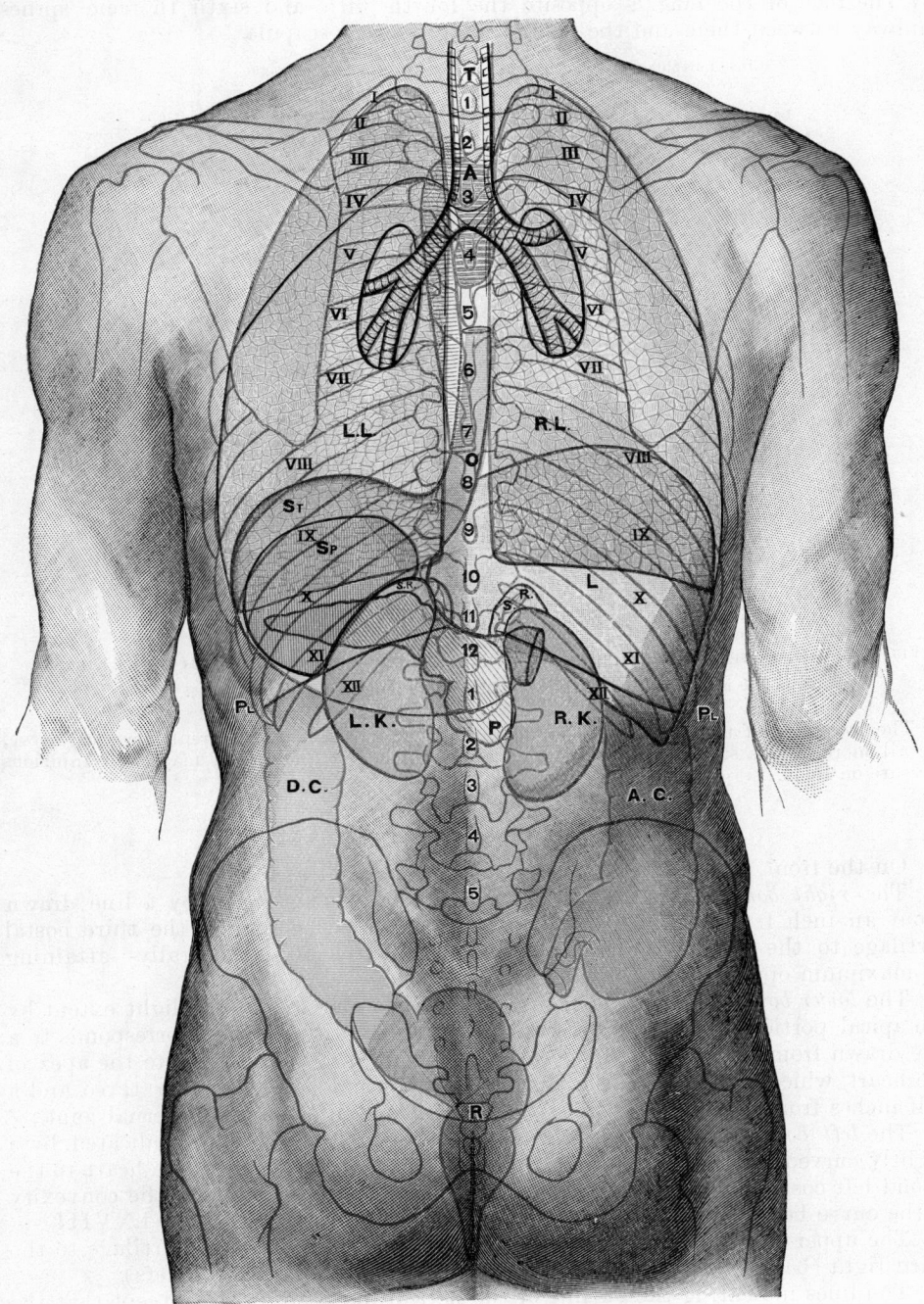

FIG. 1139.—POSTERIOR ASPECT OF TRUNK, SHOWING SURFACE TOPOGRAPHY OF VISCERA.

A. Aorta.	L.L. Left lung.	R.L. Right lung.
A.C. Ascending colon.	P. Pancreas.	Sp. Spleen.
D.C. Descending colon.	Pl. Pleura.	S.R. Suprarenal gland.
L. Liver.	R. Rectum.	St. Stomach.
L.K. Left kidney.	R.K. Right kidney.	T. Trachea.

The **root** of the **lung** is opposite the fourth, fifth, and sixth thoracic spines, midway between them and the medial margin of the scapula.

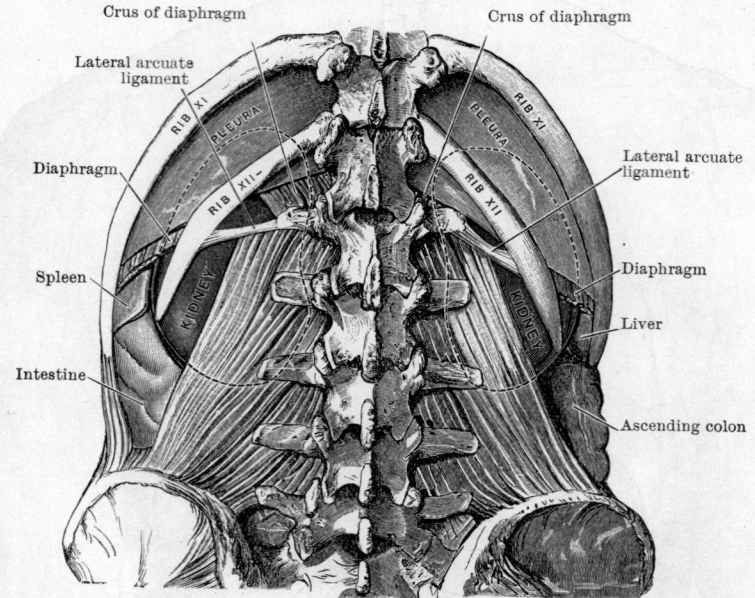

FIG. 1140.—DISSECTION FROM BEHIND TO SHOW THE RELATION OF THE PLEURAL SACS TO THE KIDNEYS. Outlines of the upper portions of the two kidneys are indicated by dotted lines. (H. J. S.)

The lower end of the trachea, the bronchi, the vagi, and the left recurrent laryngeal nerve, are all more or less surrounded by lymph glands which, when enlarged, may exert injurious pressure on them.

HEART AND GREAT VESSELS

On the front, the **outline** of the **heart** is marked out as follows :—

The *right border*, formed by the right atrium, is indicated by a line drawn about an inch from the median plane from the upper border of the third costal cartilage to the sixth; the line should be slightly convex laterally—attaining its maximum opposite the fourth intercostal space.

The *lower border*, formed by the right ventricle and to a very slight extent by the apical portion of the left ventricle, is almost horizontal, and corresponds to a line drawn from the sixth right costal cartilage to the point opposite the apex of the heart, which lies behind the fifth left intercostal space, three or three and a half inches from the median plane. The line is opposite the xiphi-sternal joint.

The *left border*, formed almost wholly by the left ventricle, is indicated by a slightly curved line extending from the point opposite the apex of the heart to the second left costal cartilage an inch and a half from the median line, the convexity of the curve being directed laterally and slightly upwards (Pls. LXV, LXVIII).

The upper border is opposite a line drawn from the second left cartilage to the third right (between the ends of the lines for the right and left borders).

The lines indicating the outline of the pericardium are similar, except that the line for the upper border passes from the second left cartilage to the second right.

The situation of the anterior part of the **atrio-ventricular sulcus** [s. coronarius] is mapped out by a line drawn from the lower border of the third left costal cartilage to the sixth right chondro-sternal junction; the line should be slightly convex upwards and to the right. The **auricle** of the **right** atrium lies in the median plane, or a little to the right of it, at the level of the second intercostal space and the upper border of the third costal cartilage. The **auricle** of the **left** atrium lies behind the second left intercostal space, close to the edge of the sternum.

The *base* or *posterior surface* of the heart is formed mainly by the **left atrium**, which is moulded posteriorly on the œsophagus, the aorta, the bronchi, and the bronchial glands—the pericardium intervening. The left atrium extends behind the right atrium for a considerable distance to the right of the median plane.

In radiographic examination in cases of general visceroptosis, the diaphragm, which should rise and fall opposite the xiphi-sternal junction, will be seen to be an inch or more lower down, while the long axis of the heart assumes an almost vertical direction (cardioptosis).

The *cardiac orifices* and *their valves* are situated below and to the left of the anterior part of the atrio-ventricular [coronary] sulcus, and lie in the following order from above downwards and from left to right, viz. pulmonary, aortic, mitral, and tricuspid.

The **pulmonary orifice**, directed upwards and backwards, is opposite the third left costal cartilage; the **aortic orifice**, directed upwards, forwards, and to the right, is farther from the surface, behind the left margin of the sternum, opposite the lower border of the third intercostal space; the **mitral orifice** is at a lower level, behind the left half of the sternum, opposite the fourth costal cartilage; it is directed downwards, forwards, and to the left. The **tricuspid orifice** is nearer the anterior wall of the chest than the mitral, and is opposite the middle of the sternum at the level of the fourth and fifth cartilages and intervening space.

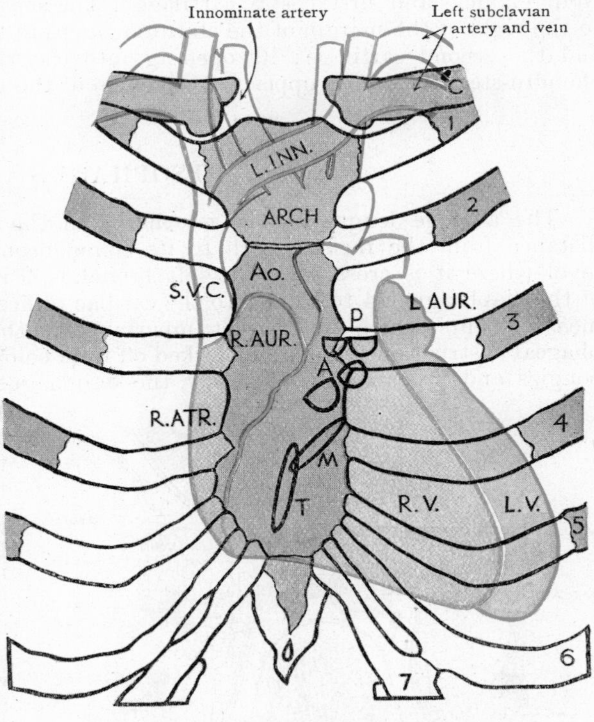

FIG. 1141.—RELATION OF THE HEART AND GREAT VESSELS TO THE ANTERIOR WALL OF THE THORAX

1 to 7. Ribs and costal cartilages.
A. Aortic orifice.
Ao. Ascending Aorta.
C. Clavicle.
L.V. Left ventricle.
M. Mitral orifice.
P. Pulmonary orifice.
R.V. Right ventricle.
S.V.C. Superior vena cava.
T. Tricuspid orifice.

Although the first and second **sounds of the heart** are heard all over the cardiac area, the sounds produced by the individual valves are heard most distinctly, not directly over their anatomical situation, but over the area where the cavity in which the valve lies is nearest the surface. Hence the mitral sound is best heard over the apex (mitral area), the tricuspid over the lower left part of the body of the sternum (tricuspid area), the aortic over the second right costal cartilage (aortic area), and the pulmonary over the third left costal cartilage (pulmonary area).

In **tapping the pericardium** (paracentesis pericardii), make the puncture through the fourth left intercostal space as close as possible to the edge of the sternum. The internal mammary vessels are thus avoided. They are avoided equally well if the puncture is made an inch from the side of the sternum—the p eura being in no danger, as it has been pushed aside by the distended pericardium.

To establish free drainage in suppurative pericarditis, the sixth left costal cartilage must be resected and the internal mammary vessels ligatured; the sterno-costalis muscle [transversus thoracis] and the pleura are then pushed aside and the pericardium exposed and incised.

To obtain surgical access to the heart, make a flap-shaped incision which exposes the fourth, fifth, and sixth costal cartilages of the left side and the corresponding half of the sternum. The base of the flap may lie medially or laterally. The fourth, fifth, and sixth ribs are divided close to their cartilages, the sternum is severed in the mid-line, and the flap so formed is lifted to one side.

The **ascending aorta** lies behind the first piece of the body of the sternum, and, unless dilated, does not project beyond its right border. The upper border of the **aortic arch** lies at or a little above the centre of the manubrium sterni, but in the child it may reach as high as the upper border of the manubrium.

The **innominate** and **left common carotid arteries** diverge from the sides of the median plane between the upper part of the manubrium sterni and the front of the trachea and pass towards the sterno-clavicular joints.

The **pulmonary trunk** lies behind the sternal end of the second interspace and the second costal cartilage.

The **left innominate vein** lies behind the medial part of the left clavicle and the upper part of the manubrium sterni, the **right** behind the medial part of the right clavicle and first costal cartilage. The **superior vena cava** lies immediately to the right of the margin of the sternum, opposite the first and second interspaces and the second cartilage; its opening into the right atrium, behind the third chondro-sternal joint, is opposite the centre of the root of the right lung.

ŒSOPHAGUS

The average length of the **œsophagus** in the adult is 10 in. (25 cm.); the distance from the incisor teeth to its commencement is 6 in.; to the point or level where it is crossed by the left bronchus, 9 in.; to the œsophageal opening of the diaphragm, 14 to 15 in.; to the cardiac orifice of the stomach, 16 in. These measurements, which are of great importance in the diagnosis of the seat of œsophageal obstructions, should be marked off from below upwards upon all œsophageal bougies and probangs. Posteriorly, the œsophagus extends from the level of the sixth cervical spine to that of the ninth thoracic, a little to the left of which is the situation at which the stethoscope is placed in order that the sound produced by the passage of fluid into the stomach may be heard (Fig. 480 and Pl. LXVII).

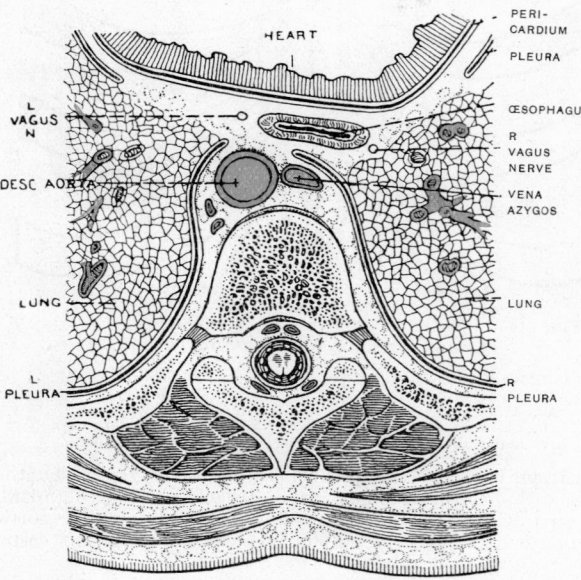

FIG. 1142.—THE RELATIONS OF THE ŒSOPHAGUS IN THE POSTERIOR MEDIASTINUM. (Testut, *Anatomie humaine.*)

There are three points in the lumen of the œsophagus at which foreign bodies are apt to become impacted, and in which neoplasms commonly occur. They are at the pharyngo-œsophageal junction (6 in. from the teeth), the level of the crossing of the left bronchus (opposite the body of the fifth thoracic vertebra), and at the passage through the diaphragm (15 in. from the teeth).

Clinically it is important to bear in mind the relation of the œsophagus to the trachea and left bronchus, to the left recurrent laryngeal nerve, to the bronchial and posterior mediastinal glands, to the descending thoracic aorta, and to the right pleura in the posterior mediastinum. Ulcers of the œsophagus are apt to open into either the trachea, the left bronchus, or the right pleura.

The *veins* of the lower end of the œsophagus open partly into the systemic veins and partly into the portal system; like those at the lower end of the rectum they are liable to become varicose in conditions which give rise to chronic interference with the portal circulation.

The *lymph vessels* of the upper part of the œsophagus open into the glands in the root of the neck, the remainder into the posterior mediastinal glands.

By means of the cinematograph X-Ray the relatively quick movements of the œsophagus have been studied. Three phases may be distinguished in the process of swallowing—

the pharyngeal, the œsophageal, and the cardiac. The upper end of the œsophagus opens secondary to contraction of the pharynx; a series of rapid peristaltic waves then appear in the œsophagus—each contraction lasting four to six seconds—and after a perceptible interval, dependent upon the type of food, the cardiac orifice of the stomach opens (Woollard, *Recent Advances in Anatomy*).

ABDOMEN

ANTERIOR WALL OF ABDOMEN

The configuration of the abdomen varies with the age, sex, obesity, and muscular development of the individual. In the child it is wider above than below, while the reverse is the case in the female adult. It is most prominent in the region of the **umbilicus**, which, in the recumbent posture, is situated below the mid-point between the xiphi-sternal joint and the pubic symphysis, usually a little above the level of the highest part of the iliac crest, and opposite the disc between the third and fourth lumbar vertebræ; but in a person standing upright it sinks to a lower level and is opposite the middle of the body of the fourth lumbar vertebra. In the obese, and especially when the abdominal muscles have lost their tone, the umbilical region becomes prominent and more or less pendulous, so that the umbilicus may come to lie considerably below the normal level. In the child it is relatively lower than in the adult, in consequence of the undeveloped state of the pelvis.

In spare subjects the lower end of the body of the sternum, the xiphoid process, and the costal margin can readily be traced. Below the xiphi-sternal joint and bounded on each side by the seventh, eighth, and ninth costal cartilages, is the **infra-sternal angle**, which varies considerably according to the shape of the chest; it is relatively wider in the child than in the adult. The lower border of the curve of the **tenth costal cartilage** is easily recognisable, and is usually the lowest point seen or felt on the costal margin when the body is examined from the front; it also marks the level of the sub-costal plane.

The anterior wall is limited below by the groove of the groin and the pubic crest. In a spare muscular subject the recti, the furrows corresponding to the tendinous intersections and the supra-umbilical portion of the **linea alba** can be readily made out. When the outline of the rectus is not visible the lateral border may be indicated by a line drawn from the tip of the ninth costal cartilage to the mid-point of a line between the umbilicus and the anterior superior iliac spine, and from there to the pubic tubercle. In the angle between the lateral border of the rectus and the ninth costal cartilage there is a slight triangular depression which, on the right side, overlies the fundus of the **gall-bladder**. Between the lower part of the lateral border of the rectus and the bulging above the anterior part of the iliac crest caused by the lower muscular fibres of the external oblique, there is another slight triangular depression which corresponds to the inferior and narrow part of the aponeurosis of the external oblique muscle.

Close above, and almost parallel to, the medial half of the inguinal ligament is the **inguinal canal**, which is traversed by the **spermatic cord** (Fig. 1143); the cord can be felt to emerge at the superficial inguinal ring immediately above the pubic tubercle. The **inguinal rings** are fully described in the chapter on Muscles. The **superficial inguinal ring** is triangular in shape, with its apex directed upwards and laterally, and its base at the pubic crest. It is to be noted that the neck of an *inguinal hernia* lies above the pubic tubercle, whereas the neck of a *femoral hernia* emerges below the medial part of the inguinal ligament, lateral to the pubic tubercle. The **deep inguinal ring** is nearly half an inch above the *mid-inguinal point*—that is a point on the inguinal ligament midway between the pubic symphysis and the anterior superior iliac spine. The **inferior epigastric artery** may be mapped out by a line drawn from the mid-inguinal point towards the umbilicus. The vessel, together with the medial third of the inguinal ligament and the lower part of the lateral border of the rectus, bounds a triangle known as the **inguinal triangle**.

As the inferior epigastric artery passes upwards and medially to disappear behind the conjoint tendon and the lateral border of the rectus, it lies behind the spermatic cord immediately medial to, and below, the deep inguinal ring. The floor of the inguinal triangle is formed throughout by the fascia transversalis, superficial to which, over the medial half or so of the triangle, is the conjoint tendon. An **oblique inguinal hernia** leaves the abdomen at the deep inguinal ring and traverses the whole length of the inguinal canal; its coverings are therefore the same as those of the spermatic cord, and the neck of the sac lies lateral to the inferior epigastric artery. A **direct inguinal hernia**, on the other hand, instead of traversing the whole length of the inguinal canal, pushes before it that part of its posterior wall which is formed by the floor of the inguinal triangle. The neck of the sac, therefore, lies medial to the inferior epigastric artery. If a direct hernia makes its way through the medial part of the inguinal triangle, it derives a covering from the conjoint tendon

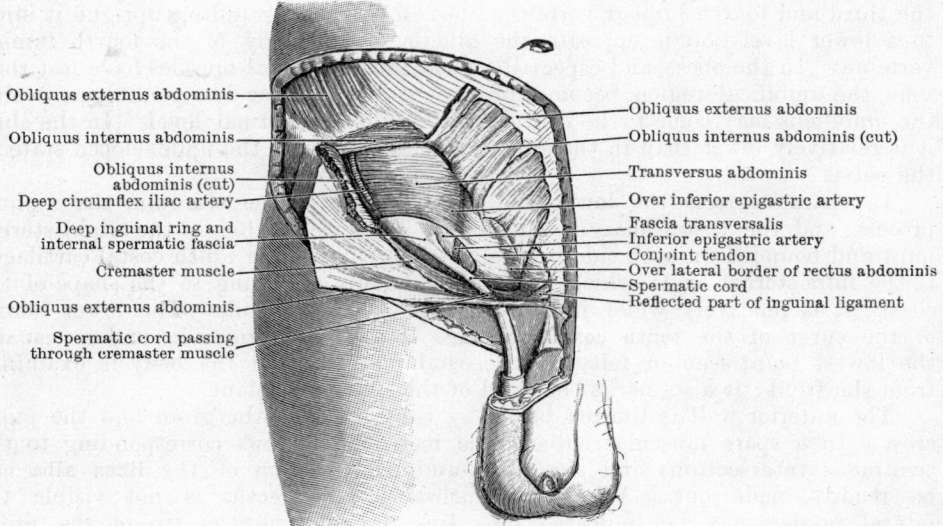

Obliquus externus abdominis
Obliquus internus abdominis
Obliquus internus abdominis (cut)
Deep circumflex iliac artery
Deep inguinal ring and internal spermatic fascia
Cremaster muscle
Obliquus externus abdominis
Spermatic cord passing through cremaster muscle

Obliquus externus abdominis
Obliquus internus abdominis (cut)
Transversus abdominis
Over inferior epigastric artery
Fascia transversalis
Inferior epigastric artery
Conjoint tendon
Over lateral border of rectus abdominis
Spermatic cord
Reflected part of inguinal ligament

FIG. 1143.—THE GROIN. The structures seen on reflexion of part of the obliquus internus abdominis. (A. M. Paterson.)

as well as from the fascia transversalis; if through the lateral part of the triangle, the lateral edge of the conjoint tendon curves round the medial side of the neck of the sac. To relieve the constriction at the neck of the sac, in the case of an *oblique inguinal hernia*, direct the edge of the knife upwards and laterally to avoid the inferior epigastric artery; in a *direct hernia* divide the constriction in an upward and medial direction in order to avoid damaging the artery. In an *oblique inguinal hernia* the sac lies within the internal spermatic fascia (fascia propria of the hernia), whereas in a *direct hernia* the fascia propria is derived from the fascia transversalis. The extraperitoneal fat which covers the outer surface of the hernial sac is sometimes hypertrophied to such an extent as to amount to a fatty tumour.

In a large number of children, at birth, the **vaginal process** of peritoneum, which connects the tunica vaginalis testis with the abdominal peritoneum, is still patent, especially on the right side. Should the bowel force its way along the patent process a **congenital inguinal hernia** arises. In the majority of the cases of congenital inguinal hernia it will be found that the tunica vaginalis testis has been shut off by closure of the lower part of the vaginal process, only the upper part remaining patent and forming the sac of the hernia.

In the child the persistence of a patent vaginal process can almost invariably be detected if the spermatic cord is rolled between the finger and thumb; for after the vas deferens and spermatic vessels have slipped away from one's grasp, the edge of the sac can be felt to follow them.   In regard to the operation for the cure of inguinal hernia, it should be borne in mind that in the acquired form the *hernia produces the sac*, whereas in the congenital variety the *sac is the cause of the hernia*; it follows, therefore, that in the operation for *acquired* hernia the closure of the canal is as important as the removal or obliteration of the sac, while in a *congenital* hernia the most essential part of the operation is the closure of the neck of the sac, and, as the muscular and fascial layers of the walls of the canal are often well developed (especially in children), they should be interfered with as little as possible.   A patent vaginal process may persist during adult life without any bowel descending into it; on the other hand, years after birth, bowel may suddenly enter it.   In practically all oblique inguinal herniæ which develop suddenly in children as well as in adolescents and young adults, the *sac* is congenital.

In the ordinary form of hydrocele the fluid is confined to the tunica vaginalis testis, but when the upper portion of the processus vaginalis remains patent, the hydrocele may extend upwards into the inguinal canal, and may or may not communicate with the general peritoneal cavity.   In the condition known as encysted hydrocele of the cord the patent vaginal process is shut off both from the tunica vaginalis testis and from the peritoneal cavity.

Abdominal Incisions

Before the abdominal cavity is dealt with reference must be made to some anatomical points connected with the more typical incisions made by surgeons in opening the abdomen.

Incisions in the Median Plane.—Median incisions through the linea alba have the advantage of being comparatively bloodless and rapid of execution, of dividing no motor nerves, and of enabling the surgeon to expose a wide area of the abdomen.   Unless special precautions are taken, however, they are more liable to be followed by a ventral hernia.

Above the umbilicus the linea alba is comparatively broad, so that the edges of the recti are separated by a distinct interval, which may be of considerable width in obese subjects and multiparous women.   Deep to the linea alba is the transversalis fascia, which is so thin and adherent that the two structures form practically a single layer.   The extraperitoneal fat, which forms a comparatively thick stratum, must not be mistaken for omentum.   The peritoneum presents itself as a thin, bluish, semi-transparent membrane.   If it is necessary to prolong the incision downwards below the level of the umbilicus, skirt its left margin in order to avoid the round ligament of the liver.   If, in closing a median supra-umbilical incision, the surgeon merely sutures the edges of the stretched linea alba without opening into the rectal sheaths, a hernia may result.   To ensure against it expose the medial borders of the recti by opening into their sheaths along each edge of the wound.   In closing the wound, make the deepest suture (continuous) include on each side the posterior layer of the rectal sheath along with the split linea alba, the transversalis fascia, and the peritoneum.   That gives a substantial "first line of defence."   The next suture takes up some of the fibres of the medial edges of the recti, along with the anterior layer of their sheaths.   The skin is sutured separately.   By this procedure the edges of the recti are brought into actual contact and a double-layered linea alba is fashioned —one layer behind the margins of the recti and the other in front of them.

Below the umbilicus the medial edges of the recti are practically in contact, and an incision between them therefore opens into the rectal sheath on both sides.

The nearer the opening into the abdomen approaches the pubic symphysis, the more likely is the bladder to be encountered; this applies more especially in children, for in them the bladder extends up out of the pelvis.   The bladder should therefore be emptied before the abdomen is opened by a low median incision; in supra-pubic cystotomy, on the other hand, the bladder is intentionally filled so as to elevate the peritoneum well above the symphysis.   Below the peritoneal layer is the **retro-pubic space**, occupied by a pad of extra-peritoneal fat which must be separated by blunt dissection before the bladder wall is actually exposed.   In opening the bladder, avoid as far as possible the veins which ramify on its surface.   Above the pubes the fascia transversalis recedes a little from the recti, leaving an interval, filled with areolar tissue, which must not be mistaken for the retro-pubic space.

If a transverse incision is added to the lower end of a supra-umbilical median incision, free access may be obtained to the hypochondrium as well as to the epigastric region.   Before dividing the fibres of the rectus, stitch the anterior layer of its sheath to them to prevent their retraction.   As the knife splits the posterior layer of the sheath, the terminal portions of the ninth and tenth intercostal nerves need not be injured, for they run in a transverse direction.

Incisions through the Recti.—In **longitudinal incisions through the rectus**, the superior epigastric artery will be encountered above the umbilicus, and the inferior epigastric below it. The nearer the opening approaches the lateral border of the rectus, the more will its nerve-supply be injured.   **Above the level of the umbilicus**, the posterior layer of the rectus sheath is well developed; and when the wound is closed this layer is included in the same suture as the transversalis fascia and the peritoneum, the three together forming a most efficient "first line of defence." The higher and more lateral the incision through the rectus is made, the more will the posterior layer of the sheath be found to be made up of muscular fibres of the transversus abdominis muscle. **Below the level of the umbilicus,** the posterior layer of the sheath is much thinner and ceases to be a definite layer, usually appearing to end at that level in a slightly thickened arched band, called the *arcuate line* [linea semicircularis], about midway between the umbilicus and the pubes. Below that level, therefore, the "deep closure" of a laparotomy wound through the rectus is less secure than it is at a higher level. It is all the more important, therefore, to see that the edges of the anterior layer of the sheath are accurately sutured.

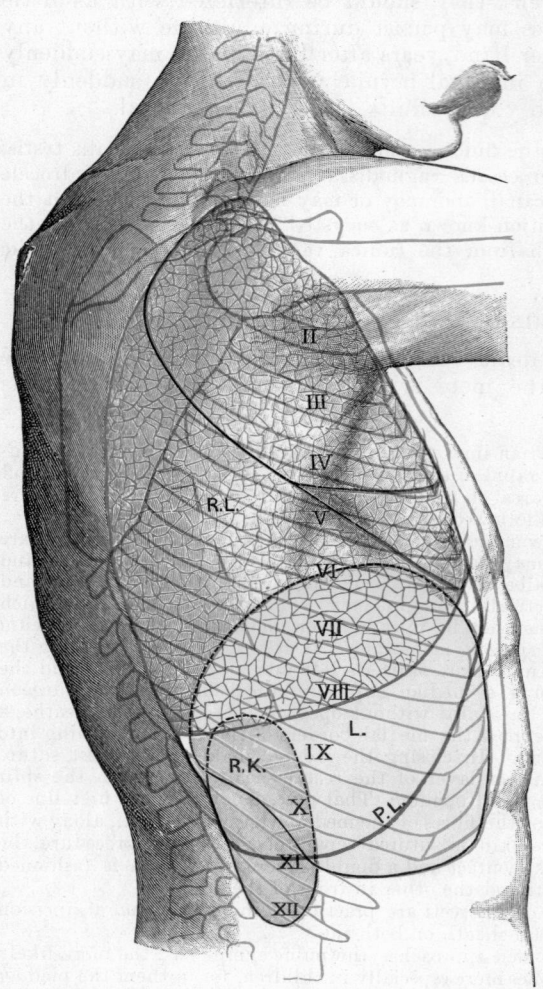

FIG. 1144.—RIGHT LATERAL ASPECT OF TRUNK, SHOWING
SURFACE TOPOGRAPHY OF VISCERA.

R.L. Right lung.	R.K. Right kidney.
L. Liver.	P.L. Pleura.

Incisions lateral to the Rectus.—Longitudinal incisions lateral and parallel to the rectus are as far as possible to be avoided because they divide the motor nerves, and also because near the rectus the abdominal wall is almost entirely aponeurotic, and a hernia is therefore apt to result.

Incisions lateral to the rectus, **above the level of the umbilicus,** are generally made more or less parallel to the costal margin. Such incisions give access to the gall-bladder and bile-ducts. The fibres of the external oblique muscles are divided transversely, but those of the internal oblique and transversus muscles may be divided more or less parallel to the fibres. The abdominal portions of the eighth, ninth, and tenth thoracic nerves lie between the two deep muscles, running in a medial and slightly downward direction, so that it is practically impossible to avoid dividing one or other of them.

In the iliac regions, to reach the cæcum and vermiform appendix on the right side, and the pelvic colon on the left side (colostomy), it is customary, by using what is known as the "grid-iron incision," to split the three abdominal muscles in the direction of their fibres. The external oblique is split in the direction of the skin incision, which is made obliquely from above downwards and medially. After retracting the edges of that muscle split the fibres of the internal oblique and transversalis muscles horizontally. The abdomen is then opened by division of the transversalis fascia and peritoneum. If a comparatively large opening is required, a branch of the deep circumflex iliac artery which ascends between the internal oblique and transversus muscles, a little medial to the anterior superior iliac spine, is divided and ligatured, while the iliohypogastric and ilio-inguinal nerves are to be avoided. If it is necessary to extend the incision in a medial direction, the lateral part of the anterior layer of the sheath of the rectus is opened and the rectus pulled medially; the inferior epigastric artery, now exposed, is pushed aside or ligatured before the opening in the fascia transversalis and peritoneum is enlarged.

DISTRIBUTION OF SENSORY NERVES IN ANTERIOR ABDOMINAL WALL

A knowledge of the segmental distribution of the sensory fibres of the anterior primary rami of the lower thoracic nerves enables us to appreciate the significance of the so-called girdle pain often associated with lesions of the spinal cord and the nerve-roots. In tuberculous disease of the vertebral column, for example, the girdle pain may be an early symptom of the disease, and when present it affords a valuable guide to the situation of the disease in the vertebral column. The seventh thoracic nerve supplies the skin at the level of the epigastric fossa, the eighth and ninth that between it and the umbilicus, the tenth that at the level of the umbilicus, the eleventh and twelfth and the ilio-hypogastric (from first lumbar) that between the umbilicus and groin.

ABDOMINAL CAVITY

Subdivisions of the Abdominal Cavity.—The cavity of the abdomen is subdivided into three zones by two imaginary planes:—

(1) The *subcostal plane*, which passes through the lowest point on the rib margins seen from the front (usually the lower edge of the tenth costal cartilage) and cuts the third lumbar vertebra.

(2) The *intertubercular plane*, which passes through the tubercles of the iliac crests (the highest part of the crests seen from the front) and cuts the fifth lumbar vertebra.

Each zone is divided into three regions by a pair of vertical planes, both of which pass through the mid-inguinal point and the ninth costal cartilage near its tip. The upper zone is thus divided into a *right* and *left hypocondrium* and an *epigastrium*, the middle zone into *lumbar* and *umbilical* regions, and the lowest zone into *iliac* and *supra-pubic* regions.

In the past too much stress has been laid on the importance and convenience of these planes and regions. A more useful line of reference is that which corresponds to the *transpyloric plane*, the convenience of which was first pointed out by Dr. Christopher Addison. This plane lies midway between the upper margin of the sternum and the upper margin of the pubic symphysis, and for easy reference may be said to be a hand's-breadth below the xiphi-sternal joint. It cuts the first lumbar vertebra, and receives its name from the fact that it passes through the pylorus.

The **peritoneal cavity** may be regarded as a large and complicated lymph sac which is intimately related to the abdominal viscera, and more especially to the gastro-intestinal canal. Inflammatory infections of the peritoneum are therefore almost always secondary to lesions of the viscera. The healthy peritoneum, in virtue of the vital action of its endothelial cells, is endowed with great absorptive properties, and, when irritated, has the power of throwing out an abundant exudation, the cell elements of which are actively phagocytic.

The reflexion of the peritoneum and its relations to the various organs have been fully described in the section on the Digestive System.

The attachment of the **transverse mesocolon** to the posterior abdominal wall is at the level of the second lumbar vertebra. The attachment, which ascends slightly as it passes from right to left, crosses the head of the pancreas, after which its attachment follows the lower border of the body of the pancreas. The *peritoneal subdivision above that attachment* is roofed in by the diaphragm, and includes the upper part of the great sac of peritoneum, and, behind it, the larger portion of the lesser sac [bursa omentalis]. The organs related to that area of the peritoneum are the liver with the bile-ducts and gall-bladder, the stomach and part of the duodenum, the spleen, the pancreas, the upper parts of the kidneys, and the suprarenal glands. Suppuration connected with any of those organs is liable to spread upwards under the cupola of the diaphragm, producing what is known as *subphrenic abscess*.

The attachment of the **mesentery** of the **small intestine** extends from the left side of the second lumbar vertebra downwards to the right iliac fossa. The attachment may be mapped out on the surface by drawing a line from a point one inch below the transpyloric line, one inch to the left of the median plane, to the intersection of the intertubercular and right vertical planes.

Subdivisions of the Peritoneal Cavity.—From the surgical point of view the peritoneal cavity may be arbitrarily divided into **four great subdivisions**: namely, a supracolic, a right infracolic, a left infracolic, and a pelvic. All those subdivisions communicate freely with one another behind the anterior abdominal wall, as well as along the gutter-like channels in the loins. It is along those gutters that pus readily makes its way from the upper part of the abdomen

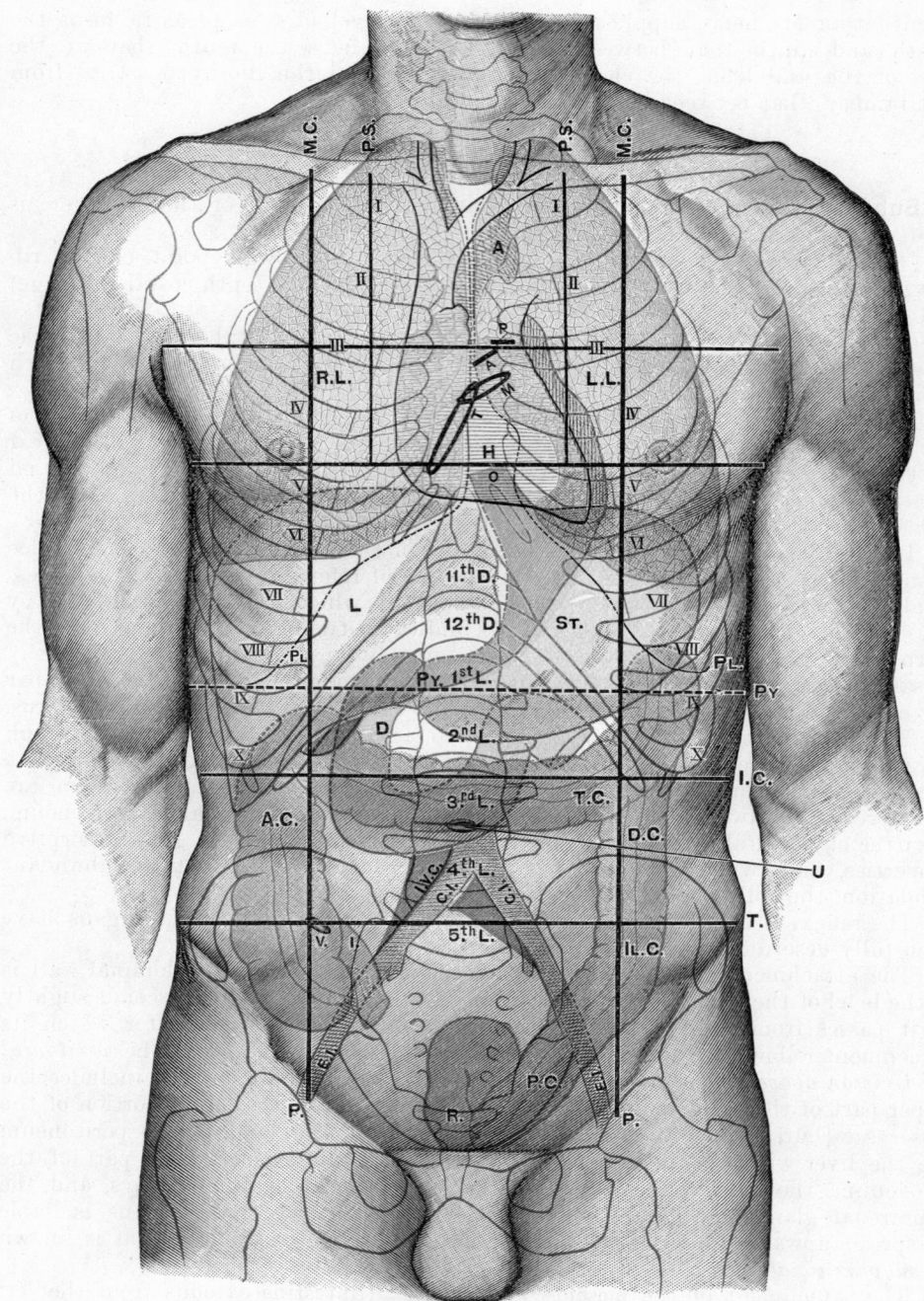

FIG. 1145.—ANTERIOR ASPECT OF TRUNK, SHOWING SURFACE TOPOGRAPHY OF VISCERA.

A.	Aorta.	I.V.C.	Inferior vena cava.	Py.	Pylorus and transpyloric
A.	Aortic orifice.	L.	Liver.		plane.
A.C.	Ascending colon.	L.L.	Left lung.	R.	Rectum.
C.I.	Common iliac artery.	M.	Mitral orifice.	R.L.	Right lung.
D.	Duodenum.	M.C.	Mid-clavicular line.	St.	Stomach.
D.C.	Descending colon.	O.	Œsophagus.	**T.**	Intertubercular line.
E.I.	External iliac artery.	**P.**	Inguinal vertical line.	T.	Tricuspid orifice.
H.	Heart.	P.	Pulmonary orifice.	T.C.	Transverse colon.
I.	Ileum.	P.C.	Pelvic colon.	U.	Umbilicus.
I.C.	Subcostal plane.	Pl.	Pleura.	V.	Ileo-colic valve.
Il.C.	Lower part of descending colon.	P.S.	Para-sternal line.		

downwards into the pelvis; and, on the other hand, the pus may ascend from the pelvis along the same channels, especially when the patient is in the recumbent posture.

The highest (subphrenic) region of the **supracolic compartment** is further subdivided into a right and left portion by the falciform ligament; and the **lesser sac** may be looked upon as a diverticulum of the right subdivision.

The subphrenic lymph plexus communicates, by means of lymph vessels which pierce the diaphragm, with the subpleural plexus on its upper surface; hence pus confined under tension in either of the subphrenic spaces is apt to give rise to secondary infection of the corresponding pleural cavity. By adhesions of the transverse colon and greater omentum to the anterior abdominal wall, the supracolic subdivision of the peritoneal cavity may become more or less completely shut off from the rest of the abdomen. Suppuration in the right half of the supracolic subdivision is generally secondary to leakage from an ulcer of the first part of the duodenum or to disease of the gall-bladder and bile-ducts; the left half of the space is more usually infected from the stomach. The best method of draining the supracolic subdivision of the peritoneal cavity is by a tube passed into the recess between the liver and the right kidney either from the wound in the anterior abdominal wall or, still better, through a puncture opening made through the loin lateral to the kidney, in the angle between the twelfth rib and the lateral border of the sacro-spinalis muscle. Another drainage route is by a tube passed from the wound in the anterior abdominal wall into the lesser sac, through either the lesser or the greater omentum.

The **right infracolic subdivision** is above and to the right of the mesentery. It is bounded laterally by the cæcum and ascending colon, and superiorly by the right and middle thirds of the transverse colon and the corresponding part of its mesocolon. At its right lower angle are the ileo-cæcal junction and the vermiform appendix; at its right upper angle is the right flexure of the colon; and at its left upper angle is the third part of the duodenum, crossed by the superior mesenteric vessels. In rare instances the third part of the duodenum is so compressed between those vessels and the vertebral column that partial, or even complete, obstruction results. The condition has been named gastro-mesenteric ileus, but a more correct term would be *duodeno-mesenteric ileus*.

The organs related to that subdivision are—in addition to the parts of the large intestine already mentioned—coils of small intestine, the lower third of the right kidney, the right ureter, the third part of the duodenum and the lower half of the second part. Suppuration in connexion with the organs in that area may extend upwards along the colon into the sub-diaphragmatic region, or downwards into the pelvis. To drain the region, introduce a tube into the right lumbar region either through the anterior abdominal wall or through a stab-wound in the loin lateral to the ascending colon.

The **left infracolic subdivision** is below and to the left of the mesentery; it narrows as it passes upwards, and reaches a higher level than the right infracolic subdivision. Inferiorly, it is directly continuous with the peritoneal cavity of the true pelvis. Above, it is bounded by the left third of the transverse colon and its mesocolon, and, still farther back, by the inferior surface of the body of the pancreas; laterally, it is bounded by the descending colon. At its right upper angle is the duodeno-jejunal flexure, lying immediately to the left of the vertebral column, on the psoas and below the pancreas. At its left upper angle is the left flexure of the colon, while at its left lower angle is the junction of descending with pelvic colon. That subdivision of the peritoneal cavity, in addition to containing the majority of the coils of the small intestine, is related to the lower third of the left kidney, the left ureter, the lower part of the abdominal aorta and vena cava, and the inferior mesenteric and common iliac vessels. Drainage of the subdivision may be established through the left loin, or by a tube introduced down to the bottom of the pelvis, namely, into the recto-vesical pouch in the male, and into or through the recto-vaginal pouch in the female.

On account of the oblique manner in which the mesentery is attached to the posterior abdominal wall, it follows that, in order to examine the organs related to the right infracolic subdivision of the abdomen, the surgeon must push coils of small intestine downwards and to the left, while to investigate the left infracolic subdivision he must displace them upwards and to the right.

ABDOMINAL VISCERA

Liver.—The *inferior margin of the liver* extends from a point a finger's-breadth below the right costal margin at the side of the trunk to the fifth left intercostal space below the nipple or in a line dropped from the middle of the clavicle; in the infracostal angle it passes from the tenth right costal cartilage to the eighth left and crosses the median plane at the transpyloric plane; in this region the position can be determined by light percussion and occasionally by palpation. The *highest part of the liver,* which corresponds also to the highest part of the right arch of the diaphragm, reaches, during expiration, to the level of the fourth intercostal space opposite the nipple or in the mid-clavicular line. To the right of the median plane the superior surface of the liver is too far removed from the anterior wall of the chest, and overlapped by too thick a layer of lung substance to be accurately determined by percussion. *Behind the sternum* the superior surface is opposite the xiphi-sternal joint. To the left of the median plane the upper limit of the liver cannot be determined by percussion, since it merges into the cardiac dullness. The base or **right lateral surface** extends from the level of the seventh rib to the level of the eleventh rib in the mid-axillary line, and is separated by the diaphragm from the lower part of the right lung and pleura.

The **falciform ligament**, at its attachment to the liver, is a little to the right of the median plane.

By dividing the *round ligament,* which passes backwards and upwards in the free margin of the falciform ligament, the surgeon is enabled to rotate the liver backwards around its transverse axis so as to expose more of its inferior surface; that procedure is sometimes taken advantage of in cases in which there is unusual difficulty in reaching the cystic duct or the bile-duct. The ligament is sutured before the abdominal wall is closed.

The **anterior surface** of the liver may be reached through a median incision extending downwards from the xiphoid process, or by an oblique incision a finger's-breadth below and parallel to the right costal margin. To obtain free access to the **superior surface** resect the eighth and ninth costal cartilages of the right side; the seventh cartilage should, if possible, be avoided, for the pleural cavity may be opened into. Division of the round and falciform ligaments allows of greater downward displacement of the liver. To reach the upper part of the **lateral surface** of the right lobe, resect portions of the seventh and eighth ribs in the mid-axillary line, and traverse both the pleural and peritoneal cavities.

Gall-Bladder.—The relation of the fundus of the **gall-bladder** to the surface of the body is subject to considerable variation. Normally it is situated behind the angle between the ninth costal cartilage and the lateral border of the right rectus; exceptionally, it is pendulous and suspended from the liver by a more or less distinct mesentery; or it may be elongated and drawn downwards by adhesion to the duodenum or colon. When displaced downwards it is liable to be mistaken for a movable kidney, but may be distinguished from that by the fact that although it may be pushed backwards into the lumbar region it returns at once to its habitual position, immediately behind the anterior abdominal wall, as soon as it ceases to be manipulated.

The **cystic duct** is enclosed in the right end of the upper border of the lesser omentum. It is about an inch and a half in length, and is sharply bent upon itself close to its origin at the neck of the gall-bladder. It joins the common hepatic duct at a very acute angle. The passage of a probe along the *normal* duct is made difficult by the marked flexure at its commencement, and also by the folded condition of its mucous membrane; hence also the frequency with which calculi become impacted at the neck of the gall-bladder.

In excising the gall-bladder, divide and ligature the cystic artery and duct before proceeding to detach the organ from the liver; by this routine bleeding is lessened and the difficult part of the operation is carried out before the field is obscured by blood.

The outline of the normal gall-bladder is demonstrable on X-ray examination following the

PLATE LXIX

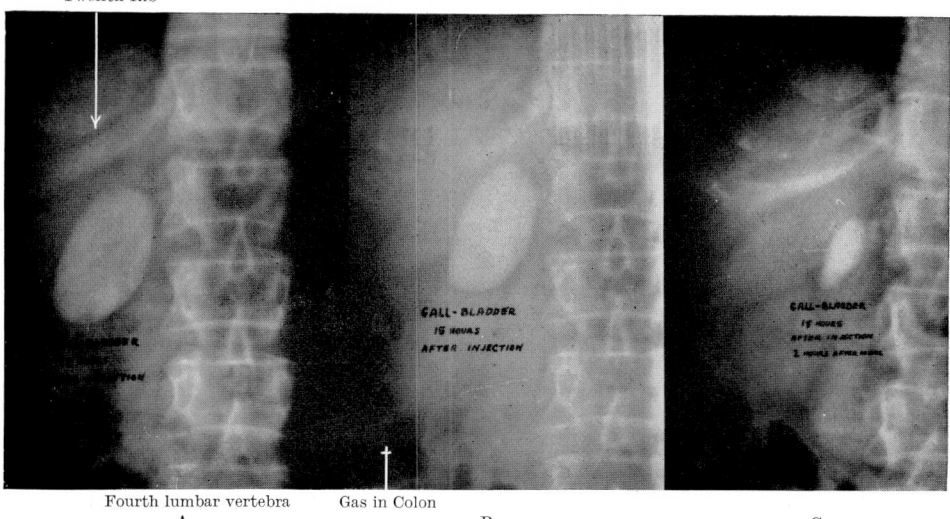

Twelfth Rib

Fourth lumbar vertebra   Gas in Colon

A   B   C

FIG. 1.—SERIAL RADIOGRAPHS OF THE SAME GALL-BLADDER SHOWING PHYSIOLOGICAL CHANGES.
(Dr. J. F. Brailsford.)

A. 12 hours after administration of tetra-iodo-phenol-phthalein.
B. 15 hours after : Concentration of Bile.
C. 18 hours after ; 2 hours after meal : Discharge of Bile into Duodenum.

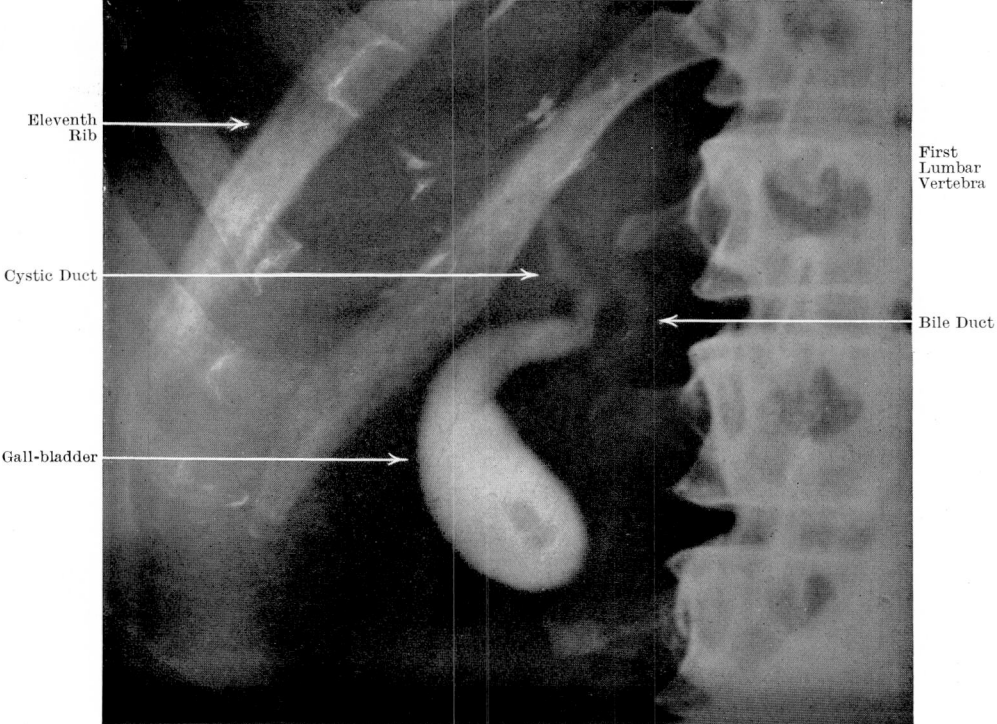

Eleventh
Rib

First
Lumbar
Vertebra

Cystic Duct

Bile Duct

Gall-bladder

FIG. 2.—RADIOGRAPH, AFTER ADMINISTRATION OF RADIO-OPAQUE DYE EXCRETED BY THE
LIVER (see p. 636), SHOWING POSITION OF THE GALL-BLADDER AND THE CYSTIC DUCT ; THE
BILE DUCT IS ALSO FAINTLY SEEN. (Dr. R. McWhirter.)

PLATE LXX

First Lumbar Vertebra

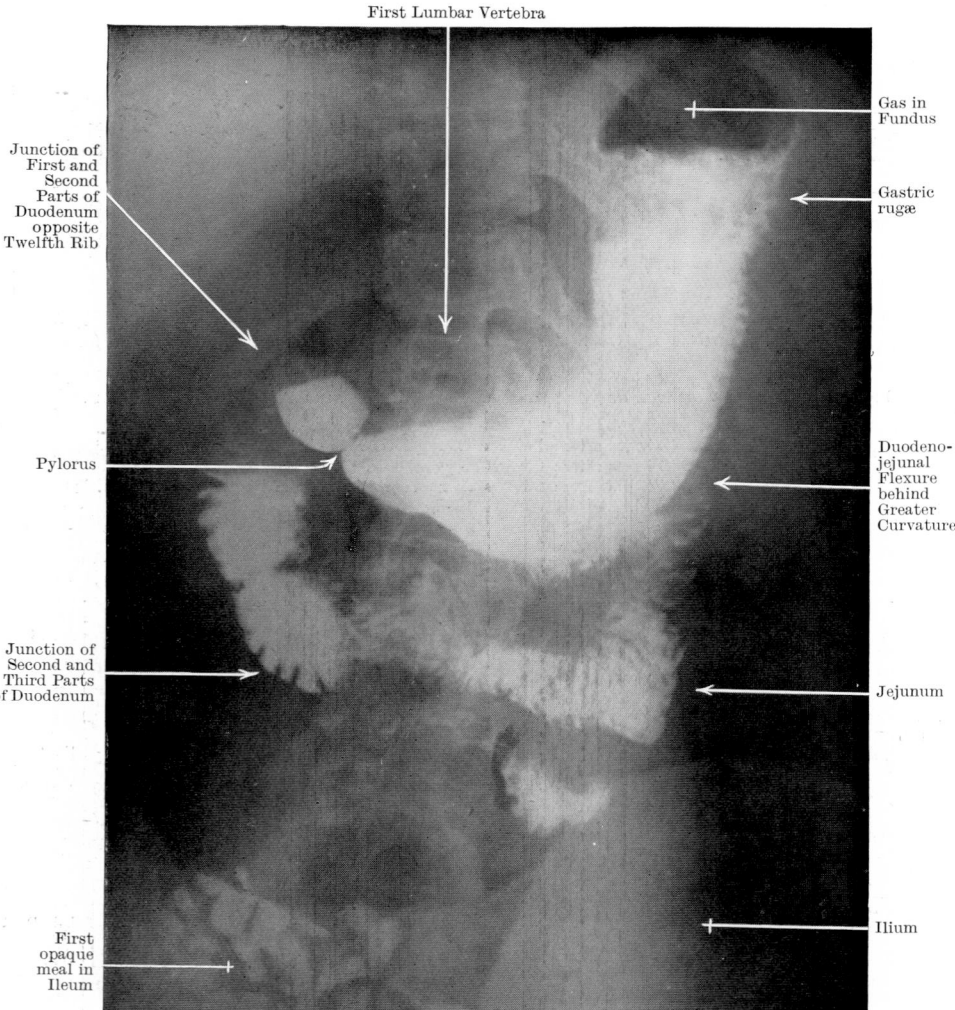

Gas in Fundus

Gastric rugæ

Junction of First and Second Parts of Duodenum opposite Twelfth Rib

Pylorus

Duodeno-jejunal Flexure behind Greater Curvature

Junction of Second and Third Parts of Duodenum

Jejunum

First opaque meal in Ileum

Ilium

PLATE LXX.—RADIOGRAPH OF STOMACH OF MAN AGED 28 IN THE ERECT POSTURE AFTER OPAQUE MEAL, SHOWING THE INTERMEDIATE FORM (see p. 592, and compare with Plates XLIII and XLV).

The Body and the Pyloric Portion of the Stomach exhibit a more continuous curvature than those of the J-shaped Stomach in Plate XLIII, the Pyloric Canal is horizontal rather than vertical, and the Pylorus lies high in the abdomen. A previous opaque meal, taken three hours before, is seen in the Ileum. Compare also with Plate XLVI in which the same stomach is seen half-filled.

PLATE LXXI

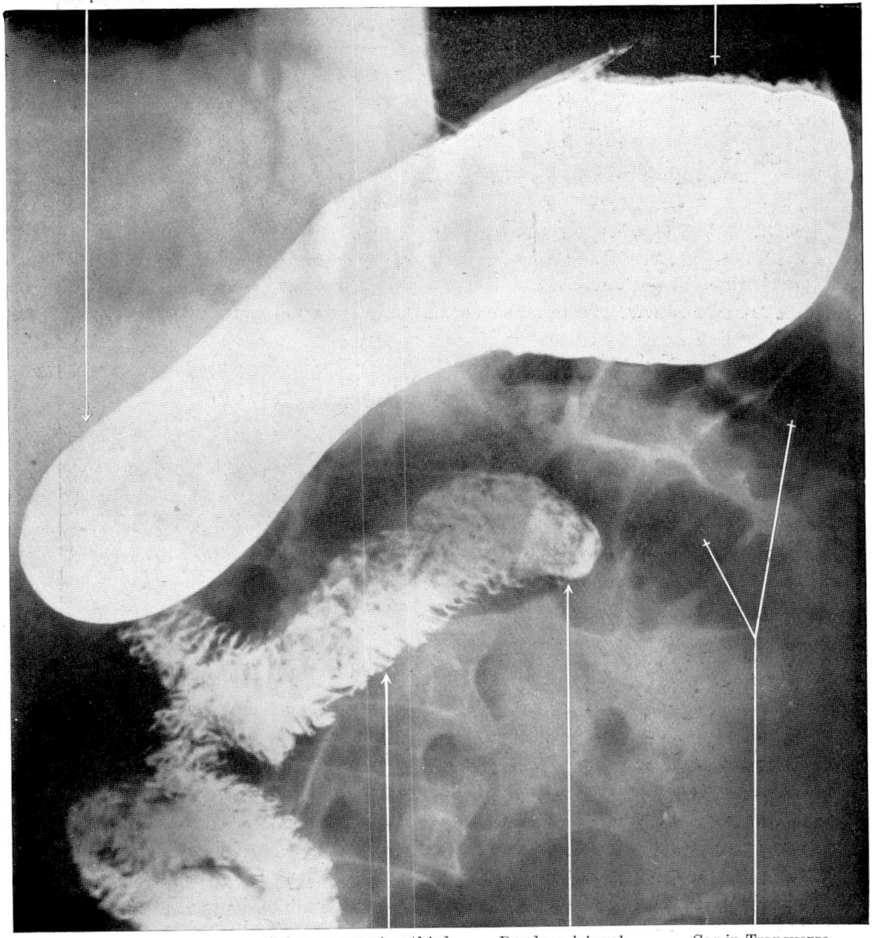

Pyloric Portion of Stomach covering
first part of Duodenum

Gas in Fundus

Jejunum crossing third
part of Duodenum

Duodeno-jejunal
Flexure

Gas in Transverse
Colon

PLATE LXXI.—RADIOGRAPH OF "STEER-HORN" STOMACH. (Dr. R. McWhirter.)

The Stomach lies almost transversely, high in the abdomen; the Pylorus and Duodenal Cap are hidden by the Pyloric Portion. The position of the gas in the Fundus shows that the radiograph was taken in the erect posture. Cf. Plates XLIII and XLIV.

PLATE LXXII

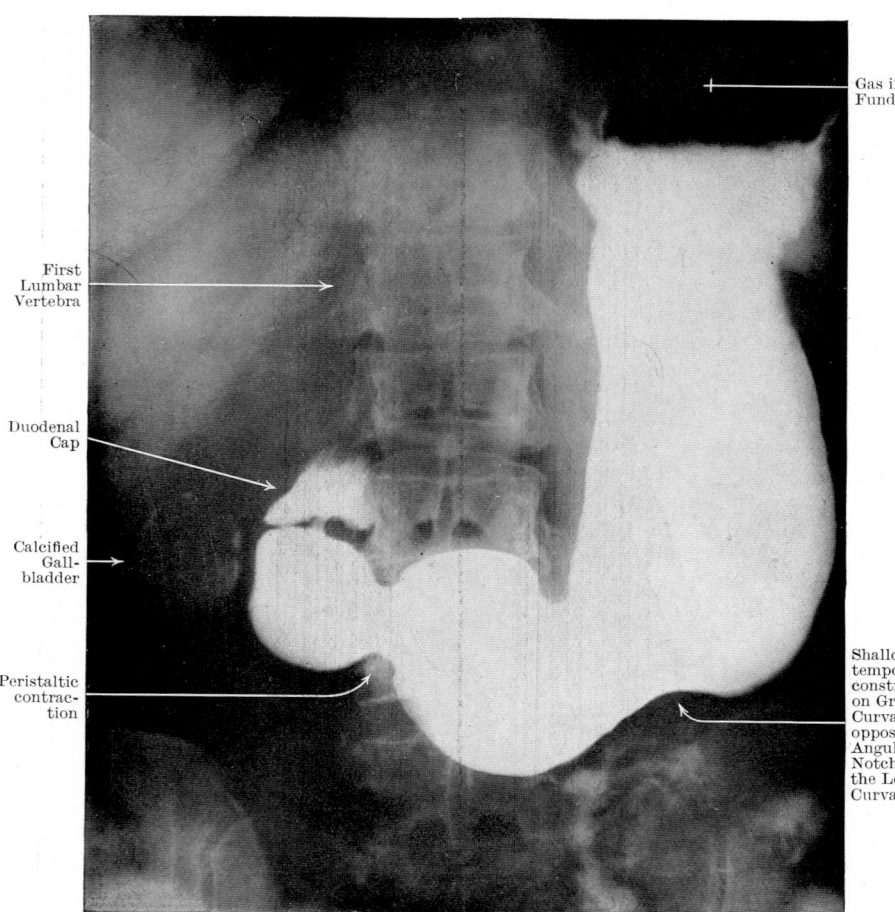

Gas in
Fundus

First
Lumbar
Vertebra

Duodenal
Cap

Calcified
Gall-
bladder

Peristaltic
contrac-
tion

Shallow
temporary
constriction
on Greater
Curvature
opposite the
Angular
Notch on
the Lesser
Curvature

PLATE LXXII.—RADIOGRAPH OF J-SHAPED STOMACH OF WOMAN
AGED 62, TAKEN IN THE ERECT POSTURE A FEW MINUTES AFTER
AN OPAQUE MEAL. (F. E. J.)

Note the low position of the Greater Curvature and of the Pylorus. Cf. Plates XLIV
and XLV. The Gall-bladder, intercepting the X-Rays because of calcification in its wall,
is seen in relation to the Pylorus. For the position of the gall-bladder see also Plate XLVIII.

administration (intravenously or by mouth) of the compound salt sodium-tetra-iodo-phenol-phthalein (Pl. LXIX). The procedure is employed in the investigation of cases of gall-stones and infections of the gall-bladder. A calcified gall-bladder may be visible in an ordinary radiograph (Pl. LXXII).

The **bile-duct** is about three and a half inches in length. Its *upper third* lies in the lesser omentum, close to the right, free border. That is the most accessible part of the duct, and, when cutting into it, draw it forwards by the finger introduced through the opening into the lesser sac; the portal vein, which must be avoided, lies immediately behind the duct. The *middle third* of the duct lies a little to the right of the gastro-duodenal artery behind the first part of the duodenum about a finger's-breadth from the pyloro-duodenal junction. The *lower third* of the duct, which passes downwards and to the right, is intimately related to the pancreas; in about two out of three bodies it is so embedded in the back of its head that it cannot be freed by blunt dissection. Close to its termination the duct is joined by the main pancreatic duct, the two opening separately, but close together, into an *ampulla* which pierces the wall of the duodenum obliquely, and opens on the summit of a small papilla situated at the middle of the medial wall of the second part of the duodenum, about four inches from the pylorus. When a calculus becomes impacted in the ampulla there is retention of the pancreatic secretion as well as of the bile. Frequently, however, the pancreas has an accessory pancreatic duct which opens into the duodenum at a higher level than the main duct, with which it also communicates.

The surgeon may reach a calculus in the ampulla either by opening the duodenum from the front (trans-duodenal route) or by freeing the duodenum and gaining access to the bile-duct from behind (retro-duodenal route). In the latter instance an incision is made, lateral to the right border of the second part of the duodenum, through that portion of the peritoneum which passes upwards and to the right from the upper layer of the transverse mesocolon, over the upper part of the second part of the duodenum on to the anterior surface of the right kidney. By blunt dissection directed medially behind the duodenum, the duodenum, along with the adjacent part of the head of the pancreas, can be separated from the kidney and vena cava, and folded over towards the left. As the bile-duct is freed from the back of the head of the pancreas a vein of considerable size will be encountered; that vein returns the blood from the pancreatico-duodenal system of arteries; it lies close to the bile-duct as it ascends behind the head of the pancreas to open into the commencement of the portal vein. Of the lymph glands related to the bile passages it is to be remembered that one lies at the neck of the gall-bladder, another at the junction of the cystic and hepatic ducts, while a third lies close to the termination of the bile-duct. When those glands are enlarged and indurated, care must be taken not to mistake them for impacted gall-stones. On account of the very free anastomosis between the lymph vessels of the gall-bladder, bile-ducts, and pancreas, infective inflammatory processes readily spread from one organ to the other.

Stomach.—The stomach lies almost entirely in the left hypochondrium and in the left half of the epigastrium. The **cardiac orifice**, which lies 1 in. below and to the left of the œsophageal opening in the diaphragm, is about 4 in. from the surface, and corresponds, on the anterior surface of the body, to a point over the seventh left costal cartilage 1 in. from the median plane. The **pylorus** lies behind the quadrate lobe of the liver in the transpyloric plane, usually a little to the right of the median plane; when the stomach is *empty* the pylorus generally lies in the median plane, when *distended* it may reach two, or even three, inches to the right of the median plane. Passing from the upper to the lower border of the pylorus at its junction with the duodenum is the **pre-pyloric vein**. That vein is a useful visible guide to the position of the pylorus. Another guide is the ring-like thickening of the pyloric sphincter, which projects into the commencement of the duodenum, and can be readily palpated through the duodenal wall. The highest part of the **fundus of the stomach** corresponds to the left vault of the diaphragm, and lies at the level of the fifth rib in the mid-clavicular line, a little above and behind the apex of the heart. The **greater curvature** crosses behind the left costal margin opposite the tip of the ninth costal cartilage. The lowest part of the great curvature, situated generally in the median plane, is a little above the level of the umbilicus. The **lesser curvature** and the adjacent part of the anterior wall of the stomach are overlapped by the left lobe of the liver.

Radiography of Stomach.—Radiographs taken after an "opaque meal" show that the form and position of the stomach in the living subject differ considerably from those which it presents in the cadaver (Pls. LXX, LXXI, LXXII).

In the cadaver, owing to loss of muscular tone, the stomach presents itself as a more or less empty pear-shaped bag with collapsed and flaccid walls.

In the living subject, the form and position of the stomach are found to vary not only according to the amount of food it contains, but also according to whether the patient occupies the erect or the recumbent posture. The most reliable, as well as the most useful, information regarding the form, the position, and the motor activity of the stomach is obtained by " screen" examinations and radiographs taken with the patient in the erect posture. When examined in that way, after the stomach is partly filled with an " opaque meal," it is seen to have a distinctly J-shaped form (Pl. LXXII). The stem of the J, which represents the **body of the stomach**, lies immediately and entirely to the left of the vertebral column. The **fundus**, which is slightly more expanded than the body, reaches up to the left cupola of the diaphragm;

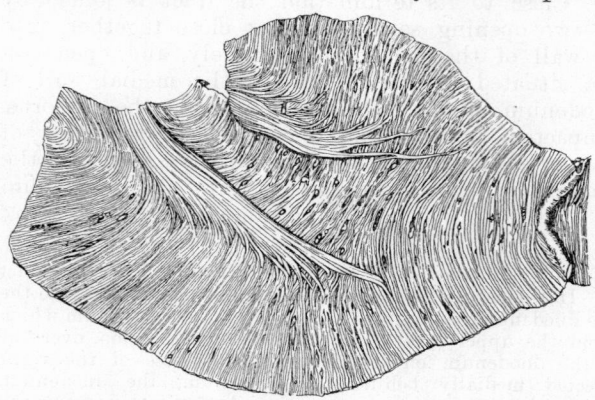

FIG. 1146.—THE LESSER CURVATURE CANAL OF THE STOMACH.

The mucous and submucous coats of the stomach have been removed and the arrangement of the inner longitudinal fibres to form the boundaries of the canal at the lesser curvature is demonstrated.

it is represented in the skiagram as a light semilunar shadow, the horizontal lower margin of which corresponds to the upper limit of the meal. That clear semilunar area is due to the rising up of the gaseous contents of the stomach to the highest part of the cavity. The **cardiac orifice** is seen to lie opposite the left side of the disc between the tenth and eleventh thoracic vertebræ. The shadow of the **pyloric portion of the stomach**, after crossing the left side of the vertebral column opposite the third and fourth lumbar vertebræ, ascends as the **pyloric canal** to join the duodenum to the right of the median plane, opposite the second (not infrequently the third) lumbar vertebra. The **pylorus** itself is represented by a light disc due to a hiatus in the continuity of the bismuth, caused by contraction of the pyloric sphincter. The lowest portion of the **greater curvature**, which generally lies at or a little to the left of the median plane, reaches, in the erect posture, down to the level of the middle of the fourth lumbar vertebra or to its lower border, or, in other words, to the highest part of the iliac crest or even lower.

As more food enters the stomach its capacity is increased by expansion sideways rather than by any elevation of its fundus or downward expansion of its greater curvature. The normal tonic action of the gastric muscle is able to hold up the meal against the action of gravity to the level of the cardiac orifice. When, as not infrequently happens, the normal muscular tonicity of the stomach is lost, the bismuth meal is no longer held up against the action of gravity, but at once sinks to the most dependent part of the stomach, where it lies as in a flaccid sac, and gives rise to a crescentic shadow which may reach down almost, or even quite, to the level of the pubes.

In gastroptosis, and in general visceroptosis, the whole stomach may be displaced downwards without any great loss of its tonicity.

During a " screen" examination after an opaque meal, the peristaltic movements of the stomach can be seen to pass in distinct wave-like indentations from left to right along the greater curvature, and to increase in force as they approach the pylorus.

When the stomach is hypertrophied and dilated, as a result of pyloric obstruction, the peristaltic waves are more pronounced, and the bismuth shadow extends well over to the right of the median plane, owing to the dilated pyloric antrum and pyloric canal being carried over to the right, in front of the first part of the duodenum. The stomach tends, therefore, to lose its J-shaped tubular form, and the axis of its body becomes more oblique. In the infant and young child the stomach is flask-shaped rather than fish-hook or J-shaped, and its axis is less vertical than in the adult. The elongated form of the adult stomach is acquired as a result of the erect posture. Occasionally the axis of the adult stomach inclines more towards the horizontal and gives rise to a radiograph shaped more like the horn of a steer (steer-horn stomach—Pl. LXXI).

When the stomach is empty it contracts into a tubular-like structure. In that condition, the free margins of two longitudinal folds of mucous membrane that lie along the line of the lesser curvature are brought into contact with each other. A canal is thus formed which leads directly from the œsophagus to the pylorus. That canal may be partially divided into an anterior and a posterior portion by a third longitudinal fold which projects downwards from the lesser curvature between the other two. Kästle, by means of cinematograph X-ray examination of the stomach, has demonstrated that the first solid food to enter the stomach travels to the pylorus along that canal, and that liquids tend to follow the same track. The arrangement is probably of significance in relation to the pathology of the stomach.

It must be remembered that the only really fixed part of the stomach is the region of the cardiac orifice, and the form and position of the organ may therefore be considerably influenced by the condition of the neighbouring organs. For example, it may be displaced downwards and to the left by enlargement of the liver, upwards by distension of the intestines, and to the right by distension of the left colic flexure.

Overlying the stomach there is an important surface area that yields a deeply tympanitic note on percussion. It is bounded, above, by the left lung; below, by the left costal margin; to the right, by the left lobe of the liver; behind and to the left, by the spleen. The line of the costo-diaphragmatic pleural reflexion crosses the space about midway between its upper and lower limits. The tympanitic area of the space is diminished superiorly by pleuritic effusion, towards the right by enlargement of the liver, and towards the left by enlargement of the spleen.

Perforation of an ulcer on the *anterior wall* of the stomach leads to extravasation into the greater sac of the peritoneum, and if the perforated ulcer is on the *posterior wall*, extravasation takes place into the lesser sac. The close relation of the splenic artery and its branches to the posterior wall of the stomach explains the severe hæmorrhage which is sometimes caused by a posterior gastric ulcer. The surgeon may reach the posterior wall of the stomach through the great omentum near the stomach, or, after throwing the greater omentum and transverse colon upwards, by traversing the transverse mesocolon; by the former route the posterior wall of the stomach is reached through the anterior wall of the lesser sac, in the latter through its posterior wall.

In **partial resection of the stomach** for malignant disease, control the bleeding by ligaturing the main vessels at an early stage of the operation. The arteries are the right and left gastrics at the lesser curvature, the gastro-duodenal behind the first part of the duodenum, and the right and left gastro-epiploics at the greater curvature. Ligature the left gastric as near the cardiac orifice as possible, in order that the whole chain of lymph glands along the lesser curvature may be removed. Remove also all the glands that lie behind the first part of the duodenum in relation to the gastro-duodenal artery and head of the pancreas, as well as those along the right half of the greater curvature in relation to the right gastro-epiploic artery. If the disease has spread to the retro-peritoneal lymph glands around the cœliac artery, above the pancreas, the chances of a permanent recovery are very remote.

In the classical "no-loop" **gastro-enterostomy operation** a longitudinal opening in the commencement of the jejunum is anastomosed by suture to an opening in the posterior wall of the stomach, near the greater curvature. The jejunum is applied to the stomach in such a way that it maintains its normal direction, namely, obliquely upwards and to the left. To bring the surfaces of the two organs in contact, surgeons are in the habit of protruding the posterior wall of the stomach through an opening made in the transverse mesocolon, on the proximal side of the arch formed by the middle and left colic arteries. A better plan, however, is to make an opening also into the lesser sac through the greater omentum a little below the gastro-epiploic vessels, and then to bring the jejunum into contact with the posterior wall of the stomach by pushing it (the jejunum) upwards through the opening in the transverse mesocolon. By that plan the posterior wall of the stomach along with the jejunum can be protruded through an opening in the greater omentum; they can then easily be delivered out of the abdominal cavity. Another advantage is that the transverse colon can be replaced into the abdominal cavity while the anastomosis is being made. When the posterior wall of the stomach and transverse colon are held down by adhesions, a long loop of jejunum is brought up in front of the greater omentum and transverse colon and anastomosed to the anterior wall of the stomach.

Duodenum.—The duodenum is the widest, thickest, and most fixed part of the small intestine. For descriptive purposes it is divided by anatomists into four parts. From the surgical standpoint it may with advantage be subdivided into a supra-colic and an infra-colic portion—above and below the attachment of the transverse colon. To expose the supra-colic portion, pull the greater omentum and the transverse colon downwards; to expose the infra-colic portion throw them upwards along with the transverse mesocolon.

The **first part** lies medial to the gall-bladder, overlapped by the quadrate lobe of the liver. As regards its **blood-supply,** it occupies the frontier zone between the cœliac and superior mesenteric vascular areas, and the vessels which supply it vary considerably in their size and mode of origin.

The peculiarity of its blood-supply may partly account for the relative frequency with which that portion of the intestine is the seat of ulceration. The first inch of the duodenum possesses some degree of mobility, being surrounded by the same two layers of peritoneum as invest the stomach. Beyond that it is in direct contact posteriorly and inferiorly with the pancreas, while descending behind it are the bile duct and the gastro-duodenal artery. The relations must be borne in mind in the operation of pylorectomy. When an ulcer of the first part perforates, extravasation takes place, in the first instance, into the supra-colic compartment of the peritoneum, thence into the recess between the liver and kidney, and subsequently down along the ascending colon into the right iliac fossa—hence the possibility of mistaking the condition for an acute appendicitis. Perforation of the ulcer into the peritoneal cavity is often prevented by the duodenum becoming adherent—especially to the pancreas, to the gall-bladder, or to the omentum.

If the finger is passed upwards, backwards, and to the left, immediately above the first part of the duodenum and behind the free border of the lesser omentum, it will pass through the opening into the lesser sac [bursa omentalis].

The **second part** of the duodenum descends from the neck of the gall-bladder to the level of the third lumbar vertebra. The transverse colon crosses it about its middle, while posteriorly it lies in front of the hilum and medial border of the right kidney, from which it is separated by loose areolar tissue. The procedure necessary to free that portion of the duodenum has been referred to already (p. 1401).

The **third part** of the duodenum crosses the inferior vena cava and the aorta about one inch above a line joining the highest part of the iliac crests; the upper part of the right ureter is behind its commencement.

The **fourth part** ascends on the left psoas opposite the third and second lumbar vertebræ.

The X-Ray shadow of the first part of the duodenum usually takes the form of a more or less vertical truncated cone ("duodenal cap") with its base directed towards the pylorus (Pls. LXX, LXXII). Owing to the fact that the opaque meal is held up for a short time in the cap, the shadow is denser than that caused by the other divisions of the duodenum, which are rapidly traversed by the meal; and as the first inch of the duodenum contains no circular folds of mucous membrane the outline of the cap is smooth and nearly symmetrical. In duodenal ulcer the outline of the cap is generally distorted—owing partly to the ulcer itself and partly to the spasm which it sets up.

The **duodeno-jejunal flexure**, which lies one inch below the transpyloric plane, one inch to the left of the median plane, is the landmark which the surgeon makes for when he wishes to identify the commencement of the jejunum (Fig. 539, p. 638, and Pls. LXX, LXXI). To find the flexure, throw the greater omentum and the transverse colon upwards and pass the finger along the lower layer of the transverse mesocolon to the left side of the vertebral column. The flexure lies in the angle between the left psoas major and the inferior surface of the body of the pancreas. With the finger in that angle the commencement of the jejunum may be hooked forward a little to the left of the superior mesenteric vessels at the root of the mesentery. There may be one or more small peritoneal recesses in the neighbourhood of the end of the duodenum. The one that is surgically the most important is the **paraduodenal recess**, which lies a little to the left of the fourth part of the duodenum, with its mouth looking towards the right. An internal hernia may develop in it ; and should strangulation occur, make the incision to relieve it in the lower margin of the mouth to avoid the inferior mesenteric vein, for the vein ascends in the peritoneal fold forming the anterior margin and curves medially in the upper margin.

Jejunum and Ileum.—To expose the coils of the jejunum and ileum completely, turn the greater omentum upwards along with the transverse colon and the greater curvature of the stomach. On account of the oblique attachment of the mesentery, the greater number of the coils lie in the left infra-colic peritoneal compartment, where they extend upwards to the left of the vertebral column as far as the attachment of the transverse mesocolon and the inferior surface of the

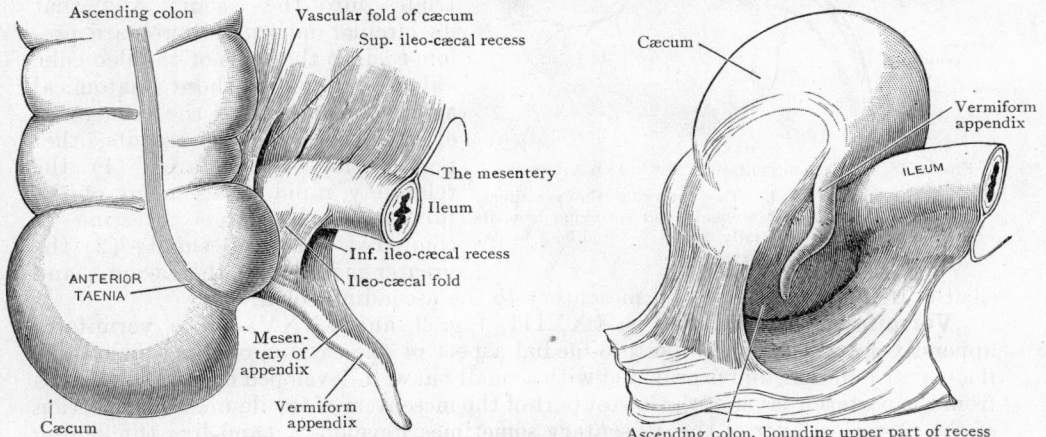

FIG. 1147.—ILEO-CÆCAL REGION AND RECESSES.

pancreas ; here they lie in front of the lower part of the left kidney, in the angle of the left colic flexure.

The only certain means which the surgeon has of distinguishing the upper from the lower coils of small intestine is by their relation to the duodeno-jejunal flexure and the ileo-cæcal junction. The lower coils of the ileum lie in the true pelvis, and the *terminal portion of the ileum*, which is attached by the lowest part of the mesentery to the floor of the right iliac fossa, crosses the brim of the pelvis, and ascends along the medial edge of the cæcum to reach its opening into the large intestine. The terminal loop of the ileum may be hooked up by the finger passed along the medial side of the cæcum downwards over the medial border of the right psoas major and the external iliac vessels into the true pelvis.

To bring out a loop of the upper jejunum in the operation of jejunostomy, open the abdomen through the left rectus muscle at the level of the umbilicus or a little above it. The duodeno-jejunal flexure is then identified and a catheter is introduced into the jejunum, and the bowel itself is then sutured to the edges of the opening in the divided peritoneum.

The **diverticulum ilei**, which is due to persistent patency of the proximal portion of the vitelline duct, is situated usually from two to three feet above the ileo-cæcal junction ; its average length is two inches. Springing from the anti-mesenteric border of the ileum, its termination is usually free, but it may be adherent either to the anterior abdominal wall, to the mesentery, or, more rarely, to one of the adjacent viscera. When its termination is fixed it may give rise to strangulation of the intestine.

Cæcum.—The cæcum occupies the right iliac region between the anterior superior iliac spine to the brim of the pelvis (Pls. LXXIII, LXXV, LXXVI). **When empty**, it is generally more or less completely overlapped by small intestine, and frequently also by the greater omentum. **When partly distended**, the cæcum comes in contact with the anterior abdominal wall immediately above the lateral half of the inguinal ligament. **In the normal condition** it is completely clothed with peritoneum, and can, therefore, along with the vermiform appendix, be readily delivered out of the abdomen. In chronic constipation, associated with intestinal atony, the cæcum is thin-walled, dilated, abnormally movable, and often sinks into the pelvis.

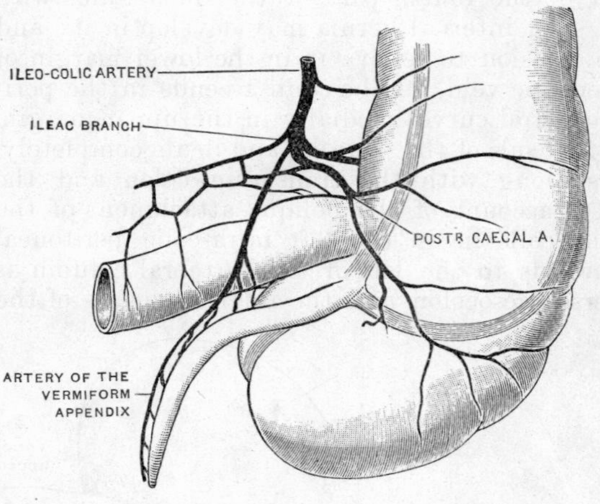

FIG. 1148.—BLOOD-SUPPLY OF CÆCUM AND APPENDIX.

The cæcum from behind. The artery of the vermiform appendix, and the three tæniæ coli springing from its root, should be specially noted. (Modified by A. Birmingham from Jonnesco.)

The position of the **ileo-colic valve** corresponds, on the surface of the body, to the lower medial angle between the intertubercular and right vertical lines, and the orifice of the vermiform appendix is one inch lower. It is to be noted that the lower end of the ileum protrudes into the cæcum, and that its circular muscular fibres are prolonged into the flaps of the ileo-colic valve. Both of those anatomical arrangements favour the occurrence of intussusception. In infants, other predisposing causes are: (1) the relatively rapid enlargement of the lumen of the large intestine as compared with the small; (2) the greater mobility of the cæcum; and (3) the frequent presence of a mesentery to the ascending colon.

Vermiform Appendix (Pls. LXXIII, Fig. 2, and LXXV).—The vermiform appendix springs from the postero-medial aspect of the cæcum, one inch below the ileo-cæcal junction, and is provided with a small but well-developed mesentery derived from the posterior layer of the lowest part of the mesentery of the ileum. That portion of the posterior layer of the mesentery sometimes develops a band-like thickening that, by dragging upon the lower end of the ileum, produces the kink to which attention was directed by Arbuthnot Lane. The vermiform appendix has only one artery; it occupies the free border of its mesentery and gives off several branches to the organ. In amputating the vermiform appendix, ligature the artery on the proximal side of its first branch in order to control the blood-supply to the stump of the appendix. The fact that the vermiform appendix is supplied by a single artery predisposes it to gangrene should the vessel become thrombosed, or should the circulation in it be interfered with by kinking as a result of adhesions.

The vermiform appendix will generally be found to pass either upwards and medially, behind the lower end of the ileum, or downwards and medially over the external iliac vessels into the pelvis; less frequently it ascends in the recess behind the cæcum. When, as not infrequently happens, the retro-cæcal recess is prolonged upwards behind the colon, the appendix almost invariably ascends into it, and should it be diseased, it may give rise to a retro-cæcal abscess. The abscess may perforate the posterior wall of the cæcum, or it may ulcerate through the posterior peritoneum; in the latter case the suppuration may spread upwards, in the loose fatty extra-peritoneal tissue behind the colon, into the lumbar and perinephric regions; and it may reach even the under surface of the diaphragm and form a subphrenic abscess. When, in the course of its development, the cæcum has failed to complete its descent, the vermiform appendix may lie in relation to the lower end of the right kidney. When it dips downwards into the pelvis it may become adherent to the pelvic colon, the rectum, or the bladder, or, in the female, to the uterine tube or the ovary.

To find the vermiform appendix, simply pull the cæcum out of the wound, and if the parts are normal the appendix will be delivered along with it; but, if the cæcum and appendix are tacked down by adhesions, find it by following the anterior tænia coli to its root.

Ascending Colon.—The ascending colon, after crossing the iliac crest, lies deeply on the fascia covering the quadratus lumborum and the adjacent aponeurotic origin of the transversus abdominis. Between the bowel and the fascia there is a quantity of loose fatty areolar tissue which may be the seat of a large abscess, secondary— (1) more especially, to disease of the colon itself, (2) to disease of a retro-colic vermiform appendix, or (3) to disease of the right kidney. The areolar tissue is directly continuous above with a thin layer that lines the lower surface of the diaphragm; the suppurative process may therefore extend upwards and give rise to one form of subphrenic abscess. The ascending colon is occasionally completely clothed with peritoneum, and it may even be provided with a mesocolon. A mesocolon is almost invariably present in infants who suffer from extensive ileo-cæcal intussusception; after the intussusception has been reduced, the mesentery proper is seen to be continuous, through the ascending mesocolon, with the transverse mesocolon.

In order to resect the cæcum and ascending colon, the surgeon frees them by dividing the peritoneum along its line of reflexion from the colon on to the side wall of the abdomen. The colon, along with the posterior peritoneum medial to it, is then stripped, from the lateral side towards the median plane, off the quadratus lumborum, the psoas, and the lower part of the right kidney. While that is being done, the branches of the ileo-colic and right colic vessels, which pass laterally to supply the gut, are secured, and the lymph vessels and associated lymph glands are removed along with the bowel. As the peritoneum is stripped off, care must be taken not to injure the important structures which lie behind it, namely, the duodenum, the ureter, and the testicular or ovarian vessels.

The **right colic flexure** lies between the lower part of the right kidney and the liver, immediately to the right of the gall-bladder, opposite the tenth costal cartilage—falling only a little short of the transpyloric plane. It is separated from the kidney by a quantity of loose areolar tissue; therefore, after the peritoneum along its right side is divided, it can readily be moved and separated from the kidney.

Transverse Colon.—The transverse colon crosses the abdomen immediately above the level of the umbilicus and below the greater curvature of the stomach (Pls. XLVI, LXXIII, LXXV, LXXVI). In cases of chronic constipation it may form a U-shaped or V-shaped loop that extends down to the level of the pubes. The natural kinking at the right and left colic flexures is then more acute, and tends, therefore, to aggravate the constipation.

The transverse colon receives its blood-supply from the arch formed by the middle and left colic arteries. The arch lies in the posterior wall of the lesser sac between the two layers of the transverse mesocolon.

In resecting portions of the stomach for malignant disease, the surgeon removes also the glands which lie in the greater omentum in relation to the right gastro-epiploic vessels. At that step of the operation care must be taken not to endanger the blood-supply of the transverse colon by injury to the middle colic artery.

The **left colic flexure** is more acute and more fixed than the right flexure; and it is at a higher level as well as deeper. A tumour originating in the flexure is generally under cover of the left costal margin, and therefore difficult to palpate.

To expose the left colic flexure, turn the omentum upwards along with the transverse colon and the body of the stomach. To free it for the purpose of resection the surgeon must divide—(1) the phrenico-colic ligament, which attaches it to the diaphragm opposite the eleventh rib; (2) the left border of the greater omentum, which attaches it to the stomach; and (3) the left portion of the transverse mesocolon, which attaches it to the pancreas.

Descending Colon.—The *upper part* of the descending colon, like the ascending, is deeply placed in the lumbar region and is related to the lower half of the lateral border of the left kidney. It is less frequently provided with a mesocolon than is the ascending colon.

The *lower part* (iliac colon) begins at the iliac crest, and ends at the inlet of the pelvis by joining the pelvic colon. It has no mesocolon, and is connected to the fascia covering the iliacus and psoas major muscles by loose areolar tissue. Towards its termination it turns medially immediately above and parallel to the inguinal ligament, and at its junction with the pelvic colon it lies in front of the testicular (or ovarian) and external iliac vessels. Although, as a rule, it is entirely overlapped by coils of small intestine, it can frequently be felt by firm palpation at the lateral part of the left iliac fossa, because its muscular wall is comparatively thick and generally is contracted.

Pelvic Colon (Pls. LXXV, LXXVI).—The pelvic colon, in consequence of having a well-developed mesocolon, is a freely movable loop which, though usually confined to the true pelvis, may, when distended, rise well up into the abdomen. It is the section of the large intestine which is opened for the purpose of making an artificial anus in malignant disease of the rectum.

The pelvic colon varies considerably in length, the average being sixteen or seventeen inches. It is relatively longer and of greater calibre in the child than in the adult. It is the part of the large intestine especially involved in the condition known as **megalocolon**—a congenital abnormality in which the large intestine is greatly dilated and its walls hypertrophied.

When the pelvic colon is thrown upwards and to the right, its mesocolon is spread out and is seen to be attached in an inverted V-shaped manner to the posterior wall of the pelvis. At the apex of the ∧ there is occasionally a small peritoneal pouch, called the **recess of the pelvic mesocolon**, situated in front of the ureter as it crosses the termination of the common iliac artery to enter the pelvis. That recess is one of the situations at which an internal retro-peritoneal hernia may originate. The mouth of the recess looks downwards and to the left, while above and to its right there is a branch of the lower left colic artery. The recess is a guide to the position of the left ureter.

It is to the proximal part of the pelvic colon that the divided lower end of the ileum is anastomosed in the short-circuiting operation of **ileo-sigmoidostomy.**

In the operation of transplanting the ureters into the large intestine for incontinence of urine—the result of epispadias in the female, and of ectopia vesicæ in either sex—the left ureter is implanted into the proximal part of the pelvic colon and the right ureter into its distal part.

By dividing the attachment of the pelvic mesocolon in the operation of excision of the rectum, the surgeon makes the pelvic colon sufficiently movable to allow of its being brought down and sutured to the skin in the sacral region or even to the anal region. Further, the mobility of the pelvic colon is such that after the whole descending colon is resected and the left colic flexure is freed, the divided ends of the bowel can be sutured together without undue traction.

Kidneys.—The kidneys lie behind the peritoneum, and are higher up than is often supposed, while laterally they are not so far away from the vertebral column as is often depicted; hence it is that, unless enlarged, the kidneys can seldom be felt through the abdominal wall. The right kidney as a rule is a little lower than the left, as well as a little farther away from the median plane. The hilum of the right kidney is 2 in. from the median plane; that of the left rather less. For practical purposes the **hilum** of the kidney may be regarded as opposite a point on the anterior abdominal wall a finger's-breadth medial to the tip of the ninth costal cartilage; and a line joining the two hila is opposite the disc between the first and second lumbar vertebræ—that is, a little below the transpyloric line. The position of the other parts can be judged from the situation of the hilum.

The student should make himself familiar with the feel of the parts in relation to the kidneys, as far as they can be made out by introducing the hand through a median abdominal incision.

A great part of the upper half of the anterior surface of the **right kidney** is covered with peritoneum, and can be felt by the hand passed upwards behind the right lobe of the liver and pressed backwards. Its lower half is felt immediately below the right lobe; and the small part of it that is covered with peritoneum lies in the angle of the right flexure of the colon. The second part of the duodenum overlaps the medial border. When the right kidney is excised by the abdominal route, the peritoneum is divided lateral to the ascending colon and right colic flexure, and those structures, along with the second part of the duodenum, are stripped off the organ in a medial direction, until the hilum and the renal vessels are reached.

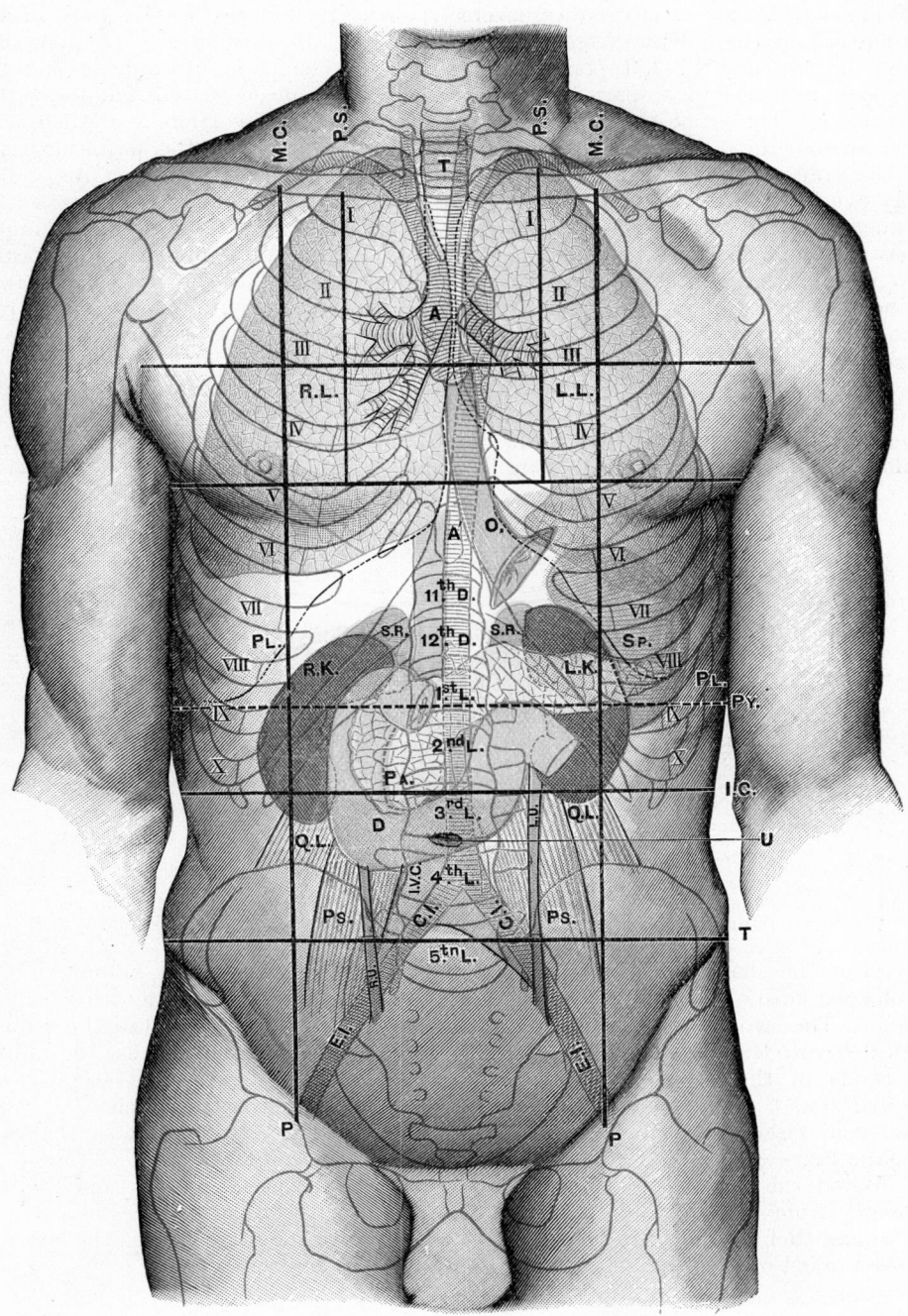

FIG. 1149.—ANTERIOR ASPECT OF TRUNK, SHOWING SURFACE TOPOGRAPHY OF VISCERA.

A.	Aorta.	M.C.	Mid-clavicular line.	R.K.	Right kidney.
C.I.	Common iliac artery.	O.	Œsophagus.	R.L.	Right lung.
D.	Duodenum.	P.	Inguinal vertical plane.	R.U.	Right ureter.
E.I.	External iliac artery.	Pa.	Pancreas.	Sp.	Spleen.
I.C.	Sub-costal plane.	Pl.	Pleura.	S.R.	Suprarenal gland.
I.V.C.	Inferior vena cava.	P.S.	Para-sternal line.	T.	Inter-tubercular plane.
L.K.	Left kidney.	Ps.	Psoas major.	T.	Trachea.
L.L.	Left lung.	Py.	Transpyloric plane.	U.	Umbilicus.
L.U.	Left ureter.	Q.L.	Quadratus lumborum.		

The **left kidney** is crossed transversely, about its middle, by the body of the pancreas and the splenic vessels. To palpate the supra-pancreatic portion, pass the hand through the left portion of the greater omentum, upwards behind the stomach, into the upper part of the lesser sac. The spleen will be felt to overlap the lateral border of the kidney. The infra-pancreatic portion is clothed with the peritoneum continued downwards from the attachment of the posterior layer of the transverse mesocolon; coils of jejunum overlie it; the descending colon may overlap its lateral border; and, underneath the peritoneum, it is crossed by branches of the upper left colic vessels. To palpate this part of the left kidney, pass the hand deeply into the upper part of the left infra-colic peritoneal compartment as far as the angle of the left flexure of the colon, and press backwards. When the left kidney is excised by the transperitoneal route, the surgeon frees the left colic flexure and the descending colon by dividing the peritoneum, and chooses the lateral side in order to avoid the branches of the left colic artery.

The kidney is surrounded by a variable quantity of **renal fat**, and is enclosed with its fat in an ill-defined sheath of **renal fascia**. Just as in the case of the prostate and thyroid gland, the kidney has thus, in addition to its true capsule, a sheath derived from the neighbouring fasciæ. The anterior and posterior

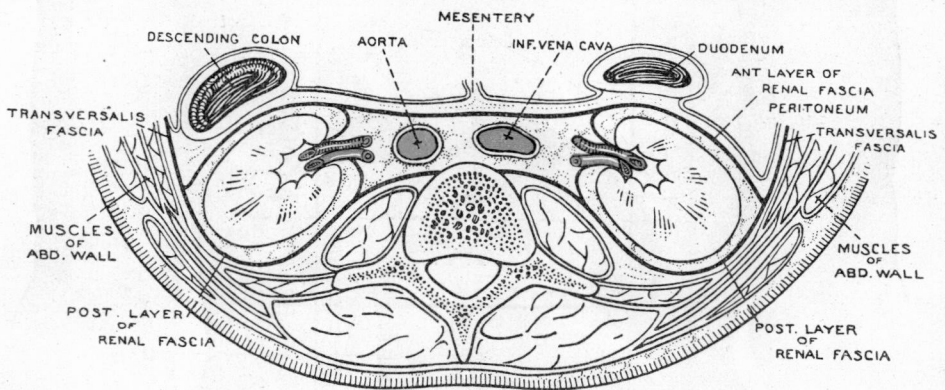

FIG. 1150.—SCHEMATIC TRANSVERSE SECTION AT THE LEVEL OF THE UPPER PART OF THE SECOND LUMBAR VERTEBRA TO SHOW THE RELATIONSHIP OF THE RENAL FASCIA.

layers of the sheath remain separate at the medial border of the kidney and are prolonged medially—the one in front of the renal vessels and the other behind them. The two layers remain separate also for some distance below the kidney, and it is into that downward extension of the fascial compartment that the kidney descends in the condition known as **movable kidney**. Above and laterally the sheath joins the fascial lining of the diaphragm and transversus muscles. Outside the renal fascia there is a second layer of fat sometimes spoken of as the **paranephric fat**.

When the lower pole of the kidney receives a special blood-supply, either directly from the aorta, or from the renal artery, the abnormal vessel may, by passing either behind or in front of the upper part of the ureter, cause the latter to be so kinked over the vessel as to cause a secondary hydronephrosis.

Brodel has shown that the branches of the renal artery are distributed to the cortex of the kidney in an anterior and a posterior group; therefore, in splitting the kidney substance to reach the pelvis of the ureter, make the incision along the frontier line between the two vascular areas, viz., about half an inch behind and parallel to the lateral border of the kidney.

The **ureters**, 10 in. (25 cm.) in length, lie behind the peritoneum on the psoas major muscles; they descend almost vertically about an inch and a half from the median plane. At the level of the pelvic brim they lie in front of the termination of the common iliac arteries, and then pass down into the true pelvis in front of the internal iliac arteries [a. hypogastrica].

The diameter of the ureter is not uniform. Its intra-vesical portion has the smallest lumen, and it is there that calculi are most likely to be impacted. A

PLATE LXXIII

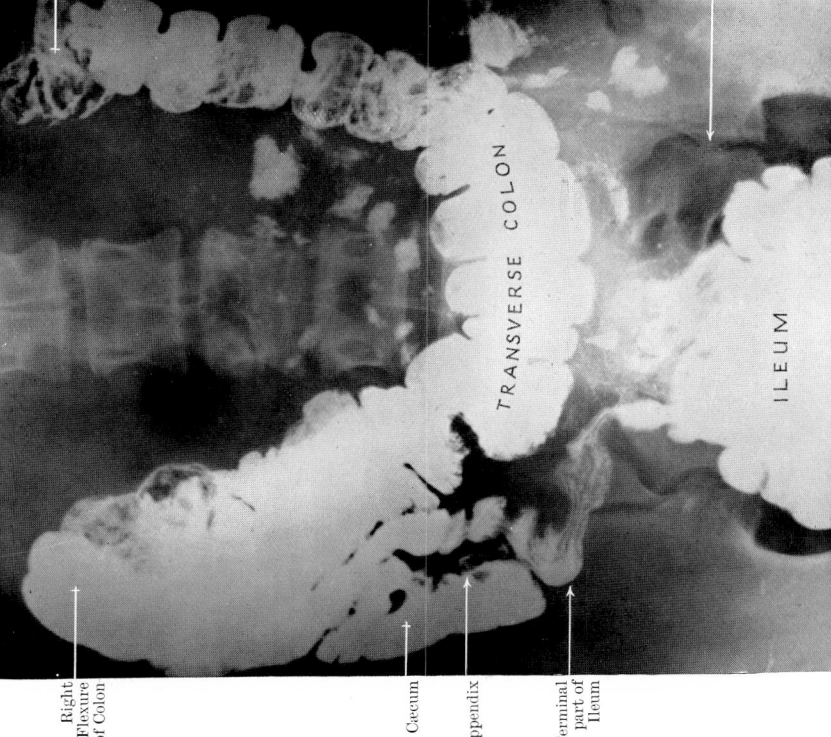

First Lumbar Vertebra

Left Flexure of Colon

Right Flexure of Colon

Caecum

Appendix

Terminal part of Ileum

Sacro-iliac Joint

TRANSVERSE COLON

ILEUM

FIG. 2.—RADIOGRAPH SHOWING ILEUM AND PART OF THE LARGE INTESTINE FILLED BY AN OPAQUE MEAL. (J. F.)

Note the high position of the Caecum (as in Fig. 1), the position of coils of the Ileum in the true pelvis, and the ascending terminal part of the Ileum. The Transverse Colon is much lower than in Fig. 1, partly because it has not contracted to pass on any of its contents to the Descending Colon.

First Lumbar Vertebra

LEFT FLEXURE

TRANSVERSE COLON

RIGHT FLEXURE

ASCENDING COLON

CAECUM

DESCENDING COLON

PELVIC COLON

RECTUM

End of Ileum

Sacro-iliac Joint

FIG. 1.—RADIOGRAPH OF THE LARGE INTESTINE OF MAN AGED 31, TAKEN 24 HOURS AFTER A BARIUM MEAL. (Dr. J. F. Brailsford.)

Note the high position of the Caecum (cf. Plates XLII and XLVII) and that the Pelvic Colon appears very short as it contains very little barium. Cf. also Plate XXXVIII and note that there is considerable variation in the time at which an opaque meal is seen throughout the large intestine.

[Facing p. 1410

PLATE LXXIV

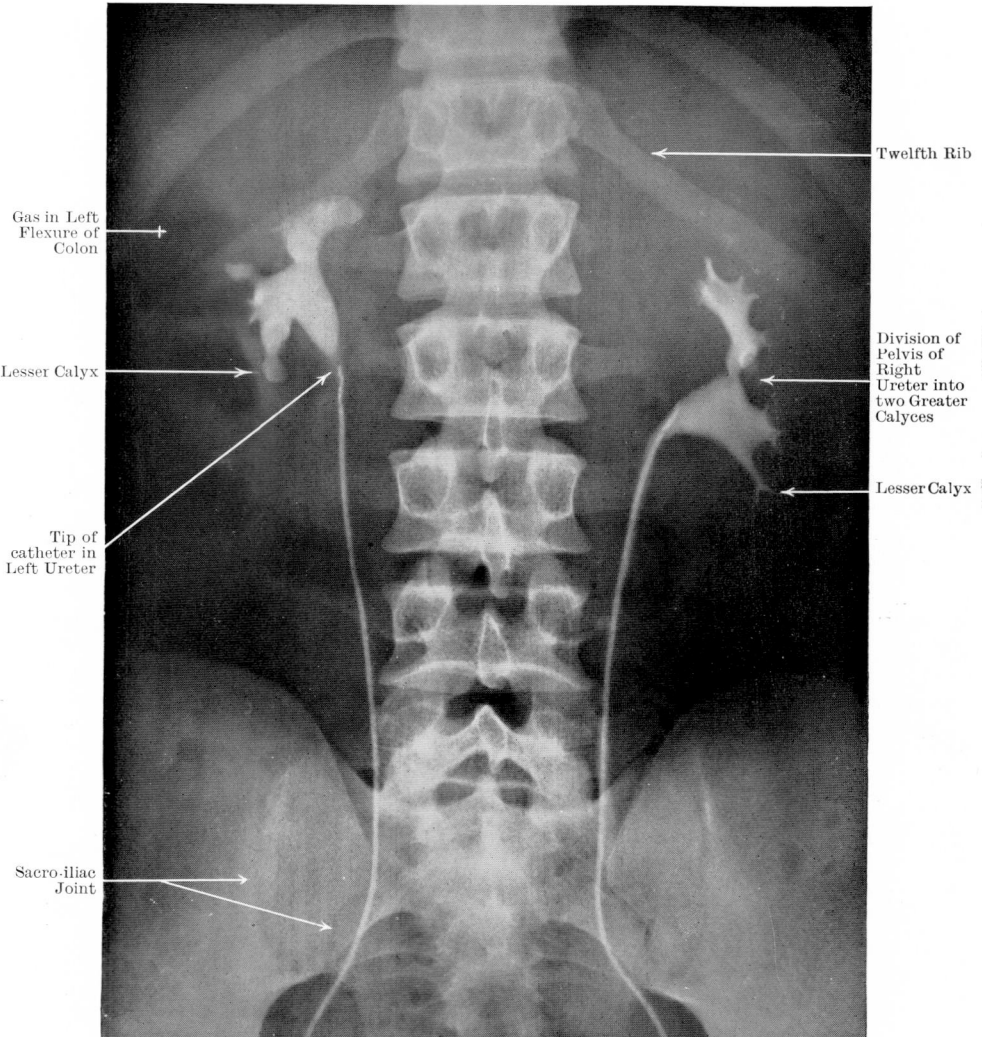

Twelfth Rib

Gas in Left
Flexure of
Colon

Division of
Pelvis of
Right
Ureter into
two Greater
Calyces

Lesser Calyx

Lesser Calyx

Tip of
catheter in
Left Ureter

Sacro-iliac
Joint

PLATE LXXIV.—RADIOGRAPH OF URETERS FROM BEHIND, AFTER THE
PASSAGE OF URETERAL CATHETERS AND THE INJECTION OF A RADIO-
OPAQUE SOLUTION INTO THE PELVES AND CALYCES. (J. F.)

The resilience of the catheters has slightly displaced the lower abdominal portions of the
ureters medially. Note the higher position of the left kidney and the form of the pelves and
calyces. Cf. Fig. 585, p. 698, and Plate LIII.

[Facing p. 1411

second narrowing occurs at or a little below the origin of the ureter proper from its pelvis, and a third where it crosses the brim of the pelvis.

The ureter has a fairly thick muscular wall, and it is therefore well adapted for suturing; and its rich blood-supply favours rapid healing. Its abdominal portion is supplied by the renal and testicular (or ovarian) arteries; its pelvic portion by the vesical, and the middle rectal arteries [a. hæmorrhoidalis media]. By their anastomoses they form a continuous and slightly tortuous chain which is generally visible through the peritoneum along the whole course of the tube.

The outline of the pelvis of the ureter and the relations of it and the ureter proper to the skeleton have assumed an additional importance now that they can be demonstrated graphically by the X-rays after injection with a solution of sodium iodide (12·5 per cent.) and mercuric chloride (1 in 3000). The shape of the normal pelvis of the ureter and the arrangement of its major and minor calyces vary considerably (Pls. LIII, LXXIV). The shadow is opposite the tips of the transverse processes of the first and second lumbar vertebræ— the upper calyces generally overlapping a portion of the twelfth rib. Normally the pelvis can contain about 7 c.c. of fluid without discomfort to the patient. The wall of the pelvis of the ureter, like that of the ureter proper, is very distensible; it is therefore capable of great expansion in cases of gradually increasing urinary obstruction; and, for the same reason, incisions into these structures heal rapidly because the edges of the wound fall into apposition. To avoid branches of the renal vessels, make incisions into the pelvis of the ureter horizontally through its posterior wall.

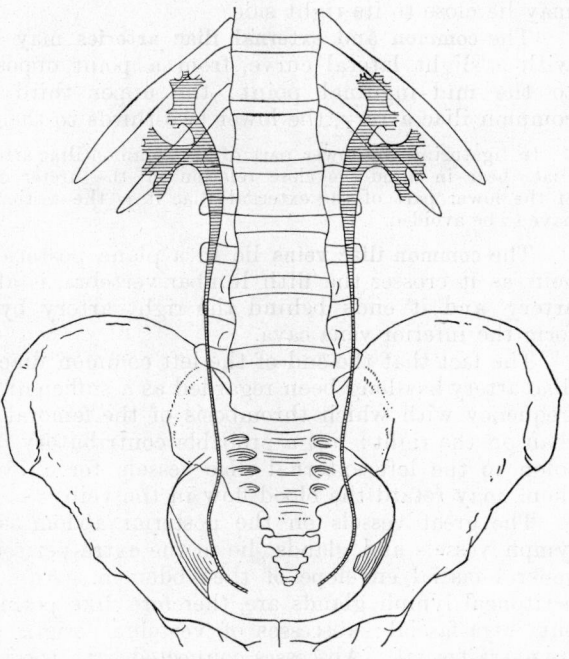

FIG. 1151.—THE OUTLINES OF THE PELVES OF THE URETERS AND THE URETERS PROPER IN RELATION TO THE SKELETON. (Drawn from an X-ray pyelogram.)

The radiographic shadow produced by an opaque catheter in the ureter crosses the tips of the transverse processes of the lumbar vertebræ and then descends to a point opposite the lower end of the sacro-iliac joint; from there the shadow descends with a curve, almost parallel to the shadow of the side of the pelvic brim, and ends opposite a point a little above and medial to the pubic tubercle. Laterally the shadow reaches almost to that caused by the ischial spine. The ureter is occasionally double throughout, or it may be bifid above or below. When the kidney is prolapsed, the abdominal portion of the ureter is more or less tortuous.

Pancreas.—The *head of the pancreas* occupies the curve of the duodenum, and is at the level of the second lumbar vertebra. The *neck* is opposite the first lumbar vertebra, in the transpyloric plane, and the body lies partly above that plane. The relations of the pancreas to the transverse mesocolon and to the neighbouring viscera have been sufficiently referred to already.

After opening the abdomen in the median line, expose the pancreas by passing through the greater omentum near the stomach; access to the organ through either the lesser omentum or the transverse mesocolon is more limited and therefore less satisfactory.

A pancreatic cyst gives rise to a tumefaction of the abdomen either in the epigastrium or in the umbilical region, depending on whether it pushes the lesser omentum before it and develops between the liver and stomach, or whether it extends forwards below the stomach. In severe contusions of the abdomen the pancreas may be ruptured against the vertebral column.

Vessels of the Abdomen.—The commencement of the **abdominal aorta** and the **cœliac artery** are situated one finger's-breadth above the transpyloric plane. The **superior mesenteric artery** arises in the transpyloric plane, the **renal arteries** a finger's-breadth below it. The **inferior mesenteric artery** arises about an inch above the level of the umbilicus. The **abdominal aorta** bifurcates a little to the left of the median plane, on a level with the highest part of the iliac crest, and about $\frac{1}{2}$ in. below the level of the umbilicus.

The **inferior vena cava** lies immediately to the right of the aorta; its most important surgical relation is the right ureter, which is to the right of it, and may lie close to its right side.

The **common** and **external iliac arteries** may be mapped out by a line drawn, with a slight lateral curve, from a point opposite the bifurcation of the aorta to the mid-inguinal point; the upper third of the line corresponds to the common iliac artery, the lower two-thirds to the external iliac.

In ligaturing the lower part of the common iliac artery, or the upper part of the external iliac, bear in mind the close relation of the ureter and the ovarian vessels; in ligature of the lower part of the external iliac it is the testicular vessels and the vas deferens that have to be avoided.

The **common iliac veins** lie in a plane posterior to their arteries; but the left vein, as it crosses the fifth lumbar vertebra, is also below and to the right of its artery, and it ends behind the right artery by uniting with the right vein to form the inferior vena cava.

The fact that the end of the left common iliac vein is *behind* the right common iliac artery has long been regarded as a sufficient explanation for the much greater frequency with which thrombosis of the femoral vein is met with on the left side than on the right; but a probable contributory factor is the close relation of the colon to the left external iliac vessels, for a loaded colon, exerting pressure on them, may retard the blood flow in the vein.

The great vessels on the posterior abdominal wall, along with the adjacent lymph vessels and glands, lie in the extra-peritoneal fat, and therefore within the general fascial envelope of the abdomen. Abscesses originating from the retro-peritoneal lymph glands are, therefore, like perinephric abscesses, extra-peritoneal but intra-fascial; abscesses of vertebral origin, whether lumbar, iliac, or psoas, are extra-fascial. Abscesses connected with the vermiform appendix are primarily intra-peritoneal; occasionally they ulcerate through the parietal peritoneum and burrow in the extra-peritoneal fat.

MALE PERINEUM

The male perineum is a heart-shaped space, the osseous boundaries of which are the same as those of the outlet of the pelvis. A line drawn transversely across the perineum between the anterior part of the tuberosities of the ischium crosses the median plane immediately in front of the anus, and divides the space into an anterior or urogenital triangle and a posterior or anal triangle.

The **urogenital triangle** is subdivided into a superficial and a deep compartment by the perineal membrane [fascia inferior diaphragmatis urogenitalis]. The **superficial compartment** contains the root of the penis, which gives rise to a longitudinal fullness on the surface. Anteriorly, the surface of the urogenital triangle is continued on to the scrotum, while on each side a distinct groove separates it from the medial surface of the thigh. The **perineal body** (central point) is the common tendon of the perineal muscles, mingled with fat and continuous with the middle of the posterior border of the perineal membrane; it lies a finger's-breadth in front of the anus. In front of it, about 1 inch from the centre of the anus, is the posterior end of the **bulb of the penis**. The *superficial compartment* of the urogenital triangle is bounded below by the membranous layer of the superficial fascia, which is attached posteriorly to the posterior border of the perineal membrane, and, on each side, to the margin of the pubic arch. Anteriorly the membranous fascia passes on to the scrotum, the penis, and spermatic cord, to become continuous with the membranous layer of the superficial fascia on the front of the abdomen.

When the urethra is ruptured below the perineal membrane, the course of infiltration of the extravasated urine is determined by the attachments of the membranous layer of fascia; at first, therefore, the urine is confined within the superficial compartment, but gradually travels forwards, on to the lower part of the anterior abdominal wall; it is prevented from passing into the front of the thigh by the attachment of the membranous fascia of the abdomen to the fascia lata a little distal to the inguinal ligament.

The **deep compartment** of the urogenital triangle is the interval between the perineal membrane and the fascia of the pelvis. The most important structures in the compartment are the membranous part of the urethra, the bulbo-urethral glands, the dorsal nerve of the penis, the internal pudendal vessels, and the artery to the bulb.

The **membranous part of the urethra** lies an inch behind the lower border of the pubic symphysis. When that division of the urethra is ruptured, the extravasated urine, after filling the deep compartment, may reach the superficial compartment by bursting through the perineal membrane where the vessels pierce it; or it may penetrate the fascia of the pelvis, infiltrate the perivesical areolar tissue and the retropubic space, and ascend on the anterior abdominal wall between the fascia transversalis and the parietal peritoneum.

The **bulbo-urethral glands** lie immediately behind the membranous part of the urethra, separated from the bulb of the penis by the perineal membrane. The **internal pudendal vessels** and the **dorsal nerve** lie just within the margin of the pubic arch. The **artery to the bulb** runs transversely medially $\frac{1}{4}$ in. in front of the posterior border of the perineal membrane.

The **male urethra** measures about eight inches from the external to the internal orifice; the narrowest point is at the external orifice; a second narrowing occurs at the perineal membrane. It is behind these narrow points that a calculus is liable to become impacted. The *most dependent part* of the urethra is the portion in the bulb, and it is there that stricture is most frequently encountered. The membranous part of the urethra, situated between the perineal membrane and the fascia of the pelvis, is surrounded by the sphincter urethræ muscle, which, when thrown into spasm, may firmly grip an instrument as it is passed into the bladder. *Rupture of the urethra* from a fall on the perineum generally involves the portion in the bulb. A *false passage* made during the passage of an instrument generally traverses the floor of the urethra at the perineal membrane; to prevent that injury direct the point of the instrument upwards, and at the same time depress the handle as soon as the instrument is felt to encounter the resistance of the perineal membrane. When the *prostate is hypertrophied* the prostatic part of the urethra is elongated, and its internal orifice may look directly forwards; and if the lateral lobes are unequally enlarged it may deviate to one side. Patients with prostatic hypertrophy are seldom able to empty the bladder completely, on account of the dependent well which is formed behind the enlarged middle lobe.

From the clinical point of view surgeons speak of an "anterior urethra," situated below the membranous portion, and a "posterior urethra," situated above it. The anterior urethra is the least sensitive portion of the canal, but the posterior urethra is highly sensitive and more vascular; and when its mucous membrane is injured toxic agents may be rapidly absorbed by the abundant blood-vessels and lymph vessels of its submucous tissue. The anterior urethra is shut off from the posterior urethra by the tonic contraction of the sphincter urethræ muscle.

Viewed with an endoscope the mucous membrane of the anterior urethra is seen to be smooth and glistening, and to have a pale yellowish-pink colour. The longitudinal row of small pit-like openings on the dorsal wall and the orifices of the lacunæ and mucous glands can be investigated. The mucous membrane of the posterior urethra is of a redder colour. The opening of the prostatic uricle is seen as a small slit-like orifice on the most prominent part of the urethral crest, while immediately on each side of it is the minute orifice of the ejaculatory duct. In the floor of the sulcus on each side of the crest are the minute openings of the majority of the prostatic ducts.

Cystoscopic Examination of the Bladder.—In a cystoscopic examination of the bladder special attention is paid to the **trigone**, as most of the pathological lesions are associated with that region. The **internal urethral orifice** is at its inferior angle; and at its supero-lateral angles there are the small oblique, slit-like **orifices of the ureters**, each surrounded by a very slight lip-like elevation of the mucous membrane. At the base of the trigone the mucous membrane is raised into a smooth *transverse ridge* which stretches between the ureteric openings, with a slight forward convexity. The ridge is caused by a bundle of transverse muscular fibres, continuous with the longitudinal fibres of the ureters. The distance of the ureteric orifices from each other is rather more than an inch, and their distance from the internal urethral orifice is slightly less than an inch.

The urine is ejected into the bladder intermittently at intervals of a minute or so. During each ejection the ureteric orifice is seen to pucker up, and as it relaxes the gush of urine takes place in the form of a characteristic whirl "resembling an injection of glycerine into water." The **mucous membrane** of the trigone is closely connected with the subjacent muscular wall, and is therefore smooth; whereas over the rest of the bladder it is thrown into folds owing to the looseness of the submucous tissue. Further, the mucous membrane of the trigone has a pink tinge, while over the rest of the bladder it is of a pale straw colour. This contrast is due to the difference in the number and arrangement of the blood-vessels. Over the trigone they are larger, more numerous, and form so close a network that, when the surface is inflamed, the dilated, congested vessels form a continuous vascular layer. Over the rest of the bladder one sees, here and there in the mucous membrane, small segments of fine vessels giving off a cluster of short branches, the finer anastomoses of which are not visible when the mucous membrane is healthy.

The form and shape of the trigone in women may be distorted by prolapse of the bladder, by alterations in the size and position of the cervix uteri, and by the presence of fibroids. In the male, distortion is usually due either to the enlargement of the prostate or to disease of the seminal vesicles.

When the normal bladder is comfortably filled, the bladder walls appear almost smooth, but when the bladder contracts the delicate muscular trabeculæ become visible through the mucous membrane. When the bladder is hypertrophied as the result of urethral obstruction the muscular trabeculæ become greatly hypertrophied, and stand out prominently, even when the bladder is full. The spaces between the trabeculæ may become so deeply pitted as to lead to the formation of little pockets known as **false diverticula.**

PROSTATE

The operation of *prostatectomy* has proved so successful in removing urinary complications associated with enlargement of the **prostate** that a fresh impetus has been given to the study of the anatomy of the organ from the surgical point of view. With the body erect the **base** of the prostate is in a horizontal plane at the level of the middle of the pubic symphysis, while its **apex** is half an inch behind and below the lower border of the symphysis. It follows, therefore, that the vesical orifice and the base of the prostate are within easy reach of the finger introduced through a supra-pubic cystotomy incision. The **anterior surface** of the prostate is about $\frac{3}{4}$ in. behind the pubes, to which it is connected by the pubo-prostatic ligaments. Above those ligaments is the *retro-pubic space*, occupied by fatty tissue which passes upwards in front of the anterior wall of the bladder, between the umbilical arteries, as far as the umbilicus, while laterally it extends on each side, between the peritoneum and pelvic fascia, as far back as the internal iliac arteries. The **posterior surface** of the prostate is related to the part of the rectal ampulla immediately above the anal canal, and is therefore accessible to palpation *per rectum*. Between the rectum and the posterior part of the fascial sheath of the prostate there is a layer of loose areolar tissue, which is taken advantage of in the operation of excision of the rectum, and when the posterior surface of the prostate is exposed in the operation of perineal prostatectomy. The areolar tissue between the rectum and the prostate is traversed by a fibrous sheet, called the *recto-vesical septum,* which extends in a coronal plane from the floor of the recto-vesical pouch of peritoneum to the perineal body and is the remains of the walls of the lower part of the recto-vesical pouch, which originally extended down behind the prostate. The **lateral surfaces** of the prostate cannot be felt through the rectum; they are related to the anterior parts of the levatores ani, from which they are separated only by the fascial sheath of the gland.

The *prostate substance* is made up of branching tubular glands supported by a fibro-muscular stroma. The gland tissue is most abundant in the posterior and lateral parts of the organ; anteriorly the stroma is more abundant and extends backwards from the capsule to the urethra to form a sort of anterior commissure. By the term "*capsule*" of the prostate is understood the immediate or proper envelope of the gland; that envelope consists of parallel layers of fibro-muscular tissue, continuous with the stroma of the organ and forming part of it. In some instances it is so thin that the gland tissue reaches almost to its surface, while in other instances it is so thick as to deserve to be regarded as the cortical portion of the gland. By the term "*sheath*" of the prostate is meant the fibrous envelope derived from the pelvic fascia; the veins of the *prostatic plexus* lie between the lamellæ of the sheath.

In what is known as "**senile**" **hypertrophy** of the prostate the organ may be uniformly enlarged, or the enlargement may affect chiefly one or other of the lateral lobes, one or both of which may enlarge more particularly in an upward direction so as to project into the bladder as a "third" lobe. The intra-vesical overgrowth may take the form of a more or less pedunculated projection, situated at the side of the internal urethral orifice or behind it, or it may surround the orifice as a prominent ring-like elevation. As the intra-vesical growth enlarges, it makes its way towards the bladder within the ring of the sphincter vesicæ, and, having pushed the internal longitudinal fibres of the bladder before it, or having separated them, it comes ultimately to be separated from the cavity of the bladder by mucous membrane only. In the operation of *supra-pubic prostatectomy* the surgeon tears through the mucous membrane overlying the prostate at a point immediately behind the internal urethral orifice. His finger then finds the plane of separation between the true capsule and the hypertrophied tissue of the gland and completes the enucleation of the gland. As the sheath is markedly thicker and denser in the hypertrophied than in the normal prostate, the enucleation can be accomplished without injuring the veins of the prostatic plexus, as they are protected by such of the outer fibres of the capsule as may be left behind. In "total" prostatectomy, practically the whole of the prostatic urethra is removed along with the prostate. The cavity, left behind after removal of the prostate, contracts at once owing to the natural shrinking of the fascial sheath and approximation of the bladder, rectum, and the two levatores ani at the sides. In some instances, instead of removing the entire prostate and its capsule along with the prostatic urethra, the surgeon, by working within the capsule, is able to enucleate each lateral glandular mass either separately or united to its fellow in the form of a horse-shoe shaped mass, the urethra and the anterior commissure being left more or less intact.

In perineal prostatectomy the posterior surface of the prostate is exposed through a horse-shoe shaped incision whose convexity reaches forwards to a point immediately behind the bulb; at the sides, the incision sinks into the ischio-rectal fossæ, its extremities ending at the anterior part of the ischial tuberosities. After reflexion of the skin and subcutaneous tissue, the incision is carried through the perineal body. The bulb, the superficial transverse perineal muscles, and the perineal membrane are then drawn forwards, and the fibres of the recto-urethral muscle (which connect the anterior wall of the rectal ampulla with the sphincter urethræ) are divided; that allows the anal canal and the lower end of the rectum to be pulled backwards. The dissection is now carried in a forward direction, between the anterior borders of the levatores ani, towards the prostate, so as to strike the loose non-vascular tissue which intervenes between the posterior part of the prostatic sheath and the thin fascia outside the muscular coat of the rectum. The posterior surface of the prostate is reached through an incision in its fascial sheath. The prostate, along with its capsule and the urethra, may either be enucleated entire from the sheath, or the capsule may be incised as well as the sheath, and the adenomatous masses removed separately. The operation is greatly facilitated if the prostate is pulled down into the wound by a special retractor (Young) inserted into the bladder through a median incision into the floor of the membranous part of the urethra.

Epididymis, Spermatic Cord and Scrotum.—The **epididymis**, which can be felt as an elongated curved body applied vertically to the posterior margin of the testis, is especially involved in gonorrhœal and tubercular infections. Occupying the posterior part of the spermatic cord is the **vas deferens**, which, when grasped between the finger and thumb, feels like a piece of whip-cord. The testicular veins form a **pampiniform plexus** in the substance of the cord; a varicose condition of those veins is known as *varicocele*. In operating for varicocele the surgeon reaches the veins by dividing, in succession, all the coats of the cord; the deepest coat, viz., the internal spermatic fascia, derived from the fascia transversalis, forms a well-marked fibrous envelope which immediately surrounds the veins and other constituents of the cord. Besides the testicular artery, the testis receives its blood-supply from the artery to the vas deferens and the artery to the cremaster muscle. The marked swelling which attends *œdema and hæmatoma of the scrotum* is due to the loose and delicate character of the areolar tissue which intervenes between the dartos muscle and the subjacent external spermatic fascia.

Anus and Anal Canal.—The **anus** is situated about $1\frac{1}{2}$ in. in front of and below the tip of the coccyx. The skin around the orifice is pigmented and thrown into radiating folds. The painful linear crack or ulcer, known as *fissure of the anus,* generally occupies one of the furrows at the posterior margin of the anus. The skin of the anus is provided with large sebaceous and sweat glands which are occasionally the site of small and very painful *anal abscesses.*

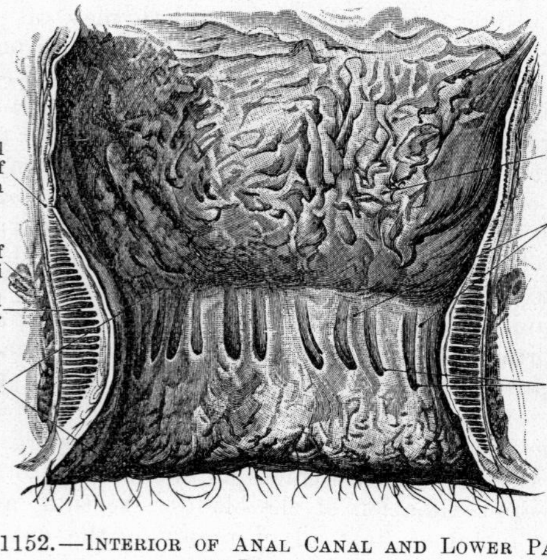

In a *rectal examination* the finger, before it reaches the cavity of the rectum, traverses the **anal canal**. That canal is directed from below upwards and forwards from the anal orifice to the ampulla of the rectum and is about an inch and a half in length.

External hæmorrhoids are developed from the anal folds situated outside the

Longitudinal fibres of rectum

Part of levator ani

Internal sphincter

Anal canal

Rugæ of mucous membrane

Anal columns

Anal sinuses and valves

Fig. 1152.—Interior of Anal Canal and Lower Part of Rectum.

The anal columns were more numerous in this specimen than usual. (Birmingham.)

white line that corresponds to the muco-cutaneous junction; *internal piles* are developed from the veins of the mucosa at the upper part of the anal canal.

In the upper half of the anal canal the mucous membrane is thrown into longitudinal ridges called *anal columns.* At the lower end of the grooves between the columns there are little flaps, called *anal valves,* which bound small pockets called the *anal sinuses* (Fig. 1152). According to Ball, fissure of the anus is generally caused by the tearing downwards of an *anal valve* during the passage of a scybalous mass.

Ischio-rectal Fossa (Fig. 1153).—The apex of the **ischio-rectal fossa** is at the origin of the levator ani from the obturator fascia; it is directed upwards towards the pelvis, and is $2\frac{1}{2}$ in. from the surface. The fossa is bounded medially by the levator ani covered with fascia (anal fascia); and laterally by the obturator internus muscle covered with the obturator fascia. An *abscess in the ischio-rectal fossa* should be opened early, otherwise it is apt to burst through the medial wall of the fossa into the rectum; should it open also on the skin surface a complete *"fistula in ano"* is formed. When a "fistula in ano" results from the bursting of a submucous abscess of the anal canal, the track of the fistula runs either medial to or through the fibres of the internal and external sphincter muscles, and the external or skin opening is, as a rule, close

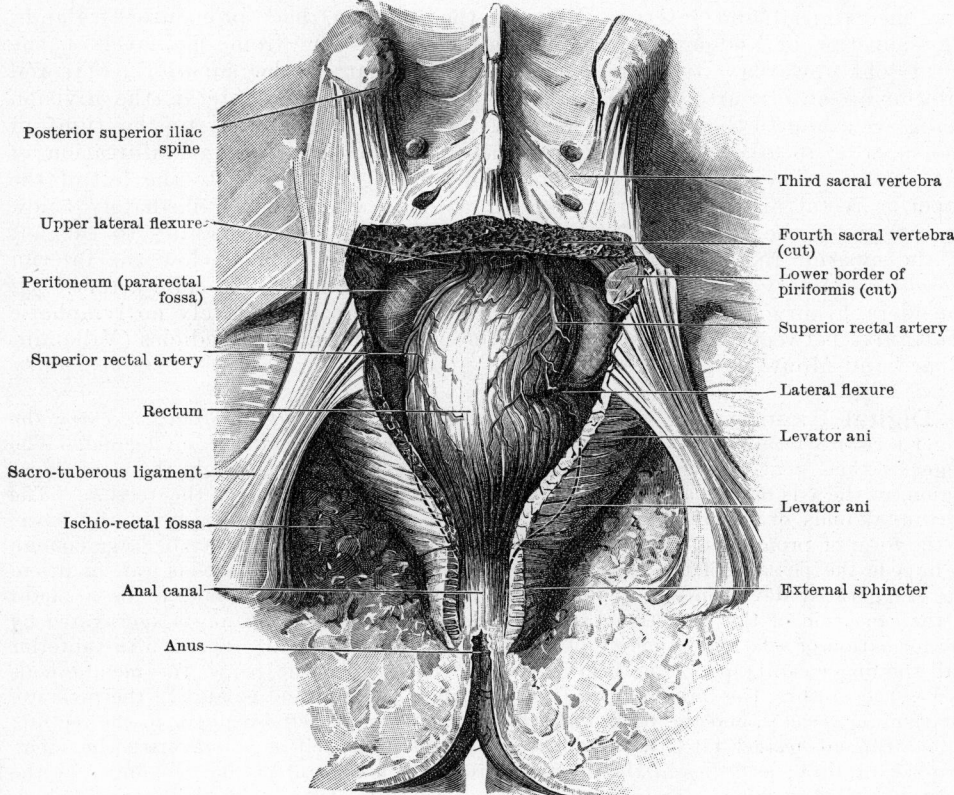

Posterior superior iliac spine

Upper lateral flexure

Peritoneum (pararectal fossa)

Superior rectal artery

Rectum

Sacro-tuberous ligament

Ischio-rectal fossa

Anal canal

Anus

Third sacral vertebra

Fourth sacral vertebra (cut)

Lower border of piriformis (cut)

Superior rectal artery

Lateral flexure

Levator ani

Levator ani

External sphincter

FIG. 1153.—THE RECTUM FROM BEHIND.

From a formalin-hardened male body, aged thirty. (Birmingham.)

to the anus, while the internal opening is generally at the upper end of the anal canal. Occasionally the ischio-rectal abscess perforates the levator ani towards the apex of the fossa; it then burrows into the areolar tissue around the rectum, and opens into the ampulla of the rectum. In other cases, the abscess starts in this areolar tissue, and it bursts either into the rectal ampulla or through the levator ani into the ischio-rectal fossa, and so reaches the surface. Or the pus may burrow between the rectum and coccyx, whence it may pass outwards through the greater sciatic foramen into the gluteal region; or, by piercing the pelvic fascia, it may reach the extra-peritoneal fatty tissue of the pelvis and ascend in it to form an iliac abscess.

The *lymph* vessels from the skin of the anus pass along the perineo-femoral grooves to the most medial glands of the groin, both superficial and deep inguinal. Those from the region of the white line end in glands which lie in front of the internal iliac artery, while those from the mucous membrane of the upper part of the anal canal and the rectum traverse a few minute glands placed between the muscular and fascial coats of the rectum, along the superior rectal [hæmorrhoidal] vein and its two branches, and pass thence to the sacral glands which lie medial to the anterior sacral foramina.

Recent work on the distribution of lymph from the ano-rectal segment indicates that the distribution is arranged in three " pedicles "—inferior, middle, and superior. The inferior pedicle collects lymph from each lateral half of the anus ; it passes to the inguinal glands, and in a lesser degree to the lateral sacral glands and to the common iliac glands that lie on the sacral promontory. The middle pedicle drains that portion of the rectum which extends from the level of the third transverse fold to the ano-rectal junction. It follows the courses of the middle rectal, the lateral sacral, and median sacral arteries, and it passes into the external and internal iliac and the common iliac (promontory) glands. The superior or abdominal pedicle drains the rectum from the level of the third fold upwards ; its course corresponds to that of the superior rectal and inferior mesenteric arteries. Three groups of vessels constitute it, the division being according to their relative lengths. The short group lies to the right of the superior rectal artery and opens into a rectal gland at the bifurcation of that vessel. The group of vessels of medium length is found to the left of the superior rectal artery and terminates in a gland which lies immediately below the origin of the lowest left colic artery. The long group also lies to the left of the superior rectal artery and passes into glands that lie below the inferior mesenteric artery at the level of the origin of the upper left colic artery. Of considerable surgical importance is the fact that there is relatively no lymphatic continuity between the lymph fields of the upper and middle pedicles (Villemin-Huard and Montagne).

Digital Examination of Rectum.—In making a *rectal examination*, carry the finger forwards from the tip of the coccyx so as to enter the anus from behind. The finger is then gently pressed upwards and slightly forwards through the sphincteric region, in the axis of the anal canal, until it reaches the ampulla of the rectum. The horizontal folds of the rectum, three in number, project into the cavity of the bowel in the form of prominent crescentic shelves ; the lower fold, which may be large enough to impede the passage of the finger, must not be mistaken for a pathological condition. An exaggerated development of one of the folds in the fœtus is said to be a factor in the causation of the condition known as *megalocolon* ; the condition is aggravated by the formation of a lateral pouching of the bowel opposite the fold. Through the anterior wall the finger can palpate from below upwards the bulb of the penis, the membranous part of the urethra, the bulbo-urethral glands (when inflamed and enlarged), the prostate, the seminal vesicles, and the back of the bladder. With the left forefinger in the rectum, an instrument passed into the bladder can be distinctly felt as it traverses the membranous urethra ; as it lies in the prostatic urethra it is separated from the finger by the prostate. Hence, when a *false passage* is made through the part of the urethra which lies in the bulb or through the membranous portion, the instrument, if pushed onwards towards the bladder, will be felt immediately outside the rectum between it and the prostate. In the child, owing to the rudimentary condition of the prostate, the instrument is distinctly felt close to the rectum, as it lies in the prostatic as well as in the membranous portion of the urethra. When the prostate is not enlarged the tip of the finger can just reach the back of the bladder, which is most distinctly felt when the bladder is full. The seminal vesicles, indistinctly felt when healthy, may be readily palpated when enlarged and indurated from disease. Through the side wall of the rectum may be palpated the ischio-rectal fossa, the bony wall of the pelvis, and, when enlarged, the internal iliac lymph glands ; through the posterior wall the sacrum and coccyx, and (when enlarged) the lymph glands lying in the retro-rectal fibro-areolar tissue.

In the child rectal examination enables one to palpate, in addition to the structures in the cavity of the pelvis, those which occupy the lower segment of the abdomen. When the bladder is empty even a small calculus can be readily felt in it by recto-abdominal palpation.

The distance of the apex of the **recto-vesical pouch** of peritoneum from the anus varies considerably, according to the degree of distension of the bladder and rectum ;

when both are empty it reaches to about 2 in. from the anus; when both are distended it is at least one inch higher (Figs. 587, 588, pp. 702, 703).

Examination by Sigmoidoscope.—In introducing the sigmoidoscope into the pelvic colon, bear in mind the direction of the anal canal and the curve of the rectum; as the instrument traverses the anal canal it must be directed forwards as well as upwards; it is then pushed onwards, in a backward and upward direction, towards the hollow of the sacrum; and, finally, in order to reach the pelvic colon, it is again directed forwards and also a little to the left so as to clear the promontory of the sacrum. The instrument is more difficult to pass in women, on account of the greater abruptness of the curvature of the sacrum.

When examined with the sigmoidoscope the mucous membrane of the rectum is seen to possess a deep red colour; and an excellent view is obtained of the horizontal folds. The most conspicuous fold projects from the right wall about the level of the recto-vesical peritoneal reflexion, *i.e.* about three inches from the anus. The highest fold gives rise to a distinct narrowing which must not be mistaken for a stricture. The pulsations of the left common iliac artery can generally be seen to be communicated, through the pelvic colon, to the postero-lateral wall of the rectum about four inches from the anus.

Removal of the Rectum.—When the rectum and anal canal are removed for malignant disease, an **incision** is carried round the anus and then upwards and backwards over the coccyx and lower part of the sacrum. The *ano-coccygeal body* is divided longitudinally and the *coccyx* (either alone or along with more or less of the lower part of the sacrum) is removed after division of the structures attached to its margins, viz. the lower fibres of the gluteus maximus, the coccygeus, and the sacro-tuberous and sacro-spinous ligaments. The **median sacral artery** is ligatured. There is now seen, stretching across the floor of the wound, a well-defined sheet of fascia; this is divided longitudinally and stripped to each side off the posterior surface of the rectum, and the branches of the **middle rectal arteries** are ligatured. Anteriorly, the anal canal is detached from the **perineal body**, after which the anterior surface of the rectum is freed from below upwards from—(1) the sphincter urethræ containing the **membranous urethra**, (2) the **prostate**, (3) the **bladder**, the **seminal vesicles** and the **vasa deferentia**. The procedure is facilitated by the existence of a layer of areolar tissue. In order to reach that tissue, the surgeon, after dividing the perineal body transversely, deepens the incision up to the apex of the prostate. In doing that he divides a band of muscular fibres (**recto-urethral muscle**) which passes from the anterior wall of the lowest part of the rectal ampulla to blend with the muscle fibres that surround the urethra at the apex of the prostate. It is those recto-urethral fibres which, by pulling forwards the ampulla, bring it into close relation with the urethra; hence it is especially at that stage of the operation that great care must be taken not to open into the rectum or to wound the urethra. After exposing the apex of the prostate he next retracts the anal canal well backwards and defines the anterior borders of the **levatores ani**. Each of those muscles is then divided well above its insertion into the anal canal. The posterior surface of the prostate, covered with recto-vesical septum, is then exposed.

Continue the separation of the rectum upwards along the layer of areolar tissue above mentioned, and the bottom of the **recto-vesical pouch** of peritoneum will be reached. The peritoneum can usually be stripped for some distance off the rectum without risk of opening into the peritoneal cavity. As the rectum is freed on each side, bands of fibro-areolar tissue containing branches of the **middle** and **superior rectal vessels** are divided. If the tumour is situated at the upper part of the rectum, the recto-vesical pouch of peritoneum is freely opened by a transverse incision. The surgeon then sets free the **colo-rectal junction** by dividing the sacral attachment of the **pelvic mesocolon** and securing the superior rectal artery. After dividing the rectum well above the tumour, he closes the opening into the peritoneal cavity by suturing together the anterior and posterior walls of the recto-vesical pouch. If a permanent colostomy has been established, the divided bowel is closed; if not, a "sacral" anus is made.

FEMALE PELVIS

When the abdomen is opened by a median incision extending from the umbilicus to the pubis, and the pelvis is looked into from above, after displacement of some coils of the small intestine upwards, the **fundus of the uterus**, directed forwards and a little upwards, is seen resting upon the upper surface of the bladder. Behind the uterus is the rectum, and between the two the **recto-uterine pouch**, containing the pelvic colon and the lower coils of the ileum. The **ovary** lies on the side of the pelvis, a little below the level of the brim, closely attached to the upper layer of the broad ligament. When the vermiform appendix hangs into the pelvis its tip may be in close relation with the right ovary—a condition which often leads to a difficulty in distinguishing an inflammation of that ovary from appendicitis.

The **round ligament** of each side is seen passing forwards and laterally from the upper part of the border of the uterus to the deep inguinal ring, which lies immediately above and in front of the termination of the external iliac artery. Inferiorly and at the medial side of the round ligament, as it enters the ring, is the **inferior epigastric artery**. If the uterus is pulled upwards the attachments of the **broad ligament** to the floor and side wall of the pelvis are brought into view, as also are the utero-vesical and recto-uterine peritoneal pouches. The utero-vesical pouch is a shallow recess ; the deepest part of the recto-uterine pouch covers the upper fourth of the posterior wall of the vagina, and is in relation, therefore, with the posterior fornix.

The utero-vesical peritoneal reflexion takes place at the junction of the body of the uterus with the cervix. The anterior wall of the cervix is in relation, therefore, with the upper part of the base of the bladder, from which, however, it is separated by a layer of loose areolar tissue. It is the existence of that areolar tissue which enables the surgeon to separate the bladder readily from the uterus in the operation of hysterectomy.

The anterior wall of the vagina is firmly united to the urethra, but its posterior wall can be readily separated from the rectum, because of the interposition of loose areolar tissue between them.

The **ureter** crosses the bifurcation of the common iliac artery and then passes backwards and downwards into the pelvis, where it lies at first on the side wall immediately below and in front of the internal iliac [hypogastric] artery, under cover of the peritoneum, through which it can be seen. It then courses medially and forwards in the parametric areolar tissue below the root of the broad ligament. In that position it lies above the lateral fornix of the vagina, about three-quarters of an inch lateral to the upper part of the cervix uteri ; finally, immediately before it pierces the lateral angle of the bladder, it inclines medially to lie in front of the upper lateral part of the vaginal wall.

The relation of the parts of the ureters that lie in the pelvis are of special importance in the female as their close relation to the cervix uteri and upper part of the vagina renders them liable to injury, more especially in the operation of hysterectomy performed for malignant disease of the uterus.

The **uterine artery**, in the first part of its course, passes downwards and forwards a little anterior and lateral to the ureter. At the level of the upper end of the cervix uteri it takes a medial direction and passes along the root of the broad ligament, and crosses above and in front of the ureter from lateral to medial side ; it then passes above the lateral fornix of the vagina and finally ascends close to the side of the body of the uterus, and ends by anastomosing with the ovarian artery below the isthmus of the uterine tube.

The **ovarian artery** enters the pelvis between the layers of that portion of the broad ligament known as the **infundibulo-pelvic ligament** ; it is there that the vessel may be most readily ligatured in abdominal hysterectomy, and in ovariotomy.

The **lymph vessels** from the lower part of the vagina pass to the inguinal and ano-rectal glands. Those from the rest of the vagina, from the cervix uteri and from the greater part of the body of the uterus, pass to the internal and external iliac, and the sacral glands. The ano-rectal glands lie on the wall of the ampulla of the rectum. The internal iliac glands are situated on the side wall of the pelvis in close relation to the origins of the branches of the internal iliac artery. The sacral glands form a chain along the medial side of the anterior sacral foramina. Some of the lymph vessels from the fundus of the uterus, and those from the uterine tube and the ovary, terminate in the glands around the aorta and inferior vena cava ; but others from the fundus run along the round ligament to the inguinal glands.

The external genitals are fully described in the chapter on the Uro-genital Organs. The **external orifice of the urethra**, surrounded by a slight annular prominence is situated about an inch behind the clitoris, in the smooth, triangular, anterior, division of the vestibule of the vagina, immediately in front of the vaginal orifice. When a *catheter* is passed the instrument is directed along the forefinger (introduced just within the vaginal orifice with the palmar surface towards the pubic symphysis) to the base of the smooth triangle, where it is tilted slightly upwards so as to bring its point opposite the urethral orifice.

The **greater vestibular glands** are a pair of glands, each about the size of a bean, placed at the sides of the posterior third of the orifice of the vagina, on the lower surface of the perineal membrane. Each has a slender duct, nearly an inch in length, which opens into the angle between the labium minus and the hymen. Abscesses and cysts not infrequently develop in connexion with these glands. The **bulbs of the vestibule** are a pair of piriform collections of erectile tissue situated one on each side of the lowest part of the vagina, between the bulbo-spongiosus muscle and the perineal membrane. Rupture of the bulbs gives rise to the condition known as *pudendal hœmatocele*.

The **cervix uteri** projects downwards and backwards into the upper part of the vagina and is separated from the vaginal wall by a distinct **fornix**. The relations of the fornix are of so much practical importance that for descriptive purposes it is customary to subdivide it into an anterior, a posterior, and two lateral portions. The **anterior fornix** is shallow, and is related to the base of the bladder and to the areolar tissue below the utero-vesical pouch of peritoneum. The **posterior fornix** is much deeper; it extends upwards for some little distance in front of the anterior wall of the lowest part of the recto-uterine pouch. The septum between the fornix and the pouch is merely the wall of the vagina; hence the readiness with which the pelvis may be drained by an incision in the posterior vaginal wall.

The **lateral fornix** (Pl. LVI) lies below the medial part of the root of the broad ligament. An incision carried through it would therefore open into the parametric areolar tissue and would expose the uterine artery as it passes transversely to the uterus, after crossing the ureter.

Vaginal Examination.—In making a *vaginal examination*, place the patient on her back, with the thighs well flexed; carry the index-finger of the right hand along the fold of the buttock towards the median plane, where it will impinge against the posterior part of the **vestibule of the vagina**, and then pass it upwards and backwards into the vagina; to make a more thorough examination introduce the middle finger also. When the uterus is in its normal position the **vaginal part of the cervix uteri** is felt as a knob-like body projecting downwards and backwards into the upper part of the vagina. In nulliparæ the external os is a small transverse slit, whereas in women who have borne children it is larger and its lips are more or less fissured. Above and behind the cervix is the **posterior fornix**, which is in close proximity to the **recto-uterine** or **recto-vaginal pouch**; the pouch, though normally occupied only by a loop of ileum or of pelvic colon, is the frequent site also of displaced abdominal and pelvic organs, and collections of intra-peritoneal effusions and exudations. A loaded rectum can be detected through the vagina by the characteristic way in which the contents can be pitted by the finger. In front of the cervix is the **anterior fornix**, through which the body of the uterus and the base of the bladder may be felt. Through the lower half of the anterior vaginal wall the **urethra** may be detected as a cylindrical, cord-like thickening which may be rolled against the lower border of the symphysis. If the **ureter** is enlarged, the finger, in the anterior part of the lateral fornix, can recognise it by compressing it against the pubic bone.

By the *bi-manual examination* the pelvic organs are steadied and pushed downwards towards the outlet of the pelvis by the pressure of the left hand applied above the pelvis, so that they can be more readily reached and palpated by the finger placed in the vagina with its palmar surface directed upwards. The **ovary** when enlarged may be felt if fingers are pushed well up into the lateral fornix towards the side wall of the pelvis. The healthy **uterine tubes** cannot, as a rule, be felt per vaginam.

Rectal Examination.—By rectal examination the finger can palpate, from below upwards, the recto-vaginal septum, the cervix uteri, the posterior fornix of the vagina, the floor of the recto-vaginal pouch, and the body of the uterus. The rectum is washed out and a speculum introduced into the bowel, with the patient in the genu-pectoral position, the rectum becomes inflated with air; the finger can now feel very distinctly the uterus and the uterine tubes, and the finger carried laterally, along the prominent fold formed by the ligament of the ovary, may feel the ovary if it is enlarged.

THE BACK

Median Line of the Back.—In the median line of the back is the **vertebral furrow**, which is deepest in the lower thoracic and upper lumbar regions. Over the upper sacral region, where the sacro-spinales muscles are tendinous, there is a flattened area forming an equilateral triangle, the angles of which correspond to the posterior superior iliac spines and the third sacral spine. The **vertebral spines** can be palpated at the bottom of the vertebral furrow, but can seldom be identified individually. It is possible to identify and count them if it is remembered that the first thoracic is the lower of the two knobs at the root of the back of the neck, that the third thoracic is on a level with the root of the spine of the scapula, the seventh thoracic with its inferior angle, the fourth lumbar with the highest part of the iliac crest, and the second sacral with the posterior superior iliac spine.

Lateral Region of the Back.—Above the spine of the scapula is the **supra-scapular region**, which is padded by a thick mass of muscle consisting of the supra-spinatus and levator scapulæ, covered by the trapezius; shrugging the shoulders brings the two trapezius muscles into relief.

In the **interscapular region** are the trapezius and rhomboid muscles, which are thrown into prominence when they brace back the shoulders.

Below the inferior angle of the scapula the last five ribs can readily be felt lateral to the sacro-spinalis muscle; when the twelfth rib does not reach beyond this muscle, the eleventh rib will be mistaken for it, unless the ribs are counted from the second rib downwards.

The **lower border of the trapezius** is indicated by a line extending upwards and laterally from the twelfth thoracic spine to the tubercle of the crest of the scapula; the **upper border of the latissimus dorsi** by a line extending from the seventh thoracic spine horizontally across the inferior angle of the scapula.

The lateral border of the **sacrospinalis** is indicated on the surface by a shallow groove on the loin about a hand's-breadth from the median line. The lateral border of the **quadratus lumborum**, which passes upwards and slightly medially, lies a little lateral to the lateral border of the sacrospinalis at the iliac crest, and a little medial to it at the twelfth rib.

The anatomy of the muscles and fasciæ which complete the abdominal wall between the last rib and the iliac crest is of great importance in connexion with operations in the **region of the loin**. The space between the last rib and the iliac crest varies greatly according to the length of the rib, and according to the general shape of the chest and slope of the ribs as a whole. As a rule, the **tip of the twelfth rib** lies about two inches vertically above the middle of the iliac crest. From a surgical point of view the costo-iliac space may be said to be limited medially by the lateral edge of the sacrospinalis, and, more deeply, by the tips of the lumbar transverse processes; laterally it is bounded by the posterior, free border of the external oblique, and, more deeply, by the line of reflexion of the peritoneum from the colon on to the side wall of the abdomen. The space is roofed over by the latissimus dorsi, except below, where a narrow, triangular interval is left between its lateral border and the posterior border of the external oblique, the base of the triangle being formed by the iliac crest just behind its middle. This **lumbar triangle** is a weak area through which a lumbar abscess may come to the surface, and through which a lumbar hernia occasionally develops. When the latissimus dorsi and the lower part of the serratus posterior inferior are removed, another triangle is exposed, which constitutes a second weak area in the loin; it is bounded above by the last rib, medially by the sacrospinalis, and laterally by the posterior muscular fibres of the internal oblique; the floor of the triangle is formed by the aponeurosis of origin of the transversus abdominis muscle; that aponeurosis splits into three layers to form two compartments, the anterior enclosing the quadratus lumborum and the posterior the sacrospinalis.

Kidneys.—The upper limit of the kidney is indicated by a line drawn transversely across the loin opposite the eleventh thoracic spine, the lower limit by a line on a level with the third lumbar spine. The upper pole reaches to the eleventh rib; the lower, which lies immediately lateral to the tip of the transverse process of

PLATE LXXV

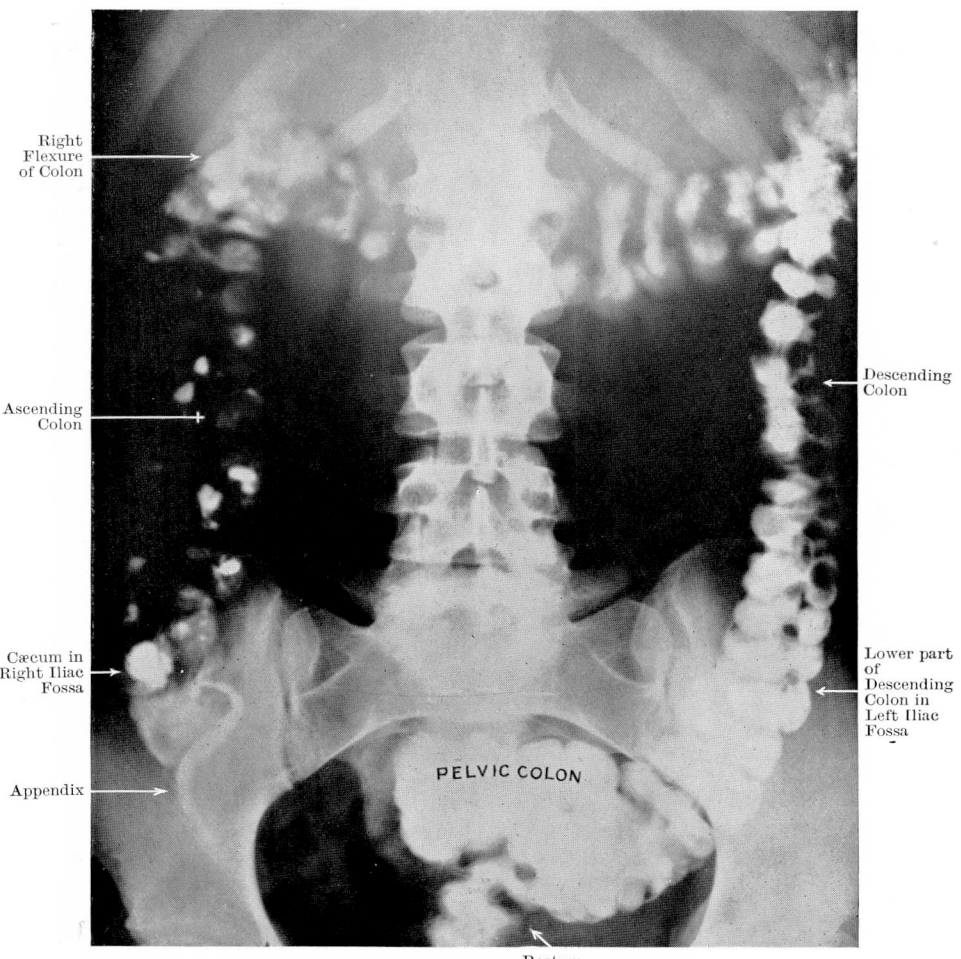

Right Flexure of Colon

Ascending Colon

Cæcum in Right Iliac Fossa

Appendix

Descending Colon

Lower part of Descending Colon in Left Iliac Fossa

PELVIC COLON

Rectum

PLATE LXXV.—Radiograph showing all the Parts of the Large Intestine. (J. F.). Most of the Opaque Meal has accumulated in the Lower part of the Descending Colon, the Pelvic Colon and the Rectum.

Note the residue of radio-opaque material in the Cæcum and Appendix, and the contraction of the Descending Colon. Compare this radiograph with Fig. 1 and Fig. 2, Plate XLI, which represent two previous stages in the filling and emptying of the Cæcum and Colon.

PLATE LXXVI

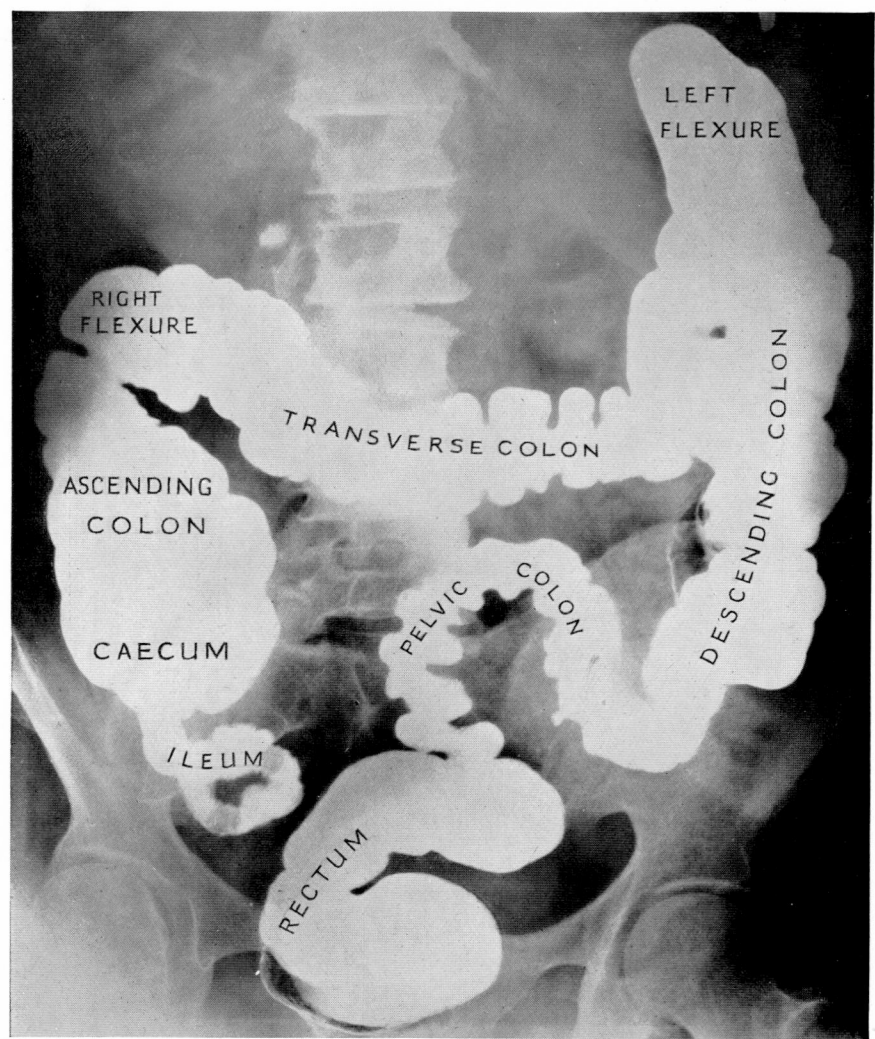

PLATE LXXVI.—RADIOGRAPH OF LARGE INTESTINE FILLED ENTIRELY (WITH THE EXCEPTION OF VERMIFORM APPENDIX) BY BARIUM ENEMA. (J. F.)

The position of the several parts of the Large Intestine is well shown. Note the loop of the Pelvic Colon, and that some of the barium injection has passed into the terminal part of the Ileum. Cf. Plate XLI, Figs. 1 and 2, and Plate XLVII.

the third lumbar vertebra, is $\frac{1}{2}$ in. to 2 in. above the iliac crest. About a third of the kidney lies above the lower margin of the twelfth rib. The left kidney is usually about $\frac{1}{2}$ in. higher than the right. The most lateral point of the lateral border is 4 in. from the median plane, while the hilum lies $1\frac{1}{2}$ or 2 ins. lateral to the median plane in front of the interval between the tips of the transverse processes of the first and second lumbar vertebræ.

The psoas major muscle intervenes between the postero-medial surface of the kidney and the transverse processes, and the kidney is therefore protected from contact with the bony processes in the event of a blow directed from the front. Between the upper end of the kidney and the eleventh and twelfth ribs is the

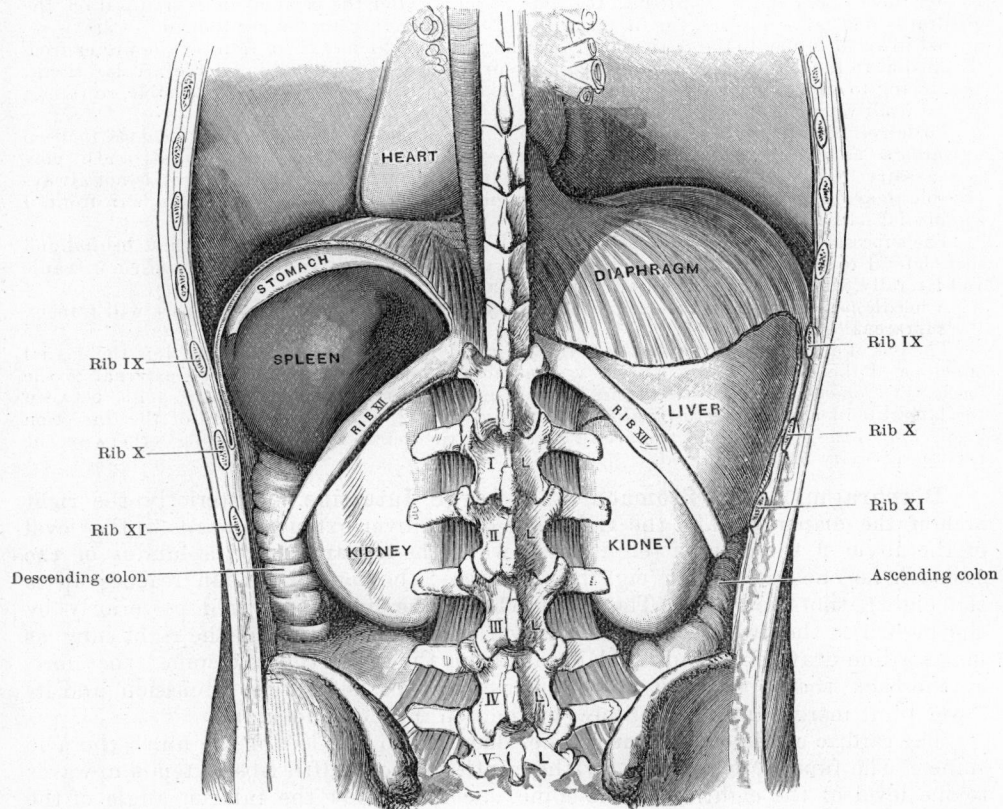

Fig. 1154.—Dissection of the Spleen, Liver, and Kidneys from behind, in a Subject hardened by Formalin Injection. (H. J. S.)

diaphragm and the costo-diaphragmatic recess of the pleura (Fig. 1140). The relations of the pleura to the last rib have been considered already (p. 1387).

On the back, the course of the upper part of the **ureter** may be indicated by a line drawn vertically upwards from the posterior superior iliac spine to the level of the second lumbar spine; the deep guides are the tips of the transverse processes of the second, third, and fourth lumbar vertebræ, covered by the psoas major muscle.

Exposure of Kidney from behind.—The kidney is exposed from the loin by a **vertical incision** between the lateral border of the sacrospinalis and the posterior border of the external oblique muscle. The following structures are divided from the superficial to the deeper parts : (1) the skin and fasciæ ; (2) the lower fibres of the latissimus dorsi and serratus posterior inferior muscles ; (3) the middle layer of the lumbar fascia, immediately lateral to the sacrospinalis compartment, and parallel to the lateral fibres of the quadratus lumborum muscles ; (4) the anterior layer of the lumbar fascia ; (5) the paranephric fat ; (6) the renal fascia and fat. The kidney may be readily shelled out of its fatty sheath with the finger. In cases of difficulty, better access to the renal vessels can be obtained if the incision is made a little nearer the median plane, and the sacrospinalis compartment of the lumbar fascia is opened. That allows of the muscle itself being pulled medially more effectively.

To expose the kidney by an **oblique incision** in the loin, divide the latissimus dorsi and serratus posterior inferior muscles at the medial part of the wound; the posterior fibres of the external and internal oblique muscles are divided at its lateral part; next, split the aponeurotic origin of the transversus muscle to expose the extra-peritoneal fat and the peritoneum as it is reflected from the colon on to the side of the abdominal wall. The peritoneum and the colon are then stripped forwards and medially off the front of the kidney, until the hilum and renal vessels are reached. The sacrospinalis and quadratus lumborum muscles are pulled well medially, and it may be necessary to divide the lateral fibres of the quadratus muscle.

To expose the upper part of the ureter, extend the division of the abdominal muscles still farther downwards and forwards into the iliac region. After the peritoneum is stripped off the quadratus and psoas muscles, the ureter will be found clinging to the peritoneum. Care is required to avoid injury to the testicular or ovarian vessels, which cross in front of the ureter from the medial to the lateral side. The ureter is surrounded by a quantity of loose areolar tissue, and, owing to an abundance of elastic fibres in its adventitious coat, is very extensible, so that it can be readily pulled up to the surface.

To deliver an enlarged kidney out of the loin, it is generally necessary to prolong the incision upwards so as to divide the lateral arcuate ligament [arcus lumbo-costalis laberalis]; and it may be necessary to divide, fracture, or resect the twelfth rib also. As that is done it is not always possible to avoid opening into the costo-diaphragmatic pleural recess, which descends in front of the medial half of the rib.

The subcostal and the ilio-hypogastric and ilio-inguinal nerves, which lie at first behind and then lateral to the organ, must not be injured; the subcostal nerve should be pulled upwards and laterally, the other two downwards and medially.

A needle passed through the medial extremity of the eleventh intercostal space will transfix the **suprarenal gland.**

The pus of a **perinephric abscess** lies in the renal fat, and is, therefore, within the fascial envelope of the abdomen; the pus in a **psoas abscess**, on the other hand, lies external to the fascia. To open a psoas abscess from behind, make a vertical incision in the angle between the lateral border of the sacrospinalis and the iliac crest; in the deeper part of the dissection keep close to the front of the transverse process of the fourth lumbar vertebra—otherwise the peritoneal cavity may be entered.

Diaphragm, Liver, Stomach, and Large Intestine.

—Posteriorly the **right arch of the diaphragm** and the right lobe of the liver extend upwards to the level of the angle of the scapula (eighth rib), while the **left arch** and the fundus of the stomach lie one inch lower (eighth interspace); the central tendon reaches up to the eighth thoracic spine. The **right lobe of the liver** is covered posteriorly by the eighth to the twelfth ribs, and is overlapped by the base of the right lung as far as a line drawn horizontally laterally from the tenth thoracic spine; therefore, on the back, the upper limit of the liver cannot be defined by percussion, and its lower limit merges into the dullness of the loin muscles and kidney.

The **cardiac orifice of the stomach** lies one inch to the left of the ninth thoracic spine. The fundus, overlapped by the ninth to the twelfth ribs, extends upwards to the level of the eighth thoracic spine, one inch below the inferior angle of the scapula. The **pyloric portion** crosses the median plane opposite the first and second lumbar spines, the **pylorus** itself being situated one inch to the right of the first lumbar spine.

Viewed from behind, the **large intestine**, on both sides, overlaps the lateral border of the kidney and lies parallel to the lateral border of the sacrospinalis muscle. The peritoneum is reflected from the colon on to the posterior abdominal wall along a line drawn vertically upwards from the middle of the iliac crest. The **right flexure** is at the level of the first lumbar spine, and the left flexure is a little higher.

Spleen.

— The *spleen* is situated in the left hypochondrium behind the stomach. It varies greatly in size and outline, but a spleen of average size is opposite the ninth, tenth, and eleventh ribs, its long axis corresponding approximately to that of the tenth rib. Between the upper third of the spleen and the chest wall (pleura and diaphragm intervening) is the lower part of the left lung, the inferior margin of which crosses the spleen horizontally at the level of the tenth thoracic spine. The costo-diaphragmatic recess of the pleura reaches down as far as the inferior angle of the spleen. The upper limit of the spleen cannot therefore be defined by percussion; and when a spleen puncture is done from behind, the needle will

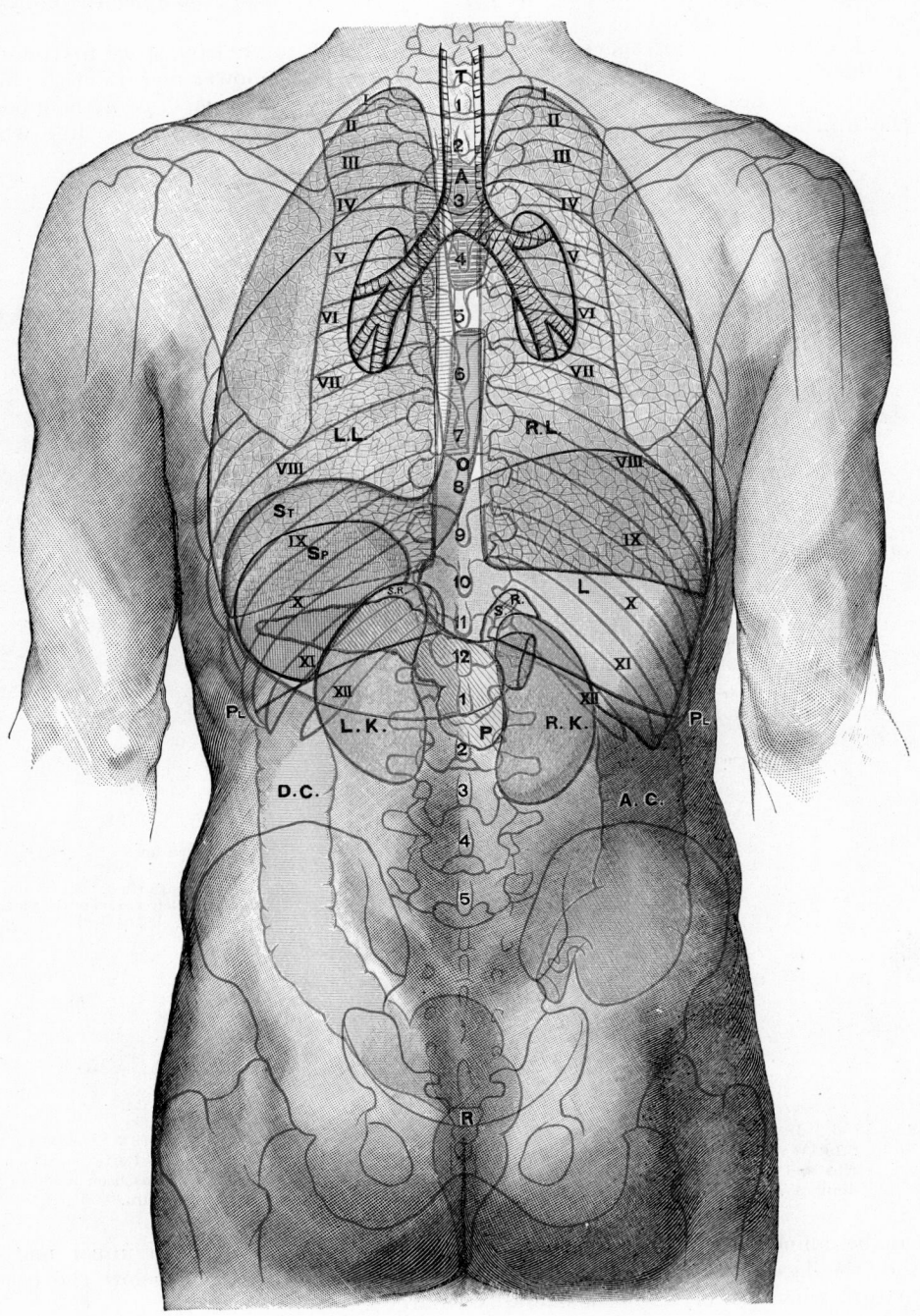

Fig. 1155.—Posterior Aspect of Trunk, showing Surface Topography of Viscera.

A. Aorta.	L.L. Left lung	R.L. Right lung.
A.C. Ascending colon.	P. Pancreas.	Sp. Spleen.
D.C. Descending colon.	Pl. Pleura.	S.R. Suprarenal gland.
L. Liver.	R. Rectum.	St. Stomach.
L.K. Left kidney.	R.K. Right kidney.	T. Trachea.

traverse the pleural as well as the peritoneal cavity unless the spleen is enlarged or displaced downwards.

The *lateral end* of the spleen reaches the ninth intercostal space in the mid-axillary line. The *medial end* is at the same level as the lower margin of the lung, about 1½ inches lateral to the tenth thoracic spine. The *highest point* is opposite the ninth rib in the scapular line. The only parts of the splenic outline which

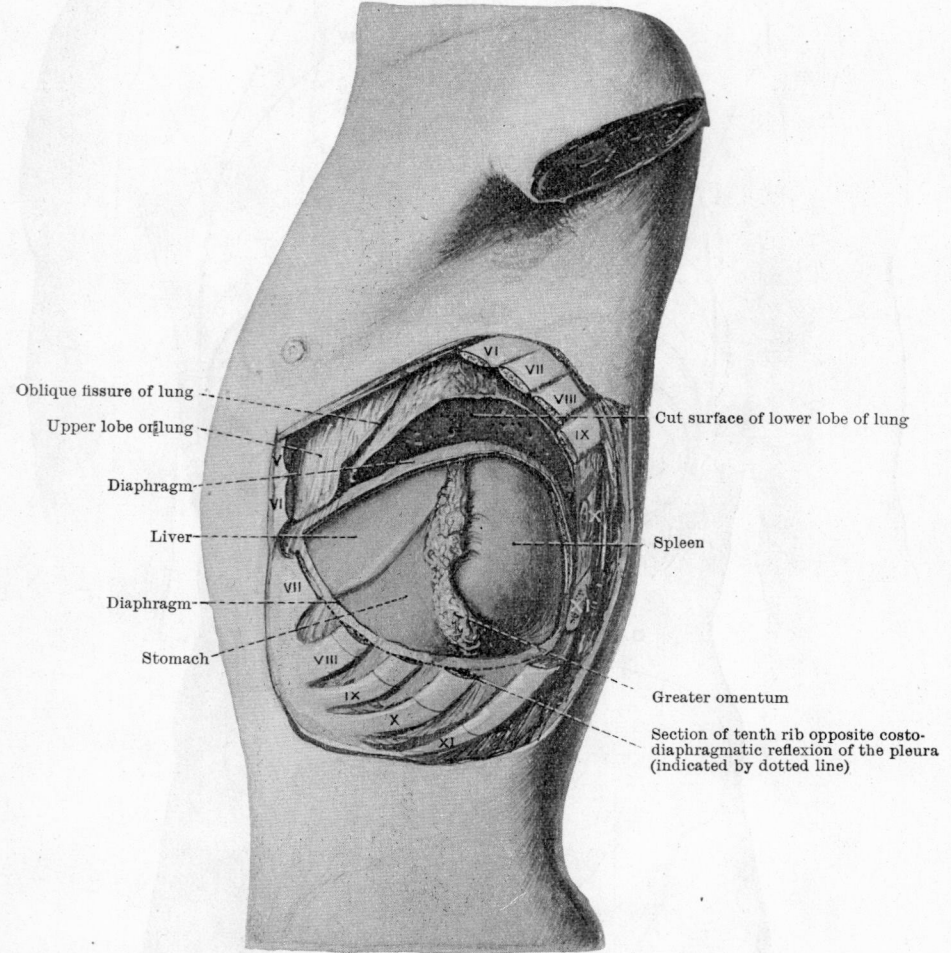

Fig. 1156.—Dissection of the Left Hypochondrium to show the Relations of the Spleen to the Side Wall of the Chest, the Diaphragm, and the Adjacent Viscera. Portions of several ribs and a part of the base of the left lung have been removed; and a window has been made in the diaphragm down almost to the level of the costo-diaphragmatic reflexion of the pleura.

can be defined by percussion are the lateral, crenated part of the upper margin and the lateral end; and it is those parts which may be felt below the costal margin when the organ is considerably enlarged.

To excise the spleen, open the abdomen by a vertical incision through the upper half of the left rectus muscle a little lateral to the middle line. Draw the spleen forwards into the wound after displacing the stomach and transverse colon downwards and to the right. The short gastric vessels are secured as they course between the two layers of the gastro-splenic ligament. The splenic vessels, which form the main pedicle, lie between the two layers of the lieno-renal ligament. Care must be taken not to injure the tail of the pancreas, which is in relation with the lower part of the gastric surface of the spleen. In a floating spleen the two peritoneal ligaments are elongated to form distinct pedicles.

Pancreas.—The head of the **pancreas** lies opposite the first and second lumbar spines; the tail lies at the same level as the left flexure of the colon.

Vertebral Column and Spinal Cord.—The spinal cord usually ends opposite the lower border of the first lumbar spine but may do so one vertebra higher or lower; in the infant it reaches the interval between the second and third lumbar spines. The *cervical enlargement*, which corresponds to the lower four cervical and the first two thoracic segments, ends opposite the first thoracic spine. The five lumbar segments are opposite the last three thoracic spines. The fourth cervical segment is opposite the third cervical spine, the eighth cervical segment opposite the interspace between the fifth and sixth cervical spines, the fourth thoracic opposite the second thoracic spine, the eighth thoracic opposite the fifth thoracic spine, the twelfth thoracic opposite the ninth thoracic spine, the second lumbar opposite the tenth thoracic spine. The sacral segments correspond to the last thoracic and first lumbar spines (see Figs. 701, 865, pp. 812, 994).

The nerve roots which arise below those of the first lumbar and form the cauda equina, are arranged in a right and a left bundle, with a median space between them. The highest roots occupy the most lateral position in the cauda, and the lowest are nearest the filum terminale.

To expose the spinal cord by the operation of laminectomy, the surgeon, after separating the muscles from the spines and laminæ, removes certain of the spines along with their supraspinous and interspinous ligaments. The next step is the removal of the corresponding laminæ. That is not difficult in the cervical region, for there they are comparatively slender and do not overlap. In the thoracic region there is more difficulty owing to the greater size of the laminæ and to their imbricated arrangement; in the lumbar region the difficulty arises from the greater depth at which the laminæ lie and their greater thickness. The bleeding comes mainly from (1) the plexus of veins on the backs of the vertebral arches, and (2) from the plexus which occupies the fatty tissue outside the dura mater. After the dura and arachnoid mater are incised, cerebro-spinal fluid escapes. The anterior and posterior nerve roots are now exposed, and are seen to be separated by the denticulate ligament, which ends below in a fork-like manner opposite the first lumbar vertebra. As the first lumbar posterior root rests on the "fork," the ligament serves as a guide to that nerve (Elsberg). Tumours which arise outside the spinal cord, but within the dura, are classified according to their relationship to the anterior and posterior nerve roots and to the denticulate ligament. The classification is therefore anterior, antero-lateral, postero-lateral, and posterior. To reach an anterior tumour divide one of the teeth of the ligament, and also one (or possibly two) adjacent posterior roots, and then displace the spinal cord (thus freed) backwards and towards the opposite side.

The **sub-dural space** extends down to the level of the second or third sacral spine. In the operation of *lumbar puncture* (Quincke) a fine trochar and cannula are introduced into the sub-arachnoid space below the level of the spinal cord, the puncture being made $\frac{1}{4}$ to $\frac{1}{2}$ in. to one side of the interspinous ligament in the interval between the third and fourth or fourth and fifth lumbar spines. The fourth spine is at the level of the highest part of the iliac crest. The instrument should be directed medially and very slightly upwards. In the adult the distance of the dura mater from the surface is from 2 to 3 in., in the infant $\frac{3}{4}$ in.

Owing to the shape and arrangement of the articular surfaces of the vertebræ, **dislocations** without fracture are practically confined to the cervical region; they are commonest between the fifth and sixth vertebræ. The dislocation may be unilateral, but it is more frequently bilateral and incomplete. In both instances the spinal cord may be only slightly bruised, and then the paralysis will be only partial. In complete bilateral dislocations the spinal cord is usually completely crushed, and when the lesion is at, or above, the level of the fourth cervical segment (origin of the phrenic nerves) death may ensue rapidly from respiratory paralysis.

Fracture-dislocations of the vertebral column are commonest in the lower cervical region and the thoraco-lumbar region—that is to say, where the movable cervical and lumbar regions join the more fixed thoracic region. The vertebral column above the injury is generally displaced forwards, and the spinal cord is often severely lacerated or completely torn across by the upper end of the portion of the column below the fracture. It is important to remember that, in consequence of the shortness of the cord as compared with the vertebral column, the origins of the spinal nerves are at a higher level than their exits from the vertebral canal. The distance between origins and exits becomes greater the farther down the nerves are—the lowest nerve roots running almost vertically downwards. The cervical nerves leave the vertebral canal *above* the vertebræ after which they are named (except the *eighth,* which is above the first thoracic vertebra) ; the thoracic, lumbar, and sacral nerves leave the canal *below* their vertebræ.

To understand the effect of **lesions of the spinal cord,** it is necessary to be familiar with the sensory and motor distributions of the various spinal segments (see Figs. 869, p. 1001, and 878, p. 1015). Transverse lesions of the cord *above the fifth cervical spine* (that is, above the disc between the fourth and fifth cervical vertebræ) are quickly fatal, owing to paralysis of respiration, as the phrenic nerves arise mainly from the fourth segment. In transverse lesions of the cervical enlargement the *cutaneous insensibility* does not extend higher than a horizontal line at the level of the second costal cartilage. The diagnosis of the particular segment involved is arrived at by testing the motor and sensory functions of each segment. The sensory areas corresponding to the *lower four cervical* and the *first two thoracic segments* are in the upper limbs, and are placed in numerical order from the lateral to the medial side of the limb. The sensory area corresponding to the *second, third,* and *fourth cervical segments* occupies the occipital region of the scalp, the back of the auricle, the masseteric region, the whole of the neck, and the shoulders and upper part of the chest down to a horizontal line at the level of the sternal angle. In a total transverse lesion of the cord in the *thoracic region,* the upper limit of the anæsthesia is horizontal, and reaches the level of the terminations of the anterior primary rami of the nerves that arise from the segment opposite the vertebral injury. The upper limit of the anæsthesia is, therefore, at a much lower level than that of the injured vertebra. For example, a fracture-dislocation at the level of the eighth thoracic vertebra involves the origin of the tenth thoracic nerve, which ends at the level of the umbilicus. The sensory zone that corresponds to the *fifth thoracic segment* is at the level of the nipples, that of the *seventh thoracic segment* is at the level of the xiphoid process, that of the *tenth* at the level of the umbilicus, while that of the *twelfth* reaches down, anteriorly, almost to the pubis. The sensory areas that correspond to the lumbar and sacral segments are seen in Fig. 887, p. 1036. See also Figs. 867, 869, 871.

Congenital Abnormalities and Postural Errors.—Abnormalities in the ossification of the bodies of the vertebræ are occasionally encountered. In some instances no clinical disturbance results, and the condition is recognised in the course of a routine X-ray examination of the vertebral column. A characteristic example is the " *slot vertebra,*" in which the anterior portions of the bodies of the thoracic vertebræ appear to be indented by a segment of unossified tissue. This appearance indicates a persistence of the intersection between the original protovertebræ. It has no clinical significance, but it is liable to be confused with pathological conditions.

In rare cases ossification of the body of the vertebræ is confined to one of the twin ossific centres, with the result that the body of the vertebra is distorted, and, if the error is a pronounced one, deformity of the vertebral column results (*scoliosis* or *kyphosis*).

Abnormal development of the laminæ and spines also occurs, and therein lies the foundation of *spina bifida.* The least serious deformity of this type implies a split or gap between the right and left halves of one or more of the spines, and through the space a band of fibrous tissue establishes continuity between the deep surface of the overlying skin and the posterior surface of the spinal meninges (*spina bifida occulta*). In the more complete malformations, where the spines are absent and the laminæ rudimentary, a saccular protrusion of meninges and nerve tissue may appear (*spina bifida* of the *meningocele, myelo-cystocele* and *myelo-meningocele* types).

In other instances development is arrested at the stage of the neural groove, so that skin, muscles, spines, laminæ and the posterior part of the spinal cord are absent over a certain area. This is the condition of *myelocele,* and it is incompatible with post-natal existence.

Abnormalities may be encountered in the *articulation between the fifth lumbar vertebra and the first piece of the sacrum.* The normal arrangement is one in which the articular processes lie in the coronal plane, the sacral articular facets being directed backwards. Recent investigations have shown that in an appreciable percentage of subjects the articular processes occupy the sagittal plane, with the result that the facets are directed medially. Such a condition results in a lessening of stability at the lumbo-sacral joint, and, in respect of this, leads to various postural disturbances in the lumbar part of the vertebral column and in the sacro-iliac joints.

The transverse processes of the fifth lumbar vertebra are sometimes abnormal in length and in shape. On one or both sides the process may pass downwards to articulate with the sacrum (*sacralisation*), or it may extend laterally to impinge upon or to articulate with the posterior portion of the ilium. These irregularities may be responsible for pain, either local or referred, along the distribution of the fifth lumbar nerve, while in some cases they appear to cause a lateral curvature of the lumbar part of the vertebral column.

It is sometimes difficult to decide from a radiograph of the pelvis, taken in the strictly supine position, whether or not the transverse process of the fifth lumbar vertebra does actually articulate with the base of the sacrum. The difficulty is due to the circumstance that in the supine position of the patient — the one usually adopted—the shadow of the posterior portion of the iliac crest is superimposed on the transverse process and the base of the sacrum just where they would join if such an articulation existed. In order to throw the shadow of the ilium completely free of the transverse process of the fifth lumbar it is necessary to tilt the pelvis towards the opposite side; the radiographer can then say definitely whether or not that process is free from the sacrum or articulates with it.

The angle of the lumbo-sacral junction in a well-developed adult is 120°. Minor variations are common and are of no significance, but a gross abnormality may lead to pain and to secondary disabilities in related parts.

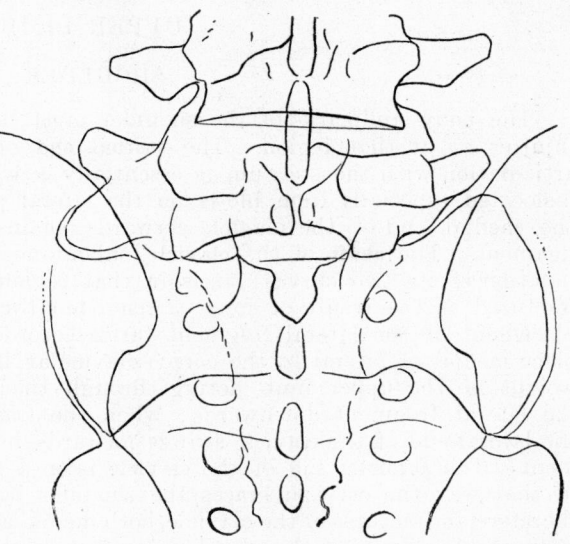

FIG. 1157.—OUTLINE DRAWING OF RADIOGRAPH OF LUMBO-SACRAL AND SACRO-ILIAC REGIONS.

On the left side there is an incomplete "sacralisation" of the transverse process of the 5th lumbar vertebra with the development of a bursa at the point of contact.

When the angle is notably increased so that the sacrum and the lumbar vertebræ are in relative alignment, or when the angle is notably diminished as the result of backward tilting of the sacrum, an additional strain is thrown upon the sacro-iliac joints, and in a certain number of cases the increased stress results in local or referred pain.

A forward displacement of the fifth lumbar vertebra upon the sacrum is sometimes encountered, and this condition is given the name of *spondylolisthesis*. At one time it was thought that the deformity was peculiar to the female, but more recently a number of examples of this error have been recorded in the male. It is apt to be associated with local pain, limitation of flexion in the lumbar region, an alteration in gait, and, if the displacement is ex-centric, pressure on the fifth lumbar nerve of the side towards which the displacement is directed may lead to weakness of the muscles supplied by the nerve. The significance of spondylolisthesis is recognised by the obstetrician, because a severe deformity of this character may interfere with parturition.

In addition to these local abnormalities, the orthopædic surgeon recognises *two general types of bodily habitus* associated with structural variation of the vertebral column— the narrow-backed, long-waisted, slender figure, and the broad-backed, thick-set, heavy one. The former, sometimes classed as the *visceroptotic type* because ptosis of the abdominal viscera is such a frequent accompaniment, is associated with a slender and unduly mobile vertebral column, and, on account of the increased mobility, postural errors are apt to arise. The lumbar part of the column loses its natural lordosis, there is increased backward displacement of the sacrum, the thoracic part of the column becomes unduly straight, while the lordotic curve of the cervical region is increased. The effect of these changes is to throw an undue strain upon the sacro-iliac joints, so that the ligaments which support them are stretched and weakened, and minor degrees of displacement occur at these joints.

In the second type, the back is thick-set and broad, and the movements of the vertebral column tend to be more restricted than is normal. The lumbar vertebræ are broad and massive, the curve of the lumbar lordosis is reduced, and the longitudinal axis of the sacrum tends to come into line with the lumbar bodies. An undue strain is thrown upon the lumbo-sacral joint, and symptoms of this may become apparent. In addition, there is limitation of flexion of the lower portion of the body, so that this movement takes place at the hip joints rather than in the vertebral area; in the same way the range of lateral movement of the lumbar part of the column is lessened.

UPPER LIMB

SHOULDER

The bony landmarks of the shoulder must be systematically examined in all injuries about that region. The **sternal end** of the **clavicle** is prominent; its articulation with the sternum is essentially a weak joint, and it is liable to be dislocated, especially from blows on the lateral part of the shoulder which drive the medial end of the clavicle forwards against the anterior sterno-clavicular ligament. The **shaft** of the **clavicle**, subcutaneous throughout, is weakest at the junction of its two curves; it is in that region that the bone is so frequently fractured as the result of force transmitted through it to the trunk. The displacement of the lateral fragment varies according to whether the break takes place medial or lateral to the coraco-clavicular ligament; in the former case the weight of the upper limb, acting through the coraco-clavicular ligament, pulls the lateral fragment downwards; when the fracture is lateral to the ligament, the lateral end of the clavicle swings forwards, but there is no downward displacement. The **acromial end** of the **clavicle** is on a plane behind its sternal end, and in that way the clavicle braces the shoulder backwards away from the thorax; therefore, in fractures of the clavicle, both medial and lateral to the coraco-clavicular ligament, the point of the shoulder swings forwards and medially. The groove that corresponds to the **acromio-clavicular joint** runs in the sagittal direction, and can be felt 1¼ in. medial to the lateral border of the acromion, immediately lateral to a slight prominence made by the acromial end of the clavicle. When the acromio-clavicular joint is dislocated the clavicle almost invariably overrides the acromion, and the summit of the shoulder presents a conical appearance.

The **tip** of the **acromion** looks directly forwards, and is a finger's-breadth lateral to and a little in front of the acromial end of the clavicle. The **lateral border** of the **acromion** can readily be followed to its junction with the spine of the scapula, and the spine can be followed to its root, which is at the level of the third thoracic spine. The **medial border** of the **acromion** and the clavicle meet at an angle into which the point of the finger can be pressed. The **upper angle** of the **scapula**, covered by the trapezius and the supraspinatus muscles, is too deeply placed to be palpated distinctly. The **inferior angle** and the **medial border**, from the root of the spine downwards, form visible prominences which are readily felt; the inferior angle overlies the seventh intercostal space at the level of the seventh thoracic spine; and the medial border is a little medial to the angles of the ribs.

To elicit crepitus in a transverse fracture of the scapula below the spine, the surgeon stands behind the patient and grasps the upper fragment by placing the forefinger on the coracoid and the thumb on the spine, while, with the other hand, he grasps the inferior angle; the two fragments are then moved the one upon the other.

The **tip** of the **coracoid process** may be felt by the finger pressed firmly on the anterior border of the deltoid at a point one inch below the junction of the middle and lateral thirds of the clavicle. Medial to the coracoid there is a triangular depression which corresponds to the upper end of the interval between the pectoralis major and deltoid muscles. Behind that triangular depression are the termination of the cephalic vein, a lymph gland, the first part of the axillary vessels, and the cords of the brachial plexus. By pressing firmly in that situation one can feel the pulsations of the **axillary artery**, and further pressure arrests the circulation in the artery by compressing the vessel against the second rib. The *first part* of the axillary artery may be cut down upon either by a transverse incision through the clavicular origin of the pectoralis major, or by a longitudinal incision in the interval between the pectoralis major and the deltoid. The **axillary vein** lies in front of the artery as well as to its thoracic side—thus adding to the difficulty of exposing the artery. In fractures of the middle third of the clavicle the subclavian vessels are protected by the subclavius muscle.

The **upper end** of the **humerus**, covered by the deltoid, gives rotundity to the shoulder. The **greater tuberosity** projects beyond the acromion, and is the most lateral bony landmark of the shoulder. When the head of the bone is dislocated, the lateral border of the acromion then becomes the most lateral bony landmark, and the shoulder presents a square contour. The **lesser tuberosity**, small but conical, can be felt through the deltoid. Pointing directly forwards, it is one inch lateral to the tip of the coracoid process and a little below its level. In examining the upper end of the humerus for fracture, grasp the tuberosities between the finger and thumb of one hand, and rotate the flexed elbow with the other hand. The **head** of the **humerus** has the same direction as the medial epicondyle; its lower part can be palpated through the axilla, the arm being meanwhile abducted to bring the head in contact with the lower part of the capsule. It is through that—the weakest part of the capsule—that the head is driven in the common varieties of dislocation of the shoulder, viz., those due to forcible abduction. The **proximal epiphysis** of the humerus includes the head and both tuberosities (Pl. IX, Fig. 1). The capsule is attached mainly to the epiphysis; in children, therefore, separation of the proximal epiphysis takes the place of dislocation. Disease in the upper part of the shaft does not necessarily involve the cavity of the joint. The **bicipital groove** [sulcus intertubercularis] is immediately lateral to the lesser tuberosity; it may be mapped out on the surface by a line, two inches in length, drawn downwards along the axis of the humerus from the tip of the acromion. When there is *effusion into the joint*, the arm becomes slightly abducted, and there is fullness in front, along the line of the long tendon of the biceps. With the elbow at the side, the lower part of the capsule of the shoulder-joint is loose and folded upon itself to form a dependent pocket; if, after an injury, the arm is retained too long in that position, the patient may be unable to abduct the arm, in consequence of the formation of adhesions in and around the pouch.

Access to the joint and to the upper end of the humerus, sufficient for excision of the joint or exploration of the bone, is obtained by an incision which begins immediately lateral to the coracoid process and follows the outline of the anterior border of the deltoid muscle downwards and laterally; a short transverse incision parallel to the clavicle from the upper end of the oblique incision may be added. That addition permits the lateral displacement of the anterior half of the deltoid muscle.

To evacuate pus from the shoulder joint, cut into the skin, fascia, deltoid, subscapularis and capsule by an incision that passes vertically downwards from the tip of the acromion.

AXILLA

The **anterior fold** of the **axilla**, formed by the lower border of the pectoralis major, extends from the fifth rib to the middle of the anterior border of the deltoid. With the arm abducted, the interval between the sternal and clavicular fibres of the pectoralis major is indicated by a slight groove that extends downwards and laterally from the sternal end of the clavicle. The sternal fibres, along with the pectoralis minor, are removed in a complete operation for malignant disease of the breast, the pectoral branches of the acromio-thoracic artery being secured as they cross the interval between the sternal and clavicular portions of the greater pectoral. The **posterior fold** of the **axilla**, formed by the latissimus dorsi and the teres major muscles, is on a lower level than the anterior fold, and leaves the chest a little in front of the inferior angle of the scapula. Between the two folds, and running in the long axis of the limb, from the axilla to the middle of the upper arm, is the prominence of the **coraco-brachialis muscle**. The pulsations of the **third part of the axillary artery** may be felt in the furrow immediately behind that prominence.

Female Mammary Gland.—The glandular tissue is arranged to form a central portion or *body*, and a peripheral portion made up of branching processes which radiate into the surrounding fat and become continuous ultimately with the fibrous septa of the subcutaneous fatty tissue. The gland has, therefore, no distinct capsule. In the young adult nullipara, the body is compact and well defined, and contains little intramammary fat, and the peripheral processes are relatively small. In the multipara, the body contains more fat, and the peripheral processes extend more widely into the surrounding fat.

The arrangement and extent of the parenchyma can be well seen when the gland is treated with a *5 per cent. solution of nitric acid.* If slices of the fresh organ are placed in that solution for a few minutes and then washed under running water, the albumin of the epithelial cells of the parenchyma is coagulated, while the fibrous tissue is made translucent and slightly gelatinous. The *ultimate lobules* of the *parenchyma* then appear as little (1 to 2 mm.), dull, opaque, white, sago-like bodies, arranged in grape-like clusters around the finer branches of the ducts.

The parenchyma is prolonged into the peripheral processes, and into the loose retromammary areolar tissue and pectoral fascia. The gland has therefore

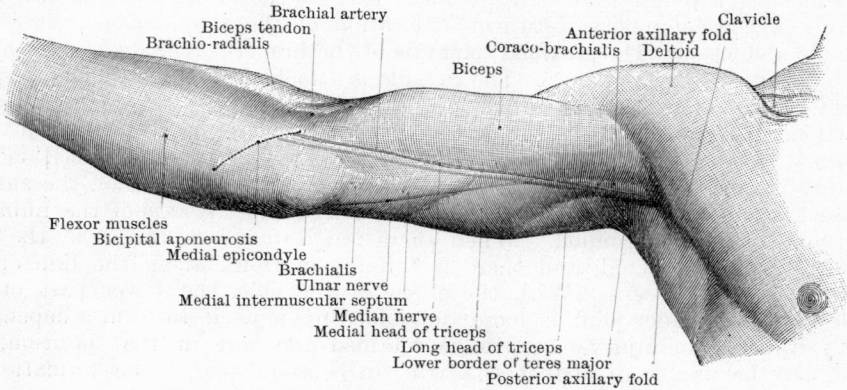

Brachial artery
Biceps tendon
Brachio-radialis
Coraco-brachialis
Biceps
Clavicle
Anterior axillary fold
Deltoid

Flexor muscles
Bicipital aponeurosis
Medial epicondyle
Brachialis
Ulnar nerve
Medial intermuscular septum
Median nerve
Medial head of triceps
Long head of triceps
Lower border of teres major
Posterior axillary fold

Fig. 1158.—Axilla and Medial Side of Arm and Elbow.

a wide range. Vertically, it extends from the second rib to the sixth costal cartilage at the angle where it begins to ascend towards the sternum ; horizontally, from a little medial to the edge of the sternum, opposite the fourth rib, to the fifth rib in the mid-axillary line. The *medial hemisphere* of the gland rests almost entirely on the pectoralis major ; at its lowest part it slightly overlies the upper part of the aponeurosis covering the rectus abdominis muscle. The *superior quadrant* of the *lateral hemisphere* rests on the greater pectoral, on the edge of the lesser pectoral, and to a slight extent on the serratus anterior ; on the serratus, however, it extends upwards into the axilla as high as the third rib, where it comes into relation with the *pectoral* group of axillary lymph glands. The *remainder of the lateral hemisphere* rests almost entirely on the serratus anterior, except the lowest part, which overlaps the digitations of the external oblique arising from the fifth and sixth ribs. It follows, therefore, that *fully one-third of the whole gland lies below and lateral to the axillary border of the pectoralis major muscle.* The surgeon must cut beyond the limits given if he wishes to remove the whole of the mammary tissue.

The axillary fascia resists the spontaneous rupture of an axillary abscess, which, therefore, tends to spread upwards under cover of the pectorals, and towards the root of the neck. To open the abscess, make the incision on the medial wall of the axilla, behind and parallel to the lateral thoracic artery, which runs under cover of the anterior fold.

The **axillary lymph glands** vary greatly in size and number ; many are no larger than a pin's head. In women some of them undergo an adipose functional involution whereby they come to resemble fat lobules. In health, one or two glands can usually be felt by the fingers thrust upwards and medially behind the anterior fold, the arm being abducted—but only slightly, so as not to stretch the axillary fascia. The *central group*, embedded in the fat immediately deep to the axillary fascia, become inflamed in poisoned wounds of the upper limb. The same group, along with the *pectoral group* (related to the medial wall of the axilla, at the infero-lateral border of the pectoralis minor), are usually the first to become diseased in malignant affections of the breast. When the disease is more advanced the *posterior* (subscapular) and the *apical* (subclavicular) groups are generally affected as well; and in a considerable number of cases diseased glands are found in the *retro-pectoral fascia*, *i.e.* between the pectoralis major and minor and, above the minor muscle, on the first intercostal space in relation to the superior thoracic artery. In operating for malignant disease of the breast, the surgeon removes, in addition to the whole gland and the greater part of the skin over it, both pectoral muscles (with the exception of the clavicular fibres of the pectoralis major), all the axillary lymph glands, and, as far as possible, all the fat and fascia, including the sheath of the axillary vein. It must be remembered that the distal part of the axillary vein lies immediately under cover of the deep fascia of the lateral wall of the axilla; as the medial wall is cleaned the nerve to the serratus anterior must not be injured; and as the posterior group of lymph glands are removed the nerve to the latissimus dorsi must be avoided, as it is very important that the action of the latissimus dorsi should be retained when the pectoral muscles have been removed.

UPPER ARM

The anterior and posterior borders of the **deltoid** may be traced from the shoulder girdle to the insertion of the muscle. The surface relations of the anterior border have been referred to already; the posterior border forms a well-marked and important landmark as it crosses the angle between the lateral margin of the scapula and the upper part of the shaft of the humerus. By making an incision along that part of the posterior border of the deltoid, and pulling the edge of the muscle upwards and laterally, the surgeon exposes the **surgical neck** of the **humerus**, and the quadrilateral opening in the posterior wall of the axilla that transmits the **posterior circumflex artery** of the humerus and the **circumflex nerve**; a little lower down is the **radial nerve**. The **coraco-brachialis**, the guide to the upper half of the brachial artery, forms a prominence that occupies the upper half of the *medial bicipital furrow*. Traced downwards the medial bicipital furrow widens out into an elongated triangle. That triangle becomes continuous, distally, with the medial part of the cubital fossa, and is limited posteriorly by the medial intermuscular septum, which may be felt as a cord-like band extending upwards from the medial epicondyle; the floor of the space is formed by the medial part of the brachialis. Within the triangle are the following important structures, enumerated from the lateral to the medial side, viz.: the **brachial artery**, the **median nerve**, the **distal part of the basilic vein**, the **medial cutaneous nerve of the forearm**, and the **supratrochlear lymph glands**, two or three in number. Extending upwards from the lateral epicondyle to the insertion of the deltoid is the lateral intermuscular septum, which is pierced at the junction of its upper and middle thirds by the **radial nerve**. Between the lateral intermuscular septum and the lateral edge of the biceps there is an ill-defined groove called the *lateral bicipital furrow*, the floor of which is formed by a strip of the brachialis, and, nearer the elbow, by the brachio-radialis and extensor carpi radialis longus.

The posterior compartment of the arm is occupied by the **triceps**, the *long head* of which can be traced upwards to the lateral margin of the scapula, in front of the posterior border of the deltoid and behind the posterior fold of the axilla. The *lateral head* of the triceps, after emerging from under cover of the distal part of the posterior border of the deltoid, is continued obliquely along the lateral side of the upper arm as a well-marked muscular elevation. Above the olecranon is the strap-like tendon of insertion of the triceps, which, when the elbow is fully flexed, forms an admirable posterior splint in fractures immediately above the epicondyles of the humerus.

The **brachial artery**—slightly overlapped in the upper half of the upper arm by the coraco-brachialis and in the lower half by the biceps—can be felt pulsating throughout the whole length of the anterior part of the medial bicipital furrow. To mark the course of the vessel on the surface draw a line from the medial border of the coraco-brachialis, at the level of the posterior fold of the axilla, to a point (opposite the neck of the radius) half an inch below the middle of the bend of the elbow. When the vessel is ligatured the edges of the coraco-brachialis and biceps muscles, together with the median nerve, furnish valuable guides to the artery, the mobility of which is often a source of trouble in the operation.

The **basilic vein** is superficial to the deep fascia in the lower third of the upper arm, and is visible in the medial epicondylar triangle and the lower part of the medial bicipital groove. The **cephalic vein** ascends in the superficial fascia over the lateral surface of the biceps to reach the interval between the deltoid and pectoralis major.

The surface guide for the **median nerve** is the same as that for the brachial artery. The **ulnar nerve** is indicated superficially by a line drawn from the lateral wall of the axilla, immediately behind the prominence of the coraco-

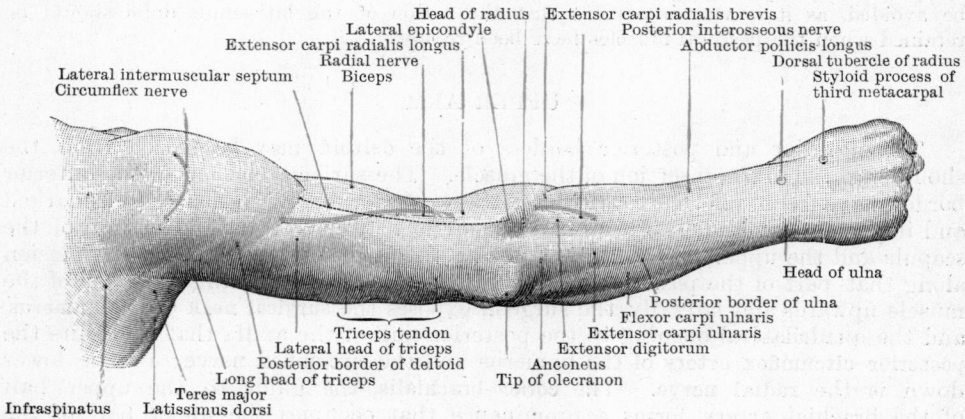

FIG. 1159.—BACK OF UPPER LIMB.

brachialis, to the back of the medial epicondyle; in the proximal half of the upper arm the nerve lies close behind the brachial artery under cover of the basilic vein; in the distal half it lies a little behind the medial intermuscular septum, partially embedded in the fibres of the medial head of the triceps. To mark the course of the **radial nerve**, first mark the point where it pierces the lateral intermuscular septum, viz., the junction of the upper and middle thirds of a line drawn from the insertion of the deltoid to the lateral epicondyle; from that point draw a line obliquely downwards and forwards to the front of the lateral epicondyle, and then onwards to the lateral side of the lower end of the radius. To map out the nerve as it lies in its spiral groove on the humerus, draw a line from the same point obliquely upwards across the prominence of the lateral head of the triceps to the junction of the posterior fold of the axilla with the arm. In fractures of the humerus in the neighbourhood of the insertion of the deltoid, the nerve is not infrequently lacerated, or so involved in the callus as to produce the condition known as "*drop-wrist*"—the result of paralysis of the extensor muscles of the forearm. To cut down on the nerve, begin the incision a little below the point where it pierces the lateral intermuscular septum, and carry it obliquely upwards and slightly backwards through the lateral head of the triceps.

The **shaft** of the **humerus**, nowhere subcutaneous, is most readily palpated in the region of the insertion of the deltoid, upwards along the lateral head of the triceps, and downwards behind the lateral supracondylar ridge. The **surgical neck** is the portion that intervenes between the tuberosities and the attachments of the muscles inserted into the lips and floor of the bicipital groove; it is related to the lateral wall of the axilla, and is on a level with the junction of the upper and middle thirds of the deltoid. The circumflex vessels and nerve are at the same level.

The shaft may be cut down upon with least injury to soft parts :—(1) In its *upper third, in front*, by an incision extending downwards through the anterior fibres of the deltoid, parallel to the bicipital groove and a little lateral to it ; the sheath of the biceps will thus be avoided, and the anterior circumflex artery will be the only vessel divided. (2) In the *upper third, behind*, by an incision through the posterior fibres of the deltoid, the bone being reached immediately lateral to the origin of the lateral head of the triceps, and the radial nerve thus avoided ; the circumflex vessels and nerve will be exposed at the upper part of the wound. (3) In the *lower third*, by an incision extending upwards from the back of the lateral epicondyle a little to the medial side of the lateral intermuscular septum.

The entire humerus, together with the shoulder joint and the elbow joint, may be exposed by an incision which begins at a point immediately lateral to the coracoid process and then follows the cephalic vein to the bend of the elbow. The incision is continued into the upper third of the forearm. Exposure of the upper third of the humerus and the shoulder joint is achieved by lateral displacement of the deltoid ; to get at the middle and lower thirds of the humerus split the brachialis muscle, a finger's-breadth lateral to the biceps. (Henry.)

ELBOW

In injuries about the elbow the diagnosis rests mainly upon the relative positions of the bony points, which are, therefore, of great importance. The **epicondyles** of the humerus are both subcutaneous and on the same level, the medial being the more prominent (Pl. XXIII). In the extended position of the elbow the tip of the **olecranon** is on a level with a line joining the epicondyles ; when the forearm is flexed the olecranon descends (Pl. XXIV), and when full flexion is reached it lies an inch distal to the epicondyles, and in a plane in front of the posterior surface of the lower end of the humerus. The **head** of the **radius**, which lies nearly an inch below the lateral epicondyle, is felt best from behind ; place the thumb on it while the semi-flexed forearm is being alternately pronated and supinated. On the lateral part of the back of the extended elbow there is a distinct dimple which overlies the **radio-humeral joint** ; that dimple, along with the hollows on each side of the olecranon, becomes effaced by synovial thickenings and effusions into the joint. The **coronoid process** is too deep to be felt distinctly. The **distal epiphysis** of the humerus includes the articular portion and the lateral epicondyle ; it is therefore almost entirely intracapsular, and, because of that, foci of disease in its neighbourhood soon invade the cavity of the joint. The medial epicondyle ossifies as a separate epiphysis which unites with the distal end of the diaphysis (Pls. VI, VII). In interpreting radiographs of the elbow of children of six years of age and upwards, take care not to mistake the centre of ossification in the lateral portion of the distal epiphysis of the humerus for a fracture (Pl. VI). In the commonest dislocation of the elbow, viz., with backward displacement of both bones of the forearm, the normal relative position of the bony points is lost, whereas in a transverse fracture above the epicondyles the normal relations are maintained. In the child the head of the radius is relatively smaller than in the adult, and is less firmly kept in position by the annular ligament ; it is liable therefore to be partially dislocated—giving rise to the condition known as "*pulled elbow.*"

To evacuate pus from the elbow joint make a vertical incision over the back of the joint, immediately lateral to the olecranon.

The **median vein** is seen to bifurcate into the median basilic and median cephalic veins half an inch below the middle of the bend of the elbow ; opposite the same point, but behind the deep fascia, is the **bifurcation** of the **brachial artery**. The **median basilic** and **median cephalic** veins diverge as they ascend one on each side of the biceps tendon ; the larger of the two veins, viz., the median basilic, is usually selected for the operations of venesection and transfusion. In the absence of a median vein (as in Figs. 1046, 1161), a **median cubital vein**, passing from the cephalic to the basilic vein, takes the place of the median basilic vein. When the elbow is flexed, the **biceps tendon** can be traced vertically through the middle of the cubital fossa almost to its insertion.　Passing downwards and medially from the medial edge of the tendon is the **bicipital aponeurosis** [lacertus fibrosus], which separates the median cubital vein from the brachial artery.　If the finger-tip is insinuated behind the medial edge of the aponeurosis it will rest on and feel the pulsations of the brachial artery.　The **median nerve** descends through the space a little medial to the brachial artery.　The **radial nerve** descends in front of the capitulum of the

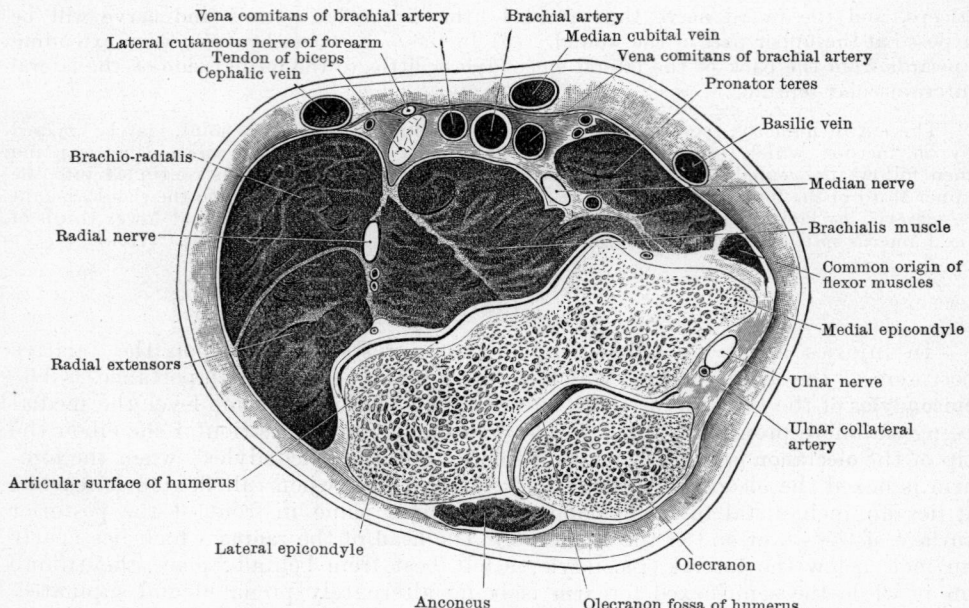

FIG. 1160.—TRANSVERSE SECTION THROUGH THE BEND OF THE ELBOW.

humerus under cover of the brachio-radialis.　The **ulnar nerve** can be rolled beneath the finger on the back of the medial epicondyle; its position renders it liable to injury in severe fractures about the elbow; and when the joint is excised care must be taken not to injure the nerve.

FOREARM AND HAND

The upper half of the **radius** is deeply placed, but the lower half is easily palpated.　The anterior border of its lower end is felt as a prominent transverse ridge about an inch above the thenar eminence; immediately below the ridge is the **wrist joint** (radio-carpal).　The **tip** of the **styloid process**—nearly half an inch lower than that of the ulna—is deeply placed at the lateral side of the wrist, in the hollow between the extensor tendons of the first and second phalanges of the thumb.　On the middle of the posterior surface of the lower end of the radius is the **dorsal tubercle of the radius**, which intervenes between the extensor pollicis longus and the short radial extensor of the wrist; the tubercle can be distinctly felt, and may be taken as a guide to the upper end of Lister's dorso-radial incision for excision of the wrist.　The **posterior border of the ulna** is subcutaneous throughout, and can be felt along the medial side of the extensor carpi ulnaris. Above the wrist, on the ulnar side of the back of the limb, when the forearm is prone, there is the well-marked rounded prominence of the **head** of the **ulna**, and in front of it the **styloid process**—on the ulnar side of the limb; the deep groove between the two is occupied by the tendon of the extensor carpi ulnaris.

The **carpal bones** are built up so as to form an arch, converted by the **flexor retinaculum** [lig. carpi transversum] into a tunnel for the transmission of the flexor tendons. At each end of the arch the two bony points to which the retinaculum is attached furnish important landmarks. Those bony points are: *laterally*, the tubercle of the scaphoid and the crest of the trapezium; *medially*, the pisiform and the hamulus of the os hamatum. The **tubercle** of the **scaphoid** [os naviculare] is felt immediately above the thenar eminence, close by the radial side of the flexor carpi radialis; half an inch below the tubercle is the **crest of the trapezium** [os multangulum majus], felt deeply in the medial part of the thenar eminence. At the upper end of the hypothenar eminence, and crossed by the crease which separates the forearm from the hand, is the **pisiform bone**, above which is the tendon of the flexor carpi ulnaris, descending to be inserted into it. The **hamulus of the os hamatum** is felt deeply in the radial part of the hypothenar eminence, and a full finger's-breadth below and lateral to the pisiform.

The bases of the **first**, **third**, and **fifth metacarpals**, all of which can be readily identified on the back, furnish a sufficient guide to the line of the carpo-metacarpal joints. At the base of the **third metacarpal** there is a tubercle, called its *styloid process*, which can be felt projecting upwards from its dorsal surface at a point $1\frac{3}{4}$ in. vertically below the dorsal tubercle of the radius. The metacarpal styloid process marks the insertion of the extensor carpi radialis brevis —the favourite site for the development of a "*ganglion*,"

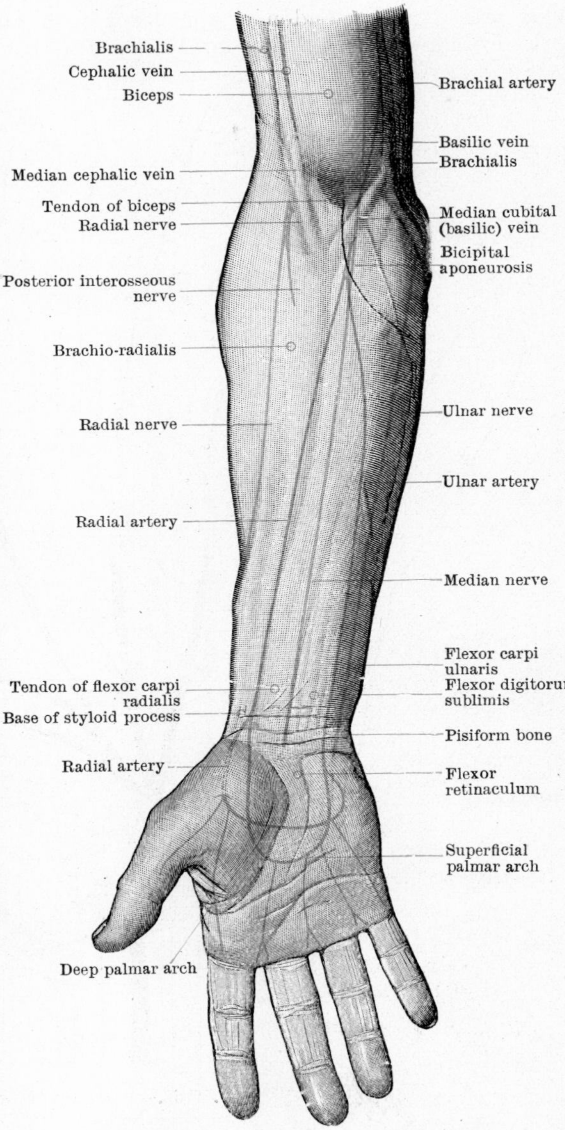

FIG. 1161.—FRONT OF ELBOW, FOREARM, AND HAND.

which in many cases can be ruptured by sudden firm pressure against the tubercle. Anteriorly, the **carpo-metacarpal joints** correspond to the distal border of the flexor retinaculum [lig. carpi transversum].

The **first row of knuckles** are the heads of the metacarpal bones. Anteriorly, the **metacarpo-phalangeal joints** are $\frac{3}{4}$ in. above the edge of the web of the fingers; posteriorly, the joints are immediately distal to the knuckles. A well-marked crease crosses obliquely over the front of the metacarpo-phalangeal joint of the thumb. The first and the terminal **inter-phalangeal joints** are opposite the most distal of the various creases that overlie the joints.

The most important *muscular* landmarks on the front of the forearm are the brachio-radialis, the flexor carpi radialis, and the pronator teres. The **brachio-radialis** is thrown into prominence when it flexes the semi-prone forearm against resistance. At the junction of the upper and middle thirds of the forearm the **pronator teres** passes under cover of the brachio-radialis; between the two is the radial artery. The tendon of the **flexor carpi radialis** forms a prominent landmark descending along the middle of the front of the forearm towards the

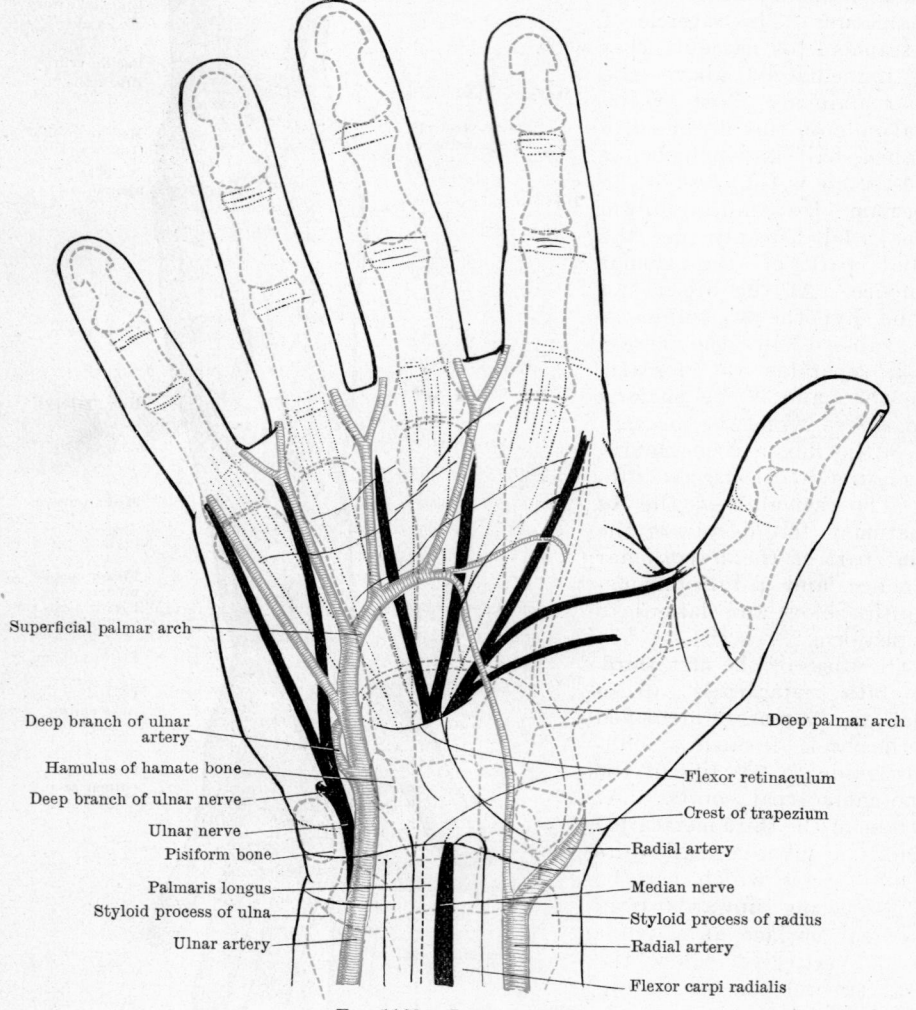

Superficial palmar arch

Deep branch of ulnar artery

Hamulus of hamate bone

Deep branch of ulnar nerve

Ulnar nerve

Pisiform bone

Palmaris longus

Styloid process of ulna

Ulnar artery

Deep palmar arch

Flexor retinaculum

Crest of trapezium

Radial artery

Median nerve

Styloid process of radius

Radial artery

Flexor carpi radialis

FIG. 1162.—PALM OF HAND.

tubercle of the scaphoid; the tendon of the **palmaris longus**, when present, is seen at its medial side.

On the back of the forearm the intermuscular septum between the radial extensors of the wrist and the extensors of the fingers corresponds to the proximal part of a line drawn from the lateral epicondyle of the humerus to the dorsal tubercle of the radius. The **posterior interosseous nerve**, at the point at which it emerges from the supinator muscle, will be found at the bottom of that septum, 2 in. below the head of the radius; below that point the septum is the best line along which to cut down upon the posterior surface of the radius. Winding across the lower third of the back of the forearm there is an oblique prominence caused by the **abductor pollicis longus** and **extensor pollicis brevis muscles.**

If the front of the hand, the fingers being extended, is inspected, it is apparent that the palm may be subdivided into three areas—(1) the thenar eminence formed by the small muscles of the thumb, (2) the hypothenar eminence in association with the muscles of the little finger, (3) the hollow of the palm. In relation to those areas, there are certain spaces filled with areolar tissue which are of importance in connection with acute pyogenic infections—they are the thenar space and the middle palmar space.

The thenar space lies to the ulnar or medial side of the flexor longus pollicis tendon. Its anterior boundaries are the short muscles of the thumb, the over-

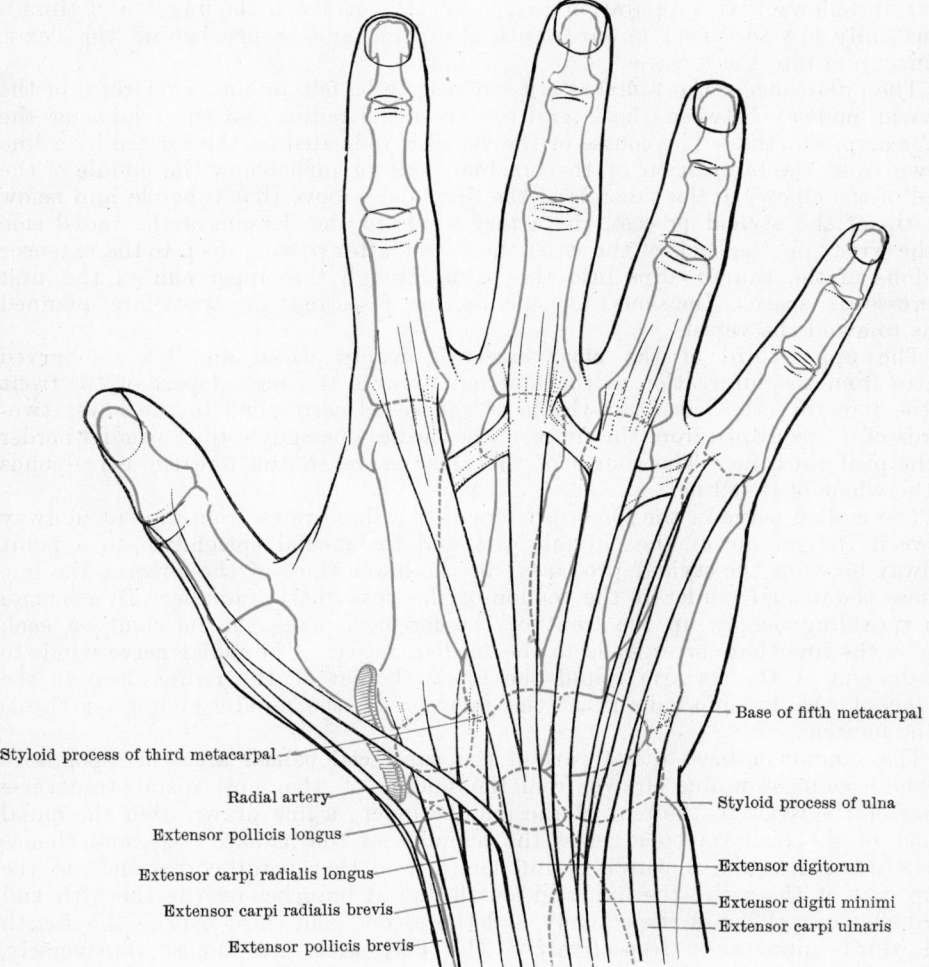

Base of fifth metacarpal

Styloid process of third metacarpal

Radial artery

Extensor pollicis longus

Extensor carpi radialis longus

Extensor carpi radialis brevis

Extensor pollicis brevis

Styloid process of ulna

Extensor digitorum

Extensor digiti minimi

Extensor carpi ulnaris

Fig. 1163.—Back of Hand.

lying deep fascia, the flexor tendons of the index finger, and the first two lumbrical muscles; posteriorly lie the transverse and oblique heads of the adductor pollicis, and a portion of the first dorsal interosseous muscle. It is separated from the middle palmar space by a fibrous septum, while the tendon of the flexor longus pollicis lies to its radial side. Deep to the flexor tendons of the third, fourth, and fifth digits is the middle palmar space — bounded posteriorly by the interosseous muscles and metacarpal bones, medially by the hypothenar muscles, and laterally by a fibrous septum which extends from the fascia behind the deep flexor tendon to the origin of the transverse head of the adductor. No definite space exists in the hypothenar region.

The synovial flexor sheaths of the palm and of the digits (Fig. 406, p. 484) are of surgical importance in consequence of their liability to suppurative inflammation. The **common flexor sheath** begins 1½ in. above the flexor retinaculum, and extends downwards behind it to a little beyond the middle of the palm. The **digital flexor sheaths** extend from the bases of the distal phalanges to the level of the distal transverse crease of the palm, opposite the necks of the metacarpal bones, *with the exception of the sheath of the little finger*, which is continuous with the common flexor sheath of the palm. The **sheath of the flexor pollicis longus** extends from the base of the terminal phalanx to a point about an inch above the retinaculum; it sometimes communicates with the common flexor sheath. From the anatomical arrangement it follows that suppuration in the sheaths of the little finger and thumb is specially apt to spread upwards into the palm, and thence behind the flexor retinaculum into the forearm.

The pulsations of the **radial artery** can readily be felt in the lower third of the forearm, midway between the lateral border of the radius and the tendon of the flexor carpi radialis. The course of the vessel is indicated on the surface by a line drawn from the bifurcation of the brachial (half an inch below the middle of the bend of the elbow) to the tubercle of the scaphoid; above that tubercle and below the tip of the styloid process, the artery winds to the dorsum of the radial side of the wrist; on the back of the wrist the vessel, after passing deep to the extensor tendons of the thumb, dips into the palm through the upper end of the first interosseous space. Incisions for opening or resecting the wrist are planned so as to avoid the vessel.

The upper third of the **ulnar artery** is deeply placed, and takes a curved course from the bifurcation of the brachial towards the medial part of the front of the forearm; the lower two-thirds of the vessel correspond to the lower two-thirds of a line drawn from the front of the medial epicondyle to the radial border of the pisiform bone. The course of the **ulnar nerve**, in the forearm, corresponds to the whole of that line.

The **median nerve** in the forearm is opposite a line drawn from a point midway between the middle of the cubital fossa and the medial epicondyle, to a point midway between the styloid processes; in the lower third of the forearm the line follows the medial border of the tendon of the flexor carpi radialis. To evacuate pus spreading deeply up the front of the forearm, make the incisions on each side of the line that corresponds to the median nerve. The **radial nerve** winds to the dorsum of the forearm round the lateral border of the radius deep to the tendon of the brachio-radialis, at the junction of the middle and lower thirds of the forearm.

The summit or most distal part of the **superficial palmar arch** corresponds to the mid-point of a line drawn from the middle of the most distal transverse crease of the wrist to the root of the middle finger; a line drawn from the radial border of the pisiform bone across the hamulus of the hamate bone, and thence in a curved direction downwards and laterally to that point, corresponds to the main part of the arch; the first and fourth digital branches overlie the fifth and third metacarpal bones respectively, and the second and third overlie the fourth and third interspaces respectively. The **deep arch** lies almost transversely, midway between the distal border of the flexor retinaculum and the superficial arch. The **radialis indicis** artery corresponds to the radial border of the index-finger.

The **ulnar nerve** and the commencement of its two divisions lie at the medial side of the superficial palmar arch; the pisiform and the hamulus are therefore the guides to the nerve. The **median nerve** emerges from behind the flexor retinaculum opposite the medial edge of the thenar eminence. It then divides into two portions—the lateral one provides (1) the three digital branches for the supply of the thumb and the radial side of the index finger, and (2) a muscular branch to the three muscles of the thenar eminence. The digital branches to the thumb run along the medial or distal edge of the eminence; incisions for the removal of foreign bodies may therefore be made into the thenar eminence with greater freedom than into the hypothenar eminence. But the muscular branch passes laterally $\frac{1}{4}$ in. below the flexor retinaculum, and must be avoided when an incision is made into the thenar space.

When pus forms in connexion with infections of the digits or hand it is encountered in one or other of the following situations : (1) the pulp of the digit ; (2) the synovial sheath of the flexor pollicis longus ; (3) the thenar space ; (4) the middle palmar space ; (5) the flexor sheaths of the middle three digits ; (6) the flexor synovial sheath of the little finger ; (7) the common synovial flexor sheath. For each situation there is an appropriate incision :—Infection of the pulp requires a horse-shoe incision which passes round the periphery of the finger pulp, so that distal end of the flap is free. The sheath of the flexor pollicis longus is drained by an incision which extends from the distal crease of the thumb to the ulnar side of the thenar eminence, finishing $1\frac{1}{2}$ in. below the distal wrist crease. The thenar space is entered through an incision made immediately dorsal to the edge of the web between the thumb and index finger ; the forceps passed through the incision deep to the muscles of the thumb enters the space. The middle palmar space is drained by an incision that

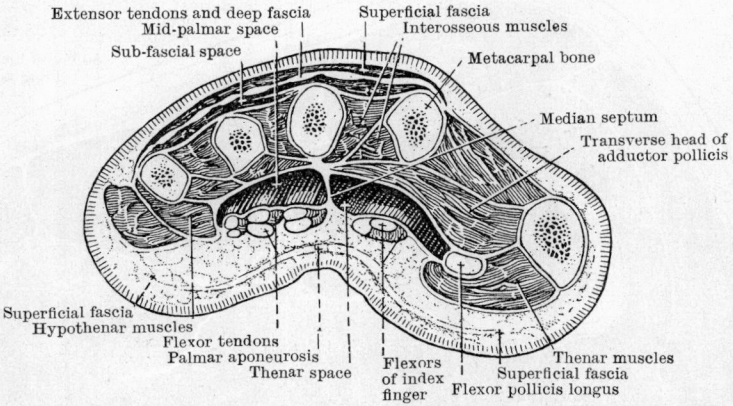

FIG. 1164.—TRANSVERSE SECTION THROUGH THE HAND TO SHOW THE THENAR AND PALMAR SPACES. (From Fifield's *Infections of the Hand*. By permission of H. K. Lewis & Co., Ltd.)

begins at the web between the middle and ring fingers and extends upwards in the inter-metacarpal space for a distance of $1\frac{1}{2}$ in.; and a similar incision may be carried upwards from the web between the ring and little fingers. To evacuate the sheath of the little finger, make an incision along the ulnar border of the palmar surface, in the line of the tendon of the little finger and slightly to its ulnar side ; from that incision the common sheath also can be explored by forceps pushed upwards, laterally and slightly backwards. A longitudinal incision between the median and ulnar nerves on the proximal side of the superficial palmar arch drains the common flexor sheath directly. To open the digital flexor sheaths, make incisions along the antero-lateral aspect of the fingers opposite the proximal and middle phalanges ; or the incision may be so made that it is in front of the digital vessels and nerves.

LOWER LIMB

GLUTEAL REGION

The region of the hip and buttock extends from the iliac crest to the fold of the buttock. The highest point of the **iliac crest**, situated a little behind its middle, is at the level of the fourth lumbar spine ; the **anterior superior iliac spine** is directed forwards, and belongs to the groin, which it limits laterally ; the **posterior superior spine**, situated in the floor of a dimple, is at the level of the second sacral spine and the middle of the **sacro-iliac joint**. Two and a half inches above and behind the anterior superior spine there is a prominence on the outer lip of the iliac crest termed the **tubercle of the crest** ; it is the most lateral part of the crest, and has been referred to already. A hand's-breadth below the tubercle of the crest is the

greater trochanter—the most lateral bony landmark of the hip. Its anterior and posterior borders are felt best between the fingers and thumb while the limb is slightly abducted to relax the ilio-tibial tract; and if the thigh is then rotated, it will be noted that the trochanter rotates round the segment of a circle the radius of which is the head and neck of the femur. *Nelaton's line,* drawn from the anterior superior spine to the most prominent part of the ischial tuberosity, crosses the hip at the level of the upper border of the greater trochanter; that line is employed to ascertain the presence or absence of upward displacement of the trochanter. John Chiene demonstrated the relative height of the trochanters by stretching two tapes across the front of the pelvis, one between the anterior superior spines, and the other between the antero-superior angles of the trochanters; the lower tape will converge towards the upper

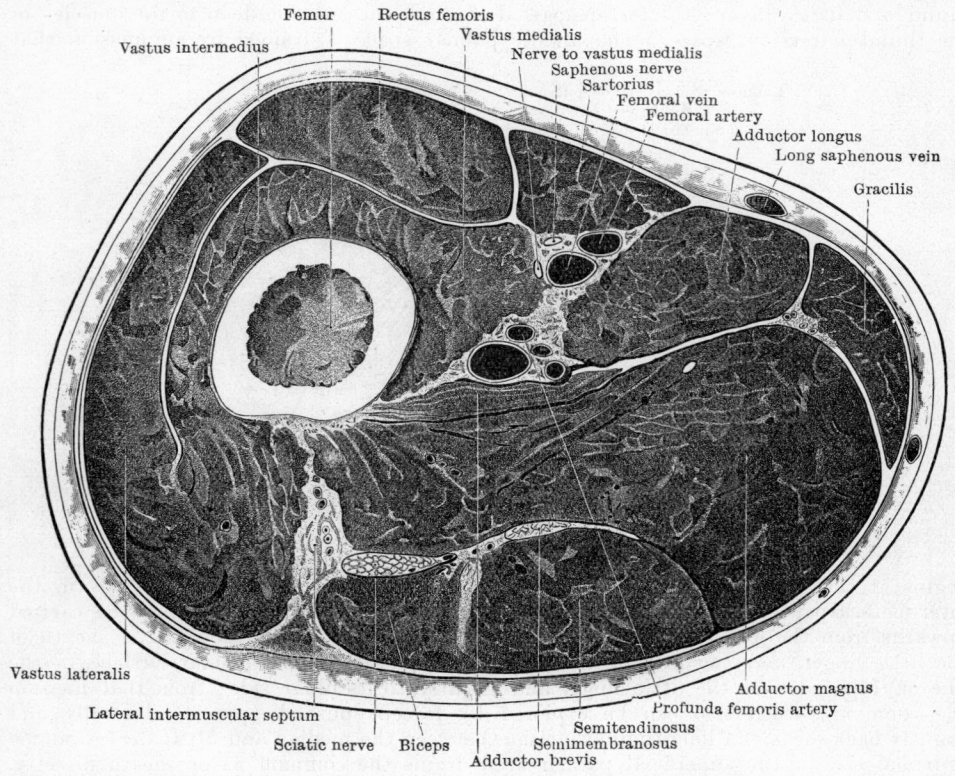

FIG. 1165.—SECTION THROUGH THIGH AT THE LEVEL OF THE UPPER PART OF SUB-SARTORIAL CANAL.

on the side of the upward displacement. The **ischial tuberosity**, in the erect posture, is overlapped by the lower border of the gluteus maximus; its most prominent part is felt a little above the medial part of the fold of the buttock. If the thigh is rotated medially, the **lesser trochanter** of the femur may be felt by deep palpation above the lateral end of that fold; it corresponds to the interval between the lower border of the quadratus femoris and the upper border of the adductor magnus, and therefore, also, to the level of the **medial circumflex artery** of the thigh.

The medial half of the **lower border** of the **gluteus maximus** lies a little above the **fold of the buttock,** crosses it about its middle, and is continued downwards and laterally to meet the upper end of the furrow of the lateral intermuscular septum, at the junction of the upper and middle thirds of the femur. The medial borders of the right and left great gluteal muscles are separated by the **natal cleft,** which extends upwards and backwards from the perineum to the level of the third sacral spine, where it opens out into the triangle on the back of the sacrum. Anteriorly the hip is limited by the prominence of the **tensor fasciæ latæ** muscle, which extends downwards and slightly backwards from the anterior part of the iliac crest to join the ilio-tibial tract below the root of the greater trochanter.

The **superior gluteal artery** reaches the gluteal region through the upper part of the greater sciatic foramen, opposite a point at the junction of the upper and middle thirds of a line drawn from the posterior superior iliac spine to the upper border of the greater trochanter. To expose the vessel make the incision along that line, which has the advantage that it is parallel to the fibres of the gluteus maximus, as well as parallel to the interval between the gluteus medius and piriformis muscles.

The **sciatic nerve** enters the gluteal region at a point opposite the junction of

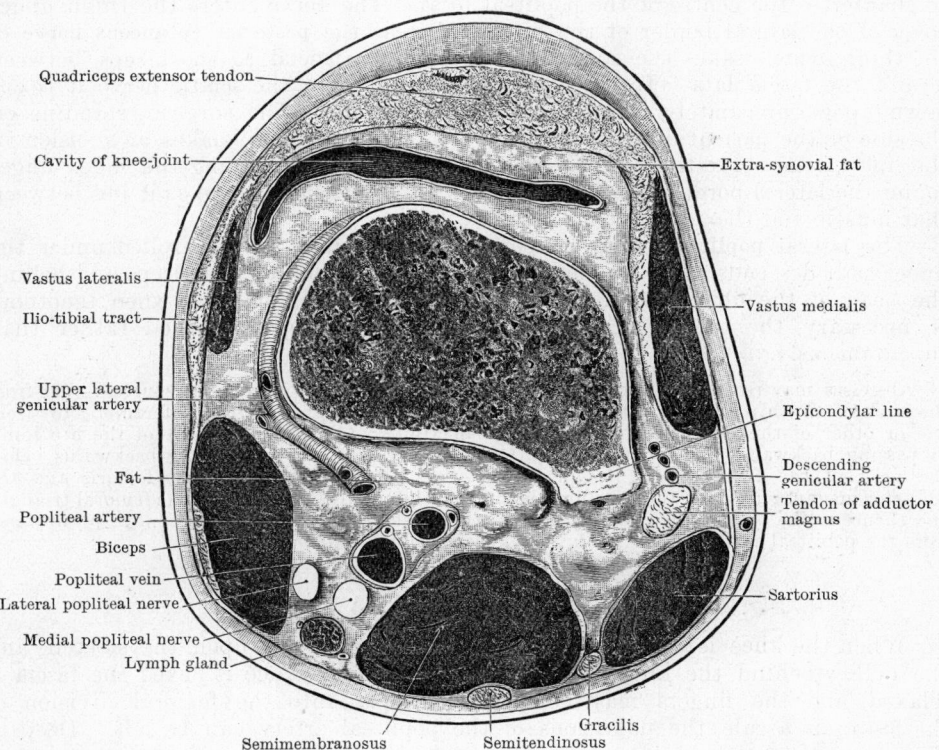

Quadriceps extensor tendon

Cavity of knee-joint

Extra-synovial fat

Vastus lateralis

Ilio-tibial tract

Vastus medialis

Upper lateral genicular artery

Epicondylar line

Fat

Descending genicular artery

Popliteal artery

Tendon of adductor magnus

Biceps

Popliteal vein

Lateral popliteal nerve

Sartorius

Medial popliteal nerve

Lymph gland

Semimembranosus   Semitendinosus   Gracilis

FIG. 1166.—SECTION THROUGH THE THIGH IMMEDIATELY ABOVE THE PATELLA.

the upper and middle thirds of a line drawn from the posterior superior iliac spine to the ischial tuberosity; from that point the nerve passes downwards and slightly laterally on the ischium to a point midway between the ischial tuberosity and the greater trochanter. The **spine of the ischium** and the **internal pudendal vessels** are opposite the junction of the lower and middle thirds of the same line. The vessels and nerves which enter the gluteal region through the greater sciatic foramen *below the piriformis* may be exposed through an incision below and parallel to that described for exposing the superior gluteal artery, viz., an incision which corresponds to the middle two-fourths of a line drawn from the upper end of the natal cleft to the root of the greater trochanter; the deep landmarks are the lower border of the piriformis and the root of the ischial spine.

BACK OF THIGH

The **hamstring muscles**, and especially the tendons of the biceps and semitendinosus, are thrown into prominence when one stands on tiptoe with the knee slightly flexed, or flexes the leg against resistance. When the hamstrings are thrown into action, the line of the **lateral intermuscular septum** of the thigh is indicated by a well-marked furrow that extends from the lower edge of the insertion of the gluteus maximus to the lateral side of the knee; behind that furrow is the **biceps femoris**, and in front of it is the **vastus lateralis**, covered by the ilio-tibial tract.   When the **shaft of the femur** has to be cut down upon, the incision that involves the least injury to the soft parts is one made along the whole length of that furrow.   The popliteal surface of the femur and deep-seated popliteal abscesses are reached most conveniently through the lower part of the same incision.

The course of the **sciatic nerve** corresponds to the upper half of a line drawn from a point midway between the ischial tuberosity and the greater trochanter to the centre of the popliteal fossa.   The nerve enters the thigh under cover of the lateral border of the biceps, whereas the **posterior cutaneous nerve** of the thigh, which takes the same line, descends superficial to the biceps, between it and the fascia lata.   In the operation of stretching the sciatic nerve it is cut down upon immediately below the gluteus maximus.   The surgeon, standing on the side of the patient opposite the limb to be operated on, makes an incision in the line of the nerve through the skin and fasciæ, and, sweeping the index-finger round the lateral border of the biceps, hooks up the sciatic nerve as it lies between that muscle and the adductor magnus.

The **lateral popliteal nerve** [n. peronæus communis] may be rolled under the finger as it descends along the medial side of the tendon of the biceps and behind the head of the fibula; so close is the nerve to the tendon that, when tenotomy is necessary, the tendon should be divided by the open method rather than subcutaneously.

Abscesses may reach the flexor compartment of the thigh from various sources :—(1) from the back of the hip joint; (2) from the pelvis, through the greater sciatic foramen; (3) from one or other of the bursæ under the gluteus maximus; (4) from the front of the hip joint, by passing backwards under cover of the tensor fasciæ latæ, or by winding backwards below the neck of the femur and through the interval between the quadratus femoris and the adductor magnus; (5) from the iliac fossa behind the inguinal ligament into the femoral triangle, and thence to the back of the thigh by one or other of the routes already mentioned; (6) upwards from the popliteal surface of the femur, the knee, a popliteal gland, or a bursa.

POPLITEAL FOSSA

When the knee is extended the **popliteal fascia** is put upon the stretch, and the hollow behind the knee is obliterated; when the knee is flexed the fascia is relaxed, and the fingers may be pressed deeply into the femoral division of the fossa; as a rule, the pulsations of the popliteal artery can be felt.   Deep to the **semitendinosus** is the **semimembranosus**, which is still fleshy in its lower part, and bulges into the space to overlap the upper part of the popliteal artery.   Between the semimembranosus and the medial head of the gastrocnemius there is the most important **bursa** in the popliteal region; it not infrequently becomes distended with fluid, and then presents usually a more or less sausage-shaped outline; sometimes the bursa communicates with the cavity of the knee-joint.

To map out the line of the **popliteal vessels** and the **medial popliteal nerve**, draw a line from a point a little medial to the upper angle of the fossa to a point midway between the condyles of the femur, and thence along the middle of the fossa to the level of the lower part of the tubercle of the tibia.   The medial popliteal nerve [n. tibialis] lies immediately under cover of the deep fascia; the artery is separated from the popliteal surface of the femur by a quantity of fat. The popliteal **lymph glands** lie near the vessels.

FRONT OF THIGH

Between the front of the thigh and the abdomen is the *groove of the groin*, in which the **inguinal ligament** can be felt as a tense band, stretching from the anterior superior iliac spine to the pubic tubercle.   The **anterior superior spine** looks directly forwards.   To make comparative measurements of the two lower limbs stretch a tape from that spine to the tip of the malleolus, taking care that the pelvis is horizontal, and the limbs in corresponding positions. The **pubic tubercle**, in a man, is felt about an inch lateral to the upper margin of the pubic symphysis, and, in a woman, rather farther from the symphysis—at the upper and lateral part of the mons pubis; between the tubercle and the symphysis is the **crest** of the pubis, the two crests together forming a rounded, bony ridge. A line drawn from the pubic tubercle horizontally across the front of the thigh crosses the front of the hip joint at the level of the lower part of the head of the femur. The cord-like **tendon** of the **adductor longus** is readily felt, and a point

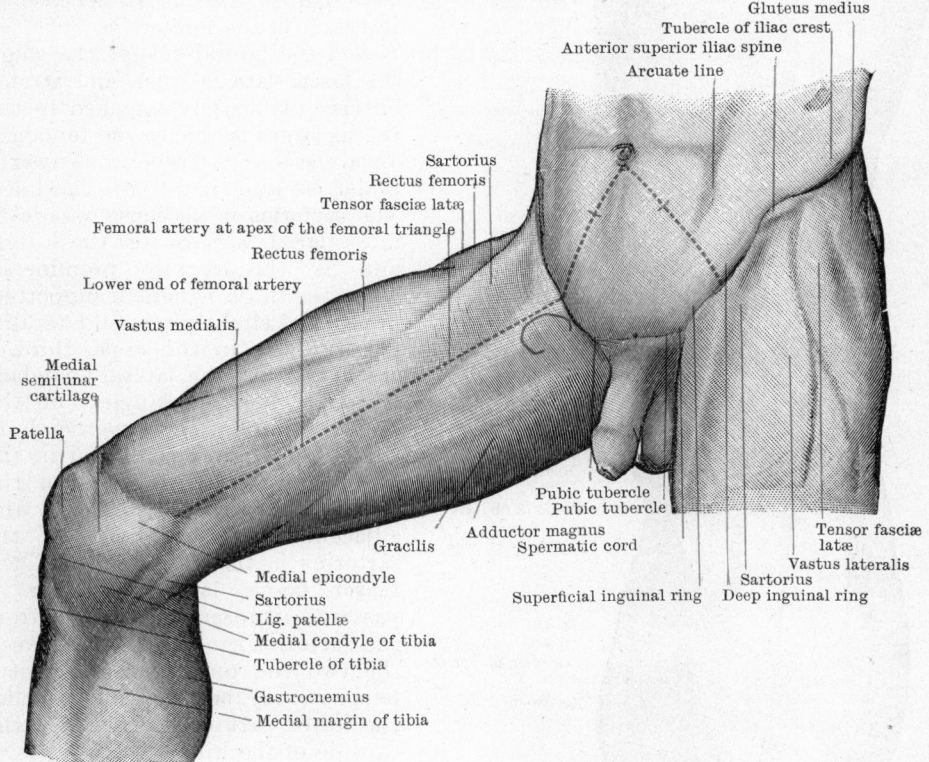

FIG. 1167.—THE THIGH AND GROIN

about an inch below the pubic tubercle is selected for performing the operation of subcutaneous tenotomy of the tendon.

The centre of the **saphenous opening** [fossa ovalis] is situated an inch and a half below and lateral to the pubic tubercle; the opening overlies the medial (hernial) and intermediate (venous) compartments of the femoral sheath; behind the lateral border of the opening is the arterial compartment of the sheath; crossing over the lower border is the terminal part of the long saphenous vein. A femoral hernia makes its way into the thigh behind the upper edge of the opening. The course of the **long saphenous vein** in the thigh is indicated by a line extending from the adductor tubercle of the femur to the lower part of the saphenous opening.

The **horizontal chain** of superficial **inguinal lymph glands** can usually be felt a little below the line of the inguinal ligament; when the glands are inflamed the surgeon should not neglect to examine the buttocks and anus as well as the external genitals. The **vertical chain** lies in close relation to the upper end of the long saphenous vein. *Deeper* glands also are met with, behind the cribriform fascia close to the medial side of the femoral vein; and there is generally one in the femoral canal. To clear out the glands in the groin, make an incision parallel to the whole length of the inguinal ligament and a finger's breadth below it.

To map out the course of the **femoral artery**, the thigh being slightly flexed and rotated laterally, draw a line from the mid-inguinal point to the adductor tubercle; rather less than the upper third of the line corresponds to the femoral artery in the femoral triangle, while rather more than its middle third corresponds to the artery as it lies in the sub-sartorial canal [c. adductorius]. The seat of election for ligature of the vessel is at the apex of the femoral triangle. To compress the femoral artery, make pressure directly backwards against the ilio-pubic eminence, and not against the head of the femur; to compress the artery in the sub-sartorial canal, press laterally against the medial surface of the shaft of the femur.

On the lateral side of the thigh the **fascia lata** is thick and strong, but is only loosely attached to the vastus lateralis; hence the tendency of abscesses to travel downwards under cover of it towards the knee. The **sartorius** is the most important muscular landmark of the thigh, and is thrown into prominence when the thigh is held unsupported, flexed, and slightly rotated laterally. Observe that in the upper third of the thigh it is the lateral boundary of the femoral triangle; in the middle third it is superficial to the sub-sartorial canal; and in the lower third it is in front of the medial hamstrings. Lateral and adjacent to the upper part of the sartorius is the prominence of the **tensor fasciæ latæ**, which, as it passes to its insertion, diverges from the sartorius; in the angle between the two the tendon of the rectus femoris may be felt as it overlies the lower part of the front of the capsule of the hip joint.

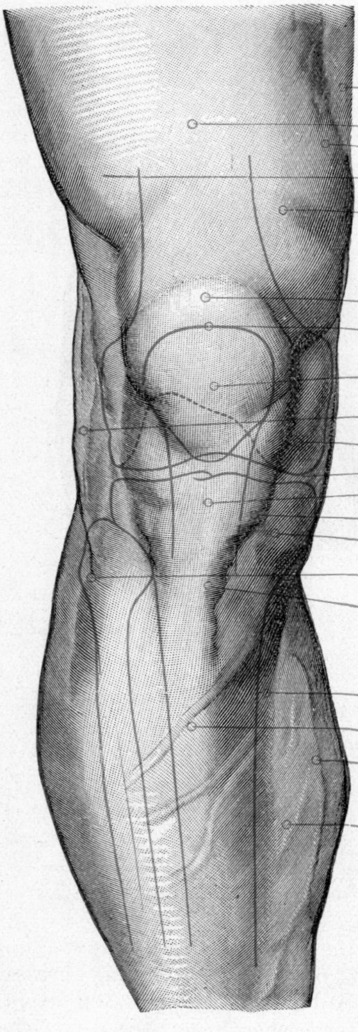

Gracilis
Rectus femoris
Sartorius
Vastus lateralis
Vastus medialis
Quadriceps extensor tendon
Upper border of patella
Patella
Ilio-tibial tract
Medial epicondyle
Medial semilunar cartilage
Ligamentum patellæ
Pad of fat
Medial condyle of tibia
Head of fibula
Tubercle of tibia
Medial border of tibia
Anterior border of tibia
Gastrocnemius
Soleus

FIG. 1168.—FRONT OF KNEE.

The medial side of the lower half of the **shaft of the femur** may be conveniently cut down upon through the vastus medialis where it comes to the surface between the sartorius and rectus muscles; make the incision along a line that begins at a point midway between the medial border of the patella and the adductor tubercle and extends towards the anterior superior iliac spine.

The front of the **hip joint** may be reached through an incision from the anterior superior iliac spine downwards along either the medial or the lateral border of the sartorius; in the former case the deeper part of the dissection passes between the iliacus and the medial border of the rectus femoris, while in the latter case the joint is reached lateral to the rectus tendon, between it and the anterior borders of the gluteus medius and minimus muscles. The *ascending branch* of the **lateral circumflex artery** of the thigh crosses the capsule parallel to the trochanteric line and immediately above it. The **ilio-psoas** crosses the anterior and the medial part of the capsule; between the two there is a **bursa** which frequently communicates with the joint through the thin part of the capsule medial to the ilio-femoral ligament; it is by way of that communication that a psoas abscess occasionally gives rise to secondary tubercular disease of the hip joint. One of the commonest situations to meet with an abscess in hip joint disease is in the fatty areolar tissue under cover of the tensor fasciæ latæ; or the pus may pass below and medial to the neck of the femur, and thence along the course of the medial circumflex artery to the back of the thigh. *To tap or explore the hip joint,* make the puncture in the interval between the sartorius and the tensor fasciæ latæ, **2** to **3** in. below the anterior superior iliac spine; if the instrument is then pushed upwards, medially and backwards behind the tendon of the rectus femoris, it will pass through the capsule a little above the trochanteric line. Regarded from the point of view of **dislocation,** the regions of the acetabular notch and of the lower part of the capsule are the weak points in the joint; it follows that abduction favours dislocation by bringing the head of the femur into relation with those two weak areas.

When particularly free access to the hip joint is required, as in the open reduction of a congenital dislocation, an angled incision may be employed. The upper limb of the incision runs parallel to the anterior third of the iliac crest and a finger's-breadth below it; the vertical or lower limb passes in the plane between the sartorius and the tensor fasciæ latæ to a point below the level of the greater trochanter.

THE KNEE

With the knee extended and the quadriceps relaxed, the **patella** can be readily outlined and moved from side to side on the femoral condyles. When the quadriceps is contracted its tendon springs forwards and is felt as a tense band above the patella; and the **ligamentum patellæ,** which has become tense and prominent, may be traced to the tubercle of the tibia. In front of the lower part of the patella and of the upper part of the ligamentum patellæ is the **pre-patellar bursa,** into which effusion takes place in the condition known as housemaid's knee. Deep to and on each side of the ligamentum patellæ there is a well-circumscribed pad of fat, palpation of which gives rise to a feeling closely resembling true fluctuation. In extension, only the distal pair of articular facets of the patella are in contact with the patellar surface of the femur (Pl. XXVI, Fig. 1). In semiflexion the middle pair of facets rests on the femur; in that position the medial margin of the medial condyle of the femur, the upper border of the medial condyle of the tibia, and the lower part of the patella are all distinctly visible, and together bound a triangular depression which overlies the line of the joint and contains the anterior part of the **medial semilunar cartilage** [meniscus]; in that triangle the surgeon searches for a displaced or thickened medial cartilage, for a loose body, and for "lipping" of the edge of the articular cartilage in chronic osteo-arthritis. A similar but less well-defined triangle may be felt immediately lateral to the lower edge of the patella. When the quadriceps is thrown into sudden or violent contraction, as in preventing oneself from falling backwards, the patella may be transversely fractured at the moment of partial flexion. In full flexion almost the whole of the patellar surface of the condyles is exposed to palpation, covered, however, by the stretched quadriceps tendon.

The upper part of the medial surface of the medial condyle of the femur is overlapped by the fleshy prominence made by the lower part of the **vastus medialis.** Leading upwards from the medial condyle there is a slight furrow that corresponds to the interval between the lower part of the vastus medialis and the sartorius; at the bottom of the furrow the **tendon of the adductor magnus** can readily be felt as a tense cord, and followed to its insertion into the **adductor tubercle**; the tubercle, situated at the junction of the medial supracondylar line with the upper and posterior part of the medial condyle, marks the level of the **epiphyseal cartilage** (Pl. XIV). Anteriorly and posteriorly the epiphyseal cartilage lies immediately above the highest part of the articular cartilage.

Disease of the lower part of the shaft of the femur generally invades the popliteal surface of the femur and the popliteal fossa rather than the cavity of the knee-joint. In *Macewen's operation for knock-knee,* carry the incision (through which the osteotome is introduced) down to the bone through the vastus medialis a little above the medial condyle—keeping a finger's-breadth above the patellar surface to avoid injury to the epiphyseal cartilage, and the same distance in front of the adductor tendon to avoid injury to the descending genicular vessels.

Below the medial condyle of the femur, the **medial condyle of the tibia** is readily felt, though it is crossed by the tendons of the sartorius, gracilis, and semi-tendinosus passing to their insertions. Between these tendons and the medial head of the gastrocnemius there is a groove which winds downwards and forwards from the popliteal fossa; an incision along that groove will expose the **long saphenous vein,** the **saphenous nerve** and the saphenous artery.

On the lateral side of the knee is the **ilio-tibial tract**, which, after crossing and obscuring the line of the joint, is attached to the **lateral condyle of the tibia**. By semiflexion of the knee the posterior border of the tract is thrown into relief, and a well-marked furrow intervenes between it and the tendon of the biceps; the lower part of the shaft of the femur and the popliteal surface may be reached through an incision along that furrow. Under cover of the ilio-tibial tract, as it crosses the line of the joint, are the **lateral semi-lunar cartilage [meniscus]**, the **lower lateral genicular artery**, and the **lateral ligament of the knee**. The **head of the fibula**, and the **tendon of the biceps** passing to be inserted into it, become distinctly visible when the knee is semi-flexed; the head of the fibula lies on a level with the tubercle of the tibia, $1\frac{1}{2}$ in. behind and a little below the most prominent part of the lateral condyle of the tibia. The termination of the **lateral popliteal nerve** [n. peronæus communis] is immediately below the head of the fibula, and is liable to be contused from blows and in fractures of the neck of the fibula.

At the lower part of the knee joint, anteriorly, the **synovial membrane** extends downwards as far as the level of the upper border of the tibia; posteriorly, it dips downwards for a short distance behind the upper end of the tibia, to form a small cul-de-sac, the close relation of which to the popliteal artery must be borne in mind in the operation of excision of

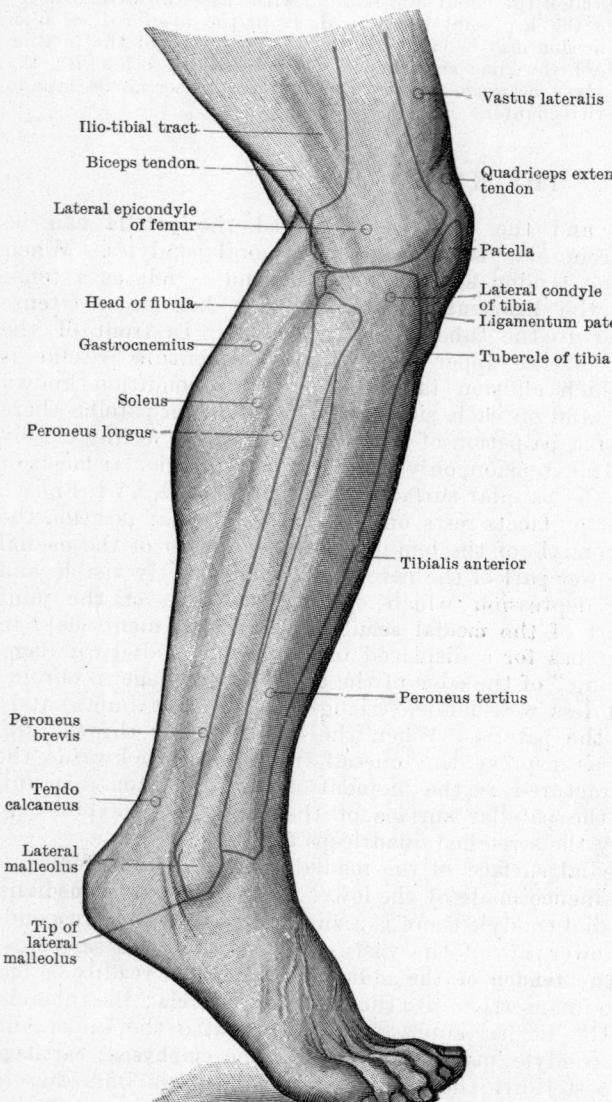

Ilio-tibial tract

Biceps tendon

Lateral epicondyle of femur

Head of fibula

Gastrocnemius

Soleus

Peroneus longus

Peroneus brevis

Tendo calcaneus

Lateral malleolus

Tip of lateral malleolus

Vastus lateralis

Quadriceps extensor tendon

Patella

Lateral condyle of tibia

Ligamentum patellæ

Tubercle of tibia

Tibialis anterior

Peroneus tertius

FIG. 1169.—LATERAL SIDE OF KNEE AND LEG.

the knee. At the upper part, anteriorly, the synovial membrane extends upwards under cover of the quadriceps in the form of a pouch which reaches a level nearly two inches above the articular surface of the femur; posteriorly, there is no extension of the synovial cavity above the condyles. At the sides of the knee the synovial membrane covers the anterior third of the superficial surface of each condyle.

In **effusion into the knee joint** the hollows become obliterated, the patella is floated up, and fluctuation may be obtained above, below, and on each side of the patella.

To pass a tube through the knee joint for drainage, make two short vertical incisions—one on each side of the joint at the level of the upper part of the patella, and a finger's-breadth behind its lateral edges. In **arthrectomy** of the knee for tubercular disease, the extra-synovial fat facilitates the separation of the supra-patellar pouch from the lower and anterior part of the shaft of the femur; to expose the **pouches behind the condyles,** divide the cruciate ligaments.

THE LEG

The medial surface of the **tibia** is subcutaneous throughout; hence the seat of a fracture of the shaft is, as a rule, easily felt, and the lower end of the upper fragment is apt to perforate the skin. The skin over the lower half of this surface is the commonest seat of varicose and callous ulcers, which are frequently prevented from healing by adhesion of the floor of the ulcer to the periosteum.

The **shaft of the fibula** is on a plane behind that of the tibia, and, with the exception of the triangular subcutaneous surface, is deeply placed among the muscles. To examine the fibula, stand on the opposite side of the patient and manipulate the bone along the line of the intermuscular septum between the peronei and the muscles of the calf.

The greater fullness of the antero-lateral surface of the leg, as compared with its medial surface, is due to the presence of the **extensor** and **peroneal groups of muscles**. When those groups are thrown into action, the individual muscles are mapped out on the surface by the grooves that correspond to their intermuscular septa. The **posterior peroneal septum** is opposite a well-marked furrow which extends from the back of the head of the fibula to the hollow behind the lateral malleolus. In front of it are two **peroneal muscles**—the *longus* giving rise to a prominence in the upper half of the leg, and the *brevis* prominent in the lower half. Behind the septum there is a prominence formed by the lateral border of the **soleus**, which projects beyond the border of the **gastrocnemius**.

It is along the line of the posterior peroneal intermuscular septum that incisions should be made to expose the fibula; to avoid the musculo-cutaneous nerve [n. peronæus superficialis], however, do not carry the incision higher than one inch below the head of the fibula.

The furrow between the extensors and the two peronei marks the **anterior peroneal septum**: it is much less distinct than the furrow of the posterior septum, and runs from the anterior border of the head of the fibula to the anterior border of the lateral malleolus; the **cutaneous portion of the musculo-cutaneous nerve** corresponds to the lower half of the furrow. At the junction of the middle and lower thirds of the leg the extensor muscles incline medially over the front of the tibia.

The **anterior tibial artery** reaches the front of the interosseous membrane an inch below the head of the fibula; in the upper two-thirds of its course it lies on the interosseous membrane; in its lower third it winds on to the front of the tibia, to terminate at a point opposite the ankle joint, midway between the two malleoli. *Incisions to expose the vessel* should strike the lateral border of the tibialis anterior, which corresponds to a line drawn from a point midway between the lateral condyle of the tibia and the head of the fibula, to the termination of the vessel.

When the muscles of the calf are thrown into action, a groove is seen between the two heads of the **gastrocnemius**, the fleshy fibres of which extend a little below the middle of the leg. The fleshy fibres of the **soleus** extend to the junction of the middle and lower thirds of the leg, and project beyond the margins of the gastrocnemius. The narrowest part of the **tendo calcaneus** is opposite the bases of the malleoli, and it is there that the tendon is divided in the operation of tenotomy. The **short saphenous vein**, which lies a little to the lateral side of the tendon, gradually reaches the middle of the calf, along which it runs upwards to the middle of the popliteal fossa. The **long saphenous vein** and the **saphenous nerve** lie along the medial margin of the tibia, except in the lower part of the leg, where they course obliquely over the medial surface of the tibia.

The course of the **posterior tibial artery** is mapped out by a line drawn from the lower angle of the popliteal fossa, at the level of the lower border of the tubercle of the tibia, to a point midway between the medial malleolus and the tendo calcaneus. *To expose the vessel* in the upper half of the leg make an incision parallel to the medial margin of the tibia and half an inch behind it; after the medial border of the gastrocnemius is retracted and the tibial origin of the soleus is divided, the artery is found lying on the tibialis posterior. When exposing the artery below the soleus, divide two layers of deep fascia and keep the knife directed towards the tibia.

The **peroneal artery** is given off 3 in. below the head of the fibula; incisions to expose the vessel are made in the direction of a line drawn from the posterior border of the head of the fibula to a point midway between the lateral malleolus and the tendo calcaneus.

FOOT AND ANKLE

The tip of the **lateral malleolus** is $\frac{1}{4}$ inch lower than the tip of the **medial malleolus** (Pl. XXVII, Fig. 1). Above the lateral malleolus is the triangular subcutaneous surface of the fibula, the apex of which corresponds to the distal end of the anterior peroneal septum.

The **line of the ankle joint** can be felt on each side of the extensor tendons, and when the foot is extended the anterior part of the upper surface of the body of the **talus** forms a visible prominence below the anterior edge of the distal end of the tibia. The posterior surface of the talus is small, but may be felt below and behind the medial malleolus, at the anterior part of the hollow between it and the heel. In *effusions into the ankle joint* the hollows in front of and behind the malleoli are obliterated, and the extensor tendons are raised from the front of the joint.

A finger's-breadth below the tip of the medial malleolus is the **sustentaculum tali**; $1\frac{1}{4}$ in. in front of the sustentaculum is the **tuberosity of the navicular bone** (the medial landmark in Chopart's amputation), which is generally visible, and always distinctly palpable. The **talo-calcanean joint** is immediately above the sustentaculum; and immediately above the joint the **tendon of the tibialis posterior** may be made visible, as it extends from behind the tip of the medial malleolus to the tuberosity of the navicular. An inch and a half in front of the tuberosity of the navicular is the **joint between the medial cuneiform and the first metatarsal**; the ridge at the base of the first metatarsal furnishes a good guide to the joint. The first **metatarso-phalangeal joint** is a little in front of the middle of the ball of the big toe.

The **base of the fifth metatarsal bone** makes a prominence on the lateral border of the foot about midway between the point of the heel and the root of the little toe. A finger's-breadth vertically below the tip of the lateral malleolus is the **peroneal tubercle** of the calcaneum [processus trochlearis], and midway between the two is the **talo-calcanean joint**; the peroneal tubercle is, when present, a trustworthy guide to the level at which the **two peroneal tendons** cross the lateral surface of the calcaneum. The anterior part of the **calcaneum** is felt in the triangular interval between the tendons of the peroneus brevis and tertius. The **calcaneo-cuboid joint**—the lateral landmark in Chopart's amputation—is barely a finger's-breadth behind the base of the fifth metatarsal (Pls. XXVII, Fig. 2 and XXVIII). To open the **lateral tarso-metatarsal joints**, enter the knife behind the base of the fifth metatarsal bone, and direct it forwards as well as medially. On the dorsum of the foot the tarsal joints are obscured by the extensor tendons. The **synovial membrane** of the **ankle joint** is prolonged on to the neck of the talus, and care must be taken to avoid opening the ankle joint in Chopart's amputation.

The **line** of the **tarso-metatarsal joints** extends nearly an inch farther forwards on the medial border of the foot than on the lateral border; and it takes a zigzag course on account of the second metatarsal bone extending backwards between the medial and lateral cuneiform bones. The joint between the second metatarsal and intermediate cuneiform is nearly half an inch behind that between the first metatarsal and medial cuneiform, and nearly a quarter of an inch behind that between the third metatarsal and the lateral cuneiform. The transverse interosseous ligament which connects the lateral surface of the medial cuneiform with the base of the second metatarsal is a strong band that must be divided in the tarsometatarsal amputation of Lisfranc. In order to preserve the insertions of the two tibialis muscles and the three peroneal muscles, the surgeon should, when possible, instead of disarticulating at joints, saw through the metatarsal bones in front of their bases.

The **metatarso-phalangeal joints** are an inch behind the web of the toes. When a toe is disarticulated, cut the plantar ligament of the joint from the

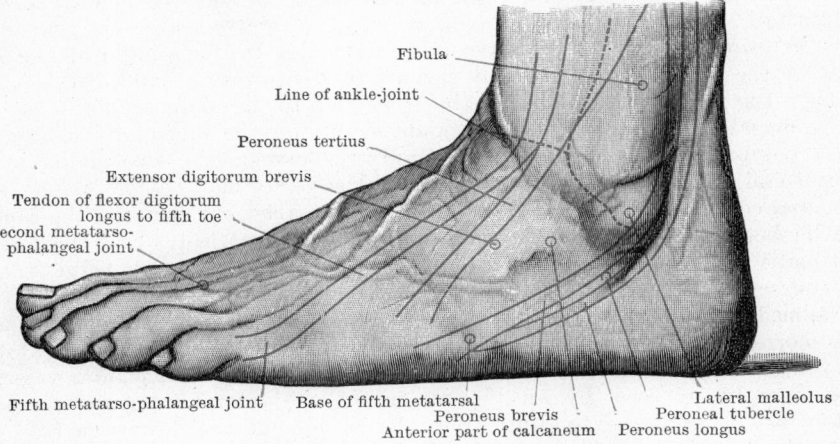

Fibula
Line of ankle-joint
Peroneus tertius
Extensor digitorum brevis
Tendon of flexor digitorum longus to fifth toe
Second metatarso-phalangeal joint
Fifth metatarso-phalangeal joint   Base of fifth metatarsal   Lateral malleolus
Peroneus brevis   Peroneal tubercle
Anterior part of calcaneum   Peroneus longus

FIG. 1170.—LATERAL SIDE OF FOOT AND ANKLE.

phalanx, but leave it otherwise uninjured, for the bands of the deep transverse ligament of the sole are attached to its margins.

The **tendon** of the **tibialis posterior** may be felt, and, when the foot is inverted, seen, as it extends from behind the tip of the medial malleolus to the tuberosity of the navicular; it crosses the deltoid ligament and the talus immediately above the sustentaculum tali.

In the commonest form of club-foot — *talipes equino-varus* — the tuberosity of the navicular is approximated to the medial malleolus, and tenotomy of the tibialis posterior should be performed therefore through a puncture a little below the tip of the medial malleolus; after dividing the tendon, carry the knife down to the bone in order to

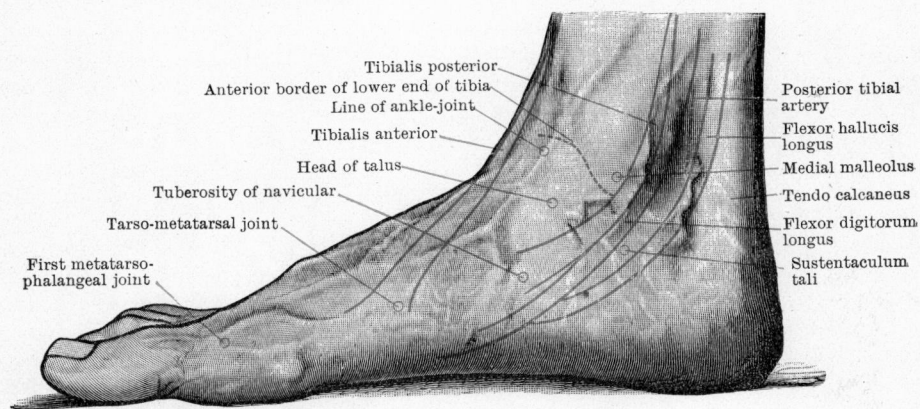

Tibialis posterior
Anterior border of lower end of tibia
Line of ankle-joint
Tibialis anterior
Head of talus
Tuberosity of navicular
Tarso-metatarsal joint
First metatarso-phalangeal joint
Posterior tibial artery
Flexor hallucis longus
Medial malleolus
Tendo calcaneus
Flexor digitorum longus
Sustentaculum tali

FIG. 1171.—MEDIAL SIDE OF FOOT AND ANKLE.

divide the **plantar calcaneo-navicular ligament** and to open the **talo-navicular joint**—a procedure called for before the foot can be brought into good position.

The following tendons—named from medial to lateral side—cross the front of the ankle-joint:—the **tibialis anterior** (the largest and most prominent), the **extensor hallucis longus**, the **extensor digitorum longus**, and the **peroneus tertius**. The **extensor digitorum brevis** makes the fleshy pad that overlies the dorsal surface of the calcaneo-cuboid joint. When the foot is everted, the tendon of the **peroneus**

brevis may be seen extending from the tip of the lateral malleolus to the base of the fifth metatarsal bone; immediately below it is the tendon of the **peroneus longus**, which, as it winds round the cuboid, is obscured by the fleshy fibres of the abductor digiti minimi muscle. The **abductor hallucis muscle**, although described along with the sole, forms a fleshy pad along the medial border of the foot below the sustentaculum tali.

An incision from the tuberosity of the navicular to the middle of the medial border of the heel will expose the various tendons, vessels, and nerves as they pass from the medial malleolus into the sole, deep to the abductor hallucis.

The **dorsalis pedis artery** may be mapped out on the surface by a line drawn from a point opposite the ankle-joint, midway between the two malleoli, to the posterior end of the first interosseous space; the vessel may be compressed against the medial column of the tarsal bones. The **long saphenous vein** and the **saphenous nerve** lie between the anterior border of the medial malleolus and the tendon of the tibialis anterior; the **short saphenous vein** and the **sural nerve** take the same course as the tendon of the peroneus brevis.

The **medial plantar vessels** and **nerves** lie along the **medial intermuscular septum**, which corresponds to a line drawn from the medial tubercle of the calcaneum to the interval between the first and second toes. The **lateral plantar vessels** and **nerves** may be exposed by an incision along the **lateral intermuscular septum**, which runs in a line extending from the middle of the lower surface of the heel to the fourth toe. To map out the course of the **plantar arch**, draw a line across the sole from the medial side of the base of the fifth metatarsal bone to the posterior end of the first interosseous space.

INDEX

THE END